TOP HAY

ENGLISH, AMERICAN, CANADIAN, HAYLAGE

FIBRE SELECT

THE RANGE OF DUST EXTRACTED
HIGH QUALITY HAY IN FULLY PACKAGED
BALES TO SUIT YOUR REQUIREMENTS

RANSLEY HAY

Contact Philip Ransley
Tel 01233 731001 / 733189   Mob 07860 915000
Email philip.ransley@ransleyhay.co.uk

For all enquiries in Ireland please contact
Tom Daly on 00353 868 220 557

EQUESTRIAN
SURFACES LTD

Expertly developed with durability, safety and consistency in mind, the composition of our racing surfaces is informed by in-depth research and over 35 years of industry experience.

THE JOCKEY CLUB
ESTATES

Olly Murphy
WARREN CHASE STABLES

WARREN
GREATREX
RACING

R·R
RICHARD HUGHES RACING

We're proud to have supplied our surfaces to the prestigious *Jockey Club Estates*, and to be relied upon by some of the industry's most respected trainers, including *Olly Murphy*, *Warren Greatrex*, *Ed Walker*, and *Richard Hughes*.

BRONCHIX PULMO

> FOR PULMONARY SUPPORT AND ELASTICITY

Richard Hughes; "I have used Bronchix Pulmo syrup and Bronchix Pulmo syringes on several horses. The product is simple and easy to use and we have had great success with it. We now would not do without it."

WINDSOR CLIVE
INTERNATIONAL

SALES, PURCHASES, LETTINGS
AND VALUATIONS
OF TRAINING YARDS AND STUD FARMS.

+44 (0)1672 521155
info@windsorclive.co.uk   windsorclive.co.uk

STAY AHEAD OF THE FIELD WITH

RACING POST
MEMBERS' CLUB

ACCESS PREMIUM CONTENT AND FEATURES

FIND OUT MORE AT
RACINGPOST.COM/MEMBERS-CLUB

HORSES
IN TRAINING 2022

132nd YEAR OF PUBLICATION

RACING POST

INDEX TO GENERAL CONTENTS

Editor   **Graham Dench**
                      E-mail: hitraceform@weatherbys.co.uk

Production Editor **Adam Cockings**
                      Weatherbys, Sanders Road, Wellingborough, NN8 4BX.

Orders   Racing Post Books, Sanders Road, Wellingborough, Northants NN8 4BX.
                      Tel: 01933 304858
                      www.racingpost.com/shop
                      E-mail: Shop@racingpost.com

Advertisements   kay.brown@archantdialogue.co.uk and
                      gary.millone@archantdialogue.co.uk

ISBN   978-1-83950-095-4

INDEX TO ADVERTISERS

2022

RACING FIXTURES

AND SALE DATES

(SUBJECT TO ALTERATION)

Flat fixtures are in **Black Type**; Jump in Light Type; Irish in *Italic*;
asterisk (★) indicates an evening or Twilight meeting;
† indicates an All Weather meeting. Sale dates are at foot of fixtures

MARCH

Sun	Mon	Tue	Wed	Thu	Fri	Sat
		1 Catterick Bridge Leicester **Newcastle†★**	**2** **Kempton Park†★** **Lingfield Park†** Musselburgh Wincanton	**3** **Chelmsford City†★** *Clonmel* Ludlow **Newcastle†** Taunton	**4** Doncaster *Dundalk (E)* **Lingfield Park†** Newbury **Newcastle†★**	**5** Doncaster Kelso **Lingfield Park†** *Navan* Newbury **Southwell†★**
6 Huntingdon *Leopardstown* Sedgefield *Wexford*	**7** *Leopardstown* Southwell Wetherby **Wolverhampton†★**	**8** Newcastle Sandown Park **Wolverhampton†★**	**9** Catterick Bridge Fontwell Park **Kempton Park†★** **Lingfield Park†**	**10** Carlisle **Newcastle†★** **Southwell†** *Thurles* Wincanton	**11** *Dundalk (E)* Exeter Leicester Newcastle **Wolverhampton†★**	**12** Ayr **Chelmsford City†★** *Gowran Park* Hereford **Lingfield Park†** *Navan* Sandown Park **Wolverhampton†**
13 Bangor-On-Dee *Limerick* *Naas* Warwick	**14** Plumpton Stratford-On-Avon Taunton **Wolverhampton†★**	**15** Cheltenham **Newcastle†★** Sedgefield **Southwell†★**	**16** Cheltenham Huntingdon **Kempton Park†★** **Newcastle†★**	**17** **Chelmsford City†★** Cheltenham *Down Royal* Hexham **Southwell†★**	**18** Cheltenham Doncaster *Dundalk (E)* Fakenham **Newcastle†★** **Wolverhampton†★**	**19** Fontwell Park Kempton Park Newcastle *Thurles* Uttoxeter **Wolverhampton†★**
20 Carlisle Chepstow *Downpatrick*	**21** Plumpton Southwell Wincanton	**22** *Clonmel* Exeter Market Rasen Wetherby	**23** Ffos Las Haydock Park Ludlow	**24** Chepstow *Cork* Huntingdon Sedgefield	**25** *Dundalk (E)* Hereford Musselburgh **Newcastle†★** Newton Abbot	**26** *Curragh* **Doncaster** Kelso **Kempton Park†** Stratford-On-Avon **Wolverhampton†★**
27 Ascot Carlisle **Doncaster** *Limerick* *Naas*	**28** Hexham Ludlow **Newcastle†★**	**29** Fontwell Park *Navan* Uttoxeter **Wolverhampton†★**	**30** **Kempton Park†★** **Lingfield Park†** Market Rasen Wincanton	**31** **Chelmsford City†★** **Lingfield Park†** *Naas* Warwick Wetherby		

APRIL

Sun	Mon	Tue	Wed	Thu	Fri	Sat
■	■	■	■	■	**1** Ayr *Dundalk (E)* **Leicester** Newbury **Southwell†★** *Dundalk (AW-E)* *Wexford (E)*	**2** Ayr Chepstow *Leopardstown* **Lingfield Park†** Newbury **Wolverhampton†★**
3 *Cork* *Fairyhouse* Hereford Plumpton	**4** Kelso **Redcar** **Windsor**	**5** Exeter **Pontefract** Southwell	**6** **Catterick Bridge** **Kempton Park†★** *Leopardstown* **Lingfield Park★** **Nottingham**	**7** Aintree **Chelmsford City†★** Ffos Las *Gowran Park (E)* *Limerick* Taunton	**8** Aintree *Ballinrobe (E)* *Dundalk (E)* Fontwell Park **Kempton Park★** Sedgefield	**9** Aintree Bangor-On-Dee Newcastle **Thirsk** **Wolverhampton†★**
10 *Curragh* Stratford-On-Avon *Tramore* Wincanton	**11** Hexham **Pontefract** *Tramore (E)* **Windsor** Tattersalls Sale	**12** Ayr *Dundalk (E)* **Newmarket** **Wolverhampton†★** Tattersalls Sale	**13** **Beverley** Cheltenham *Gowran Park (E)* Kempton Park★ **Newmarket** Southwell★	**14** **Bath★** Cheltenham *Clonmel (E)* Exeter★ **Newmarket** **Ripon**	**15** **Chelmsford City†** **Lingfield Park†** **Newcastle†**	**16** **Brighton★** Carlisle *Cork* *Fairyhouse* Haydock Park **Musselburgh** **Newbury** Newton Abbot **Nottingham★**
17 *Cork* *Fairyhouse* Ffos Las Market Rasen **Newbury** Plumpton **Southwell†**	**18** Chepstow *Cork* *Fairyhouse* Fakenham Huntingdon **Kempton Park★** Plumpton **Redcar** **Wolverhampton†**	**19** **Epsom Downs** Sedgefield **Wolverhampton†★** Worcester★ **Yarmouth**	**20** *Bellewstown (E)* **Catterick Bridge** **Lingfield Park†★** Ludlow Perth **Salisbury★**	**21** **Beverley** **Chelmsford City†★** *Kilbeggan (E)* Perth Taunton★ *Tipperary (E)* Warwick	**22** Chepstow★ **Doncaster** *Kilbeggan (E)* Perth **Sandown Park** Southwell★	**23** **Doncaster★** Haydock Park **Leicester** *Limerick* *Navan* **Ripon** Sandown Park **Wolverhampton†★**
24 **Bath** Wetherby	**25** Ayr **Lingfield Park†** *Naas (E)* **Southwell†** **Thirsk★** **Windsor★**	**26** **AYR★** **Brighton** **Nottingham** *Punchestown (E)* **Yarmouth** Tattersalls Sale	**27** **Ascot** **Brighton★** **MUSSELBURGH★** **Pontefract** *Punchestown (E)* **Wolverhampton†** Tattersalls Sale	**28** **Chelmsford City†★** **CHEPSTOW★** **Lingfield Park†** **Musselburgh** *Punchestown (E)* **Redcar** Tattersalls Sale	**29** Cheltenham★ **Goodwood** **Newcastle†★** **Newmarket** *Punchestown (E)* **Wolverhampton†**	**30** **Doncaster★** **Goodwood** Hexham★ **Newmarket** *Punchestown* **Thirsk** Uttoxeter

MAY

Sun	Mon	Tue	Wed	Thu	Fri	Sat
1 **Hamilton Park** **Newmarket** **Salisbury** *Sligo*	**2** **Bath** **Beverley** *Curragh* *Down Royal* Kempton Park Warwick **Windsor**	**3** *Ayr* *Ballinrobe (E)* Fakenham Sedgefield★ **Lingfield Park**† **Wetherby**★	**4** Fontwell Park★ *Gowran Park (E)* Kelso **Kempton Park**†★ Newton Abbot	**5** **Chelmsford City**†★ **Chester** Huntingdon *Tipperary (E)* Worcester	**6** **Ascot** **Chester** *Cork (E)* *Downpatrick (E)* Market Rasen **Nottingham**★ **Ripon**★ **Wolverhampton**†★	**7** **Ascot** *Cork* Haydock Park Hexham **Lingfield Park** *Naas* **Nottingham** **Thirsk**★ Warwick★
8 **Hamilton Park** *Leopardstown* Ludlow Plumpton	**9** **Catterick Bridge** **Musselburgh** *Roscommon (E)* Southwell★ **Windsor**★ **Wolverhampton**†	**10** **Beverley** **Chepstow** **Newcastle**†★ Sedgefield	**11** **Bath**★ Gowran Park Newton Abbot Perth★ Worcester **York**	**12** *Clonmel (E)* Fontwell Park★ **Newmarket**★ Perth **Salisbury** **York**	**13** Aintree★ **Hamilton Park**★ *Kilbeggan (E)* *Leopardstown (E)* **Newbury** **Newmarket** **York**	**14** Bangor-On-Dee **Chelmsford City**† **Doncaster**★ *Navan* **Newbury** **Newmarket** **Thirsk** Uttoxeter★ *Wexford*
15 *Killarney* *Naas* **Ripon** Stratford-On-Avon	**16** **Carlisle** Ffos Las *Killarney (E)* **Leicester**★ **Redcar** **Windsor**★	**17** **Brighton** Hexham★ Huntingdon★ *Killarney (E)* **Nottingham** *Sligo (E)* **Wolverhampton**†	**18** *Ayr* *Cork (E)* **Kempton Park**†★ Southwell★ Warwick **Yarmouth**	**19** **Chelmsford City**†★ **Lingfield Park** Market Rasen **Sandown Park**★ *Tipperary (E)* **Wolverhampton**†	**20** **Bath** **Catterick Bridge**★ *Curragh (E)* *Downpatrick (E)* **Goodwood** **Haydock Park** Worcester★	**21** *Curragh* **Goodwood** **Haydock Park** **Lingfield Park**★ **Musselburgh** Stratford-On-Avon★ **York**
22 *Curragh* Fakenham **Nottingham** **York**	**23** Huntingdon★ **Leicester** Ludlow *Roscommon (E)* **Windsor**★ **Wolverhampton**†	**24** Bangor-On-Dee *Gowran Park (E)* **Lingfield Park**†★ **Newcastle**†★ Southwell	**25** **Beverley** **Hamilton Park** Newton Abbot **Ripon**★ Warwick★ *Wexford (E)*	**26** Carlisle★ **Haydock Park** *Limerick (E)* **Ripon** **Sandown Park**★ **Yarmouth**	**27** **Brighton** **Carlisle** **Chepstow** *Fairyhouse (E)* **Haydock Park**★ *Limerick (E)* **Pontefract**★ Stratford-On-Avon★ BBAG Sale	**28** **Beverley** Cartmel **Catterick Bridge** **Chelmsford City**† **Chester** Ffos Las★ **Haydock Park** *Navan* Punchestown **Salisbury**★
29 Fontwell Park Kelso Punchestown Uttoxeter	**30** **AYR** *Ballinrobe (E)* Cartmel **Lingfield Park** **Redcar** **Windsor**	**31** *Ballinrobe (E)* **Brighton** **Leicester** **Newbury** **Thirsk**★ *Tipperary (E)* **Yarmouth**★				

JUNE

Sun	Mon	Tue	Wed	Thu	Fri	Sat
			1 Cartmel *Curragh (E)* **Kempton Park**★ Newton Abbot **Nottingham** **Ripon**★	**2** **Chelmsford City**†★ Ffos Las **Hamilton Park** **Leicester** *Leopardstown (E)* **Redcar** Uttoxeter	**3** Bath★ Catterick Bridge **Doncaster**★ *Down Royal (E)* **Epsom Downs** **Goodwood**★ Huntingdon Market Rasen *Tramore (E)*	**4** Chepstow★ **Doncaster** **Epsom Downs** Hexham **Lingfield Park**★ *Listowel* **Musselburgh** *Tramore* Worcester
5 **Goodwood** *Kilbeggan* *Listowel* **Musselburgh** Perth	**6** *Curragh (E)* *Gowran Park* **Lingfield Park** *Listowel* **Pontefract**★ Southwell **Windsor**★	**7** **Brighton** **Chelmsford City**†★ **Salisbury** **Wetherby**★	**8** *Cork (E)* Fontwell Park **Hamilton Park** **Haydock Park** **Kempton Park**★ *Wexford* **Yarmouth**	**9** **Haydock Park**★ *Leopardstown (E)* **Newbury** **Nottingham** Uttoxeter★ **Yarmouth**	**10** Aintree★ **Chepstow** *Clonmel (E)* *Fairyhouse (E)* **Goodwood**★ Newton Abbot★ **Sandown Park** **York**	**11** Bath Chester *Downpatrick* Hexham **Leicester**★ *Limerick* **Sandown Park** Worcester★ **York**
12 Doncaster *Downpatrick* *Gowran Park* **Salisbury**	**13** Carlisle *Kilbeggan (E)* **Lingfield Park**† **Nottingham**★ **Windsor**★	**14** Ascot **Beverley** **Brighton**★ *Roscommon (E)* Stratford-On-Avon **Thirsk**	**15** Ascot **Hamilton Park** **Nottingham**★ Ripon★ Uttoxeter *Wexford (E)*	**16** Ascot **Chelmsford City**† Ffos Las★ *Leopardstown (E)* **Lingfield Park**†★ Ripon	**17** Ascot Ayr★ *Down Royal (E)* **Goodwood**★ *Limerick (E)* Market Rasen **Newmarket**★ **Redcar**	**18** Ascot Ayr *Down Royal* **Haydock Park**★ **Lingfield Park**★ **Newmarket** Perth **Redcar**
19 Hexham **Pontefract** Worcester	**20** *Ballinrobe (E)* **Chepstow** Southwell **Windsor**★ **Wolverhampton**†★	**21** **Beverley** **Brighton** **Newbury**★ Newton Abbot★ *Sligo (E)*	**22** Bath★ Carlisle **Kempton Park**†★ *Naas (E)* **Salisbury** Worcester	**23** **Hamilton Park**★ **Leicester**★ **Newcastle**† **Newmarket** **Nottingham**	**24** Cartmel **Chester**★ *Curragh (E)* **Doncaster** **Newcastle**†★ **Newmarket**★ **Yarmouth**	**25** Chester *Curragh* **Doncaster**★ **Lingfield Park**★ **Newcastle**† **Newmarket** **Windsor**
26 Cartmel *Curragh* Uttoxeter **Windsor**	**27** **Musselburgh**★ **Pontefract** Southwell **Windsor**★	**28** **Brighton** **Chepstow**★ **Hamilton Park** *Roscommon (E)* Stratford-On-Avon★	**29** Bath★ **Kempton Park**★ **Musselburgh** **Thirsk** *Tipperary (E)* Worcester	**30** *Bellewstown (E)* **Epsom Downs**★ **Haydock Park** **Newbury**★ Perth *Tipperary (E)* **Yarmouth**		

JULY

Sun	Mon	Tue	Wed	Thu	Fri	Sat
31 Chester *Galway* Market Rasen					**1** *Bellewstown (E)* Beverley★ Doncaster Haydock Park★ *Newton Abbot* Sandown Park	**2** *Bellewstown (E)* Beverley Carlisle★ Haydock Park Leicester *Naas* Nottingham★ Sandown Park
3 *Ayr* Chelmsford City† Market Rasen *Tramore*	**4** Ayr Ffos Las★ Ripon★ Worcester	**5** Brighton★ Pontefract *Roscommon (E)* Uttoxeter★ Wolverhampton† Tattersalls Sale	**6** Bath★ Catterick Bridge *Fairyhouse (E)* Kempton Park★ Lingfield Park Yarmouth Tattersalls Sale	**7** *Bellewstown (E)* Carlisle Doncaster Epsom Downs★ *Leopardstown (E)* *Limerick (E)* Newbury★ Newmarket Tattersalls Sale	**8** Ascot Chepstow★ Chester★ *Cork (E)* *Kilbeggan (E)* Newmarket York Tattersalls Sale	**9** Ascot Chester Hamilton Park★ *Navan* Newmarket Salisbury★ York
10 *Fairyhouse* Perth *Sligo* Stratford-On-Avon	**11** Ayr *Killarney (E)* Newton Abbot Windsor★ Wolverhampton†★	**12** Bath Beverley Chelmsford City†★ *Dundalk* *Killarney (E)* Southwell★	**13** Brighton Catterick Bridge *Downpatrick* *Killarney (E)* Lingfield Park★ Uttoxeter Yarmouth★	**14** Chepstow Epsom Downs★ Hamilton Park *Killarney (E)* Leicester *Leopardstown (E)* Worcester★	**15** Hamilton Park★ Haydock Park *Kilbeggan (E)* *Killarney* Newbury Newmarket★ Nottingham Pontefract★	**16** Cartmel Chester *Curragh* Doncaster★ Haydock Park★ Market Rasen Newbury Newmarket Ripon
17 *Curragh* Newton Abbot Redcar Stratford-On-Avon *Tipperary*	**18** Ayr *Ballinrobe (E)* Beverley★ Cartmel Windsor★	**19** *Ballinrobe (E)* Chelmsford City†★ Musselburgh Southwell Wolverhampton†★	**20** Bath Catterick Bridge Leicester★ *Limerick (E)* Lingfield Park *Naas (E)* Sandown Park★	**21** Doncaster★ *Leopardstown (E)* *Limerick (E)* Newbury★ Sandown Park Worcester Yarmouth	**22** Ascot Chepstow★ *Cork (E)* *Down Royal (E)* Newmarket★ Thirsk Uttoxeter York★	**23** Ascot *Gowran Park* Lingfield Park★ Newcastle† Newmarket Salisbury★ York
24 Chelmsford City† Pontefract Uttoxeter	**25** Ayr Ffos Las★ *Galway (E)* Newton Abbot Windsor★	**26** Beverley *Galway (E)* Goodwood Perth★ Worcester★ Yarmouth	**27** *Galway (E)* Goodwood Leicester★ Perth Redcar Sandown Park★	**28** Epsom Downs★ *Galway* Goodwood Nottingham SALISBURY★ Stratford-On-Avon	**29** Bangor-On-Dee Bath★ *Galway (E)* Goodwood Musselburgh★ Newmarket★ Wolverhampton†	**30** Doncaster *Galway* Goodwood Hamilton Park★ Lingfield Park★ Newmarket Thirsk

AUGUST

Sun	Mon	Tue	Wed	Thu	Fri	Sat
	1 Ayr Carlisle★ *Cork* *Naas* **Ripon** Windsor★	**2** Catterick Bridge Chelmsford City†★ **Ffos Las** Kempton Park†★ *Roscommon (E)*	**3** Brighton Kempton Park†★ Newcastle†‡ Pontefract *Sligo (E)* Yarmouth★	**4** AYR★ Brighton *Leopardstown (E)* Nottingham Sandown Park★ *Sligo (E)* Yarmouth	**5** Brighton Haydock Park★ Musselburgh Newmarket★ Thirsk *Tipperary (E)* *Wexford (E)*	**6** Ascot Ayr★ *Curragh* Haydock Park *Kilbeggan (E)* Lingfield Park★ Newmarket Redcar
7 *Downpatrick* **Haydock Park** Leicester Windsor	**8** *Ballinrobe (E)* *Cork* Kempton Park† *Naas* **Ripon**★ Windsor★ Wolverhampton†	**9** Carlisle★ Chelmsford City†★ Lingfield Park Nottingham	**10** Beverley Ffos Las★ *Gowran Park (E)* Kempton Park†★ Salisbury Yarmouth	**11** Beverley *Leopardstown (E)* Lingfield Park Salisbury *Tramore (E)*	**12** *Cork (E)* Newbury Newmarket★ Nottingham Thirsk★ *Tramore (E)* Wolverhampton†	**13** Bath★ *Curragh* Doncaster Market Rasen★ Newbury Newmarket *Perth* **Ripon** *Tramore (E)*
14 Chelmsford City† Pontefract Southwell† *Tramore*	**15** *Bangor-On-Dee*★ Catterick Bridge *Dundalk* Lingfield Park★ *Roscommon (E)* Windsor★	**16** Chelmsford City†★ Hamilton Park Kempton Park† Wolverhampton†★	**17** Bath Kempton Park†★ Musselburgh *Sligo (E)* Worcester★ York	**18** Chepstow Fontwell Park★ *Killarney (E)* Leicester★ Stratford-on-Avon York	**19** Carlisle *Kilbeggan (E)* *Killarney (E)* Newbury Newcastle†★ Salisbury★ Wolverhampton†★ York	**20** Chelmsford City†★ Chester *Curragh* *Killarney* Lingfield Park†★ *Newton Abbot* Sandown Park York
21 Brighton *Naas* Sandown Park Yarmouth	**22** *Ballinrobe (E)* Brighton Chepstow Southwell†★ Stratford-on-avon★	**23** Bangor-On-Dee *Bellewstown (E)* Fontwell Park★ Worcester	**24** *Bellewstown (E)* Catterick Bridge Kempton Park†★ Lingfield Park Musselburgh	**25** BATH★ Carlisle Chelmsford City† Ffos Las *Navan* Sedgefield★	**26** *Down Royal (E)* Ffos Las Goodwood★ Hamilton Park★ Newmarket Thirsk *Tipperary (E)*	**27** Beverley *Cartmel* *Curragh* Goodwood Newmarket Redcar★ Windsor★
28 Beverley Goodwood Yarmouth	**29** *Cartmel* Chepstow *Downpatrick* **Epsom Downs** **Ripon** *Roscommon (E)* Southwell†	**30** Carlisle★ **Epsom Downs** *Newton Abbot*★ **Ripon**	**31** Bath *Gowran Park* Hamilton Park★ Lingfield Park Wolverhampton† Worcester★			
		Tattersalls Sale	Tattersalls Sale			

SEPTEMBER

Sun	Mon	Tue	Wed	Thu	Fri	Sat
				1 *Clonmel (E)* **Ffos Las**★ **Haydock Park** **Salisbury** *Sedgefield* **Windsor**★ *Tattersalls Sale*	**2** **Ascot** *Down Royal (E)* **Haydock Park** **Kempton Park**† *Kilbeggan (E)* **Newcastle**† *BBAG Sale*	**3** **Ascot** **Haydock Park** **Kempton Park**† *Navan* Stratford-On-Avon **Thirsk** *Wexford* **Wolverhampton**†★
4 *Fontwell Park* **York** *Tattersalls Sale*	**5** **Brighton** *Galway (E)* **Newcastle**†★ *Newton Abbot* *Perth* *Tattersalls Sale*	**6** **Catterick Bridge** *Galway (E)* **Goodwood** *Hexham*★ **Leicester**	**7** **Carlisle** *Cork (E)* **Doncaster** **Kempton Park**†★ *Uttoxeter*	**8** **Chelmsford City**†★ **Chepstow** **Doncaster** **Epsom Downs** *Laytown (E)*	**9** *Ballinrobe (E)* **Chester** *Clonmel (E)* **Doncaster** **Salisbury**★ **Sandown Park**	**10** **Bath** **Chelmsford City**† **Chester** **Doncaster** *Leopardstown* **Lingfield Park** **Musselburgh**★
11 **Bath** *Curragh* **Musselburgh**	**12** **Brighton** **Kempton Park**†★ **Thirsk** *Worcester*	**13** *Punchestown* **Redcar** *Uttoxeter* **Wolverhampton**†★ **Yarmouth**	**14** **Beverley** *Kelso*★ **Sandown Park** *Sligo* **Yarmouth**	**15** **Ayr** **Chelmsford City**†★ *Naas* **Pontefract** **Yarmouth**	**16** **Ayr** *Downpatrick* *Dundalk (E)* **Kempton Park**†★ **Newbury** *Newton Abbot*	**17** **Ayr** **Catterick Bridge** *Gowran Park* *Navan* **Newbury** **Newmarket** **Wolverhampton**†★
18 **Hamilton Park** *Listowel* *Plumpton*	**19** *Fairyhouse (E)* **Hamilton Park** **Leicester** *Listowel* *Warwick* **Wolverhampton**†★	**20** **Beverley** **Lingfield Park**† *Listowel* **Newcastle**†★ *Warwick*	**21** **Goodwood** **Kempton Park**†★ *Listowel* *Perth* **Redcar**	**22** *Listowel* **Newmarket** *Perth* **Pontefract** **Southwell**†★	**23** *Dundalk (E)* **Haydock Park** *Listowel* **Newcastle**†★ **Newmarket** *Worcester*	**24** **Chelmsford City**†★ **Chester** *Curragh* **Haydock Park** *Listowel* Market Rasen **Newmarket** **Ripon**
25 *Curragh* **Epsom Downs** **Ffos Las**	**26** **Bath** *Down Royal (E)* **Hamilton Park** **Newcastle**†★ *Newton Abbot* *Roscommon*	**27** **Ayr** *Cork* *Sedgefield* *Southwell* **Wolverhampton**†★	**28** *Bangor-On-Dee* *Bellewstown* **Catterick Bridge** **Kempton Park**†★ **Nottingham**	**29** *Bellewstown* **Chelmsford City**†★ *Clonmel* **Lingfield Park**† **Salisbury** *Warwick*	**30** **Ascot** *Dundalk (E)* *Fontwell Park* *Gowran Park* *Hexham* **Newcastle**†★	

OCTOBER

Sun	Mon	Tue	Wed	Thu	Fri	Sat
30 Carlisle *Galway* Huntingdon *Wexford*	**31** *Galway* Hereford **Kempton Park†** Plumpton *Wexford* **Wolverhampton†★**					**1** **Ascot** Fontwell Park *Gowran Park* *Killarney* **Newmarket** **Redcar** **Wolverhampton†★**
2 Kelso *Killarney* *Tipperary* Uttoxeter	**3** **Pontefract** Stratford-On-Avon *Tipperary* **Windsor** **Wolverhampton†★**	**4** **Brighton** *Galway* Huntingdon **Leicester** **Southwell†★**	**5** **Kempton Park†★** Ludlow *Navan* **Nottingham** Sedgefield	**6** **Ayr** **Chelmsford City†★** Exeter *Thurles* Worcester	**7** Chepstow *Downpatrick* *Dundalk (E)* **Newcastle†★** **Newmarket** **York**	**8** **Chelmsford City†★** Chepstow *Curragh* *Fairyhouse* Hexham **Newmarket** **York**
		Tattersalls Sale	Tattersalls Sale	Tattersalls Sale		
9 Ffos Las **Goodwood**	**10** *Gowran Park* *Killarney* **Musselburgh** **Windsor** **Wolverhampton†★** **Yarmouth**	**11** Hereford Huntingdon **Leicester** **Newcastle†★** *Punchestown*	**12** **Bath** **Kempton Park†★** **Nottingham** *Punchestown* Wetherby	**13** **Brighton** Carlisle **Chelmsford City†★** *Curragh* *Tramore* Wincanton	**14** *Dundalk (E)* Fakenham **Haydock Park** **Newcastle†★** **Redcar** Uttoxeter	**15** **Ascot** **Catterick Bridge** *Leopardstown* Market Rasen Newton Abbot Stratford-On-Avon **Wolverhampton†★**
	Tattersalls Sale	Tattersalls Sale	Tattersalls Sale	Tattersalls Sale	Tattersalls Sale BBAG Sale	Tattersalls Sale BBAG Sale
16 *Cork* Kempton Park *Naas* Sedgefield	**17** Plumpton **Pontefract** **Windsor** **Wolverhampton†★**	**18** Exeter *Gowran Park* **Kempton Park†★** **Newcastle†** **Yarmouth**	**19** Fontwell Park **Kempton Park†★** *Navan* **Newmarket** Worcester	**20** Carlisle Ludlow **Southwell†** *Thurles* **Wolverhampton†★**	**21** Cheltenham **Doncaster** *Dundalk (E)* **Newbury** **Newcastle†★** *Sligo*	**22** **Chelmsford City†★** Cheltenham **Doncaster** Kelso *Leopardstown* **Newbury**
23 Aintree *Curragh* *Limerick* Wincanton	**24** Ayr **Leicester** **Newcastle†★** **Redcar**	**25** Bangor-On-Dee **Catterick Bridge** Chepstow **Newcastle†★**	**26** *Curragh* Fakenham **Kempton Park†★** **Nottingham** Taunton	**27** **Chelmsford City†★** *Clonmel* **Lingfield Park†** Stratford-On-Avon Worcester	**28** *Dundalk (E)* **Newmarket** **Southwell†★** Uttoxeter Wetherby	**29** Ascot Ayr *Galway* **Newmarket** Wetherby **Wolverhampton†★**
	Tattersalls Sale	Tattersalls Sale	Tattersalls Sale	Tattersalls Sale	Tattersalls Sale	

NOVEMBER

Sun	Mon	Tue	Wed	Thu	Fri	Sat
		1 Newcastle†★ **Redcar** **Southwell†** Warwick	**2** Chepstow *Dundalk* **Kempton Park†★** Musselburgh **Nottingham**	**3** **Chelmsford City†★** Ludlow Newbury Sedgefield *Thurles*	**4** *Down Royal* *Dundalk (E)* Exeter Fontwell Park Hexham **Newcastle†★**	**5** Aintree **Chelmsford City†★** **Doncaster** *Down Royal* Kelso Wincanton
6 Cork Ffos Las *Naas* Sandown Park	**7** Carlisle Kempton Park **Wolverhampton†★**	**8** **Chelmsford City†★** *Fairyhouse* Hereford Huntingdon Lingfield Park	**9** Ayr Bangor-On-Dee *Dundalk* **Kempton Park†★**	**10** **Chelmsford City†★** Market Rasen Sedgefield Taunton	**11** Cheltenham *Dundalk (E)* **Newcastle†** Southwell **Wolverhampton†★**	**12** Cheltenham **Lingfield Park†** *Naas* Uttoxeter Wetherby **Wolverhampton†★**
13 Cheltenham Fontwell Park *Navan*	**14** Exeter Leicester Plumpton **Wolverhampton†★**	**15** *Fairyhouse* Fakenham Hereford Lingfield Park **Newcastle†★**	**16** *Dundalk* Hexham **Kempton Park†★** **Southwell†** Warwick	**17** **Chelmsford City†★** *Clonmel* Market Rasen Newcastle Wincanton	**18** Ascot Catterick Bridge Chepstow *Dundalk (E)* **Kempton Park†★**	**19** Ascot Haydock Park Huntingdon **Lingfield Park†** *Punchestown* **Wolverhampton†★**
20 Cork Exeter *Punchestown* Uttoxeter	**21** Kempton Park Ludlow Musselburgh ... Tattersalls Sale	**22** *Limerick* Sedgefield Southwell	**23** *Dundalk* Hereford Wetherby ... Tattersalls Sale	**24** Kelso Lingfield Park Taunton *Thurles* ... Tattersalls Sale	**25** Doncaster *Dundalk (E)* Ffos Las Newbury ... Tattersalls Sale	**26** Bangor-On-Dee Doncaster *Gowran Park* Newbury Newcastle **Wolverhampton†★** ... Tattersalls Sale
27 Carlisle Leicester *Navan*	**28** Catterick Bridge **Kempton Park†** **Wolverhampton†★** ... Tattersalls Sale	**29** Ayr **Lingfield Park†** *Punchestown* Southwell **Wolverhampton†★** ... Tattersalls Sale	**30** *Dundalk* Haydock Park **Kempton Park†★** **Lingfield Park†** Ludlow ... Tattersalls Sale			

DECEMBER

Sun	Mon	Tue	Wed	Thu	Fri	Sat
				1 **Chelmsford City†★** Leicester Market Rasen *Thurles* Wincanton Tattersalls Sale	**2** *(E)* *Exeter* **Newcastle†★** Sandown Park Sedgefield	**3** Aintree Chepstow *Fairyhouse* Sandown Park Wetherby **Wolverhampton†★**
4 *Fairyhouse* Huntingdon Kelso	**5** Lingfield Park Musselburgh **Wolverhampton†★**	**6** Fontwell Park Wincanton **Southwell†★** *Tramore* Uttoxeter	**7** *Dundalk* Hexham **Kempton Park†★** Leicester **Lingfield Park†**	**8** **Chelmsford City†★** *Clonmel* Newcastle Taunton Warwick	**9** Bangor-On-Dee Cheltenham Doncaster *Dundalk (E)* **Southwell†★**	**10** Cheltenham Doncaster Hereford *Navan* **Newcastle†** **Wolverhampton†**
11 Carlisle *Cork* *Punchestown* Southwell	**12** Market Rasen Plumpton *Thurles* **Wolverhampton†★**	**13** Catterick Bridge Wincanton **Wolverhampton†★**	**14** *Dundalk* **Kempton Park†★** **Lingfield Park†** Newbury	**15** **Chelmsford City†★** Exeter *Ffos Las* *Naas* **Southwell†**	**16** Ascot *Dundalk (E)* **Kempton Park†★** **Southwell†** Uttoxeter	**17** Ascot *Fairyhouse* Haydock Park **Lingfield Park†** Newcastle
18 Fakenham *Navan* *Thurles* **Wolverhampton†**	**19** **Chelmsford City†★** Lingfield Park Musselburgh	**20** Ludlow **Newcastle†★** Plumpton **Southwell†**	**21** *Dundalk (E)* Lingfield Park Taunton **Wolverhampton†★**	**22** Ayr **Lingfield Park†** **Southwell†★**	**23**	**24**
25	**26** *Down Royal* Fontwell Park Huntingdon Kempton Park *Leopardstown* *Limerick* Market Rasen Sedgefield Wetherby Wincanton **Wolverhampton†**	**27** Chepstow Kempton Park *Leopardstown* *Limerick* Wetherby **Wolverhampton†★**	**28** Catterick Bridge Leicester *Leopardstown* *Limerick* **Newcastle†★**	**29** Doncaster Kelso *Leopardstown* *Limerick* **Southwell†★**	**30** Haydock Park Taunton **Wolverhampton†★**	**31** **Lingfield Park†** Newbury *Punchestown* Uttoxeter Warwick

DATES OF PRINCIPAL RACES

(SUBJECT TO ALTERATION)

JANUARY

The Paddy Power Millionaire Handicap Steeple Chase (Grade 3)	CHELTENHAM	Sat 01
The Paddy Power Novices' Steeple Chase (Registered As The Dipper Novices' Steeple Chase) (Grade 2)	CHELTENHAM	Sat 01
The Dornan Engineering Relkeel Hurdle Race (Grade 2)	CHELTENHAM	Sat 01
The Cheltenham Pony Club "Junior" National Hunt Flat Race (Listed Race)	CHELTENHAM	Sat 01
The Ballymore Novices' Hurdle Race (Listed Race)	FAIRYHOUSE	Sat 01
The John Fowler Memorial Mares Chase (Grade 3)	FAIRYHOUSE	Sat 01
The Metal Man Chase (Grade 3)	TRAMORE	Sat 01
The Slaney Novice Hurdle (Grade 1)	NAAS	Sun 02
The Unibet Tolworth Novices' Hurdle Race (Grade 1)	SANDOWN PARK	Sat 08
The Unibet 'You're On' Mares' Hurdle Race (Listed Race)	SANDOWN PARK	Sat 08
The Dan Moore Mem Handicap Chase (Grade A)	FAIRYHOUSE	Sun 09
The Pertemps Network Mares' Steeple Chase (Listed Race)	LEICESTER	Wed 12
The Ladbrokes Silviniaco Conti Chase (Grade 2)	KEMPTON PARK	Sat 15
The Ladbrokes Lanzarote Handicap Hurdle Race (Listed Race)	KEMPTON PARK	Sat 15
The Ballymore Leamington Novices' Hurdle Race (Grade 2)	WARWICK	Sat 15
The Mccoy Contractors Civil Engineering Classic Handicap Steeple Chase (Grade 3)	WARWICK	Sat 15
The Mccoy Contractors Civils And Infrastructure Hampton Novices' Steeple Chase (Grade 2)	WARWICK	Sat 15
The Killiney Novice Chase (Grade 3)	PUNCHESTOWN	Sun 16
The Moscow Flyer Novice Hurdle (Grade 2)	PUNCHESTOWN	Sun 16
The Alan Swinbank Mares' Standard Open National Hunt Flat Race (Listed Race)	MARKET RASEN	Fri 21
The Matchbook Betting Exchange Clarence House Steeple Chase (Grade 1)	ASCOT	Sat 22
The Matchbook Betting Podcast Mares' Hurdle Race (Grade 2) (Registered As The Warfield)	ASCOT	Sat 22
The Matchbook Better Way To Bet Holloway's Handicap Hurdle Race (Grade 3)	ASCOT	Sat 22
The Peter Marsh Handicap Steeple Chase (A Limited Handicap) (Grade 2)	HAYDOCK PARK	Sat 22
The Read Nicky Henderson's Unibet Blog Novices' Steeple Chase (Grade 2) (Registered As The Altcar Novices' Steeple Chase)	HAYDOCK PARK	Sat 22
The Sky Bet Supreme Trial Rossington Main Novices' Hurdle Race (Grade 2)	HAYDOCK PARK	Sat 22
The New One Unibet Hurdle Race (Grade 2) (Registered As The Champion Hurdle Trial Race)	THURLES	Sun 23
The Coolmore EBF Mares Novice Chase (Grade 2)	THURLES	Sun 23
The Kinloch Brae Chase (Grade 2)	GOWRAN PARK	Thu 27
The Galmoy Hurdle (Grade 2)	GOWRAN PARK	Thu 27
The Goffs Thyestes Handicap Chase (Grade A)	GOWRAN PARK	Thu 27
The Sky Bet Fillies' Juvenile Hurdle Race (Listed Race)	DONCASTER	Fri 28
The Pertemps Lady Protectress Mares' Steeple Chase (Listed Race)	HUNTINGDON	Fri 28
The Paddy Power Millionaire Trophy Handicap Steeple Chase (Grade 3)	CHELTENHAM	Sat 29
The Ballymore Novices' Hurdle Race (Registered As The Classic Novices' Hurdle Race) (Grade 2)	CHELTENHAM	Sat 29
The Paddy Power Cleeve Hurdle Race (Grade 2)	CHELTENHAM	Sat 29
Cheltenham' Cotswold Steeple Chase (Grade 2)	CHELTENHAM	Sat 29
The Jcb Triumph Trial Juvenile Hurdle Race (Grade 2) (Registered As The Finesse)	CHELTENHAM	Sat 29
The Sky Bet Handicap Steeple Chase (Listed Race)	DONCASTER	Sat 29
The Irish Thoroughbred Marketing Yorkshire Rose Mares' Hurdle Race (Grade 2)	DONCASTER	Sat 29
The Irish Thoroughbred Marketing Lightning Novices' Steeple Chase (Grade 2)	DONCASTER	Sat 29
The Albert Bartlett River Don Novices' Hurdle Race (Grade 2)	DONCASTER	Sat 29
The Solerina Mares Novice Hurdle (Grade 3)	FAIRYHOUSE	Sat 29
The Limestone Lad Hurdle (Grade 3)	NAAS	Sun 30
The Woodlands Novice Chase (Grade 3)	NAAS	Sun 30

FEBRUARY

The Chanelle Pharma Irish Champion Hurdle (Grade 1)	LEOPARDSTOWN	Sat 05
The Ladbrokes Dublin Chase (Grade 1)	LEOPARDSTOWN	Sat 05
The Arkle Novice Chase (Grade 1)	LEOPARDSTOWN	Sat 05
The Goffs (C and G) INH Flat Race (Grade 2)	LEOPARDSTOWN	Sat 05
The Nathaniel Lacy Golden Cygnet Novice Hurdle (Grade 1)	LEOPARDSTOWN	Sat 05
The Betway Kachy Stakes (Listed Race) (All-Weather Championships Fast-Track Qualifier)	LINGFIELD PARK	Sat 05
The Betway Winter Derby Trial Stakes (Listed Race) (All-Weather Championships Fast-Track Qualifier)	LINGFIELD PARK	Sat 05
The Virgin Bet Heroes Handicap Hurdle Race (Grade 3)	SANDOWN PARK	Sat 05
The Virgin Bet Scilly Isles Novices' Steeple Chase (Grade 1)	SANDOWN PARK	Sat 05
The Virgin Bet Contenders Hurdle Race (Listed Race)	SANDOWN PARK	Sat 05
The William Hill Towton Novices' Steeple Chase (Grade 2)	WETHERBY	Sat 05
The Brave Inca Novice Hurdle (Grade 1)	LEOPARDSTOWN	Sun 06
The Flogas Novice Chase (Grade 1)	LEOPARDSTOWN	Sun 06
The Coolmore Stud NH Sires Deep Run Mares INH Flat Race (Grade 2)	LEOPARDSTOWN	Sun 06
The Tattersalls Ireland Spring 4yo Hurdle (Grade 1)	LEOPARDSTOWN	Sun 06
The Paddy Power Irish Gold Cup (Grade 1)	LEOPARDSTOWN	Sun 06
The Bet365 Scottish Triumph Hurdle (A Juvenile Hurdle Race) (Listed Race)	MUSSELBURGH	Sun 06
The Ballymore Sidney Banks Memorial Novices' Hurdle Race (Listed Race)	HUNTINGDON	Thu 10
The Opera Hat Mares Chase (Listed Race)	NAAS	Sat 12
The Betfair Hurdle Race (Handicap) (Grade 3)	NEWBURY	Sat 12

The Betfair Denman Steeple Chase (Grade 2) .... NEWBURY .... Sat 12
The Cheltenham Free Bet Pot Builder Steeple Chase (Grade 2) (Registered As The Game Spirit Steeple Chase) ...... NEWBURY .... Sat 12
The Read Tony Calvin's Tips On Betting.Betfair (Listed Race) .... NEWBURY .... Sat 12
The Agetur UK Kingmaker Novices' Steeple Chase (Grade 2) .... WARWICK .... Sat 12
The Close Brothers Warwick Mares' Hurdle Race (Listed Race) .... WARWICK .... Sat 12
The Bet At Racingtv.com Novices' Hurdle Race (Listed Race) .... EXETER .... Sun 13
The Join Racing TV Now Mares' Steeple Chase (Listed Race) .... EXETER .... Sun 13
The EBF Novice Hurdle (Listed Race) .... PUNCHESTOWN .... Sun 13
The Grand National Trial Handicap Chase (Grade B) .... PUNCHESTOWN .... Sun 13
The Surehaul Mercedes-Benz Powerstown Novice Hurdle (Grade 3) .... CLONMEL .... Thu 17
The Jane Seymour Mares' Novices' Hurdle Race (Grade 2) .... SANDOWN PARK .... Thu 17
The 'My Oddsboost' On Betfair Swinley Chase (A Limited Handicap) (Listed Race) ...... ASCOT .... Sat 19
The Ascot Steeple Chase (Grade 1) .... ASCOT .... Sat 19
The Bateaux London Reynoldstown Novices' Steeple Chase (Grade 2) .... ASCOT .... Sat 19
The Red Mills Chase (Grade 2) .... GOWRAN PARK .... Sat 19
The Red Mills Trial Hurdle (Grade 3) .... GOWRAN PARK .... Sat 19
The Albert Bartlett Prestige Novices' Hurdle Race (Grade 2) .... HAYDOCK PARK .... Sat 19
The William Hill Grand National Trial Handicap Steeple Chase (Grade 3) .... HAYDOCK PARK .... Sat 19
The William Hill Rendlesham Hurdle Race (Grade 2) .... HAYDOCK PARK .... Sat 19
The Betway Kingwell Hurdle Race (Grade 2) .... WINCANTON .... Sat 19
The Boyne Hurdle (Grade 2) .... NAVAN .... Sun 20
The Ten Up Novice Chase (Grade 2) .... NAVAN .... Sun 20
The Quevega Mares Hurdle .... PUNCHESTOWN .... Wed 23
The Michael Purcell Novice Hurdle (Grade 3) .... THURLES .... Thu 24
The Bobbyjo Chase (Grade 3) .... FAIRYHOUSE .... Sat 26
The Winning Fair Juvenile Hurdle (Grade 3) .... FAIRYHOUSE .... Sat 26
The Sky Bet Dovecote Novices' Hurdle Race (Grade 2) .... KEMPTON PARK .... Sat 26
The Close Brothers Pendil Novices' Steeple Chase (Grade 2) .... KEMPTON PARK .... Sat 26
The Close Brothers Handicap Steeple Chase (Grade 3) .... KEMPTON PARK .... Sat 26
The Close Brothers Adonis Juvenile Hurdle Race (Grade 2) .... KEMPTON PARK .... Sat 26
The Betway Winter Derby Stakes (Group 3) (All-Weather Championships Fast-Track Qualifier) ...... LINGFIELD PARK .... Sat 26
The Betway Hever Sprint Stakes (Listed Race) .... LINGFIELD PARK .... Sat 26
The Loch Lomond Whiskies National Spirit Hurdle Race (Grade 2) .... FONTWELL PARK .... Sun 27
The Paddy Power Johnstown Novice Hurdle (Grade 2) .... NAAS .... Sun 27
The Paddy Power Newlands Chase (Grade 3) .... NAAS .... Sun 27

MARCH

The Patton Stakes (Listed Race) .... DUNDALK .... Fri 04
The Virgin Bet Mares' Novices' Hurdle Race (Listed Race) .... DONCASTER .... Sat 05
The Bet365 Premier Steeple Chase (Listed Race) .... KELSO .... Sat 05
The Bet365 Premier Novices' Hurdle Race (Grade 2) .... KELSO .... Sat 05
The Get Your Ladbrokes Daily Odds Boost Spring Cup Stakes (Listed Race) (All-Weather Championships Fast-Track Qualifier) ...... LINGFIELD PARK .... Sat 05
The Flyingbolt Novice Chase (Grade 3) .... NAVAN .... Sat 05
The Betvictor Greatwood Gold Cup Handicap Steeple Chase (Grade 3) .... NEWBURY .... Sat 05
The TRI Equestrian Carrickmines Handicap Chase (Grade B) .... LEOPARDSTOWN .... Sun 06
The Shamrock Handicap Chase (Grade B) .... GOWRAN PARK .... Sat 12
The An Uaimh Chase (Grade 2) .... NAVAN .... Sat 12
The EBF Novice Final Handicap Chase (Grade B) .... NAVAN .... Sat 12
The Paddy Power Imperial Cup Handicap Hurdle Race (Grade 3) .... SANDOWN PARK .... Sat 12
The Paddy's Rewards Club Novices' Handicap Steeple Chase (Listed Race) .... SANDOWN PARK .... Sat 12
The European Breeders' Fund Paddy Power 'National Hunt' Novices' Handicap Hurdle Race Final (Grade 3) ...... SANDOWN PARK .... Sat 12
The British Stallion Studs EBF Mares' Standard Open National Hunt Flat Race (Listed Race) ...... SANDOWN PARK .... Sat 12
The Bombardier Lady Wulfruna Stakes (Listed Race) (All-Weather Championships Fast-Track Qualifier) ...... WOLVERHAMPTON .... Sat 12
The Shannon Spray EBF Mares Novice Hurdle (Grade 3) .... LIMERICK .... Sun 13
The Directors Plate Novice Chase (Grade 3) .... NAAS .... Sun 13
The Kingsfurze Novice Hurdle (Grade 3) .... NAAS .... Sun 13
The Leinster National (Grade A) .... NAAS .... Sun 13
The Unibet Champion Hurdle Challenge Trophy (Grade 1) .... CHELTENHAM .... Tue 15
The Close Brothers Mares' Hurdle Race (Registered As The David Nicholson Mares' Hurdle) (Grade 1) ...... CHELTENHAM .... Tue 15
The Sky Bet Supreme Novices' Hurdle Race (Grade 1) .... CHELTENHAM .... Tue 15
The Sporting Life Arkle Challenge Trophy Novices' Steeple Chase (Grade 1) .... CHELTENHAM .... Tue 15
The Sam Vestey National Hunt Challenge Cup Novices' Steeple Chase (Grade 2) ...... CHELTENHAM .... Tue 15
The Ultima Handicap Steeple Chase (Grade 3) .... CHELTENHAM .... Tue 15
The Boodles Juvenile Handicap Hurdle Race (Registered As The Fred Winter) (Grade 3) ...... CHELTENHAM .... Tue 15
The Johnny Henderson Grand Annual Challenge Cup Handicap Steeple Chase (Grade 3) ...... CHELTENHAM .... Wed 16
The Coral Cup Handicap Hurdle Race (Grade 3) .... CHELTENHAM .... Wed 16
The Brown Advisory Novices' Steeple Chase (Grade 1) (Registered As The Broadway Novices' Chase) ...... CHELTENHAM .... Wed 16
The Betway Queen Mother Champion Steeple Chase (Grade 1) .... CHELTENHAM .... Wed 16
The Ballymore Novices' Hurdle Race (Grade 1) (Registered As The Baring Bingham) ...... CHELTENHAM .... Wed 16
The Weatherbys Champion Bumper (Grade 1) .... CHELTENHAM .... Wed 16
The Marsh Novices' Steeple Chase (Grade 1) (Registered As The Golden Miller) ...... CHELTENHAM .... Thu 17
The Paddy Power Stayers' Hurdle Race (Grade 1) .... CHELTENHAM .... Thu 17
The Parnell Properties Mares' Novices' Hurdle Race (Grade 2) (Registered As The Dawn Run Mares' Novices' Hurdle) ...... CHELTENHAM .... Thu 17
The Pertemps Network Final Handicap Hurdle Race (Grade 3) .... CHELTENHAM .... Thu 17

The Ryanair Steeple Chase (Registered As The Festival Trophy) (Grade 1) ....CHELTENHAM ....Thu 17
The Paddy Power Plate Handicap Steeple Chase (Grade 3) ....CHELTENHAM ....Thu 17
The Mrs Paddy Power Mares' Steeple Chase (Registered As The Liberthine Mares' Steeple Chase) (Grade 2) ...CHELTENHAM ....Fri 18
The Mccoy Contractors County Handicap Hurdle Race (Grade 3) ....CHELTENHAM ....Fri 18
The Albert Bartletts Novices' Hurdle Race (Grade 1) (Registered As The Spa Novices' Hurdle Race) ....CHELTENHAM ....Fri 18
The Cheltenham Gold Cup Steeple Chase (Grade 1) ....CHELTENHAM ....Fri 18
The JCB Triumph Hurdle Race (Grade 1) ....CHELTENHAM ....Fri 18
The Native Upmanship Novice Chase (Grade 3) ....THURLES ....Sat 19
The Marston's 61 Deep Midlands Grand National (Listed Race) ....UTTOXETER ....Sat 19
The Paddy Power Irish Lincolnshire ....CURRAGH ....Sat 26
The Unibet Cammidge Trophy Stakes (Listed Race) ....DONCASTER ....Sat 26
The Unibet Doncaster Mile Stakes (Listed Race) ....DONCASTER ....Sat 26
The Ladbrokes Magnolia Stakes (Listed Race) ....KEMPTON PARK ....Sat 26
The Hugh McMahon Mem Novice Chase (Grade 3) ....LIMERICK ....Sun 27
The Kevin McManus Bumper (Listed Race) ....LIMERICK ....Sun 27
The EBF Park Express Stakes (Group 3) ....NAAS ....Sun 27
The Devoy Stakes Stakes (Listed Race)..NAAS ....Sun 27

APRIL

The Jordan Electrics Ltd Future Champion Novices' Steeple Chase (Grade 2) ....AYR ....Sat 02
The Coral Scottish Grand National Handicap Steeple Chase (Grade 3) ....AYR ....Sat 02
The Coral Scottish Champion Hurdle Race (A Limited Handicap) (Grade 2) ....AYR ....Sat 02
The Scotty Brand Handicap Steeple Chase (Listed Race) ....AYR ....Sat 02
The Ballysax Stakes Stakes (Group 3) ....LEOPARDSTOWN ....Sat 02
The Leopardstown 1,000 Guineas Trial Stakes (Group 3) ....LEOPARDSTOWN ....Sat 02
The Leopardstown 2,000 Guineas Trial Stakes (Listed Race)..LEOPARDSTOWN ....Sat 02
The Easter Festival Novice Hurdle (Grade 2) ....FAIRYHOUSE ....Sun 03
The Hardy Eustace Novice Hurdle (Grade 2) ....FAIRYHOUSE ....Sun 03
The Total Enjoyment Mares Bumper (Listed Race) ....FAIRYHOUSE ....Sun 03
The Maid Of Money Mares Chase (Listed Race) ....FAIRYHOUSE ....Sun 03
The Heritage Stakes (Listed Race) ....LEOPARDSTOWN ....Wed 06
The Mansionbet Barry Hills Further Flight Stakes (Listed Race) ....NOTTINGHAM ....Wed 06
The Close Brothers Red Rum Handicap Steeple Chase (Grade 3) ....AINTREE ....Thu 07
The Doom Bar Anniversary 4-Y-O Juvenile Hurdle Race (Grade 1) ....AINTREE ....Thu 07
The Goffs UK Nickel Coin Mares' Standard Open National Hunt Flat Race (Grade 2) ....AINTREE ....Thu 07
The Betway Bowl Steeple Chase (Grade 1) ....AINTREE ....Thu 07
The SSS Super Alloys Manifesto Novices' Steeple Chase (Grade 1) ....AINTREE ....Thu 07
The Aintree Hurdle Race (Grade 1) ....AINTREE ....Thu 07
The Betway Top Novices' Hurdle Race (Grade 1) ....AINTREE ....Fri 08
The Marsh Steeple Chase (Registered As The Melling Steeple Chase) (Grade 1) ....AINTREE ....Fri 08
The Randox Topham Handicap Steeple Chase (Grade 3) ....AINTREE ....Fri 08
The Doom Bar Sefton Novices' Hurdle Race (Grade 1) ....AINTREE ....Fri 08
The Betway Mildmay Novices' Steeple Chase (Grade 1) ....AINTREE ....Fri 08
The Pertemps Network Handicap Hurdle Race (Grade 3) ....AINTREE ....Fri 08
The Betway Mersey Novices' Hurdle Race (Grade 1) ....AINTREE ....Sat 09
The Betway Handicap Steeple Chase (Grade 3) ....AINTREE ....Sat 09
The Randox Grand National Handicap Steeple Chase (Grade 3) ....AINTREE ....Sat 09
The Ryanair Stayers Hurdle Race (Registered As The Liverpool Hurdle Race) (Grade 1) ....AINTREE ....Sat 09
The Weatherbys Nhstallions.co.uk Standard Open National Hunt Flat Race (Grade 2) ....AINTREE ....Sat 09
The Doom Bar Maghull Novices' Steeple Chase (Grade 1) ....AINTREE ....Sat 09
The EFT Systems Handicap Hurdle Race (Grade 3) ....AINTREE ....Sat 09
The Alleged Stakes (Group 3) ....CURRAGH ....Sun 10
The Gladness Stakes (Group 3) ....CURRAGH ....Sun 10
The Hillhouse Quarry Handicap Steeple Chase (Listed Race) ....AYR ....Tue 12
The Bet365 European Free Handicap Stakes (Listed Race) ....NEWMARKET ....Tue 12
The Bet365 Earl Of Sefton Stakes (Group 3) ....NEWMARKET ....Tue 12
The Lanwades Stud Nell Gwyn Stakes (Group 3) ....NEWMARKET ....Tue 12
The Ballymore Silver Trophy Handicap Steeple Chase (Grade 2) (A Limited Handicap) ....CHELTENHAM ....Wed 13
The Bet365 Craven Stakes (Group 3) ....NEWMARKET ....Wed 13
The Bet365 Abernant Stakes (Group 3) ....NEWMARKET ....Wed 13
The Whitsbury Manor Stud/British EBF Lansdown Stakes (Listed Race) ....BATH ....Thu 14
The Citipost Mares' Handicap Hurdle Race (Listed Race) ....CHELTENHAM ....Thu 14
The British EBF Mares' Novices' Handicap Steeple Chase Final (Listed Race) ....CHELTENHAM ....Thu 14
The Irish Thoroughbred Marketing Mares' Novices' Hurdle Race (Listed Race) ....CHELTENHAM ....Thu 14
The NAF Fillies' Juvenile Handicap Hurdle Race (Grade 3) ....CHELTENHAM ....Thu 14
The Bet365 Feilden Stakes (Listed Race) ....NEWMARKET ....Thu 14
The Ladbrokes All-Weather Fillies' And Mares' Championships Conditions Stakes ....LINGFIELD PARK ....Fri 15
The Ladbrokes 3 Year Old All-Weather Championships Apprentice Handicap Stakes ....LINGFIELD PARK ....Fri 15
The Bombardier All-Weather Championships Apprentice Handicap Stakes ....LINGFIELD PARK ....Fri 15
The Betway All-Weather Sprint Championships Conditions Stakes ....LINGFIELD PARK ....Fri 15
The Betway Easter Classic All-Weather Middle Distance Championships Conditions Stakes ....LINGFIELD PARK ....Fri 15
The Bombardier All-Weather Mile Championships Conditions Stakes ....LINGFIELD PARK ....Fri 15
The Betway All-Weather Marathon Championships Conditions Stakes ....LINGFIELD PARK ....Fri 15
The Ladbrokes Burradon Stakes (Listed Race) ....NEWCASTLE ....Fri 15

The Cork Sprint Stakes (Listed Race)..CORK...............................Sat 16
The Noblesse Stakes Stakes (Listed Race)...CORK...............................Sat 16
The RYBO Glascarn Handicap Hurdle (Grade A)..FAIRYHOUSE....................Sat 16
The Imperial Call Chase (Grade 3)..CORK...............................Sun 17
The EBF Mares Novice Hurdle Final (Grade 1)..FAIRYHOUSE....................Sun 17
The Gold Cup Novice Chase (Grade 1)..FAIRYHOUSE....................Sun 17
The Boylesports Irish Grand National (Grade A)..FAIRYHOUSE....................Mon 18
The Ballybin Hurdle (Grade 2)..FAIRYHOUSE....................Mon 18
The Percy Maynard 4yo Hurdle (Grade 2)..FAIRYHOUSE....................Mon 18
The Devenish Fairyhouse Chase (Grade 2)...FAIRYHOUSE....................Mon 18
The William Hill Fair Maid Of Perth Mares' Steeple Chase (Listed Race)........................PERTH.............................Fri 22
The Bet365 Gordon Richards Stakes (Group 3)..SANDOWN PARK..............Fri 22
The Bet365 Mile (Group 2)...SANDOWN PARK..............Fri 22
The Bet365 Classic Trial (Group 3)...SANDOWN PARK..............Fri 22
The Elusive Bloodstock EBF Stallions King Richard III Stakes (Listed Race)..................LEICESTER......................Sat 23
The Committed Stakes (Listed Race)..NAVAN............................Sat 23
The Salsabil Stakes (Listed Race)..NAVAN............................Sat 23
The Vintage Crop Stakes (Group 3)..NAVAN............................Sat 23
The Bet365 Oaksey Steeple Chase (Grade 2) (For The Menorah Challenge Trophy)......SANDOWN PARK..............Sat 23
The Bet365 Select Hurdle Race (Grade 2)..SANDOWN PARK..............Sat 23
The Bet365 Celebration Steeple Chase (Grade 1)...SANDOWN PARK..............Sat 23
The Bet365 Gold Cup Handicap Steeple Chase (Grade 3)...SANDOWN PARK..............Sat 23
The Woodlands Sprint Stakes (Listed Race)..NAAS..............................Mon 25
The British EBF Supporting Racing To School Nottinghamshire Oaks Stakes (Listed Race)..NOTTINGHAM...................Tue 26
The Champion Chase (Grade 1)..PUNCHESTOWN................Tue 26
The Champion Novice Hurdle (Grade 1)...PUNCHESTOWN................Tue 26
The Ellier Novice Chase (Grade 1)..PUNCHESTOWN................Tue 26
The Kilashee Handicap Hurdle (Grade B)...PUNCHESTOWN................Tue 26
The QIPCO British Champions Series Horseracinghof.com Pavilion Stakes (A Commonwealth Cup Trial) (Group 3)..ASCOT............................Wed 27
The Longines Sagaro Stakes (Group 3) (A Gold Cup Trial)..ASCOT............................Wed 27
The Charlie Waller Trust Paradise Stakes (A Queen Anne Stakes Trial) (Listed Race)......ASCOT............................Wed 27
The Champion Bumper (Grade 1)..PUNCHESTOWN................Wed 27
The Punchestown Gold Cup (Grade 1)..PUNCHESTOWN................Wed 27
The Guinness Handicap Chase (Grade A)...PUNCHESTOWN................Wed 27
The Irish Daily Mirror War of Attrition Novice Hurdle (Grade 1)......................................PUNCHESTOWN................Wed 27
The Liss A Paoraigh Mares Bumper (Grade 3)..PUNCHESTOWN................Wed 27
The Chelmer Fillies' Stakes (Listed Race)..CHELMSFORD CITY..........Thu 28
The Ladbrokes World Series Hurdle (Grade 1)..PUNCHESTOWN................Thu 28
The Shawiya Mares Novice Hurdle (Listed Race)..PUNCHESTOWN................Thu 28
The Ryanair Novice Chase (Grade 1)..PUNCHESTOWN................Thu 28
The Black Hills Handicap Steeplechase (Grade B)...PUNCHESTOWN................Thu 28
The British Stallion Studs EBF Daisy Warwick Fillies' Stakes (Listed Race)...................GOODWOOD.....................Fri 29
The Betfair Newmarket Stakes (Listed Race)..NEWMARKET....................Fri 29
The Betfair Exchange Jockey Club Stakes (Group 2)...NEWMARKET....................Fri 29
The Glencarraig Lady Mares Handicap Chase (Grade 2)..PUNCHESTOWN................Fri 29
The Punchestown Champion Hurdle (Grade 1)..PUNCHESTOWN................Fri 29
The Punchestown Novice Handicap Chase (Grade A)...PUNCHESTOWN................Fri 29
The Tickell Champion Novice Hurdle (Grade 1)..PUNCHESTOWN................Fri 29
The Mansionbet Best Odds Guaranteed Conqueror Fillies' Stakes (Listed Race)............GOODWOOD.....................Sat 30
The QIPCO 2000 Guineas Stakes (Group 1) (British Champions Series)........................NEWMARKET....................Sat 30
The Betfair Palace House Stakes (Group 3)..NEWMARKET....................Sat 30
The Champion 4yo Hurdle (Grade 1)...PUNCHESTOWN................Sat 30
The EBF Mares Champion Hurdle (Grade 1)..PUNCHESTOWN................Sat 30

MAY

The Betfair Pretty Polly Stakes (Listed Race)...NEWMARKET....................Sun 01
The QIPCO 1000 Guineas Stakes (Group 1) (British Champions Series).........................NEWMARKET....................Sun 01
The Betfair Dahlia Stakes (Group 2)..NEWMARKET....................Sun 01
The Coolmore Athasi Stakes (Group 3)..CURRAGH.........................Mon 02
The Coolmore Mooresbridge Stakes (Group 2)..CURRAGH.........................Mon 02
The Coolmore Tetrarch Stakes (Listed Race)...CURRAGH.........................Mon 02
The First Flier Stakes Stakes (Listed Race)...CURRAGH.........................Mon 02
The Weatherbys ePassport Cheshire Oaks (For The Robert Sangster Memorial Cup)....CHESTER.........................Wed 04
The Chester Vase Stakes (Group 3)..CHESTER.........................Wed 04
The Victor McCalmont Stakes (Listed Race)..GOWRAN PARK.................Wed 04
The Vintage Tipple Stakes (Listed Race)...GOWRAN PARK.................Wed 04
The Tote+ Biggest Dividends At Tote.co.uk Dee Stakes (Listed Race)...........................CHESTER.........................Thu 05
The Tote+ Pays You More At Tote.co.uk Ormonde Stakes (Group 3)..............................CHESTER.........................Thu 05
The Melodi Media Huxley Stakes (Group 2)...CHESTER.........................Thu 05
The Polonia Stakes (Listed Race)...CORK...............................Fri 06
The Tote+ Pays More At Tote.co.uk Buckhounds Stakes (Listed Race)..........................ASCOT............................Sat 07
The Pertemps Network Spring Trophy Stakes (Listed Race)..HAYDOCK PARK...............Sat 07
The Pertemps Network Swinton Handicap Hurdle Race (Grade 3).................................HAYDOCK PARK...............Sat 07

The Novibet Derby Trial Stakes (Listed Race) .... LINGFIELD PARK .... Sat 07
The Novibet Chartwell Fillies' Stakes (Group 3) .... LINGFIELD PARK .... Sat 07
The Novibet Oaks Trial Fillies' Stakes (Listed Race) .... LINGFIELD PARK .... Sat 07
The Blue Wind Stakes (Group 3) .... NAAS .... Sat 07
The British Stallion Studs EBF Kilvington Stakes (Listed Race) .... NOTTINGHAM .... Sat 07
The Amethyst Stakes (Group 3) .... LEOPARDSTOWN .... Sun 08
The Leopardstown 1,000 Guineas Trial Stakes (Group 3) .... LEOPARDSTOWN .... Sun 08
The Leopardstown Derby Trial Stakes (Group 3) .... LEOPARDSTOWN .... Sun 08
The Racing Welfare Royal Windsor Stakes (Listed Race) .... WINDSOR .... Mon 09
The Tattersalls Musidora Stakes (Group 3) .... YORK .... Wed 11
The Duke Of York Clipper Logistics Stakes (Group 2) .... YORK .... Wed 11
The British Stallion Studs EBF Westow Stakes (Listed Race) .... YORK .... Thu 12
The Al Basti Equiworld Dubai Dante Stakes (Group 2) .... YORK .... Thu 12
The Al Basti Equiworld Dubai Middleton Fillies' Stakes (Group 2) .... YORK .... Thu 12
The Savel Beg Stakes (Listed Race) .... LEOPARDSTOWN .... Fri 13
The Matchbook Yorkshire Cup Stakes (Group 2) (British Champions Series) ...... YORK .... Fri 13
The Oaks Farm Stables Fillies' Stakes (Registered As The Michael Seely Memorial Fillies' Stakes) (Listed Race) .... YORK .... Fri 13
The Langleys Solicitors British EBF Marygate Fillies' Stakes (Listed Race) .... YORK .... Fri 13
The Yeats Stakes (Listed Race) .... NAVAN .... Sat 14
The Betvictor Carnarvon Stakes (Listed Race) .... NEWBURY .... Sat 14
The Haras De Bouquetot Fillies' Trial Stakes (Listed Race) .... NEWBURY .... Sat 14
The Al Rayyan Stakes (Registered As The Aston Park Stakes) (Group 3) .... NEWBURY .... Sat 14
The Al Shaqab Lockinge Stakes (Group 1) (British Champions Series) .... NEWBURY .... Sat 14
The Betway King Charles II Stakes (Listed Race) .... NEWMARKET .... Sat 14
The Betway Fairway Stakes (Listed Race) .... NEWMARKET .... Sat 14
The Tourist Attraction Mares Hurdle (Listed Race) .... KILLARNEY .... Sun 15
The Coolmore Stud Juvenile Fillies Stakes (Group 3) .... NAAS .... Sun 15
The Lacken Stakes (Group 3) .... NAAS .... Sun 15
The Whitehead Memorial Stakes (Listed Race) .... NAAS .... Sun 15
The Sole Power Stakes (Listed Race) .... NAAS .... Sun 15
The An Riocht Chase (Grade 3) .... KILLARNEY .... Mon 16
The Weatherbys ePassport Stakes (Registered As The Leisure Stakes) (Listed Race) ... WINDSOR .... Mon 16
The British Stallion Studs EBF Rothesay Stakes (Listed Race) .... AYR .... Wed 18
The Casumo Best Odds Guaranteed Heron Stakes (Listed Race) .... SANDOWN PARK .... Thu 19
The British Stallion Studs EBF Cocked Hat Stakes (Listed Race) .... GOODWOOD .... Fri 20
The Height Of Fashion Stakes (Listed Race) .... GOODWOOD .... Fri 20
The EBF British Stallion Studs Cecil Frail (Listed Race) .... HAYDOCK PARK .... Fri 20
The Lanwades Stud Stakes Stakes (Group 3) .... CURRAGH .... Sat 21
The GAIN Marble Hill Stakes (Group 3) .... CURRAGH .... Sat 21
The Tattersalls Irish 2,000 Guineas Stakes (Group 1) .... CURRAGH .... Sat 21
The Weatherbys Greenlands Stakes Stakes (Group 2) .... CURRAGH .... Sat 21
The Mansionbet Beaten By A Head Festival Stakes (Listed Race) .... GOODWOOD .... Sat 21
The Mansionbet Best Odds Guaranteed Tapster Stakes (Listed Race) .... GOODWOOD .... Sat 21
The Casumo Bet10Get10 Sandy Lane Stakes (Group 2) .... HAYDOCK PARK .... Sat 21
The Casumo Best Odds Guaranteed Temple Stakes (Group 2) .... HAYDOCK PARK .... Sat 21
The William Hill Bronte Cup Fillies' Stakes (Group 3) .... YORK .... Sat 21
The Tattersalls Irish 1,000 Guineas Stakes (Group 1) .... CURRAGH .... Sun 22
The Heider Family Stables Gallinule Stakes (Group 3) .... CURRAGH .... Sun 22
The Tattersalls Gold Cup Stakes (Group 1) .... CURRAGH .... Sun 22
The Coral Henry II Stakes (Group 3) .... SANDOWN PARK .... Thu 26
The Coral 'Beaten By A Length' National Stakes (Listed Race) .... SANDOWN PARK .... Thu 26
The Coral Brigadier Gerard Stakes (In Memory Of Joe Mercer) (Group 3) .... SANDOWN PARK .... Thu 26
The Betway Pinnacle Stakes (Group 3) .... HAYDOCK PARK .... Sat 28
The Betway John Of Gaunt Stakes (Group 3) .... HAYDOCK PARK .... Sat 28
The Betway Achilles Stakes (Listed Race) .... HAYDOCK PARK .... Sat 28
The Mayo Grand National (Grade B) .... BALLINROBE .... Tue 31

JUNE

The Ballyogan Stakes Stakes (Group 3) .... CURRAGH .... Wed 01
The Sky Bet Orby Stakes (Listed Race) .... CURRAGH .... Wed 01
The Glencairn Stakes (Listed Race) .... LEOPARDSTOWN .... Thu 02
The Nijinsky (for King George V Cup) Stakes (Listed Race) .... LEOPARDSTOWN .... Thu 02
The Cazoo Oaks (Group 1) (British Champions Series) .... EPSOM DOWNS .... Fri 03
The Coral Coronation Cup (Group 1) (British Champions Series) .... EPSOM DOWNS .... Fri 03
The Play Coral 'Racing-Super-Series' For Free Surrey Stakes (Listed Race) ...... EPSOM DOWNS .... Fri 03
The Princess Elizabeth Stakes (Sponsored By Cazoo) (Group 3) .... EPSOM DOWNS .... Sat 04
The Derby (Group 1) .... EPSOM DOWNS .... Sat 04
The Cazoo Diomed Stakes (Group 3) .... EPSOM DOWNS .... Sat 04
The Every Race Live On Racingtv Maggie Dickson Stakes (Listed Race) .... MUSSELBURGH .... Sat 04
The Midsummer Sprint Stakes (Listed Race) .... CORK .... Wed 08
The Munster Oaks Stakes (Group 3) .... CORK .... Wed 08
The Ballycorus Stakes Stakes (Group 3) .... LEOPARDSTOWN .... Thu 09
The Betfair British EBF Stakes (Registered As The Abingdon Stakes) (Listed Race) (Formerly The Ballymacoll Stakes) .... NEWBURY .... Thu 09

The Sky Bet Ganton Stakes (Listed Race) .... YORK .... Fri 10
The Coral "Beaten By A Length" Free Bet Scurry Stakes (Listed Race) .... SANDOWN PARK .... Sat 11
The Sky Bet Race To The Ebor Grand Cup Stakes (Listed Race) .... YORK .... Sat 11
The British Stallion Studs EBF Cathedral Stakes (Listed Race) .... SALISBURY .... Sun 12
The Coventry Stakes (Group 2) .... ASCOT .... Tue 14
The Queen Anne Stakes (Group 1) (British Champions Series) .... ASCOT .... Tue 14
The Wolferton Stakes (Listed Race) .... ASCOT .... Tue 14
The King's Stand Stakes (Group 1) (British Champions Series) .... ASCOT .... Tue 14
The St James's Palace Stakes (Group 1) (British Champions Series) .... ASCOT .... Tue 14
The Duke Of Cambridge Stakes (Group 2) .... ASCOT .... Wed 15
The Queen Mary Stakes (Group 2) .... ASCOT .... Wed 15
The Queen's Vase (Group 2) .... ASCOT .... Wed 15
The Windsor Castle Stakes (Listed Race) .... ASCOT .... Wed 15
The Prince Of Wales's Stakes (Group 1) (British Champions Series) .... ASCOT .... Wed 15
The Gold Cup (Group 1) (British Champions Series) .... ASCOT .... Thu 16
The Hampton Court Stakes (Group 3) .... ASCOT .... Thu 16
The Ribblesdale Stakes (Group 2) .... ASCOT .... Thu 16
The Norfolk Stakes (Group 2) .... ASCOT .... Thu 16
The Commonwealth Cup (Group 1) (British Champions Series) .... ASCOT .... Fri 17
The Albany Stakes (Group 3) .... ASCOT .... Fri 17
The Coronation Stakes (Group 1) (British Champions Series) .... ASCOT .... Fri 17
The King Edward Vii Stakes (Group 2) .... ASCOT .... Fri 17
The Martin Molony Stakes (Listed Race) .... LIMERICK .... Fri 17
The Diamond Jubilee Stakes (Group 1) (British Champions Series) .... ASCOT .... Sat 18
The Chesham Stakes (Listed Race) .... ASCOT .... Sat 18
The Jersey Stakes (Group 3) .... ASCOT .... Sat 18
The Hardwicke Stakes (Group 2) .... ASCOT .... Sat 18
The Irish Stallion Farms EBF Land O'Burns Fillies' Stakes (Listed Race) .... AYR .... Sat 18
The Sky Bet Pontefract Castle Fillies' Stakes (Listed Race) .... PONTEFRACT .... Sun 19
The British Stallion Studs EBF Eternal Stakes (Listed Race) .... CARLISLE .... Wed 22
The Naas Oaks Trial Stakes (Listed Race) .... NAAS .... Wed 22
The William Hill Hoppings Fillies' Stakes (Group 3) .... NEWCASTLE .... Fri 24
The Dubai Duty Free Belgrave Stakes (Listed Race) .... CURRAGH .... Sat 25
The Dubai Duty Free Celebration Stakes (Listed Race) .... CURRAGH .... Sat 25
The Dubai Duty Free Irish Derby Stakes (Group 1) .... CURRAGH .... Sat 25
The GAIN Railway Stakes (Group 2) .... CURRAGH .... Sat 25
The William Hill Chipchase Stakes (Group 3) .... NEWCASTLE .... Sat 25
The Close Brothers Criterion Stakes (Group 3) .... NEWMARKET .... Sat 25
The Close Brothers Fred Archer Stakes (Listed Race) .... NEWMARKET .... Sat 25
The Maureen Brittain Memorial Empress Fillies' Stakes (Listed Race) .... NEWMARKET .... Sat 25
The Fitzdares Midsummer Stakes (Listed Race) .... WINDSOR .... Sat 25
The Comer International Curragh Cup Stakes (Group 2) .... CURRAGH .... Sun 26
The Airlie Stud Balanchine Stakes (Group 2) .... CURRAGH .... Sun 26
The ARM Holding International Stakes (Group 3) .... CURRAGH .... Sun 26
The Alwasmiyah Pretty Polly Stakes (Group 1) .... CURRAGH .... Sun 26
The Bet365 Summer Cup (An Open Handicap Steeple Chase) (Listed Race) .... UTTOXETER .... Sun 26
The Lenebane Stakes (Listed Race) .... ROSCOMMON .... Tue 28
The Tipperary Stakes (Listed Race) .... TIPPERARY .... Wed 29
The Grimes Hurdle (Grade 3) .... TIPPERARY .... Thu 30

JULY

The Davies Insurance Services Gala Stakes (Listed Race) .... SANDOWN PARK .... Fri 01
The Coral Marathon (Listed Race) (Registered As The Esher Stakes) .... SANDOWN PARK .... Fri 01
The Coral Dragon Stakes (Listed Race) .... SANDOWN PARK .... Fri 01
The Bet365 Lancashire Oaks (Group 2) .... HAYDOCK PARK .... Sat 02
The Coral Charge (Group 3) (Registered As The Sprint Stakes) .... SANDOWN PARK .... Sat 02
The Coral Distaff (Listed Race) .... SANDOWN PARK .... Sat 02
The Coral-Eclipse (Group 1) (British Champions Series) .... SANDOWN PARK .... Sat 02
The Totepool Queen Charlotte Fillies' Stakes (Listed Race) .... CHELMSFORD CITY ..... Sun 03
The Weatherbys Bloodstock Pro Pipalong Stakes (Listed Race) .... PONTEFRACT .... Tue 05
The Princess Of Wales's Tattersalls Stakes (Group 2) .... NEWMARKET .... Thu 07
The Tattersalls July Stakes (Group 2) .... NEWMARKET .... Thu 07
The Bahrain Trophy Stakes (Group 3) .... NEWMARKET .... Thu 07
The Edmondson Hall Solicitors Sir Henry Cecil Stakes (Listed Race) .... NEWMARKET .... Thu 07
The Midlands Grand National (Grade B) .... KILBEGGAN .... Fri 08
The Tattersalls Falmouth Stakes (Group 1) (British Champions Series) .... NEWMARKET .... Fri 08
The Duchess Of Cambridge Stakes (Sponsored By Bet365) (Group 2) .... NEWMARKET .... Fri 08
The William Hill Summer Stakes (Group 3) .... YORK .... Fri 08
The Betfred Summer Mile Stakes (Group 2) .... ASCOT .... Sat 09
The Homeserve Back On Track City Plate Stakes (Listed Race) .... CHESTER .... Sat 09
The Bet365 Superlative Stakes (Group 2) .... NEWMARKET .... Sat 09
The Darley July Cup Stakes (Group 1) (British Champions Series) .... NEWMARKET .... Sat 09
The John Smith's City Walls Stakes (Listed Race) .... YORK .... Sat 09
The John Smith's Silver Cup Stakes (Group 3) .... YORK .... Sat 09

The Brownstown Stakes Stakes (Group 3) .... FAIRYHOUSE .... Sun 10
The Cairn Rouge Stakes (Listed Race) .... KILLARNEY .... Wed 13
The Green Room Meld Stakes Stakes (Group 3) .... LEOPARDSTOWN .... Thu 14
The British Stallions Studs EBF Glasgow Stakes (Listed Race) .... HAMILTON PARK .... Fri 15
The Bourn Vincent Memorial Handicap S'chase (Grade B) .... KILLARNEY .... Fri 15
The Ire Incentive, It Pays To Buy Irish Rose Bowl Stakes (Listed Race) .... NEWBURY .... Fri 15
The Juddmonte Irish Oaks Stakes (Group 1) .... CURRAGH .... Sat 16
The Jebel Ali Anglesey Stakes Stakes (Group 3) .... CURRAGH .... Sat 16
The Romanised Minstrel Stakes Stakes (Group 3) .... CURRAGH .... Sat 16
The Betway Summer Plate Handicap Steeple Chase (Grade 3) .... MARKET RASEN .... Sat 16
The Bet365 Stakes (Registered As The Steventon Stakes) (Listed Race) .... NEWBURY .... Sat 16
The Weatherbys Super Sprint Stakes .... NEWBURY .... Sat 16
The Bet365 Hackwood Stakes (Group 3) .... NEWBURY .... Sat 16
The Ric And Mary Hambro Aphrodite Fillies' Stakes (Listed Race) .... NEWMARKET .... Sat 16
The Kilboy Estate Stakes (Group 2) .... CURRAGH .... Sun 17
The Sapphire Stakes Stakes (Group 2) .... CURRAGH .... Sun 17
The Sweet Mimosa Stakes (Listed Race) .... NAAS .... Wed 20
The Marwell Stakes (Listed Race) .... NAAS .... Wed 20
The Silver Flash Stakes Stakes (Group 3) .... LEOPARDSTOWN .... Thu 21
The JRA Tyros Stakes Stakes (Group 3) .... LEOPARDSTOWN .... Thu 21
The British Stallion Studs EBF Star Stakes (Listed Race) .... SANDOWN PARK .... Thu 21
The Her Majesty's Plate Stakes (Listed Race) .... DOWN ROYAL .... Fri 22
The British Stallion Studs EBF Lyric Fillies' Stakes (Listed Race) .... YORK .... Fri 22
The King George Vi And Queen Elizabeth QIPCO Stakes (Group 1) (British Champions Series) ... ASCOT .... Sat 23
The British Racecourses Join Sunflower Lanyard Scheme Valiant Stakes (Group 3) .... ASCOT .... Sat 23
The Pat Eddery Stakes (Listed Race) (Formerly The Winkfield Stakes) .... ASCOT .... Sat 23
The Princess Margaret Keeneland Stakes (Group 3) .... YORK .... Sat 23
The Sky Bet York Stakes (Group 2) .... YORK .... Sat 23
The Sky Bet Go-Racing-In-Yorkshire Summer Festival Pomfret Stakes (Listed Race) ..... PONTEFRACT .... Sun 24
The Castlegar Novice Hurdle (Listed Race) .... GALWAY .... Tue 26
The Unibet Lennox Stakes (Group 2) .... GOODWOOD .... Tue 26
The Unibet Vintage Stakes (Group 2) .... GOODWOOD .... Tue 26
The Al Shaqab Goodwood Cup Stakes (Group 1) (British Champions Series) .... GALWAY .... Wed 27
The Tote Galway Plate (Handicap Chase) (Grade A) .... GOODWOOD .... Wed 27
The Qatar Sussex Stakes (Group 1) (British Champions Series) .... GOODWOOD .... Wed 27
The Markel Molecomb Stakes (Group 3) .... GOODWOOD .... Wed 27
The Whispering Angel Oak Tree Stakes (Group 3) .... GOODWOOD .... Wed 27
The Corrib EBF Fillies Stakes (Listed Race) .... GALWAY .... Thu 28
The Ballybrit Novice Chase (Grade 3) .... GALWAY .... Thu 28
The Guinness Galway Hurdle (Handicap) (Grade A) .... GALWAY .... Thu 28
The Unibet Richmond Stakes (Group 2) .... GOODWOOD .... Thu 28
The John Pearce Racing Gordon Stakes (Group 3) .... GOODWOOD .... Thu 28
The Qatar Nassau Stakes (Group 1) (British Champions Series) .... GOODWOOD .... Fri 29
The King George Qatar Stakes (Group 2) .... GOODWOOD .... Fri 29
The L'Ormarins Queen's Plate Glorious Stakes (Group 3) .... GOODWOOD .... Fri 29
The Bonhams Thoroughbred Stakes (Group 3) .... GALWAY .... Sat 30
The Mervue Handicap Hurdle (Grade B) .... GOODWOOD .... Sat 30
The Qatar Lillie Langtry Stakes (Group 2) .... NEWMARKET .... Sat 30
The British Stallion Studs EBF Chalice Stakes (Listed Race) .... CHESTER .... Sun 31
The Children's Air Ambulance Queensferry Stakes (Listed) ....

AUGUST

The Irish EBF Ballyhane Stud Median Sires Stakes .... NAAS .... Mon 01
The Grant Thornton Ballyroan Stakes Stakes (Group 3) .... LEOPARDSTOWN .... Thu 04
The El Gran Senor Stakes (Listed Race) .... TIPPERARY .... Fri 05
The Keeneland Phoenix Stakes (Group 1) .... CURRAGH .... Sat 06
The Rathasker Stud Phoenix Sprint Stakes (Group 3) .... CURRAGH .... Sat 06
The British Stallion Studs EBF Dick Hern Stakes (Listed Race) .... HAYDOCK PARK .... Sat 06
The Mansionbet Rose Of Lancaster Stakes (Group 3) .... HAYDOCK PARK .... Sat 06
The 100% RacingTV Profits Back To Racing Sweet Solera Stakes (Group 3) .... NEWMARKET .... Sat 06
The Hurry Harriet Stakes (Listed Race) .... GOWRAN PARK .... Wed 10
The British Stallion Studs EBF Upavon Fillies' Stakes (Listed Race) .... SALISBURY .... Wed 10
The Invesco Desmond Stakes Stakes (Group 3) .... LEOPARDSTOWN .... Thu 11
The Vinnie Roe Stakes (Listed Race) .... LEOPARDSTOWN .... Thu 11
The D & N Construction Sovereign Stakes (Group 3) .... SALISBURY .... Thu 11
The Platinum Stakes (Listed Race) .... CORK .... Fri 12
The Betvictor St Hugh's Stakes (Listed Race) .... NEWBURY .... Fri 12
The Fitzdares Royal Whip Stakes (Group 3) .... CURRAGH .... Sat 13
The Betvictor Hungerford Stakes (Group 2) .... NEWBURY .... Sat 13
The Betvictor Geoffrey Freer Stakes (Group 3) .... NEWBURY .... Sat 13
The Denford Stakes (Listed Race) (Formerly The Washington Singer Stakes) .... NEWBURY .... Sat 13
The EBF Stallions Highfield Farm Flying Fillies' Stakes (Listed Race) .... PONTEFRACT .... Sun 14
The Sky Bet Great Voltigeur Stakes (Group 2) .... YORK .... Wed 17
The Tattersalls Acomb Stakes (Group 3) .... YORK .... Wed 17

The Juddmonte International Stakes (British Champions Series) (Group 1) .... YORK .... Wed 17
The Ruby Stakes (Listed Race) .... KILLARNEY .... Thu 18
The Sky Bet Lowther Stakes (Group 2) .... YORK .... Thu 18
The Darley Yorkshire Oaks (Group 1) (British Champions Series) .... YORK .... Thu 18
The British EBF & Sir Henry Cecil Galtres Stakes (Listed Race) .... YORK .... Thu 18
The Mount Brandon Handicap Hurdle (Grade B) .... KILLARNEY .... Fri 19
The Longines Irish Champions Weekend EBF Stonehenge Stakes (Listed Race) .... SALISBURY .... Fri 19
The Coolmore Wootton Bassett Nunthorpe Stakes (Group 1) (British Champions Series) .... YORK .... Fri 19
The Al Basti Equiworld Dubai Gimcrack Stakes (Group 2) .... YORK .... Fri 19
The Weatherbys Hamilton Lonsdale Cup Stakes (Group 2) (British Champions Series) .... YORK .... Fri 19
The Stella Artois Chester Stakes (Listed Race) .... CHESTER .... Sat 20
The Alpha Centauri Debutante Stakes (Group 2) .... CURRAGH .... Sat 20
The Galileo Futurity Stakes (Group 2) .... CURRAGH .... Sat 20
The Lough Leane Handicap Chase (Grade B) .... KILLARNEY .... Sat 20
The Betway Atalanta Stakes (Group 3) .... SANDOWN PARK .... Sat 20
The Betway Solario Stakes (Group 3) .... SANDOWN PARK .... Sat 20
The Julia Graves Roses Stakes (Listed Race) .... YORK .... Sat 20
The Sky Bet City Of York Stakes (Group 2) .... YORK .... Sat 20
The Sky Bet And Symphony Group Strensall Stakes (Group 3) .... YORK .... Sat 20
The Abergwaun Stakes (Listed Race) .... TIPPERARY .... Fri 26
The Fairy Bridge Stakes (Group 3) .... TIPPERARY .... Fri 26
The William Hill Beverley Bullet Sprint Stakes (Listed Race) .... BEVERLEY .... Sat 27
The Flame Of Tara Stakes (Group 3) .... CURRAGH .... Sat 27
The Heider Family Stables Round Tower Stakes (Group 3) .... CURRAGH .... Sat 27
The Snow Fairy Stakes (Group 3) .... CURRAGH .... Sat 27
The Tote Celebration Mile (Group 2) .... GOODWOOD .... Sat 27
The Tote Prestige Stakes (Group 3) .... GOODWOOD .... Sat 27
The Tote March Stakes (Group 3) (In Memory Of John Dunlop) .... GOODWOOD .... Sat 27
The Close Brothers Hopeful Stakes (Listed Race) .... NEWMARKET .... Sat 27
The Sytner Bmw Sunningdale & Maidenhead August Stakes (Listed Race) .... WINDSOR .... Sat 27
The Sytner Bmw Sunningdale & Maidenhead Winter Hill Stakes (Group 3) .... WINDSOR .... Sat 27
The Weatherbys Hamilton Supreme Stakes (Group 3) .... GOODWOOD .... Sun 28
The British Stallion Studs EBF Ripon Champion Two Yrs Old Trophy Stakes (Listed Race) .... RIPON .... Mon 29

SEPTEMBER

The Ire Incentive Scheme Dick Poole Fillies' Stakes (Group 3) .... SALISBURY .... Thu 01
The Betfair Double Daily Rewards Superior Mile Stakes (Group 3) .... HAYDOCK PARK .... Sat 03
The Betfair Exchange Ascendant Stakes (Listed Race) .... HAYDOCK PARK .... Sat 03
The Betfair Sprint Cup Stakes (Group 1) (British Champions Series) .... HAYDOCK PARK .... Sat 03
The Unibet September Stakes (Group 3) .... KEMPTON PARK .... Sat 03
The Unibet 3 Uniboosts A Day Sirenia Stakes (Group 3) .... KEMPTON PARK .... Sat 03
The Biowavego Garrowby Stakes (Listed Race) .... YORK .... Sun 04
The Oyster Stakes Stakes (Listed Race) .... GALWAY .... Tue 06
The Japan Racing Association Sceptre Fillies' Stakes (Group 3) .... DONCASTER .... Wed 07
The Cazoo Scarbrough Stakes (Listed Race) .... DONCASTER .... Wed 07
The Cazoo May Hill Stakes (Group 2) .... DONCASTER .... Thu 08
The Park Hill Fillies' Stakes (Group 2) .... DONCASTER .... Thu 08
The Wainwright Flying Childers Stakes (Group 2) .... DONCASTER .... Fri 09
The Cazoo Flying Scotsman Stakes (Group 3) .... DONCASTER .... Fri 09
The Doncaster Cup Stakes (Group 2) (British Champions Series) .... DONCASTER .... Fri 09
The Tote+ Stand Cup Stakes (Listed Race) .... CHESTER .... Sat 10
The Champagne Stakes (Group 2) .... DONCASTER .... Sat 10
The Cazoo St Leger Stakes (Group 1) (British Champions Series) .... DONCASTER .... Sat 10
The Cazoo Park Stakes (Group 2) .... DONCASTER .... Sat 10
The Ingabelle Stakes Stakes (Listed Race) .... LEOPARDSTOWN .... Sat 10
The Irish Stallion Stakes (Group 1) .... LEOPARDSTOWN .... Sat 10
The Clipper Logistics Solonoway Stakes Stakes (Group 2) .... LEOPARDSTOWN .... Sat 10
The Coolmore Matron Stakes (Group 1) .... LEOPARDSTOWN .... Sat 10
The KPMG Golden Fleece Stakes (Group 2) .... LEOPARDSTOWN .... Sat 10
The Comer Group International St Leger Stakes (Group 1) .... CURRAGH .... Sun 11
The Derrinstown Stud Flying Five Stakes (Group 1) .... CURRAGH .... Sun 11
The Goffs Vincent O'Brien National Stakes (Group 1) .... CURRAGH .... Sun 11
The Moyglare Stud Blandford Stakes (Group 2) .... CURRAGH .... Sun 11
The Moyglare Stud Stakes (Group 1) .... CURRAGH .... Sun 11
The Chasemore Farm Fortune Stakes (Listed Race) .... SANDOWN PARK .... Wed 14
The EBF Stallions John Musker Fillies' Stakes (Listed Race) .... YARMOUTH .... Wed 14
The British EBF Stallions Rosebery Stakes (Listed Race) .... AYR .... Fri 16
The Arran Scottish Sprint EBF Fillies' Stakes (Listed Race) .... AYR .... Fri 16
The Dubai Duty Free Cup Stakes (Listed Race) .... NEWBURY .... Fri 16
The Ayrshire Agricultural Challenge Cup) .... AYR .... Sat 17
The Virgin Bet Doonside Cup Stakes (Listed Race) .... AYR .... Sat 17
The Cordell Lavarack Stakes Stakes (Group 3) .... GOWRAN PARK .... Sat 17
The Dubai Duty Free Mill Reef Stakes (Group 2) .... NEWBURY .... Sat 17
The Dubai Duty Free Legacy Cup Stakes (Group 3) (Formerly The Arc Trial) .... NEWBURY .... Sat 17

The Dubai International Airport World Trophy Stakes (Group 3) .... NEWBURY .... Sat 17
The Ballyhane Blenheim Stakes (Listed Race).. FAIRYHOUSE .... Mon 19
The Listowel Stakes Stakes (Listed Race) .... LISTOWEL .... Mon 19
The Latrigue 4yo Handicap Hurdle (Grade B) .... LISTOWEL .... Tue 20
The Tote Foundation Stakes (Listed Race) .... GOODWOOD .... Wed 21
The Guinness Kerry National (Handicap Chase) (Grade A).. LISTOWEL .... Wed 21
The Ladbrokes Handicap Hurdle (Grade B).. LISTOWEL .... Thu 22
The Tattersalls Stakes (Registered As The Somerville Tattersalls Stakes) (Group 3) .... NEWMARKET .... Thu 22
The Jockey Club Rose Bowl Stakes (Listed Race) .... NEWMARKET .... Thu 22
The Diamond Stakes Stakes (Group 3) .... DUNDALK .... Fri 23
The Rockfel Stakes (Group 2) .... NEWMARKET .... Fri 23
The Princess Royal Stakes (Group 3) .... NEWMARKET .... Fri 23
The Joel Stakes (Group 2) .... NEWMARKET .... Fri 23
The British EBF Rosemary Stakes (Listed Race) .... NEWMARKET .... Fri 23
The Godolphin Stakes (Listed Race) .... NEWMARKET .... Fri 23
The Juddmonte Cheveley Park Stakes (Group 1) .... NEWMARKET .... Sat 24
The Juddmonte Royal Lodge Stakes (Group 2) .... NEWMARKET .... Sat 24
The Juddmonte Middle Park Stakes (Group 1) .... NEWMARKET .... Sat 24
The Smurfit Beresford Stakes Stakes (Group 2) .... CURRAGH .... Sun 25
The Weld Park Stakes (Group 3) .... CURRAGH .... Sun 25
The Raa Atoll Loughbrown Stakes (Group 3) .... CURRAGH .... Sun 25
The Renaissance Stakes Stakes (Group 3) .... CURRAGH .... Sun 25
The Kilbegnet Novice Chase (Grade 3) .... ROSCOMMON .... Mon 26
The Navigation Stakes (Listed Race).. CORK .... Tue 27
The Ascot Noel Murless Stakes (Listed Race) .... ASCOT .... Fri 30
The Star Appeal Stakes (Listed Race) .... DUNDALK .... Fri 30
The Legacy Stakes (Listed Race) .... DUNDALK .... Fri 30
The Mucklemeg Mares Bumper (Listed Race).. GOWRAN PARK .... Fri 30

OCTOBER

The Oakman Group Rous Stakes (Listed Race) .... ASCOT .... Sat 01
The John Guest Racing Bengough Stakes (Group 3) .... ASCOT .... Sat 01
The John Guest Racing British EBF Stakes (Registered As The October Stakes) (Listed Race) .. ASCOT .... Sat 01
The Cumberland Lodge Stakes (Group 3) .... ASCOT .... Sat 01
The Gowran Champion Chase (Grade 2) .... GOWRAN PARK .... Sat 01
The Kingdom Of Bahrain Sun Chariot Stakes (Group 1) (British Champions Series) .... NEWMARKET .... Sat 01
The William Hill Two Year Old Trophy (Listed Race) .... REDCAR .... Sat 01
The Racing TV EBF Stallions Guisborough Stakes (Listed Race) .... REDCAR .... Sat 01
The Concorde Stakes Stakes (Group 3) .... TIPPERARY .... Sun 02
The Joe Mac Novice Hurdle (Grade 3) .... TIPPERARY .... Sun 02
The Like A Butterfly Novice Chase (Grade 3).. TIPPERARY .... Sun 02
The Tipperary Hurdle (Grade 2).. TIPPERARY .... Sun 02
The Unibet Persian War Novices' Hurdle Race (Grade 2) .... CHEPSTOW .... Fri 07
The Newmarket Academy Godolphin Beacon Project Cornwallis Stakes (Group 3) .... NEWMARKET .... Fri 07
The Newmarket Pony Academy Pride Stakes (Group 3) .... NEWMARKET .... Fri 07
The Bet365 Fillies' Mile (Group 1) .... NEWMARKET .... Fri 07
The Godolphin Stud & Stable Staff Awards Challenge Stakes (Group 2) .... NEWMARKET .... Fri 07
The Godolphin Lifetime Care Oh So Sharp Stakes (Group 3) .... NEWMARKET .... Fri 07
The Dunraven Windows Novices' Steeple Chase (Listed Race) (For The Robert Mottram Memorial Trophy) .. CHEPSTOW .... Sat 08
The Wasdell Group Silver Trophy Handicap Hurdle Race (Grade 3) .... CHEPSTOW .... Sat 08
The Waterford Testimonial Stakes (Listed Race) .... CURRAGH .... Sat 08
The Darley Stakes (Group 3) .... NEWMARKET .... Sat 08
The Dubai British EBF Boadicea Stakes (Listed Race) .... NEWMARKET .... Sat 08
The Emirates Autumn Stakes (Group 3) .... NEWMARKET .... Sat 08
The Godolphin Flying Start Zetland Stakes (Group 3) .... NEWMARKET .... Sat 08
The Darley Dewhurst Stakes (Group 1) .... NEWMARKET .... Sat 08
The Coral.co.uk Rockingham Stakes (Listed Race) .... YORK .... Sat 08
The British Stallion Studs EBF Beckford Stakes (Listed Race) .... BATH .... Wed 12
The Buck House Novice Chase (Grade 3).. PUNCHESTOWN .... Wed 12
The Carvills Hill Chase (Grade 3).. PUNCHESTOWN .... Wed 12
The Mercury Stakes (Group 3) .... DUNDALK .... Fri 14
The Queen Elizabeth II Stakes (Sponsored By QIPCO) (Group 1) (British Champions Mile) .. ASCOT .... Sat 15
The QIPCO British Champions Sprint Stakes (Group 1) (British Champions Series) .... ASCOT .... Sat 15
The QIPCO Champion Stakes (British Champions Middle Distance) (Group 1) .... ASCOT .... Sat 15
The QIPCO British Champions Long Distance Cup (Group 2) (British Champions Series) ...... ASCOT .... Sat 15
The QIPCO British Champions Fillies & Mares Stakes (Group 1) (British Champions Series) .. ASCOT .... Sat 15
The Killavullan Stakes Stakes (Group 3).. LEOPARDSTOWN .... Sat 15
The Trigo Stakes (Listed Race) .... LEOPARDSTOWN .... Sat 15
The Racing TV Novices' Hurdle Race (Listed Race) .... KEMPTON PARK .... Sun 16
The Racing TV Hurdle Race (Listed Race) .... KEMPTON PARK .... Sun 16
The Bluebell Stakes (Listed Race) .... NAAS .... Sun 16
The Garnet Stakes (Listed Race) .... NAAS .... Sun 16
The British Stallion Studs EBF Silver Tankard Stakes (Listed Race) .... PONTEFRACT .... Mon 17
The Vertem Futurity Trophy Stakes (Group 1) .... DONCASTER .... Sat 22

The Virgin Bet Doncaster Stakes (Listed Race)	DONCASTER	Sat 22
The Eyrefield Stakes (Group 3)	LEOPARDSTOWN	Sat 22
The Knockaire Stakes (Listed Race)	LEOPARDSTOWN	Sat 22
The Virgin Bet Horris Hill Stakes (Registered As The Horris Hill Stakes) (Group 3)	NEWBURY	Sat 22
The Virgin Bet St Simon Stakes (Registered As The St Simon Stakes) (Group 3)	NEWBURY	Sat 22
The Galloping To Give 10 Years With A Transplant Stakes (Registered As The Radley Stakes) (Listed Race)	NEWBURY	Sat 22
The Monet's Garden Old Roan Limited Handicap Steeple Chase (Grade 2)	AINTREE	Sun 23
The Ladbrokes Munster National Handicap Chase (Grade A)	LIMERICK	Sun 23
The Cailain Alainn Mares Hurdle (Listed Race)	LIMERICK	Sun 23
The Ladbrokes EBF River Eden Fillies' Stakes (Listed Race)	LINGFIELD PARK	Thu 27
The Ladbrokes EBF Fleur De Lys Fillies' Stakes (Listed Race) (All Weather Championships Fast-Track Qualifier)	LINGFIELD PARK	Thu 27
The Cooley Stakes (Listed Race)	DUNDALK	Fri 28
The Irish Stallion Farms EBF 'Bosra Sham' Fillies' Stakes (Listed Race)	NEWMARKET	Fri 28
The Cash Out At Bet365 Handicap Steeple Chase (Listed Race)	WETHERBY	Fri 28
The Weatherbys Hamilton Wensleydale Juvenile Hurdle Race (Listed Race)	WETHERBY	Fri 28
The Sodexo Handicap Hurdle Race (Listed Race)	ASCOT	Sat 29
The Sodexo Gold Cup Handicap Steeple Chase (Grade 3)	ASCOT	Sat 29
The Byrne Group Handicap Steeple Chase (Listed Race) (L.H.O-150)	ASCOT	Sat 29
The Price Bailey Ben Marshall Stakes (Listed Race)	NEWMARKET	Sat 29
The British Stallion Studs EBF Montrose Fillies' Stakes (Listed Race)	NEWMARKET	Sat 29
The Weatherbys James Seymour Stakes (Listed Race)	NEWMARKET	Sat 29
The Bet365 Mares' Hurdle Race (Listed Race)	WETHERBY	Sat 29
The Bet365 Hurdle Race (Grade 2) (Registered As The West Yorkshire Hurdle)	WETHERBY	Sat 29
The Bet365 Charlie Hall Steeple Chase (Grade 2)	WETHERBY	Sat 29
The Colin Parker Memorial Intermediate Steeple Chase (Listed Race)	CARLISLE	Sun 30
The Bettyville Steeplechase (Listed Race)	WEXFORD	Sun 30
The Unibet 3 Uniboosts A Day Floodlit Stakes (Listed Race)	KEMPTON PARK	Mon 31

NOVEMBER

The Hamptons EBF Mares Novice Hurdle (Grade 3)	DOWN ROYAL	Fri 04
The WKD Hurdle (Grade 2)	DOWN ROYAL	Fri 04
The Haldon Gold Cup (A Limited Handicap Steeple Chase) (Grade 2)	EXETER	Fri 04
The British EBF Gillies Fillies' Stakes (Listed Race)	DONCASTER	Sat 05
The Virgin Bet Wentworth Stakes (Listed Race)	DONCASTER	Sat 05
The Kauto Star Chase (Grade 1)	DOWN ROYAL	Sat 05
The Skymas Chase (Grade 2)	DOWN ROYAL	Sat 05
The 'Rising Stars' Novices' Steeple Chase (Grade 2)	WINCANTON	Sat 05
The 60th Badger Beer Handicap Steeple Chase (Listed Race)	WINCANTON	Sat 05
The Unibet Elite Hurdle Race (Grade 2)	WINCANTON	Sat 05
The Paddy Power Cork Grand National Handicap Chase (Grade B)	CORK	Sun 06
The Paddy Power EBF Novice Chase (Grade 3)	CORK	Sun 06
The Paddy Power EBF Novice Hurdle (Listed Race)	CORK	Sun 06
The Finale Stakes (Listed Race)	NAAS	Sun 06
The Future Stars Intermediate Chase (Listed Race)	SANDOWN PARK	Sun 06
The Bangor On Dee Racecourse Mares' Novices' Steeple Chase (Listed Race)	BANGOR-ON-DEE	Wed 09
The Bud Booth Mares' Steeple Chase (Listed Race)	MARKET RASEN	Thu 10
The Ballymore Novices' Hurdle Race (Grade 2) (Registered As The Hyde Novices' Hurdle)	CHELTENHAM	Fri 11
The Paddy Power Gold Cup Handicap Steeple Chase (Grade 3)	CHELTENHAM	Sat 12
The Jcb Triumph Trial Juvenile Hurdle Race (Registered As The Prestbury Juvenile Hurdle Race) (Grade 2)	CHELTENHAM	Sat 12
The From The Horse's Mouth Podcast Novices' Steeple Chase (Grade 2) (Registered As The November)	CHELTENHAM	Sat 12
The Paddy Power Games Handicap Hurdle Race (Listed Race)	CHELTENHAM	Sat 12
The Karndean Designflooring Mares' Open National Hunt Flat Race (Listed Race)	CHELTENHAM	Sat 12
The Betway Churchill Stakes (Listed Race) (All Weather Championships Fast-Track Qualifier)	LINGFIELD PARK	Sat 12
The Betway Golden Rose Stakes (Listed Race) (All Weather Championships Fast-Track Qualifier)	LINGFIELD PARK	Sat 12
The Fishery Lane 4yo Hurdle (Grade 3)	NAAS	Sat 12
The Poplar Square Chase (Grade 3)	NAAS	Sat 12
The Shloer Chase (Registered as The Cheltenham Steeple Chase) (Grade 2)	CHELTENHAM	Sun 13
The High Sheriff Of Gloucestershire Open National Hunt Flat Race) (Listed Race)	CHELTENHAM	Sun 13
The Sky Bet Supreme Trial Novices' Hurdle Race (Registered As The Sharp Novices' Hurdle) (Grade 2)	CHELTENHAM	Sun 13
The Unibet Greatwood Handicap Hurdle Race (Grade 3)	CHELTENHAM	Sun 13
The Winchcombe Handicap Steeple Chase (Grade 3)	CHELTENHAM	Sun 13
The For Auction Novice Hurdle (Grade 3)	NAVAN	Sun 13
The Fortria Chase (Grade 2)	NAVAN	Sun 13
The Lismullen Hurdle (Grade 2)	NAVAN	Sun 13
The Clonmel Oil Chase (Grade 2)	CLONMEL	Thu 17
The EBF TA Morris Mem Mares Chase (Listed Race)	CLONMEL	Thu 17
The Chanelle Pharma 1965 Steeple Chase (Grade 2)	ASCOT	Sat 19
The Coral Hurdle (Registed as The Ascot Hurdle Race) (Grade 2)	ASCOT	Sat 19
The Betfair Weighed In Podcast Newton Novices' Hurdle Race (Listed Race)	HAYDOCK PARK	Sat 19
The Betfair Steeple Chase (Grade 1) (Registered As The Lancashire Steeple Chase)	HAYDOCK PARK	Sat 19
The Betfair Exchange Stayers' Handicap Hurdle Race (Grade 3)	HAYDOCK PARK	Sat 19
The Morgiana Hurdle (Grade 1)	PUNCHESTOWN	Sat 19
The Craddockstown Novice Chase (Grade 2)	PUNCHESTOWN	Sat 19
The Florida Pearl Novice Chase (Grade 2)	PUNCHESTOWN	Sun 20

The Grabel Mares Hurdle (Listed Race)..PUNCHESTOWN.................Sun 20
The Racing TV Mares' Hurdle Race (Listed Race) ....KEMPTON PARK................Mon 21
The Thurles Chase (Listed Race) ....THURLES..........................Thu 24
The Ladbrokes Committed To Safer Gambling Novices' Steeple Chase (Grade 2) (Registered As The Berkshire) NEWBURY.........................Fri 25
The Ladbrokes Long Distance Hurdle Race (Grade 2) ....NEWBURY.........................Fri 25
The Ladbrokes Committed To Safer Gambling Intermediate Hurdle (Listed Race) (A Limited Handicap) (Registered As The Gerry Fielden Hurdle).... NEWBURY.........................Sat 26
The Play Ladbrokes 5-A-Side On Football Mares' Novices' Hurdle Race (Listed Race) ......NEWBURY.........................Sat 26
The Ladbrokes John Francome Novices' Steeple Chase (Grade 2) ....NEWBURY.........................Sat 26
The Ladbrokes Trophy Steeple Chase (Handicap) (Grade 3) ....NEWBURY.........................Sat 26
The Betfair Fighting Fifth Hurdle Race (Grade 1) ....NEWCASTLE.....................Sat 26
The Betfair Exchange Rehearsal Handicap Steeple Chase (Listed Race) ....NEWCASTLE.....................Sat 26
The Houghton Mares' Steeple Chase (Listed Race) ....CARLISLE.........................Sun 27
The Aries Girl Mares Bumper (Listed Race) ....NAVAN............................Sun 27
The Ladbrokes Troytown Handicap Chase (Grade B) ....NAVAN............................Sun 27
The Monksfield Novice Hurdle (Grade 3) ....NAVAN............................Sun 27
The British Stallion Studs EBF Hyde Stakes (Listed Race) (All Weather Championships Fast-Track Qualifier) ......KEMPTON PARK................Mon 28
The Unibet Wild Flower Stakes (Listed Race) ....KEMPTON PARK................Wed 30

DECEMBER

The Ballymore Winter Novices' Hurdle Race (Grade 2) ....SANDOWN PARK...............Fri 02
The William Hill Becher Handicap Steeple Chase (Grade 3) ....AINTREE..........................Sat 03
The William Hill Many Clouds Steeple Chase (Grade 2) ....AINTREE..........................Sat 03
The Williamhill.Com Best Odds Guaranteed Fillies' Juvenile Hurdle Race (Listed Race) ......AINTREE..........................Sat 03
The Ballyhack Handicap Chase (Grade B) ....FAIRYHOUSE....................Sat 03
The Planteur At Chapel Stud Henry VII Novices' Steeple Chase (Grade 1) ....SANDOWN PARK...............Sat 03
The Betfair Tingle Creek Steeple Chase (Grade 1) ....SANDOWN PARK...............Sat 03
The Betfair Exchange December Handicap Hurdle Race (Listed Race) ....SANDOWN PARK...............Sat 03
The Bar One Drinmore Novice Chase (Grade 1)..FAIRYHOUSE....................Sun 04
The Bar One Hattons Grace Hurdle (Grade 1) ....FAIRYHOUSE....................Sun 04
The Bar One Royal Bond Novice Hurdle (Grade 1)...FAIRYHOUSE....................Sun 04
The Porterstown Handicap Chase (Grade B) ....FAIRYHOUSE....................Sun 04
The Winter Festival Juvenile Hurdle (Grade 3) ....FAIRYHOUSE....................Sun 04
The Peterborough Steeple Chase (Grade 2) ....HUNTINGDON...................Sun 04
The Fitzdares Club Salutes Henrietta Knight Mares' Open National Hunt Flat Race (Listed Race) ...HUNTINGDON...................Sun 04
The Wigley Group Lady Godiva Mares' Novices' Steeple Chase (Listed Race) ....WARWICK.........................Thu 08
The December Handicap Steeple Chase (Grade 3) ....CHELTENHAM...................Fri 09
The Caspian Caviar Gold Cup Handicap Steeple Chase (Grade 3) ....CHELTENHAM...................Sat 10
The Albert Bartlett Novices' Hurdle Race (Registered As The Bristol Novices' Hurdle Race) (Grade 2) ....CHELTENHAM...................Sat 10
The Unibet International Hurdle Race (Grade 2) ....CHELTENHAM...................Sat 10
The Bet365 Summit Juvenile Hurdle Race (Grade 2) ....DONCASTER......................Sat 10
The Bet365 December Novices' Steeple Chase (Grade 2) ....DONCASTER......................Sat 10
The Klairon Davis EBF Novice Chase (Grade 3)...NAVAN............................Sat 10
The Navan Novice Hurdle (Grade 2) ....NAVAN............................Sat 10
The Foxrock Handicap Chase (Grade B) ....NAVAN............................Sat 10
The Proudstown Handicap Hurdle (Grade B) ....NAVAN............................Sat 10
The Kerry Group Cork Stayers Novice Hurdle (Grade 3) ....CORK..............................Sun 11
The Kerry Group Hilly Way Chase (Grade 2) ....CORK..............................Sun 11
The Lombardstown EBF Mares Novice Chase (Grade 2) ....PUNCHESTOWN.................Sun 11
The John Durkan Mem Chase (Grade 1)...NEWBURY.........................Wed 14
The Pertemps Network Mares' Steeple Chase (Listed Race) ....ASCOT.............................Fri 16
The Enter Itv7 Tonight Open National Hunt Flat Race (Listed Race) ....ASCOT.............................Fri 16
The Ascot Noel Novices' Steeple Chase (Grade 2) ....ASCOT.............................Sat 17
The Sky Bet Supreme Trial Novices' Hurdle Race (Grade 2) (Registered As The Kennel Gate) ....ASCOT.............................Sat 17
The Betfair Exchange Trophy (A Handicap Hurdle Race) (Grade 3) ....ASCOT.............................Sat 17
The Wokingham Silver Cup Handicap Steeple Chase (Listed Race) ....ASCOT.............................Sat 17
The Porsche Long Walk Hurdle Race (Grade 1) ....ASCOT.............................Sat 17
The Back And Lay On The Betfair Exchange Abram Mares' Novices' Hurdle Race (Listed Race) ....HAYDOCK PARK................Sat 17
The Betway Quebec Stakes (Listed Race) ....LINGFIELD PARK...............Sat 17
The Future Champions Bumper (Listed Race) ....NAVAN............................Sun 18
The Boreen Belle EBF Mares Novice Hurdle (Listed Race)..THURLES..........................Sun 18
The Ladbrokes Kauto Star Novices' Steeple Chase (In Memory Of Nigel Clark) (Grade 1) ....KEMPTON PARK................Mon 26
The Ladbrokes Christmas Hurdle Race (Grade 1) ....KEMPTON PARK................Mon 26
The Ladbrokes King George VI Steeple Chase (Grade 1) ....KEMPTON PARK................Mon 26
The Knight Frank Juvenile Hurdle (Grade 2) ....LEOPARDSTOWN..............Mon 26
The Racing Post Novice Chase (Grade 1)...LIMERICK.........................Mon 26
The Greenmount Park Novice Chase (Grade 1)..LEOPARDSTOWN..............Mon 26
The William Hill Rowland Meyrick Handicap Steeple Chase (Grade 3) ....WETHERBY.......................Mon 26
The Coral Welsh Grand National Handicap Steeple Chase (Grade 3) (Run In Memory Of Kim Gingell) ....CHEPSTOW......................Tue 27
The Coral Finale Juvenile Hurdle Race (Grade 1) ....CHEPSTOW......................Tue 27
The Ladbrokes Wayward Lad Novices' Steeple Chase (Grade 2) ....KEMPTON PARK................Tue 27
The Ladbrokes Desert Orchid Steeple Chase (Grade 2) ....KEMPTON PARK................Tue 27
The Paddy Power Dial A Bet Chase (Grade 1)...LEOPARDSTOWN..............Tue 27
The Paddy Power Future Champions Novice Hurdle (Grade 1) ....LEOPARDSTOWN..............Tue 27
The Paddy Power Handicap Chase (Grade B) ....LEOPARDSTOWN..............Tue 27

The Dorans Pride Novice Hurdle (Grade 2) .... LIMERICK .... Tue 27
The Savills Christmas Chase (Grade 1) .... LEOPARDSTOWN .... Wed 28
The Christmas Hurdle (Grade 1) .... LEOPARDSTOWN .... Wed 28
The Tim Duggan Mem Handicap Chase (Grade B) .... LIMERICK .... Wed 28
The Dawn Run EBF Mares Novice Chase (Grade 2) .... LIMERICK .... Wed 28
The Yorkshire Silver Vase Mares' Steeple Chase (Listed Race) .... DONCASTER .... Thu 29
The Fort Leney Novice Chase (Grade 1) .... LEOPARDSTOWN .... Thu 29
The Matheson December Hurdle (Grade 1) .... LEOPARDSTOWN .... Thu 29
The EBF Mares Hurdle (Grade 3) .... LEOPARDSTOWN .... Thu 29
The Sporting Limerick 4yo Hurdle (Grade 2) .... LIMERICK .... Thu 29
The Byerley Stud Mares' Novices' Hurdle Race (Listed Race) .... TAUNTON .... Fri 30
The Mansionbet Challow Novices' Hurdle Race (Grade 1) .... NEWBURY .... Sat 31

The list of Principal Races has been supplied by the BHA and Horse Racing Ireland and is provisional.
In all cases, the dates, venues, and names of sponsors are correct at time of going to press, but also subject to possible alteration.

INDEX TO TRAINERS
†denotes Permit to train under N.H. Rules only

N

NAYLOR, DR JEREMY 391
†NEEDHAM, MRS FIONA 392
NELMES, MRS HELEN 393
NEWCOMBE, MR TONY 394
NEWLAND, DR RICHARD 395
NEWTON-SMITH, MISS ANNA 396
NICHOLLS, MR ADRIAN 397
NICHOLLS, MR PAUL 398
NICOL, MR ADAM 399
NIVEN, MR PETER 400
NORTON, MR JOHN 401

O

O'BRIEN, MR A. P. 402
O'BRIEN, MR DONNACHA 403
O'BRIEN, MR FERGAL 404
O'KEEFFE, MR JEDD 405
O'MEARA, MR DAVID 406
†O'NEILL, MRS DANIELLE 407
O'NEILL, MR JOHN 408
O'NEILL, MR JONJO 409
O'ROURKE, MR BRIAN 410
O'SHEA, MR JOHN 411
OLDROYD, MR GEOFFREY 412
OLIVER, MR HENRY 413
OSBORNE, MR JAMIE 414
OWEN, MISS EMMA 415
OWENS, MR PATRICK 416

P

PALMER, MR HUGO 417
PARR, MR JOSEPH 418
PATTINSON, MR MARK 419
PAULING, MR BEN 420
PEARCE, MR SIMON 421
PEARS, MR OLLIE 422
PERRATT, MISS LINDA 423
PERRETT, MRS AMANDA 424
PHELAN, MR PAT 425
PHILIPPART DE FOY, MR KEVIN 426
PHILLIPS, MR RICHARD 427
PIPE, MR DAVID 428
POGSON, CHARLES AND ADAM 429

PONTING, MR JOE 430
PORTMAN, MR JONATHAN 431
POTTER, MR RYAN 432
POULTON, MRS CAMILLA 433
PRESCOTT BT, SIR MARK 434
PRICE, MISS KATY 435
PRICE, MR RICHARD 436
PRITCHARD, MR PETER 437

Q

QUINN, MR DENIS 438
QUINN, MR JOHN 439

R

RALPH, MR ALASTAIR 440
REED, MR TIM 441
REES, MR DAVID 442
†REES, MRS HELEN 443
RICHARDS, MRS LYDIA 444
RICHARDS, MR NICKY 445
RICHES, MR JOHN DAVID 446
RIMELL, MR MARK 447
ROBERTS, MR DAVE 448
ROBERTS, MR MIKE 449
ROBINSON, MISS SARAH 450
ROBSON, MR PAUL D. 451
ROBSON, MISS PAULINE 452
†ROSS, MR RUSSELL 453
ROTHWELL, MR BRIAN 454
ROWE, MR RICHARD 455
ROWLAND, MISS MANDY 456
ROWLEY, MRS MELANIE 457
RUSSELL, MS LUCINDA 458
RYAN, MR JOHN 459
RYAN, MR KEVIN 460

S

SADIK, MR AYTACH 461
SAUNDERS, MR MALCOLM 462
SAYER, MRS DIANNE 463
SCARGILL, DR JON 464
†SCOTT, MR DERRICK 465
SCOTT, MR GEORGE 466
SCOTT, MR JEREMY 467
SCOTT, MISS KATIE 468

STAY AHEAD OF THE FIELD WITH

RACING POST
MEMBERS' CLUB

ACCESS PREMIUM CONTENT AND FEATURES

FIND OUT MORE AT
RACINGPOST.COM/MEMBERS-CLUB

PROPERTY OF HER MAJESTY
The Queen

Colours: Purple, gold braid, scarlet sleeves, black velvet cap with gold fringe

Trained by **Sir Michael Stoute**, Newmarket

FOUR-YEAR-OLDS

1   **JUST FINE (IRE),** b g Sea The Stars (IRE) - Bint Almatar (USA)

THREE-YEAR-OLDS

2   **KITEFLYER,** b c Iffraaj - Star Value (IRE)
3   **NAVAL COLLEGE,** b g Darmouth - Sequence (IRE)

Trained by **William Haggas**, Newmarket

THREE-YEAR-OLDS

4   **EDUCATOR,** br c Deep Impact (JPN) - Diploma
5   **GENERAL IDEA,** b c Galileo (IRE) - Sweet Idea (AUS)
6   **CLEAR DAY (FR),** b g Camelot - Dawn Glory
7   **MELLOW YELLOW (IRE),** b f Dubawi (IRE) - Yellow Rosebud (IRE)
8   **PERFECT ALIBI,** b f Le Havre (IRE) - Daphne

Richard Hannon, Marlborough

Trained by **Harry and Roger Charlton**, Beckhampton

THREE-YEAR-OLDS

9   **CHANCERY LANE (IRE),** b g Recorder - Queen's Prize
10   **DISCRETION,** b f Dubawi (IRE) - Momentary (Nayef (USA))
11   **FRESH FANCY (IRE),** b f New Approach (IRE) - Pure Fantasy (Fastnet Rock (AUS))

Trained by **Michael Bell**, Newmarket

THREE-YEAR-OLDS

12   **SPRING IS SPRUNG (FR),** b c Oasis Dream - Kinematic (Kyllachy)
13   **LOUDSPEAKER,** b g Recorder - Daring Aim (Daylami (IRE))
14   **GOLD BELT,** b f Golden Horn- Hypoteneuse (IRE) (Sadler's Wells (USA))
15   **IMPROVISE (FR),** b f Iffraaj - Set To Music (IRE) (Danehill Dancer (IRE))

PROPERTY OF HER MAJESTY
The Queen

Trained by **Andrew Balding**, Kingsclere

OLDER HORSES

16 **KING'S LYNN,** 5 b g Cable Bay (IRE) - Kinematic
17 **TACTICAL,** 4 b c Toronado (IRE) - Make Fast

THREE-YEAR-OLDS

18 **DUTY BOUND,** b c Kingman - Key Point (IRE)
19 **TACK (FR),** b c Iffraaj - Make Fast (Makfi)
20 **DISTANT LIGHT,** b f Fastnet Rock (AUS) - Light Music (Elusive Quality (USA))
21 **IMMINENT,** b f Dubawi (IRE) - Enticement (Montjeu (IRE))

Trained by **John and Thady Gosden**, Newmarket

THREE-YEAR-OLDS

22 **REACH FOR THE MOON,** b c Sea The Stars (IRE) - Golden Stream (IRE) (Sadler's Wells (USA))
23 **SAGA,** b gr c Invincible Spirit (IRE) - Emily Bronte (Machiavellian (USA))
24 **DUKEDOM (IRE),** b g Dubawi (IRE) - Nathra (IRE) (Iffraaj)
25 **PARK STREET,** b g New Approach (IRE) - City Chic (USA) (Street Cry (IRE))

Trained by **Richard Hughes**, Upper Lambourn

THREE-YEAR-OLDS

26 **INTELLIGENTSIA (IRE),** ch f Exceed And Excel (AUS) - Discernable (Elusive Quality (USA))

Trained by **Clive Cox**, Hungerford

THREE-YEAR-OLDS

27 **SILVER SCREEN,** b f Lope de Vega (IRE) - Silver Mirage (Oasis Dream)
28 **YARRALUMLA,** ch f Australia - Free Verse (Danehill Dancer (IRE))

Trained by **Nicky Henderson**, Lambourn

29 **STEAL A MARCH,** 7 b g Mount Nelson - Side Step
30 **KINCARDINE,** 5 b g Kayf Tara - Side Step
31 **BLUE HEAVEN,** 5 b f Blue Bresil (FR) - Spring Flight (Groom Dancer (USA))

Trained by **Charlie Longsdon**, Chipping Norton

32 **HIGH YIELD,** 5 b g Yeats (IRE) - Midsummer Magic

PROPERTY OF HER MAJESTY
The Queen

To be allocated

TWO-YEAR-OLDS

33 **CIRCLE OF FIRE,** br c 28/1 Almanzor (FR) - Fiery Sunset (Galileo (IRE))
34 **CONSTITUTION,** b c 19/2 Churchill (IRE) - Pack Together (Paco Boy (IRE))
35 **CROSSTICH,** ch c 4/3 Recorder - Craftiness (Al Kazeem)
36 **DESERT HERO,** ch c 29/1 Sea The Stars (IRE) - Desert Breeze (Dubawi (IRE))
37 **GARNER,** b c 23/2 Recorder - Dawn Glory (Oasis Dream)
38 **JURYMAN,** b c 21/3 Recorder - Kinematic (Kyllachy)
39 **PERSIAN GOLD (IRE),** b c 24/1 Night of Thunder (IRE) - Huma Bird (Invincible Spirit (IRE))
40 **SLIPOFTHEPEN,** ch c 18/4 Night of Thunder (IRE) - Free Verse (Danehill Dancer (IRE))
41 **SPANISH SERENADE (IRE),** b c 29/2 Lope de Vega (IRE) - Pink Rose (Shirocco (GER))
42 **THEME PARK,** b c 22/2 Lope de Vega (IRE) - Queen's Prize (Dansili)
43 **BARRIER (FR),** ch f 11/4 Australia - Pure Fantasy (Fastnet Rock (AUS))
44 **BLUE MISSILE,** b f 26/1 Galileo (IRE) - Nathra (IRE) (Iffraaj)
45 **CALMLY,** br f 17/1 Dubawi (IRE) - Shama (IRE) (Danehill Dancer (IRE))
46 **CANDLE OF HOPE,** br f 8/3 Cable Bay (IRE) - Good Hope (Cape Cross (IRE))
47 **CAPE POINT,** b f 5/4 Muhaarar - Key Point (IRE) (Galileo (IRE))
48 **CLEAR THINKING,** b f 19/4 Dubawi (IRE) - Sweet Idea (AUS) (Snitzel (AUS))
49 **GENTLE LIGHT,** ch f 29/4 Frankel - Light Music (Elusive Quality (USA))
50 **KEEN MELODY,** b f 25/4 Le Havre (IRE) - Set To Music (IRE) (Danehill Dancer (IRE))
51 **LOVE AFFAIRS,** b f 22/1 Showcasing - Fond Words (IRE) (Shamardal (USA))
52 **MARKET VALUE (IRE),** b f 27/3 Siyouni (FR) - Estimate (IRE) (Monsun (GER))
53 **PLAYBACK,** b f 26/1 Recorder - Make Fast (Makfi)
54 **QUIET LIFE,** b f 26/4 Oasis Dream - Humdrum (Dr Fong (USA))
55 **REMINDER,** b f 3/3 Dubawi (IRE) - Memory (IRE) (Danehill Dancer (IRE))
56 **SILVER PAGEANT,** b f 27/2 Iffraaj - Silver Mirage (Oasis Dream)
57 **TORCHLIGHT,** b f 14/4 Invincible Spirit (IRE) - Fireglow (Teofilo (IRE))

1 MR N. W. ALEXANDER, Kinneston

Postal: Kinneston, Leslie, Glenrothes, Fife, KY6 3JJ
Contacts: PHONE 01592 840774 MOBILE 07831 488210
EMAIL nicholasalexander@kinneston.com WEBSITE www.kinneston.com

1 **ARNICA**, 9, b g Champs Elysees—Cordoba **Mr J. K. McGarrity**
2 **ARTIC MANN**, 8, b g Sulamani (IRE)—Line Artic (FR) **Alexander, Baxter & Jardine-Paterson**
3 **ATLANTIC DANCER (IRE)**, 9, b m Waky Nao—Sarika (IRE) **Mr C. Lynn**
4 **BLAZING PORT (IRE)**, 7, b g Yeats (IRE)—Despute (IRE) **Turcan, Borwick, Dunning & McGarrity**
5 **BROADWAY JOE (IRE)**, 8, b g Milan—Greenhall Rambler (IRE) **Clan Gathering**
6 **CALIVIGNY (IRE)**, 13, b g Gold Well—Summer Holiday (IRE) **Alexander Family**
7 **CANCAN (FR)**, 6, b m Al Namix (FR)—Kestrel Mail (FR) **The Dregs Of Humanity**
8 **CHANTING HILL (IRE)**, 8, b m Milan—Kitty Dillon (IRE) **Quandt & Cochrane**
9 **CHARM OFFENSIVE (IRE)**, 8, b m Le Triton (USA)—Go Lison (FR) **The Nags to Riches Partnership**
10 **CLAN LEGEND**, 12, ch g Midnight Legend—Harrietfield **Clan Gathering**
11 **COUNTERMAND**, 10, b g Authorized (IRE)—Answered Prayer **Team Kinneston Club**
12 **CREAM OF THE WEST (IRE)**, 6, b g Westerner—Clare Hogan (IRE) **Quandt & Cochrane**
13 **DIOCLETIAN (IRE)**, 7, b g Camelot—Saturday Girl **Mr R. J. C. Wilmot-Smith**
14 **DONNY BOY (IRE)**, 6, b g Westerner—Lady Roania (IRE) **Mrs L. Maclennan**
15 **DUBAI DAYS (IRE)**, 8, b g Dubai Destination (USA)—Comeragh Girl (IRE) **Alexander, McGarrity, Morris & Parker**
16 **EAGLE RIDGE (IRE)**, 11, b g Oscar (IRE)—Azaban (IRE) **Ken McGarrity and Murray Cameron**
17 **EBONY JEWEL (IRE)**, 8, b g Westerner—Lady Roania (IRE) **Mrs L. Maclennan**
18 **ELOI DU PUY (FR)**, 4, b g Jeu St Eloi (FR)—Martalina (FR)
19 **ELVIS MAIL (FR)**, 8, gr g Great Pretender (IRE)—Queenly Mail (FR) **The Ladies Who**
20 **ETOILE D'ECOSSE (FR)**, 8, gr m Martaline—Etoile de Mogador (FR) **Douglas Miller, Coltman, Dunning, Turcan**
21 **FERNHILL LAD (IRE)**, 7, b g Dylan Thomas (IRE)—Sarahall (IRE) **Coltman Cundall Matterson & Stephenson**
22 **FINAL REMINDER (IRE)**, 10, b m Gold Well—Olde Kilcormac (IRE) **Katie & Brian Castle**
23 **FORTESCUE WOOD (IRE)**, 7, b g Westerner—Primrose Time **Bowen & Nicol**
24 **GAILLIMH A STOR (IRE)**, 6, b g Presenting—Gaillimh A Chroi (IRE)
25 **GINGER MAIL (FR)**, 6, gr g Sinndar (IRE)—Queenly Mail (FR) **David & J Miller**
26 **GIPSY LEE ROSE (FR)**, 8, gr m Walk In The Park (IRE)—Vanoo d'Orthe (FR) **Mrs S. M. Irwin**
27 **GUSTAV'S DREAM (IRE)**, 5, ch m Mahler—Lindy Lou **Hugh Hodge Ltd**
28 **HALF TRACK (IRE)**, 6, b g Fame And Glory—Presenting Brook (IRE) **Drew & Ailsa Russell**
29 **HIGH ROLLER (IRE)**, 5, gr g Al Namix (FR)—Mandchou (FR) **Turcan Dunning Borwick & Wemyss**
30 **LACILA BLUE (FR)**, 4, b f Muhaymin (USA)—Hispanola (FR) **Coltman, Douglas Miller, Matterson**
31 **LAKE VIEW LAD (IRE)**, 12, gr g Oscar (IRE)—Missy O'Brien (IRE) **Exors of the Late Mr T. J. Hemmings**
32 **LEWA HOUSE**, 6, b g Yeats (IRE)—Primrose Time **Bissett Racing**
33 4, B g Soldier of Fortune (IRE)—Lindy Lou **Hugh Hodge Ltd**
34 4, B f Blue Bresil (FR)—Little Glenshee (IRE) **Mr N. W. Alexander**
35 **LUCKY SOLDIER (IRE)**, 4, br g Soldier of Fortune (IRE)—Kilbarry Flame (IRE) **Dudgeon, Loudon, Monroe & Morris**
36 **MANETTI (IRE)**, 10, b g Westerner—Mrs Wallensky (IRE) **Sandy's Angels**
37 **MELCHOIR (FR)**, 5, b m Montmartre (FR)—Arvicaya
38 **MEMORS (IRE)**, 7, b m Shirocco (GER)—Mtpockets (IRE) **Miss A. R. Harper**
39 **NED TANNER (IRE)**, 6, b g Milan—Rose Tanner (IRE) **Hands and Heels**
40 **NICEANDEASY (IRE)**, 9, b g Kalanisi (IRE)—High Priestess (IRE) **Katie & Brian Castle**
41 **NOT THE CHABLIS (IRE)**, 8, b g Scorpion (IRE)—De Street (IRE) **Turcan, Dunning, Price, Stewart, Burnham**
42 **OFF THE HOOK (IRE)**, 10, b m Getaway (GER)—Call Her Again (IRE) **Mrs I. Hodge**
43 **PENNY RIVER**, 7, b m Kayf Tara—River Alder **Katie & Brian Castle**
44 **RACING PILE (IRE)**, 13, b g Garuda (IRE)—Jacks Sister (IRE) **Mr N. W. Alexander**
45 **RYEDALE RACER**, 11, b g Indian Danehill (IRE)—Jontys'lass **Bissett Racing**
46 **SANOSUKE (IRE)**, 4, b g Galileo (IRE)—Fix (NZ) **H Turcan S Dunning E Skinner & F Skinner**
47 **SCALLOWAY BAY (IRE)**, 6, br g And Beyond (IRE)—Gretton **J Matterson & J Douglas Miller**
48 **SILK OR SCARLET (IRE)**, 10, ch g Mahler—Spirit of Clanagh (IRE) **Ken McGarrity & Dudgeon, Cundall, Liddle**
49 **SKIPTHESCALES (IRE)**, 10, b g Winged Love (IRE)—Waterland Gale (IRE) **Alexander Family**
50 5, B m Gentlewave (IRE)—Spinning Away **Mr N. W. Alexander**
51 4, B f Clovis du Berlais (FR)—Swift Getaway (IRE) **Mr N. W. Alexander**

MR NICK ALEXANDER - continued

52 **TANGIERS (FR)**, 4, b f Masked Marvel—Jacira (FR) **Bowen & Nicol**
53 **THAT'S A GIVEN (FR)**, 8, b g Great Pretender (IRE)—Aulne River (FR) **Kinneston Racing**
54 **TRAVAIL D'ORFEVRE (FR)**, 6, gr g Martaline—Lady Needles (IRE) **Bowen & Nicol**
55 **ULTRA VIOLET (GER)**, 4, b g Sea The Moon (GER)—United Germany (GER) **Quandt, Cochrane, Lysaght**
56 **UP HELLY AA KING**, 11, ch g And Beyond (IRE)—Gretton **Jean Matterson & J Douglas Miller**
57 **UPANDATIT (IRE)**, 7, b g Winged Love (IRE)—Betty Beck (IRE) **Miss J. G. K. Matterson**
58 **WAKOOL (FR)**, 6, gr g Motivator—Symba's Dream (USA) **Turcan, Borwick, Dunning & Fleming**
59 **WARRIORS STORY**, 6, b g Midnight Legend—Samandara (FR) **The Warriors**
60 **WAVELENGTH (FR)**, 7, b g Gentlewave (IRE)—Mrs Percival

Other Owners: Mr N. W. Alexander, Mr L. Borwick, Mr A. J. Bowen, Lady Burnham, Mr M. Cameron, Mr B. C. Castle, Mrs C. Castle, The Hon T. H. V. Cochrane, Mrs M. C. Coltman, Mr R. H. Cundall, Mrs J. Douglas Miller, Dudgeon, Cundall, Liddle, Sir Simon Dunning, Miss D. F. Fleming, C. Lysaght, Miss J. G. K. Matterson, Mr J. K. McGarrity, Mr A. G. Nicol, Mrs D. C. S. Price, Miss S. Quandt, Mrs A. Russell, A. J. R. Russell, Mrs E. Skinner, Mrs F. L. Skinner, Mr O. G. Stephenson, A. D. Stewart, H. W. Turcan, Mrs C. M. Weymyss.

Assistant Trainer: Catriona Bissett.

Amateur Jockey: Mr Kit Alexander.

MISS LOUISE ALLAN, Newmarket
Postal: 2 London Road, Newmarket, Suffolk, CB8 0TW
Contacts: **MOBILE 07703 355878**
EMAIL **louiseallan1@hotmail.co.uk**

1 **CALTON HILL (IRE)**, 4, b g No Nay Never (USA)—Aljumar (IRE) **Mr R. P. Holley**
2 **HARD TOFFEE (IRE)**, 11, b g Teofilo (IRE)—Speciale (USA) **Miss V. L. Allan**
3 **INDURO DE FONTAINE (FR)**, 5, b g Manduro (GER)—Indian View (GER)
                                    Mr R. P. Holley, Clifton,Banks,Bona,Kelleway & Ashbrook
4 **PIPERS DREAM**, 5, b m Beat All (USA)—High Meadow Rose **Mr R. Moore**
5 **REALMS OF FIRE**, 9, ch g Malinas (GER)—Realms of Gold (USA) **J. W. Whyte**

THREE-YEAR-OLDS

6 **BOND SPIRIT**, ch g Monsieur Bond (IRE)—Spirit Na Heireann (IRE) **The Early Birds**
7 **ROYAL CYGNET**, b f Hot Streak (IRE)—Air Biscuit (IRE) **Mr N. Budden**

MR CONRAD ALLEN, Newmarket
Trainer did not wish details of their string to appear

4 MR SAM ALLWOOD, Whitchurch

Postal: **Church Farm, Church Lane, Ash Magna, Whitchurch, Shropshire, SY13 4EA**
Contacts: **PHONE 07738 413579**
EMAIL office@samallwood.co.uk

1 **ALRIGHT CHIEF (IRE)**, 10, b br g Daylami (IRE)—Lee Valley Native (IRE) **Beverley & Steve Evason**
2 **ALTUMANINA**, 7, b m Helmet (AUS)—Tanwir **Mr P. J. Harney**
3 **AQUILA SKY (IRE)**, 7, b g Arcadio (GER)—Starventure (IRE) **The Lygon Lot**
4 **AUSTRIANA (IRE)**, 4, b f Teofilo (IRE)—Flute Enchante (FR) **Thomas and friends**
5 **BEMPTON CLIFFS (IRE)**, 7, gr g Canford Cliffs (IRE)—Grand Lili **Mr M Dunlevy & Mrs H McGuinness**
6 **BITASWEETSYMPHONY (IRE)**, 7, b g Mahler—Libertango (IRE) **Bostock Dunlevy McGuinness Bradshaw**
7 **BIZERTA (FR)**, 6, ch g Le Havre (IRE)—Blue Blue Sea **R. B. Francis**
8 **CONINGBEG (IRE)**, 7, b m Flemensfirth (USA)—Blue Gale (IRE) **Church Farm Racing Club**
9 **DOOBY**, 4, b f Pearl Secret—Moonshine Ridge (IRE) **Mr D. J. Todd**
10 4, b g Arcadio (GER)—Full of Spirit (IRE) **Mr D. J. Astbury**
11 **HOWYOUPLAYTHEGAME (FR)**, 6, b g Montmartre (FR)—Maille Asie (FR) **R. B. Francis**
12 **JOBSONFIRE**, 10, b g Sulamani (IRE)—Seviot **Paul Clifton & Sarah Thomas**
13 **MONEY FOR JAM (IRE)**, 5, b g Westerner—She's All Talk (IRE) **Ashton & Gittins**
14 **OUT ON THE TEAR (IRE)**, 8, b g Arcadio (GER)—Madame Coco (IRE) **Sam Allwood Racing Club**
15 4, b g Pether's Moon (IRE)—Queen's Law **S. J. Allwood**
16 **R BERNARD**, 6, b g Norse Dancer (IRE)—Channel Treat **Mr R. J. W. Broadley**
17 **ROB THE GETAWAY (IRE)**, 9, b g Getaway (GER)—Kinard True (IRE) **Mr C. H. Gittins**
18 4, B c Heeraat (IRE)—Shemriyna (IRE) **S. J. Allwood**
19 **SINNDARELLA (FR)**, 6, b m Sinndar (IRE)—Ludwig Von (FR) **Maximum Racing**
20 **VON MELAS (IRE)**, 4, b g Battle of Marengo (IRE)—Rock Magic (IRE) **Church Farm Racing Club**
21 **YAMBOCHARLIE**, 5, ch g Gentlewave (IRE)—Materiality **S. J. Allwood**

THREE-YEAR-OLDS

22 **FAST STYLE (IRE)**, b g Camacho—That's My Style **Mr M. Dunlevy**

Other Owners: Mr G. J. Ashton, Mrs B. A. Bostock, Mr P. E. Bradshaw, Mr P. Clifton, Mr M. Dunlevy, Mr S. Evason, Mr C. H. Gittins, Mrs H. A. McGuinness, Miss S. M. Thomas.

5 MR ERIC ALSTON, Preston

Postal: **Edges Farm Stables, Chapel Lane, Longton, Preston, Lancashire, PR4 5NA**
Contacts: **PHONE 01772 619600 MOBILE 07879 641660 FAX 01772 619600**
EMAIL eric1943@supanet.com

1 **BOUDICA BAY (IRE)**, 7, b m Rip Van Winkle (IRE)—White Shift (IRE) **The Grumpy Old Geezers**
2 **CAPTAIN CORCORAN (IRE)**, 5, b g Anjaal—Hms Pinafore (IRE) **Whitehills Racing Syndicate 2**
3 **DESERT CAT**, 4, b f Bobby's Kitten (USA)—Wonderful Desert **The Horses Mouth Racing Club**
4 **FOX HILL**, 6, b m Foxwedge (AUS)—Siryena **Whitehills Racing Syndicate**
5 **HARRY'S RIDGE (IRE)**, 7, b g Acclamation—Dani Ridge (IRE) **Mr L. Carlisle**
6 **KASPERENKO**, 8, b g Archipenko (USA)—Jardin **Mr C. F. Harrington**
7 **REDROSEZORRO**, 8, b g Foxwedge (AUS)—Garter Star **Red Rose Partnership**

THREE-YEAR-OLDS

8 B g Free Eagle (IRE)—Elusive Ellen (IRE) **Mr C. F. Harrington**
9 **GABRIELLA'S SPIRIT (IRE)**, b f Invincible Spirit (IRE)—Ridge Ranger (IRE) **Mr C. F. Harrington**

TWO-YEAR-OLDS

10 **FELIX NATALIS (IRE)**, br c 26/04 Harry Angel (IRE)—Newtown Pippin (Dubawi (IRE)) (17007) **Sleeve It Ltd**
11 **ONEFORSUE**, b f 20/03 Bated Breath—Unveiling (Mayson) (26000) **Paul Buist & Mike Taylor**

Assistant Trainer: Mrs Sue Alston.

6 MR CHARLIE APPLEBY, Newmarket
Postal: Godolphin Management Co Ltd, Moulton Paddocks, Newmarket, Suffolk, CB8 7PJ
WEBSITE www.godolphin.com

1 **ADAYAR (IRE)**, 4, b c Frankel—Anna Salai (USA)
2 **AL SUHAIL**, 5, b g Dubawi (IRE)—Shirocco Star
3 **BANDINELLI**, 4, ch g Dubawi (IRE)—Indian Petal
4 **CREATIVE FORCE (IRE)**, 4, ch g Dubawi (IRE)—Choose Me (IRE)
5 **DHAHABI (IRE)**, 4, b c Frankel—Fleche d'Or
6 **ECHO POINT (IRE)**, 4, ch g Dubawi (IRE)—Yodelling (USA)
7 **HIGHLAND AVENUE (IRE)**, 4, gr g Dubawi (IRE)—Lumiere
8 **HURRICANE LANE (IRE)**, 4, ch c Frankel—Gale Force
9 **KEMARI**, 4, b g Dubawi (IRE)—Koora
10 **KINGSWEAR**, 5, b g Dubawi (IRE)—Galatee (FR)
11 **LA BARROSA (IRE)**, 4, b g Lope de Vega (IRE)—Bikini Babe (IRE)
12 **LAZULI (IRE)**, 5, b g Dubawi (IRE)—Floristry
13 **MAN OF PROMISE (USA)**, 5, b h Into Mischief (USA)—Involved (USA)
14 **MANOBO (IRE)**, 4, b g Sea The Stars (IRE)—Tasaday (USA)
15 **MASTER OF THE SEAS (IRE)**, 4, b g Dubawi (IRE)—Firth of Lorne (IRE)
16 **MODERN NEWS**, 4, ch g Shamardal (USA)—Modern Ideals
17 **NAVAL CROWN**, 4, b c Dubawi (IRE)—Come Alive
18 **NOBLE DYNASTY**, 4, b g Dubawi (IRE)—Alina (IRE)
19 **ONE RULER (IRE)**, 4, b g Dubawi (IRE)—Fintry (IRE)
20 **QUINTILLUS**, 4, ch g Dubawi (IRE)—Epitome (IRE)
21 **REBEL'S ROMANCE (IRE)**, 4, br g Dubawi (IRE)—Minidress
22 **ROYAL FLEET**, 4, b g Dubawi (IRE)—Zibelina (IRE)
23 **SILENT FILM**, 4, ch g New Approach (IRE)—Dibajj (FR)
24 **VALIANT PRINCE (IRE)**, 4, b g Dubawi (IRE)—Chachamaidee (IRE)
25 **YIBIR**, 4, ch g Dubawi (IRE)—Rumh (GER)

THREE-YEAR-OLDS

26 **AL NAFIR (IRE)**, ch c Dubawi (IRE)—Nightime (IRE)
27 **AL SAHARA (IRE)**, b f Galileo (IRE)—Lumiere
28 **ALBAHR**, ch g Dubawi (IRE)—Falls of Lora (IRE)
29 **ALNILAM (FR)**, b br g Sea The Stars (IRE)—Awareness (USA)
30 **BAY OF HONOUR (IRE)**, b c Shamardal (USA)—Kazimiera
31 **BEDOUIN QUEEN**, b f Teofilo (IRE)—Anna Salai (USA)
32 **BLUE TRAIL (IRE)**, b c Teofilo (IRE)—Pietrafiore (IRE)
33 **COROEBUS (IRE)**, b c Dubawi (IRE)—First Victory (IRE)
34 **ETERNAL PEARL**, b f Frankel—Pearly Steph (FR)
35 **FALLING SHADOW (IRE)**, b c Invincible Spirit (IRE)—Belonging
36 **FIRST RULER**, b c Dubawi (IRE)—Zhukova (IRE)
37 **GOLDSPUR (IRE)**, b c Dubawi (IRE)—Pomology (USA)
38 **HAFIT (IRE)**, b c Dubawi (IRE)—Cushion
39 **HIGH RENAISSANCE**, b c Farhh—Patroness
40 **IMPERIAL CROWN**, b c Frankel—Attraction
41 **INDEPENDENT ACT (IRE)**, b c Dubawi (IRE)—Hand Puppet (IRE)
42 **INNER LIGHT**, b c Dubawi (IRE)—Shawanda (IRE)
43 **JAVAKHETI (IRE)**, b f Teofilo (IRE)—Lava Flow (IRE)
44 **KHATHAK**, b g Iffraaj—Mujarah (IRE)
45 **KING OF TIME (IRE)**, b g Kingman—Lombatina (FR)
46 **LAST AMMO (IRE)**, ch c Teofilo (IRE)—Hawsa (USA)
47 **LIFE OF DREAMS**, b f Dubawi (IRE)—Endless Time (IRE)
48 **MAKKARI**, b f Galileo (IRE)—Sobetsu
49 **MODERN GAMES (IRE)**, ch c Dubawi (IRE)—Modern Ideals
50 **NAHANNI**, ch c Frankel—Final Stage
51 **NATIONS PRIDE (IRE)**, b c Teofilo (IRE)—Important Time (IRE)
52 **NATIVE TRAIL**, b c Oasis Dream—Needleleaf
53 **NATURAL WORLD (IRE)**, b c Frankel—Skiffle
54 **NEW COMEDY (IRE)**, b g Sea The Stars (IRE)—Tearless
55 **NEW KINGDOM**, ch c Dubawi (IRE)—Provenance

MR CHARLIE APPLEBY - continued

56 **NEW LONDON (IRE),** b c Dubawi (IRE)—Bright Beacon
57 **NEW SCIENCE,** b c Lope de Vega (IRE)—Alta Lilea (IRE)
58 **NOBLE ORDER (IRE),** b c Dubawi (IRE)—Zibelina (IRE)
59 **NOBLE TRUTH (FR),** b c Kingman—Speralita (IRE)
60 **OTTOMAN FLEET,** b c Sea The Stars (IRE)—Innevera (FR)
61 **PARLANDO,** b c Dubawi (IRE)—Discourse (USA)
62 **PEARL BORDER (IRE),** b f Ribchester (IRE)—Firth of Lorne (IRE)
63 **PRINCESSE D'OR (IRE),** b f Frankel—Fleche d'Or
64 **PRIVATE SIGNAL,** b g Sea The Stars (IRE)—Smoulder
65 **ROYAL SYMBOL (IRE),** b c Sea The Stars (IRE)—Measured Tempo
66 **RULING DYNASTY,** ch c Night of Thunder (IRE)—Indian Petal
67 **SARANGANI,** ch c Shamardal (USA)—Tasaday (USA)
68 **SECRET IMAGE (IRE),** b g Dark Angel (IRE)—Pimpernel (IRE)
69 **SECRET STATE (IRE),** ch c Dubawi (IRE)—Jacqueline Quest (IRE)
70 **SENSE OF POWER (IRE),** b g Invincible Spirit (IRE)—Boldarra (USA)
71 **SENSE OF WISDOM,** b c Shamardal (USA)—Tajriba (IRE)
72 **SILENT SPEECH,** ch c Dubawi (IRE)—Epitome (IRE)
73 **SILK ROMANCE (IRE),** b f Shamardal (USA)—Lyric of Light
74 **SOVEREIGN PRINCE,** b g Dubawi (IRE)—Gamilati
75 **STATE EVENT,** br c Shamardal (USA)—Blue Bunting (USA)
76 **STORMY OCEAN,** b c Frankel—As Good As Gold (IRE)
77 **SYMBOL OF LIGHT,** b g Shamardal (USA)—Pure Diamond
78 **TIMELESS MELODY (IRE),** b f Teofilo (IRE)—Dufay (IRE)
79 **TRANQUIL NIGHT,** b g Invincible Spirit (IRE)—Serene Beauty (USA)
80 **WALK OF STARS,** b c Dubawi (IRE)—Sound Reflection (USA)
81 **WESTERN WRITER (IRE),** b c Shamardal (USA)—Yodelling (USA)
82 **WHISPERING ROMANCE (IRE),** b f Kingman—Sante (IRE)
83 **WILD BEAUTY,** b f Frankel—Tulips (IRE)
84 **WILD CRUSADE,** b c Dubawi (IRE)—Rumh (GER)
85 **WITH THE MOONLIGHT (IRE),** b f Frankel—Sand Vixen
86 **YANSOON,** b g Dark Angel (IRE)—Bean Feasa
87 **YANTARNI,** ch c Dubawi (IRE)—Villarrica (USA)
88 **YUKON STAR (IRE),** b g Oasis Dream—Easy Victory

TWO-YEAR-OLDS

89 B c 29/03 Shamardal (USA)—Adoringly (IRE) (Dubawi (IRE))
90 B f 29/03 Fastnet Rock (AUS)—Aim of Artemis (IRE) (Leroidesanimaux (BRZ))
91 B c 23/04 Lope de Vega (IRE)—Aniseed (IRE) (Dalakhani (IRE)) (350000)
92 B f 24/04 Invincible Spirit (IRE)—Anjaz (USA) (Street Cry (IRE))
93 B c 05/04 Frankel—Anna Salai (USA) (Dubawi (IRE))
94 B c 26/02 Frankel—As Good As Gold (IRE) (Oasis Dream) (900000)
95 B f 15/04 Shamardal (USA)—Autumn Lily (USA) (Street Cry (IRE))
96 B f 13/03 Night of Thunder (IRE)—Avongrove (Tiger Hill (IRE))
97 Ch f 21/01 Teofilo (IRE)—Award Winning (IRE) (Dubawi (IRE)) (187075)
98 B c 21/02 Dubawi (IRE)—Baisse (High Chaparral (IRE))
99 Ch c 01/04 Almanzor (FR)—Beach Frolic (Nayef (USA)) (425000)
100 Ch f 16/04 Cracksman—Bean Feasa (Dubawi (IRE))
101 B c 18/03 Invincible Spirit (IRE)—Berengaria (IRE) (Teofilo (IRE))
102 Ch f 30/01 Sea The Stars (IRE)—Best Terms (Exceed And Excel (AUS)) (1500000)
103 B c 11/04 Dubawi (IRE)—Blossomtime (Shamardal (USA))
104 B f 21/04 Frankel—Blue Bunting (USA) (Dynaformer (USA))
105 B c 16/02 Dubawi (IRE)—Bound (IRE) (Galileo (IRE)) (550000)
106 B c 03/04 Kingman—Bristol Bay (IRE) (Montjeu (IRE)) (750000)
107 B c 01/04 Teofilo (IRE)—Calare (IRE) (Dubawi (IRE))
108 Ch c 01/03 Lope de Vega (IRE)—Carriwitchet (IRE) (Dubawi (IRE))
109 B c 23/02 Exceed And Excel (AUS)—Certify (USA) (Elusive Quality (USA))
110 Ch f 07/02 Lope de Vega (IRE)—Come Alive (Dansili)
111 Ch c 24/02 Galileo (IRE)—Dancing Rain (IRE) (Danehill Dancer (IRE))
112 B c 09/03 New Approach (IRE)—Dancing Sands (IRE) (Dubawi (IRE))

MR CHARLIE APPLEBY - continued

113 Br c 17/02 Dubawi (IRE)—Dane Street (USA) (Street Cry (IRE))
114 Ch c 08/03 Dubawi (IRE)—Davantage (FR) (Galileo (IRE)) (552721)
115 Ch c 03/02 Showcasing—Delphinidae (IRE) (Sepoy (AUS))
116 B f 27/03 Dubawi (IRE)—Devonshire (IRE) (Fast Company (IRE))
117 B c 01/04 Teofilo (IRE)—Discursus (Dubawi (IRE))
118 B c 19/02 Dubawi (IRE)—Duchess of Berry (New Approach (IRE))
119 B c 11/03 Kingman—Eartha Kitt (Pivotal) (525000)
120 B c 19/02 Teofilo (IRE)—Emirates Rewards (Dubai (IRE))
121 Ch c 18/03 Exceed And Excel (AUS)—Endless Charm (Dubawi (IRE))
122 Ch c 29/04 New Approach (IRE)—Entertains (AUS) (Street Cry (IRE))
123 B c 30/03 Kingman—Epitome (IRE) (Nashwan (USA))
124 Ch c 09/01 Farhh—Ethereal Sky (IRE) (Invincible Spirit (IRE))
125 Ch c 02/04 Dubawi (IRE)—Extra Mile (Frankel)
126 B c 08/02 New Approach (IRE)—Falls of Lora (IRE) (Street Cry (IRE))
127 Ch c 07/02 Teofilo (IRE)—Finata (Dubawi (IRE))
128 B c 15/02 Fastnet Rock (AUS)—Fintry (IRE) (Shamardal (USA))
129 B c 04/05 Shamardal (USA)—First Victory (IRE) (Teofilo (IRE))
130 B f 13/03 Dark Angel (IRE)—Firth of Lorne (IRE) (Danehill (USA))
131 B f 01/05 Shamardal (USA)—Floristry (Fasliyev (USA))
132 B f 29/02 Siyouni (FR)—Gaterie (USA) (Dubai Destination (USA))
133 B c 21/03 Lope de Vega (IRE)—God Given (Nathaniel (IRE)) (725000)
134 B c 03/05 Shamardal (USA)—Gonbarda (GER) (Lando (GER))
135 B f 06/02 Invincible Spirit (IRE)—Grecian Light (IRE) (Shamardal (USA))
136 B f 16/02 Dubawi (IRE)—Hadith (IRE) (New Approach (IRE))
137 B f 27/03 Invincible Spirit (IRE)—Hand Puppet (IRE) (Manduro (GER))
138 B f 02/02 Deep Impact (JPN)—Hibaayeb (Singspiel (IRE))
139 B f 22/04 Dubawi (IRE)—Hidden Gold (IRE) (Shamardal (USA))
140 B c 14/03 Kingman—Horseplay (Cape Cross (IRE)) (350000)
141 B f 11/02 Lope de Vega (IRE)—How (IRE) (Galileo (IRE)) (475000)
142 Ch f 06/05 Dubawi (IRE)—Indian Petal (Singspiel (IRE))
143 B c 26/04 Sea The Stars (IRE)—Karenine (High Chaparral (IRE))
144 B f 21/02 New Approach (IRE)—Khawlah (IRE) (Cape Cross (IRE))
145 Ch c 07/02 Dubawi (IRE)—Lacey's Lane (Street Cry (IRE))
146 B c 25/03 Exceed And Excel (AUS)—Lacily (USA) (Elusive Quality (USA))
147 Ch f 06/05 Exceed And Excel (AUS)—Laugh Aloud (Dubawi (IRE))
148 Ch c 31/03 Shamardal (USA)—Lava Flow (IRE) (Dalakhani (IRE))
149 Ch c 15/02 Dubawi (IRE)—Lucida (IRE) (Shamardal (USA))
150 B f 15/03 Sea The Stars (IRE)—Lumiere (Shamardal (USA))
151 B f 27/04 Kingman—Marie de Medici (USA) (Medicean)
152 Ch c 19/04 Dubawi (IRE)—Marigold Hotel (IRE) (Galileo (IRE)) (600000)
153 Ch f 07/03 Dubawi (IRE)—Midnight Fair (IRE) (Raven's Pass (USA))
154 B c 04/02 Frankel—Mindress (Street Cry (IRE))
155 MISCHIEF MAGIC (IRE), b c 07/02 Exceed And Excel (AUS)—Veil of Silence (IRE) (Elusive Quality (USA))
156 B gr f 06/03 Dark Angel (IRE)—Miss Lucifer (FR) (Noverre (USA))
157 B f 15/04 Frankel—Mujarah (IRE) (Marju (IRE))
158 MYSTERIOUS NIGHT (IRE), b c 08/03 Dark Angel (IRE)—Mistrusting (IRE) (Shamardal (USA))
159 B br f 13/02 New Approach (IRE)—Najoum (USA) (Giant's Causeway (USA))
160 B f 15/02 Kingman—Needleleaf (Observatory (USA)) (807823)
161 B br f 06/02 Kodiac—New Style (USA) (Street Cry (IRE))
162 Ch c 17/03 Lope de Vega (IRE)—Normandel (FR) (Le Havre (IRE)) (297619)
163 Ch c 22/04 Dubawi (IRE)—Panegyric (Monsun (GER))
164 B f 13/03 Frankel—Patroness (Dubawi (IRE))
165 B f 14/02 Dark Angel (IRE)—Peace Trail (Kyllachy)
166 Ch c 10/04 Dubawi (IRE)—Phiz (GER) (Galileo (IRE)) (425000)
167 B f 27/04 Invincible Spirit (IRE)—Pietrafiore (IRE) (Dubawi (IRE))
168 B f 07/03 Kodiac—Policoro (IRE) (Pivotal)
169 B c 23/01 Sea The Stars (IRE)—Powder Snow (USA) (Dubawi (IRE))
170 B f 27/02 Frankel—Pure Diamond (Street Cry (IRE))
171 B c 21/03 Shamardal (USA)—Rainswept (Frankel)
172 B c 05/03 Dubawi (IRE)—Really Special (Shamardal (USA))

MR CHARLIE APPLEBY - continued

173 B c 06/02 New Approach (IRE)—Right Direction (IRE) (Cape Cross (IRE))
174 B c 29/04 Golden Horn—Rumh (GER) (Monsun (GER))
175 B f 26/02 Sea The Stars (IRE)—Sahraah (USA) (Kingmambo (USA))
176 B f 02/03 Cracksman—Sand Vixen (Dubawi (IRE))
177 B f 21/03 Shamardal (USA)—Secret Gesture (Galileo (IRE))
178 B c 31/03 Dubawi (IRE)—Serena's Storm (IRE) (Statue of Liberty (USA)) (625000)
179 B c 02/04 New Approach (IRE)—Serene Beauty (USA) (Street Cry (IRE))
180 B f 29/03 Kingman—Show Day (IRE) (Shamardal (USA))
181 B f 17/02 Exceed And Excel (AUS)—Silk Words (Dubawi (IRE))
182 Ch f 07/04 Frankel—Sobetsu (Dubawi (IRE))
183 Ch f 19/04 New Approach (IRE)—Sound Reflection (USA) (Street Cry (IRE))
184 B c 05/02 Dubawi (IRE)—Speirbhean (IRE) (Danehill (USA))
185 B c 29/02 Kingman—Sperry (IRE) (Shamardal (USA))
186 B c 04/02 Dubawi (IRE)—Spring Mist (Dansili)
187 B f 17/03 Dubawi (IRE)—Switching (USA) (Street Cry (IRE))
188 Ch c 03/05 New Approach (IRE)—Tasaday (USA) (Nayef (USA))
189 B f 13/03 Dubawi (IRE)—Usherette (IRE) (Shamardal (USA))
190 Ch c 24/01 Lope de Vega (IRE)—Via Condotti (IRE) (Galileo (IRE)) (550000)
191 B c 14/04 Kingman—Via Pisa (FR) (Pivotal) (722789)
192 B f 16/03 Frankel—Violante (USA) (Kingmambo (USA))
193 Ch f 23/02 Teofilo (IRE)—Voice of Truth (IRE) (Dubawi (IRE))
194 B c 06/04 Teofilo (IRE)—Waitress (USA) (Kingmambo (USA))
195 B f 02/03 Dubawi (IRE)—Winter Lightning (IRE) (Shamardal (USA))
196 B f 28/04 Dubawi (IRE)—Winters Moon (IRE) (New Approach (IRE))
197 Ch f 06/04 Galileo (IRE)—Wuheida (Dubawi (IRE))
198 B f 22/04 Sea The Stars (IRE)—Yodelling (USA) (Medaglia d'Oro (USA))
199 B c 05/02 Dubawi (IRE)—Zhukova (IRE) (Fastnet Rock (AUS))

Owners: S. Ali, Godolphin Management Company Ltd.

Assistant Trainer: Alex Merriam, Marie Murphy, **Racing Secretary:** Hannah Pollard.

Flat Jockey: William Buick, James Doyle.

---

7 MR MICHAEL APPLEBY, Oakham
Postal: **The Homestead, Langham, Oakham, Leicestershire, LE15 7EJ**
Contacts: **PHONE 01572 722772 MOBILE 07884 366421**
EMAIL **mickappleby@icloud.com WEBSITE www.mickappleby.com**

1 ALEXANDER JAMES (IRE), 6, b g Camelot—Plying (USA) **Magna Carter Bloodstock**
2 ASAD (IRE), 6, ch g Lope de Vega (IRE)—Venus de Milo (IRE) **The Weston Super Mares**
3 AYR HARBOUR, 5, b g Harbour Watch (IRE)—Sorella Bella (IRE) **JP's Racing Syndicate**
4 BABE ALICIOUS (IRE), 4, b f Kodiac—Forgiving Flower **Diamond Racing Ltd**
5 BALDOMERO (IRE), 4, b g Shalaa (IRE)—Besotted **The Horse Watchers**
6 BANCNUANAHEIREANN (IRE), 15, b g Chevalier (IRE)—Alamanta (IRE) **Mr W. Sewell & Mr Michael Appleby**
7 BARRINGTON (IRE), 8, b g Casamento (IRE)—Mia Divina **Mr Frank McAleavy & Mr Ian McAleavy**
8 BLISSFUL SONG (IRE), 4, b f Mehmas (IRE)—Kummel Excess (IRE) **Mr N. Brereton**
9 BOUNDLESS POWER (IRE), 5, br g Slade Power (IRE)—Boundless Joy (AUS) **ValueRacingClub.co.uk**
10 BRONZE RIVER, 5, b g Archipenko—Avon Lady **Mr M. J. Taylor**
11 BY JOVE, 5, b g Nathaniel (IRE)—Calima Breeze **T. R. Pryke**
12 CASARUAN, 5, b g Casamento (IRE)—Aruan **B. D. Cantle**
13 CASHEL (IRE), 7, b g Sepoy (AUS)—Snow Dust **Mr L. A. Bellman**
14 CHANNEL PACKET, 8, b h Champs Elysees—Etarre (IRE) **Howdale Bloodstock**
15 CLIPSHAM TIGER (IRE), 6, b g Bungle Inthejungle—Texas Queen **Mr F. Morley**
16 COME ON GIRL, 5, gr m Outstrip—Floating **Mrs D. Hopkins**
17 CRIMSON KING (IRE), 6, b g Kingman—Toi Et Moi (IRE) **T. R. Pryke**

MR MICHAEL APPLEBY - continued

18 **DANZENO**, 11, b g Denounce—Danzanora **Mr W. C. Wragg**
19 **DARUAN**, 4, b f Dunaden (FR)—Aruan **B. D. Cantle**
20 **DEW YOU BELIEVE (IRE)**, 4, b g Make Believe—Dew (IRE) **Mr D. B. Gillett**
21 **EAGLE EYED FREDDIE**, 4, b g Gleneagles (IRE)—Spice Trail **Mr E. Foster**
22 **EDRAAK (IRE)**, 6, b g Elzaam (AUS)—So Blissful (IRE) **Michael & Tommy Wickins**
23 **EL CAMINO**, 4, gr g Gleneagles (IRE)—Silver Clouds (IRE) **Fosnic Racing**
24 **ELEKTRONIC (IRE)**, 4, b g Kodiac—Elektra Marino **Mr M. J. Taylor**
25 **EPONINA (IRE)**, 8, b m Zoffany (IRE)—Dame Rochelle (IRE) **Mrs E. Cash**
26 **FASHION FREE**, 5, b m Muhaarar—Ighraa (IRE) **Mr L. J. M. J. Vaessen**
27 **FENNAAN (IRE)**, 7, br g Footstepsinthesand—Sanadaat **Honestly Racing**
28 **FINERY**, 5, b m Al Kazeem—Elysian **Mr M. O. Ward**
29 **FOR PEAT'S SAKE**, 4, b g Showcasing—Peacehaven (IRE) **Mr I. Lawrence**
30 **FOX POWER (IRE)**, 6, gr g Dark Angel (IRE)—Zenella **Mr M. J. Taylor**
31 **HA'AN**, 4, b c Black Sam Bellamy (IRE)—Luna de Ventura **Howdale Bloodstock**
32 **HATHLOOL (IRE)**, 4, b g Awtaad (IRE)—Majestic Jasmine (IRE) **The Horse Watchers 1**
33 **HE'S A LEGEND**, 7, b g Schiaparelli (GER)—Midnight Fun **M. Appleby**
34 **HELMORA**, 4, ch f Helmet (AUS)—Demora **Mr W. C. Wragg**
35 **IN THE BREEZE (IRE)**, 4, b g Harzand (IRE)—Its In The Air (IRE) **J & A Young (Leicester) Ltd**
36 **INTERVENTION**, 5, b g Swiss Spirit—Lady Lube Rye (IRE) **The Horse Watchers 8**
37 **KABUTO**, 4, b g Helmet (AUS)—Bochafina (FR) **M. Appleby**
38 **KATIE'S KITTEN**, 4, ch f Bobby's Kitten (USA)—Freedom Reigns (IRE) **Fosnic Racing**
39 **KATTANI (IRE)**, 6, b g Tamayuz—Katiola (IRE) **Kaizen Racing**
40 **KHATWAH (IRE)**, 4, ch f Lope de Vega (IRE)—Accipiter **Mr R. Oliver**
41 **KING OF STARS (IRE)**, 5, gr g Starspangledbanner (AUS)—Glowing Star (IRE) **Mr William Esdaile**
42 **LADY MONICA**, 6, b m Bated Breath—Sina (GER) **Mr M. Hollier**
43 **LARADO (FR)**, 4, b g Shalaa (IRE)—Suertez (USA) **Mrs E. Cash**
44 **LIAMBA**, 7, b m Equiano (FR)—Hisaronu (IRE) **Diamond Racing Ltd**
45 **LIBERATION POINT (IRE)**, 5, b g Iffraaj—Botanique (IRE) **The Horse Watchers**
46 **MACS GIRL (IRE)**, 4, b f Buratino (IRE)—Encore Encore (FR) **Honestly Racing**
47 **MAWKEB (USA)**, 4, b g Kitten's Joy (USA)—Illegal Search (USA) **Mrs D. Hopkins**
48 **MEHMO (IRE)**, 4, ch g Mehmas (IRE)—Baltic Belle (IRE) **Mr T. O. Bownes**
49 **MOHAREB**, 6, b g Delegator—Irrational **Mr I. Lawrence**
50 **MOONRAKER**, 10, ch g Starspangledbanner (AUS)—Licence To Thrill **The Kettlelites**
51 **MOP'S A LEGEND**, 5, b g Schiaparelli (GER)—Midnight Fun **Mick Appleby Racing**
52 **MOPS GEM**, 4, b f Equiano (FR)—Mops Angel **Mick Appleby Racing**
53 **MOSTALLIM**, 5, b g Bated Breath—Lifting Me Higher (IRE) **The Hobbits**
54 **MOTAWAAFEQ (FR)**, 6, b g Wootton Bassett—Crossed Fingers (IRE) **Middleham Park Racing XX**
55 **MUST BE ROYALE**, 4, b g Mustajeeb—Sofia Royale **Mr Wayne Brackstone, Mr Steve Whitear**
56 **NIGEL NOTT**, 6, ch g Dutch Art—Baileys Jubilee **Mr N. Brereton**
57 **NIGHT ON EARTH (IRE)**, 4, b g Kodiac—Eternal View (IRE) **The Horse Watchers 4**
58 **PETTINGER**, 5, b m Hot Streak (IRE)—Joshua's Princess **Mr T. O. Bownes**
59 **PLASTIC PADDY**, 4, b g Buratino (IRE)—Bereka **Mr M. J. Goggin**
60 **RAASEL**, 5, ch g Showcasing—Dubai Affair **The Horse Watchers**
61 **RESTLESS ENDEAVOUR (IRE)**, 5, b m Dandy Man (IRE)—Belgique (IRE) **Craig & Laura Buckingham**
62 **RIVER SONG (IRE)**, 5, b m Battle of Marengo (IRE)—Yurituni **Riverwood Racing**
63 **SAATTY (IRE)**, 4, gr g Markaz (IRE)—Rashaaqa **The Horse Watchers 2**
64 **SAMPERS SEVEN (IRE)**, 5, b m Anjaal—Sampers (IRE) **ValueRacingClub.co.uk**
65 **SANDYMAN**, 6, ch g Footstepsinthesand—Quiz Mistress **The Rocket Racing Club**
66 **SEAGULLS NEST**, 5, b m Camelot—Mare Imbrium (USA) **The Horse Watchers 4**
67 **SIEGE OF ZARA**, 4, b f Olden Times—Zaras Legend **Mick Appleby Racing**
68 **SIR GREGORY (FR)**, 4, ch g Equiano (FR)—Tegara **B & M Pallets Ltd**
69 **SNOW BERRY (IRE)**, 4, b f Dragon Pulse (IRE)—Primal Snow (USA) **J & A Young (Leicester) Ltd**
70 **SPIDERSTEVE**, 7, b g Schiaparelli (GER)—Di's Dilemma **Mr S. J. Elmer**
71 **SPRING ROMANCE (IRE)**, 7, gr g Zebedee—Love And Devotion **Mr N. Hassan**
72 **SWINTON NOON**, 4, b g Sepoy (AUS)—Marasil (IRE) **Star of Aspire Racing**
73 **THRAVE**, 7, b g Sir Percy—Feis Ceoil (IRE) **MIDEST 1**
74 **TWILLEY**, 4, b f Nathaniel (IRE)—Poppy Bond **North Cheshire Trading & Storage Ltd**
75 **UNITED FRONT (USA)**, 5, b g War Front (USA)—Shell House (IRE) **Mr N. Brereton**
76 **VOCATUS (IRE)**, 6, b g Vocalised (USA)—Beyond Intensity (IRE) **ValueRacingClub.co.uk**
77 **WHITTLE LE WOODS**, 4, b g Lethal Force (IRE)—Lady Loch **The Horse Watchers 4**

MR MICHAEL APPLEBY - continued

78 **WRATH OF HECTOR**, 5, b g Mayson—Dutch Mistress **Mr A. S. Griffiths**
79 **ZAPPER CASS (FR)**, 9, b g Elusive City (USA)—Moonlight Cass (IRE) **M. Appleby**
80 **ZIM BABY**, 5, b m Roderic O'Connor (IRE)—Kenyan Cat **Fosnic Racing**
81 **ZOOM ZOOM BABE**, 5, b m Footstepsinthesand—Blues In Cee (IRE) **Mrs L. White**
82 **ZUUL**, 4, ch c Black Sam Bellamy (IRE)—Sharp Dresser (USA) **Howdale Bloodstock**

THREE-YEAR-OLDS

83 **ANNAF (IRE)**, br c Muhaarar—Shimah (USA) **Fosnic Racing**
84 **BOND BOY**, b c Equiano (FR)—Poppy Bond **North Cheshire Trading & Storage Ltd**
85 **CLIPSHAM GOLD (IRE)**, ch f Galileo Gold—Tilly Two (IRE) **Mr F. Morley**
86 **DE VEGA'S WARRIOR (IRE)**, b g Lope de Vega (IRE)—Oh Sedulous (IRE) **J & A Young (Leicester) Ltd**
87 **GLASSTREES**, gr f Heeraat (IRE)—Goadby **Cleartherm Glass Sealed Units Ltd**
88 **HOT MOP**, b f Hot Streak (IRE)—Mops Angel **S & M Appleby**
89 **JENNYS JACK DANIEL**, b c Jack Hobbs—Vodka Island (IRE) **Mr D. G. Skelton**
90 **KOTYONOK**, b c Bobby's Kitten (USA)—Nezhenka **ValueRacingClub.co.uk**
91 **LADYMAC**, b f Camacho—Prim (USA) **Honestly Racing**
92 **LUXOR FLUSH (IRE)**, b g Cappella Sansevero—Flip Flop (IRE) **Mr N. Brereton**
93 **MEGA MARVEL**, b c Equiano (FR)—Megaleka **North Cheshire Trading & Storage Ltd**
94 **MINESBIGGERTHANURS**, b gr c Brazen Beau (AUS)—Laguna Belle **B & M Pallets Ltd**
95 **NAUGHTY NADINE**, b f The Last Lion (IRE)—Glen Molly (IRE) **Mr N. Brereton**
96 **TAKEUSTOTHEMOON**, gr g Sea The Moon (GER)—Frosty Welcome (USA) **B & M Pallets Ltd**
97 **TWISTALINE**, b f Showcasing—Tongue Twista **ValueRacingClub.co.uk**

TWO-YEAR-OLDS

98 **ARTISTIC DREAMER**, b f 22/03 Caravaggio (USA)—So You Dream (IRE) (So You Think (NZ)) (8000) **Magna Carter Bloodstock**

Other Owners: M. Appleby, Mr W. M. Brackstone, Mr C. Buckingham, Mrs L. K. Buckingham, Mr C. Dixon, Mr M. Harris, Mr R. Hoiles, Mr F. McAleavy, Mr I. McAleavy, Mr S. G. Morris, Rod In Pickle Partnership, Exors of the Late Mr W. J. Sewell, Mr S. Sutton, Mr S. J. Whitear, Mr T. Wickins.

Assistant Trainer: Jonathan Clayton.

Flat Jockey: Alistair Rawlinson, Jason Watson. **Apprentice Jockey:** Theodore Ladd, Frederick Larson.

MR RICHARD ARMSON, Melbourne
Postal: **Scotlands Farm, Burney Lane, Staunton-Harold, Melbourne, Derbyshire, DE73 8BH**

1 **ALBURN**, 12, b g Alflora (IRE)—Burn Brook **R. J. Armson**
2 **KILCARAGH BOY (IRE)**, 13, b g King's Theatre (IRE)—Histologie (FR) **R. J. Armson**
3 **MACKIE DEE (IRE)**, 10, b g Westerner—Whatdoyouthinkmac (IRE) **R. J. Armson**
4 5, B g Sans Frontieres (IRE)—Shannon Pearl (IRE)

9 **MR PETER ATKINSON, Northallerton**
Postal: **Yafforth Hill Farm, Yafforth, Northallerton, North Yorkshire, DL7 0LT**
Contacts: **PHONE 01609 772598 MOBILE 07751 131215**

1 **BLACK MINSTER**, 7, bl g Trans Island—Mini Minster **Mr P. G. Atkinson**
2 **CENTIMENTALJOURNEY**, 5, b m Telescope (IRE)—Elusive Swallow **Mrs L. Atkinson**
3 **FINGAL'S HILL (IRE)**, 6, b g Shirocco (GER)—Fingal's Sister (IRE) **Mr P. G. Atkinson**
4 **PRIDE PARK (IRE)**, 6, b g Yeats (IRE)—Ballyallia Pride (IRE) **Mr P. G. Atkinson**
5 **RIBEYE**, 7, b g Lucarno (USA)—Elusive Swallow **Mrs L. Atkinson**

10 **MR MICHAEL ATTWATER, Epsom**
Postal: **Tattenham Corner Stables, Tattenham Corner Road, Epsom Downs, Surrey, KT18 5PP**
Contacts: **PHONE 01737 360066 MOBILE 07725 423633**
EMAIL Attwaterracing@hotmail.co.uk WEBSITE www.attwaterracing.com

1 **BIG TIME MAYBE (IRE)**, 7, b g Dandy Man (IRE)—Divine Design (IRE) **Lamprell Roofing Ltd**
2 **BREGUET BOY (IRE)**, 5, br g Requinto (IRE)—Holly Hawk (IRE) **Haxted Racing**
3 **CAPPANANTY CON**, 8, gr g Zebedee—Fairmont (IRE) **Dare To Dream Racing**
4 **CHROMIUM**, 5, gr m Cable Bay (IRE)—Ghedi (IRE) **Dare To Dream Racing**
5 **CONCIERGE (IRE)**, 6, br g Society Rock (IRE)—Warm Welcome **Dare To Dream Racing**
6 **DELAGATE THE LADY**, 6, b m Delegator—Lady Phill **Mrs M. S. Teversham**
7 **EZZRAH**, 6, b g Garswood—Tessie **Dare To Dream Racing**
8 **FAR TOO BEAUTIFUL**, 4, b f Farhh—Four Miracles **BG Racing Partnership**
9 **FUJAIRA KING (USA)**, 6, b g Kitten's Joy (USA)—Cat On a Tin Roof (USA) **Dare To Dream Racing**
10 **GAVLAR**, 11, b g Gentlewave (IRE)—Shawhill **Canisbay Bloodstock**
11 **JOEY'S GIFT**, 5, b g War Command (USA)—Cadeau Speciale **The Attwater Partnership**
12 **KINGSTON KURRAJONG**, 9, b g Authorized (IRE)—Kingston Acacia **Canisbay Bloodstock**
13 **LAWN RANGER**, 7, b g Cityscape—Baylini **Canisbay Bloodstock**
14 **LETTER AT DAWN (IRE)**, 4, b g Dawn Approach (IRE)—Christmas Letter (IRE) **Dare To Dream Racing**
15 **LOTHIAN**, 4, b g Coach House (IRE)—Gracilia (FR) **Haxted Racing**
16 **MAAHI VE (IRE)**, 4, ch f Havana Gold (IRE)—Elsa T (IRE) **The Attwater Partnership**
17 **MINHAAJ (IRE)**, 5, b m Invincible Spirit (IRE)—Sharqeyih **Dare To Dream Racing**
18 **MR MONEYPENNY**, 4, b g Monsieur Bond (IRE)—Normandy Maid **Haxted Racing**
19 **MY KIND OF LADY**, 4, b f Proconsul—Lady Suesanne (IRE) **The Attwater Partnership**
20 **NOBLE DEED**, 12, ch g Kyllachy—Noble One **Canisbay Bloodstock**
21 **PASSING CLOUDS**, 7, b g Kheleyf (USA)—Steppin Out **Canisbay Bloodstock**
22 **PHYSICS (IRE)**, 6, b g Acclamation—Precipitous (IRE) **Dare To Dream Racing**
23 **REAL ESTATE (IRE)**, 7, b g Dansili—Maskunah (IRE) **Mr A. C. D. Main**
24 **RHUBARB BIKINI (IRE)**, 5, b g Zoffany (IRE)—Pearlitas Passion (IRE) **Dare To Dream Racing**
25 **SAVOY BROWN**, 6, b g Epaulette (AUS)—Kindia (IRE) **Canisbay Bloodstock**
26 **SOMETHING LUCKY (IRE)**, 10, gr g Clodovil (IRE)—Lucky Leigh **Dare To Dream & the Attwater Partnership**
27 **STREET PARADE**, 6, b g Swiss Spirit—Jollification (IRE) **Dare To Dream Racing**
28 **TADREEB (IRE)**, 4, b c Oasis Dream—Wake Up Call **Canisbay Bloodstock**
29 **VANDAD (IRE)**, 5, b g Dandy Man (IRE)—Ruby Girl (IRE) **Dare To Dream Racing**

THREE-YEAR-OLDS

30 **ACADIAN CITY**, ch f Cityscape—Cajun Moon **Canisbay Bloodstock**
31 **ARD UP**, b g Ardad (IRE)—Oriental Romance (IRE) **The Attwater Partnership**
32 **BEAR TO DREAM (IRE)**, b f Kodi Bear (IRE)—Wind In Her Sails (IRE) **Dare To Dream Racing**
33 **BEAUEN ARROWS**, b g Brazen Beau (AUS)—Kindia (IRE) **Canisbay Bloodstock**
34 **CABEZA DE LLAVE**, ch g Pearl Secret—Speed Princess (IRE) **Dare To Dream Racing**
35 **LONG TIME COMIN**, ch f Postponed (IRE)—Bowstar **Canisbay Bloodstock**
36 **LUV U MUM**, b f Heeraat (IRE)—Lady Suesanne (IRE) **The Attwater Partnership**
37 **MARY OF MODENA**, b f Bated Breath—Miss Chicane **Haxted Racing**
38 **MISS SHIRLEY (IRE)**, b f Dandy Man (IRE)—Shirley (IRE) **Mr B. Neaves**
39 **MY JOKER (IRE)**, b g Free Eagle (IRE)—Redoutable (IRE) **The Attwater Partnership**

MR MICHAEL ATTWATER - continued

40 **NORDIC GLORY (IRE)**, ch g Cotai Glory—Norwegian Highness (FR) **Dare To Dream Racing**
41 **RULES OF ORDER (IRE)**, b g Acclamation—Lightning Mark (IRE) **The Attwater Partnership**
42 **STRAWBERRY LOLA**, b f Mayson—Strawberry Sorbet **Dare To Dream Racing**
43 **THANK THE LORD**, ch g Coach House (IRE)—Lady Phill **Mrs M. S. Teversham**

TWO-YEAR-OLDS

44 **BIG DRIFT**, b c 01/03 Brazen Beau (AUS)—Posy Fossil (USA) (Malibu Moon (USA)) (16000)
The Attwater Partnership

45 Gr c 27/01 Havana Grey—Eleusis (Elnadim (USA)) (12000) **The Attwater Partnership**
46 B c 10/04 Dandy Man (IRE)—Mercifilly (FR) (Whipper (USA)) (11000) **Dare To Dream Racing**

Other Owners: Mr B. M. Attwater, Mr M. J. Attwater, Dare To Dream Racing, R. F. Kilby, Mr A. C. D. Main, Mrs L. Main, Mr I. Sharrock, Mr W. Smith, Miss M. E. Stopher, The Attwater Partnership.

Assistant Trainer: S. Sawyer.

---

11 MR JEAN-RENE AUVRAY, Calne
Postal: **West Nolands Farm, Nolands Road, Yatesbury, Calne, Wiltshire, SN11 8YD**
Contacts: **MOBILE 07798 645796**
EMAIL **jr.auvray@outlook.com** WEBSITE **www.jrauvrayracing.co.uk**

1 **MAGNIFIQUE (FR)**, 4, ro f Dansili—Classe Vendome (FR) **Nigel Kelly & Stuart McPhee**
2 **STREETS OF FIRE (IRE)**, 8, br m Milan—Flaming Brandy (IRE) **Lady E. Mays-Smith**
3 **TRIGGER HAPPY (IRE)**, 5, b g Gutaifan (IRE)—Boom And Bloom (IRE) **Nigel Kelly & Jr Auvray Racing**

THREE-YEAR-OLDS

4 **KHARSHUF (USA)**, ch f Kitten's Joy (USA)—Aroosah (IRE) **Mr S. K. McPhee**
5 **MY FRIEND WOODY**, br g Garswood—Wotnot (IRE) **The Yatesbury Racing Syndicate**
6 **UMMSUQUAIM (USA)**, br f More Than Ready (USA)—Jiwen (CAN) **Nigel Kelly & Stuart McPhee**

---

12 MRS CAROLINE BAILEY, Holdenby
Postal: **Holdenby Lodge, Spratton, Northants, NN6 8LG**
Contacts: **HOME 01604 883729 PHONE 01604 770234 MOBILE 07831 373340 FAX 01604 770423**
EMAIL **caroline.bailey66@yahoo.com** WEBSITE **www.carolinebaileyracing.co.uk**

1 **ANNIE DAY (IRE)**, 7, br m Arcadio (GER)—Aunt Annie (IRE) **BDRSyndicates**
2 **ANOTHER NIGHTCAP (IRE)**, 6, gr ro g Dylan Thomas (IRE)—Silver Proverb
A Lofts K Nicholson P Proctor B Robinson
3 **BEGIN THE LUCK (IRE)**, 6, b g Le Fou (IRE)—Bobsyourdad (IRE) **Vaughan-jones, Bailey & Mellor**
4 **BOLDMERE**, 9, b g Multiplex—Pugnacious Lady **W. J. Odell**
5 **COBRA DE MAI (FR)**, 10, b g Great Pretender (IRE)—Miria Galanda (FR) **Mrs S. Carsberg**
6 **COOLE LION (IRE)**, 8, br g Presenting—Kayanti (IRE) **Mrs W. M. Wesley**
7 **CROSSPARK**, 12, b g Midnight Legend—Blue Shannon (IRE) **Mrs W. M. Wesley**
8 **ELKSTONE**, 11, b g Midnight Legend—Samandara (FR) **Tredwell, Robinson, Proctor & Nicholson**
9 **HOWYA HUN (IRE)**, 8, b m Stowaway—Glencree Rose (IRE) **Mrs J. M. Dixon Smith**
10 **HUNKY (FR)**, 5, b g Tirwanako (FR)—Funkia (FR) **G. T. H. Bailey**
11 **JUST A DEAL**, 7, b g Arvico (FR)—Monte Mayor Golf (IRE) **G. T. H. Bailey**
12 **LADY MASTER**, 9, b m Native Ruler—Elmside Katie **Mr P. Dixon Smith**
13 **LORD SPARKY**, 8, ch g Sulamani (IRE)—Braybrooke Lady (IRE) **The On The Bridle Partnership**

MRS CAROLINE BAILEY - continued

14 MATCHMAKING (GER), 7, ch g Mastercraftsman (IRE)—Monami (GER) **G. T. H. Bailey**
15 READY TO PLEASE, 6, b m Kayf Tara—Ready To Crown (USA) **Braybrooke Lodge Partnership**

Other Owners: G. T. H. Bailey, Mrs A. L. Lofts, Mrs S. Mellor, Mr K. M. Nicholson, Mr P. S. C. Proctor, Mrs B. D. Robinson, J. Tredwell, Mrs A. Vaughan-Jones.

NH Jockey: Sean Bowen, Harry Skelton. **Amateur Jockey:** Mr Thomas McClorey.

---

13 MR KIM BAILEY, Cheltenham

Postal: **Thorndale Farm, Withington Road, Andoversford, Cheltenham, Gloucestershire, GL54 4LL**
Contacts: **PHONE 01242 890241 MOBILE 07831 416859 FAX 01242 890193**
EMAIL info@kimbaileyracing.com WEBSITE www.kimbaileyracing.com

1 AJERO (IRE), 7, b g Red Jazz (USA)—Eoz (IRE) **Julie & David R Martin & Dan Hall**
2 ALNITAK, 5, b g Blue Bresil (FR)—Youngstar (FR) **Mr C. J. Courage**
3 ARCTIC SAINT (IRE), 4, gr g Saint des Saints (FR)—Nomad Attitude (FR) **Lady M. B. Dulverton**
4 BALLETICON (IRE), 8, br g Arakan (USA)—Miss Garbo (IRE) **Inn For A Penny**
5 BLAZON, 9, b g Dansili—Zante **The Blazing Optimists**
6 BOBHOPEORNOHOPE (IRE), 7, b g Westerner—Bandelaro (IRE) **Mr J. F. Perriss**
7 CAPTAIN ROSE, 5, b g Telescope (IRE)—Fragrant Rose **Park View**
8 CHARMING GETAWAY (IRE), 5, b g Getaway (GER)—Charming Leader (IRE) **Ever The Optimists**
9 CHAZZA (IRE), 8, b g Mahler—Presenting Proform (IRE) **The Azza Chance Syndicate**
10 CHIANTI CLASSICO (IRE), 5, b g Shantou (USA)—Ballinderry Lady (IRE) **Brooke Pilkington**
11 DESTROYTHEEVIDENCE, 4, b g Kayf Tara—Mathine (FR) **Mr P. J. Andrews**
12 DOES HE KNOW, 7, b g Alkaased (USA)—Diavoleria **Yes He Does Syndicate**
13 EL PRESENTE, 9, b g Presenting—Raitera (FR) **Davies Pilkington Yarborough Brooke**
14 EQUUS DREAMER (IRE), 7, ch g Getaway (GER)—Thornleigh Blossom (IRE)
                                                Mr & Mrs M Laws & Mr & Mrs P Woodhall
15 ESPOIR DE ROMAY (FR), 8, b g Kap Rock (FR)—Miss du Seuil (FR) **The Midgelets**
16 FAIR FRONTIERES (IRE), 7, ch g Sans Frontieres (IRE)—Cappawhite Lass (IRE) **The Front Ears**
17 FIRST FLOW (IRE), 10, b g Primary (USA)—Clonroche Wells (IRE) **A. N. Solomons**
18 FIRTH OF GOLD (IRE), 5, ch g Flemensfirth (USA)—Muance (FR) **The Flemmings**
19 FLIRTATIOUS GIRL (IRE), 6, b m Flemensfirth (USA)—Another Gaye (IRE)
                                                Mrs I. C. Sellars & Major & Mrs P. Arkwright
20 GALANTE DE ROMAY (FR), 6, gr m Lord du Sud (FR)—Miss du Seuil (FR) **The Galante Gallopers**
21 GALAXY MOON (FR), 4, b g Spanish Moon (USA)—Porquerollaise (FR) **Wendy Prince Racing**
22 GERARD MENTOR (FR), 6, b g Policy Maker (IRE)—Trephine du Sulon (FR) **Garrett, Meacham & Woodhall**
23 GETAWEAPON (IRE), 7, b m Getaway (GER)—Milan Serenade (IRE) **Mr J. F. Perriss**
24 GLANCING GLORY (IRE), 6, br m Presenting—Littlemissthistle (IRE) **Turf 2020 & Mrs D Johnson**
25 HALLIGATOR (FR), 5, b g Saddler Maker (IRE)—Quick des Sacart (FR) **Imperial Racing Partnership 2016**
26 HAMILTON DICI (FR), 5, b g Coastal Path—Umbria Dici (FR) **Lady M. B. Dulverton**
27 I SPY A DIVA, 5, b m Telescope (IRE)—Molly's A Diva **Mr J. F. Perriss**
28 IMPERIAL AURA (IRE), 9, b g Kalanisi (IRE)—Missindependence (IRE) **Imperial Racing Partnership 2016**
29 IMPERIAL HURRICANE, 5, b g Black Sam Bellamy (IRE)—Silverlined **Imperial Racing & Mr John Blackburn**
30 IMPERIAL ICON (IRE), 7, ch g Shantou (USA)—Bobomy (IRE) **Imperial Racing Partnership**
31 INCA ROSE, 7, ch g Malinas (GER)—Cinderella Rose **The Coln Valley Partnership**
32 INFLAGRANTE (IRE), 6, ch g Getaway (GER)—Maggie Connolly (IRE) **Mrs V. W. H. Johnson**
33 KYNTARA, 6, b g Kayf Tara—Speed Bonnie Boat **Lady M. B. Dulverton**
34 LADY OF THE NIGHT, 9, b m Midnight Legend—Even Flo **Mr J. F. Perriss**
35 4, b g Getaway (GER)—Liane de Pougy (FR)
36 LOTS OF LUCK (IRE), 8, b g Millenary—Lovely Hand (IRE) **Mr J. F. Perriss**
37 MAGICAL ESCAPE (IRE), 4, b g Getaway (GER)—Chestnut (IRE) **Surprise Syndicate**
38 MARTON ABBEY, 6, br g Orientor—Naywye **Jockey Club Ownership (SW 2020) Limited**
39 MIKHAILOVICH (IRE), 5, b g Sholokhov (IRE)—Putland's Bridge (IRE) **The Cossacks**
40 MR GREY SKY (IRE), 8, gr g Fame And Glory—Lakil Princess (IRE) **Mr P. J. Andrews**
41 PARC D'AMOUR (IRE), 5, b g Walk In The Park (IRE)—Mal d'Amour (IRE) **The Strollers**

MR KIM BAILEY - continued

42 **PARTY FUZZ**, 7, b g Great Pretender (IRE)—Very Special One (IRE) **Mr P. J. Andrews**
43 **PAY THE PILOT**, 5, b g Telescope (IRE)—Becky B **Julie & David R Martin & Dan Hall**
44 **PEAKED TOO SOON**, 5, b g Iffraaj—Libys Dream (IRE) **Julie & David R Martin & Dan Hall**
45 **PERCY VEERING**, 5, ch g Sir Percy—Saltpetre (IRE) **The Percy Vera's**
46 **PHANTOM GETAWAY (IRE)**, 5, ch g Getaway (GER)—Belle Provence (FR) **The P G Tipsters**
47 **QUEENOHEARTS (IRE)**, 9, ch m Flemensfirth (USA)—Chars (IRE) **The Sherington Partnership**
48 **ROCKY'S TREASURE (IRE)**, 11, b g Westerner—Fiddlers Bar (IRE) **Mr J. F. Perriss**
49 **ROSE AND THISTLE**, 5, b m Blue Bresil (FR)—Cinderella Rose **Jones Broughtons Wilson Weaver**
50 **SAINT BIBIANA (IRE)**, 5, b m Sholokhov (IRE)—En Vedette (FR) **Miss M. Peterson**
51 **SAMATIAN (IRE)**, 5, bl g Sageburg (IRE)—Bodhran Davis (FR) **Mr N. Carter**
52 **SAYADAM (FR)**, 5, b g Saint des Saints (FR)—Catmoves (FR) **Lady M. B. Dulverton**
53 **SHANACOOLE PRINCE (IRE)**, 9, ch g Primary (USA)—Shanacoole Rose (IRE) **Mr & Mrs Mark Laws**
54 **SHANTOU EXPRESS (IRE)**, 7, ch g Shantou (USA)—Spanker **The Second Chancers**
55 **SHINOBI (IRE)**, 6, ch g Iffraaj—Ninja Lady **Shinobithemoney**
56 **STARVOSKI (IRE)**, 7, b m Aizavoski (IRE)—Telstar (IRE) **The Grapevine Syndicate**
57 **SUBWAY SURF (IRE)**, 8, b g Shantou (USA)—Duck (IRE) **Surf On The Turf**
58 **TALK OF THE MOON**, 5, b m Pether's Moon (IRE)—Tara The Gossip (IRE) **E Hawkings A Lofts B Harding M Harris**
59 **TANTOLI**, 5, ch g Norse Dancer (IRE)—Aoninch **99 problems but the horse ain't 1**
60 **THE BULL MCCABE (IRE)**, 8, b g Yeats (IRE)—Twilight View (IRE) **Park View**
61 **THE EDGAR WALLACE (IRE)**, 7, b g Flemensfirth (USA)—Annalecky (IRE) **Mr P. J. Andrews**
62 **THOSE TIGER FEET (IRE)**, 8, b g Shantou (USA)—Luca Lite (IRE) **Mr P. J. Andrews**
63 **THRUTHELOOKINGLASS**, 5, b g Kayf Tara—Amazing d'Azy (IRE) **Mr & Mrs K. R. Ellis**
64 **TIME FOR HOLLIE**, 6, b m Black Sam Bellamy (IRE)—Any Pearl **Roy & Louise Swinburne**
65 **TREGELE (IRE)**, 4, b g Mahler—Emily Gray (IRE) **Julie & David R Martin & Dan Hall**
66 **TRELAWNE**, 6, b g Geordieland (FR)—Black Collar **The Real Partnership**
67 **TWO FOR GOLD (IRE)**, 9, b g Gold Well—Two of Each (IRE) **May We Never Be Found Out Partnership 2**
68 **UNDERCOVER LOVER (IRE)**, 4, b g Cloudings (IRE)—Another Gaye (IRE)
                                                                Mrs I. C. Sellars & Major & Mrs P. Arkwright
69 **VOYBURG (IRE)**, 6, br g Sageburg (IRE)—Slevoy Ahoy (IRE) **The Ten Sages**
70 **WANDRIN STAR (IRE)**, 11, b g Flemensfirth (USA)—Keralba (USA) **Mrs P. A. Perriss**

Other Owners: Major P. W. F. Arkwright, Mrs Sandra G. E. Arkwright, Mrs C. Bailey, Mr K. C. Bailey, Mr R. H. Beevor, Mr O. S. W. Bell, Sir F. Brooke, Sir M. F. Broughton, Mr D. J. Burke, Mr S. R. Cannon, Mr A. N. Cheyne, Mr K. T. Clancy, Mrs V. Clancy, M. E. T. Davies, Lady M. B. Dulverton, Mrs E. Ellis, K. R. Ellis, D. A. Hall, Mr B. C. Harding, Mr M. T. Harris, Lady M. P. Hatch, Mr E. J. Hawkings, Mrs V. W. H. Johnson, Mrs N. Jones, Mrs J. M. Laws, Mr M. J. Laws, Mrs A. L. Lofts, Col A. J. E. Malcolm, D. R. Martin, Mrs J. M. T. Martin, Mr R. A. Pilkington, Mrs N. P. Sellars, Mr R. Sheppard, Turf Club 2020, Mrs R. B. Weaver, Mr J. Webber, T. C. Wilson, Mrs F. M. Woodhall, Mr P. W. Woodhall, The Earl Of Yarborough.

Assistant Trainer: Matthew Nicholls.

NH Jockey: David Bass, Ciaran Gethings.

---

14 **MR LIAM BAILEY, Middleham**
Postal: **2 Little Spigot, Coverham, Middleham, Leyburn, North Yorkshire, DL8 4TL**
Contacts: **PHONE 07807 519220**
EMAIL liambailey_foulricefarm@hotmail.com

1 **ABEL HANDY (IRE)**, 7, b g Arcano (IRE)—Belle Isle **Mrs C M Clarke, Foulrice Park Racing Ltd**
2 **CANFORD'S JOY (IRE)**, 7, b g Canford Cliffs (IRE)—Joyful (IRE) **Mrs C M Clarke, Foulrice Park Racing Ltd**
3 **CEASE AND DESIST (IRE)**, 4, b g No Nay Never (USA)—Mackenzie's Friend **Oakfield Racing**
4 **CITY CENTRAL (IRE)**, 4, b f Camacho—Boucheron **Mrs C M Clarke, Foulrice Park Racing Ltd**
5 **CLANSMAN (IRE)**, 4, b g Nathaniel (IRE)—Pearl Dance (USA) **Mrs C M Clarke, Foulrice Park Racing Ltd**
6 **FANZONE (IRE)**, 5, b g Gutaifan (IRE)—Dame Alicia (IRE) **Foulrice Park Racing Limited**
7 **FRAMLEY GARTH (IRE)**, 10, b g Clodovil (IRE)—Two Marks (USA) **FPR Yorkshire Syndicate**
8 **GORDONSTOUN (IRE)**, 4, b g Gleneagles (IRE)—Elusive Girl (IRE) **Mrs C M Clarke, Foulrice Park Racing Ltd**
9 **HAJJAM**, 8, b g Paco Boy (IRE)—Amanda Carter **Mrs C M Clarke, Foulrice Park Racing Ltd**

MR LIAM BAILEY - continued

10 **HOW BIZARRE**, 7, ch g Society Rock (IRE)—Amanda Carter **Foulrice Park Racing Limited**
11 **INSIDE INTEL (IRE)**, 5, b m Intello (GER)—Polar Eyes **Mrs C M Clarke, Foulrice Park Racing Ltd**
12 **MARKAZI (FR)**, 8, gr g Dark Angel (IRE)—Marasima (USA) **Foulrice Park Racing Limited**
13 **QUANAH (IRE)**, 6, ch g Dandy Man (IRE)—Boucheron **Mrs A. M. Stirling**
14 **STRONSAY (IRE)**, 6, b g Gale Force Ten—Perfect Blossom **Mrs C M Clarke, Foulrice Park Racing Ltd**
15 **THREE SAINTS BAY (IRE)**, 7, b g Kodiac—Fiuise (IRE) **Mr C. R. Stirling**

THREE-YEAR-OLDS

16 **KATA HEART'S**, b g Mondialiste (IRE)—Just The Tonic **Wyndrinkers Racing**
17 B g Dragon Dancer—Lil Sophella (IRE) **Foulrice Park Racing Limited**

TWO-YEAR-OLDS

18 Ch c 01/03 Mondialiste (IRE)—Just The Tonic (Medicean) **Wyndrinkers Racing**

MR GEORGE BAKER, Chiddingfold
Postal: **Robins Farm, Fisher Lane, Chiddingfold, Godalming, Surrey, GU8 4TB**
Contacts: **PHONE 01428 682059 MOBILE 07889 514881**
EMAIL gbakerracing@gmail.com WEBSITE www.georgebakerracing.com

1 **ATOMIC JACK**, 7, b g Nathaniel (IRE)—Indigo River (IRE) **George Baker and Partners - Super Six**
2 **BONNET**, 4, ch f Helmet (AUS)—Tanda Tula (IRE) **Seaton Partnership**
3 **BOWLING RUSSIAN (IRE)**, 5, b g Lope de Vega (IRE)—Minute Limit (IRE) **Nigel Jones & Paul Bowden**
4 **CEMHAAN**, 5, b g Muhaarar—Shalwa **PJL Racing**
5 **CONFILS (FR)**, 6, b m Olympic Glory (IRE)—Mambo Mistress (USA) **Confidence Partnership**
6 **CONFRERIE (IRE)**, 7, b g Society Rock (IRE)—Intellibet One **New Confidence Partnership**
7 **DANTE'S VIEW (IRE)**, 6, ch g Galileo (IRE)—Daivika (USA) **Goodwin Racing Ltd**
8 **DAWAAM (USA)**, 6, b g Kitten's Joy (USA)—Nereid (USA) **George Baker Racing Bahrain Syndicate**
9 **DEVORGILLA**, 4, ch f Mukhadram—Sweetheart Abbey **Miss S. Bannatyne**
10 **DYAMI (FR)**, 5, b br g Bated Breath—Zaltana (USA) **Mark & Lavinia Sherwood**
11 **ETON BLUE (IRE)**, 4, b g Starspangledbanner (AUS)—Naturotopia (FR) **The Eton Ramblers**
12 **FAME N FORTUNE**, 6, b h Thewayyouare (USA)—Acapella Star (IRE) **Fame N Fortune Syndicate**
13 **GRAIGNES (FR)**, 6, b g Zoffany (IRE)—Grey Anatomy **Delancey Real Estate Asset Management Limited**
14 **HIERONYMUS**, 6, b g Dutch Art—Sleek **Mrs Pao, Mr Stafford & Mr Tucker**
15 **HIGHWAY ONE (USA)**, 8, b m Quality Road—Kinda Wonderful (USA) **Mr G. Baker**
16 **HONEYSUCKLE MOON**, 5, b m Make Believe—Zerka **Lady S. K. Marchwood**
17 **KAYARNAH**, 6, b m Mount Nelson—Sparkling Montjeu (IRE) **Mrs C. E. Cone**
18 **LA MAQUINA**, 7, b g Dutch Art—Miss Meltemi (IRE) **George Baker Racing Bahrain Syndicate**
19 **LOCKDOWN**, 4, b g Charm Spirit (IRE)—Bounty Box **Mrs Benjamin Newton & Friends**
20 **MAMILLIUS**, 9, b g Exceed And Excel (AUS)—Laika Lane (USA) **The Mamillius Partnership**
21 **MAY REMAIN**, 7, b g Mayson—Ultimate Best **Guards Club Racing Limited**
22 **PASSIONOVA (IRE)**, 4, b c Bated Breath—Passionable
                                           Mr G. Baker, Sir John Ritblat & Suki Ritblat, Mr P. Bowden
23 **PINWHEEL (IRE)**, 4, b g Exceed And Excel (AUS)—Quilting (USA) **Mr J R Wallis & Partners**
24 **RUN FORREST RUN (IRE)**, 4, b g Bobby's Kitten (USA)—Minute Limit (IRE) **Mr J R Wallis & Partners**
25 **SPIRIT WARNING**, 6, b g Charm Spirit (IRE)—Averami **Mr G. Baker**
26 **STUDY THE STARS**, 4, b g Due Diligence (USA)—Celestial Bay **Homebred Racing**
27 **SURREY PRINCESS**, 4, b f Kingman—Terre du Vent (FR) **Surrey Racing (SPR)**
28 **TAMPERE (IRE)**, 5, b m Sea The Moon (GER)—Brigitta (IRE) **The Tampere Partnership**
29 **THE LAMPLIGHTER (FR)**, 7, b g Elusive City (USA)—Plume Rouge **The Lamplighter Syndicate**

THREE-YEAR-OLDS

30 **AWESOME DANCER (IRE)**, ch g Highland Reel (IRE)—Adutchgirl (GER) **Carbine of London Racing (2)**
31 **BONDI SPICE (IRE)**, b c Australia—La Spezia (IRE) **One Day Rodney Partnership**

MR GEORGE BAKER - continued

32 **BOTANIST,** b c Bated Breath—Sunflower **Highclere ThoroughbredRacing-Dream Again**
33 **DESTINY QUEEN (FR),** b f Al Wukair (IRE)—Trissa (FR) **The Wise Old Al Partnership**
34 **FAT GLADIATOR (IRE),** b g Cotai Glory—New Magic (IRE) **The Fat Gladiators**
35 **GALACTIQUE,** b f Fast Company (IRE)—Lulu The Rocket **Hot To Trot Racing 1 & Theakston Stud**
36 **HECTOR (IRE),** b g Bated Breath—Typhoon Della (FR) **Sir John Ritblat & Suki Ritblat**
37 **IKKARI (IRE),** b f Mehmas (IRE)—Ease The Jets **Mr Rupert Williams & Friends**
38 **JOHN BALLIOL,** b g Sixties Icon—Sweetheart Abbey **Miss S. Bannatyne**
39 **LE FORBAN,** b g Showcasing—Compton Bird **Team Le Forban**
40 **RAWYAAN,** b g Markaz (IRE)—Rathaath (IRE) **Mr C. S. Norman, Highclere Thoroughbred Racing Ltd**
41 **RILEY'S AYADA,** b f Churchill (IRE)—Tobacco Bay (IRE) **Miss Riley Carson & Partner, Mr M. Doerr**
42 **RILEY'S POSITANO (IRE),** br g Bated Breath—Metal Precious (FR) **Miss Riley Carson & Partner, Mr M. Doerr**
43 **ROCHEBRUNE,** b f Postponed (IRE)—Singuliere (IRE) **Adams, Baker, Buckland & Green**
44 **SENSE OF SECURITY,** b f Havana Gold (IRE)—Lilly Junior **Fellowship Racing**
45 **SHE'S A LADY,** b c Telescope—Acapella Star **Fame N Fortune Syndicate**
46 **SHOWLAN SPIRIT,** ch f Showcasing—Seolan (IRE) **Sir John Ritblat & Suki Ritblat**
47 **SURREY MIST (FR),** gr g Kendargent (FR)—Kindly Dismiss (FR) **Surrey Racing (sm) & Partner**
48 **TRAMONTANE,** ch g Le Havre (IRE)—Paris Winds (IRE) **Mr G. Baker**
49 **WARHOL (IRE),** b g Belardo (IRE)—Darsan (IRE) **Mr C. S. Norman, Mr F. McKay**

TWO-YEAR-OLDS

50 **BABY BILL,** b c 03/04 Belgian Bill—Billie Jean (Bertolini) **PJL Racing**
51 **ELECTRIC AVENUE,** b c 19/03 Outstrip—School Fees (Royal Applause) **Mrs Benjamin Newton & Friends**
52 B c 01/02 New Approach (IRE)—Expecting To Fly (USA) (Iffraaj) (47000)
53 **OUT OF CAMELOPARDALIS,** b c 11/03 Brazen Beau—Camelopardalis (Tobougg) **Greens Racing**
54 B f 23/02 Bated Breath—Quiet Queen (Sulamani (IRE)) (25000)
55 Gr f 05/02 Cracksman—Runner Runner (IRE) (Dark Angel (IRE)) (59524) **Tucker, Stafford, Pao & McCormack**
56 **SURREY CHARM,** b f 26/02 Havana Gold (IRE)—Stacey Sutton (FR) (Tertullian (USA)) (26000) **Surrey Racing (SC)**

Other Owners: Mr Peter Andre, Mr G. Baker, Mrs Nona Baker, Mrs Valerie Baker, Mr P. Bowden, Bowden & Baker, Mrs Angela Bray, Sir Francis Brooke, Mr Willie Carson, Mr AN Cheyne, Turf Club, Mr Adrian Coleman, Miss Rebecca Curtis, Sir Alex Ferguson, Mr A. Flintoff, Mr S. Grubb, Mr C. R. Hadingham, Mr R. S. Hoskins, Mr David Howden, Mr Chris Humber, Miss L Hurley, Mrs EL James, Mrs Cherry Jones, Mr Bernard Kantor, David Kidd, E. McCormack, Mr G. Pariente, The Chriselliam Partnership, Mr Harry Phillips, Richard Pilkington, Sir Tommy Pilkington, Julian Pittam, Mr Jake Ritblat, Mr Jamie Ritblat, Mr M. A. C. Rudd, Edward Russell, Sir William Russell, Mr Don Shanks, Earl Spencer, Mrs Muffy Spencer, Alvediston Stud, Theakston Stud Syndicate, Mr M. J. Tracey, URSA Major Racing, J. R. Wallis, Mr Michael Watt, Mr Christopher Wright.

Assistant Trainer: Barney Baker, Patrick Murphy, Valerie Murphy.

Flat Jockey: Pat Cosgrave, Trevor Whelan. **NH Jockey:** Marc Goldstein.

---

16 **MR ANDREW BALDING, Kingsclere**
Postal: **Park House Stables, Kingsclere, Newbury, Berkshire, RG20 5PY**
Contacts: **PHONE 01635 298210**
EMAIL admin@kingsclere.com WEBSITE www.kingsclere.com

1 **ACHELOIS (IRE),** 4, b f Zoffany (IRE)—Fontley **Thurloe for Royal Marsden Cancer Charity**
2 **ALCOHOL FREE (IRE),** 4, b f No Nay Never (USA)—Plying (USA) **J. C. Smith**
3 **ALOUNAK (FR),** 7, b g Camelot—Awe Struck **King Power Racing Co Ltd**
4 **AURIA,** 4, b f Muhaarar—Tiana **Mrs F. Denniff**
5 **AURIFEROUS (IRE),** 4, b g Golden Horn—Sequester **Mick and Janice Mariscotti**
6 **BELL ROCK,** 6, b g Kingman—Liberally (IRE) **Mrs F. H. Hay**
7 **BERKSHIRE ROCCO (FR),** 5, ch g Sir Percy—Sunny Again **Berkshire Parts & Panels Ltd**
8 **BEYOND BOUNDARIES (IRE),** 4, ch g Australia—What A Treasure (IRE) **King Power Racing Co Ltd**
9 **BOUNCE THE BLUES (IRE),** 5, ch m Excelebration (IRE)—Jazz Up **Mrs B. M. Keller**
10 **CAROLUS MAGNUS (IRE),** 4, b g Holy Roman Emperor (IRE)—Izola **Kennet Valley Thoroughbreds III**

MR ANDREW BALDING - continued

11 **CHIL CHIL**, 6, b m Exceed And Excel (AUS)—Tiana **King Power Racing Co Ltd**
12 **COLTRANE (IRE)**, 5, b g Mastercraftsman (IRE)—Promise Me (IRE) **Mick and Janice Mariscotti**
13 **EIKONIX**, 4, b g Paco Boy (IRE)—Slide Show **Mr Daniel Hunt & Mrs Eileen Markham**
14 **FIESTA DE VEGA**, 5, ch g Lope de Vega (IRE)—Party (IRE) **PDR Properties**
15 **FIVETHOUSANDTOONE (IRE)**, 4, b c Frankel—Promised Money (IRE) **King Power Racing Co Ltd**
16 **FLYIN' HIGH**, 4, b c Siyouni (FR)—Zee Zee Top **Castle Down Racing**
17 **FOX CHAIRMAN (IRE)**, 6, b g Kingman—Starfish (IRE) **King Power Racing Co Ltd**
18 **FOX TAL**, 6, b g Sea The Stars (IRE)—Maskunah (IRE) **King Power Racing Co Ltd**
19 **FOXES TALES (IRE)**, 4, b c Zoffany (IRE)—Starfish (IRE) **King Power Racing Co Ltd**
20 **GOOD BIRTHDAY (IRE)**, 6, b g Dabirsim (FR)—Chica Loca (FR) **King Power Racing Co Ltd**
21 **GOOLWA (IRE)**, 4, b f Australia—Pivotalia (IRE) **Sheikh J. D. Al Maktoum**
22 **GROUP ONE POWER**, 5, b g Lope de Vega (IRE)—Lady Aquitaine (USA) **King Power Racing Co Ltd**
23 **HAPPY POWER (IRE)**, 6, gr h Dark Angel (IRE)—Tamarisk (GER) **King Power Racing Co Ltd**
24 **INVITE (IRE)**, 4, b f The Gurkha (IRE)—Katiyra (IRE) **Team Valor LLC**
25 **JOHNNY DRAMA (IRE)**, 7, b g Lilbourne Lad (IRE)—Quelle Histoire (IRE) **King Power Racing Co Ltd**
26 **KING'S LYNN**, 5, b g Cable Bay (IRE)—Kinematic **Her Majesty The Queen**
27 **KINGSOFTHEMIDLANDS (FR)**, 4, b g Kingman—Spin (IRE) **King Power Racing Co Ltd**
28 **MAY NIGHT**, 4, ch g Mayson—Dream Melody **M. Payton**
29 **MELLOW MAGIC**, 4, b f Nathaniel (IRE)—Lady Brora **Kingsclere Racing Club**
30 **MORANDO (FR)**, 9, gr g Kendargent (FR)—Moranda (FR) **King Power Racing Co Ltd**
31 **NAPPER TANDY**, 4, b c Mukhadram—Diktalina **Lisahully Investments Ltd**
32 **NATE THE GREAT**, 6, b g Nathaniel (IRE)—Theladyinquestion **Mildmay Racing & D. H. Caslon**
33 **NOTRE BELLE BETE**, 4, gr g Zoffany (IRE)—Angelic Guest (IRE) **King Power Racing Co Ltd**
34 **OO DE LALLY (IRE)**, 4, b g Vadamos (FR)—In Dubai (USA) **J. Palmer-brown & Partner 2**
35 **OPERA GIFT**, 5, b g Nathaniel (IRE)—Opera Glass **J. C. Smith**
36 **PIVOINE (IRE)**, 8, b g Redoute's Choice (AUS)—Fleur de Cactus (IRE) **King Power Racing Co Ltd**
37 **RANCH HAND**, 6, b g Dunaden (FR)—Victoria Montoya **Kingsclere Racing Club**
38 **ROSCIOLI**, 4, b g Territories (IRE)—Never Lose **Mr Philip Fox & Partner**
39 **SCAMPI**, 4, b g Nayef (USA)—Preveza (FR) **Mr M. W. Pendarves**
40 **SECRET SHADOW (IRE)**, 4, b f Camelot—Secret Pursuit (IRE) **Mr G. C. B. Brook**
41 **SHINE SO BRIGHT**, 6, gr h Oasis Dream—Alla Speranza **King Power Racing Co Ltd**
42 **SILENCE PLEASE (IRE)**, 5, b b r m Gleneagles (IRE)—Crazy Volume (IRE) **Team Valor LLC**
43 **SOMETHING ENTICING (IRE)**, 4, b f Fascinating Rock (IRE)—La Chapelle (IRE)
44 **SPIRIT MIXER**, 4, ch g Frankel—Arabian Queen (IRE) **J. C. Smith**
45 **SPRING GLOW**, 5, gr m Mukhadram—Spring Dream (IRE) **Rainbow Racing**
46 **STAR CABER**, 4, b br g Golden Horn—Lombatina (IRE) **King Power Racing Co Ltd**
47 **STONE OF DESTINY**, 7, b g Acclamation—Irishstone (IRE) **King Power Racing Co Ltd**
48 **SYMBOLIZE (IRE)**, 5, ch g Starspangledbanner (AUS)—French Flirt **Sheikh J. D. Al Maktoum**
49 **TACTICAL**, 4, b c Toronado (IRE)—Make Fast **Her Majesty The Queen**
50 **TRIBAL CRAFT**, 6, ch m Mastercraftsman (IRE)—Snoqualmie Star **J. C. Smith**
51 **VALLEY FORGE**, 4, b g Dansili—Lixirova (FR) **G. Strawbridge**
52 **WE'LL MEET AGAIN**, 4, b f Cityscape—Sweet Mandolin **J. C. & S. R. Hitchins**

THREE-YEAR-OLDS

53 **AEGIS POWER**, b c Nathaniel (IRE)—Robema **King Power Racing Co Ltd**
54 **AFTER EIGHT**, b c Rock of Gibraltar (IRE)—Peppermint Green **Park House Partnership**
55 **AL MARMAR (IRE)**, br c Kodiac—Fraulein **Al Shaqab Racing UK Limited**
56 **ALL GO**, b f Bobby's Kitten (USA)—Alboretta **Miss K. Rausing**
57 **ANGEL'S POINT**, b c Dark Angel (IRE)—Madonna Dell'orto **Sheikh Mohammed Obaid Al Maktoum**
58 **ANTIPHON (IRE)**, b c Kodiac—Freedom's Light **G. Strawbridge**
59 **ATTACHE (IRE)**, b g Declaration of War (USA)—Go Kart (IRE) **Kennet Valley Thoroughbreds VII**
60 **AUSTRALIAN ANGEL**, ch f Australia—Angel Terrace (USA) **G. Strawbridge**
61 **AZTEC EMPIRE (IRE)**, b c Sea The Stars (IRE)—Azanara (IRE) **Sheikh I. S. Al Khalifa**
62 **BERKSHIRE BREEZE (IRE)**, b c Mastercraftsman (IRE)—Bright And Shining (IRE) **Berkshire Parts & Panels Ltd**
63 **BERKSHIRE REBEL (IRE)**, b c Sir Percy—Silicon Star (FR) **Berkshire Parts & Panels Ltd**
64 **BERKSHIRE SHADOW**, gr c Dark Angel (IRE)—Angel Vision (IRE) **Berkshire Parts & Panels Ltd No1 Fanclub**
65 **BIZARRE LAW**, b c Lawman (FR)—Bizzarria **Apollo Racing, Opulence T-breds**
66 **BLACKBIRD POWER**, gr f Dark Angel (IRE)—Delevigne **King Power Racing Co Ltd**
67 **CADMUS (IRE)**, b g Gleneagles (IRE)—Allegrezza **Ellipsis & Partner**

MR ANDREW BALDING - continued

68 **CAPTAIN SQUARE**, ch g Sir Percy—Primobella **Mrs L E Ramsden & Partner**
69 **CITY STREAK**, ch g Cityscape—Daffydowndilly **Lord J. Blyth**
70 **CONFLICT (IRE)**, b c No Nay Never (USA)—Sound of Guns **Qatar Racing, M Detampel, D Howden**
71 **DISTANT LIGHT**, b f Fastnet Rock (AUS)—Light Music **Her Majesty The Queen**
72 **DUBAI JEWEL**, b f Showcasing—Diamond Blaise **Sheikh Mohammed Obaid Al Maktoum**
73 **DUCAL CROWN**, b c Duke of Marmalade (IRE)—Ebony Flyer (SAF) **Team Valor, Cayton Park Stud, Mr.A.Singh**
74 **DUTY BOUND**, b c Kingman—Key Point (IRE) **Her Majesty The Queen**
75 **ELOGIO (IRE)**, b g Aclaim (IRE)—Scholarly **J. Palmer-brown & Partner 2**
76 **EMULATION**, b f Ulysses (IRE)—My Hope (USA) **Cheveley Park Stud Limited**
77 **ESPADA (IRE)**, ch c Lope de Vega (IRE)—Lady Pimpernel **Mick and Janice Mariscotti**
78 **FAR AWAY THOUGHTS**, b c Storm The Stars (USA)—War Effort (USA) **Sheikh J. D. Al Maktoum**
79 **FILBERT POWER**, ch c Night of Thunder (IRE)—Candleberry **King Power Racing Co Ltd**
80 **FLAG HIGH (IRE)**, b g Starspangledbanner (AUS)—Acid **J Maldonado/ Pip Elson & Partner**
81 **FOLLOW THAT STAR**, b f Almanzor (FR)—Queen of The Stars **Mr Sultan Ali**
82 **FRANKLIN WILLIAM**, b c Frankel—Kiyoshi **Qatar Racing Limited**
83 **GREEN AND PLEASANT**, b f Pivotal—Grace And Favour **N. M. H. Jones**
84 **GRIFFIN PARK**, ch c Elm Park—Know The Truth **Kingsclere Racing Club**
85 **GROUNDBREAKER (GER)**, b c Oasis Dream—Guajara (GER) **Sheikh Mohammed Obaid Al Maktoum**
86 **HARROW (IRE)**, gr c El Kabeir (USA)—School Run (IRE) **Highclere Thoroughbred Racing - Wisteria**
87 **HESPERANTHA**, ch f The Gurkha (IRE)—Conservatory **Mrs P. I. Veenbaas**
88 **HOFFMAN (IRE)**, ch c New Bay—Nordkappe (GER) **The Yippees & Partner**
89 **HOO YA MAL**, b c Territories (IRE)—Sensationally **A. Al Shaikh**
90 **I'LL BE THERE**, ch f Starspangledbanner (AUS)—Hanella (IRE) **Mrs A. Althani**
91 **IMMINENT**, b f Dubawi (IRE)—Enticement **Her Majesty The Queen**
92 **IMPERIAL FIGHTER (IRE)**, b c The Gurkha (IRE)—Endure (IRE) **Mr M. A. R. Blencowe**
93 **JUAN BERMUDEZ**, ch c Nathaniel (IRE)—Long Face (USA) **The Bermuda Salman Morris Partnership**
94 **KITTEN HEELS**, b f Bobby's Kitten (USA)—Bossybobby **Lord J. Blyth**
95 **KOY KOY**, b c Acclamation—Lynique (IRE) **Mrs A. Althani**
96 **LADY CLEMENTINE**, b f Churchill (IRE)—Wind Fire (USA) **Qatar Racing Limited**
97 **LADY LABELLE (IRE)**, ch f The Gurkha (IRE)—Duchess of Marmite (IRE) **Team Valor LLC**
98 **LITTLE HUSTLE**, b c Fastnet Rock (AUS)—Amser **Park House Partnership**
99 **LOVE MYSTERY**, ch c Frankel—Mix And Mingle (IRE) **King Power Racing Co Ltd**
100 **MAJESTIC GLORY**, b f Frankel—Bella Nouf **Mrs D. A. Tabor**
101 **MASEKELA (IRE)**, b c El Kabeir (USA)—Lady's Purse **Mick and Janice Mariscotti**
102 **MOMENT DE REVE**, b f Equiano (FR)—Dreamily (IRE) **Ms S. M. Pritchard-Jones, Byerley Racing Club**
103 **MONT ATHENA**, ch f Nathaniel (IRE)—Le Badie (IRE) **Farleigh Racing**
104 **MR ZIPPI**, b c Intello (GER)—Izzi Top **Castle Down Racing**
105 **NASIM**, ch g Galileo Gold—Ashwaq **Al Rabban Racing**
106 **NEANDRA (GER)**, gr f Jukebox Jury (IRE)—Noble Rose (GER) **DJT Racing & Partner**
107 **NIETZSCHE'S STAR**, b g Exceed And Excel (AUS)—Whim **Colbert Racing**
108 **NOBEL (IRE)**, ch c Lope de Vega (IRE)—Starlet (IRE) **Qatar Racing Limited**
109 **NOBLE RUN (USA)**, b c Noble Mission—Toxis (USA) **Another Bottle Racing 2**
110 **NYMPHADORA**, b f No Nay Never (USA)—Bewitchment **St Albans Bloodstock Limited**
111 **OLD HARROVIAN**, ch c Sea The Stars (IRE)—Daivia (USA) **Mr M. A. R. Blencowe**
112 **ORZO**, b f Aclaim (IRE)—Chibola (ARG) **Mrs A. Wigan**
113 **PRINCE OF REBELS (IRE)**, b g Estidhkaar (IRE)—Cute **Mr M. A. R. Blencowe**
114 **RENDITION (IRE)**, ch f Ulysses (IRE)—Penny Lane Forever **Cheveley Park Stud Limited**
115 **RETICENT**, b f Sixties Icon—Inhibition **Kingsclere Racing Club**
116 **RING FENCED**, b f Haafhd—Victoria Pollard **Kingsclere Racing Club**
117 **ROSEBERRY TOPPING**, b f Mayson—Our Poppet (IRE) **Hot To Trot Racing 1**
118 **SANDRINE**, b f Bobby's Kitten (USA)—Seychelloise **Miss K. Rausing**
119 **SAORLA**, ch f Charming Thought—Lizzie Tudor **Ms K. Gough**
120 **SCHMILSSON**, b c Muhaarar—Zee Zee Top **Mick and Janice Mariscotti**
121 **SEA GREY**, gr c Ulysses (IRE)—Sensory (IRE) **Mrs A. Althani**
122 **SHARP FRANK**, b c Frankel—Sharp Susan (USA) **Cayton Park Stud Limited**
123 **SIR HENRY COTTON (IRE)**, gr g Gutaifan (IRE)—Findhorn Magic **Mr B Greenwood/Mrs K Greenwood/Pip Elson**
124 **SOUL STOPPER**, b c Postponed (IRE)—Perfect Spirit (IRE) **Sheikh Mohammed Obaid Al Maktoum**
125 **SOUTHERLY STORM**, b g Fastnet Rock (AUS)—Opera Gal (IRE) **J. C. Smith**
126 **SPEAK**, gr f Sea The Moon (GER)—Lixirova (FR) **G. Strawbridge**
127 **STAR FROM AFARHH**, b f Farhh—Tears of The Sun **Dr Bridget Drew & Partners**

MR ANDREW BALDING - continued

128 B f Nayef (USA)—Sweet Mandolin **J. C. & S. R. Hitchins**
129 SWILCAN BRIDGE, b c Helmet (AUS)—Avon Lady **Mick and Janice Mariscotti**
130 TACK (FR), b c Iffraaj—Make Fast **Her Majesty The Queen**
131 TEUMESSIAS FOX (IRE), ch c Lope de Vega (IRE)—Princess Serena (USA) **King Power Racing Co Ltd**
132 TYPEWRITER (IRE), b f Gleneagles (IRE)—On Location (USA) **Mrs F. H. Hay**
133 UPTON PARK (FR), ch c Elm Park—Sienna Bella **Qatar Racing Ltd & A M Balding**
134 VAZIRE (IRE), b f Frankel—Aricia (IRE) **G. Strawbridge**
135 VE DAY (IRE), b c Churchill (IRE)—Cochabamba (IRE) **Mrs F. H. Hay**
136 VEGA SICILIA, ch c Lope de Vega (IRE)—Stone Roses (FR) **Apollo Racing & Srb Equine**
137 VIRTUOSO, b f Passing Glance—Make Music **Kingsclere Racing Club**
138 WAR IN HEAVEN (IRE), b c Exceed And Excel (AUS)—Burma Sun (IRE) **Mr M. A. R. Blencowe**
139 WHIMSY, ch f Charming Thought—Cape Victoria **Kingsclere Racing Club**
140 WILDERNESS GIRL (IRE), br f No Nay Never (USA)—Novantae **Cornthrop Bloodstock Limited**
141 WODETON (FR), b br g Wootton Bassett—Amanda Carter **Thurloe Thoroughbreds Ll**
142 WOLSEY (USA), b br c Kitten's Joy (USA)—Justaroundmidnight (IRE) **Qatar Racing Limited**

TWO-YEAR-OLDS

143 B c 22/04 Cracksman—Al Mahmeyah (Teofilo (IRE)) (55000) **Hamad Rashed Bin Ghedayer**
144 B c 22/04 No Nay Never (USA)—Aljaazya (USA) (Speightstown (USA)) (260000) **Mrs F. H. Hay**
145 Gr c 10/02 Kingman—America Nova (FR) (Verglas (IRE)) **Al Wasmiyah Stud**
146 ANOTHER RUN (IRE), b c 09/05 Zoffany (IRE)—Mais Si (Montjeu (IRE)) (80000) **Another Bottle Racing 2**
147 ARABIAN STORM, b c 09/03 Kingman—Arabian Queen (IRE) (Dubawi (IRE)) **J. C. Smith**
148 B c 15/03 Cracksman—Astrelle (IRE) (Makfi) (200000) **King Power Racing Co Ltd**
149 B c 20/03 Time Test—Aurelia (Rainbow Quest (USA)) (400000) **King Power Racing Co Ltd**
150 B c 10/04 Nathaniel (IRE)—Averami (Averti (IRE)) **Kingsclere Racing Club**
151 B c 29/02 Cracksman—Bahia Breeze (Mister Baileys) (75000) **Mr S. Suhail**
152 B f 30/04 Time Test—Bari (IRE) (Cape Cross (IRE)) (72000) **Sheikh J. D. Al Maktoum**
153 BATISTET, b c 05/02 Bated Breath—Bermondsey Girl (Bertolini (AUS)) (19048) **Miss S. Phipps Hornby**
154 B f 21/02 Zoustar (AUS)—Beldale Memory (IRE) (Camacho) **Qatar Racing Limited**
155 BERKSHIRE BRAVE (IRE), b c 21/04 Churchill (IRE)—Mitzi Winks (Lookin At Lucky (USA)) (55000)
                                                                            Berkshire Parts & Panels Ltd
156 BERKSHIRE CRUZ, b c 08/02 Exceed And Excel (AUS)—Special Dancer (Shareef Dancer (USA)) (75000)
                                                                            Berkshire Parts & Panels Ltd
157 BERKSHIRE PHANTOM, gr c 10/03 Expert Eye—Silver Step (FR) (Silver Frost (IRE)) (75000)
                                                                            Berkshire Parts & Panels Ltd
158 BERKSHIRE SUNDANCE, ch c 23/02 Decorated Knight—Hugs 'n Kisses (IRE) (Noverre (USA)) (34014)
                                                                            Berkshire Parts & Panels Ltd
159 BETTERMENT, b f 12/05 Bobby's Kitten (USA)—Beta (Selkirk (USA)) **Miss K. Rausing**
160 B c 07/04 Zoustar (AUS)—Bewitchment (Pivotal) **Mr D. P. Howden**
161 BRITANNICA, ch f 06/03 Lope de Vega (IRE)—Guerriere (Invincible Spirit (IRE)) (310000)
                                                                            St Albans Bloodstock Limited
162 B c 08/03 Dark Angel (IRE)—Bulrushes (Byron) (90000) **Al Wasmiyah Stud**
163 B c 18/04 Bobby's Kitten (USA)—Cape Spirit (IRE) (Cape Cross (IRE)) **Kingsclere Racing Club**
164 B c 16/02 Cityscape—Casual Glance (Sinndar (IRE)) **Kingsclere Racing Club**
165 B c 23/02 Siyouni (FR)—Cercle de La Vie (Galileo (IRE)) (1275510) **H.H. Sheikh Nasser Al Khalifa**
166 CHARITABLE, b f 10/02 Iffraaj—Send Up (IRE) (Fastnet Rock (AUS)) (65000) **Highclere - Ernest Hemingway**
167 B f 04/02 Sea The Stars (IRE)—Childa (IRE) (Duke of Marmalade (IRE)) **H.H. Sheikh Nasser Al Khalifa**
168 CONSTITUTION, b c 19/02 Churchill (IRE)—Pack Together (Paco Boy) **Her Majesty The Queen**
169 B f 05/04 Sea The Stars (IRE)—Crafty (AUS) (Manhattan Rain (AUS)) **Qatar Racing Limited**
170 B c 30/04 U S Navy Flag (USA)—Cristielle (Australia) **Imad Alsagar**
171 B c 11/05 Zoffany (IRE)—Danidh Dubai (IRE) (Noverre (USA)) (60000) **Thurloe Thoroughbreds Ll**
172 DESERT COP, b c 19/04 Oasis Dream—Speed Cop (Cadeaux Genereux) **J. C. Smith**
173 Ch c 25/02 Dawn Approach (IRE)—Dorraar (IRE) (Shamardal (USA)) **Sheikh Hamed Dalmook Al Maktoum**
174 DUTIFUL, b f 06/02 Ulysses (IRE)—Verity (Redoute's Choice (AUS)) **Cheveley Park Stud Limited**
175 Ch f 20/04 Gleneagles (IRE)—Elbereth (Mount Nelson) (110000) **Magnier, Tabor, Smith & Westerberg**
176 ELEANOR CROSS, b f 09/05 Pivotal—Field of Miracles (IRE) (Galileo (IRE)) **Cheveley Park Stud Limited**
177 EMBRACE (IRE), b f 16/01 Lope de Vega (IRE)—Whazzis (Desert Prince (IRE)) (70000) **Mr A. A. Alkhallafi**
178 ENBORNE, b f 16/02 Tamayuz—Highest (Dynaformer (USA)) **Denford Stud**
179 B c 10/02 Acclamation—Fashion Theory (Dubawi (IRE)) (68027) **Mr M. A. R. Blencowe**

MR ANDREW BALDING - continued

180 FEYHA (IRE), b f 31/01 Sir Percy—Mariana (IRE) (Manduro (GER)) (23810) **Ellipsis Ii & Partner**
181 B c 23/04 Time Test—Flashing Colour (GER) (Pivotal) (15238) **Pimlico Racing - Time Test**
182 B c 20/04 Time Test—Four Miracles (Vettori (IRE)) (25000) **Mrs A. Althani**
183 Ch c 21/04 Zoffany (IRE)—Frabjous (Pivotal) (35238) **Mr M. A. R. Blencowe**
184 FRANKNESS, ch f 18/02 Frankel—Cosmopolitan Queen (Dubawi (IRE)) **J. C. Smith**
185 B gr c 12/04 Dark Angel (IRE)—Fregate First (Le Havre (IRE)) (40000) **Mrs A. Althani**
186 GALACTIC JACK, b c 06/04 Galileo (IRE)—Galileo (Champs Elysees) J. C. Smith
187 GETOVERIT, b c 11/02 Gutaifan (IRE)—Titova (Halling (USA)) (7619) **Park House Partnership**
188 GLENFINNAN, b c 21/03 Harry Angel (IRE)—Fatanah (IRE) (Green Desert (USA)) (100000)
Mick and Janice Mariscotti
189 GOLDSBOROUGH, ch c 31/03 2011 Pearl Secret—Emily Carr (IRE) (Teofilo (IRE)) **Ms S. M. Pritchard-Jones**
190 Gr c 27/04 Tasleet—Gone Sailing (Mizzen Mast (USA)) (52000) **Kennet Valley Thoroughbreds VII**
191 GRENHAM BAY (IRE), gr c 12/04 Dark Angel (IRE)—Dawn of Empire (USA) (Empire Maker (USA)) (35000)
Martin & Valerie Slade & Partner
192 B f 07/01 El Kabeir (USA)—Hidden Steps (Footstepsinthesand) (15000) **Simon Davies**
193 B f 21/02 Lightning Spear—Hidden Valley (Haafhd) **Kingsclere Racing Club**
194 B f 02/02 Shirocco (GER)—Highland Pass (Passing Glance) **Kingsclere Racing Club**
195 B f 06/04 Caravaggio (USA)—Honourably (IRE) (Galileo (IRE)) (83420) **Mr J Wright**
196 Gr c 18/01 Kessaar (IRE)—Hope And Faith (IRE) (Zebedee) (52000) **Sheikh A. H. F. M. A. Al Sabah**
197 B c 09/03 Nathaniel (IRE)—Indian Love Bird (Efisio) (25000) **A. Al Shaikh**
198 Ch c 17/03 Mehmas (IRE)—Interweave (Dutch Art) (109524) **Sheikh A. H. F. M. A. Al Sabah**
199 B c 17/04 Dubawi (IRE)—J Wonder (USA) (Footstepsinthesand) (450000) **MyRacehorse.com, Mr A Rosen**
200 JURYMAN, b c 21/03 Recorder—Kinematic (Kyllachy) **Her Majesty The Queen**
201 KAY CERAAR, b c 19/03 Kessaar (IRE)—Love To Dream (IRE) (Dream Ahead (USA)) (24762)
Park House Partnership
202 B c 02/04 Mehmas (IRE)—Kibara (Sadler's Wells (USA)) (45714) **Mr M. A. R. Blencowe**
203 KING'S VANITY, b c 03/02 Kingman—Pant's Vanity (Poet's Voice) (150000) **Mrs C. J. Wates**
204 B f 29/02 Passing Glance—Know The Truth (Lawman (FR)) (952) **Kingsclere Racing Club**
205 Gr c 20/04 Dark Angel (IRE)—Kurland (IRE) (Kheleyf (USA)) **Sheikh J. D. Al Maktoum**
206 Br c 05/04 Raven's Pass (USA)—Lady Bee (IRE) (Lawman (FR)) (17143) **The Merry Pranksters & Partner**
207 Ch c 28/04 Roaring Lion (USA)—Lady Dragon (IRE) (Galileo (IRE)) **Qatar Racing Limited**
208 B f 12/03 Saxon Warrior (JPN)—Lady Perignon (Poet's Voice) **Mrs F. H. Hay**
209 B c 26/04 Oasis Dream—Lavender And Lace (Barathea (IRE)) (67000) **Abdullatif M Al-Abdulrazzaq**
210 B f 19/02 No Nay Never (USA)—Light The Stars (IRE) (Sea The Stars (IRE)) (170068) **Qatar Racing Limited**
211 B c 15/03 Gregorian (IRE)—Macarthurs Park (IRE) (Equiano (FR)) (115000) **Saeed Bin Mohammed Al Qassimi**
212 B c 10/04 Intello (GER)—Make Music (Acclamation) **Kingsclere Racing Club**
213 MARZOCCO, gr c 01/03 Roaring Lion (USA)—Sand Shoe (Footstepsinthesand) (85000) **Mick and Janice Mariscotti**
214 MATCHING SOX (IRE), b c 17/02 Camacho—Follow My Lead (Night Shift (USA)) (32381)
The Pink Hat Racing Partnership
215 B c 08/03 Havana Gold (IRE)—Mirzam (IRE) (Mastercraftsman (IRE)) (16000) **Simon Davies**
216 MLLE CHANEL, b f 18/04 Bobby's Kitten (USA)—Miss Cap Ferrat (Darshaan) **Miss K. Rausing**
217 B c 09/05 Cracksman—Mount Elbrus (Barathea (IRE)) **Mr Sultan Ali**
218 B c 08/02 Kuroshio (AUS)—My Better Half (Rip Van Winkle (IRE)) (102041) **King Power Racing Co Ltd**
219 Ch c 30/04 Ulysses (IRE)—Nashama (IRE) (Pivotal) (21905) **Relentless Dreamers Racing & Partner**
220 NIGHT AT SEA, br f 12/02 Sea The Stars (IRE)—Wordless (IRE) (Rock of Gibraltar (IRE)) **Denford Stud**
221 OPERA FOREVER, b f 25/03 No Nay Never (USA)—Opera Gal (IRE) (Galileo (IRE)) **J. C. Smith**
222 PERISTYLE, ch f 08/02 Ulysses (IRE)—Verandah (Medicean) **Cheveley Park Stud Limited**
223 PLATINUM JUBILEE, b f 15/04 Oasis Dream—Marisol (IRE) (Teofilo (IRE)) (65000) **Royal Ascot Racing Club**
224 B f 24/04 Sea The Moon (GER)—Plume Rose (Marchand de Sable (USA)) (170000) **Mr J Wright**
225 B c 22/04 Dandy Man (IRE)—Plying (USA) (Hard Spun (USA)) **Clipper Logistics**
226 Ch c 05/03 Dream Ahead (USA)—Private Cashier (Leroidesanimaux (BRZ)) **Mr R. J. C. Wilmot-Smith**
227 B c 11/03 Australia—Queen Arabella (Medicean) (100000) **Mr S. Suhail**
228 B c 23/03 Sea The Moon (GER)—Queen's Dream (GER) (Oasis Dream) **Sir Alex Ferguson**
229 B f 20/02 Saxon Warrior (JPN)—Remember You (IRE) (Invincible Spirit (IRE)) **Healthy Wood Co**
230 Br c 04/02 Roaring Lion (USA)—Rich Legacy (IRE) (Holy Roman Emperor (IRE)) (140000) **Qatar Racing Limited**
231 Ch c 09/04 Showcasing—Roodle (Xaar) (130000) **Mr S. Suhail**
232 Gr c 24/03 Havana Grey—Roxie Lot (Exceed And Excel (AUS)) (55238) **J. Palmer-brown & Partner 2**
233 ROYAL WOOTTON, b f 21/03 Wootton Bassett—Rimth (Oasis Dream) **Denford Stud**
234 B f 27/02 Nathaniel (IRE)—Same Jurisdiction (SAF) (Mambo In Seattle (USA)) **Cayton Park Stud Limited**
235 SCINTILLANTE, gr c 17/03 Roaring Lion (USA)—Freesia (IRE) (Dansili) (62000) **Mr Philip Fox & Partner**

MR ANDREW BALDING - continued

236 B c 16/05 Kodiac—Serafina's Flight (Fantastic Light (USA)) (60000) **Sheikh A. H. F. M. A. Al Sabah**
237 Br f 06/02 Camelot—Shamlahar (Shamardal (USA)) **Hussain Alabbas Lootah**
238 B c 28/04 Le Havre (IRE)—Shutka (FR) (Holy Roman Emperor (IRE)) (63776) **Mr M. A. R. Blencowe**
239 SPRING DAY, ch f 30/03 Bobby's Kitten (USA)—So In Love (Smart Strike (CAN)) **Miss K. Rausing**
240 B f 02/02 Pour Moi (IRE)—St Mary's (Siyouni (FR)) **Kingsclere Racing Club**
241 STORM BUSTER, b c 12/02 Dubawi (IRE)—Barshiba (FR) (Barathea (IRE)) **J. C. Smith**
242 B f 08/02 Saxon Warrior (JPN)—Summer Chorus (Exceed And Excel (AUS)) **Sheikh J. D. Al Maktoum**
243 SYDNEY MEWS (IRE), ch f 23/02 New Bay—La Superba (IRE) (Medicean) (47619) **Chelsea Thoroughbreds**
244 B c 27/03 Churchill (IRE)—Tanaghum (Darshaan) (440000) **King Power Racing Co Ltd**
245 THE GOAT, ch c 22/03 Cracksman—My Hope (AUS) (Afleet Alex (USA)) (45000) **The True Acre Partnership 1**
246 THERAPIST, b f 19/02 Le Havre (IRE)—Homeopathic (Dark Angel (IRE)) **Cheveley Park Stud Limited**
247 TORRE DE ORO, b c 08/02 Almanzor (FR)—Roystonia (IRE) (Redoute's Choice (AUS)) (55000)
Mick and Janice Mariscotti
248 TOSTADO (IRE), b c 15/04 Kessaar (IRE)—Zaindera (IRE) (Acclamation) (38095) **Mr J. Maldonado**
249 TOTNES (IRE), b f 10/03 Kingman—Havant (Halling (USA)) **Mrs A. Wigan**
250 VERMILION (IRE), b f 19/02 Kodiac—Western Sky (Barathea (IRE)) (120000) **Highclere - Sir Alexander Fleming**
251 VETIVER, ch f 05/02 Twilight Son—Poana (FR) (New Approach) **Cheveley Park Stud Limited**
252 B c 20/04 Sea The Moon (GER)—Victoria Pollard (Sir Percy) **Kingsclere Racing Club**
253 Ch c 24/01 Sioux Nation (USA)—Volute (FR) (Rock of Gibraltar (IRE)) (65476) **Sheikh A. H. F. M. A. Al Sabah**
254 WINNARETTA (IRE), b gr f 06/05 No Nay Never (USA)—Freezy (IRE) (Dalakhani (IRE)) (60000)
Mr J Gladstone & Partner

Other Owners: Sheikh I. S. Al Khalifa, Apollo Racing, Mr A. M. Balding, Berkshire Parts & Panels Ltd, Cayton Park Stud Limited, Cornthrop Bloodstock Limited, Dr Bridget Drew & Partners, Mr D. P. Howden, Mr D. Hunt, Mr J. Maldonado, Mildmay Racing, Qatar Racing Limited, Team Valor LLC.

Assistant Trainer: Paul Morkan.

Flat Jockey: Rob Hornby, Oisin Murphy, David Probert, Jason Watson. **Apprentice Jockey:** William Carver, William Cox, Harry Davies, Callum Hutchinson.

17	**MR RICHARD J. BANDEY, Kingsclere** Postal: **Plantation House, Wolverton, Tadley, Hampshire, RG26 5RP** Contacts: **MOBILE 07887 535615**

1 ALL THE FAME (IRE), 7, b g Fame And Glory—Abhainn Ri (IRE) **Miss A. M. Reed**
2 BLUE MOONLIGHT, 4, br f Blue Bresil (FR)—Taniokey (IRE) **Mr M. A. Burton**
3 CORRAN CROSS (IRE), 7, b g Doyen (IRE)—Steel Lady (IRE) **Miss A. M. Reed**
4 DELTA RUN (IRE), 5, b g Ocovango—Curragheen (IRE) **Wendy & Malcolm Hezel**
5 DIESEL D'ALLIER (FR), 9, gr g Kap Rock (FR)—Iena d'Allier (FR) **The French Link**
6 ECLAIR MAG (FR), 8, b g Network (GER)—Katerinette (FR) **R. M. Kirkland**
7 ECUME ATLANTIQUE (FR), 8, b g Satri (IRE)—Force Atlantique (FR) **R. M. Kirkland**
8 ELYAQIM (FR), 8, b g Spider Flight (FR)—Sinceres (FR) **Mr C. J. Boreham**
9 EXTRACURICULAR, 4, b f Coach House (IRE)—First Term **The Plantation Picnic Club**
10 FIRST ASSEMBLY (IRE), 8, b g Arcadio (GER)—Presenting Katie (IRE) **Mr S. R. Cross**
11 FLINTARA, 7, b m Kayf Tara—Flinders **Leith Hill Chasers**
12 GIVE ME A MOMENT (IRE), 7, b g Mountain High (IRE)—Maryann (IRE) **The Plantation Picnic Club**
13 GODREVY POINT, 6, b g Coastal Path—Quetzalya (FR) **Mr T. D. J. Syder**
14 HORS GUARD (FR), 5, br g Kitkou (FR)—Soulte (FR) **Mr C. J. Boreham**
15 LIBERTY POWER, 5, b g Makfi—Liberty Cheri **Mr R. J. Bandey**
16 OAKLEY (IRE), 9, b g Oscar—Tirolean Dance (IRE) **Mr T. D. J. Syder**
17 PASS ME BY, 6, ch g Shirocco (GER)—Materiality **Wendy & Malcolm Hezel**
18 PEBBLY LUNAR LADY, 5, b m Sea Moon—Spanker **R. M. Kirkland**
19 PEBBLY NEW MOON (IRE), 7, b g Mahler—Pharney Fox (IRE) **Mr J. Beswick**
20 SAINT PALAIS (FR), 5, b g Saint des Saints (FR)—Ladies Choice (FR) **Mr T. D. J. Syder**
21 SOUTHERN SAM, 8, b g Black Sam Bellamy (IRE)—Pougatcheva (FR) **Mr T. D. J. Syder**

MR RICHARD J. BANDEY - continued

22 **WEWILLGOWITHPLANB (IRE)**, 5, b g Fame And Glory—Our Polly (IRE) **The Test Valley Partnership**

THREE-YEAR-OLDS
23 **SHIPTON MOYNE**, b f Coach House (IRE)—Blissamore **Miss R. Jones**

18	**MISS CHELSEA BANHAM, Newmarket**

Postal: **Mulligans Cottage, Cowlinge, Newmarket, Suffolk, CB8 9HP**
Contacts: **PHONE 07387 169781**

1 **ADMIRABLE LAD**, 4, ch g Bated Breath—Admirable Spirit **Mulligans Racing club**
2 **AT YOUR SERVICE**, 8, b g Frankel—Crystal Gaze (IRE)
3 **AXEL JACKLIN**, 6, b g Iffraaj—Reroute (IRE) **Mr A. Searle**
4 **CAFE ESPRESSO**, 6, b m Sir Percy—Forest Express (AUS) **Chelsea Banham Pre Training ltd**
5 **CAPRICIOUS**, 4, b f Harzand (IRE)—Adaptability **Longview Stud & Bloodstock Ltd**
6 **CHOCCO STAR (IRE)**, 6, b m Lawman (FR)—Sharplaw Star **Mulligans Racing club**
7 **GHAALIYA (IRE)**, 4, b f Frankel—Shumoos (USA) **Mr M. Bartram**
8 **HANDEL (USA)**, 4, b c Pioneerof The Nile (USA)—Party Starter (USA) **Chelsea Banham Pre Training ltd**
9 **INDEPENDENCE DAY (IRE)**, 9, b g Dansili—Damson (IRE) **Chelsea Banham Pre Training ltd**
10 **KALOOR**, 6, b g Nathaniel (IRE)—Blinking **Chelsea Banham Pre Training ltd**
11 **KAWAALEES**, 4, gr g Havana Gold (IRE)—Blanc de Chine (IRE) **Mulligans Racing club**
12 **LADY OF YORK**, 8, b m Sir Percy—Parsonagehotelyork (IRE) **Chelsea Banham Pre Training ltd**
13 **MAKAMBE (IRE)**, 7, gr g Dark Angel (IRE)—Pink Diva (IRE) **Chelsea Banham Pre Training ltd**
14 **MARIONETTE (IRE)**, 5, b m Dark Angel (IRE)—Hand Puppet (IRE) **Mr M. Bartram**
15 **MUNIFICENT**, 4, b c Pearl Secret—Hulcote Rose (IRE) **Mulligans Racing club**
16 **RUSHMORE**, 4, b g Lope de Vega (IRE)—Qushchi **Chelsea Banham Pre Training ltd**
17 **SUPER JULIUS**, 8, ch g Bated Breath—Paradise Isle **Mulligans Racing club**
18 **TOKYO CHIC**, 4, b f Sir Percy—Lady Bling **Mulligans Racing club**
19 **TOPLIGHT**, 4, b g Bated Breath—Operettist **Longview Stud & Bloodstock Ltd**

THREE-YEAR-OLDS

20 **BANKRUPT (IRE)**, b g Adaay (IRE)—Scintillating (IRE) **Mulligans Racing club**
21 B f Free Eagle (IRE)—Dundel's Spirit (IRE)
22 **HEAVENS LIGHT (IRE)**, gr g Dark Angel (IRE)—Kurland (IRE)
23 **NIGHT TRAVELLER**, ch f Night of Thunder (IRE)—Travelling **Longview Stud & Bloodstock Ltd**
24 **OXYGEN THIEF (IRE)**, gr g Prince of Lir (IRE)—Spavento (IRE)
25 **SECRET STRIPPER**, ch f Outstrip—Secret Advice **Chelsea Banham Pre Training ltd**
26 **SHOT TO THE HEART**, b g Brazen Beau (AUS)—Trick Shot Jenny **Mulligans Racing club**

TWO-YEAR-OLDS

27 **OVERLAND**, b c 14/03 Territories (IRE)—Authoritarian (Authorized (IRE)) (30476) **Longview Stud & Bloodstock Ltd**

---

19 | MR JACK BARBER, Crewkerne
Postal: **Higher Peckmoor, Henley, Crewkerne, Somerset, TA18 8FF**
Contacts: **PHONE 01460 76555 MOBILE 07904 185720**
EMAIL **info@jackbarberracing.co.uk** WEBSITE **www.jackbarberracing.co.uk**

1 **BLACKJACK MAGIC,** 7, b g Black Sam Bellamy (IRE)—One Wild Night
T Hayward, O'Gorman, Walker & Patersons
2 **DOCTOR FOLEY (IRE),** 5, b g Malinas (GER)—Quarryanna (IRE) **Newton, Gaunt**
3 **DOYANNIE (IRE),** 8, ch m Doyen (IRE)—Annie May (IRE) **Barber, Dolan-abrahams & Shortland**
4 **EARTH KING (IRE),** 6, b g Shirocco (GER)—Beach Beauty (IRE) **Mrs C. E. Penny**
5 **EARTH STAR (IRE),** 6, br g Presenting—Madam Bovary (IRE) **R. M. Penny**
6 **ECHO OF PROMISE,** 4, ch f Shantou (USA)—Topette (FR)
7 **ELECTRIC ANNIE (IRE),** 7, b m Fame And Glory—Decent Dime (IRE) **Mr P. A. Hiscock**
8 **FENRIR BINDING,** 7, b g Norse Dancer (IRE)—Bethany Lewis **Racing Dreams**
9 **FLYING SARA,** 7, b m Malinas (GER)—Samandara (FR) **Peckmoor Flyers**
10 **JITTERBUG GEORDIE,** 4, gr g Geordieland (FR)—Dancingtilmidnight **Mrs S. J. Maltby**
11 **KEEPITFROMBECKY (IRE),** 4, b g Diamond Boy (FR)—Tobetall **Mr J J Barber & Mr J French**
12 **LAMANVER BEL AMI,** 8, b g Black Sam Bellamy (IRE)—Lamanver Homerun **Wessex Racing Club**
13 **LYDFORD LAD (IRE),** 7, b g Yeats (IRE)—Shannon Rose (IRE) **Mr David Martin & Mr Paul Barber**
14 **MIDNIGHT MALIN,** 6, b m Malinas (GER)—Dancingtilmidnight **Mrs S. J. Maltby**
15 **NORTON HILL (IRE),** 6, b g Fame And Glory—Charming Leader (IRE) **Mr & Mrs J. J. Barber & Mr A. Norman**
16 **ONEUPMANSHIP (IRE),** 7, ch g Mahler—Letthisbetheone (IRE) **Charlie Walker & Phil Fry**
17 **SHINTORI (FR),** 10, b g Enrique—La Masai (FR) **Mrs R. E. Vicary**
18 **TIPSY HALL,** 6, b m Gentlewave (IRE)—Lush Lady (IRE) **Mr R. Hall**

Other Owners: Mr J. J. Barber, P. K. Barber, Mr E. J. Dolan-Abrahams, Mr O. P. Farrer, Mr J. M. French, R. P. Fry, Mr R. Gaunt, A. A. Hayward, Mr D. J. Martin, Mr M. Newton, A. J. Norman, Mr J. Shortland, C. C. Walker.

20 | MRS STELLA BARCLAY, Garstang
Postal: **Lancashire Racing Stables, The Paddocks, Strickens Lane, Barnacre, Garstang, Lancashire, PR3 1UD**
Contacts: **PHONE 01995 605790 MOBILE 07802 764094**
EMAIL **paul@lancashireracingstables.co.uk**

1 **AUSSIE BREEZE,** 6, ch m Australia—Terre du Vent (FR) **Keep Knocking Syndicate & Stella Barclay**
2 4, B f Telescope (IRE)—Classic Fantasy **Andy Clarke & the Four Aces**
3 **DANZART (IRE),** 4, b g Dandy Man (IRE)—Surava **Carl Pye, Gary Prescott & Stella Barclay**
4 **DARE TO BEGIN (IRE),** 7, b b g Recital (FR)—Everybodys Dream (IRE) **Winks Racing**
5 **DEOLALI,** 8, b g Sleeping Indian—Dually **Matt Watkinson Racing Club**
6 **ELSPETH ROSE,** 5, b m Coach House (IRE)—Ella Rosie **Matt Watkinson Racing Club**
7 **ENSEL DU PERCHE (FR),** 8, b g Anabaa Blue—Onvavoir (FR) **Matt Watkinson Racing I**
8 **GHOSTLY,** 4, gr g Outstrip—Alpha Spirit **Stella Barclay Racing Club**
9 **GIANT STEPS (IRE),** 5, b g Footstepsinthesand—Saysim West (IRE) **Stella Barclay Racing Club**
10 **GLORIOUS RIO (IRE),** 5, b g Gutaifan (IRE)—Renaissance Rio (IRE) **Matt Watkinson Racing Club**
11 **GRACEFUL MOMENT (IRE),** 4, gr ro f Fast Company (IRE)—Silver Grey (IRE) **Matt Watkinson Racing II**
12 4, B f Telescope (IRE)—Halo Flora **The Coz Syndicate**
13 **LADY OF DESIRE,** 4, ch f Territories (IRE)—Fantacise **Matt Watkinson Racing Club**
14 **LANCASHIRE LIFE,** 4, b f Coach House (IRE)—Betty's Pride **Betty's Brigade**
15 **MANJAAM (IRE),** 9, ch g Tamayuz—Priory Rock (IRE) **Matt Watkinson Racing III**
16 **MANSFIELD,** 9, b g Exceed And Excel (AUS)—Jane Austen (IRE) **The Style Council**
17 4, B gr f Leading Light (IRE)—Road To Freedom (FR) **The Cataractonium Racing Syndicate**
18 **ROSE OF LANCASHIRE,** 4, b f Coach House (IRE)—Ella Rosie **The Most Wanted Partnership**
19 **SELECTO,** 5, b g Paco Boy (IRE)—Telescopic **The Haydock Badgeholders**
20 **SHARRABANG,** 6, b g Coach House (IRE)—Dually **Matt Watkinson Racing Club**
21 **SIR BENEDICT (IRE),** 4, ch g Dandy Man (IRE)—Kingdomforthebride (IRE) **Village Racing**
22 **STORM TIGER,** 6, b g Shirocco (GER)—Lucys Pet **G Seward & Stella Barclay**

MRS STELLA BARCLAY- continued

23 **WILDMOUNTAINTHYME,** 6, b m Doncaster Rover (USA)—Awaywithefairies **Mr P. J. Metcalfe**
24 **ZANEVSKY,** 9, b g And Beyond (IRE)—Nevsky Bridge **Miss A. Lea**

THREE-YEAR-OLDS

25 **BUACHAILL (IRE),** b g Gregorian—Anazah **Tony Culhane Racing Club**
26 B g Coach House (IRE)—Ella Rosie **Stella Barclay**

TWO-YEAR-OLDS

27 B f 09/05 Coach House (IRE)—Ella Rosie **Stella Barclay**
28 B g 24/03 Coach House (IRE)—Melanna **Brandsby Racing**

Other Owners: Howard Anderson, Alan Appleton, Steve & Eve Atkinson, John Ball, Tony Ball, Jim & Judy Barnes, John Booth, Paul Bushell, Paul Clarkson, Katie Dalton, Keith Dodd, Craig Harrison, Chris Hickey, Steve Hicks, Shirley Hurst, Dave Kay, David & Trish Maitland-Price, Richard Mattinson, Geoff & Jan Metcalfe, Alan Pierce, Martin Prince, Peter Sedgwick, Dave Simpson, Chris Smith, Trevor Willis.

21
MRS TRACEY BARFOOT-SAUNT, Wotton-under-Edge
Postal: **Cosy Farm, Huntingford, Charfield, Wotton-under-Edge, Gloucestershire, GL12 8EY**
Contacts: **PHONE 01453 520312 MOBILE 07976 360626 FAX 01453 520312**

1 **EARTH SPIRIT,** 9, b g Black Sam Bellamy (IRE)—Samandara (FR) **Mrs T. M. Barfoot-Saunt**
2 **HERE COMES MOLLY (IRE),** 11, ch m Stowaway—Grange Melody (IRE) **BS Racing**
3 **MRS JONES,** 6, b m Multiplex—Gertrude Webb **BS Racing**
4 **NUMERO UNO,** 6, b g Dubawi (IRE)—Casual Look (USA) **A Good Days Racing**
5 **TENSION TIME (IRE),** 8, b g Dubai Destination (USA)—Leader's Hall (IRE) **Mr G. C. Barfoot-Saunt**

22
MR MAURICE BARNES, Brampton
Postal: **Tarnside, Farlam, Brampton, Cumbria, CA8 1LA**
Contacts: **PHONE 016977 46675 MOBILE 07760 433191**
EMAIL anne.barnes1@btinternet.com

1 **BAFANA BLUE,** 11, b g Blueprint (IRE)—Anniejo **Hogarth, Morris, Percival & Irving**
2 **BALKALIN (FR),** 10, ch g Balko (FR)—Rose Caline (FR) **Mr M. A. Barnes**
3 **BREAKING RECORDS (IRE),** 7, b g Kodiac—Querulous (USA) **Burgan,Fosberg & Rowan**
4 **DAPPER GENT,** 5, b h Dapper—Overpriced
5 **DEERFOOT,** 5, b g Archipenko (USA)—Danceatdusk **Mr M. A. Barnes**
6 **DOLLY DANCER (IRE),** 8, b m Yeats (IRE)—Scrapper Jack (IRE) **Mr E. Cassie**
7 **FARLAM KING,** 9, br g Crosspeace (IRE)—Second Bite **Mr M. A. Barnes**
8 **FAROCCO (GER),** 9, b g Shirocco (GER)—Fantasmatic (GER) **Miss A. P. Lee**
9 **GET 'EM IN (IRE),** 6, b g Getaway (GER)—Swap Shop (IRE) **Miss H. M. Crichton**
10 **KNOCKOURA (IRE),** 10, b g Westerner—Lisselton Thatch (IRE) **Mr M. A. Barnes**
11 **LOULOUMILLS,** 12, b m Rob Roy (USA)—Etching (USA) **Mr M. A. Barnes**
12 **MABLEABLE,** 6, b m Black Sam Bellamy (IRE)—Lady Jinks **Miss A. P. Lee**
13 **MRINDEPENDANT,** 5, b g Recharge (IRE)—Lady Jinks **Miss A. P. Lee**
14 **MY MACHO MAN (IRE),** 5, ch g Camacho—Mypreciousblue **Mr E. Cassie**
15 **OH NO,** 10, b g Indian Danehill (IRE)—See My Girl **Mr M. A. Barnes**
16 **OISHIN,** 10, b g Paco Boy (IRE)—Roshina (IRE) **Mr M. A. Barnes**
17 **PEAK TIME,** 9, ch g Distant Peak (IRE)—Ruby Redwing **J. Wade**

MR MAURICE BARNES - continued

18 **PLACEDELA CONCORDE,** 9, b g Champs Elysees—Kasakiya (IRE) **Mr M. A. Barnes**
19 **ROMA BANGKOK,** 6, b g Mount Nelson—Magika **Mr M. A. Barnes**
20 **SAINT ARVANS (FR),** 8, b g Motivator—Castellina (USA) **D & A Lee**
21 **SKIDDAW TARA,** 8, b g Kayf Tara—Bob Back's Lady (IRE) **Exors of the Late J. R. Wills**
22 **VICTORY ECHO (IRE),** 9, b g Cloudings (IRE)—Serendipity (IRE) **Mr M. A. Barnes**

23	**MR BRIAN BARR, Sherborne**

Postal: **Tall Trees Stud, Longburton, Sherborne, Dorset, DT9 5PH**
Contacts: **PHONE 01963 210173 MOBILE 07826 867881**
EMAIL brianbarrracing@hotmail.com WEBSITE www.brianbarrracing.co.uk
TWITTER @brianbarrracing

1 **ANNIEMATION (IRE),** 5, b g Acclamation—Cafetiere **Alan Rogers & Partner**
2 **BENANDGONE,** 5, b g Hallowed Crown (AUS)—Peaceful Soul (USA) **Mr G. Hitchins**
3 **CHUMLEE (IRE),** 7, b g Recital (FR)—Oceanna Mist (IRE) **Troika Racing**
4 **DAN MCGRUE (IRE),** 10, b g Dansant—Aahsaypasty (IRE) **Miss D. Hitchins**
5 5, Gr g Born To Sea (IRE)—Danealla (IRE) **Mr P. Bona**
6 **EPIC PASS (IRE),** 4, b c Awtaad (IRE)—Kanes Pass (IRE) **Roofnet Limited**
7 **GET SUPREME (IRE),** 9, ch g Getaway (GER)—Supreme Supreme (IRE) **Alan Rogers & Partner**
8 **ICE AGE (IRE),** 9, b g Frozen Power (IRE)—Incendio **Troika Racing**
9 **INDEPENDENCE (USA),** 6, br g More Than Ready (USA)—Frivolous Alex (USA) **Chris Clark & Daisy Hitchins**
10 **KATELLI (IRE),** 5, br g Dragon Pulse (IRE)—Kateeva (IRE) **Roofnet Limited**
11 **MADAME BIJOUX,** 4, b f Geordieland (FR)—Madame Be **Brian Barr Racing Club**
12 **MANOR PARK,** 7, b g Medicean—Jadeel **Miss D. Hitchins**
13 **MISTER MORETTI (IRE),** 7, b g Masterofthehorse (IRE)—Lost It (IRE) **Troika Racing**
14 **SAOIRSE AWAY (IRE),** 6, b m Getaway (GER)—Ms Monroe (IRE) **Chris Clark & Daisy Hitchins**
15 **TORONTO (IRE),** 5, b g Galileo (IRE)—Mrs Marsh **Troika Racing**

THREE-YEAR-OLDS

16 **BEERENBERG,** b g National Defense—Mademoiselle Marie (FR) **Mrs Caroline Louise Balmer & Partner**

Assistant Trainer: Daisy Hitchins.

NH Jockey: Paul O'Brien. **Amateur Jockey:** Mr A Butterfield.

24	**MR RON BARR, Middlesbrough**

Postal: **Carr House Farm, Seamer, Stokesley, Middlesbrough, Cleveland, TS9 5LL**
Contacts: **PHONE 01642 710687 MOBILE 07711 895309**
EMAIL christinebarr1@aol.com

1 **COLLETTE (IRE),** 5, ch m New Approach (IRE)—Shallow Lake (USA) **D Thomson & C Barr**
2 **DOMINANNIE (IRE),** 9, b m Paco Boy (IRE)—English Rose (USA) **Mrs V. G. Davies**
3 4, B g Eagle Top—Karate Queen **Mrs C. Barr**
4 **MIGHTASWELLSMILE,** 8, b m Elnadim (USA)—Intishaar (IRE) **R. E. Barr**
5 4, Ch g Eagle Top—Pay Time **Mrs V. G. Davies**
6 **ROSE ALL DAY,** 4, b f Oasis Dream—May Rose (IRE) **Mrs V. G. Davies**

MR RON BARR - continued

7 **SKEDADDLED (IRE),** 4, b f Fast Company (IRE)—Knock Twice (USA) **D Thomson & C Barr**

Other Owners: Mrs C. Barr, D. Thomson.

Assistant Trainer: C. Barr, **Head Girl:** V. Barr.

---

25 MR DAVID BARRON, Thirsk
Postal: **Maunby House, Maunby, Thirsk, North Yorkshire, YO7 4HD**
Contacts: **PHONE 01845 587435 FAX 01845 587331**
EMAIL david.barron@maunbyhouse.com

1 **ABOVE THE REST (IRE),** 11, b g Excellent Art—Aspasias Tizzy (USA) **L. G. O'Kane**
2 **ANNIE ROSE,** 4, b f Equiano (FR)—Tebee's Oasis **Minster Stud & Partner**
3 **ANOTHER BATT (IRE),** 7, ch g Windsor Knot (IRE)—Mrs Batt (IRE) **L. G. O'Kane**
4 **ATIYAH,** 4, br f Swiss Spirit—Jofranka **Mrs Anne Atkinson & Partner**
5 **BARYSHNIKOV,** 6, ch g Mastercraftsman (IRE)—Tara Moon **Mr John Knotts & Partner**
6 **BERT KIBBLER,** 4, b g Fountain of Youth (USA)—Annie Beach (IRE) **Mrs D. Dalby & Harrowgate Bloodstock Ltd**
7 **CLASS CLOWN (IRE),** 5, ch g Intense Focus (USA)—Joli Elegant **Dr N. J. Barron**
8 **CONTACT (IRE),** 4, gr c Gutaifan (IRE)—La Tulipe (FR) **Mr H. D. Atkinson**
9 **DEEVIOUS BEAU,** 5, b g Brazen Beau (AUS)—Vespasia **Harrowgate Bloodstock Ltd**
10 **ESTICKY END (IRE),** 4, b g Estidhkaar (IRE)—Hay Now (IRE) **Dr N. J. Barron**
11 **HOMER STOKES,** 4, b g Stimulation (IRE)—Thicket **Harrowgate Bloodstock Ltd**
12 **HUDDLE UP (IRE),** 4, ch g Anjaal—Red Red Rose
13 **LILIKOI (IRE),** 4, b f Alhebayeb (IRE)—Passion Fruit **Mr James A Cringan & Partner**
14 **MODULAR MAGIC,** 5, b g Swiss Spirit—Lucy Parsons (IRE) **Mr P McKenna, Mr L O Kane & Partner**
15 **MOSSBAWN,** 5, b g Brazen Beau (AUS)—Maziona **Mrlaurenceo'Kane/Harrowgatebloodstockltd**
16 **NORTH WIND (IRE),** 6, b g No Nay Never (USA)—Kawn **Penton Hill Racing Limited**
17 **ON A SESSION (USA),** 6, b g Noble Mission—Destiny Calls (USA) **Penton Hill Racing Limited & Mr L O'Kane**
18 **OTTO OYL,** 4, b g Mayson—Olive Mary **Dr N. J. Barron**
19 **PERSUASION (IRE),** 5, b g Acclamation—Effervesce (IRE) **L. G. O'Kane**
20 **POET'S LADY,** 5, gr m Farhh—La Gessa **L. G. O'Kane**
21 **POLAM LANE,** 4, b g Swiss Spirit—La Zamora **Mr David A Jones & Partner**
22 **VENTUROUS (IRE),** 9, ch g Raven's Pass (USA)—Bold Desire **Mrlaurenceo'Kane/Harrowgatebloodstockltd**
23 **VIVA VOCE (IRE),** 5, b g Intense Focus (USA)—Moonbi Haven (IRE) **Dr N. J. Barron**
24 **WESTERN MUSIC (IRE),** 4, b f Epaulette (AUS)—Western Tune (IRE) **Harrowgate Bloodstock Ltd**
25 **WILLARD CREEK,** 4, br g Havana Gold (IRE)—Zaaneh (IRE) **Mrs S. C. Barron**
26 **ZARZYNI (IRE),** 5, b g Siyouni (FR)—Zunera (IRE) **Mrlaurenceo'Kane/Harrowgatebloodstockltd**

THREE-YEAR-OLDS

27 **AHAMOMENT (IRE),** b g Alhebayeb (IRE)—Taispeantas (IRE) **D P Van Der Hoeven & D G Pryde**
28 **ARDOM'S LADY,** b f Ardad (IRE)—Xenon **Mr A. C. Cook**
29 **COAXING,** b f Outstrip—Blandish (USA) **Harrowgate Bloodstock Ltd**
30 **GENTLE ELLEN (IRE),** b f Bungle Inthejungle—Art of Gold **D Ellis & Partner**
31 **HENERY HAWK,** b g Heeraat (IRE)—Rosecomb (IRE) **Harrowgate Bloodstock Ltd**
32 B f Scorpion (IRE)—Hula Ballew **Tees Components Ltd**
33 **MERESIDE ANGEL (IRE),** b gr g Gutaifan (IRE)—Mary Thomas (IRE) **Mereside Racing Limited & Partner**
34 Ch f Outstrip—Pledge of Honour (FR) **Mr A. C. Cook**
35 **STREETSCAPE,** ch g Cityscape—Maziona **Dr N. J. Barron**
36 **SUNDAY JUSTICE (IRE),** b g Gutaifan (IRE)—Knapton Hill **Dr N. J. Barron**
37 **THUNDER CHAP,** b c Night of Thunder (IRE)—Percys Princess **Penton Hill Racing Limited**
38 **TIDEWELL,** ch g Sixties Icon—Lucy Parsons (IRE) **Harrowgate Bloodstock Ltd & Associate**

MR DAVID BARRON - continued

TWO-YEAR-OLDS
39 B c 05/03 Camacho—Basira (FR) (Azamour (IRE)) (13605)
40 **BROWNLEE (IRE)**, ch c 21/04 Bungle Inthejungle—Flashy Queen (IRE) (Bahamian Bounty) (20000)
41 **DALEY T (IRE)**, ch c 14/03 Dragon Pulse (IRE)—Elizabeth Swann (Bahamian Bounty) (23810)
42 **GOLD GUY (IRE)**, ch c 13/02 Gustav Klimt (IRE)—Lella Beya (Diktat) (20952)
43 B f 09/04 Equiano (FR)—High On Light (Makfi)
44 **HOY,** b c 03/02 Havana Grey—Fair Maiden (JPN) (Carnegie (IRE)) (25000)
45 Gr c 12/05 Galileo Gold—Morethanafeeling (IRE) (Verglas (IRE)) (35714)
46 Ch f 28/03 Ivawood (IRE)—Mujaesce (ITY) (Mujahid (USA)) (12755)
47 **RANZINI (IRE)**, b c 22/01 Zoffany (IRE)—Bellajeu (Montjeu (IRE)) (44000) **Mr H. D. Atkinson**
48 B c 01/03 Massaat (IRE)—Rosecomb (IRE) (Rip Van Winkle (IRE))
49 B c 12/02 Ruler of The World (IRE)—Sweet Surprise (IRE) (Danetime (IRE)) (13605)

Other Owners: Mrs A. Atkinson, Mrs S. C. Barron, Exors of the Late E. Carson, W. F. H. Carson, J. A. Cringan, Mrs D. Dalby, Mr D. B. Ellis, Harrowgate Bloodstock Ltd, Mr D. A. Jones, Mr J. Knotts, Mr P. McKenna, Mereside Racing Limited, Minster Stud, L. G. O'Kane, Penton Hill Racing Limited, D. G. Pryde, Mr J. Wells, Mr D. P. van der Hoeven.

Assistant Trainer: Nicola-Jo Barron.

26	**MR RALPH BECKETT, Kimpton** Postal: **Kimpton Down Stables, Kimpton, Andover, Hampshire, SP11 8QQ** Contacts: **PHONE 01264 772278** **EMAIL trainer@rbeckett.com**

1 **ALBAFLORA,** 5, gr m Muhaarar—Almiranta **Miss K. Rausing**
2 **ALLOWED,** 4, b f Al Kazeem—Sign of Life **Mrs D. M. Swinburn**
3 **BIGGLES,** 5, b g Zoffany (IRE)—At A Clip **Lady N. F. Cobham**
4 **BULLACE,** 4, b g Toronado (IRE)—Redstart **Mr A. D. G. Oldrey & Mr G. C. Hartigan**
5 **DIOCLES OF ROME (IRE),** 7, b g Holy Roman Emperor (IRE)—Serisia (FR) **Mrs Philip Snow & Partners**
6 **FOX CHAMPION (IRE),** 6, b g Kodiac—Folegandros Island (FR) **King Power Racing Co Ltd**
7 **FOX VARDY (USA),** 6, b g Frankel—Dance With Another (IRE) **King Power Racing Co Ltd**
8 **KINROSS,** 5, b g Kingman—Ceilidh House **Mr M. Chan**
9 **LORD PROTECTOR (GER),** 4, b br g Pastorius (GER)—Lady Jacamira (GER) **Quantum Leap Racing X & Partner**
10 **LUCANDER (IRE),** 5, b g Footstepsinthesand—Lady Sefton **Mrs M. E. Slade & Mr B. Ohlsson**
11 **MAX VEGA (IRE),** 5, ch g Lope de Vega (IRE)—Paraphernalia (IRE) **The Pickford Hill Partnership**
12 **NEW MANDATE (IRE),** 4, b g New Bay—Mishhar (IRE) **Mr M. Chan**
13 **OMAN (IRE),** 4, ch g Australia—Awohaam (IRE) **Mr Y. M. Nasib**
14 **ROCK EAGLE,** 7, ch g Teofilo (IRE)—Highland Shot **J. C. Smith**
15 **SAM COOKE (IRE),** 6, b g Pour Moi (IRE)—Saturday Girl **Chelsea Thoroughbreds - Wonderful World**
16 **SCOPE (IRE),** 4, ch c Teofilo (IRE)—Look So **J. H. Richmond-Watson**
17 **SKY POWER (IRE),** 5, b g Fastnet Rock (AUS)—Dame Blanche (IRE) **King Power Racing Co Ltd**
18 **STAR OF ORION (IRE),** 4, b g Footstepsinthesand—Harpist (IRE) **Miss T. A. Ashbee**
19 **STATE OCCASION,** 4, b f Iffraaj—Forest Crown **The Eclipse Partnership**
20 **TAKE MY CHANCES (FR),** 4, b f Frankel—Take the Ribbon (USA) **John Gunther & Tanya Gunther**
21 **TOMFRE,** 5, b g Cable Bay (IRE)—Kurtanella **Mrs Philip Snow & Partners**
22 **VICTORY CHIME (IRE),** 7, b g Campanologist (USA)—Patuca (IRE) **Mr A. Nevin**
23 **VULCAN (IRE),** 5, b g Free Eagle (IRE)—Quixotic **Valmont**
24 **YESYES,** 4, b f Camelot—Shared Account **Juddmonte Farms Ltd**

THREE-YEAR-OLDS
25 **ALLEMANDE,** gr f Sea The Moon (GER)—Almiranta **Miss K. Rausing**
26 **ALTERNATIVA,** b f Invincible Spirit (IRE)—Alyssa **Miss K. Rausing**
27 **ANGEL BLEU (FR),** b c Dark Angel (IRE)—Cercle de La Vie (IRE) **Mr M. Chan**
28 **BE LUCKY MY SON,** b g Dandy Man (IRE)—Ceol Loch Aoidh (IRE) **Mr P. Mellett**
29 **CENTRALLIA,** ch f Cityscape—Pivotal Drive (IRE) **Melody Racing**

MR RALPH BECKETT - continued

30 **CONVECTION**, b f Oasis Dream—Mechanism **Juddmonte Farms Ltd**
31 **CRESTA DE VEGA (IRE)**, b g Lope de Vega (IRE)—Bibury **Mr M. Chan**
32 **CYGNETURE**, br f Kingman—Dark Swan (IRE) **The Prince of Wales & The Duchess of Cornwall**
33 **DAIQUIRI DREAM**, b f Dubawi (IRE)—Cocktail Queen (IRE) **J. C. Smith**
34 **DAIQUIRI FRANCAIS**, b f Havana Gold (IRE)—Moretta Blanche **Absolute Solvents Ltd**
35 **DEFINITE**, b g Kingman—Zulema **Juddmonte Farms Ltd**
36 **DELOREAN (IRE)**, b g Time Test—Dawn of Empire (USA) **The Lucra Partnership II**
37 **DEODAR**, br g Bated Breath—Tested **Juddmonte Farms Ltd**
38 **ECHO CHAMBER (FR)**, b f Postponed (IRE)—Wall of Sound **Chasemore Farm LLP**
39 **EDINBURGH ROCK (IRE)**, b g Highland Reel (IRE)—Sixpenny Sweets (IRE) **The Lucra Partnership II**
40 **ELECTRESS**, b f Galileo (IRE)—Just The Judge (IRE) **Qatar Racing Limited**
41 **ELENA'S GIFT**, ch f Frankel—Sant Elena **The Eclipse Partnership**
42 **FASHION LOVE**, b f Fastnet Rock (AUS)—Felicity (GER) **Cornthrop Bloodstock Limited**
43 **GIRL ON FILM (FR)**, b f Dabirsim (FR)—Pretty Paper (IRE) **John Gunther & Tanya Gunther**
44 **GOOD AMERICAN**, b f American Pharoah (USA)—Parvaneh (IRE) **Mr A. Rosen**
45 **GREENSCAPE**, b f Cityscape—Green Room (FR) **Aylesfield Farms Stud**
46 **HAM AND JAM (IRE)**, gr g Champs Elysees—Artistica (IRE) **Quantum Leap Racing VI**
47 **HELVETIQUE**, b f Bobby's Kitten (USA)—Helvetia (USA) **Miss K. Rausing**
48 **HIGH FIBRE (IRE)**, b c Vadamos (FR)—Multi Grain **The Lucra Partnership II**
49 **HOSANA (IRE)**, b f Acclamation—Chantrea (IRE) **Airlie Stud & Mrs S.Rogers**
50 **JIMI HENDRIX (IRE)**, ch c New Bay—Planchart (USA) **Chelsea Thoroughbreds - Purple Haze**
51 **JUPITER AND MARS**, b g Camelot—At A Clip **Lady N. F. Cobham**
52 **LADY SHOTGUN**, b f Night of Thunder (IRE)—She Is No Lady **D & J Newell**
53 **LE DESIGNE (IRE)**, b f Siyouni (FR)—Oh Goodness Me **Mr M. Chan**
54 **LUNA DORADA (IRE)**, b f Golden Horn—Lunar Spirit **Team Valor & Steven Rocco**
55 **MATCHED**, b c Teofilo (IRE)—Treat Gently **Juddmonte Farms Ltd**
56 **MISS BLENNERHASSET (IRE)**, b f Nathaniel (IRE)—Elizabelle (IRE) **The Anagram Partnership**
57 **MOON DE VEGA**, b f Lope de Vega (IRE)—Lunesque (IRE) **Regents Consulting**
58 **NARANCO**, b c Kingman—Patsy Boyne (IRE) **Mr I. Gomez-Pineda**
59 **NEW YEAR HONOURS**, b f Nathaniel (IRE)—Coquette Noire (IRE) **Qatar Racing Limited**
60 **ORIOLE**, b f Nathaniel (IRE)—Redstart **Mr A. D. G. Oldrey & Mr G. C. Hartigan**
61 **PLAYDAY**, b f Frankel—Posset **John Gunther & Tanya Gunther**
62 **POSTMARK**, b g Postponed (IRE)—Dream Wild **The Audax Partnership**
63 **PROSPEROUS VOYAGE (IRE)**, b f Zoffany (IRE)—Seatone (USA) **Mr M. Chan, Mr A. Rosen**
64 **PUFFING (IRE)**, b f Kingman—Puff (IRE) **Mr & Mrs David Aykroyd**
65 **QUAVERING (IRE)**, b g Vocalised (USA)—Halla Na Saoire (IRE) **The Lucra Partnership II**
66 **RECHERCHER**, b f Nathaniel (IRE)—Regardez **J. H. Richmond-Watson**
67 **RICH RHYTHM**, b g Profitable (IRE)—Gift of Music (IRE) **J. C. Smith**
68 **RIVER OF STARS (IRE)**, b f Sea The Stars (IRE)—Amazone (GER) **Woodford Thoroughbreds LLC**
69 **SEATTLE KING**, b g Kingman—Snoqualmie Star **J. C. Smith**
70 **SHOUTOUT**, ch f Havana Gold (IRE)—Lady Dragon (IRE) **Qatar Racing Limited**
71 **SKY BLUE PINK**, ch f Showcasing—Miss Work of Art **Absolute Solvents Ltd**
72 **SPEYCASTER**, b c Highland Reel (IRE)—Examinee (GER) **Quantum Leap Racing Xiv & Partner**
73 **STAR FORTRESS (IRE)**, br gr f Sea The Stars (IRE)—Lady Aquitaine (USA) **John Gunther & Tanya Gunther**
74 **STREGA DE VEGA (IRE)**, b f Lope de Vega (IRE)—Witches Brew (IRE) **Rfz Technology & Apollo Racing**
75 **SUSPICIOUS**, b f Nathaniel (IRE)—White Cay **Qatar Racing Limited**
76 **SWEET FANTASY**, b f Wootton Bassett—Parnell's Dream **Mr & Mrs David Aykroyd**
77 **THANKS MONICA (IRE)**, b f Teofilo (IRE)—Wedding Wish (IRE) **Mr M. Chan**
78 **THE GADGET MAN**, b g Jack Hobbs—Kallisha **D & J Newell**
79 **TIEMPO STAR**, b g Time Test—Tanaasub (IRE) **Michael and Roya Rembaum**
80 **TINKERS CROSS (IRE)**, b c Wootton Bassett—Born Cross (IRE) **The Lucra Partnership II**
81 **UNSPOKEN (IRE)**, b g Territories (IRE)—Silent Secret (IRE) **The Audax Partnership**
82 **UPTIME**, b f Nathaniel (IRE)—Time On **R. Barnett**
83 **VEE SIGHT**, b g Churchill (IRE)—Look So **J. H. Richmond-Watson**
84 **WESTOVER**, b c Frankel—Mirabilis (USA) **Juddmonte Farms Ltd**

TWO-YEAR-OLDS

85 **ALBA LONGA**, b f 07/04 Muhaarar—Alla Speranza (Sir Percy) **Miss K. Rausing**
86 **ALBANY**, ch f 16/04 Lope de Vega (IRE)—Alyssa (Sir Percy) **Miss K. Rausing**

MR RALPH BECKETT - continued

87 Gr c 01/05 Iffraaj—Amona (IRE) (Aussie Rules (USA)) (56973) **Quantum Leap Racing I & Partner**
88 B f 23/03 Camelot—Angel Wing (Barathea (IRE)) **J. C. Smith**
89 B c 27/03 Nathaniel (IRE)—Australian Queen (Fastnet Rock (AUS)) **J. C. Smith**
90 BACCARAT BABY, b f 26/01 Gleneagles (IRE)—Volunteer Point (IRE) (Footstepsinthesand) (68571)
Valmont & Partner
91 BALANCE PLAY (IRE), ch c 06/05 Lope de Vega (IRE)—Bezique (Cape Cross (IRE)) (280000) **Valmont**
92 B c 24/01 Frankel—Baltic Duchess (IRE) (Lope de Vega (IRE)) (136054) **Mr M. Chan**
93 BOOM BOOM POW, gr f 27/04 Havana Grey—Sunburnt (Haafhd) **Absolute Solvents Ltd**
94 BRIGHT SIDE GIRL (IRE), b f 01/04 Churchill (IRE)—Pussycat Lips (IRE) (Holy Roman Emperor (IRE)) (100000)
Mr P Stokes & Mr S Krase
95 B f 30/03 Sea The Stars (IRE)—Buying Trouble (USA) (Hat Trick (JPN)) (250000) **Valmont**
96 CAMPAIGN TRAIL (IRE), b c 07/05 Mastercraftsman (IRE)—Greta (FR) (High Chaparral (IRE)) (32313)
The Lucra Partnership III
97 CAPTAIN WIERZBA, ch c 24/03 Night of Thunder (IRE)—Return Ace (Zamindar (USA)) (280000) **Valmont**
98 CHELSEA SQUARE (IRE), b c 03/05 Exceed And Excel (AUS)—Miss Liguria (Galileo (IRE)) (75000)
Chelsea Thoroughbreds Ltd
99 B f 13/04 Havana Gold (IRE)—Coquette Noire (IRE) (Holy Roman Emperor (IRE)) (9524) **Qatar Racing Limited**
100 DANDY ALYS (IRE), b f 14/03 Dandy Man (IRE)—Alyssum (IRE) (New Approach (IRE)) (42857)
The Sunshine Partnership & Partner
101 B f 21/01 Roaring Lion (USA)—Diamonds Pour Moi (Pour Moi (IRE)) **Qatar Racing Limited**
102 B f 10/02 Kodiac—Emeriya (USA) (Giant's Causeway (USA)) (155000) **Mr M. Chan**
103 B f 28/01 Havana Grey—Funny Enough (Dansili) **Mrs M.E.Slade & Whitsbury Manor Stud**
104 B f 06/04 Zoffany (IRE)—Genuine Quality (USA) (Elusive Quality (USA)) (110544)
Andrew Rosen and Barry K Schwartz
105 GLENCALVIE (IRE), b f 28/03 Gleneagles (IRE)—Considered Opinion (Redoute's Choice (AUS))
The Eclipse Partnership
106 B c 28/02 Galileo (IRE)—Here to Eternity (USA) (Stormy Atlantic (USA)) (230000) **Valmont**
107 B f 24/03 Lope de Vega (IRE)—Honor Bound (Authorized (IRE)) (89286) **Valmont**
108 B f 04/01 Invincible Spirit (IRE)—Hypothetically (IRE) (Medicean) (200000) **King Power Racing Co Ltd**
109 B c 05/04 New Bay—Inconceivable (IRE) (Galileo (IRE)) (110544) **Valmont & Ballylinch Stud**
110 B c 03/02 Churchill (IRE)—Katiyra (IRE) (Peintre Celebre (USA)) (200000) **Valmont**
111 KEEP BIDDING (IRE), b f 12/02 Ribchester (IRE)—Coolfitch (IRE) (Roderic O'Connor (IRE)) (46000)
The Obank Partnership
112 LUCKY FIFTEEN, ch c 10/04 Lope de Vega (IRE)—Bess of Hardwick (Dansili) (200000) **Valmont**
113 B c 06/03 New Bay—Lunar Spirit (Invincible Spirit (IRE)) **Mr & Mrs David Aykroyd**
114 B c 16/04 Galileo (IRE)—Madame Chiang (Archipenko (USA)) (200000) **Mrs F. H. Hay**
115 B c 06/04 Invincible Spirit (IRE)—Marie Celeste (IRE) (Galileo (IRE)) (150000) **Mr M. Chan**
116 B c 09/02 Territories (IRE)—Matron of Honour (Teofilo (IRE)) (55272) **Miss T. A. Ashbee**
117 Ch f 22/02 Lope de Vega (IRE)—Megan Lily (IRE) (Dragon Pulse (IRE)) (120000) **Regents Consulting**
118 MILDYJAMA (IRE), b f 20/02 Zoffany (IRE)—Moment Juste (Pivotal) (95000) **Mr P Stokes & Mr S Krase**
119 MISTER STAPLE (IRE), b c 03/03 U S Navy Flag (USA)—Media Luna (Oasis Dream) (42517)
The Obank Partnership
120 B f 09/02 Lope de Vega (IRE)—Moi Meme (Teofilo (IRE)) (160000) **Andrew Rosen and Barry K Schwartz**
121 B f 13/04 Showcasing—Moretta Blanche (Dansili) **P. K. Gardner T/A Springcombe Park Stud**
122 B c 20/02 Sea The Moon (GER)—Nada (GER) (Authorized (IRE)) (33163) **The Lucra Partnership III**
123 B c 27/05 Galileo (IRE)—Nechita (AUS) (Fastnet Rock (AUS)) **J. C. Smith**
124 NIGIRI (IRE), ch f 15/02 Lope de Vega (IRE)—Disclose (Dansili) (300000) **Valmont**
125 B f 09/03 Sioux Nation (USA)—Novantae (Pivotal) (160000) **Mr M. Chan**
126 Br c 27/05 Sea The Stars (IRE)—Olympienne (IRE) (Sadler's Wells (USA)) (102041) **Valmont**
127 OVERACTIVE, b c 09/04 Awtaad (IRE)—Hyperactive (Rip Van Winkle (IRE)) (45000) **The Lucra Partnership III**
128 B c 24/03 Postponed (IRE)—Parnell's Dream (Oasis Dream) **Mr & Mrs David Aykroyd**
129 B c 19/04 Gleneagles (IRE)—Pink Symphony (Montjeu (IRE)) **Mrs F. H. Hay**
130 B c 09/03 Dubawi (IRE)—Posset (Oasis Dream) (200000) **John Gunther & Tanya Gunther**
131 B f 16/02 Time Test—Prairie Flower (IRE) (Zamindar (USA)) **J. H. Richmond-Watson**
132 PRIDE OF THE PACK, b f 16/03 Roaring Lion (USA)—Dark Swan (IRE) (Zamindar (USA))
The Prince of Wales & The Duchess of Cornwall
133 PROMOTER, ch c 04/03 Showcasing—Hereawi (Dubawi (IRE)) **J. H. Richmond-Watson**
134 B f 04/05 Kodiac—Puff (IRE) (Camacho) **Mr & Mrs David Aykroyd**
135 B f 27/04 Galileo (IRE)—Quiet Oasis (IRE) (Oasis Dream) (800000) **Michael Tabor**
136 REMARQUEE, b f 15/03 Kingman—Regardez (Champs Elysees) **J. H. Richmond-Watson**

MR RALPH BECKETT - continued

137 **SALT BAY (GER)**, ch c 21/02 Farhh—Saltita (IRE) (Galileo (IRE)) (350000) **Valmont**
138 **SEAHOUSES**, b c 01/02 Sea The Moon (GER)—Ceilidh House (Selkirk (USA)) **J. H. Richmond-Watson**
139 B f 04/04 Roaring Lion (USA)—Simple Verse (IRE) (Duke of Marmalade (IRE)) **Qatar Racing Ltd & Mr M. Al Kubaisi**
140 Ch c 11/03 Mastercraftsman (IRE)—Snoqualmie Star (Galileo (IRE)) **J. C. Smith**
141 **SOFIA CAT**, b f 27/02 Jungle Cat (IRE)—Finalize (Firebreak) (40000) **The Obank Partnership**
142 **SOLUTION**, b c 19/01 New Approach (IRE)—Luisa Calderon (Nayef (USA)) (38265) **The Lucra Partnership III**
143 B f 20/02 Sea The Stars (IRE)—Son Macia (GER) (Soldier Hollow) (119048) **Valmont**
144 B c 12/03 Cracksman—Starring Guest (IRE) (Teofilo (IRE)) (80000) **The Lucra Partnership III**
145 B f 19/02 Expert Eye—Time Honoured (Sadler's Wells (USA)) **R. Barnett**
146 **UNDERSTATED**, b f 29/03 Nathaniel (IRE)—Catalyst (IRE) (Makfi) (56973) **Peter Jensen & Partners**
147 **WHERE DO YOU GO TO (IRE)**, b f 30/04 Australia—Pleasantry (Johannesburg (USA)) (130000) **Valmont**
148 B f 27/03 Lope de Vega (IRE)—Witches Brew (IRE) (Duke of Marmalade (IRE)) (161565)
　　　　Marc Chan & Michael Tabor
149 Ch c 11/02 Frankel—Without You Babe (USA) (Lemon Drop Kid (USA)) (360000) **John Gunther & Tanya Gunther**
150 **YOU SAW BRIGADOON (IRE)**, b c 11/04 Kingman—Stirring Ballad (Compton Place) (221088) **Valmont**

Assistant Trainer: Gary Plasted.

Flat Jockey: Hector Crouch, Rob Hornby, Rossa Ryan. **Apprentice Jockey:** Laura Pearson.

---

27 **MISS JESSICA BEDI, Yarm**
Postal: **Hill House Farm, Kirklevington, Yarm, Cleveland, TS15 9PY**
Contacts: **PHONE 01642 780202**

1 **BUCK DANCING (IRE)**, 13, b g King's Theatre (IRE)—Polly Anthus **Mrs S. M. Barker**
2 **DEFINITE WARRIOR (IRE)**, 9, b g Definite Article—Waist Deep (IRE) **Hill House Racing Club**
3 **DERRICK D'ANJOU (IRE)**, 11, b g Double Eclipse (IRE)—Belle d'Anjou (FR) **Hill House Racing Club**
4 **FILOU DES ISSARDS (FR)**, 7, ch g Network (GER)—Rapiere (FR) **Hill House Racing Club**
5 **LUCA BRASI'S BOY (IRE)**, 8, b g Court Cave (IRE)—Luca Brasi (IRE) **Hill House Racing Club**
6 **OLIVER'S ISLAND (IRE)**, 10, b g Milan—Leading Rank (IRE) **Mr S. Conway**
7 **PATEEN (IRE)**, 10, b br g Vinnie Roe (IRE)—Richards Claire (IRE) **Hill House Racing Club**
8 **THAT SHIPS SAILED (IRE)**, 7, b g Califet (FR)—Mill Lady (IRE) **Capt M. Anderson**
9 **TUFF MCCOOL (IRE)**, 8, gr g Arcadio (GER)—Mrs Wallensky (IRE) **Hill House Racing Club**

---

28 **MR MICHAEL BELL, Newmarket**
Postal: **Fitzroy House, Newmarket, Suffolk, CB8 0JT**
Contacts: **PHONE 01638 666567 MOBILE 07802 264514**
EMAIL office@fitzroyhouse.co.uk WEBSITE www.michaelbellracing.co.uk

1 **ACE ROTHSTEIN (USA)**, 4, b g More Than Ready (USA)—A P Cindy (USA) **Mr K. Sohi**
2 **BEOWULF (IRE)**, 4, b g Camelot—Hug And A Kiss (USA) **Peter Trainor & Partner**
3 **DIAMONDS AT DUSK**, 4, b f Twilight Son—Diamond Run **Mascalls Stud**
4 **HEARTBREAKER**, 5, b br m Cable Bay (IRE)—Intishaar (IRE) **King Power Racing Co Ltd**
5 **KING FRANCIS (IRE)**, 4, b g Le Havre (IRE)—Princess Nada **Mr Peter Trainor & Partner 1**
6 **NATURAL PATH (IRE)**, 5, b g Toronado (IRE)—Panda Spirit (USA) **Mr P. Trainor**
7 **PLATFORM NINETEEN (IRE)**, 6, ch g Australia—Susan Stroman **The Royal Ascot Racing Club**
8 **PRINCE ALEX**, 5, b g Excelebration (IRE)—Interchange (IRE) **Amo Racing Limited**
9 **STONE CIRCLE (IRE)**, 5, ch g No Nay Never (USA)—Candlehill Girl (IRE) **The Fitzrovians 3**
10 **TRUE COURAGE**, 4, br g Le Havre (IRE)—Pearly Steph (FR) **Mr S. Mizon**
11 **ZEEBAND (IRE)**, 5, b g Sea The Stars (IRE)—Zeeba (IRE) **Mr K. Sohi**

MR MICHAEL BELL - continued

THREE-YEAR-OLDS

12 **ADJUVANT (IRE),** b g New Bay—Levanto (IRE) **Mr A. Bound**
13 **AT LIBERTY (IRE),** b g Muhaarar—Federation **Mr David Fish & Partner**
14 **BALTIMORE BOY (IRE),** b c Starspangledbanner (AUS)—Biaraafa (IRE) **M.B. & I Hawtin Family & Corbani**
15 **BELLSTREET BRIDIE,** b f Sir Percy—Mambo Gold (USA) **Mr Jim Biggane & Partner**
16 **BETWEEN THE SHEETS (IRE),** gr f El Kabeir (USA)—Shena's Dream (IRE) **Mr C. N. Wright**
17 **BOLTHOLE (IRE),** b c Free Eagle (IRE)—Weekend Getaway (IRE) **Michael & Fiona Mahony**
18 **CANDY KITCHEN (IRE),** ch f Lope de Vega (IRE)—Bristol Bay (IRE) **The Hawtin Family and Partners**
19 **DAIRERIN,** b g Spill The Beans (AUS)—Sakhya (IRE) **Mr P. Trainor**
20 **DILLIAN (IRE),** b c Camelot—Debdebdeb **Mr D. Hanafin**
21 **FIFTY SENT,** br g Dabirsim (FR)—Sentaril **Mr Kulbir Sohi & Partner**
22 **FIREBOLT (IRE),** b f Galileo (IRE)—Lightning Thunder **Qatar Racing Limited**
23 **GOLD BELT,** b f Golden Horn—Hypoteneuse (IRE) **Her Majesty The Queen**
24 **GREAT MAX (IRE),** b c Wootton Bassett—Teeslemee (FR) **Amo Racing Limited**
25 **HAARAR,** b g Muhaarar—Interchange (IRE) **D.W. & L.Y. Payne and G. & T. Blackiston**
26 **HEATHERDOWN HERO,** b c Sea The Moon (GER)—Mariee **The Heatherdonians 1**
27 **IMPROVISE (FR),** b f Iffraaj—Set To Music (IRE) **Her Majesty The Queen**
28 **JOHN O'GROATS (FR),** b g Dabirsim (FR)—Ecume du Jour (FR) **Mr D. T. Fish, Sarah & Wayne Dale**
29 **KING EAGLE (IRE),** b c Frankel—The Lark **Lady Bamford**
30 **KING OF THE KIPPAX (IRE),** b g Almanzor (FR)—Timepecker (IRE) **Middleham Park Racing Xliii & Partner**
31 **LILA GIRL (IRE),** b f Pride of Dubai (AUS)—The Shrew **Amo Racing Limited & Mrs Patricia Burns**
32 **LOUDSPEAKER,** b g Recorder—Daring Aim **Her Majesty The Queen**
33 **MISS HARMONY,** ch f Tamayuz—Muaamara **Mr C Philipps Mr T Redman & Mr T Trotter**
34 **MOONLIT WARRIOR,** ch g Sea The Moon (GER)—Claiomh Solais (IRE) **Sarah & Wayne Dale & Mr David Fish**
35 **MORAG MCCULLAGH,** b f Exceed And Excel (AUS)—Whazzat **The Gredley Family**
36 **ONE MORNING (IRE),** b f Gleneagles (IRE)—All's Forgotten (USA) **Lady Bamford**
37 **POWER TO LOVE (IRE),** b f Zoffany (IRE)—Gypsy Eyes (IRE) **Mrs B. V. Sangster & Mrs P. Shanahan**
38 **PRESENT MOMENT (IRE),** b f No Nay Never (USA)—Danehill's Dream (IRE) **Magnier, Sangster Mrs Shanahan**
39 **PUB CRAWL (IRE),** b g Noble Mission—Water Hole (IRE) **Mrs I. Corbani, Mrs W. O'Leary**
40 **SHIVRAJ,** b g Invincible Spirit (IRE)—Sariska **Lady Bamford**
41 **SPLENDID ISOLATION (IRE),** b g Bungle Inthejungle—Lavender List (IRE) **Mr David Kilburn & Partner**
42 **SPRING IS SPRUNG (FR),** b c Oasis Dream—Kinematic **Her Majesty The Queen**
43 **TARDIS,** b f Time Test—Twizzell **Wood Hall Stud Limited and Partner**

TWO-YEAR-OLDS

44 **ATLANTIC DREAM (IRE),** b c 02/02 Starspangledbanner (AUS)—Tafawoq (Oasis Dream) (52381)
Mr D. T. Fish, Sir A. Ferguson, Mr T. Fish, Miss C. A. D. Fish
45 **BLETCHLEY STORM,** ch f 11/02 Night of Thunder (IRE)—Mystery Code (Tobougg (IRE)) (35000) **The Fitzrovians 3**
46 **CREME CHANTILLY (IRE),** b f 17/04 New Bay—Creme Anglaise (Motivator) (30612)
Mrs G. Rowland Clark & Mr J. O'Connor
47 **CROSSTITCH,** ch c 04/03 Recorder—Craftiness (Al Kazeem) **Her Majesty The Queen**
48 B c 20/02 Sioux Nation (USA)—Cynthia Calhoun (Exceed And Excel (AUS)) (40000) **Mrs I Corbani & Partner**
49 **DOVES OF PEACE (IRE),** b c 10/02 Camacho—Petits Potins (IRE) (Verglas (IRE)) (65476) **Mr J Lonsdale & Partner**
50 **DUKE OF OXFORD,** b c 14/01 Kingman—Miss Marjurie (IRE) (Marju (IRE)) (27000)
Mr J. Biggane, Mr A Cope, Mr B Roberts
51 **FOR A LAUGH (IRE),** ch c 06/02 Australia—Savoy Showgirl (IRE) (Kyllachy) (80000) **Valmont**
52 Ch c 24/02 Lope de Vega (IRE)—Glamorous Approach (IRE) (New Approach (IRE)) (95000)
Oti Racing, Ballylinch Stud & Partner
53 B c 29/02 Toronado (IRE)—Highborne (FR) (Anabaa (USA)) (60000) **Stuart & Lee Baker**
54 **IBRAHIMOVIC (IRE),** gr c 25/03 Le Havre (IRE)—Isanous (FR) (Zamindar (USA)) (90000) **Mr P. Trainor**
55 B c 26/02 Dandy Man (IRE)—Image (Sepoy (AUS)) (33000)
Mr David Fravigar and Kathy Dixon Racing, Mr S.Jones and Partner
56 **KYOGO (IRE),** ch c 14/02 Ribchester (IRE)—Saint Lucia (IRE) (Whipper (USA)) (36190) **Mr P. Trainor**
57 **LADY D'ASCOYNE,** ch f 01/03 Showcasing—Victory Garden (New Approach (IRE)) (45000)
Mrs D M Swinburn, Mrs H Breitmeyer
58 B c 08/03 New Bay—Millport (Zamindar (USA)) (75000) **Mr P. Trainor**
59 **NO SAINT,** b c 05/03 Koropick (IRE)—Lady Kyllar (Kyllachy) (18095) **The Fitzrovians 3**
60 **SERAPHIA,** b f 20/02 Dark Angel (IRE)—Lolwah (Pivotal) (100000) **Dr A. Harter, Ms L. Bacon**
61 **SILVER PAGEANT,** b f 27/02 Iffraaj—Silver Mirage (Oasis Dream) **Her Majesty The Queen**

MR MICHAEL BELL - continued

62 SINDRI, b f 08/05 New Approach (IRE)—Marie Baa (FR) (Anabaa (USA)) (32000) **Mr R. S. Matharu**
63 Ch c 21/01 New Approach (IRE)—Tight Lines (Fastnet Rock (AUS)) (52000) **Mr E. J. Ware**
64 B f 23/04 Sea The Moon (GER)—Wood Chorus (Singspiel (IRE)) **Mrs B. Farr**

Other Owners: Amo Racing Limited, Mr L. Baker, Ballylinch Stud, Mr M. L. W. Bell, Mr N. Bell, Mr J. Biggane, M. A. C. Buckley, Mrs Patricia J. Burns, Mrs I. Corbani, Sarah & Wayne Dale, Mr W. R. Dale, Mr L. Dickinson, Mr A. C. Elliott, T C & Alex Ferguson, Mr D. T. Fish, Lily & Andy Harter, Mrs M. B. Hawtin, M. B. Hawtin, B. M. W. Hearn, Mrs S. J. Hearn, Mr T. Henderson, D. Kilburn, Mr J. L. S. Lonsdale, M. L. W. Bell Racing Ltd, Mrs E. Magnier, Mrs F. Mahony, Middleham Park Racing XLIII, Mr S. Mizon, Mr J. P. M. O'Connor, Mr S. O'Donnell, I. & E. O'Leary, O.T.I. Racing, T. S. Palin, Mr C. E. L. Philipps, M. Prince, Mr A. J. Ramsden, Mr T. S. Redman, Mrs G. E. Rowland-Clark, B. V. Sangster, Mrs L. O. Sangster, Mrs L. M. Shanahan, Mr K. Sohi, Mr P. Trainor, Mr T. Trotter, Wood Hall Stud Limited.

Assistant Trainer: Nick Bell.

Apprentice Jockey: Joe Bradnam.

---

29   **MR JAMES BENNETT, Wantage**
Postal: **2 Filley Alley, Letcombe Bassett, Wantage, Oxfordshire, OX12 9LT**
Contacts: **PHONE 01235 762163 MOBILE 07771 523076**
EMAIL jbennett345@btinternet.com

1 GONZAGA, 7, b g Oasis Dream—Symposia **Miss J. C. Blackwell**
2 PARISIAN PRINCESSE, 6, ch m Schiaparelli (GER)—Princesse Katie (IRE) **Miss J. C. Blackwell**
3 THE LAST MELON, 10, ch g Sir Percy—Step Fast (USA) **Miss J. C. Blackwell**

Assistant Trainer: Jackie Blackwell.

Flat Jockey: Jane Elliott. **NH Jockey:** David Bass. **Conditional Jockey:** Harriet Tucker.

---

30   **MR ALAN BERRY, Cockerham**
Postal: **Moss Side Racing Stables, Crimbles Lane, Cockerham, Lancashire, LA2 0ES**
Contacts: **PHONE 01524 791179 MOBILE 07880 553515**
EMAIL berryracing@hotmail.com

1 BARRISTER BLASTER, 4, b g Toronado (IRE)—Dansante **A Parr & A Berry**
2 ECONOMIC CRISIS (IRE), 13, ch m Excellent Art—Try The Air (IRE) **William Burns & Alan Berry**
3 I'LL BE GOOD, 13, b g Red Clubs (IRE)—Willisa **Mr A. Berry**
4 LEANNES LADY (IRE), 10, b m Ask—Wizzy (IRE) **Mr A. Berry**
5 LITTLE GEM, 4, b f Bobby's Kitten (USA)—Harlequin Twist **A Parr & A Berry**
6 NAGASAKI DREAM, 4, b g Bated Breath—Calakanga **Mr R. P. Quinn**
7 ONE FOR BRAD (IRE), 7, b m Watar (IRE)—Our Jaffa (IRE) **Kirkby Lonsdale Racing**
8 VERMILION DANCER, 4, b f Helmet (AUS)—King's Guest (IRE) **Mr S. J. Allen**

THREE-YEAR-OLDS

9 B f Elzaam (AUS)—Atlantic Cycle (IRE) **Mr A. Berry**
10 CAPPLE GIRL (IRE), b f Battle of Marengo (IRE)—Cliff Walk (IRE) **Kirkby Lonsdale Racing**
11 CASSIEL (IRE), b g Dark Angel (IRE)—Masaya **A Parr & A Berry**
12 HOLLIS BROWN, b g Bobby's Kitten (USA)—Akranti **William Burns & Alan Berry**
13 LAOCH GACH LA, gr g Lethal Force (IRE)—Poetic Dancer **Mr R. P. Quinn**
14 SOOTHING (IRE), b f Twilight Son—Feathery **A Parr & A Berry**

Assistant Trainer: John A. Quinn.

31 MR JOHN BERRY, Newmarket

Postal: **Beverley House Stables, Exeter Road, Newmarket, Suffolk, CB8 8LR**
Contacts: **PHONE 01638 660663**
EMAIL johnwathenberry@yahoo.co.uk WEBSITE www.johnberryracing.com

1 BERYL BURTON, 4, b f Sixties Icon—Miss Moses (USA) **J. C. De P. Berry**
2 BIG PETE, 5, b g Nayef (USA)—Sweet Child O'Mine **Mr J. A. Byrne**
3 CLOUDY ROSE, 4, ch f Proconsul—Zarosa (IRE) **Runfortheroses**
4 DAS KAPITAL, 7, b g Cityscape—Narla **J. C. De P. Berry**
5 DEAR ALIX, 7, b g Schiaparelli (GER)—Desiree (IRE) **McArthur, Nastanovich E Berry**
6 DEREHAM, 6, b g Sir Percy—Desiree (IRE) **Mrs E. L. Berry**
7 ELJAYTEE (IRE), 4, br g Rock of Gibraltar (IRE)—Yukon Girl (IRE) **Mr D. Tunmore**
8 HIDDEN PEARL, 6, ch m Dunaden (FR)—Volkovkha **The Sisters of Mercy & John Berry**
9 KRYPTOS, 8, b g Cacique (IRE)—Posteritas (USA) **Mr A. W. Fordham**
10 LOVING PEARL, 6, b m Dunaden (FR)—Forever Loved **Mr A. W. Fordham**
11 MERRIJIG, 4, b g Schiaparelli (GER)—Near Wild Heaven **Mrs E. L. Berry**
12 SUROOJ, 5, br m Mukhadram—Eldalil **J. C. De P. Berry**
13 4, B g Mukhadram—Sweet Child O'Mine **Mr J. A. Byrne**
14 SYLVIA PLATH (IRE), 5, ch m Poet's Voice—Speak Softly (JPN) **J. C. De P. Berry**
15 THE ROCKET PARK (IRE), 9, b g Rock of Gibraltar (IRE)—Snowpalm **L. C. Wadey**
16 THE SIMPLE TRUTH (FR), 5, gr g Rajsaman (FR)—Minnie's Mystery (FR) **Mr A. W. Fordham**
17 TURN OF PHRASE, 5, ch m Kitten's Joy (USA)—Gotcha Good (USA) **The Sisters of Mercy & John Berry**

THREE-YEAR-OLDS

18 MRS MAISEL, b f Dunaden (FR)—Minnie's Mystery (FR) **J. C. De P. Berry**
19 TARBAT NESS, br gr g Reliable Man—Ethics Girl (IRE) **The 1997 Partnership & Rhd**
20 TRUMPER, b g Jack Hobbs—Indira **J. C. De P. Berry**

Other Owners: Mrs E. L. Berry, J. C. De P. Berry, Mr T. W. Deadman, Mr J. McArthur, Mr R. A. Nastanovich, RHD, RHD Research Limited, The 1997 Partnership, The Sisters Of Mercy, L. C. Wadey.

Flat Jockey: Nicola Currie, John Egan, Josephine Gordon. **NH Jockey:** Will Kennedy, Jack Quinlan.

Amateur Jockey: Mr R. Birkett.

32 JOHN BEST AND KAREN JEWELL, Sittingbourne

Postal: **Eyehorn Farm, Munsgore Lane, Borden, Sittingbourne, Kent, ME9 8JU**
Contacts: **PHONE 07889 362154**
EMAIL office@bestjewellracing.com

1 ALL ABOUT LOGAN, 5, b g Casamento (IRE)—Atabaas Allure (FR) **Smarden Thoroughbreds**
2 BELLA COLOROSSA, 4, b f Toronado (IRE)—Shesells Seashells **Smarden Thoroughbreds**
3 BERRAHRI (IRE), 11, b g Bahri (USA)—Band of Colour (IRE) **White Turf Racing UK**
4 CHASING HIGHS (IRE), 9, b g September Storm (GER)—Rusada (IRE) **Valence Racing Too**
5 ELMEJOR (IRE), 6, b g Xtension (IRE)—Lyca Ballerina **T & B Partnership**
6 4, B g Dansant—Goodthyne Miss (IRE) **Mr H J Jarvis & Mrs P Jarvis**
7 HOW HARD CAN IT BE, 4, b f Style Vendome (FR)—Louya (IRE) **T & B Partnership**
8 IMPACOBLE, 4, ch g Paco Boy (IRE)—Fashionable Gal (IRE) **Mrs L. C. Jewell**
9 INTEL, 4, b g Telescope (IRE)—Phantom Ridge (IRE) **Mr H J Jarvis & Mrs P Jarvis**
10 MARAKAN (IRE), 6, b m Arakan (USA)—Goodthyne Miss (IRE) **H. J. Jarvis**
11 MILLIES MITE (IRE), 6, ch m Zoffany (IRE)—Charmingly (USA) **CS Partnership**
12 MISS MALARKY (IRE), 9, b m Presenting—The Shan Gang (IRE) **Mr R. Churcher**
13 PABLO PRINCE, 4, b gr g Outstrip—French Accent **Mr J. R. Best**
14 PENTIMENTO, 6, b g Garswood—M'Selle (IRE) **Walter & Geraldine Paine**
15 PLANTADREAM, 7, b g Planteur (IRE)—Phantom Ridge (IRE) **Mr H J Jarvis & Mrs P Jarvis**
16 PLEASURE GARDEN (USA), 5, b g Union Rags (USA)—Garden of Eden (USA) **Mr H J Jarvis & Mrs P Jarvis**
17 4, B f Garswood—Princess Spirit **Mr N. Dyshaev**

JOHN BEST AND KAREN JEWELL - continued

18 **RED FLYER (IRE)**, 4, ch g Free Eagle (IRE)—Hip **Mrs L. C. Jewell**
19 **SANTIBURI SPIRIT**, 4, gr ro f Outstrip—Santiburi Spring **Hill Paine & Partners**
20 4, B f Walk In The Park (IRE)—Serpentine River (IRE)
21 **TORBELLINO**, 6, b m Maxios—Tiny Smile (IRE) **Ballantine, Curtis, Malt & Iandolo**
22 **TREGURRIAN**, 5, ch g Equiano (FR)—Hvasavi **Mr H J Jarvis & Mrs P Jarvis**
23 **UALLRIGHTHARRY (IRE)**, 10, b g Craigsteel—Enchanted Valley (IRE) **Mrs S. M. Stanier**
24 4, B g Elzaam (AUS)—Uncharted Waters (IRE) **Mr H J Jarvis & Mrs P Jarvis**

THREE-YEAR-OLDS

25 **BURABACK (IRE)**, b g Buratino (IRE)—Gailes First (IRE) **Mr B. P. Keogh**
26 Gr g Lethal Force (IRE)—Elounta **Laura Malcolm & Partners**
27 B f Iffraaj—Fashion Darling (IRE)
28 **GISELLES IZZY (IRE)**, b f Camacho—Miss Cape (IRE) **Mr B. P. Keogh**
29 **LADY BEACONSFIELD (IRE)**, b f Lawman (FR)—Belanoiva (IRE) **Mr S. D. Malcolm**
30 B c Alhebayeb (IRE)—Maria Milena
31 **SMARDEN FLYER (IRE)**, gr g Markaz (IRE)—Seminole Sun (IRE) **Mr K. De la Plain**

TWO-YEAR-OLDS

32 B f 24/02 U S Navy Flag (USA)—Counterpoise (Cape Cross (IRE))
33 B f 25/02 Golden Horn—Ever Love (BRZ) (Nedawi) **Keaveney & Butcher**
34 **INVINCIBLE HEIR**, b c 07/03 Brazen Beau (AUS)—Santiburi Spring (Mullionmileanhour (IRE)) **Hill Paine & Partners**
35 Ch f 24/04 Jack Hobbs—Madam Anna (IRE) (Papal Bull) **Mr T. Betteridge**
36 B c 01/04 Outstrip—Princess Spirit (Invincible Spirit (IRE)) **Mr N. Dyshaev**

Other Owners: Mr P. I. Beckett, Mr J. R. Best, Mr S. D. Bradley, Mr P. Butcher, Mr N. Couldrey, Mr M. G. Fitzjohn, Mrs S. M. Fitzjohn, Mrs H. J. Fitzsimons, Mrs A. P. Giggins, Mr B. J. Hensman, H. J. Jarvis, Mrs P. Jarvis, Mr D. A. Jones, Mr A. Keaveney, Mr M. Keaveney, Mrs L. C. G. Malcolm, Mr S. D. Malcolm, Mr J. Miller, Mr K. Pinder, Mr J. J. Saxton, Mr M. Thomson, Miss H. J. Williams, Reverend T. Wyatt.

---

33 **MRS SUZI BEST, Lewes**
Postal: **The Bungalow, Grandstand Stables, The Old Racecourse, Lewes, East Sussex, BN7 1UR**
Contacts: **MOBILE 07804 487296**
EMAIL sbestracing@yahoo.com

1 **EVENTFUL**, 5, b m Oasis Dream—Spectacle **Guy Dunphy, Chris Dillon, Mr C Seeney**
2 6, B m El Salvador (IRE)—Flora May
3 **FORLANO (FR)**, 5, b g Papal Bull—Floriana (GER) **South Downs Super 6 & If Only Partnershp**
4 **GLOBAL WONDER (IRE)**, 7, b g Kodiac—Traveller's Tales
5 **GOOD TIME AHEAD (IRE)**, 8, b g Iffraaj—Good Time Sue (IRE) **Mark & Guy Dunphy**
6 **GRANDEE (IRE)**, 8, b g Lope de Vega (IRE)—Caravan of Dreams (IRE) **B Hepburn, A C Dillon**
7 **GRANGECLARE NORTH (IRE)**, 5, ch m Presenting—Hayabusa **If Only Partnership**
8 **GUINESSED (IRE)**, 5, b m Sageburg (IRE)—Swap Shop (IRE) **If Only Partnership**
9 5, B m El Salvador (IRE)—Hester Lady (IRE)
10 **LEWESIAN LASS (IRE)**, 5, b m Yeats (IRE)—O Mio My (IRE) **Lewes Dream Syndicate**
11 **MAJOR REWARD (IRE)**, 6, b g Dawn Approach (IRE)—Zanzibar Girl (USA) **A & Brian Hepburn**
12 **MATEWAN (IRE)**, 7, b g Epaulette (AUS)—Cochin (USA) **The Best Partnership**
13 **NAUTICAL HAVEN**, 8, b g Harbour Watch (IRE)—Mania (IRE) **Mr Chris Dillon & Mr D G Edmonston**
14 5, Br m Malinas (GER)—Neat 'n Nimble
15 **NESS TA RAH**, 4, br f Cable Bay (IRE)—Point Perfect **Miss L. McGrath**
16 **POUR ME A DRINK**, 6, ch g Nathaniel (IRE)—Euroceleb (IRE) **Mr L. Best**
17 **PROMISES (IRE)**, 5, b m Bated Breath—Symposia **F. A. O'Sullivan & John Collins**
18 **THE TRAMPOLINIST (IRE)**, 7, b m Flemensfirth (USA)—D'Gigi **If Only Partnership**
19 **WELLS GLORY (IRE)**, 6, b g Fame And Glory—Annas Theatre **Milldean Racing Syndicate**

MRS SUZI BEST - continued

Other Owners: Mr M. J. Benton, Cheam Marketing Consultants Limited, Mr J. Collins, Mr A. R. Coupland, Mr C. J. Dillon, Mr G. Dunphy, Mr D. Edmonston, Mr B. Hepburn, Miss F. O'Sullivan, Miss M. Price, Mr C. A. Seeney, South Downs Super 6, Mr B. Vasey.

Assistant Trainer: Mr Tom Best.

---

34 MR EDWARD BETHELL, Middleham
Postal: **Thorngill House, Middleham, Leyburn, Yorkshire, DL8 4TJ**
Contacts: **PHONE 07767 622921**
EMAIL edward@bethellracing.co.uk

1 **ARTISTIC RIFLES (IRE),** 6, b g War Command (USA)—Chatham Islands (USA) **Mr Zaro Srl**
2 **BRIARDALE (IRE),** 10, b g Arcano (IRE)—Marine City (JPN) **Mr J. Carrick & Clarendon Thoroughbred Racing**
3 **EAGLE'S FOOT (IRE),** 5, b g Free Eagle (IRE)—Carmens Fate **Eagles Foot Syndicate**
4 **GAINSBOURG,** 4, b g Sixties Icon—Aromatherapy **Mr W.H. Carson**
5 **MOSS GILL (IRE),** 6, b g No Nay Never (USA)—Sharaarah (IRE) **Mr G Van Cutsem, J & S Bethell**
6 **MUDAWWAN (IRE),** 8, b g Invincible Spirit (IRE)—Louve Sacree (USA) **Clarendon Thoroughbred Racing**
7 **REGIONAL,** 4, b g Territories (IRE)—Favulusa **Future Champions Racing Regional**
8 **RICH DREAM (IRE),** 4, b g Make Believe—Poppet's Lovein **The Vickers & Clark Racing Partnership**
9 **STOCKBRIDGE TAP,** 5, ch g Nayef (USA)—Last Supper **Mr R. F. Gibbons**
10 **TASKHEER (IRE),** 4, b g Golden Horn—Shaarfa (USA) **Future Champions Racing Taskheer**
11 **TROLLEY BOY,** 4, b g Casamento (IRE)—Where I Be **Mrs E. A. Cyzer**
12 **ULSHAW BRIDGE (IRE),** 7, b g High Chaparral (IRE)—Sharaarah (IRE)
Mr J. Carrick & Clarendon Thoroughbred Racing

THREE-YEAR-OLDS
13 **BIG CHEESE (FR),** b c New Approach (IRE)—Kunegunda **Earl of Halifax**
14 **BRIGHT BLUE (IRE),** ch c Nathaniel (IRE)—Colour Bright (IRE) **Mr Zaro Srl**
15 **CARTRIDGE,** b g Time Test—Donatia **Hurworth Bloodstock Ltd**
16 **CHILLINGHAM (IRE),** b g Ulysses (IRE)—Last Jewel (IRE) **Mr J. Carrick, Mr S. Taylor**
17 **EIDIKOS,** b f Ardad (IRE)—Elpida (USA) **St Albans Bloodstock Limited**
18 **EMILY POST,** b f Charming Thought—Mary Read **Mrs F. Denniff, Hot To Trot Racing 2**
19 **EXMINSTER (IRE),** b g Ribchester (IRE)—Surface of Earth (USA) **Clarendon Thoroughbred Racing**
20 **FAST BEAUTY (IRE),** b f Kodi Bear (IRE)—Taqneyya (IRE) **Mrs S. Bethell**
21 **FEARBY (IRE),** b c Havana Gold (IRE)—Coolminx (IRE) **Clarendon Thoroughbred Racing**
22 **KHURUMBI (IRE),** b f The Gurkha (IRE)—Sharaarah (IRE) **Mr G Van Cutsem & Partners**
23 Ch c Mayson—Lady Hen **Mr Andrew Coombs**
24 **NOONIE,** b f Almanzor (FR)—Gallice (IRE) **Earl of Ronaldshay**
25 **POINT LYNAS (IRE),** b c Iffraaj—Initially **Julie & David R Martin & Dan Hall**
26 **REEL ROSIE (IRE),** b f Highland Reel (IRE)—Lady Canford (IRE) **The Reel Wheelers and Dealers**
27 **RICH KING,** b g Gleneagles (IRE)—Hairspray **Vickers Racing**
28 **ROUND ACRE,** ch f Garswood—Winter's Night (IRE) **Clarendon Thoroughbred Racing**
29 **SANDBECK,** b f Ardad (IRE)—Astley Park **Mr D.W. Armstrong**
30 **SKYE BREEZE (IRE),** ch g Pride of Dubai (AUS)—Zelloof (IRE) **Mr M. J. Dawson**
31 **SWINTON,** ch g Lope de Vega (IRE)—Valtina (IRE) **Clarendon Thoroughbred Racing**
32 **THEWAYTOTHESTARS,** b f Due Diligence (USA)—Last Supper **Mr R. F. Gibbons**

TWO-YEAR-OLDS
33 Ch c 02/04 Mayson—Azpeitia (Showcasing) **Mr D.W. Armstrong**
34 **CHAOTIC,** gr c 09/03 Bungle Inthejungle—Silver Games (IRE) (Verglas (IRE))
The Hon Mrs C. Corbett, Mr C. N. Wright
35 **COVERDALE (IRE),** b c 11/04 Expert Eye—Brynica (FR) (Desert Style (IRE)) (22000)
Clarendon Thoroughbred Racing
36 **DEEPDALE,** b f 25/02 Tasleet—Movementneverlies (Medicean) (22857) **Clarendon Thoroughbred Racing**
37 B c 10/02 Mukhadram—Fen Ali (Harbour Watch (IRE)) (10000) **Mr M.M. Foulger, Mr D. Tunmore**

MR EDWARD BETHELL - continued

38 B c 15/02 Lope de Vega (IRE)—Gallitea (IRE) (Galileo (IRE)) (127551) **Ms F. Carmichael, Ballylinch Stud**
39 **INDIANA BE,** b c 26/04 Sioux Nation (USA)—Because (IRE) (Sadler's Wells (USA)) (27000)

Mr J. Carrick, Mr S. Taylor

40 **KARDIA,** b f 14/02 Kingman—Elpida (USA) (Giant's Causeway (USA)) **St Albans Bloodstock Limited**
41 B f 20/04 Footstepsinthesand—Lady Canford (IRE) (Canford Cliffs (IRE)) (17007) **The Reel Wheelers and Dealers**
42 B c 24/03 Bobby's Kitten (USA)—Lady Clair (IRE) (Canford Cliffs (IRE)) **White Rose Racing**
43 **LADY ROAMER,** b f 08/02 Oasis Dream—Royal Eloquence (IRE) (Duke of Marmalade (IRE)) **C. Lewis (UK) Ltd**
44 **LERWICK,** b c 12/03 Awtaad (IRE)—Mystique (Oasis Dream) (30000) **The Marquess of Zetland**
45 B f 19/04 Make Believe—Majestic Dancer (IRE) (Danehill Dancer (IRE)) (18707) **Julie Martin and David R Martin**
46 **MINT EDITION,** b c 05/03 Showcasing—Starflower (Champs Elysees) (75000) **Titanium Racing Club**
47 **MOUNTAIN WARRIOR,** b c 22/03 Brazen Beau (AUS)—Plucky (Kyllachy) (25000)

Mr P. R. C. Morrison, Mr J. S. Lambert

48 B c 22/03 Brazen Beau (AUS)—Plucky (Kyllachy) (25000)
49 **ROCK OF ENGLAND (IRE),** ch c 15/03 Unfortunately (IRE)—Miss Fay (IRE) (Sayif (IRE)) (25714)

Mr J. Morris, Mr R. M. Phillips

50 B c 31/03 Zoustar (AUS)—Rohlindi (Red Ransom (USA)) (90000) **Titanium Racing Club**
51 B c 09/04 Churchill (IRE)—Springlike (IRE) (Acclamation) (52000) **Mr P. B. Moorhead**
52 **SWANLAND (IRE),** b c 01/02 Profitable (IRE)—Water Hole (IRE) (Oasis Dream) (100000)

Mr G Van Cutsem, Mrs B. D. M. Fenton

53 **TRIUMPHAL ARCH (IRE),** b c 17/02 Kodiac—Pearl of The Night (IRE) (Sea The Stars (IRE)) (82000)

Mr G Van Cutsem, Mrs B. D. M. Fenton

Other Owners: Mr D.W. Armstrong, Mrs S. Bethell, Mr J. Carrick, Clarendon Thoroughbred Racing, Clipper Logistics, Mr G Van Cutsem.

---

35 MISS HARRIET BETHELL, Arnold
Postal: **Arnold Manor, Black Tup Lane, Arnold, Hull, Yorkshire, HU11 5JA**
EMAIL **harrietbethell@hotmail.co.uk**

1 **BROKEN RIFLE,** 5, b g Havana Gold (IRE)—Peace Concluded **W. A. Bethell**
2 **CHINESE WHISPERER (FR),** 5, b g Poet's Voice—Shanghai Noon (FR) **W. A. Bethell**
3 **DHARAN (FR),** 9, b g Slickly Royal (FR)—Kelle Home (FR) **W. A. Bethell**
4 **GALIDERMES (FR),** 5, b g Hunter's Light (IRE)—Angie Eria (FR) **Miss H. Bethell**
5 **ISLE OF WOLVES,** 6, b g Nathaniel (IRE)—L'lle Aux Loups (IRE) **W. A. Bethell**
6 **LOPES DANCER (IRE),** 10, b g Lope de Vega (IRE)—Ballet Dancer (IRE) **W. A. Bethell**
7 **MIAMI PRESENT (IRE),** 12, b br g Presenting—Miami Nights (GER) **W. A. Bethell**
8 **NEWBERRY NEW (IRE),** 10, b g Kodiac—Sunblush (UAE) **W. A. Bethell**
9 **STEEL HELMET (IRE),** 8, ch g Helmet (AUS)—Marine City (JPN) **W. A. Bethell**
10 **YANIFER,** 4, b g Dandy Man (IRE)—Fondie (IRE) **W. A. Bethell**

Trainer did not supply details of their two-year-olds.

Flat Jockey: Josephine Gordon, Cam Hardie, Jo Mason. **NH Jockey:** Harry Banister.

---

36 MR WILLIAM BETHELL, Arnold
Postal: **Arnold Manor, Arnold, Hull, North Humberside, HU11 5JA**
Contacts: **PHONE 01964 562996**
EMAIL **wabethell@btinternet.com**

1 **FITSAOHA (FR),** 7, b m Barastraight—Kelle Home (FR) **W. A. Bethell**

37 **MR ROBERT BEVIS, Duckington**
Postal: The White House, Old Coach Road, Duckington, Cheshire, SY14 8LH
EMAIL robertjbevis66@aol.com

1 CRAZY JACK (IRE), 14, b g Royal Anthem (USA)—Cindy's Fancy (IRE) **R. J. Bevis**
2 DANILO D'AIRY (FR), 9, ch g Anzillero (GER)—Monita d'Airy (FR) **R. J. Bevis**
3 SARTENE'S SON (FR), 9, ch g Linda's Lad—Sartene (FR) **R. J. Bevis**
4 TURNING GOLD, 8, ch g Pivotal—Illusion **R. J. Bevis**
5 UNBLINKING, 9, b g Cacique (IRE)—Deliberate **R. Bevis**

---

38 **MR GEORGE BEWLEY, Appleby-In-Westmorland**
Postal: Jerusalem Farm, Colby, Appleby-In-Westmorland, Cumbria, CA16 6BB
Contacts: PHONE 017683 53003 MOBILE 07704 924783
EMAIL bewleyracing@outlook.com WEBSITE www.georgebewleyracing.co.uk

1 ASKALLI (IRE), 5, b g Ask—Gift Wrapped (IRE) **J. Wade**
2 AZOF DES MOTTES (FR), 5, b g Sinndar (IRE)—Wavy (FR) **Montgomerie, Mandle, Annett & Davidson**
3 BREAKING THE ICE (IRE), 7, b g Frozen Power (IRE)—Specific (IRE) **Montgomerie & Bewley**
4 BROOMFIELDS KAN (IRE), 7, gr g Arakan (USA)—Roses And Wine (IRE) **Southdean Racing Club**
5 CLASSICAL MILANO (IRE), 11, b g Milan—Miss Baden (IRE) **Victoria Bewley,John Gibson&e G Tunstall**
6 CLONDAW FIXER (IRE), 10, b g Court Cave (IRE)—The Millers Tale (IRE) **Mrs C. J. Todd**
7 FAMOUS RESPONSE (IRE), 8, b g Fame And Glory—Any Response (IRE) **Mr R Fisher & Bewley**
8 FOLLOW YOUR ARROW (FR), 6, b br g Crillon (FR)—Rakane Rouge (FR) **Todd & Bewley**
9 GLENBEG LAKE (IRE), 6, b g Mahler—Far From Here (IRE) **Mr A. Udale**
10 HUNGRY TIGER (IRE), 8, b g Morozov (USA)—Ballinamona Wish (IRE) **Mrs C. Holland**
11 MAH MATE BOB (IRE), 10, b g Mahler—Bobset Leader (IRE) **J. Wade**
12 MINNIMO, 7, ch g Motivator—Alessandra **Miss V. F. Bewley**
13 OUR MORRIS (IRE), 11, b g Milan—Broken Gale (IRE) **Mr R Fisher & Bewley**
14 PADDY THE HORSE (IRE), 7, b g Imperial Monarch (IRE)—Dendelady (IRE) **Mr A. Udale**
15 RAISE YOUR HAND (IRE), 7, br g Imperial Monarch (IRE)—Midnight Dasie (IRE) **Mrs E. Annett**
16 5, Ch g Getaway (GER)—Rathleek **Mr A. Udale**
17 RUSSELL'S QUARTER (IRE), 7, b g Imperial Monarch (IRE)—Native Bev (IRE) **Southdean Racing Club**
18 STAR VANTAGE (IRE), 5, b g Ocovango—Laura's Star (IRE) **J. Wade**
19 STRIKE OF LIGHTING (IRE), 6, ch g Jet Away—Will She Smile (IRE)
20 TOMMY TUNT, 5, b h Lucarno (USA)—Newdane Dancer (IRE) **Mr E. G. Tunstall**
21 WAR AT SEA (IRE), 8, gr g Mastercraftsman (IRE)—Swirling (IRE) **Mrs Lesley Bewley & Mr John Gibson**

Other Owners: Mrs E. Annett, G. T. Bewley, Mrs L. Bewley, Miss V. F. Bewley, Mr L. J. Davidson, Mr R. A. Fisher, Mr J. H. Gibson, Mrs R. J. Mandle, D. H. Montgomerie, Mrs C. J. Todd, Mr E. G. Tunstall.

NH Jockey: Jonathon Bewley, Colm McCormack, Craig Nichol.

---

39 **MR SAEED BIN SUROOR, Newmarket**
Postal: Godolphin Office, Snailwell Road, Newmarket, Suffolk, CB8 7YE
Contacts: PHONE 01638 569956
WEBSITE www.godolphin.com

1 ARABIAN WARRIOR, 5, b g Dubawi (IRE)—Siyaadah **Godolphin Management Company Ltd**
2 BEDOUIN'S STORY, 7, b g Farhh—Time Crystal (IRE) **Godolphin Management Company Ltd**
3 BIG MEETING (IRE), 5, b br g Shamardal (USA)—Beta **Godolphin Management Company Ltd**
4 BIG TEAM (USA), 5, b br g Speightstown (USA)—Kotuku **Godolphin Management Company Ltd**
5 BIN BATTUTA, 8, ch g Dubawi (IRE)—Land of Dreams **Godolphin Management Company Ltd**

MR SAEED BIN SUROOR - continued

6 **BRIGHT START (USA)**, 5, b br g Medaglia d'Oro (USA)—Blue Petrel (USA) **Godolphin Management Company Ltd**
7 **BRILLIANT LIGHT**, 5, b g Sea The Stars (IRE)—Flame of Gibraltar (IRE) **Godolphin Management Company Ltd**
8 **CITY WALK (IRE)**, 5, b g Brazen Beau (AUS)—My Lucky Liz (IRE) **Godolphin Management Company Ltd**
9 **COLOUR IMAGE (IRE)**, 5, b g Kodiac—Chroussa (IRE) **Godolphin Management Company Ltd**
10 **DESERT FIRE (IRE)**, 7, b g Cape Cross (IRE)—Crystal House (CHI) **Godolphin Management Company Ltd**
11 **DUBAI FUTURE**, 6, b g Dubawi (IRE)—Anjaz (USA) **Godolphin Management Company Ltd**
12 **DUBAI HOPE (IRE)**, 4, b br f Invincible Spirit (IRE)—City Glam (ARG) **Godolphin Management Company Ltd**
13 **DUBAI HORIZON**, 8, b g Poet's Voice—Chibola (ARG) **Godolphin Management Company Ltd**
14 **DUBAI ICON**, 6, b h New Approach (IRE)—Arabian Beauty (IRE) **Godolphin Management Company Ltd**
15 **DUBAI LEGACY (USA)**, 6, b g Discreet Cat (USA)—Afsana (IRE) **Godolphin Management Company Ltd**
16 **DUBAI LOVE**, 5, b m Night of Thunder (IRE)—Devotion (IRE) **Godolphin Management Company Ltd**
17 **DUBAI MIRAGE (IRE)**, 5, ch g Dubawi (IRE)—Calipatria **Godolphin Management Company Ltd**
18 **DUBAI SOUQ (IRE)**, 5, b g Dubawi (IRE)—Balsamine (USA) **Godolphin Management Company Ltd**
19 **DUBAI WELCOME**, 5, gr ro g Dubawi (IRE)—Emily Bronte **Godolphin Management Company Ltd**
20 **ELECTRICAL STORM**, 5, b g Dubawi (IRE)—Mujarah (IRE) **Godolphin Management Company Ltd**
21 **FINAL SONG (IRE)**, 5, b m Dark Angel (IRE)—Rahiyah (USA) **Godolphin Management Company Ltd**
22 **FIRST VIEW (IRE)**, 5, b g Exceed And Excel (USA)—Love Charm **Godolphin Management Company Ltd**
23 **FUTURE KING (IRE)**, 5, b g Dark Angel (IRE)—Relation Alexander (IRE) **Godolphin Management Company Ltd**
24 **GLOBAL HEAT (IRE)**, 6, b g Toronado (IRE)—Raskutani **Godolphin Management Company Ltd**
25 **GLOBAL WALK (IRE)**, 5, b g Society Rock—Shehila (IRE) **Godolphin Management Company Ltd**
26 **GREAT HUNTER (IRE)**, 4, gr c Dark Angel (IRE)—Floristry **Godolphin Management Company Ltd**
27 **GREAT NEWS**, 4, gr g Shamardal (USA)—Nahoodh (IRE) **Godolphin Management Company Ltd**
28 **LAND OF LEGENDS (IRE)**, 6, b br h Iffraaj—Homily **Godolphin Management Company Ltd**
29 **LAST LOOK (IRE)**, 6, b m Pivotal—Gonbarda (GER) **Godolphin Management Company Ltd**
30 **LAST SUNSET (IRE)**, 4, b br f Teofilo—Dufay (IRE) **Godolphin Management Company Ltd**
31 **LIVE YOUR DREAM (IRE)**, 5, b g Iffraaj—Dream Book **Godolphin Management Company Ltd**
32 **LONE FIGHTER (IRE)**, 4, b g Dawn Approach (IRE)—Pulcinella (USA) **Godolphin Management Company Ltd**
33 **LOST GOLD (IRE)**, 4, b br g Dark Angel (IRE)—Windsor County (USA) **Godolphin Management Company Ltd**
34 **LOST IN TIME**, 5, b g Dubawi (IRE)—Reunite (USA) **Godolphin Management Company Ltd**
35 **MAJOR PARTNERSHIP (IRE)**, 7, gr g Iffraaj—Roystonea **Godolphin Management Company Ltd**
36 **MARCHING ARMY**, 4, ch g Iffraaj—Show Day (IRE) **Godolphin Management Company Ltd**
37 **MILITARY MARCH**, 5, b h New Approach (IRE)—Punctilious **Godolphin Management Company Ltd**
38 **MO'ASSESS (IRE)**, 4, ch c Pivotal—Hush Money (CHI) **Godolphin Management Company Ltd**
39 **MOVING LIGHT (IRE)**, 5, ch h Night of Thunder (IRE)—North East Bay (USA) **Godolphin Management Company Ltd**
40 **MUTAFAWWIJ**, 6, b g Oasis Dream—Reunite (USA) **Godolphin Management Company Ltd**
41 **NIGHT HUNTER (USA)**, 5, gr g Tapit (USA)—Wickedly Wise (USA) **Godolphin Management Company Ltd**
42 **PASSION AND GLORY (IRE)**, 6, b g Cape Cross (IRE)—Potent Embrace (USA) **Godolphin Management Company Ltd**
43 **PIECE OF HISTORY (IRE)**, 7, b g Iffraaj—Moonlife (IRE) **Godolphin Management Company Ltd**
44 **QUIET EVENING (IRE)**, 5, b m Teofilo (IRE)—Prussian **Godolphin Management Company Ltd**
45 **RAAEB (IRE)**, 5, ch h Raven's Pass (USA)—Kalaatah (USA) **Godolphin Management Company Ltd**
46 **REAL WORLD (IRE)**, 5, b h Dark Angel (IRE)—Nafura **Godolphin Management Company Ltd**
47 **RICH WATERS (IRE)**, 4, b g Showcasing—Springlike (IRE) **Godolphin Management Company Ltd**
48 **ROYAL INVITATION**, 4, ch c New Approach (IRE)—Nadia **Godolphin Management Company Ltd**
49 **ROYAL MARINE (IRE)**, 6, b g Raven's Pass (USA)—Inner Secret (USA) **Godolphin Management Company Ltd**
50 **SECRET MOMENT (IRE)**, 5, b g Exceed And Excel (AUS)—Devotee (USA) **Godolphin Management Company Ltd**
51 **SHINING EXAMPLE (IRE)**, 5, b h Shamardal (USA)—Kailani **Godolphin Management Company Ltd**
52 **SILENT HUNTER**, 6, b g Dutch Art—Yellow Rosebud (IRE) **Godolphin Management Company Ltd**
53 **SMART START**, 4, b g Teofilo (IRE)—Haughtily (IRE) **Godolphin Management Company Ltd**
54 **SOFT WHISPER (IRE)**, 4, b f Dubawi (IRE)—Placidia (IRE) **Godolphin Management Company Ltd**
55 **STORM DAMAGE**, 4, b g Night of Thunder (IRE)—Sundrop (JPN) **Godolphin Management Company Ltd**
56 **STORM FRONT**, 4, ch g Helmet (AUS)—Vituisa **Godolphin Management Company Ltd**
57 **STUNNING BEAUTY**, 5, ch m Shamardal (USA)—Short Skirt **Godolphin Management Company Ltd**
58 **TOMOUH (IRE)**, 5, b m Dubawi (IRE)—Sundrop (JPN) **Godolphin Management Company Ltd**
59 **UNTOLD STORY**, 5, ch h Teofilo (IRE)—Tanzania (USA) **Godolphin Management Company Ltd**
60 **VOLCANIC SKY**, 7, b g Street Cry (IRE)—Short Skirt **Godolphin Management Company Ltd**
61 **WARM SMILE**, 4, ch f New Approach (IRE)—Adoringly (IRE) **Godolphin Management Company Ltd**
62 **WHITE MOONLIGHT (USA)**, 5, b m Medaglia d'Oro (USA)—Fitful Skies (IRE) **Godolphin Management Company Ltd**
63 **WILD HURRICANE (IRE)**, 4, b g Dubawi (IRE)—Wavering (USA) **Godolphin Management Company Ltd**
64 **WILD LION (IRE)**, 4, ch g The Last Lion (IRE)—Snow Powder (IRE) **Godolphin Management Company Ltd**

MR SAEED BIN SUROOR - continued

THREE-YEAR-OLDS

65 **ARMY SERGEANT (IRE),** ch g Iffraaj—Voice of Truth (IRE) **Godolphin Management Company Ltd**
66 **BEAUTIFUL COLOUR,** b f Iffraaj—Mar Mar (IRE) **Godolphin Management Company Ltd**
67 **CLOUDY WATERS (IRE),** b f The Gurkha (IRE)—First Blush (IRE) **Godolphin Management Company Ltd**
68 **CRYSTAL CLOUD,** b f Teofilo (IRE)—Blue Illusion **Godolphin Management Company Ltd**
69 **DARK COLOURS (IRE),** b f Dark Angel (IRE)—Karenine **Godolphin Management Company Ltd**
70 **FEEL THE MOMENT,** b f Invincible Spirit (IRE)—Country Music **Godolphin Management Company Ltd**
71 **GAME MASTER,** b g Postponed (IRE)—Sundrop (JPN) **Godolphin Management Company Ltd**
72 **HOME CITY (IRE),** b c Profitable (IRE)—Nafura **Godolphin Management Company Ltd**
73 **ISLAND FALCON (IRE),** b br c Iffraaj—Adoringly (IRE) **Godolphin Management Company Ltd**
74 **LABIBA,** b f Night of Thunder (IRE)—Wedding March (IRE) **Godolphin Management Company Ltd**
75 Ch c Exceed And Excel (AUS)—My Call **Godolphin Management Company Ltd**
76 **NADER,** b c Iffraaj—Manaboo (USA) **Godolphin Management Company Ltd**
77 **NIGHT OF LUXURY,** b g Postponed (IRE)—Moonlife (IRE) **Godolphin Management Company Ltd**
78 **ONE COLOUR (IRE),** ch f Teofilo (IRE)—Bluefire **Godolphin Management Company Ltd**
79 **OPEN MIND,** br g Cable Bay (IRE)—Bonhomie **Godolphin Management Company Ltd**
80 **RACING ROYALTY,** b g Fast Company (IRE)—Patent Joy (IRE) **Godolphin Management Company Ltd**
81 **RAYAT (IRE),** b c Starspangledbanner (AUS)—Violet's Gift (IRE) **Godolphin Management Company Ltd**
82 **RETURN TO DUBAI (IRE),** ch c Ribchester (IRE)—Farthing (IRE) **Godolphin Management Company Ltd**
83 **SHAMEKH,** ch c New Bay—Ever Love (BRZ) **Godolphin Management Company Ltd**
84 **SKI DUBAI (IRE),** b f Teofilo (IRE)—Snow Powder (IRE) **Godolphin Management Company Ltd**
85 **SPECIAL DESIGN,** ch c Iffraaj—Forte **Godolphin Management Company Ltd**
86 **SWISS VALLEY,** b f Teofilo (IRE)—Trieste **Godolphin Management Company Ltd**
87 **VALLEY MIST,** b f Dubawi (IRE)—Mise En Rose (USA) **Godolphin Management Company Ltd**
88 **WHITE WOLF (IRE),** b c Invincible Spirit (IRE)—Long Lashes (USA) **Godolphin Management Company Ltd**
89 **WILD PLACE (IRE),** b f Mehmas (IRE)—Turuqaat **Godolphin Management Company Ltd**
90 **WILD TIGER,** b c Frankel—Antara (GER) **Godolphin Management Company Ltd**

TWO-YEAR-OLDS

91 B f 10/04 Invincible Spirit (IRE)—Aiming For Rio (FR) (Rio de La Plata (USA)) **Godolphin Management Company Ltd**
92 B f 12/05 Dark Angel (IRE)—Albasharah (USA) (Arch (USA)) **Godolphin Management Company Ltd**
93 B f 28/03 Teofilo (IRE)—All Clear (Dubawi (IRE)) **Godolphin Management Company Ltd**
94 B c 03/04 Invincible Spirit (IRE)—Aurora Leigh (Dubawi (IRE)) **Godolphin Management Company Ltd**
95 B c 29/02 Fast Company (IRE)—Belle Boyd (Oasis Dream) **Godolphin Management Company Ltd**
96 B f 04/03 Lope de Vega (IRE)—Bint Almatar (USA) (Kingmambo (USA)) **Godolphin Management Company Ltd**
97 B f 13/02 Exceed And Excel (AUS)—Bitter Lake (USA) (Halling (USA)) **Godolphin Management Company Ltd**
98 B gr c 23/04 Dark Angel (IRE)—Dark Orchid (USA) (Dansili) **Godolphin Management Company Ltd**
99 B f 15/03 Exceed And Excel (AUS)—Days of Old (New Approach (IRE)) **Godolphin Management Company Ltd**
100 B f 07/04 Iffraaj—Flora Sandes (USA) (War Front (USA)) **Godolphin Management Company Ltd**
101 Gr c 16/03 Dark Angel (IRE)—Good Place (USA) (Street Cry (IRE)) **Godolphin Management Company Ltd**
102 Ro f 16/04 Mastercraftsman (IRE)—Hawsa (Rahy (USA)) **Godolphin Management Company Ltd**
103 Gr f 03/03 Dubawi (IRE)—Heart's Content (IRE) (Daylami (IRE)) **Godolphin Management Company Ltd**
104 B c 03/04 Exceed And Excel (AUS)—Heartily (IRE) (Dubawi (IRE)) **Godolphin Management Company Ltd**
105 B c 27/02 Iffraaj—La Rosetta (New Approach (IRE)) **Godolphin Management Company Ltd**
106 B c 09/02 Nathaniel (IRE)—Lura (USA) (Street Cry (IRE)) **Godolphin Management Company Ltd**
107 B c 05/05 Ribchester (IRE)—Michita (USA) (Dynaformer (USA)) **Godolphin Management Company Ltd**
108 B f 24/04 Exceed And Excel (AUS)—Modern Ideals (New Approach (IRE)) **Godolphin Management Company Ltd**
109 B f 02/03 Postponed (IRE)—Moonsail (Monsun (GER)) **Godolphin Management Company Ltd**
110 Ch c 18/02 Postponed (IRE)—Perfect Light (IRE) (Galileo (IRE)) **Godolphin Management Company Ltd**
111 B c 02/04 Dubawi (IRE)—Pleascach (IRE) (Teofilo (IRE)) **Godolphin Management Company Ltd**
112 B f 25/01 Farhh—Pulcinella (USA) (Dubawi (IRE)) **Godolphin Management Company Ltd**
113 B f 12/01 Iffraaj—Ragsah (IRE) (Shamardal (USA)) **Godolphin Management Company Ltd**
114 Ch f 01/02 Harry Angel (IRE)—Saoirse Abu (USA) (Mr Greeley (USA)) **Godolphin Management Company Ltd**
115 Ch c 02/04 Cracksman—Summer Flower (IRE) (Oasis Dream) **Godolphin Management Company Ltd**
116 B gr c 19/04 Caravaggio (USA)—Tandragee (USA) (Bernardini (USA)) **Godolphin Management Company Ltd**
117 B c 15/05 Teofilo (IRE)—West Wind (Machiavellian (USA)) **Godolphin Management Company Ltd**

Assistant Trainer: Anthony Paul Howarth.

40 MRS EMMA-JANE BISHOP, Cheltenham
Postal: **Brockhill, Naunton, Cheltenham, Gloucestershire, GL54 3BA**
Contacts: **MOBILE 07887 845970 FAX 01451 850199**
EMAIL emmabishopracing@hotmail.com WEBSITE www.emmabishopracing.com

1 **ANOTHER GLANCE**, 6, br m Passing Glance—Roberta Back (IRE) **Emma Bishop Racing Club**
2 **GLANCE BACK**, 11, b g Passing Glance—Roberta Back (IRE) **Mrs J. Arnold**
3 **HAAFBACK**, 4, b g Haafhd—Roberta Back (IRE) **Mrs J. Arnold**
4 **HAAFBOURD**, 4, b g Haafhd—Bourdello
5 **LUMINATION**, 6, b g Toronado (IRE)—Sparkling Eyes **Manton Park Racing**
6 **MASTER MALCOLM**, 5, ch g Mastercraftsman (IRE)—Desert Sage **Mrs C. Richmond-Watson**
7 **MAX DYNAMO**, 12, b g Midnight Legend—Vivante (IRE) **Mrs M. J. Wilson**
8 **RUBY'S PEARL**, 5, b m Passing Glance—Ruby Valentine (FR) **Mrs M. J. Wilson**
9 **STAAR (IRE)**, 8, b g Sea The Stars (IRE)—Bitooh **Mrs J. Arnold**
10 **THEOULE (FR)**, 6, b br g Le Havre (IRE)—Santa Louisia **Emma Bishop Racing Club**

41 MR FRANK BISHOP, Kidderminster
Postal: **Parkside, Blakeshall, Wolverley, Kidderminster, Worcestershire, DY11 5XW**
Contacts: **MOBILE 07900 407647**

1 **GUNMETAL (IRE)**, 9, gr g Clodovil (IRE)—March Star (IRE) **Mr F. A. Bishop**
2 **HURRICANE ALERT**, 10, b g Showcasing—Raggle Taggle (IRE) **Mr M. R. Baldry**
3 **MAZAMINSKY**, 4, b f Mazameer (IRE)—Pursuit of Purpose **Mr M. R. Baldry**
4 **SEEKING PERFECTION**, 4, b f Twilight Son—Arabian Music (IRE) **Mr N. P. Hardy**
5 **SPARKLING DIAMOND**, 5, b m Cable Bay (IRE)—Read Federica **Mr F. A. Bishop**
6 **WIN WIN POWER (IRE)**, 5, b g Exceed And Excel (AUS)—Spesialta **Mr N. P. Hardy**

THREE-YEAR-OLDS

7 **ANK MARVIN**, b c Garswood—Miss Toldyaso (IRE) **Mr F. A. Bishop**
8 B f Equiano (FR)—Broughtons Charm (IRE) **Mr F. A. Bishop**
9 **HI HOH TONTO**, gr c Captain Gerrard (IRE)—Blakeshall Diamond **Mr F. A. Bishop**
10 Ch c Mazameer (IRE)—Laurel Star **Mr M. R. Baldry**
11 B c Epaulette (AUS)—Twilight Belle (IRE) **Mr F. A. Bishop**

Assistant Trainer: Mr Martin Bishop.

42 MISS LINDA BLACKFORD, Tiverton
Postal: **Shortlane Stables, Rackenford, Tiverton, Devon, EX16 8EH**
Contacts: **PHONE 01884 881589 MOBILE 07887 947832**
EMAIL overthelast@outlook.com WEBSITE www.overthelast.com

1 **BAILY GORSE (IRE)**, 8, b g Milan—Lillies Bordello (IRE) **Mrs V. W. Jones & Mr B. P. Jones**
2 **LURE DES PRES (IRE)**, 10, b g Robin des Pres (FR)—Pinkeen Lady (IRE) **Mr M. J. Vanstone**
3 **POET'S REFLECTION (IRE)**, 7, b m Dylan Thomas (IRE)—Lola's Reflection **Mrs S. H. Livesey-Van Dorst**
4 **PRINCE RHINEGOLD (IRE)**, 4, b g Getaway (GER)—Water Rock **Mrs D Robinson Mrs&mrs Livesey-van Dorst**
5 **RANGATIRA JACK**, 4, ch g Mount Nelson—Woodland Walk **Mrs D Robinson Mrs&mrs Livesey-van Dorst**

Other Owners: Mr B. P. Jones, Mrs V. W. Jones, Mrs J. Livesey-Van Dorst, Mrs S. H. Livesey-Van Dorst, Mrs D. Robinson.

Assistant Trainer: M. J. Vanstone.

NH Jockey: James Best, Micheal Nolan, Nick Scholfield. **Conditional Jockey:** Sean Houlihan.

43 **MR MICHAEL BLAKE, Trowbridge**
Postal: Staverton Farm, Trowbridge, Wiltshire, BA14 6PE
Contacts: PHONE 01225 782327 MOBILE 07971 675180
EMAIL mblakestavertonfarm@btinternet.com WEBSITE www.michaelblakeracing.co.uk

1 **ATHEEB**, 5, b g Muhaarar—Lady Francesca **Mr A. D. Potts**
2 **BOUNTY PURSUIT**, 10, b g Pastoral Pursuits—Poyle Dee Dee **Racing For A Cause**
3 **CHAMPS DE REVES**, 7, b g Champs Elysees—Joyeaux **Staverton Owners Group**
4 **CLEARANCE**, 8, b g Authorized (IRE)—Four Miracles **Joseph & Kirk Warr**
5 **FARD**, 7, b g Dutch Art—Rose Blossom **Mr R. Gould**
6 **FREEDOM AND WHEAT (IRE)**, 6, b g Fast Company (IRE)—Rustam **Racing For A Cause**
7 **HURRICANE ARCADIO (IRE)**, 8, b g Arcadio (GER)—Back To Favour (IRE) **Staverton Owners Group**
8 **LOVE DREAMS (IRE)**, 8, b g Dream Ahead (USA)—Kimola (IRE) **Mr A. D. Potts**
9 **MR ZEE (IRE)**, 5, b g Zebedee—Monsusu (IRE) **Staverton Owners Group**
10 **POSH GIRL**, 4, gr f Outstrip—Sauvage (FR) **In the Mix Racing**
11 **TENTH CENTURY**, 4, b g Fountain of Youth (IRE)—Sukuma (IRE) **Allie & John Burchell**

Other Owners: Mr J. Blake, Mrs A. Burchell, Mr J. R. Burchell, Ms E. C. Chivers, Mr P. J. Gadsden, Mr K. Warr.

Assistant Trainer: Sharon Blake.

---

44 **MISS GILLIAN BOANAS, Saltburn**
Postal: Groundhill Farm, Lingdale, Saltburn-By-The-Sea, Cleveland, TS12 3HD
Contacts: MOBILE 07976 280154
EMAIL gillianboanas@aol.com

1 **ARMY'S DREAM (IRE)**, 5, b g Dylan Thomas (IRE)—Cappa Or (IRE) **WASPS Syndicate**
2 **BABY JANE (IRE)**, 7, b m Oscar (IRE)—Young Lady (IRE) **Miss G Boanas & Mr M Foxton**
3 **BESTIARIUS (IRE)**, 10, b g Vinnie Roe (IRE)—Chione (IRE) **Gillianboanas,Douglasrenton,Lesdonaldson**
4 **BROCTUNE RED**, 7, ch g Haafhd—Fairlie **Mrs M. B. Thwaites**
5 **BUSY STREET**, 10, b g Champs Elysees—Allegro Viva (USA) **Mr J. A. Swinbank**
6 **CRIXUS'S ESCAPE (IRE)**, 9, ch g Beneficial—Tierneys Choice (IRE) **Mr R. Collins**
7 **FAME AND HOPE (IRE)**, 7, b m Fame And Glory—Kaituna (IRE) **Miss G. L. Boanas**
8 **FLEXI FURLOUGH (IRE)**, 6, gr m Milan—Young Lady (IRE) **Douglas & David Barclay**
9 **GENERALISATION (IRE)**, 9, b g Arcadio (GER)—Will She Smile (IRE) **Miss G. L. Boanas**
10 **GREAT COLACI**, 9, b g Sulamani (IRE)—Fairlie **Rug, Grub & Pub Partnership**
11 **GUIDEDBYTHESCIENCE (IRE)**, 6, b m Shirocco (GER)—Kaffie **Mr John Coates Mr Richard Smith**
12 **JACK OF ALL SHAPES (IRE)**, 6, b g Arcadio (GER)—Arequipa (IRE) **Rug, Grub & Pub Partnership**
13 **JUST CALL ME AL (IRE)**, 9, br g Presenting—Tonaphuca Girl (IRE) **M.B.Thwaites G Halder**
14 **KARAPIRO DOUG**, 6, ch g Mr Medici (IRE)—Littlemiss **J. Binks**
15 **LADY VINETTA**, 7, b m Sulamani (IRE)—Vinetta **The Thoughtful Partnership**
16 **LOCH LINNHE**, 10, b g Tobougg (IRE)—Quistaquay **Miss G Boanas & Mr M Foxton**
17 **LUNAR GLOW**, 4, b f Pether's Moon (IRE)—Just For Pleasure (IRE)
18 **POUND OFF YOU**, 6, ch m Haafhd—Let It Be **Miss G. L. Boanas**
19 **SILVER DUST (IRE)**, 6, gr g Clodovil (IRE)—Silesian (IRE) **Miss G. L. Boanas**
20 **SO MACHO (IRE)**, 7, ch g Camacho—Turban Heights (IRE) **Mr J. A. Swinbank**
21 **SULTANS PRIDE**, 10, b g Sulamani (IRE)—Pennys Pride (IRE) **Reveley Racing 1**
22 **TEESCOMPONENTS LAD**, 9, b g Midnight Legend—Northern Native (IRE) **Gillian Boanas Racing**
23 **TEESCOMPONENTSTRIG**, 7, ch g Black Sam Bellamy (IRE)—La Calinda **Tees Components Ltd**
24 **TRY TEESCOMPONENTS**, 5, br g Shirocco (GER)—Northern Native (IRE) **Tees Components Ltd**
25 **WHOOPSA DAYZEE**, 5, ch m Black Sam Bellamy (IRE)—La Calinda **Miss G. L. Boanas**

Other Owners: Mr D. J. S. Barclay, Miss G. L. Boanas, J. W. Coates, Mr W. L. Donaldson, M. E. Foxton, Mr G. S. Halder, D. C. Renton, R. V. Smith, Mrs M. B. Thwaites.

45 MRS MYRIAM BOLLACK-BADEL, Chantilly-Lamorlaye
Postal: 20 Rue Blanche, 60260 Lamorlaye, France
Contacts: HOME +33 3 44 21 33 67 MOBILE +33 6 10 80 93 47 FAX +33 3 44 21 33 67
EMAIL myriam.bollack@gmail.com

1 **AVEC LAURA,** 9, ch h Manduro (GER)—Sign of Life **Mme M. Bollack-Badel**
2 **COGOLIN (FR),** 4, ch c Goken (FR)—Albicocca (FR) **Mr Patrick Fellous**
3 **DARE,** 5, b m Bated Breath—Heronetta **Oscar Ortmans**
4 **GREEN SPIRIT (FR),** 5, b g Charm Spirit (IRE)—Green Speed (FR) **Mr J. C. Smith**
5 **ZYGFRYD (FR),** 4, ch c Literato (FR)—Zython (FR) **Zygfryd Partnership**

THREE-YEAR-OLDS
6 **ACREGATE,** b f Ribchester (IRE)—Green Speed (FR) **Mr J. C. Smith**
7 **LUNE DE RIO (FR),** ch f Rio de La Plata (USA)—Rocheville (FR) **Mr Henri d'Aillieres**
8 **NUMERO (FR),** b f Myboycharlie (IRE)—Numerologie (FR) **Alain Badel**
9 **PENTAOUR (FR),** ch c Toronado (IRE)—Perpetual Glory **Ecurie Noel Forgeard**
10 **SINNDARILLO (FR),** b c Amarillo (IRE)—Sinnderelle (FR) **Philippe Stein**
11 **WELCOME SIGHT,** br f Aclaim (IRE)—Loch Mirage **Mr J. C. Smith**
12 **ZINNIA (FR),** ch c Waldpark (GER)—Zython (FR) **Mme M. Bollack-Badel**

TWO-YEAR-OLDS
13 Ch f 15/03 Fast Company (IRE)—Cline (Pivotal) (7653) **Mrs Eva Crone**
14 B c 23/04 Exceed And Excel (AUS)—Cocktail Queen (IRE) (Motivator) **Mr J. C. Smith**
15 Ch c 23/02 Sea The Moon (GER)—Dawn Dash (Dawn Approach (IRE)) **Mr J. C. Smith**
16 **SMART STYLE (IRE),** b f 05/02 Raven's Pass (USA)—Some Style (IRE) (Kodiac) (20408) **Mr J. C. Smith**
17 **ZERETH (FR),** b c 21/04 Literato—Zython (FR) (Kabool) **Mme M. Bollack-Badel**

Assistant Trainer: Alain Badel, **Travelling Head:** Philippe Celier, **Racing Secretary:** Marie Helene Coulomb.

Flat Jockey: Stephane Pasquier.

46 MR MARTIN BOSLEY, Chalfont St. Giles
Postal: Bowstridge Farm, Bowstridge Lane, Chalfont St. Giles, Buckinghamshire, HP8 4RF
Contacts: PHONE 01494 875533 MOBILE 07778 938040
EMAIL martin@martinbosley.com WEBSITE www.martinbosleyracing.com

1 **ASSEMBLED,** 6, gr g Iffraaj—Bezique **Ms J. Williams**
2 **DRUNKEN PIRATE,** 9, b g Black Sam Bellamy (IRE)—Peel Me A Grape **Mrs E. A. Prowting**
3 **FIBONACCI,** 8, ch g Galileo (IRE)—Tereschenko (USA) **Mrs E. A. Prowting**
4 **FULLY LOADED,** 5, ch g Lucarno (USA)—Mayberry **Mrs E. A. Prowting**
5 **HURCLE (IRE),** 5, b g Exceed And Excel (AUS)—Switcher (IRE) **Quartet Racing**
6 **NAWAR,** 7, b g Henrythenavigator (USA)—Nouriya **Quartet Racing**
7 **NORSE CASTLE,** 7, b g Norse Dancer (IRE)—Hursley Hope (IRE) **M.A.S.A.**
8 **SENNEN,** 4, gr ro g Outstrip—Makara **Mr M. R. Bosley**
9 **WHYTEHALL ROSE,** 4, b f Heeraat (IRE)—Meebo (IRE) **Whytehall Partnership**
10 **ZEFFERINO,** 8, ch g Frankel—Turama **J. Carey**

THREE-YEAR-OLDS
11 Ch g Proconsul—Meebo (IRE) **Whytehall Partnership**

Other Owners: Mr M. J. Bond, Mr D. Chapman, Mr M. Gannon, Mr H. Vlatas.

47 MR MARCO BOTTI, Newmarket

Postal: **Prestige Place, Snailwell Road, Newmarket, Suffolk, CB8 7DP**
Contacts: **PHONE 01638 662416 MOBILE 07775 803007 FAX 01638 662417**
EMAIL office@marcobotti.co.uk WEBSITE www.marcobotti.co.uk

1 **ALJARI**, 6, b g Quality Road (USA)—Rhagori **Mr R. El Youssef**
2 **AMALFI SALSA (IRE)**, 4, gr f Mastercraftsman (IRE)—Lemon Rock **Middleham Park Racing Lxxiv & Partner 2**
3 **BLUENOSE BELLE (USA)**, 4, b f Noble Mission—Poster Girl (USA) **Middleham Park Racing CXXVI & Les Boyer**
4 **CASINA DI NOTTE (IRE)**, 8, ch g Casamento (IRE)—Nightswimmer (IRE) **Mrs L. Botti**
5 **COSMIC GEORGE**, 4, b g Dawn Approach (IRE)—Badalona **Middleham Park Racing Xcviii & Partner**
6 **COUNTY WICKLOW (USA)**, 4, b g War Front (USA)—Coolmore (IRE) **Mr Manfredini & Partner**
7 **DIVINE MAGIC**, 4, b f Farhh—Magika **Les Boyer Partnership**
8 **DREAM A LITTLE**, 4, b f Oasis Dream—Got To Dream **Milan Racing Club**
9 **FELIX**, 6, ch g Lope de Vega (IRE)—Luminance (IRE) **Gary Allsopp & Partner**
10 **HABIT ROUGE**, 5, b g Helmet (AUS)—Hurricane Harriet **Ambrosiana Racing & Partner**
11 **INVINCIBLE LASS (IRE)**, 4, b br f Invincible Spirit (IRE)—Polygon (USA) **Heart of the South Racing 124**
12 **MOBASHR (USA)**, 4, b g Mshawish (USA)—Refreshing **Ahmad Bintouq & Partner**
13 **MOJAZAFFAH (IRE)**, 4, b f New Approach (IRE)—Almashooqa (USA) **Jonny & Boyer**
14 **MOLIWOOD**, 4, b g Fastnet Rock (AUS)—Shalwa **Les Boyer Partnership 1**
15 **NAO DA MAIS (BRZ)**, 6, b h T H Approval (USA)—Espetacular (BRZ) **Mr B. Steinbruch**
16 **NUBLE (URU)**, 6, gr m Brilliant Speed (USA)—Hero of The Night (BRZ) **Mr B. Steinbruch**
17 **NUSHAFREEN**, 4, b f Holy Roman Emperor (IRE)—Day Away (IRE) **Milan Racing Club**
18 **RISING STAR**, 4, b f Fast Company (IRE)—Ile Flottante **Mamba Racing & Partner**
19 **SAIGON**, 4, b g Frankel—Silk Sari **Bengough, Booth, Silver, Steed, Fittocks**
20 **SILVER GUNN (IRE)**, 4, gr g Lope de Vega (IRE)—Claba di San Jore (IRE) **Mr P. Hunt**
21 **SILVER SAMURAI**, 5, gr g Cable Bay (IRE)—High Tan **What A Time To Be Alive 1**
22 **SUMMERTIME ROMANCE**, 4, b f Declaration of War (USA)—Montjess (IRE)
Middleham Park Xxii & Steven Rocco 1
23 **THE CONQUEROR**, 7, ch h Excelebration (IRE)—March Madness **Mr R Bruni & Partner**
24 **TRICOLORE (ITY)**, 4, b g Twilight Son—Tribulina **La Tesa Spa & Partner**
25 **VALENTINKA**, 4, ch f Helmet (AUS)—Pantile **Mrs L. Botti**

THREE-YEAR-OLDS

26 **AGUAPLANO**, b c Outstrip—Ile Flottante **Les Boyer Partnership**
27 **ALMODOVAR DEL RIO (IRE)**, b c Dabirsim (FR)—Everglow (FR) **Keep Kicking Racing & Partner**
28 **AUGUST PLACE**, b g Postponed (IRE)—Brandybend (IRE) **A J Suited Partnership**
29 **BULLISH (IRE)**, gr g Gutaifan (IRE)—Fanciful Dancer **Middleham Park Racing V & Partner**
30 **CHURCHILL COLLEGE (IRE)**, b g Churchill (IRE)—Alazeya (IRE) **Mamba Racing & Partner**
31 **DELPHI DREAMER**, b c Iffraaj—Dixie Dreamer **Promenade Bloodstock Limited**
32 **DUBAI IMMO (IRE)**, ch c The Gurkha (IRE)—Bright Glow **Middleham Park Racing CXXI & Partners**
33 **EL BELLO**, gr g El Kabeir (USA)—Ya Halla (IRE) **Scuderia Blueberry & Partner**
34 **EL FELICIA (IRE)**, gr f El Kabeir (USA)—Luminance (IRE) **K Sohi & Partner**
35 **ESSENCIAL (IRE)**, b c Awtaad (IRE)—Passionable **Keep Kicking Racing & Partner**
36 **FIFTEENTHAMENDMENT (USA)**, b c Noble Mission—Volver (IRE) **Kings Court Racing**
37 **GIAVELLOTTO (IRE)**, ch c Mastercraftsman (IRE)—Gerika (FR) **La Tesa SPA**
38 **GOLDEN WARRIOR (IRE)**, ch g Cotai Glory—Jayla **Mr Abbas Alalawi & Partner**
39 **LA DUCHESSE (GER)**, b f Iffraaj—La Reine Noir (GER) **Scuderia Blueberry & Partner**
40 **LAHEG (FR)**, b c Dabirsim (FR)—Sierra Leona (FR) **Mr R. El Youssef**
41 **LIMITED ABILITY**, b c Postponed (IRE)—Ruffled **Mr C. J. Murfitt**
42 **LUCKYBOYLOVELYWIFE**, b f Oasis Dream—Iridescence **Middleham Park Racing I & Partners**
43 **MALORIE (IRE)**, b f Churchill (IRE)—Ghurfah **Les Boyer Partnership 1**
44 **MASTER OF COLOURS**, gr c Muhaarar—Maglietta Fina (IRE) **Scuderia Archi Romani & Partner**
45 **MINO PICO (FR)**, b f Dabirsim (FR)—Meeting Waters **Mr E. Elhrari**
46 **MONELISA**, b f Havana Gold (IRE)—Moma Lee **Milan Racing Club**
47 **NIGHT GLASS (IRE)**, b c Galileo Gold—Hen Night (IRE) **Mr Manfredini & Partner**
48 **ODISSEO**, ch c Ulysses (IRE)—Atalis **Blueberry R. & Boyer Boyer**
49 **PENNA ROSSA (IRE)**, b g Belardo (IRE)—Alpine **Scuderia Blueberry & Partner**
50 **RIBBON ROSE**, b f Time Test—Kelowna (IRE) **Scuderia Archi Romani & Partner**
51 **SANDIE'S DREAM**, b f Belardo (IRE)—Alexandrite **Nick Bradley Racing 30 & Partner**
52 **SOUSA (IRE)**, b c Exceed And Excel (AUS)—Broadway Melody **The Honorable Earle I. Mack & Partner**
53 **VIDHAATA (IRE)**, b c New Approach (IRE)—Hanzada (USA) **Mr A. Anne**

MR MARCO BOTTI - continued

54 WAR HORSE (IRE), b g Sea The Stars (IRE)—Santa Anabaa **E. I. Mack**
55 WARD CASTLE (IRE), b c Flintshire—Endless Light **Milan Racing Club 1**
56 WAY TO WIN (IRE), b c The Gurkha (IRE)—Siesta Time **Mr Ahmad Alrashidi & Partner**

TWO-YEAR-OLDS

57 Ch c 29/04 Night of Thunder (IRE)—American Endeavour (USA) (Distorted Humor (USA)) (42000)
London Calling Syndicate & Partner

58 B f 24/04 Cracksman—At A Clip (Green Desert (USA)) (33333)
59 B f 10/02 Massaat (IRE)—Beta Tauri (USA) (Oasis Dream) (30000) **Scuderia Sagam Srls & Partner**
60 BLENHEIM PRINCE, b c 26/03 Churchill (IRE)—Snow Dust (First Defence (USA)) (25510)
Keep Kicking Racing 1 & Partner

61 B c 17/02 Camacho—Boodley (Acclamation) (50000) **Rabbah Racing**
62 Ch c 04/02 New Approach (IRE)—Brazilian Bride (IRE) (Pivotal) (25000) **Keep Kicking Racing 1 & Partner**
63 Ch f 14/03 Tasleet—Buttercross (Zamindar (USA)) (12000) **Ahmad Bintouq & Partner**
64 B c 25/03 Outstrip—Capla Ishtar (Moohaajim (IRE)) **Milan Racing Club**
65 COME MUSICA (ITY), b c 01/03 Muhaarar—Winter Serenade (ITY) (Fastnet Rock (AUS))
66 B c 12/03 Kodiac—Dark Promise (Shamardal (USA)) (42000) **R. & Kicking Racing**
67 B c 18/01 Starspangledbanner (AUS)—Fou Rire (IRE) (Iffraaj) (72279) **Mr I. Bin Haider**
68 B f 22/04 Australia—Juno Moneta (IRE) (Holy Roman Emperor (IRE)) (16000)
69 Ch f 28/04 Saxon Warrior (JPN)—Kittens (Marju (IRE)) (16000) **Scuderia Archi Romani & Partner**
70 B c 20/04 Churchill (IRE)—Komedy (IRE) (Kodiac) (104762) **Mr R. El Youssef**
71 B c 28/03 Siyouni (FR)—Lady Darshaan (IRE) (High Chaparral (IRE)) **Newsells Park Stud & Partner**
72 Ch c 07/02 Ribchester (IRE)—Merseybeat (New Approach (IRE)) (20000) **Mr C. J. Murfitt & Partner**
73 B c 15/01 Lightning Spear—Moonlight Rhapsody (IRE) (Danehill Dancer (IRE)) (12000)
74 Ch c 20/04 Night of Thunder (IRE)—Notary (Lawman (FR)) (100000) **Mr A. Bintouq**
75 B c 17/04 Holy Roman Emperor (IRE)—Primrose Gate (IRE) (Verglas (IRE)) (9524)
76 B c 25/04 Ulysses (IRE)—Rhagori (Exceed And Excel (AUS)) (16000)
77 B c 10/04 Exceed And Excel (AUS)—Simmy's Temple (Royal Applause) (68571) **Middleham Park Racing & Partner**
78 B f 28/02 Footstepsinthesand—Storyline (IRE) (Kodiac) (39000) **La Tesa SPA**
79 STRATEGIA (ITY), b c 14/02 Shalaa (IRE)—Tribulina (Dansili)
80 B f 18/03 Starspangledbanner (AUS)—Valkyries (FR) (Le Havre (IRE)) (25714) **Scuderia Sagam Srls & Partner**
81 B f 09/02 Golden Horn—Vandergirl (IRE) (Dutch Art) (28000) **Mr A. Bintouq**
82 VICTORS DREAM, b c 01/03 Oasis Dream—Victors Lady (IRE) (Society Rock (IRE)) **Mr P. Hunt**
83 B f 25/03 Oasis Dream—Za Za Zoom (IRE) (Le Vie Dei Colori) **Scuderia Archi Romani**
84 B f 08/03 Gleneagles (IRE)—Zenara (IRE) (Sea The Stars (IRE)) (18000) **Ahmad Bintouq & Partner**

Other Owners: Mrs E. Agostini, Mr P. Agostini, Mr A. Al Alawi, Mr J. Allison, Mr G. Allsopp, Mr A. M. M. H. A. Alrashidi, Ambrosiana Racing, Mr A. Baragiola, Miss E. M. Baragiola, Mr A. N. C. Bengough, Mr L. Biffi, Mr A. Bintouq, Mr P. Booth, Mrs L. Botti, Mr N. Bradley, Mr R. Bruni, Mr A. J. Driver, Fittocks Stud, Miss S. Holden, Keep Kicking Racing, Keep Kicking Racing 1, La Tesa SPA, Les Boyer Partnership, London Calling Syndicate, E. I. Mack, Mamba Racing, Mr G. Manfredini, Middleham Park Racing LXXXVII, Middleham Park Racing CXXI, Middleham Park Racing CXXVI, Middleham Park Racing I, Middleham Park Racing LXXIV, Middleham Park Racing V, Middleham Park Racing XCVIII, Middleham Park XXII & Steven Rocco, Milan Racing Club, Mr C. J. Murfitt, Newsells Park Stud Limited, Nick Bradley Racing 30, Mr C. C. Norris, Mr M. A. O'Connell, T. S. Palin, Mr C. Pizarro, M. Prince, Scuderia Sagam SRLS, Scuderia Archi Romani, Scuderia Blueberry SRL, Mr P. G. S. Silver, Mr K. Sohi, Mr G. Steed, What A Time To Be Alive.

Assistant Trainer: Alberto Baragiola, Lucie Botti, **Pupil Assistant:** Conor Norris.

Apprentice Jockey: Christian Howarth, Ellie Norris.

48

MR GEORGE BOUGHEY, Newmarket
Postal: **Saffron House Stables, Hamilton Road, Newmarket, Suffolk, CB8 0NY**
Contacts: PHONE **07765 132508**
EMAIL george@georgeboughey.com

1 **AIR TO AIR**, 4, ch g Toronado (IRE)—Blossom Mills
2 **ANOTHER DAWN**, 4, b f Exceed And Excel (AUS)—Queen Philippa (USA)
3 **ANYTHINGTODAY (IRE)**, 8, b g Zoffany (IRE)—Corking (IRE)
4 **COLOMBE (IRE)**, 4, b f Mehmas (IRE)—Symbol of Peace (IRE)
5 **DESERT LIME**, 4, b f Sepoy (AUS)—Scallop
6 **DUBAI LADY (IRE)**, 4, b f Invincible Spirit (IRE)—Long Lashes (USA)
7 **INVER PARK**, 4, b g Pivotal—Red Baton
8 **JEAN BAPTISTE (IRE)**, 5, b g Invincible Spirit (IRE)—Pioneer Bride (USA)
9 **MORNING SYMPHONY (IRE)**, 4, b f Shamardal (USA)—Country Music
10 **NEEDLE LACE**, 4, b f Golden Horn—Rosaline (IRE)
11 **PERIPETEIA**, 4, b f Sir Percy—Archduchess
12 **PRETTY SWEET (IRE)**, 4, b f Iffraaj—Majenta (IRE)
13 **PURPLE POWER**, 5, b m Slade Power (IRE)—Peace Summit
14 **SONGKRAN (IRE)**, 6, b g Slade Power (IRE)—Choose Me (IRE)
15 **TOTALLY CHARMING**, 4, b g Charming Thought—Totally Millie

THREE-YEAR-OLDS

16 **AL AMEEN (IRE)**, b c Aclaim (IRE)—Kendal Mint
17 **APRIL IN PARIS (IRE)**, b f Zoffany (IRE)—Aurora Borealis (IRE)
18 **ARIES LAD**, b g Adaay (IRE)—Angie And Liz (IRE)
19 **BAYLASAN**, b f Ardad (IRE)—Dabyah (IRE)
20 **BRASIL POWER (FR)**, b c Dark Angel (IRE)—Venturous Spirit (FR)
21 **CACHET (IRE)**, b br f Aclaim (IRE)—Poyle Sophie
22 **CASHEW (IRE)**, b f Bated Breath—Taste The Salt (IRE)
23 **CHARLES ST**, b c Outstrip—Under The Rainbow
24 **CHATTONAGA GIRL (IRE)**, ch f Highland Reel (IRE)—Gabardine
25 **CLEMENT DANES**, b f Ribchester (IRE)—Blossom Mills
26 **CORAZON (IRE)**, b f Markaz (IRE)—Disko (IRE)
27 **FIORINA**, b f Showcasing—Bird Key
28 **FORCA BRASIL (IRE)**, ch c Cotai Glory—Naias (IRE)
29 **FOXY RASCAL (FR)**, b f Dabirsim (FR)—Whipcorse (FR)
30 **HELLOMYDARLIN (IRE)**, b f Galileo Gold—Speed Freak
31 **IMPERIAL ECLIPSE**, br g Bated Breath—Queen of Mean
32 **JASTAR**, b g Showcasing—Foxcatcher
33 **JUDY'S PARK (IRE)**, ch f Charming Thought—Sarah Park (IRE)
34 **LITTLE RAVEN (IRE)**, b c Iffraaj—Azameera (IRE)
35 **LOVELY MANA (IRE)**, b f Dabirsim (FR)—Enraptured (IRE)
36 **LUCIA JOY**, b f Ulysses (IRE)—Synergy (FR)
37 **MEDAL OF GLORY (IRE)**, ch f Cotai Glory—Cape Elizabeth (IRE)
38 **MR ALAN**, ch c Ulysses (IRE)—Interlace
39 **MY LITTLE TIP (IRE)**, b c Belardo (IRE)—How Sweet It Is (IRE)
40 **MYSTIC WELLS (USA)**, b f Kitten's Joy (USA)—Cat On a Tin Roof (USA)
41 **NAVELLO**, b g Ivawood (IRE)—Caprella
42 **OSCULA (IRE)**, b f Galileo Gold—Bisous Y Besos (IRE)
43 **PHANTASY MAC (IRE)**, b f Bobby's Kitten (USA)—Phantasmagoric (IRE)
44 **POCKET THE PROFIT**, b g Mayson—Musical Beat (IRE)
45 **SALONICA**, br f Showcasing—All Time
46 **SASSY RASCAL (IRE)**, b f Mehmas (IRE)—Luna Forest (IRE)
47 B f Charming Thought—See Emily Play (IRE)
48 **SHURUT**, ch f Showcasing—Qawaasem (IRE)
49 **SIMPLY SONDHEIM (IRE)**, b c Pivotal—Finishingthehat
50 **SIP AND SMILE (IRE)**, b c Acclamation—Marisol (IRE)
51 **SUPERIOR FORCE**, b br g Ardad (IRE)—Locharia
52 **THE CEILING JOB (IRE)**, ch f Galileo Gold—Elshamms
53 **THE PROVENIST**, b c Bated Breath—Saniyaat
54 **TOLLARD ROYAL (IRE)**, b c Ribchester (IRE)—Dew Line (IRE)

MR GEORGE BOUGHEY - continued

55 WOODERS DREAM, ch f Equiano (FR)—Psychic's Dream

TWO-YEAR-OLDS

56 B c 10/03 Showcasing—A Huge Dream (IRE) (Refuse To Bend (IRE)) (28000)
57 Br f 17/03 Brazen Beau (AUS)—Aldana (Slade Power (IRE)) (9000)
58 B f 17/04 Camacho—Angel Grace (IRE) (Dark Angel (IRE)) (92000)
59 APEX (IRE), b c 28/03 Kessaar (IRE)—Bisous Y Besos (IRE) (Big Bad Bob (IRE)) (85034)
60 B f 20/02 Profitable (IRE)—Asking Price (USA) (First Defence (USA)) (21905)
61 B f 29/04 Fast Company (IRE)—Aurora Butterfly (IRE) (Born To Sea (IRE)) (30000)
62 B f 26/01 Zoffany (IRE)—Beat The Stars (IRE) (Verglas (IRE)) (93537)
63 BEAU ROC, b f 02/02 Brazen Beau (AUS)—Kicker Rock (Fastnet Rock (AUS)) (5500)
64 B f 20/03 Time Test—Bridge Poseidon (IRE) (Dark Angel (IRE)) (37000)
65 CANTORA, b br f 18/03 Time Test—Umthoulah (IRE) (Unfuwain (USA))
66 B f 13/03 U S Navy Flag (USA)—Celestial Bow (IRE) (Raven's Pass (USA)) (9048)
67 CONCORDE, ch c 26/03 Sixties Icon—Silca Chiave (Pivotal) (90000)
68 CORAJE, b f 29/01 Expert Eye—Omneeya (Frankel) (6000)
69 B f 17/03 Iffraaj—Ego (Green Desert (USA)) (170000)
70 ESTEHWADH (IRE), b c 10/03 Profitable (IRE)—Packed House (Azamour (IRE)) (24000)
71 EVENSTAR, b f 06/04 Havana Grey—Star Squared (Sea The Stars (IRE))
72 B c 17/02 Twilight Son—Fascinator (Helmet (AUS)) (38095)
73 B c 09/02 Kodiac—Fine If (IRE) (Iffraaj) (170000)
74 B br f 31/01 Air Force Blue (USA)—Giant Cruiser (USA) (Giant Oak (USA)) (19558)
75 HIGHLAND MAC (IRE), b f 13/02 Gleneagles (IRE)—Little Empress (IRE) (Holy Roman Emperor (IRE)) (14286)
76 B f 17/04 Elzaam (AUS)—Instant Memories (IRE) (Ad Valorem (USA)) (7653)
77 Ch f 02/04 Starspangledbanner (AUS)—Intermittent (Cacique (IRE)) (180000)
78 B f 02/04 Kodiac—Inverse (IRE) (Oasis Dream) (191327)
79 B c 20/03 Churchill (IRE)—Its All For Luck (IRE) (Fast Company (IRE))
80 B f 03/04 Zoffany (IRE)—Jollification (IRE) (Acclamation) (25000)
81 Ch f 15/03 Dandy Man (IRE)—Kendal Mint (Kyllachy) (49524)
82 B f 02/03 Territories (IRE)—La Roumegue (USA) (Henrythenavigator (USA)) (14000)
83 B f 16/03 Holy Roman Emperor (IRE)—Maoineas (IRE) (Teofilo (IRE)) (16667)
84 MIAMI BAY (IRE), b f 17/04 Tamayuz—Carioca (IRE) (Rakti) (47000)
85 Ch f 16/04 Dragon Pulse (IRE)—Miss Cogent (IRE) (Clodovil (IRE)) (9524)
86 MISS VALCHOPE (FR), b f 01/03 Born To Sea (IRE)—First Chope (FR) (Indian Rocket) (23810)
87 B c 01/05 Scissor Kick (AUS)—Mixfeeling (IRE) (Red Ransom (USA))
88 Ch c 23/03 Lightning Spear—Molly Mayhem (IRE) (Casamento (IRE)) (78000)
89 NAXOS, ch c 30/03 Saxon Warrior (JPN)—Ecureuil (FR) (Lope de Vega (IRE)) (21259)
90 Gr f 19/01 Caravaggio (USA)—New Terms (New Approach (IRE)) (40952)
91 B f 11/02 Exceed And Excel (AUS)—Oziris (Sepoy (AUS)) (32000)
92 B f 16/02 Ulysses (IRE)—Panova (Invincible Spirit (IRE))
93 PASTICHE, ch f 16/02 Zoustar (AUS)—Crying Lightening (IRE) (Holy Roman Emperor (IRE)) (105000)
94 Gr f 14/03 Gregorian (IRE)—Queen Zain (IRE) (Lawman (FR)) (11000)
95 B f 19/01 Profitable (IRE)—Roxelana (IRE) (Oasis Dream) (11429)
96 B f 08/05 Kingman—Ruby Rocket (IRE) (Indian Rocket) (130000)
97 B c 10/02 Acclamation—Sea Meets Sky (FR) (Dansili)
98 B f 06/04 Mehmas (IRE)—Star of Kings (Sea The Stars (IRE)) (53333)
99 Gr f 10/03 El Kabeir (USA)—Taraeff (USA) (Cape Cross (IRE)) (23810)
100 Br f 28/02 Nathaniel (IRE)—Theladyinquestion (Dubawi (IRE)) (270000)
101 B f 26/01 American Pharoah (USA)—Tiburtina (IRE) (Holy Roman Emperor (IRE)) (70000)
102 B f 07/04 Fastnet Rock (AUS)—Wittgenstein (IRE) (Shamardal (USA)) (18000)
103 ZARRAFINA, b f 16/04 Oasis Dream—Primo Lady (Lucky Story (USA))
104 ZO FE CHOPE (FR), ch f 15/02 Kheleyf (USA)—Laureva Chope (FR) (Panis (USA)) (13605)

Racing Secretary: Mrs Nicky Pellatt.

49 MR DARAGH BOURKE, Lockerbie
Postal: Cherrybank, Waterbeck, Lockerbie, Dumfries and Galloway, DG11 3EY
Contacts: **MOBILE 07495 948493**

1 CORAL BLUE (IRE), 7, b g Big Bad Bob (IRE)—Eva's Time (IRE) **Mr A. Kanji**
2 DIXIELAND SWING (IRE), 7, b g Red Jazz (USA)—Kathleen Rafferty (IRE) **Mr D. F. Bourke**
3 EVER READY EDDIE (IRE), 6, b g Ocovango—Youngvicky (IRE) **Mrs J. Lowther**
4 EVITA DU MESNIL (FR), 8, gr m Gris de Gris (IRE)—Perle du Mesnil (FR) **Mrs L. J. McLeod**
5 GALLAHERS CROSS (IRE), 10, b g Getaway (GER)—Raheen Lady (IRE) **Mr D. F. Bourke**
6 GOLDEN CHANCER, 8, b g Gold Well—Princess Oriane (IRE) **Mr S. Lowther**
7 MASTER OF THE MALT, 6, b g Yeats (IRE)—Mrs Malt (IRE) **Mr S. Lowther**
8 OCH ONE MORE GIN (IRE), 5, b g Ocovango—No More Gin (IRE) **Mr S. Lowther**
9 OLD JEWRY (IRE), 8, b g Le Fou (IRE)—Clerken Bridge (IRE) **Origin**
10 PADDY THE PANDA (IRE), 7, b g Flemensfirth (USA)—Pandorama Lady (IRE) **Mr S. Lowther**
11 PRESENTEDWITHWINGS (IRE), 8, br g Presenting—Rosa Rugosa (IRE) **Cherrybank Crusaders**
12 SOIVEGOTACHANCE (IRE), 7, b g Imperial Monarch (IRE)—Spirit of Youth (IRE) **Mrs L. J. McLeod**
13 WEE BAZ (IRE), 4, b g Getaway (GER)—Flame Supreme (IRE) **Mrs J. Lowther**

50 MR DANIEL JOHN BOURNE, Varteg
Postal: Tyddau Farm, Penylan Fields, Varteg, Pontypool, Gwent, NP4 7SA
Contacts: **PHONE 01495 772444**
EMAIL bournegroundworks@gmail.com

1 ASOCKASTAR (IRE), 14, b g Milan—Baie Barbara (IRE) **Mr D. J. Bourne**
2 BLUE MISTAKE (IRE), 6, b g Blueprint (IRE)—Fastnet Light (IRE) **Mr D. J. Bourne**
3 HARDE FASHION, 6, b g Schiaparelli (GER)—La Harde (FR) **Mr D. J. Bourne**
4 PASCHALS DREAM (IRE), 10, b g Primary (USA)—State Ur Case (IRE) **James Bourne Daniel Bourne**

51 MR PETER BOWEN, Haverfordwest
Postal: Yet-Y-Rhug, Letterston, Haverfordwest, Pembrokeshire, SA62 5TB
Contacts: **PHONE 01348 840486 MOBILE 07811 111234 FAX 01348 840486**
EMAIL info@peterbowenracing.co.uk **WEBSITE** www.peterbowenracing.co.uk

1 ALFA DAWN (IRE), 6, b m No Nay Never (USA)—Aitch (IRE) **Mr H. Jones & Mrs E. Evans**
2 CALICOJACK (IRE), 10, b g Beneficial—Ballyoscar (IRE) **Mr M. G. Robinson**
3 COUGAR'S GOLD (IRE), 11, b g Oscar (IRE)—Top Her Up (IRE) **Mr W. E. V. Harries**
4 DALKINGSTOWN (IRE), 8, ch g Malinas (GER)—True Rose (IRE) **R. R. Owen**
5 DICEY RIELLY (IRE), 5, b m Getaway (GER)—Saintly Lady (IRE) **Mr D. Devereux**
6 DOWNTOWN GETAWAY (IRE), 9, b g Getaway (GER)—Shang A Lang (IRE) **Bucks Racing Club**
7 DR DES (IRE), 11, b g Double Eclipse (IRE)—Dans Belle (IRE) **Mac Mediation Ltd**
8 DREAMS OF DIAMONDS (IRE), 5, ch g Malinas (GER)—Double Dream (IRE) **Mrs N. Unsworth**
9 DRIFT ROCK (IRE), 8, ch g Malinas (GER)—Araucaria (IRE) **Amanda & Patrick Bancroft**
10 EASY BUCKS (IRE), 7, b g Getaway (GER)—Tushana (IRE) **Bucks Racing Club**
11 EMRAAN (IRE), 6, b g Invincible Spirit (IRE)—Wissal (USA) **Mr M. B. Bowen**
12 EQUUS DANCER (IRE), 8, b g Jeremy (USA)—Celtic Cailin (IRE) **R. R. Owen**
13 FAIRLAWN FLYER, 6, b g Dr Massini (IRE)—She's Our Native (IRE) **Mr R. Williams**
14 FOREVER FORWARD (IRE), 4, b g Exceed And Excel (AUS)—Teofilo's Princess (IRE)
Mr Simon Munir & Mr Isaac Souede
15 FRANCKY DU BERLAIS (FR), 9, b g Saint des Saints (FR)—Legende du Luy (FR) **R. R. Owen**
16 FREDDIE DARLING (IRE), 7, b g Shantou (USA)—Baby Lenson (IRE) **Peter Bowen Racing Group**

MR PETER BOWEN - continued

17 **GAME LINE (IRE)**, 8, ch g Sandmason—Superline (IRE) **Roggie Crew**
18 **GET A HIGH (IRE)**, 7, b m Getaway (GER)—Top Nurse (IRE) **Mrs K. Bowen**
19 **GET AN OSCAR (IRE)**, 8, ch m Getaway (GER)—Lady Perspex (IRE) **Peter Bowen Racing Club**
20 **GETASTAR (IRE)**, 6, ch g Getaway (GER)—Metro Star (IRE) **Amanda & Patrick Bancroft**
21 **JACKTOT**, 5, b m Gentlewave (IRE)—Tot of The Knar **Steve & Jackie Fleetham**
22 **JUDGE EARLE (IRE)**, 10, b g Court Cave (IRE)—Louis's Teffia (IRE) **G. J. Morris**
23 **LADY SAMSON (IRE)**, 4, b f Court Cave (IRE)—Lady Kadina (IRE) **Mr M. B. Bowen**
24 **LANDOFSMILES (IRE)**, 9, b g Beneficial—Sadie Supreme (IRE) **Miss Jayne Brace & Mr Gwyn Brace**
25 **LE TUEUR (IRE)**, 7, ch g Flemensfirth (USA)—Golden Odyssey (IRE) **Peter Bowen Racing Club**
26 **LERMOOS LEGEND**, 7, b g Midnight Legend—Absalom's Girl **Mr J. A. Martin**
27 **LORD BRYAN (IRE)**, 11, b g Brian Boru—Run Cat (IRE) **Miss Jayne Brace & Mr Gwyn Brace**
28 **LORD NAPIER (IRE)**, 9, b g Galileo (IRE)—Jacqueline (IND) **F. Lloyd**
29 **MAC TOTTIE**, 9, b g Midnight Legend—Tot of The Knar **Steve & Jackie Fleetham**
30 **MASTER OF SPIN (IRE)**, 7, b br g Arcadio (GER)—Railway Adella (IRE) **Mr R. A. Jones**
31 **MO TOTTIE**, 8, b m Midnight Legend—Tot of The Knar **Steve & Jackie Fleetham**
32 **MONTANNA**, 8, ch g Notnowcato—Asi (USA) **F. Lloyd**
33 **NO QUARTER ASKED (IRE)**, 7, b g Jeremy (USA)—Louis's Teffia (IRE) **R. R. Owen**
34 **PILGRIMS KING (IRE)**, 6, b g Sholokhov (IRE)—So You Said (IRE) **Mr W. E. V. Harries**
35 **SHAKE HIM UP (IRE)**, 6, br g Jet Away—Lady Howe **Mr M. B. Bowen**
36 **SHANTOU CHAMPAGNE (IRE)**, 5, b m Shantou (USA)—Couture Daisy (IRE) **Mrs J. Iddon**
37 **SHAREEF STAR**, 7, b g Sea The Stars (IRE)—Gotlandia (FR) **F. Lloyd**
38 **STATUARIO**, 7, b g Helmet (AUS)—Cat Hunter **Mrs N. Unsworth**
39 **TWILIGHT PRINCE**, 4, b g Twilight Son—Honour **Mr M. B. Bowen**

Other Owners: Mrs A. Bancroft, P. A. Bancroft, D. G. Brace, Miss M. J. Brace, Mrs E. G. Evans, Mr H. Jones, S. E. Munir, Mr I. Souede.

Assistant Trainer: Karen Bowen, Michael Bowen.

NH Jockey: James Bowen, Sean Bowen.

---

52 | **MISS SARAH BOWEN, Bromsgrove**
Postal: New House, Forest Farm, Forest Lane, Hanbury, Bromsgrove, Worcestershire, B60 4HP
Contacts: **PHONE 07718 069485**
EMAIL sarah.bowen25@hotmail.com

1 **AL KHERB**, 7, b g Al Kazeem—Perfect Spirit (IRE) **Mrs S. A. Bowen**
2 **KING FRANK**, 9, b g Fantastic Spain (USA)—Elegant Accord (IRE) **Mrs S. A. Bowen**

---

53 | **MR ROY BOWRING, Edwinstowe**
Postal: Fir Tree Farm, Edwinstowe, Mansfield, Nottinghamshire, NG21 9JG
Contacts: **PHONE 01623 822451 MOBILE 07973 712942**
EMAIL srbowring@outlook.com

1 **ABOUT GLORY**, 8, b g Nayef (USA)—Lemon Rock **S. R. Bowring**
2 **ARTILLERY**, 5, b g Brazen Beau (AUS)—Malpas Missile (IRE) **Mr R. Wheatley**
3 **BACK FROM DUBAI (IRE)**, 5, b g Exceed And Excel (AUS)—Emirates Rewards **Mr K. Nicholls**
4 **CLIFFCAKE (IRE)**, 4, b c Canford Cliffs (IRE)—Cake (IRE) **S. R. Bowring**
5 **DECISION MAKER (IRE)**, 8, b g Iffraaj—Consensus (IRE) **Mr K. Nicholls**
6 **DYLAN'S LAD (IRE)**, 5, b g G Force (IRE)—Chizzler (IRE) **S.R. & Malc Hancock**
7 **HIYA MAITE**, 4, b g Heeraat (IRE)—Misu's Maite **S. R. Bowring**

MR ROY BOWRING - continued

8 **JEANS MAITE**, 6, b m Burwaaz—Misu's Maite **S. R. Bowring**
9 **NINE ELMS (USA)**, 7, ch g Street Cry (IRE)—Nawaiet (USA) **Mr K. Nicholls**
10 **TOPTIME**, 4, b g Gregorian (IRE)—Dominance **S. R. Bowring**
11 **TRULIE GOOD**, 4, b f Heeraat (IRE)—Exceedingly Good (IRE) **S. R. Bowring**

THREE-YEAR-OLDS
12 **SHE'S THE DANGER (IRE)**, b f Pride of Dubai (AUS)—Moment In The Sun

---

54	**MR JIM BOYLE**, Epsom

Postal: **South Hatch Stables, Burgh Heath Road, Epsom, Surrey, KT17 4LX**
Contacts: **WORK 07719 554147 MOBILE 07719 554147**
WORK EMAIL info@jamesboyle.co.uk HOME EMAIL Jimboyle17@hotmail.com
EMAIL pippaboyle@hotmail.com WEBSITE www.jamesboyle.co.uk

1 **ANGELS ROC**, 5, b g Roderic O'Connor (IRE)—Divine Pamina (IRE) **Lady R. M. Prosser**
2 **AVENTURINA**, 4, b f Charming Thought—Clearing **Dr Pamela Wilson & Partners**
3 **BAD COMPANY**, 5, b g Fast Company (IRE)—Clearing **The Clean Sweep Partnership**
4 **BEAT THE HEAT**, 5, b g Hot Streak (IRE)—Touriga **Inside Track Racing Club**
5 **BONUS**, 5, b g Roderic O'Connor (IRE)—Spring Clean (FR) **The Clean Sweep Partnership**
6 **DESERT LAND (IRE)**, 6, b g Kodiac—La Chicana (IRE) **Epsom Equine Spa Partnership**
7 **DOLPHIN VISTA (IRE)**, 9, b g Zoffany (IRE)—Fiordiligi **The BeeGeeZ**
8 **DOWNSMAN (IRE)**, 4, b g Fast Company (IRE)—Hawk Dance (IRE) **The Paddock Space Partnership 2**
9 **GOING GONE (IRE)**, 4, b g Le Havre (IRE)—Sea The Sun (GER) **Taylor & O'Dwyer**
10 **HOPE SPRINGS**, 4, b f Mukhadram—Spring Clean (FR) **The Clean Sweep Partnership**
11 **LADY SUSIE (IRE)**, 4, b f Equiano (FR)—Seduct (IRE) **Epsom Equine Spa Partnership**
12 **LEROY LEROY**, 6, b g Compton Place—Small Fortune **The Reserve Tankers**
13 **MARLAY PARK**, 4, b br g Cable Bay (IRE)—Lovers' Vows **Inside Track Racing Club**
14 **OTAGO**, 5, b g Cable Bay (IRE)—Spinning Top **Mr P and Mrs L Rowe and Mr John Turner**
15 **PEACE PREVAILS**, 7, ch m Declaration of War (USA)—Miss Mediator (USA) **Mr M. Aljoe**
16 **PURE PURFECTION (IRE)**, 5, b m Dream Ahead (USA)—Rose of Africa (IRE) **Maid In Heaven Partnership**
17 **SHINING**, 6, b m Lethal Force (IRE)—Spring Clean (FR)

THREE-YEAR-OLDS
18 **EY UP ITS JAZZ**, ch g Pastoral Pursuits—Mad Jazz **Jastar Ltd, Murt Khan & Harry Wigan**
19 **HODLER (GER)**, b g Sea The Moon (GER)—Herzprinzessin (GER) **Taylor & O'Dwyer**
20 **ICE FURY (IRE)**, gr f El Kabeir (USA)—Trading Places **Mrs M. Doyle**
21 **JUST AN INKLING**, b f Equiano (FR)—Inke (IRE) **Harrier Racing 2**
22 **MELERI**, b f Nathaniel (IRE)—Divine Pamina (IRE) **Lady R. M. Prosser**
23 **NONSUCH LAD (IRE)**, ch g Tamayuz—Solandia (IRE) **South Hatch Partners**
24 **SPARKED**, b f Night of Thunder (IRE)—Clearing **The Clean Sweep Partnership**
25 **TWINING (IRE)**, ch f Fast Company (IRE)—Interlacing **Inside Track Racing Club**
26 **WATCHING OVER YOU**, ch g Nathaniel (IRE)—Sonnetation (IRE)

Other Owners: Mr J. R. Boyle, Mrs P. Boyle, M. C. Cook, Ms J. E. Harrison, Mr J. Hillier, Jastar Capital Limited, M. Khan, Mr H. E. Wigan, Dr P. Wilson.

55 **MR RICHARD BRABAZON, Curragh**
Postal: **Rangers Lodge, The Curragh, Co. Kildare, R56 Y443, Ireland**
Contacts: **MOBILE +353 87 251 5626**
EMAIL Brabazonrichard@gmail.com WEBSITE www.richardbrabazon.ie

1 APPLE OF HIS EYE (IRE), 4, b f Mehmas (IRE)—Maridiyna (IRE) **Leon Carrick & Michelle Gibbons**
2 FAIR DAMSEL (IRE), 4, b f Dragon Pulse (IRE)—Placere (IRE) **Richard Brabazon**
3 GORDON BENNETT (IRE), 4, b g Prince of Lir (IRE)—Laureldean Lady (IRE) **Out All Night Syndicate**
4 LET'S BELIEVE (IRE), 4, b f Epaulette—Doubt **Cafe Du Journal Syndicate**

THREE-YEAR-OLDS
5 GOD KNOWS (IRE), b f Divine Prophet (AUS)—Placere (IRE) **Richard Brabazon**

Assistant Trainer: Heidi Brabazon.

56 **MR DAVID BRACE OBE, Bridgend**
Postal: **Llanmihangel Farm, Pyle, Bridgend, Mid Glamorgan, CF33 6RL**
Contacts: **HOME 01656 742313 MOBILE 07900 495510**

1 BRIN MO, 5, ch g Mountain High (IRE)—Betty The Bog **Mr D. Brace**
2 COLORADO DOC, 11, b g Dr Massini (IRE)—First Royal (GER) **Mr D. Brace**
3 DARIYA (USA), 7, b m Include (USA)—Dubai (IRE) **Mr D. Brace**
4 GATS AND CO, 7, b g Dr Massini (IRE)—Vineuil (FR) **Mr D. Brace**
5 LOOKSNOWTLIKEBRIAN (IRE), 11, b g Brian Boru—Sheebadiva (IRE) **Mr D. Brace**
6 PATCH ME UP, 6, b g Dr Massini (IRE)—Betty The Bog **Mr D. Brace**
7 PINK EYED PEDRO, 3, b g Dr Massini (IRE)—Poacher's Paddy (IRE) **Mr D. Brace**
8 QUILAURA (FR), 5, b m Lauro (GER)—Qualite Controlee (FR) **Mr D. Brace**
9 RIVER LLYNFI (IRE), 6, b g Ocovango—La Lambertine (FR) **Mr D. Brace**
10 ROBIN DES PEOPLE (IRE), 12, br g Robin des Pres (FR)—Zelea (IRE) **Mr D. Brace**
11 ROKOCOKO BLUE (IRE), 4, b f Shirocco (GER)—Freefairngenuine (IRE) **Mr D. Brace**
12 THATZA DAZZLER, 4, b g Blue Bresil (FR)—Sainte Fortuna (FR) **Mr D. Brace**
13 WATCHING BRIEF (IRE), 9, b g Rudimentary (USA)—Miss Tsigalko (IRE) **Mr D. Brace**

NH Jockey: Connor Brace.

57 **MR MARK BRADSTOCK, Wantage**
Postal: **Old Manor Stables, Foresters Lane, Letcombe Bassett, Wantage, Oxfordshire, OX12 9NB**
Contacts: **WORK 01235 760780 HOME 01235 760780 PHONE 01235 760754 MOBILE 07887 686697**
EMAIL mark.bradstock@btconnect.com WEBSITE www.markbradstockracing.co.uk

1 BENDY BOW, 7, br g Malinas (GER)—Maid of Oaksey **The BB Partnership**
2 CRAWFORD, 6, b g Kayf Tara—Maid of Oaksey **The Billy Partnership**
3 EGLANTIER (FR), 8, b g Bonbon Rose (FR)—Kyalami (FR) **M. F. Bradstock**
4 HELIX, 5, ch g Helmet (AUS)—Child Bride (USA) **The Leiter Partnership**
5 HERMIN D'OUDAIRIES (FR), 5, b g Masterstroke (USA)—Ukalee (FR)
6 IDOLS'S EYE (FR), 7, b g Diamond Boy (FR)—Rose Caline (FR) **M. F. Bradstock**
7 JAISALMER (IRE), 10, b g Jeremy (USA)—Shara (IRE) **Dartbridge Manor Racing Club**
8 JAKAMANI, 8, b g Sulamani (IRE)—Kentford Grebe **Miss C Fordham & Mr C Vernon**
9 STEP BACK (IRE), 12, ch g Indian River (IRE)—Stepitoutmary (IRE) **Cracker and Smodge Partnership**

Other Owners: Miss C. Fordham, Mr J. B. G. Macleod, Mr J. Reilly, C. A. Vernon.

MR MARK BRADSTOCK - continued

Assistant Trainer: Sara Bradstock, **Head Girl:** Lily Bradstock, **Racing Secretary:** Samantha Partridge.

NH Jockey: Nico De Boinville.

---

58 **MR BARRY BRENNAN, Lambourn**
Postal: **2 Rockfel Road, Lambourn, Hungerford, Berkshire, RG17 8NG**
Contacts: **MOBILE 07907 529780**
EMAIL barrybrennan2@hotmail.co.uk WEBSITE www.barrybrennanracing.co.uk

1 **CREM FRESH**, 8, b m Malinas (GER)—Clotted Cream (USA) **D. R. T. Gibbons**
2 **DANCING DORIS**, 7, b m Malinas (GER)—Peggies Run **F. J. Brennan**
3 **DEBBONAIR (IRE)**, 6, b g Slade Power (IRE)—Bryanstown Girl (IRE) **D. R. T. Gibbons**
4 **DOLLY MCQUEEN**, 6, b m Canford Cliffs (IRE)—Caterina de Medici (FR) **Mrs L. Osborne**
5 **HIGH HOPES LADY**, 4, b f Linda's Lad—Lady Arbella **F. J. Brennan**
6 **KALAYA (IRE)**, 6, b m Thewayyouare (USA)—Kalabaya (IRE) **D. R. T. Gibbons**

---

59 **MR JOHN BRIDGER, Liphook**
Postal: **Upper Hatch Farm, Liphook, Hampshire, GU30 7EL**
Contacts: **PHONE 01428 722528 MOBILE 07785 716614**
EMAIL jbridger@sky.com

1 **AMNAA**, 5, b m Bungle Inthejungle—She Mystifies
　　　　　　　　　　　　　　　Mr J. J. Bridger, Watts & Spooner, Mr M. Watts, Mr W. J. Spooner
2 **BE PREPARED**, 5, b g Due Diligence (USA)—Chicklade **Mr P. Cook**
3 **BEAU JARDINE (IRE)**, 4, b g Make Believe—Akira (IRE) **Rachel Cook**
4 , B f Kier Park (IRE)—Devils In My Head **Mr J. J. Bridger**
5 **ESSME**, 4, b f Twilight Son—Desert Kiss **Mrs D. J. Ellison**
6 **FIRENZE ROSA (IRE)**, 7, b m Zebedee—Our Nana Rose (IRE) **Mr & Mrs K. Finch, Mrs D. Finch, K. Finch**
7 **JULIE JOHNSTON**, 4, b f Acclamation—Jeanie Johnston (IRE) **Mrs E. Gardner**
8 **LAW BROOK BELLE**, 4, b f Dunaden (FR)—Belle Blonde (IRE)
　　　　　　　　　　　　　　Mr M J Evans & Mr T M Jones, Mr M. J. Evans, T. M. Jones
9 **LETHAL BLAST**, 5, b m Lethal Force (IRE)—Having A Blast (USA) **Mr J. J. Bridger**
10 **PETTOCHSIDE**, 13, b g Refuse To Bend (IRE)—Clear Impression (IRE) **Mr P. Cook**
11 **RUBEE FORTY**, 5, b m Lethal Force (IRE)—Desert Kiss **Mrs D. J. Ellison**
12 **SANTORINI SAL**, 5, b m Gregorian (IRE)—Aegean Mystery **Mr J. J. Bridger**
13 **VICE ROYAL**, 5, b g Swiss Spirit—Ivory Lace **Vice Royal Partnership, Mrs P. M. Tyler, Dr J. A. H. Miles**

THREE-YEAR-OLDS

14 **ARBOY WILL**, b g Ardad (IRE)—High 'n Dry (IRE) **Mr J. J. Bridger, Mr D Paton, Mrs D Stewart & Mrs J
　　Trueman, Mrs D. Stewart, Mr D. J. C. Paton, Mr M. J. Trueman**
15 **DEBBIE'S CHOICE (IRE)**, b f Ardad (IRE)—Alnawiyah **The Deer's Hut**
16 , Ch f Eastern Anthem (IRE)—One Big Surprise **Double-R-Racing**

TWO-YEAR-OLDS

17 , B f 08/04 Havana grey—Chicklade **Mr P. Cook**
18 **LAHINA BAY (IRE)**, b f 08/04 Cracksman—Serendipitously (IRE) (Kodiac) (5000)
　　　　　　　　　　　　　　　Mr & Mrs K. Finch, Mrs D. Finch, K. Finch
19 **RHYTHM DANCER**, b f 03/04 Expert Eye—Haydn's Lass (Sir Percy) (8000)
　　　　　　　　　　　　　　　Mr & Mrs K. Finch, Mrs D. Finch, K. Finch

Assistant Trainer: Rachel Cook.

MR DAVID BRIDGWATER, Stow-on-the-Wold

60

Postal: **Wyck Hill Farm, Wyck Hill, Stow-on-the-Wold, Cheltenham, Gloucestershire, GL54 1HT**
Contacts: PHONE **01451 830349** MOBILE **07831 635817** FAX **01451 830349**
EMAIL **sales@bridgwaterracing.co.uk** WEBSITE **www.bridgwaterracing.co.uk**

1 5, B g Authorized (IRE)—Ahdaaf (USA) **Mr S. Hunt**
2 4, Bl g Great Pretender (IRE)—Athinea (FR) **Mr S. Hunt**
3 **BARNAVIDDAUN (IRE)**, 9, b g Scorpion (IRE)—Lucy Murphy (IRE) **Graham Clarkson & Andrew Smelt**
4 **CAPTAIN TOMMY (IRE)**, 8, b g Court Cave (IRE)—Freemantle Doctor (IRE) **Mr R. J. Gurr**
5 **CARPE DIEM (FR)**, 4, b g Walzertakt (GER)—Chance Bleue (FR) **Terry & Sarah Amos**
6 **COBY NINE (IRE)**, 9, b g Arcadio (GER)—Timing **The Roworth Family Syndicate**
7 **DAME DU SOIR (FR)**, 9, br m Axxos (GER)—Kassing (FR) **Graham Clarkson & Andrew Smelt**
8 **DOM OF MARY (FR)**, 6, b g Saddler Maker (IRE)—Antinea Marie (FR) **P. J. Cave**
9 **DUTCH ADMIRAL (IRE)**, 5, ch g Dutch Art—Apasionata Sonata (USA) **P. J. Cave**
10 **ENRICHISSANT (FR)**, 8, b br g Speedmaster (GER)—Quibble (FR) **Simon & Liz Hunt**
11 **EPPLETON COLLIER (FR)**, 6, b g Balko (FR)—Golden Firebird (IRE) **Mr S. Hunt**
12 **EXTRAORDINARY MAN (FR)**, 6, b g No Risk At All (FR)—Argovie (FR) **Mr S. Hunt**
13 **FORTUNEDEFORTUNATA (IRE)**, 5, b g Soldier of Fortune (IRE)—Glenda King (IRE)
14 **FREDDY BOY**, 6, b g Midnight Legend—Aster (IRE) **P. J. Cave**
15 **GAIA VALLIS (FR)**, 6, b m Saint des Saints (FR)—Toccata Vallis (FR) **David Bridgwater Racing**
16 **IT'S FOR YOU MUM (FR)**, 4, gr f Lord du Sud (FR)—Odile (FR) **Mr S. Hunt**
17 **KIMIFIVE (IRE)**, 7, ch g Born To Sea (IRE)—Appletreemagic (IRE) **Mr R. J. Gurr**
18 5, B g Diamond Boy (FR)—Lazoukine (FR) **Mr S. Hunt**
19 **PASDDATTENTES (FR)**, 4, b f Walzertakt (GER)—Line Tzigane (FR) **Terry & Sarah Amos**
20 **PIRATE SAM**, 7, b g Black Sam Bellamy (IRE)—Teenero **JA & RJ Chenery & Partners**
21 **SA ALORS (FR)**, 6, b m Nicaron (GER)—Line Tzigane (FR) **Terry & Sarah Amos**
22 **SALTY BOY (IRE)**, 9, b g Stowaway—Ballons Oscar (IRE) **Premier Plastering (UK) Limited**
23 **SAQUEBOUTE (FR)**, 5, b m Slickly Royal (FR)—Grande Cavale (FR) **Mr S. Hunt**
24 4, B g Telescope (IRE)—September Blaze
25 **SIROBBIE (IRE)**, 8, br g Arakan (USA)—Presentbreeze (IRE) **Mr R. J. Gurr**
26 **SUKAT (IRE)**, 5, b g War Command (USA)—Precious Gem (IRE) **Constructive Equine**
27 **TELLAIRSUE (GER)**, 4, ch g Zoffany (IRE)—Tiangua **Mr R. Wilson**
28 **TIGERTEN**, 5, b g Born To Sea (IRE)—Morning Bride (IRE) **Mr R. J. Gurr**
29 **URANUS DES BORDES (FR)**, 6, b g Kapgarde (FR)—Queen des Bordes (FR) **Mr S. Hunt**
30 **VAN MEEGEREN (IRE)**, 6, ch g Gale Force Ten—Ashdali (IRE) **Mrs J. A. Chenery & Mr R. J. Chenery**
31 **ZAMANI (GER)**, 6, ch g Mamool (IRE)—Zuccarella (GER) **Mr R. Wilson**

THREE-YEAR-OLDS

32 **CHARLIFAN (IRE)**, b g Gutaifan (IRE)—Appletreemagic (IRE) **Mr R. J. Gurr**

Other Owners: Mrs S. P. Amos, T. P. Amos, D. G. Bridgwater, Mrs J. A. Chenery, Mr R. J. Chenery, Mrs J. A. Chenery & Mr R. J. Chenery, David Bridgwater Racing, Mrs E. A. Hunt, Mr S. Hunt, Mr M. Kempley, Mr T. J. Payton.

Assistant Trainer: Mrs Lucy K. Bridgwater.

NH Jockey: Tom Scudamore. **Conditional Jockey:** Daniel Hiskett, Callum McKinnes.

MR ROBYN BRISLAND, Stockbridge

61

Postal: **Stud House, Danebury , Stockbridge, Hampshire SO20 6JX**
Contacts: MOBILE **07771 656081**
EMAIL **robbris@me.com**

1 4, B f Outstrip—Absent Amy (IRE)
2 **ALBA DEL SOLE (IRE)**, 7, b m Dandy Man (IRE)—Winterwell (USA) **Mr M. Seedel**
3 **ANDRE AMAR (IRE)**, 6, b g Dandy Man (IRE)—Heaven's Vault (IRE) **Mr M. Seedel**
4 **APACHE CHARM**, 4, b f Swiss Spirit—Nizhoni (USA) **Ferrybank Properties Limited**

MR ROBYN BRISLAND- continued

5 **APACHE JEWEL (IRE)**, 4, b f Teofilo (IRE)—Floating Along (IRE) **Ferrybank Properties Limited**
6 **BIG IMPACT**, 5, b g Lethal Force (IRE)—Valandraud (IRE) **Mr D. R. J. Freeman**
7 **BLACK BOX**, 5, b m Iffraaj—Perfect Story (IRE) **Cross Channel Racing Club**
8 **BOMBASTIC (IRE)**, 7, ch g Raven's Pass (USA)—Star of The West **Cross Channel Racing Club**
9 **BRASS CLANKERS**, 5, b g Helmet (AUS)—Millsini **Cross Channel Racing & Partner**
10 **BUTCHEROFSTOCKHOLM**, 5, b m Toronado (IRE)—Anna's Vision (IRE) **Cross Channel Racing & Partner**
11 **CALONNE (IRE)**, 6, gr g Alhebayeb (IRE)—Lady Pastrana (IRE) **Cross Channel Racing Club**
12 **CAMPACHOOCHOO (IRE)**, 4, b f Kodi Bear (IRE)—Divert (IRE) **Cross Channel Racing & Partner**
13 **CLIFFS OF FREEDOM (IRE)**, 5, b g Canford Cliffs (IRE)—By Jupiter **Mrs J. Brisland**
14 **COLD HARBOUR**, 7, b g North Light (IRE)—Pilcomayo (USA) **Royale Racing Syndicate & Partner**
15 **COMPASS POINT**, 7, b g Helmet (AUS)—Takarna (IRE) **Cross Channel Racing & Partner**
16 **COOL VIXEN (IRE)**, 5, b m Dandy Man (IRE)—Cool Tarifa (IRE)
17 **COOLAGH MAGIC**, 6, b g Sepoy (AUS)—Miliika **Mrs J. Brisland**
18 **DANSING BEAR (IRE)**, 4, b g Kodi Bear (IRE)—Atlas Silk **Cross Channel Racing Club**
19 **DEEDS NOT WORDS (IRE)**, 11, b g Royal Applause—Wars (IRE) **Cross Channel Racing & Partner**
20 **DON'T ASK ME**, 4, b f Sixties Icon—Tenpence
21 **DYNAKITE**, 4, b g Adaay (IRE)—Ahwahnee **Cross Channel Racing Club**
22 **ELLIE PIPER**, 4, b f Acclamation—Corncockle **Luther Lives On**
23 **ESSGEE NICS (IRE)**, 9, b g Fairly Ransom (USA)—Vannuccis Daughter (IRE) **Cross Channel Racing & Partner**
24 **EVASIVE POWER (USA)**, 6, b g Elusive Quality (USA)—Casting Director (USA) **Cross Channel Racing Club**
25 **FAREWELL KISS (IRE)**, 5, ch m Exceed And Excel (AUS)—Kiss Me Goodbye **Cross Channel Racing Club**
26 **HARBOUR STORM**, 7, br g Sayif (IRE)—Minette **Mr C. J. Harding**
27 **HOWZAK**, 4, b g Sepoy (AUS)—Alys Love **Cross Channel Racing & Partner**
28 **JUSCOMINPASTY**, 4, b f Bobby's Kitten (USA)—Chatalong (IRE) **Mrs A. L. Heayns**
29 **KODIAC HARBOUR (IRE)**, 7, b g Kodiac—Operissimo **Cross Channel Racing Club**
30 **LUA DE MEL (IRE)**, 5, b m Casamento (IRE)—Selfara **Cross Channel Racing Club**
31 **MANDM**, 4, b g Haafhd—Bonne de Fleur **Cross Channel Racing & Partner**
32 **MONSIEUR PATAT**, 5, b g Coach House (IRE)—Miss Trish (IRE) **Wackey Racers Harefield**
33 **NAVAL COMMANDER**, 4, b g French Navy—Quail Landing **Mrs Jackie Cornwell & Mrs Jo Brisland**
34 **NAVAL FLEET**, 4, ch f French Navy—Straviethirteen **Mrs J. A. Cornwell**
35 **NICK VEDDER**, 4, b g Rip Van Winkle (IRE)—Devotion (IRE) **Wackey Racers Harefield**
36 **PORTERINTHEJUNGLE (IRE)**, 6, ch m Bungle Inthejungle—Porto Calero **Cross Channel Racing & Partner**
37 **POWER OVER ME (IRE)**, 5, b g Ivawood (IRE)—Bridge Note (USA) **Cross Channel Racing & Partner**
38 **REVOLUTIONARY MAN (IRE)**, 7, b g Exceed And Excel (AUS)—Bint Almukhtar (IRE) **Cross Channel Racing Club**
39 **RIVERS LAD**, 4, b g Adaay (IRE)—Siena Gold **Cross Channel Racing & Partner**
40 **ROBY MILL (IRE)**, 6, b f Dandy Man (IRE)—Charlie Em **Houghton Bloodstock**
41 **ROUNDEL**, 4, b g Dawn Approach (IRE)—Revered **Cross Channel Racing Club**
42 **SEESAWING**, 5, br g Music Master—Stunning In Purple (IRE) **Mr J. C. Levey**
43 **SERGEANT TIBBS**, 4, b g Bobby's Kitten (USA)—Beautiful View **Nick Andersen & Partner**
44 **SETTLE PETAL**, 8, b m Peintre Celebre (USA)—Shall We Dance **Cross Channel Racing & Partner**
45 **SHOOT TO KILL (IRE)**, 5, b g Dandy Man (IRE)—Nancy Astor **Mrs A. L. Heayns**
46 **SIX TIL TWELVE (IRE)**, 6, b g Bungle Inthejungle—Cuiseach (IRE) **Cross Channel Racing & Partner**
47 **SOLENT SCENE**, 5, b g Footstepsinthesand—Stravie (IRE) **Mrs J. A. Cornwell**
48 **SOURIRE SECRET**, 4, b g Monsieur Bond (IRE)—Smile That Smile **Royale Racing Syndicate & Partner**
49 **SWORD EXCEED (GER)**, 8, b g Exceed And Excel (AUS)—Sword Roche (GER) **Cross Channel Racing Club**
50 **TACKLESLIKEAFERRET (IRE)**, 5, b g Alhebayeb (IRE)—Regal Kiss **Cross Channel Racing & Partner**
51 **TOPARIAN**, 4, b f Gregorian (IRE)—Topaling **Mrs J. Brisland**
52 **TROOPER COOPER (IRE)**, 4, b g Fast Company (IRE)—Miss Lillie **Cross Channel Racing Club**
53 **TRUE WARRIOR**, 4, b g Marcel (IRE)—Eleanor Eloise (USA) **Mrs J. A. Cornwell**
54 **WHISTLING SANDS**, 6, b g Gregorian (IRE)—Sea Whisper **Mrs J. Brisland**
55 **YUFTEN**, 11, b g Invincible Spirit (IRE)—Majestic Sakeena (IRE) **Mrs J. Brisland**

THREE-YEAR-OLDS

56 **APACHE PORTIA**, b f Twilight Son—Nizhoni (USA) **Ferrybank Properties Limited**
57 **BLUE COLLAR LAD**, b c Ardad (IRE)—Wonderful Life (IRE) **Cross Channel Racing & Partner**
58 **BLUE COLLAR LASS**, b f Due Diligence (USA)—Night Premiere (IRE)
59 B f Estibhkaar (IRE)—Cantaloupe
60 **CARPE FORTUNA (IRE)**, b g Camacho—Phoenix Clubs (IRE) **Mrs J. Brisland**
61 **CLARITY SPIRIT**, b f Time Test—Matron of Honour (IRE) **Cross Channel Racing & Partner**

MR ROBYN BRISLAND- continued

62 **DADS ARMY,** b c Ardad (IRE)—Romantic Comedy (IRE) **Mrs Jackie Cornwell & Mrs Jo Brisland**
63 **HOLD THE PRESS (IRE),** b g Profitable (IRE)—Hairicin (IRE) **Mrs J. Brisland**
64 **KALKA RIVER (IRE),** b g Exceed And Excel (AUS)—Arjeed (IRE)
65 **MALAKYE (IRE),** b g Elzaam (AUS)—Sweet Chilli (IRE) **Mr A. M. Al Jasmi**
66 B f Aclaim (IRE)—Sea Regatta (IRE)
67 B f Brazen Beau (AUS)—Six Diamonds
68 **SWATCH (IRE),** b c Time Test—Gliding (IRE) **Mrs J. Brisland**
69 **THEREHEGOES,** b g Charming Thought—Chatalong (IRE) **Mrs A. L. Heayns**
70 **ZANDORA (IRE),** b f Ulysses (IRE)—Mayberain (IRE) **Cross Channel Racing & Partner**

Other Owners: Mr N. Andersen, Mrs J. Brisland, Mrs J. A. Cornwell, Cross Channel Racing Club, Mr A. Fellowes, Miss M. Hancox, Mr M. J. Hocking, Royale Racing Syndicate, Mr M. Seedel, Mr D. M. Standring.

Flat Jockey: Martin Harley, Luke Morris.

MR ANTONY BRITTAIN, Warthill
Postal: **Northgate Lodge, Warthill, York, YO19 5XR**
Contacts: **PHONE 01759 371472 FAX 01759 372915**
EMAIL email@antonybrittain.co.uk WEBSITE www.antonybrittain.co.uk

1 **ABNAA,** 5, b g Dark Angel (IRE)—Along Came Casey (IRE) **John & Tony Jarvis & Partner**
2 **ANOTHER ANGEL (IRE),** 8, b g Dark Angel (IRE)—Kermana (IRE) **Mr Antony Brittain**
3 **ASADJUMEIRAH,** 4, b c Adaay (IRE)—Place In My Heart **Made Profiles Ltd & Partner**
4 **BELLAGIO MAN (IRE),** 4, b g Dandy Man (IRE)—Rouge Noir **Paul Musson & Antony Brittain**
5 **CANFORD BAY (IRE),** 8, b g Canford Cliffs (IRE)—Maundays Bay (IRE) **Northgate Racing**
6 **DAAFR (IRE),** 6, b g Invincible Spirit (IRE)—Kitty Love (USA) **Mrs C. Brittain**
7 **EL JAD (IRE),** 4, ch g Shamardal (USA)—Doors To Manual (USA) **Mrs C. Brittain**
8 **INEXPLICABLE (IRE),** 5, gr g Dark Angel (IRE)—Bikini Babe (IRE) **R Wherritt & Partner**
9 **INTERNATIONAL LAW,** 8, gr g Exceed And Excel (AUS)—Cruel Sea (USA) **John & Tony Jarvis & Partner**
10 **MABDAA,** 4, b g Oasis Dream—Darajaat (USA) **Tykes & Terriers Racing Club**
11 **MONDAMMEJ,** 5, b g Lope de Vega (IRE)—Lamps of Heaven (IRE) **Mrs C. Brittain**
12 **MUTABAAHY (IRE),** 7, b g Oasis Dream—Habaayib **King For A Day & Antony Brittain**
13 **QAARAAT,** 7, b g Acclamation—Ladyship **Mr Antony Brittain**
14 **RAABEH,** 5, b g Showcasing—Twinkle Twinkle **John & Tony Jarvis & Partner**
15 **ROOT SIXTY SIX,** 5, ch g Monsieur Bond (IRE)—Mozayada (USA) **Mr Antony Brittain**
16 **SPARTAN FIGHTER,** 5, b g Dutch Art—Survived **John & Tony Jarvis & Partner**
17 **TATHMEEN (IRE),** 7, b g Exceed And Excel (AUS)—Deyaar (USA) **King For A Day & Antony Brittain**
18 **THAWRY,** 7, b g Iffraaj—Salacia (IRE) **Mr Antony Brittain**
19 **THE SEDBERGHIAN (IRE),** 4, b f Kodi Bear (IRE)—Shirley Blake (IRE) **The Pointless Partnership**
20 **TISTAAHAL,** 4, b g Showcasing—Blue Bayou **Mr Antony Brittain**
21 **UBAHHA,** 4, ch g Dubawi (IRE)—Taqaareed (IRE) **Mr Antony Brittain**
22 **VAN DIJK,** 5, b g Cable Bay (IRE)—Stresa **Mr Antony Brittain**

THREE-YEAR-OLDS

23 **DALGLISH (IRE),** b c Aclaim (IRE)—Lamps of Heaven (IRE) **Mrs C. Brittain**
24 **ELDEYAAR (IRE),** br g Slade Power (IRE)—Wardat Dubai **Made Profiles Ltd & Partner**
25 **MURBIH (IRE),** b g Kodiac—Leyburn **Paul Musson & Antony Brittain**
26 **YAAHOBBY (IRE),** b g Kodiac—Nations Alexander (IRE) **Styler, Chambers A Brittain**

TWO-YEAR-OLDS

27 B f 17/04 Pastoral Pursuits—Ananda Kanda (USA) (Hero's Tribute (USA))
28 B f 21/03 Pastoral Pursuits—Certral (Iffraaj)

Other Owners: Mr Antony Brittain, Mr K. S. Chambers, Mr I. Harle, Mr A. Jarvis, Mr J. Jarvis, King For A Day Club, Made Profiles Ltd, Mr P. W. Musson, M. J. Styler, Mr R. Wherritt.

Flat Jockey: Cam Hardie.

63 MR DANIEL BROOKE, Middleham
Postal: **Brough Farm, Middleham, Leyburn, North Yorkshire, DL8 4SG**
Contacts: **PHONE 01969 625259**
EMAIL danny.brooke@yahoo.com

1 **CONTREBASSE**, 7, b g Champs Elysees—Viola da Braccio (IRE) **MT Buckley & Brough Farm Racing Partners**
2 **DERWENT DEALER (IRE)**, 6, gr g Cloudings (IRE)—Feenakilmeedy (IRE) **& Barker**
3 **DIABOLEO (FR)**, 6, ch g Galileo (IRE)—Beautifix (GER) **Alan Court & Brough Farm Racing Partners**
4 **FASCINATING NEWS**, 4, b g Fascinating Rock (IRE)—Morning News (IRE) **Mr & Mrs G. Turnball**
5 **FLAVIUS TITUS**, 7, ch g Lethal Force (IRE)—Furbelow **Mr Foster & Partner**
6 **FRISCO QUEEN (IRE)**, 6, b m Kalanisi (IRE)—Brownlow Castle (IRE)
7 **GET PHAR (IRE)**, 6, b g Getaway (GER)—Lasado (IRE) **The Rolypoly Partnership**
8 **GLOBETROTTER (IRE)**, 8, ch g Helmet (AUS)—Shimna **Sowray Brothers, Brooke & Platts**
9 **GREY ATLANTIC WAY (IRE)**, 9, gr g Dahjee (USA)—Altregan Touch (IRE) **Maurice Friel & Mrs Mary Sadler**
10 **HATS OFF TO LARRY**, 8, b g Sixties Icon—Highland Jig **Miss A. S. White**
11 **LORD CONDI (IRE)**, 9, ch g Papal Bull—Wings To Soar (USA) **Absolutely Average Partnership**
12 **MELVICH BAY**, 5, b m Telescope (IRE)—Douryna **Mr A. Grant**
13 **ROCCO STORM (IRE)**, 7, b g Shirocco (GER)—Line White (FR) **The Rolypoly Partnership**
14 **SILKSTONE (IRE)**, 6, b g Alhebayeb (IRE)—Fine Silk (USA) **The Dalby Family**
15 **WESTDANTE (IRE)**, 7, b g Westerner—Mydante (IRE) **MT Buckley & Brough Farm Racing Partners**

THREE-YEAR-OLDS
16 **DREAM DEAL**, b g Due Diligence (USA)—Triveni (FR) **& Barker**
17 **PUCCINI (IRE)**, b g Exceed And Excel (AUS)—Madame Butterfly (IRE) **The Sportsmans Syndicate**
18 **RIVER RIBBLE (FR)**, b g Ribchester (IRE)—Barsemdara (FR)

Other Owners: Mr D. Barker, Mrs S. J. Barker, Mrs J. A. Brooke, Brough Farm Racing Partnership, Mr M. T. Buckley, Mr A. Court, Mrs J. A. Dalby, Mr P. N. Dalby, Mr S. C. Foster, Mr M. Friel, Mr J. Platts, Mr H. Redknapp, Mrs M. Sadler, Mr S. A. Sowray.

64 MR ROY BROTHERTON, Pershore
Postal: **Mill End Racing Stables, Netherton Road, Elmley Castle, Pershore, Worcestershire, WR10 3JF**
Contacts: **PHONE 01386 710772 MOBILE 07973 877280**

1 **AUNTIE JUNE**, 6, ch m Piccolo—Basle **Mr M. A. Geobey**
2 **DUN BAY CREEK**, 11, b g Dubai Destination (USA)—Over It **Elmley Queen 2**
3 **LANZAROTE SUNSHINE**, 5, b m Music Master—Basle **Mr M. A. Geobey**
4 **MIRACLE GARDEN**, 10, ch g Exceed And Excel (AUS)—Sharp Terms **R. Brotherton**
5 **WHERE'S THE DOG**, 4, ch f Mortga (FR)—So Belle **Miss S. C. Longford**

THREE-YEAR-OLDS
6 **PRETTY MAHRA**, bl f Silver Pond (FR)—Mara Grey (IRE) **R. Brotherton**

Other Owners: R. Brotherton, Mr N. A. Lavender Jones, Mr M. A. Savage.

Assistant Trainer: Justin Brotherton.

NH Jockey: Jamie Moore.

65 MR ALAN BROWN, Malton
Postal: **Lilac Farm, Yedingham, Malton, North Yorkshire, YO17 8SS**
Contacts: **PHONE 01944 728090 MOBILE 07970 672845**
EMAIL ad.brown@hotmail.co.uk WEBSITE www.alanbrownracing.co.uk

1 **ATRAFAN (IRE)**, 8, b g Atraf—Up Front (IRE) **Mr F. E. Reay**
2 **BLACKCURRENT**, 6, b g Kuroshio (AUS)—Mamounia (IRE) **Max Europe Limited**
3 **BLACKJACK**, 5, b g Sleeping Indian—Medam **The Hon Mrs E. S. Cunliffe-Lister**
4 **BOBS TEAL**, 5, b g Assertive—Teals Deal **Mr C. I. Ratcliffe**
5 **DYLANS CROSS (IRE)**, 6, ch g Vita Venturi (IRE)—Commanche Rise (IRE) **Mr D. McGillicuddy**
6 **EMBLA**, 4, b f Albaasil (IRE)—Medam **The Hon Mrs E. S. Cunliffe-Lister**
7 **INITIAL APPROACH (IRE)**, 6, b m Dawn Approach (IRE)—Coquette Noire (IRE) **A. D. Brown**
8 **JEMS BOND**, 5, ch g Monsieur Bond (IRE)—Saphire **Frank & A Brown**
9 **LIZZIANNA (IRE)**, 5, ch m Libranno—Perhaps Love (IRE) **Mr D. McGillicuddy**
10 **OASIS LAW (IRE)**, 5, b m Lawman (FR)—Lus Na Greine (IRE) **Mr D. McGillicuddy**
11 **SHEILA'S LEGACY**, 4, ch f Medicean—Fairy Shoes **The Odd Partnership**

THREE-YEAR-OLDS
12 **ICE SHADOW (IRE)**, b g Buratino (IRE)—Chicane **G. Morrill**
13 **THORDIAC**, b f Night of Thunder (IRE)—Nefetari **Mr F. E. Reay**
14 **TIME SHADOW (IRE)**, b f Cotai Glory—Queen Celeste (IRE) **G. Morrill**
15 **URBAN ROAD**, ch g Monsieur Bond (IRE)—Normandy Maid **Max Europe Limited**
16 **WAVERLEY STAR**, b c Peace Envoy (FR)—Redalani (IRE) **S. E. Pedersen**

Other Owners: Mrs B. V. Benthall, A. D. Brown, Mr D. D. Oakes, Mr F. E. Reay.

66 MR ANDI BROWN, Newmarket
Postal: **Southfields Stables, Hamilton Road, Newmarket, Suffolk, CB8 7JQ**
Contacts: **PHONE 01638 669652 MOBILE 07980 393263 FAX 01638 669652**
EMAIL southfieldsstables@btinternet.com WEBSITE www.southfieldsstables.co.uk

1 **KIRTLING**, 11, gr g Araafa (IRE)—Cape Maya **Faith Hope and Charity**
2 **MAKTER**, 5, b g Sepoy (AUS)—Perfect Silence **Miss L. J. Knocker**
3 **MR FUSTIC (IRE)**, 4, b g Epaulette (AUS)—Marion Antoinette (IRE) **Dave Tonge, Steph Collins. Phil Mills**

Other Owners: A. S. Brown, Mrs S. Collins, Mr P. Mills, Mr D. Tonge.

Assistant Trainer: Miss Linsey Knocker.

67 MR DAVID BROWN, Whitby
Postal: **6 Linden Lane, Newholm, Whitby, North Yorkshire, YO21 3QX**
Contacts: **PHONE 01636 613793 MOBILE 07889 132931**
EMAIL david@davidbrownracing.com

1 **CAN CAN GIRL (IRE)**, 4, b f Champs Elysees—Osthurry (IRE) **Bratwa**
2 **HARWORTH (IRE)**, 4, b g Showcasing—Kiyra Wells (IRE) **Mr R. Hull**
3 **LADY ZIANA**, 4, b f Dawn Approach (IRE)—Heartlines (USA) **Mount Pleasant Farm Syndicate**
4 **MAGIC GEM**, 4, ch g Garswood—Thorntoun Piccolo **Mr R. Hull**
5 **MIGHTY FINE (FR)**, 4, b f Acclamation—Toute Famille **Thomas, Thomas, Wright**
6 **SOVEREIGN MOON**, 4, b f Swiss Spirit—Rivas Rhapsody (IRE) **Mr R. Hull**
7 **TRUE HERO**, 6, b g Charm Spirit (IRE)—Beldale Memory (IRE) **Mr R. Hull**

MR DAVID BROWN - continued

THREE-YEAR-OLDS

  8 BEAU LILLY, b f Elzaam (AUS)—Katie Elder (FR) **Jack Thomas & Ben Thomas**
  9 BILLY MCGARRY, b g Night of Thunder (IRE)—Anosti **Mr R. Hull**
10 DRAKEHOLES, b g Gutaifan (IRE)—Elfine (IRE) **Mr R. Hull**
11 LETHAL VISION, b f Lethal Force (IRE)—Pigeon Point **New Vision Bloodstock and Partner**
12 SUN RISING (IRE), ch f Dawn Approach (IRE)—Beauty Pageant (IRE)
                                                D H Brown, Mr Clive Watson & Mr J. R. Atherton

Other Owners: Mr J. R. Atherton, Mr N. J. Blencowe, Mr D. H. Brown, Mrs F. Denniff, Mr G. S. Felston, Mr M. Lenton, New Vision Bloodstock, Mr B. M. Thomas, Mr J. F. Thomas, Mr C. Watson, Mr S. Wright.

Assistant Trainer: Dushyant Dooyea.

Flat Jockey: Tom Eaves.

68	**MR GARY BROWN, Compton** Postal: **East Yard, Hamilton Stables, Hockham Road, Compton, Berkshire, RG20 6QJ** Contacts: **PHONE 07545 915253** **EMAIL gbrownracing@hotmail.co.uk**

  1 ALIOSKI, 5, b g Kodiac—Luluti (IRE) **G. Cheshire**
  2 CARDS ARE DEALT (IRE), 6, ch g Mastercraftsman (IRE)—High Praise (USA) **Mr K. W. Sneath**
  3 HE CAN DANCE (IRE), 4, b g Es Que Love (IRE)—Balqaa (USA) **Mrs K. Hickmott**
  4 HE IS A CRACKER (IRE), 6, b g Califet (FR)—She Is A Cracker (FR) **Mr N. Byrne**
  5 MAKE A DEAL (IRE), 6, b g Shantou (USA)—Miss Denman (IRE) **G. Brown**
  6 SHALOTT (IRE), 5, b g Camelot—Nasanice (IRE) **Mr G. Costelloe**

THREE-YEAR-OLDS

  7 B f Holy Roman Emperor (IRE)—Hannahs Turn **Mr K. W. Sneath**
  8 Ch g Highland Reel (IRE)—Sweet Martoni **Mr K. W. Sneath**

69	**MISS HARRIET BROWN, Sturminster Newton** Postal: **Blenheim Cottage,Quar Close, Mappowder, Sturminster Newton, Dorset, DT10 2EN** Contacts: **MOBILE 07798 613111** **EMAIL harriet_brown1@hotmail.co.uk**

  1 AR MEST (FR), 9, bl g Diamond Boy (FR)—Shabada (FR)
  2 4, B g Yeats (IRE)—Ashbury (IRE)
  3 COAL STOCK (IRE), 7, ch g Red Jazz (USA)—Scar Tissue
  4 COUP DE PINCEAU (FR), 10, b g Buck's Boum (FR)—Castagnette III (FR)
  5 DESIGNER JET (IRE), 6, gr g Jet Away—Casa Queen (IRE)
  6 ELUSIVE INTENTIONS (IRE), 8, b g Presenting—Roses Dreams (IRE)
  7 FAMOSO (IRE), 6, b g Fame And Glory—Mucho Macabi (IRE)
  8 HARLEM SOUL, 4, ch g Frankel—Giants Play (USA)
  9 IRON MIKE, 6, gr g Gregorian (IRE)—Regal Velvet
10 KALYPTRA (FR), 6, b g Fair Mix (IRE)—Lovely Origny (FR)
11 LIEUTENANT ROCCO (IRE), 7, ch g Shirocco (GER)—Five Star Present (IRE)
12 5, B g Shirocco (GER)—Lithai (GER)
13 LUCKY LARA (IRE), 7, ch m Mahler—Honour Own (IRE)
14 M'LADY MELODY, 5, br m Royal Anthem (USA)—Carissima (IRE)
15 MASCAT, 5, ch g Zoffany (IRE)—Critical Acclaim

MISS HARRIET BROWN - continued

16 **MESSAGE MAN (IRE)**, 6, b g Ocovango—Maidofthemountain (IRE)
17 **MILANFORD (IRE)**, 8, b g Milan—Tabachines (FR)
18 **MONETE (GER)**, 5, gr m Jukebox Jury (IRE)—Mayumi (IRE)
19 **MYSTIC COURT (IRE)**, 9, b g Court Cave (IRE)—My Mystic Rose (IRE)
20 **NOMOREDANCING**, 6, b m Norse Dancer (IRE)—Morebutwhen
21 **PAUDIE (IRE)**, 6, b g Fame And Glory—Honeyed (IRE)
22 4, B g Shirocco (GER)—Pixie Dust (IRE)
23 **PLENTY OF TIME (IRE)**, 6, b m Robin des Champs (FR)—Give It Time
24 **PROMISING MILAN (IRE)**, 7, b g Milan—French Promise (IRE)
25 **SHE'S OUT OF REACH**, 4, ch f Phoenix Reach (IRE)—Beat Seven
26 **TAKODA (IRE)**, 6, b g Doyen (IRE)—Crimson Bow (GER)
27 **TOWTHELINE**, 6, b m Black Sam Bellamy (IRE)—Tiger Line
28 **TRUMP LADY (IRE)**, 7, b m Doyen (IRE)—Kris Krystal (IRE)
29 4, B g Soldier of Fortune (IRE)—Whisky Rose (IRE)

---

70   **MISS MICHELLE BRYANT, Lewes**
Postal: **Bevern Bridge Farm Cottage, South Chailey, Lewes, East Sussex, BN8 4QH**
Contacts: **PHONE 01273 400638 MOBILE 07976 217542**
EMAIL bear_2009@live.co.uk

1 **CHURCHTOWN GLEN (IRE)**, 9, b g Getaway (GER)—Annagh Lady (IRE) **Miss M P Bryant, David & Eileen Bryant**
2 **FITZY**, 6, b g Epaulette (AUS)—Zagarock **Miss M. P. Bryant**
3 **FLOWERS ON VENUS (IRE)**, 10, ch g Raven's Pass (USA)—Chelsea Rose (IRE) **Miss M. P. Bryant**

Amateur Jockey: Miss M. P. Bryant.

---

71   **MR BOB BUCKLER, Bridgwater**
Postal: **Gibb Hill, Courtway, Spaxton, Bridgwater, Somerset, TA5 1DR**
Contacts: **PHONE 01278 671268 MOBILE 07785 773957**
EMAIL rbuckler@btconnect.com WEBSITE www.robertbucklerracing.co.uk

1 **BARBARIAN**, 6, b g Black Sam Bellamy (IRE)—Mizzurka **The Five Fedoras**
2 **CUSHUISH**, 9, b m Yeats (IRE)—My Petra **Cushuish Syndicate**
3 **FLOWING CADENZA**, 8, b m Yeats (IRE)—Over The Flow **Mrs H. R. Dunn**
4 **MIZZ MOONDANCE**, 7, b m Yeats (IRE)—Mizzurka **The Five Fedoras**

Head Lad: Giles Scott.

Conditional Jockey: Sean Houlihan.

72 MR TOBY BULGIN, Thetford
Postal: **High Fen, Thornham Road, Methwold, Thetford, Norfolk, IP26 4PJ**
EMAIL **toby@beatbushfarm.co.uk**

1 **ARTHUR'S SEAT (IRE)**, 5, b g Champs Elysees—Sojitzen (FR) **Mrs N. H. Bulgin**
2 **DARLING ALKO (FR)**, 9, b g Al Namix (FR)—Padalko Tatou (FR) **Mrs N. H. Bulgin**
3 **GERRITZEN**, 7, ch m Geordieland (FR)—Wibble Wobble **Mrs N. H. Bulgin**
4 7, B m Librettist (USA)—Jessie May (IRE) **Mrs N. H. Bulgin**
5 **LUCKOFTHEDRAW (FR)**, 9, gr g Martaline—La Perspective (FR) **Mrs M.E.Latham Mr John R Latham**
6 4, B f Clovis du Berlais (FR)—Mere Detail (IRE) **Mrs N. H. Bulgin**
7 **RAPAPORT**, 10, b m Dr Massini (IRE)—Seemarye **Mrs N. H. Bulgin**
8 **SOLAR SOVEREIGN (IRE)**, 7, b g Multiplex—Royal Roxy (IRE) **Mrs N. H. Bulgin**
9 **TRICOMI**, 7, b br m Getaway (GER)—Annaghbrack (IRE) **Mrs N. H. Bulgin**

TWO-YEAR-OLDS
10 B f 21/05 Kayf Tara—Mere Detail (IRE) (Definite Article) (4762) **Mrs N. H. Bulgin**

73 MR K. R. BURKE, Leyburn
Postal: **Spigot Lodge, Middleham, Leyburn, North Yorkshire, DL8 4TL**
Contacts: PHONE **01969 625088** MOBILE **07778 458777** FAX **01969 625099**
EMAIL **karl@karlburke.co.uk** WEBSITE **www.karlburke.co.uk**

1 **ADABBAH (IRE)**, 4, b f No Nay Never (USA)—Seeking Solace **Promenade Bloodstock Limited**
2 **ALYARA**, 4, b f Cable Bay (IRE)—Norway Cross **Mr M. S. Al Shahi**
3 **ASTRO JAKK (IRE)**, 6, b g Zoffany (IRE)—By The Edge (IRE) **Titanium Racing Club**
4 **BARON RUN**, 12, ch g Bertolini (USA)—Bhima **Mr Eric Burke & Partner**
5 **BOOGIE TIME (IRE)**, 4, b g Kodiac—Get Up And Dance **Mr Carl Waters & Mrs E Burke**
6 **BORN TO BE ALIVE (IRE)**, 8, b g Born To Sea (IRE)—Yaria (IRE) **Mr T Dykes & Mrs E Burke**
7 **DABIRSTAR (FR)**, 4, b f Dabirsim (FR)—Aster Nox (USA) **Hold Your Horses Racing & Mrs E Burke**
8 **DISTINCTION (IRE)**, 4, b g Kodiac—Tajbell (IRE) **Mrs E. M. Burke**
9 **EILEAN DUBH (IRE)**, 4, b c Vadamos (FR)—Kenwana (FR) **Pau - Perth Partnership**
10 **EXALTED ANGEL (FR)**, 6, b g Dark Angel (IRE)—Hurryupharriet (IRE) **Pau-perth Partnership & Mrs E Burke**
11 **FRONTLINE PHANTOM (IRE)**, 15, b g Noverre (USA)—Daisy Hill **Mr Eric Burke & Partner**
12 **INVINCIBLY (IRE)**, 4, b g Invincible Spirit (IRE)—Recite (JPN) **Apple Tree Stud**
13 **KELLY'S DINO (FR)**, 9, b g Doctor Dino (FR)—Sabolienne (FR) **Mr Liam Kelly & Mrs E Burke**
14 **LEAD STORY (IRE)**, 4, b f New Bay—Newsletter (IRE) **Ballylinch Stud**
15 **LORD OBERON**, 7, b g Mayson—Fairy Shoes **Mr D J MacKay & Mrs E Burke**
16 **LORD OF THE LODGE (IRE)**, 5, b h Dandy Man (IRE)—Archetypal (IRE) **Mrs E. M. Burke**
17 **MISS SEAFIRE (IRE)**, 4, b f Dandy Man (IRE)—Solstice **Mrs E. M. Burke**
18 **PARALLEL WORLD (IRE)**, 6, b g Morpheus—Miss Glitters (IRE) **Ontoawinner 14 & Mrs E Burke**
19 **RAYONG**, 5, b g Mayson—Lydiate (IRE) **King Power Racing Co Ltd**
20 **REBEL AT DAWN (IRE)**, 4, b g Dandy Man (IRE)—Ragtime Dancer **Mr Carl Waters & Mrs E Burke**
21 **RIVELLINO**, 12, b g Invincible Spirit (IRE)—Brazilian Bride (IRE) **Mrs E. M. Burke**
22 **SHALLOW HAL**, 6, b g Mayson—Bazelle **Ontoawinner 14 & Mrs E Burke**
23 **SHE'S NO ANGEL (IRE)**, 4, ch f Libertarian—Angel Voices (IRE) **Mrs E. M. Burke**
24 **SIGNIFICANTLY**, 4, b g Garswood—Rosebride **Mr J Laughton & Mrs E Burke**
25 **SOCIALLY SHADY**, 5, ch g Zoffany (IRE)—Executrix **Mrs E. M. Burke**
26 **SPYCATCHER (IRE)**, 4, b c Vadamos (FR)—Damask (IRE) **Highclere T'BredRacing-Adriana Zaefferer**
27 **TIPPERARY TIGER (IRE)**, 4, b g Mayson—Tipperary Boutique (IRE) **Get & E Lets Get Racing & Mrs E Burke**
28 **WIZARD D'AMOUR**, 4, gr ro g Dutch Art—Holistic **Mr Carl Waters & Mrs E Burke**

THREE-YEAR-OLDS
29 **AASSER (FR)**, bl c Dabirsim (FR)—Iffraja (IRE) **Mr M. S. Al Shahi**
30 **AL QAREEM (IRE)**, b g Awtaad (IRE)—Moqla **Nick Bradley Racing 33 + Burke**

MR K. R. BURKE - continued

31 **ALMOHANDESAH**, b f Postponed (IRE)—Chocolate Hills (FR) **Sheikh Mohammed Obaid Al Maktoum**
32 **ANGEL IN THE WINGS**, b f Showcasing—Infamous Angel **Hj Racing & Mrs E Burke**
33 **ATTAGIRL**, br f Wootton Bassett—Catalina Bay (IRE) **Clipper Group Holdings Ltd**
34 **BACKSTAGE**, b f Showcasing—Modesty's Way (USA) **Dykes, Hughes E Burke**
35 **BALLYNAVEEN BOY (IRE)**, gr g El Kabeir (USA)—Ballet Move **Get & E Lets Get Racing & Mrs E Burke**
36 **BEGGARMANS ROAD (IRE)**, b g Elzaam (AUS)—Kiralik **Lilley, Buckle & Burke**
37 **BENEFICIARY**, b g Profitable (IRE)—La Roumegue (USA) **Almohamediya Racing & Mrs E Burke**
38 **BULLET FORCE (IRE)**, b c Cable Bay (IRE)—Ard Na Sidhe (IRE) **Amo Racing Limited**
39 **CHAMPAGNE DIAL**, ch f Recorder—Urban Art (FR) **R & B Barker**
40 **CHASING RAINBEAUS**, b f Brazen Beau (AUS)—Raggle Taggle (IRE) **Hold Your Horses Racing & Mrs E Burke**
41 **EL CABALLO**, b c Havana Gold (IRE)—Showstoppa **Grange Park Racing Xviii & Ofo Partners**
42 **EMERALD LADY (IRE)**, ch f Garswood—Bahia Emerald (IRE) **Mrs E. M. Burke**
43 B g Vadamos (FR)—Fashionable Spirit (IRE) **Mrs E. M. Burke**
44 **FAST RESPONSE (IRE)**, b f Fast Company (IRE)—Deemah (IRE) **Nick Bradley Racing 39**
45 **FEMME PATRONNE (IRE)**, gr f El Kabeir (USA)—Little Audio (IRE) **More Turf Racing & Mrs E Burke**
46 **GIFTED GOLD (IRE)**, ch f Galileo Gold—Flare of Firelight (USA) **Mr Carl Waters & Mrs E Burke**
47 **GUILDED (IRE)**, gr f Mastercraftsman (IRE)—Lajatico **Nick Bradley Racing 1 & Mrs E Burke**
48 **HONEY SWEET (IRE)**, b f Adaay (IRE)—Sweet Sienna **Nick Bradley Racing 14 & Mrs E Burke**
49 **HOOKED ON YOU (IRE)**, b f Starspangledbanner (AUS)—Plying (USA) **John & Jessica Dance**
50 **ILLUSTRATING**, b f Showcasing—Maids Causeway (IRE) **Clipper Group Holdings Ltd**
51 **KABOO (USA)**, b br c More Than Ready (USA)—Follow Moon (USA) **Nick Bradley Racing 49 & Mrs E Burke**
52 **KANZINO (IRE)**, gr g El Kabeir (USA)—Katrine (USA) **G & E Burke**
53 **KORKER (IRE)**, b g Dandy Man—Adaptation **Claret & Racing**
54 **LAST CRUSADER (IRE)**, b c Oasis Dream—Spanish Fly (IRE) **Clipper Group Holdings Ltd**
55 **LATENIGHTMISTAKE (IRE)**, b f Estidhkaar (IRE)—Wishyouwerehere (IRE) **Nick Bradley Racing 25 & E Burke**
56 **LIAMARTY DREAMS**, b g Oasis Dream—Heavenly Verse **Mr Liam Kelly & Mrs E Burke**
57 **LIGHTENING GESTURE**, b g Estidhkaar (IRE)—Cornlaw **Nick Bradley Racing 12 & Mrs E Burke**
58 **LULLABY BAY**, b f Profitable (IRE)—Dubai Affair **Bearstone Stud Limited**
59 **MACCHIAVELLO (IRE)**, b g No Nay Never (USA)—Mona Vale (IRE) **Amo Racing & Michael Tabor**
60 **MAGGIE'S JOY**, b f Time Test—Pure Joy **Nick Bradley Racing 34 & Mrs E Burke**
61 **MONTINEY**, ch g Monsieur Bond (IRE)—Arculinge **G & E Burke**
62 **MUVERAN**, b c Iffraaj—Karmadal (IRE) **David & Yvonne Blunt**
63 **NEGWAH (IRE)**, b f Mukhadram—Sounds of April (IRE) **Mr A. Mohamdi**
64 **PINK STORM**, b f Aclaim (IRE)—Rowan Brae **E & B Partnership**
65 **POLYPHONIC (IRE)**, b c Sea The Stars (IRE)—Aim To Please (FR) **John & Jessica Dance**
66 **POPTRONIC**, b f Nathaniel (IRE)—Alpine Dream (IRE) **David & Yvonne Blunt**
67 **QUICK CHANGE**, b f New Approach (IRE)—Ensemble (FR) **The All About York Partnership**
68 **RHINOPLASTY (IRE)**, ch f Buratino (IRE)—Alta Definizione (IRE) **Nick Bradley Racing 16 + Burke**
69 **ROAMIN IN GLOAMIN**, b g Twilight Son—Madame Mere (IRE) **Heaton, Buckle & Burke**
70 **ROYAL EMERTHER (IRE)**, b g Mehmas (IRE)—Tifariti (USA) **R & B Barker**
71 **RUN TEDDY RUN (FR)**, b g Mayson—Idealist **C & E Burke**
72 **SHERDIL (IRE)**, b g Dandy Man—Chicago Fall (IRE) **K. A. Dasmal**
73 **SILKY WILKIE (IRE)**, b g Mehmas (IRE)—Vasoni (IRE) **Middleham Park Racing Lxxxi & E Burke**
74 **SOPHIE'S STAR**, b f Cotai Glory—Overheard (IRE) **Nick Bradley Racing 5 & E Burke**
75 **SPECIAL LOVE**, b f Heeraat (IRE)—Canford Kilbey (IRE) **Mr T. Kilbey**
76 **TAJ ALOLA (IRE)**, b g El Kabeir (USA)—Girl Ranger (IRE) **Mr F. F. A. Almandeel**
77 **TAJ ALRIYADH (IRE)**, b c Mehmas (IRE)—Next Trial (IRE) **Mrs E. M. Burke**
78 **TEDDY'S PROFIT (IRE)**, b g Profitable (IRE)—Newsroom (IRE) **C & E Burke**
79 **TOTHENINES (IRE)**, gr g Dandy Man (IRE)—Ultimate Best **Middleham Park Racing Ci & Mrs E Burke**
80 **TRUE JEM (FR)**, b f Dabirsim (FR)—Vally Jem (FR) **Nick Bradley Racing 47**

TWO-YEAR-OLDS

81 Gr f 14/04 Havana Grey—Asia Minor (IRE) (Pivotal) (20000) **Nick Bradley Racing 15 & Mrs E Burke**
82 Ch f 15/04 Intello (GER)—Augusta Ada (Byron) **L C & A E Sigsworth**
83 **BEYOND REPROACH (IRE)**, b c 03/02 Dandy Man (IRE)—Ultimate Best (King's Best (USA)) (52000)
     Mr D J MacKay & Mrs E Burke
84 Ch f 19/04 Dandy Man (IRE)—Born To Spend (IRE) (Born To Sea (IRE)) (42000)
     Nick Bradley Racing 9 & Mrs E Burke
85 B f 12/02 Shalaa (IRE)—Crystal War (IRE) (Declaration of War (USA)) (93537) **Mr R. Kent**

MR K. R. BURKE - continued

86 B f 09/04 Massaat (IRE)—Delizia (IRE) (Dark Angel (IRE)) (42857) **Mr C R. Hirst**
87 **DESIGN,** b c 31/03 Expert Eye—Betty Loch (Pivotal) (65000) **Highclere T'Bred Racing -Mother Teresa**
88 **DISTRICT COUNCIL,** b c 12/04 Washington DC (IRE)—Bold Bidder (Indesatchel (IRE)) (27000)
                                                                                    Bearstone Stud Limited
89 **EDMUND IRONSIDE,** b c 15/03 Saxon Warrior (JPN)—Garden Row (IRE) (Invincible Spirit (IRE)) (82000)
                                                                                    Claret & Racing
90 B c 08/02 Farhh—Formidable Kitt (Invincible Spirit (IRE)) (125000) **Sheikh Mohammed Obaid Al Maktoum**
91 Bl f 28/02 Dabirsim (FR)—Fresh Laurels (IRE) (Rock of Gibraltar (IRE)) (22109) **Nick Bradley Racing 45**
92 **GEORGIAVA,** gr f 14/03 Havana Grey—Shohrah (IRE) (Giant's Causeway (USA)) (17000) **G & E Burke**
93 **GREYCIOUS ANNA,** gr f 05/03 Havana Grey—Annawi (Dubawi (IRE)) (8000) **Pau - Perth Partnership**
94 B c 25/02 Brazen Beau (AUS)—Hafaawa (IRE) (Mukhadram) (12000) **Poppy Holdings (UK) Limited**
95 **JAHIDIN (FR),** b c 20/01 Kheleyf (USA)—Loda (FR) (Zieten (USA)) (3401) **Pau - Perth Partnership**
96 **KELLIA BERE (FR),** b f 02/04 Whitecliffsofdover (USA)—Ajab Bere (FR) (Peer Gynt (JPN)) (18707)
                                                                                    Nick Bradley Racing 2 & Mrs E Burke
97 B c 28/01 Showcasing—Killermont Street (IRE) (Dream Ahead (USA)) (160000)
                                                                                    Sheikh Mohammed Obaid Al Maktoum
98 **KISA BERE (FR),** b f 21/03 Pedro The Great (USA)—Sanisa (FR) (Panis (USA)) (6378)
                                                                                    Nick Bradley Racing 28 & E Burke
99 B c 13/03 Showcasing—Little Kim (Garswood) **R & B Barker**
100 LOOKING FOR LYNDA (IRE), ch c 17/03 Unfortunately (IRE)—Designated (Dutch Art) (12000) **D & E Burke**
101 B c 19/03 Mayson—Loving Touch (Nathaniel (IRE))
102 Gr f 03/04 Havana Grey—Mayfair Rock (IRE) (Society Rock (IRE)) (5714) **Grange Park Racing Xviii & the Tara Five**
103 B f 21/01 Dark Angel (IRE)—Meydan Princess (IRE) (Choisir (AUS)) (64762) **Nick Bradley Racing 40**
104 MISS BRAZEN, b f 16/04 Brazen Beau (AUS)—Quelle Affaire (Bahamian Bounty) (7619) **Fitzwilliams, Railton**
105 MISS JUNGLE CAT, b f 07/02 Jungle Cat (IRE)—Honky Tonk Sally (Dansili) (60000) **Hunscote Stud & Mrs E Burke**
106 B c 29/03 Camacho—Newsroom (IRE) (Manduro (GER)) (30476)
107 B f 16/04 Kodiac—Nijah (IRE) (Pivotal) (45000) **Nick Bradley Racing 7 & E Burke**
108 Ch f 11/03 Showcasing—Pilates (IRE) (Shamardal (USA)) (120000) **Sheikh J. D. Al Maktoum**
109 B f 31/03 Roaring Lion (USA)—Rive Gauche (Fastnet Rock (AUS)) (38000)
110 B gr c 12/03 Havana Grey—Ruby Slippers (Sir Percy) (26667)
111 SHINE HONEY SHINE, b f 19/02 Havana Grey—Military Madame (IRE) (Epaulette (AUS)) (12000)
                                                                                    Gove & Shaw 02 & Whitsbury Manor Stud
112 B f 07/03 Decorated Knight—Sounds of April (IRE) (Exceed And Excel (AUS)) **Mr A. Mohamdi**
113 Ch c 14/04 Havana Gold (IRE)—Storybook (UAE) (Halling (USA)) (92000) **Mr M. S. Al Shahi**
114 B f 03/02 Unfortunately (IRE)—Sugar Hiccup (IRE) (Refuse To Bend (IRE)) (5000) **Wolf Pack 6 & Partners**
115 Ch c 03/03 Ulysses (IRE)—Sultry (Pivotal) (60000)
116 B f 21/03 Profitable (IRE)—Teeline (IRE) (Exceed And Excel (AUS)) (59048) **Nick Bradley Racing 35 & E Burke**
117 B f 09/04 Ribchester (IRE)—Tides (Bahamian Bounty) (33333)
118 B f 16/02 Dandy Man (IRE)—Tilly Trotter (IRE) (Kodiac) (33333)
119 B f 26/01 Jungle Cat (IRE)—Time To Exceed (IRE) (Exceed And Excel (AUS)) **Hunscote Stud Limited**
120 B f 15/04 Dark Angel (IRE)—Umniyah (IRE) (Shamardal (USA)) (260000) **Sheikh Mohammed Obaid Al Maktoum**
121 UNITARIAN, b c 29/02 Tasleet—Mysterious Girl (IRE) (Teofilo (IRE)) (23000)
                                                                                    Pau-perth Partnership & Mrs E Burke
122 B f 21/02 Showcasing—Weisse Socken (IRE) (Acclamation) (23000) **Nick Bradley Racing 17 + Burke**

Other Owners: Sheikh N. Al Khalifa, Sheikh N. M. H. Al Khalifa, AlMohamediya Racing, Amo Racing Limited, Mr D. A. Bardsley, Mr B. L. Barker, Mr N. Bradley, Mr S. Bridge, Miss K. Buckle, Mr E. J. Burke, Mrs E. M. Burke, Mrs F. H. B. Cork, Mr J. F. P. Cork, Mr A. D. Crombie, Mr G. Curnow, Mr D. Curran, Mrs J. Dance, Mr J. E. Dance, Mr A. Denham, Mr P. Doughty, Mr T. J. Dykes, Tim Dykes & Jon Hughes, Mr A. C. Elliott, Dr C. I. Emmerson, Chris Emmerson & Jon Hughes, Mr J. J. Fildes, Fine Claret Racing, Mr G. F. Fitzwilliams, Mr A. Gove, Grange Park Racing XVIII, H/J Racing, Mr E. J. Harper, Mr P. Harper, Mrs R. L. Heaton, Mr C. R. Hirst, Hold Your Horses Racing, Miss S. Holden, Mr S. G. Hope, G. Horsford, Mr E. J. Hughes, Mrs J. Hughes, Hunscote Stud Limited, Mr K. W. Jarvis, Mr L. Kelly, Mr R. Kent, Mr J. Laughton, Let's Get Racing Ltd, Mr A. J. R. Lilley, Mr D. J. MacKay, Mr R. C. McKeown, Middleham Park Racing CI, Middleham Park Racing LXXXI, More Turf Racing, P.Newton, Nick Bradley Racing 1, Nick Bradley Racing 12, Nick Bradley Racing 14, Nick Bradley Racing 15, Nick Bradley Racing 16, Nick Bradley Racing 17, Nick Bradley Racing 2, Nick Bradley Racing 25 & Sohi, Nick Bradley Racing 28, Nick Bradley Racing 33, Nick Bradley Racing 34, Nick Bradley Racing 35, Nick Bradley Racing 49, Nick Bradley Racing 5, Nick Bradley Racing 7, Nick Bradley Racing 9, Mr N. J. O'Brien, Ontoawinner 14, T. S. Palin, Pau - Perth Partnership, M. Prince, Mr J. Railton, Mr D. A. Shaw, Mrs A. E. Sigsworth, L. C. Sigsworth, Mrs D. M. Swinburn, M. Tabor, The Tara Five, Mr C. J. Waters.

MR K. R. BURKE - continued

Assistant Trainer: Mrs Elaine Burke, Kelly Burke, Lucy Burke, Joe O'Gorman, **Pupil Assistant:** Ian Hickey.

Flat Jockey: Ben Curtis, Clifford Lee. **Apprentice Jockey:** Rhona Pindar, Harrison Shaw.

---

74   **MR KEIRAN BURKE, Sturminster Newton**
Postal: **Rudge Hill Farm, Rivers Corner, Sturminster Newton, Dorset**
Contacts: **MOBILE 07855 860993**

1 5, B m Black Sam Bellamy (IRE)—Aphrodisias (FR) **Glanvilles Stud Partners**
2 **DANZINI (IRE),** 6, br m Ocovango—Grainne Delight (IRE) **Kingsbere Racing**
3 5, Gr g Geordieland (FR)—Drop The Hammer
4 **GOLDEN POET (IRE),** 10, b g Urban Poet (USA)—Little Linnet **Mr K. M. F. Burke**
5 **HIGHERMONARCHY (IRE),** 6, b g Imperial Monarch (IRE)—Ballinamona Belle (IRE) **K B Racing**
6 **LADY WILBERRY,** 5, br m Montmartre (FR)—Lady Willa (IRE) **Balham Hill Racing**
7 **LAST ROYAL,** 7, b g Sulamani (IRE)—First Royal (GER) **Glanvilles Stud Partners**
8 7, Ch g Tiger Groom—Laureldean Belle (IRE)
9 **LOVE ACTUALLY (IRE),** 6, br m Shirocco (GER)—Elsie (IRE) **Mrs M. A. Crook**
10 **MAROOCHI,** 5, b m Presenting—Makadamia **Whitcombe Racing Club**
11 **PUTDECASHONTHEDASH (IRE),** 9, b g Doyen (IRE)—Be My Adelina (IRE) **Goodfellers Racing**
12 **SCRUMPY BOY,** 10, b g Apple Tree (FR)—Presuming **SMLC Racing**
13 **SOUL ICON,** 5, b g Sixties Icon—Solitary Girl **Glanvilles Stud Partners**
14 **SPIRIT OF ROME (IRE),** 8, ch m Mastercraftsman (IRE)—Zagreb Flyer **Whitcombe Racing Club**
15 **TARKS HILL,** 8, b m Brian Boru—Risky May **Glanvilles Stud Associates**
16 **THE HEIGHT OF FAME,** 5, b m Fame And Glory—Good Thinking **Barrow Hill**
17 4, B f Blue Bresil (FR)—West River (USA) **K B Racing**

TWO-YEAR-OLDS

18 B f 25/03 Profitable (IRE)—Magic Minor (IRE) (Montjeu (IRE)) (2857)

---

75   **MR HUGH BURNS, Alnwick**
Postal: **Rose Cottage, Hedgeley Hall, Powburn, Alnwick, Northumberland, NE66 4HZ**
Contacts: **PHONE 01665 578647 MOBILE 07503 539571**
EMAIL hughburns123@hotmail.co.uk

1 6, B g Kalanisi (IRE)—Balinacary **Mr H. Burns**
2 **COUNTRY DELIGHTS (IRE),** 9, b m Mahler—Nadwell (IRE) **Mr H. Burns**
3 **IN HIS PRIME (IRE),** 6, b g Primary (USA)—Simply Erin (IRE) **Mr H. Burns**
4 **MASH POTATO (IRE),** 12, b g Whipper (USA)—Salva **Mr H. Burns**
5 **MAUREEN'S STAR (IRE),** 9, b m Gold Well—Serpentine Mine (IRE) **Mr H. Burns**
6 **SHADY KATIE (IRE),** 6, gr m Well Chosen—Loughaderra Rose (IRE) **Mr H. Burns**
7 **SPIRIT OF DREAMS (IRE),** 7, b m Dream Ahead (USA)—Easy To Thrill **Mr H. Burns**

---

76 **MR OWEN BURROWS, Lambourn**
Postal: **Farncombe Down Stables, Baydon Road, Lambourn Woodlands, Hungerford, Berkshire, RG17 7AQ**
Contacts: **PHONE 01488 71631**
WORK EMAIL rquinn@kingwoodhousestables.co.uk

1 **ALBASHEER (IRE)**, 4, ch c Shamardal (USA)—Mutebah (IRE) **Shadwell Estate Company Ltd**
2 **ANMAAT (IRE)**, 4, b g Awtaad (IRE)—African Moonlight (UAE) **Shadwell Estate Company Ltd**
3 **HUKUM (IRE)**, 5, b h Sea The Stars (IRE)—Aghareed (USA) **Shadwell Estate Company Ltd**
4 **MINZAAL (IRE)**, 4, b c Mehmas (IRE)—Pardoven (IRE) **Shadwell Estate Company Ltd**
5 **MURAAD (IRE)**, 6, gr g Dark Angel (IRE)—Hidden Girl (IRE) **Shadwell Estate Company Ltd**

THREE-YEAR-OLDS

6 **ALFLAILA**, b c Dark Angel (IRE)—Adhwaa **Shadwell Estate Company Ltd**
7 **ALSAAQY (IRE)**, ro c Sea The Stars (IRE)—Natagora (FR) **Shadwell Estate Company Ltd**
8 B f Exceed And Excel (AUS)—Bahjtee **Sheikh Ahmed Al Maktoum**
9 **BAYRAQ (USA)**, ch c Kitten's Joy (USA)—Fly Past **Shadwell Estate Company Ltd**
10 **MEREDIF**, b f Muhaarar—Moonlit Garden (IRE) **Sheikh Ahmed Al Maktoum**
11 B f Muhaarar—Nasmatt **Sheikh Ahmed Al Maktoum**
12 B c Dark Angel (IRE)—Soraaya (IRE) **Sheikh Ahmed Al Maktoum**
13 **WASHRAA (IRE)**, b f Ribchester (IRE)—Aneedah (IRE) **Sheikh Ahmed Al Maktoum**
14 **ZAGHAAREED**, b f Intello (GER)—Aghareed (USA) **Shadwell Estate Company Ltd**

TWO-YEAR-OLDS

15 B f 08/03 Dubawi (IRE)—Alaflaak (USA) (War Front (USA)) **Shadwell Estate Company Ltd**
16 **ANA EMARAATY**, b c 22/02 Acclamation—Inpromptu (IRE) (Cacique (IRE)) (25000) **A. Al Shaikh**
17 B c 22/02 Siyouni (FR)—Anasheed (Frankel) **Shadwell Estate Company Ltd**
18 B c 09/04 Kodiac—Deleyla (Acclamation) **Sheikh Ahmed Al Maktoum**
19 B c 18/02 Showcasing—Evita Peron (Pivotal) (105000) **Sheikh Ahmed Al Maktoum**
20 **HEILAY YA MLAY (IRE)**, b c 04/04 Expert Eye—Soft Ice (Kingmambo (USA)) **A. Al Shaikh**
21 Ch c 14/03 Dubawi (IRE)—Into The Mystic (IRE) (Galileo (IRE)) **Sheikh Ahmed Al Maktoum**
22 Ch f 28/03 Iffraaj—Lady of Persia (JPN) (Shamardal (USA)) **Sheikh Ahmed Al Maktoum**
23 B f 24/03 Kingman—Mudawanah (Dansili) **Shadwell Estate Company Ltd**
24 B f 25/03 Dubawi (IRE)—Mutebah (IRE) (Marju (IRE)) **Shadwell Estate Company Ltd**
25 B c 26/03 Churchill (IRE)—Myturn (IRE) (Rock of Gibraltar (IRE)) (160000) **Sheikh Ahmed Al Maktoum**
26 B f 18/03 Dandy Man (IRE)—Ocean Myth (Acclamation) (77000) **Sheikh Ahmed Al Maktoum**
27 B c 20/03 Exceed And Excel (AUS)—Raaqyah (USA) (Elusive Quality (USA)) **Sheikh Ahmed Al Maktoum**
28 B c 04/02 Lope de Vega (IRE)—Romaana (Iffraaj) **Sheikh Ahmed Al Maktoum**
29 Ro f 28/04 Mastercraftsman (IRE)—Soraaya (Elnadim (USA)) **Sheikh Ahmed Al Maktoum**
30 Ch f 12/04 Siyouni (FR)—Wohileh (Cape Cross (IRE)) **Sheikh Ahmed Al Maktoum**

Assistant Trainer: Robert McDowall.

---

77 **MR JOHN BUTLER, Newmarket**
Postal: **The Cottage, Charnwood Stables, Hamilton Road, Newmarket, Suffolk, CB8 7JQ**
Contacts: **MOBILE 07764 999743**
EMAIL johnbutler1@btinternet.com

1 4, B g Helmet (AUS)—A Lulu Ofa Menifee (USA)
2 **ADMODUM (USA)**, 9, ch g Majestic Warrior (USA)—Unbridled Treasure (USA) **Mr A. Campbell**
3 **ALBA DE TORMES (IRE)**, 4, gr g Lope de Vega (IRE)—Danaskaya (IRE) **Mr D. J. Cupit**
4 **ARABESCATO**, 5, gr g Outstrip—Cat Hunter **D. Cohen**
5 **AVARICE (IRE)**, 5, b g Zoffany (IRE)—Spirit Watch (IRE) **Power Geneva Ltd**
6 **CIGOLI (IRE)**, 5, b g Galileo (IRE)—Posset **Mr J. Butler**
7 **CONNEMERA QUEEN**, 9, ch m Major Cadeaux—Cashleen (USA) **Power Geneva Ltd**
8 **COURTSIDE (FR)**, 7, ch g Siyouni (FR)—Memoire (FR) **Power Geneva Ltd**

MR JOHN BUTLER - continued

9 **CURRANAITOR,** 4, ch f French Navy—Costa Del Fortune (IRE) **Power Geneva Ltd**
10 **DECLARING LOVE,** 5, gr m Dubawi (IRE)—Wedding March (IRE) **Miss M. L. Evans**
11 **FAIR POWER (IRE),** 8, b g Power—Pitrizzia **Mr N. Holmes**
12 **FARHAN (IRE),** 4, b c Zoffany (IRE)—Market Forces **Mr N. Buresli**
13 **GOLD COAST (IRE),** 5, ch g Galileo (IRE)—Come To Heel (IRE) **Mr A. A. A. Bin Ghalita Almheiri**
14 **GREYED FIRST (IRE),** 4, gr f Fascinating Rock (IRE)—Grey Thou Art (IRE) **Mr J. Butler**
15 **HAVEONEYERSELF (IRE),** 7, b g Requinto (IRE)—Charismas Birthday (IRE) **Mr J. Butler**
16 **INAAM (IRE),** 9, b g Camacho—Duckmore Bay (IRE) **Power Geneva Ltd**
17 **IT'S A LOVE THING,** 4, b g Intrinsic—Lady Kyllar **Mr D. Pittack**
18 **IVASECRET (IRE),** 4, b g Ivawood (IRE)—Ziggy's Secret **C Benham/ D Whitford/ L Quinn/ K Quinn**
19 **IZAR (GER),** 4, ch g Isfahan (GER)—Irun (GER) **Miss S. B. Nakelski**
20 **KATALAN (GER),** 9, b g Adlerflug (GER)—Kalla **Mr J. Butler**
21 **KING CRIMSON,** 10, ch g Captain Gerrard (IRE)—Elegant Lady **Power Brothers**
22 **KINGSLEY KLARION (IRE),** 9, b g Arcano (IRE)—May Day Queen (IRE) **Madeira Racing**
23 **KNIGHT OF KINGS,** 4, b g New Approach (IRE)—Night Lily (IRE) **Mr K. Snell**
24 **LASTING BEAUTY (FR),** 4, gr f Dark Angel (IRE)—War Effort (USA) **Mr J. Butler**
25 **LIGHT LILY,** 5, ch m Iffraaj—Night Lily (IRE) **Mr K. Snell**
26 **LIMITED EDITION,** 4, b g Al Kazeem—Hope And Fortune (IRE) **K. J. Quinn**
27 **LUCKY BE,** 4, b f Nathaniel (IRE)—Where's Susie **Recycled Products Limited**
28 **MARTINEO,** 7, b g Declaration of War (USA)—Woodland Scene (IRE) **Power Geneva Ltd**
29 **MUTARABBY (IRE),** 8, ch g Tamayuz—Shaarfa (USA) **Whiterok Ltd**
30 **NEVER SURRENDER (IRE),** 8, b g High Chaparral (IRE)—Meiosis (USA) **Mr A. Campbell**
31 **NO DIGGITY (IRE),** 6, b g Sir Prancealot (IRE)—Monarchy (IRE) **R Reed, L Reed R Favarulo**
32 **POWER ON (IRE),** 4, b g Power—Intermittent **Rowley Racing & Partner**
33 **PRECISELY,** 5, b m Al Kazeem—Easter Diva (IRE) **C Benham/ D Whitford/ L Quinn/ K Quinn**
34 5, B m First Samurai (USA)—Principle Equation (IRE) **Mrs A. J. Nicol**
35 **QUTEY ZEE (IRE),** 5, b m Ivawood (IRE)—Cute Cait **Mr J. Butler**
36 **RHYTHM N ROCK (IRE),** 4, b c Fascinating Rock (IRE)—Rythmic **Newtown Anner Stud Farm Ltd**
37 **SEAS OF ELZAAM (IRE),** 5, b g Elzaam (AUS)—Ocean Sands (IRE) **Power Geneva Ltd**
38 **SILVERHILL STAMP (IRE),** 5, b g Getaway (GER)—Tramp Stamp (IRE) **Level Par Racing**
39 **SOAR ABOVE,** 7, gr ro g Lethal Force (IRE)—Soar **Miss M. Bishop-Peck**
40 **SOPHAR SOGOOD (IRE),** 5, b g French Navy—Cloud Break **Rowley Racing**
41 **SPLIT ELEVENS,** 4, b g Ajaya—Woodland Scene (IRE) **Mr D. James**
42 **STRATEGIC FORTUNE (IRE),** 5, b g Power—Jenniings (IRE) **B. N. Fulton**
43 **SWEET BERTIE (IRE),** 4, ch g Dandy Man (IRE)—Tartiflette **Power Brothers**
44 **SWISS ROWE (IRE),** 4, b g Swiss Spirit—Hucking Hot **Level Par Racing**
45 **TIME TO SEA (IRE),** 8, b g Born To Sea (IRE)—Eastern Glow **C Benham/ D Whitford/ L Quinn/ K Quinn**
46 **UZINCSO,** 6, b g Mayson—Capacious **Recycled Products Limited**
47 **WARRIOR GODDESS,** 7, b m Henrythenavigator (USA)—Azenzar **Mr J. Butler**
48 **WELOOF (FR),** 8, b g Redoute's Choice (AUS)—Peinted Song (USA) **Power Geneva Ltd**
49 **WINDRUSH SONG,** 5, b m Gentlewave (IRE)—Dayia (IRE) **Lady J. Green**

THREE-YEAR-OLDS

50 **ANNULMENT (IRE),** b c Fascinating Rock (IRE)—Imdancinwithurwife (IRE)
51 **BRAZEN GIRL,** b f Brazen Beau (AUS)—Easter Diva (IRE) **K. J. Quinn**
52 **CONTROL,** b f Havana Gold (IRE)—Love And Cherish (IRE) **Mr N. Buresli**
53 **DESIGNER,** ch f Pearl Secret—Curly Come Home **Mr A. L. Al Zeer**
54 **HAKU (IRE),** b c Dragon Pulse (IRE)—Quiania (USA) **Level Par Racing**
55 **MEASURED MOMENTS,** b f Time Test—Hope And Fortune (IRE) **K. J. Quinn**
56 **MIDNIGHT GLOW (IRE),** b f Fascinating Rock (IRE)—Campfire Glow (IRE) **Newtown Anner Stud Farm Ltd**
57 B f Mount Nelson—Mountain Law (USA) **Mrs A. J. Nicol**
58 **MUSKATEER ONE,** b f Charm Spirit (IRE)—Satulagi (USA) **Miss M. L. Evans**
59 **MUSKATEER TWO,** b f Slade Power (IRE)—Scattered Petals (IRE) **Miss M. L. Evans**
60 B f Speightstown (USA)—Principle Equation (IRE) **Mrs A. J. Nicol**
61 B c Zoffany (IRE)—Red Stars (IRE) **Mr J. Butler**
62 B g Due Diligence (USA)—Showbizzy **Mr J. Butler**
63 B c Gleneagles (IRE)—So In Love **Mr J. Butler**
64 **SOLANNA,** ch c Helmet (AUS)—Night Lily (IRE) **Mr K. Snell**
65 **STANDARDS (IRE),** b f Fast Company (IRE)—Alerted (USA) **Mr N. Buresli**

MR JOHN BUTLER - continued

66 **STRANGE CARGO (IRE)**, ch g Camacho—Fancy Feathers (IRE) **M M Stables**
67 **THATSTHEFINEST (IRE)**, b g Camacho—Not Misbegotten (IRE) **Mr J. Butler**
68 **TOTAL LOCKDOWN**, b g Finjaan—Diamondsaretrumps (IRE) **Mr R. Favarulo**

Other Owners: Mr C. F. Benham, Mr J. Butler, Mr P. A. Cafferty, Mr P. W. D'Arcy, Mrs S. I. D'Arcy, Mr R. Favarulo, Mrs S. Horne, K. J. Quinn, Mr L. M. Quinn, K. Quinn/ C. Benham, Mrs E. J. Reed, R. W. Reed, Rowley Racing, Mr D. Tiernan, Mr D. L. Whitford.

Assistant Trainer: Alice Haynes.

---

78 MR PADDY BUTLER, Lewes
Postal: **Homewood Gate Racing Stables, Novington Lane, East Chiltington, Lewes, East Sussex, BN7 3AU**
Contacts: **PHONE 01273 890124 MOBILE 07973 873846**
EMAIL homewoodgate@aol.com

1 **AHORSECALLEDWANDA**, 5, b m Music Master—Lady Mascot (IRE) **Mrs E. Lucey-Butler**
2 **ART OF AMERICA**, 7, br g American Post—Marigay's Magic **Mrs E. A. Elliott**
3 **ENGAGING SAM**, 5, ch g Casamento (IRE)—Engaging **Mrs E. Lucey-Butler**
4 **ESTIBDAAD (IRE)**, 12, b g Haatef (USA)—Star of Siligo (USA) **Miss M. P. Bryant**
5 **FRANZI FURY (IRE)**, 7, b m Carlo Bank (IRE)—Sara Cara (IRE) **Homewoodgate Racing Club**
6 **HARAZ (IRE)**, 9, b g Acclamation—Hanakiyya (IRE) **Christopher W Wilson & Partner**
7 **JUMPING JACK (IRE)**, 8, b g Sir Prancealot (IRE)—She's A Character **Homewoodgate Racing Club**
8 **MERCERS**, 8, b m Piccolo—Ivory's Joy **Homewoodgate Racing Club**
9 **REMEMBERTHETITANS**, 6, ch g Bated Breath—Summers Lease **Miss M. P. Bryant**
10 **UAE SOLDIER (USA)**, 7, b g Dansili—Time On **Mrs E. Lucey-Butler**

Other Owners: Mrs E. Lucey-Butler, C. W. Wilson.

Assistant Trainer: Mrs E Lucey-Butler.

Amateur Jockey: Miss M. Bryant, Miss J. Oliver.

---

79 MRS BARBARA BUTTERWORTH, Appleby
Postal: **Bolton Mill, Bolton, Appleby-in-Westmorland, Cumbria, CA16 6AL**
Contacts: **PHONE 017683 61363 MOBILE 07778 104118**

1 **AGE OF GLORY**, 13, b g Zamindar (USA)—Fleeting Moon **Miss E. Butterworth**
2 **CHERRY PRINCESS**, 12, gr m Act One—Francia **Mrs B. Butterworth**
3 **COEUR AIMANT (FR)**, 7, b g Maresca Sorrento (FR)—Babet (IRE) **Mrs B. Butterworth**
4 **KITTY HALL (IRE)**, 8, b m Fame And Glory—Set In Her Ways (IRE) **Miss E. Butterworth**
5 **SNOWED IN (IRE)**, 13, gr g Dark Angel (IRE)—Spinning Gold **Miss E. Butterworth**
6 **SUBTLE INNUENDO (IRE)**, 4, gr g Lawman (FR)—Whistling Straits (FR) **Miss E. Butterworth**
7 **THATSY (FR)**, 8, gr g Martaline—Rainallday (FR) **Mrs B. Butterworth**

Assistant Trainer: Miss Elizabeth Butterworth.

NH Jockey: Sean Quinlan.

80 MISS JULIE CAMACHO, Malton

Postal: **Star Cottage, Welham Road, Norton, Malton, North Yorkshire, YO17 9QE**
Contacts: **PHONE 01653 696205 MOBILE 07950 356440, 07779 318135 FAX 01653 696205
EMAIL julie@jacracing.co.uk WEBSITE www.juliecamacho.com**

1 **ARMY OF INDIA (IRE)**, 4, gr g Sepoy (AUS)—Sudfah (USA) **Ian Clements & Julie Camacho**
2 **BABA REZA**, 4, ch g Garswood—Friendship Is Love **Judy & Richard Peck**
3 **BALLYCONNEELY BAY (IRE)**, 4, b g Fast Company (IRE)—Kathy Sun (IRE) **Mr M. B. Hughes**
4 **BIG LES (IRE)**, 7, b g Big Bad Bob (IRE)—Love Match **Stockdale Racing**
5 **BILL CODY (IRE)**, 7, b g Declaration of War (USA)—Call This Cat (IRE) **Judy & Richard Peck**
6 **BRIDGETOWN**, 4, br g Mayson—Marigot Bay **Owners Group 069**
7 **BURTONWOOD**, 10, b g Acclamation—Green Poppy **Judy & Richard Peck & Partner**
8 **CAPTAIN CORELLI (IRE)**, 5, ch g Anjaal—Disprove (IRE) **Judy & Richard Peck**
9 **DELUXE MUSIC**, 5, b m Lope de Vega (IRE)—Divergence (IRE) **G. B. Turnbull Ltd**
10 **I KNOW HOW (IRE)**, 7, b g Epaulette (AUS)—Blue Crystal (IRE) **Judy & Richard Peck & Partner**
11 **JUDICIAL (IRE)**, 10, b g Iffraaj—Marlinka **Elite Racing Club**
12 **LAZYITIS**, 4, b f Swiss Spirit—Horsforth **Morecool Racing**
13 **LOOK OUT LOUIS**, 6, b g Harbour Watch (IRE)—Perfect Act **Miss Victoria Watt & Graeme Howard**
14 **LOWESWATER**, 4, b f Adaay (IRE)—Oilinda **Miss J. A. Camacho**
15 **MAKANAH**, 7, b g Mayson—Diane's Choice **Axom LXXI**
16 **MAKEEN**, 5, b g Dubawi (IRE)—Estidraaj (USA) **Verity, Pritchard & Simpson**
17 **MAPLE JACK**, 4, ch c Mayson—Porcelain (IRE) **Owners Group 075**
18 **NORTHBOUND (IRE)**, 4, b g Fast Company (IRE)—Natalisa (IRE) **Edwards Harland & Hitchman**
19 **PROCLAIMER**, 5, b g Free Eagle (IRE)—Pious **Owners Group 033**
20 **QAASID (IRE)**, 4, b g Awtaad (IRE)—Nisriyna (IRE) **Mr M. B. Hughes**
21 **QUEST FOR FUN**, 4, ch g Lope de Vega (IRE)—Craic Agus Spraoi (IRE) **Mr & Mrs G. Turnbull**
22 **RAATEA**, 5, b g Invincible Spirit (IRE)—Darajaat (USA) **Mr M. B. Hughes**
23 **RIGGSBY (IRE)**, 4, b g Acclamation—Silk Affair (IRE) **The Hands & Heels Partnership**
24 **RONGWAYRILEY (IRE)**, 5, ch g Farhh—Caerlonore (IRE) **S & J Camacho**
25 **SECRET EQUITY**, 5, ch m Equiano (FR)—Secret Charge **Mr B. A. McGarrigle**
27 **SHAKE A LEG (IRE)**, 5, b g Excelebration (IRE)—Sos Brillante (CHI) **Hey Ho**
27 **SEPARATE**, 5, b m Cable Bay (IRE)—Miss Moses (USA) **Martin Hughes & Mark Murphy**
28 **THE GREY BAY (IRE)**, 5, gr g Gutaifan (IRE)—Coursing **Judy & Richard Peck**
29 **WETHER FELL**, 5, b g Due Diligence (USA)—Triveni (FR) **Miss J. A. Camacho**

THREE-YEAR-OLDS

30 **BOASTED**, b f Showcasing—Tinted (IRE) **Mr M. B. Hughes**
31 **BURNING EMOTION**, b f Mondialiste (IRE)—Flame Out **Mr & Mrs G. Turnbull**
32 **DIRTY LEEDS**, b c Swiss Spirit—New Road Side **Morecool Racing**
33 **EASTER ISLAND**, b g Teofilo (IRE)—Pacific Pride (USA) **Mr & Mrs G. Turnbull**
34 **ENRAGED**, b f Adaay (IRE)—Little Lady Katie (IRE) **Mr A Barnes & Cliff Stud**
35 **FELIX ADLER**, b f Mondialiste (IRE)—Craic Agus Spraoi (IRE) **Mr & Mrs G. Turnbull**
36 **FLASH THE DASH (IRE)**, b c Estidhkaar (IRE)—Anamarka **Cliff Stud Limited**
37 **HELPFUL**, b c Oasis Dream—Magic (IRE) **Mr M. B. Hughes**
38 **INSPIRATIONELLIE (IRE)**, ch f Dandy Man (IRE)—Bahamian Wishes (IRE) **Judy & Richard Peck**
39 **LESS IS MORE**, b f Tamayuz—Vassaria (IRE) **Miss J. A. Camacho**
40 **MISTER FALSETTO**, b c Twilight Son—Bint Arcano (FR) **Edwards, Rush & Camacho**
41 **NEVERBATSANEYELID**, b f Due Diligence (USA)—Lady Lube Rye (IRE) **D. & S. L. Tanker Transport Limited**
42 **RED HOW**, ch f Equiano (FR)—Diane's Choice **G B Turnbull Ltd & Julie Camacho**
43 **ROSHAMBO**, b f Due Diligence (USA)—Horsforth **Morecool Racing**
44 **RUGGLES**, b f Exceed And Excel (AUS)—Madame Defarge (IRE) **Mr N. Edwards**
45 **WORLD CRUISE**, b g Mondialiste (IRE)—Ocean Princess (IRE) **Mr & Mrs G. Turnbull**

Other Owners: Hon T. W. Barber, A. R. Barnes, Mr S. Bland, Miss J. A. Camacho, Mrs S. Camacho, Mr I. R. Clements, Cliff Stud Limited, Mr E. Cosgrove, Mr J. J. Cosgrove, Mr N. Edwards, G. B. Turnbull Ltd, Mr G. Harland, Mr D. P. Harrison, Mr R. Heath, Mr S. Hitchman, Mr G. P. Howard, Mrs J. M. Peck, Judy & Richard Peck, Mr R. S. Peck, Mrs R. E. Pritchard, Mrs D. J. Rush, Mrs J. K. Simpson, Mr P. Simpson, Mr M. N. Slater, Mr C. Verity, Miss V. Watt.

Assistant Trainer: Steve Brown. **Flat Jockey:** Paul Mulrennan, Callum Rodriguez.

81 **MR MARK CAMPION, Malton**
Postal: **Whitewell House Stables, Whitewall, Malton, North Yorkshire, YO17 9EH**
Contacts: **PHONE 01653 692729 MOBILE 07973 178311 FAX 01653 600066**
EMAIL info@markcampion-racing.com WEBSITE www.markcampion-racing.com

1 BALLYWOOD (FR), 8, b g Ballingarry (IRE)—Miss Hollywood (FR) **Whitewall Racing**
2 BURGUNDY MAN (FR), 5, b g Manduro (GER)—Kapirovska (FR) **Whitewall Racing**
3 CIVIL ENSIGN (FR), 8, b g Rob Roy (USA)—Petillante Royale (FR) **Whitewall Racing**
4 DINONS (FR), 9, b g Balko (FR)—Beni Abbes (FR) **Whitewall Racing**
5 ISLE OF OIR (IRE), 8, b g Gold Well—Patsy Cline (IRE) **Whitewall Racing**
6 LAAFY (USA), 6, b g Noble Mission—Miner's Secret (USA) **Whitewall Racing**
7 LAXEY (IRE), 8, b g Yeats (IRE)—Nerissa (IRE) **Whitewall Racing**
8 LORD WARBURTON (IRE), 5, ch g Zoffany (IRE)—Portrait of A Lady (IRE) **Whitewall Racing**
9 MELDRUM WAY (IRE), 9, b g Getaway (GER)—Meldrum Hall (IRE) **Mark Campion Racing Club**
10 MOUNTAIN RAPID (IRE), 10, ch m Getaway (GER)—Founding Daughter (IRE) **Whitewall Racing**
11 SE YOU, 7, b g Sepoy (AUS)—Lady Hestia (USA) **Mark Campion Racing Club**
12 TROIS BON AMIS (IRE), 8, gr g Lilbourne Lad (IRE)—Vanozza (FR) **Whitewall Racing**

Assistant Trainer: Mrs F. Campion.

---

82 **MS JENNIE CANDLISH, Leek**
Postal: **Basford Grange Farm, Basford, Leek, Staffordshire, ST13 7ET**
Contacts: **PHONE 07925 825134, 07889 413639 FAX 01538 360324**
EMAIL jenniecandlish@yahoo.co.uk WEBSITE www.jenniecandlishracing.co.uk

1 ANNIES PRAYER (IRE), 5, b g Sageburg (IRE)—Slate Lady (IRE) **Brian Verinder & Alan Baxter**
2 ASK THE JUDGE (IRE), 6, ch g Ask—Connemara Kate (IRE) **Ms J. Candlish**
3 BARNAY, 7, b g Nayef (USA)—Barnezet (GR) **D. Ashbrook**
4 BASFORD (IRE), 5, b g Soldier of Fortune (IRE)—Be My Present **Brian Verinder & Alan Baxter**
5 BRIDGE ROAD (IRE), 6, b g Sholokhov (IRE)—Lucy's Legend (IRE) **Alan Baxter & Brian Hall**
6 CADDYHILL (IRE), 7, b g Arcadio (GER)—Ring Hill **J. L. Marriott**
7 CATCHMEIFYOUCAN (IRE), 8, b m Touch of Land (FR)—Irish Honey (IRE) **A Baxter, C Burke & N Sobreperez**
8 CHEDDLETON, 7, br g Shirocco (GER)—Over Sixty **Mr P. & Mrs G. A. Clarke**
9 CLICK AND COLLECT, 10, b g Humbel (USA)—Galena (GER) **D. Ashbrook**
10 COSHESTON, 9, ch g Black Sam Bellamy (IRE)—Rare Ruby (IRE) **Mrs J. M. Ratcliff**
11 CRACK DU NINIAN (FR), 7, b g Le Houssais (FR)—Syphaline (FR) **Mr P. & Mrs G. A. Clarke**
12 FOLLOW YOUR FIRE (IRE), 7, b g Le Fou (FR)—Jollie Bollie (IRE) **Jennie Candlish & Jillian McKeown**
13 FOR JIM (IRE), 10, gr g Milan—Dromhale Lady (IRE) **Ms J. Candlish**
14 FORTIFIED BAY (IRE), 10, b g Makfi—Divergence (USA) **Alan Baxter & Terry Hastie**
15 GETAWAY GLENDA (IRE), 7, b br m Getaway (GER)—Dangan Juliet (IRE) **Don't tell the girls**
16 GOLAN CLOUD (IRE), 9, b g Golan (IRE)—Mite Be Cloudy (IRE) **Ms J. Candlish**
17 HACHERT, 5, b g Lope de Vega (IRE)—Sense of Joy **Jonathan & Catherine Williams**
18 HAPPY HOLLOW, 10, b g Beat Hollow—Dombeya (IRE) **Alan Baxter & Jennie Candlish**
19 IT'S GOOD TO LAUGH (IRE), 5, b g Tamayuz—London Plane (IRE) **Brian Verinder & Alan Baxter**
20 LIGNOU (FR), 7, b g Rajsaman (FR)—Lady Meydan (FR) **Alan Baxter & Brian Hall**
21 MARTHA YEATS (IRE), 7, b m Yeats (IRE)—Stratosphere **Mrs F. M. Draper**
22 MCGOWAN'S PASS, 11, b g Central Park (IRE)—Function Dreamer **Mrs A. E. Lee**
23 MINT CONDITION, 8, b g Black Sam Bellamy (IRE)—Winning Counsel (IRE) **Whites Property Limited**
24 NAYWAY, 5, b g Nayef (USA)—Sharway Lady **W. Cox**
25 NERO ROCK (IRE), 7, b g Shirocco (GER)—Gilt Benefit (IRE) **J. L. Marriott**
26 OSCARS LEADER (IRE), 9, b g Oscar (IRE)—Lead'er Inn (IRE) **J. L. Marriott**
27 PAKIE'S DREAM (IRE), 8, b g Arcadio (GER)—Emily's Princess (IRE) **Alan Baxter & Jennie Candlish**
28 QUICK PICK (IRE), 11, b g Vinnie Roe (IRE)—Oscars Arrow (IRE) **4 Left Footers & A Blewnose**
29 RED GIANT (IRE), 11, ch g Beneficial—Barrack Star (IRE) **Mr V. A. Healy**
30 STOP TALKING (IRE), 10, b m Gamut (IRE)—Miss Snapdragon (IRE) **Anthony,Barrett,Baxter,Corbett,Deane,Lloyd**
31 TANARPINO, 11, ch g Tobougg (IRE)—Got Tune (FR) **Mr P. & Mrs G. A. Clarke**

MS JENNIE CANDLISH - continued

32 **TOO MUCH TO ASK (IRE)**, 9, b g Ask—Chinara (IRE) **Whites Property Limited**
33 **ULVERSTON (IRE)**, 7, b g Yeats (IRE)—So Supreme (IRE) **Mr P. & Mrs G. A. Clarke**
34 **ZOLFO (IRE)**, 10, gr g Cloudings (IRE)—Hardy Lamb (IRE) **Matt Barrett & Alan Baxter**
35 **ZUCKERBERG (GER)**, 6, b g Kamsin (GER)—Zazera (FR) **J. L. Marriott**

Other Owners: Mr M. Barrett, Mr A. J. Baxter, Mr C. Burke, Ms J. Candlish, Mrs G. A. Clarke, Mr P. Clarke, Mr B. J. Hall, Mr T. Hastie, Mrs J. McKeown, Mr N. Sobreperez, Mr B. W. Verinder, Mrs C. Williams, Mr J. Williams.

Assistant Trainer: Alan O'Keeffe.

Flat Jockey: Joe Fanning. **NH Jockey:** Sean Quinlan.

83	**MR HENRY CANDY, Wantage** Postal: **Kingstone Warren, Wantage, Oxfordshire, OX12 9QF** Contacts: **PHONE 01367 820276 MOBILE 07836 211264** EMAIL henrycandy@btconnect.com

1 **ALFRED BOUCHER**, 6, gr g Aussie Rules (USA)—Policy Term (IRE) **Mr R. Allcock**
2 **BIBULOUS (IRE)**, 4, b g Camacho—Cant Hurry Love **Mr A. Davis**
3 **BY STARLIGHT (IRE)**, 5, b m Sea The Stars (IRE)—Step Lightly (IRE) **Mr A. Davis**
4 **FOUR FEET (IRE)**, 6, b g Harbour Watch (IRE)—Royal Connection **Henry D. N. B Candy**
5 **GEORGE MORLAND**, 4, b c Camacho—Baharah (USA) **Mr R. Allcock**
6 **HOORAY HENRY**, 5, gr g Brazen Beau (AUS)—All That Jas (IRE) **Henry D. N. B Candy**
7 **LUCKY BAY**, 4, b f Beat Hollow—Free Offer **Earl Cadogan**
8 **MAIDEN CASTLE**, 6, b g Nayef (USA)—Danae **Girsonfield Ltd**
9 **PEARL BAY**, 4, b f Cable Bay (IRE)—Pavonine **Henry Candy & Partners V**
10 **POLLINATE**, 4, b f Oasis Dream—Spring Fling **Henry D. N. B Candy**
11 **RING OF LIGHT**, 4, gr g Mayson—Silver Halo **T A Frost & Simon Broke & Partners**
12 **RUN TO FREEDOM**, 4, b c Muhaarar—Twilight Mistress **G. A. Wilson**
13 **SOVEREIGN DUKE (GER)**, 7, b g Jukebox Jury (IRE)—Shadow Queen (GER) **One Too Many Partners**
14 **SOVEREIGN SLIPPER**, 4, b c Charm Spirit (IRE)—Last Slipper **Mr D B Clark & Mr H Candy**
15 **TWILIGHT CALLS**, 4, b g Twilight Son—Zawiyah **Cheveley Park Stud Limited**
16 **UNFOOLISH (IRE)**, 4, b f Fastnet Rock (AUS)—Foolish Act (IRE) **Mr A. Davis**

THREE-YEAR-OLDS

17 **AUTUMNAL DANCER (IRE)**, gr f El Kabeir (USA)—Autumn Tide (IRE) **Autumn Decs**
18 **BOMBINATE**, b g Cable Bay (IRE)—Rock Follies **Mr A. Davis**
19 **BRUSH CREEK**, b f Twilight Son—Resort **Cheveley Park Stud Limited**
20 **BUSSELTON**, b g Dark Angel (IRE)—Pirouette **Earl Cadogan**
21 **CENTRE DRIVE**, b f Iffraaj—Upper Street (IRE) **Major M. G. Wyatt**
22 **CHANGE OF FORTUNE**, ch g Cityscape—Secret Dream (IRE) **Fortune Racing**
23 **CLOUD CUCKOO**, b g Mayson—Crimson Cloud **Henry D. N. B Candy**
24 **CYRUS KINGOFPERSIA**, b g Holy Roman Emperor (IRE)—La Persiana **Mr T. V. Speight**
25 **HEARTBREAK LASS**, b f Cotai Glory—Motion Lass **Mr A. Davis**
26 **JACK LESLIE**, b g Twilight Son—Fenella Rose **P. G. Jacobs**
27 **NEPHALIST (IRE)**, b f Elzaam (AUS)—Cant Hurry Love **Mr A. Davis**
28 **NIARBYL BAY**, b g Nayef (USA)—Danae **Girsonfield Ltd**
29 **NIVELLE'S MAGIC**, b f Hellvelyn—Nihal (IRE) **Mr M. V. Aram, Henry D. N. B Candy**
30 **PENGUIN ISLAND**, b f The Gurkha (IRE)—In Secret **Earl Cadogan**
31 **RAVELLO SUNSET**, b g Twilight Son—Amalfi (IRE) **Henry D. N. B Candy**
32 **RENOIR**, b c Nathaniel (IRE)—Feis Ceoil (IRE) **Mr R. Allcock**
33 **SAINTE COLETTE**, gr f Mastercraftsman (IRE)—La Chapelle (IRE) **T A Frost, Candy, Clayton & Lamb**
34 **SIR PHILIP**, b g Heeraat (IRE)—Sea of Hope (IRE) **Mr A. Davis**
35 **TWILIGHT MISCHIEF**, b f Twilight Son—Cardrona **Candy, Pritchard & Thomas**

MR HENRY CANDY - continued

TWO-YEAR-OLDS
36 **ARAMINTA**, ch f 23/04 Gleneagles (IRE)—Mince (Medicean) (82000) **St Albans Bloodstock, Acloque & Frost**
37 **CAPE VINCENT**, b g 13/05 Kuroshio (AUS)—Cape Violet (IRE) (Cape Cross (IRE)) **Henry D. N. B Candy**
38 **COVETABLE**, b f 28/01 Twilight Son—Invaluable (Invincible Spirit (IRE)) **Cheveley Park Stud Limited**
39 B f 12/02 Aclaim (IRE)—Dream On Me (GER) (Kendargent (FR)) (27619) **Mr A. Davis**
40 **FITZROY RIVER**, b f 17/03 Oasis Dream—In Secret (Dalakhani (IRE)) **Earl Cadogan**
41 **GOSMORE**, b f 21/03 Oasis Dream—Gosbeck (Dubawi (IRE)) **Major M. G. Wyatt**
42 **HIGH SPIRITED**, b f 05/04 Belardo (IRE)—Spirited Charm (Invincible Spirit (IRE)) (45000) **T. A. F. Frost**
43 B f 29/03 Zoustar (AUS)—Pearly Spirit (FR) (Invincible Spirit (IRE)) (18000) **Mr Clive Brandon**
44 B f 16/03 Aclaim (IRE)—Quiet Protest (USA) (Kingmambo (USA)) (47619) **Mr A. Davis**
45 B f 18/03 Harry Angel (IRE)—Totally Lost (IRE) (Rip Van Winkle (IRE)) **Henry D. N. B Candy**
46 **TWIZ**, b f 10/02 Twilight Son—Ortiz (Havana Gold (IRE)) **P. G. Jacobs**
47 **WALL GAME**, b g 11/03 Shalaa (IRE)—Wall of Light (Zamindar (USA)) (8000) **Henry D. N. B Candy**

Assistant Trainer: Amy Scott.

---

84 MR GRANT CANN, Lower Hamswell
Postal: **Park Field, Hall Lane, Lower Hamswell, Bath, Gloucestershire, BA1 9DE**
Contacts: **PHONE 01225 891674 MOBILE 07968 271118**

1 **CADEAU DU BRESIL (FR)**, 10, b g Blue Bresil (FR)—Melanie du Chenet (FR) **J. G. Cann**
2 **DISTANT VIEW**, 5, b m Telescope (IRE)—Ruby Crown **J. G. Cann**
3 **LADY STANHOW**, 7, br m Getaway (GER)—Loxhill Lady **J. G. Cann**
4 **MR PALM (IRE)**, 7, ch g Mountain High (IRE)—Miss Palm (IRE) **Mrs P. J. Pengelly**
5 **QUEEN OF THE COURT (IRE)**, 9, b m Court Cave (IRE)—Waydale Hill **J. G. Cann**

---

85 MR DON CANTILLON, Newmarket
Postal: **63 Exeter Road, Newmarket, Suffolk, CB8 8LP**
Contacts: **PHONE 01638 668507 MOBILE 07709 377601**

1 **ADMIRING GLANCE (IRE)**, 5, b m Shantou (USA)—As I Am (IRE) **D. E. Cantillon**
2 **BOLD VISION (IRE)**, 6, b g Shirocco (GER)—As I Am (IRE) **D. E. Cantillon**
3 4, B f Court Cave (IRE)—Faucon **D. E. Cantillon**
4 **NAVARRA PRINCESS (IRE)**, 7, b m Intense Focus (USA)—Navarra Queen **D. E. Cantillon**

THREE-YEAR-OLDS
5 **FIERCELY PROUD (IRE)**, b g Iffraaj—Estiqaama (USA) **D. E. Cantillon**

---

86 MRS LOUISA CARBERRY, Senonnes
Postal: **Les Fosses, Senonnes, Pays de la Loire, 53390, France**
Contacts: **WORK +33 6 24 86 63 69**
WORK EMAIL louisacarberryracing@gmail.com

1 **ADORABLE DE BALLON (FR)**, 6, ch m Barastraight—Nile Breeze (FR)
2 **AMANHA (FR)**, 4, b f Authorized (IRE)—My Glitters (FR)

MRS LOUISA CARBERRY - continued

3 **CADMOON (FR)**, 4, b c Spanish Moon (USA)—Cadeau de Shuil (IRE)
4 **CANICHETTE (FR)**, 5, b m Prince Gibraltar (FR)—Noanoa (FR)
5 **CESAR DE BALLON (FR)**, 5, b h Doctor Dino (FR)—Nile Altesse (FR)
6 **DINETTE DE BALLON (FR)**, 10, b m Doctor Dino (FR)—Nile Altesse (FR)
7 **DOCTEUR DE BALLON (FR)**, 10, ch g Doctor Dino (FR)—Nile Breeze (FR)
8 **GILOU JAGUEN (FR)**, 4, b g Bathyrhon (GER)—Don'aristarque (FR)
9 **GRAN DIOSE (FR)**, 6, b g Planteur (IRE)—Noanoa (FR)
10 **INVITED (FR)**, 4, b f Nidor (FR)—Baracoa
11 **IRIS DE GRUGY (FR)**, 4, b f Masterstroke (USA)—Diane de Grugy (FR)
12 **KALINSKI (IRE)**, 8, b g Kalanisi (IRE)—Blonde Ambition (IRE)
13 **KINCSEM PARK (FR)**, 5, b m Turgeon (USA)—Baracoa
14 **LADY LIZZY**, 6, ch m Rio de La Plata (USA)—Elzebieta (IRE)
15 **SOME OPERATOR (IRE)**, 8, b g September Storm (GER)—Emilies Pearl (IRE)
16 **TOP ROCK TALULA (IRE)**, 7, b m Lord Shanakill (USA)—Spirit Watch (IRE)

THREE-YEAR-OLDS

17 **RISKY GIRL (FR)**, b f Manatee—Risky Mix (FR)

| **87** | **MRS RUTH CARR, Stillington** |

Postal: **Mowbray House Farm, Easingwold Road, Stillington, York, North Yorkshire, YO61 1LT**
Contacts: WORK **01347 823776** MOBILE **07721 926772**
EMAIL **ruth@ruthcarrracing.co.uk, chrissie@ruthcarrracing.co.uk**
WEBSITE **www.ruthcarrracing.co.uk**

1 **ATHMAD (IRE)**, 6, b g Olympic Glory (IRE)—Black Mascara (IRE) **R J H Limited & Ruth Carr**
2 **BADRI**, 5, b g Dark Angel (IRE)—Penny Drops **RJH Ltd & Mr D Padgett**
3 **BOBBY JOE LEG**, 8, ch g Pastoral Pursuits—China Cherub **Mrs A. Clark**
4 **CAPTAIN CLARET**, 5, b g Medicean—Shirazz **Mrs R. A. Carr, Mrs S. J. Doyle**
5 **CITY WANDERER (IRE)**, 6, b g Kodiac—Viletta (GER) **Mrs S Hibbert & Mrs R Carr**
6 **COPPER AND FIVE**, 6, ch g Paco Boy (IRE)—Peachez **Mrs R. A. Carr, Mrs S. J. Doyle**
7 **CORNDAVON LAD (IRE)**, 5, b g Camacho—Wild Ways **G. Murray**
8 **EMBOUR (IRE)**, 7, b g Acclamation—Carpet Lady (IRE) **Formulated Polymer Products Ltd**
9 **FINAL FRONTIER (IRE)**, 9, b g Dream Ahead (USA)—Polly Perkins (IRE) **V. Khosla**
10 **FORESEEABLE FUTURE (FR)**, 7, b g Harbour Watch (IRE)—Russian Spirit **RHD & Ruth Carr**
11 **FREEDOM FLYER (IRE)**, 5, b g Invincible Spirit (IRE)—Liberating **Mrs R. A. Carr**
12 **HOSTELRY**, 5, ch m Coach House (IRE)—Queens Jubilee **Dennis Clayton & Ruth Carr**
13 **KATHEEFA (USA)**, 8, gr g Street Cry (IRE)—Wid (USA) **Mrs R. A. Carr**
14 **KYLIE RULES**, 7, br m Aussie Rules (USA)—Africa's Star (IRE) **Mr J. A. Knox and Mrs M. A. Knox**
15 **LOQUACIOUS BOY (IRE)**, 4, b g Camacho—Talkative **Mrs Marion Chapman & Mrs Ruth A. Carr**
16 **MAC MCCARTHY (IRE)**, 5, ch g Anjaal—Kitty Softpaws (IRE) **The Venturers & Mrs R Carr**
17 **MAGICAL EFFECT (IRE)**, 10, ch g New Approach (IRE)—Purple Glow (IRE) **Miss Vanessa Church**
18 **MISS CONNAISSEUR**, 4, ch f Monsieur Bond (IRE)—China Cherub **Mrs A. Clark**
19 **MONAADHIL (IRE)**, 8, b g Dark Angel (IRE)—Urban Daydream (IRE) **Mrs R. A. Carr**
20 **MUTANAASEQ (IRE)**, 7, ch g Red Jazz (USA)—Indaba (IRE) **Grange Park Racing VIII & Ruth Carr**
21 **NIGHT TERRORS (IRE)**, 4, b g Zoffany (IRE)—Dream of Tara (IRE) **G. Murray**
22 **O'REILLY'S PASS**, 5, b g Australia—Dynaglow (USA) **Mr J. A. Swinburne & Mrs Ruth A. Carr**
23 **POWER PLAYER**, 6, b g Slade Power (IRE)—Varnish **Grange Park Racing XIII & Ruth Carr**
24 **REPUTATION (IRE)**, 9, b g Royal Applause—Semaphore **Mrs K. John**
25 **RHYTHM (IRE)**, 4, b f Acclamation—Strasbourg Place **Mr D. Padgett**
26 **SEVEN FOR A POUND (USA)**, 6, b g Scat Daddy (USA)—Gimlet Witha Twist (USA) **Mr E. D. Broadwith**
27 **SPANISH ANGEL (IRE)**, 5, br g Gutaifan (IRE)—City Dazzler (IRE)
                                          Mrs R. A. Carr, Mrs M. Chapman, Mr G. A. Shields
28 **STREAK LIGHTNING (IRE)**, 5, ch g Night of Thunder (IRE)—Emreliya (IRE) **Grange Park Racing Club & Ruth Carr**
29 **SWISS ACE**, 4, b g Kingman—Swiss Lake (USA) **The Bottom Liners & Mrs R. Carr**
30 **TREVIE FOUNTAIN**, 5, b g Fountain of Youth (IRE)—Fantacise **Grange Park Racing Vii & Ruth Carr**

MRS RUTH CARR - continued

THREE-YEAR-OLDS

33 **DANBY WISKE (IRE)**, b f Dandy Man (IRE)—Serafina Sunset (IRE) **Reach For The Moon & Mrs R Carr**
34 **MAKALU (IRE)**, b g Mehmas (IRE)—Jolly Juicester (IRE) **Bruce Jamieson & Ruth Carr**
35 **MIDAS (IRE)**, ch g Galileo Gold—Keeper's Ring (USA) **The Beer Stalkers & Ruth Carr**
36 **NEXT SECOND**, b f Hot Streak (IRE)—Millisecond **J Greaves, R Willcock & Ruth Carr**
37 **PEPPER ARDEN**, b g Brazen Beau (AUS)—Scarlet Royal **Mr J. A. Knox and Mrs M. A. Knox**
38 **REIGNING PROFIT (IRE)**, ch g Profitable (IRE)—Reign (IRE) **The Chancers**
39 **SIRAJU**, b g Showcasing—Bereka **Mr S. R. Jackson**
40 **VAN ZANT**, b g Lethal Force (IRE)—Emmuska **Ged Martin Nick & Mrs R Carr**

TWO-YEAR-OLDS

41 Ch g 21/04 Pastoral Pursuits—China Cherub (Inchinor) **Mrs A. Clark**
42 **ROCKIN ROSA**, ch f 28/01 Bated Breath—Rosalie Bonheur (Siyouni (FR)) (14000) **The Beer Stalkers & Ruth Carr**
43 **SHOTLEY ROYALE**, b g 26/02 Hot Streak (IRE)—Royal Pardon (Royal Applause)
                                                        Mr J. A. Swinburne & Mrs Ruth A. Carr

Other Owners: T. J. E. Brereton, Mrs R. A. Carr, Sally & Ruth Carr, M Mrs Carr, G Shields, Mrs M. Chapman, Miss V. A. Church, Mr D. G. Clayton, Mr A. D. Crombie, Mr T. W. Deadman, Mr C. Dufferwiel, Mr F. H. Eales, Ged Martin Nick, Grange Park Racing Club, Grange Park Racing VII, Grange Park Racing VIII, Grange Park Racing XIII, Mr J. A. Greaves, J. P Hames, Mr A. R. G. Harris, Mrs S. Hibbert, Hollinbridge Partnership, Mr A. B. Jamieson, Mr D. R. Kelly, Mr P. Newell, Mr D. Padgett, R J H Limited, RHD Research Limited, A. Riaz, Mr G. A. Shields, Mr E. T. Surr, Mr J. A. Swinburne, The Beer Stalkers, The Bottom Liners, Mr R. Willcock, Mr R. W. Wilson.

Assistant Trainer: Mrs M. Chapman, **Racing Secretary:** Mrs Chrissie Skyes.

Flat Jockey: James Sullivan. **Amateur Jockey:** Miss Emily Bullock.

88	**MR DECLAN CARROLL, Malton** Postal: **Santry Stables, Langton Road, Norton, Malton, North Yorkshire, YO17 9PZ** Contacts: MOBILE **07801 553779** EMAIL **declancarrollracing@gmail.com**

1 **ASMUND (IRE)**, 5, b g Zebedee—Suffer Her (IRE) **Mrs S. A. Bryan**
2 **BALLYCOMMON (IRE)**, 4, b g Dabirsim (FR)—Luxie (IRE) **B&E Partnership**
3 **EMIYN (FR)**, 5, b g Invincible Spirit (IRE)—Edelmira (IRE) **Fab Five**
4 **FIRST COMPANY (IRE)**, 4, b g Fast Company (IRE)—Pira Palace (IRE) **Northern Marking Ltd**
5 **IRELAND'S EYE (IRE)**, 4, b g Canford Cliffs (IRE)—Sofi's Spirit (IRE) **Mrs S. A. Bryan**
6 **ISLE OF DREAMS**, 4, gr f Gutaifan (IRE)—Munaa's Dream **J. A. Duffy**
7 **JACK DANIEL (IRE)**, 4, b c Equiano (FR)—Mirdhak **Danny Fantom Racing Ltd**
8 **JACKAMUNDO (FR)**, 6, b g Fast Company (IRE)—Luxie (IRE) **Danny Fantom Racing Ltd**
9 **JAKACAN (IRE)**, 4, b g Acclamation—Masonbrook Lady (IRE) **Mr Ray Flegg & Mr John Bousfield**
10 **KING OF TONGA (IRE)**, 6, gr g Dark Angel (IRE)—Bronze Queen (IRE) **Mrs S. A. Bryan**
11 **LE CHEVAL RAPIDE (IRE)**, 4, b g Estidhkaar (IRE)—Greek Spirit (IRE) **Dreams**
12 **LOUBY LOU**, 4, b f Awtaad (IRE)—Na Zdorovie **Danny Fantom Racing Ltd**
13 **MOTAHASSEN (IRE)**, 8, br g Lonhro (AUS)—Journalist (IRE) **Mrs S. A. Bryan**
14 **MUSIC SEEKER (IRE)**, 8, b g Henrythenavigator (USA)—Danehill Music (IRE) **Mrs S. A. Bryan**
15 **NATCHEZ TRACE**, 5, b g Invincible Spirit (IRE)—Passage of Time **Second Chancers**
16 **PHOTOGRAPH (IRE)**, 5, b g Kodiac—Supreme Occasion (IRE) **Mr Ray Flegg & Mr John Bousfield**
17 **SIR SEDRIC (FR)**, 4, b g Dragon Pulse (IRE)—Rajastani (IRE) **Miss A. Walton**
18 **TRINITY LAKE**, 6, b g Dansili—Mirror Lake **Dreams**
19 **TWEET TWEET**, 4, ch f Twilight Son—Tweety Pie (IRE) **Mrs P A Johnson & Mr C H Stephenson**

THREE-YEAR-OLDS

20 Br g Fast Company (IRE)—All In Green (IRE)
                           Dr Faisal Maassarani, Mr Johnathan Brown, Mr Michael Murphy, Mr David Lloyd

MR DECLAN CARROLL - continued

21 **GANNON GLORY (IRE)**, b g Cotai Glory—Folegandros Island (FR) **Northern Marking Ltd**
22 **LISA'S DREAM (IRE)**, gr f Caravaggio (USA)—Cape Sunshine (IRE) **Danny Fantom Racing Ltd**
23 **PASCHA**, b f Garswood—Sirenuse (IRE) **Andy Turton & Terry Johnston**
24 Ch f Gleneagles (IRE)—Portentous **Mr Brian Chambers**
25 **SLATE CRACKER**, b g Bated Breath—Songseeker (IRE) **Mr Brian Chambers**
26 **VICTORY FLAGSHIP**, b g Garswood—Mis Chicaf (IRE) **Highgreen Partnership**
27 **YELLOW BEAR**, ch g Poet's Voice—Roman Holiday (IRE) **Mr Ray Flegg & Mr John Bousfield**

TWO-YEAR-OLDS

28 B c 04/04 Estidhkaar (IRE)—Dancing Soprano (IRE) (Jeremy (USA)) (1701) **Ms Victoria Watt**
29 Ch c 24/02 Sioux Nation (USA)—Dusty (Paco Boy (IRE)) **Mr B Cooney**
30 **FORTUNATE STAR (IRE)**, ch c 08/04 Unfortunately (IRE)—Effusive (Starspangledbanner (AUS)) (4677)
Mr Ray Flegg & Mr John Bousfield.
31 B c 20/03 Camacho—Latina Reach (IRE) (Arcano (IRE)) (25510) **Santry Racing**
32 Ch c 30/03 Dandy Man (IRE)—Sundown Sally (IRE) (Iffraaj) (11429) **Santry Racing**
33 **TEN BOB NOTE**, b c 13/03 Muhaarar—Ha'penny Beacon (Erhaab (USA))
P A Johnson ,C H Stephenson & A Stephenson
34 **WHATACRACKER**, ch g 14/03 Cracksman—Isa (Approve (IRE)) **Mrs P A Johnson & Mr C H Stephenson**

Assistant Trainer: Kym Dee.

Flat Jockey: Harrison Shaw. **Apprentice Jockey:** Zak Wheatley. **Amateur Jockey:** Donovan Goucher.

| **89** | **MR TONY CARROLL, Cropthorne**
Postal: Mill House Racing, Cropthorne, Pershore, Worcs
Contacts: **PHONE** 01386 861020 **MOBILE** 07770 472431 **FAX** 01386 861628
EMAIL a.w.carroll@btconnect.com **WEBSITE** www.awcarroll.co.uk |
|---|---|

1 **APATITE**, 4, b f Gleneagles (IRE)—Rainfall Radar (USA) **Lycett Racing Ltd**
2 **ASTROPHYSICS**, 10, ch g Paco Boy (IRE)—Jodrell Bank (IRE) **Lynn Siddall Memorial Syndicate**
3 **BE FAIR**, 6, b g Kyllachy—Going For Gold **Surefire Racing & Partner**
4 **BE MY SEA (IRE)**, 11, b g Sea The Stars (IRE)—Bitooh **Mr Layton T. Cheshire L. T. Cheshire**
5 **BEAU GESTE (IRE)**, 6, b g Lilbourne Lad (IRE)—Valbonne (IRE) **The Bbc Partnership**
6 **BELEK BULLFINCH**, 4, b f Cameron Highland (IRE)—Farmers Dream (IRE) **D. J. Oseman**
7 **BEZZAS LAD (IRE)**, 5, b g Society Rock (IRE)—Red Rosanna **KHDRP**
8 **BLACK BUBLE (FR)**, 9, b g Valanour (IRE)—Miss Bubble Rose (FR) **Northway Lodge Racing**
9 **BLUE VENTURE**, 5, b m Bated Breath—Blue Goddess (IRE) **G. A. Wilson**
10 **BOOM THE GROOM (IRE)**, 11, b g Kodiac—Ecco Mi (IRE) **Mr B. J. Millen**
11 **CAFE SYDNEY (IRE)**, 6, ch m Foxwedge (AUS)—Carafe **Contubernium Racing**
12 **CALIN'S LAD**, 7, ch g Equiano (FR)—Lalina (GER) **Lycett Racing Ltd**
13 **CAMACHO MAN**, 5, ch g Camacho—Ezilii (IRE) **Whites Property Limited**
14 **CHERISH (FR)**, 5, b m Hunter's Light (IRE)—Agent Kensington **Wedgewood Estates**
15 **CHETAN**, 10, b g Alfred Nobel (IRE)—Island Music (IRE) **L Judd T Stamp J Hardcastle R Miles**
16 **CHRISTINES ANGEL**, 5, gr m Gutaifan (IRE)—Salmon Rose (IRE) **Mr A. W. Carroll**
17 **COLDEN'S PASSION (IRE)**, 4, ch g Twilight Son—Coco Rouge (IRE) **& Gosden J Coles M Sharp**
18 4, Gr g Hot Streak (IRE)—Cool Angel (IRE) **Mr A. W. Carroll**
19 **DE VEGAS KID (IRE)**, 8, b g Lope de Vega (IRE)—Fravolina (USA) **The Rebelle Boys**
20 **DELLA MARE**, 6, b m Delegator—Golbelini **The Fine Gild Racing Partnership**
21 **DESTINADO**, 4, b g Lope de Vega (IRE)—Contribution **Green lighting Ltd**
22 **DOC SPORTELLO (IRE)**, 10, b g Majestic Missile (IRE)—Queen of Silk (IRE) **International Racing Club & Partner**
23 **DRAGOON SPRINGS (IRE)**, 6, br g Arcadio (GER)—Lunar Star (IRE) **Mr I. Slatter**
24 **DYLAN'S RUBY (IRE)**, 5, b m Dylan Thomas (IRE)—Rose Garnet (IRE) **J. A. Dewhurst**
25 **EASTERN STAR (IRE)**, 6, b m Dylan Thomas (IRE)—Sweet Surprise (IRE) **The Fruit Flow Partners**
26 **ELEGANT LOVE**, 6, b m Delegator—Lovellian **H. M. W. Clifford**
27 **ELUSIVE ARTIST (IRE)**, 4, ch g Zoffany (IRE)—Lady Pimpernel **KHDRP**

MR TONY CARROLL - continued

28 **ENDOWED**, 5, gr g Dark Angel (IRE)—Muqantara (USA) **KHDRP**
29 **EQUION**, 4, b g Mayson—Eleodora **Mr A. W. Carroll**
30 **ESSAKA (IRE)**, 10, b g Equiano (FR)—Dream Vision (USA) **Mrs J. Carrington**
31 **FIELDSMAN (USA)**, 10, b g Hard Spun (USA)—R Charlie's Angel (USA) **SF Racing Club**
32 **FLY THE NEST (IRE)**, 6, b g Kodiac—Queen Wasp (IRE) **Mr B. J. Millen**
33 **FORBEARING (IRE)**, 4, b g Kodi Bear (IRE)—Mercifilly (FR) **Keith Cosby & Partners**
34 **GLOBAL STYLE (IRE)**, 7, b g Nathaniel (IRE)—Danaskaya (IRE) **Curry House Corner & Partner**
35 **GOLD STANDARD (IRE)**, 6, ch g Casamento (IRE)—Goldplated (IRE) **Mr J. M. Wall**
36 **HARBOUR PROJECT**, 5, b g Harbour Watch (IRE)—Quelle Affaire **Mrs Y. T. Wallace**
37 **HE'S OUR STAR (IRE)**, 7, b g Lord Shanakill (USA)—Afilia **Mrs S. R. Keable**
38 **HEADSHOT**, 4, b g Awtaad (IRE)—Kesara **Lycett Racing Ltd**
39 **HERE AT NIGHT**, 4, b g Heeraat (IRE)—Endless Night (GER) **Patrick Thompson Roger Musson & Partners**
40 **HOLBACHE**, 4, b g Coach House (IRE)—By Rights **Last Day Racing Partnership**
41 **HOOVES LIKE JAGGER (IRE)**, 4, b g Sir Prancealot (IRE)—Roseisarose (IRE) **Mr A. Mills**
42 **HOT DESERT**, 4, ch g Hot Streak (IRE)—Saharan Song (IRE) **Cole, Green & Wellbelove**
43 **HOT HOT HOT**, 5, ch m Hot Streak (IRE)—Just Emma **Mrs Susan Keable & Partner**
44 **ICONIC KNIGHT (IRE)**, 7, b g Sir Prancealot (IRE)—Teutonic (IRE) **Mill House Racing Syndicate**
45 **ILHABELA FACT**, 8, b gr h High Chaparral (IRE)—Ilhabela (IRE) **Cooke & Millen**
46 **IT'S WONDERFUL (FR)**, 5, b m Orpen (USA)—Heaven **Wedgewood Estates**
47 **JACK'S POINT**, 6, b g Slade Power (IRE)—Electra Star **Mr P. A. Downing**
48 **KELLS (IRE)**, 5, b g Galileo (IRE)—Christmas Kid (USA) **Lycett Racing Ltd**
49 **KING CARNEY**, 5, ch g Australia—Petit Trianon **The Risk Takers Partnership**
50 **KONDRATIEV WAVE (IRE)**, 5, ch g Dragon Pulse (IRE)—Right Reason (IRE) **Mr B. J. Millen**
51 **LATENT HEAT (IRE)**, 6, b g Papal Bull—Taziria (SWI) **Mr J. M. Wall**
52 **LEQUINTO (IRE)**, 5, b g Requinto (IRE)—Moss Nation **Mrs Y. T. Wallace**
53 **LIGHT UP OUR STARS (IRE)**, 6, b g Rip Van Winkle (IRE)—Shine Like A Star **Mr D. Boocock**
54 **LONG CALL**, 9, b g Authorized (IRE)—Gacequita (URU) **Northway Lodge Racing**
55 **MADRINHO (IRE)**, 9, ch g Frozen Power (IRE)—Perfectly Clear (USA) **Mr A. Mills**
56 **MAGICAL MIST**, 4, ch f Dunaden (FR)—Bernisdale **Mr D. M. Mathias**
57 **MAN OF THE NORTH**, 9, b g And Beyond (IRE)—Latin Beauty (IRE) **Last Day Racing Partnership**
58 **MANY WORDS (IRE)**, 4, b g Kodi Bear (IRE)—Few Words **Northway Lodge Racing**
59 **MASTER SULLY**, 4, b g Coach House (IRE)—Dawn Catcher **Mayden Stud**
60 **MID DAY RUSH (IRE)**, 4, ch f Dandy Man (IRE)—Que Sera Sera **Mr A. W. Carroll**
61 **MR PC (IRE)**, 4, b g Acclamation—Beramana (IRE) **Mill House Racing Syndicate**
62 **NELSON RIVER**, 7, b g Mount Nelson—I Say (IRE) **CCCP Syndicate**
63 **NIGHT BEAR**, 5, ch g Dragon Pulse (IRE)—Contenance (IRE) **Mr R. Bellamy**
64 **OEIL DE TIGRE (FR)**, 11, b g Footstepsinthesand—Suerte **Mr A. W. Carroll**
65 **OKAIDI (USA)**, 5, ch g Anodin (IRE)—Oceanique (USA) **Mr A. W. Carroll**
66 **PAYMASTER**, 4, ch g Hot Streak (IRE)—High 'n Dry (IRE) **Mrs Susan Keable & Partner**
67 **PILOT WINGS (IRE)**, 7, b g Epaulette (AUS)—Intaglia (GER) **Green lighting Ltd**
68 **POETIC FORCE (IRE)**, 8, ch g Lope de Vega (IRE)—Obligada (IRE) **International Racing Club & Partner**
69 **POP DANCER (IRE)**, 5, b g Kodiac—Pop Art (IRE) **Mr B. J. Millen**
70 **PRAIRIE TOWN (IRE)**, 11, b g High Chaparral (IRE)—Lake Baino **Cooke & Millen**
71 5, Ch m Schiaparelli (GER)—Princess Sabaah (IRE) **Mr D. Boocock**
72 **QUEEN SARABI (IRE)**, 4, b f The Last Lion (IRE)—Tango Tonic (IRE) **Ms E. A. Judd**
73 **RECON MISSION (IRE)**, 6, b g Kodiac—Ermine Ruby **Mr B. J. Millen**
74 **RED ALERT**, 8, b g Sleeping Indian—Red Sovereign **KHDRP**
75 **RELAY RUNNER (IRE)**, 5, b g Due Diligence (USA)—Audrey Brown **Mr A. W. Carroll**
76 **RIVER WHARFE**, 4, ch g Showcasing—Wahylah (IRE) **Mr B. J. Millen**
77 **ROSE HIP**, 7, b m Acclamation—Poppy Seed **Lady Whent**
78 **SCHERBOBALOB**, 4, gr ro g Cityscape—Cloudy Spirit **Mrs N. S. Harris**
79 **SECOND COLLECTION**, 6, b m Delegator—Quelle Affaire **Mr Ian Furlong & Partner**
80 **SEND IN THE CLOUDS**, 5, b g Delegator—Saharan Song (IRE) **Mrs Y. T. Wallace**
81 **SHANI**, 5, b m Heeraat (IRE)—Limegrove **China Racing Club**
82 **SIR TITAN**, 8, b g Aqlaam—Femme de Fer **Wedgewood Estates**
83 **TAYLORS THREE ROCK (IRE)**, 6, ch m Roderic O'Connor (IRE)—Miss Me **Ms K. J. Austin**
84 **TEMUR KHAN**, 7, br g Dansili—Slink **Mrs H. Hogben**
85 **THE WORTHY BRAT (IRE)**, 5, b g Worthadd (IRE)—Khibraat **Wayne Clifford & Ian Gosden**
86 **THUNDEROAD**, 6, b g Street Sense (USA)—Royal Crystal (USA) **Mrs L. Hunt**
87 **TOO SHY SHY (IRE)**, 5, gr m Kodiac—Satwa Ruby (FR) **Mill House Racing Syndicate**

MR TONY CARROLL - continued

88 **TOP BOY,** 12, b g Exceed And Excel (AUS)—Injaaz **Mrs S. A. Bowen**
89 **TRUSTY RUSTY,** 5, ch m Roderic O'Connor (IRE)—Madame Rouge **H. M. W. Clifford**
90 **UNDER CURFEW,** 6, ch g Stimulation (IRE)—Thicket **Mr M. J. Wellbelove**
91 **URBAN HIGHWAY,** 6, b g Kodiac—Viking Fair **Millen & Partner**
92 **VAPE,** 5, gr g Dark Angel (IRE)—Puff (IRE) **Mill House Racing Syndicate**
93 **VIVE LE ROI (IRE),** 11, b g Robin des Pres (FR)—Cappard View (IRE) **Surefire Racing**
94 **VOLTAIC,** 6, ch g Power—Seramindar **SF Racing Club**
95 **WINNETKA (IRE),** 5, ch g Camacho—Little Audio (IRE) **International Racing Club**

THREE-YEAR-OLDS

96 **AUTUMN ANGEL (IRE),** b f Dark Angel (IRE)—Elshabakiya (IRE) **Mr A. W. Carroll**
97 Ch f Coach House (IRE)—By Rights **Mayden Stud**
98 **DARKE HORSE,** br c Outstrip—Atyaab **Wedgewood Estates**
99 Ch f Coach House (IRE)—Dawn Catcher **Mayden Stud**
100 **EL HIBRI (IRE),** b g Havana Gold (IRE)—Shawka **Mr M. I. Greaves**
101 Ch f Leading Light (IRE)—Fujara **China Racing Club**
102 **GUN DOG (IRE),** b g Dandy Man (IRE)—Shesthebiscuit **International Racing Club**
103 **HUNTSMANS MOON (FR),** b c Hunter's Light (IRE)—Song of India **Wedgewood Estates**
104 **KENSINGTON AGENT (FR),** b f Elusive City (USA)—Agent Kensington **Wedgewood Estates**
105 **MAYBE TONIGHT,** b g Muhaarar—Night Affair **Lady Whent**
106 B c Jack Hobbs—Norma Hill **Mr G. Lloyd**
107 **PRETTY GREEN,** b f Dabirsim (FR)—Crowning Glory (FR) **Mr D. Allen**
108 **SAPPHIRE'S MOON,** b f Ardad (IRE)—Shifting Moon **Curry House Corner**
109 **THIS IS MY HALF (IRE),** b g Muhaarar—Satin Kiss (USA) **Mill House Racing Syndicate**
110 **THREE DONS (IRE),** b g Fast Company (IRE)—Avizare (IRE) **KHDRP**
111 **YOU ARE EVERYTHING (FR),** b br f Belardo (IRE)—Sensa (FR) **Wedgewood Estates**

TWO-YEAR-OLDS

112 B c 22/03 Gleneagles (IRE)—Rockshine (Fastnet Rock (AUS)) (28000) **Mr D. Boocock**
113 B c 10/03 Hunter's Light (IRE)—Sensa (FR) (Pivotal) **Wedgewood Estates**
114 B c 13/04 Tasleet—Wedgewood Estates (Assertive) **Wedgewood Estates**

Other Owners: Mr J. A. Barber, Mr D. R. Blake, Mr R. Buckland, Mr A. W. Carroll, H. M. W. Clifford, Mr D. J. Coles, Mr M. S. Cooke, Mr K. A. Cosby, Curry House Corner, Mr J. P Da Mata, Mrs D. S. Dewhurst, J. A. Dewhurst, Mr I. Furlong, Mrs E. C. Gosden, Mr I. F. Gosden, International Racing Club, Mr I. Johnson, Mrs S. R. Keable, R. Kent, Mr J. Lawrence, Mr B. J. Millen, R. D. Musson, Mr W. J. Musson, Mr M. L. Sharp, Surefire Racing, Mr P. S. Thompson, Mr V. Thompson, Mr A. N. Waters.

---

90 MR TONY CARSON, Newmarket
Postal: **Cedar Lodge Racing Stables, Hamilton Road, Newmarket, Suffolk, CB8 0NQ**
Contacts: **MOBILE 07837 601867**
WORK EMAIL tcarsonracing@gmail.com INSTAGRAM tcarsonracing

1 **AGENT OF FORTUNE,** 7, ch m Kheleyf (USA)—Royal Bloom (IRE) **Billy and The Boys**
2 **CAHORS,** 4, gr f Lethal Force (IRE)—Surprise (IRE) **Mr C. T. Dennett**
3 **CECILIA BEAUX,** 4, b f Oasis Dream—Lizzie Siddal **Mr A. T. Carson**
4 **DENABLE,** 6, b g Champs Elysees—Surprise (IRE) **Mr C. T. Dennett**
5 5, B m Nayef (USA)—Distant Florin **Mr C. T. Dennett**
6 **FLAMINGO ROSE,** 5, gr m Casamento (IRE)—Distant Waters **Mrs J. O'Neill**
7 **HENRY THE FIFTH (IRE),** 4, ch g Dawn Approach (IRE)—Vincennes **Mr M. R. Francis**
8 **LETHAL ANGEL,** 7, gr m Lethal Force (IRE)—Heliograph **Billy and The Boys**
9 **MUTALAAQY (IRE),** 4, br g Dark Angel (IRE)—Misdaqeya **Well Connected Electrics UK Ltd**
10 **NEEDWOOD BLOSSOM,** 4, b f Garswood—Fangfoss Girls **Miss Michelle B Fernandes & Partners**
11 **NOZIERES,** 4, b f Mayson—Cool Catena **Mr C. T. Dennett**
12 **STARRY EYES (USA),** 6, ch m Animal Kingdom (USA)—Starship Elusive (USA) **Billy and The Boys**

THREE-YEAR-OLDS

13 **CANTERS WELL (IRE),** gr g Caravaggio (USA)—Gali Gal (IRE) **Mr P. Foster**
14 **MARADENN,** b f Bobby's Kitten (USA)—Bright Girl (IRE) **Mr C. T. Dennett**

MR TONY CARSON - continued

15 **NITRO NEMO,** b g Marcel (IRE)—Believe In Dreams
16 **ROSELEA GIRL,** ch f Garswood—Roslea Lady (IRE) **Mr C. Butler**

Flat Jockey: William Carson. **NH Jockey:** Mr Graham Carson. **Amateur Jockey:** Kerryanne Alexander.

91

MR LEE CARTER, Epsom
Postal: **The Old Yard, Clear Height Stables, Epsom, Surrey, KT18 5LB**
Contacts: **PHONE 01372 740878 MOBILE 07539 354819 FAX 01372 740898**
EMAIL leecarterracing@aol.co.uk WEBSITE www.leecarterracing.com

1 **AL TARMAAH (IRE),** 5, b g Muhaarar—How's She Cuttin' (IRE) **Mr J. J. Smith**
2 **ALBUM (IRE),** 5, gr g Clodovil (IRE)—Michael's Song (IRE) **Only One Bid Partnership**
3 **CREATIONIST (USA),** 6, b g Noble Mission—Bargain Blitz (USA) **Mr J. J. Smith**
4 **DREAM TALE,** 6, b g Shamardal (USA)—Dream Book **Mr R. M. C. Barney**
5 **DUTUGAMUNU (IRE),** 5, ch g Ivawood (IRE)—Bunditten (IRE) **Clear Racing**
6 **ENOUGH ALREADY,** 6, b g Coach House (IRE)—Funny Enough **Mr R. M. C. Barney**
7 **MAAZEL (IRE),** 8, b g Elzaam (AUS)—Laylati (IRE) **Mr J. J. Smith**
8 **MISS ELSA,** 6, b m Frozen Power (IRE)—Support Fund (IRE) **Mr J. J. Smith**
9 **OLIVIA MARY (IRE),** 4, b gr f Dark Angel (IRE)—Lapis Blue (IRE) **Mr R. M. C. Barney**
10 **PERFECT FOCUS (IRE),** 5, b g Acclamation—Tonle Sap (IRE) **Mr R. M. C. Barney**
11 **PLYMOUTH ROCK (IRE),** 5, b g Starspangledbanner (AUS)—Welcome Spring (IRE) **Ewell Never Know**
12 **REPARTEE (IRE),** 5, br g Invincible Spirit (IRE)—Pleasantry **Mr R. M. C. Barney**
13 **SENSE OF WORTH (IRE),** 6, b g Street Sense (USA)—Desert Song (USA) **Mr R. M. C. Barney**
14 **SHYRON,** 11, b g Byron—Coconut Shy **Mr J. J. Smith**
15 **SILENT QUEEN (IRE),** 4, b f Gutaifan (IRE)—Gold Hush (USA) **Mr J. J. Smith**
16 **TREBLE CLEF,** 7, b g Helmet (AUS)—Musical Key **Mrs K. T. Carter**
17 **VILLEURBANNE,** 4, b g Iffraaj—Ninas Rainbow **Mr J. J. Smith**

THREE-YEAR-OLDS

18 **MISS HOUDINI (IRE),** gr f Gutaifan (IRE)—Starlite Sienna (IRE) **Mr R. M. C. Barney**

92

MR BEN CASE, Banbury
Postal: **Wardington Gate Farm, Edgcote, Banbury, Oxfordshire, OX17 1AG**
Contacts: **PHONE 01295 750959 MOBILE 07808 061223**
EMAIL info@bencaseracing.com WEBSITE www.bencaseracing.com TWITTER @bencaseracing
INSTAGRAM bencaseracing

1 **ANNABELLE ROAD (IRE),** 5, b m Sholokhov (IRE)—Alexander Road (IRE)
2 **BASHERS REFLECTION,** 5, ch g Mount Nelson—Dungarvan Lass (IRE) **Mrs S. R. Bailey**
3 **BATTLE OF PAVIA (IRE),** 6, b g Milan—First Battle (IRE) **Lady Jane Grosvenor**
4 **BOLEYN BOY (IRE),** 4, b g Elusive Pimpernel (USA)—Fuchsia Delight (IRE) **Mr D P Walsh & Mr A Barry**
5 **CELESTIAL PARK (IRE),** 4, b f Walk In The Park (IRE)—Corona Moon (IRE) **Foran & Harrison**
6 **COBBLERS DREAM (IRE),** 6, br g Yeats (IRE)—Miss Parkington (IRE) **Lady Jane Grosvenor**
7 **CODED MESSAGE,** 9, b m Oscar (IRE)—Ring Back (IRE) **Wardington Hopefuls**
8 **CONCEROE (IRE),** 6, br g Yeats (IRE)—Made In Kk (IRE) **Lady Jane Grosvenor**
9 **DASH OF BLUE,** 7, b g Great Pretender (IRE)—Madame Bleue **Bluebuyu**
10 **DORADO DOLLAR (IRE),** 8, ch g Golden Lariat (USA)—Stability Treaty (IRE) **Miss P. Murray**
11 **ELECTORAL LADY (IRE),** 5, gr m Westerner—Milford Maggie (IRE) **Hardman, Walsh, Warren, Wright**
12 **FELTON BELLEVUE (FR),** 7, b g Kap Rock (FR)—Sister du Berlais (FR) **Mrs H Munn, Mr R E Good, Mr B Case**
13 **FERN HILL (IRE),** 7, b g Dylan Thomas (IRE)—Water Rock **Cross Foran Harrison**
14 **GAZETTE BOURGEOISE (FR),** 6, b m Spanish Moon (USA)—Jasmine (FR) **Mr A. H. Harvey**

MR BEN CASE - continued

15 4, Ch f Poet's Voice—Hymn To Love (FR) **Mr B. I. Case**
16 **KASABA BAY,** 5, ch g Universal (IRE)—Emmaslegend **Mrs L. R. Lovell**
17 **KILBREW BOY (IRE),** 9, b g Stowaway—Bean Ki Moon (IRE) **Case Racing Partnership**
18 **MIDNIGHTREFLECTION,** 7, b m Midnight Legend—Hymn To Love (FR) **Case Racing Partnership & Anita J Lush**
19 **NORVICS REFLECTION (IRE),** 7, b g Mahler—Finallyfree (IRE) **Mrs S. R. Bailey**
20 **REBEL ROYAL (IRE),** 9, b g Getaway (GER)—Molly Duffy (IRE) **Case Racing Partnership**
21 **SHANTY ALLEY,** 8, b g Shantou (USA)—Alexander Road (IRE) **Jerry Wright Adam Lucock Patricia Murray**
22 **STARGAZER BELLE,** 4, b f Telescope (IRE)—Theatre Belle **Pat Murray Martin Redman Maurice Thomas**
23 **THE GOLDEN REBEL (IRE),** 8, b g Gold Well—Good Thought (IRE) **The Golden Rebels**
24 **TROUVILLE LADY,** 5, b m Boris de Deauville (IRE)—Artofmen (FR) **Foran Lovell Moore**
25 **UNIKA ETOILE,** 4, b f Telescope (IRE)—Unika La Reconce (FR) **Meads, Redman, Smith, Thomas**

Other Owners: Mr A. K. Barry, Mr B. I. Case, Mrs S. L. Case, Case Racing Partnership, Mr R. Cross, Mrs S. P. Foran, Mr R. Freeman, Mr R. E. Good, Lady Jane Grosvenor, Mr S. Hardman, Mr J. E. Harrison, Mrs M. A. Howlett, Mrs L. R. Lovell, Mr A. W. Lucock, Miss A. J. Lush, Mr P. Meads, Mr T. W. Moore, Mrs H. M. Munn, Miss P. Murray, Mr M. W. Redman, Mr D. W. Smith, Mr M. H. Thomas, D. P. Walsh, Mr M. K. Warren, J. Wright.

NH Jockey: Harry Bannister, Jack Quinlan. **Conditional Jockey:** Jack Andrews, Bryan Carver. **Amateur Jockey:** Charlie Case.

---

93 | MR PATRICK CHAMINGS, Baughurst
Postal: **Inhurst Farm Stables, Baughurst, Tadley, Hampshire, RG26 5JS**
Contacts: **PHONE 0118 981 4494 MOBILE 07831 360970 FAX 0118 982 0454**
EMAIL chamingsracing@talk21.com

1 **AMATHUS (IRE),** 5, b g Anjaal—Effige (IRE) **Mr D. F. Henery**
2 **ARMADAR,** 4, b g Sinndar (IRE)—Amba **The Foxford House Partnership**
3 **BHUBEZI,** 4, ch g Starspangledbanner (AUS)—Lulani (IRE) **The Foxford House Partnership**
4 **COCO BEAR (IRE),** 4, br g Kodi Bear (IRE)—House of Roses **Trish and Colin Fletcher-Hall**
5 **DARVEL (IRE),** 4, b g Dark Angel (IRE)—Anthem Alexander (IRE) **& Symonds**
6 **DOURADO (IRE),** 8, b h Dark Angel (IRE)—Skehana (IRE) **Mrs B. C. Wickens**
7 **EMERALD FOX,** 7, b m Foxwedge (AUS)—Roshina (IRE) **The Foxford House Partnership**
8 **EMINENT HIPSTER (IRE),** 4, b g Make Believe—Organza **Mr D. F. Henery**
9 **GHEPARDO,** 7, b m Havana Gold (IRE)—Clincher **The Foxford House Partnership**
10 **GLOBAL ACCLAMATION,** 6, b g Acclamation—High Luminosity (USA) **Inhurst Players**
11 **GUILTY PARTY (IRE),** 5, b m Lawman (FR)—Coolree Marj (IRE) **Mrs R. Lyon & Mr P. R. Chamings**
12 **LOOKSEE,** 4, b g Passing Glance—Orphina (IRE) **Mr J. A. Mould**
13 **MAGICAL DRAGON (IRE),** 5, b g Dragon Pulse (IRE)—Place That Face **Mr H. R. Symonds & Mrs S. A. Symonds**
14 **MISTER FREEZE (IRE),** 8, ch g Frozen Power (IRE)—Beacon of Hope (IRE) **G N Hunt, G E Bassett**
15 **MOTATAABEQ (IRE),** 4, b c Kodiac—Jabhaat (USA) **Mr P. R. Chamings**
16 **MY LADY CLAIRE,** 6, ch m Cityscape—Lady Sylvia **The Foxford House Partnership**
17 **RAQRAAQ (USA),** 4, b g War Front (USA)—Firdaws (USA) **The Foxford House Partnership**
18 **RINTY MAGINTY (IRE),** 6, b g Camacho—Peanut Butter (IRE) **Mr P. R. Chamings**
19 **SHIP TO SHORE,** 4, b g Famous Name—Sea Regatta (IRE) **Jackie Cornwell & Patrick Chamings**
20 **SPANISH STAR (IRE),** 7, b g Requinto (IRE)—Rancho Star (IRE) **Shirley Symonds & Fred Camis**
21 **TAWTHEEF (IRE),** 5, b g Muhaarar—Miss Beatrix (IRE) **Trolley Action**
22 **VELVET AND STEEL (USA),** 4, ch f Union Rags (USA)—Beyond Our Reach (IRE) **Mr S. Thompson**
23 **VINCENZO COCCOTTI (USA),** 10, gr ro g Speightstown (USA)—Ocean Colors (USA) **Mr D. F. Henery**

TWO-YEAR-OLDS
24 B f 05/05 Requinto (IRE)—Rancho Star (IRE) (Soviet Star (USA)) **Shirley Symonds & Fred Camis**
25 **SPANISH STORM (IRE),** b g 23/03 Requinto (IRE)—Mezogiorno (IRE) (Zamindar (USA)) (14000) **F. D. Camis**

MR PATRICK CHAMINGS - continued

Other Owners: Mr G. E. Bassett, F. D. Camis, Mr P. R. Chamings, Mrs J. A. Cornwell, Mr C. M. Fletcher, Mrs P. A. Hall, Mr G. N. Hunt, Mrs R. Lyon, Mr H. R. Symonds, Mrs S. A. Symonds.

Assistant Trainer: Phillippa Chamings.

---

94 — MR MICK CHANNON, West Ilsley
Postal: **West Ilsley Stables, West Ilsley, Newbury, Berkshire, RG20 7AE**
Contacts: **PHONE 01635 281166 FAX 01635 281177**
EMAIL **mick@mick-channon.co.uk** WEBSITE **www.mickchannon.tv**

1 5, B m Gleneagles (IRE)—Al Manaal
2 **AMY BEACH (IRE),** 4, b f New Approach (IRE)—Isabella Bird **Jon & Julia Aisbitt**
3 **BAREST OF MARGINS (IRE),** 6, b g Shirocco (GER)—Holly Baloo (IRE) **The Tailenders**
4 **CERTAIN LAD,** 6, b g Clodovil (IRE)—Chelsey Jayne (IRE) **Mr C. R. Hirst**
5 **CHAIRMANOFTHEBOARD (IRE),** 6, b g Slade Power (IRE)—Bound Copy (USA)
　　　　　　　　　　　　　　　　　　　　　　　David Kilburn, David Hudd & Chris Wright
6 **DALANIJUJO (IRE),** 5, ch m Night of Thunder (IRE)—Kiss From A Rose **Mr C. R. Hirst**
7 **DIAMONDS DANCING,** 4, b f Swiss Spirit—Crazee Diamond **M. R. Channon**
8 **FANGORN,** 4, b g Bungle Inthejungle—Inffiraaj (IRE) **Ann Black & Partner**
9 **GEARING'S POINT,** 4, b f Harbour Watch (IRE)—Amahoro **Dave & Gill Hedley**
10 **HIROMICHI (FR),** 4, gr g Dabirsim (FR)—Pachelbelle (FR) **Jon & Julia Aisbitt**
11 **HUNDRED ISLES (IRE),** 5, b g Fastnet Rock (AUS)—Gallic Star (IRE) **Jon & Julia Aisbitt**
12 **INDIAN CREEK (IRE),** 5, b g Camacho—Ushindi (IRE) **Peter Taplin & Susan Bunney**
13 **JOHAN,** 5, b g Zoffany (IRE)—Sandreamer (IRE) **Jon & Julia Aisbitt**
14 **KOEMAN,** 8, b g Dutch Art—Angelic Note (IRE) **Peter Taplin & Susan Bunney**
15 **MAHALE,** 4, b f Kodiac—Zarafa **Dave & Gill Hedley**
16 **MAJESTIC (IRE),** 4, b g Conduit (IRE)—Grevillea (IRE) **Mr N. J. Hitchins**
17 **SINGLE (IRE),** 5, ch m Nathaniel (IRE)—Solita (USA) **The Sweet Partnership**
18 **SMEATON'S LIGHT (IRE),** 4, b g Dragon Pulse (IRE)—Clenaghcastle Lady (IRE) **Mr R. O'Rourke & Partner**
19 **STORM CHASER (FR),** 5, b m Hurricane Run (IRE)—Pachelbelle (FR) **Box 41**
20 **STORTING,** 6, b g Iffraaj—Stella Point (IRE) **Jon & Julia Aisbitt**
21 **TRAIS FLUORS,** 8, b br g Dansili—Trois Lunes (IRE) **M. R. Channon**
22 **URBAN VIOLET,** 4, b f Cityscape—Just Violet **Eternal Folly Partnership**

THREE-YEAR-OLDS

23 **BAROQUE STAR (IRE),** ch f Lope de Vega (IRE)—Gallic Star (IRE) **Jon & Julia Aisbitt**
24 **BASS STRAIT,** b f Cityscape—Rough Courte (IRE) **Aston Bloodstock**
25 **BAZALGETTE (IRE),** br gr g Clodovil (IRE)—Irene Adler (IRE) **Mr R. O'Rourke & Partner**
26 **BLUEBELL WAY,** b f Sixties Icon—Whiteley (IRE) **Peter Taplin & Susan Bunney**
27 **BONITA B,** b f Oasis Dream—Effie B **Bastian Family**
28 **BURTONLODGE BEAUTY (IRE),** b f Bungle Inthejungle—Katevan (IRE) **Mrs T. Burns**
29 **DANCE OF DRAGONS,** b br f Gutaifan (IRE)—Sahafh (USA) **M. R. Channon**
30 **EASTER ICON,** ch c Sixties Icon—Vive Ma Fille (GER) **Mr J. M. Mitchell**
31 **FLASH BETTY,** b f Gregorian (IRE)—Bridie Ffrench **Paul Humphreys & Jonathan Sweeney**
32 **GRAFFITI,** b g Sixties Icon—Outside Art **Mrs Janet Evans & Partners**
33 **GREATNESS AWAITS (IRE),** b g Clodovil (IRE)—Top Act (IRE) **M. R. Channon**
34 **INGRA TOR (IRE),** b c Churchill (IRE)—Kassia (USA) **Jon & Julia Aisbitt**
35 **JACOVEC CAVERN,** b g Sixties Icon—Siri **Dave & Gill Hedley**
36 **KINRARRA,** b f Australia—Miss Lahar **Barry Walters Farms**
37 **LARK LANE,** b g Sixties Icon—Ann Without An E **Barry Walters Farms & Partner**
38 **LORD'S BELL,** b g Jack Hobbs—Delightful Belle (USA) **Mr W.H. Carson**
39 **MINNAMOOLKA (IRE),** b f Anjaal—Lucky Leigh **Mrs Theresa Burns & Partner**
40 **MIVVI,** b f Sixties Icon—Dozen (FR) **M. R. Channon**

MR MICK CHANNON - continued

41 **MR FREEDOM,** b g Sixties Icon—Waitingforachance **M. R. Channon**
42 **PENUMBRA,** b f Sixties Icon—Shadows Ofthenight (IRE) **M. R. Channon**
43 **PYROTECHNIC,** b g Territories (IRE)—Bright Flash **M. R. Channon**
44 **QUAKER HOUSE,** gr g Garswood—Tigrilla (IRE) **M. R. Channon**
45 **QUEEN OF FASHION,** b f Sixties Icon—Shrimpton **Box 41**
46 **RUBY GLOW,** b f Sixties Icon—Zaatar (IRE) **Jolly Folly Syndicate**
47 **SABYINYO,** gr g Gregorian (IRE)—Amahoro **Dave & Gill Hedley**
48 **SIGNORINA MERISI,** b grf Caravaggio (USA)—Novalina (IRE) **David Kilburn, David Hudd & Chris Wright**
49 **STEVENSON,** b c Havana Gold (IRE)—In Your Time **Hunscote Stud Limited**
50 **TWENTYFIRST LANCER,** b g Churchill (IRE)—Zarafa **Dave & Gill Hedley**
51 **WHISTLEDOWN,** gr f Gregorian (IRE)—El Che **Mr Peter Taplin & Partner**
52 **WONDERFUL WORLD,** b c Bungle Inthejungle—La Gifted **George Materna & Roger Badley**

TWO-YEAR-OLDS

53 B c 06/02 Camacho—Amaany (Teofilo (IRE)) (11429)
54 B f 06/04 Bated Breath—Amahoro (Sixties Icon) **Dave & Gill Hedley**
55 B g 24/01 Kessaar (IRE)—Balaawy (Bated Breath) **Insignia Racing**
56 B f 24/03 Sixties Icon—Bridie Ffrench (Bahamian Bounty) **Six or Sticks (Sixties)**
57 Ch f 23/02 Zoffany (IRE)—Chelsey Jayne (IRE) (Galileo) **Mrs MV. Magnier & Mrs P. Shanahan**
58 B f 26/04 Sixties Icon—Chicago Star (Exceed And Excel (AUS))
59 B c 15/04 Sixties Icon—Dark Blue (IRE) (Dark Angel (IRE))
60 B f 29/04 Sixties Icon—Dozen (FR) (Mastercraftsman (IRE))
61 B c 02/03 Captain Gerrard (IRE)—El Che (Winker Watson) **Mr Peter Taplin & Partner**
62 B f 23/02 Sixties Icon—Estrellada (Oasis Dream) **Six or Sticks (Sixties)**
63 B f 21/03 Coulsty (IRE)—Evanesce (Lujain (USA)) **Dave & Gill Hedley**
64 B f 26/01 New Approach (IRE)—Faeroes (IRE) (Fastnet Rock (AUS)) (5000) **Mr D. Elsworth**
65 B c 07/04 Sixties Icon—Featherweight (IRE) (Fantastic Light (USA)) **Mr R. Windridge**
66 **FERROUS (IRE),** b c 29/04 Dark Angel (IRE)—Grizzel (IRE) (Kodiac) (35000) **Recycled Products Ltd & Partner**
67 B c 07/04 Charm Spirit (IRE)—Fiumicino (Danehill Dancer (IRE)) **Mr P. Trant**
68 B c 20/04 Bungle Inthejungle—Good Morning Lady (Compton Place)
69 B f 19/04 Bungle Inthejungle—Hi Note (Acclamation)
70 B f 14/02 Postponed (IRE)—Indicia (Bated Breath) **Mr J. M. Mitchell**
71 B f 25/02 Sixties Icon—Inffiraaj (IRE) (Iffraaj) **Insignia Racing**
72 B c 06/04 Washington DC (IRE)—Intrusion (Indesatchel (IRE)) (20952) **Six or Sticks (Washington DC)**
73 B f 21/04 Bungle Inthejungle—Jillnextdoor (IRE) (Henrythenavigator (USA)) (30000)
74 **JOHNJAY,** b c 27/03 Sixties Icon—Jersey Breeze (IRE) (Dark Angel (IRE)) **Mrs S. G. Bunney**
75 B c 23/03 Captain Gerrard (IRE)—Jollyhockeysticks (Fantastic Light (USA))
76 **KANAWHA,** b f 22/03 Kodiac—Kassia (IRE) (Acclamation) **Jon & Julia Aisbitt**
77 B f 10/03 Highland Reel (IRE)—Lady Lahar (Fraam) **Barry Walters Farms**
78 **METAL MERCHANT (IRE),** b c 06/04 Make Believe—Whipped (IRE) (Whipper (USA)) (29524)

Recycled Products Ltd & Partner

79 B c 01/04 New Bay—Nour'spirit (IRE) (Invincible Spirit (IRE)) (36000)
80 **OASIS ANGEL,** b f 01/03 Harry Angel (IRE)—Sandreamer (IRE) (Oasis Dream) **Jon & Julia Aisbitt**
81 B c 26/04 Oasis Dream—Opal Tiara (IRE) (Thousand Words) **The Filly Folly & Sweet Partnership**
82 B c 25/04 Sixties Icon—Outside Art (Excellent Art) **Mrs Janet Evans & Partners**
83 B f 07/04 Dandy Man (IRE)—Pastoral Star (Pastoral Pursuits) (19048) **Norman Court Stud**
84 B c 21/04 Sixties Icon—Potternello (IRE) (Captain Marvelous (IRE))
85 **RATHGAR,** ch c 20/03 Ulysses (IRE)—Why We Dream (IRE) (Al Kazeem) **Jon & Julia Aisbitt**
86 B f 11/04 Cityscape—Rebecca Romero (Exceed And Excel (AUS)) **Mr S. Taplin**
87 B c 15/04 Sixties Icon—Rough Courte (IRE) (Clodovil (IRE))
88 B f 11/04 Cityscape—Royal Ffanci (Royal Applause) **Hunscote Stud Limited**
89 Ch c 05/04 Sixties Icon—Section Onesixsix (IRE) (Dandy Man (IRE))
90 Ch c 08/04 Sixties Icon—Shadows Ofthenight (IRE) (Fastnet Rock (AUS))
91 B f 09/04 Sixties Icon—Shine Likeadiamond (Atlantic Sport (USA))
92 B c 14/04 Sixties Icon—Siri (Atlantic Sport (USA)) **Dave & Gill Hedley**
93 B f 17/05 Massaat (IRE)—Stella Rise (IRE) (Dutch Art) **Mr R. Windridge**
94 Ch c 27/04 Sixties Icon—Tanojin (IRE) (Thousand Words)
95 B f 17/05 Sixties Icon—Vilnius (Imperial Dancer)
96 B c 18/03 Territories (IRE)—Weigelia (Raven's Pass (USA)) (22000)

MR MICK CHANNON - continued

97 B f 14/04 Coulsty (IRE)—Winkaway (Winker Watson) **Norman Court Stud**
98 WOODSTOCK, b c 24/03 Sixties Icon—Isabella Bird (Invincible Spirit (IRE)) **Jon & Julia Aisbitt**

Other Owners: Mrs J. M. Aisbitt, J. R. Aisbitt, Jon & Julia Aisbitt, Mr R. Badley, Barry Walters Farms, Mr E. I. R. Bastian, Mr W. Bastian, Bastian Family, Mrs A. C. Black, Mrs S. G. Bunney, Mrs T. Burns, M. R. Channon, Mrs J. A. Evans, Ms G. H. Hedley, Mr A. Leader, Mrs E. Leader, Mr G. D. P Materna, Mr. E. Mills-Webb, Mr W. Mula, Mr R. O'Rourke, Stoneham Park Stud, Mr A. Prickett, Mrs C. Prickett, P Taplin.

Assistant Trainer: Jack Channon, Allana Mason, Suzannah Stevens.

---

95 **MR MICHAEL CHAPMAN, Market Rasen**
Postal: **Woodlands Racing Stables, Woodlands Lane, Willingham Road, Market Rasen, Lincolnshire, LN8 3RE**
Contacts: **PHONE 01673 843663 MOBILE 07971 940087**
EMAIL woodlands.stables@btconnect.com WEBSITE www.woodlandsracingstables.co.uk

1 FAST DEAL, 5, ch g Fast Company (IRE)—Maven **Mrs M. M. Chapman**
2 GLACIER FOX, 7, ch g Foxwedge (AUS)—Beat Seven **Mrs M. M. Chapman**
3 L'ES FREMANTLE (FR), 11, b g Orpen (USA)—Grand Design **Mrs M. M. Chapman**
4 LUDUAMF (IRE), 8, ch g Tamayuz—Aphorism **Mrs M. M. Chapman**
5 4, B f Pether's Moon (IRE)—Materiality
6 NOLANS HOTSPUR (IRE), 10, b g Bushranger (IRE)—Cayambe (IRE) **Mr G. Nolan**
7 4, Ch f Gentlewave (IRE)—Precious Lady

THREE-YEAR-OLDS

8 B f Dariyan (FR)—Cross Section (USA)

Assistant Trainer: Mrs M. Chapman.

---

96 **MR RYAN CHAPMAN, St Mawgan**
Postal: **Trevenna Forge, St Mawgan, Newquay, Cornwall, TR8 4EZ**

1 AWESOME TUNES (IRE), 12, b g Milan—Europet (IRE) **Mr R. G. Chapman**
2 BALLY DUN (IRE), 7, b g Arcadio (GER)—Queen's Forest (IRE) **Mr R. G. Chapman**
3 BLUE RIBBON, 7, b g Sayif (IRE)—Mar Blue (FR) **Mr R. G. Chapman**
4 CLOUNCERNA (IRE), 9, b g Presenting—Kinincha Girl (IRE) **Mr R. G. Chapman**
5 COMERAGH LAD (IRE), 8, b g Morozov (USA)—Fox Glacier (IRE) **Mr R. G. Chapman**
6 LEADING KNIGHT (IRE), 6, b g Leading Light (IRE)—Miss McGoldrick (IRE) **Mr R. G. Chapman**
7 THE RIGHT PROFILE (IRE), 9, b g Milan—Bonnie And Bright (IRE) **Mr R. G. Chapman**

THREE-YEAR-OLDS

8 Ch g Linda's Lad—Onwegoagain (IRE) **Mr R. G. Chapman**

97 MR FABRICE CHAPPET, Chantilly

Postal: **29 Avenue de Joinville, Chantilly, 60500, France**
Contacts: PHONE **+33 3 44 21 03 00**
EMAIL **chappet.office@chappetracing.fr** WEBSITE www.chappetracing.com

1 **AFGHANY (FR)**, 4, b c The Gurkha—Texaloula **Infinity Nine Horses**
2 **ALBA POWER (IRE)**, 7, b g Fast Company (IRE)—Shehila (IRE) **F. J. Carmichael**
3 **ALL THE KING'S MEN (FR)**, 4, b c Kingman—Gooseley Chope (FR) **F. J. Carmichael**
4 **BEL ARISTO (FR)**, 4, b c New Approach (IRE)—Baroness Daniela **A. Gilibert**
5 **EARLY LIGHT (FR)**, 4, b c Wootton Bassett—Accalmie **H. Saito**
6 **FOREST OF WISDOM**, 4, b c Ifraaj—Wiesenlerche **R. Shaykhutdinov**
7 **KEN COLT (IRE)**, 7, b g Kendargent (FR)—Velvet Revolver (IRE)
8 **KILFRUSH MEMORIES (FR)**, 6, b h Shakespearean (IRE)—Elusive Lily **S. Vidal**
9 **NEPALAIS**, 4, b c The Gurkha—Daltiana (FR) **A. Gilibert**
10 **PRINCE LANCELOT**, 4, b c Sir Prancealot (IRE)—Rainbow Vale (FR) **A. Gilibert**
11 **ROC ANGEL (FR)**, 8, ch g Rock of Gibraltar (IRE)—Forewarned (IRE) **A. Gilibert**
12 **ROYAUMONT (FR)**, 5, b g Dabirsim (FR)—Rosie Thomas (IRE) **A. Gilibert**
13 **VAL BASSETT (FR)**, 4, b g Wootton Bassett—Val d'Hiver **Haras de Saint Julien**
14 **WATCHMEN (FR)**, 5, b g Elvstroem—Watchful **A. Tamagni**
15 **WHITE WHISKY**, 4, b c Kodiac—Mambo Light (USA) **R. Shaykhutdinov**

THREE-YEAR-OLDS

16 **AD LIBITUM (FR)**, ch c Amaron—Timocita **H. de Pracomtal**
17 **AREGAI (FR)**, b g Le Havre—Sur Choix **C. Marzocco**
18 **ASPEN (FR)**, b g Dabirsim (FR)—Aquamerica (USA) **S. Amar**
19 **BAMBITA (IRE)**, ch f De Treville—Bambara **R. Shaykhutdinov**
20 **BARON PALATCHI (FR)**, b c Myboycharlie (IRE)—Costanza (IRE) **F. Bianco**
21 **BLAST OF WIND (FR)**, b c Shalaa (IRE)—Changing Skies (IRE) **Al Shaqab Racing**
22 **BOARDING TIME (FR)**, b g Elvstroem—Bijou a toi **Haras de Saint Julien**
23 **CANDLE STICK (FR)**, ch c Lope de Vega—Attractive Lady **H. Saito**
24 **CELESTINE (FR)**, b f Shamalgan (FR)—Celesteville (IRE) **Ecurie Normandie Pur Sang**
25 **CHATEAU FORT (FR)**, ch c Footstepinthesand—Gargotiere **Al Shaqab Racing**
26 **CHAUSSONS ROSES (IRE)**, ch f New Approach (IRE)—Go Lovely Rose (IRE) **A-M. Hayes**
27 **CHILLY BOY**, b c De Treville—Cherry Bee **R. Shaykhutdinov**
28 **DEKABRISTKA**, b f Nyquist (USA)—Dyning Out (USA) **R. Shaykhutdinov**
29 **DIADEMA (FR)**, b f De Treville—Panja (IRE) **R. Shaykhutdinov**
30 **DOCTOR ARI (IRE)**, ch c No Nay Never—Virginia **H. Guy**
31 **DUBAI MEMORIES (FR)**, b g Recorder—Elusive Lily **S. Vidal**
32 **DUCHESS OF DUBAI (IRE)**, b f Sea The Stars (IRE)—Duchess of France (IRE) **Ecurie des Monnaies**
33 **ERIDA (FR)**, ch f De Treville—Edda **R. Shaykhutdinov**
34 **ETATIQUE (FR)**, b c Wootton Bassett—Engage **A. Jathiere**
35 **FEDE GALIZIA (IRE)**, b f Lawman (FR)—Loanne (FR) **C. Marzocco**
36 **FREJA (FR)**, b f Toronado (IRE)—No Wind No Rain **A. Gilibert**
37 **GADZART (USA)**, gr g Biogenic—Proud Commander **B. Chalmel**
38 **GEMMA (IRE)**, b f Siyouni (FR)—Signe (IRE) **F. J. Carmichael**
39 **GOODNESS (FR)**, b br f Muhaarar—Sweet Electra (FR)
40 **GREGARINA (FR)**, ch f De Treville—Gagarina (FR) **R. Shaykhutdinov**
41 **GUESS WHAT (FR)**, ch c Sea The Stars (IRE)—Witty Guess (FR) **Al Shaqab Racing**
42 **HEALING OASIS (FR)**, b f Oasis Dream—Healing Dream (FR) **Haras de Saint Julien**
43 **KALGANOV**, b c Gutaifan—Nidina **A. Jathiere**
44 **KALINA (FR)**, b f Wootton Bassett—Texanne (FR) **LG Bloodstock**
45 **KELIADE (IRE)**, b f Le Havre (IRE)—Consumer Credit (USA) **F. Sauque**
46 **LADY MILLION (FR)**, b f Brametot—Libbard **Haras de Saint Julien**
47 **LAW STAR (FR)**, b g Lawman—Holy Roman **C. Marzocco**
48 **LOVE TREVILLE (IRE)**, b f De Treville—Love Dance **R. Shaykhutdinov**
49 **MACHETE (IRE)**, b c Myboycharlie (IRE)—Maid To Believe **R. Shaykhutdinov**
50 **MADEMOISELLE ROSE**, b f Shalaa (IRE)—Brasileira **A. Lallemand**
51 **MASTER GATSBY (FR)**, ch c The Grey Gatsby (IRE)—Moonee Valley (FR) **A. Tamagni**
52 **MEA DOMINA (FR)**, b f Pivotal—Regina Mundi **San Paolo Agri Stud**
53 **MILAD'ID (FR)**, b f Johnny Barnes (IRE)—Coup d'Eclat (IRE) **G. Larrieu**
54 **ONCE (IRE)**, b f Tamayuz—Bikini Babe (IRE) **A-M. Hayes**

MR FABRICE CHAPPET - continued

55 **ONESTO (IRE)**, ch c Frankel—Onshore **J-P. Dubois**
56 **PLESENT JANE**, b f Pivotal—Jane the star **R. Shaykhutdinov**
57 **POURQUOI PAS (IRE)**, b f Dark Angel—Peut Etre **A-M. Hayes**
58 **PRIVATE LOUNGE**, ch f Toronado (IRE)—Polarized **Haras de Saint Julien**
59 **QUIETLY CONFIDENT**, br f Dabirsim (FR)—Quiet **F. Chappet**
60 **SAN TEODORICO (FR)**, b c Farhh—Belle Croix **T. de la Heronnière**
61 **SANTA GIULIA (FR)**, b f Shalaa (IRE)—Alpine Rose (FR) **Ecurie F. Defosse**
62 **SAVING GRACE (FR)**, b f Almanzor (FR)—Desiree Clary (GER) **Ecurie J-L. Bouchard**
63 **SHE'S COSMIC**, b f Sea The Stars (IRE)—Kosmische (IRE) **R. Shaykhutdinov**
64 **SHUMI LA SHUMI LA (FR)**, b f Motivator—Trevise (FR) **S. B. Al Kuwari**
65 **SICILIA**, b f Shalaa—Nigwah **Al Shaqab Racing**
66 **SLOANE RANGER (FR)**, ch f Nathaniel—Chelsea **C.N. Wright**
67 **STELLA DUCET (FR)**, b f Dubawi—Steip Amach **Riviera Equine**
68 **STIRLING (FR)**, b c Frankel—Some Spirit (IRE) **A. Gilibert**
69 **SUNSET APPROACH (FR)**, b f Dawn Approach (IRE)—Testina (IRE) **C. Marzocco**
70 **SWEETHEART (FR)**, bl f Al Wukair (IRE)—Santa Christiana (FR) **A. Tamagni**
71 **TOPGEAR (FR)**, b c Wootton Bassett—Miss Lech (USA) **H. Saito**
72 **TWICE (IRE)**, gr f Fast Company (IRE)—Kapria (FR) **A-M. Hayes**
73 **UTOPISTE (FR)**, b c Almanzor (FR)—Unaided **Haras d'Etreham**
74 **VARENNES (FR)**, b g Dark Angel—Vadariya **A. Gilibert**
75 **VICTOR LAZZLO (USA)**, b c Runhappy—Do the Danse **A. Gilibert**

Trainer did not supply details of their two-year-olds.

98	**MRS JANE CHAPPLE-HYAM, Newmarket** Postal: **Abington Place Racing Stables, 44 Bury Road, Newmarket, Suffolk, CB8 7BT** Contacts: PHONE **07899 000555** MOBILE **07899 000555** FAX **01638 661335** EMAIL **janechapplehyam@hotmail.co.uk, janechapplehyamracing@outlook.com**

1 **AMBASSADORIAL (USA)**, 8, b g Elusive Quality (USA)—Tactfully (IRE) **Ms J. F. Chapple-Hyam**
2 **APLOMB (IRE)**, 6, b g Lope de Vega (IRE)—Mickleberry (IRE) **Mrs F. J. Carmichael**
3 **AZETS (IRE)**, 6, b g Dubawi (IRE)—Nashmiah (IRE) **Mr M. N. M. A. Almutairi**
4 **BELLOSA (IRE)**, 4, b f Awtaad (IRE)—Poole Belle (IRE) **Sir E. J. Loder**
5 **CLEGANE**, 5, ch m Iffraaj (IRE)—Cradle of Life (IRE) **Abigail Harrison & Jane Chapple-hyam**
6 **COPINET**, 4, b f Mehmas (IRE)—Dominatrix **Mrs A Cantillon & Jane Chapple-hyam**
7 **EMOJIE**, 8, b g Captain Gerrard (IRE)—Striking Pose (IRE) **Jakes Family**
8 **EX GRATIA**, 4, b f Exceed And Excel (AUS)—Beta **Miss K. Rausing**
9 **FULL AUTHORITY (IRE)**, 5, b g Kingman—Ashley Hall (USA) **H.H. & Chapple-hyam**
10 **HALA JOUD (IRE)**, 4, gr f Belardo (IRE)—Sifter (USA) **Mr M. Al Daihani**
11 **INTERNATIONALANGEL (IRE)**, 5, gr m Dark Angel (IRE)—Wrong Answer **SBZ Corporation Limited**
12 **MAID MILLIE**, 6, b m Dream Ahead (USA)—Maid A Million **Ms J. F. Chapple-Hyam**
13 **MCCANN THE MAN**, 4, b g Fountain of Youth (IRE)—Rememberance Day **Mr B. J. Hirst**
14 **NIZAAKA (FR)**, 4, b f New Bay—Dusky Queen (IRE)
15 **PALIFICO**, 4, ch f Siyouni (FR)—Montalcino (IRE) **Mrs L. O. Sangster**
16 **PRINCE OF ABINGTON (IRE)**, 4, b g Prince of Lir (IRE)—Greatest Dancer (IRE) **Morriss, Harrison, Chapple-hyam**
17 **RADETSKY (USA)**, 5, b g Speightstown (USA)—Brooch (USA) **Mr S. A. Almutairi**
18 **SAFFRON BEACH (IRE)**, 4, ch f New Bay—Falling Petals (IRE) **Mrs B. V. Sangster, J Wigan & O Sangster**
19 **STAMFORD RAFFLES**, 9, b g Champs Elysees—Romantic Retreat **Ms J. F. Chapple-Hyam**
20 **SUZI'S CONNOISSEUR**, 11, b g Art Connoisseur (IRE)—Suzi Spends (IRE) **Ms J. F. Chapple-Hyam**
21 **UBER COOL (IRE)**, 8, b g Born To Sea (IRE)—My Uptown Girl **Fiona Carmichael & Jane Chapple-hyam**

THREE-YEAR-OLDS

22 **ARIKA (USA)**, b c Speightstown (USA)—Josette (IRE) **Kenjiro Private Office Limited**
23 **ATHEBY**, b c Gutaifan (IRE)—Meet Marhaba (IRE) **Mr B. J. Hirst**
24 **BONDI GIRL (IRE)**, b f Ivawood (IRE)—Bond's Girl **Ms J. F. Chapple-Hyam**

MRS JANE CHAPPLE-HYAM - continued

25 **CHORUS SONG,** b f Havana Gold (IRE)—Angelic Note (IRE) **Mrs B. V. Sangster & Mr B. V. Sangster**
26 **CLAYMORE (FR),** b c New Bay—Brit Wit **Mrs M. Slack**
27 **CRAFTY LADY,** gr f Mastercraftsman (IRE)—Kindu **B Sangster & Middleham Park Racing Lxvi**
28 **HEAT OF THE MOMENT,** ch f Bobby's Kitten (USA)—Heat of The Night **Miss K. Rausing**
29 **KICKBOX,** b br g Dabirsim (FR)—Rich Legacy (IRE)
30 **MARWAD,** br g Intello (GER)—Murahana (IRE)
31 **MISS CANDY (IRE),** b f Equiano (FR)—Candycakes (IRE) **Mr J. Acheson**
32 **MUBAARAK,** b c Cable Bay (IRE)—Madhaaq (IRE) **Mr M. N. M. A. Almutairi**
33 **NAFEE (IRE),** b g Mehmas (IRE)—Something Magic **Mr B. Alshraika**
34 **NIAMH AND OONAGH (IRE),** b f Free Eagle (IRE)—Crystal Mountain (USA) **Mrs A. Cantillon**
35 **PLANTATREE,** b f Helmet (AUS)—Chatline (IRE) **The Gredley Family**
36 **POPPY BOUCHET,** b f Havana Gold (IRE)—Audacia (IRE) **Mrs F. J. Carmichael**
37 **ROCKET YOGI (IRE),** ch c Fast Company (IRE)—Yogi's Girl (IRE) **Mr G. W. Y. Li**
38 **STREAKY BAY,** b f Hot Streak (IRE)—Lyra's Daemon **W & Chapple-hyam**
39 **SWASHBUCKLER,** b c Sea The Stars (IRE)—Majestic Jasmine (IRE) **Mr H. J. Merry**

TWO-YEAR-OLDS

40 **I AM LEGEND (SWE),** b f 13/03 Barocci (JPN)—Rock The Legend (IRE) (Rock of Gibraltar (IRE)) (4660)

Other Owners: Mrs A. Cantillon, Mrs F. J. Carmichael, Ms J. F. Chapple-Hyam, Ms A. Harrison, Mr J. C. Jakes, Mrs T. M. A. Jakes, Middleham Park Racing LXVI, Mrs M. D. Morriss, T. S. Palin, M. Prince, Mr W. J. S. Prosser, B. V. Sangster, Mrs L. O. Sangster, Mr O. R. J. Sangster, J. Wigan.

Assistant Trainer: Abi Harrison.

---

99 **MR PETER CHAPPLE-HYAM, Newmarket**
Postal: **St Gatien Stables, All Saints Road, Newmarket, Suffolk, CB8 8HJ**

1 **BHARANI STAR (GER),** 5, ch m Sea The Stars (IRE)—Bay of Islands (FR)
2 **DEJA (FR),** 7, b g Youmzain (IRE)—Atarfe (IRE) **Fairlawns Racing Ltd**
3 **FAST MEDICINE (IRE),** 4, b g Iffraaj—Annie The Doc **Fairlawns Racing Ltd**
4 **FRANCO GRASSO,** 4, b g Frankel—Oakley Girl
5 **ISLE OF LIGHT,** 4, b g Twilight Son—Belle Isle
6 **LORD MARBURY (IRE),** 4, b c Galileo (IRE)—Convocate (USA)
7 **MAKINITUP (IRE),** 4, b f Marcel (IRE)—Waterways (IRE) **Miss Sally Wall & Partners**
8 **MARTINENGO (IRE),** 7, b g Elusive Pimpernel (USA)—Albiatra (USA) **Miss S. E. Wall**
9 **MASTER OF SOULS (IRE),** 4, b g Kodiac—Soul Searcher (IRE) **Fairlawns Racing Ltd**
10 **SAYF AL DAWLA,** 4, b c Frankel—Attraction
11 **SWISS MISTRESS (IRE),** 4, ch f Mastercraftsman (IRE)—Arosa (IRE)
12 **UNION SPIRIT,** 5, b br g Outstrip—Nouvelle Lune **Miss Sally Wall & Star Pointe Ltd**

THREE-YEAR-OLDS

13 **QUEENS BALLET,** b f Frankel—Ballet De La Reine (USA) **Fairlawns Racing Ltd**

Other Owners: Mr P. W. Chapple-Hyam, Mr D. A. Farrington, Star Pointe Ltd, Miss S. E. Wall.

100 MR PETER CHARALAMBOUS, Newmarket
Postal: **30 Newmarket Road, Cheveley, Newmarket, Suffolk, CB8 9EQ**
Contacts: **PHONE 07921 858421**
EMAIL camalotracing@btinternet.com

1 **ALPHA KING**, 4, b g Kingman—Kilo Alpha **Mr C. Pigram**
2 **APOLLO ONE**, 4, ch g Equiano (FR)—Boonga Roogeta **pcracing.co.uk**
3 **INTREPIDLY (USA)**, 8, b g Medaglia d'Oro (USA)—Trepidation (USA) **C Pigram & T Hind**
4 **LEVENDI**, 4, b g Toronado (IRE)—Ela Goog La Mou **pcracing.co.uk**
5 **MAKARIOS**, 4, b g Toronado (IRE)—Ela Gorrie Mou **pcracing.co.uk**

THREE-YEAR-OLDS
6 **MAN ON A MISSION**, b g Swiss Spirit—Loveatfirstsight **Miss K. L. Squance**
7 **SHES MY GIRL**, b f Helmet (AUS)—Theydon Girls **pcracing.co.uk**

TWO-YEAR-OLDS
8 Ch c 04/04 Lethal Force (IRE)—Boonga Roogeta (Tobougg (IRE)) **pcracing.co.uk**
9 B c 29/02 Mayson—kalon brama **pcracing.co.uk**
10 B f 07/04 Charming Thought—Theydon Girls (Poet's Voice) (800) **pcracing.co.uk**

101 HARRY AND ROGER CHARLTON, Beckhampton
Postal: **Beckhampton House, Marlborough, Wiltshire, SN8 1QR**
Contacts: **PHONE 01672 539533 MOBILE 07710 784511**
EMAIL office@beckhamptonstables.com WEBSITE www.rogercharlton.com

1 **AMALFI BAY**, 4, b g Lope de Vega (IRE)—Affinity **Elite Racing Club**
2 **IMPERIUM (IRE)**, 6, ch g Frankel—Ramruma (USA) **Weston Brook Farm & Bromfield**
3 **JUMBY BREEZE**, 4, b f Dubawi (IRE)—Annabelle's Charm (IRE) **Merry Fox Stud Limited**
4 **KING ZAIN**, 4, b c Kingman—Shreyas **Jaber Abdullah**
5 **NAJEEBA**, 4, gr f Dansili—Rose of Miracles **Mr I. Alsagar**
6 **RUMI**, 4, br g Harzand (IRE)—Donatia **Dr J. Ahmadzadeh**
7 **SINJAARI (IRE)**, 6, b g Camelot—Heavenly Song (IRE) **Mohammed Jaber**
8 **SLEEPING LION (USA)**, 7, ch g Teofilo (IRE)—Flame of Hestia (IRE) **Merry Fox Stud Limited**
9 **UMM HURAIR (IRE)**, 4, br f Awtaad (IRE)—Oasis Sunset (IRE) **Mohammed Jaber**
10 **WITHHOLD**, 9, b g Champs Elysees—Coming Back **Mr A. G. Bloom**

THREE-YEAR-OLDS
11 **ALBION PRINCESS**, b f Kingman—Langlauf (USA) **Mr A. G. Bloom**
12 **APHELIOS**, b g Kodiac—Homily **Kingwood Stud Management Co Ltd**
13 **ASHKY (IRE)**, gr f Caravaggio (USA)—Pannonia (USA) **Mohammed Jaber**
14 **AVE MARIA**, b f Kingman—Lustrous **St Albans Bloodstock Limited**
15 Gr g Caravaggio (USA)—Azeema (IRE) **Mr & Mrs Paul & Clare Rooney**
16 **BRAYDEN STAR**, b c Twilight Son—Desert Liaison **Chris Kiely Racing Limited**
17 **CHANCERY LANE**, b g Recorder—Queen's Prize **Her Majesty The Queen**
18 **CHARLIE'S NUMBERS**, b c Frankel—September Stars (IRE) **Andrew Rosen & Edward W Easton**
19 **CHEF DE PARTIE**, b c Siyouni (FR)—Nessina **Brook Farm Bloodstock**
20 B f Kingman—Choumicha **Mohammed Jaber**
21 **DANCING EAGLE**, b f Gleneagles (IRE)—Maid To Dream **Fishdance Ltd**
22 **DANCING EMPRESS (IRE)**, b f Holy Roman Emperor (IRE)—Aspasias Tizzy (USA) **Fishdance Ltd**
23 **DANCING TANGO (IRE)**, b f Camelot—Dream Approach (IRE) **Fishdance Ltd**
24 **DISCRETION**, b f Dubawi (IRE)—Momentary **Her Majesty The Queen**
25 **FLORA MACDONALD**, b f Gleneagles (IRE)—Ship's Biscuit **P. Newton**
26 Gr f Caravaggio (USA)—French Friend (IRE) **Mr & Mrs Paul & Clare Rooney**
27 **FRESH FANCY (IRE)**, b f New Approach (IRE)—Pure Fantasy **Her Majesty The Queen**
28 **GOLDEN SHEEN**, ch f Frankel—Yellow Band (USA) **Merry Fox Stud Limited**

HARRY AND ROGER CHARLTON - continued

29 **GRAPH,** b f Frankel—Photographic **Juddmonte**
30 **HONKY TONK MAN (IRE),** b c Tamayuz—Dance Hall Girl (IRE) **de Zoete, Inglett & Jones**
31 **JUMBLY,** b f Gleneagles (IRE)—Thistle Bird **Emmy Rothschild & Partner**
32 **KING OF WAR,** b g Churchill (IRE)—Materialistic **Mohammed Jaber**
33 B gr f Mastercraftsman—Kinni **Mrs S. A. J. Kinsella**
34 **LA PULGA (IRE),** b g Kodiac—Nijah (IRE) **Mohammed Jaber**
35 **LEAF MOTIF,** ch f Bated Breath—Palmette **Juddmonte**
36 **LUDUS,** b c New Approach (IRE)—Comeback Queen **Kingwood Stud Management Co Ltd**
37 **MAGGIE AND ME,** gr f Time Test—Sell Out **Mr & Mrs Paul & Clare Rooney**
38 **MAJESTIC FIGHTER (IRE),** ch g Teofilo (IRE)—Majestic Manner **Mr Saeed Jaber**
39 **MAOKAI,** b g Showcasing—Towards (USA) **Kingwood Stud Management Co Ltd**
40 **MARS MAGIC (IRE),** b g Magician (IRE)—Celerina (IRE) **Ms L. A. Mars**
41 **METABOLT,** ch c Night of Thunder (IRE)—Something Exciting **Kingwood Stud Management Co Ltd**
42 **MOON ISLAND,** b f Oasis Dream—Dhan Dhana (IRE) **Mohammed Jaber**
43 **MR WHITE SOCKS,** b g Frankel—Hana Lina **Mr Saeed Jaber**
44 **MUDEERAH,** ch f Exceed And Excel (AUS)—Areyaam (USA) **Ahmed Jaber**
45 **NOISY NIGHT,** b g Night of Thunder (IRE)—Ya Hajar **Mr Saeed Jaber**
46 **NOYA,** b f Shamardal (USA)—Sooraah **Mohammed Jaber**
47 **OKEECHOBEE,** b c Time Test—Scuffle **Juddmonte**
48 **OUT FROM UNDER,** b c Dubawi (IRE)—Koora **White Birch Farm & Fittocks Stud**
49 **PERSIAN ROYAL,** b g Al Kazeem—Poplin **D. J. Deer**
50 **PIROUZ,** b g El Kabeir (USA)—President's Seal **Dr J. Ahmadzadeh**
51 **SEASCAPE GIRL,** b f Time Test—Marine Girl **Clipper Logistics**
52 B f Night of Thunder (IRE)—Sharaakah (IRE) **Mohammed Jaber**
53 **SHARED,** b g Almanzor (FR)—Between Us **Mohammed Jaber**
54 **SILVER BULLET LADY (IRE),** ch f Decorated Knight—Lost Icon (IRE) **Mr I. Alsagar**
55 **SMALL PRINT,** b f Siyouni (FR)—Privacy Order **Clipper Logistics**
56 Ch f Postponed (IRE)—Starscape (IRE) **Mohammed Jaber**
57 **SWEET SUMMER,** b f Muhaarar—Spring Fling **Chasemore Farm**
58 **TEAGARDEN JAZZ,** b f Golden Horn—Zamoura **D. J. Deer**
59 **THESIS,** b c Kingman—Nimble Thimble **Juddmonte**
60 **TIME LOCK,** b f Frankel—Time Chaser **Juddmonte**
61 **VALSAD (IRE),** b c Intello (GER)—Vuela **Mr S. A. Stuckey**
62 **WHITEBEAM,** gr f Caravaggio (USA)—Sleep Walk **Juddmonte**
63 **ZAIN NIGHTS,** b c Decorated Knight—Missy O' Gwaun (IRE) **Mr A. Al Banwan**

TWO-YEAR-OLDS

64 **ABBRISHAM,** b f 03/05 Havana Gold (IRE)—Donatia (Shamardal (USA)) (28000)
65 **ALGERNON,** b c 17/02 Showcasing—Caponata (USA) (Selkirk (USA)) (105000)
66 Gr c 10/02 Kodiac—Aphrodite's Angel (IRE) (Dark Angel (IRE)) (105000)
67 **BALTIC,** b c 21/03 Frankel—Baltic Best (IRE) (King's Best (USA))
68 B f 26/04 Kingman—Be My Gal (Galileo)
69 **BILLABONG,** b c 14/03 Oasis Dream—Carding (USA) (Street Cry (USA)) (42000)
70 Ch c 14/02 Shamardal—Choumicha (Paco Boy)
71 B c 17/03 Kodiac—Chupalla (Helmet (AUS)) (160000)
72 **CLENCHED,** ch f 11/04 Cityscape—Grasped (Zamindar (USA))
73 B c 09/03 Churchill (IRE)—Damselfly (IRE) (Power) (85000)
74 **DARK JADE,** gr c 27/04 Dark Angel (IRE)—African Rose (Observatory (USA))
75 B f 19/02 Muhaarar—Dhan Dhana (Dubawi (IRE))
76 **ELEGANCIA,** b f 14/03 Lope De Vega—So Sleek (Lawman)
77 B c 22/03 Oasis Dream—Encore Moi (Exceed And Excel (AUS)) (80000)
78 B c 11/01 Showcasing—Floria Tosca (IRE) (Shamardal (USA)) (110000)
79 **FROM BEYOND,** b f 10/04 Zoustar (AUS)—Via Lazio (Lawman (FR)) (50000)
80 **GARNER,** b c 23/02 Recorder—Dawn Glory (Oasis Dream)
81 B f 18/01 Zoustar (AUS)—Gee Kel (Danehill Dancer)
82 B c 08/02 Starspangledbanner (AUS)—Heavenly Song (IRE) (Oratorio (IRE))
83 Gr f 10/03 Zoustar (AUS)—Langlauf (Raven's Pass)
84 **PRIMEVAL,** b f 23/01 Lope de Vega (IRE)—Passage of Time (Dansili)
85 **ROARIN' SUCCESS,** ch f 16/03 Roaring Lion—Random Success (Shamardal)

HARRY AND ROGER CHARLTON - continued

86 B c 21/02 Kodiac—Savida (IRE) (King's Best (USA)) (50000)
87 B f 22/02 Kingman—September Stars (IRE) (Sea The Stars)
88 B c 06/03 Al Kazeem—Serenada (Anaba)
89 B c 30/03 Golden Horn—Souville (Dalakhani (IRE)) (30000)
90 B c 12/01 Camelot—Sweet Gentle Kiss (IRE) (Henrythenavigator (USA)) (120000)
91 B f 14/02 Ardad (IRE)—Talqaa (Exceed And Excel (AUS)) (35238)

Pupil Assistant: Matt Fielding.

Apprentice Jockey: Thomas Greatrex.

102
MR HARRY CHISMAN, Moreton-In-Marsh
Postal: **25 Coachmans Court, Station Road, Moreton-In-Marsh, Gloucestershire, GL56 0DE**
Contacts: **PHONE 07787 516723**
WEBSITE www.harrychisman.co.uk

1 CALL HIS BLUFF (IRE), 10, b g Westerner—Gaza Strip (IRE) **Mr M. Comley**
2 FOYLESIDEVIEW (IRE), 10, b g Dark Angel (IRE)—Showerproof **Harry Chisman & Wendy Summers**
3 ROCKINGHAM SOUTH, 6, b g Kayf Tara—Safari Run (IRE) **Mr M. Comley**
4 TANGO PETE, 5, ch g Norse Dancer (IRE)—Ellway Prospect **The Tango Syndicate**

Assistant Trainer: G. Charles-Jones.

Flat Jockey: Robert Havlin. **NH Jockey:** Tom O'Brien, Sean Quinlan. **Conditional Jockey:** Daniel Hiskett.

103
MR BEN CLARKE, Chard
Postal: **Puthill Barn, Cricket St Thomas, Chard, Somerset, TA20 4EJ**
EMAIL benclarkeracing@gmail.com

1 ARAWELO (IRE), 4, b br f Ocovango—Macs Magic (IRE) **Mr A. Paterson**
2 BOBALOT, 5, gr g Camelot—Riva Snows (IRE) **Fusion Racing Club**
3 CAST'S TASHA (IRE), 5, b m Westerner—Samsha (IRE) **Sue & Clive Cole & Ann & Tony Gale**
4 CASTKITELLO (IRE), 6, b m Milan—Correctandpresent (IRE) **Sue & Clive Cole & Ann & Tony Gale**
5 CREATIVE INERTA (IRE), 12, br g Balakheri (IRE)—Rambling Liss (IRE) **Monica Tory & N J McMullan**
6 DR KANANGA, 8, b g Dapper—Crepe de Chine (FR) **Mike Tootell & Monica Tory**
7 HAVING A BARNEY (IRE), 5, ch g Getaway (GER)—Batren's Garden (IRE) **Mr A. Paterson**
8 JELLICLE JEWEL (IRE), 6, b m Shirocco—Strike's Oscar (IRE) **Mr M. Tootell**
9 JUNIOR DOCTOR, 5, b g Millenary—Crepe de Chine (FR) **Mr M. Tootell**
10 LETTIE LUTZ (IRE), 6, b m Mahler—Grange Oscar (IRE) **Mr A. Paterson**
11 LITTLE JESSTURE (IRE), 6, b m Dylan Thomas (IRE)—The Legislator (IRE) **Mr R. Butler**
12 PIXIE LOC, 7, gr m Lucarno (USA)—Ixora (IRE) **Mr R. Butler**
13 SO SOCKSY (FR), 8, b m Coastal Path—South Island (IRE) **Mr A. Paterson**
14 THE GALLOPING BEAR, 9, b g Shantou (USA)—Cheshire Kat **Mr A. Paterson**
15 TIME BANDIT (IRE), 5, b g Arcadio (GER)—Good Times Had (IRE) **The Time Bandit Partnership**

Other Owners: Mr C. Cole, Mrs S. S. Cole, Mrs A. G. Gale, Mr A. P. Gale, Mr H. W. G. Geering, N. J. McMullan, Mr A. Paterson, Mr M. Tootell, Mrs M. A. Tory, Mr L. D. C. Usher.

104 MR NICOLAS CLEMENT, Chantilly
Postal: **37, Avenue de Joinville, 60500 Chantilly, France**
Contacts: **PHONE +33 3 44 57 59 60 MOBILE +33 6 07 23 46 40**
EMAIL office@nicolasclement.com WEBSITE www.nicolasclement.com

1 **BLLUSHING**, 4, ch c Sepoy (AUS)—Convention
2 **CAPRICE DES DIEUX (FR)**, 4, b c Declaration of War—Neko (FR)
3 **CONTROL TOWER (FR)**, 5, b m Youmzain (IRE)—La Tour Rouge
4 **FENELON (FR)**, 4, b c Fastnet Rock (AUS)—Aigue Marine
5 **GALIFA (IRE)**, 4, b f Frankel—Viva Rafaela (BRZ)
6 **HAVANA BOUND**, 5, ch m Havana Gold (IRE)—Exceedingly Rare (IRE)
7 **HOPISSIME (FR)**, 4, b f Camelot—Baino Hope (FR)
8 **LAZY (GER)**, 4, b c Siyouni (FR)—Larella (GER)
9 **MERCIELAGO (FR)**, 4, b c Teofilo (IRE)—Mondalay
10 **NOW WE KNOW (FR)**, 5, gr h Kendargent (FR)—Now Forever (GER)
11 **SCHOONER RIDGE (IRE)**, 4, b f Siyouni (FR)—Surprisingly (IRE)
12 **SCILIAR (IRE)**, 4, ch c Raven's Pass (USA)—Snake Dancer (IRE)
13 **WILDWOOD (FR)**, 4, b br f Maxios—Walayta (GER)

THREE-YEAR-OLDS

14 B f Ectot—Across The Sky (IRE)
15 **ANAMANDA (FR)**, gr f Reliable Man—Anyana
16 **BRIGHT SPIRIT**, b f Dubawi (IRE)—Local Time
17 **CAP SAN ROMAN (FR)**, b f Muhaarar—Cap Verite (IRE)
18 **COMMANDER BUZZKILL**, b f Lope de Vega (IRE)—Centime
19 **DADDY LONG LEGS (FR)**, ch c Almanzor (FR)—Private Eyes
20 **GALBEN (FR)**, b f Sir Percy—Odense
21 **GREEN MAXIOS (IRE)**, b f Maxios—Green Swallow (FR)
22 **ILE DE CIRCE (IRE)**, ch f Ulysses (IRE)—Sea Chanter (USA)
23 **ISCA (IRE)**, b f Mehmas (IRE)—Pretty Priceless (IRE)
24 **L'ILE AU TRESOR**, b f Iffraaj—Diamond Bangle (IRE)
25 B f Fastnet Rock (AUS)—La Conquerante
26 **LA TOUR DES REVES (FR)**, b f Oasis Dream—La Tour Rouge
27 **LADY ARIELLA (FR)**, ch f Ruler of The World (IRE)—Sea The Future (IRE)
28 **MAJAL (FR)**, b f Shalaa (IRE)—Peaceful Love (GER)
29 **MARMELET (IRE)**, b f Kingman—Cherriya (FR)
30 **MIDNIGHT FEVER (IRE)**, b f Shalaa (IRE)—Fregate First
31 **MORNING CALL (FR)**, ch f New Bay—Morgenlicht (GER)
32 **NORTHERN PROJECT**, b c Ribchester (IRE)—North Mare (GER)
33 **NOW SHE KNOWS (FR)**, b f Kendargent (FR)—Now Forever (GER)
34 **ONE O'CLOCK JUMP (FR)**, b g Shalaa (IRE)—Dynamite (FR)
35 **PAGGANE**, b f Muhaarar—Penelopa
36 **PRINCESS GLITTERS (FR)**, b f Zarak (FR)—Lady Glitters (FR)
37 **RADIANT SKY (FR)**, ch f Almanzor (FR)—Glowing Cloud
38 **RIMBAULT (GER)**, b c Zoffany (IRE)—Rock My World (GER)
39 **ROSETTA STONE (FR)**, ch c Rock of Gibraltar (IRE)—Forewarned (IRE)
40 **SEA OF GEMS**, b f Siyouni (FR)—Aigue Marine
41 **SELWAN (IRE)**, b c Zelzal (FR)—Al Wathna
42 **SIRIUS (FR)**, b f Ectot—Across The Sky (IRE)
43 **SOUTHWEST HARBOR (IRE)**, b f Churchill (IRE)—Squeeze (IRE)
44 **SUNRAY (IRE)**, ch f Dawn Approach (IRE)—Snake Dancer (IRE)
45 **THEORETICAL (FR)**, ch f Tamayuz—Game Theory (IRE)
46 **THETYS (FR)**, b f Camelot—Tasharowa (FR)
47 **TOLEDE (USA)**, b f Curlin—Taste Of Heaven
48 **WHITE NOISE (FR)**, ch f Mastercraftsman (IRE)—Peppermint
49 **WINGS OF FIRE (FR)**, b c Wings of Eagles (FR)—Sajida (FR)
50 **YOU'VE GOT SAIL (FR)**, b c Pomellato (GER)—Yachtclubgenoa (IRE)
51 **ZENITH (FR)**, b g Zelzal (FR)—Zalal

MR NICOLAS CLEMENT - continued

TWO-YEAR-OLDS

52 **AMINATU,** b f 10/01 Frankel—Just Sensual (SAF) (Dynasty (SAF)) (246599)
53 **COUP DE SOLEIL (FR),** b f 25/04 Showcasing—Evaporation (Red Ransom)
54 Br f 08/04 Saxon Warrior (JPN)—Demeanour (Giant's Causeway)
55 **DRUM ROLL (FR),** br f 01/05 Gleneagles (IRE)—Douda (Sea The Stars (IRE))
56 **GALISIA (FR),** ch f 17/04 Galiway—Temsia (FR) (Delfos (IRE))
57 B c 19/02 Territories (IRE)—Harvestide (IRE) (Duke of Marmalade (IRE)) (61224)
58 **KOREA (GER),** ch f 17/02 Amaron—Konigsbraut (GER) (Lord of England (GER)) (34014)
59 **LUNALA (FR),** b f 28/03 Penny's Picnic (IRE)—Noella (FR) (American Post) (38265)
60 **NARIMAN POINT (IRE),** ch f 12/03 Dubawi (IRE)—Traffic Jam (IRE) (Duke of Marmalade (IRE)) (170068)
61 **NEAR AMORE (GER),** b f 10/05 Amaron—Near Galante (GER) (Galileo (IRE)) (28912)
62 B c 02/06 Invincible Spirit (IRE)—Olga Prekrasa (USA) (Kingmambo (USA)) (100000)
63 **RAGNAROK (FR),** br c 18/02 Churchill (IRE)—Anna Simona (Slip Anchor)
64 B f 30/03 Mendelssohn (USA)—Royal Story (USA) (Lemon Drop Kid (USA)) (199830)
65 **SAGMIRJA (FR),** b f 01/04 Pedro The Great—Albicocca (Naaqoos)
66 **SEA TOWER (FR),** b f 05/04 Sea The Stars (IRE)—La Tour Rouge (Monsun (GER))
67 **SEA URCHIN (FR),** b c 12/02 Seahenge (USA)—Lady of Light (IRE) (Shamardal (USA)) (39116)
68 B f 03/04 Lope de Vega (IRE)—Special Gal (FR) (Galileo (IRE)) (102041)
69 **SUNSHINEFLED (FR),** b f 12/05 Seabhac—Winshine (Chineur)
70 B f 12/04 Motivator—Theoricienne (Kendor)
71 **TROPEIRA (FR),** b f 26/01 Cloth Of Stars—Tropa De Elite (Street Cry (IRE))
72 **VEGA STAR,** b c 26/02 Lope de Vega (IRE)—With Your Spirit (FR) (Invincible Spirit (IRE)) (85034)
73 B f 29/04 Cloth Of Stars—Vejer (Dalakhani (IRE))

Flat Jockey: Sebastien Maillot, Stephane Pasquier, Thomas Truillier. **Apprentice Jockey:** Aaron Mackay.

105
MR TOM CLOVER, Newmarket
Postal: **Kremlin House Stables, Fordham Road, Newmarket, Suffolk, CB8 7AQ**
Contacts: PHONE 07795 834960, 01638 660055
EMAIL thomaspwclover@gmail.com WEBSITE www.tomcloverracing.com

1 **ADELITA (IRE),** 4, b f Territories (IRE)—Sibling Honour **Mrs G. J. Davey**
2 **BALGAIR,** 8, gr f Foxwedge (AUS)—Glencal **Newmarket Racing Club HQi**
3 **CELSIUS (IRE),** 6, ch g Dragon Pulse (IRE)—Grecian Artisan (IRE) **J. Collins, C. Fahy & S. Piper**
4 **ELECTRIC LOVE,** 4, b f Equiano (FR)—Electric Feel **Joseph Barton & Partner**
5 **FABRICATED,** 4, b f Pride of Dubai (AUS)—Unnatural (USA) **Clipper Group Holdings Ltd**
6 **HOLY KINGDOM (IRE),** 6, gr h Australia—Cable (USA) **The Rogues Gallery**
7 **RAAJIL (IRE),** 4, br g Awtaad (IRE)—Qaadira (USA) **Mr M. J. Bringloe**
8 **RAJMEISTER,** 4, b c Showcasing—Brilliant Sunshine **Mr R. S. Matharu**
9 **ROCKETT MAN,** 4, ch g Equiano (FR)—Flamenco Dancer **The Rogues Gallery**
10 **ROGUE BEAR (IRE),** 4, br g Kodiac—Rancho Montoya (IRE) **The Rogues Gallery**
11 **ROGUE FORCE,** 4, b g Iffraaj—Lonely Rock **The Rogues Gallery**

THREE-YEAR-OLDS

12 **AL BAREZ,** b c Dark Angel (IRE)—Jet Setting (IRE) **Mr R. El Youssef**
13 **ANGEL OF TRAFALGAR,** b c Dark Angel (IRE)—Learned Friend (GER) **& John Alston**
14 **ANJALA (IRE),** ch f Anjaal—Dreaming Lady (IRE) **Carroll House Racing**
15 **CAPUCHINERO,** b f Holy Roman Emperor (IRE)—Ape Attack **Chasemore Farm LLP**
16 **CASTLEBERG ROCK,** b g Fastnet Rock (AUS)—Banzari **Carroll House Racing**
17 **GOLD SPLASH,** ch g Bobby's Kitten (USA)—Caribana **Carroll House Racing**
18 **GRAND LIBYA,** b c Churchill (IRE)—Sprinkling (USA) **Mr E. Elhrari**
19 **JUNGLE RUN (IRE),** b g Bungle Inthejungle—Malekat Jamal (IRE) **D. M. Proos**
20 **LANDERMERE,** b g New Approach (IRE)—Sharnberry **Carroll House Racing**
21 **LUMBERJACK,** gr g Mastercraftsman (IRE)—Wood Chorus **Carroll House Racing**
22 **MR BEAUFORT,** b g Cable Bay (IRE)—Tan Tan **The Mr Beaufort Syndicate**

MR TOM CLOVER - continued

23 **MUSICAL ROMANCE**, b f Marcel (IRE)—Carenot (IRE) **Mrs M. C. Hancock**
24 **MY BOY JACK**, ch g No Nay Never (USA)—Great Court (IRE) **Mr M. J. Bringloe**
25 **MZAHEM (IRE)**, ch c Mastery (USA)—Parade Militaire (IRE) **Mr R. El Youssef**
26 **PAPA COCKTAIL (IRE)**, b g Churchill (IRE)—Anklet (IRE) **K. A. Dasmal**
27 **REY ARTURO (IRE)**, b g Zoffany (IRE)—Atlantic Isle (GER) **Carroll House Racing**
28 **ROGUE BULL**, b g Lawman (FR)—Fizzi Top **The Rogues Gallery**
29 **ROGUE MILLENIUM (IRE)**, b f Dubawi (IRE)—Hawaafez **The Rogues Gallery**
30 **ROGUE MISSION (IRE)**, gr g El Kabeir (USA)—Ascot Lady (IRE) **The Rogues Gallery**
31 **ROGUE ROCKET (FR)**, ch c Recorder—Eva Kant **The Rogues Gallery**
32 **ROGUE STAR (FR)**, br c Zelzal (FR)—Magical Flower **The Rogues Gallery**
33 **SANFELICE (IRE)**, b f Acclamation—Mickleberry (IRE) **Halcyon Thoroughbreds**
34 **THEBEAUTIFULGAME**, b f Slade Power (IRE)—Imasumaq (IRE) **The Tripletto Partnership & Partner**
35 **WILD ABOUT HARRY**, b g Mahsoob—Long Embrace
36 **ZAIN SARINDA (IRE)**, b c Churchill (IRE)—Sarinda **Mr E. Elhrari**

TWO-YEAR-OLDS

37 B c 12/03 El Kabeir (USA)—Angel Bright (IRE) (Dark Angel (IRE)) (40000)
38 B c 17/02 Washington DC (IRE)—Citron (Reel Buddy (USA)) (22000)
39 **FISHING RIGHTS**, ch c 03/05 Le Havre (IRE)—Puzzler (IRE) (New Approach (IRE)) (2857)
40 B f 06/03 Brazen Beau (AUS)—Jumeirah Street (USA) (Street Cry (IRE)) (2000)
41 B c 11/03 Brazen Beau (AUS)—Madame Lafite (Dutch Art)
42 B c 25/01 Dark Angel (IRE)—Moghamarah (Dawn Approach (IRE)) (153061) **Mr R. El Youssef**
43 B c 31/03 Dark Angel (IRE)—Quite Sharp (New Approach (IRE)) (11000) **The Rogues Gallery**
44 **ROGUE LION**, gr c 29/04 Roaring Lion (USA)—Welsh Angel (Dubai Destination (USA)) (65000) **The Rogues Gallery**
45 B c 30/04 Washington DC (IRE)—Romany Gypsy (Indesatchel (IRE)) (50000)

Other Owners: Mrs J. A. Alston, Mr J. P. Alston, J. Barton, Mr T. P. Clover, Mr A. J. Driver, El Catorce, Mr A. R. Elliott, Mrs G. A. S. Jarvis, Mr T. Muller, Mr C. Pizarro, Mrs K. Pizarro, Tripletto Partnership, Mr J. Tuthill.

---

106   MR DENIS COAKLEY, West Ilsley
Postal: **Keeper's Stables, West Ilsley, Newbury, Berkshire, RG20 7AH**
Contacts: **PHONE 01635 281622 MOBILE 07768 658056**
EMAIL racing@deniscoakley.com WEBSITE www.deniscoakley.com

1 **BOBBY KENNEDY**, 4, b g Bobby's Kitten (USA)—All Annalena (IRE) **Ms I. Coakley**
2 **EAGLES DARE**, 4, b g Free Eagle (IRE)—Fasten Up **Keeper's 12**
3 **LISDARRAGH (USA)**, 4, b g Hit It A Bomb (USA)—Thewholeshebang (USA) **Mrs U. M. Loughrey**
4 **NELL QUICKLY (IRE)**, 4, b f The Gurkha (IRE)—Burke's Rock **Chris van Hoorn Racing**
5 **PARTY ISLAND**, 5, ch g Tagula (IRE)—Pretty Demanding (IRE) **Mr T. A. Killoran**
6 **PATROON (USA)**, 4, b g Blame (USA)—Inventing Paradise (USA) **Chris van Hoorn Racing**
7 **RUSKIN RED (IRE)**, 5, ch g Mastercraftsman (IRE)—Firey Red (IRE) **Mrs B. Coakley**
8 **SONNETINA**, 6, b m Poet's Voice—Tebee's Oasis **The Good Mixers**
9 **SUPERSONIQUE**, 4, b f Cable Bay (IRE)—La Concorde (FR) **Poachers' Dozen**
10 **WATERLOO SUNSET**, 4, b g Adaay (IRE)—Atwix **Mrs B. Coakley**
11 **WONDER STARELZAAM (IRE)**, 4, b g Elzaam (AUS)—Ava Star (IRE) **J. C. Kerr**

THREE-YEAR-OLDS

12 **HOORNBLOWER**, ch c Ulysses (IRE)—Tulip Dress **Chris van Hoorn Racing**
13 **ISKAHEEN (IRE)**, b g Profitable (IRE)—Scarlet Rosefinch **Mrs U. M. Loughrey**
14 **JUANITA**, b f Adaay (IRE)—Kip **Ms A. Dunphy**
15 **MY AMBITION (IRE)**, ch c Galileo Gold—Rise Up Lotus (IRE) **Mrs B. Coakley**
16 **UNA NOTTE**, b f Time Test—Goodnightsuzy (IRE) **West Ilsley Racing**

TWO-YEAR-OLDS

17 Ch f 21/03 Gustav Klimt (IRE)—Amour Fou (IRE) (Piccolo) (8000)

MR DENIS COAKLEY - continued

18 **MILVUS (IRE)**, b c 31/01 Dark Angel (IRE)—Redmaven (IRE) (Teofilo (IRE)) (35000) **Sparkling Partners**
19 B f 30/01 Churchill (IRE)—Short Call (IRE) (Kodiac) (75000) **Chris van Hoorn Racing**

Other Owners: Miss A. D. Swift, Mr C. T. Van Hoorn.

107	**MRS HEATHER COBB, Pulborough**

Postal: Kilbrannan Stud Farm, Gay Street, Pulborough, West Sussex, RH20 2HJ
EMAIL kilbrannanstud@aol.com

1 **IRON IN THE SOUL**, 10, ch g Sulamani (IRE)—Go Classic **Mrs H. J. Cobb**
2 **MANO CORNUTO (IRE)**, 9, b g Grandera (IRE)—Martin's Oscar (IRE) **Mrs H. J. Cobb**
3 **STATISTICAL (IRE)**, 10, b g Robin des Champs (FR)—Lusty Beg (IRE) **Mrs H. J. Cobb**

108	**MS DEBORAH COLE, Solihull**

Postal: 1577 Warwick Road, Knowle, Solihull, West Midlands, B93 9LF
EMAIL dbrh.cole@gmail.com

1 **CABAYO LADY**, 5, b m Midnight Legend—Santera (IRE) **Knowle Racing Stables Limited**
2 **CABAYO LORD BRYAN**, 7, b g Norse Dancer (IRE)—Daurica **Knowle Racing Stables Limited**
3 **CABAYO LORD GEORGE**, 6, gr g Geordieland (FR)—Daurica **Knowle Racing Stables Limited**
4 **DORUNRON (IRE)**, 5, ch g Zebedee—Green Briar **Knowle Racing Stables Limited**
5 **DUCA DE THAIX (FR)**, 9, b g Voix du Nord (FR)—Nouca de Thaix (FR) **Knowle Racing Stables Limited**
6 **HAURAKI GULF**, 7, b g Kayf Tara—Leading On **Knowle Racing Stables Limited**
7 **SIR JACK WEST (IRE)**, 6, b g Westerner—Star Sprinkled Sky (IRE) **Knowle Racing Stables Limited**
8 **SOME BUCKLE (IRE)**, 13, b g Milan—Miss Moppit (IRE) **Knowle Racing Stables Limited**
9 **TRICKALIGHT (IRE)**, 6, b m Leading Light (IRE)—Horner Mill (IRE) **Knowle Racing Stables Limited**

109	**PAUL AND OLIVER COLE, Whatcombe**

Postal: Whatcombe Racing Stables, Whatcombe, Wantage, Oxfordshire, OX12 9NW
Contacts: PHONE 01488 638433
EMAIL admin@paulcole.co.uk

1 **GENERAL LEE (IRE)**, 4, b c Lope de Vega (IRE)—Hall Hee (IRE) **Mrs F. H. Hay**
2 **IVATHEENGINE (IRE)**, 5, br g Ivawood (IRE)—Sharp Applause (IRE) **P. F. I. Cole Ltd**
3 **MAJESTIC DAWN (IRE)**, 6, ch h Dawn Approach (IRE)—Jolie Chanson (FR) **Green & Norman**
4 **MANY A STAR (IRE)**, 5, ch g Starspangledbanner (AUS)—Many Hearts (USA) **Mrs L. P. Hobby**
5 **STRICTLY SPICY**, 4, b g Nathaniel (IRE)—Spicy Dal **Ben & Sir Martyn Arbib**
6 **ZHANG FEI (FR)**, 4, b c Camelot—Mambomiss (FR) **P. F. I. Cole Ltd**

THREE-YEAR-OLDS

7 **DEACS DELIGHT**, ch g Tamayuz—Keene Dancer **R & P I Cole**
8 **ERNIE'S VALENTINE**, gr c Havana Gold (IRE)—Eastern Destiny **Williams, Campbell, Sennett & Cole**
9 **FIRTH OF CLYDE (IRE)**, b g Gleneagles (IRE)—Chrysanthemum (IRE) **Mrs F. H. Hay**
10 **GEELONG (FR)**, b c Australia—Tioga Pass **The Fairy Story Partnership**
11 **GRAND CRU GAGA**, gr f Clodovil (IRE)—Comfort In Sound (USA) **Mr C. N. Wright**

PAUL AND OLIVER COLE - continued

12 **JACK DARCY (IRE)**, b g Gleneagles (IRE)—Pretty Face **Flm Ltd, Williams, Vincent & 3d Transport**
13 **LEAP ABROAD (IRE)**, b c Gregorian (IRE)—Norfolk Broads (IRE) **Middleham Park Racing Civ, Cole & Deacon**
14 **SANITISER**, b c The Gurkha (IRE)—Spicy Dal **Ben & Sir Martyn Arbib**
15 **SPLENDENT (IRE)**, b c Fast Company (IRE)—Sweet Lilly **Mrs F. H. Hay**
16 **TARTAN CHIEF**, gr c Dark Angel (IRE)—Pink Symphony **Mrs F. H. Hay**
17 **TARTARUS**, b c Ruler of The World (IRE)—Respectfilly **The Fairy Story Partnership**
18 **WILD MOUNTAIN (IRE)**, b c Aclaim (IRE)—Rochitta (USA) **Mrs F. H. Hay**

TWO-YEAR-OLDS

19 B c 16/04 New Bay—Cornlaw (Lawman (FR)) (37000)
20 B c 29/04 Gleneagles (IRE)—Enrol (Pivotal) (125000)
21 Ch c 02/04 Gleneagles (IRE)—Fashion Statement (Rainbow Quest (USA)) (50000)
22 **FLEET FEET**, ch c 24/02 Footstepsinthesand—Seramindar (Zamindar (USA))
23 Gr c 10/02 Mastercraftsman (IRE)—Ghurfah (Tamayuz) (17000)
24 B c 10/02 Acclamation—Mesaria (IRE) (Montjeu (IRE)) (20000)
25 Ch f 24/02 Cracksman—Nunavik (IRE) (Indian Ridge) (30000) **Christopher Wright & David Kilburn**
26 B c 25/04 Kingman—Shapes (IRE) (So You Think (NZ)) (170000)
27 **SUMO SAM**, b gr f 26/02 Nathaniel (IRE)—Seaduced (Lope de Vega (IRE))
28 **THUNDER BALL**, ch c 29/05 Night of Thunder (IRE)—Seradim (Elnadim (USA))
29 Ch f 03/04 Sioux Nation (USA)—Timely Words (Galileo (IRE)) (16000)
30 Ch c 03/03 Kessaar (IRE)—Turkana Girl (Hernando (FR)) (45000)
31 **WYOMING**, b f 08/04 Motivator—Tioga Pass (High Chaparral (IRE))

Other Owners: 3D Transport Limited, Mr B. G. Arbib, M. Arbib, Mr R. H. Deacon, Financial Lifestyle Management Limited, Mrs J. Green, D. Kilburn, Middleham Park Racing ClV, Mr C. S. Norman, P. F. I. Cole Ltd, T. S. Palin, M. Prince, Mr T. Sennett, Mr C. Vincent, Mr L. Vincent, Mr C. M. Williams, Mrs R. L. Williams, Mr C. N. Wright.

---

110   **MR TJADE COLLIER, Wilsden**
Postal: **Salter Royd House, Shay Lane, Wilsden, Bradford, West Yorkshire, BD15 0DJ**
Contacts: **PHONE 01535 271445**
EMAIL tjade331@icloud.com

1 **AVABELLA (IRE)**, 5, ch m Sans Frontieres (IRE)—All Eyes On Me (IRE) **Mr S. Smith**
2 5, Ch m Lucky Speed (IRE)—Bealath Champ (IRE) **Mr S. Smith**
3 **BLUE HAWAII (IRE)**, 7, b m Jeremy (USA)—Luanna (IRE) **R. Banks & J. Sheard**
4 5, B g Native Ruler—Bold Tara **T. Collier**
5 **CALL ME JEZZA (IRE)**, 7, b g Jeremy (USA)—Fair Astronomer (IRE) **Mr J. N. Sheard**
6 **CHEMICAL WARFARE (IRE)**, 5, b g Fame And Glory—Blazing Sky (IRE) **Sendemon**
7 5, B g Black Sam Bellamy (IRE)—Damascena (GER) **T. Collier**
8 **DOORS BREAKER (FR)**, 5, b g American Post—Polyandry (IRE) **Sendemon**
9 **FRANKEUR (FR)**, 7, b g Khalkevi (IRE)—Razia (FR) **T C Racing Syndicate**
10 5, Gr g Recharge (IRE)—Inthesettlement **T. Collier**
11 4, Br g Soldier of Fortune (IRE)—Jessies Delight **T C Racing Syndicate**
12 **LADRONNE (FR)**, 8, b g Linda's Lad—Worldeta (FR) **T C Racing Syndicate**
13 **MIDNIGHT ANTICS (IRE)**, 8, b m Midnight Legend—Toungara (FR) **T C Racing Syndicate**
14 **POSH SPICE**, 6, b m Kayf Tara—Alflora's Girl (IRE) **T C Racing Syndicate**
15 **RAYTHEHANDYMAN (IRE)**, 6, br g Westerner—La Femme Blanche (IRE) **T C Racing Syndicate**
16 **SHANTOU BOUDICCA**, 6, ch m Shantou (USA)—Toubeera **T C Racing Syndicate**
17 **VALIRANN EXPRESS (IRE)**, 5, b m Valirann (FR)—Sharps Express (IRE) **T C Racing Syndicate**
18 **VINDOBALA (IRE)**, 4, b f Pride of Dubai (AUS)—Sphere of Grace (FR) **The Marina Partnership**
19 **WAR WHISPER (IRE)**, 9, b g Royal Applause—Featherweight (IRE) **The Marina Partnership**

TWO-YEAR-OLDS

20 B f 06/03 Frontiersman—Blackjax (Black Sam Bellamy (IRE)) (952) **Mr S. Smith**
21 Ch g 13/03 Bated Breath—Spin Doctor (Mayson) (22857) **Mr R. Banks**

111 MR PAUL COLLINS, Saltburn-By-The-Sea
Postal: **Groundhill Farm, Lingdale, Saltburn-By-The-Sea, Cleveland, TS12 2WP**
Contacts: **MOBILE 07779 794684**

1 **BREAKEVEN (IRE)**, 7, b g Scorpion (IRE)—Lady Marnay (IRE) **Mr G. R. Vasey**
2 **GOLD VENTURE (IRE)**, 5, ch m Dandy Man (IRE)—Monroe
3 **LUCKY LIGHT**, 6, b m Leading Light (IRE)—Oscar Annie (IRE) **Mr G. R. Vasey**
4 **SONGBIRD'S TALE**, 7, b m Sulamani (IRE)—She Likes To Boogy (IRE) **Mrs P. A. Cowey**
5 **THE LAST KNIGHT (IRE)**, 4, b g The Last Lion (IRE)—Kyanight (IRE) **Mr P. Collins**

THREE-YEAR-OLDS
6 **LADY HOBBS**, b f Jack Hobbs—Definite Artist (IRE)

---

112 MR STUART COLTHERD, Selkirk
Postal: **Clarilawmuir Farm, Selkirk, Selkirkshire, TD7 4QA**
Contacts: **PHONE 01750 21251 MOBILE 07801 398199 FAX 01750 21251**
EMAIL wscoltherd@gmail.com

1 **ANNIES REGATTA**, 6, b m Flemensfirth (USA)—Queens Regatta (IRE) **Mercer Campbell Stanners**
2 **ARCANDY (IRE)**, 6, b m Arcadio (GER)—Turf (FR) **Gillie,Scott,Swinton,Robertson,Tawse**
3 **ARCHI'S AFFAIRE**, 8, ch g Archipenko (USA)—Affaire d'Amour **Coltherd Racing Club**
4 **ARD CHROS (IRE)**, 10, b g Publisher (USA)—Threecrossmammies (IRE) **Coltherd McDougal**
5 **AUGHARUE (IRE)**, 5, b g Rule of Law (USA)—Abbans Aunt (IRE) **Perryman Coltherd**
6 **BUDARRI**, 9, b g Supreme Sound—Amtaar **Cruikshank Coltherd**
7 **CHANCEANOTHERFIVE (IRE)**, 10, b g Dubai Destination (USA)—Ryhall (IRE) **Mr Richard & Mrs Lisa McCulloch**
8 **CLOUDLAND**, 4, ch f Dawn Approach (IRE)—Dream Book **Coltherd Racing Club**
9 **COOPER'S CROSS (IRE)**, 7, b g Getaway (GER)—Rocella (GER) **The Vacuum Pouch Company Limited**
10 **DEEP CHARM**, 8, b g Kayf Tara—Reel Charmer **Mr Richard & Mrs Lisa McCulloch**
11 **DEQUALL**, 6, ch g Zoffany (IRE)—Bark (IRE) **W. S. Coltherd**
12 **GETADAY (IRE)**, 9, ch g Getaway (GER)—Wintry Day (IRE)
13 **GRAND VOYAGE (FR)**, 6, b g Network (GER)—Cape Noir (FR) **Shire Dreamers**
14 **GRAYSTOWN (IRE)**, 10, b g Well Chosen—Temple Girl (IRE) **Ursa Major Coltherd**
15 **JACK YEATS (IRE)**, 6, b g Galileo (IRE)—Fire Lily (IRE) **Coltherd Racing Club**
16 **JIMMY RABBITTE (IRE)**, 9, b g Dubai Destination (USA)—Time To Act **Coltherd Racing Club**
17 **MAID O'MALLEY**, 9, b m Black Sam Bellamy (IRE)—Jolie (IRE) **Debbie Crawford & Stuart Coltherd**
18 **MIDNIGHT SHUFFLE**, 7, b r m Midnight Legend—Lifestyle **Mr A. McCormack**
19 **MISS MISTRAL (IRE)**, 6, gr m War Command (USA)—Drifting Mist **Coltherd Racing Club**
20 **MOONACURA (IRE)**, 5, b g Fame And Glory—Monks Charm (IRE) **Flannigan Newitt French Valender Herriot**
21 **NOTNOWBOB (IRE)**, 5, b g Notnowcato—Meldrum Hall (IRE) **W. S. Coltherd**
22 **OSCAR WILDE (IRE)**, 8, b g Oscar (IRE)—Deep Supreme (IRE)
23 **POOKIE PEKAN (IRE)**, 9, b g Putra Pekan—Shii-Take's Girl **Mr J. Muir**
24 5, B m Yorgunnabelucky (USA)—Pugnacious Lady
25 **RING PRETENDER (FR)**, 6, b m Great Pretender (IRE)—Ring Blood (FR) **The Vacuum Pouch Company Limited**
26 **ROLLERRULER**, 8, b g Native Ruler—Roll Over Rose (IRE) **Mr R. W. Powell**
27 **SILKEN MOONLIGHT**, 8, b m Aqlaam—Silk (IRE) **Coltherd Racing Club**
28 **TO THE LIMIT (IRE)**, 7, gr g Carlotamix (FR)—Miss Kilkeel (IRE) **Border Eagles**
29 **WARENDORF (FR)**, 9, b g Speedmaster (GER)—Hyllisia (FR) **Howard Coltherd Flannigan Newitt**
30 **WHEELBAHRI**, 8, b g Bahri (USA)—Midlem Melody **Coltherd Racing Club**

Other Owners: Mr D. T. Campbell, W. S. Coltherd, Mrs D. Crawford, Mr N. J. Cruikshank, Mr I. R. Flannigan, Mr R. Flannigan, Miss J. French, Mr E. Gillie, Mr B. Herriot, Mr G. P. Howard, Mrs L. J. McCulloch, Mr R. McCulloch, Mr G. McDougal, Mr K. Mercer, Mrs S. C. Newitt, Mr R. J. Perryman, Mr B. A. Robertson, Mr M. J. Scott, Mr M. Stanners, Mr S. Swinton, Mr C. Talbot, Mrs S. Tawse, URSA Major Racing, Mr J. Valender, Mrs G. B. Walford.

Conditional Jockey: Sam Coltherd.

113 MRS SUSAN CORBETT, Otterburn
Postal: **Girsonfield, Otterburn, Newcastle upon Tyne, Tyne and Wear, NE19 1NT**
Contacts: **PHONE 01830 520771 MOBILE 07713 651215 FAX 01830 520771**
EMAIL girsonfield@outlook.com WEBSITE www.girsonfield.co.uk

1 **ANDANTE (IRE)**, 5, b g Califet (FR)—Court Over **King For A Day & W F Corbett**
2 **ASK MY HEATHER (IRE)**, 4, ch g Ask—Tilly Ann (IRE) **Mr R. Payne**
3 **ATOMIC ANGEL**, 7, gr m Geordieland (FR)—Sovereignoftheseas **Castle View Racing**
4 **AVOID DE MASTER (IRE)**, 8, b g Getaway (GER)—Tanit **Castle View Racing**
5 **CLEAR ANGEL**, 4, b g Dark Angel (IRE)—Calypso Beat (USA) **Castle View Racing**
6 **DEVOUR (IRE)**, 9, b g Milan—Marble Desire (IRE) **Girsonfield Racing Club**
7 **DR LYNAS**, 4, ch f Ruler of The World (IRE)—Ogaritmo **Ms J. E. Maggs**
8 **DRUMFIRE**, 4, ch g Night of Thunder (IRE)—Rosewater (IRE) **Girsonfield Racing Club**
9 **FUGACIOUS (IRE)**, 6, b g Fast Company (IRE)—Dazzling Day **Castle View Racing**
10 **GORGEOUS GOBOLINA**, 6, b m Captain Gerrard (IRE)—Gorgeous Goblin (IRE) **Mr S. Humphries**
11 **GOWANBUSTER**, 7, b g Bahri (USA)—Aahgowangowan (IRE) **Gowan Racing**
12 **JODY**, 9, ch m Kheleyf (USA)—Canis Star
13 **LES'S LEGACY**, 5, b g Kutub (IRE)—Morning With Ivan (IRE) **Mr L. P. Richards**
14 5, B m Millenary—Listen Tarablue
15 **ORLAS' ABBEY**, 7, b m Multiplex—Evelith Abbey (IRE) **Girsonfield Racing Club**
16 **REDESDALE ANGEL**, 4, ch f Cityscape—First Harmony **Castle View Racing**
17 **REDESDALE REBEL**, 6, ch g Mayson—Jubilee **Castle View Racing**
18 **SISU**, 4, b f Lawman (FR)—Salonmare (GER) **The Race4fun Syndicate**
19 **STAR DREAMER**, 5, b m Nathaniel (IRE)—Queen's Dream (IRE) **Castle View Racing**
20 **WOR VERGE**, 9, b g Virtual—Hanover Gate **The Goodfellow Partnership**

Other Owners: Castle View Racing, Mr D. J. Clarke, Mrs S. Corbett, Mr W. F. Corbett, Mr M. D. Foden, Girsonfield Racing Club, Mr I. Harle, Mr S. Humphries, King For A Day Club, Mr L. Waugh, Mrs V. M. Waugh.

Assistant Trainer: Mr James Corbett, **Travelling Head:** Emma Tully, **Yard Sponsor:** Finnies Heavy Haulage.

114 MR JOHN CORNWALL, Melton Mowbray
Postal: **April Cottage, Pasture Lane, Hose, Melton Mowbray, Leicestershire, LE14 4LB**
Contacts: **PHONE 01664 444453 MOBILE 07939 557091 FAX 01664 444754**
EMAIL johncornwall7@gmail.com

1 **LESKINFERE (IRE)**, 9, b g Darsi (FR)—Taipans Girl (IRE) **Mr J. R. Cornwall**
2 **TORRENT DES MOTTES (FR)**, 11, gr g Montmartre (FR)—Wavy (FR) **Mr J. R. Cornwall**

115 MR JAKE COULSON, Heaton
Postal: **Bent End Farm, Bearda Hill Racing, Heaton, Macclesfield, Cheshire, SK11 0SJ**
Contacts: **MOBILE 07460 471492**
EMAIL beardahillracing@gmail.com

1 **CHAPATI (FR)**, 8, gr g Fragrant Mix (IRE)—Bessouba (FR) **Horses Over Diamonds**
2 **COOLE WELL (IRE)**, 9, b g Gold Well—Bobs Lass (IRE) **Horses Over Diamonds**
3 **FARM THE ROCK (IRE)**, 11, b g Yeats (IRE)—Shades of Lavender (IRE) **Mr N. Carter**
4 **FOREVER A DOVE (IRE)**, 4, b f Westerner—Drumderry (IRE) **Mr K. Dove**
5 **GALLOWAY DU LIA (FR)**, 6, gr g Turgeon (USA)—Valinka du Lia (FR) **Proper mon Racing**
6 **GETALADY (IRE)**, 6, b m Getaway (GER)—Knocksouna Lady (IRE) **Barrow-yates, Walsh S Hargreaves**
7 **GIBBERWELL (IRE)**, 6, b g Getaway (GER)—Unique Snoopy (IRE) **All Or Nothing Racing Club**
8 **HUBBLE**, 5, gr g Telescope—Tomintoul Star **North West Racing**
9 **IMPERIAL LORD (IRE)**, 6, b g Imperial Monarch (IRE)—Grannys Kitchen (IRE) **Mr N. Carter**
10 **LADY P (IRE)**, 6, ch m Sans Frontieres—Johny's Lantern (IRE) **Mr N. Carter**
11 **NO REACTION (IRE)**, 6, ch m Camacho—Fruit O'The Forest (IRE) **Mr N. Carter**

MR JAKE COULSON - continued

12 **ROB ROYAL (FR)**, 10, gr g Rob Roy (USA)—Royale Trophy (FR) **Mr N. Carter**
13 **SNAP CHAP (IRE)**, 4, b g Vocalised (USA)—Style Queen (IRE) **Mr N. Carter**
14 **TANGLEWOOD TALES**, 4, ch g Nathaniel (IRE)—Camdora (IRE) **The Farnworth Secret Circle**

THREE-YEAR-OLDS
15 **FIFTEEN SUMMERS (IRE)**, b f Zoffany (IRE)—Chase The Light (IRE) **MPS Racing Ltd**

Other Owners: Mrs D. Barrow - Yates, Mr S. Hargreaves, Mrs S. Walsh.

Assistant Trainer: Sarah Carter.

---

116   MISS JACQUELINE COWARD, Dalby
Postal: **Low Moor Farm, Dalby, Yorkshire, YO60 6PF**
Contacts: **PHONE 01653 628995**

1 **ALRIGHT MARLENE (IRE)**, 9, b m Stowaway—One Theatre (IRE) **Mr J. W. Nellis**

---

117   MR ROBERT COWELL, Newmarket
Postal: **Bottisham Heath Stud, Six Mile Bottom, Newmarket, Suffolk, CB8 0TT**
Contacts: **PHONE 01638 570330 MOBILE 07785 512463**
EMAIL robert@robertcowellracing.co.uk WEBSITE www.robertcowellracing.co.uk

1 **AISH**, 4, b f Twilight Son—Chandresh **Manor Farm Stud & Partner**
2 **ARAIFJAN**, 5, ch g Kyllachy—Light Hearted **Mr T. W. Morley**
3 **ARECIBO (FR)**, 7, b g Invincible Spirit (IRE)—Oceanique (USA) **Mr T. W. Morley**
4 **ATALIS BAY**, 4, b c Cable Bay (IRE)—Atalis **Mr T W Morley & Middleham Park Racing**
5 **AUTUMN FLIGHT (IRE)**, 6, b g Dandy Man (IRE)—Swallow Falls (IRE)
              Mrs M. J. Morley, Mrs Morley, R Penney & A Rix
6 **BLUE DE VEGA (GER)**, 9, b g Lope de Vega (IRE)—Burning Heights (GER) **Mrs M. J. Morley**
7 **CLARENDON HOUSE**, 4, b c Mehmas (IRE)—Walaaa (IRE) **Middleham Park Racing VIII**
8 **COMETH THE MAN (IRE)**, 4, b g Dandy Man (IRE)—Be My Queen (IRE) **Mrs M. J. Morley**
9 **COOPERATION (IRE)**, 4, b g Mehmas (IRE)—Ripalong (IRE) **Mrs M. J. Morley**
10 **CORVAIR (IRE)**, 5, b g Toronado (IRE)—Nagham (IRE) **Mrs M. J. Morley**
11 **DUBAI STATION**, 5, b g Brazen Beau (AUS)—Princess Guest (IRE) **Middleham Park, Michael Watt & K Dasmal**
12 **FAUSTUS**, 4, b g Mayson—Israfel **Mrs J. Hadida**
13 **GOLDEN AGE (FR)**, 5, b g Golden Horn—Farnesina (FR) **Mr C Humphris & Partner**
14 **GRANDFATHER TOM**, 7, b g Kheleyf (USA)—Kassuta **Mr J. Sargeant**
15 **GREEN DOOR (IRE)**, 11, b g Camacho—Inourhearts (IRE) **Bottisham Heath Stud**
16 **HAN SOLO BERGER (IRE)**, 7, b g Lord Shanakill (USA)—Dreamaway (IRE) **Mrs B. J. Berresford**
17 **ISLE OF LISMORE (IRE)**, 4, b g Zebedee—Spring Bouquet (IRE) **Mr P. S. Ryan**
18 **LIPSINK (IRE)**, 5, b g Kodiac—Iron Lips **Mr J. Sargeant**
19 **NAVY DRUMS (USA)**, 4, b br g Super Saver (USA)—Beat to Quarters (USA) **Bottisham Heath Stud**
20 **PRIVILEGE (FR)**, 4, b f Elusive City (USA)—Helen Fourment **C. Humphris**
21 **SHANGHAI ROCK**, 4, b g Dark Angel (IRE)—Red Lady (IRE) **Mr R. J. Moore**
22 **SHOW ME A SUNSET**, 6, b g Showcasing—Sunrise Star **The Cool Silk Partnership**
23 **SICILIAN BELLE**, 4, b f Brazen Beau (AUS)—Sciacca (IRE) **Bottisham Heath Stud**
24 **SWELL SONG**, 6, ch m Kyllachy—Racina **Mr I. A. Southcott**
25 **TEMPLE MAN**, 4, b g Showcasing—Kendal Mint **Mr T. W. Morley**
26 **TOMSHALFBROTHER**, 6, b g Sir Percy—Kassuta **Bottisham Heath Stud**
27 **YAZAMAN (IRE)**, 4, b g Kodiac—Online Alexander (IRE) **Mr T. W. Morley**

MR ROBERT COWELL - continued

THREE-YEAR-OLDS

28 **ANGLE LAND**, b f Mayson—Jumeirah Star (USA) **K Dasmal, A Rix, R Penney**
29 **CALIFORNIA CHERRY**, b f Heeraat (IRE)—Rappel **Dachel Stud**
30 **CITY JEWEL**, b f Intrinsic—Chantilly Jewel (USA) **Bottisham Heath Stud**
31 **DREAMS OF THUNDER (IRE)**, b f Night of Thunder (IRE)—Militate **The Cool Silk Partnership**
32 **DYNAMIC FORCE (IRE)**, b c Kodiac—Dream Dana (IRE) **Middleham Park & T W Morley**
33 **EXPLICIT THOUGHTS**, b f Charming Thought—Sciacca (IRE) **Bottisham Heath Stud**
34 **JAZZY PRINCESS**, b f Prince of Lir (IRE)—Street Jazz **The Cool Silk Partnership**
35 **JUSTJAMIE**, b g Sir Percy—Slewtoo **Dachel Stud**
36 **KING OF SPEED (IRE)**, b g Acclamation—Music And Dance **K. A. Dasmal**
37 **KRYPTON**, bl f Farhh—Hot Reply **Mrs V. Machen**
38 **LITTLE EARL (IRE)**, b g Havana Gold—Majestic Alexander (IRE) **Mrs F. H. Hay**
39 **PRINCE OF FLIGHT**, b g Prince of Lir (IRE)—Falsify **Bottisham Heath Stud**
40 **PRINCE OF SPEED**, b g Havana Gold (IRE)—Liberty Chery **K. A. Dasmal**
41 **SHAMILLA**, b f Mayson—Most Tempting **Mrs M Ferguson & Partner**
42 **THAKRAH**, b f Dubawi (IRE)—Thafeera (USA) **Mr T W Morley & Mrs M Ferguson**

TWO-YEAR-OLDS

43 **AGOSTINO**, b c 21/04 Harry Angel (IRE)—Firenze (Efisio) (37000) **Mr P. S. Ryan**
44 **ASIAN QUEEN**, b f 04/04 Twilight Son—Alsium (IRE) (Invincible Spirit (IRE)) (25000) **Mr R. J. Moore**
45 **CUBAN GREY**, gr c 14/04 Havana Grey—Tout Va Bien (IRE) (Verglas (IRE)) (27000) **Mr R. J. Moore**
46 B f 12/04 Tasleet—Falsify (Compton Place)
47 B f 12/04 Intrinsic—Jumeirah Star (USA) (Street Boss (USA)) **Mr Khalifa Dasmal & Bottisham Heath Stud**
48 Ch c 04/03 Night of Thunder (IRE)—Kassuta (Kyllachy) **Mr J. Sargeant**
49 B c 25/02 Oasis Dream—Looks All Right (IRE) (Danehill Dancer (IRE)) (60000) **Mrs F. H. Hay**
50 B f 12/02 Prince Of Lir—Mia Tia (Equiano)
51 **MISS MARIANNE**, b f 03/02 Showcasing—Little Voice (USA) (Scat Daddy (USA))
52 **MOONLIGHT DREAMER**, b c 30/03 Oasis Dream—Peace Dreamer (IRE) (Sir Prancealot (IRE)) **Mrs J. Hadida**
53 Ch c 28/03 Rajasinghe (IRE)—Most Tempting (Showcasing)
54 **POETIC JACK**, b c 06/04 Peace Envoy (FR)—Suzi Spends (IRE) (Royal Applause)
55 **POWEREDBYLOVE**, b f 14/02 Cracksman—Sitar (Aqlaam) (35000) **Mr R. J. Moore**
56 B c 15/01 Mayson—Sciacca (IRE) (Royal Applause)
57 B c 08/04 Profitable (IRE)—Zenella (Kyllachy) (120000) **Mrs F. H. Hay**

Other Owners: Bottisham Heath Stud, Mr R. M. H. Cowell, K. A. Dasmal, Mrs M. Ferguson, C. Humphris, O. H. Kingsley, MPR LIX, Manor Farm Stud & Partner, Manor Farm Stud (Rutland), Middleham Park Racing LXXII, Middleham Park Racing XCIV, Mr T. W. Morley, Mrs R. J. Norman, T. S. Palin, Mr R. C. Penney, M. Prince, Mr A. J. Rix, M. H. Watt.

Head Lad: Mark Gadsby, Gavin Hernon. **Racing Secretary:** Holly Roeder. **Secretary:** Katy Warren.

---

118 **MR CLIVE COX, Hungerford**
Postal: Beechdown Farm, Sheepdrove Road, Lambourn, Hungerford, Berkshire, RG17 7UN
Contacts: WORK 01488 73072 MOBILE 07740 630521
EMAIL clive@clivecox.com WEBSITE www.clivecox.com

1 **ARATUS (IRE)**, 4, b g Free Eagle (IRE)—Shauna's Princess (IRE) **A. Butler**
2 **ASCOT ADVENTURE**, 4, ch g Mayson—Kasumi **Woodhurst Ltd & Withernsea**
3 **CHEERS STEVE**, ch g Lethal Force (IRE)—Dartrix **Clive Cox Racing Ltd**
4 **CHURCHILL BAY**, 4, b g The Last Lion (IRE)—Cape Cay **J. C. Smith**
5 **DANCE FEVER (IRE)**, 5, b g Sir Prancealot (IRE)—Silk Fan (IRE) **Kennet Valley Thoroughbreds VIII**
6 **DILIGENT HARRY**, 4, b c Due Diligence (USA)—Harryana To **The Dilinquents**
7 **FERNANDO RAH**, 4, b g Lethal Force (IRE)—Lacing **Mr P. N. Ridgers**
8 **GLOBAL ACCLAIM**, 4, b f Acclamation—Oeuvre d'Art (IRE) **P. J. Gleeson**
9 **IMPRESSIONS DREAM**, 4, gr f Lethal Force (IRE)—Silken Skies (IRE) **Clive Cox Racing Ltd**
10 **INVINCIBLE SOLDIER (IRE)**, 4, b g The Gurkha (IRE)—Guessing (USA) **Ms A. E. Bilton**

MR CLIVE COX - continued

11 **JUST AMBER,** 4, ch f Lethal Force (IRE)—Milly's Gift **Ken Lock Racing**
12 **LITTLE MISS LILLY,** 7, b m Lethal Force (IRE)—Malilla (IRE) **Clive Cox Racing Ltd**
13 **LITTLE PALAVER,** 10, b g Showcasing—Little Nymph **Mr T. H. S. Fox**
14 **LOUIE DE PALMA,** 10, b g Pastoral Pursuits—Tahirah **Mr P. N. Ridgers**
15 **MILLE MIGLIA,** 4, b f Pride of Dubai (AUS)—Millestan (IRE) **Hot To Trot Racing & D B Clark**
16 **MINE'S A DOUBLE,** 4, b c Mukhadram—Mosa Mine **Maywood Stud**
17 **NIGHT NARCISSUS (IRE),** 4, b f Kodi Bear (IRE)—Midnight Martini **AlMohamediya Racing**
18 **POSITIVE,** 5, b h Dutch Art—Osipova **Mr Alan Spence**
19 **PROP FORWARD,** 4, b g Iffraaj—My Propeller (IRE) **J. C. Smith**
20 **RIVER NYMPH,** 5, b g Cable Bay (IRE)—Little Nymph **Mr T. H. S. Fox**
21 **ROYAL SCIMITAR (IRE),** 4, b g Territories (IRE)—Prequel (IRE) **AlMohamediya Racing**
22 **SADIQAA (IRE),** 4, b g Estidhkaar (IRE)—Tatiana Romanova (USA) **Mr Amigos Partnership**
23 **SPIRIT OF THE BAY (IRE),** 4, b f Cable Bay (IRE)—Decorative (IRE) **The Baywatchers**
24 **TIS MARVELLOUS,** 8, b g Harbour Watch (IRE)—Mythicism **Miss J. Deadman & Mr S. Barrow**
25 **TREGONY,** 4, ch f New Bay—Timarwa (IRE) **S R Hope & S W Barrow**

THREE-YEAR-OLDS

26 **ADAAY ATATIME (IRE),** b g Adaay (IRE)—Glacier Point **B Allen, G Hill & N Wagland**
27 **ADATORIO,** br g Adaay (IRE)—Belatorio (IRE) **The Daydreamers**
28 **APPLAUD NOW,** b c Acclamation—Straight Away **J. C. Smith**
29 **ARGONAULT,** ch g Ulysses (IRE)—Frosting **Philip Booth & Peter Gleeson**
30 **ASCENDING (IRE),** b g Awtaad (IRE)—Midnight Martini **Mr J. Goddard**
31 **AUTUMN MAGIC,** b f Brazen Beau (AUS)—Heliograph **Mr P. N. Ridgers**
32 **BARE NECESSITY (IRE),** b f Kodi Bear (IRE)—Malilla (IRE) **Clive Cox Racing Ltd**
33 **BENEFIT,** b f Acclamation—Boost **Cheveley Park Stud Limited**
34 **BERMUDA,** b f Kodiac—Poana (FR) **Cheveley Park Stud Limited**
35 **BEST BOY ALFIE (IRE),** b g Footstepsinthesand—Harpist (IRE) **Mr & Mrs Paul & Clare Rooney**
36 **CAMBAY SCOUT (IRE),** b c Profitable (IRE)—Throne **AlMohamediya Racing**
37 **CATURRA (IRE),** b c Mehmas (IRE)—Shoshoni Wind **Mr S. B. M. Al Qassimi**
38 **CAVE DIVER,** b f Ulysses (IRE)—Fellbeck **Cheveley Park Stud Limited**
39 **CODIFY (IRE),** b g Lawman (FR)—Bayja (IRE) **Mr J. Goddard**
40 **COMBAT STYLE (IRE),** b c Profitable (IRE)—Thakafaat (IRE) **Clipper Group Holdings Ltd**
41 **DARK SWANSONG (IRE),** b c Dark Angel (IRE)—Pixeleen **Mr A. G. Craddock**
42 **DOUBLE DARE YOU,** b g Bated Breath—Miskin Diamond (IRE) **Maywood Stud**
43 **ELETTARIA (IRE),** b f Mehmas (IRE)—Rayon Rouge (IRE) **Mr S. B. M. Al Qassimi**
44 B c Due Diligence (USA)—Endow (IRE) **AlMohamediya Racing**
45 **FAITHFUL SPIRIT,** b f Cable Bay (IRE)—Don't Forget Faith (USA) **The Beechdown Faithful**
46 **FRUITLOOP,** ch c Profitable (IRE)—Frabjous **Mr & Mrs Paul & Clare Rooney**
47 **GET AHEAD,** ch f Showcasing—Suelita **Hot To Trot Racing V**
48 **HARRY THREE,** b c Adaay (IRE)—Harryana To **Clive Cox Racing Ltd**
49 **INITIATE,** b f Ardad (IRE)—Present Danger **Clipper Group Holdings Ltd**
50 **ISAKOVA,** ch f Pivotal—Russian Heroine **Cheveley Park Stud Limited**
51 **KEEPING HOPING (IRE),** ch f Profitable (IRE)—Sassy Gal (IRE) **Mr & Mrs Paul & Clare Rooney**
52 **KINGDOM COME (IRE),** b c Kingman—Monami (GER) **China Horse Club Int Ltd & Gandharvi Uk**
53 **LET'S FLY AGAIN,** b g Kodiac—Kinnaird (IRE) **Mr Simon Munir & Mr Isaac Souede**
54 **LETHAL NYMPH,** b g Lethal Force (IRE)—Little Nymph **Mr T. H. S. Fox**
55 **MAMBO BEAT (IRE),** ch g Red Jazz (USA)—Bulrushes **Middleham Park Racing CXIV**
56 **MIDNIGHT TRAIN,** b c Iffraaj—Amarysia (FR) **A.D. & A.J. Pearson**
57 **MILITARY ALLIANCE (IRE),** b c Churchill (IRE)—Dusty In Memphis (USA) **Clipper Group Holdings Ltd**
58 **MOHI,** b c Acclamation—Minalisa **AlMohamediya Racing**
59 **MURPHY'S DREAM,** br c Due Diligence (USA)—Chicklade **Mr & Mrs Paul & Clare Rooney**
60 **OLYMPIC EAGLE,** ch c Gleneagles (IRE)—Olympic Runner **J. C. Smith**
61 **PAVLODAR (FR),** ch g Recorder—Sampaquita (FR) **N. Bizakov**
62 **PERFECT CHARMER,** gr c Charming Thought—Secret Night **Hants & Herts**
63 **REGAL ENVOY (IRE),** b c Ardad (IRE)—Regina **Kennet Valley Thoroughbreds I**
64 **RETURN VOYAGE (USA),** ch f Street Boss (USA)—Sail Away Home (USA) **Mr P Stokes & Mr S Krase**
65 **RUM COCKTAIL,** b f Muhaarar—Tropical Treat **J. C. Smith**
66 **SAFETY FIRST,** b f New Bay—Soteria (IRE) **China Horse Club International Limited**
67 **SAUSALITO,** b g Frankel—One Last Dance (AUS) **Mr J. M. Camilleri**

MR CLIVE COX - continued

68 B f Zoffany (IRE)—Savannah Belle **Mrs Patricia J. Burns**
69 **SECOND STAR (IRE),** b f Sea The Stars (IRE)—Minute Limit (IRE) **Celbridge Estates Ltd**
70 **SECRET SERVICE,** ch c Churchill (IRE)—Ighraa (IRE) **Mrs J Magnier M Tabor D Smith Westerberg**
71 Gr ro g Lethal Force (IRE)—Silken Skies (IRE) **Clive Cox Racing Ltd**
72 **SILVER SCREEN,** b f Lope de Vega (IRE)—Silver Mirage **Her Majesty The Queen**
73 **SPECIAL TIMES,** b f Time Test—Salonmare (GER) **Windmill Racing III**
74 **STELLAR QUEEN,** b f Muhaarar—Bella Lulu **Mr I. Alsagar**
75 **SURAC (IRE),** b g Frankel—Belesta **Mr Simon Munir & Mr Isaac Souede**
76 **TRANS MONTANA,** b f Mondialiste (IRE)—Tarqua (IRE) **Earl of Carnarvon**
77 **UBERRIMA FIDES,** b c Exceed And Excel (AUS)—Baileys Showgirl (FR) **Mr Simon Munir & Mr Isaac Souede**
78 **WATCHYA,** gr c Dark Angel (IRE)—Barroche (IRE) **Mr A. L. Cohen**
79 **WHOPUTFIFTYINYOU (IRE),** ch c Twilight Son—Poyle Meg **Mr & Mrs Paul & Clare Rooney**
80 **WINGS OF WAR (IRE),** gr c Dark Angel (IRE)—Futoon (IRE) **Sheikh I. S. Al Khalifa**
81 **WINTER GAMES (IRE),** b c Mehmas (IRE)—Keukenhof (GER) **Mr M. Rashid**
82 **WOWZERS,** gr c Kodiac—Vallado (IRE) **Mr A. L. Cohen**
83 **YARRALUMLA,** ch f Australia—Free Verse **Her Majesty The Queen**

TWO-YEAR-OLDS

84 B c 20/04 Kodiac—Alluring Park (IRE) (Green Desert (USA)) (475000)
85 **BONNY ANGEL,** b f 25/03 Harry Angel (IRE)—Timeless Gift (IRE) (Camacho) **Mr P. N. Ridgers**
86 B c 12/04 U S Navy Flag (USA)—Cherished (IRE) (Kodiac) (76190) **AlMohamediya Racing**
87 Ch c 11/04 Harry Angel (IRE)—Dance Hall Girl (IRE) (Dansili) (47619) **Sheikh A. H. F. M. A. Al Sabah**
88 B c 13/04 Kodi Bear (IRE)—Dazzling Valentine (Oratorio (IRE)) (95000) **Mr S. B. M. Al Qassimi**
89 **DUE DATE,** b c 23/04 Due Diligence (USA)—Harryana To (Compton Place) (52381) **N. Bizakov**
90 B c 27/01 Sioux Nation (USA)—Edessa (IRE) (Lawman (FR)) (140000)

                                 Mrs J Magnier M Tabor D Smith Westerberg
91 Gr c 15/02 Free Eagle (IRE)—Evening Frost (IRE) (Invincible Spirit (IRE)) (50000) **A. Butler**
92 Br f 03/04 Cracksman—Garanciere (FR) (Anabaa (USA)) (70000)
93 **HAVANA BLUE,** gr c 10/03 Havana Grey—Exrating (Exceed And Excel (AUS)) (104762) **Teme Valley**
94 **HIGHER WIRE (IRE),** gr f 15/03 Dark Angel (IRE)—Layla Jamil (IRE) (Exceed And Excel (AUS)) (80000)

                                 Mr P Stokes & Mr S Krase
95 B c 09/04 Kodi Bear (IRE)—Ice Haven (IRE) (Verglas (IRE)) (17857) **Mrs O. A. Shaw**
96 **JUST BRING IT (IRE),** ch c 25/03 Harry Angel (IRE)—Just Joan (IRE) (Pour Moi (IRE)) (130000) **Atlantic Equine**
97 Gr c 23/02 Gregorian (IRE)—Kabaya (FR) (Stormy River (FR)) (18000) **Kennet Valley Thoroughbreds I**
98 Gr c 19/03 Havana Grey—Kendamara (FR) (Kendargent (FR)) (72279) **Mr J. Goddard**
99 B c 12/04 Washington DC (IRE)—La Cabana (Havana Gold (IRE)) (3810) **Bearstone Stud Limited**
100 B c 29/02 Invincible Spirit (IRE)—Liberating (Iffraaj) (85034) **Mr J. Goddard**
101 B c 08/03 Kodiac—Light Glass (IRE) (Lope de Vega (IRE)) (76190)
102 **LOST ANGEL (IRE),** gr f 11/04 Dark Angel (IRE)—Last Bid (Vital Equine (IRE)) (150000) **Atlantic Equine**
103 Ch f 06/04 Starspangledbanner (AUS)—Our Joy (IRE) (Kodiac) (50000)
104 B f 13/02 Kingman—Place In My Heart (Compton Place) (75000) **C. J. Harper**
105 B f 18/04 Ribchester (IRE)—Puff Pastry (Pivotal) (39116) **Mr J. Goddard**
106 **QUEEN OF THRONES (IRE),** b f 25/02 Profitable (IRE)—Throne (Royal Applause) (38095) **The Profiteers**
107 **QUIET LIFE,** b f 26/04 Oasis Dream—Humdrum (Dr Fong (USA))
108 B c 05/02 Exceed And Excel (AUS)—Quinta Verde (IRE) (Tamayuz) (55000) **Woodhurst Construction Ltd**
109 **REDEMPTION TIME,** b c 06/03 Harry Angel (IRE)—Red Box (Exceed And Excel (AUS)) (209524) **Atlantic Equine**
110 B c 23/04 Gleneagles (IRE)—Relevant (IRE) (So You Think (NZ)) (75000) **Clive Cox Racing Ltd**
111 B c 30/01 Dragon Pulse (IRE)—Rosa Gialla (IRE) (Diamond Green (FR)) (43810) **Miss J. Deadman & Mr S. Barrow**
112 B c 28/02 Shalaa (IRE)—Rowan Brae (Haafhd) (64762) **Miss J. Deadman & Mr S. Barrow**
113 B c 04/02 Profitable (IRE)—Sahaayef (IRE) (Mawatheeq (USA)) (36190) **AlMohamediya Racing**
114 B c 21/03 Twilight Son—Samasana (IRE) (Redback) (135000) **AlMohamediya Racing**
115 **SCHOLARSHIP (IRE),** b c 30/04 Profitable (IRE)—Thakerah (IRE) (New Approach (IRE)) (60000)

                                 Sheikh I. S. Al Khalifa
116 B c 06/02 Lethal Force (IRE)—Secret Night (Dansili)
117 Ch f 18/02 Havana Grey—Showstoppa (Showcasing) (61905)
118 B c 22/01 Kodiac—Supporter (Dubawi (IRE)) **N. Bizakov**
119 B f 02/04 War Front (USA)—Susan B Anthony (IRE) (Galileo (IRE))
120 B br c 08/02 Sioux Nation (USA)—Swing Out Sister (IRE) (Kodiac) (140000) **Sheikh I. S. Al Khalifa**
121 B c 25/04 Dark Angel (IRE)—The Hermitage (IRE) (Kheleyf (USA)) (59524) **Mr J. Goddard**

MR CLIVE COX - continued

122 TICKET TO ALASKA (IRE), b c 21/04 Kodiac—Jira (Medicean) (47619) **Browns & Hornbys**
123 Ch c 22/01 Cotai Glory—Wee Jean (Captain Gerrard (IRE)) (31000) **Sheikh A. H. F. M. A. Al Sabah**
124 B c 26/02 Ardad (IRE)—Wild Mimosa (IRE) (Dynaformer (USA)) (100000) **Woodhurst Construction Ltd**

Other Owners: Miss B. Allen, Mr S. W. Barrow, Mr P. Booth, D. R. Brown, Mrs E. E. Brown, China Horse Club International Limited, D. B. Clark, Mr D. J. Cox, Miss J. Deadman, Mr A. C. Elliott, Gandharvi UK Ltd, P. J. Gleeson, C. J. Harper, Mr I. C. Higginson, Mr G. I. Hill, S. R. Hope, Mr A. H. Hornby, Mr R. S. Hoskins, Hot To Trot Racing 1, Hot To Trot Racing 2, K. T. Ivory, Mr S. D. Krase, L. Lillingston, Mrs S. Magnier, S. E. Munir, Mr A. Pearson, Ms Z. L. Pinchbeck, Mr A. J. Ramsden, D. Smith, Mr I. Souede, Mr Alan Spence, Mr P. G. C. A. Stokes, M. Tabor, Mr N. Wagland, Westerberg, Withernsea Thoroughbred Limited, Woodhurst Construction Ltd.

Flat Jockey: Hector Crouch, Liam Keniry, Adam Kirby. **Apprentice Jockey:** Amelia Glass, Deon Le Roux, Owen Lewis.

119
MR TONY COYLE, Norton
Postal: **Long Row Stables, Beverley Road, Norton, Malton, North Yorkshire, YO17 9PJ**
Contacts: **MOBILE 07976 621425**
EMAIL tonycoyleracing@hotmail.co.uk

1 BROKEN SPEAR, 6, b g Pastoral Pursuits—My Pretty Girl **Morecool Racing**
2 EY UP IT'S MAGGIE, 4, b f Equiano (FR)—Velvet Jaguar **Mrs M. Lingwood**
3 EY UP ITS MICK, 6, b g Milk It Mick—Silky Silence **Mrs M. Lingwood**
4 FLEETING BLUE (FR), 4, ch f French Navy—My Pretty Girl **David Bishop & Tony Coyle**
5 NEWGATE ANGEL, 6, b m Heeraat (IRE)—Rio's Girl **Alison Johnson & Tony Coyle**
6 5, Ch m Proclamation (IRE)—Qualitee **C. R. Green**
7 SCORCHED EARTH (IRE), 6, ch g Zoffany (IRE)—How's She Cuttin' (IRE) **Mr R. Postlethwaite**
8 WOTS THE WIFI CODE, 5, b g Fast Company (IRE)—Velvet Jaguar **Mrs M. Lingwood**
9 YOUARENOTFORGIVEN, 4, b g Starspangledbanner (AUS)—Spiliada (FR) **Mr R. Postlethwaite**

THREE-YEAR-OLDS
10 EY UP ITS THE BOSS, br g Pastoral Pursuits—Velvet Jaguar **M. & S. Bland**
11 GOLDEN PROSPERITY (IRE), ch g Galileo Gold—April (IRE) **Mr A. C. Coyle**
12 PEACE ANGEL, b f War Command (USA)—Bridge Poseidon (IRE) **Mr D F L Bishop & Partner**
13 SELBY'S PRIDE, b f Lethal Force (IRE)—Vibrant **Mrs A. M. Johnson**

TWO-YEAR-OLDS
14 Ch g 25/02 Pastoral Pursuits—Mad Jazz (Sir Percy)
15 Ch c 21/03 Dandy Man (IRE)—Pretty Pebble (IRE) (Cape Cross (IRE)) (28000)
16 Br f 14/01 Pastoral Pursuits—Velvet Jaguar (Hurricane Run (IRE))
17 B f 23/05 Massaat (IRE)—Vibrant (Pivotal) **Mrs A. M. Johnson**

Other Owners: Mr D. F. L. Bishop, Mr S. Bland, Mr A. C. Coyle, Mrs A. M. Johnson, Mrs M. Lingwood, Mr J. Walsh.

Flat Jockey: Barry McHugh.

120
MR RAY CRAGGS, Sedgefield
Postal: **East Close Farm, Sedgefield, Stockton-On-Tees, Cleveland, TS21 3HW**
Contacts: **PHONE 01740 620239 FAX 01740 623476**

1 AMELIA R (IRE), 6, b m Zoffany (IRE)—Xaloc (IRE) **R. Craggs**
2 AMOURI GLEAM, 7, b m Arabian Gleam—Tour d'Amour (IRE) **R. Craggs**
3 AMOURIE, 6, ch m Haafhd—Tour d'Amour (IRE) **R. Craggs**

MR RAY CRAGGS- continued

4 **GLEAMING MAIZE**, 6, b m Arabian Gleam—Mrs Quince **R. Craggs**
5 **KHABIB (IRE)**, 4, b br g Mehmas (IRE)—Lady Mega (IRE) **R. Craggs**
6 **QUAY QUEST**, 8, ch g Shami—Quay Four (IRE) **R. Craggs**
7 **SPYCRACKER**, 5, b g Monsieur Bond (IRE)—Tour d'Amour (IRE) **R. Craggs**
8 **WELL I NEVER**, 10, b g Josr Algarhoud (IRE)—Tour d'Amour (IRE) **R. Craggs**

THREE-YEAR-OLDS

9 **BRASS CASTLE**, b g Intrinsic—Fleurtille **R. Craggs**

Assistant Trainer: Miss J. N. Craggs.

121
MR MATTHEW CRAWLEY, Newmarket
Postal: **73 Manderston Road, Newmarket, Suffolk, CB8 0NL**
Contacts: PHONE **07719 616402**
EMAIL **matcrawley73@hotmail.co.uk**

1 **CENDRILLON**, 4, ch f Bobby's Kitten (USA)—Midnight Ransom **Ms S. J. Humber**
2 **DREAM GAME**, 5, bl m Brazen Beau (AUS)—Dreamily (IRE) **Ms S. J. Humber**
3 **NO TIME TO DIE**, 4, b f Proconsul—The Last Daughter
4 **OWEN LITTLE**, 4, b g Sakhee (USA)—Three Heart's **Ms S. J. Humber**
5 **STRANGER THINGS**, 4, ch f Mukhadram—Fairy Steps **Ms S. J. Humber**

THREE-YEAR-OLDS

6 **WAR BONNET**, b c Helmet (AUS)—House Maiden (IRE) **Ms S. J. Humber**

122
SIMON AND ED CRISFORD, Newmarket
Postal: **Gainsborough Thoroughbreds Limited, Gainsborough Stables, Hamilton Road,
Newmarket, Suffolk, CB8 0TE**
Contacts: PHONE **01638 662661**
EMAIL **info@gainsboroughoffice.com** WEBSITE **www.gainsboroughthoroughbreds.com**
TWITTER **@gainsboroughhq** INSTAGRAM **@gainsboroughhq**

1 **AADDEEY (IRE)**, 5, b g New Approach (IRE)—Feedyah (USA)
2 **CHANCE**, 6, ch g Lope de Vega (IRE)—Harem Lady (FR)
3 **FINEST SOUND (IRE)**, 5, b g Exceed And Excel (AUS)—Amplifier
4 **ILZA'EEM (FR)**, 4, b g Olympic Glory (IRE)—Money Time (IRE)
5 **INTUITIVE (IRE)**, 6, b g Haatef (USA)—Majraa (FR)
6 **JADOOMI (FR)**, 4, b c Holy Roman Emperor (IRE)—South Sister
7 **LATEST GENERATION**, 4, b g Frankel—Rizeena (IRE)
8 **MISS MARBLE**, 4, b f Iffraaj—Lottie Dod (IRE)
9 **NANKEEN**, 4, b g Dubawi (IRE)—Yellow Rosebud (IRE)
10 **ROULSTON SCAR (IRE)**, 6, b g Lope de Vega (IRE)—Pussycat Lips (IRE)
11 **SALEYMM (IRE)**, 4, b c Dubawi (IRE)—Talmada (USA)
12 **WITHOUT A FIGHT (IRE)**, 5, b g Teofilo (IRE)—Khor Sheed

THREE-YEAR-OLDS

13 **AL AGAILA (IRE)**, b f Lope de Vega (IRE)—L'Amour de Ma Vie (USA)
14 **AMMOLITE (IRE)**, ch f Profitable (IRE)—Romie's Kastett (GER)
15 B c Gleneagles (IRE)—Anaamil (IRE)
16 **ANGLESEY ABBEY**, b g New Approach (IRE)—Summer Flower (IRE)

SIMON AND ED CRISFORD - continued

17 B c Lope de Vega (IRE)—Anna's Rock (IRE)
18 ANOTHER ROMANCE (IRE), ch f Night of Thunder (IRE)—Late Romance (USA)
19 ANTHEM NATIONAL (IRE), b c Dark Angel (IRE)—Anthem Alexander (IRE)
20 ARTAOIS, b c Kodiac—La Patria
21 B f Ribchester (IRE)—Artisti
22 ASWAN (IRE), b g Caravaggio (USA)—Spring Garden (IRE)
23 B f Shamardal (USA)—Baheeja
24 BASE NOTE, b c Shamardal (USA)—Fragrancy (IRE)
25 BEAU RIVAGE, b f Nathaniel (IRE)—Baisse
26 BENZINE, b c Almanzor (FR)—Holberg Suite
27 BOLD PRESENCE, b c Siyouni (FR)—Appearance
28 CAESAR'S PALACE, b g Holy Roman Emperor (IRE)—Return Ace
29 CENTRAL HALL (IRE), b c Dubawi (IRE)—Megaron
30 COURT OF SESSION, br g Iffraaj—Sibilance
31 CROUPIER (IRE), b g Invincible Spirit (IRE)—Aaraamm (USA)
32 CYNICAL POINT (USA), br c Point of Entry (USA)—Cynical Storm (USA)
33 DANEH, b f Dubawi (IRE)—Rizeena (IRE)
34 DESERT TEAM (IRE), b f Invincible Spirit (IRE)—Kilmah
35 B c Holy Roman Emperor (IRE)—Dream Wedding
36 DUKEMAN (IRE), b c Kingman—She's Mine (IRE)
37 ELITE ARTIST, ch f Shamardal (USA)—Aquatinta (GER)
38 FAST ATTACK (IRE), b f Kodiac—Fort Del Oro (IRE)
39 FINE BALANCE (IRE), b f Siyouni (FR)—Cash In The Hand (USA)
40 B f Kingman—Fine Time
41 FLOTUS (IRE), b f Starspangledbanner (AUS)—Floriade (IRE)
42 GOLDEN GLANCE, b f Golden Horn—Zeeba (IRE)
43 HAMAAMM (FR), b f Le Havre (IRE)—Equity Card (FR)
44 B c Animal Kingdom (USA)—Hawana (USA)
45 B f Exceed And Excel (AUS)—Hushing
46 B c Kingman—Into The Mystic (IRE)
47 KAASIRR (IRE), gr c Dark Angel (IRE)—Majeyda (USA)
48 KAATIBB, b g Siyouni (FR)—Newton's Night (IRE)
49 B f Iffraaj—Lady of Persia (JPN)
50 B c Dabirsim (FR)—Mambomiss (FR)
51 MISS FEDORA (IRE), b f Helmet (AUS)—Shahabad
52 NAJAT, b f Ardad (IRE)—Ouja
53 NEW NATION (IRE), b c Starspangledbanner (AUS)—Intermittent
54 NIGHT SPARKLE (IRE), b f Postponed (IRE)—Rose Diamond (IRE)
55 PHILOSOPHY, b f Exceed And Excel (AUS)—Greatest Virtue
56 B f Fastnet Rock (AUS)—Pivotal Mission
57 POKER FACE (IRE), b g Fastnet Rock (AUS)—Stars At Night (IRE)
58 POSITIVE IMPACT (IRE), ch c Shamardal (USA)—Masarah (IRE)
59 Ch g Sea The Moon (GER)—Proserpine (USA)
60 PUNTO BANCO (IRE), b g Zoffany (IRE)—Dewdrop (IRE)
61 B f Churchill (IRE)—Pussycat Lips (IRE)
62 QUEEN OF CHANGE (IRE), b f Sea The Stars (IRE)—Salacia (IRE)
63 READY TO SHINE (IRE), b f Camelot—Matorio (FR)
64 B c Australia—Reset In Blue (IRE)
65 SAFRA (USA), b f War Front (USA)—Tell Me Now (IRE)
66 SASSI NERI, b f Nathaniel (IRE)—Secret Soul
67 SEA THE CASPER (IRE), ch c Sea The Stars (IRE)—October Queen (IRE)
68 SMART CONTENDER (IRE), b c Shamardal (USA)—Dark Liberty (IRE)
69 SOOGHAN, b c Iffraaj—Feedyah (USA)
70 B f Churchill (IRE)—South Bay
71 SPRINGTIME, b c Postponed (IRE)—Frangipanni (IRE)
72 Gr ro f Dubawi (IRE)—Summer Fete (IRE)
73 TYLOS (FR), b c Night of Thunder (IRE)—New Arrival (FR)
74 B g Wootton Bassett—Vega Sicilia (FR)
75 VESPASIAN (IRE), b c Acclamation—Lady Livius (IRE)
76 WEST WIND BLOWS (IRE), b c Teofilo (IRE)—West Wind

SIMON AND ED CRISFORD - continued

TWO-YEAR-OLDS

77 B c 29/03 Exceed And Excel (AUS)—Bahjtee (Pivotal)
78 **BOLSTER,** b c 16/04 Invincible Spirit (IRE)—Quilting (USA) (King's Best (USA))
79 B c 20/03 Cracksman—Buntingford (IRE) (Manduro (GER))
80 **BYSTANDER (IRE),** b c 31/03 Dark Angel (IRE)—Witnessed (Authorized (IRE)) (150000)
81 B f 30/03 New Approach (IRE)—Cairncross (IRE) (Cape Cross (IRE))
82 **CATORI,** b f 16/02 Invincible Spirit (IRE)—Lilian Baylis (IRE) (Shamardal (USA))
83 B c 11/03 Kingman—Cercle d'Or (IRE) (Acclamation) (400000)
84 B c 01/04 Shamardal (USA)—Dark Liberty (IRE) (Dark Angel (IRE))
85 B f 12/02 Cracksman—Dresden Doll (USA) (Elusive Quality (USA))
86 B c 07/03 Frankel—Feedyah (USA) (Street Cry (IRE))
87 B c 15/04 Mehmas (IRE)—Fidaaha (IRE) (New Approach (IRE)) (210000)
88 Ch c 18/02 New Approach (IRE)—First Priority (Street Cry (IRE))
89 Ch f 12/05 Night of Thunder (IRE)—Fragrancy (IRE) (Singspiel (IRE))
90 B c 01/02 Showcasing—Fresh Air (IRE) (Montjeu (IRE)) (119048)
91 B c 31/03 Dubawi (IRE)—Golden Valentine (FR) (Dalakhani (IRE)) (637755)
92 Ch c 09/04 Pivotal—Greatest Virtue (Poet's Voice)
93 Ch f 08/02 Showcasing—Intense Pink (Pivotal) (130000)
94 Ch c 31/01 New Approach (IRE)—Jadeyra (Dubawi (IRE))
95 B c 05/02 New Approach (IRE)—Lady Marian (GER) (Nayef (USA))
96 B f 21/04 Postponed (IRE)—Lady Zonda (Lion Cavern (USA))
97 B f 13/04 Camacho—Lavande (FR) (Style Vendome (FR))
98 **LUFU,** b f 23/02 Muhaarar—Melody of Love (Haafhd) (16000)
99 B f 15/05 Lope de Vega (IRE)—Majeyda (USA) (Street Cry (IRE))
100 **MISKA (IRE),** b f 26/01 Kodiac—Shobobb (Shamardal (USA)) (210000)
101 B c 13/04 Territories (IRE)—Miss Carbonia (IRE) (Lilbourne Lad (IRE))
102 C f 18/02 Sea The Stars (IRE)—Nezwaah (Dubawi (IRE))
103 B c 09/04 Kingman—Pirouette (Pivotal) (130000)
104 **ROTATIONAL,** b br f 23/03 Kingman—Pivotiue (Pivotal)
105 B c 23/02 Kingman—Sajjhaa (King's Best (USA))
106 B c 08/05 Teofilo (IRE)—Special Guest (Dubawi (IRE))
107 **STAR PLAYER,** b c 09/02 Zoffany (IRE)—Lunar Phase (Galileo (IRE)) (31429)
108 **TARLO (IRE),** b c 20/03 Kodiac—Pious Alexander (IRE) (Acclamation) (230000)
109 Ch f 08/05 New Approach (IRE)—Time To Blossom (Cape Cross (IRE))
110 **TRIBUTE (IRE),** b c 03/03 Acclamation—Party Whip (IRE) (Whipper (USA)) (90000)
111 Gr c 02/05 Wootton Bassett—Tubereuse (IRE) (Cape Cross (IRE)) (263605)
112 B f 20/04 Shamardal (USA)—Tutu Nguru (USA) (Blame (USA))

123	**MR ANDREW CROOK, Middleham**

Postal: **Ashgill Stables (Yard 2), Tugpill Park, Coverham, Middleham, North Yorkshire, DL8 4TJ**
Contacts: **PHONE 01969 640303 MOBILE 07764 158899**
EMAIL andycrookracing@gmail.com **WEBSITE** www.andrewcrookracing.co.uk

1 **BUBBLES'N'TROUBLES,** 5, b m Flemensfirth (USA)—Jontys'lass **Mr D. Carter**
2 **CRAKEHALL LAD (IRE),** 11, ch g Manduro (GER)—My Uptown Girl **Mrs K. M. Savage**
3 **DAKOTA MOIRETTE (FR),** 9, b g Voix du Nord (FR)—Rahana Moirette (FR) **The Golden Dream**
4 **DANKING,** 5, b g Dansili—Time Saved **Mrs H. Sinclair**
5 **EMPORTEPARLAFOULE (FR),** 8, gr g Smadoun (FR)—Sempiternelle (FR) **Mr D. Carter**
6 **HAUT BERRY (FR),** 5, bl g My Risk (FR)—Bonjour Madame (FR) **R. P. E. Berry**
7 **HUBBEL BUBBEL,** 4, b g Telescope (IRE)—Cormorant Cove **Mr D. Carter**
8 **KNACKER TRAPPER (IRE),** 4, b g Court Cave (IRE)—Present Line (IRE) **Mr D. Carter**
9 **LADY BABS,** 8, br m Malinas (GER)—Jontys'lass **Ashgill Stud**
10 4, B f Night Wish (GER)—Message Personnel **R. P. E. Berry**
11 **ORCHID ROSE (IRE),** 4, b f Mehmas (IRE)—Pale Orchid (IRE) **Mr D. Carter**

MR ANDREW CROOK - continued

12 **OUR CILLA**, 8, gr m Sixties Icon—Kinetix **The 100 Club**
13 **OUR STAR IN HEAVEN (IRE)**, 4, b g Sea The Stars (IRE)—Rich Jade (USA) **Miss A. M. Crook**
14 **RACEMAKER**, 8, b g Stimulation (IRE)—Sophies Heart **Mrs H. Sinclair**
15 **TILTILYS ROCK (IRE)**, 5, ch g Society Rock (IRE)—Tiltili (IRE) **Mr D. Carter**
16 **VESHENSKAYA (IRE)**, 7, b m Sholokhov (IRE)—Manorville (IRE) **Signify Partnership**
17 **ZARA'S UNIVERSE**, 6, b m Universal (IRE)—Jontys'lass **Ashgill Stud 2**

Other Owners: R. P. E. Berry, Mr D. Carter, Mr R. Chapman, Miss A. M. Crook, Miss M. Hodgson, Mrs C. Hopper, Mrs K. M. Savage, Mr J. A. Saxby, Mr E. Skeels, O. R. Weeks.

Assistant Trainer: Amy Crook.

NH Jockey: John Kington.

---

124 **MR SEAN CURRAN, Swindon**
Postal: **Twelve Oaks, Lechlade Road, Highworth, Swindon, Wiltshire, SN6 7QR**
Contacts: **MOBILE 07774 146169**

1 **ALL YOURS (FR)**, 11, ch g Halling (USA)—Fontaine Riant (FR) **Power Geneva Ltd**
2 **ALMUFEED (IRE)**, 5, b g Mukhadram—Anqooda (USA) **Power Geneva Ltd**
3 **BRAVE GOZZY (BEL)**, 6, b g Brave Mansonnien (FR)—God's Rescape (FR) **12 Oaks Racing**
4 **BUCKLAND BOY (IRE)**, 7, b g Bated Breath—Rancho Montoya (IRE) **Mr P. S. McNally**
5 **C'EST QUELQU'UN (FR)**, 5, br g Buck's Boum (FR)—Sangrilla (FR) **Mr R. Cooper**
6 **DOMAINE DE L'ISLE (FR)**, 9, b g Network (GER)—Gratiene de L'Isle (FR) **Oaks & Ian Hutchins**
7 **DOUKAROV (FR)**, 7, b g Le Havre (FR)—Landskia (FR) **Mr A. J. White**
8 **GIVE US A SWIG**, 7, b g Trans Island—Touch of Ivory (IRE) **Power Geneva Ltd**
9 **GRAND KNIGHT (FR)**, 6, b g Slickly (FR)—La Grande Dame (FR) **Mr N. Byrne**
10 **GRIGGY (IRE)**, 6, b g Dandy Man (IRE)—Joint Destiny (IRE) **Power Geneva Ltd**
11 **GROOM DE COTTE (FR)**, 6, b g Tiger Groom—Traviata Valtat (FR) **Mr W. J. M. Byrne**
12 **KERRKENNY GOLD (IRE)**, 8, ch g Sans Frontieres (IRE)—Cailins Honour (IRE) **12 Oaks Racing**
13 **PINK JAZZ (IRE)**, 5, br g Red Jazz (USA)—Marveloftheledge (IRE) **Power Geneva Ltd**
14 **RUBY RED EMPRESS (IRE)**, 5, b m Holy Roman Emperor (IRE)—Rougette **Power Geneva Ltd**
15 **TALKING ABOUT YOU**, 5, b m Sixties Icon—Ificaniwill (IRE) **I. M. McGready**
16 **UNFORGIVING MINUTE**, 11, b g Cape Cross (IRE)—Ada River **Power Geneva Ltd**

---

125 **MISS REBECCA CURTIS, Newport**
Postal: **Fforest Farm, Newport, Pembrokeshire, SA42 0UG**
Contacts: PHONE 01348 811489 MOBILE 07970 710690
EMAIL rebcurtis@hotmail.com

1 **ANAX (IRE)**, 8, b g Oscar (IRE)—Limetree Leader (IRE) **Mr N. D. Morris**
2 **BARNARD CASTLE (IRE)**, 7, b g Oscar (IRE)—Rambling Liss (IRE) **Conyers, O'Reilly, Roddis, Zeffman**
3 **BEATTHEBULLET (IRE)**, 8, br g Flemensfirth (USA)—Top Quality **Conyers, O'Reilly, Roddis, Zeffman**
4 **BLACK SAM MELODY**, 6, b m Black Sam Bellamy (IRE)—Moonlight Music (IRE) **Mr M. A. Sherwood**
5 **BOLEY BAY (IRE)**, 7, b g Yeats (IRE)—Print It On Lips (IRE) **Fforest Star Racing Ltd**
6 **BOSTON JOE (IRE)**, 6, b g Sageburg (IRE)—Supreme Millie (IRE) **Miss R. Curtis**
7 **CARDIGAN ISLE**, 6, br m Kalanisi (IRE)—Sacred Isle (IRE) **Mrs G. A. Davies**
8 **COMETH THE HOUR (IRE)**, 5, b g Imperial Monarch (IRE)—Back And Fore (IRE) **Diamond Racing Ltd**
9 **CUBAO (IRE)**, 8, b g Fame And Glory—Rematch (IRE) **Primus Partners**
10 **FANAMIX (FR)**, 7, gr g Al Namix (FR)—Fanfan Du Fanil (FR) **Mrs G. A. Davies**
11 **FIDDLERS TRACKER (IRE)**, 7, b g Pour Moi (IRE)—Tracker **Mr R. Hyde**
12 **GEORDIE DES CHAMPS (IRE)**, 11, br g Robin des Champs (FR)—Kilcoleman Lady (IRE) **Mr J. P. McManus**
13 **HARD GROUND**, 8, b g Malinas (GER)—Poppy Come Running (IRE) **Mrs C Lockett & The Welsh Rugby Rockets**
14 4, B g Dahjee (USA)—Haven't A Notion **Mr G. S. Gammond**

MISS REBECCA CURTIS - continued

15 **HIS OSCAR (IRE)**, 7, b g Oscar (IRE)—St Helans Bay (IRE) **Got There In the End Partnership**
16 **HOUSE OF STORIES (IRE)**, 6, b br g Presenting—Liss Aris (IRE) **O'Reilly, Zeffman.**
17 **INDIGO BOY (FR)**, 4, b g Diamond Boy (FR)—Perle Irlandaise (FR) **Miss R. Curtis**
18 **JOUEUR BRESILIEN (FR)**, 10, b g Fuisse (FR)—Fille du Bresil (FR) **Inthewayboy Group**
19 **LEGENDS GOLD (IRE)**, 8, b m Gold Well—Fu's Legend (FR) **Lockett,Hyde,Mountford,Bishop&Outhart**
20 **LISNAGAR OSCAR (IRE)**, 9, b g Oscar (IRE)—Asta Belle (FR) **Racing For Fun**
21 **LISSITZKY (IRE)**, 7, b g Declaration of War (USA)—Tarfshi **Mr N. D. Morris**
22 **LUBEAT FORAS (IRE)**, 7, ch g Aizavoski (IRE)—Roomier (IRE) **Relentless Dreamers Racing**
23 **MINELLA BOBO (IRE)**, 9, gr g Oscar (IRE)—Line Kendie (FR) **Moran, Outhart, McDermott, Hyde & Hill**
24 **MONBARI (FR)**, 4, b g Zanzibari (USA)—Mondovi (FR) **Miss R. Curtis**
25 **MR KATANGA (IRE)**, 8, b g Flemensfirth (USA)—Pomme Tiepy (FR) **Miss R. Curtis**
26 **NELSONS GIFT (IRE)**, 4, b g Mount Nelson—Real Revival (IRE) **Mr S Hubble, Mr M Doocey & Mr P Mayling**
27 **PATS FANCY (IRE)**, 7, b g Oscar (IRE)—Pat's Darling (IRE) **Hydes,McDermott,Spencer,Frobisher & Lee**
28 **PENNYFORAPOUND (IRE)**, 8, b g Winged Love (IRE)—Recession Lass (IRE)
                                                             R & J Farnham,P Burns,S Gammond,F Street
29 5, B g Califet (FR)—Quintara (IRE) **Fforest Star Racing Ltd**
30 **RANIERI (IRE)**, 7, b g Westerner—Carrigmoorna Storm (IRE) **The Brizzle Boys**
31 **RUTHLESS ARTICLE (IRE)**, 9, b g Definite Article—Lady Kamando **J Rymer R Farnham C Rymer J Farnham**
32 **SUNSET SHOWDOWN (IRE)**, 9, b g Flemensfirth (USA)—Sunset Queen (IRE) **Mr J. P. McManus**
33 **THE BOOLA BOSS (IRE)**, 6, ch g Quest For Peace (IRE)—Hy Kate (IRE) **Hyde, Frobisher, Cullen, Waters & Hyde**
34 4, B g Sageburg (IRE)—The Right Thing (IRE) **Miss R. Curtis**
35 **UNIVERSAL BROOK (IRE)**, 6, b m Universal (IRE)—Alfies Gift **Mrs G. A. Davies**
36 **WAYFINDER (IRE)**, 8, br g Shantou (USA)—Sibury (IRE) **The Wayfinders**
37 **ZOFFALAY (IRE)**, 4, b c Zoffany (IRE)—Layalee (IRE) **Miss R. Curtis**

Other Owners: Mr D. J. Bishop, Mr P. Burns, Mr A. R. Clerkson, Mr J. Conyers, Mr J. A. Cullen, Miss R. Curtis, Mr M. A. Doocey, Mrs J. L. Farnham, Mr R. A. Farnham, Mr S. Frobisher, Mr G. S. Gammond, Mr L. Gardner, Mr I. Glendenning, Mr N. Goulden, Mr N. J. Guttridge, M. Hill, Mr K. Hopgood, Mr S. J. Hubble, Mr M. Hyde, Mr R. Hyde, Mr R. J. Line, Mrs C. M. Lockett, Mr P. Mayling, Mr D. P. McDermott, Ms J. A. Moran, Mr N. D. Morris, Mrs K. M. Mountford, Mr J. P. O'Reilly, Mr W. J. O'Reilly, A. J. Outhart, Mr S. Palmer, Mr S. C. Prowting, Mr N. M. Roddis, Mr C. A. Rymer, Mr J. Rymer, Mr A. Spencer, Mrs F. Street, Mr C. R. Trembath, Mr K. D. Waters, D. C. Zeffman.

Assistant Trainer: Paul Sheldrake.

126

MR LUKE DACE, Billingshurst
Postal: **Copped Hall Farm and Stud, Okehurst House, Okehurst Lane, Billingshurst, West Sussex, RH14 9HR**
Contacts: **MOBILE 07949 401085 FAX 01403 612176**
EMAIL lukedace@yahoo.co.uk WEBSITE www.lukedace.co.uk

1 **EXECUTIVE**, 4, b f Swiss Spirit—Stylistick
2 **GALACTIC GLOW (IRE)**, 5, b g No Nay Never (USA)—Shine Like A Star
3 **SAMEER (FR)**, 6, b g Nathaniel (IRE)—Sanabyra (FR)

THREE-YEAR-OLDS

4 **KING CABO (USA)**, b br c Carpe Diem (USA)—Cabo Queen (CAN)
5 **YOUTHFUL KING**, b c Fountain of Youth (IRE)—Lady Moscou (IRE)

Assistant Trainer: Mrs L. Dace.

---

127 MR KEITH DALGLEISH, Carluke
Postal: **Belstane Racing Stables, Carluke, Lanarkshire, ML8 5HN**
Contacts: **PHONE 01555 773335**
EMAIL dalgleish.racing@outlook.com

1 **ABERAMA GOLD**, 5, b g Heeraat (IRE)—Nigella
2 **AIN'T NO SUNSHINE (IRE)**, 6, b g Shantou (USA)—Screaming Witness (IRE)
Middleham Park Racing Xx & Partner
3 **ALPINE SIERRA (IRE)**, 4, br g Distorted Humor (USA)—Unaccompanied (IRE) **Mr J S Morrison**
4 **ALRIGHT SUNSHINE (IRE)**, 7, b g Casamento (IRE)—Miss Gibraltar **Richard & Katherine Gilbert**
5 **AMALFI DOUG (FR)**, 12, gr g Network (GER)—Queissa (FR) **The County Set (seven) & Partner**
6 **AYR EMPRESS (IRE)**, 4, b f Holy Roman Emperor (IRE)—Miss Anneliese (IRE)
Ken McGarrity and Murray Cameron
7 **BRINGITONBORIS (USA)**, 5, gr g Distorted Humor (USA)—Miss Fontana (USA) **Mr J S Morrison & Partner**
8 **CABALLERO (IRE)**, 6, ch g Camacho—Dame d'Honneur (IRE) **Mr J. K. McGarrity**
9 **CHICHESTER**, 5, b g Dansili—Havant **Sir Ian & Ms Catriona Good**
10 **CHOOKIE DUNEDIN**, 7, b g Epaulette (AUS)—Lady of Windsor (IRE) **Raeburn Brick Limited**
11 **CORTON LASS**, 7, gr m Showcasing—Elbow Beach **Mr J. J. Hutton**
12 **DENZIL'S LAUGHING (IRE)**, 4, b g Mehmas (IRE)—Question (USA) **Mr K. W. Dalgleish**
13 **EL PICADOR (IRE)**, 6, b g Dansili—West of Venus (USA) **Sir Ian & Ms Catriona Good**
14 **EVALUATION**, 4, b g Dubawi (IRE)—Estimate (IRE) **Sir Ian & Ms Catriona Good**
15 **FASHION ADVICE**, 5, ch m Dandy Man (IRE)—Secret Advice **A. R. M. Galbraith**
16 **FIRST ACCOUNT**, 8, b br g Malinas (GER)—Kind Nell **The County Set (Two)**
17 **GARDE DES CHAMPS (IRE)**, 6, b g Robin des Champs (FR)—La Reine de Riogh (IRE) **I. T. Buchanan**
18 **GIOIA CIECA (USA)**, 4, b c Kitten's Joy (USA)—Dynacielo (USA) **Weldspec Glasgow Limited**
19 **GOD OF DREAMS**, 6, b g Morpheus—Bella Chica (IRE)
20 **GOMETRA GINTY (IRE)**, 6, b m Morpheus—Silver Cache (USA) **Ken McGarrity & Partner**
21 **GOODWOOD GLEN**, 4, b g Territories (IRE)—Bonnie Brae
22 **HAIZOOM**, 4, ch f Sea The Stars (IRE)—Sortita (GER) **Mr J S Morrison**
23 **HEAR ME OUT (IRE)**, 5, b g Kingston Hill—Waha (IRE) **Richard & Katherine Gilbert**
24 **HEIGHTS OF ABRAHAM (IRE)**, 4, b g Starspangledbanner (AUS)—High Vintage (IRE) **Two Goldfish & A Balloon 1**
25 **HIGHWAY COMPANION (IRE)**, 8, b g Milan—Niffyrann (IRE) **Weldspec Glasgow Limited**
26 **HOWZER BLACK (IRE)**, 6, b g Requinto (IRE)—Mattinata **Middleham Park Racing LXXVI**
27 **I'M TO BLAME (IRE)**, 9, b g Winged Love (IRE)—Swap Shop (IRE) **The Gilbert's & Mr Campbell**
28 **KRAKEN FILLY (IRE)**, 4, b f Camacho—Tip It On The Top (IRE) **Mr J. Fyffe**
29 **LE MAGNIFIQUE (GER)**, 5, ch g Kamsin (GER)—La Poesie (GER)
30 **MI CAPRICHO (IRE)**, 7, b g Elzaam (AUS)—Mavemacullen (IRE) **Mr C. Jones**
31 **MONSIEUR CO (FR)**, 9, b g Turgeon (USA)—Cayras Style (FR) **Ken McGarrity & Partner**
32 **NEWTOWN BOY (IRE)**, 9, b g Beneficial—Tanit Lady (IRE) **The County Set Eight**
33 **ONE NIGHT IN MILAN (IRE)**, 9, b g Milan—Native Mo (IRE) **Mr J. K. McGarrity**
34 **PRINCE KAYF**, 8, b g Kayf Tara—Annie's Answer (IRE)
35 **RAYMOND (IRE)**, 7, b g Tobougg (IRE)—Crack The Kicker (IRE) **Richard & Katherine Gilbert**
36 **RED BOND (IRE)**, 6, b g Red Jazz (USA)—Faithfulbond (IRE) **Middleham Park Racing XXVII**
37 **ROYAL ADVICE (IRE)**, 4, ch g Anjaal—Tamara Love (IRE) **Mr E. M. Sutherland**
38 **SEXTANT**, 7, b g Sea The Stars (IRE)—Hypoteneuse (IRE) **Richard & Katherine Gilbert**
39 **SOLDIER'S MINUTE**, 7, b g Raven's Pass (USA)—Hadba (IRE) **Weldspec Glasgow Limited**
40 **SUMMA PETO (USA)**, 4, gr g Dialed In (USA)—Unbridled Gem (USA) **Weldspec Glasgow Limited**
41 **TAXMEIFYOUCAN (IRE)**, 8, b g Beat Hollow—Accounting
42 **TEFNUT (USA)**, 5, b m American Pharoah (USA)—Virginia Waters (USA) **Weldspec Glasgow Limited**
43 **THE THIN BLUE LINE (IRE)**, 4, b br g Mehmas (IRE)—Rahlah **Middleham Park Racing LI & Partner**
44 **THREE CASTLES**, 6, b g Zoffany (IRE)—Fountain of Honour (IRE) **Mr J. K. McGarrity**
45 **VENTURA FLAME (IRE)**, 5, b m Dandy Man (IRE)—Kramer Drive (IRE) **Middleham Park Racing Lxxxiii & Partner**
46 **VOLATILE ANALYST (USA)**, 4, b g Distorted Humor (USA)—Gentle Caroline (USA) **Mr K. W. Dalgleish**
47 **WHAT'S THE STORY**, 8, b g Harbour Watch (IRE)—Spring Fashion (IRE) **Weldspec Glasgow Limited**
48 **WILL HE DANCE (IRE)**, 4, b g Fast Company (IRE)—Dubai's Success **Richard & Katherine Gilbert**

THREE-YEAR-OLDS

49 **AMOUGE (IRE)**, b f Churchill (IRE)—Imtiyaaz (IRE) **Weldspec Glasgow Limited I**
50 **BELLE OF ANNANDALE (IRE)**, ch f Australia—Fountain of Honour (IRE) **W. M. Johnstone**
51 **BELLSLEA (IRE)**, b g Churchill (IRE)—Miss Anneliese (IRE) **W. M. Johnstone**
52 **BELTANE (IRE)**, ch g Fast Company (IRE)—Northern Affair (IRE) **Middleham Park Racing Lxiv & Partner**

MR KEITH DALGLEISH - continued

53 **CELESTIAL STAR (IRE)**, ch f Ribchester (IRE)—Praskovia (IRE) **Weldspec Glasgow Limited**
54 **EDWARD CORNELIUS (IRE)**, b c Bungle Inthejungle—Calorie **John Kelly & John McNeill**
55 **ETERNAL HALO (IRE)**, b f Night of Thunder (IRE)—Quenched **Weldspec Glasgow Limited**
56 **FERGIE TIME (IRE)**, b g Tamayuz—Armoise **Weldspec Glasgow Limited I**
57 **FRIENDLY VEGAN (IRE)**, b f El Kabeir (USA)—Avomcic (IRE) **Weldspec Glasgow Limited I**
58 **HEIGHTS OF ARAN (IRE)**, b g Camacho—High Vintage (IRE) **Two Goldfish & A Balloon**
59 **HOT DIGGITY DOG (IRE)**, b g Dandy Man (IRE)—Unusually Hot (IRE) **Weldspec Glasgow Limited I**
60 **LADY LADE**, b f Havana Gold (IRE)—Accolade **Partick Partnership**
61 **LOOSE LIPS**, b g War Command (USA)—Cheeseandpickle **The Gilbert's & Mr Campbell**
62 B c Nathaniel (IRE)—Maleficent Queen **Weldspec Glasgow Limited**
63 **MISTY AYR (IRE)**, b f Kodi Bear (IRE)—Rasana **Middleham Park Racing Iii & Partner**
64 **NINKY NONK (IRE)**, ch g Raven's Pass (USA)—Firey Red (IRE) **Weldspec Glasgow Limited I**
65 B f Dialed In (USA)—Pin Up (IRE) **Weldspec Glasgow Limited**
66 **PRETTY BOUQUET (IRE)**, b f Champs Elysees—Catwalk Queen (IRE) **Mr & Mrs Paul & Clare Rooney**
67 B f Highland Reel (IRE)—Spirit of The Sea (IRE)
68 **TIMBUKONE (IRE)**, b g Zoffany (IRE)—High Figurine (IRE) **Mr & Mrs Paul & Clare Rooney**

TWO-YEAR-OLDS

69 **ANGEL FROM ABOVE (IRE)**, b f 24/04 Galileo Gold—Cartoon (Danehill Dancer (IRE)) (40000) **Mr F. Brady**
70 Ch f 17/02 Camacho—Avomcic (IRE) (Avonbridge) (20000)
71 **LOVELY LADY**, ch f 31/03 Mastercraftsman (IRE)—Kylia (USA) (Mr Greeley (USA)) (85000) **Mr F. Brady**
72 **RUTHERGLEN ROSE**, ch f 08/04 Orientor—Nanjoe (Helmet (AUS)) **Mr F. Brady**
73 B c 06/02 Free Eagle (IRE)—Scatina (IRE) (Samum (GER)) (38265) **Richard & Katherine Gilbert**
74 Ch c 03/04 Bungle Inthejungle—Weston Angel (IRE) (Lilbourne Lad (IRE)) (15306)
75 B f 01/02 Saxon Warrior (JPN)—Wishing Star (IRE) (Galileo (IRE)) (35000) **Richard & Katherine Gilbert**

Other Owners: Mr M. Cameron, Mr J. J. Campbell, County Set Seven, Mr K. W. Dalgleish, Mrs K. E. Gilbert, Mr R. P. Gilbert, Richard & Katherine Gilbert, G. Godsman, Ms C. Good, Sir Ian Good, Mr T. Huntingford, Keith Dalgleish Racing Limited, Mr J. Kelly, Robert Macgregor, Mr J. K. McGarrity, Mr J. McNeill, Middleham Park Racing Iii, Middleham Park Racing Li, Middleham Park Racing LXIV, Middleham Park Racing LXXXIII, Middleham Park Racing XX, Mr J S Morrison, M. Prince, Mr E. M. Sutherland, Mr P. B. Tann, Mr D. A. Walker, Weldspec Glasgow Limited, Mrs S. A. Wood.

Assistant Trainer: Kevin Dalgleish, **Racing Secretary:** Leanne Gordon.

---

128 **MR HENRY DALY, Ludlow**
Trainer did not wish details of their string to appear

---

129 **MR PHILLIP DANDO, Peterston-Super-Ely**
Postal: Springfield Court, Peterston-Super-Ely, Cardiff, South Glamorgan, CF5 6LG
Contacts: **PHONE 01446 760012 MOBILE 07872 965395**

1 **BEAU HAZE**, 9, b g Black Sam Bellamy (IRE)—Bella Haze **P. C. Dando**
2 **CHANTILLY HAZE**, 7, b m Black Sam Bellamy (IRE)—Bella Haze **P. C. Dando**
3 **HARRY HAZE**, 10, b g Dr Massini (IRE)—Gypsy Haze **Mr Phillip Dando & Mr Anthony Brown**
4 **SAM HAZE**, 8, b g Black Sam Bellamy (IRE)—Bella Haze **P. C. Dando**
5 **TARA HAZE**, 6, b m Kayf Tara—Bella Haze **P. C. Dando**

Other Owners: Mr H. A. Brown, P. C. Dando.

Assistant Trainer: Mrs Rebecca Davies.

---

130 MR VICTOR DARTNALL, Barnstaple
Postal: **Higher Shutscombe Farm, Charles, Brayford, Barnstaple, Devon, EX32 7PU**
Contacts: **PHONE 01598 710280 MOBILE 07974 374272 FAX 01598 710708**
EMAIL victordartnall@gmail.com WEBSITE www.victordartnallracing.com

1 **ADARE WAY (IRE)**, 7, b g Getaway (GER)—Toscar (IRE)
2 **ARAUCANA**, 4, b f Swiss Spirit—Presto Levanter **Mrs D. J. Fleming**
3 **ARTHALOT (IRE)**, 5, b g Camelot—Annina (IRE) **Thethrillofitall**
4 **ATJIMA (IRE)**, 7, b m Mahler—Qui Plus Est (FR) **Mr N. Viney**
5 **AURIGNY MILL (FR)**, 5, b g Diamond Boy (FR)—Fresh Princess (FR) **Mrs E. S. Weld**
6 **BILINGUAL**, 5, b m Le Havre (IRE)—Downhill Dancer (IRE) **Miss K. M. George**
7 **BUCK N SKIP**, 8, b g Bollin Eric—April Attraction (FR) **Mrs J. Scrivens**
8 **DANCING SHADOW (IRE)**, 13, br g Craigsteel—Be My Shadow (IRE) **The Dancing Shadows**
9 **EXMOOR EXPRESS (IRE)**, 6, b g Sans Frontieres (IRE)—Blue Article (IRE) **The First Shutscombe Syndicate**
10 **FISHERMANS COVE (IRE)**, 8, b g Getaway (GER)—Toscar (IRE) **G. D. Hake**
11 **HALDON HILL (IRE)**, 9, b g Mahler—Qui Plus Est (FR) **Mr J. P. McManus**
12 **HARTNOLL HERO (IRE)**, 6, br g Sageburg (IRE)—Skyra (IRE) **Mrs.S.De Wilde,Mr.B.Dallyn,Mrs.C.Carter**
13 **LHEBAYEB (GER)**, 4, b f Alhebayeb (IRE)—Lady Gabrielle (IRE) **Boddy, George, Kilby, Oram & Partner**
14 **MELODOR**, 4, ch f Cannock Chase (USA)—Legal Art **Mr V. R. A. Dartnall**
15 **MINNIE ESCAPE**, 10, b m Getaway (GER)—Minnie Hill (IRE) **The Second Brayford Partnership**
16 **PATH HILL**, 7, bl g Malinas (GER)—Minnie Hill (IRE) **Mrs L. M. Northover**
17 **POCKET TOO**, 4, b g Cannock Chase (USA)—Dance A Daydream **Mr V. R. A. Dartnall**
18 **PRIDE OF PARIS (IRE)**, 4, b g Champs Elysees—Bincas Beauty (IRE) **Dallyn, De Wilde, Haggett, Metters, Yeo**
19 **RIVER BRAY (IRE)**, 9, ch g Arakan (USA)—Cill Fhearga (IRE) **The River Bray Syndicate**
20 **RUN TO MILAN (IRE)**, 10, b g Milan—Run Supreme (IRE) **Barber, Birchenhough, De Wilde**

THREE-YEAR-OLDS
21 **CURB APPEAL**, b f Ardad (IRE)—Powerfulstorm **Ashton,Boddy,George,Harris & Senior**
22 **I MATTER (IRE)**, b br f Slade Power (IRE)—Piccola Sissi (IRE) **B. McDaid & K. George**
23 **SALTA RESTA**, bl f Brazen Beau (AUS)—Be Joyful (IRE) **Senior, George S. Greig**

Other Owners: Mr M. Ashton, Mrs C. M. Barber, Mrs K. Birchenhough, Mr D. Boddy, Ms C. Carter, Mr B. C. Dallyn, Mr V. R. A. Dartnall, Mrs S. De Wilde, Miss K. M. George, Mr S. Greig, Mr N. Haggett, Mrs S. M. Hall, Mr B. Harris, Mr S. Kilby, Mr M. Masters, Mr B. McDaid, Mr M. N. Metters, Mr R. D. Oram, Mr R. Paver, Mr C. Perrin, Mr C. A. Poulter, Mr A. Senior, Mr G. Stead, Mr E. T. Yeo.

Assistant Trainer: Mr G. A. Dartnall.

131 MR TRISTAN DAVIDSON, Carlisle
Postal: **Bellmount, Laversdale, Irthington, Carlisle, Cumbria, CA6 4PS**
Contacts: **MOBILE 07789 684290**

1 **ALL THINGS BRIGHT (IRE)**, 4, b f Acclamation—Avenue Montaigne (IRE) **Edward Cassie & T Davidson**
2 **ASKGARMOR (IRE)**, 10, b g Ask—Karmafair (IRE) **Mr E. G. Tunstall**
3 **BOOTLEGGER (IRE)**, 9, b g Kayf Tara—Sweetbitter (FR) **The Risk Takers Partnership**
4 **CRESSWELL QUEEN**, 7, b m Brian Boru—Cresswell Willow (IRE) **The Mag & the Mackem**
5 **ECLAIR DES SABLONS (FR)**, 8, b g Noroit (GER)—Jolie Fari (FR) **Mr P. Drinkwater**
6 **FRANKIE BABY (IRE)**, 7, b g Yeats (IRE)—Belsalsa (FR)
7 **GREENGAGE (IRE)**, 7, b m Choisir (AUS)—Empowermentofwomen (IRE) **Poker & Davidson**
8 **INAJIFFY (IRE)**, 9, b m Mahler—Spirit of Clanagh (IRE) **Mrs J. Lloyd**
9 **IRIS DANCER**, 4, b f Kodiac—Rainbow's Arch (IRE) **Auld Pals**
10 **NASTASIYA**, 4, ch f Archipenko (USA)—Nezhenka **ValueRacingClub.co.uk**
11 **OCTAVIUS SABINI (IRE)**, 5, b g Yeats (IRE)—Feathard Lady (IRE) **Aldsworth, Ellison & Stevens**
12 **PEARL OF QATAR**, 6, gr m Footstepsinthesand—Musical Molly (IRE) **Border Raiders & T Davidson**
13 **PROTON (IRE)**, 6, b g Slade Power (IRE)—Singing Bird (IRE) **The Risk Takers Partnership**
14 **RUBENESQUE (IRE)**, 10, b m Getaway (GER)—Shouette (IRE) **Toby Noble & Andy Bell**
15 **SOPHIE OLIVIA (IRE)**, 10, gr m Ask—Gill's Honey (IRE) **Mr A. Bell**
16 **THORSDA**, 5, ch m Norse Dancer (IRE)—Wheyaw
17 **TOMORROW'S ANGEL**, 7, ch m Teofilo (IRE)—Funday **Adamson, Etheridge**

MR TRISTAN DAVIDSON- continued

18 **TORNGAT (FR)**, 6, ch g Kapgarde (FR)—Loin de Moi (FR) **Mr G. Curnow**
19 **UGO DU MISSELOT (FR)**, 8, b g Irish Wells (FR)—Princesse Pauline (FR) **Graeme Curnow & T Davidson**
20 **UP THE TEMPO**, 4, ch g Belardo (IRE)—Paulinie **Mrs Hugh Fraser**
21 **WESTCOAST TIGER (IRE)**, 7, b m Doyen (IRE)—Dabiyra (IRE) **R Harwood**

THREE-YEAR-OLDS

22 **SONOFAMADAM**, b c Sixties Icon—Madam Lilibet (IRE)

Other Owners: Mr G. G. Adamson, Mr L. G. Aldsworth, Mr A. Bell, Border Raiders, Carlisle Poker Club, Mr E. Cassie, Mr G. Curnow, J. T. Davidson, Mr A. L. Ellison, Mr Gary Etheridge, & Harwood, Mrs B. C. Harwood, Mr P. T. C. Harwood, Mr D. A. Knowles, Mr D. Lamonby, Mr T. Noble, Mrs R. A. Robson, Mr B. Stevens.

Racing Secretary: Mrs Sharon McManus.

---

132 MR JOHN DAVIES, Darlington
Postal: **Denton Grange, Piercebridge, Darlington, County Durham, DL2 3TZ**
Contacts: **PHONE 01325 374366 MOBILE 07746 292782**
EMAIL johndavieshorses@live.co.uk WEBSITE www.johndaviesracing.com

1 **CORNELL**, 4, b g Cannock Chase (USA)—Tsarina Louise **The Red and White Stripes**
2 4, Br f Cannock Chase (USA)—Floradorado **J. J. Davies**
3 **HIGHJACKED**, 6, b g Dick Turpin (IRE)—Vera Richardson (IRE) **J. J. Davies**
4 **OOH LA LAH**, 5, b m Champs Elysees—Cameo Tiara (IRE)
               The Frenchship, Mrs M. J. Collins, Mr C. W. Davies, Mrs D. Walton
5 **PIXIE CARTER**, 4, ch f Monsieur Bond (IRE)—Wedgewood Star **Mr C. W. Davies**
6 **TYKENWEAR**, 4, b f Cannock Chase (USA)—La Hoofon **The Red and White Stripes**

THREE-YEAR-OLDS

7 B f Mahsoob—Rise Up Singing **J. J. Davies**

TWO-YEAR-OLDS

8 B f 22/02 Havana Gold (IRE)—Code Cracker (Medicean) (9524)
9 B f 02/04 Mondialiste (IRE)—Croftamie (Selkirk (USA)) **J. J. Davies**
10 B f 18/05 Mondialiste (IRE)—Vera Richardson (IRE) (Dutch Art) **K. Kirkup**

---

133 MISS SARAH-JAYNE DAVIES, Leominster
Postal: **The Upper Withers, Hundred Lane, Kimbolton, Leominster, Herefordshire, HR6 0HZ**
Contacts: **PHONE 01584 711138 MOBILE 07779 797079**
EMAIL sarah@sjdracing.co.uk WEBSITE www.sjdracing.co.uk

1 **ABSOLUTE ALTITUDE**, 5, b g Cacique (IRE)—Nougaboo (USA) **Miss N. Thompson**
2 **ACCESSALLAREAS (IRE)**, 17, ch g Swift Gulliver (IRE)—Arushofgold (IRE) **Miss S. J. Davies**
3 **BLUE BEIRUT (IRE)**, 6, b g Lilbourne Lad (IRE)—Ornellaia (IRE) **Mr A. J. Gough**
4 **CELESTIAL LIGHT**, 6, b m Universal (IRE)—Miss Lightning **Pipannsue Partnership**
5 **EQUUS MILLAR (IRE)**, 9, b g Masterofthehorse (IRE)—Lets Get Busy (IRE) **Mrs J. N. Mansfield**
6 **EST ILLIC (IRE)**, 8, b br g Court Cave (IRE)—Ten Friends (IRE) **Mr A. J. Gough**
7 **FAIR TO DREAM**, 9, b g Fair Mix (IRE)—Sahara's Dream **K. E. Stait**
8 **FITZROY (IRE)**, 8, b g Fame And Glory—Forces of Destiny (IRE) **Michael & Lesley Wilkes**
9 **FORT NELSON**, 5, b g Mount Nelson—Iron Butterfly **Miss S. J. Davies**
10 **GRIMM STAR (FR)**, 6, b g Cokoriko (FR)—Beauty Blue (FR) **K. E. Stait**
11 **HIGGS (IRE)**, 9, b g Scorpion (IRE)—Captain Supreme (IRE) **Mr A. J. Gough**
12 **INVINCIBLE WISH (IRE)**, 10, b g Vale of York (IRE)—Moonlight Wish (IRE) **Michael & Lesley Wilkes**
13 4, B f Black Sam Bellamy (IRE)—Kansas City (FR) **Miss S. J. Davies**
14 **LUIS VAN ZANDT (IRE)**, 8, b g Scorpion (IRE)—Banrion Na Boinne **Moorland Racing**
15 **MACEY MILAN (IRE)**, 6, b m Milan—Zoeys Dream (IRE) **Moorland Racing**
16 **MADAM MILLER**, 6, b m Lucarno (USA)—Still Runs Deep **Miss S. J. Davies**

MISS SARAH-JAYNE DAVIES - continued

17 **MOUNT OLIVER (IRE)**, 12, b g Mountain High (IRE)—Little Nancy (IRE) **Withers Winners**
18 **NAUGHTY LINES**, 4, ch f Black Sam Bellamy (IRE)—Blurred Lines (IRE) **Miss S. J. Davies**
19 **PEMBROKE HOUSE**, 15, gr g Terimon—Bon Coeur **Miss S. J. Davies**
20 **PROSOPAGNOSIA**, 6, ch m Black Sam Bellamy (IRE)—Clever Liz **Mr A. J. Gough**
21 **ROYAL ACT**, 10, br g Royal Anthem (USA)—Native's Return (IRE) **Moorland Racing & Mark Hammond**
22 **SECRET MELODY**, 9, b g Sakhee's Secret—Montjeu's Melody (IRE) **Moorland Racing & Mark Hammond**
23 **STORM GIRL**, 6, b m Paco Boy (IRE)—Evenstorm (USA) **Mr A. J. Gough**
24 **THEQUEENBEE (IRE)**, 7, b m Stowaway—Accordeon Royale (IRE) **Michael & Lesley Wilkes**
25 **VOLATORE**, 6, b g Lucarno (USA)—Rocking Robin **Quadriga Racing**

Other Owners: Miss S. J. Davies, Mrs S. M. Davies, Mr M. J. Hammond, Mrs A. M. Mace, S. A. Mace, Moorland Racing, Mrs C. Tucker, Mr M. J. F. Tucker, Mrs P. Vaughan, Mrs B. Vincent, Mr J. F. Vincent, Mrs L. Wilkes, Mr M. H. A. Wilkes.

Head Man: Ryan Bradford.

NH Jockey: William Kennedy.

134
MISS JO DAVIS, Highworth
Postal: **Eastrop, Highworth, Wiltshire, SN6 7PP**
Contacts: **PHONE** 01793 762232 **MOBILE** 07879 811535 **FAX** 01793 762232
EMAIL jo@jodavisracing.com **WEBSITE** www.jodavisracing.com

1 **CATLOW (IRE)**, 9, b g Let The Lion Roar—Jon Jon's Grace (IRE) **The Ab Fab Patsy Partnership**
2 **CLAUDE ALMIGHTY (FR)**, 5, br g Fuisse (FR)—Belle Sauvage (FR) **TheseGirlsCan Racing Club**
3 **DEMOCRITUS**, 3, b g Universal (IRE)—Nant Y Mynydd **Tony Worth & Vic Bedley**
4 **DREAMINGOFASONG**, 6, b m Epaulette (AUS)—No Frills (IRE) **Mrs P. M. Brown**
5 **FIAMETTE (IRE)**, 4, ch f Free Eagle (IRE)—High Reserve **Mr C. Butler**
6 **GALLIC DESTINY (IRE)**, 11, b g Champs Elysees—Cross Your Fingers (USA) **Mrs P. M. Brown**
7 **GREAT COMMISSION**, 4, b g Nathaniel—Duchess of Gazeley (IRE) **The Unstoppables**
8 **MORVAL (FR)**, 4, b br g Morandi (FR)—Valley Girl (FR) **Jo Davis & Chris Butler**
9 **MR FITZROY (IRE)**, 12, ch g Kyllachy—Reputable **Mrs P. M. Brown**
10 **PIANISSIMO**, 6, b g Teofilo (IRE)—Perfect Note **Mr C. Butler**
11 **SAND IN MY SHOES (FR)**, 4, b grg Mastercraftsman (IRE)—Suquia (GER) **The Unstoppables**
12 **TOUCHTHESOUL (ITY)**, 7, b g Red Rocks (IRE)—Easy Hawk **Mr C. Butler**
13 **UNSTOPPABLE (FR)**, 4, b g Morandi (FR)—Perdicilla (FR) **The Unstoppables**

THREE-YEAR-OLDS

14 **JOLIE BAIE (FR)**, b f Gris de Gris (IRE)—Belle Sauvage (FR) **Mr C. Butler**

Other Owners: Mr R. C. C. Baker, V. R. Bedley, Mr G. P. Bendall, Mr C. Butler, Miss J. S. Davis, Mrs M. A. Davis, Mr A. G. Worth.

Assistant Trainer: Gregg Whitehead.

135
MISS KATHARINE DAVIS, Reading
Postal: **Brewery Fields Farm, Southend, Reading, Berkshire, RG7 6JP**
EMAIL katharinedavisracing@gmail.com

1 **CHANTECLER**, 11, b g Authorized (IRE)—Snow Goose **Mr D. White**
2 **DUKE OF CHALFONT (FR)**, 6, b g Alianthus (GER)—Bonne Mere (FR) **Mr D. White**
3 **GIVEHIMHISDEW (IRE)**, 7, b g Shirocco (GER)—Tarantella Lady **Mr D. White**
4 **KING LEWLEW**, 5, b g Swiss Spirit—Aura **Mr D. White**
5 **PISTOL SMOKE (IRE)**, 7, b g Califet (FR)—Free Lift **Mr D. White**
6 **POLLYAMOROUS (IRE)**, 7, b m Califet (FR)—Our Polly (IRE) **Mr D. White**
7 **SILENT OCEAN (IRE)**, 7, b g Jeremy (USA)—Elodie Eile (IRE) **Mr D. White**
8 **TELLEROFTALES (IRE)**, 7, b g Yeats (IRE)—Sweetbitter (FR) **Mr D. White**

MISS KATHARINE DAVIS - continued

9 **UBERMAN (IRE)**, 8, b g Mahler—Super Sammy **Mr D. White**
10 **WHISKEY TIMES (IRE)**, 9, br m Olden Times—Tomcoole Oscar (IRE) **Mr D. White**
11 **WORTH KNOWING (IRE)**, 7, b g Stowaway—Duclair Duck (IRE) **Mr D. White**

---

136 MR ANTHONY DAY, Hinckley
Postal: **Wolvey Fields Farm, Coalpit Lane, Wolvey, Hinckley, Leicestershire, LE10 3HD**

1 **FAMOUS OISIN (IRE)**, 6, br g Famous Name—Peig Alainn (IRE) **Mrs K. D. Day**
2 **GETTYSBURGH (IRE)**, 7, b m Presenting—Rhapsody In Blue (GER) **Mrs K. D. Day**
3 **LAVERTEEN (FR)**, 11, b g Laveron—Manson Teene (FR) **Mrs K. D. Day**
4 **STRIPE OF HONOUR (IRE)**, 9, b g Court Cave (IRE)—Miss Top (IRE) **Mrs K. D. Day**

---

137 MR WILLIAM DE BEST-TURNER, Lambourn
Postal: **Coppington Stables , Greenways , Lambourn , Berkshire , RG17 7LG**
Contacts: **HOME 01249 813850 PHONE 01249 811944 MOBILE 07977 910779**
EMAIL **debestracing@hotmail.co.uk**

1 **CALGARY TIGER**, 7, b g Tiger Groom—Sachiko **W. de Best-Turner**
2 **MOLLY'S ANGEL**, 5, ch m Arvico (FR)—Sterling Moll **Debestracing**
3 **NELSON'S HILL**, 12, b g Mount Nelson—Regal Step **Debestracing**
4 **TIGER PRINT**, 7, b m Tiger Groom—Maylan (IRE) **Debestracing**

Assistant Trainer: Mrs I. de Best.

---

138 MR ED DE GILES, Ledbury
Postal: **Lilly Hall Farm, Little Marcle, Ledbury, Herefordshire, HR8 2LD**
Contacts: **PHONE 01531 637369 MOBILE 07811 388345**
EMAIL **ed@eddegilesracing.com** WEBSITE **www.eddegilesracing.com**

1 **ALPINE STROLL**, 4, b g Nathaniel (IRE)—Kammaan **The LAM Partnership**
2 **CHIFA (IRE)**, 5, gr g Gutaifan (IRE)—Inca Trail (USA) **Mr J. P. Carrington**
3 **FITZROVIA**, 7, br g Poet's Voice—Pompey Girl **Clarissa Casdagali & Partners**
4 **FRANCISCO BAY**, 6, b g Paco Boy (IRE)—Lucky Breeze (IRE) **Mr C. C. Shand Kydd & Partner**
5 **KALAMITY KITTY**, 4, b f Cityscape—Lucky Breeze (IRE) **Fair Wind Partnership & Partner**
6 **LUCKY DRAW**, 5, b m Roderic O'Connor (IRE)—Lucky Breeze (IRE) **Mr C. C. Shand Kydd & Partner**
7 **OVERHAUGH STREET**, 9, b g Bahri (USA)—Born Chicka Wah Wah (USA) **Sharron & Robert Colvin**
8 **ROAR (IRE)**, 8, b g Pour Moi (IRE)—Evening Rushour (IRE) **Mr P. Inglett**
9 **TREACHEROUS**, 8, b g Paco Boy (IRE)—Black Baroness **Woodham Walter Partnership**
10 **URBAN FOREST**, 4, ch g Cityscape—Tijuca (IRE) **Friends In Low Places**
11 **ZLATAN (IRE)**, 9, b g Dark Angel (IRE)—Guard Hill (USA) **Casdagli & Partners**

THREE-YEAR-OLDS

12 **AE FOND KISS**, b f Time Test—Aurora Gray **Simon Treacher, Robert Colvin & Partner**
13 **GOODISON GIRL**, b f Helmet (AUS)—Cloudchaser (IRE) **The Tully Family**
14 B c Helmet (AUS)—Lucky Breeze (IRE) **Mr E. B. de Giles**
15 **MACON BELLE**, b f Due Diligence (USA)—Disco Ball **Woodham Walter Partnership**
16 **TROJAN TRUTH**, b g Ulysses (IRE)—Verity **Woodham Walter Partnership**

MR ED DE GILES - continued

TWO-YEAR-OLDS
17 B f 20/03 Sea The Moon (GER)—Kammaan (Diktat) **The LAM Partnership**
18 **RACING DEMON**, b c 29/02 Muhaarar—Whatdoiwantthatfor (IRE) (Kodiac) **John Manser & Simon Treacher**
19 **TWO PLUS TWO (IRE)**, ch c 11/04 Free Eagle (IRE)—Pivotal's Princess (IRE) (Pivotal) **The LAM Partnership**

Other Owners: Mr J. P. Carrington, Mrs C. R. Casdagli, R. Colvin, Mrs S. Colvin, Ms A. P. M. Cunningham, Fair Wind Partnership, Dr M. F. Ford, Mr P. J. Manser, Ms L. M. Mulcahy, C. C. Shand Kydd, Mr S. Treacher, A. J. Viall, Mr E. B. de Giles.

---

139 **MR GEOFFREY DEACON, Compton**
Postal: **Hamilton Stables, Hockham Road, Compton, Newbury, Berkshire, RG20 6QJ**
Contacts: **MOBILE 07967 626757**
EMAIL **geoffdeacon5@gmail.com** WEBSITE **www.geoffreydeacontraining.com**

1 **APRICOT STAR (IRE)**, 5, ch m Anjaal—Allegrissimo (IRE) **Allinc Property Services**
2 **CAPTAIN RYAN**, 11, b g Captain Gerrard (IRE)—Ryan's Quest (IRE) **Geoffrey Deacon Racing Crew**
3 **CHARLIE MAGRI**, 6, b g Midnight Legend—Psychosis **Reed Truan & Spershott**
4 **DANCING JO**, 6, b g Mazameer (IRE)—Remix (IRE) **R.E.F.TEN**
5 **DARK CROCODILE (IRE)**, 7, b g Dark Angel (IRE)—Heaven's Vault (IRE) **Mr M. D. Drake**
6 **DOLLY DRAKE**, 4, b f Havana Gold (IRE)—Farletti **Mr M. D. Drake**
7 5, Gr m Heeraat (IRE)—Elderberry **Geoffrey Deacon Racing Crew**
8 **ENCHANTEE (IRE)**, 5, b m Gale Force Ten—Love Valentine (IRE) **Geoffrey Deacon Racing Crew**
9 **FOLLOWTHEFOOTSTEPS (IRE)**, 4, b f Footstepsinthesand—Gush (USA) **Allinc Property Services**
10 5, Gr m Fast Company (IRE)—Glastonberry **Mr G. Deacon**
11 **JUST ALBERT**, 5, gr ro g Toronado (IRE)—Deire Na Sli (IRE) **Mr and Mrs Duckett**
12 6, B m Born To Sea (IRE)—Khajool (IRE) **Geoffrey Deacon Racing Crew**
13 **LA ROCA DEL FUEGO (IRE)**, 6, br g Rock of Gibraltar (IRE)—Reign (IRE) **Mr M. D. Drake**
14 **NIGHT N GALE (IRE)**, 6, b m Gale Force Ten—Hadya (IRE) **Geoffrey Deacon Racing Crew**
15 **SAHHAB (USA)**, 5, b m Declaration of War (USA)—Princess Consort (USA) **Mr A. Altazi**
16 **WUDASHUDACUDA**, 4, b c Awtaad (IRE)—Chicita Banana **Geoffrey Deacon Racing Crew**

THREE-YEAR-OLDS
17 Gr g Heeraat (IRE)—Glastonberry **Mr G. Deacon**
18 **ORLANDO LAMMY**, b c Showcasing—One Pixel **The Sunset Crew**

TWO-YEAR-OLDS
19 B c 17/04 Captain Gerrard (IRE)—Aunt Minnie (Night Shift (USA)) (6000) **Mr G. Deacon**

Other Owners: Miss J. E. Reed, Mr D. G. Spershott, Mr M. R. Truan.

Assistant Trainer: Sally Duckett.

---

140 **MR ROBIN DICKIN, Alcester**
Postal: **Hill Farm, Park Lane, Great Alne, Alcester, Warwickshire, B49 6HS**
Contacts: **MOBILE 07979 518594, 07979 518593**
EMAIL **claire@robindickinracing.org.uk** WEBSITE **www.robindickinracing.org.uk**

1 **BALLINSLEA BRIDGE (IRE)**, 10, b g Pierre—Feelin' Looser (IRE) **NHRE Racing Club**
2 **CHEER'S DELBOY (IRE)**, 9, ch g Golan (IRE)—Lindy Lou **Just 4 Fun**
3 **EL DIABLO (IRE)**, 6, gr g Cloudings (IRE)—Mayfly **Mrs C. M. Dickin**

MR ROBIN DICKIN - continued

4 **FITZ THE BRIEF (IRE)**, 6, ch g Sholokhov (IRE)—Roxy Beat
Mrs C. M. Dickin, Fitzwell Partners & Rd Racing Club, Mr M. Fitzgerald, Robin Dickin Racing Club, The Fitz Well Songsters
5 **FITZ WELL (IRE)**, 7, b g Milan—La Sentinelle (FR) **The Fitz Well Songsters**
6 **GALACTIC POWER (IRE)**, 12, ch g Gamut (IRE)—Celtic Peace (IRE) **Robin Dickin Racing Club**
7 **HOOKY STREET (IRE)**, 6, ch g Shirocco (GER)—Academy Miss (IRE) **The Goodies & Tricksters & Mr D Gillett**
8 **MOON OVER GERMANY (IRE)**, 11, ch g Germany (USA)—Elea Moon (IRE) **The Moggy Syndicate**
9 **MR PALMTREE (IRE)**, 9, gr g Robin des Pres (FR)—Mattys Joy (IRE) **Mr C. J. Dickin, The Tricksters, The Cocoa Nuts & the Tricksters, The Cocoa Nuts**
10 **PHOEBUS LESCRIBAA (FR)**, 10, b g Policy Maker (IRE)—Mia Lescribaa (FR) **Medbourne Racing**
11 **ROYAL BASSETT (FR)**, 5, b g Wootton Bassett—Donna Roberta (GER) **The Bertie Allsorts**
12 **THAT'S THE SPIRIT**, 4, b g Swiss Spirit—Shilpa (IRE) **The Point Of Attack Partnership**
13 **THREE BULLET GATE (IRE)**, 9, b g Touch of Land (FR)—Brave Hope (IRE) **The Point Of Attack Partnership**
14 **WILLIAMDECONQUEROR**, 6, b g Native Ruler—Dancing Daffodil **Mrs M A Cooper & Mrs C M Dickin**

Other Owners: Mrs M. A. Cooper, Mr C. J. Dickin, Mrs C. M. Dickin, D. J. Hern, Graham & Lynne Knight, Mr T. P. Poulson, The Goodies, The Tricksters.

Assistant Trainer: Harriet Dickin.

NH Jockey: Jack Quinlan, Tabitha Worsley. **Conditional Jockey:** Lorcan Murtagh.

---

141 | MR JOHN DIXON, Carlisle
Postal: **Moorend, Thursby, Carlisle, Cumbria, CA5 6QP**
Contacts: **PHONE 01228 711019**

1 **CAPTAIN ZEBO (IRE)**, 10, b g Brian Boru—Waydale Hill **Mrs S. F. Dixon**
2 **PISTOL (IRE)**, 13, b g High Chaparral (USA)—Alinea (USA) **Mrs S. F. Dixon**
3 **PRESENCE FELT (IRE)**, 14, br g Heron Island (IRE)—Faeroe Isle (IRE) **Mrs S. F. Dixon**
4 **ROAD TO ROSLEY**, 5, b g Millenary—Ballela Road (IRE) **Mrs S. F. Dixon**

Amateur Jockey: Mr J. J. Dixon.

---

142 | MR SCOTT DIXON, Retford
Postal: **Haygarth House Stud, Haygarth House, Babworth, Retford, Nottinghamshire, DN22 8ES**
Contacts: **PHONE 01777 869079, 01777 701818, 01777 869300**
MOBILE 07976 267019 FAX 01777 869326
EMAIL scottdixon1987@hotmail.com, mrsyvettedixon@gmail.com
WEBSITE www.scottdixonracing.com

1 **A PINT OF BEAR (IRE)**, 4, gr g Kodi Bear (IRE)—Heart of An Angel **The Bear Partnership**
2 4, b f Kodi Bear (IRE)—Al Jamal
3 **ALEX GRACIE**, 5, b m Fountain of Youth (IRE)—Kyllarney **Winning Connections Racing**
4 **ARFINN ROSE**, 4, br g Swiss Spirit—Ginger Cookie **The Scott Dixon Racing Partnership**
5 **BOND ANGEL**, 7, gr m Monsieur Bond (IRE)—Angel Grigio
6 4, b f Pride of Dubai (AUS)—Camille's Secret (FR) **The Scott Dixon Racing Partnership**
7 **CATESBY**, 5, b g Slade Power (IRE)—Bonfire Heart **Winning Connections Racing**
8 **COBH KID**, 5, b g Kyllachy—Never A Quarrel (IRE) **Winning Connections Racing**
9 **CRACKLING (IRE)**, 6, b g Vale of York (IRE)—Almatlaie (USA) **The Scott Dixon Racing Partnership**
10 **DARK SHOT**, 9, b g Acclamation—Dark Missile **Chappell Rose & Radford**
11 **EBURY**, 6, ch g Iffraaj—Alabelle **Chappell & Dixon**
12 **FEEL THE THUNDER**, 6, b g Milk It Mick—Totally Trusted **Ne-chance & Dixon**
13 **FINE WINE (FR)**, 5, b g Dream Ahead (USA)—Mulled Wine (FR) **Paul Dixon Kevin Brennan & Partners**
14 **GENTLY SPOKEN (IRE)**, 5, b gr m Gutaifan (IRE)—Always Gentle (IRE) **The Scott Dixon Racing Partnership**

15 **GIOGIOBBO**, 9, b h Bahamian Bounty—Legnani **ARC Racing Syndicate**
16 **GOSSIP**, 5, b m Exceed And Excel (AUS)—Al Sharood **ARC Racing Club**
17 **GYPSY WHISPER**, 5, b m Helmet (AUS)—Secret Insider (USA) **Mr P. Wright-Bevans**
18 **HARBOUR VISION**, 7, gr g Harbour Watch (IRE)—Holy Nola (USA) **Southwell Racing Club**
19 **HARMONIOUS**, 5, b b g New Approach (IRE)—Clear Voice (USA) **Winning Connections Racing**
20 **HEADLAND**, 6, b g Harbour Watch (IRE)—Bazzana **ARC Racing Club**
21 **INVINCIBLE LARNE (IRE)**, 6, b g Invincible Spirit (IRE)—Caphene **Middleham Park & Scott Dixon Racing**
22 **KITTEN'S DREAM**, 5, b g Kitten's Joy (USA)—Strathnaver **Southwell Racing Club**
23 4, B f Fountain of Youth (IRE)—Kyllarney
24 4, Ch c Monsieur Bond (IRE)—La Capriosa **Winning Connections Racing**
25 **MARNIE JAMES**, 7, b g Camacho—Privy Garden (IRE) **Redknapp Dixon Chappell Baker**
26 **MAY THE SIXTH**, 5, b m Mayson—Six Wives **Sexy Six Partnership**
27 **MYKONOS ST JOHN**, 5, b g Swiss Spirit—Royal Pardon **Southwell Racing Club**
28 **NOT NOW NEB (IRE)**, 5, ch g Zebedee—Why Not Now **& Family**
29 **ONE NIGHT STAND**, 5, b g Swiss Spirit—Tipsy Girl **Chappell & Dixon**
30 **POP FAVORITE**, 4, br g Fastnet Rock (AUS)—Soundstrings **Southwell Racing Club**
31 **REBEL REDEMPTION**, 5, gr g Lethal Force (IRE)—Tempting **Southwell Racing Club**
32 **SAMARA STAR**, 4, b f Adaay (IRE)—Starlight Walk **Southwell Racing Club**
33 **SEA FERN**, 4, b f Acclamation—Scots Fern **Southwell Racing Club**
34 **SHACKABOOAH**, 5, b g Swiss Spirit—Ginger Cookie **Winning Connections Racing**
35 **SOCIOLOGIST (FR)**, 7, ch g Society Rock (IRE)—Fabiola (GER) **Rob Massheder, A J Turton & Partners**
36 **SYCAMORE (IRE)**, 5, b g Kingman—Scarborough Fair **P Dixon & A Turton**
37 **THEOTHERSIDE (IRE)**, 5, b m Dandy Man (IRE)—New Magic (IRE) **The Scott Dixon Racing Partnership**
38 **VALENTINE BLUES (IRE)**, 5, gr m Clodovil (IRE)—Grecian Artisan (IRE) **Southwell Racing Club**
39 **VISIBILITY (IRE)**, 5, b g Raven's Pass (USA)—Cry Pearl (USA)
40 **ZARGUN (GER)**, 7, b g Rock of Gibraltar (IRE)—Zenaat **Sexy Six Partnership**

THREE-YEAR-OLDS

41 **AL TILAL (IRE)**, ch f Anjaal—Anythingknappen (IRE) **Southwell Racing Club**
42 **AMBER DEW**, b f Showcasing—Roxy Star (IRE) **The Scott Dixon Racing Partnership**
43 **CANDY WARHOL (USA)**, b c Twirling Candy (USA)—Costume **The Scott Dixon Racing Partnership**
44 **COAST**, b f Aclaim (IRE)—Rio's Cliffs **Southwell Racing Club**
45 **KING OF YORK (IRE)**, b g Kingman—Archangel Gabriel (USA) **The Scott Dixon Racing Partnership**
46 **SIX O' HEARTS**, b c Finjaan—Six Wives **Sexy Six Partnership**
47 **THERMOMETER (IRE)**, b g Excelebration (IRE)—Celsius Degre (IRE) **Southwell Racing Club**
48 B c Aclaim (IRE)—Waterways (IRE) **The Scott Dixon Racing Partnership**

Other Owners: Mr A. D. Baker, Mr K. Brennan, Mr S. E. Chappell, P. J. Dixon, S. P. J. Dixon, Mrs Y. Dixon, Mr M. Hilton, Mr R. Massheder, Ne-Chance, T. S. Palin, Mr H. Redknapp, Mr A. Severn, Paul J Dixon & Ashley Severn, The Scott Dixon Racing Partnership, Mr A. Turton, Mr P. Wright-Bevans.

Assistant Trainer: Mr K. Locking.

Amateur Jockey: Mr Kevin Locking.

---

143 **MRS ROSE DOBBIN, Alnwick**
Postal: **South Hazelrigg Farm, Chatton, Alnwick, Northumberland, NE66 5RZ**
Contacts: **PHONE 01668 215151, 01668 215395 MOBILE 07969 993563 FAX 01668 215114**
EMAIL hazelriggracing1@btconnect.com WEBSITE www.rosedobbinracing.co.uk

1 **AAZZA (IRE)**, 6, b m Beat Hollow—Kalygarde (FR) **Helen Ray & Isabel Tebay**
2 **BIGIRONONHISHIP (IRE)**, 11, b g Beneficial—Portobello Lady (IRE) **Mr & Mrs Duncan Davidson**
3 **CAILIN DEARG (IRE)**, 7, ch m Getaway (GER)—Lepidina (IRE) **Ronnie Jacobs & Rose Dobbin**
4 **CAPTAIN QUINT (IRE)**, 6, b g Flemensfirth (USA)—Vics Miller (IRE) **Mr & Mrs Duncan Davidson**
5 **CHOSEN FLAME (IRE)**, 10, b g Well Chosen—Flaming Misty (IRE) **S & G Soils Limited**
6 **COOLE HALL (IRE)**, 10, b g Flemensfirth (USA)—Coole Assembly (IRE) **Mr & Mrs Duncan Davidson**
7 **COSMIC OUTLAW (IRE)**, 6, b g Arctic Cosmos (USA)—Golden Moro (IRE) **Mr & Mrs Duncan Davidson**

MRS ROSE DOBBIN - continued

8 **DEFINITE WISDOM (IRE)**, 9, b g Definite Article—Wisdom And Light (IRE)

M & M Edwardson, M Hunter & J Matterson

9 **DO NOT DISTURB (IRE)**, 9, b g Mahler—Galbertstown Run (IRE) **Mr & Mrs Duncan Davidson**
10 **DOKTOR GLAZ (FR)**, 12, b g Mount Nelson—Deviolina (IRE) **Mr & Mrs D Davidson & The Friday Lions**
11 **EAGLE DE GUYE (FR)**, 8, b g Buck's Boum (FR)—Balibirds (FR) **Mr & Mrs D Davidson & Thistle Racing Ltd**
12 **ESPOIR MORIVIERE (FR)**, 8, ch g Saddex—Sagesse Moriviere (FR) **Dunkley, Ray & Roberts**
13 **FAMOUS MOMENT (IRE)**, 7, b g Fame And Glory—Endless Moments (IRE) **Mr & Mrs Duncan Davidson**
14 **FETE CHAMPETRE (IRE)**, 7, b g Robin des Champs (FR)—John's Eliza (IRE) **Mr & Mrs Duncan Davidson**
15 **FIRTH OF FORTH (IRE)**, 6, b g Flemensfirth (USA)—Gypsy Mo Chara (IRE) **M. S. Hunter & Mrs C. H. C. Hunter**
16 **GENTLEMAN DE MAI (FR)**, 6, b g Saddler Maker (IRE)—Ula de Mai (FR) **Mr & Mrs Ducan Davidson**
17 **GET WITH IT (IRE)**, 7, b g Getaway (GER)—Listening (IRE) **Mr & Mrs Duncan Davidson**
18 **HERE COMES THE MAN (IRE)**, 7, b g Flemensfirth (USA)—Nifty Nuala (IRE) **Mr & Mrs Duncan Davidson**
19 **HITMAN FRED (IRE)**, 9, b g Getaway (GER)—Garravagh Lass (IRE) **The Friday Lions 2**
20 **JACK DEVINE (IRE)**, 10, b g Kalanisi (IRE)—Sybil Says (IRE) **Mr & Mrs Duncan Davidson**
21 **LAST ONE TO SHOW (IRE)**, 7, b g Arcadio (GER)—Garravagh Lass (IRE) **Mrs R. Dobbin**
22 **LE CHEVAL NOIR (IRE)**, 8, b g Le Fou (IRE)—Bonny Lass **Mr & Mrs Duncan Davidson**
23 **LIMERICK LEADER (FR)**, 5, b g Joshua Tree (IRE)—Out Law d'Oc (FR) **Mr & Mrs Duncan Davidson**
24 **MONFASS (IRE)**, 11, b g Trans Island—Ajo Green (IRE) **Mrs Dobbin & The Dimhorns**
25 **OKAVANGO DELTA (IRE)**, 6, b g Ocovango—Court My Eye **One For the Road Flower**
26 **PLANET NINE (IRE)**, 10, b g Flemensfirth (USA)—Old Moon (IRE) **Mr & Mrs Duncan Davidson**
27 **PURCELL'S BRIDGE (FR)**, 15, b g Trempolino (USA)—Theatrical Lady (USA) **Mrs R. Dobbin**
28 **RAE DES CHAMPS (IRE)**, 5, ch m Robin des Champs (FR)—Dani Salamanca (IRE) **Mr & Mrs Duncan Davidson**
29 **RATH AN IUIR (IRE)**, 9, b g Flemensfirth (USA)—Amathea (FR) **Mr & Mrs Duncan Davidson**
30 **ROMULUS DU DONJON (IRE)**, 11, gr g Stormy River (FR)—Spring Stroll (USA) **Jacobs, Ray & Roberts**
31 **SEVEN EYE BRIDGE (IRE)**, 7, b g Sans Frontieres (IRE)—Woodland Path (IRE) **Mr J. A. F. Filmer-Wilson**
32 **SHANBALLY ROSE (IRE)**, 8, b m Court Cave (IRE)—Amy's Song (IRE) **Mrs C Hunter & Mr & Mrs M Edwardson**
33 **SLANELOUGH (IRE)**, 10, b g Westerner—Tango Lady (IRE) **Miss J. Matterson & Mrs D. Davidson**
34 **SMUGGLER'S STASH (IRE)**, 12, ch g Stowaway—Sweetasanu (IRE) **The Friday Lions 2**
35 **SOME REIGN (IRE)**, 11, b g Kayf Tara—Bridge Love (FR) **Mr & Mrs Duncan Davidson**
36 **STYLE NELSON (FR)**, 7, b g Mount Nelson—Ana Style (FR) **Mr & Mrs Duncan Davidson**
37 **SWEET AS CANDY (IRE)**, 8, b g Morozov (USA)—Sweet Nancy (IRE) **Mr & Mrs Duncan Davidson**
38 **THE PLAYER QUEEN (IRE)**, 6, b m Yeats (IRE)—Seductive Dance **Mr & Mrs Duncan Davidson**
39 **TROOPER TURNBULL (IRE)**, 8, b g Arcadio (GER)—Clover Pearl (IRE) **Hunter & McKie**
40 **VINTAGE GLEN (IRE)**, 10, b g Ask—Rare Vintage (IRE) **Jacobs, Macconnachie & Dickson**
41 **WHELANS BRIDGE (IRE)**, 6, b g Finsceal Fior (IRE)—Saintly Wish (USA) **Ian Macconnachie & Rose Dobbin**
42 **WILD POLLY (IRE)**, 8, ch m Mahler—Dalzenia (IRE) **Mr & Mrs Duncan Davidson**
43 **WORCESTER PEARMAIN (IRE)**, 12, b m Beat All (USA)—Granoski Gala **Mr & Mrs Duncan Davidson**

Other Owners: D. H. Davidson, Mr & Mrs Duncan Davidson, Mrs S. K. Davidson, Mr J. L. Dickson, Mr L. Dimsdale, Mrs R. Dobbin, Miss E. Dunkley, J. M. Edwardson, J. M. & Mrs M. R. Edwardson, Mrs M. R. Edwardson, Mrs S. Helmont, Mr R. Houghton, Mrs C. H. C. Hunter, M. S. Hunter, Mrs R. A. Jacobs, J. R. Jeffreys, Miss C. L. Jones, Mr I. G. Macconnachie, Miss J. G. K. Matterson, Mrs V. J. McKie, Mrs M. H. Ray, Mr E. Renwick, Mr R. Roberts, Mr D. A. C. Spencer-Churchill, Mrs I. Tebay, The Friday Lions, Thistle racing club.

Assistant Trainer: Tony Dobbin.

NH Jockey: Craig Nichol.

144 | **MR ASHLEY DODGSON, Thirsk**
Postal: **Southerby House, Catton, Thirsk, North Yorkshire, YO7 4SQ**

1 **MR DEALER (IRE)**, 10, b g Mr Dinos (IRE)—Vera Glynn (IRE) **Mrs F. M. G. Dodgson**

145 MR MICHAEL DODS, Darlington

Postal: Denton Hall Farm, Piercebridge, Darlington, County Durham, DL2 3TY
Contacts: **PHONE 01325 374270 MOBILE 07860 411590, 07773 290830 FAX 01325 374020**
EMAIL dods@michaeldodsracing.co.uk **WEBSITE** www.michaeldodsracing.co.uk

1 **A BOY NAMED IVY (IRE)**, 4, gr g Markaz (IRE)—St Athan **Mr F. Lowe**
2 **AQUAMAS (IRE)**, 4, b f Mehmas (IRE)—Acquaint (IRE) **M. J. K. Dods**
3 **ARCH MOON**, 5, b g Sea The Moon (GER)—Archduchess **Mr Allan Mcluckie & Mr M. J. K. Dods**
4 **BERRY EDGE (IRE)**, 4, b g Mukhadram—Amaany **Elliott Brothers And Peacock**
5 **BILLY NO MATES (IRE)**, 6, b g Clodovil (IRE)—Sabaidee (IRE) **Mr J Sagar & Mr M Dods**
6 **BLACKHEATH**, 7, b g Excelebration (IRE)—Da's Wish (IRE) **Game on Racing**
7 **BLOWING WIND (IRE)**, 4, b g Markaz (IRE)—Wojha (IRE) **Denton Hall Racing Ltd**
8 **BOLD TERRITORIES (IRE)**, 4, ch g Territories (IRE)—Amberley Heights (IRE) **Tg Racing**
9 **COMMANCHE FALLS**, 5, br g Lethal Force (IRE)—Joyeaux **Mr Doug Graham, Davison & Drysdale**
10 **DAKOTA GOLD**, 8, b g Equiano (FR)—Joyeaux **Doug Graham, Ian Davison, Alan Drysdale 1**
11 **DANIELSFLYER (IRE)**, 8, b g Dandy Man (IRE)—Warm Welcome **Elliott Brothers And Peacock**
12 **DEPUTY (IRE)**, 4, b br g Lawman (FR)—Finagle (IRE) **Mr V Spinks & Partner**
13 **DIAMOND HAZE (IRE)**, 4, b g Coulsty (IRE)—Cannot Give (USA) **Denton Hall Racing Ltd**
14 **DIAMONDONTHEHILL**, 4, b g Al Kazeem—It's My Time **Sekura Group & John Burns**
15 **FIRST GREYED (IRE)**, 4, gr g Gutaifan (IRE)—Hidden Girl (IRE) **The Gorijeb Partnership**
16 **FLEETWOOD PIER**, 4, ch g Garswood—Lilbourne Lass **High Hopes Partnership**
17 **GALE FORCE MAYA**, 6, ch m Gale Force Ten—Parabola **Mr F. Lowe**
18 **HAVAGOMECCA**, 4, ch f Havana Gold (IRE)—Bikini **Mr David T J Metcalfe & Mr M J K Dods**
19 **HEAR ME ROAR (IRE)**, 4, b g The Last Lion (IRE)—Dutch Heiress **Mr P Appleton & Mrs Anne Elliott**
20 **JAWWAAL**, 7, ch g Bahamian Bounty—Avenbury **Sekura Trade Frames Ltd**
21 **JOMONT (FR)**, 5, b g Motivator—Sea Life (FR) **Teresa Blackett & M Dods**
22 **LANGHOLM (IRE)**, 6, b g Dark Angel (IRE)—Pindrop **Dods Racing Club**
23 **MARCELLO SI**, 4, b g Marcel (IRE)—Serenata Mia **Mrs H. I. S. Calzini**
24 **MAYMOON (IRE)**, 4, b f Mayson—Moonstone Magic **Mrs E. Kennedy**
25 **NORTHERN EXPRESS (IRE)**, 4, ch g Zoffany (IRE)—Hint of a Tint (IRE) **Sekura Trade Frames Ltd**
26 **PENDLETON**, 6, b g Garswood—Anglezarke (IRE) **Dods Racing Club**
27 **QUEEN'S SARGENT (FR)**, 7, gr g Kendargent (FR)—Queen's Conquer **Mr D. Stone**
28 **QUEENSFERRY (USA)**, 4, gr f Flintshire—Mortgage the House (USA) **Qatar Racing Limited**
29 **RICCIRELLA**, 4, gr ro f Rajsaman (FR)—Agnese **Mrs H. I. S. Calzini**
30 **SIN E SHEKELLS**, 5, ch g Bated Breath—Meddling **Mrs C. E. Dods**
31 **SIR TITUS (IRE)**, 4, ch g Dandy Man (IRE)—Moss Top (IRE) **Mr Michael Moses & Mr Terry Moses**
32 **STALLONE (IRE)**, 6, b g Dandy Man (IRE)—Titian Queen **Dods Racing Club**
33 **TINTO**, 6, b g Compton Place—Amirah (IRE) **F. Watson**
34 **WOR WILLIE**, 4, b g Mukhadram—Caterina de Medici (FR) **D. Neale**

THREE-YEAR-OLDS

35 **ALETHIOMETER (FR)**, b f Aclaim (IRE)—Live Love Laugh (FR) **Mrs C. Dods & Mr D Stone**
36 **AUDIT (IRE)**, b g Footstepsinthesand—Bayan Kasirga (IRE) **The Bottom Liners**
37 **AZURE BLUE (IRE)**, gr f El Kabeir (USA)—Sea of Dreams (IRE) **Mr P Appleton & Mrs Anne Elliott**
38 **CAPERCAILLIE (IRE)**, b f Coulsty (IRE)—Awwal Malika (USA) **Mrs T Burns, Mr M D Pearson & M Dods**
39 **CHIELLINI (IRE)**, b c Aclaim (IRE)—Onomatomania (USA) **Mrs T. Burns**
40 **CIRCOLOCO (IRE)**, b f Mehmas (IRE)—Special Focus (IRE) **Mrs C. Dods & Mr D Stone**
41 **CLARETS GLORY (IRE)**, b g Cotai Glory—Puddles (IRE) **D & M Dods**
42 **JOEYREMY (IRE)**, b g Gutaifan (IRE)—School Holidays (USA) **Top House 4**
43 **MASTER ELLIS (IRE)**, gr g Markaz (IRE)—Grecian Artisan (IRE) **Mr F. Lowe**
44 B g Excelebration (IRE)—Monroe
45 **OLIVER'S ARMY (FR)**, b g Pedro The Great (USA)—Douriya (USA) **Mr D. Stone**
46 **PURPLE ICE (IRE)**, gr g El Kabeir (USA)—Maybe Now Baby (IRE) **High Hopes Partnership & Partner**
47 **QUEEN SPIRIT (IRE)**, ch f Tagula (IRE)—Falabelle (IRE) **M. J. K. Dods**
48 **RED WARNING (IRE)**, ch g Bungle Inthejungle—Red Red Rose **Ian Davison & Geoff Thompson**
49 Ch g Twilight Son—Scarborough (IRE) **Taylor's Bloodstock Ltd**
50 **SEZAAM (IRE)**, gr g Elzaam (AUS)—Sesmen **Dunham Trading & Carole Dods**
51 **THIN LIZZY**, br f Brazen Beau (AUS)—Romp **Mr Michael Moses & Mr Terry Moses**
52 **VACCINE (IRE)**, b c Vadamos (FR)—Strike A Light **Rjh Ltd & D Stone**
53 **YEEEAAH (IRE)**, gr g El Kabeir (USA)—Red Savina **J & Dods**

MR MICHAEL DODS - continued

TWO-YEAR-OLDS

54 B c 26/04 Aclaim (IRE)—Azhar (Exceed And Excel (AUS)) (35000) **Trevor Scothern & Dave Stone**
55 B f 28/02 Gutaifan (IRE)—Capomento (IRE) (Casamento (IRE)) (16500) **Denton Hall Racing Ltd**
56 B g 15/03 Bungle Inthejungle—Fol O'Yasmine (Dubawi (IRE)) (16190) **Mr D. R. Graham**
57 B c 24/03 Caravaggio (USA)—Hand On Heart (IRE) (Mastercraftsman (IRE)) (35238) **Mr F. Lowe**
58 HILLS OF GOLD, ch c 12/03 Pivotal—Posterity (IRE) (Indian Ridge) (45000) **Sekura Trade Frames Ltd**
59 B g 22/04 Equiano (FR)—Lavetta (Peintre Celebre (USA)) (11429)
60 B c 16/03 New Bay—Lola Ridge (IRE) (Excelebration (IRE)) (48000) **F & M Dods**
61 B g 20/03 Fast Company (IRE)—Lydia Becker (Sleeping Indian) (20000)
62 B c 26/03 Bungle Inthejungle—Nafa (IRE) (Shamardal (USA)) (70000) **Mrs C. Dods & Mr D Stone**
63 NAVY WREN (IRE), b f 06/05 U S Navy Flag (USA)—Front House (IRE) (Sadler's Wells (USA)) (16190)
                                                                                    Mr W. R. Arblaster
64 POL ROGER (IRE), b c 17/02 Churchill (IRE)—Passegiata (Mastercraftsman (IRE)) (15000)
                                                                                    Mr J Sagar & Mr S Lowthian
65 PRAIRIE FALCON, b c 22/03 Belardo (IRE)—New Falcon (IRE) (New Approach (IRE)) (17000)
                                                                                    Bearstone Stud Limited
66 B c 13/02 Caravaggio (USA)—Princesse de San (IRE) (Mastercraftsman (IRE)) (32000)
67 B f 15/02 Sea The Moon (GER)—Realt Eile (IRE) (Dark Angel (IRE)) (18707) **The Gorijeb Partnership**
68 B c 03/03 Roaring Lion (USA)—Seychelloise (Pivotal) (65000) **Mr F. Lowe**
69 SPARKLING RED (IRE), b f 21/02 Bungle Inthejungle—Hint of Red (IRE) (Fast Company (IRE)) (32313)
                                                                                    R Saunders,G Thompson,I Davison
70 B c 12/03 Time Test—Summers Lease (Pivotal) (35000) **D. Neale**
71 VORTIGAN, ch c 15/03 Ulysses (IRE)—Aristocratic (Exceed And Excel (AUS)) (42000) **Mr D. A. Bardsley**
72 B f 19/01 El Kabeir (USA)—Wings Of The Rock (Rock of Gibraltar (IRE)) (37000) **D. T. J. Metcalfe**
73 ZUFFOLO (IRE), b c 02/05 Bungle Inthejungle—Red Red Rose (Piccolo) (26361)
                                                                                    Thompson,Saunders,Drysdale,Davison

Other Owners: Mr P. Appleton, Mr D. A. Bardsley, Mr J. N. Blackburn, Mr P. R. Blackett, Mr J. Burns, Mrs T. Burns, Mr L. H. Christie, Mr Ian Davison, Mrs C. E. Dods, M. J. K. Dods, Mr A. Drysdale, Dunham Trading Ltd, Mrs A. E. Elliott, Mr M. P. Glass, Mr D. R. Graham, Mr J. B. Hart, High Hopes Partnership, Mr R. Homburg, Mr A. S. Kelvin, Mr R. A. Little, Mr F. Lowe, Mr S. R. Lowthian, Mr A. McLuckie, D. T. J. Metcalfe, Mr R. I. Moffatt, Mr M. Moses, Mr T. J. Moses, Mr M. D. Pearson, R J H Limited, Mr J. Sagar, Mr R. R. D. Saunders, T. A. Scothern, Sekura Trade Frames Ltd, V. J. Spinks, Mr D. Stone, Mr N. H. Taylor-Garthwaite, Mr P. E. Taylor-Garthwaite, Mr S. A. Taylor-Garthwaite, Mr G. C. Thompson.

Assistant Trainer: Carole Dods, **Head Lad:** Steve Alderson, David Dickenson.

Flat Jockey: Connor Beasley, Paul Mulrennan. **Amateur Jockey:** Miss Chloe Dods, Miss Sophie Dods.

146

MR SIMON DOW, Epsom
Postal: **Clear Height Stable, Derby Stables Road, Epsom, Surrey, KT18 5LB**
Contacts: **PHONE 01372 721490 MOBILE 07860 800109**
EMAIL simon@simondow.co.uk WEBSITE www.simondow.co.uk TWITTER @SimonDowRacing

1 ARCTICIAN (IRE), 4, gr c Dark Angel (IRE)—Atlantic Drift **R. A. Murray-Obodynski**
2 ARENAS DEL TIEMPO, 4, b br f Footstepsinthesand—Vezere (USA) **Mr R. J. Moss**
3 BLUE BERET, 4, ch f Helmet (AUS)—Vivid Blue **Bantry Boy's Partnership**
4 CAFE MILANO, 5, bg Al Kazeem—Selka (FR) **S. L. Dow**
5 CANAGAT, 5, ch g Zoffany (IRE)—Caskelena (IRE) **Mr C. G. J. Chua**
6 CORAZON ESPINADO (IRE), 7, b h Iffraaj—Three Decades (IRE) **Mr R. J. Moss**
7 GOSNAY GOLD (FR), 4, b g Goken (FR)—Vesly (FR) **The Gg Racing Partnership**
8 HEADLEY GEORGE (IRE), 5, b g Due Diligence (USA)—Silent Secret (IRE) **Mr M. J. Convey**
9 HECTOR LOZA, 5, b g Kodiac—Queen Sarra **Mr R. J. Moss**
10 JEREMIAH JOHNSON (IRE), 4, b c Camacho—Lady Lassie (IRE) **J J's Syndicate & Simon Dow**
11 MOOSMEE (IRE), 5, br g Society Rock (IRE)—Tara Too (IRE) **Miss S. D. Groves**
12 NEFARIOUS (IRE), 6, ro g Zebedee—Tellelle (IRE) **R Moss, H Redknapp**

MR MICHAEL DODS - continued

13 **OLIVERS PURSUIT,** 5, br g Pastoral Pursuits—Deep Blue Sea **Roundabout Magic Racing**
14 **PABLO DEL PUEBLO (IRE),** 4, b g Kodiac—Solar Event **Mr R. J. Moss**
15 **PRINCE ROCK (IRE),** 7, ch g Society Rock (IRE)—She's A Queen (IRE) **Mr M. McAllister**
16 **QEYAADY,** 4, b g Muhaarar—Starflower **S. L. Dow**
17 **RECUERDAME (USA),** 6, b g The Factor (USA)—B R's Girl (USA) **Mr R. J. Moss**
18 **SHERPA TRAIL (USA),** 6, gr ro g Gio Ponti (USA)—Vapour Musing **S. L. Dow**
19 **SUBLIMINAL,** 7, b g Arcano (IRE)—Rare Virtue (USA) **Mr M. McAllister**
20 **THE GAME IS ON,** 6, b g Garswood—Paquerettza (FR) **Mr B. R. Lindley**
21 **WAKE UP HARRY,** 4, b g Le Havre (IRE)—Regatta (FR) **Mr H. Redknapp**

THREE-YEAR-OLDS

22 **AURELIA GOLD,** b f Havana Gold (IRE)—Dainty Dandy (IRE) **The Fat Jockey Partnership**
23 **CABLE MOUNTAIN,** b g Cable Bay (IRE)—Esteemed Lady (IRE) **The Fat Jockey Partnership**
24 **EDDY MAY (IRE),** b f Profitable (IRE)—Hollow Green (IRE) **Eddy May Racing Partnership**
25 **HUL AH BAH LOO (IRE),** b g Raven's Pass (USA)—Susiescot (USA) **Mr M. McAllister**
26 **RIKONA,** b f Shalaa (IRE)—Paradise Sea (USA) **The Fat Jockey Partnership**
27 **ROMAN TEMPEST (FR),** b c Tiberius Caesar (FR)—Seasonal Cross **Malcolm & Alicia Aldis**
28 **ROUNDABOUT SILVER,** gr g Silver Pond (FR)—Mumtaza **Roundabout Magic Racing**
29 **TORIOUS,** ch f Lethal Force (IRE)—Authora (IRE) **The Fat Jockey Partnership**
30 **WOE BETIDE,** b g Siyouni (FR)—Kenzadargent (FR) **Chasemore Farm LLP**

TWO-YEAR-OLDS

31 **DESFONDADO (IRE),** b c 25/03 Australia—Baroness (IRE) (Declaration of War (USA)) (90000) **Mr R. J. Moss**
32 **EL PEQUENO PULPO,** ch c 01/03 Proconsul—Vezere (USA) (Point Given (USA)) (1400) **Mr R. J. Moss**
33 **MUY MUY GUAPO,** b c 25/03 Ardad (IRE)—Belvoir Diva (Exceed And Excel (AUS)) (115000) **Mr R. J. Moss**
34 **RICARDO OFWORTHING (IRE),** b c 26/04 Dandy Man (IRE)—Shamardyh (IRE) (Shamardal (USA)) (20000)
Miss S. D. Groves

Other Owners: Mrs A. Aldis, Mr M. S. Aldis, Mr S. Buy, S. L. Dow, Mr D. L. Galway, J J's Syndicate, A. M. G. Mackenzie, Mr R. J. Moss, Mr B Phillpott, Mr H. Redknapp, Mr N. S. Scandrett, Dr C. Stam, Mr I. R. Steadman, Mr A. Webb, Mr N. White.

147	**MR CHRIS DOWN, Cullompton** Postal: **Upton, Cullompton, Devon, EX15 1RA** Contacts: **PHONE 01884 32212 MOBILE 07828 021232 FAX 01884 32212** EMAIL cjdownracing@gmail.com

1 **ALKHATAAF,** 4, b g Mukhadram—Rewaaya (IRE) **Knights of Ni**
2 **BALLYGOE (IRE),** 6, ch g Shantou (USA)—Paradise Lily (IRE) **P. D. Holland, Mrs V. Holland**
3 **BATTLE MARCH (USA),** 5, b g War Front (USA)—Lahinch Classics (IRE) **Chris Down Racing**
4 **BRYHER,** 5, b g Dream Eater (IRE)—Angel Sprints **Miss V. M. Halloran**
5 **DAYTIME AHEAD (IRE),** 11, gr m Daylami (IRE)—Bright Times Ahead (IRE) **R. J. Hodges**
6 **FRANKINCENSE (IRE),** 7, b g Galileo (IRE)—Anna Karenina (IRE) **The Almost Hopeful Partnership**
7 **JOHNNY B (IRE),** 8, b g Famous Name—Zoudie **Mrs P. Roffe-Silvester**
8 **LIGHT IN THE SKY (FR),** 6, b g Anodin (IRE)—Arsila (IRE) **C. J. Down**
9 **MERRY MONTY,** 5, b g Arvico (FR)—Red Mimi **Mrs S. M. Trump**
10 **MIDNIGHT MIDGE,** 8, b g Midnight Legend—Posh Emily **A Midgley, R J Hodges**
11 **MISS MARETTE,** 6, b m Passing Glance—La Marette **Culm Valley Racing**
12 **MR SOCIABLE,** 7, b g Geordieland (FR)—Secret Queen **Kittymore Racing**
13 **NOSTALGICA,** 5, b m She The Moon (GER)—Neige d'Antan **The Down & Dennis Partnership**
14 **OPENING BID,** 7, b g Native Ruler—Clifton Encore (USA) **Mr T Hamlin & Mr J M Dare**
15 **PUZZLE CACHE,** 8, b m Phoenix Reach (IRE)—Secret Queen **Kittymore Racing**
16 **RADDON TOP (IRE),** 9, ch g Getaway (GER)—Knockbrack Vic (IRE) **Mrs S. M. Trump**
17 **REGAL 'N BOLD,** 5, bl m Royal Anthem (USA)—Secret Queen **Kittymore Racing**
18 **RUSSIES DREAM,** 6, b g Dream Eater (IRE)—Russie With Love **Howzat Partnership**
19 **SECRET POTION (GER),** 6, b g Dabirsim (FR)—Sola Gratia (IRE) **C. J. Down**

MR CHRIS DOWN - continued

20 **SILVER CHORD**, 4, gr f Linda's Lad—Lily Potts **C. J. Down**
21 **WHAT A PLEASURE**, 6, b gr m Al Namix (FR)—Emergence (FR) **Mr D. Lockwood**

Other Owners: Mr J. M. Dare, R. A. Davies, Mr R. G. Dennis, C. J. Down, T. Hamlin, R. J. Hodges, & Holland, A. M. Midgley, Ms K. H. Smith.

NH Jockey: James Davies, Paige Fuller, David Noonan. **Conditional Jockey:** Jo Anderson, Harriet Tucker.

148
MR CLIVE DREW, Rampton
Postal: **Fox End Stables, 83 King Street, Rampton, Cambridgeshire, CB24 8QD**
Contacts: **PHONE 01954 250772 MOBILE 07917 718127**
EMAIL polly.drew@googlemail.com

1 **MAISON BRILLET (IRE)**, 15, b g Pyrus (USA)—Stormchaser (IRE) **C. Drew**
2 **MONSIEUR ROYALE**, 12, ch g Monsieur Bond (IRE)—Bond Royale **C. Drew**
3 4, B c Alhebayeb (IRE)—Ur Secret Is Safe (IRE)

Assistant Trainer: Miss Polly Drew.

149
MR SAMUEL DRINKWATER, Strensham
Postal: **The Granary, Twyning Road, Strensham, Worcester, Worcestershire, WR8 9LH**
Contacts: **MOBILE 07747 444633**
EMAIL samdrinkwater@gmail.com

1 **ATHGARVAN (IRE)**, 5, b g Soldier of Fortune (IRE)—Foildearg (IRE) **Drinkwater Family & Cheltenham Boys**
2 **BALLYBREEZE**, 6, b g Schiaparelli (GER)—Cottstown Gold (IRE) **Mr K. J. Price**
3 **BENNY'S BRIDGE (IRE)**, 9, b g Beneficial—Wattle Bridge (IRE) **Biddestone Racing I**
4 **BEST PAL (IRE)**, 5, b g Soldier of Fortune (IRE)—Shapley Shadow **All Bar None Racing**
5 **BUZZ DE TURCOING (FR)**, 8, b g Maresca Sorrento (FR)—Panora Night (FR) **Prestbury Thoroughbreds - Buzz**
6 **CAPTAIN JACK**, 9, b g Mount Nelson—Court Princess **Mr & Mrs D. C. Holder**
7 **COACHELLA GREEN (IRE)**, 10, b m Westerner—Turquoise Green (IRE) **Mr D. A. Hunt**
8 5, B g Mount Nelson—Court Princess
9 **CUP OF COFFEE (FR)**, 8, b m Dragon Dancer—Danser Sur La Lune (FR) **Mr D. A. Hunt**
10 **FLIGHT COMMAND (IRE)**, 5, br g War Command (USA)—Regency Girl (IRE) **Prestbury Thoroughbreds**
11 **FONTANA ELLISSI (FR)**, 6, b g Sinndar (IRE)—Leni Riefenstahl (IRE) **Anthony & Family**
12 **GALLIC GEORDIE**, 9, b g Geordieland (FR)—Je Ne Sais Plus (FR) **Glastonbury & On the Gallops 1**
13 **GENERAL CONSENSUS**, 10, br g Black Sam Bellamy (IRE)—Charlottes Webb (IRE) **Mrs K. Drinkwater**
14 **GENTLE FIRE**, 6, b m Phoenix Reach (IRE)—Pugnacious Lady **Court Reclamation & Salvage Ltd**
15 **HELLO BOB**, 7, ch m Cityscape—Maid of Perth **Mrs J. Drinkwater**
16 **HOWLING MILAN (IRE)**, 8, b g Milan—Fantasia Filly (FR) **P. Drinkwater**
17 **JEN'S GEORGIE**, 7, gr m Geordieland (FR)—Je Ne Sais Plus (FR) **Glastonburys & On the Gallops 2**
18 **KICKONMYSON**, 6, b g Schiaparelli (GER)—Madam Min **The Cheltenham Boys Racing Club**
19 **LA FILLE FRANCAISE (FR)**, 9, b m Kapgarde (FR)—Pondimari (FR) **Mrs J. C. Venvell**
20 **LIGHTNING BLUE**, 5, b m Harbour Watch (IRE)—Blue Beacon **Premier Thoroughbred Racing Ltd**
21 **NIGHTBOATTOCLYRO**, 6, ch g Sulamani (IRE)—Wychwoods Legend
22 **RUSSIAN SERVICE**, 10, b g Robin des Champs (FR)—Just Kate **Stephen Mattick & Mr D.P. Drinkwater**
23 **SAWPIT SAMANTHA**, 4, b f Champs Elysees—Sawpit Supreme **Mr D. A. Hunt**
24 **SAWPIT SIENNA**, 5, b m Dylan Thomas (IRE)—Sawpit Supreme **Mr D. A. Hunt**
25 **SPIKE JONES**, 5, b g Walk In The Park (IRE)—Mathine **Drinkwater Family & Cheltenham Boys**
26 **STORMING CARLOS (IRE)**, 5, b g Carlotamix (FR)—Storming Run (IRE) **Mick Coulson, Karen Drinkwater**
27 **STRENSHAM COURT**, 7, b g Great Pretender (IRE)—Diktalina **P. Drinkwater**

MR SAMUEL DRINKWATER - continued

28 **THE BRIMMING WATER (IRE)**, 7, b g Yeats (IRE)—Dollar's Worth (IRE) **Mrs K. Drinkwater**
29 **TOP DECISION (IRE)**, 9, ch g Beneficial—Great Decision (IRE) **Prestbury Thoroughbreds**

Other Owners: Mr M. D. Coulson, Mr D. P. Drinkwater, Mrs K. Drinkwater, P. Drinkwater, Mrs A. J. Glastonbury, Mr K. J. Glastonbury, Kevin & Anne Glastonbury, Mr M. Glastonbury, Mr R. Glastonbury, Mrs C. R. Holder, D. C. Holder, Mr A. Hunt, Mr V. Martin, Mr S. J. Mattick, On The Gallops Racing Club, The Cheltenham Boys Racing Club.

150

MISS JACKIE DU PLESSIS, Saltash
Postal: **Burell Farm, Longlands, Saltash, Cornwall, PL12 4QH**
Contacts: **PHONE 01752 842362 MOBILE 07970 871505**
EMAIL ziggerson@aol.com

1 **BOTUS FLEMING**, 7, ch g Tiger Groom—Chelsea Express **Miss J. M. du Plessis**
2 **ERICAS LAD**, 11, b g Mutazayid (IRE)—Kingsmill Quay **Miss J. M. du Plessis**
3 **FORGET YOU NOT (FR)**, 7, ch g Smadoun (FR)—Baby Sitter (FR) **Mr R. C. Dodson**
4 **HALOA MAIL (FR)**, 5, gr m Zanzibari (USA)—Queenly Mail (FR)
5 **KINGSMILL GIN**, 9, b m Fair Mix (IRE)—Kingsmill Lake **Miss J. M. du Plessis**
6 **LITTLE PEACHEY (IRE)**, 6, b m September Storm (GER)—Mrs Peachey (IRE) **Miss J. M. du Plessis**
7 **MABEL KINGSMILL**, 7, b m Lucarno (USA)—Kingsmill Lake **Miss J. M. du Plessis**
8 **MARTHA BURELL**, 7, ch m Lucarno (USA)—Theatre Diva (IRE) **Miss J. M. du Plessis**
9 **ST ERNEY**, 11, ch g Kadastrof (FR)—Ticket To The Moon **Miss J. M. du Plessis**
10 **THEATRE MIX**, 9, gr m Fair Mix (IRE)—Theatre Diva (IRE) **The Cornish Barmies**
11 **VALENTINO**, 7, b g Sulamani (IRE)—Romance Dance **Jackie Du Plessis & Sarah Pridham**

Other Owners: Miss S. Pridham, Miss J. M. du Plessis.

151

MRS ANN DUFFIELD, Leyburn
Postal: **Sun Hill Racing Ltd, Sun Hill Farm, Constable Burton, Leyburn, North Yorkshire, DL8 5RL**
Contacts: **PHONE 01677 450303 MOBILE 07802 496332 FAX 01677 450993**
EMAIL ann@annduffield.co.uk WEBSITE www.annduffield.co.uk

1 **ARNOLD**, 8, b g Equiano (FR)—Azurinta (IRE) **Duffield & Shewring, Patterson, Joyce**
2 **CLOTHERHOLME (IRE)**, 5, b g Sir Prancealot (IRE)—Giorgi (IRE) **Mr T. S. Ingham & Mrs Liz Ingham**
3 **COLLABORATING (IRE)**, 5, b g Bated Breath—Insieme (USA) **Mr K. Jardine**
4 **CUPPACOCO**, 7, b m Stimulation (IRE)—Glen Molly (IRE) **Mrs C. A. Gledhill**
5 **FAVOURITE NIECE**, 4, b f Fountain of Youth (IRE)—Ambella (IRE) **Mr T. S. Ingham & Mrs Liz Ingham**
6 **FUSAIN (FR)**, 7, gr g Lord du Sud (FR)—Savigny (FR) **Mr E. McElligott**
7 **GLENTRUAN (IRE)**, 7, b g Getaway (GER)—Mac Idol (IRE) **Mrs A. Duffield**
8 **GO FOX**, 7, ch g Foxwedge (AUS)—Bling Bling (IRE) **Mr E. McElligott**
9 **LADY NECTAR (IRE)**, 5, b m Zebedee—Mitchelton (FR) **Mr T. S. Ingham & Mrs Liz Ingham**
10 **MACCLOUD (IRE)**, 7, b g Cloudings (IRE)—Macville (IRE) **Mr A. McNamara**
11 **MR TREVOR (IRE)**, 4, b g Kodi Bear (IRE)—Muscadelle **Mr T. S. Ingham & Mrs Liz Ingham**
12 **N'GOLO (IRE)**, 7, gr g Galileo (IRE)—Dame Again (AUS) **K Jardine R Griffiths S Greig**
13 **OLYMPUS (IRE)**, 4, b g Kingman—Carpe Vita (IRE) **Mr E. McElligott**
14 **QUERCUS (IRE)**, 5, b g Nayef (USA)—Dufoof (IRE) **Mrs C. A. Gledhill**
15 **RUNNINWILD**, 4, b g Fountain of Youth (IRE)—Dont Tell Nan **Mr Ian Farrington & Partner**
16 **SUNTORY STAR (IRE)**, 4, ch f Starspangledbanner (AUS)—Sunbula (USA) **Racing Knights**
17 **THE REAL WHACKER (IRE)**, 6, b g Mahler—Credit Box (IRE) **Mrs A. Duffield**
18 **THE RED JET (IRE)**, 7, ch g Mahler—Carraigeen (IRE)

MRS ANN DUFFIELD - continued

THREE-YEAR-OLDS

19 **BILLYB (FR),** b g Raven's Pass (USA)—Aztec Queen **D. K. Barker**
20 **MADAME HELEN (FR),** b f Attendu (FR)—Spring Star (FR) **Mr T. S. Ingham & Mrs Liz Ingham**
21 **MASTER RICHARD,** b g Aclaim (IRE)—Movementneverlies **Mr T. S. Ingham & Mrs Liz Ingham**
22 **MISS DEMEANOUR (FR),** b f Shalaa (IRE)—Lady Tipperary (FR) **Ms J. F. Bianco**
23 Ch f Dragon Pulse (IRE)—Miss Frime (IRE)
24 **SIR DUKE,** b g Swiss Spirit—Prima Pagina **K Jardine R Griffiths**
25 **SYDNEY BAY,** b g Australia—Sudu Queen (GER) **Mr J. A. Kay**

Other Owners: Mrs A. Duffield, Mr I. J. Farrington, Mr S. Greig, Mr R. M. Griffiths, Mrs M. E. Ingham, Mr T. S. Ingham, Mr K. Jardine, Mr S. Joyce, K Jardine R Griffiths, Mr L. S. Patterson, Mr D. J. Shewring, Mrs S. A. Shewring.

---

152   MR BRENDAN W. DUKE, The Curragh
Postal: **Fenway House, Pollardstown, Curragh, Co. Kildare, Ireland**
Contacts: **MOBILE +353 85 818 9724**
EMAIL **brendanwduke@hotmail.com**

1 **CHUFFER DANDRIDGE (IRE),** 6, b g So You Think (NZ)—I'm Sheikra (IRE)
2 **FIZZY RAZZA (IRE),** 5, ch g Dunelight (IRE)—Pretty Kittiwake (IRE)
3 **JOAN OF PIMLICO (IRE),** 5, b m Free Eagle (IRE)—Poplar Close (IRE)
4 4, Ch c Rule of Law (USA)—Jodi's Oscar (IRE)
5 **LEAGAN GAEILGE (IRE),** 6, b m Vocalised (USA)—Feile Bride (IRE)
6 **MADE IN PIMLICO (IRE),** 5, ch h Dragon Pulse (IRE)—Runway Giant (USA)
7 **MARKETTA,** 4, b f Markaz (IRE)—Liscoa (IRE)
8 **MOVING (IRE),** 5. b g Gleneagles (IRE)—National Swagger (IRE)
9 4, B c Parish Hall (IRE)—Odisha (USA)
10 **PERCY PI,** 6, b g Sir Percy—Clifton Encore (USA)
11 **PRIDE OF PIMLICO (IRE),** 6, ch g Casamento (IRE)—Casina Valadier (IRE)
12 **SPEAK NOW (IRE),** 5, b g Vocalised (USA)—Heir Today (IRE)
13 **THE BILLY COCK (IRE),** 5, b g Rule of Law (USA)—Jodi's Oscar (IRE)
14 **THE BLUE GARTER (IRE),** 4, b f Kodi Bear—You're My Cracker
15 **VOCAL QUEEN (IRE),** 7, b m Vocalised (USA)—Silver Queen

THREE-YEAR-OLDS

16 **DARRABY,** br c Danon Ballade (JPN)—Patronne
17 B c Dragon Pulse—I'm Sheikra (IRE)
18 B c Fulbright—Stella Etoile (IRE)
19 B f Peace Envoy—Testing (FR)
20 **VICTORY LANTERN (IRE),** b f Mehmas (IRE)—Faddwa (IRE)

TWO-YEAR-OLDS

21 B c 26/04 Parish Hall (IRE)—Odisha (USA) (Drosselmeyer (USA))

Flat Jockey: Rory Cleary, Kevin Manning, Ronan Whelan. **NH Jockey:** Sean Flanagan. **Apprentice Jockey:** Luke McAteer.

---

153   MR IAN DUNCAN, Coylton
Postal: **Sandhill Farm, Coylton, Ayr, Ayrshire, KA6 6HE**
Contacts: **PHONE 01292 571118 MOBILE 07731 473668 FAX 01292 571118**
EMAIL **idracing@outlook.com**

1 **BANNSIDE (IRE),** 6, b g Robin des Champs (FR)—Milogan (IRE) **Dr S. Sinclair**
2 **BOLT MAN,** 4, b g Millenary—Miss Chatterbox **Mrs V. C. Macdonald**
3 **CELESTIAL FASHION,** 4, b f Telescope (IRE)—French Fashion (IRE)
4 **FAME VALLEY (IRE),** 7, b g Fame And Glory—Miss Island (IRE) **Dr S. Sinclair**
5 **GUINNESS VILLAGE (IRE),** 6, bl g Sholokhov (IRE)—Lowroad Cross (IRE) **Mr C. Davidson**
6 **JESSIEMAC (IRE),** 8, br m Sholokhov (IRE)—All Our Blessings (IRE) **Alan & Barry Macdonald**

MR IAN DUNCAN - continued

7 **KING OF FASHION (IRE)**, 12, ch g Desert King (IRE)—French Fashion (IRE) **Dr S. Sinclair**
8 **LARGY PROSPECT (IRE)**, 10, b g Stowaway—Thrilling Prospect (IRE) **Sinclair, Hammersley & Davidson**
9 **NORDIC EXPRESS**, 5, ch m Norse Dancer (IRE)—Belfast Central (IRE) **Stephen Sinclair & Ian Duncan**
10 4, Ch f Ask—Red Card (IRE)
11 **STARSINHEREYES**, 5, b m Kayf Tara—French Fashion (IRE) **Mrs V. C. Macdonald**
12 **STRONG ECONOMY (IRE)**, 10, ch g Sandmason—Odd Decision (IRE) **Alan & Barry Macdonald**

Other Owners: Mr C. Davidson, I. A. Duncan, Mr G. Hammersley, Dr S. Sinclair.

154

MR NIGEL DUNGER, Pulborough
Postal: **17 Allfrey Plat, Pulborough, West Sussex, RH20 2BU**
Contacts: **PHONE 07494 344167 MOBILE 07790 631962**
EMAIL debdunger05@gmail.com

1 **HIER ENCORE (FR)**, 10, ch g Kentucky Dynamite (USA)—Hierarchie (FR) **N. A. Dunger**
2 **PRIDE OF PEMBERLEY (IRE)**, 10, ch g Flemensfirth (USA)—On Galley Head (IRE) **N. A. Dunger**
3 **SAFE PASSAGE**, 4, b f Paco Boy (IRE)—Daring Aim **N. A. Dunger**

Assistant Trainer: Mrs D Dunger.

155

MR ED DUNLOP, Newmarket
Postal: **La Grange Stables, Fordham Road, Newmarket, Suffolk, CB8 7AA**
Contacts: **PHONE 01638 661998 MOBILE 07785 328537 FAX 01638 667394**
EMAIL edunlop@eddunlopracing.co.uk WEBSITE www.edunlop.com

1 **AMAZING RED (IRE)**, 9, b g Teofilo (IRE)—Artisia (IRE)
2 **ARTHUR'S REALM (IRE)**, 4, b g Camelot—Morning Line (FR)
3 **BLUE FLAME (IRE)**, 5, gr g Dark Angel (IRE)—Bluefire
4 **GLOBAL ART**, 7, b g Dutch Art—Constant Dream
5 **JOHN LEEPER (IRE)**, 4, b c Frankel—Snow Fairy (IRE)
6 **JUAN LES PINS**, 5, b g Invincible Spirit (IRE)—Miss Cap Ferrat
7 **LENNY'S SPIRIT (FR)**, 4, b br g Intello (GER)—Moonee Valley (FR)
8 **MASTER THE STARS (GER)**, 5, b g Sea The Stars (IRE)—Magma (GER)
9 **PARIKARMA (IRE)**, 5, b m Canford Cliffs (IRE)—Pushkar
10 **RED VERDON (USA)**, 9, ch g Lemon Drop Kid (USA)—Porto Marmay (IRE)
11 **ROYAL HEART (FR)**, 4, b g Wootton Bassett—Gift of Life (USA)
12 **SOCIETY LION**, 5, b g Invincible Spirit (IRE)—Pavlosk (USA)
13 **VERREAUX EAGLE**, 4, gr f Free Eagle (IRE)—Evening Frost (IRE)
14 **VIRGIN SNOW**, 5, b m Gleneagles (IRE)—Snow Fairy (IRE)

THREE-YEAR-OLDS

15 **ALPHONSE LE GRANDE (IRE)**, b g Sea The Stars (IRE)—Dolce Strega (IRE)
16 **BAY OF BAKU (FR)**, b g Wootton Bassett—Maiden Tower
17 **BELLARENA LADY**, b f Due Diligence (USA)—Eshq (IRE)
18 **BURNING BUSH (IRE)**, b g Fulbright—Practicallyperfect (IRE)
19 **BY YOUR SIDE**, b g Lope de Vega (IRE)—Indiscrete (FR)
20 **CAPRICIOUS CAITLIN**, b f Iffraaj—Capricious Cantor (IRE)
21 **CITIZEN GENERAL (IRE)**, b c Camelot—Capriole
22 **COMMANDMENT (IRE)**, b f Acclamation—Heavenly Note
23 **DRAWING CLOCKS**, b c Time Test—Lynnwood Chase (USA)
24 **FEARLESS BAY (IRE)**, b g Siyouni (IRE)—Monroe Bay (IRE)

MR ED DUNLOP - continued

25 **FESTIVAL OF LIGHT,** b f Time Test—Luminda (IRE)
26 **GIRL INTHE PICTURE (IRE),** b f Lawman (FR)—Hidden Girl (IRE)
27 **GOT CARTER (IRE),** ch c Australia—Aegean Girl (IRE)
28 **HAUNTED DREAM (IRE),** gr g Oasis Dream—Red Halo (IRE)
29 **HEATHEN,** b c Lope de Vega (IRE)—Great Heavens
30 **HOMER'S GIRL,** ch f Ulysses (IRE)—Last Echo (IRE)
31 **INDY MOON,** b f Sea The Moon (GER)—Deserted
32 **MANHATTANVILLE (IRE),** ch g Tamayuz—Carol (IRE)
33 **MANNIKIN (IRE),** b g Buratino (IRE)—Musical Review (UAE)
34 **MISS CLEMENTINE (IRE),** b f Churchill (IRE)—Indigo Lady
35 **MUHTASHIM,** b g Muhaarar—Shurfah (IRE)
36 **MY SILENT SONG,** b f Postponed (IRE)—Sky Crystal (GER)
37 **NIKKI'S GIRL (IRE),** b f Mehmas (IRE)—Dame Judi (IRE)
38 **PENSA TE (IRE),** ch f Mehmas (IRE)—Araajmh (USA)
39 **PURPLE REIGN (IRE),** b g Camelot—Button Up (IRE)
40 **RICHARD P SMITH,** b g Belardo (IRE)—Illico
41 **ROSE'S GIRL,** ch f Ribchester (IRE)—Ballerina Rose
42 **SARKHA (IRE),** b c The Gurkha (IRE)—Saga Celebre (FR)
43 **SEAL OF SOLOMON (IRE),** b g Make Believe—Sapphire Waters (IRE)
44 **SELENE'S DREAM,** b f Dark Angel (IRE)—A Huge Dream (IRE)
45 **STERLING KNIGHT,** b g Camelot—Sterling Sound (USA)
46 **SUMMEREYES (IRE),** b f Lawman (FR)—Dream High (IRE)
47 **TADITA TWITCH,** b f Siyouni (FR)—Twitch (IRE)
48 **TOPAZ DREAM,** b f Dark Angel (IRE)—Dreamlike
49 **TURNER GIRL (IRE),** b f Mastercraftsman (IRE)—Music In My Heart
50 **WENDELL'S LAD,** b g New Approach (IRE)—Radhaadh (IRE)
51 **WENDELL'S LASS,** ch f New Approach (IRE)—Autumn Leaves (FR)
52 **WESTERN STARS (FR),** b g Almanzor (FR)—Waikika (FR)
53 **WILD TIDES (IRE),** b c Lope de Vega (IRE)—Wild Irish Rose (IRE)

TWO-YEAR-OLDS

54 B c 20/04 Caravaggio (USA)—Allegrezza (Sir Percy) (70000)
55 B f 23/04 Territories (IRE)—Angelic Note (IRE) (Excellent Art) (38000)
56 B c 12/04 Teofilo (IRE)—Balakera (IRE) (Dansili) (30000)
57 B f 26/03 Le Havre (IRE)—Capricious Cantor (IRE) (Cape Cross (IRE))
58 B c 25/03 Fast Company (IRE)—Chantilly Cream (IRE) (Acclamation) (74286)
59 Gr f 14/03 Zoustar (AUS)—Cheetah (Tiger Hill (IRE)) (38000)
60 B c 29/03 Acclamation—Cravin Raven (USA) (Raven's Pass (USA)) (50000)
61 B f 29/03 Brazen Beau (AUS)—Cue's Folly (Nathaniel (IRE))
62 B f 23/02 U S Navy Flag (USA)—Epsom Icon (Sixties Icon) (170068)
63 B br f 20/02 Ribchester (IRE)—Etesian Flow (Bated Breath) (119048)
64 Gr f 04/03 Camacho—Guiletta (IRE) (Dalakhani (IRE)) (24762)
65 B f 23/01 Sea The Moon (GER)—Gulden Gorl (GER) (Iffraaj) (97789)
66 B c 24/01 Almanzor (FR)—Just Gorgeous (IRE) (Galileo (IRE)) (110000)
67 Ch c 06/03 Belardo (IRE)—Kodiac Island (Kodiac) (17143)
68 B c 24/04 Showcasing—Landmark (USA) (Arch (USA)) (200000)
69 B f 13/04 Sea The Moon (GER)—Lonely Rock (Fastnet Rock (AUS)) (85000)
70 B c 08/03 Holy Roman Emperor (IRE)—Marthamydear (USA) (Tapizar (USA)) (14286)
71 B c 05/02 Massaat (IRE)—Miss Lesley (Needwood Blade) (40952)
72 B f 03/04 Ulysses (IRE)—Miss Pinkerton (Danehill (USA)) (120000)
73 B c 27/02 Golden Horn—Optica (FR) (Hernando (FR)) (4252)
74 Ch f 07/04 Mukhadram—Oulianovsk (IRE) (Peintre Celebre (USA)) (27211)
75 Ch c 20/04 Fast Company (IRE)—Portico (Pivotal) (85714)
76 B c 18/04 Gleneagles (IRE)—Queen Myrine (IRE) (Oratorio (IRE)) (55000)
77 Ch f 29/02 Decorated Knight—Queen Sarra (Shamardal (USA)) (35000)
78 Ch f 27/02 Galileo Gold—Rahaala (IRE) (Indian Ridge) (61905)
79 Ch c 06/04 Iffraaj—Ravensburg (Raven's Pass (USA)) (28000)
80 B f 27/04 Muhaarar—Red Fantasy (IRE) (High Chaparral (IRE)) (11000)
81 B f 14/03 Garswood—Royal Seal (Dansili) (61905)

MR ED DUNLOP - continued

82 B c 02/03 Muhaarar—Royale Danehill (IRE) (Danehill (USA)) (6000)
83 B f 17/03 Zoffany (IRE)—Roystonea (Polish Precedent (USA)) (100000)
84 B f 18/04 Cracksman—Sea Horn (FR) (Fastnet Rock (AUS)) (50000)
85 Gr c 18/03 Mastercraftsman (IRE)—Shanjia (GER) (Soldier Hollow) (140000)
86 B c 28/03 Muhaarar—Shingwedzi (SAF) (Trippi (USA))
87 B f 26/04 Muhaarar—South Bay (Exceed And Excel (AUS)) (15000)
88 **STREETSTORM,** b f 16/04 Night of Thunder (IRE)—Upper Street (IRE) (Dansili)
89 Br f 29/02 Awtaad (IRE)—Taarkod (IRE) (Singspiel (IRE)) (26361)
90 B c 10/01 Starspangledbanner (AUS)—Tammy Wynette (IRE) (Tamayuz) (80952)
91 B f 03/03 Time Test—Vallila (Dunkerque (FR)) (55000)
92 B f 03/04 Harry Angel (IRE)—Via Lattea (IRE) (Teofilo (IRE)) (75000)

Owners: Mrs J. Allison, S. A. Allison, Anamoine Ltd, Andy and Julie White and Partner, Mr R. J. Arculli, Mrs J. E. Ball, Cayton Park Stud Limited, The Earl Of Derby, Mr E. A. L. Dunlop, Mrs R. S. Dunlop, Mr D. G. Hicken, La Grange Partnership, Mr A. Leopold, Mr A. Leopold & Ms L. Norman, Lord Derby & Ors, Miltil Consortium, Ms L. C. Norman, Mrs W. O'Leary, Old Road Securities Limited, P Deals & H-Bs, Mr I. Quy, Serendipity Racing, St Albans Bloodstock Limited, The Isjamala Crew, The Old Etonian Racing Syndicate II, The Serendipity Partnership, Mr P. Turner, Sir J. R. Weatherby, Mrs S. F. Weatherby, Mr A. J. D. White, Windflower Overseas Holdings Inc, Major M. G. Wyatt.

Assistant Trainer: Jack Morland, **Head Lad:** Joey Brown.

---

156 **MR HARRY DUNLOP, Lambourn**
Postal: Frenchmans Lodge Stables, Upper Lambourn, Hungerford, Berkshire, RG17 8QW
Contacts: **PHONE 01488 73584 MOBILE 07880 791895**
EMAIL info@harrydunlopracing.com WEBSITE www.harrydunlopracing.com

1 ANGEL ON HIGH (IRE), 5, b g Dark Angel (IRE)—Angel of The Gwaun (IRE) **The Gehrings & Partners**
2 BRANSON MISSOURI (IRE), 6, b m Fame And Glory—Virtue **Harry Dunlop Racing Partnership**
3 LAWMANS BLIS (IRE), 4, b g Lawman (FR)—Megec Blis (IRE) **Mr J. R. Dwyer**
4 MAKETH BELIEVETH (IRE), 4, b g Make Believe—Lady Penko (FR) **Haven't A Pot**
5 MAXINE (IRE), 4, b f Maxios—Saltita (IRE) **Friends of John Dunlop**
6 MINISTER FOR MAGIC (IRE), 4, b f Make Believe—Rose of Africa (IRE) **Haven't A Pot**
7 MISS ZENLINGUS (IRE), 4, b f Kodiac—Orpha **Haven't A Pot**
8 POINT LOUISE, 4, b f Free Eagle (IRE)—Cape Mystery **Simon Birdseye & Velocity Racing**
9 SEA OF CHARM (FR), 4, b f Charm Spirit (IRE)—Sea Meets Sky (FR) **Mrs C. A. M. Dunlop**
10 SKY BLUE THINKING, 4, b f Charming Thought—Powder Blue **Haven't A Pot & William Dunlop**

THREE-YEAR-OLDS

11 ADAAY IN ASIA, b f Adaay (IRE)—Asia Minor (IRE) **The 2 Under Partnership**
12 ESCAPE FREE (IRE), b f Free Eagle (IRE)—Calatrava Cape (IRE) **Windflower Overseas Holdings Inc**
13 GRENADA, b c Oasis Dream—Pina **Mr & Mrs D. Hearson**
14 NEW ROSE, b f Ardad (IRE)—Litewska (IRE) **The Megsons**
15 NORDIC PEARL, gr f Pearl Secret—Skiing **MTWB Racing**
16 SOLAR PROPHET, b c Profitable (IRE)—Starring Guest (IRE) **The Sungayne Partnership**

TWO-YEAR-OLDS

17 BINGLEY CROCKER (IRE), b c 29/04 Bungle Inthejungle—Ellbeedee (IRE) (Dalakhani (IRE)) (13000) **The Megsons**
18 CHARMING LILY, b f 09/03 Charm Spirit (IRE)—Lilly Junior (Cape Cross (IRE)) (5500)
Frenchmans Lodge Stables Partnership
19 ENTRANCEMENT (FR), b f 29/04 Expert Eye—Entree (Halling (USA)) (6667) **Be Hopeful (2)**
20 MAGNIFICENT MILLIE, b f 20/01 Tasleet—Voicemail (Poet's Voice) (11000) **The 2 Under Partnership**
21 POLLY POTT, b f 09/02 Muhaarar—Must Be Me (Trade Fair) (21000) **The Megsons**

Other Owners: Mr S. C. Birdseye, Mr M. T. W. Blanshard, Mrs E. J. Clarke, Mr M. J. Cross, Mr A. S. Dudgeon, Mrs C. A. M. Dunlop, H. J. L. Dunlop, R. P. Foden, Mr G. Freeman, Mr K. C. Freeman, Haven't A Pot, D. N. Hearson, Mrs D. S. Hearson, Velocity Racing, Mr D. A. Woodley.

157   MRS ALEXANDRA DUNN, Wellington
Postal: **The Gallops, West Buckland, Wellington, Somerset, TA21 9LE**
Contacts: **MOBILE 07738 512924**
WEBSITE www.alexandradunnracing.com

1 **AFFWONN (IRE)**, 5, b g Free Eagle (IRE)—Shauna's Princess (IRE) **Racehorse Ownership Club**
2 **ALDRICH BAY (IRE)**, 5, b g Xtension (IRE)—Sail With The Wind **West Buckland Bloodstock Ltd**
3 **ANNIE NAIL (IRE)**, 5, ch m Doyen (IRE)—Castletown Girl **Racehorse Ownership Club**
4 **ARGUS (IRE)**, 10, b g Rip Van Winkle (IRE)—Steel Princess (IRE) **Helium Racing LTD**
5 **BEAT THE STORM (IRE)**, 4, b g Dragon Pulse (IRE)—Before The Storm **Gangbusters**
6 **BLACKHILLSOFDAKOTA (IRE)**, 7, b g Galileo (IRE)—Aymara **The Profile Partnership 2**
7 **BLACKWATER BRAMBLE (IRE)**, 11, b g King's Theatre (IRE)—Don't Be Upset (IRE) **Mrs K. R. Smith-Maxwell**
8 **BLITZ SPIRIT (IRE)**, 4, b f Free Eagle (IRE)—All Clear **Racehorse Ownership Club**
9 **BOOLAMORE GLORY (IRE)**, 5, b g Ocovango—Go Sandy Go (IRE) **Racehorse Ownership Club**
10 **CITY FLAME**, 6, b m Cityscape—High Drama (IRE) **Mr M. Vaughan**
11 **COLD SHOULDER**, 8, b g Passing Glance—Averami **Lycett Racing Ltd**
12 **CRY WOLF**, 9, ch g Street Cry (IRE)—Love Charm **W.B.B. & G.J. Daly**
13 **DARK MOON (FR)**, 4, b f Spanish Moon (USA)—Vida Sure Bailly (FR) **Team Dunn**
14 **DIDO**, 12, b g Killer Instinct—Bowdlane Barb **Mr R. H. Fox**
15 5, B m Kayf Tara—Double Mead **Mrs K. R. Smith-Maxwell**
16 **ESTATE ITALIANA (USA)**, 5, b br g Elusive Quality (USA)—Unaccompanied (IRE) **Team Dunn**
17 **ETOILE BRILLANTE (FR)**, 4, ch f Sholokhov (IRE)—Dam Royale (FR) **Racehorse Ownership Club**
18 **FREESTYLE (FR)**, 4, b br f Magadino (FR)—Fristar (FR)
19 **HELIAN (IRE)**, 6, b g Shamardal (USA)—Amathia (IRE) **Racehorse Ownership Club**
20 **HO QUE OUI (FR)**, 5, ch m Network (GER)—Highest Card (FR) **West Buckland Bloodstock Ltd**
21 4, B f Haafhd—Holy Veil
22 **JERSEY GREY (FR)**, 5, gr g Rajsaman (FR)—Akoyama **Racehorse Ownership Club**
23 **KAPITALISTE (FR)**, 6, b g Intello (GER)—Kapitale (GER) **The Profile Partnership 2**
24 **KAYF BREAK**, 6, b g Kayf Tara—Ishka Baha (IRE) **West Buckland Bloodstock Ltd**
25 **KEPALA**, 5, gr m Mastercraftsman (IRE)—Kebaya **Racehorse Ownership Club**
26 **MASTER MEAD**, 7, b g Malinas (GER)—Double Mead **Mrs K. R. Smith-Maxwell**
27 **MINELLA VOUCHER**, 11, b g King's Theatre (IRE)—All Rise (GER) **Taunton Town Peacocks**
28 **MONAAJEZ (USA)**, 4, gr g Speightstown (USA)—Broadway Show (USA) **Racehorse Ownership Club**
29 **NO FAME NO GAME (IRE)**, 7, b m Fame And Glory—Grande Milan (IRE) **Ms L. L. Clune**
30 **REGULATOR (IRE)**, 7, b g Acclamation—Rasana **S. Towens & W.B.B.**
31 **ROCK OF STAR (FR)**, 5, b g Nom de d'La (FR)—Rolie de Vindecy (FR) **Racehorse Ownership Club**
32 **SARCEAUX (FR)**, 5, gr m Rajsaman (FR)—Sainte Adresse **Racehorse Ownership Club**
33 **SAUSALITO SUNRISE (IRE)**, 14, b g Gold Well—Villaflor (IRE) **Mrs K. R. Smith-Maxwell**
34 **SIGNAL TWENTY NINE**, 5, gr g Gregorian (IRE)—Beacon Lady **West Buckland Bloodstock Ltd**
35 **THAHAB IFRAJ (IRE)**, 9, ch g Frozen Power (IRE)—Penny Rouge (IRE) **The Dunnitalls & Partner**
36 **THE EAGLE'S NEST (IRE)**, 8, ch g Lope de Vega (IRE)—Follow My Lead **Helium Racing LTD**
37 **THE RAIN KING (IRE)**, 5, b g No Nay Never (USA)—Brigids Cross (IRE) **Racehorse Ownership Club**
38 **TOAD OF TOAD HALL**, 6, b g Universal (IRE)—Double Mead **Team Dunn**

THREE-YEAR-OLDS

39 B g Passing Glance—Holy Veil

Other Owners: Mr D. R. Arthur, Mr S. Cullum, G. J. Daly, Mrs A. Dunn, Mr T. Dunn, Team Dunn, The Dunnitalls, The Profile Partnership, Mr N. Towens, West Buckland Bloodstock Ltd, Mrs C. M. Wheatley, Mr T. Wheatley.

158 MRS CHRISTINE DUNNETT, Norwich
Postal: **College Farm, Hingham, Norwich, Norfolk, NR9 4PP**
Contacts: **PHONE 01953 851364 MOBILE 07775 793523**
EMAIL christine@christinedunnett.com WEBSITE www.christinedunnett.com

1 4, B g Lethal Force (IRE)—Barathea Dancer (IRE) **Mr P. D. West**
2 **BRAZEN ARROW**, 4, b g Brazen Beau (AUS)—Patience **Pete West & Christine Dunnett**
3 **ENCHANTED NIGHT**, 4, ch f Night of Thunder (IRE)—Khaseeb **Paul Eggett & Christine Dunnett**
4 **FLOWER OF THUNDER (IRE)**, 5, b m Night of Thunder (IRE)—Flower Fairy (USA)
Sparkes, Machin, Amey & Dunnett
5 **GRAFFA**, 4, b g Bobby's Kitten (USA)—Marigay's Magic **Sparkes & Dunnett**
6 **JONATHANS PRINCESS**, 4, ch f Garswood—College Doll **Jonathan Butcher & Christine Dunnett**
7 **KRAKA (IRE)**, 7, b g Dark Angel (IRE)—Manuelita Rose (ITY) **Team Kraka**
8 4, B f Epaulette (AUS)—No Nightmare (USA) **Jonathan Butcher & Christine Dunnett**
9 **PERCY TOPLIS**, 8, b g Kheleyf (USA)—West Lorne (USA) **Christine Dunnett Racing (Arryzona)**
10 **ROSETINTEDGLASSES (IRE)**, 4, b f Gutaifan (IRE)—Manuelita Rose (ITY)
Christine Dunnett & Alan & Barbara Brown
11 **SHYJACK**, 7, ch g Archipenko (USA)—Coconut Shy **Christine Dunnett Racing (Arryzona)**
12 **SWOOPER**, 4, b g Brazen Beau (AUS)—Most Tempting **Pete West & Christine Dunnett**
13 **WALK IN THE STARS (IRE)**, 5, b m Walk In The Park (IRE)—Chiroule (IRE)

THREE-YEAR-OLDS
14 **BELOVED OF ALL (IRE)**, ch c Starspangledbanner (AUS)—Midnight Oasis **Christine Dunnett Racing (Arryzona)**
15 **DOVES CRY (IRE)**, b f Footstepsinthesand—Fickle Feelings (IRE) **Mr A. Machin & Mrs C. Dunnett**
16 **FAST FLO**, b f Garswood—College Doll **HSWHO Syndicate**
17 **JUST PERCY (IRE)**, b c Sir Percy—Sandtail (IRE) **Mr A. Brown & Mrs B. I. Brown**
18 **LATE BLOOM**, b f Charm Spirit (IRE)—Lovely Memory (IRE) **Mr P. Eggett**
19 **SONNY BROWN**, b g Mayson—Sand And Deliver **Mr A. Brown & Mrs B. I. Brown**
20 **SPIRIT OF THE AGE**, b f Mehmas (IRE)—Enterprising **Mr A. S. Machin**
21 **TIMES TWO**, b f Time Test—Time Crystal (IRE) **Mr A. Machin & Mrs C. Dunnett**

Other Owners: Mr P. Amey, Mr A. Brown, Mrs B. I. Brown, Mr J. G. Butcher, Mrs C. A. Dunnett, Mr P. Eggett, Mr A. S. Machin, Mr A. P. Scriggins, Mr E. N. Sparkes, Mr P. D. West.

159 MR SEAMUS DURACK, Upper Lambourn
Postal: **The Croft Stables, Upper Lambourn, Hungerford, Berkshire, RG17 8QH**
Contacts: **PHONE 01488 491480 MOBILE 07770 537971**
EMAIL sd.111@btinternet.com WEBSITE www.seamusdurack.com

1 **CAYIRLI (FR)**, 10, b g Medicean—Clarinda (FR) **S. P. Tucker**
2 **DARKEST DREAM**, 6, b m Albaasil (IRE)—Rare Ruby (IRE) **Mr R. S. Fiddes**
3 **FAST ART (IRE)**, 6, b g Fast Company (IRE)—Poulkovo (IRE) **Mr & Mrs A Archer & Mr & Mrs M Leonard**
4 **HERESY**, 6, b m Albaasil (IRE)—Straversjoy **Mr R. S. Fiddes**
5 **PHOENIX AQUILUS (IRE)**, 5, b g Slade Power (IRE)—Permsiri (IRE) **Mr S. E. Durack**
6 **PROPHECY**, 6, b g Albaasil (IRE)—Littlemoor Lass **Mr R. S. Fiddes**
7 **REFLECT**, 5, b m Albaasil (IRE)—True Rose (IRE) **Mr R. S. Fiddes**
8 **THUNDER LILY (IRE)**, 4, b f Night of Thunder (IRE)—Permsiri (IRE) **Mr Stephen Tucker and Mr S Durack**
9 **TWILIGHT HEIR**, 4, b g Twilight Son—Xtrasensory **Mr R. S. Fiddes**

THREE-YEAR-OLDS
10 **DARCY'S ROCK**, b f Heeraat (IRE)—Rock On Candy **Mrs W. Edwards**
11 **MY LOVELY SYLV**, b f Equiano (FR)—Royal Obsession (IRE) **Mr S. King**

Other Owners: Mr A. Archer, Mrs J. Archer, Mr S. E. Durack, Mr M. A. Leonard, Mrs M. E. Leonard, S. P. Tucker.

Assistant Trainer: Sam Beddoes.

160 MR CHRIS DWYER, Newmarket
Postal: **Paddocks View, Brickfield Stud, Exning Road, Newmarket, Suffolk, CB8 7JH**
EMAIL getadwyer@aol.com

1 ALETOILE, 4, ch f Sea The Stars (IRE)—Alamode **Strawberry Fields Stud**
2 DARK SIDE DIAMOND, 4, b f Equiano (FR)—Dark Side Princess **Mr M. M. Foulger**
3 ENDURED (IRE), 5, b g Shamardal (USA)—Wadaat **Mr B. C. M. Wong**
4 EPIC EXPRESS, 4, ch g Twilight Son—Keep The Secret **Mr M. M. Foulger**
5 GLOBAL ESTEEM (IRE), 5, b g Kodiac—Baltic Belle (IRE) **Dr J. Hon**
6 GLOBAL PROSPECTOR (USA), 6, b br g Scat Daddy (USA)—Alegendinmyownmind **Dr J. Hon**
7 GLOBAL VISION (IRE), 4, gr ro g Markaz (IRE)—Vision of Peace (IRE) **Dr J. Hon**
8 GLOBAL WARNING, 6, b g Poet's Voice—Persario **Dr J. Hon**
9 LONDON EYE (USA), 6, ch g Australia—Circle of Life (USA) **Dr J. Hon**
10 SIR OLIVER (IRE), 5, b g Dark Angel (IRE)—Folga **Dr J. Hon**
11 THAKI (IRE), 5, b g Lope de Vega (IRE)—Mickleberry (IRE) **Mrs S. Dwyer**
12 WORLD OF WINDHOVER (IRE), 5, b g Showcasing—City Image (IRE) **Mrs N. S. L. Thorne**

THREE-YEAR-OLDS

13 BE BE EX (IRE), b g Harzand (IRE)—Juno Moneta (IRE) **Strawberry Fields Stud**
14 GLOBAL GRANDEUR, b f Fastnet Rock (AUS)—Raggety Ann (IRE) **Dr J. Hon**
15 GLOBAL MIRAGE, b f Mayson—Jeanie Johnston (IRE) **Dr J. Hon**
16 GLOBAL ROMANCE (IRE), ch f Iffraaj—Katawi **Dr J. Hon**
17 GLOBAL TYCOON (IRE), br gr g Caravaggio (USA)—Much Faster (IRE) **Dr J. Hon**
18 GLOBAL WISDOM (FR), b g No Nay Never (USA)—Shahinda (FR) **Dr J. Hon**

TWO-YEAR-OLDS

19 GLOBAL MERIT (IRE), b c 31/03 No Nay Never (USA)—Casila (IRE) (High Chaparral (IRE)) (100000) **Dr J. Hon**
20 GLOBAL RESOLVE (IRE), b c 25/03 Starspangledbanner (AUS)—Laurelita (IRE) (High Chaparral (IRE)) (90000)
Dr J. Hon
21 Ch c 24/02 Territories (IRE)—Global Rose (IRE) (Dark Angel (IRE)) **Dr J. Hon**
22 GLOBAL VOLITION, br c 29/02 Mayson—Global Spring (Kodiac) **Dr J. Hon**
23 Ch c 09/02 Gleneagles (IRE)—Irish Madam (Equiano (FR)) (10476)
24 B br c 16/03 Muhaarar—Sprinkling (USA) (Quality Road (USA)) (24000)

161 MISS CLAIRE DYSON, Evesham
Postal: **Froglands Stud Farm, Froglands Lane, Cleeve Prior, Evesham, Worcestershire, WR11 8LB**
Contacts: **PHONE 01789 774000, 07803 720183 FAX 01789 774000**
EMAIL cdyson@live.co.uk WEBSITE www.clairedysonracing.co.uk

1 5, B g Universal (IRE)—Adiynara (IRE) **Miss C. Dyson**
2 CLASSIC TUNE, 12, b g Scorpion (IRE)—Classic Fantasy **D. J. Dyson**
3 HY BRASIL (IRE), 5, b g Fastnet Rock (AUS)—Kahyasi Moll (IRE) **DYDB Marketing Limited**
4 LINGER (IRE), 9, b g Cape Cross (IRE)—Await So **Dydb Marketing & C Dyson**
5 MIDNIGHT OWLE, 12, ch g Midnight Legend—Owlesbury Dream (IRE) **FSF Racing**
6 MIND'S EYE (IRE), 10, b g Stowaway—Joleen (IRE) **DYDB Marketing Limited**
7 PASSAM, 10, b g Black Sam Bellamy (IRE)—One Wild Night **FSF Racing**
8 6, B g Harbour Watch (IRE)—Pigeon Pie **D. J. Dyson**
9 SNEAKY FEELING (IRE), 10, b g Oscar (IRE)—Shuil Aris (IRE) **Guy Sainsbury & D J Dyson**
10 STUNSAIL (FR), 6, b g Davidoff (GER)—Rio Athenas (FR) **DYDB Marketing Limited**
11 4, B c Telescope (IRE)—Tarbay **D. J. Dyson**
12 THE COME BACK DUDE (IRE), 8, ch g Stowaway—Bells Glory (IRE) **FSF Racing**

Other Owners: DYDB Marketing Limited, Miss C. Dyson, D. J. Dyson, Mr G. T. Sainsbury.

NH Jockey: David Noonan. **Conditional Jockey:** Charlie Hammond.

162 MR SIMON EARLE, Sutton Veny
Postal: **The Lower Barn, The Beeches Farm, Deverill Road, Sutton Veny, Wiltshire, BA12 7BY**
Contacts: **PHONE 01985 840450 MOBILE 07850 350116 FAX 01985 840450**
EMAIL simonearleracing@btinternet.com WEBSITE www.simonearleracing.co.uk

1 **ASHTON COURT (IRE)**, 8, b g Court Cave (IRE)—Hayabusa
2 4, b f Malinas (GER)—Avichi (IRE)
3 **BIG TREE (IRE)**, 9, b g Scorpion (IRE)—Montecateno (IRE)
4 **GOLDEN DOVE**, 4, b f Golden Horn—Laughing Dove (IRE)
5 **GOLDEN MILLIE**, 4, b f Walk In The Park (IRE)—Mille Et Une (FR)
6 **KILKEASKIN MOLLY (IRE)**, 8, b br m Mountain High (IRE)—Nicola's Girl (IRE)
                                                                Mrs P Bridel, Mr C Marment, Mr C Church
7 **MERAKI MIST (FR)**, 4, gr g Tin Horse (IRE)—Merka (FR)
8 **NOWYOUVEBINANDUNIT**, 5, b m Roderic O'Connor (IRE)—Oceana Blue
9 **RARE CLOUDS**, 8, b g Cloudings (IRE)—Rare Vintage (IRE)
10 **ROBBER'S BRIDGE (IRE)**, 4, b g Frammassone (IRE)—Mille Et Une Nuits (FR)
11 **WITCH FROM ROME**, 11, b g Holy Roman Emperor (IRE)—Spangle

THREE-YEAR-OLDS

12 **JOUR D'ORAGE (FR)**, b g Great Pretender (IRE)—Ne M'Oubliez Pas (FR)

Other Owners: Mrs P. L. Bridel, Mr C. Church, Mr S. A. Earle, Mr K. M. Harris, Mr C. V. Marment, Mr R. H. J. Martin, Mrs M. Williams.

Racing Secretary: Mrs Katie Earle.

163 MICHAEL AND DAVID EASTERBY, Sheriff Hutton
Postal: **New House Farm, Stittenham Farms, Sheriff Hutton, York, Yorkshire, YO60 6TN**
EMAIL office@stittenham.com

1 **A DAY IN DONOSTIA (IRE)**, 5, b g Nathaniel (IRE)—Dreaming of Stella (IRE)
                                                        Mr L. J. Westwood, Golden Equinox Racing 1
2 **ALBERT'S BACK**, 8, b g Champs Elysees—Neath **Golden Ratio & J Blackburn**
3 **ALSITHEE**, 4, b g Summer Front (IRE)—Secret Dream (IRE) **Mr Andrew Stott Racing**
4 **AU JUS**, 6, ch m Nayef (USA)—Serraval (FR) **J. T. Brown**
5 **BANKAWI**, 5, b m Coach House (IRE)—Whitby (IRE) **South Bank Racing 2**
6 **BAVARDAGES (IRE)**, 5, b g Dream Ahead (USA)—Petits Potins (IRE) **The Laura Mason Syndicate**
7 **CALCUTTA DREAM (IRE)**, 4, b g Iffraaj—Short Affair **Mr A Saha Racing**
8 **CASILLI**, 5, b m Cacique (IRE)—Lilli Marlane **Tinning, Wallis & Hollings**
9 **EAGLE CREEK (IRE)**, 8, b g Raven's Pass (USA)—Blue Angel (IRE) **M. W. Easterby**
10 **ELIGIBLE**, 6, b g Dark Angel (IRE)—Secrets Away (IRE) **M & L Westwood**
11 **ENLIGHTEN**, 8, b g Kayf Tara—Rapturous **The Laura Mason Syndicate**
12 **FIRE IN THE RAIN**, 4, b f Starspangledbanner (AUS)—Downhill Dancer (USA)
13 **HARVEST DAY**, 7, b m Harbour Watch (IRE)—Miss Wells (IRE) **Mrs C E Mason & Partner**
14 **LA RAV (IRE)**, 8, b g Footstepsinthesand—Swift Acclaim (IRE) **Mr B Hoggarth, Mr S Hull & Mr S Davis**
15 **LATE ARRIVAL (IRE)**, 5, b g Night of Thunder (IRE)—Powdermill **A & S Windle**
16 **LOU MARVELOUS (FR)**, 5, b g Masked Marvel—Lou Emerald (FR) **Mrs Bartram & Mrj Goodrick**
17 **LUKE**, 5, b g Lucarno (USA)—More Ballet Money **Falcon's Line Ltd**
18 **MARWARI (IRE)**, 6, b g Exceed And Excel (AUS)—Miss Polaris **Stittenham Racing**
19 **MAYELF**, 4, ch g Mayson—Delft **Mr D Scott & Partner**
20 **NEVERWRONGFORLONG**, 4, ch f Eagle Top—Pretty Verse **Mr J. N. Blackburn**
21 **REACH (IRE)**, 4, b f Sea The Stars (IRE)—Ameliorate (IRE)
22 **REFUGE**, 5, b g Harbour Watch (IRE)—Beldale Memory (IRE) **Laura Mason Syndicate & Julia Lukas**
23 **RING OF GOLD**, 5, b g Havana Gold (IRE)—Pitter Patter **Gay & Peter Hartley Racing**
24 **ROCKET DANCER**, 5, b g Toronado (IRE)—Opera Dancer **Southbank Racing, S Hull & S Hollings**

MICHAEL AND DAVID EASTERBY - continued

25 **SAM'S CALL**, 5, b g Finjaan—Winner's Call **Westy Partnership**
26 **SO GRATEFUL**, 4, b g Swiss Spirit—Bow Bridge
27 **SPICE STORE**, 4, gr f Mastercraftsman (IRE)—Night Carnation **The Laura Mason Syndicate**
28 **TWO BROTHERS**, 4, b g Sir Percy—Blandish (USA) **Thompson Brothers**
29 **UNPLUGGED (IRE)**, 6, b g Alhebayeb (IRE)—Crown Light **Pellon Racing**
30 **WHERE'S HECTOR**, 5, b g Schiaparelli (GER)—Diavoleria **Mr J Goodrick Racing**
31 **WHERE'S JEFF**, 7, b g Haafhd—Piece of Magic **A G Pollock & Golden Ratio Partnership**
32 **WHITWELL**, 5, b g Cable Bay (IRE)—Blissamore **H. Mrs A. & C Wallis**
33 **WILD THUNDER (IRE)**, 5, b g Night of Thunder (IRE)—Shama's Song (IRE) **B & A Morse**
34 **YORKSHIRE LADY**, 4, gr f Mukhadram—Brave Mave **Munroe, McHale K Wreglesworth**

THREE-YEAR-OLDS

35 **ARMO**, b f Ardad (IRE)—Amitola (IRE) **J Blackburn & B Padgett**
36 **BIG STAR**, b f Linda's Lad—Tinotara **Mr G. F. Mugleston**
37 Br c Outstrip—Bow Bridge **M. W. Easterby**
38 Gr g El Kabeir (USA)—Cesca (IRE) **M. W. Easterby**
39 **COPPER MOUNTAIN**, b f Sir Percy—Aetna **Laura Mason Syndicate Racing**
40 **DECONTRACTE**, b g Ardad (IRE)—Natural Appeal (IRE) **Mr B. Hoggarth**
41 B f Forever Now—Diavoleria **M. W. Easterby**
42 Br g Galileo Gold—Empress Rock (IRE) **Southbank Racing, Mr B. Padgett**
43 **FIERY DAWN (IRE)**, b g Lawman (FR)—Maidin Maith (IRE) **Imperial Racing & Mr J Blackburn**
44 **GRANTLEY HALL**, b f Ardad (IRE)—Combustible (IRE) **Imperial Racing P'Ship & Mr J Blackburn**
45 **HEEROSE GIRL**, bl f Heerat (IRE)—Rose Bien **Rose 2 Riches**
46 **JAZZ SAMBA (IRE)**, gr f El Kabeir (USA)—Sensational Samba (IRE) **M. W. Easterby**
47 **KING OF EUROPE (IRE)**, b g Ardad (IRE)—High Cross (IRE) **The Lee Westwood Partnership**
48 **LE BEAU GARCON**, b g Brazen Beau (AUS)—Bacall **Bernard Hoggarth Racing**
49 **MIN TILL**, b f Al Kazeem—Avessia **Mrs C E Mason & Partner**
50 **MISTER CAMACHO (IRE)**, b g Camacho—Drifting Mist **The Lee Westwood Partnership**
51 Gr g Sea The Moon (GER)—Neige d'Antan **Imperial Racing Partnership 2016**
52 **NOSEY MARE**, gr f Pastoral Pursuits—Brave Mave **Laura Mason Syndicate Racing**
53 **ON THE HOOK**, b g Coach House (IRE)—Elegant Pursuit **Southbank Racing & Partner**
54 **OSCAR DOODLE**, br gr g Outstrip—Dusty Blue **Miss V. Watt**
55 **PIRANHEER**, b g Heeraat (IRE)—Piranha (IRE) **Mr M. Hancock**
56 B c Pivotal—Queen's Castle **Mr J Blackburn & Imperial Racing P'ship**
57 Ch g Kantharos (USA)—Raging Atlantic (USA) **Mr B. Padgett**
58 **SHIMMERING SANDS**, b g Teofilo (IRE)—Milady **Stittenham Racing, Imperial Racing Partnership 2016**
59 Gr g Lawman (FR)—Skyline Dancer **Imperial Racing Partnership 2016, M. W. Easterby**
60 **STRAWBERRY DREAM**, ch f Havana Gold (IRE)—Strawberry Martini **Mr J Blackburn & Imperial Racing P'ship**
61 **SUN HILL**, b g Dabirsim (FR)—Spirit of India
62 **THE GREY LASS**, ro f Outstrip—Be Lucky **The Lee Westwood Partnership**
63 B c Estidhkaar (IRE)—Viva Diva **Southbank Racing**
64 **WABA DABA DO (IRE)**, b f Caravaggio (USA)—Spirit of Cuba (IRE) **Southbank Racing & Partner**

TWO-YEAR-OLDS

65 B c 20/02 Bungle Inthejungle—Al Sultana (Charm Spirit (IRE)) (9524) **Mr B. Hoggarth**
66 B c 26/03 Washington DC (IRE)—Alle Stelle (Sea The Stars (IRE))
67 B g 17/02 Sir Percy—Apalis (FR) (Mastercraftsman (IRE)) **Mr J. N. Blackburn**
68 B f 25/01 Harry Angel (IRE)—Blue Maiden (Medicean) (20000)
69 B c 09/03 Bungle Inthejungle—Bonne (Namid) (9524)
70 B c 31/03 Awtaad (IRE)—Butoolat (Oasis Dream) (3810)
71 B c 20/04 Camacho—Cape Joy (IRE) (Cape Cross (IRE)) (16190)
72 Ch c 13/04 Highland Reel (IRE)—Don't Forget Faith (USA) (Victory Gallop (CAN)) (11429)
73 B g 08/02 Camacho—Embroidery (Mastercraftsman (IRE)) (1500)
74 Ch f 17/03 Cityscape—Englishwoman (Acclamation) (5000)
75 B f 01/02 Dark Angel (IRE)—Everglades (Teofilo (IRE)) (4762)
76 Ch c 24/01 Tasleet—Feint (Teofilo (IRE)) (17000)
77 Ch f 09/02 Ulysses (IRE)—Ferrier (Iffraaj)
78 Ch f 14/02 Decorated Knight—Fligaz (FR) (Panis (USA)) (15000) **Mr B. Hoggarth**
79 Gr c 29/04 Gregorian (IRE)—Generous Heart (Sakhee's Secret) (8000)

MICHAEL AND DAVID EASTERBY - continued

80 B c 24/03 El Kabeir (USA)—Hazardous (Night Shift (USA)) (20000) **Mr B. Padgett**
81 B g 01/05 Mayson—La Gessa (Largesse) (1750)
82 LADY DOUGLAS, b f 29/03 Massaat (IRE)—Angel Grigio (Dark Angel (IRE)) (14286)
83 B f 17/05 Massaat (IRE)—Lady Suesanne (IRE) (Cape Cross (IRE)) (4762) **Mr S. A. Windle**
84 B f 16/02 Zoffany (IRE)—Midnight Dance (IRE) (Danehill Dancer (IRE)) (16190) **Mr S. A. Windle**
85 B c 12/04 Farhh—Miss Sheridan (IRE) (Lilbourne Lad (IRE)) (3810) **Mr J. N. Blackburn**
86 B f 10/01 Aclaim (IRE)—On A Whim (Tamayuz) (20952)
87 B f 13/03 Massaat (IRE)—Otrooha (IRE) (Oasis Dream) (9524) **Mr S. A. Windle**
88 B c 19/02 Cable Bay (IRE)—Selka (FR) (Selkirk (USA)) (9524)
89 B f 01/02 New Approach (IRE)—Some Site (IRE) (Nayef (USA)) (8000) **Capla Developments Racing**
90 Y B SOBER, b f 30/04 Outstrip—Brave Mave (Daylami (IRE)) **Munroe, McHale K Wreglesworth**

Other Owners: Altitude Racing, Mrs J. A. Bartram, Mr C. Bennett, Mr J. N. Blackburn, Mr J Blackburn & Imperial Racing P'ship, Mr J. E. Bray, Mr R. H. Cooper, Mr S. G. Davis, M. W. Easterby, Golden Equinox Racing, Mr J. Goodrick, Mr M. Grayson, Gay & Peter Hartley, P. A. H. Hartley, Mrs R. C. Hartley, Mr B. Hoggarth, Mr S. A. Hollings, S. Hull, Imperial Racing & Mr J Blackburn, Imperial Racing Partnership 2016, Mrs A. Jarvis, Mr H. Jones, The Laura Mason Syndicate, Mrs J. K. Lukas, Mrs C. E. Mason, Mr M. McHale, Mr A. Morse, Mr J. Munroe, Mr B. Padgett, Mr A. G. Pollock, Mr I. Robinson, Mr A. Saha, D. Scott, Mr P.G. Scott, Southbank Racing, Stittenham Racing, Mr A. F. Stott, Mr P. Stubbins, Miss M. L. Taylor, Mr G. Thompson, Mr O. Thompson, Mrs J. A. Tinning, W. H. Tinning, Mr L. J. Vincent, Mrs C. M. Wallis, Mr L. J. Westwood, Mr S. A. Windle, Mr C. J. Woods, K. Wreglesworth.

---

164 **MR TIM EASTERBY, Malton**
Postal: **Habton Grange, Great Habton, Malton, North Yorkshire, YO17 6TY**
Contacts: **PHONE 01653 668566 FAX 01653 668621**
EMAIL easterby@habtonfarms.co.uk WEBSITE www.timeasterby.co.uk

1 AASHEQ (IRE), 9, b g Dubawi (IRE)—Beach Bunny (IRE) **Ryedale Partners No1**
2 ALBEGONE, 4, b g Alhebayeb (IRE)—Pacngo **Mr D B & Mrs C Lamplough & Partner**
3 ART POWER (IRE), 4, gr h Dark Angel (IRE)—Evening Time (IRE) **King Power Racing Co Ltd**
4 AVA GO JOE (IRE), 4, b g Dragon Pulse (IRE)—Elusive Ellen (IRE) **Mr B Valentine & Partner**
5 BARNEY'S BAY, 4, b g Cable Bay (IRE)—Fisadara **Mr J. R. Saville**
6 BETTY BALOO, 6, b m Schiaparelli (GER)—Tarabaloo **R. W. Metcalfe**
7 BITE YA LEGS, 4, b g Pastoral Pursuits—Cheers For Thea (IRE) **ALAW**
8 BOARDMAN, 6, b g Kingman—Nimble Thimble (USA) **Mr Ball, Mr Hodkinson, Mr Malley & Ptr**
9 BOLLIN JOAN, 7, b m Mount Nelson—Bollin Greta **N Arton, P Hebdon, R Taylor & Prtnr**
10 BOLLIN MARGARET, 5, b m Fountain of Youth (IRE)—Bollin Greta **Mr D B & Mrs C Lamplough & Partner**
11 BOLLIN NEIL, 6, ch g Haafhd—Bollin Nellie **Habton Racing**
12 BOLLIN PHOENIX, 5, b g Phoenix Reach (IRE)—Bollin Annabel **Ryedale Partners No 5**
13 BOSSIPOP, 9, ch g Assertive—Opopmil (IRE) **A. R. Turnbull**
14 BRANDY BAY, 4, b f Cable Bay—Shaken And Stirred **Mr D. A. West & Partner**
15 CANARIA PRINCE, 4, b g Alhebayeb (IRE)—Gran Canaria Queen **The Senators**
16 CARRIGILLIHY, 4, gr g New Bay—Spectacle **The Harmonious Lot & Partner**
17 CASSY O (IRE), 5, b g Camacho—Hawaajib (FR) **R. Taylor & Mr P. Hebdon**
18 CHIEF CRAFTSMAN, 8, gr ro g Mastercraftsman (IRE)—Eurolink Raindance (IRE) **Habton Racing**
19 CILLUIRID (IRE), 8, b g Arcadio (GER)—Garw Valley **Reality Partnerships IV**
20 COPPER KNIGHT (IRE), 8, b g Sir Prancealot (IRE)—Mystic Dream **Middleham Park, Ventura Racing 6&partner**
21 COUNT D'ORSAY (IRE), 6, b g Dandy Man (IRE)—Deira (USA) **Mr Ambrose Turnbull & John Cruces**
22 COURT AT SLIP (IRE), 5, b g Court Cave (IRE)—Lady Fame (IRE) **Mrs Anne Dawson & Partner**
23 CRAGSIDE, 4, b g Pride of Dubai (AUS)—Umneeyatee (AUS) **Elsa Crankshaw, Gordon Allan & Partner**
24 CRUYFF TURN, 5, ch g Dutch Art—Provenance **Aberdeen Park & Partner**
25 DAN DE LIGHT (IRE), 4, ch g Twilight Son—Nancy Astor **Reality Partnerships X**
26 DANCE KING, 12, ch g Danehill Dancer (IRE)—One So Wonderful **Habton Racing**
27 DANZAN (IRE), 7, b g Lawman (FR)—Charanga **Reality Partnerships XVII**
28 DARK JEDI (IRE), 6, b g Kodiac—Whitefall (USA) **Mr Evan M Sutherland & Partner**
29 DELGREY BOY, 5, b g Delegator—Maybeagrey **Reality Partnerships XIV**

MR TIM EASTERBY - continued

30 **DEVILWALA (IRE)**, 4, b c Kodiac—Najraan **Mr M. J. Macleod**
31 4, B gr f Mastercraftsman (IRE)—Double High **Exors of the Late Mr T. J. Hemmings**
32 **DREAMSELLER (IRE)**, 6, ch g Dream Ahead (USA)—Picture of Lily **Ryedale Partners No. 2**
33 **EAST STREET REVUE**, 9, ch g Pastoral Pursuits—Revue Princess (IRE) **Mr S. A. Heley & Partner**
34 **ECLIPSE DE LUNAR (IRE)**, 4, b g Sea The Moon (GER)—Scoville (GER) **Bulmer, Hebdon R Taylor**
35 **EXCESSABLE**, 9, ch g Sakhee's Secret—Kummel Excess (IRE) **Mr B Guerin & Habton Racing**
36 **EYE KNEE**, 4, b g Territories (IRE)—Western Pearl **A. Ali**
37 **FISHABLE**, 5, b g Dutch Art—Sweet Stream (ITY) **Mr B Guerin & Habton Racing**
38 **GARDEN OASIS**, 7, b g Excelebration (IRE)—Queen Arabella **Mr T. A. Scothern & Partner**
39 **GIVE IT SOME TEDDY**, 8, b g Bahamian Bounty—Croeso Cariad **Mr L. Bond**
40 **GLENCADAM GLORY**, 8, b g Nathaniel (IRE)—Lady Grace (IRE) **MPR, Ventura Racing 15 & Partner**
41 **GOLDEN APOLLO**, 8, ch g Pivotal—Elan **Mr David Scott & Partner**
42 **GOLDEN MELODY (IRE)**, 4, ch f Belardo (IRE)—Chanter **Mr M. J. Macleod**
43 **GRAND PIANOLA**, 5, b g Firebreak—Grand Liaison **Mr J. C. Mowat**
44 **HARD TO FAULT**, 4, b g Harzand (IRE)—Polly Floyer **Mr J Clarke & Partner**
45 **HELLENISTA**, 4, b f Nathaniel (IRE)—Maven **Habton Racing**
46 **HIGHWAYGREY**, 6, b g Dick Turpin (IRE)—Maybeagrey **Reality Partnerships VII**
47 **HILDENLEY**, 5, ch g Teofilo (IRE)—Alpine Storm (IRE) **Elsa Crankshaw, Gordon Allan & Partner**
48 **HYPERFOCUS (IRE)**, 8, b br g Intense Focus (USA)—Jouel (FR) **Ryedale Partners No 14**
49 **IMPELLER**, 4, b g Pivotal—Musical Beat (IRE) **D Scott & Co (pattern Makers) Ltd & Ptr**
50 **JEWEL MAKER (IRE)**, 7, b g Invincible Spirit (IRE)—Sapphire (IRE) **Reality Partnerships I**
51 **JUST HISS**, 9, b g Lawman (FR)—Feather Boa (IRE) **The Sandmoor Partnership**
52 **KIND REVIEW**, 6, b g Kodiac—Melodique (FR) **Elsa Crankshaw Gordon Allan**
53 **KODIELLEN (IRE)**, 4, b m Kodiac—Newellen (IRE) **Habton Racing**
54 **LAMPANG (IRE)**, 5, b g Dandy Man—Black Mascara (IRE) **King Power Racing Co Ltd**
55 **LICIT (IRE)**, 5, b m Poet's Voice—Deserted **Habton Racing**
56 **LISTEN AGAIN (IRE)**, 4, b f Make Believe—Though (IRE) **Ryedale Partners No 8**
57 **LITTLE TED**, 5, ch g Cityscape—Speedy Utmost Meg **Mr M. J. Macleod**
58 **LOST MY SOCK (IRE)**, 4, ch g Bungle Inthejungle—Changari (USA) **Ryedale Partners No 4**
59 **LULU BALOO**, 7, b m Schiaparelli (GER)—Tarabaloo **R. W. Metcalfe**
60 **MAC AILEY**, 6, ch g Firebreak—Rosabee (IRE) **Dubelem (racing) Limited & Partner**
61 4, B f Sepoy (AUS)—Magic Music (IRE) **R. Bailey**
62 **MANIGORDO (USA)**, 5, b br g Kitten's Joy (USA)—Cutting Edge (USA) **Mr M. J. Macleod**
63 **MILL RACE KING (IRE)**, 9, b g Scorpion (IRE)—Oso Special **Reality Partnerships IX**
64 **MOROZOV COCKTAIL (IRE)**, 6, b g Morozov (USA)—Gold Platinum (IRE) **Mr & Mrs N Wrigley & Partner**
65 **MOTARAJEL**, 5, b g Camacho—Vereri Senes **Reality Partnerships XVIII**
66 **MR CARPENTER**, 6, gr ro g Mastercraftsman (IRE)—Satwa Pearl **Mr B Valentine & Partner**
67 **MUSIC SOCIETY (IRE)**, 7, gr g Society Rock (IRE)—Absolutely Cool (IRE) **R. Taylor & Mr P. Hebdon**
68 **MYRISTICA (IRE)**, 4, br f Harzand (IRE)—Black Mascara (IRE) **King Power Racing Co Ltd**
69 **NAUGHTY ANA (IRE)**, 4, b f Anodin (IRE)—Boldarra (USA) **A. R. Turnbull**
70 **NEARLY A GONNA**, 5, ro g Helmet (AUS)—Clodova (IRE) **E. A. Brook**
71 **OBEE JO (IRE)**, 6, b g Kodiac—Maleha (IRE) **Mrs Joanne Boxcer & Partner**
72 **PARYS MOUNTAIN (IRE)**, 8, gr g Dark Angel (IRE)—Muzdaan (IRE) **Reality Partnerships XII**
73 **PERFECT SWISS**, 6, b g Swiss Spirit—Perfect Practice **Mr Craig Wilson & Partner**
74 **PIVOTING**, 4, b g Charming Thought—Poppy Pivot (IRE) **A. R. Turnbull**
75 **POET'S DAWN**, 7, ch g Poet's Voice—Dudley Queen (IRE) **Mr Timothy O'Gram & Partner**
76 **PREMIER POWER**, 5, ch g Siyouni (FR)—Pelerin (FR) **King Power Racing Co Ltd**
77 **REGAL MIRAGE (IRE)**, 8, ch g Aqlaam—Alzaroof (USA) **Ryedale Partners No 7**
78 **RELKADAM (FR)**, 8, ch g Muhtathir—Gloirez (FR) **Ryedale Partners No 12**
79 5, B g Norse Dancer (IRE)—Rule Britannia **Mr E. A. Brook & Partner**
80 **SAMEEM**, 6, b g New Approach (IRE)—Ahla Wasahl **The Sandmoor Partnership**
81 **SAN ROCH (FR)**, 5, ch g Le Havre (IRE)—Four Green (FR) **Ryedale Partners No 13**
82 **SAULIRE STAR (IRE)**, 4, b f Awtaad (IRE)—Gallic Star (IRE) **Habton Racing**
83 **SHERIFF GARRETT (IRE)**, 8, b g Lawman (FR)—Few Are Chosen (IRE) **Ontoawinner 10 & Partner 4**
84 **SHOWALONG**, 4, ch g Showcasing—Muaamara **The Showalong Partnership**
85 **SKIPNESS**, 7, b g Desideratum—Gwyre (IRE) **The Racing Emporium & Partner**
86 **SNASH (IRE)**, 4, b g Markaz (IRE)—Wardat Dubai **Habton Racing**
87 **SOLLER BAY (IRE)**, 4, b f Iffraaj—Ahazeej (IRE) **Mrs Joanne Boxcer & Partner**
88 **STRONGBOWE (FR)**, 6, b g Siyouni (FR)—Landing Site (FR) **Ryedale Partners No 6**
89 **STROXX (IRE)**, 5, b g Camacho—Labisa (IRE) **Stroxx Partnership**

MR TIM EASTERBY - continued

90 **SUNDAY SOVEREIGN,** 5, b g Equiano (FR)—Red Sovereign **King Power Racing Co Ltd**
91 **TAR HEEL (IRE),** 4, b g Zoffany (IRE)—Nidhaal (IRE) **Mr Evan M Sutherland & Partner**
92 **TEMPER TRAP,** 5, br g Slade Power (IRE)—Sloane Square **Ontoawinner 10 & Partner**
93 **TRUE BLUE MOON (IRE),** 7, gr g Holy Roman Emperor (IRE)—Fancy Intense **Grange Park Racing Club & Hr**
94 **UGO GREGORY,** 6, gr g Gregorian (IRE)—Raajis (IRE) **Mr F. Gillespie**
95 **UNDER FOX (IRE),** 4, b g Dandy Man (IRE)—Lily's Rainbow (IRE) **King Power Racing Co Ltd**
96 4, B f Casamento (IRE)—Upton Seas **Habton Racing**
97 **VOLKOVA (IRE),** 4, b f The Gurkha (IRE)—Tilthe End of Time (IRE) **T. C. Stewart**
98 **WADE'S MAGIC,** 5, gr g Lethal Force (IRE)—Miliika **Reality Partnerships XVI**
99 **WAR DEFENDER,** 5, b g War Command (USA)—Never Lose **Ryedale Partners No.15**
100 **WELLS FARHH GO (IRE),** 7, b h Farhh—Mowazana (IRE) **Mr S A Heley & Partner**
101 **WINTER POWER (IRE),** 3, b f Bungle Inthejungle—Titian Saga (IRE) **King Power Racing Co Ltd**

THREE-YEAR-OLDS

102 **ALBEGREY,** b gr g Alhebayeb (IRE)—Maybeagrey **Reality Partnerships Xiii**
103 **ANGELS TALE (IRE),** gr f Caravaggio (USA)—Angels Story (IRE) **Habton Racing**
104 **ATOMIC LADY (FR),** b f Kodiac—Fusion (IRE) **Reality Partnerships II**
105 Gr g Dark Angel—Bastet (IRE)
106 **BAY BREEZE,** b g Buratino (IRE)—Midnight Mojito **Mr D. A. West & Partner**
107 **BERRA GO (IRE),** ch g Buratino (IRE)—Silent Serenade **Mr B Valentine & Partner**
108 **BRAZILIAN BEACH (IRE),** b f Fast Company (IRE)—Dutota Desejada (BRZ) **Mr M. J. Macleod**
109 **BUNGLEY (IRE),** b f Bungle Inthejungle—Milly's Secret (IRE) **Mr Craig Wilson & Partner**
110 B g Bobby's Kitten (USA)—Cassique Lady (IRE) **Habton Racing**
111 B f Bungle Inthejungle—Changari (USA) **Habton Racing**
112 **CLAIM THE STARS,** b g Starspangledbanner (AUS)—Ponty Acclaim (IRE) **Habton Racing**
113 **CLODOVEA,** b f Mondialiste (IRE)—Clodova (IRE) **Nick Bradley Racing 10 & Partner**
114 **COGNOCENTI (IRE),** b g Intello (GER)—Shanghai Rose **Sir R. Ogden C.B.E., LLD**
115 **COMBATANTCOMMANDER,** b c Ulysses (IRE)—Finidaprest (IRE) **Mr M. J. Macleod**
116 **COPPERLINE (IRE),** ch g Dandy Man (IRE)—Meduse Bleu **Reality Partnerships**
117 **DANDY BAY (IRE),** b f Dandy Man (IRE)—Harmony Bay (IRE) **Hart Inn Racing & Partner**
118 **ERUPTION (IRE),** b f Bungle Inthejungle—Volcanic Lady (IRE) **Mr Evan M Sutherland & Partner**
119 **FLIPPIN' ECK (IRE),** b g Gleneagles (IRE)—Sweet Serendipity **Nick Rhodes & Partner**
120 **FORGIVABLE,** ch g Iffraaj—All For Laura **Mr B Guerin & Habton Racing**
121 **FYLINGDALE (IRE),** b f National Defense—Pulp Idol (USA) **Mr Martin Adams, Mr Neil Arton & Partner**
122 **GIBSIDE,** b g Time Test—Ardbrae Tara (IRE) **Elsa Crankshaw, Gordon Allan & Partner**
123 **GNAT ALLEY (IRE),** gr f Caravaggio (USA)—Winter Snow (IRE) **Mr J. C. Davies**
124 **GOLDEN GEORGE (IRE),** ch g Galileo Gold—Fuaigh Mor (IRE) **Mr Lee Bond & Partner**
125 **GRACELANDS GIRL,** b f Iffraaj—Stella Point (IRE) **The Wolf Pack 2 & Partner**
126 Bl f Mattmu—Gran Canaria Queen **Habton Racing**
127 Ch g Exceed And Excel (AUS)—Ivory Gala (FR) **Mr B Valentine & Partner**
128 **JUNGLE BEE (IRE),** ch g Bungle Inthejungle—Hint of Red (IRE) **Mrs Joanne Boxcer & Partner**
129 **LIKE A LION (IRE),** b g Kodiac—Termagant (IRE) **Habton Racing**
130 **LORENZO LOTTO (IRE),** b gr g Caravaggio (USA)—Instant Sparkle (IRE) **Mr M. J. Macleod**
131 **MAHANAKHON,** b c Siyouni (FR)—Belle Josephine **King Power Racing Co Ltd**
132 **MANILA SCOUSE,** b g Aclaim (IRE)—Forever Excel (IRE) **Mr Ambrose Turnbull & John Cruces**
133 **MARBUZET,** b g Farhh—Estournel
134 **MARIMBA,** b f Territories (IRE)—Xylophone **Habton Racing**
135 **MATTICE,** b g Mattmu—Ice Mayden **Mr B Valentine & Partner**
136 **MATTY TOO,** b g Mattmu—Bustling Darcey **Mr B Valentine & Partner**
137 **MAY PUNCH,** ch f Mayson—Russian Punch **Lovely Bubbly Racing**
138 **MICKY MICHAELIS,** b g Fountain of Youth (IRE)—Katie Boo (IRE) **Mr J. F. Bowers**
139 **MOONBI (IRE),** b g Fascinating Rock (IRE)—Moonbi Ridge (IRE) **Mr D Lumley, Mrs A Dawson & Partner**
140 **MOVING IMAGE,** b f Aclaim (IRE)—Killermont Street (IRE) **J Shack, G Barnard & James Mj Moore**
141 **MR MOONSTORM,** b g Sea The Moon (GER)—Bracing Breeze **Ashfield Caravan Park**
142 **NO TOMORROW,** ch f Territories (IRE)—Present Day **Habton Racing**
143 **NOTIME TO PASS (IRE),** b g Postponed (IRE)—Red Raven (IRE) **Mr S A Heley & Partner**
144 **PANAMA CITY,** b g Iffraaj—Guavia (GER) **Habton Racing**
145 B f Fountain of Youth (IRE)—Penny Garcia **Mr J. F. Bowers**
146 **PROPHESISE (IRE),** b g Divine Prophet (AUS)—Hecuba **Habton Racing**

MR TIM EASTERBY - continued

147 **RED ASTAIRE,** ch g Intello (GER)—Barynya **The Wolf Pack 2 & Partner**
148 **REVOQUABLE,** b g Pastoral Pursuits—Breakable **Ryedale Partners No 9**
149 **ROACH POWER (IRE),** gr c Ribchester (IRE)—Evening Time (IRE) **King Power Racing Co Ltd**
150 **RUBY PORT,** b f Territories (IRE)—Tawaasul **Lovely Bubbly Racing**
151 **SIXSTAR,** b g Pivotal—Chantry **Mr David Scott & Partner**
152 **SNAKE PASS (IRE),** ch c Raven's Pass (USA)—Tadkhirah **Habton Racing**
153 **SONELLA,** b f Ardad (IRE)—Love Action (IRE) **Grange Park Racing Club & Hr**
154 **STREETSENSE BERTIE (USA),** b br g Street Sense (USA)—Juliastown (USA) **Mr J. R. Saville**
155 **STRIPZEE,** gr gr f Outstrip—Zeela (IRE) **The Senators**
156 **THAKURI (IRE),** b f The Gurkha (IRE)—Lone Survivor (IRE) **Habton Racing**
157 **THE DUNKIRK LADS,** b g Pivotal—Spatial **Mr David Scott & Partner**
158 **THE GREY WOLF (IRE),** gr g Dark Angel (IRE)—Penny Pepper (IRE) **The Wolf Pack 2 & Partner**
159 B g Fountain of Youth (IRE)—Upton Seas **Habton Racing**
160 **WAKEY WAKEY (IRE),** b g Estidhkaar (IRE)—Sleeping Princess (IRE) **Hp Racing Wakey Wakey & Partner**
161 **WHISKY WOLF,** ch g Territories (IRE)—Cartimandua **Mr Lee Bond & Partner**
162 **ZIMMERMAN,** ch g Poet's Voice—Cresta Gold **Linkenholt Racing & Partner**

TWO-YEAR-OLDS

163 **AMAZING ARTHUR,** b c 23/03 Showcasing—Majestic Song (Royal Applause) (23000)
Mr Evan M Sutherland & Partner
164 **BOWLAND PRINCE (IRE),** b c 08/05 Ribchester (IRE)—Lady Catherine (Bering) (23000) **Ryedale Partners No 3**
165 **BUGGERLUGS,** b c 10/02 Shalaa (IRE)—Isole Canarie (IRE) (Rip Van Winkle (IRE)) (25714) **Nick Rhodes & Partner**
166 **EMERALD DUCHESS,** b f 02/04 Massaat (IRE)—Caledonia Duchess (Dutch Art) (20000)
The 1891 Group & Partners
167 B f 28/04 Harry Angel (IRE)—First Destinity (FR) (Lawman (FR)) (13000)
168 **HARDY ANGEL,** b c 27/04 Harry Angel (IRE)—Cadeaux Power (Major Cadeaux) (13333) **Mr R Hardgrave & Partner**
169 Ch c 23/03 Ribchester (IRE)—Liel (Pivotal) (27000) **Aberdeen Park & Partner**
170 **MOON FRIEND (IRE),** ch c 26/03 Camacho—Acushladear (IRE) (Tagula (IRE)) (16190) **Kate Barrett & Partner**
171 **NORTHCLIFF (IRE),** ch c 24/03 Dandy Man (IRE)—Colgin (Canford Cliffs (IRE)) **Bulmer, Hebdon R Taylor**
172 B c 19/05 Washington DC (IRE)—Rose Eclair (Major Cadeaux) **Mr J. F. Bowers**
173 **SEABREEZES,** ch f 05/02 Washington DC (IRE)—Seamisst (Sepoy (AUS)) **Bearstone Stud Limited**
174 **THE GO TO (IRE),** b f 24/03 Ribchester (IRE)—Laura's Oasis (Oasis Dream) (21000)
Jonathan Shack, Gawain Barnard & Partner

Other Owners: Mr M. Adams, Mr G. Allan, Mr N. F. Arton, Mr J. Ball, G. M. Barnard, Mrs K. E. Barrett, Mr L. Bond, Mrs J. Boxcer, Mr N. Bradley, Mr S. Bridge, E. A. Brook, Mr S. N. Bulmer, Mr J. Clarke, Miss E. Crankshaw, Mr A. D. Crombie, Mr J. Cruces, David Scott & Co (Pattern Makers) Ltd, Mrs A. Dawson, Mr A. Denham, Mr T. Denham, Dubelem (Racing) Limited, Mr H. P. Easterby, P. Easterby, Mr G. Fox, Mr A. Gemmell, A. J. J. Gompertz, Grange Park Racing Club, Mr J. H. Green, Mr B. M. P. R. Guerin, HP Racing Wakey Wakey, Habton Racing, Mr R. Hardgrave, Mr P. F. Hebdon, S. A. Heley, Mr A. S. Hodkinson, Miss S. Holden, Mr I. P. Homer, R. Kent, Mr M. Kershaw, Mrs D. Lamplough, D. B. Lamplough, Linkenholt Racing, Mr David John Lumley, Mr M. A. Madden, Mr P. Malley, Middleham Park and Ventura Racing 15, Middleham Park and Ventura Racing 6, Mr P. H. Milmo, Mr J. Moore, Mr J. E. Mott, Nick Bradley Racing 10, Mr N. J. O'Brien, T. J. O'Gram, Ontoawinner 10, Mr W. M. Oxley, T. S. Palin, W. H. Ponsonby, Mr N. A. Rhodes, Mr A. J. Scaife, T. A. Scothern, D. Scott, Mr J. Shack, Mr J. F. Strain, Mr T. J. Strain, Mr E. M. Sutherland, Mr R. Taylor, The 1891 Group, The Harmonious Lot, The Racing Emporium, A. R. Turnbull, Mr B. Valentine, D. A. West, Mr C. Wilson, N. H. T. Wrigley, Mrs V. A. Wrigley.

165 MR BRIAN ECKLEY, Brecon
Postal: Closcedi Farm, Llanspyddid, Brecon, Powys, LD3 8NS
Contacts: PHONE 01874 622422 MOBILE 07891 445409
EMAIL brian.eckley@live.co.uk

1 **JAUNTY EXPRESS**, 6, b g Yorgunnabelucky (USA)—Jaunty Spirit **B. J. Eckley**
2 **JAUNTY FREYJA**, 7, b m Norse Dancer (IRE)—Jaunty Walk **B. J. Eckley**
3 **JAUNTY VIKING**, 7, b g Norse Dancer (IRE)—Jaunty Spirit **B. J. Eckley**
4 **JAUNTY ZING**, 5, b m Yorgunnabelucky (USA)—Jaunty Walk **B. J. Eckley**
5 **LIBBERTY HUNTER**, 6, b g Yorgunnabelucky (USA)—Classy Crewella **B. J. Eckley**
6 **TIMEFORADANCE**, 7, b g Norse Dancer (IRE)—Timeforagin **B. J. Eckley**

166 MR ROBERT EDDERY, Newmarket
Postal: Robert Eddery Racing Limited, Heyward Place Stables,
Hamilton Road, Newmarket, Suffolk, CB8 7JQ
Contacts: PHONE 01638 428001 MOBILE 07938 898455
EMAIL info@roberteddery.com WEBSITE www.robertedderyracing.com

1 **CLASSY DAME (IRE)**, 4, b f Belardo (IRE)—Scholarly **Graham & Lynn Knight & R J Creese**
2 **EEVILYNN DREW**, 5, b g Epaulette (AUS)—Halicardia **Graham & Lynn Knight**
3 **HOTSPUR HARRY (IRE)**, 5, b g Zoffany (IRE)—Dark Crusader (IRE) **R. J. Creese**
4 **SILVER DOLLAR (IRE)**, 4, gr g Markaz (IRE)—Bunditten (IRE) **Mr B. Lawrence**
5 **SPRING BLOOM**, 5, ch g Power—Almond Branches **Mrs P. Aitken**
6 **TYNECASTLE PARK**, 9, b g Sea The Stars (IRE)—So Silk **Mr C. R. Eddery**
7 **VINO SANTO**, 4, b g Cable Bay (IRE)—Sugar Free (IRE) **Julia Rayment & Robert Eddery**

THREE-YEAR-OLDS
8 **ASTONBURY (IRE)**, b f Profitable (IRE)—Namaadhej (USA) **R. J. Creese**
9 **DIZZY ED (IRE)**, b c Tamayuz—Maroochydore (IRE) **E. S. Phillips**
10 B g Exceed And Excel (AUS)—Fairywren (IRE)
11 **HOMEMADE ANDREA (IRE)**, ch f Showcasing—Sas (IRE) **Horseshoe Bay**
12 **NEW SHEPARD (IRE)**, b c No Nay Never (USA)—Caelis **Julia Rayment & Brett Lawrence**
13 **TRUGANINI (IRE)**, b f Lawman (FR)—Tazmania (IRE) **Graham & Lynn Knight**

TWO-YEAR-OLDS
14 **DRUM BRAE BOY**, ch c 08/02 Bobby's Kitten (USA)—Wilbury Twist (Pivotal) (6000)
Mrs P. Aitken, Mr P. H. Matthews
15 **O'MHAIRE**, b f 14/04 Scorpion—Kompete (Komaite) **World Racing Network**
16 **RHEA OF THE YEAR**, b f 30/03 Postponed—Equimou (Equiano) **E. S. Phillips**

Other Owners: R. J. Creese, Mr C. R. Eddery, G. Knight, Graham & Lynn Knight, Mrs L. C. Knight, Mr B. Lawrence, Pam & Phil Matthews, Mrs J. M. Rayment.

Flat Jockey: Andrea Atzeni. **Apprentice Jockey:** Molly Presland. **Amateur Jockey:** Mr George Eddery.

167 MR STUART EDMUNDS, Newport Pagnell

Postal: **6 Fences Farm, Tyringham, Newport Pagnell, Buckinghamshire, MK16 9EN**
Contacts: **PHONE 01908 611369, 01908 611406 MOBILE 07778 782591 FAX 01908 611255**
EMAIL Trishandstu@aol.com

1 **ADDOSH**, 4, b f The Gurkha (IRE)—Wild Storm **Stuart Edmunds Racing Club**
2 **ARIZONA CARDINAL**, 6, b g Kayf Tara—Mathine (FR) **Mr D. Mitson**
3 **BLACKFINCH**, 7, ch g Black Sam Bellamy (IRE)—Grassfinch **The Long Hop Syndicate**
4 **BLUE CATO (IRE)**, 5, b g Notnowcato—Heart of Love (IRE) **The Horwoods Partnership**
5 **BUBBLE DUBI (FR)**, 5, b g Waldpark (GER)—Miss Bubble Rose (FR) **The Garratt Family**
6 **CLASSIC BEN (IRE)**, 9, b g Beneficial—Dark Daisy (IRE) **The Lavendon Partnership**
7 **COOLAMAINE LAD (IRE)**, 4, b g Champs Elysees—Coolamaine Star (IRE) **The Coolamaine Lad Syndicate**
8 **DOIREANN (IRE)**, 5, b m Shirocco (GER)—Sew N Sew (IRE) **Stuart Edmunds Racing Club**
9 **GENTLEMAN AT ARMS (IRE)**, 5, gr g Reliable Man—Sworn Sold (GER) **D & B Partnership**
10 **GO MILLIE GO (IRE)**, 9, b m Milan—Another Present (IRE) **The Chicheley Partnership**
11 **GOELETTE (FR)**, 6, b m Muhtathir—Tamara (FR) **Mr D. Mitson**
12 **GRAND LORD (FR)**, 6, gr g Lord du Sud (FR)—Toscane des Fleurs (FR) **The Garratt Family**
13 **HAVANA HERMANO (IRE)**, 8, b g Flemensfirth (USA)—Senorita Rumbalita **The Golf Victor Charlie Syndicate**
14 **HERE COMES HENRY**, 5, b g Walk In The Park (IRE)—Castlefleming (IRE) **The Danum Partnership**
15 **HILLFINCH**, 5, ch m Hillstar—Grassfinch **BDRSyndicates**
16 **HOMETOWN BOY (IRE)**, 7, ch g Curtain Time (IRE)—Mercy Mission **The Garratt Family**
17 **KRYPTON GOLD (IRE)**, 4, b g Holy Roman Emperor (IRE)—Red Planet **The Danum Partnership**
18 **LARUSSO (IRE)**, 5, ch g Doyen (IRE)—Muckle Flugga (IRE) **The Larusso Partnership**
19 **MANDOCELLO (FR)**, 6, b g Motivator—Serenada (FR) **Mrs R. L. Banks**
20 **MARSH WREN**, 6, b m Schiaparelli (GER)—Carolina Wren **Far Bihoue Partnership**
21 **MASKADA (FR)**, 6, b m Masked Marvel—Mandina (FR) **M. Kehoe**
22 **MEGAN (GER)**, 5, ch m Lord of England (GER)—Mrs Summersby (IRE) **Stuart Edmunds Racing Club**
23 **MEXICO (GER)**, 6, b g Sea The Moon (GER)—Mexicali (IRE) **Mr D. Mitson**
24 **MIDNIGHT MARY**, 6, b m Midnight Legend—Epee Celeste (FR) **Mr S A Richards & Louise Kemble**
25 **MISS MCGUGEN (IRE)**, 7, b m Arakan (USA)—Sixties Girl (IRE) **BDRSyndicates**
26 **MY GIRL LOLLIPOP (IRE)**, 6, b m Mahler—Pop Princess **Mrs N. C. Kappler**
27 **ONE EYE ON VEGAS**, 5, b g Blue Bresil (FR)—Savingforvegas (IRE) **Mr B. H. Turner**
28 **RAMURE (FR)**, 4, b f Maresca Sorrento (FR)—Rasara (FR) **The Holryale Partnership**
29 **RED ROYALIST**, 8, b g Royal Applause—Scarlet Royal **Mrs R. L. Banks**
30 **ROWLAND WARD**, 6, b g Sea The Stars (IRE)—Honor Bound **Mr D. Mitson**
31 **SANTESA**, 5, b m Telescope (IRE)—Santia **Rebels Without A Claus**
32 **SEDGE WREN**, 4, b f Blue Bresil (FR)—Carolina Wren **Exors of the Late Mr P. D. Robeson**
33 **SOME CAN SING (IRE)**, 7, b g Recital (FR)—Our Fair Lady (IRE) **Mr D. Mitson**
34 **SWAFFHAM BULBECK (IRE)**, 8, b g Jeremy (USA)—Ballygologue (IRE) **D Bassom & P Cardosi**
35 **TREEFINCH**, 4, b f Telescope (IRE)—Grassfinch **Exors of the Late Mr P. D. Robeson**
36 **WHO'S THE BOSS (IRE)**, 7, b br m Oscar (IRE)—Final Episode (IRE) **Mr D. Mitson**
37 **YOUNG OFFENDER (IRE)**, 7, b g Rule of Law (USA)—Cayetina **Mr D. Mitson**

THREE-YEAR-OLDS

38 Gr c Gleneagles (IRE)—Mussoorie (FR) **Mr D. Mitson**

Other Owners: Mr D. Bassom, Mr P Cardosi, Mrs D. E. Gardiner, Mr D. B. Iseton, Ms L. M. Kemble, Mr K. J. Orchard, Mr S. A. Richards, Mr D. A. M. R. Shuttle, Mr J. A. Tabb, Mr B. H. Turner.

Assistant Trainer: Miss Harriet Edmunds.

168 MR GORDON EDWARDS, Minehead

Trainer did not wish details of their string to appear

169 **MISS CLARE ELLAM, Market Drayton**
Postal: **Lostford Manor Stables, Mickley, Tern Hill, Market Drayton, Shropshire, TF9 3QW**
Contacts: **MOBILE 07974 075042**
EMAIL clareellam@btinternet.com WEBSITE www.clareellamracing.com

1 **ARCHIE STEVENS**, 12, b g Pastoral Pursuits—Miss Wells (IRE) **Miss Clare L. Ellam**
2 **GLORVINA (IRE)**, 8, b m Dragon Pulse (IRE)—Hawk Dance (IRE) **Miss Clare L. Ellam**
3 **KILCASEY GOLD (IRE)**, 7, b g Le Fou (IRE)—Annie Be Quick (IRE) **Mr R. P. Clarke**
4 **MOUNTAIN HAWK (IRE)**, 10, b g Mountain High (IRE)—Septembers Hawk (IRE) **Mr R. P. Clarke**
5 **ROCK UP IN STYLE**, 6, b g Showcasing—Flora Trevelyan **The Double Six Racing Partnership**
6 **SAW THE SEA**, 6, b g Sea The Moon (GER)—Frances Stuart (IRE) **Mr R. P. Clarke**

Assistant Trainer: Amy Myatt.

170 **MR BRIAN ELLISON, Malton**
Postal: **Spring Cottage Stables, Langton Road, Norton, Malton, North Yorkshire, YO17 9PY**
Contacts: **PHONE 01653 690004 MOBILE 07785 747426 FAX 01653 690008**
EMAIL office@brianellisonracing.co.uk WEBSITE www.brianellisonracing.co.uk

1 **ASHINGTON**, 7, b g Canford Cliffs (IRE)—Kadoma **Mr T. Alderson**
2 **BARON DE MIDLETON (IRE)**, 9, b g Brian Boru—Present Climate (IRE) **Phil & Julie Martin**
3 **BRANCASTER (IRE)**, 8, ch g Casamento (IRE)—Makheelah **Brian Ellison Racing Club**
4 **COOL JET (IRE)**, 6, b g Jet Away—Cool Trix (IRE) **Mr P. Boyle**
5 **CORMIER (IRE)**, 6, b g Born To Sea (IRE)—Scotch Bonnet (IRE) **Mr D. R. Gilbert**
6 **FAIR STAR (IRE)**, 6, b g Sea The Stars (IRE)—Night Fairy (IRE) **Dan Gilbert & Andrew Bruce**
7 **GOLD MINER**, 9, b g Goldmark (USA)—Sly Empress (IRE) **Mr M. M. Allen**
8 **GORDON'S JET (IRE)**, 6, ch g Jet Away—Rose Brook (IRE) **Mr P. Boyle**
9 **HACKBERRY**, 5, b g Nathaniel (IRE)—Dumfriesshire **J Blackburn, Imperial Racing & B Ellison**
10 **HANGARD**, 10, b g Black Sam Bellamy (IRE)—Empress of Light **Mr D. C. Blake**
11 **HIGHLAND SKY (IRE)**, 7, b g Camelot—Healing Music (FR) **Mr P Boyle & Mr Brian Ellison**
12 **HOOFLEPUFF (IRE)**, 6, b g Gale Force Ten—Hflah (IRE) **Mr K. Brown**
13 **INSTANT REPLAY (IRE)**, 10, ch g Fruits of Love (USA)—Ding Dong Belle **Brian Ellison Racing Club**
14 **JOHNNY BOOM (IRE)**, 4, ch g New Bay—Moody Blue (IRE) **Dan Gilbert & Andrew Bruce**
15 **JOHNNY COME LATELY**, 5, ch h Black Sam Bellamy (IRE)—Kilkenny Kim (IRE) **Mr M. M. Allen**
16 **KEARNEY HILL (IRE)**, 7, b g Dylan Thomas (IRE)—Sunny Glen (IRE) **Julie & Phil Martin**
17 **KILTORCAN BOY (IRE)**, 7, b g Stowaway—Hathamore **Chris Lowther, Ian Smith & Partner**
18 **KING VIKTOR**, 4, ch g Cityscape—Ananda Kanda (USA) **Mr K. J. Strangeway**
19 **KISS MY FACE**, 5, b g Nathaniel (IRE)—Bridle Belle **Dan Gilbert & Andrew Bruce**
20 **LEESWOOD LILY**, 9, b m Alflora (IRE)—Showtime Annie **Mr M. M. Allen**
21 **LOCOMOTIVE BRETH (IRE)**, 4, b g Exceed And Excel (AUS)—Perfect Fun **Mr T. Alderson**
22 **LUCKY ROBIN (IRE)**, 10, ch g Mister Fotis (USA)—Bewilderment (IRE) **Brian Ellison Racing Club**
23 **MIDRARR (IRE)**, 5, b m Dubawi (IRE)—Oojooba **Strawberry Fields Stud**
24 **MING DYNASTY (FR)**, 10, b g King's Best (USA)—Memoire (FR) **Mr P. Boyle**
25 **MR WHIPPED (IRE)**, 9, br g Beneficial—Dyrick Daybreak (IRE) **Mrs J. A. Martin**
26 **NIETZSCHE**, 9, ch g Poet's Voice—Ganga (IRE) **Gilbert, Bruce, Wills**
27 **NIGHT RANGER**, 5, br g Dansili—Sleep Walk **Ellison, Lyons and Thompson**
28 **ONEHUNDREDPERCENT (FR)**, 6, b g Great Pretender—Combloux (USA) **The Mount Fawcus Partnership**
29 **ONESMOOTHOPERATOR (USA)**, 4, br g Dialed In (USA)—Sueno d'Oro (USA) **Mr P. Boyle**
30 **PADDY ELLIOTT (IRE)**, 5, b g French Navy—Siphon Melody (USA) **Brian Ellison Racing Club**
31 **PALLAS DANCER**, 5, b g War Command (USA)—Dance Card **Spring Cottage Syndicate 3**
32 **PALLAS LORD (IRE)**, 4, b g Dandy Man (IRE)—Nutshell **Linsey & Ian Pallas**
33 **PUNXSUTAWNEY PHIL (IRE)**, 5, b g Shirocco (GER)—Chilly Filly (IRE) **Mr D. R. Gilbert**
34 **RAMIRO (IRE)**, 6, ch g Born To Sea (IRE)—Whispering Lady (IRE) **Brian's Mates 2**
35 **RECLAIM VICTORY (IRE)**, 5, b h Helmet (AUS)—Doctor's Note **Quickly Group Holdings Ltd & Partner**
36 **SALSADA (IRE)**, 5, ch m Mukhadram—Mokaraba **Geoff & Sandra Turnbull & Partner**
37 **SAM'S ADVENTURE**, 10, b g Black Sam Bellamy (IRE)—My Adventure (IRE) **Julie & Phil Martin**

MR BRIAN ELLISON - continued

38 **SEZINA**, 5, ch m Cityscape—Sorcellerie **Mr K. J. Strangeway**
39 **SNOOKERED (IRE)**, 8, b g Born To Sea (IRE)—Secret Quest **Brian Ellison Racing Club**
40 **SON OF THE SOMME (IRE)**, 7, b g Yeats (IRE)—Present Venture (IRE) **Mr D. C. Blake**
41 **SPICY DUBAI (IRE)**, 4, b f Pride of Dubai (AUS)—Sugarformyhoney (IRE) **The Hopeful Hombres & Partner**
42 **TASHKHAN (IRE)**, 4, b g Born To Sea (IRE)—Tarziyna (IRE) **Mr P. Boyle**
43 **THE DANCING POET**, 6, ch g Poet's Voice—Caldy Dancer (IRE) **Spring Cottage Syndicate**
44 **THE KING OF MAY (FR)**, 8, b g High Rock (IRE)—Waltzing (IRE) **Phil & Julie Martin**
45 **TIGER JET (IRE)**, 6, ch g Jet Away—Just A Moment (IRE) **Mr S Gale & Partner**
46 **TOMMY TITTLEMOUSE (IRE)**, 4, b g Sir Prancealot (IRE)—French Doll (IRE) **Linsey & Ian Pallas**
47 **TUPELO MISSISSIPPI (IRE)**, 7, b g Yeats (IRE)—Misleain (IRE) **Phil & Julie Martin**
48 **TYCHE**, 5, b m Due Diligence (USA)—Szabo's Art **Spring Cottage Syndicate 3**
49 **VICTORIANO (IRE)**, 6, b g Teofilo (IRE)—Victorian Beauty (USA) **Mr L. Taylor**
50 **WEAKFIELD (IRE)**, 9, b g Court Cave (IRE)—Thats The Lot (IRE) **Phil & Julie Martin**
51 4, B f Soldier of Fortune (IRE)—What A Lark (IRE)
52 **WHISKEY AND WATER**, 6, b g Harbour Watch (IRE)—Bahamamia **Dan Gilbert & Andrew Bruce**
53 **WINDSOR AVENUE (IRE)**, 10, b g Winged Love (IRE)—Zaffarella (IRE) **Phil & Julie Martin**

THREE-YEAR-OLDS

54 **CIANCIANA**, ch f Cityscape—Golden Valley **Mrs C Ellison & Miss Anna Morton**
55 **FREDDY ROBINSON**, b g Adaay (IRE)—Bling Bling (IRE) **Linsey Pallas & Claire Ellison**
56 **LANGTON WOLD (IRE)**, b g Cotai Glory—Ceylon Round (FR) **Mr B Dunn & Partner**
57 **LITTLE EMMA LOULOU**, ch f Jack Hobbs—Reaf **Linsey Pallas & Claire Ellison**
58 **MYTHICAL MOLLY (IRE)**, b f Profitable (IRE)—The Tempest **Linsey & Ian Pallas**
59 **PERSEPTION**, b f Helmet (AUS)—Xtrasensory **Mr K. Brown**
60 **THEORETICAL (IRE)**, ch f Bungle Inthejungle—Entitled **Mr K. Brown**
61 **TOP NOTCH TOMMY**, b g Brazen Beau (AUS)—Mexican Milly (IRE) **Hughes Bros Construction LTD**

TWO-YEAR-OLDS

62 B f 25/04 Postponed (IRE)—Al Rowaiyah (Kheleyf (USA)) (6000) **Mr K. Brown**
63 B g 10/04 Adaay (IRE)—Amelia Grace (IRE) (Starspangledbanner (AUS)) **Northern Water Services & Brian Ellison**
64 B f 10/04 Muhaarar—Blushing Rose (Dalakhani (IRE)) (1000) **Mr K. Brown**
65 Ch f 22/04 Bated Breath—Bronte Sister (IRE) (Acclamation) (3500) **Mr K. Brown**
66 B br c 22/04 Mondialiste (IRE)—Dame Hester (IRE) (Diktat) (22857)
67 **GEORDIE MACKEM**, b g 24/01 Jack Hobbs—The Pirate's Queen (IRE) (King's Theatre (IRE)) (38095)
                                                                        The Cat & The Mag Partnership
68 **GRANDAD**, b c 30/01 War Command (USA)—Livia Drusilla (IRE) (Holy Roman Emperor (IRE)) **Mrs C. L. Ellison**
69 **IMAGINEER (IRE)**, b c 24/03 Make Believe—Abilene (Samum (GER)) (45000) **The Artis Partnership**
70 **MY ROXANNE (IRE)**, b f 04/03 James Garfield (IRE)—Magic Motif (USA) (Giant's Causeway (USA)) (30612)
                                                                        Mr P. Boyle
71 B g 12/04 Ulysses (IRE)—Perfect Persuasion (Myboycharlie (IRE)) **Mr K. J. Strangeway**
72 B g 18/02 Pastoral Pursuits—Run Fat Lass Run (Sakhee (USA)) **Mr K. J. Strangeway**
73 Ch c 19/04 Free Eagle (IRE)—Shauna's Princess (IRE) (Soviet Star (USA)) (50000) **Mr Steve Bradley and Partner 2**
74 **SILVERLODE (IRE)**, gr c 26/03 Gutaifan (IRE)—Freedom Pass (USA) (Gulch (USA)) (26000) **The Artis Partnership**
75 **SUNFYRE**, ch g 19/02 Twilight Son—Lunar Corona (Dansili) (26000) **The Artis Partnership**
76 Ch f 17/04 Ulysses (IRE)—Topatoo (Bahamian Bounty) (10000) **Mr K. Brown**

Other Owners: Mr J. N. Blackburn, Mr P. Boyle, Mr A. Bruce, B. Dunn, Mr Brian Ellison, Mrs C. L. Ellison, Mr S. Gale, Mr D. R. Gilbert, C. P. Lowther, Mr N. P. Lyons, Mrs J. A. Martin, Mr P. J. Martin, Ms J. Matthews, Mrs L. Pallas, Quickly Group Holdings Limited, Mr I. Robinson, Mr I. Smith, Mr K. J. Strangeway, Miss M. L. Taylor, The Hopeful Hombres, Mr D. Thompson, Exors of the Late Mr G. Turnbull, Mr & Mrs G. Turnbull, Mrs S. E. Turnbull, Mr D. Whetton, Mr G. Wills.

Assistant Trainer: Jessica Robinson.

Flat Jockey: Cam Hardie, Ben Robinson. **NH Jockey:** Henry Brooke, Sam Coltherd, Brian Hughes, Sean Quinlan.

Conditional Jockey: Oakley Brown. **Apprentice Jockey:** Harry Russell.

171 MISS SARA ENDER, Malton
Postal: **Swallows Barn, East Heslerton, Malton, North Yorkshire, YO17 8RN**
Contacts: **MOBILE 07983 462314**
EMAIL seequineservices@hotmail.com WEBSITE www.enderracing.co.uk

1 **ACCOMPANIED (USA)**, 6, b g Distorted Humor (USA)—Unaccompanied (IRE) **Mr N. P. Ender**
2 **CALCULUS (IRE)**, 5, b g Frankel—Vital Statistics **Yorkshire Horseracing**
3 **DEMI SANG (FR)**, 9, b g Gris de Gris (IRE)—Morvandelle (FR) **Mr I. Ender**
4 **DURLINGTON (FR)**, 9, ch g Montmartre (FR)—Dalyonne (FR) **Mr N. P. Ender**
5 **EVISCERATING (IRE)**, 10, gr g Court Cave (IRE)—Titanic Quarter (IRE) **Malton Racing Club**
6 **INDIAN SUNBIRD (IRE)**, 5, b g Hillstar—Mausin (IRE) **Mr N. P. Ender**
7 **KING ATHELSTAN (IRE)**, 7, b g Mayson—Ashtaroute (USA) **Mr N. P. Ender**
8 **LORD SPRINGFIELD (IRE)**, 9, ch g Well Chosen—Super Thyne (IRE) **Mr N. P. Ender**
9 5, B g Morozov (USA)—Ms Jilly Maaye (IRE)
10 **MURCHISON RIVER**, 8, b g Medicean—Free Offer **Mr N. P. Ender**
11 **NORTHANDSOUTH (IRE)**, 12, ch g Spadoun (FR)—Ennel Lady (IRE)
12 **ROGAN'S FANCY (IRE)**, 6, b g Frozen Power (IRE)—Kanuri (IRE) **Yorkshire Horseracing**
13 **SPEEDY HOOVES**, 5, b g Montmartre (FR)—Cantzagua (FR) **Mr L. Murray**
14 **WELLS GOLD (IRE)**, 11, b g Gold Well—Exit Baby (IRE) **Mr N. P. Ender**
15 **WHEREWOULDUGETIT (IRE)**, 8, b g Morozov (USA)—Matinee Show (IRE) **Mr N. P. Ender**

Assistant Trainer: Mr Neville Ender.

172 MRS SAM ENGLAND, Guiseley
Postal: **Brentwood, Manor Farm, Guiseley, Leeds, West Yorkshire, LS20 8EW**
Contacts: **MOBILE 07921 003155**

1 **ARIJ (IRE)**, 5, b g Charm Spirit (IRE)—Aquarelliste (FR)
2 **ASK PADDY (IRE)**, 10, ch g Ask—Dalzenia (IRE) **Gremot Racing 2**
3 **BILLY RAY**, 7, b g Sixties Icon—Fiumicino **Mrs S. A. England**
4 **CHEF D'OEUVRE (FR)**, 11, b g Martaline—Kostroma (FR) **The Sandmoor Partnership 2**
5 **CROAGH PATRICK (IRE)**, 7, b g Mountain High (IRE)—Benedicta Rose (IRE) **R. J. Hewitt**
6 **FENLAND TIGER**, 6, ch g Schiaparelli (GER)—La Calinda **Mr J C England and Valerie Beattie**
7 **GENNADY (IRE)**, 8, b g Arakan (USA)—Topathistle (IRE) **Cragg Wood Racing**
8 **GOING MOBILE**, 7, b g Arcano (IRE)—Next To The Top **Cragg Wood Racing**
9 **GOLD RUNNER (IRE)**, 10, b m Gold Well—Copper Coast (IRE) **Itsnotabadlife**
10 **KINONDO KWETU**, 6, b g Casamento (IRE)—Asinara (GER) **Mrs S. A. England**
11 **LARGY MOUTH**, 7, b g Court Cave (IRE)—Leblon (IRE) **The Atkin Partnership**
12 **LIFFEYDALE DREAMER (IRE)**, 7, b m Azamour (IRE)—Owega Dale (IRE) **Worcester Racing Club & Partner**
13 **MAGIC OF MILAN (IRE)**, 9, b m Milan—Laughing Lesa (IRE) **On the Road Again 2**
14 **MANWELL (IRE)**, 12, b g Gold Well—Roborette (FR) **Sam England Racing Club**
15 **MARK'S CHOICE (IRE)**, 6, b g Bungle Inthejungle—Ramamara (IRE) **Cragg Wood Racing**
16 **MIRACULOUS GETAWAY (IRE)**, 7, b g Getaway (GER)—Miracle Millie (IRE) **& Racing**
17 **NEAR KETTERING**, 8, ch g Medicean—Where's Broughton **Mrs S. A. England**
18 **NO CRUISE YET**, 7, b g Passing Glance—Claradotnet **Rgm Partnership**
19 **OKSANA**, 9, b m Midnight Legend—La Harde (FR) **Sam England Racing Club**
20 **ONE FOR NAVIGATION (IRE)**, 5, b g Born To Sea (IRE)—Valmari (IRE) **Moorland Racing & Mark Hammond**
21 **RUKWA (FR)**, 8, b g Soldier Hollow—So Oder So (FR) **John Birtles, Gary Ellis , Gary Smith**
22 **SIR APOLLO (IRE)**, 7, b g Westerner—Fieldtown (IRE) **Nmus**
23 **SOUNDSLIKETHUNDER (IRE)**, 4, ch g Night of Thunder (IRE)—Dust Flicker
24 **SPOT ON SOPH (IRE)**, 6, b m Walk In The Park (IRE)—Gwenadu (FR) **Mowbray Park**
25 **TANORA (IRE)**, 7, b m Court Cave (IRE)—Muscova Rose (IRE) **Pink & Purple Partnership**
26 **TARA MILL (IRE)**, 9, b g Kalanisi (IRE)—Eileens Dream (IRE) **Simon & Angela Gillie**
27 **THE TRADER (IRE)**, 6, gr g Mastercraftsman (IRE)—Chinese White (IRE)

MRS SAM ENGLAND - continued

THREE-YEAR-OLDS
28 **RAMAMARAS BOY (IRE)**, ch g Anjaal—Ramamara (IRE) **Cragg Wood Racing**
29 **TMEEMA**, ch f Night of Thunder (IRE)—Robbie Roo Roo

Other Owners: Mr M. Atkinson, Mr M. V. Atkinson, Mr P. H. Ayre, Mrs V. A. Beattie, Mr J. Birtles, Mr D. Brooks, Mr A. J. Cooper, Mr F. A. D. Currie, Mr T. K. Davis, Mrs J. E. Drake, Mr G. G. Edwards, Mr G. Ellis, Mr J. C. England, Mrs S. A. England, Mrs S. Fawcett, Mr H. M. A. Fojt, Mr G. Fox, Mr D. N. French, Mrs A. Gillie, Mr S. P. Gillie, Mr J. H. Green, Mr M. J. Hammond, R. J. Hewitt, M. P. Hill, Mrs J. Holgate, Mr I. Janotta, Mrs A. M. Mace, S. A. Mace, Mr G. Malanga, Moorland Racing, Mr J. E. Mott, Mrs J. M. Mott, Mr G. Smith, Mr J. J. Wilkinson, Worcester Racing Club.

---

173 | MR HARRY EUSTACE, Newmarket
Postal: **Park Lodge Stables, Newmarket, Suffolk, CB8 8AX**
Contacts: **WORK 01638 664277 MOBILE 07733 413771**
WORK EMAIL harry@harryeustaceracing.com, office@harryeustaceracing.com
WEBSITE www.harryeustaceracing.com

1 **AMSBY**, 5, b g Sir Percy—Astrodiva **Judi Dench, Bryan Agar & Mystic Meg Ltd.**
2 **ANCIENT TIMES**, 4, b g Exceed And Excel (AUS)—Oriental Step (IRE) **The MacDougall Two**
3 **ASTROMAN**, 5, b g Garswood—Mega (IRE) **Mystic Meg Limited**
4 **AT A PINCH**, 4, b f Lope de Vega (IRE)—Inchina **Mr A. J. McGladdery & Park Lodge Stables**
5 **POTENZA (IRE)**, 6, b g Born To Sea (IRE)—Cranky Spanky (IRE) **The MacDougall Two**
6 **REINE DU BAL**, 4, b f Mukhadram—She's Gorgeous (IRE) **Johnstone Partnership**
7 **TOPANTICIPATION**, 5, b m Mount Nelson—Topatoo **M. P. Bowring & R. Smith**
8 **ZIGGY**, 4, b g Sixties Icon—Brushing **Sarabex & Aragon Racing**

THREE-YEAR-OLDS
9 **ALDBOURNE (IRE)**, b g Awtaad (IRE)—Always Gentle (IRE) **Mr D. H. Batten**
10 **ALNWICK CASTLE**, b f Sir Percy—Iron Butterfly **H. D. Nass**
11 **ALNWICK ROSE**, b f Sir Percy—Juniper Girl (IRE) **Andrew McGladdery & Wye Not**
12 **ASTROBRIO**, ch f Garswood—Astrosecret **Mystic Meg Limited**
13 **BE GLORIOUS**, b f Kodiac—Spirit Raiser (IRE) **Glentree Pastoral R & L Jones & Families**
14 **BELHAVEN (IRE)**, ch f Belardo (IRE)—Park Haven (IRE) **A. M. Mitchell**
15 **CHASING APHRODITE**, b c Profitable (IRE)—Tutti Frutti **Gullwing Enterprises W.L.L.**
16 **CLARITUDO**, b g Nathaniel (IRE)—Clarentine **Jackson XV**
17 **FLAMING LORD**, ch g Zarak (FR)—Elusive Flame **J. C. Smith**
18 **FOSHAN (IRE)**, b g The Last Lion (IRE)—China In My Hands **The MacDougall Two**
19 **J'ADORE (IRE)**, b f Australia—Dillydallydo (IRE) **Gullwing Enterprises W.L.L.**
20 **LATIN LOVER (IRE)**, b g Starspangledbanner (AUS)—Blue Dahlia (IRE) **Candour House & Partner**
21 **LUMLEY (IRE)**, b f The Gurkha (IRE)—Anestasia (IRE) **Thunder From Down Under**
22 **MAKINMEDOIT (IRE)**, b f Golden Horn—Tranquil Star (IRE) **Mr. R. M. Levitt & Mr A. Bromley**
23 **POSTWICK**, b g Postponed—Sated **Major M. G. Wyatt**
24 **POWER GENERATION (IRE)**, b g Profitable (IRE)—Dame Alicia (IRE) **Chief Singer Racing III**

TWO-YEAR-OLDS
25 Ch f 02/05 Mastercraftsman (IRE)—Beshayer (FR) (Galileo (IRE)) **Major M. G. Wyatt**
26 **BETWEEN THE COVERS (IRE)**, ch f 02/03 Belardo (IRE)—Novel Fun (IRE) (Noverre (USA)) (15238)
Chief Singer Racing II
27 **DOCKLANDS**, b c 30/04 Massaat (IRE)—Icky Woo (Mark of Esteem (IRE)) (15238) **O.T.I. Racing**
28 **GOLD ROBBER**, b c 12/04 Cracksman—Prize Diva (Motivator) **J. C. Smith**
29 B f 15/02 Cityscape—Liberisque (Equiano (FR)) (12000) **Bart Ryan-Beswick & Warwick Ryan-Beswick**
30 **MAN OF A'AN (IRE)**, b c 27/01 Highland Reel (IRE)—Three Decades (IRE) (Invincible Spirit (IRE)) (30000)
Aragon Racing 2
31 **MUSICAL TRIBUTE**, b f 14/03 Acclamation—Gift of Music (IRE) (Cadeaux Genereux) **J. C. Smith**

MR HARRY EUSTACE - continued

32 **MYSTICAL APPLAUSE**, b c 03/04 Aclaim (IRE)—Siren's Gift (Cadeaux Genereux) **J. C. Smith**
33 **REALISED**, b f 13/04 Wootton Bassett—Wake Up Call (Noverre (USA)) (60000) **Park Lodge Racing**
34 **STARLIGHT MAGIC**, b f 08/03 Ribchester (IRE)—Celestial Secret (Sakhee's Secret) **J. C. Smith**

174	**MR DAVID EVANS**, Abergavenny

Postal: **Ty Derlwyn Farm, Pandy, Abergavenny, Monmouthshire, NP7 8DR**
Contacts: PHONE **07834 834775, 01873 890837** MOBILE **07860 668499** FAX **01873 890837**
EMAIL **pdevansracing@btinternet.com** WEBSITE **www.pdevansracing.co.uk**

1 **AL MUHAAJIR (IRE)**, 5, ch g Tamayuz—Lemon Rock
2 **ALABLAQ (IRE)**, 4, ch g Lope de Vega (IRE)—Tributary **T. H. Gallienne**
3 **ARE YOU ABLE**, 5, b m Cable Bay (IRE)—Jacaranda Ridge **Mr P. Harrington**
4 **CUBAN BREEZE**, 4, b f Bated Breath—Madam Mojito (USA) **Dalwhinnie Bloodstock Limited**
5 **DELTA RIVER**, 7, b g Kodiac—Waterways (IRE)
6 **FOOL PROOF (IRE)**, 5, b g Fulbright—Church Road (IRE) **Mrs I. M. Folkes**
7 **GLASVEGAS (IRE)**, 5, gr g Zebedee—Rejuvenation (IRE) **T. H. Gallienne**
8 **KODI GOLD (IRE)**, 4, b g Kodi Bear (IRE)—Labisa (IRE) **Shropshire Wolves 3**
9 **LIHOU**, 6, ch g Mayson—Kodiac Island **T. H. Gallienne**
10 **MABRE (IRE)**, 5, gr g Make Believe—Slope **Mr K. McCabe**
11 **MILLION REASONS (IRE)**, 4, ch g Mehmas (IRE)—Yasmeena (USA) **Mr Z. Austin**
12 **NEFYN SANDS**, 4, b f Havana Gold (IRE)—Raiysina **T & R Kent**
13 **OLD PORT (IRE)**, 4, b g The Gurkha (IRE)—Misty Lane (IRE) **Mr K. McCabe**
14 **OOH IS IT**, 4, ch g Es Que Love (IRE)—Candleberry **Mr K. McCabe**
15 **PORTELET BAY**, 4, b g Mayson—Fenella Rose **T. H. Gallienne**
16 **RIGHT ACTION**, 8, b g Dandy Man (IRE)—Rockaby Baby (IRE) **Mr Stuart Morgan & Partner, Mr S. Morgan**
17 **ROHAAN (IRE)**, 4, b g Mayson—Vive Les Rouges **Chris Kiely Racing Ltd & Mr J Tomkins**
18 **STAGE LIGHTS (IRE)**, 4, b br f Showcasing—Trempjane
19 **WINKLEVI (FR)**, 7, br g Maxios—Wild Star (IRE) **T. H. Gallienne**
20 **WOO WOO**, 4, b f Heeraat (IRE)—Icky Woo

THREE-YEAR-OLDS

21 **AMJAD**, ch g Decorated Knight—Shaden (IRE) **Spiers & Hartwell Ltd & Mrs E. Evans, Spiers & Hartwell Ltd**
22 **BASTOGNE**, b br g Holy Roman Emperor—Wavebreak
23 **DECORATED DOLL (IRE)**, ch f Decorated Knight—Dolphina (USA) **Miss M. L. Evans**
24 **DORA PENNY**, b f Mayson—Aubrietia **Shropshire Wolves**
25 **FABIOSA**, b f Havana Gold (IRE)—Delizia (IRE) **Richard Kent & Richard & Pam Dawson**
26 **FIDHA**, b f Havana Gold (IRE)—Shafafya **Mr E. A. R. Morgans**
27 **HONORARY MEMBER**, ch f Iffraaj—Red Lady (IRE) **Clipper Group Holdings Ltd**
28 **JACKS PROFIT (IRE)**, b c Profitable (IRE)—Violet Flame (IRE) **D. E. Edwards**
29 **LORD GORGEOUS (IRE)**, b c Bated Breath—Dawreya (IRE) **Mrs I. M. Folkes**
30 **MIDGETONAMISSION (IRE)**, b f Holy Roman Emperor—Kramer Drive (IRE) **Mrs I. M. Folkes**
31 **PROFIT AND LOSS (FR)**, b g Profitable (IRE)—Narva (USA) **Mr E. R. Griffiths**
32 **ROSIE BOBBIE**, gr f Adaay (IRE)—Processional (USA) **Mr F. P. Maghery**
33 **RUSSELLINTHEBUSHES (IRE)**, ch f Bungle Inthejungle—Princess Banu
                                                                    John Abbey & Mike Nolan, J. E. Abbey, M. F. Nolan
34 **SHE'S SOPHIE**, b f Equiano (FR)—Wenden Belle (IRE) **Amazing Racing**
35 **THE ORMER GATHERER**, b gr g Outstrip—Camp Fire (IRE) **T. H. Gallienne**
36 **WIND YOUR NECK IN (IRE)**, ch c Decorated Knight—Samite (USA) **Mr & Mrs Paul & Clare Rooney**

TWO-YEAR-OLDS

37 B f 12/02 Dragon Pulse (IRE)—Amthal (IRE) (Dalakhani (IRE)) **P. D. Evans**
38 B f 18/02 Brazen Beau (AUS)—Aubrietia (Dutch Art) (26000) **Shropshire Wolves**
39 B f 29/03 Massaat (IRE)—Erica Bing (Captain Gerrard (IRE)) **Mr S. W. Banks**

MR DAVID EVANS - continued

40 Ch f 11/04 Prince of Lir (IRE)—Girl Invader (Foxwedge (AUS)) (5527)
        Mr E A R Morgans & Partner, Mr E. A. R. Morgans
41 B f 05/02 Fast Company (IRE)—Kathy Sun (IRE) (Intikhab (USA)) (36190) **Mr S. W. Banks**
42 B f 27/04 Acclamation—Lismore (USA) (Tiznow (USA)) (43000) **T. H. Gallienne**
43 B c 10/04 Cotai Glory—Majestic Alexander (IRE) (Bushranger (IRE)) (68571) **Mr K. McCabe**
44 Gr c 18/04 Clodovil (IRE)—Princess Banu (Oasis Dream) (45000)
        J. E. Abbey, Mrs E. Evans, John Abbey & Emma Evans
45 B gr f 04/02 Havana Grey—Radio Gaga (Multiplex) (47619) **Mr B Mould & Partner**
46 B f 04/03 Tamayuz—Scent of Roses (IRE) (Invincible Spirit (IRE)) (4762) **Mr E A R Morgans & Partner**
47 B c 11/04 Tagula (IRE)—She's A Pistol (IRE) (Danehill Dancer (IRE)) **Mr E. R. Griffiths**
48 STREETLADY (USA), ch f 01/04 Street Boss (USA)—Donna D (USA) (Dixie Union (USA)) (46647)
49 STREETLADY (USA), ch f 01/04 Street Boss (USA)—Donna D (USA) (Dixie Union (USA)) (46647)
50 B f 15/04 Camacho—Wavebreak (Tiger Hill (IRE)) (48571) **John Abbey & Mike Nolan, J. E. Abbey, M. F. Nolan**
51 Gr c 11/04 Havana Gold (IRE)—Ya Halla (IRE) (Dark Angel (IRE)) **P. D. Evans**
52 Ch f 13/04 Bungle Inthejungle—Zuzinia (IRE) (Mujadil (USA)) (13000)
        Rob Emmanuelle, T Burns & P D Evans, Mrs T. Burns

Other Owners: Mr J. Babb, Mrs L. Buckley, Chris Kiely Racing Limited, Mr R. Emmanuel, Mrs E. Evans, P. D. Evans, Mrs I. M. Folkes, Mr T. Johnson, R. Kent, Mr E. A. R. Morgans, Mr B. J. Mould, Shropshire Wolves, R. Simpson, Mr J. O. C. Tomkins, Mr D. White.

Assistant Trainer: Emma Evans.

---

175 **MR HYWEL GWYN EVANS, Kidwelly**
Postal: **Llwynpiod Farm, Llangyndeyrn, Kidwelly, Carmarthenshire, SA17 5HD**
Contacts: PHONE **01267 231501**
EMAIL hywelgevans@hotmail.co.uk

1 DEBACLE, 9, b g Bach (IRE)—De Blanc (IRE) **Mr H. G. Evans**
2 PERSAVERANCE, 9, b g Sir Percy—Marliana (IRE) **Mr H. G. Evans**

---

176 **MR JAMES EVANS, Worcester**
Postal: **14-16 Kinnersley Severn Stoke, Worcester, Worcestershire**
Contacts: MOBILE **07813 166430**
EMAIL herbie_evans@hotmail.com WEBSITE www.hjamesevans.co.uk

1 CROESO CYMRAEG, 8, b g Dick Turpin (IRE)—Croeso Cusan **Richard Evans Bloodstock**
2 DOONBEG FARMER (IRE), 4, br g Vadamos (FR)—Risk A Look **Peter Clarke Racing Partners**
3 DREAM COMPOSER (FR), 4, b g Dream Ahead (USA)—High Spice (USA) **Peter Clarke Racing Partners**
4 FRENCH DE GUYE (FR), 7, gr g Lord du Sud (FR)—Kasibelle de Guye (FR) **Elegant Clutter & Mr S D Faiers**
5 FRIENDSHIP BAY, 18, b g Midnight Legend—Friendly Fairy **Mrs J. Evans**
6 GERROTS (FR), 4, b g Rajsaman (FR)—Gonzeville (FR) **Peter Clarke Racing Partners**
7 HALFACROWN (IRE), 5, b g Hallowed Crown (AUS)—Ava's World (IRE)
8 KENTUCKY KINGDOM (IRE), 6, b g Camacho—Venetian Rhapsody (IRE) **The Cheltenham Flyers**
9 LAST MISSION (FR), 4, br g Invincible Spirit (IRE)—Magic Mission **Peter Clarke Racing Partners**
10 LORD GETAWAY (IRE), 10, b g Getaway (GER)—Terre d'Orient (FR) **Mrs J. Evans**
11 MALINDI BAY (FR), 9, b m Malinas (GER)—La Grande Villez (FR) **Mr S. D. Faiers**
12 MASQOOL (IRE), 4, br g Invincible Spirit (IRE)—Eshaadeh (USA) **Peter Clarke Racing Partners**
13 MOSSING, 10, b m Passing Glance—Missy Moscow (IRE) **Mrs J. Evans**
14 NOBEL LEADER (IRE), 12, b g Alflora (IRE)—Ben Roseler (IRE) **Mr S. D. Faiers**

MR JAMES EVANS - continued

15 **OPTIMISTIC BIAS (IRE)**, 13, b g Sayarshan (FR)—Dashers Folly (IRE) **Elegant Clutter Ltd**
16 **PRINCE OF STEAL (IRE)**, 12, b g Craigsteel—Princess Gloria (IRE) **The Cheltenham Flyers**
17 **RISK AND ROLL (FR)**, 8, b g No Risk At All (FR)—Rolie de Vindecy (FR) **Mr B. W. Preece**
18 **SANDS COVE (IRE)**, 15, b g Flemensfirth (USA)—Lillies Bordello (IRE) **Mrs J. Evans**
19 4, B g Cityscape—Wise Little Girl **Richard Evans Bloodstock**

THREE-YEAR-OLDS
20 **CROESO CYNNES**, ch c Hot Streak (IRE)—Croeso Cusan **Richard Evans Bloodstock**
21 **JUSTCALLMEPETE**, b g Bated Breath—Firenze **Peter Clarke Racing Partners**

TWO-YEAR-OLDS
22 Gr f 12/04 Havana Grey—Catmint (Piccolo) (5714) **Mr B. W. Preece**
23 B c 22/03 City of Light (USA)—Dream (USA) (Malibu Moon (USA)) (40000) **Mr B. W. Preece**
24 B f 07/04 Cityscape—Malindi Bay (FR) (Malinas (GER)) **Mr B. W. Preece**
25 B f 09/04 Washington DC (IRE)—Mortitia (Dansili) (14286) **Mr B. W. Preece**
26 B g 07/05 Falco (USA)—Whocalledmespeedy (IRE) (Rip Van Winkle (IRE)) (762) **Mr B. W. Preece**

Other Owners: Elegant Clutter Ltd, Mr S. D. Faiers.

Assistant Trainer: Mrs Jane Evans.

---

177 MRS NIKKI EVANS, Abergavenny
Postal: **Penbiddle Farm, Penbidwal, Pandy, Abergavenny, Gwent, NP7 8EA**
Contacts: **MOBILE 07977 753437**
EMAIL penbiddleracing@gmail.com WEBSITE NikkiEvansracing.com FACEBOOK NikkiEvansRacing
TWITTER @PenbiddleRacing WHATSAPP 07977753437

1 **AHEAD OF SCHEDULE (IRE)**, 7, ch g Shirocco (GER)—Colleen Bawn (FR) **Mr R. Singh**
2 **CARNAGE**, 7, b g Holy Roman Emperor (IRE)—Sylvestris (IRE) **Mr J. Berry**
3 **CORINTO (IRE)**, 9, br g Flemensfirth (USA)—Fashion Target (IRE) **P. T. Evans**
4 **DANCING DANI (IRE)**, 7, ch m Stowaway—Nodelay (IRE) **Hanford's Chemist Ltd & Partner**
5 **FITTLETON FERRY**, 4, br f Equiano (FR)—Sasheen **Evans & Donlin**
6 **GLOBAL FRONTIER (IRE)**, 8, b g Sans Frontieres (IRE)—Avoca Star (IRE) **Mr M Donlin and Partner**
7 **HOWDY PARTNER (IRE)**, 6, b g Califet (FR)—Areyououtofurmind (IRE) **P. T. Evans**
8 **JUKEBOX JUNIOR**, 6, gr g Jukebox Jury (IRE)—Street Fire (IRE) **Mrs M. E. Gittings-Watts**
9 **LATE SHIPMENT**, 11, b g Authorized (IRE)—Time Over **P. T. Evans**
10 **MONTY'S MISSION (IRE)**, 8, b m Arctic Cosmos (USA)—Montys Miss (IRE) **Hanford's Chemist Ltd**
11 **MORE THAN LIKELY**, 6, b m Coach House (IRE)—Moss Likely (IRE) **Mr A. T. L. Clayton**
12 **OCEAN'S OF MONEY (IRE)**, 6, b m Califet (FR)—Black Money **Mike Sheridan & Partner**
13 **ORANGE GINA**, 6, ch m Schiaparelli (GER)—Bobs Present **Martin Donlin & Lynne Bodman**
14 **PEDRO DE STYLES (FR)**, 7, b g Pedro The Great (USA)—Toscabella (FR) **Mike Sheridan & Partner**
15 **PRO ANNIE**, 4, ch f Proconsul—Come On Annie **Mrs E. V. A. Trotman**
16 **RAKISH PADDY (IRE)**, 4, ch g Mustajeeb—Pink Ivory **Mr M. S. Donlin**
17 **RESTRICTED AREA (IRE)**, 4, b g Lethal Force (IRE)—L'lle Aux Loups (IRE) **Tip of the Sword Racing**
18 **RITA THE CHEETAH**, 4, b f Prince of Lir (IRE)—Munaawashat (IRE) **Tip of the Sword Racing**
19 **SPIRITUS MUNDI (IRE)**, 7, b g Yeats (IRE)—Maiden City (IRE) **P. T. Evans**
20 **SUE BE IT (IRE)**, 11, b m Presenting—Runaround Sue (IRE) **Hanford's Chemist Ltd**
21 **WELSH WARRIOR**, 6, b g Harbour Watch (IRE)—Crimson Queen **Mr A. T. L. Clayton**

Other Owners: Mr J. Berry, Mrs L. Bodman, Mr M. S. Donlin, Mrs N. S. Evans, P. T. Evans, Hanford's Chemist Ltd, Mr M. Huntington, Nikki Evans Racing, Mr M. Sheridan.

Assistant Trainer: Mr P. T. Evans.

178 MR JAMES EWART, Langholm
Postal: **James Ewart Racing Limited, Craig Farm, Westerkirk, Langholm, Dumfriesshire, DG13 0NZ**
Contacts: **PHONE 013873 70707 MOBILE 07786 995073**
EMAIL office@jeracing.co.uk WEBSITE www.jamesewartracing.com

1 ASCOT DE BRUYERE (FR), 12, b br g Kapgarde (FR)—Quid de Neuville (FR) **The Steel Bonnets**
2 BEAT BOX (FR), 6, b g Cokoriko (FR)—Niemen (FR) **Exors of the Late J. D. Gordon**
3 BENACK (IRE), 6, b g Shirocco (GER)—Maggies Oscar (IRE) **Team Benack**
4 BIGBADMATTIE (IRE), 8, b g Big Bad Bob (IRE)—Arcuate **Bb Racing Club & Partner**
5 BLACK PIRATE, 10, b g Black Sam Bellamy (IRE)—Proper Posh **Leeds Plywood & Doors Ltd**
6 BOTTLE HILL, 6, bl g Malinas (GER)—Minnie Hill (IRE) **Mrs Hugh Fraser**
7 BRAYHILL (IRE), 7, b g Sholokhov (IRE)—Definite Love (IRE) **J Fyffe & N M L Ewart**
8 CELLAR VIE, 8, gr g Tikkanen (USA)—Branceilles (FR) **Percy, Graham&carruthers**
9 CHARMANT (FR), 10, b g Balko (FR)—Ravissante (FR) **Mr A Phillips & Mrs N Sperling**
10 CLONDAW FAME (IRE), 5, b g Fame And Glory—Aguida (FR) **N. M. L. Ewart**
11 EMPIRE DE MAULDE (FR), 8, b g Spanish Moon (USA)—Ondine de Brejoux (FR) **Mr S Murrills & Mr J Ewart**
12 ERIMITIS, 4, b f Black Sam Bellamy (IRE)—Think Green
13 ESCAPEANDEVADE (IRE), 6, b g Westerner—Sandrinechoix (FR) **N. M. L. Ewart**
14 ETTILA DE SIVOLA (FR), 8, gr g Noroit (GER)—Wild Rose Bloom (FR) **Kesson,Phillips,Humbert,Ogilvie,Graham**
15 FAST SCENIC (FR), 7, b g Brave Mansonnien (FR)—Scenaria (FR) **Mrs J. E. Dodd**
16 FOR THREE (IRE), 8, b g Pour Moi (IRE)—Asmaa (USA) **Craig Farm,Percy,Palmer,Graham,Higgins**
17 FOSTERED PHIL (IRE), 8, b g Arcadio (GER)—Knock Na Shee (IRE) **N. M. L. Ewart**
18 HOLD ONTO THE LINE (IRE), 5, br g Westerner—Dedoctorsdaughter (IRE) **Carruthers, Drew, Kesson & Phillips**
19 HONOURARY GIFT (IRE), 9, b g City Honours (USA)—Zaffalong (IRE) **Ewart,Elliot,Carruthers,Palmer**
20 JIMS APPLE (IRE), 6, br m Sageburg (IRE)—Good Thyne Lucy (IRE) **The Craig Farm Syndicate**
21 JUGE ET PARTI (FR), 9, gr g Martaline—Nakota Rag (FR) **The Jp's**
22 KNOT ANOTHER ONE (IRE), 5, ch g Ocovango—Nora's Flame (IRE) **Mr A. M. Phillips**
23 LAKE TAKAPUNA (IRE), 11, b g Shantou (USA)—Close To Shore (IRE) **Carruthers,Graham,Hughes,Kesson**
24 LORD ROCO, 6, b g Rocamadour—Dolly Penrose **N. M. L. Ewart**
25 MUHTAMAR (FR), 7, ch g Muhtathir—Martalina (FR) **Mrs J. E. Dodd**
26 NIKGARDE (FR), 7, b g Kapgarde (FR)—Nikoline (FR) **Mrs J. E. Dodd**
27 SAO MAXENCE (FR), 9, b g Saint des Saints (FR)—Primadona (FR) **Mrs J. E. Dodd**
28 SCARLET N' BLACK, 4, b f Black Sam Bellamy (IRE)—Overlady
29 THE BLAME GAME (IRE), 8, b g Getaway (GER)—Tribal Princess (IRE) **Exors of the Late J. D. Gordon**
30 THE CARETAKER, 6, b g Mukhadram—Perfect Story (IRE) **Exors of the Late J. D. Gordon**

THREE-YEAR-OLDS
31 LEMOINE, b g Black Sam Bellamy (IRE)—Think Green
32 O'ERBURN, ch f Black Sam Bellamy (IRE)—Overlady

Other Owners: B B Racing Club, Mr R. Carruthers, Mr A. Didlick, Mrs L. J. Drew, Mr J. J. Elliot, Mr J. Ewart, N. M. L. Ewart, Mr J. Fyffe, W. Graham, Mrs M. Higgins, Mr D. M. C. Hughes, Mrs A. G. Humbert, Dr C. M. Kesson, Mr S. A. Murrills, Mr P. M. Ogilvie, Dr R. A. Palmer, Mrs J. D. Percy, Mr A. M. Phillips, Mr D. I. Rolinson, Mr R. E. Smith, The South Hayrigg Partnership, Mrs J. Sperling, Mr D. R. Stanhope, The Craig Farm Syndicate, Mr A. I. D. Todd, Ms H. K. Walker, Mr James Westoll.

Assistant Trainer: Briony Ewart.

NH Jockey: Rachael McDonald.

179 MR LES EYRE, Beverley
Postal: **Ivy House Stables, Main Street, Catwick, Beverley, North Humberside, HU17 5PJ**
Contacts: **MOBILE 07864 677444**
EMAIL leseyreracing@hotmail.co.uk

1 BEDFORD FLYER (IRE), 4, b c Clodovil (IRE)—Nafa (IRE) **RP Racing Ltd**
2 BLADES EQUAL, 4, b f Equiano (FR)—Blades Girl **Dr V. Webb**
3 COSMIC STAR, 4, b gr f Charm Spirit (IRE)—Reaching Ahead (USA) **Melissa Cooke & Val Webb**

MR LES EYRE - continued

4 **COTE D'AZUR**, 9, ch g Champs Elysees—Florentia **Billy Parker & Steven Parker**
5 **FAME AND ACCLAIM (IRE)**, 5, b g Acclamation—Applause (IRE) **RP Racing Ltd**
6 **HEY MR**, 4, b g Territories (IRE)—Filona (IRE) **Billy Parker & Steven Parker**
7 **JUST FRANK**, 4, b g Epaulette (AUS)—Mabinia (IRE) **Billy Parker & Steven Parker**
8 **LE BAYOU (FR)**, 5, b g Dabirsim (FR)—Kastiya (FR) **RP Racing Ltd**
9 **MORETTI (IRE)**, 7, b m Requinto (IRE)—Hassaya (IRE) **Mr G. Parkinson & Mr J. L. Eyre**
10 **QUEEN OF KALAHARI**, 7, b m Lethal Force (IRE)—Aromatherapy **Les Eyre Racing Partnership I**
11 **RON O**, 4, ch g Toronado (IRE)—Xaloc (IRE) **Mr M. J. Rozenbroek**

THREE-YEAR-OLDS

12 **ARKID**, b g Ardad (IRE)—Lady Vermeer **Mr G. Parkinson & Mr J. L. Eyre**
13 **BEARCARDI (IRE)**, b g Kodi Bear (IRE)—Mojita (IRE) **RP Racing Ltd**
14 **FLASHY BEAR (IRE)**, b g Kodiac—Stylish Design (FR) **RP Racing Ltd**
15 **HILARY'S BOY**, b g Lethal Force (IRE)—Mitigate **RP Racing Ltd**
16 **JUST ANOTHER (IRE)**, ch g Bungle Inthejungle—Labyrinthine (IRE) **B Parker, S Parker J Blackburn**
17 **LADY ARDAD**, gr f Ardad (IRE)—My Angel **Sunpak Racing**
18 **REEL TIMBA (IRE)**, b g Highland Reel (IRE)—Timba **Mr M. J. Rozenbroek**

TWO-YEAR-OLDS

19 B c 04/05 Dandy Man (IRE)—Lily's Rainbow (IRE) (Intikhab (USA)) (35000) **RP Racing Ltd**

Other Owners: Mr J. N. Blackburn, Mrs M. A. Cooke, Mr J. L. Eyre, Mr B. Parker, Mr S. Parker, Mr G. Parkinson, Dr V. Webb.

Assistant Trainer: Tracy Johnson.

180

MR RICHARD FAHEY, Malton
Trainer did not wish details of their string to appear

181

MR CHRIS FAIRHURST, Middleham
Postal: Glasgow House, Middleham, Leyburn, North Yorkshire, DL8 4QG
Contacts: PHONE 01969 622039 MOBILE 07889 410840
EMAIL cfairhurst@tiscali.co.uk

1 **BENADALID**, 7, b g Assertive—Gambatte **Mrs S. France**
2 **KAYLYN**, 4, b f Charm Spirit (IRE)—Dark Quest **Mr A. Davies**
3 **MASHAM MOOR**, 5, b g Music Master—Jane's Payoff (IRE) **Mrs C. Arnold**
4 **RED TORNADO (FR)**, 10, ch g Dr Fong (USA)—Encircle (USA) **Richard III Partnership**
5 **THE ARMED MAN**, 9, b g Miso Bond (IRE)—Accamelia **Mrs C. Arnold**
6 **TOP ATTRACTION**, 5, b g Fountain of Youth (IRE)—Symphonic Dancer (USA) **The PQD Partnership**
7 **VALLAMOREY**, 4, gr f Outstrip—Zagaleta **Mrs A. M. Leggett**
8 **VELMA**, 5, b m Fast Company (IRE)—Valoria **Mr A. Davies**

THREE-YEAR-OLDS

9 **HEZMIE (IRE)**, b f Divine Prophet (AUS)—Zoumie (IRE) **Mr A. Davies**
10 **MADAM ARKATI**, br f Pastoral Pursuits—Accamelia **Mrs C. Arnold**

TWO-YEAR-OLDS

11 **GREY FORCE ONE**, gr g 18/04 Lethal Force (IRE)—Flamenco (Showcasing) (7619) **Hugh T. Redhead**
12 **VIXEY**, b f 05/05 Cable Bay (IRE)—Valoria (Hernando (FR)) (4000) **Mr A. Davies**

182 MR JAMES FANSHAWE, Newmarket

Postal: **Pegasus Stables, Snailwell Road, Newmarket, Suffolk, CB8 7DJ**
Contacts: **PHONE 01638 664525 FAX 01638 664523**
EMAIL **james@jamesfanshawe.com**
WEBSITE **www.jamesfanshawe.com, www.fredarcherracing.com**

1 BLUE ARTEMIS, 4, b f Showcasing—Azure Amour (IRE) **Fred Archer Racing - Dutch Oven**
2 CROWN POWER (IRE), 5, b m Camelot—Causeway Queen (IRE) **King Power Racing Co Ltd**
3 DEVILRY, 4, b f Sea The Moon (GER)—Diablerette **Miss K. Rausing**
4 ENCOURAGED (IRE), 4, br g Elzaam (AUS)—Gangster Squad (FR) **Mr B. C. M. Wong**
5 FLOWER OF SCOTLAND, 5, b m Gleneagles (IRE)—Seal of Approval **T. R. G. Vestey**
6 FRESH, 5, b g Bated Breath—Kendal Mint **Clipper Group Holdings Ltd**
7 GREEK FLAME (FR), 4, ch f Siyouni (FR)—Flame of Hestia (IRE) **Merry Fox Stud Limited**
8 HICKORY (IRE), 4, b g Free Eagle (IRE)—Badr Al Badoor (IRE) **Fred Archer Racing - Galliard**
9 ISOLA ROSSA, 4, b f Iffraaj—Isola Verde **Jan & Peter Hopper & Michelle Morris**
10 JASMINE JOY (IRE), 4, b f Lope de Vega (IRE)—Pecking Order (IRE) **Merry Fox Stud Limited**
11 LAST PICASSO (IRE), 4, ch g Lope de Vega (IRE)—Alvee (IRE) **Merry Fox Stud Limited**
12 MURAU, 4, b g Mukhadram—Entitlement **Dr C. M. H. Wills**
13 SECOND SLIP (IRE), 5, b g Lope de Vega (IRE)—Arkadina (IRE) **Merry Fox Stud Limited**
14 SERENADING, 6, br m Iffraaj—Constant Dream **Mr John E Rose & Manor Farm Stud**
15 VIOLA (IRE), 5, ch m Lope de Vega (IRE)—Sistine **Elite Racing Club**

THREE-YEAR-OLDS

16 ANNIE GALE (IRE), b f No Nay Never (USA)—Double Fantasy (GER) **Fred Archer Racing - Minting**
17 BIG NEWS (IRE), b f Dubawi (IRE)—Biz Bar **Qatar Racing Limited**
18 BLUEBIRD, b f Acclamation—Blues Sister **Michelle Morris & Jan & Peter Hopper**
19 CARUSO, ch g Lope de Vega (IRE)—Carpe Vita (IRE) **Sir R. Ogden C.B.E., LLD**
20 CITRUS GROVE (IRE), b f Oasis Dream—Zest (IRE) **Elite Racing Club**
21 CLIPPER CLASS, b f Frankel—Speedy Boarding **Helena Springfield Ltd**
22 COERCION, b f Kitten's Joy (USA)—Cat's Claw (IRE) **Qatar Racing Limited**
23 COMPLIANT, b f Pivotal—Royal Seal **Cheveley Park Stud Limited**
24 B f Muhaarar—Crystal Gal (IRE) **Clipper Group Holdings Ltd**
25 B f Storm The Stars (USA)—Daintily Done **Sheikh J. D. Al Maktoum**
26 EURAQUILO, b g Raven's Pass (USA)—Air Kiss **Dr C. M. H. Wills**
27 ISCHIA, ch f Equiano (FR)—Isola Verde **Fred Archer Racing - Lady Golightly**
28 LAILAH, b f Australia—Wedding Speech (IRE) **Mr G. Marney**
29 LIBERTUS, b g Equiano (FR)—Italian Connection **Fred Archer Racing - Peeping Tom**
30 B f Golden Horn—Moonlight Sonata **Mrs M. Slack**
31 MOONLIGHT TIARA, ch f Helmet (AUS)—Amarylis (IRE) **Mrs M Bacon**
32 NOVEL LEGEND (IRE), b c Nathaniel (IRE)—Majestic Dubawi **Mr Boniface Ho Ka Kui**
33 QUEEN OF NAVARRE (IRE), ch f Bated Breath—Queen Andorra (IRE) **Clipper Group Holdings Ltd**
34 ROYAL SCANDAL, ch f Dubawi (IRE)—Seal of Approval **T. R. G. Vestey**
35 SECLUDED, b f Intello (GER)—Cosseted **Mr J. R. Fanshawe**
36 STORMBREAKER, b c Proconsul—Shadows' Whispers (IRE) **Somerton Sporting Club**
37 TAYCAN, b f Postponed (IRE)—Act Fast **Mrs M. L. Morris**
38 TELEMACHUS, b g Ulysses (IRE)—Tallulah Rose **Cheveley Park Stud Limited**
39 TUXEDO JUNCTION, b c Iffraaj—Dash To The Front **Castle Down Racing**
40 WANDERING ROCKS, ch g Ulysses (IRE)—West of The Moon **Cheveley Park Stud Limited**
41 WANNABE BRAVE (IRE), b g Fastnet Rock (AUS)—Wannabe Special **Mrs G. J. Davey**
42 WILLEM TWEE, b c Ribchester (IRE)—Paulinie **Chris van Hoorn Racing**

TWO-YEAR-OLDS

43 ALPINE GIRL (IRE), b f 21/03 Acclamation—Almond Brook (Mayson) (70000) **Owners Group 097**
44 AMERICAN BELLE, b f 20/03 Starspangledbanner (AUS)—Syndicate (Dansili) (38000)
Fred Archer Racing - Little Sister
45 AUBAZINE (IRE), b f 18/04 Shamardal (USA)—Ambassadrice (Oasis Dream) (210000) **T. C. Stewart**
46 CALIBRE, b c 02/03 Camacho—Isis (USA) (Royal Academy (USA)) **Dr C. M. H. Wills**
47 CRACKSKING, ch c 07/02 Frankel—Calyxa (Pivotal) (403912) **Janet Ostermann**
48 B f 10/05 Teofilo (IRE)—Dubai Fashion (IRE) (Dubawi (IRE)) (135000) **Mrs A. M. Swinburn**
49 B f 29/01 Belardo (IRE)—Elle Gala (IRE) (Galileo (IRE)) (60000) **The Macaroni Beach Society**
50 FAST AFFAIR, b f 13/04 Cracksman—Felicity (GER) (Inchinor) **Janet Ostermann**

MR JAMES FANSHAWE - continued

51 **FIRST OF MAY,** b f 22/01 Mayson—Roubles (USA) (Speightstown (USA)) **Elite Racing Club**
52 B c 09/01 Dark Angel (IRE)—Frankel Light (IRE) (Frankel) (180000) **Mr B. C. M. Wong**
53 B c 20/04 Roaring Lion (USA)—Granny Franny (USA) (Grand Slam (USA)) **Qatar Racing Limited**
54 B f 09/05 Wootton Bassett—Harem Lady (FR) (Teofilo) (178571) **Mrs A. M. Swinburn**
55 B c 18/03 Bobby's Kitten (USA)—Interstella (Sea The Stars (IRE)) (27000) **Fred Archer Racing Thunder**
56 **KLIMOVA,** ch f 25/03 Intello (GER)—Queen of Ice (Selkirk (USA)) **Cheveley Park Stud Limited**
57 **LADY WORMSLEY (IRE),** ch f 12/02 Twilight Son—Dutch Princess (Dutch Art)

W Russell, B McManus, Mrs S Roy

58 **MASTER DANDY (IRE),** ch c 17/03 Dandy Man (IRE)—Honeymead (IRE) (Pivotal) (30000)

Fred Archer Racing - Grandmaster

59 B f 17/02 Lope de Vega (IRE)—Millistar (Galileo (IRE)) **Helena Springfield Ltd**
60 B c 06/04 Churchill (IRE)—Opportuna (Rock Hard Ten (USA)) (33000) **Mrs A. M. Swinburn**
61 **PERSEVERANDO,** ch gr f 15/04 Mastercraftsman (IRE)—Starlet (IRE) (Sea The Stars (IRE)) **Lord Halifax**
62 B f 20/02 Roaring Lion (USA)—Quiza Quiza Quiza (Golden Snake (USA)) **Qatar Racing Limited**
63 **SEA OF TRANQUILITY,** b c 28/02 Sea The Moon (GER)—She's Gorgeous (IRE) (Acclamation)

Johnstone Partnership

64 B f 16/03 Acclamation—Spirit Raiser (IRE) (Invincible Spirit (IRE)) **Lord Vestey**
65 **STARBASE,** b c 17/04 Sea The Stars (IRE)—Silk Sari (Dalakhani (IRE)) (85000)

Bengough, Booth, Silver, Steed, Fittocks

66 **TABERNACLE,** b f 14/04 Unfortunately (IRE)—Pious (Bishop of Cashel) **Cheveley Park Stud Limited**
67 **UPDATE,** b f 24/03 Free Eagle (IRE)—Upshot (Pivotal) **Cheveley Park Stud Limited**
68 **YEOMAN,** b c 24/01 Tamayuz—Harmonica (Pivotal) **Elite Racing Club**

Assistant Trainer: Tom Fanshawe.

183	**MISS JULIA FEILDEN, Newmarket**

Postal: **Harraton Stud, Laceys Lane, Exning, Newmarket, Suffolk, CB8 7HW**
Contacts: **MOBILE 07974 817694**
EMAIL **juliafeilden@gmail.com** WEBSITE **www.juliafeildenracing.com**

1 **ALIBABA,** 5, b g Lawman (FR)—Fantasy In Blue **Miss J. D. Feilden,**

Ahamed Farook & Julia Feilden, Mr A. R. Farook

2 **ENGRAVE,** 6, gr m Dark Angel (IRE)—Hot Wired **Newmarket Equine Tours Racing Club**
3 **FEN TIGER (IRE),** 4, b g Vadamos (FR)—Three Knots (IRE) **Mrs C. T. Bushnell**
4 **HEER'S SADIE,** 4, b f Heeraat (IRE)—Sadiigah **Mr J. W. Ford**
5 **HOT ROMANCE,** 4, b f Hot Streak (IRE)—Vintage Steps

Miss J. D. Feilden, Million To One Partnership, Mr R. A. Birkett

6 **MAEVE'S MEMORY (IRE),** 4, b f Kodiac—Startori **Newmarket Equine Tours Racing Club**
7 **MRS MEADER,** 6, b m Cityscape—Bavarica **Miss J. D. Feilden, Nj Bloodstock, Mr N. Child**
8 **OUD METHA BRIDGE (IRE),** 8, ch g Helmet (AUS)—Central Force **In It To Win Partnership**
9 **SMOKEY MALONE,** 4, gr g Outstrip—Trixie Malone **The Sultans of Speed**
10 **SPANISH MANE (IRE),** 7, b g Havana Gold (IRE)—Kiva **Stowstowquickquickstow Partnership**
11 **SUNSET SALUTE,** 4, b g Twilight Son—Hill Welcome **Mrs J. E. Lambert**
12 **YOU DIDN'T DID YOU,** 4, ch f Twilight Son—Castaway Queen (IRE) **Mr D. A. Clark**

THREE-YEAR-OLDS

13 **ARPINA (IRE),** ch f Starspangledbanner (AUS)—Lara Amelia (IRE)

Miss J. D. Feilden, Mr S. J. Clarke, Steve Clarke & Partner

14 **KITI SUNSET,** b f Charming Thought—Sunset Kitty (USA)

Steve Clarke & Partners 3, Miss J. D. Feilden, Mr S. J. Clarke, Mr O. A. Wideson

15 **QUEEN'S COMPANY,** b f Siyouni (FR)—Queen's Charter **Good Company Partnership**
16 **SCOTCH MIST,** gr f Time Test—Positive Spin **Carol Bushnell & Partners**
17 **THE MOUSE KING (IRE),** gr g El Kabeir (USA)—Empress Anna (IRE) **Mrs C. T. Bushnell**

MISS JULIA FEILDEN - continued

TWO-YEAR-OLDS

18 B f 29/02 Adaay (IRE)—Displaying Amber (Showcasing)
19 **HURRICANE KIKO (IRE)**, gr c 25/04 Kuroshio (AUS)—Madame Thunder (IRE) (Zebedee) (15000)
    Carol Bushnell & Partners
20 **LADY CLEMMIE**, b f 16/02 Churchill (IRE)—Joquina (IRE) (Big Bad Bob (IRE)) (1000)
21 **SAVANNAH SONG**, gr f 24/02 Roaring Lion (USA)—Dynaglow (USA) (Dynaformer (USA)) (13000)
    Carol Bushnell & Partners
22 **STINTINO SUNSET**, b f 02/04 Twilight Son—Sunset Kitty (USA) (Gone West (USA)) (2500)
    Steve Clarke & Partners 3, Miss J. D. Feilden, Mr S. J. Clarke, Mr O. A. Wideson
23 **TRINIDAD CALYPSO**, gr f 25/01 Roaring Lion (USA)—My Only One (Frankel) (18000) **Mrs C. T. Bushnell**
24 **ZANAGOR**, b f 03/04 Zarak (FR)—Jasmiralda (FR)
25 **ZANY IDEA (IRE)**, b f 19/01 Zoffany (IRE)—Novel Concept (IRE) (Fastnet Rock (AUS))
    Newmarket Equine Tours Racing Club

Assistant Trainer: Ross Birkett.

Flat Jockey: Dylan Hogan. **Apprentice Jockey:** Mr Sam Feilden. **Amateur Jockey:** Mr R. Birkett.

---

184 **MR ROGER FELL, Nawton**
Postal: **Arthington Barn House, Highfield Lane, Nawton, York, North Yorkshire, YO62 7TU**
Contacts: **PHONE 01439 770184**
EMAIL rogerfellracing@gmail.com WEBSITE www.rogerfell.co.uk

1 **ADMIRALITY**, 8, b g Mount Nelson—Dialma (USA) **MPR, Ventura Racing, Salthouse&Fell**
2 **COCKALORUM (IRE)**, 7, b g Cape Cross (IRE)—Opinionated (IRE) **K Hardy & R Fell**
3 **DANDY SPIRIT (IRE)**, 5, b g Dandy Man (IRE)—Spirit of Grace **Mr R. G. Fell**
4 **DANDYS GOLD (IRE)**, 8, b m Dandy Man (IRE)—Proud Penny (IRE) **Nick Bradley Racing 8 & Partner**
5 **DAPPER MAN (IRE)**, 8, b g Dandy Man (IRE)—Gist (IRE) **Colne Valley Racing & Partner**
6 **DAVE DEXTER**, 6, b g Stimulation (IRE)—Blue Crest (FR) **The Wolf Pack & Partner**
7 **END ZONE**, 5, b g Dark Angel (IRE)—Brown Eyed Honey **Middleham Park Racing Xix & Partner 1**
8 **ERICH BLOCH (IRE)**, 6, b g Dandy Man (IRE)—Star Bonita (IRE) **Swales & Fell**
9 **GINATO (IRE)**, 4, b g Footstepsinthesand—Jacquelin Jag (IRE) **Mr R. G. Fell**
10 **GLOBAL SPIRIT**, 7, b g Invincible Spirit (IRE)—Centime **Swales & Fell**
11 **HAROME (IRE)**, 8, ch g Bahamian Bounty—Clytha **Middleham Park Racing Lxxi & Partner**
12 **HARSWELL DUKE**, 4, b g Garswood—Grafitti **Harswell Thoroughbred Racing**
13 **HIGHLIGHT REEL (IRE)**, 7, b g Big Bad Bob (IRE)—Dance Hall Girl (IRE) **Grange Park Racing Club & R Fell**
14 **IRON SHERIFF (IRE)**, 4, b g Lawman (FR)—Rebelline (IRE) **Mr R. G. Fell**
15 **KAPONO**, 6, b g Kuroshio (AUS)—Fair Maiden (JPN) **Mr S. M. Al Sabah**
16 **LARGE ACTION**, 6, b g Iffraaj—Titian's Pride (USA) **Nick Bradley Racing 46**
17 **MARIE'S DIAMOND (IRE)**, 6, b br h Footstepsinthesand—Sindiyma (IRE) **The Wolf Pack & Partner**
18 **MUNTADAB (IRE)**, 10, b g Invincible Spirit (IRE)—Chibola (ARG) **Swales & Fell**
19 **OSO RAPIDO (IRE)**, 5, b g Kodiac—Burke's Rock **Woodhurst Construction & G Chrysanthou**
20 **PRESIDENTIAL (IRE)**, 8, b g Invincible Spirit (IRE)—Poetical (IRE) **Mr R. G. Fell**
21 **THE FLYING GINGER (IRE)**, 4, ch f Showcasing—Law of The Range **Mr S. M. Al Sabah**
22 **USTATH**, 6, ch g Exceed And Excel (AUS)—Adorn **MPR LXXXII & Peter Hewitson & Partner**
23 **ZIHAAM**, 8, ch g Dutch Art—Hymnsheet **Nick Bradley Racing 29 & Partner**

THREE-YEAR-OLDS

24 **BELLSHILL BEAUTY (IRE)**, ch f Decorated Knight—Ellbeedee (IRE) **Nick Bradley Racing 6 & Partner**
25 **ELDRICKJONES (IRE)**, b c Cotai Glory—Dream Impossible (IRE) **Nick Bradley Racing 42,Salthouse&Partner**
26 **JONNY BOXER (IRE)**, b g Profitable (IRE)—Gala Style (IRE) **Fell & Salthouse**
27 B g Vadamos (FR)—Last Hooray
28 **LOTUS ROSE**, b f Showcasing—Ealaan (USA) **The Roses Partnership & R G Fell**
29 **LUCY LULU**, b f Muhaarar—Melody of Love **Nick Bradley Racing 16 and Partner**
30 **MAKHAN KING (IRE)**, b g Bated Breath—Passionatta (IRE) **Harswell Racing, Salthouse & Fell**

MR ROGER FELL - continued

31 **METHINKS (IRE),** b g Showcasing—Landale **Mr S. M. Al Sabah**
32 B g Kodiac—Miss Glitters (IRE)
33 **MISS WOMBLETON (IRE),** ch f Galileo Gold—Eponastone (IRE) **Mr R. G. Fell**
34 **PRIMO,** b g Acclamation—Border Bloom **Mr S. M. Al Sabah**
35 **RAYDOUN (IRE),** b c Moohaajim (IRE)—Add Up (IRE) **Nick Bradley Racing 13,Salthouse&Partner**
36 **ROBBIE ROGER (IRE),** b g Galileo Gold—Mediska **Nick Bradley Racing 13,Salthouse&Partner**
37 **WHERE'S DIANA (IRE),** b f Markaz (IRE)—Maid In Heaven (IRE) **Mr R. G. Fell**

TWO-YEAR-OLDS

38 B f 29/04 Adaay (IRE)—Ealaan (USA) (Invasor (ARG)) (12381)
39 B c 21/02 Elzaam (AUS)—Juste Pour Moi (IRE) (Pour Moi (IRE)) (9524)
40 B f 24/02 Bungle Inthejungle—Khayrat (IRE) (Polar Falcon (USA)) (42857)
41 B f 21/03 Holy Roman Emperor (IRE)—Mambo Paradise (Makfi) (11500)
42 B f 03/03 Twilight Son—Private View (Exceed And Excel (AUS)) (17143)
43 Ch f 20/04 Decorated Knight—Rooney O'Mara (Dragon Pulse (IRE)) (5000) **Mr S. M. Al Sabah**
44 B f 02/05 Union Rags (USA)—Sea of Laughter (USA) (Distorted Humor (USA)) **Mr S. M. Al Sabah**
45 Ch c 25/03 Dandy Man (IRE)—Shesastar (Bahamian Bounty) (12000)
46 B f 13/02 Shalaa (IRE)—Trainnah (Pivotal) (34014)

Other Owners: P. Bamford, Mr J. M. Binns, Mr N. Bradley, Mr G. Chrysanthou, Colne Valley Racing, Mr A. D. Crombie, Mr A. Denham, Mr T. Denham, Mr R. G. Fell, Grange Park Racing Club, Mrs K. L. Hardy, Harswell Thoroughbred Racing, Miss S. Holden, Mr M. Kirby, Mr P. M. Lockwood, MPR LXXXII & Peter Hewitson, Middleham Park Racing LXXI, Middleham Park Racing XIX, Middleham Park and Ventura Racing 6, Nick Bradley Racing 13, Nick Bradley Racing 16, Nick Bradley Racing 29, Nick Bradley Racing 42, Nick Bradley Racing 6, Nick Bradley Racing 8, T. S. Palin, M. Prince, Mr W. J. Salthouse, Mr D. A. Swales, Mr M. Taylor, The Roses Partnership, Woodhurst Construction Ltd.

Assistant Trainer: Sean Murray.

185
MR CHARLIE FELLOWES, Newmarket
Postal: Bedford House Stables, 7 Bury Road, Newmarket, Suffolk, CB8 7BX
Contacts: **PHONE 01638 666948 MOBILE 07968 499596**
EMAIL charlie@charliefellowesracing.co.uk WEBSITE www.charliefellowesracing.co.uk

1 **AMARILLO STAR (IRE),** 5, ch g Society Rock (IRE)—Neutrina (IRE) **Lady De Ramsey**
2 **BLOW YOUR HORN (IRE),** 5, b g Golden Horn—She's Complete (IRE) **Mr J. Soiza**
3 **CHIEFOFCHIEFS,** 9, b g Royal Applause—Danvers **M. L. Ayers**
4 **DIAVOLO (IRE),** 4, b g Dubawi (IRE)—Sultanina **Normandie Stud Ltd**
5 **DUBIOUS AFFAIR (IRE),** 6, b m Frankel—Dubian To (IRE) **M. Obaida**
6 **DUEL IN THE SUN (IRE),** 5, ch g Sea The Stars (IRE)—Queen's Conquer **Mrs S. M. Roy**
7 **EJTILAAB (IRE),** 6, b g Slade Power (IRE)—Miranda Frost (IRE) **Mr P. E. Wildes**
8 **FREE AS AN EAGLE (IRE),** 4, b g Free Eagle (IRE)—Silirisa (FR) **The Staying Syndicate**
9 **GOLDEN FORCE,** 6, b g Lethal Force (IRE)—Malilla (IRE) **A. M. Mitchell**
10 **ICONIQUE,** 4, b gr f Sixties Icon—Rose Cheval (USA) **Newmarket Racing Club HQii**
11 **INJAZATI (IRE),** 4, ch c Night of Thunder (IRE)—Mathanora (IRE) **M. Obaida**
12 **IVYNATOR (IRE),** 4, b g Muhaarar—Venturous Spirit (FR) **The Accession Partners**
13 **KATYUSHA,** 4, b f Siyouni (FR)—Akhmatova **Mr D. S. Lee**
14 **LASTING LEGACY,** 5, gr m Lethal Force (IRE)—Araminte **Darivas,Soiza,Sohi,Morjaria & Fellowes**
15 **LIGHTENING SHORE,** 4, bl g Showcasing—Zora Seas (IRE) **Darivas,Soiza,Sohi,Morjaria & Fellowes**
16 **MADAME PELTIER (IRE),** 5, b m Exceed And Excel (AUS)—Airline Hostess (IRE)
Mr P Hickman, Mr G Johns & Mr D King
17 **MOUNTAIN BRAVE,** 5, b m Sepoy (AUS)—Plucky **K Sohi & C Fellowes**
18 **MR CURIOSITY,** 5, b g Frankel—Our Obsession (IRE) **A. E. Oppenheimer**
19 **PIRATE KING,** 7, br g Farhh—Generous Diana **Daniel MacAuliffe & Anoj Don**

MR CHARLIE FELLOWES - continued

20 **PURPLE RIBBON,** 4, b f Gleneagles (IRE)—Crimson Ribbon (USA) **A. E. Oppenheimer**
21 **SEASETT,** 4, b g Wootton Bassett—Sea Horn (FR) **Mr P. E. Wildes**
22 **SHOULDERING (IRE),** 5, b m Epaulette (AUS)—Abhasana (IRE) **Darivas,Soiza,Sohi,Morjaria & Fellowes**
23 **THE KODI KID (IRE),** 4, b g Kodi Bear (IRE)—Dat II Do **Mr P. E. Wildes**
24 **VADREAM,** 4, b f Brazen Beau (AUS)—Her Honour (IRE) **Mr D. R. J. King**
25 **VANITY AFFAIR (IRE),** 5, b g Mayson—Height of Vanity (IRE) **Dun Lee & Charlie Fellowes**
26 **VIA SERENDIPITY,** 8, b g Invincible Spirit (IRE)—Mambo Light (USA) **J Soiza & D Lovatt**
27 **VIRGO (IRE),** 4, b g Sea The Stars (IRE)—Bibury **Mr J. Soiza**

THREE-YEAR-OLDS

28 **ALBERT (IRE),** b g Fastnet Rock (AUS)—Fallen In Love **Normandie Stud Ltd**
29 **ATOMISE,** b f Ardad (IRE)—Eolith **Miranda Duchess of Beaufort**
30 **ATRIUM,** b g Holy Roman Emperor (IRE)—Hail Shower (IRE) **Highclere Thoroughbred Racing - Pergola**
31 **BENEDICT WILDES (IRE),** b g Ribchester (IRE)—Black Pearl (IRE) **Mr P. E. Wildes**
32 **BLAITHIN,** b f Night of Thunder (IRE)—Venus Marina **M. L. Ayers**
33 **COOKIES AND CREME,** ch f Siyouni (FR)—Coconut Creme **Normandie Stud Ltd**
34 **CRUMBIES (IRE),** gr g Gutaifan (IRE)—Miranda Frost (IRE) **Mr P. E. Wildes**
35 **CUMULONIMBUS (IRE),** ch c Night of Thunder (IRE)—Queen's Novel **Mr P Hickman and Mr D King**
36 **DOROTHEA,** b f Equiano (FR)—Persario **Hot to Trot Racing 2 and Mrs E Grundy**
37 **EASY WITH ACES (IRE),** b g Zoffany (IRE)—Abbasharjah (GER) **Mr C. H. Huggan**
38 **EVE LODGE,** b f Ardad (IRE)—Sandy Times (IRE) **Mathis Stables LLC**
39 **FAI FAI,** b c Acclamation—Sabratah **Mr A. F. Abukhadra**
40 **FRESH HOPE,** b f New Approach (IRE)—Wiener Valkyrie **The Eclipse Partnership**
41 **GRAND ALLIANCE (IRE),** b c Churchill (IRE)—Endless Love (IRE) **Mrs S. M. Roy**
42 **INCHBAE,** b f Golden Horn—Inchina **A. E. Oppenheimer**
43 **MARTHA EDLIN,** b f Intello (GER)—Tempest Fugit (IRE) **Middleham Park Racing LXXV**
44 **PROSPECTING,** ch f Spill The Beans (AUS)—Elvira Delight (USA) **Mr F. J. Perry**
45 **SAN FRANCISCO BAY (IRE),** b c Muhaarar—Stor Mo Chroi (IRE) **Mr A Dee & Mr Graham Smith-Bernal**
46 **SCARLET WILLOW (IRE),** b f Kodiac—Sona **Lady Bamford**
47 **SEA TRUE (IRE),** ch f Sea The Stars (IRE)—Crafty (AUS) **Dahab Racing**
48 **SIR MIN (IRE),** b g Caravaggio (USA)—Danehurst **Mr P. E. Wildes**
49 **SOUS LES ETOILES,** b f Sea The Stars (IRE)—Nyarhini **A. E. Oppenheimer**
50 **STAR ZINC (IRE),** b c Kodiac—Night Queen (IRE) **Dahab Racing**
51 **SURREY KNIGHT (FR),** b c Le Havre—Millionaia (IRE) **Surrey Racing (SK)**
52 **TEQUILAMOCKINGBIRD,** ch f New Approach (IRE)—Tequila Sunrise **Mr C. N. Wright**
53 **TRAVESURAS (USA),** b br g Hit It A Bomb (USA)—Heart's Song (USA) **Mr J. L. Kung**
54 **WANNABE KIND (USA),** b f Harzand (IRE)—Wannabe Posh (USA) **Normandie Stud Ltd**
55 **WYNTER WILDES,** b f Tamayuz—Khazeena **Mr P. E. Wildes**
56 **YOUNG AT HEART (IRE),** br f Golden Horn—Missunited (IRE) **Normandie Stud Ltd**
57 **YOUNG ENDLESS,** b g Champs Elysees—Eternity Ring **The Endless Acres Five**

TWO-YEAR-OLDS

58 B f 17/02 Unfortunately (IRE)—Abonos (IRE) (Approve (IRE)) (15000) **Offthebridle Podcast**
59 B c 02/05 Invincible Spirit (IRE)—Afdhaad (Nayef (USA)) **Sheikh Ahmed Al Maktoum**
60 B c 27/04 Mehmas (IRE)—Asmeen (IRE) (Shamardal (USA)) (27000) **Mr P Wildes & Mr C Fellowes**
61 B c 04/05 Gleneagles (IRE)—Bibury (Royal Applause) **Mr C. H. Huggan**
62 B c 09/03 Muhkadram—Carsulae (IRE) (Marju (IRE)) (17143) **Moore, Clark, Loftus, Jubb & Fellowes**
63 Br f 06/03 Sea The Stars (IRE)—Deveron (USA) (Cozzene (USA)) (200000) **Mr D. R. J. King**
64 B c 06/03 Australia—Hyper Dream (IRE) (Oasis Dream) (22000) **Dahab Racing**
65 B f 12/03 Dandy Man (IRE)—Kayak (Singspiel (IRE)) (221088)
66 B c 12/02 Le Havre (IRE)—Manaha (FR) (Elusive City (USA)) **Sheikh Ahmed Al Maktoum**
67 Ch f 05/02 Sea The Stars (IRE)—Nectar de Rose (FR) (Shamardal (USA)) (60000) **Mr P Hickman and Mr D King**
68 B f 19/04 Kodiac—Night Queen (IRE) (Rip Van Winkle (USA)) (80000) **Mr D. R. J. King**
69 Ch f 16/04 Sea The Stars (IRE)—Parade Militaire (IRE) (Peintre Celebre (USA)) (70000) **Dahab Racing**
70 **REFLEX (IRE),** gr c 13/02 El Kabeir (USA)—Knapton Hill (Zamindar (USA)) (38095) **Highclere - Ernest Rutherford**
71 B c 28/04 Ulysses (IRE)—Regal Heiress (Pivotal) (150000) **Mathis Stables LLC**
72 **ROYAL RAZZMATAZZ (IRE),** ch c 04/04 Tasleet—Royal Visit (IRE) (King's Best (USA)) (75000) **Mr A. C. Waney**
73 **SHAHBAZ (IRE),** b c 02/05 Free Eagle (IRE)—Middle Persia (Dalakhani (IRE)) (38095)
The Wolfpack and Partners Five

74 B c 18/02 Time Test—Speed Date (Sakhee's Secret) (55000) **Mathis Stables, J Soiza & C Fellowes**
75 STRENGTH N' HONOUR, b c 27/03 Showcasing—Wiener Valkyrie (Shamardal (USA)) **Car Colston Hall Stud**
76 SURREY NOIR (FR), b c 07/04 Dream Ahead (USA)—Model Black (IRE) (Trade Fair) (37415) **Surrey Racing SN**
77 B c 26/02 Sea The Stars (IRE)—Waldnah (New Approach (IRE)) (320000) **Mr P Hickman and Mr D King**
78 B c 04/03 Oasis Dream—Zahoo (IRE) (Nayef (USA)) **Sheikh Ahmed Al Maktoum**

Other Owners: M. L. Ayers, Mr Eric Buddle, Dahab Racing, Mr A. Darivas, Mr A. Dee, Mr C. H. Fellowes, Mrs E. M. Grundy, Mr P. J. Hickman, Mr R. S. Hoskins, Hot To Trot Racing 2, Mr G. Johns, Mr D. R. J. King, Mr D. S. Lee, L. Lillingston, D. S. Lovatt, Mathis Stables LLC, Mr S. Morjaria, Mr G. F. Smith-Bernal, Mr K. Sohi, Mr J. Soiza, Mr P. E. Wildes.

Flat Jockey: Stevie Donohoe.

---

186 MR JAMES FERGUSON, Newmarket

Postal: **Saville House Stables, St Mary's Square, Newmarket, Suffolk, CB8 0HZ**
Contacts: **WORK** 01638 599581 **MOBILE** 07826 889571
WORK EMAIL james@jamesfergusonracing.com

1 ACROSS THE NILE, 4, b f Iffraaj—Meeting Waters **The Saville House Syndicate**
2 CRYSTAL STARLET, 4, b f Frankel—Crystal Zvezda **Mr J. P. Ferguson**
3 DIDEROT, 4, br g Bated Breath—Modern Look **Owners Group 091**
4 FIRST FOLIO, 4, gr g Dark Angel (IRE)—Lilian Baylis (IRE) **Owners Group 083**
5 RIDGEWAY AVENUE (USA), 4, ch g Kitten's Joy (USA)—Trensa (USA) **Mr L. J. Williams**
6 U S S MICHIGAN (USA), 6, gr g War Front (USA)—Photograph (USA) **Mr L. J. Williams**

THREE-YEAR-OLDS

7 ALBERT BRIDGE, b c Iffraaj—Sloane Square
8 ARISTOBULUS, b c Adaay (IRE)—Salome (FR)
9 AUTUMN (IRE), gr f Bated Breath—Excellent View **Mr D. Redvers**
10 AXOPAR, ch c Helmet (AUS)—Bella Dubai (USA) **Mr I. Nagem**
11 CARAFFINI (IRE), b br c Lope de Vega (IRE)—Hukamaa **Mr J. P. Ferguson**
12 CITY OF LIFE, b g Cityscape—Sign of Life **Mrs D. M. Swinburn**
13 DEAUVILLE LEGEND (IRE), b g Sea The Stars (IRE)—Soho Rose (IRE) **Mr K. K. B. Ho**
14 EL BODEGON (IRE), b c Kodiac—Al Andalyya (USA) **Nas Syndicate & A. F. O'Callaghan**
15 HARBOUR BRIDGE, b c Australia—Sweet Dream **Morea Partnership**
16 INVINCIBLE KING (IRE), b g Invincible Spirit (IRE)—Lulawin **Mrs S. M. Roy**
17 MISE EN SCENE, b f Siyouni (FR)—Gadfly **Qatar Racing Limited**
18 MUSIC BANNER (IRE), ch g Starspangledbanner (AUS)—Jazz Cat (IRE)
19 NEWTON DANCER (IRE), ch g Frankel—Ventura (IRE) **Nas Syndicate & Partners**
20 OCEANIA LEGEND (IRE), ch g Australia—Ame Bleue **Mr K. K. B. Ho**
21 STATE LEGEND (IRE), b c Churchill (IRE)—Zibeling (IRE) **Mr K. K. B. Ho**
22 THE WRITER, ch g Ulysses (IRE)—Arwaah (IRE) **Quantum Leap Racing Viii & Partner**
23 VIADELAMORE (IRE), b g Invincible Spirit (IRE)—Love Street (USA) **Nas Syndicate**
24 WINEGLASS BAY (IRE), b g New Bay—Lady Penko (FR) **Nas Syndicate & Ballylinch Stud**

TWO-YEAR-OLDS

25 B c 22/02 Tamayuz—Alors Quoi (IRE) (Siyouni (FR)) (130000) **Nas Syndicate, M Buckley & Mrs A M Hayes**
26 BEAUTIFUL SUNRISE (IRE), b c 02/03 Exceed And Excel (AUS)—Spanish Fly (IRE) (Iffraaj) (50000) **Mr S. Siddiqui**
27 CHEALAMY, br f 29/03 Siyouni (FR)—Carnachy (IRE) (Mastercraftsman (IRE))
28 B f 27/02 Lightning Spear—Dainty's Daughter (Cape Cross (IRE)) (17000)
29 B c 12/02 Roaring Lion (USA)—Dubara (Dubawi (IRE)) **Qatar Racing Limited**
30 B c 24/02 Sea The Stars (IRE)—Fondly (Dansili) (52000) **NAS Syndicate II**
31 B c 20/03 Roaring Lion (USA)—Gertrude Versed (Manduro (GER)) (30476) **Qatar Racing Limited**
32 B f 28/03 Teofilo (IRE)—Hadeeqa (IRE) (Cape Cross (IRE)) (25510)
33 B c 21/02 Dark Angel (IRE)—Hay Chewed (IRE) (Camacho) (110000) **Nas Syndicate Ii & Partners**
34 B f 26/04 Kingman—Hundi (Fastnet Rock (AUS)) (60000)
35 B c 15/03 Australia—Imalwayshotforyou (USA) (Discreetly Mine (USA)) (34014) **Mr K. K. B. Ho**
36 LADY CHAPEL (IRE), b f 27/03 Dandy Man (IRE)—Sistine (Dubai Destination (USA))
37 Ch c 26/03 Galileo (IRE)—Landikusic (IRE) (Dansili) (85034) **Mr K. K. B. Ho**

MR JAMES FERGUSON - continued

38 **LIKE A TIGER,** ch c 17/02 Farhh—Last Tango Inparis (Aqlaam) (50000) **Nas Syndicate Ii, Castledown & L Lynam**
39 Gr c 16/03 Roaring Lion (USA)—Mutatis Mutandis (IRE) (Mastercraftsman (IRE)) (95000) **Qatar Racing Limited**
40 **OUTWARD BOUND,** b f 26/02 Outstrip—Shamara (IRE) (Spectrum (IRE)) (2500)
41 B c 08/03 Zoustar (AUS)—Peach Melba (Dream Ahead (USA)) **Qatar Racing Limited**
42 Gr c 27/04 Dark Angel (IRE)—Prontamente (More Than Ready (USA)) (57000)
43 **ROARING LEGEND (FR),** gr ro c 04/04 Roaring Lion (USA)—Amarysia (FR) (Medicean) (93537) **Mr K. K. B. Ho**
44 Ch c 24/04 Australia—Rocana (Fastnet Rock (AUS)) (35000) **Mr K. K. B. Ho**
45 B f 08/04 Bungle Inthejungle—Scarlet Wings (Sir Percy) (15000) **Hasmonean Racing & Mr A Chapman**
46 B f 27/05 Starspangledbanner (AUS)—Short Affair (Singspiel (IRE)) (44000)
47 B f 12/04 Fastnet Rock (AUS)—Stars At Night (IRE) (Galileo (IRE)) (150000) **NAS Syndicate II**
48 B c 10/04 Dark Angel (IRE)—Todegica (Giant's Causeway (USA)) (37000)
49 B f 11/02 Galileo Gold—Victoria Montoya (High Chaparral (IRE)) (40000)

Head Girl: Aideen Marshall. **Travelling Head:** Alyson West.

 ## MR DOMINIC FFRENCH DAVIS, Lambourn
Postal: **College House, 3 Oxford Street, Lambourn, Hungerford, Berkshire, RG17 8XP**
Contacts: **HOME 01488 72342 PHONE 01488 73675 MOBILE 07831 118764 FAX 01488 73675**
EMAIL ffrenchdavis@btinternet.com **WEBSITE** www.ffrenchdavis.com

1 **BOY GEORGE,** 5, b g Equiano (FR)—If I Were A Boy (IRE) **Mr R. F. Haynes**
2 **BRECKLAND,** 4, ch g Helmet (AUS)—Cherry Orchard (IRE) **Stapleford Racing Ltd**
3 **BRICKLAGGER (IRE),** 7, ch g Frozen Power (IRE)—Annaofcompton (IRE) **D. J. S. Ffrench Davis**
4 **CALL MY BLUFF (IRE),** 5, b g Make Believe—Ocean Bluff (IRE) **The Ffrench Connection**
5 **CAPONE (GER),** 7, br g Nathaniel (IRE)—Codera (GER) **D. J. S. Ffrench Davis**
6 **EGYPSYAN CRACKAJAK,** 5, b g Kutub (IRE)—Three Scoops **G. King Haulage Ltd**
7 **HEATON CHAPEL (IRE),** 5, b g Requinto (IRE)—Coastal Storm **Mr T. Gibbons**
8 4, B f Haafhd—If I Were A Boy (IRE) **Mr R. F. Haynes**
9 **IVILNOBLE (IRE),** 9, b g Alfred Nobel (IRE)—Almutamore (IRE) **D. J. S. Ffrench Davis**
10 **JAMES PARK WOODS (IRE),** 6, b g Australia—Happy Holly (IRE) **Philip Banfield & Dominic Ffrench Davis**
11 **ROCK AND BEL (FR),** 9, b g Laverock (IRE)—Belmiesque (FR) **D. J. S. Ffrench Davis**

THREE-YEAR-OLDS

12 **EGYPSYAN CRACKELLI,** b c Sixties Icon—Three Scoops **G. King Haulage Ltd**
13 **PULL THE LEVER (IRE),** b c Tagula (IRE)—Hi Milady (IRE) **Drop the Flag**

TWO-YEAR-OLDS

14 **CHERRYHAWK,** ch f 22/02 Hawkbill (USA)—Cherry Orchard (IRE) (King's Best (USA)) **Stapleford Racing Ltd**
15 Ch f 11/03 Lightning Spear—Ellen Gates (Mayson)
16 Ch c 16/04 Ulysses (IRE)—Eyeshine (Dubawi (IRE)) (35000) **The Agincourt Partnership**
17 **J J STINGLETON,** ch c 17/04 Washington DC (IRE)—Bee Ina Bonnet (Helmet (AUS)) (16000) **Ffrench Polish**
18 B c 12/03 National Defense—Thanks (IRE) (Kheleyf (USA)) (31000)

Assistant Trainer: Ben Ffrench Davis.

188 MR GUISEPPE FIERRO, Hednesford
Postal: **Brook House, Rawnsley Road, Hednesford, Cannock, Staffordshire, WS12 1RB**
Contacts: **PHONE 01543 879611 MOBILE 07976 321468**

1 5, B g Multiplex—Eternal Legacy (IRE) **G. Fierro**
2 **JUST LIKE BETH,** 14, b m Proclamation (IRE)—Just Beth **G. Fierro**
3 **LAFILIA (GER),** 7, b m Teofilo (IRE)—Labrice **G. Fierro**
4 **LITTLE DOTTY,** 13, br m Erhaab (USA)—Marsh Marigold **G. Fierro**
5 **RAMBLING RIVER,** 11, b g Revoque (IRE)—Just Beth **G. Fierro**
6 **SUNDANCE BOY,** 13, gr g Proclamation (IRE)—Just Beth **G. Fierro**
7 5, Gr g Geordieland (FR)—Woodland Retreat

Assistant Trainer: M Fierro.

189 MR JOHN FLINT, Bridgend
Postal: **Woodland Lodge, Waunbant Road, Kenfig Hill, Bridgend, Mid Glamorgan, CF33 6FF**
Contacts: **MOBILE 07581 428173 FAX 01656 744347**
EMAIL johnflint900@gmail.com WEBSITE www.johnflintracing.com

1 **AMATEUR (IRE),** 9, ch g Giant's Causeway (USA)—Adja (IRE) **Burnham Plastering & Drylining Ltd**
2 **BLAZE A TRAIL (IRE),** 8, b g Morozov (USA)—Bright Blaze (IRE) **Belly's Heroes**
3 **CANFORD STAR (IRE),** 9, b m Canford Cliffs (IRE)—Alexander Alliance (IRE) **Mrs S. M. Farr**
4 **CARP KID (IRE),** 7, b g Lope de Vega (IRE)—Homegrown (IRE) **JACK Racing**
5 **CHEEKY AZ,** 4, b g Teofilo (IRE)—Azma (USA)
6 **EDDIEMAURICE (IRE),** 11, ch g Captain Rio—Annals **Mr D. M. Mathias**
7 **GIBRALTARIAN (IRE),** 6, b m War Command (USA)—Star of Gibraltar **Mr D. A. Poole**
8 **GRAVITY WAVE (IRE),** 8, br g Rip Van Winkle (IRE)—Phrase **J. L. Flint**
9 **ISLA DI MILANO (IRE),** 11, b g Milan—Monagee Island (IRE) **Mr J. M. H. Hearne**
10 **ITSALLABOUTLUCK (IRE),** 5, b g Kodiac—Lucky (IRE) **E. R. Clough**
11 **LILANDRA (FR),** 5, b m Equiano (FR)—Indigo River (IRE) **Katchar Racing**
12 **LOVE AND BE LOVED,** 8, b m Lawman (FR)—Rightside **J. L. Flint**
13 **LYNDON B (IRE),** 6, b g Charm Spirit (IRE)—Kelsey Rose **P.DuffyD.SemmensVWilliamsRHarperMLoveday**
14 **MARTY BYRDE,** 5, b g Blue Bresil (FR)—Dancing Emily (IRE) **Burnham Plastering & Drylining Ltd**
15 **OUTER SPACE,** 11, b g Acclamation—Venoge (IRE) **Mr D. A. Poole**
16 **RIVAL,** 4, b g Iffraaj—Pamona (IRE)
17 **SISTER RAPHAEL (IRE),** 6, b m Ask—Sunny South East (IRE) **J. L. Flint**
18 **THE WIRE FLYER,** 7, b g Champs Elysees—Good Morning Star (IRE) **Aled Evans & Tommy Williams**
19 **TIME INTERVAL,** 4, b g Adaay (IRE)—Kuriosa (IRE)
20 **TWIGGYS PRIDE,** 6, b g Monsieur Bond (IRE)—Sea Crest **Aled Evans/lynn Evans/ Tommy Williams**
21 **WINKLEMANN (IRE),** 10, br g Rip Van Winkle (IRE)—Kykuit (IRE) **J. L. Flint**
22 **WITH PLEASURE,** 9, b g Poet's Voice—With Fascination (USA) **J. L. Flint**

Assistant Trainer: Mrs Martine Louise Flint, Rhys Flint.

190 MR DAVID FLOOD, Swindon
Postal: **15 High Street, Chiseldon, Swindon, Wiltshire, SN4 0NG**
Contacts: PHONE **07919 340619**
EMAIL **davidflood1@hotmail.co.uk**

1 **DUSK CHORUS (FR)**, 4, b f War Command (USA)—Diamond Light (USA) **Hildare Stud Farm**
2 **GLENCOE BOY (IRE)**, 5, b g Gleneagles (IRE)—Eastern Appeal (IRE) **Mrs A. Cowley**
3 **KENDERGARTEN KOP (IRE)**, 7, ch g Kendargent (FR)—Elsa T (IRE) **Royal Wootton Bassett Racing Limited**
4 **PEDESTAL (IRE)**, 8, b g Invincible Spirit (IRE)—Ashley Hall (USA) **Mrs A. Cowley**

191 MR TONY FORBES, Uttoxeter
Postal: **Hill House Farm, Poppits Lane, Stramshall, Uttoxeter, Staffordshire, ST14 5EX**
Contacts: PHONE **01889 562722** MOBILE **07967 246571**
EMAIL **tony@thimble.net**

1 **CHEF DE TROUPE (FR)**, 9, b g Air Chief Marshal (IRE)—Tazminya **Mr A. L. Forbes**
2 **FLEURSALS**, 6, b m Poet's Voice—Entitlement **Mr A. L. Forbes**
3 **SWEET DIME**, 6, b br m Toronado (IRE)—Rainbow's Edge **Mr A. L. Forbes**

Assistant Trainer: Mr Tim Eley.

192 MRS RICHENDA FORD, Blandford Forum
Postal: **Garlands Farm, The Common, Okeford Fitzpaine, Blandford Forum, Dorset, DT11 0RT**
Contacts: MOBILE **07800 634846**
WORK EMAIL **Richendafordracing@gmail.com** WEBSITE **www.richendafordracing.co.uk** FACEBOOK
RichendaFordRacing INSTAGRAM **RichendaFordRacing**

1 **DON'T SAY NEVER (FR)**, 7, b g No Risk At All (FR)—Sleeping Jane (FR) **Richenda Ford Racing Club**
2 **DONT BE ROBIN (IRE)**, 10, b g Robin des Pres (FR)—Rainbow Times (IRE) **Mr & Mrs K. B. Snook**
3 **FLAMENCO DE KERSER (FR)**, 7, b g Vendangeur (IRE)—Nouba de Kerser (FR)
   Sturminster Newton Building Supplies Ltd
4 **HENZO DES BOULLATS (FR)**, 5, b g Saddler Maker (IRE)—Becky des Boulats (FR) **Mr & Mrs K. B. Snook**
5 **LEAVE MY ALONE (IRE)**, 9, br m Getaway (GER)—Glenda King (IRE) **Mr & Mrs K. B. Snook**
6 **MASTER MIKEY DEE (IRE)**, 7, b g Fame And Glory—Miss Lauren Dee (IRE) **Mr & Mrs K. B. Snook**
7 **MR P (IRE)**, 7, br g Malinas (GER)—La Belle Sauvage **Mr C. Pistaszczuk**
8 **NOAH'S LIGHT (IRE)**, 5, b g Leading Light (IRE)—Scrapper Jack (IRE)
9 **O'FAOLAINS LAD (IRE)**, 8, b g Oscar (IRE)—O'Faolains Fancy (IRE) **Lloyd Builders Investments Ltd**
10 **SHANROE SMOOCH (IRE)**, 9, b g Ask—Lady Quesada (IRE) **Mr & Mrs K. B. Snook**
11 5, B m Pether's Moon (IRE)—Sovereignsflagship (IRE) **Mr & Mrs K. B. Snook**

193 MISS SANDY FORSTER, Kelso

Postal: **Halterburn Head, Yetholm, Kelso, Roxburghshire, TD5 8PP**
Contacts: **PHONE 01573 420615 MOBILE 07976 587315, 07880 727877 FAX 01573 420615**
EMAIL clivestorey@btinternet.com

1 **ASHJAN**, 9, b g Medicean—Violet (IRE) **Dave Skeldon & Sandy Forster**
2 **BALLYTOBIN (IRE)**, 7, ch g Salutino (GER)—Restless Dreams (IRE) **Dave Skeldon & Sandy Forster**
3 **CHARLIE SNOW ANGEL**, 13, b g Overbury (IRE)—Sister Seven (IRE) **C. Storey**
4 **CLEAR WHITE LIGHT**, 6, b g Dubawi (IRE)—Dalkova **The cosy at home family and friends**
5 **DIVAS DOYEN (IRE)**, 5, b m Doyen (IRE)—Sleeping Diva (FR) **The Unlikely Tenors**
6 **DR SHIROCCO (IRE)**, 7, ch g Shirocco (GER)—Uncommited (IRE) **I I F T F**
7 **DUTY CALLS (IRE)**, 9, b g Arcadio (GER)—Inniskeen (IRE) **Dont Mind If We Do**
8 **FOG ON THE TYNE (IRE)**, 5, b m Malinas (GER)—Flaming Poncho (IRE) **The cosy at home family and friends**
9 **FORTCANYON (IRE)**, 6, b g Yeats (IRE)—Thegoodwans Sister (IRE) **Ms A. G. Long**
10 **GYPSEY'S SECRET (IRE)**, 7, b m Dylan Thomas (IRE)—Lady Howe **Mr M. H. Walton**
11 **KITTY FISHER (IRE)**, 12, b m Scorpion (IRE)—Luck of The Deise (IRE) **C. Storey**
12 **LASTIN' MEMORIES (IRE)**, 10, b g Overbury (IRE)—Dusky Dante (IRE) **Dave Skeldon & Sandy Forster**
13 **LISSEN TO THE LADY (IRE)**, 8, b m Fame And Glory—Liss Rua (IRE) **Mr M. H. Walton**
14 **MORNINGSIDE**, 9, b g Kayf Tara—Bouncing Bean **I I F T F**
15 **PIPERS CROSS (IRE)**, 5, b m Soldier of Fortune (IRE)—Oatfield Lady (IRE) **Mr M. H. Walton**
16 **STOWAWAY JOHN (IRE)**, 8, b g Stowaway—Figlette **Dave Skeldon & Clive Storey**

Other Owners: Miss S. E. Forster, Mr D. S. Oliver, Mrs M. A. H. Shanks, Mr D. A. Skeldon, C. Storey, Mrs I. H. Thomson.

Assistant Trainer: C. Storey.

Amateur Jockey: Miss J. Walton.

194 MISS JO FOSTER, Ilkley

Postal: **The Old Mistal, Brookleigh Farm, Burley Road, Menston, Ilkley, West Yorkshire, LS29 6NS**
Contacts: **PHONE 07980 301808 MOBILE 07980 301808**
EMAIL info@jofosterracing.co.uk WEBSITE www.jofosterracing.co.uk

1 **BALLYNAGRAN (IRE)**, 7, br g Imperial Monarch (IRE)—Fancyfacia (IRE) **The Yorkshire Racing Partnership**
2 **BIT ON THE SIDE (IRE)**, 7, b m Presenting—Tara Rose **Mr J. Nixon**
3 **CAIRNSHILL (IRE)**, 11, gr g Tikkanen (USA)—Ilikeyou (IRE) **The Yorkshire Racing Partnership**
4 **CHASE THE WIND (IRE)**, 13, ch g Spadoun (FR)—Asfreeasthewind (IRE) **Mr J. Nixon**
5 **DA VINCI HAND (IRE)**, 7, b g Champs Elysees—Thousandkissesdeep (IRE) **Mr J. Nixon**
6 **DILLARCHIE**, 5, b m Sulamani (IRE)—Cute N You Know It **J Saxby, M Simmons Partnership**
7 **ONE STEP TOO FAR (IRE)**, 5, br g Footstepsinthesand—High Society Girl (IRE) **SMASHBLOCK**
8 **SEAPOINT (IRE)**, 8, b m Footstepsinthesand—Genuinely (IRE) **Give It A Go Partners**
9 **SIGURD (GER)**, 10, ch g Sholokhov (GER)—Sky News (GER) **Mrs E. A. Verity**

Other Owners: Mr M. Collins, Miss J. E. Foster, Mr D. Liddle, Mrs C. Potter, Mr J. A. Saxby, Mr M. Simmons.

Assistant Trainer: P. Foster.

NH Jockey: Henry Brooke.

195 MR JIMMY FOX, Marlborough
Postal: **Highlands Farm Stables, Herridge, Collingbourne Ducis, Marlborough, Wiltshire, SN8 3EG**
Contacts: **PHONE 01264 850218, 07931 724358 MOBILE 07702 880010**
EMAIL jcfoxtrainer@aol.com

1 **DOYOUKNOWMYUNCLES**, 4, b f Proconsul—Elle Rebelle **SP9 RACING CLUB**
2 **GRACEFUL JAMES (IRE)**, 9, ch g Rock of Gibraltar (IRE)—Little Miss Gracie **Abacus Employment Services Ltd**
3 **GRACIOUS GEORGE (IRE)**, 12, b g Oratorio (IRE)—Little Miss Gracie **Highlands Farm Racing Partnership**
4 **LADY HOLLY**, 4, b f Sepoy (AUS)—Night Affair **SP9 RACING CLUB**
5 **MARCHETTI (IRE)**, 5, b m Camelot—Though (IRE) **Mr Y. T. Mehmet**
6 **PURPLE PADDY**, 7, b g Swiss Spirit—Stunning In Purple (IRE) **The Brazen Racing Club**
7 **PURPLE POPPY**, 4, b f Swiss Spirit—Stunning In Purple (IRE) **Mrs B. A. Fuller**
8 **THEY CALL ME PETE**, 4, b g Shirocco (GER)—Pectora (IRE) **Mrs S. J. Fox**
9 **TRIDEVI**, 4, b f Sepoy (AUS)—Female Spring **SP9 RACING CLUB**

THREE-YEAR-OLDS
10 **ALBUS ANNE**, b f Mayson—Asmahan **Miss F. L. Thomas**

Assistant Trainer: Sarah-Jane Fox.

196 MISS SUZZANNE FRANCE, Norton on Derwent
Postal: **Cheesecake Hill House, Highfield, Beverley Road,
Norton on Derwent, North Yorkshire, YO17 9PJ**
Contacts: **PHONE 07904 117531 MOBILE 07904 117531 FAX 01653 691947**
EMAIL suzzanne@newstartracing.co.uk
WEBSITE www.suzzannefranceracing.com, www.newstartracing.co.uk

1 **ARCHIVE (FR)**, 12, b g Sulamani (IRE)—Royale Dorothy (FR) **Newstart Partnership**
2 **BILLY DYLAN (IRE)**, 7, b g Exceleration (IRE)—It's True (IRE) **Newstart Partnership**
3 **STAND FREE**, 5, b m Helmet (AUS)—Ivory Silk **Miss Kate Dobb & Mr Stuart Dobb**

THREE-YEAR-OLDS
4 **KITTYBREWSTER**, br f Brazen Beau (AUS)—Ivory Silk **Miss Kate Dobb & Mr Stuart Dobb**

Assistant Trainer: Mr Aaron James.

197 MR DEREK FRANKLAND, Brackley
Postal: **Springfields, Mixbury, Brackley, Northamptonshire, NN13 5RR**
Contacts: **MOBILE 07763 020406 FAX 01280 847334**
EMAIL dsfrankland@aol.com

1 **CANNY TOM (IRE)**, 12, b g Jimble (FR)—Tombazaan (IRE) **Mr D. S. Frankland & Mr D. J. Trott**
2 **JOINT ACCOUNT (IRE)**, 9, b g Jimble (FR)—Late Back (IRE) **Mr D. S. Frankland & Mr D. J. Trott**

198 MR ALEX FRENCH, Newmarket
Postal: **Phantom House, Fordham Road, Newmarket, Suffolk, CB8 7AA**
Contacts: **PHONE 07776 306588**
EMAIL a.french@outlook.com

1 **BREATHLESSLY (IRE)**, 4, b f Bated Breath—Zainda (IRE) **Ms J. A. French**
2 **CHARMING BERRY (IRE)**, 4, gr g Charm Spirit—Frosty Berry **Ms J. A. French**
3 5, B g Casamento (IRE)—Devonelli (IRE) **Ms J. A. French**
4 **FLYING INSTRUCTOR (IRE)**, 4, b g Nayef (USA)—Devonelli (IRE) **Jam Tomorrow Partnership**
5 **KARATAYKA (IRE)**, 4, b f Dariyan (FR)—Karamaya (IRE)
6 **OUT OF SIGHT (IRE)**, 4, b g Outstrip—Bountiful Girl **Ms J. A. French**
7 4, Ch f Dutch Art—Spellcraft **Ms J. A. French**
8 **TEA GARDEN**, 4, ch f Helmet (AUS)—Tea Gown (IRE) **Ms J. A. French**
9 5, Ch g Farhh—Zainda (IRE) **Ms J. A. French**

THREE-YEAR-OLDS
10 Gr f Markaz (IRE)—Ariyfa (IRE) **Ms J. A. French**
11 B gr f New Bay—Frosty Berry **Ms J. A. French**
12 B g Muhaarar—Mu'ajiza **Ms J. A. French**
13 B g Dawn Approach (IRE)—Spellcraft **Ms J. A. French**
14 B g War Command (USA)—Zainda (IRE) **Ms J. A. French**

TWO-YEAR-OLDS
15 B f 17/03 Ulysses (IRE)—Cheerfilly (IRE) (Excelebration (IRE)) (14000)

199 MR JAMES FROST, Buckfastleigh
Postal: **Hawson Stables, Buckfastleigh, Devon, TQ11 0HP**
Contacts: **HOME 01364 642332 PHONE 01364 642267 MOBILE 07860 220229 FAX 01364 643182**
EMAIL info@frostracingclub.co.uk

1 **ANTIDOTE (IRE)**, 6, gr g Dark Angel (IRE)—Mood Indigo (IRE) **Frost Racing Club**
2 **BOGOSS DU PERRET (FR)**, 11, b br g Malinas (GER)—Lady Paques (FR) **Mrs J. Bury**
3 **DEMOTHI (IRE)**, 7, b g Le Fou (IRE)—Tuscarora (IRE) **Mr P. Tosh & Partner**
4 **FINDUSATGORCOMBE**, 10, b g Tobougg (IRE)—Seemma **Mr P. R. Meaden**
5 **FIREFLY LANE (IRE)**, 6, b m Milan—More Equity **Firefly Racing**
6 **FLASH GORCOMBE**, 5, b g Alqaahir (USA)—Seem of Gold **Mr P. R. Meaden**
7 **FOILLMORE (IRE)**, 7, gr g Carlotamix (FR)—Beale Native (IRE) **Frost Racing Club**
8 **GORCOMBE MOONSHINE**, 5, b g Alqaahir (USA)—Seemma **Mr P. R. Meaden**
9 **GORCOMBE'S RASCAL**, 9, b g Fantastic View (USA)—Seem of Gold **Mr P. R. Meaden**
10 **GRACEFULL DANCER**, 4, ch g Alqaahir (USA)—Miss Grace **4Racing Owners Club**
11 **LITTLE MISS ALICE**, 6, b m Alqaahir (USA)—Miss Grace **J. D. Frost**
12 4, B g Swiss Spirit—Love Is More **J. D. Frost**
13 **OTTER LYNN**, 7, b m Alqaahir (USA)—Definite Lynn (IRE) **Frost Racing Club**
14 **PRESGRAVE (IRE)**, 5, b g Camelot—Alamouna (IRE) **J. D. Frost**
15 **SAINTEMILION (FR)**, 9, b g Diamond Green (FR)—Matakana (FR) **J. D. Frost**
16 **THE CILLEENS (IRE)**, 7, ch m Le Fou (IRE)—Petite Mielle (IRE) **G. T. Chambers**
17 **TREACYS JIM (IRE)**, 8, b g Milan—Bridge Hotel Lilly (IRE) **Frost Racing Club**
18 **WHAT A BALOO (IRE)**, 7, b g Jeremy (USA)—Luca Lite (IRE) **Share My Dream**

Other Owners: Mr G. P. Budd, Mrs J. Bury, Mr E. A. Darke, J. D. Frost, Mr A. J. Shepherd, Mr P. M. Tosh.

Assistant Trainer: G. Frost.

NH Jockey: Bryony Frost.

200   MR KEVIN FROST, Newark

Postal: Hill Top Equestrian Centre, Danethorpe Lane, Danethorpe Hill, Newark, Nottinghamshire, NG24 2PD
Contacts: PHONE 07748 873092 MOBILE 07919 370081
EMAIL info@kevinfrostracing.co.uk WEBSITE www.kevinfrostracing.co.uk

1 **ATACAMA DESERT (IRE)**, 4, ch c Galileo (IRE)—Ikat (IRE) **Rocky Canzone Partnership**
2 **BEAGNACH SASTA (IRE)**, 4, b f Dawn Approach (IRE)—Sasamh (IRE) **Mrs A. Frost**
3 **BILLIEBROOKEDIT (IRE)**, 7, ch g Dragon Pulse (IRE)—Klang (IRE) **Mr Matthew & Mrs Rachael Gavin**
4 **CLONDAW SECRET (IRE)**, 7, b g Court Cave (IRE)—Secret Can't Say (IRE) **Mr K. Frost**
5 **DOCUMENTING**, 9, b g Zamindar (USA)—Namaskar **Kf Racing Club, Humphreys, Jones & Orr**
6 **FIFTYSHADESOFRED (FR)**, 4, b g Siyouni (FR)—Candinie (USA) **Mr D Orr & Mr M Humphreys**
7 **FRANCIS XAVIER (IRE)**, 8, b g High Chaparral (IRE)—Missionary Hymn (USA) **Curzon House Partnership**
8 **HART FELL**, 6, b g Nayef (USA)—Dumfriesshire **Total Asbestos Solutions Limiited**
9 **HELVETIAN**, 7, b g Swiss Spirit—Lucky Dip **Ms T. Keane**
10 **INFINITI (IRE)**, 9, b m Arcano (IRE)—Seraphina (IRE) **Total Asbestos Solutions Ltd & A Frost**
11 **MASTER OF COMBAT (IRE)**, 4, b g Invincible Spirit (IRE)—Sharja Queen **Law Abiding Citizens**
12 **MOTARAJJA (IRE)**, 4, b g Frankel—Rumoush (USA) **D & A Frost**
13 **O CONNELL STREET (IRE)**, 8, b g Fame And Glory—Victorine (IRE) **D & A Frost**
14 **OWENS LAD**, 4, b g Harbour Watch (IRE)—Dancing Primo **L. R. Owen**
15 **POSTER CHILD (IRE)**, 5, b m Fracas (IRE)—Rachida (IRE) **Mr K. Frost**
16 **STEAL THE SCENE (IRE)**, 10, b g Lord Shanakill (USA)—Namoos (USA) **Curzon House Partnership & Friends**
17 **THE THROSTLES**, 7, b g Poet's Voice—Stylish Dream (USA) **Kevin Frost Racing Club & Trisha Keane**
18 **THUNDER SUN (FR)**, 4, b g Siyouni (FR)—Bal de La Rose (IRE) **Mrs V. Kinder**
19 **VIENNA GIRL**, 4, b f Golden Horn—Bint Doyen **Mr K. Frost**
20 **WHITE MOCHA (USA)**, 7, ch g Lope de Vega (IRE)—Lastroseofsummer (IRE) **Curzon House Partnership**

THREE-YEAR-OLDS

21 **ELSHAAMEQ**, b c Awtaad (IRE)—Elraazy **Rocky Canzone Partnership**
22 **FERRO D'ORR (IRE)**, b g Dawn Approach (IRE)—Miss Cogent (IRE) **D & A Frost**
23 **MAFFEO BARBERINI (IRE)**, b c Caravaggio (USA)—Rain Goddess (IRE) **Mr K. Frost**
24 **SWIFT REMARK**, ch g Bated Breath—Kite Mark **P & K Frost**

TWO-YEAR-OLDS

25 B c 28/04 Estidhkaar (IRE)—Cathie's Dream (USA) (More Than Ready (USA)) **Mr K. Frost**
26 **SKINWALKER**, ch c 30/03 Lethal Force (IRE)—Xylophone (Medicean) (3810) **Mr K. Frost**

Other Owners: Curzon House Partnership, Mrs A. Frost, Mr K. Frost, Mr M. Gavin, Mrs R. Gavin, Mr M. A. Humphreys, Mr H. Jones, Miss J. Jones, Ms T. Keane, Mr D. Orr, Mr P. Swift, The Kevin Frost Racing Club, Total Asbestos Solutions Limiited.

201   MR HARRY FRY, Dorchester

Postal: Corscombe, Dorchester, Dorset, DT2 0PD
Contacts: WORK 01935 350330 PHONE 01935 350330
EMAIL info@harryfryracing.com WEBSITE www.harryfryracing.com

1 **ALTOBELLI (IRE)**, 4, b g Maxios—Atiana **C. C. Walker, Mr Johnny Craib**
2 **ASK ME EARLY (IRE)**, 8, gr g Ask—Cotton Ali (IRE) **The Dare Family**
3 **BEAT THE BAT (IRE)**, 4, b g Walk In The Park (IRE)—Dani Salamanca (IRE) **Twelfth Man Partnership 6**
4 **BEN BULBEN (IRE)**, 5, b g Yeats (IRE)—Mystic Masie (IRE) **Tom Chadney and More Friends**
5 **BOOTHILL (IRE)**, 7, b br g Presenting—Oyster Pipit (IRE) **Brian & Sandy Lambert**
6 **BURROWS TREAT (FR)**, 6, b m Muhtathir—La Vie de Boitron (FR) **Mr M. Stenning**
7 **CAPTAIN DRAKE (IRE)**, 9, b g Getaway (GER)—Julika (GER) **Gary Stevens & Brian & Sandy Lambert**
8 **CAPTURED MY HEART (FR)**, 6, br gr g Geordieland (FR)—Woodland Retreat **Ian & Claire Gosden**
9 **DEEPER BLUE (FR)**, 6, ch g Muhtathir—Divine Cayras (FR) **C. C. Walker**
10 **DUBROVNIK HARRY (IRE)**, 6, b g Yeats (IRE)—Kashmir Lady (FR) **Manhole Covers Ltd**

MR HARRY FRY - continued

11 5, B g Soldier of Fortune (IRE)—Fair Present (IRE)
12 FAIRY GEM (IRE), 6, b m Shantou (USA)—Mystic Masie (IRE) **Chasing Gold Limited**
13 FOREVER BLESSED (IRE), 4, b g Zoffany (IRE)—Yet Again **Thornton, Gibbs, Davies & Andrews**
14 FORTUNES MELODY, 5, b m Yorgunnabelucky (USA)—Fulgora **Mr Simon Munir & Mr Isaac Souede**
15 GAOT (FR), 6, b m Crillon (FR)—Truffe (FR) **Mr J. P. McManus**
16 GET BACK GET BACK (IRE), 7, b g Lord Shanakill (USA)—Bawaakeer (USA) **Get Back Get Back**
17 GIN COCO (FR), 6, b g Cokoriko (FR)—Qlementine (FR) **David's Partnership**
18 GOLD IN DOHA (FR), 6, b g Spanish Moon (USA)—Utah Bald (FR) **Brian & Sandy Lambert**
19 GOUDHURST STAR (IRE), 6, b g Yeats (IRE)—Baliya (IRE) **Nigel & Barbara Collison**
20 HAY THERE MONA (IRE), 5, b m Mustameet (USA)—Turf (FR) **Ms M. E. Hannaford**
21 HOT ROD LINCOLN (IRE), 6, b g Westerner—Flaming Annie (IRE)
22 HOW WILL I KNOW (IRE), 5, b g Ocovango—Balleen Rose (IRE) **Wait & See Partnership**
23 HURRICANE MITCH (IRE), 7, b g Shirocco (GER)—Miss Mitch (IRE) **Tom Chadney and Friends**
24 HYMAC (IRE), 6, b g Ask—Katie Cranny (IRE)
25 IF THE CAP FITS (IRE), 10, b g Milan—Derravaragh Sayra (IRE) **Mr Simon Munir & Mr Isaac Souede**
26 IMPERIAL ESPRIT (IRE), 8, b g Scorpion (IRE)—Shesourpresent (IRE) **Imperial Racing Partnership 2016**
27 KING ALEXANDER, 4, b g Mount Nelson—Pale Face (IRE) **Mr J. I. Neocleous**
28 LADY ADARE (IRE), 6, b m Sholokhov (IRE)—En Vedette (FR) **Dare & Dolan-Abrahams Families**
29 LAST OF A LEGEND, 5, b m Midnight Legend—Blue Buttons (IRE) **Hot To Trot Jumping**
30 LAUGHING BRAVE (FR), 5, b g Choeur du Nord (FR)—Laughing (FR) **The Eyre Family**
31 LIGHTLY SQUEEZE, 8, b g Poet's Voice—Zuleika Dobson **J Davies & Govier & Brown**
32 LITTERALE CI (FR), 9, b m Soldier of Fortune (IRE)—Cigalia **Mr J. P. McManus**
33 LORD RAVENSLEY (IRE), 4, b g Walk In The Park (IRE)—Fentara **Chasing Gold Limited**
34 LOVE ENVOI (IRE), 6, b m Westerner—Love Divided (IRE) **Noel Fehily Racing Syndicates Love Envoi**
35 MA BELLE NOIRE, 5, br m Soldier of Fortune (IRE)—Loxhill Lady **The Zoomers**
36 MASTER DEBONAIR, 8, br g Yeats (IRE)—Swincombe Flame **The Gosden Mob**
37 METIER (IRE), 6, b g Mastercraftsman (IRE)—We'll Go Walking (IRE) **G. C. Stevens**
38 MIGHT I (IRE), 6, b g Fame And Glory—Our Honey (IRE) **Brian & Sandy Lambert**
39 MILLBANK FLYER (IRE), 7, b g Milan—The Last Bank (IRE) **Somerset Racing**
40 MILLE SUSSURRI (IRE), 7, b g Milan—Silent Whisper (IRE) **The Jago Family Partnership**
41 MOMELLA (IRE), 10, ch m Sholokhov (IRE)—Missing Link (IRE) **Holt, Clark, Macnabb, Nugent & Robinson**
42 MUY BIEN (IRE), 6, b g Cloudings (IRE)—Sari Rose (FR) **Peter Dawes & Nick Pitcher**
43 ON MY COMMAND (IRE), 6, b m War Command (USA)—Highindi **Mr J. I. Neocleous**
44 OUR SURPRISE (IRE), 7, b br g Jeremy (USA)—Cadia's Lady (IRE) **Mr Simon Munir & Mr Isaac Souede**
45 PHOENIX WAY (IRE), 9, b g Stowaway—Arcuate **Mr J. P. McManus**
46 PICNIC IN THE PARK, 5, b m Walk In The Park (IRE)—Cherry Pie (FR) **Exors of the Late Mr T. J. Hemmings**
47 PIRATE MOON, 5, b g Pether's Moon (IRE)—Celestial Island **Mrs C. Fry**
48 POGO I AM, 8, b m Passing Glance—Orbital Orchid **Sandie & David Newton**
49 PURE BLISS, 7, ch m Mount Nelson—Burton Ash **Jago & Allhusen**
50 REE OKKA, 6, b g Getaway (GER)—Presentea (IRE) **The Jago Family Partnership**
51 REVELS HILL (IRE), 7, b g Mahler—Chlolo Supreme (IRE) **Noel Fehily Racing Syndicates-Revels Hil**
52 SAN GIOVANNI (IRE), 6, b g Milan—Down By The Sea (IRE) **GDM Partnership**
53 SECRET PROPHET (IRE), 5, b g Lucky Speed (IRE)—Grangeclare Rhythm (IRE)
Holt,Macnabb,Taylor,Clark,Nugent,Peters
54 SIR IVAN, 12, b g Midnight Legend—Tisho **The Eyre Family**
55 SONG OF THE HUNTER (FR), 8, gr g Network (GER)—Kittewhistle (FR) **Manhole Covers Ltd**
56 THE SCIENTIST (FR), 5, gr g Al Namix (FR)—Lady of Good Hope (FR) **Somerset Racing**
57 WALK ON HIGH, 5, b g Walk In The Park (IRE)—Highland Retreat **The Highland Walkers**
58 WHISKY EXPRESS, 6, ch m Imperial Monarch (IRE)—Loxhill Lady **Lorna Squire, R Metherell, D German**
59 WHITE HART LADY (IRE), 8, b m Doyen (IRE)—Hats And Heels (IRE) **Chasing Gold Limited**
60 WHITEHOTCHILLIFILI (IRE), 8, b m Milan—Mhuire Na Gale (IRE) **Chasing Gold Limited**
61 WINNINGSEVERYTHING (IRE), 8, b g Flemensfirth (USA)—Baliya (IRE) **Jago & Allhusen**
62 WINTERWATCH (GER), 4, b g Lord of England (GER)—Wildlife Lodge (GER) **Dolan-Abrahams, Jago & Allhusen.**

THREE-YEAR-OLDS

63 B f Yeats (IRE)—Miss McGoldrick (IRE)

MR HARRY FRY - continued

Other Owners: Mr N. C. Allhusen, Mr P. Andrews, G. S. Brown, Mrs S. Cameron, Mr D. Charlesworth, G. Charlesworth, Mr C. N. Clark, Mrs B. Collison, Mr N. Collison, Mr N. Collison, Mr J. M. Dare, Mrs J. M. Dare, Mr J. Davies, Mr P. L. Dawes, Viscountess S. J. Dilhorne, Mr E. J. Dolan-Abrahams, Mrs P. E. Dolan-Abrahams, Mr A. L. Ellison, Mrs C. A. Eyre, Mr C. G. S. Eyre, Mr H. Eyre, & Families, Mrs C. Fry, Dr C. E. Fry, Mr D. S. J. German, Mr R. Gibbs, Mrs D. J. Goodall, Mrs E. C. Gosden, Mr I. F. Gosden, Mr P. Govier, Mr P. F. Govier, Govier & Brown, Mr A. Holt, Mr F. C. A. Jago, Mrs J. L. Jago, Miss M. L. A. Jago, Mr P. J. A. Jago, Mr I. N. Kingham, Mr B. Lambert, Mr J. Lloyd-Townshend, Mr I. Macnabb, Mr J. D. Mayo, Mr T. F. McGowan, R. J. Metherell, S. E. Munir, Mr D. Newton, Mrs J. S. Newton, Mr J. O. Nugent, Mr D. G. Peters, Mr N. C. Pitcher, Mr J. D. Robinson, Mr M. L. Sharp, Mr M. Smith, Mr I. Souede, SprayClad UK, Mrs L. Squire, G. C. Stevens, Mr A. Taylor, The Gosden Mob, Mr G. M. Thornton, Mr J. P. G. Turner, Mr J. D. Wallen, Mrs R. E. Young.

Assistant Trainer: Ciara Fry.

NH Jockey: Sean Bowen. **Conditional Jockey:** Lorcan Murtagh. **Amateur Jockey:** Miss A. B. O'Connor.

202	**MS CAROLINE FRYER, Wymondham**

Postal: **Browick Hall Cottage, Browick Road, Wymondham, Norfolk, NR18 9RB**
Contacts: **PHONE 07768 056076 MOBILE 07768 056076**
EMAIL caroline@carolinefryerracing.co.uk, c.fryer528@btinternet.com
WEBSITE www.carolinefryerracing.co.uk

1 **GOODNIGHT CHARLIE,** 12, gr m Midnight Legend—Over To Charlie **Miss C. Fryer**
2 **MANOFTHEMOMENT (IRE),** 8, b g Jeremy (USA)—Endless Ambition (IRE) **Miss C. Fryer**
3 **RATOUTE YUTTY,** 9, b m Midnight Legend—Easibrook Jane **C J Underwood & Caroline Fryer**
4 **TIME PLEASE,** 5, b g Millenary—Saffron's Song (IRE) **Miss C. Fryer**

Other Owners: Miss C. Fryer, C. J. Underwood.

203	**MRS CHARLOTTE FULLER, Penwood**

Postal: **Penwood Grange, Penwood, Newbury, Berkshire, RG20 9EW**
Contacts: **PHONE 01635 250658 MOBILE 07775 713107**
EMAIL charlotte.fuller@me.com

1 **ARVIKA ROYAL,** 6, b m Arvico (FR)—Tamara King (IRE)
2 **SKANDIBURG (FR),** 8, b g Sageburg (IRE)—Skandia (FR) **R. H. F. Fuller**
3 **WINTER HOLIDAY,** 8, b m Dubai Destination (USA)—Tamara King (IRE) **Mr & Mrs R. H. F. Fuller**

204	**MR IVAN FURTADO, Newark**

Postal: **The Old Stables, Averham Park Farm, Averham, Newark, Nottinghamshire, NG23 5RU**
Contacts: **MOBILE 07783 520746**
EMAIL ivan.furtado@hotmail.co.uk

1 **ATYAAF,** 7, b g Invincible Spirit (IRE)—Eshaadeh (USA) **GB Civil Engineering (Leicester) LTD**
2 **BALQAA,** 4, b f Cable Bay (IRE)—Angels Wings (IRE) **J. C. Fretwell**
3 **BRISTOL HILL (IRE),** 4, b g New Bay—Bristol Bay (IRE) **J. C. Fretwell**

MR IVAN FURTADO - continued

4 **BYFORD (FR)**, 5, b g Toronado (IRE)—Verba (FR) **Mr C. Hodgson**
5 **CAPTAIN ST LUCIFER**, 5, b g Casamento (IRE)—Delaware Dancer (IRE) **Stuart Dobb & Kate Dobb**
6 **CERULEAN (FR)**, 4, b g Siyouni (FR)—Fugitive Angel (USA) **The Cerulean Partnership**
7 **CHANTREYS**, 5, gr ro m Mayson—Raajis (IRE) **The Giggle Factor Partnership**
8 **CHIPIRON (FR)**, 6, ch g Rio de la Plata (USA)—Chicago May (FR) **Mr D. Croot**
9 **CRAZY SPIN**, 6, b m Epaulette (AUS)—George's Gift
10 **DARK ZEAS (IRE)**, 4, b g Dark Angel (IRE)—Carallia (IRE) **AR Racing**
11 **DESERT EMPEROR**, 5, b g Camelot—Praia (GER) **J. L. Marriott**
12 **EAGLEWAY (FR)**, 6, b g Sakhee's Secret—Tearsforjoy (USA) **J. L. Marriott**
13 **ELEVEN ELEVEN (FR)**, 4, b g Olympic Glory (IRE)—Pretty Panther (FR) **The Giggle Factor Partnership**
14 **GIORGIO VASARI (FR)**, 4, b g Air Force Blue (USA)—Dream The Blues (IRE) **333racing**
15 **HEALING POWER**, 6, b g Kodiac—Loch Ma Naire (IRE) **Mr D. Croot**
16 **HECTOR'S HERE**, 6, b g Cityscape—L'Addition **The Giggle Factor Partnership**
17 **I'M GRATEFUL**, 4, b g Assertive—Tanning **Mr E. P. Spain**
18 **JUNGLE SPEED (FR)**, 6, b g Bungle Inthejungle—Velvet Revolver (IRE) **J. L. Marriott**
19 **KENYX (FR)**, 5, b g Kendargent (FR)—Onyx (FR) **Mr G. White**
20 **KOOLA BUALA (IRE)**, 5, ch m Raven's Pass (USA)—Naizah (IRE) **Mr P. Tait**
21 **LAST DATE**, 5, br g Music Master—Tanning **Mr E. P. Spain**
22 **LEDNIKOV**, 4, b g Footstepsinthesand—Ledena
23 **LEGAL REFORM (IRE)**, 5, b g Lawman (FR)—Amhrasach (IRE) **GB Civil Engineering (Leicester) LTD**
24 **LIBBY AMI (IRE)**, 4, b f The Gurkha (IRE)—Moore's Melody (IRE) **S & R Racing Partnership**
25 **LINCOLN GAMBLE**, 5, gr g Zebedee—Lincolnrose (IRE) **G.P.S. Heart of Racing (Bloodstock) Ltd**
26 **MATCHLESS (IRE)**, 4, b g Galileo (IRE)—Bye Bye Birdie (IRE) **J. L. Marriott**
27 **MUTARAAFEQ (IRE)**, 4, b g Estidhkaar (IRE)—Cumbfree (IRE) **J. C. Fretwell**
28 **NOBLE DAWN (GER)**, 5, ch m Dawn Approach (IRE)—Neuquen (IRE) **J. L. Marriott**
29 **ROCKET ACTION**, 6, gr g Toronado (IRE)—Winning Express (IRE) **Mr D. Croot**
30 **SHARIB (IRE)**, 4, b g Invincible Spirit (IRE)—Thamarat **21st Century Racing & The Giggle Factor**
31 **STARTER FOR TEN**, 5, b g Bated Breath—Scariff Hornet (IRE) **21st Century Racing & The Giggle Factor**
32 **STRAITOUTTACOMPTON**, 4, b g Compton Place—Red Mischief (IRE) **Golden Equinox Racing**
33 **TESTON**, 7, ch g Rio de la Plata (USA)—Tianshan (FR) **Daniel MacAuliffe & Anoj Don**
34 **THE NAIL GUNNER (IRE)**, 4, b g Tough As Nails (IRE)—Remediate (USA) **Mr W. P. Flynn**
35 **TOM MIX**, 4, ch g Sepoy (AUS)—Golden Dirham **Mrs S Nicholls Mrs R J Mitchell**
36 **TREVOLLI**, 4, b g Outstrip—Petit A Petit (IRE) **AR Racing**
37 **WALLAROO (IRE)**, 4, b g Australia—Dancequest (IRE) **Mr C. Hodgson**

THREE-YEAR-OLDS

38 **CRAZY MAISIE (IRE)**, b f Belardo (IRE)—Circleofinfluence (USA)
    Mr N. P. Sennett, Mr J. R. Holt, The Giggle Factor Partnership, Mr G. White, Gary White & the Giggle Factor
39 **DARK ENCHANTMENT (IRE)**, br f Vadamos (FR)—Listen Alexander (IRE)
40 **DOWN TO THE KID (IRE)**, ch g Pride of Dubai (AUS)—Classic Lass
41 **DUTCH LACE**, b f Garswood—Tiptree Lace **N & Factor**
42 **FAIRY FOOTPRINTS**, b f Free Eagle (IRE)—Maggie Lou (IRE) **The Giggle Factor Partnership**
43 **FRUSTRATING**, b g Ardad (IRE)—Miss Villefranche **J. C. Fretwell**
44 **GREY BELLE (FR)**, gr f Johnny Barnes (IRE)—Coldgirl (FR) **Daniel MacAuliffe & Anoj Don**
45 **KIRITIMATI ISLAND**, b gr g Lethal Force (IRE)—Camposanto **Civil & Giggle Factor**
46 **KODIACLAIM**, b f Aclaim (IRE)—Gumhrear (IRE) **Mr P. L. Coe**
47 **LIZZIE JEAN**, b f Nathaniel (IRE)—Mensoora (SAF) **Civil & Giggle Factor**
48 **MAD ARTYMAISE (IRE)**, ch f Dandy Man (IRE)—El Mirage (IRE) **Smith, White G Wood**
49 **MADAME MARMALADE**, b f Fountain of Youth (IRE)—Cuppatee (IRE) **Mr A. H. Proenca**
50 **PARACELSUS (IRE)**, b g Muhaarar—Peloponnese (FR) **Mr C. Hodgson**
51 Gr f Territories (IRE)—Raajis (IRE) **The Giggle Factor Partnership**
52 **ROARING ROSA (IRE)**, b f Buratino (IRE)—Heart's Desire (IRE) **Civil & Giggle Factor**
53 **RUMOURMONGER (IRE)**, ch f Galileo Gold—Village Gossip (IRE) **Alchemy Bloodstock**
54 **TICKETS**, b c Aclaim (IRE)—Czarna Roza **J. C. Fretwell**
55 **VIEGO (IRE)**, b f Charm Spirit (IRE)—Riptide Wave (IRE) **The Giggle Factor Partnership**

TWO-YEAR-OLDS

56 B f 25/03 Muhaarar—Adjudicate (Dansili) (10000)
57 B f 03/02 Raven's Pass (USA)—Margie (IRE) (Marju (IRE)) (6000) **The Giggle Factor Partnership**

MR IVAN FURTADO - continued

58 Gr c 12/02 Zoffany (IRE)—Modern Love (IRE) (Dark Angel (IRE)) (12000)
59 B f 09/05 Fast Company (IRE)—Pearlitas Passion (IRE) (High Chaparral (IRE)) (18095)
60 PERDIKA, b f 03/03 Unfortunately (IRE)—Golden Dirham (Kheleyf (USA))
61 B c 30/01 Cracksman—Rajar (Archipenko (USA)) (9524) **Mr G. White**
62 RAVANELLI (IRE), gr c 15/03 Dark Angel (IRE)—Sacred Aspect (IRE) (Haatef (USA)) **Mr G. White**
63 B c 25/02 Kodiac—Stage Name (Famous Name) (30000) **J. L. Marriott**
64 Ch c 01/01 Profitable (IRE)—Tantivy (USA) (Giant's Causeway (USA)) (20408) **Daniel MacAuliffe & Anoj Don**

Other Owners: 21st Century Racing, A. W. Catterall, Mrs B. Catterall, Mr A. R. Culumbarapitiyage Don, Miss K. M. Dobb, Mr S. Dobb, Civil & Giggle Factor, Mr S. Furniss, GB Civil Engineering (Leicester) LTD, Mr J. R. Holt, Mr D. P. MacAuliffe, Daniel MacAuliffe & Anoj Don, Mr R. Maddocks, Mrs R. J. Mitchell, Mrs S. E. Nicholls, Mr N. P Sennett, Mr D. Smith, The Giggle Factor Partnership, Mrs N. J. Welby, Mr G. White, Mr G. D. Wood.

205	**MR JOHN GALLAGHER, Moreton-In-Marsh** Postal: **Grove Farm, Chastleton, Moreton-In-Marsh, Gloucestershire, GL56 0SZ** Contacts: **PHONE** 01608 674492 **MOBILE** 07780 972663 **EMAIL** gallagherracing@phonecoop.coop **WEBSITE** www.gallagherracing.com

1 BATCHELOR BOY (IRE), 5, ch g Footstepsinthesand—Kathoe (IRE) **C. R. Marks (Banbury)**
2 BEATRIX ENCHANTE, 6, b m Phoenix Reach (IRE)—Bailadeira **World Wide Racing Partners**
3 GREEN POWER, 7, b g Kheleyf (USA)—Hakuraa (IRE) **Nino's Partnership**
4 INTERCESSOR, 5, b g Due Diligence (USA)—Miss Meticulous **The LAM Partnership**
5 JUNOESQUE, 8, b m Virtual—Snake Skin **Andrew Bell & Michael Wright**
6 LOS CAMACHOS (IRE), 7, b g Camacho—Illuminise (IRE) **Mr A. Bell**
7 PUSEY STREET, 4, ch f Equiano (FR)—Pusey Street Lady **C R Marks (banbury) & J Gallagher**
8 RIVAS ROB ROY, 7, ch g Archipenko (USA)—Rivas Rhapsody **Mr T. J. F. Smith**
9 SARAS HOPE, 5, b g Swiss Spirit—Rivas Rhapsody (IRE) **Max Europe Limited**
10 SECRET HANDSHEIKH, 4, b g Mayson—Descriptive (IRE) **The Old Deer Racing Partnership**
11 SILVER DIVA, 4, gr f Hellvelyn—Heartsong (IRE) **J & L Wetherald - M & M Glover**
12 THORN, 6, b g Dansili—Thistle Bird **Mr R G Robinson & Mr R D Robinson**

THREE-YEAR-OLDS

13 ANIMIST, b gr g Equiano (FR)—Iseemist (IRE) **Mr K. Marsden**
14 BUDDY'S BEAUTY, b f Equiano (FR)—Hollybell **Mr T. J. F. Smith**
15 EDINSON KEVANI (IRE), b g Kodiac—Lucrezia **Caveat Emptor Partnership**
16 GRAND BOBBY, gr g Bobby's Kitten (USA)—Grand Myla (IRE) **HCN Racing**
17 KATIE K, b f Garswood—Princess Luna (GER) **Andrew Bell & Michael Wright**
18 LADY ANNE BLUNT, b f Brazen Beau (AUS)—Ada Lovelace **Mr D. A. Clark**
19 PADDY K, b g Ardad (IRE)—Bella Catalina **Andrew Bell & Michael Wright**
20 PLANXTY, b c Telescope (IRE)—Snake Skin **Mr M. Park**
21 RUNNER BEAN, b f Heeraat (IRE)—Miss Meticulous **The LAM Partnership**
22 STUNGBYTHEMASTER, ch g Jack Hobbs—Scorpion Princess (IRE) **Mr J. N. Greenley**

TWO-YEAR-OLDS

23 GET BUSY, ch c 30/01 Unfortunately (IRE)—Heartsong (IRE) (Kheleyf (USA)) **J & L Wetherald - M & M Glover**
24 HAVANA PUSEY, b f 16/04 Havana Grey—Pusey Street Lady (Averti (IRE)) **C. R. Marks (Banbury)**
25 Gr c 24/04 Havana Grey—Iseemist (IRE) (Verglas (USA)) **Mr K. Marsden**

Other Owners: Mr A. Bell, Dr M. F. Ford, John Gallagher, Ms M. E. Glover, M. P Glover, Mrs S. E. Kirk, Mr J. P W. Lawrie, Mrs B. A. Long, J. F. Long, C. R. Marks (Banbury), Ms L. M. Mulcahy, Mr O. M. Parsons, Mr R. D. Robinson, Mr R. G. Robinson, Mr J. A. Wetherald, Mrs L. T. Wetherald, Mr M. F. Wright.

Assistant Trainer: Mr B Denvir.

206 **MR THOMAS GALLAGHER, Borehamwood**
Postal: **5 Old Priory Park, Old London Road, St. Albans, Hertfordshire, AL1 1QF**
Contacts: **MOBILE 07786 025427**

1 4, B g Dandy Man (IRE)—Cafe Lassere (USA) **Mr J. Reddington**
2 **D'ORVEL (FR)**, 5, ch g Masked Marvel—Dima d'Or (FR) **Mr J. Reddington**
3 4, B g Harzand (IRE)—Deep Winter **Mr J. Reddington**
4 **FERN ARABLE**, 8, b m Fair Mix (IRE)—Charlottes Webb (IRE) **Mr J. Reddington**
5 4, B g Raven's Pass (USA)—Freya Tricks **Mr J. Reddington**
6 **GOLD CONTI (FR)**, 6, ch g Network (GER)—Regina Conti (FR) **Mr J. Reddington**
7 **GREAT UNIVERSE**, 6, b g Universal (IRE)—As Was **Mr J. Reddington**
8 **I'M DIGBY (IRE)**, 5, gr ro g Gutaifan (IRE)—Lathaat **Mr J. Reddington**
9 **ICARE COLOMBE (FR)**, 4, b g Cokoriko (FR)—Valse de Touzaine (FR) **Mr J. Reddington**
10 **LOST IN THE MIST (IRE)**, 6, ch g Shirocco (GER)—Spirit Rock (IRE) **Mr J. Reddington**
11 **MR HARP (IRE)**, 9, b g Court Cave (IRE)—Chapel Wood Lady (IRE) **Mr J. Reddington**
12 **SECOND SUBALTERN (USA)**, 6, b g Declaration of War (USA)—Queen of The Night **Mr J. Reddington**
13 **THAMES CITY (FR)**, 5, b g Casamento (IRE)—Mooizo (IRE) **Mr J. Reddington**

207 **MRS ILKA GANSERA-LEVEQUE, Newmarket**
Postal: **Saint Wendreds, Hamilton Road, Newmarket, Suffolk, CB8 7JQ**
Contacts: **PHONE 01638 454973 MOBILE 07855 532072**
EMAIL office@gansera-leveque.com WEBSITE www.gansera-leveque.com

1 **JUST ONCE**, 6, b m Holy Roman Emperor (IRE)—Nur Jahan (IRE) **Vantage Point Racing Club**
2 **MERCI PERCY (FR)**, 4, b f Sir Percy—Acacalia (GER) **Downlands Racing**
3 **MISS BELLA BRAND**, 4, b f Poet's Voice—Miss Toldyaso (IRE) **Mr R. A. G. Robinson**
4 **RABAT (IRE)**, 4, b f Mehmas (IRE)—Refuse To Give Up (IRE) **Vantage Point Racing Club**
5 **RETROUVAILLES**, 4, b br f Iffraaj—Badweia (USA) **Vantage Point Racing Club**

THREE-YEAR-OLDS

6 Ch g Charming Thought—Bexandella **Mr S. D. Bradley**
7 **HAMMERHEAD**, b g Aclaim (IRE)—La Pieta (AUS)
8 **KINGWELL**, b c Kingman—Frenzified **Mrs I. Gansera-Leveque**

TWO-YEAR-OLDS

9 **DARING GREATLY**, ch f 08/04 Decorated Knight—Epiphany (Zafonic (USA)) (4000)
10 B f 18/03 Aclaim (IRE)—La Pieta (AUS) (Redoute's Choice (AUS))
11 B f 05/04 Aclaim (IRE)—Linet (IRE) (Oasis Dream)
12 **ONCE ADAAY**, b c 22/03 Adaay (IRE)—Sonko (IRE) (Red Clubs (IRE)) (15000) **Mrs A. M. Sturges**
13 B f 10/04 Pearl Secret—Zophilly (IRE) (Zoffany (IRE))

Assistant Trainer: Stephane Leveque.

208 **MRS SUSAN GARDNER, Longdown**
Postal: Woodhayes Farm, Longdown, Exeter
Contacts: **PHONE 01392 811213 MOBILE 07936 380492**
EMAIL woodhayesstudfarm@btinternet.com WEBSITE www.suegardnerracing.co.uk

1 **ALRAMZ**, 6, b g Intello (GER)—Rewaaya (IRE) **Clear Racing**
2 **ASTRONOMIC VIEW**, 5, ch g Schiaparelli (GER)—Winter Scene (IRE) **Mr D. V. Gardner**
3 **BLUFFMEIFYOUCAN**, 5, br g Yorgunnabelucky (USA)—Cita Verda (FR) **A & D Gardner**
4 **CLARENDON CROSS**, 4, b g New Approach (IRE)—Meet Me Halfway **Mrs L. Osborne**
5 **EMMPRESSIVE LADY (IRE)**, 7, b m Jeremy (USA)—Court Lexi (IRE) **Clear Racing**
6 **ENDLESS FLIGHT (IRE)**, 8, b g Winged Love (IRE)—Lady Oakwell (IRE) **Miss Jane Edgar & Mr D. V. Gardner**
7 **GINGE**, 6, ch g Cityscape—Lupa Montana (USA) **J. L. Rowsell**
8 **HARDTOROCK (IRE)**, 13, b g Mountain High (IRE)—Permissal (IRE) **Mr N. A. Eggleton**
9 **HAVACUPPA**, 8, b m Dream Eater (IRE)—Darjeeling (IRE) **Mr D. V. Gardner**
10 **KING ORRY (IRE)**, 7, b g Oscar (IRE)—Deer Island Peg (IRE) **Gardner Wheeler**
11 **LIGHTONTHEWING (IRE)**, 7, b g Winged Love (IRE)—Neat 'n Nimble **Mr D. V. Gardner**
12 **MILITARY TACTIC (IRE)**, 6, b g Iffraaj—Lunar Spirit **Mrs L. Osborne**
13 5, B g Kayf Tara—Molly Flight (FR) **Mrs B. Russell & Mr D. V. Gardner**
14 **SAFFRON TIGER**, 7, br g Tiger Groom—Miss Saffron **P. A. Tylor**
15 **SIROP DE MENTHE (FR)**, 12, ch g Discover d'Auteuil (FR)—Jolie Menthe (FR) **Clear Racing & Partner**
16 **SNUG AS A BUG (IRE)**, 7, b m Shirocco (GER)—More Equity **Mrs L. Osborne**
17 **TACTICAL MANOEUVRE (IRE)**, 11, b g Marienbard (IRE)—Pride O'Fleet (IRE) **The Tacticians**
18 **TEA TIME ON MARS**, 10, ch g Schiaparelli (GER)—Darjeeling (IRE) **Mrs B. Russell & Mr D. V. Gardner**
19 **THE GENEROUS JOKER**, 6, b g Le Fou (IRE)—Too Generous **Mr D. V. Gardner**
20 **TRANS EXPRESS (IRE)**, 12, br g Trans Island—Hazel Fastrack **Mr D. V. Gardner**
21 **WOULDUADAMANDEVEIT (IRE)**, 9, b g Stowaway—Figlette **Keith Harris & Tom Gardner**
22 **ZILLION (IRE)**, 8, b g Zebedee—Redelusion (IRE) **Miss Jane Edgar & Mr D. V. Gardner**

Other Owners: Miss J. E. Edgar, Mr V. P. Finn, Mr D. V. Gardner, Mr T. A. Gardner, Mr B. J. Greening, Mrs M. M. Greening, Mr K. T. Harris, Mr S. Hill, Mr A. I. Leach, Mrs B. A. Russell, Mr N. J. Wheeler.

Assistant Trainer: D. V. Gardner.

NH Jockey: Lucy Gardner.

---

209 **MRS ROSEMARY GASSON, Banbury**
Postal: Alkerton Grounds, Balscote, Banbury, Oxfordshire, OX15 6JS
Contacts: **PHONE 01295 730248 MOBILE 07769 798430**
EMAIL arb@agf.myzen.co.uk

1 **BIGNORM (IRE)**, 10, b g Mahler—Merry Heart (IRE) **Mrs R. Gasson**
2 **IRISH OCTAVE (IRE)**, 12, b g Gamut (IRE)—Fairytaleofnewyork (IRE) **Mrs R. Gasson**
3 **MASKIA (FR)**, 5, b g Masked Marvel—Rasia (FR) **Mrs R. Gasson**
4 **MEETMELATER (IRE)**, 5, b g Mustameet (USA)—Emilies Pearl (IRE) **Mrs R. Gasson**
5 **SIDEWAYSINMILAN (IRE)**, 7, b g Milan—Erins Love (IRE) **Mrs R. Gasson**

NH Jockey: Ben Poste.

210 MR MICHAEL GATES, Stratford-Upon-Avon
Postal: **Comfort Park Stud & Racing Stables, Campden Road, Clifford Chambers, Stratford-Upon-Avon, Warwickshire, CV37 8LW**
Contacts: **PHONE 07581 246070**
EMAIL comfortparkstud@hotmail.co.uk

1 **DAYBREAK BOY (IRE)**, 9, b br g Kingsalsa (USA)—Aloisi **Mr M. Gates**
2 **DRUMNAGREAGH (IRE)**, 9, b m September Storm (GER)—Saffron Pride (IRE) **Mr M. Gates**
3 **TICKENWOLF (IRE)**, 12, gr g Tikkanen (USA)—Emma's Choice (IRE) **SprayClad UK**

211 MR PAUL GEORGE, Crediton
Postal: **Higher Eastington, Lapford, Crediton, Devon, EX17 6NE**
Contacts: **MOBILE 07733 171112**
EMAIL paul.george1@icloud.com WEBSITE www.paulgeorgeracing.co.uk

1 **ACCRINGTON STANLEY**, 4, ch g Outstrip—Round Midnight **P. J. H. George**
2 **RATHAGAN**, 5, b g Kyllachy—Ardessie **P. J. H. George**
3 **SOPHIE**, 4, ch f Farhh—Poyle Sophie **Miss K. M. George**
4 **SYMPATHISE (IRE)**, 4, b f Kodi Bear (IRE)—Starfly (IRE) **Karen George & Adrian Parr**

Assistant Trainer: Cassie Haughton.

Apprentice Jockey: Rhiain Ingram.

212 MR TOM GEORGE, Slad
Postal: **Down Farm, Slad, Stroud, Gloucestershire, GL6 7QE**
Contacts: **PHONE 01452 814267 MOBILE 07850 793483**
EMAIL tom@trgeorge.com WEBSITE www.tomgeorgeracing.co.uk

1 **ABOVE SUSPICION (IRE)**, 7, b g Oscar (IRE)—The Sailors Bonnet (IRE) **O'Donohoe, Cavanagh, Robinson, Nelson**
2 4, B g Westerner—An Banog (IRE) **R. S. Brookhouse**
3 4, B c Telescope (IRE)—Arctic Lady (IRE) **Mr S. W. Clarke**
4 **BABY KING (IRE)**, 13, b g Ivan Denisovich (IRE)—Burn Baby Burn (IRE) **About Two Weeks**
5 **BALLON ONABUDGET (IRE)**, 9, b g Arcadio (GER)—Little Present (IRE)
6 **BANNISTER (FR)**, 5, gr g Olympic Glory (IRE)—Amou Daria (FR) **Crossed Fingers Partnership**
7 **BIG BRESIL**, 7, b g Blue Bresil (FR)—Cutielilou (FR) **R. S. Brookhouse**
8 **BLACK OP (IRE)**, 11, br g Sandmason—Afar Story (IRE) **R. S. Brookhouse**
9 **BLUE HOP (IRE)**, 5, b g Soldier of Fortune (IRE)—Afaraka (IRE) **R. S. Brookhouse**
10 **BOAGRIUS (IRE)**, 10, ch g Beneficial—Greenhall Rambler (IRE) **The MerseyClyde Partnership**
11 **BOBBY THE GREAT**, 5, b g Frankel—Riberac **R. S. Brookhouse**
12 **BOYHOOD (IRE)**, 11, b g Oscar (IRE)—Glen Dubh (IRE) **H Stephen Smith & The Gabbertas Family**
13 **BUCK'S BOGGLE (FR)**, 6, b g Tiger Groom—Buck's Bravo (FR) **R. S. Brookhouse**
14 **BUN DORAN (IRE)**, 11, b g Shantou (USA)—Village Queen (IRE) **Crossed Fingers Partnership**
15 **CALL ME RAFA (IRE)**, 5, b g Mahler—Annie Grit (IRE) **Mr C. B. Compton**
16 **CASA TALL (FR)**, 8, b g No Risk At All (FR)—Gribouille Parcs (FR) **Nelson, O'Donohoe, Mcdermott**
17 **CHAMPAGNE MYSTERY (IRE)**, 8, b g Shantou (USA)—Spanker **The Franglais Partnership**
18 **CHAPTAL (FR)**, 6, b g Le Havre (IRE)—Amacali (FR) **D Thompson & The Magic Ten**
19 **CHARLES RITZ**, 6, b g Milan—Miss Ballantyne
20 **CLEAR ON TOP (IRE)**, 6, b g Robin des Champs (FR)—Homelander (IRE) **Nelson, Bovington, Taylor, Delarocha**
21 **CLONDAW CASTLE (IRE)**, 10, b g Oscar (IRE)—Lohort Castle (IRE) **J French, D McDermott, S Nelson, T Syder**
22 **COME ON GRUFF (IRE)**, 6, b g Mahler—Annie Grit (IRE) **Mr N T Griffith & H M Haddock**

MR TOM GEORGE - continued

23 **COME ON TEDDY (IRE)**, 8, b g Fame And Glory—Theatre View (IRE) **Noel Fehily Racing Syndicates-Teddy**
24 **COTTUN (FR)**, 6, b g Le Havre (IRE)—Montebella (FR) **Sharon Nelson & Katya Taylor Delarocha**
25 **COUPDEBOL (FR)**, 7, gr g Rajsaman (FR)—Chance Bleue (FR) **Terry Warner & Tim Syder**
26 **CREALION (FR)**, 6, b g Creachadoir (IRE)—Lady La Lionne (FR) **S Nelson, T Keelan, H Polito, C Compton**
27 **DARLING DU LARGE (FR)**, 9, b m Kapgarde (FR)—Dissidente (FR) **Mr S. W. Clarke**
28 **DOM BOSCO**, 5, b g Blue Bresil (FR)—Definitely Better (IRE) **Miss J. A. Hoskins**
29 **DOUBLE SHUFFLE (IRE)**, 12, b g Milan—Fiddlers Bar (IRE) **Crossed Fingers Partnership**
30 **ESPOIR DE TEILLEE (FR)**, 10, b g Martaline—Belle de Lyphard (FR) **R. S. Brookhouse**
31 **FANFAN DU SEUIL (FR)**, 7, b g Racinger (FR)—Nina du Seuil (FR) **Crossed Fingers Partnership**
32 **FARO DE KERSER (FR)**, 7, b g Ungaro (GER)—Nuit de Kerser (FR) **The Twenty One Partnership**
33 **FORGOT TO ASK (IRE)**, 10, b g Ask—Lady Transcend (IRE) **Miss J. A. Hoskins**
34 **GET BYE (IRE)**, 7, b g Getaway (GER)—Cappa Or (IRE) **Mr C. B. Compton**
35 **GETAWAY GUILLAUME (IRE)**, 7, b m Getaway (GER)—Corrie Hall (IRE) **The Twelve Minimum Racing Club**
36 **GLOBAL EFFECT (IRE)**, 7, b br g Presenting—Ella Watson (IRE) **S Nelson, R Blunt, K Delarocha, D Savell**
37 **GO ON BRYCEY LAD (FR)**, 6, b g Saddler Maker (IRE)—Lonita d'Airy (FR) **The MerseyClyde Partnership**
38 **GREAT D'ANGE (FR)**, 6, b g Great Pretender (IRE)—Vickx (FR) **Mr T. D. J. Syder**
39 **HOODLUM (FR)**, 4, b g Aizavoski (IRE)—Lough Ennell (IRE) **Sharon Nelson & Vicki Robinson**
40 **HOOLIGAN (IRE)**, 7, b g Aizavoski (IRE)—Victory Run (IRE) **O'Donohoe, Cavanagh, Robinson, Nelson**
41 **JAVA POINT (IRE)**, 7, b g Stowaway—Classic Sun (GER) **Fanning, Griffith, Haddock**
42 **JOBESGREEN GIRL**, 5, b m Passing Glance—Overnight Fame (IRE) **Mr R. T. Cornock**
43 **JOBESGREEN LAD**, 7, b g Passing Glance—Overnight Fame (IRE) **Mr R. T. Cornock**
44 **JUST A STING (IRE)**, 10, b g Scorpion (IRE)—Shanann Lady (IRE) **Nigel & Barbara Collison**
45 **KAKAMORA**, 7, b g Great Pretender (IRE)—Roche d'Or **Mr T. D. J. Syder**
46 **LETS GO CHAMP (IRE)**, 7, b g Jeremy (USA)—Dark Mimosa (IRE) **R. S. Brookhouse**
47 **LYDIA VIOLET (IRE)**, 7, b rm Kalanisi (IRE)—Anne Hathaway (IRE) **Chasing Gold Limited**
48 **MAXIMUM DEX (IRE)**, 5, b g Westerner—Parsons Hall (IRE) **Crossed Fingers Partnership**
49 **MILLIE ROUND (IRE)**, 6, b m Fame And Glory—Molly Round (IRE) **The Borris Partnership**
50 **MISS CHANTELLE**, 5, b m Yorgunnabelucky (USA)—Miss Estela (IRE) **R. S. Brookhouse**
51 **OLD DUKE (IRE)**, 5, br g Shirocco (GER)—Sunlight (IRE) **Aniol & Burslem**
52 **OSCAR ROBERTSON (IRE)**, 8, b g Oscar (IRE)—Beaus Polly (FR) **Crossed Fingers Partnership**
53 **OUR NOBBY**, 5, b g Native Ruler—Patacake **Nobbys Mates**
54 **OVERALL MAJORITY (IRE)**, 6, b g Sholokhov (IRE)—Liss Alainn (IRE)
                                                                      S Nelson K Delarocha T Keelan J Edgedale
55 **RABBLE ROUSER (IRE)**, 5, b g Aizavoski (IRE)—The Flaming Matron (IRE)
                                                                      O'Donohoe, Cavanagh, Robinson, Nelson
56 **RASCAL**, 6, b g Blue Bresil (FR)—Fairy Theatre (IRE) **Sharon Nelson & Vicki Robinson**
57 **RAYA TIME (FR)**, 9, gr g Al Namix (FR)—Ruthenoise (FR) **R. S. Brookhouse**
58 **ROCK ON ROCCO (IRE)**, 8, b g Shirocco (GER)—Katalina **R. S. Brookhouse**
59 **ROYAL REGARD (FR)**, 4, b g Shalaa (IRE)—Royal Highness (GER) **Noel Fehily Racing Syndicates-Royal Rega**
60 **SEPTEMBER DAISY**, 7, b m September Storm (GER)—Alleged To Rhyme (IRE) **Mrs E. A. Fletcher**
61 **SMUGGLER'S BLUES (IRE)**, 10, b g Yeats (IRE)—Rosy de Cyborg (IRE) **D Rea & K Bebbington**
62 **SOMERWAY (IRE)**, 4, b f Getaway (GER)—Way Back When **Somerset Racing**
63 **SPRINGFIELD FOX**, 9, gr g Sagamix (FR)—Marlbrook Fox **O'Donohoe, Cavanagh, Robinson, Nelson**
64 **STORMIN CROSSGALES (IRE)**, 5, b g Saganburg (IRE)—Nodelay (IRE) **Noel Fehily Racing Syndicates-Stormin Cr**
65 **SUMMERVILLE BOY (IRE)**, 10, b g Sandmason—Suny House **R. S. Brookhouse**
66 **THE BRASS MAN (IRE)**, 8, b g Milan—The Brass Lady (IRE) **S Nelson G Birrell K Delarocha D Savell**
67 4, B c Walk In The Park (IRE)—Toungara (FR) **Mr S. W. Clarke**
68 **WHAT A STEAL (IRE)**, 5, b g Flemensfirth (USA)—Misty Heather (IRE) **O'Donohoe, Delchar, Jack, Nelson**
69 **WRITTENINTHESAND (IRE)**, 8, b g Milan—Sommer Sonnet (IRE) **Wilkin, Orr, Boileau & Douglas**

THREE-YEAR-OLDS

70 **FRENCH EXIT (FR)**, b f Spanish Moon (USA)—Kavatina (FR)
71 **IHAVEAUSEFORYOU**, b f Night Wish (GER)—Roche d'Or **DASH Racing**
72 **JACHAR (FR)**, b g Cokoriko (FR)—Creatina (FR) **Mr & Mrs R. G. Kelvin-Hughes**
73 **JAR DU DESERT (FR)**, b g Kapgarde (FR)—Dora du Desert (FR) **Crossed Fingers Partnership**
74 **THE LIKELY LAD (FR)**, b g Great Pretender (IRE)—Turgotine (FR) **Mr & Mrs R. G. Kelvin-Hughes**
75 **TIBIA (FR)**, b br g Manduro (GER)—Triceps (IRE) **Mr T. George**
76 **ZOEMAN (FR)**, b g Great Pretender (IRE)—Voulay (FR) **Silkword Racing Partnership**

MR TOM GEORGE - continued

TWO-YEAR-OLDS

77 B g 10/03 Lawman (FR)—Cry of Love (SPA) (Sakhee (USA)) (18707)
78 B g 23/04 Spanish Moon (USA)—Lucky Flower (FR) (Soldier of Fortune (IRE)) (29762)
79 **RABELLOISE (FR)**, ch f 14/02 Gemix (FR)—Boliche (Key of Luck (USA)) (11905) **Mr T. George**
80 **SHINJUKU (FR)**, b g 20/04 Creachadoir (IRE)—Susukino (FR) (Great Journey (JPN)) (6803)

Other Owners: Mr M. Aniol, Mr K. M. Bebbington, Mrs E. G. A. Birrell, Mr R. J. Blunt, Mrs H. L. Boileau, Mr D. A. Bovington, Mr P. R. Burslem, Mr J. P. Cavanagh, Mr S. W. Clarke, Mrs B. Collison, Mr N. Collison, Mr C. B. Compton, Mrs J. C. E. Crichton, Mr S. M. Delchar, Mr J. S. A. Douglas, Mr J. W. Edgedale, Mr O. Fanning, Mr J. M. Fawbert, Mr C. P. L. Francklin, Mr A. R. R. French, Mr J. M. Gabbertas, Mr R. K. Gabbertas, Mrs S. P. Gabbertas, Mr T. George, Mr N. Griffith, Mrs H. M. Haddock, Mr P. Jack, Mrs A. J. Jamieson, Mr T. J. Keelan, Lady A. J. Kiszely, Mr D. P. McDermott, Mr A. McMorrough Kavanagh, Mrs S. C. Nelson, Mr D. J. O'Donohoe, Mrs S. Orr, Mr D. Osullivan, Mrs H. W. Polito, Sir C. A. Ponsonby, Mr David Rea, Ms V. Robinson, Mr D. A. Savell, H. S. Smith, Mr T. D. J. Syder, Mr J. Taylor, Mrs K. Torres de la Rocha, J. T. Warner, Mr R. C. Wilkin, Mr N. Williamson.

Assistant Trainer: Noel George, Darren O'Dwyer, **Pupil Assistant:** Lawrence Jordan, **Travelling Head:** Sarah Peacock, **Secretary:** Lauren Thompson.

NH Jockey: Jonathan Burke, Ciaran Gethings. **Conditional Jockey:** Thomas Doggrell.

---

213 MR NICK GIFFORD, Findon
Postal: **The Downs, Stable Lane, Findon, West Sussex, BN14 0RT**
Contacts: **PHONE 01903 872226 MOBILE 07940 518077**
WORK EMAIL giffordracing@outlook.com **WEBSITE** www.nickgiffordracing.co.uk

1 BELARGUS (FR), 7, b g Authorized (IRE)—Belga Wood (USA) **Mr J. P. McManus**
2 CHURCHILLS BOY (IRE), 5, b g Malinas (GER)—Lindas Last (IRE)
3 COBBS CORNER (IRE), 6, b g Ocovango—A Long Way **Mr M. P. Jones**
4 4, B f Califet (FR)—Cove (IRE) **Mrs R. E. Gifford**
5 DIDTHEYLEAVEUOUTTO (IRE), 9, ch g Presenting—Pretty Puttens (IRE) **Mr J. P. McManus**
6 FAIRWAY FREDDY (IRE), 9, b g Elusive Pimpernel (USA)—Silent Supreme (IRE) **New Gold Dream**
7 FIRST OFFENCE (IRE), 5, gr h Ask—Umadachar (FR) **Mrs T. J. Stone-Brown**
8 FOLLOW INTELLO (IRE), 7, b g Intello (GER)—Sauvage (FR) **Findon Flyers**
9 ITSNOTWHATYOUTHINK (IRE), 7, b br g Westerner—Baladiva (IRE) **Mrs L Bowtell & Mrs S Cotty**
10 JUNGLE PROSE (IRE), 7, b br m Yeats (IRE)—Spring Baloo (IRE) **Nick Gifford Racing Club**
11 KILFORDS QUEEN (IRE), 5, b m Dylan Thomas (IRE)—Lunar Gift (IRE) **Nick Gifford Racing Club**
12 KINGS KRACKERTARA, 7, b m Kayf Tara—Firecracker Lady (IRE) **J.C.Harrison Lee & T.Howard Partnership**
13 LEGENDARY GRACE, 5, b m Multiplex—Fairyinthewind (IRE) **Mr R. J. Delnevo**
14 MARINE JAG (FR), 5, b m Saint des Saints (FR)—Soif d'Aimer (FR) **Paul & Louise Bowtell**
15 4, Ch g Jet Away—Miss Penny Pincher (IRE) **Hope Springs Too**
16 MISSFIT (IRE), 5, gr m Kalanisi (IRE)—Miss Miracle **Mrs J A Thomas & Heart Racing**
17 MY BAD LUCY, 6, b g Kayf Tara—Luci di Mezzanotte **Mr M. K. O'Shea**
18 NORTHERN POET (IRE), 7, b g Yeats (IRE)—Crowning Virtue (IRE) **The Hope Springs Syndicate**
19 ONESTEPTWOSTEPS (IRE), 5, b br g Getaway (GER)—Total Gossip (IRE) **Paul & Louise Bowtell**
20 PADDY'S POEM, 11, b g Proclamation (IRE)—Ashleys Petale (IRE) **Mrs T. J. Stone-Brown**
21 RIVER TYNE, 7, b m Geordieland (FR)—Not Now Nellie **Mr T Allan and Mrs H Allan**
22 ROSE OF AGHABOE (IRE), 9, b m Gold Well—Shillinglee Spring **The Rose Tinted Partnership**
23 RUM COVE, 4, ch g Black Sam Bellamy (IRE)—First Wonder (FR) **Hope Springs Too**
24 SALLYANN (IRE), 5, ch m Soldier of Fortune (IRE)—Golden Bay **Mrs S. A. Addington-Smith**
25 SIMPLY SUPREME (IRE), 7, b m Robin des Champs (FR)—Old Dreams (IRE) **Ledwardian Legacy Partnership**
26 THE MIGHTY DON (IRE), 10, ch g Shantou (USA)—Flying Answer (IRE) **Golden Rose Partnership**
27 ZUBA, 6, b g Dubawi (IRE)—Purr Along **The South Downs Partnership**

Other Owners: Mr A. C. Allan, Mrs H. F. Allan, Miss R Bailey, Mr J. P. M. Bowtell, Mrs L. Bowtell, Mr G. F. Brooks, Mrs S. Cotty, Heart Racing, Mr J. Kyle, Mrs J. A. Thomas, Mrs L. Wolfe.

NH Jockey: James Davies, Tabitha Worsley.

214 MR MARK GILLARD, Dorset

Postal: **Hawkes Field Farm, Hilton, Blandford Forum, Dorset, DT11 0DN**
Contacts: **PHONE 01258 881111 MOBILE 07970 700605**
EMAIL office@markgillardracing.com WEBSITE www.markgillardracing.com

1 AVITHOS, 12, b m Kayf Tara—Digyourheelsin (IRE) **Mr N J McMullan & Mr T Winzer**
2 BANNERGIRL (IRE), 4, ch f Starspangledbanner (AUS)—Scarlet Belle **Mr R. M. Rivers**
3 BLUEBLOOD (IRE), 6, b br g Dawn Approach (IRE)—Ghany (IRE) **Mr I. T. Booth**
4 CAPTAIN CUCKOO, 10, ch g Black Sam Bellamy (IRE)—Shiny Thing (USA) **Mr M. W. Hoskins**
5 COALBROOK BRIDGE (IRE), 8, b g Bollin Eric—Crews Hill (IRE) **The Family Goes Racing**
6 DON'T JUMP GEORGE (IRE), 7, b g Canford Cliffs (IRE)—My Sweet Georgia (IRE) **Mrs P. M. R. Gillard**
7 GIRANDOLE (FR), 4, b g No Nay Never (USA)—Laber Ildut (IRE) **Mr S. J. Garnett**
8 HAZMAT (IRE), 4, br f Harzand (IRE)—Suite (IRE) **Mr R. M. Rivers**
9 JOHN BETJEMAN, 6, b g Poet's Voice—A Great Beauty **Robin Gillard & Rory Gillard**
10 4, Ch g Linda's Lad—Midnight Seranade (IRE) **Mrs P. M. R. Gillard**
11 NO NO TONIC, 8, b m Sulamani (IRE)—Karinga Madame **N. J. McMullan**
12 OLLY'S FOLLY, 8, b g Poet's Voice—Pearl Diva (IRE) **Mrs P. M. R. Gillard**
13 SANDS CHORUS, 10, b g Footstepsinthesand—Wood Chorus **Mrs P. M. R. Gillard**
14 UNDERCOVER AGENT (IRE), 4, b g Kodiac—Multicolour Wave (IRE) **Mr S. J. Garnett**
15 VANDERBILT (IRE), 8, ch g Intense Focus (USA)—Star of The West **T. J. C. Seegar**

Other Owners: Mr R. Gillard, Mr R. Gillard, N. J. McMullan, T. O. Winzer.

Assistant Trainer: Mrs Pippa Gillard, **Yard Sponsor:** Ascot Park Polo Club.

Conditional Jockey: Fergus Gillard, Theo Gillard.

215 MR JIM GOLDIE, Glasgow

Postal: **Libo Hill Farm, Uplawmoor, Glasgow, Lanarkshire, G78 4BA**
Contacts: **PHONE 01505 850212 MOBILE 07778 241522**
WEBSITE www.jimgoldieracing.com

1 AIGHEAR, 4, b f Farhh—Kabjoy (IRE)
2 ANNANDALE (IRE), 4, ch c Australia—Fountain of Honour (IRE) **Ms S. Johnstone**
3 AYR POET, 7, b g Poet's Voice—Jabbara (IRE) **The Reluctant Suitor's**
4 BE PROUD (IRE), 6, b g Roderic O'Connor (IRE)—Agnista (IRE) **Whitestonecliffe Racing Partnership**
5 BOBBY SHAFTOE, 4, ch g Mazameer (IRE)—Sister Red (IRE) **Mr James Callow & Mr J. S. Goldie**
6 BRAES OF DOUNE, 4, b g Orientor—Gargoyle Girl **Johnnie Delta Racing**
7 CALL ME GINGER, 6, ch g Orientor—Primo Heights **Johnnie Delta Racing**
8 COSA SARA (IRE), 4, b f Gleneagles (IRE)—Antique Platinum (IRE) **Summerstorm Bloodstock Ltd**
9 EUCHEN GLEN, 9, b g Authorized (IRE)—Jabbara (IRE) **W. M. Johnstone**
10 GEREMIA (IRE), 4, b g Fastnet Rock (AUS)—Gerika (FR) **Mr James Fyffe & Mr Scott Fyffe**
11 GLEN LOMOND, 4, ch g Orientor—Glenlini **Johnnie Delta Racing**
12 GLOBAL HUMOR (USA), 7, b g Distorted Humor (USA)—In Bloom (USA) **Mr P. Stewart**
13 GRACES QUEST, 4, b f Telescope (IRE)—Ballinargh Girl (IRE) **Summerstorm Bloodstock Ltd**
14 GRAND CANAL (IRE), 5, b g Australia—Loreto (IRE) **Summerstorm Bloodstock Ltd**
15 JESSIE ALLAN (IRE), 11, b m Bushranger (IRE)—Ishimagic **Mr R. W. C. McLachlan**
16 KRAKEN POWER (IRE), 4, b g The Last Lion (IRE)—Throne **Mr James Fyffe & Mr Scott Fyffe**
17 LOCHNAVER, 4, b f Frankel—Strathnaver **Summerstorm Bloodstock Ltd**
18 LORD OF THE GLEN, 7, b g Orientor—Glenlini **Johnnie Delta Racing**
19 MAZALITA, 4, b br f Mazameer (IRE)—Miss Ippolita **The Vital Sparks**
20 MAZAMIX, 5, br m Mazameer (IRE)—Crosby Millie **The Vital Sparks**
21 MILLIEMIX, 4, gr ro f Mazameer (IRE)—Crosby Millie **The Vital Sparks**
22 NICHOLAS T, 10, b g Rail Link—Thorntoun Piccolo **Mr James Callow & Mr J. S. Goldie**
23 ONE LAST HUG, 7, b g Orientor—Gargoyle Girl **Mr James Callow & Mr J. S. Goldie**
24 ORIENTAL LILLY, 8, ch m Orientor—Eternal Instinct **Johnnie Delta Racing**
25 PAMMI, 7, b m Poet's Voice—Bright Girl (IRE) **Ayrshire Racing & Partner**

26 **PINK SILK**, 4, b f Mazameer (IRE)—Pnyka (IRE) **Mr James Callow & Mr J. S. Goldie**
27 **PRIMO'S COMET**, 7, b g Orientor—Primo Heights **Whitestonecliffe Racing Partnership**
28 **RAINY CITY (IRE)**, 12, b g Kalanisi (IRE)—Erintante (IRE) **Mr James Callow & Mr J. S. Goldie**
29 **RORY**, 4, ch g Orientor—Eternal Instinct **Mr H. Connor**
30 **SARVI**, 7, br m Intello (GER)—Crystal Swan (IRE) **Johnnie Delta Racing**
31 **SCOTS SONNET**, 8, b g Poet's Voice—Jabbara (IRE) **Mr James Callow & Mr J. S. Goldie**
32 **SIR CHAUVELIN**, 10, b g Authorized (IRE)—Jabbara (IRE) **Mr J. Fyffe & Mr J. S. Goldie**
33 **SOUND OF IONA**, 6, ch m Orientor—Eternal Instinct **Mr & Mrs G Grant & the Reluctant Suitors**
34 **SUMMER HEIGHTS**, 5, b m Orientor—Primo Heights **Johnnie Delta Racing**
35 **TANASOQ (IRE)**, 9, b g Acclamation—Alexander Youth (IRE) **Mr P. Stewart**
36 **TARA KAY**, 6, b m Kayf Tara—La Vecchia Scuola (IRE) **The Reluctant Suitor's**
37 **TOMMY G**, 9, ch g Makfi—Primo Heights **Johnnie Delta Racing**

THREE-YEAR-OLDS

38 **AUTUMN SYMPHONY (IRE)**, ch f Profitable (IRE)—Comeraincomeshine (IRE) **Racing Connexions 12**
39 B g Orientor—Eternal Instinct
40 B f Orientor—Eternalist **Johnnie Delta Racing**
41 B g Orientor—Glenlini
42 **SOPHISTICATE (IRE)**, b f War Command (USA)—Lenoire **W. M. Johnstone**
43 **TAFSIR (USA)**, b f Tamarkuz (USA)—Jannattan (USA) **Summerstorm Bloodstock Ltd**

TWO-YEAR-OLDS

44 **DIAMOND DANDY (IRE)**, ch f 23/04 Dandy Man (IRE)—Saga Celebre (FR) (Peintre Celebre (USA)) (28571)
Chris Giles & Sandra Giles
45 B c 29/02 Gustav Klimt (IRE)—Dream Scenario (Araafa (IRE)) (17000) **ASAP Racing**
46 **HUMBLE SPARK (IRE)**, b c 20/02 Acclamation—Maiden Approach (New Approach (IRE)) (45000) **Mr F. Brady**

Other Owners: Ayrshire Racing, Mr N. Boyle, Mr J. R. Callow, Mr J. Fyffe, Mr S. Fyffe, Mrs A. E. Giles, Mr C. M. Giles, Mrs D. I. Goldie, Mr J. S. Goldie, Mrs C. H. Grant, Mr G. R. Grant, Mr D. W. McIntyre, The Reluctant Suitor's.

Assistant Trainer: George Goldie, James Goldie.

216	**MR CHRIS GORDON, Winchester** Postal: **Morestead Farm Stables, Morestead, Winchester, Hampshire, SO21 1JD** Contacts: **PHONE 01962 712774 MOBILE 07713 082392** **EMAIL chrisgordon68@hotmail.co.uk WEBSITE www.chrisgordonracing.com**

1 **ALTO ALTO (FR)**, 5, ch g Falco (USA)—Beautyful (IRE) **Mrs C. New**
2 **ANNUAL INVICTUS (IRE)**, 7, b g Mount Nelson—Shantou Rose (IRE) **Mr T. M. Smith**
3 **AUCUNRISQUE (FR)**, 6, b g No Risk At All (FR)—Saintheze (FR) **Goodwin Racing Ltd**
4 **BADDESLEY (IRE)**, 7, b g Presenting—Fox Theatre (IRE) **Mr Richard & Mrs Carol Cheshire**
5 **BELLE JOUR (IRE)**, 7, ch g Presenting—Belle Glory (IRE) **L. Gilbert**
6 **BLACK CENTAUR (IRE)**, 9, b g Oscar (IRE)—Arcanum (IRE) **Davies King Selway Wavish**
7 **BLADE RUNNER (IRE)**, 6, b g Great Pretender (IRE)—Cutting Edge (FR) **C. E. Gordon**
8 **BLAME THE GAME (IRE)**, 7, b g Darsi (FR)—Lucy Walters (IRE) **Redz Together**
9 **CADMAR**, 8, b g Shirocco (GER)—Raitera (FR) **Mr Richard & Mrs Carol Cheshire**
10 **CAN'T STOP NOW (IRE)**, 5, ch g Starspangledbanner (AUS)—Sorry Woman (FR) **Let's Be Lucky Racing 30**
11 **CARD DEALER (IRE)**, 5, ch g Aizavoski (IRE)—Oscar Invitation (IRE) **Mr D. S. Dennis**
12 5, B g Diamond Boy (FR)—Clochette de Sou (FR) **Mrs J. L. Gordon**
13 **COMMANCHE RED (IRE)**, 9, ch g Mahler—Auntie Bob **Mr Richard & Mrs Carol Cheshire**
14 **COOLVALLA (IRE)**, 6, b g Westerner—Valleyboggan (IRE) **L. Gilbert**
15 **CORONADO JOE**, 6, ch g Norse Dancer (IRE)—Hopatina (IRE) **E Hawkingsb Hardingj Baigentg Hawkings**
16 4, B g Mahler—Deianira (IRE) **Mrs J. L. Gordon**
17 **DIAMOND EGG (FR)**, 4, b g Diamond Boy (FR)—Chamoss World (FR) **Henrietta Knight Racing Club**
18 **DON'T TELL GEORGE (FR)**, 9, b g Enrique—Anowa (FR) **Mrs K. Digweed**
19 **FOREST ECHO**, 5, b g Norse Dancer (IRE)—Sunley Spirit **Mrs I. D. Colderick**

MR CHRIS GORDON - continued

20 **FOREST JUMP (IRE)**, 5, b g Mahler—Deianira (IRE) **Mrs N. Morris**
21 **GERICO VILLE (FR)**, 6, b g Protektor (GER)—Jadoudy Ville (FR) **Cox, Russell, Lloyd, Finnegan & Scanlon**
22 **GO WHATEVER (IRE)**, 8, b g Gold Well—And Whatever Else (IRE) **A. C. Ward-Thomas**
23 **GOODWIN RACING (IRE)**, 5, b g Califet (FR)—Ballinahow Tara (IRE) **Goodwin Racing Ltd**
24 **HAPPY BOY (FR)**, 5, gr g Rail Link—Vrai Bonheur (FR) **Brenda Ansell & Jane Goddard**
25 **HARDY FELLA (IRE)**, 5, b g Libertarian—Combustible Spirit (IRE) **Mighty Acorn Stables**
26 **HIGHWAY ONE O FOUR (IRE)**, 4, b g Saghero (IRE)—Good Time In Milan (IRE) **A. C. Ward-Thomas**
27 **HIGHWAY ONE O TWO (IRE)**, 7, b br g Shirocco (GER)—Supreme Dreamer (IRE) **A. C. Ward-Thomas**
28 **HIWAY ONE O THREE (IRE)**, 5, b g Saghero (IRE)—Good Time In Milan (IRE) **Ward-thomas & Dennis**
29 4, B f Universal—Hopatina (IRE) **Mr E. J. Hawkings**
30 **INVICTUS DE BRION (FR)**, 4, b c Vespone (IRE)—Assemblee A Brion (FR) **Mrs J. L. Gordon**
31 **IPSO FALCO (FR)**, 4, b c Falco (USA)—Roselaine (FR)
32 **LEAVE OF ABSENCE (FR)**, 5, ch g Masked Marvel—To Much Fun **Mr Richard & Mrs Carol Cheshire**
33 **LORD BADDESLEY (IRE)**, 7, b br g Doyen (IRE)—Tropical Ocean (IRE) **Mr Richard & Mrs Carol Cheshire**
34 **MELLOW BEN (IRE)**, 9, b g Beneficial—Mellowthemoonlight (IRE) **Broadsword Group Ltd**
35 4, B g Champs Elysees—Mount Corkish Girl (IRE) **C. E. Gordon**
36 **MY TICKETYBOO (IRE)**, 4, b g Shirocco (GER)—Subtle Hint (IRE) **L. Gilbert**
37 **NOTLONGTILLMAY**, 6, b g Malinas (GER)—Tara Croft **Mr A. Rogers**
38 **ON THE SLOPES**, 8, b g Librettist (USA)—Dalriath **Skill Scaffolding Ltd**
39 **ONE FOR THE WALL (IRE)**, 6, br g Yeats (IRE)—Abinitio Lady (IRE) **The Select Syndicate**
40 **ONLY MONEY (IRE)**, 8, ch g Getaway (GER)—Kings Diva (IRE) **Mr D. S. Dennis**
41 **PASVOLSKY (IRE)**, 7, ch g Aizavoski (IRE)—Snowlaw (IRE) **The Augean Stables Syndicate**
42 **POPEYETHESAILORMAN**, 4, b g Norse Dancer (IRE)—Olive Oyl **Mrs C. E. Burton**
43 **PRESENTING A QUEEN**, 5, br m Presenting—Queens Regatta (IRE) **Mr Richard & Mrs Carol Cheshire**
44 **PRESS YOUR LUCK (IRE)**, 7, b g Doyen (IRE)—Merry Gladness (IRE) **Cox, Lloyd & Finden**
45 **PSYCHE**, 5, b h Lope de Vega (IRE)—Ode To Psyche (IRE) **L. Gilbert**
46 **RAMORE WILL (IRE)**, 11, gr g Tikkanen (USA)—Gill Hall Lady **E. J. Farrant**
47 **RED WINDSOR (IRE)**, 5, b g Elusive Pimpernel (USA)—Pros 'n' Cons (IRE) **Party People 2**
48 **RWANDA MIST**, 4, b g Maxios—Nyanza (GER) **The Mountain Gorillas**
49 **SAMI BEAR**, 6, b g Sulamani (IRE)—Dalriath **Team ABC**
50 **SANDY BROOK (IRE)**, 7, ch g Sandmason—Lovely Lolly (IRE) **Goodwin Racing Ltd**
51 **SHUT THE BOX (IRE)**, 8, ch g Doyen (IRE)—Bond Holder (IRE) **The Shut The Box Syndicate**
52 **SMURPHY ENKI (FR)**, 7, b g Blue Bresil (FR)—Creme Veloutee (IRE) **Miss J. A. Goddard**
53 **SPANISH HUSTLE**, 4, b g Pearl Secret—Dos Lunas (IRE) **Let's Be Lucky Racing 31**
54 **STANLEY PINCOMBE (IRE)**, 5, b g Multiplex—Allez Zane **Ms E. J. Southall**
55 **STORM DENNIS (IRE)**, 6, b g Libertarian—Lady Eile (IRE) **Mr D. S. Dennis**
56 **STRAIGHT SWAP (IRE)**, 7, b br g Yeats (IRE)—Alittlebitofheaven **Ward-thomas & Dennis**
57 **THE DOMINO EFFECT (IRE)**, 8, b g Oscar (IRE)—Lively Lass (IRE) **Mighty Acorn Stables**
58 **THE TIN MINER (IRE)**, 11, br g Presenting—Sidalcea (IRE) **Mrs B. M. Ansell**
59 **TOP MAN (IRE)**, 8, b g Milan—Get In There (IRE) **Broadsword Group Ltd**
60 **TWOMINUTES TURKISH (IRE)**, 7, ch g Mahler—Kilbarry Cliche (IRE) **The Cabal**
61 **UNANSWERED PRAYERS (IRE)**, 6, b g Ocovango—Fitanga Speed (IRE) **The Pres Partnership**
62 **WHO IS THAT (IRE)**, 6, ch g Shirocco (GER)—Nodelay (IRE) **Mr D. S. Dennis**

THREE-YEAR-OLDS

63 **CASTEL FOU (FR)**, ch g Castle du Berlais (FR)—Fol' Allegria (USA)
64 **JEFE TRIUNFO (FR)**, gr g Cima de Triomphe (FR)—Assemblee A Brion (FR)

Other Owners: Mrs B. M. Ansell, Mr J. R. Baigent, Mrs C. L. Cheshire, Mr R. Cheshire, Mr P. Cox, Mrs C. E. Davies, Mr D. S. Dennis, W. E. Enticknap, Mr A. P. Finden, Miss J. A. Goddard, C. E. Gordon, Mr B. C. Harding, Mr E. J. Hawkings, Miss G. Hawkings, Mr D. Horsman, Mrs L. M. King, Mr P. D. Lloyd, Mrs N. Morris, Mr B. Ralph, A. G. Selway, A. C. Ward-Thomas, Mr P. T. J. Wavish, Mr J. Williams.

Assistant Trainer: Jenny Gordon.

NH Jockey: Tom Cannon. **Conditional Jockey:** Nathan Brennan.

217 JOHN AND THADY GOSDEN, Newmarket
Postal: Clarehaven, Bury Road, Newmarket, Suffolk, CB8 7BY

1 **AL RUFAA (FR)**, 5, b g Kingman—Clarmina (IRE)
2 **AMTIYAZ**, 5, b h Frankel—Rose of Miracles
3 **BEAU NASH (IRE)**, 4, b c Golden Horn—What Style (IRE)
4 **BLUE DIAMOND (IRE)**, 4, b f Galileo (IRE)—Pearling (USA)
5 **CORDOUAN (FR)**, 4, b g Shalaa (IRE)—Piler Lann (FR)
6 **COUNSEL**, 4, ch g Frankel—Honorina
7 **DARAMETHOS (IRE)**, 4, b g Sea The Stars (IRE)—Dark Orchid (USA)
8 **DARLECTABLE YOU**, 4, b f Dubawi (IRE)—Dar Re Mi
9 **DEAR HEART**, 4, b f Kingman—Lyrique (IRE)
10 **EMBLEM EMPIRE (IRE)**, 4, ch c Gleneagles (IRE)—Hurricane Emma (USA)
11 **ETERNAL SUMMER**, 4, b f Kingman—Rose Blossom
12 **EVANIA**, 4, b f Golden Horn—Hanami
13 **FOREST OF DEAN**, 6, b g Iffraaj—Forest Crown
14 **FREE WIND (IRE)**, 4, b f Galileo (IRE)—Alive Alive Oh
15 **GLEN SAVAGE (IRE)**, 4, b c Gleneagles (IRE)—Rocksavage (IRE)
16 **HARROVIAN**, 6, b g Leroidesanimaux (BRZ)—Alma Mater
17 **LAW OF THE SEA**, 4, b g Golden Horn—Leaderene
18 **LORD NORTH (IRE)**, 6, b g Dubawi (IRE)—Najoum (USA)
19 **MAGICAL MORNING**, 5, b g Muhaarar—The Lark
20 **MARSHALL PLAN**, 4, b c Golden Horn—Manaboo (USA)
21 **MEGALLAN**, 4, b c Kingman—Eastern Belle
22 **MISHRIFF (IRE)**, 5, b h Make Believe—Contradict
23 **MOSTAHDAF (IRE)**, 4, br c Frankel—Handassa
24 **PENNYMOOR**, 4, b f Frankel—Penelopa
25 **PETER THE GREAT**, 4, b g New Approach (IRE)—Palitana (USA)
26 **POLLING DAY (IRE)**, 4, b g Sea The Stars (IRE)—Pollyana (IRE)
27 **RAINBOW FIRE (IRE)**, 4, b c Kodiac—Heroine Chic (IRE)
28 **STOWELL**, 4, b c Zoffany (IRE)—Marywell
29 **STRADIVARIUS (IRE)**, 8, ch h Sea The Stars (IRE)—Private Life (FR)
30 **SUNRAY MAJOR**, 5, b h Dubawi (IRE)—Zenda
31 **TRAWLERMAN (IRE)**, 4, b g Golden Horn—Tidespring (IRE)
32 **UNFORGOTTEN (IRE)**, 4, gr ro g Exceed And Excel (AUS)—Souviens Toi
33 **WALDKONIG**, 5, b h Kingman—Waldlerche
34 **YOUCOULDHAVESAIDNO**, 4, b f Shalaa (IRE)—Tara's Force (IRE)

THREE-YEAR-OLDS

35 **A CAPPELLA**, b f Frankel—Sivoliere (IRE)
36 **A E HOUSMAN**, b c Oasis Dream—Astronomy's Choice
37 **AEROSPACE**, b c Sea The Stars (IRE)—Talent
38 **ALDOUS HUXLEY (IRE)**, b c Dubawi (IRE)—Albasharah (USA)
39 **ALMUHIT (IRE)**, b c Sea The Stars (IRE)—Ezima (IRE)
40 **ALOTAIBI (IRE)**, b c Acclamation—Lady of The Lamp (IRE)
41 **ANTARAH (IRE)**, ch c Sea The Stars (IRE)—Adool (IRE)
42 **ATLANTIS**, gr f Sea The Stars (IRE)—Alla Speranza
43 **AUDIENCE**, b c Iffraaj—Ladyship
44 **AUYOUNI**, b f Siyouni (FR)—Cercle d'Or (IRE)
45 **BALTIC BIRD**, b c Frankel—Baltic Baroness (GER)
46 **BELT BUCKLE**, br f Golden Horn—Bible Belt (IRE)
47 **BLUEBERRY HILL (IRE)**, b c Showcasing—Because (IRE)
48 **BOUQUET**, gr f Dark Angel (IRE)—Bound (IRE)
49 **BUGLE BOY**, b c Golden Horn—Bustling
50 **COMPLEMENTARY (IRE)**, ch f Churchill (IRE)—Miss Mariduff (USA)
51 **COURAGE MON AMI**, b c Frankel—Crimson Ribbon (USA)
52 **DAMAAR**, b c Decorated Knight—Arwa (IRE)
53 **DAME ETHEL SMYTH**, b f Golden Horn—Lyrique (IRE)
54 **DARMOISELLE**, b f Dubawi (IRE)—Dar Re Mi
55 **DHABAB (IRE)**, ch c No Nay Never (USA)—Habbat Reeh (IRE)

JOHN AND THADY GOSDEN - continued

56 **DIGNIFIED,** b f Galileo (IRE)—Jack Naylor
57 **DREAM BY DAY,** b g Shalaa (IRE)—Illaunmore (USA)
58 **DUKEDOM (IRE),** b g Dubawi (IRE)—Nathra (IRE)
59 **ELEGANT VERSE,** b f Galileo (IRE)—Special Duty
60 **EMILY UPJOHN,** b f Sea The Stars (IRE)—Hidden Brief
61 **EMOTION,** ch f Frankel—Molly Malone (FR)
62 **FILISTINE (IRE),** c c Almanzor (FR)—Desire To Win (IRE)
63 **FIND,** b g Frankel—Spring In The Air (CAN)
64 **FRANCESCO CLEMENTE (IRE),** b c Dubawi (IRE)—Justlookdontouch (IRE)
65 **FRANTASTIC,** b c Frankel—Rhadegunda
66 **FRANZ STRAUSS,** b br c Golden Horn—Favulusa
67 **FRENCH TOAST,** b c Dark Angel (IRE)—French Dressing
68 **GEORGE ELIOT,** b c Golden Horn—Mary Anne Evans
69 **GIA DARLING,** b f Churchill (IRE)—Dona Viola
70 **GLORIOUS ROMANCE,** b f Nathaniel (IRE)—Magical Romance (IRE)
71 **GOVERNOR OF INDIA (IRE),** b c Invincible Spirit (IRE)—Sarita
72 **GRANDE DAME,** b f Lope de Vega (IRE)—Minwah (IRE)
73 **GULFAM,** b c Golden Horn—Golden Lilac (IRE)
74 **HIGH MOOR (USA),** b c War Front (USA)—Midday
75 **HIGHLAND FROLIC (FR),** b g Highland Reel (IRE)—Beach Frolic
76 **HOMERIC,** ch c Ulysses (IRE)—Fools In Love (USA)
77 **HONITON (IRE),** gr c Dark Angel (IRE)—Lacily (USA)
78 **IFTIKHAAR (IRE),** b c Dubawi (IRE)—Intisaar (USA)
79 **INSPIRAL,** b f Frankel—Starscope
80 **ISRAR,** b c Muhaarar—Taghrooda
81 **JUDITH,** b f Almanzor (FR)—Stella Bellissima (IRE)
82 **KENSINGTON (IRE),** b f Frankel—Canonbury (IRE)
83 **KIND OF BEAUTIFUL,** b f Frankel—Melesina (IRE)
84 **KINGS JOY,** b f Kingman—Golden Laughter (IRE)
85 **KNIGHT OF HONOUR (IRE),** b c Decorated Knight—Princess Noor (IRE)
86 **LADY EROS (USA),** b f War Front (USA)—Agreeable Miss (USA)
87 **LADY LOULOU (IRE),** b f Dark Angel (IRE)—Light The Stars (IRE)
88 **LOVING CARE (IRE),** b c Fastnet Rock (AUS)—Loving Things
89 **MAGISTERIAL (IRE),** b c Frankel—Hoity Toity
90 **MARCH MOON (IRE),** ch c Frankel—Snow Moon
91 **MASTER SERGEANT (IRE),** b c Shamardal (USA)—Mandinga (BRZ)
92 **MELFET (IRE),** b c Shalaa (IRE)—Al Jassasiyah (IRE)
93 **MHAJIM (IRE),** b c Teofilo (IRE)—Cape Magic (IRE)
94 **MIGHTY ULYSSES,** b c Ulysses (IRE)—Token of Love
95 **MIMIKYU,** b f Dubawi (IRE)—Montare (IRE)
96 **MIZMAR,** b g Muhaarar—Magnolea (IRE)
97 **MOON WATCH (IRE),** ch c Dubawi (IRE)—Moonlight Cloud
98 **MORNING POEM,** b f Kingman—Mill Springs
99 **NASHWA,** b f Frankel—Princess Loulou (IRE)
100 **NATASHA,** ch f Frankel—Darkova (USA)
101 **ONE EVENING,** ch f Galileo (IRE)—Seta
102 **OPERATING (USA),** b c War Front (USA)—Good Vibes (USA)
103 **PACIFIC,** b f Zoffany (IRE)—California (IRE)
104 **PEACE MAN,** b c Kingman—Peacehaven (IRE)
105 **PEACHY KEEN,** b f Pivotal—Perfectly Spirited
106 **PLUPERFECT,** b f Invincible Spirit (IRE)—Present Tense
107 **QUEEN OF IPANEMA (IRE),** ch f Teofilo (IRE)—Aiming For Rio (FR)
108 **QUEEN OF THE SKIES,** ch f Lope de Vega (IRE)—Westwiththenight (IRE)
109 **RAKURAI,** b br f Deep Impact (JPN)—Lightening Pearl (IRE)
110 **RASHMI,** b f Frankel—Ridafa (IRE)
111 **REACH FOR THE MOON,** b c Sea The Stars (IRE)—Golden Stream (IRE)
112 **REEL POWER,** b c Highland Reel (IRE)—Ensaya (IRE)
113 **ROYAL PARADE (IRE),** b g Kodiac—Supreme Occasion (IRE)
114 **ROYAL VERSE,** b c Frankel—Simple Verse (IRE)
115 **SAGA,** gr ro c Invincible Spirit (IRE)—Emily Bronte

JOHN AND THADY GOSDEN - continued

116 SALVATOR MUNDI (IRE), b c Galileo (IRE)—Bufera (IRE)
117 SAMBURU, b c Kingman—Tempera
118 SECURITY CODE, b c Territories (IRE)—Moment of Time
119 SHAARA, b f Shamardal (USA)—Yasmeen
120 SHADOWFAX, gr c Galileo (IRE)—Golden Valentine (FR)
121 SHIBORI (IRE), b gr f Dark Angel (IRE)—Made By Hand (IRE)
122 SHINING AL DANAH (IRE), b f Iffraaj—Signora Queen (FR)
123 SOBEGRAND, b c Decorated Knight—Nouriya
124 SPECIAL ENVOY, b c Frankel—Marlinka
125 SPINAROUND (IRE), b g Kodiac—Spinamiss (IRE)
126 STEPMOTHER (IRE), b f Dark Angel (IRE)—Divorces (AUS)
127 STORM CASTLE, b c Invincible Spirit (IRE)—Journey
128 SUPER CHIEF, b c Kingman—Eastern Belle
129 SUPER MORNING (IRE), b f Sea The Stars (IRE)—Sweet Firebird (IRE)
130 SWIFT ADVANCE, b f Golden Horn—Swift Campaign (IRE)
131 SYLVIA BEACH, b f Ulysses (IRE)—Furbelow
132 TATTERED FLAG (USA), gr c Union Rags (USA)—Careless Jewel (USA)
133 THAQEB, b c Invincible Spirit (IRE)—African Skies
134 THUNDERSHOWER (IRE), ch f Iffraaj—Rainswept
135 TOLSTOY (IRE), b g Kingman—War And Peace
136 WONDERFUL TIMES (IRE), b f Golden Horn—Wonderfully (IRE)
137 YUMMYLICIOUS, b f Dubawi (IRE)—Yummy Mummy

Trainer did not supply details of their two-year-olds.

Flat Jockey: L. Dettori, Martin Harley, Robert Havlin, Kieran O'Neill. **Apprentice Jockey:** Benoit De La Sayette.

218

HARRIET GRAHAM AND GARY RUTHERFORD, Jedburgh
Postal: **Strip End, Jedburgh, Roxburghshire, TD8 6NE**
Contacts: **PHONE 01835 840354 MOBILE 07843 380401**
EMAIL hgrahamracing@aol.com

1 AYE RIGHT (IRE), 9, b g Yeats (IRE)—Gaybric (IRE) **Mr G. F. Adam & Mrs E. Adam**
2 BIG ARTHUR, 5, b g Passing Glance—Xpectations (IRE) **The Potassium Partnership 2**
3 BRANDY MCQUEEN (IRE), 5, b g Yeats (IRE)—Down Ace (IRE) **Mr S. Townshend**
4 CLARET DABBLER, 8, ch g Haafhd—Floreana (GER) **Mrs A. J. Boswell**
5 DON BROCCO, 6, gr g Shirocco (GER)—Brantingham Breeze **Rutherford Racing**
6 MIDNIGHT FIDDLER, 6, ch g Midnight Legend—Overlady **Mr W. F. Jeffrey**
7 MILLARVILLE (IRE), 9, b m Court Cave (IRE)—Portavoe (IRE) **Mr G. F. Adam & Mrs E. Adam**
8 RACKS CROSS (IRE), 8, b m Jeremy (USA)—Lemons Legend **Mr G. F. Adam & Mrs E. Adam**
9 SHOUGHALL'S BOY (IRE), 6, b g Watar (IRE)—Lady Shackleton (IRE) **Mr R. Chapman**
10 STAR OF MARKINCH (IRE), 6, b m Watar (IRE)—Gibboghstown (IRE) **Mr R. Chapman**

Assistant Trainer: R D Graham.

219 MR CHRIS GRANT, Billingham
Postal: **Low Burntoft Farm, Wolviston, Billingham, Cleveland, TS22 5PD**
Contacts: **PHONE 01740 644054 MOBILE 07860 577998**
EMAIL chrisgrantracing@gmail.com WEBSITE www.chrisgrantracing.co.uk

1 **BALLINTOGHER BOY (IRE)**, 8, b g Flemensfirth (USA)—Room Seven (IRE) **Chris Grant Racing Club**
2 **BEBSIDE BANTER (IRE)**, 5, b g Westerner—Hard Fought (IRE) **D&D Armstrong Limited**
3 **CHASE A FORTUNE**, 4, b g Cannock Chase (IRE)—Lucematic **Chasing the Dream**
4 **DARIUS DES SOURCES (FR)**, 9, gr g Irish Wells (FR)—Lionata (FR) **D & D Armstrong Ltd & Mr L Westwood**
5 **DONNA'S DIVA**, 7, b m Oscar (IRE)—Micro Mission (IRE) **D&D Armstrong Limited**
6 **FEARLESS ACTION (IRE)**, 6, b g Yeats (IRE)—Hello Kitty (IRE) **G. F. White**
7 **FIADH (IRE)**, 6, b m Fame And Glory—Lady Charisma **G. F. White**
8 **FLAKARNA**, 7, b m Lucarno (USA)—Flaybay **Miss A. P. Lee**
9 **FRANKS FANCY (IRE)**, 7, b g Stowaway—Palesa Accord (IRE) **G. F. White**
10 **GLORY HIGHTS**, 6, b g Fame And Glory—Lady High (FR) **John & Grant**
11 **JACQANINA**, 7, b m Fame And Glory—Ninna Nanna (FR) **Mr J. Kenny**
12 **LENNY (IRE)**, 6, b g Notnowcato—Golden Misti (IRE) **Chris Grant Racing Club**
13 **LYNDALE**, 7, gr g Mountain High (IRE)—Grey Clouds **C. Grant**
14 **RED OCHRE**, 9, b g Virtual—Red Hibiscus **Mrs M Nicholas & Chris Grant**
15 **RED REMINDER**, 8, b m Mount Nelson—Red Hibiscus **Mrs H. N. Eubank**
16 **RULEOUT (IRE)**, 6, b g Rule of Law (USA)—Galingale (IRE)
17 **SIX ONE NINE (IRE)**, 7, b g Cloudings (IRE)—Indian Athlete (IRE) **D&D Armstrong Limited**
18 **SLANEMORE HILL (IRE)**, 10, br g Court Cave (IRE)—Goodonyou-Polly (IRE) **The Hon Mrs D. J. Faulkner**
19 **STRONG TEAM (IRE)**, 9, b g Exceed And Excel (AUS)—Star Blossom (USA) **Chris Grant Racing Club**
20 **THEATRE LEGEND**, 9, b g Midnight Legend—Theatre Belle **Division Bell Partnership**
21 **UNCLE GEZ (IRE)**, 6, b g Califet (FR)—Louis's Teffia (IRE) **D&D Armstrong Ltd & Mr Chris Grant**

Other Owners: D&D Armstrong Limited, C. Grant, Mrs M. Nicholas, J. Wade, Mr L. J. Westwood.

Assistant Trainer: Mrs S. Grant.

NH Jockey: Callum Bewley, Brian Hughes.

220 MR MICHAEL GRASSICK, Curragh
Postal: **Fenpark House, Pollardstown, Curragh, Co. Kildare, Ireland**
Contacts: **MOBILE +353 86 364 8829**
EMAIL michaelgrassick1@gmail.com WEBSITE www.michaelcgrassick.com

1 **ALQABEELA (IRE)**, 4, b f Awtaad (IRE)—Intimacy (IRE) **Eoin Connolly**
2 **ANDROMEDAS KINGDOM (IRE)**, 4, b f Holy Roman Emperor (IRE)—Boundless Joy (AUS) **Renata Coleman**
3 **BOMBAY GLORY (IRE)**, 5, b m Fame And Glory—Backinthere (IRE) **Aidan Gleeson**
4 **CACTUS TREE (IRE)**, 6, b h Camelot—Limetree Lady **Alotdonemoretodo Syndicate**
5 **ELANORA (IRE)**, 4, br f No Nay Never (USA)—Vestavia (IRE) **J. Keeling**
6 **ELUSIVE NICOLE (IRE)**, 5, b m Elusive Pimpernel (USA)—Princess Nicole (IRE) **John Walshe**
7 **INDY SYSTEM (IRE)**, 8, gr m Raven's Pass (USA)—Perruche Grise (FR) **Aidan Gleeson**
8 **LOINGSEOIR (IRE)**, 6, b g Henrythenavigator (USA)—Only Exception (IRE) **William Keeling, Roisin Walshe**
9 **MISS MYERS (IRE)**, 5, b m Zoffany (IRE)—Jabroot (IRE) **J. Keeling**
10 **MOLLYS GLORY (IRE)**, 7, b m Fame And Glory—Pellerossa (IRE) **Aidan Gleeson**
11 **NOTALOSSLA (IRE)**, 6, b m Sholokhov (IRE)—Dixie Chick (IRE) **Eoin Connolly**
12 **STELLIUM (IRE)**, 4, b g Elzaam (AUS)—Gleaming Silver (IRE) **J. Keeling**
13 **TEXAS ROCK (IRE)**, 11, b g Rock of Gibraltar (IRE)—Vestavia (IRE) **J. Keeling**
14 **VERHOYEN (IRE)**, 7, b g Piccolo—Memory Lane **P. Cullen**
15 **WHISPER IN COURT (IRE)**, 7, b m Court Cave (IRE)—Dizzy's Whisper (IRE) **Mary Brennan**

THREE-YEAR-OLDS
16 **AMANIRENAS (IRE)**, b f War Command (USA)—Via Aurelia (IRE) **Renata Coleman**
17 **BROWN EAGLE (IRE)**, b g Gleneagles (IRE)—Blueberry Gal (IRE) **J. Keeling**

MR MICHAEL GRASSICK - continued

18 **FAIRY LOVE (IRE)**, b f Raven's Pass (USA)—Only Exception (IRE) **P. Cullen**
19 B c Pride of Dubai (AUS)—Malibu Magic (IRE) **T. Geary**
20 B f Fascinating Rock (IRE)—Mood Indigo (IRE) **William Keeling**
21 B f Elusive Pimpernel (USA)—Pine Valley (IRE) **Conor O'Daly**

TWO-YEAR-OLDS

22 **BEAUMADIER (IRE)**, b c 11/04 Kuroshio (AUS)—Bird of Light (IRE) (Elnadim (USA)) (8078) **P. Cullen**
23 B f 28/04 Australia—Blueberry Gal (IRE) (Bushranger (IRE)) **J. Keeling**
24 B f 20/01 Churchill (IRE)—Flowers Will Bloom (IRE) (Fastnet Rock (AUS)) (51020) **J. Keeling**
25 **LARANJAL (IRE)**, b f 26/03 Camacho—Lexington Sky (IRE) (Iffraaj) (17007) **Alotdonemoretodo Syndicate**
26 B c 30/04 Gregorian (IRE)—Maqueda (USA) (Rock Hard Ten (USA)) (7619) **Shane Doyle**
27 **MIMOSA PARK (IRE)**, b f 01/05 Dragon Pulse (IRE)—Vestavia (IRE) (Alhaarth (IRE)) (2551) **M. C. Grassick**
28 Gr c 09/05 Beat Hollow—Perruche Grise (FR) (Mark of Esteem (IRE)) **Roisin Walshe**

Flat Jockey: W. J. Lee.

MR CARROLL GRAY, Bridgwater
Postal: **The Little Glen, Peartwater Road, Spaxton, Bridgwater, Somerset, TA5 1DG**
Contacts: **MOBILE 07989 768163**

1 **BELLAMY'S GREY**, 10, gr g Black Sam Bellamy (IRE)—Lambrini Queen **Riverdance Consortium 2**
2 **FRAME RATE**, 7, b g Arcano (IRE)—Miss Quality (USA) **Mrs M. E. Gittings-Watts**
3 **LADY IRONSIDE (IRE)**, 5, gr m Lawman (FR)—Expedience (USA) **Mr S. A. Reeves**
4 **SCEALOGHAN (IRE)**, 6, b m Mahler—Mayo Mystique (IRE) **Riverdance Consortium 3**
5 **VINNIE'S ICON (IRE)**, 8, b m Vinnie Roe (IRE)—Iconic Events (IRE) **Mr R. J. Napper & Mr S Reeves**

Other Owners: Mr R. J. Napper, Mr S. A. Reeves.

Assistant Trainer: Mrs C. M. L. Gray.

NH Jockey: Micheal Nolan.

MR WARREN GREATREX, Upper Lambourn
Postal: **Rhonehurst, Upper Lambourn, Hungerford, Berkshire, RG17 8QN**
Contacts: **PHONE 01488 670279 MOBILE 07920 039114**
EMAIL info@wgreatrexracing.com WEBSITE www.wgreatrexracing.com

1 **ABUFFALOSOLDIER (IRE)**, 5, br g Mahler—Adderstonlee (IRE) **Mahler & The Wailers**
2 **ALLANAH'S BOY (IRE)**, 5, b g Westerner—Countess Eileen (IRE) **Fitorfat Racing**
3 **AMERICAN LEGACY**, 6, ch g Shirocco (GER)—Karingas Legacy **Jim and Claire Limited**
4 **ANOTHER EMOTION (FR)**, 9, gr g Turgeon (USA)—Line Perle (FR) **Fitorfat Racing**
5 **ART OF ILLUSION (IRE)**, 5, b g Malinas (GER)—Zara (IRE) **Mr A. Pegley**
6 **BAMFORD EDGE (IRE)**, 5, b g Flemensfirth (USA)—Black Rock Lady (IRE) **Jim and Claire Limited**
7 **BEL MARE**, 4, b f Pether's Moon (IRE)—Uppermost **Mr A. Pegley**
8 **BIG JIM BEAM (IRE)**, 6, b g Westerner—Brighid (IRE)
9 **BILL BAXTER (IRE)**, 6, gr g Milan—Blossom Rose (IRE) **Glassex Holdings Ltd**
10 **BOLD SOLDIER**, 7, b g Kayf Tara—Major Hoolihan **Alan & Andrew Turner**
11 **BOLSOVER BILL (IRE)**, 5, b g Getaway (GER)—Peripheral Vision (USA) **Jim and Claire Limited**
12 **DANCINGWITH STORMS (IRE)**, 8, ch g New Approach (IRE)—Mad About You (IRE) **Jim and Claire Limited**
13 **DHOWIN (IRE)**, 8, b g Yeats (IRE)—On The Way Home (IRE) **Mrs Jill Eynon & Mr Robin Eynon**

MR WARREN GREATREX - continued

14 **DREADPOET'SSOCIETY (IRE)**, 4, b g Mahler—Deadly Pursuit (IRE) **Mr A. Pegley**
15 **DRUMLEE WATAR (IRE)**, 9, ch g Watar (IRE)—Dolly of Dublin (IRE) **Fitorfat Racing**
16 **ELLEON (FR)**, 7, b g Martaline—Ailette **The Spero & Batting Partnership**
17 **EMITOM (IRE)**, 8, b g Gold Well—Avenging Angel (IRE) **The Spero Partnership Ltd**
18 **FRAUGHAN HILL (IRE)**, 6, b g Jet Away—Miss Foaley (IRE) **Fitorfat Racing**
19 **GALLOPADE**, 6, b g Schiaparelli (GER)—Shikra **Mr N. J. Hussey**
20 **GANGSTER (IRE)**, 12, ch g Green Tune (USA)—Dahlia's Krissy (USA) **Jim and Claire Limited**
21 **GO PHARISEE FLYER (FR)**, 6, b g Cokoriko (FR)—Rosalie Malta (FR) **Glassex Holdings Ltd**
22 **GOLDEN ROC (IRE)**, 7, b g Shirocco (GER)—Sovereign Lass (IRE) **Keith Hunter & Francis Ong**
23 4, B f Walk In The Park (IRE)—Hannah's Princess (IRE) **Swanee River Partnership**
24 **HENSCHKE (IRE)**, 8, b g Mahler—Reserve The Right (IRE) **Mrs T. J. Stone-Brown**
25 **HERAKLES (FR)**, 5, b g Saddler Maker (IRE)—Une Histoire (FR) **The Albatross Club**
26 **HERE HARE HERE (FR)**, 5, b g Masterstroke (USA)—Valence (FR) **Mr A. Pegley**
27 **HERMES LE GRIS (FR)**, 5, gr g Gris de Gris (IRE)—Lola Lolita (FR) **David Turner & Ellie Lines**
28 **HEY SOUL SISTER (FR)**, 5, b m Diamond Boy (FR)—Unique Star (FR) **Mr W. J. Greatrex**
29 **HIGH STAKES (IRE)**, 8, b g Scorpion (IRE)—High Performer (IRE) **Jim and Claire Limited**
30 **ICONIC ROCK (IRE)**, 6, b m Yeats (IRE)—Forgotten Lady (IRE) **Million in Mind Partnership**
31 **ISLE OF RONA**, 5, gr m Kayf Tara—Wassailing Queen **Jim and Claire Limited**
32 **IVY AVENUE (IRE)**, 5, ch m Ivawood (IRE)—Dance Avenue (IRE) **Fitorfat Racing**
33 **JARAMILLO**, 4, b g Oasis Dream—Guajara (GER) **Owners Group 098**
34 **KICKSAFTERSIX (IRE)**, 6, b g Scorpion (IRE)—Astalanda (FR) **The Spero Partnership Ltd**
35 4, B g Telescope (IRE)—La Grande Villez (FR)
36 **LINE OF DESCENT (IRE)**, 4, b g Nathaniel (IRE)—Joys of Spring (IRE) **Jim and Claire Limited**
37 **MAHLERVOUS (IRE)**, 9, b g Mahler—Brook Style (IRE) **The Marvellous Partnership**
38 **MANDALAYAN (IRE)**, 7, b g Arakan (USA)—Danza Nera (IRE) **Alan & Andrew Turner**
39 4, Br gr g Shirocco (GER)—Marta Mes (FR) **Mr W. J. Greatrex**
40 **MILITAIRE**, 5, b g Soldier of Fortune (IRE)—La Dame Brune (FR) **Jim and Claire Limited**
41 **MINELLA EXAMINER**, 9, b g Beat Hollow—Bold Fire **The Examiners**
42 **MISSED VACATION (IRE)**, 5, b m Sholokhov (IRE)—Liss Na Piseoga (IRE) **Alan & Andrew Turner**
43 **MOUSETRAP**, 5, gr m Al Namix (FR)—Mickie **Miss A Gibson Fleming&selwood Bloodstock**
44 **MULCAHYS HILL (IRE)**, 10, b g Brian Boru—Belsalsa (FR) **Jim and Claire Limited**
45 **NORTH STAR OSCAR (IRE)**, 8, b g Oscar (IRE)—North Star Poly (IRE) **The North Star Oscar Partnership**
46 **PILOT SHOW (IRE)**, 5, b g Yeats (IRE)—Castle Jane (IRE) **Eynon, Bryce & Rowley**
47 4, B f Presenting—Reine Angevine (FR) **Mrs Julien Turner & Mr Andrew Merriam**
48 6, Gr m Apple Tree (FR)—Rivers Daydream (IRE) **Mr N. J. Hussey**
49 **ROCCOWITHLOVE**, 8, b g Shirocco (GER)—Love Train (IRE) **Crimbourne Bloodstock**
50 **SALAMANCA SCHOOL (FR)**, 5, b g Rock of Gibraltar (IRE)—Princess Sofia (UAE) **As Sutch Partnership**
51 **SARIM (IRE)**, 7, b g Declaration of War (USA)—Silver Star **Fitorfat Racing**
52 **SILVER AND GOLD**, 6, gr g Martaline—Raitera (FR) **Jim and Claire Limited**
53 **STAR FLYER (IRE)**, 5, ch g Jet Away—Gaye Mercy **Jim and Claire Limited**
54 **SUPREME SUNSET**, 5, b m Kayf Tara—Supreme Present **Little Lodge Farm**
55 **THEYSEEKHIMTHERE (IRE)**, 4, b g Elusive Pimpernel (USA)—Wild Spell (IRE) **BadJams 5 Syndicate**
56 **TIPPERARY STAR**, 4, b f Getaway (GER)—Presenteea (IRE) **Glassex Holdings Ltd**
57 **TOP BRASS**, 4, b g Gleneagles (IRE)—California (IRE) **Glassex Holdings Ltd**
58 **WIND FROM THE WEST**, 5, b m Shirocco (GER)—Free Thinking **Mr R. B. Waley-Cohen**

Other Owners: AWR Consultancy Ltd, Mr T. J. Batting, Mr L. A. Bolingbroke, Mrs J. S. Chugg, Mr R. D. Chugg, Mr B. W. Enright, Mrs J. M. Eynon, R. A. F. Eynon, Mrs Jill Eynon & Mr Robin Eynon, Miss A. Gibson Fleming, Mr T. R. Gittins, Mr W. J. Greatrex, Mr M. W. Gregory, Mr M. Helyar, Mr G. P. Howard, K. L. Hunter, Jim and Claire Limited, Ms E. J. Lines, Mr S. M. Little, Mr P. Martin, Mr M. McLoughlin, A. W. K. Merriam, Mr P. Molony, Mr K. O'Brien, Mr F. Ong, Mr C. M. Parker, Mrs M. Parker, Mr D. A. Roberts, Mr M. N. Scott, Selwood Bloodstock, Mr C. J. Sutton, The Spero Partnership Ltd, Mr D. A. Turner, Ms J. B. Turner, Mrs N. C. Turner, Mrs N. J. White, Mr S. Williams.

Assistant Trainer: Oliver Kozak, **Head Lad:** Trigger Plunkett, Ian Yeates.

Flat Jockey: Thomas Greatrex. **NH Jockey:** Harry Bannister, Gavin Sheehan. **Conditional Jockey:** Caoilin Quinn.

223 MR OLIVER GREENALL, Malpas
Postal: Stockton Hall Farm, Oldcastle, Malpas, Cheshire, SY14 7AE
Contacts: **PHONE 01948 861207 MOBILE 07771 571000**
EMAIL ocg@stocktonhall.co.uk **WEBSITE** www.olivergreenall.co.uk

1 **ADJOURNMENT (IRE)**, 6, b g Court Cave (IRE)—Cherry Eile (IRE) **Stockton Hall Farm Racing**
2 **ANDONNO**, 4, b g Dansili—Lavender And Lace **The Andonno Syndicate**
3 **ARCTIC ROAD**, 9, b g Flemensfirth (USA)—Arctic Actress **Mr J. F. Wilson**
4 **ASK THE DOC (IRE)**, 6, b g Ask—Benedicta Rose (IRE) **The Mystery Machine**
5 **AUTHORIZO (FR)**, 7, b g Authorized (IRE)—Street Lightning (FR) **The Deesiders**
6 **BARNIE BEETLE**, 5, b g Firebreak—Helamis **Mr F. W. Dronzek**
7 **BASHFUL**, 4, b g Manduro (GER)—Inhibition **Lycett Racing Ltd**
8 **BLACKWELL BAY (IRE)**, 5, ro g Carlotamix (FR)—Koochie Baby (IRE) **Ratkatcha Racing**
9 **BLUE COLLAR GLORY (IRE)**, 5, b m Fame And Glory—Rosy de Cyborg (FR)
10 **BOUNDSY BOY**, 4, b g Awtaad (IRE)—Wadaat **E. A. Brook**
11 **BRAVETHEWAVES**, 5, b g Gentlewave (IRE)—Miss Lucky Penny **The Brave Bunch**
12 **CAWTHORNE**, 8, b g Sulamani (IRE)—Kings Maiden (IRE) **Back to the Track Syndicate**
13 **CHRIS COOL**, 6, b g Sulamani (IRE)—Cool Friend (IRE) **Evason, Harney & Greenall**
14 **CLONDAW PRETENDER**, 7, br g Great Pretender (IRE)—Shropshire Girl **Peavoy Emdells Daresbury Adams Lewis**
15 **COISA BLANCO (IRE)**, 9, b g Jeremy (USA)—Moon Legend (USA) **Mr O. C. Greenall**
16 **DIEU VIVANT (FR)**, 9, b g Network (GER)—Panique Pas (FR) **Mr P. J. Chesters**
17 5, b m Multiplex—Do It On Dani **Mr O. C. Greenall**
18 **DONAIRE (IRE)**, 6, b g Califet (FR)—Grangeclare Lark (IRE) **Ratkatcha Racing**
19 **DONDIAM (FR)**, 5, b g Diamond Boy (FR)—Nouvelle Donne (FR) **Ratkatcha Racing**
20 **DOOYORK (IRE)**, 6, b m Shantou (USA)—Hannah Rose (IRE) **Manchester Tennis & Racquet Club Racing**
21 **DRAGONFRUIT**, 7, ch g Black Sam Bellamy (IRE)—Fruity Farm **Mrs B. A. Bostock**
22 **DRUK (FR)**, 4, br g Sea The Stars (IRE)—Solita (USA) **Bate, Daresbury & Studholme**
23 **DUKE OF DECEPTION (IRE)**, 5, b g September Storm (GER)—Mrs Peachey (IRE) **Salmon Racing**
24 **ECOSSAIS (FR)**, 8, b g Saddler Maker (IRE)—Sacade (FR) **Oliver Greenall Racing Club**
25 **EL BORRACHO (IRE)**, 7, b g Society Rock (IRE)—Flame of Hibernia (IRE) **El Borracho Syndicate**
26 **EMMA BLUE (IRE)**, 5, b m Mahler—Rhapsody In Blue (GER) **Ratkatcha Racing**
27 **ESCALADE (IRE)**, 5, b m Canford Cliffs (IRE)—Sliding Scale **Bcc Racing Partnership**
28 **EVANDER (IRE)**, 7, b g Arcadio—Blazing Belle (IRE) **Highclere Tbracing Henry Moore & Partner**
29 **FARO (FR)**, 7, b g Cokoriko (FR)—Teskaline (FR) **The Oldcastle Racing Syndicate**
30 **FFREE PEDRO (IRE)**, 6, b g Yeats (IRE)—Ain't Misbehavin (IRE) **Ratkatcha Racing**
31 **FIRST GLANCE**, 8, b m Passing Glance—Call Me A Star **Ratkatcha Racing**
32 **FIRST MAN (IRE)**, 7, b g Lilbourne Lad (IRE)—Dos Lunas (IRE) **The Haydock Park Racing Syndicate**
33 **FIST PUMPING TIME (IRE)**, 6, b m Fame And Glory—That's The Goose (IRE) **Foxtrot Racing Kubinski**
34 **FIVE BAR BRIAN**, 8, br g Elusive Pimpernel (USA)—Vayenga (FR) **Deva Racing Five Bar Brian**
35 **FRATERCULUS (IRE)**, 5, ch g Teofilo (IRE)—Sanaara (USA) **Coxon, Daresbury, Greenall & Macechern**
36 **FURIUS DE CIERGUES (FR)**, 7, gr g Lord du Sud (FR)—Java de Ciergues (FR) **Ratkatcha Racing**
37 **GAMESTERS GIRL**, 4, b f Telescope (IRE)—Gamesters Lady **Gamesters Partnership**
38 **GAMESTERS ICON**, 7, b m Sixties Icon—Gamesters Lady **Gamesters Partnership**
39 **GARETH CAEL (FR)**, 6, gr g Montmartre (FR)—Dallia (FR) **The Good Friends Syndicate**
40 **GESSKILLE (FR)**, 6, b g Network (GER)—Nashkille (FR) **The Nevers Racing Partnership I**
41 **GO ON CHEZ**, 6, b g Malinas (GER)—Who's Afraid **The Lads & Her**
42 **GOLD DESERT**, 5, ch g Mastercraftsman (IRE)—Tendency (IRE) **Harbour Rose Partnership**
43 **GOOD WORK (FR)**, 6, gr g Network (GER)—Teskaline (FR) **The Cool Runnings Syndicate**
44 **GOUET DES BRUYERES (FR)**, 6, b g Policy Maker (IRE)—Innsbruck (FR)

Daresbury,Buckley,R Mills,D Mills,Walsh
45 **HERBIERS (FR)**, 5, b g Waldpark (GER)—Qualanke (FR) **The Nevers Racing Partnership**
46 **HERITIER (FR)**, 5, b g Fuisse (FR)—Toscane (FR) **Gardiner & the Cool Runnings Team**
47 **HOMME PUBLIC (FR)**, 5, b g Cokoriko (FR)—Uddy (FR) **The Nevers Racing Partnership Ii**
48 **HORACIO APPLE'S (FR)**, 5, ch g Saddex—Apple's Noa (FR) **Highclere Tb Racing - Apple & Dudgeon**
49 **IMPERIAL SUN**, 4, b g Sea The Stars (IRE)—Abunai **Ratkatcha Racing**
50 **IROKO (FR)**, 4, b g Cokoriko (FR)—Boscraie (FR) **Mr J. P. McManus**
51 **JET OF MAGIC (IRE)**, 6, b g Jet Away—Ginandit (IRE) **Ratkatcha Racing**
52 **JUST GOT TO GET ON**, 8, ch g Malinas (GER)—Just Cliquot **Mrs C. Swarbrick**
53 **KILBARRY LEADER (IRE)**, 6, b m Leading Light (IRE)—Eternal Lady (IRE)
54 **KUBINSKI (IRE)**, 5, br g Aizavoski (IRE)—Gone Wrong (IRE) **Foxtrot Racing Kubinski**
55 **LADY TARA MOSS**, 5, b m Kayf Tara—Brackenmoss (IRE) **The Lady Tara Moss Syndicate & Partner**

MR OLIVER GREENALL - continued

56 **LATE ROMANTIC (IRE),** 12, b g Mahler—Mere Gaye (IRE) **Spitalized Racing**
57 **LETTHETRUTHBEKNOWN (IRE),** 6, b m Shirocco (GER)—Pescetto Lady (IRE) **Mr G. C. Myddelton**
58 **LUCKY LOVER BOY (IRE),** 7, b g Teofilo (IRE)—Mayonga (IRE) **The Lucky Lovers Partnership**
59 **MCPHERSON,** 4, b br g Golden Horn—Moonlight Sonata **Mr O. C. Greenall**
60 **MIDNIGHT MOSS,** 10, ch g Midnight Legend—Brackenmoss (IRE) **Midnight Moss Partnership**
61 **MISS DELIGHTED (IRE),** 9, b m Getaway (GER)—Abhainn Ri (IRE) **Blumtolhurstonionsdaresbury**
62 **MISS TARA MOSS,** 7, b m Kayf Tara—Brackenmoss (IRE) **Miss Tara Moss Syndicate & Partner**
63 **MONTE IGUELDO (FR),** 5, b g Cokoriko (FR)—Petite Nany (FR) **Mr S. Beetham**
64 **MY POEM,** 5, ch m Poet's Voice—Watchoverme **Back to the Track Syndicate**
65 **OCEANS RED,** 6, ch g Yorgunnabelucky (USA)—Djess **Spitalized Racing**
66 **OLDGRANGEWOOD,** 11, b g Central Park (IRE)—Top of The Class (IRE) **Mr G. C. Myddelton**
67 4, B g Gentlewave (IRE)—Onetwobeat
68 **OUTBACK BOY (IRE),** 4, ch g Australia—Permission Slip (IRE) **The Zigzaggers**
69 **PATAGONIA (FR),** 5, b g Ballingarry (IRE)—Daramour (FR) **Mr S. Beetham**
70 **PATIENT DREAM (FR),** 4, b g Al Kazeem—Parnell's Dream **More Turf Racing**
71 **PEPITE DE BELLE,** 7, br m Great Pretender (IRE)—Pepite de Soleil (FR) **Mr M. Fennessy**
72 **PHIL DE PAIL (FR),** 5, gr g Silver Frost (IRE)—Dame de Pail (FR) **Stockton Hall Farm Racing**
73 **POST CHAISE (IRE),** 5, b g Shirocco (GER)—Trazona Kit (IRE) **Mr G. Cardwell**
74 **PYM (IRE),** 9, b g Stowaway—Liss Rua (IRE) **Ratkatcha Racing**
75 **SHADY CHARACTER,** 9, b g Malinas (GER)—Shady Anne **Jocelyn Rosenberg & Roger Weatherby**
76 **SHE'S ALL IN GOLD (IRE),** 5, b m Golden Horn—Simonetta (IRE) **The Gold Diggers**
77 **SIMPLY RED,** 4, ch f Proconsul—Ssafa **Bolingbroke, Mickley**
78 **SNOWY EVENING (IRE),** 5, b g Snow Sky—Sherwolf (IRE) **The Stockton Hopefuls**
79 **SOMEONE YOU LOVE,** 6, b m Schiaparelli (GER)—Perjury **Mr G. Malanga**
80 **STEEL YARD (IRE),** 7, ch g Frozen Fire (GER)—Banphrionsa (IRE) **Mrs J. Smith**
81 **SUCELLUS,** 6, b g Dansili—Primevere (IRE) **P. G. Evans**
82 **THAI TERRIER (USA),** 6, b g Kitten's Joy (USA)—Perfect Agility (USA) **Hardscrabble**
83 **THE QUESTIONER (IRE),** 6, ch g Ask—Cush Bach (IRE) **Salmon Racing**
84 **THE WILD WILD SEA,** 4, b m Gentlewave (IRE)—Sting In The Gale **The Oldcastle Racing Syndicate**
85 **THUMUR (USA),** 5, b br g Golden Horn—Time Being **Mr D. J. Astbury**
86 **TORINO (IRE),** 4, b g Fastnet Rock (AUS)—Sacrosanct (IRE) **The Early Doors Syndicate**
87 **TRE A PENI,** 5, b m Pether's Moon (IRE)—Cerise Bleue (FR) **The Malpas Syndicate**
88 **TWOTWOTHREE (IRE),** 9, b g Shantou (USA)—Sibury (IRE) **Evason, Hewitt, Tolhurst & Walsh**
89 **VANDEMERE (IRE),** 7, b g Jeremy—Victoria Bridge (IRE) **Mr S. Burns**
90 **WASASTYLEQUEEN,** 7, b m Schiaparelli (GER)—As Was **The Burling Family Ltd**
91 **WHITE RHINO (IRE),** 6, b g Doyen (IRE)—Aventia (IRE)
92 **WHODINI (IRE),** 5, ch g Conduit (IRE)—Mosey On Molly (IRE) **Malcolm Jones & John Norbury**
93 **ZINC WHITE (IRE),** 4, gr g Vadamos (FR)—Chinese White (IRE) **Mr S. Beetham**

THREE-YEAR-OLDS

94 **BAZZA THE BARREL,** b g Postponed (IRE)—Weigelia **Mr D. J. Astbury**
95 **PADDY'S FANCY,** gr f New Bay—Likelihood (USA) **Zoe Hassall & George Hassall**
96 **SHETLAND TONY,** b g Sea The Moon (GER)—St Aye (USA) **Ratkatcha Racing**

TWO-YEAR-OLDS

97 Ch g 06/03 Free Eagle (IRE)—Only Together (IRE) (Montjeu (IRE))

Other Owners: Mr G. F. C. Adams, Mr B. Allan, Mr M. Astbury, Mr N. J. Bate, Mr P. R. Billington, Mr W. B. B. Blum Gentilomo, Mr L. A. Bolingbroke, Mrs B. A. Bostock, Mr K. J. Buckley, Mr S. Bullough, S. Cannon, Mr S. A. Coxon, Lord Daresbury, Mr P. A. Davies, Mr G. Dewhurst, Mr K. J. Dodd, Mr B. H. Dolan, Mr A. S. Dudgeon, Mr S. Evason, Mr T. Gardiner, Mr O. C. Greenall, Mr P. J. Harney, Mr G. A. Hassall, Mr N. A. D. Hassall, Mrs Z. L. Hassall, Mr C. A. J. Hathorn, R. J. Hewitt, Highclere TBred Racing -Henry Moore, Highclere Thoroughbred Racing - Apple, Highclere Thoroughbred Racing Ltd, M. B. Jones, R. Kent, Mr M. H. Lampton, Mr K. P. Leggett, Gavin MacEchern, Mr C. P. A. McDonagh, Mr J. McInerney, Mrs L. J. Midgley, Mr D. P. Mills, Mr R. Mills, Miss Tara Moss Syndicate, Mr R. J. Nicholas, Mr J. D. Norbury, Mr A. W. Onions, Reveley Farms, Mr J. L. Roberts, Mr K. J. Roscoe, Mrs J. P. Rosenberg, Mr D. B. Salmon, Mrs Lynn Salmon, Mr M. W. Salmon, Mr M. Smyth, Mr D. Studholme, The Cool Runnings Syndicate, The Lady Tara Moss Syndicate, Mr A. M. Tolhurst, Mr M. Trounce, Mr D. J. Walsh, Mr S. M. Walsh, Mr R. N. Weatherby.

Assistant Trainer: J. Guerriero.

224 MRS CAMILLA GREENWOOD, Horsington
Postal: **Hazeldene, High Road, Horsington, Templecombe, Somerset, BA8 0DN**
Contacts: **PHONE 07855 798126**
EMAIL **cagreenwood1@hotmail.com**

1 **HATARI (IRE)**, 10, b g Vinnie Roe (IRE)—Quinnsborooldvic (IRE) **Mr T. P. Greenwood**
2 **RUNNING WITH ERIC**, 6, b g Bollin Eric—Running Hotter **Mrs C. Greenwood**

225 MR TOM GRETTON, Inkberrow
Postal: **C/o Gretton & Co Ltd, Middle Bouts Farm, Bouts Lane, Inkberrow, Worcester**
Contacts: **PHONE 01386 792240 MOBILE 07866 116928 FAX 01386 792472**
EMAIL **tomgretton@hotmail.co.uk WEBSITE www.tomgrettonracing.com**

1 **COMMITTEE OF ONE**, 7, b m Universal (IRE)—Inkberrow Rose (IRE) **Lewis Family & Tom Gretton Racing Club**
2 **GETBAZOUTOFHERE**, 6, ch m Gentlewave (IRE)—Present Your Case (IRE) **Mr I. M. Lewis**
3 **IGGY IGGINS**, 6, b g Norse Dancer (IRE)—La Creole (FR) **T. R. Gretton & Mr D. T. B. Griffiths**
4 **JEAN BART (FR)**, 6, ch g Muhtathir—Jacira (FR) **T. R. Gretton**
5 **JOHNNY MAC (IRE)**, 7, b g Imperial Monarch (IRE)—Killowen Pam (IRE) **Mr M. Slingsby**
6 **KAUTO RIKO (FR)**, 11, b g Ballingarry (IRE)—Kauto Relstar (FR) **Mr & Mrs J.Dale & Partners**
7 **LICKPENNY LARRY**, 11, gr g Sagamix (FR)—Myriah (IRE) **Alan Clarke & Tom Gretton Racing Club**
8 **LINCOLN LYN**, 6, b m Universal (IRE)—Altesse de Sou (FR) **Team Burton, Ray & Warburton**
9 **ONE LAST GLANCE**, 5, b g Passing Glance—Lillie Lou **Fred Camis, Ray Fielder & Mel Clarke**
10 **PASSING SECRETS**, 6, bl g Passing Glance—Tabora **T. R. Gretton**
11 **PERSUER**, 6, ch m Intello (GER)—Chase The Lady (USA) **G1 Racing Club Ltd**
12 **PRETTY FANTASY (IRE)**, 6, b m Casamento (IRE)—Pixie Belle (IRE) **T. R. Gretton**
13 **SADLER'S BAY**, 5, b g Black Sam Bellamy (IRE)—Cormorant Cove **Mr T. Wheeler**
14 **URBLEREAGH (FR)**, 5, ch g High Rock (IRE)—Kelly des Cotieres (FR) **D. R. & E. E. Brown**
15 **WILDKATZE (GER)**, 6, b m Kamsin (GER)—Zaynaat **Mr J. P. Edwards**

THREE-YEAR-OLDS
16 **FASHION DELIGHT (USA)**, b f Overanalyze (USA)—Where Woody Bea (USA) **Mr B. P. Keogh**

Other Owners: D. R. Brown, Mrs E. E. Brown, Mr A. J. Burton, F. D. Camis, Mr A. S. Clarke, Mr M. D. Clarke, Mrs J. S. Dale, Mr J. W. Dale, Mr B. Dennehy, R. Fielder, Mrs L. Gretton, T. R. Gretton, Mr D. T. B. Griffiths, Mr I. M. Lewis, Mr G. C. Parkins, Dr D. J. M. Ray, Mr T. Rees, Tom Gretton Racing Club, Mr N. D. Warburton.

Assistant Trainer: Laura Gretton.

226 MR DAVID C. GRIFFITHS, Bawtry
Postal: **Martin Hall Farm, Martin Common, Bawtry, Doncaster, South Yorkshire, DN10 6DA**
Contacts: **PHONE 01302 714247 MOBILE 07816 924621**
EMAIL **davidgriffiths250@hotmail.com WEBSITE www.davidgriffithsracing.co.uk**

1 **CANZONE**, 5, ch g Siyouni (FR)—Stirring Ballad **Jason Adlam & Martin Hall Farm Racing**
2 **COOL SPIRIT**, 7, b g Swiss Spirit—Marmot Bay (IRE) **Mr D. Milthorp**
3 **DUKE OF FIRENZE**, 13, ch g Pivotal—Nannina **Adlam & Griffiths**
4 **FIREWATER**, 6, ch g Monsieur Bond (IRE)—Spirit Na Heireann (IRE) **Ladies & The Tramps**
5 **LUCKY BEGGAR (IRE)**, 12, gr g Verglas (IRE)—Lucky Clio (IRE) **Mr D. C. Griffiths**
6 **ORNATE**, 9, b g Bahamian Bounty—Adorn **Kings Road Racing Partnership**
7 **TERUNTUM STAR (FR)**, 10, ch g Dutch Art—Seralia **Mrs E. Jepson**

MR DAVID C. GRIFFITHS - continued

THREE-YEAR-OLDS
8 **MR QUIGLEY**, b g Iffraaj—White Rosa (IRE) **Flash Figs Racing Mhf & Mr D Thomas**

TWO-YEAR-OLDS
9 Ch c 11/04 Mazameer (IRE)—Black Diamond Girl (Kheleyf (USA)) **Martin Hall Farm Racing**
10 B f 13/03 Heeraat (IRE)—Lookalike (Multiplex) **Martin Hall Farm Racing**

Other Owners: Mr J. P. Adlam, Mr M. Bartlett, Mr G. Davidoff, Flash Figs Racing, Mrs N. Forrest, Mr D. C. Griffiths, Mrs S. E. Griffiths, Mr D. W. Thomas.

Assistant Trainer: Mrs S. E. Griffiths.

Flat Jockey: David Allan, Phil Dennis.

227

MRS DIANA GRISSELL, Robertsbridge
Postal: **Brightling Park, Robertsbridge, East Sussex, TN32 5HH**
Contacts: **PHONE 01424 838241 MOBILE 07950 312610**
EMAIL digrissell@aol.com WEBSITE www.brightlingpark.com

1 **ISKRABOB**, 12, ch g Tobougg (IRE)—Honour Bolton **Mrs S. B. Bolton**
2 **JAPPELOUP (IRE)**, 13, b br g Presenting—Crackin' Liss (IRE) **Mrs C. A. Bailey**
3 6, B m Dunaden (FR)—Miltara (IRE)
4 **MILTON**, 10, br g Nomadic Way (USA)—Jesmund **Mrs C. A. Webber**
5 **SQUIRE HOCKEY**, 9, b g Green Horizon—Luisa Miller (IRE) **Mr M. Park**

Assistant Trainer: Paul Hacking, **Head Girl:** Donna French.

Amateur Jockey: Mr James Rawdon-Mogg.

228

MR JOHN GROUCOTT, Much Wenlock
Postal: **Dairy Cottage, Bourton, Much Wenlock, Shropshire, TF13 6QD**
Contacts: **PHONE 01746 785603**

1 **ALDERSON**, 9, b g Zamindar (USA)—Claradotnet **Mr G. D. Kendrick**
2 **CABHFUILFUNGI (IRE)**, 6, b g Mahler—Maggie Andy (IRE) **C. J. Tipton**
3 **EL SCORPIO (IRE)**, 10, b g Scorpion (IRE)—El Monica (IRE) **Mrs B. Clarke**
4 **HAND AND DIAMOND**, 7, b m Westerner—Heels Overhead **Miss J. Balmer**
5 **HAPPY NEWS**, 9, gr m Fair Mix (IRE)—Welcome News **Mrs C. L. Shaw**
6 **HEDGEBIRD**, 8, b m Black Sam Bellamy (IRE)—Morville **Mrs B. Clarke**
7 **JESSIE LIGHTFOOT**, 8, b m Yeats (IRE)—Needle Doll (IRE) **Mr C. Bartley**
8 **LADY MALARKEY (IRE)**, 7, b m Scorpion (IRE)—Heather Feather (IRE) **Mr P. Price**
9 **MAISIEBELLA**, 9, b m Black Sam Bellamy (IRE)—Lucylou (IRE) **Mrs B. Clarke**
10 **MASSINI MAN**, 9, b g Dr Massini (IRE)—Alleged To Rhyme (IRE) **Mrs E. A. Fletcher**
11 **MONITION (IRE)**, 9, b g Stowaway—Forever Bubbles (IRE) **Mr G. D. Bower**
12 **MUSE OF FIRE (IRE)**, 8, b g Getaway (GER)—Maria Sophia (IRE) **C. J. Tipton**
13 **MYTHICAL FORTUNE**, 5, b m Phoenix Reach (IRE)—Alleged To Rhyme (IRE) **Mrs E. A. Fletcher**
14 **ON THE PLATFORM (IRE)**, 6, b g Valirann (FR)—Coca's Lady (IRE) **Mrs B. Clarke**
15 **POT OF PAINT**, 5, b g New Approach (IRE)—Regency (JPN) **Mr D. R. Passant**
16 **RATTLING ROSIE**, 4, gr f Lethal Force (IRE)—Lady Red Oak **Mr D. R. Passant**
17 **RICHARDSON**, 7, ch g Kirkwall—Makeover **Mr G. D. Kendrick**
18 **ROSIERITA**, 8, b m Black Sam Bellamy (IRE)—Mtilly **Mrs B. Clarke**
19 **SAMMIX**, 5, gr g Black Sam Bellamy (IRE)—Morville **Mrs B. Clarke**
20 **STAR OF RORY (IRE)**, 8, b g Born To Sea (IRE)—Dame Alicia (IRE) **Mr D. R. Passant & Hefin Williams**

229 MR RAE GUEST, Newmarket

Postal: **Chestnut Tree Stables, Hamilton Road, Newmarket, Suffolk, CB8 0NY**
Contacts: **WORK** 01638 661508 **MOBILE** 07711 301095
EMAIL raeguest@raeguest.com **WEBSITE** www.raeguest.com

1 **ARAMIS GREY (IRE)**, 5, gr m Gutaifan (IRE)—Sveva (IRE) **The Musketeers**
2 **ARRIVISTE**, 5, b m Sea The Moon (GER)—Apparatchika **Miss K. Rausing**
3 **AUTUMN TRAIL**, 5, b m Sixties Icon—Boleyna (USA) **Mr P. J. Smith**
4 **BAHIA STAR**, 4, b f Twilight Son—Bahia Breeze **BB Bloodstock**
5 **CAPE SUNSET**, 5, b g Gutaifan (IRE)—Cape Factor (IRE) **Mr D. J. Willis**
6 **CRY HAVOC (IRE)**, 5, b m War Command (USA)—Na Zdorovie **The Musketeers**
7 **EVENING SONG**, 4, b f Twilight Son—Zerka **The Good Reason Partners**
8 **FAUVETTE (IRE)**, 5, gr m Dark Angel (IRE)—Falsafa **Mr R. Guest**
9 **JEWEL IN MY CROWN**, 4, gr f Mukhadram—Rosa Grace **Mr E. P. Duggan**
10 **KISS KISS (IRE)**, 4, b f Power—Formidable Guest **Miss V. Markowiak**
11 **LAND OF WINTER (FR)**, 6, b g Camelot—Gaselee (USA) **Paul Smith & Rae Guest**
12 **NATURE (IRE)**, 4, b f Nathaniel (IRE)—Chantrea (IRE) **Celbridge Estates Partnership**
13 **WALTZING QUEEN (IRE)**, 4, b f Helmet (AUS)—Alsaaden **BB Thoroughbreds**

THREE-YEAR-OLDS

14 **BELLA VENETA**, b f Belardo (IRE)—World Class **The Chestnut Tree Syndicate**
15 **DAYS LIKE THIS**, b f Iffraaj—Safiyna (FR) **Mr D. J. Willis, Mr R. Guest**
16 **EKLIL**, b c Invincible Spirit (IRE)—Raaqy (IRE) **Mr D. J. Willis**
17 **FAMOUS FOOTSTEPS (FR)**, b f Dabirsim (FR)—Darysina (USA) **Mr R. Guest**
18 **KUTAIBA (IRE)**, b f Golden Horn—Maktaba (IRE) **Mr R. Guest**
19 **LUNA BREEZE**, b f Nathaniel (IRE)—Bahia Breeze **BB Bloodstock**
20 **MELODRAMATICA**, b f Bobby's Kitten (USA)—Memory Lane **Miss K. Rausing**
21 **MIZZEN YOU**, gr f Mizzen Mast (USA)—Preferential **The Chestnut Tree Syndicate**
22 **PHOTO BOMB (IRE)**, b f Haatef (USA)—Formidable Guest **Miss V. Markowiak**
23 **RIBTICKLER (IRE)**, b f Ribchester (IRE)—Folk Singer **The Storm Again Syndicate**
24 **SAY GRACE (IRE)**, b f Kodiac—Break Bread (IRE) **The Rainy Day Partnership**
25 **WALTZING INTIME (IRE)**, b f Australia—Alsaaden **BB Thoroughbreds**

TWO-YEAR-OLDS

26 B f 12/03 Australia—Alsaaden (Acclamation) **BB Thoroughbreds**
27 B f 21/04 Tamayuz—Baliyka (IRE) (Cape Cross (IRE)) (5000) **The 'Can't Say No' Syndicate**
28 B f 15/02 Golden Horn—Beautiful Forest (Nayef (USA)) (20952) **Top Hat and Tails**
29 B c 28/04 Dariyan (FR)—Boleyna (USA) (Officer (USA)) **Mr P. J. Smith**
30 **CARIWINA**, b f 24/02 Bobby's Kitten (USA)—Catadupa (Selkirk (USA)) **Mr R. Guest**
31 B f 13/02 Mayson—Corps de Ballet (IRE) (Fasliyev (USA)) (10000) **Mr R. Guest**
32 **GRAND DUCHESS OLGA**, b f 26/01 Sir Percy—Archduchess (Archipenko (USA)) **Miss K. Rausing**
33 Gr f 21/04 Havana Grey—Inagh River (Fasliyev (USA)) (9000) **The Unusual Suspects Syndicate**
34 Ch f 16/04 Australia—Jane's Memory (IRE) (Captain Rio) (45000) **Mr R. Guest**
35 Ch f 09/02 Decorated Knight—Maid To Master (IRE) (Danehill Dancer (IRE)) (14000) **The Unusual Suspects Syndicate**
36 **SHOW OF HANDS**, b f 19/03 Showcasing—Yali (IRE) (Orpen (USA)) (28571) **Mr Colin Joseph**
37 Ch f 02/04 Profitable—Showbird (Showcasing) (20000) **The Unusual Suspects Syndicate**
38 B f 15/02 Postponed (IRE)—Velvet Charm (Excelebration (IRE)) **Mr Colin Murfitt**
39 **VIA AEMILIA**, b f 31/03 Oasis Dream—Sea The Queen (IRE) (Sea The Stars (IRE)) (20000) **Paul Smith & Rae Guest**

Other Owners: Celbridge Estates Ltd, R. T. Goodes, Derek & Rae Guest, Mr R. Guest, Mr A. P. Rogers, Mrs S. Rogers, Mr P. J. Smith, Mr B. Stewart.

230 MS POLLY GUNDRY, Ottery St Mary

Postal: **Holcombe Brook, Holcombe Lane, Ottery St Mary, Devon, EX11 1PH**
Contacts: **PHONE** 01404 811181 **MOBILE** 07932 780621
EMAIL pollygundrytraining@live.co.uk **WEBSITE** www.pollygundrytraining.co.uk

1 **DAWSON CITY**, 13, b g Midnight Legend—Running For Annie **Kim Franklin & Polly Walker**
2 **DON'T RIGHTLY KNOW**, 7, ch m Malinas (GER)—Thebelloftheball **Mr J. P. Selby**
3 **GIDLEIGH PARK**, 4, b g Walk In The Park (IRE)—Lindeman (IRE) **Mr & Mrs R. G. Kelvin-Hughes**

MS POLLY GUNDRY - continued

4 **MADAME POMPADOUR,** 4, b f Pour Moi (IRE)—Tinagoodnight (FR) **Mr & Mrs R. G. Kelvin-Hughes**
5 **MISS GHILLIE,** 4, b f Policy Maker (IRE)—Miss Ballantyne **Mr & Mrs R. G. Kelvin-Hughes**
6 **MISS HARRIETT,** 6, b m Arvico (FR)—Ivorsagoodun **Mr P. G. Gibbins**
7 **RIVARAMA,** 4, b f Milan—Chomba Womba (IRE) **Mr & Mrs R. G. Kelvin-Hughes**
8 **SANTINI,** 10, b g Milan—Tinagoodnight (FR)
9 **SMITH'S BAY,** 9, b g Midnight Legend—Takotna (IRE) **Kim Franklin & Polly Walker**
10 **SWEET NIGHTINGALE,** 5, b m Excelebration (IRE)—Night Symphonie **Sweet Nightingale Partnership**

Other Owners: Mr P. R. Carter, Miss K. M. Franklin, Miss P. Gundry, Mr N. R. Shires.

Assistant Trainer: Edward Walker.

NH Jockey: James Best, Nick Schofield. **Amateur Jockey:** Mr Josh Newman.

MR WILLIAM HAGGAS, Newmarket
Postal: **Somerville Lodge, Fordham Road, Newmarket, Suffolk, CB8 7AA**
Contacts: **PHONE 01638 667013 MOBILE 07860 282281 FAX 01638 660534**
EMAIL **william@somerville-lodge.co.uk** WEBSITE www.somerville-lodge.co.uk

1 **ADDEYBB (IRE),** 8, ch g Pivotal—Bush Cat (USA) **Sheikh Ahmed Al Maktoum**
2 **AL AASY (IRE),** 5, b g Sea The Stars (IRE)—Kitcara **Shadwell Estate Company**
3 **ALDAARY,** 4, ch g Territories (IRE)—Broughtons Revival **Shadwell Estate Company**
4 **ALENQUER (FR),** 4, b c Adlerflug (GER)—Wild Blossom (GER) **M M Stables**
5 **AMETIST,** 5, ch g Dutch Art—Zykina **Cheveley Park Stud**
6 **ARAMAIC (IRE),** 4, b br g Le Havre (IRE)—Middle Persia **Sheikh Isa Salman**
7 **AROUSING,** 4, b f Kodiac—Enticing (IRE) **Lael Stable**
8 **ARTEMISIA LOMI (IRE),** 4, b f Galileo (IRE)—Sharp Susan (USA) **Cayton Park Stud**
9 **BAAEED,** 4, b c Sea The Stars (IRE)—Aghareed (USA) **Shadwell Estate Company**
10 **BARTZELLA,** 4, b f Golden Horn—Primevere (USA) **A. E. Oppenheimer**
11 **BASHKIROVA,** 4, b f Pivotal—Russian Finale **Cheveley Park Stud**
12 **BOOSALA (IRE),** 5, b g Dawn Approach (IRE)—Zoowraa **Sheikh Ahmed Al Maktoum**
13 **CANDLEFORD (IRE),** 4, b g Kingman—Dorcas Lane **Barnane Stud**
14 **DUBAI HONOUR (IRE),** 4, b g Pride of Dubai (AUS)—Mondelice **Mohamed Obaida**
15 **FIREWORKS (FR),** 4, b g Kingman—Miss Plimsoll (USA) **Fiona Carmichael**
16 **GAASSEE (IRE),** 4, b c Sea The Stars (IRE)—Oojooba **Sheikh Ahmed Al Maktoum**
17 **GROCER JACK (GER),** 5, b h Oasis Dream—Good Donna (GER) **Prince Faisal Khaled**
18 **HAMISH,** 6, b g Motivator—Tweed **Brian Haggas**
19 **HURRICANE IVOR (IRE),** 5, b g Ivawood (IRE)—Quickstep Queen **Fiona Carmichael**
20 **ILARAAB (IRE),** 5, b h Wootton Bassett—Belova (IRE) **Sheikh Ahmed Al Maktoum**
21 **IRISH ADMIRAL (IRE),** 5, b g French Navy—Magadar (USA) **Sheikh Ahmed Al Maktoum**
22 **LILAC ROAD (IRE),** 4, ch f Mastercraftsman (IRE)—Lavender Lane (IRE) **Jon & Julia Aisbitt**
23 **MAHRAJAAN (USA),** 4, ch g Kitten's Joy (USA)—Lahudood **Shadwell Estate Company**
24 **MOHAAFETH (IRE),** 4, ch c Frankel—French Dressing **Shadwell Estate Company**
25 **MUJTABA,** 4, b g Dubawi (IRE)—Majmu (USA) **Shadwell Estate Company**
26 **MY ASTRA (IRE),** 4, b f Lope de Vega (IRE)—My Titania (IRE) **Sunderland Holding Inc.**
27 **MY OBERON (IRE),** 5, b g Dubawi (IRE)—My Titania (IRE) **Sunderland Holding Inc.**
28 **NAHAARR (IRE),** 6, b h Dark Angel (IRE)—Charlotte Rua (IRE) **Sheikh Ahmed Al Maktoum**
29 **PRIDE OF PRIORY,** 4, b g Pivotal—Millennium Star (IRE) **Tim Bridge**
30 **ROBERTO ESCOBARR (IRE),** 5, b h Galileo (IRE)—Bewitched (IRE) **Hussain Lootah**
31 **SACRED,** 4, b f Exceed And Excel (AUS)—Sacre Caroline (USA) **Cheveley Park Stud**
32 **SEA LA ROSA (IRE),** 4, ch f Sea The Stars (IRE)—Soho Rose (IRE) **Sunderland Holding Inc.**
33 **SEA SPEEDWELL (IRE),** 4, ch f Sea The Stars (IRE)—Flower Market **Sunderland Holding Inc.**
34 **SKYRUNNER (IRE),** 4, b g Invincible Spirit (IRE)—Maidservant (USA) **Graham Smith-Bernal**
35 **SUBSTANTIAL,** 4, b br c Siyouni (FR)—Sentaril **Lael Stable**
36 **SWEET BELIEVER (IRE),** 4, b f Make Believe—Olivia Pope (IRE) **Sheikh Rashid Dalmook**
37 **TARHIB (IRE),** 4, b f Dark Angel (IRE)—Allez Alaia (IRE) **Shadwell Estate Company**

MR WILLIAM HAGGAS - continued

THREE-YEAR-OLDS

38 **ADDINGHAM,** b g Intello (GER)—Tweed **Brian Haggas**
39 **AL MUBHIR,** ch c Frankel—Muffri'Ha (IRE) **Sheikh Juma Dalmook**
40 **ALVEDISTON (IRE),** ch g New Bay—Ebbesbourne (IRE) **James Wigan**
41 **AMANZOE (IRE),** b f Fastnet Rock (AUS)—Starship (IRE) **The Starship Partnership II**
42 **BALGOWAN (IRE),** ch g Australia—Star Search **Nick Jonsson**
43 **BREWING,** b c Showcasing—Cloud Line **Lael Stable**
44 **CANONIZED,** b f Acclamation—Sainted **Cheveley Park Stud**
45 **CANTERBURY BELL (IRE),** b f Ribchester (IRE)—Lavender Lane (IRE) **Jon & Julia Aisbitt**
46 **CET HORIZON,** b f Iffraaj—Dawn Horizons **Sheikh Juma Dalmook**
47 **CHIPOTLE,** b c Havana Gold (IRE)—Lightsome **Prince Faisal Khaled**
48 **CRIOLLO,** gr f Dark Angel (IRE)—La Rioja **Qatar Racing**
49 **CRYSTAL CAVES (FR),** b f Almanzor (FR)—Vivacity **Bermuda Racing**
50 **ENSHRINE,** b f Ulysses (IRE)—Sacre Caroline (IRE) **Cheveley Park Stud**
51 **ESTIDAMA,** b f Farhh—Kitty For Me **Sheikh Rashid Dalmook**
52 **FINAL DECISION,** ch f Iffraaj—Adjudicate **Sheikh Rashid Dalmook**
53 **FOOTSY,** ch c Siyouni (FR)—Barter **White Birch Farm & Fittocks Stud**
54 **FRANTANCK,** b c Frankel—Janey Muddles (IRE) **Mr Y. L. A. Lee**
55 **GLORY AND GOLD,** b f Havana Gold (IRE)—Grace And Glory (IRE) **Nicholas Jones**
56 **GOLDEN LYRA (IRE),** ch f Lope de Vega (IRE)—Sea The Sun (GER) **Sunderland Holding Inc.**
57 **GOLDEN VOICE,** ch c Havana Gold (IRE)—Granola **Saeed Suhail**
58 **GOOD MEASURE,** b c Havana Gold (IRE)—Superstar Leo (IRE) **Lael Stable**
59 **GRENOBLE,** b g Siyouni (FR)—Giants Play (USA) **Newsells Park Stud**
60 **HAMAKI (IRE),** b g Churchill (IRE)—Sarawati (IRE) **Mr Simon Munir & Mr Isaac Souede**
61 **HEBRIDES (IRE),** ch g Mehmas (IRE)—Woodland Maiden (IRE) **Highclere Thoroughbred Racing - Oak Tree**
62 **HELLO SYDNEY (IRE),** b c Zoffany (IRE)—Queen of Stars (USA) **Abdulla Belhabb**
63 **HOLOCENE,** ch f Ulysses (IRE)—Heaven Sent **Cheveley Park Stud**
64 **I AM THE SEA,** b g Sea The Stars (IRE)—Polly's Mark (IRE) **The Bermuda Salman Morris Partnership**
65 **ICE HOUSE,** ch f Ulysses (IRE)—Ice Palace **Cheveley Park Stud**
66 **ICYKEL (IRE),** ch f Frankel—Cold As Ice (SAF) **Barnane Stud**
67 **IRRESISTABLE,** gr f Dark Angel (IRE)—Sommesnil (IRE) **Yvonne Jacques**
68 **JUST A TAD (IRE),** b f Intello (GER)—Tadpole **Ian & Christine Beard & Family**
69 **JUST WONDER,** b c Siyouni (FR)—Wonderstruck (IRE) **Lael Stable**
70 **KHANJAR (IRE),** b g Kodiac—Naafer **Shadwell Estate Company**
71 **KIDWAH (IRE),** b f Kodiac—Areeda (IRE) **Shadwell Estate Company**
72 **KING OF ICE,** ch g Ulysses (IRE)—Queen of Ice **Cheveley Park Stud**
73 **LAATANSA (FR),** ch c New Bay—Louve Rare (IRE) **Prince Faisal Khaled**
74 **LATTAM (IRE),** ch g Lope de Vega (IRE)—Alaata (USA) **Wrigleys & Wyatts**
75 **LYSANDER,** br c New Approach (IRE)—Darting **Highclere Thoroughbred Racing - Beehives**
76 **MANDOBI (IRE),** b c Iffraaj—Oojooba **Sheikh Ahmad Al Maktoum**
77 **MARMALASHES (IRE),** ch f Australia—Marmalady (AUS) **Barnane Stud**
78 **MORGAN FAIRY (IRE),** b f Lope de Vega (IRE)—My Fairy (IRE) **Sunderland Holding Inc.**
79 **MY PROSPERO (IRE),** b c Iffraaj—My Titania (IRE) **Sunderland Holding Inc.**
80 **NATHANAEL GREENE,** b c Nathaniel (IRE)—My Special J's (USA) **Sheikh Isa Salman**
81 **NATIONAL CHARTER,** b f Lawman (FR)—Debuetantin **Sheikh Isa Salman**
82 **PAWAPURI,** b f Golden Horn—Palitana (USA) **A. E. Oppenheimer**
83 **PERFECT NEWS,** b f Frankel—Besharah (IRE) **Sheikh Rashid Dalmook**
84 **PERSIST,** b f Frankel—Persuasive **Cheveley Park Stud**
85 **POST IMPRESSIONIST (IRE),** b g Teofilo (IRE)—Island Remede **Richard Green**
86 **PUBLIC OPINION,** gr f Dark Angel (IRE)—Katie's Diamond (FR) **Clipper Logistics**
87 **PUNDA MARIA (IRE),** b f Oasis Dream—Shingwedzi (SAF) **Cayton Park Stud**
88 **QOYA,** b f Almanzor (FR)—Plume Rose **Louisa Stone & St Albans Bloodstock**
89 **QUEEN AMINATU,** br f Muhaarar—Zeb Un Nisa **A. E. Oppenheimer**
90 **QUEENLET (IRE),** b f Kingman—Tesoro (IRE) **James Wigan**
91 **RAZEYNA (IRE),** b f Kodiac—Deleyla **Sheikh Ahmed Al Maktoum**
92 **REMEMBERING (IRE),** ch f Frankel—Remember You (IRE) **Sheikh Juma Dalmook**
93 **ROMANTIC ART,** ch g The Gurkha (IRE)—Fauran (IRE) **Richard Green**
94 **RUBYLINA,** b f Muhaarar—Ruby Rocket (IRE) **Sir Peter Vela & New England Stud**
95 **SCATTERING,** b g Showcasing—Seed Corn **Nicholas Jones**

MR WILLIAM HAGGAS - continued

96 **SEA CLARE (IRE)**, br f Sea The Stars (IRE)—Creggs Pipes **Sunderland Holding Inc.**
97 **SEA FLAWLESS (IRE)**, br f Sea The Stars (IRE)—Kitcara **Sunderland Holding Inc.**
98 **SEA FORMULA (IRE)**, b f Sea The Stars (IRE)—Seas of Wells (IRE) **Sunderland Holding Inc.**
99 **SEA GALAXY (IRE)**, ch f Sea The Stars (IRE)—Ninas Terz (GER) **Sunderland Holding Inc.**
100 **SEA ON TIME (IRE)**, ch f Sea The Stars (IRE)—My Timing **Sunderland Holding Inc.**
101 **SEA SILK ROAD (IRE)**, b f Sea The Stars (IRE)—Oriental Magic (GER) **Sunderland Holding Inc.**
102 **SEA THE SEVEN**, b f Sea The Stars (IRE)—Nadia Glory **Graham & Marcela Smith-Bernal**
103 **SEA TSARINA (IRE)**, b f Sea The Stars (IRE)—Tayma (IRE) **Sunderland Holding Inc.**
104 **SECOND WIND (IRE)**, b g Kodiac—Princess Janie (USA) **Wrigleys & Wyatts**
105 **SENSE OF DUTY**, b br f Showcasing—Margaret's Mission (IRE) **St Albans Bloodstock**
106 **SERENITY (IRE)**, b gr f Mastercraftsman (IRE)—Break of Day (USA) **Mr Michael Buckley & Mrs Paul Shanahan**
107 **SHIGAR (IRE)**, b c Farhh—Diala (IRE) **Sheikh Abdulla Al Khalifa**
108 **SMART DEAL**, b c Kingman—Bargain Buy **Sheikh Rashid Dalmook**
109 **SOULCOMBE**, b c Frankel—Ribbons **Sir Martyn Arbib,Ben Arbib,Chris Budgett**
110 **SPANISH (IRE)**, ch f Lope de Vega (IRE)—Czabo **Sheikh Isa Salman**
111 **SPIRIT OF NGURU (IRE)**, b c Invincible Spirit (IRE)—Tutu Nguru (USA) **Sheikh Juma Dalmook**
112 **TAMILLA**, b f Nathaniel (IRE)—Miss Pinkerton **Abdulla Belhabb**
113 **TATHBEET**, b c Lope de Vega (IRE)—Momentus (IRE) **Sheikh Rashid Dalmook**
114 **TESSITURA**, b f Frankel—Soundstrings **Lael Stable**
115 **THREE START (IRE)**, b g Muhaarar—Front House (IRE) **Brian Haggas**
116 **TIBER FLOW (IRE)**, br gr c Caravaggio (USA)—Malabar **Jon & Julia Aisbitt**
117 **TRUE ICON (IRE)**, ch f Churchill (IRE)—Purple Glow (IRE) **Clipper Logistics**
118 **TRUEMAN**, b c Wootton Bassett—Dazzling Rose **Clipper Logistics**
119 **VINTAGE CHOICE (IRE)**, ch c Lope de Vega (IRE)—Effervesce (IRE) **Sheikh Isa Salman**
120 **WILKINS**, b g Lope de Vega (IRE)—Tiptree (IRE) **Mr & Mrs M. Morris**
121 **YONAFIS**, b c Golden Horn—Modeyra **Sheikh Ahmed Al Maktoum**
122 **ZAIN FARHH**, ch c Farhh—Local Spirit (USA) **Sheikh Juma Dalmook**

TWO-YEAR-OLDS

123 B c 01/04 Nathaniel—Aghareed (Kingmambo) **Shadwell Estate Company**
124 **ALPHA CAPTURE (IRE)**, b c 27/04 Cotai Glory—York Express (Vale of York) **Mr Simon Munir & Mr Isaac Souede**
125 B c 28/03 Australia—Baheeja (Dubawi) **Sheikh Ahmed Al Maktoum**
126 B c 26/03 No Nay Never—Balankiya (Darshaan) **Michael Buckley**
127 B f 13/03 Dubawi—Besharah (Kodiac) **Sheikh Rashid Dalmook**
128 B c 31/01 Wootton Bassett—Bhageerathi (IRE) (Motivator) (425170) **Fiona Carmichael**
129 **BLUEBOTTLE BLUE**, ch f 06/02 Zoffany—Ebbesbourne (Teofilo) **Tim Bridge**
130 **BUGLE BEADS**, b f 04/03 Pivotal—Glitter Girl (Invincible Spirit) **Cheveley Park Stud**
131 **CHARMING STAR (IRE)**, b c 25/02 Sea The Stars (IRE)—Baino Hope (FR) (Jeremy (USA)) (153061)
                                                                              Abdulla bin Mutaib Al Saud
132 B c 04/05 Galileo (IRE)—Cloth of Cloud (SAF) (Captain Al (SAF)) **Kantor, Nagle & Coolmore**
133 **COCO ROYALE**, b f 11/04 Frankel—Coconut Creme (Cape Cross) **Newsells Park Stud/T Johnson**
134 Ch f 19/02 Frankel—Cold As Ice (SAF) (Western Winter) **Barnane Stud**
135 Ch b 19/03 Australia—Cumbree (IRE) (Footstepsinthesand) (125000) **Prince Faisal Khaled**
136 **DAY MEMBER**, b f 02/02 Twilight Son—Clubbable (Mayson) **Cheveley Park Stud**
137 Br c 28/01 Kingman—Deep Inside (Redoute's Choice) **Shadwell Estate Company**
138 B c 14/02 Camelot—Delta Dreamer (Oasis Dream) (200000) **K K Ho**
139 B c 19/03 Fastnet Rock—Enticing (Pivotal) **Lael Stable**
140 B f 06/02 Invincible Spirit (IRE)—Ertiyad (Dark Angel (IRE)) **Sheikh Juma Dalmook**
141 B c 25/03 Harry Angel—Exacting (Excelebration) **Sheikh Juma Dalmook**
142 B c 09/03 Dubawi—Ferdoos (Dansili) **Sheikh Ahmed Al Maktoum**
143 Gr f 25/02 Farhh—Fire Orchid (Lethal Force) **Sheikh Rashid Dalmook**
144 **GODWINSON**, b c 30/05 Saxon Warrior (JPN)—Malabar (Raven's Pass (USA)) **Jon & Julia Aisbitt**
145 **GOOD GRACIOUS**, b f 04/02 Kingman—Give And Take (Cityscape) **Nicholas Jones**
146 Ch c 03/04 No Nay Never (USA)—Gravity Flow (IRE) (Exceed And Excel (AUS)) **Sheikh Juma Dalmook**
147 B f 29/03 Lord Kanaloa—Guilty Twelve (Giant's Causeway) **Merry Fox Stud**
148 Ch f 18/02 No Nay Never—In The Fast Lane (SAF) (Jet Master) **Barnane Stud**
149 B c 09/02 Dubawi—Intricately (Fastnet Rock) **Mr & Mrs M. Morris**
150 Ch f 20/03 Lope De Vega—Ionic (Intello) **SBA Racing**
151 **KINGFISHER KING**, ch c 09/05 Farhh—Queen Consort (Kingmambo) **Tim Bridge**

MR WILLIAM HAGGAS - continued

152 B br f 28/04 Australia—Kitcara (Shamardal) **Sunderland Holding Inc.**
153 KODERA (IRE), ch f 02/02 Zoffany—Shamwari Lodge (Hawk Wing) **Mr Simon Munir & Mr Isaac Souede**
154 B c 29/04 Galileo (IRE)—Koora (Pivotal) (600000) **Jonsson, Cumani & Coolmore**
155 KYEEMA, b c 20/02 Siyouni—Karisma (Lawman (FR)) **Yvonne Jacques**
156 B c 14/02 Le Havre (IRE)—Lady Francesca (Montjeu (IRE)) (230000) **Sheikh Isa Salman**
157 Ch gr f 14/02 Mastercraftsman—Legerete (Rahy) **Newsells Park Stud/Merry Fox Partnership**
158 LOHENGRIN, b c 04/04 Ulysses—Diyavania (Pivotal) **Cheveley Park Stud**
159 LORDSHIP (GER), ch c 05/03 Lord of England (GER)—La Caldera (Hernando (FR)) (32313)
Ian & Christine Beard & Family
160 B c 06/05 Saxon Warrior (JPN)—Love And Bubbles (USA) (Loup Sauvage (USA)) (120000) **M M Stables**
161 Gr f 13/05 Kingman—Majmu (Redoute's Choice) **Shadwell Estate Company**
162 B c 31/01 Showcasing—Maleficent Queen (Mount Melson) **Saeed Suhail**
163 B f 21/02 Sea The Stars (IRE)—Mayhem (Whipper) **Sheikh Juma Dalmook**
164 Bl c 15/03 Camelot—Mill Springs (Shirocco (GER)) (130000) **Teme Valley/Rebecca Phillips**
165 B f 08/03 Iffraaj—Miskin Diamond (IRE) (Diamond Green (FR)) (61905) **Sheikh Juma Dalmook**
166 B f 13/05 Oasis Dream—Modeyra (Shamardal) **Sheikh Ahmed Al Maktoum**
167 B br c 04/02 Dubawi—Muffri'Ha (Iffraaj) **Sheikh Juma Dalmook**
168 B c 16/02 Sea The Stars—Muneyra (Dubawi) **Sheikh Ahmed Al Maktoum**
169 B f 17/05 Lope De Vega—My Titania (Sea The Stars) **Sunderland Holding Inc.**
170 NINE TENTHS (IRE), b f 02/05 Kodiac—Covetous (Medaglia D'Oro) **St Albans Bloodstock**
171 B c 21/01 Night of Thunder—Operettist (Singspiel) **K K Ho**
172 PICCADILLY CIRCUS, ch c 12/03 Australia—Piccadilly Filly (IRE) (Exceed And Excel (AUS)) (95000)
Royal Ascot Racing Club
173 PLINK, b c 15/02 Zoustar—Soundstrings (Oasis Dream) **Lael Stable**
174 B f 22/01 Iffraaj—Posh Claret (Royal Applause) **Sheikh Hamed Dalmook**
175 Br c 02/02 Dark Angel—Propel (Dubawi) **K K Ho**
176 B f 01/04 Invincible Spirit (IRE)—Proserpine (Hat Trick) **Sheikh Hamed Dalmook**
177 Gr c 04/02 Australia—Prosper (Exceed And Excel (AUS)) (140000) **K K Ho**
178 RAMENSKY, b c 28/02 Cracksman—Agathe Sainte (Holy Roman Emperor (IRE)) (20000)
Highclere Thoroughbred Racing - Martin Luther King
179 RIVER NAVER (FR), ch f 14/05 Showcasing—Imperialistic Deva (Haafhd) **St Albans Bloodstock**
180 SABALENKO, gr f 05/03 Dark Angel—Safina (Pivotal) **Cheveley Park Stud**
181 SANCTION, b f 15/03 Camelot—Margaret's Mission (Shamardal) **St Albans Bloodstock**
182 B c 13/03 Zoustar—Saniyaat (Galileo) **Sheikh Ahmed Al Maktoum**
183 B c 09/02 Sea The Stars (IRE)—Selyl (Oasis Dream) (180000) **Sheikh Ahmed Al Maktoum**
184 B f 21/05 Kingman—Signe (Sea The Stars) **Fiona Carmichael**
185 B c 07/02 Kodiac—Soul Searcher (Motivator) **Sheikh Ahmed Al Maktoum**
186 STAR AHOY, b c 14/03 Sea The Stars (IRE)—Infallible (Pivotal) **Cheveley Park Stud**
187 B f 30/04 Fastnet Rock—Starship (Galileo (IRE)) **The Starship Partnership II**
188 B c 20/05 Shamardal—Taqaareed (Sea The Stars) **Shadwell Estate Company**
189 Gr c 25/02 Roaring Lion—Tiger Eye (Frankel) **Qatar Racing**
190 B c 03/02 Fast Company—Tilthe End of Time (Acclamation) **M M Stables**
191 TRUTHFUL (IRE), b f 06/04 Sea The Stars (IRE)—My Timing (Street Cry)
Highclere Thoroughbred Racing - Nelson Mandela
192 B f 07/03 Mukhadram—Undress (IRE) (Dalakhani (IRE)) **Brian Haggas**
193 UNEQUAL LOVE, ch f 16/02 Dutch Art—Heavenly Dawn (Pivotal) **Cheveley Park Stud**
194 VITERBO (IRE), b c 10/04 Mehmas (IRE)—Statenice (Montjeu (IRE)) (130000) **Newsells Park Stud**
195 VIVA BOLIVIA, b f 12/03 Galileo—Aljaazi (Shamardal) **Newsells Park Stud**
196 B f 26/04 Kingman—Wonderstruck (Sea The Stars) **Lael Stable**
197 Gr c 17/02 Pivotal—Yanabeeaa (Street Cry) **Sheikh Ahmed Al Maktoum**
198 B c 01/04 Sea The Stars (IRE)—Zarzali (AUS) (Hussonet (USA)) (52000) **Sheikh Juma Dalmook**
199 Ch f 08/02 No Nay Never—Zoowraa (Azamour) **Sheikh Ahmed Al Maktoum**

Assistant Trainer: Josh Hamer, Andy McIntyre, Isabella Paul.

Flat Jockey: Cieren Fallon, Tom Marquand. **Apprentice Jockey:** Adam Farragher.

232 MR ALEX HALES, Edgecote

Postal: **Trafford Bridge Stables, Edgecote, Banbury, Oxfordshire, OX17 1AG**
Contacts: PHONE 01295 660131 MOBILE 07771 511652 FAX 01295 660128
EMAIL alex@alexhalesracing.co.uk WEBSITE www.alexhalesracing.co.uk

1 **ABINGTON PARK**, 7, br g Passing Glance—Epicurean **Red Cap Racing**
2 **AVEC PERMISSION (FR)**, 5, b m Authorized (IRE)—Naive (IRE) **Bloomsbury Stud**
3 **BOOK OF GOLD (IRE)**, 10, b g Flemensfirth (USA)—Ballerina Queen (IRE) **Mr A Lousada & Mr A Kaplan**
4 **BOURBON BEAUTY**, 7, b m Great Pretender (IRE)—It Doesn't Matter **Old Stoics Racing Club 2**
5 **BROOKLYN BELLE**, 7, b m Olden Times—Andromache **Mr A. M. Hales**
6 **CRONK Y KNOX (IRE)**, 7, gr g Cloudings (IRE)—Exit Baby (IRE) **Mr D. L. Simkins**
7 **DON'T ASK (IRE)**, 9, b g Ask—Outback Ivy (IRE) **Gumbrills Racing Partnership**
8 **DON'T TELL WILLY (IRE)**, 6, ch g Vita Venturi (IRE)—Katies Pet (IRE) **Mr M. W. Redman**
9 **DRAGON'S FIRE**, 4, b g Equiano (FR)—Annawi **Millard Charter Chapman Pearce & Partner**
10 **EZ TIGER (IRE)**, 5, b g Sholokhov (IRE)—Miss Opera **Mr N Rodway & Partner**
11 **FAGAN**, 12, gr g Fair Mix (IRE)—Northwood May **Mr S. N. Brackenbury**
12 **FAMILY TIME**, 4, b g Exceleberation (IRE)—Porcini **Mr S. N. Brackenbury**
13 **FEEL LIKE DE BAUNE (FR)**, 6, b g Feel Like Dancing—Sofia de Baune (FR) **Mr S. N. Brackenbury**
14 **FOR PLEASURE (IRE)**, 7, ch g Exceleberation (IRE)—Darsan (IRE) **Premier Plastering (UK) Limited**
15 **FOX'S SOCKS (FR)**, 7, br g Crillon (FR)—Queva de Sarti (FR) **The Lost My Socks Racing Syndicate**
16 **GET YOUR OWN (IRE)**, 7, b br g Getaway (GER)—Western Girl (IRE) **The The Get Your Own Racing Partnership**
17 **GONE IN SIXTY**, 5, b g Sixties Icon—Gib (IRE) **Golden Equinox Racing**
18 **HAPPY AND FINE (FR)**, 5, b g Balko (FR)—Richona (FR) **Mr T Acott, Mr L Cross, Mr S Cross**
19 **HARA KIRI (FR)**, 5, b g Diamond Boy (FR)—Beauty du Bidou (FR) **Premier Plastering (UK) Limited**
20 **HAS TROKE (FR)**, 5, b g Masterstroke (USA)—Shifa (FR) **The Arty Syndicate**
21 **HICONIC**, 5, b m Sixties Icon—Hi Note **Golden Equinox Racing & Partner**
22 **HOUSTON BERE (FR)**, 5, b g Hurricane Cat (USA)—Kunoichi (USA)
23 **I AM DE CHAILLAC (FR)**, 4, b g Jeu St Eloi (FR)—Vivaldi du Pecos (FR) **Mr Michael & Mrs Norma Tuckey**
24 **INCLEMENT WEATHER**, 4, b f Bated Breath—Rapid Recruit (IRE) **Golden Equinox Racing**
25 **JACK THUNDER**, 8, b g Masterofthehorse (IRE)—Acqua Pesante (IRE) **Mr D. G. Christian**
26 **JIMMI CHEW (IRE)**, 9, br g Jimble (FR)—Katie Baby (IRE) **Mr A. M. Hales**
27 **KANKIN**, 6, ch g Archipenko (USA)—Touriga **Mr A. L. Cohen**
28 **LAURELDEAN CROSS (IRE)**, 6, b g Cape Cross (IRE)—Laureldean Spirit (IRE) **Mrs J. M. Mayo**
29 **MARIA MAGDALENA (IRE)**, 6, b m Battle of Marengo (IRE)—Few Words **The Problem Solvers**
30 **METHAG (FR)**, 9, b m Pour Moi (IRE)—Kyria **The One For Us**
31 **MIDNIGHTINBRESIL**, 5, b m Blue Bresil (FR)—Farewellatmidnight **Mrs J. Way**
32 **MILLERS BANK**, 8, b g Passing Glance—It Doesn't Matter **Millers Bank Partnership**
33 **MISS WACHIT (IRE)**, 6, b m Flemensfirth (USA)—Miss Mitch (IRE) **Claxby & Co**
34 **NEXTDOORTOALICE (IRE)**, 6, b m Mahler—Lady Zephyr (IRE) **The Syndicate Next Door**
35 **OMAR MARETTI (IRE)**, 8, b g Fame And Glory—Parsons Hall (IRE) **J. T. B. Hunt**
36 **OUR BILL'S AUNT (IRE)**, 6, b m Blueprint (IRE)—Carrigmoorna Oak (IRE) **The 25 Club**
37 **PARSONS PLEASURE (FR)**, 6, gr g Planteur (IRE)—Netrebko (IRE) **Mr R. J. Tompkins**
38 **PETITE DAME (IRE)**, 6, b m Shantou (USA)—Offside Rule (IRE) **Edging Ahead**
39 **POLLYPOCKETT (IRE)**, 5, b m Presenting—Mtpockets (IRE) **Edging Ahead**
40 **QUEENS HIGHWAY (IRE)**, 6, br m Presenting—Augusta Bay **Golden Equinox Racing**
41 **SAY NOTHING**, 6, b m Nathaniel (IRE)—I Say (IRE) **The The Silent Partners**
42 **SEA PRINCE**, 6, b g Born To Sea (IRE)—Briery (IRE) **The Sea Prince Racing Partnership**
43 **SID HOODIE (IRE)**, 8, b m Rip Van Winkle (USA)—Universe **Mr D. G. Christian**
44 **SMOOTH STEPPER**, 13, b g Alflora (IRE)—Jazzy Refrain (IRE) **Mr S. N. Brackenbury**
45 **STIGWOOD (IRE)**, 4, b g Kodiac—Time Honoured **In The Pink Partnership**
46 **THE DUBAI WAY (IRE)**, 10, b g Dubai Destination (USA)—Britway Lady (IRE) **N.W.A. Bannister & M.J.R. Bannister**
47 **THE LION DANCER (IRE)**, 10, b g Let The Lion Roar—Shesadoll (IRE) **The 25 Club**
48 **TICKET TO L A (IRE)**, 7, b m Westerner—In Bloom (IRE) **Golden Equinox Racing & Partner**
49 **TIME FOR TIMONE (IRE)**, 7, b g Mahler—Lettermaney (IRE) **Mr S. N. Brackenbury**
50 **TORADORA**, 7, br m Sakhee (USA)—Sainte Gig (FR) **Miss S. M. L. Parden**

THREE-YEAR-OLDS

51 B f Mukhadram—Anqooda (USA)

233 **MR MICHAEL HALFORD, Kildare**
Postal: **Copper Beech Stables, Doneaney, Kildangan Road, Kildare, Co. Kildare, R51 TC79, Ireland**
Contacts: WORK **+353 45 526 119** MOBILE **+353 87 257 9204** WORK FAX **+353 45 526 157**
WORK EMAIL **info@michaelhalford.com** WEBSITE **www.michaelhalford.com**

1 **ARCANEARS (IRE)**, 7, b g Arcano (IRE)—Ondeafears (IRE) **Mrs Caroline Roper**
2 **ARDLA (IRE)**, 7, b g Delegator—Tamaletta (IRE) **Ms Fiona Wentges**
3 **BEAR STORY (IRE)**, 4, b c Kodiac—Angels Story (IRE) **Mr John Connaughton**
4 **BRIGHT GLORY**, 4, br c Starspangledbanner (AUS)—Luminance (IRE) **Mr P Rooney**
5 **CHALLY CHUTE (IRE)**, 4, ch g Fast Company (IRE)—Edith Somerville (IRE) **Ms. Julie White**
6 **COLLEEN'S PRINCE (IRE)**, 4, b g Prince of Lir (IRE)—Blondie's Esteem (IRE) **Mr Brian Gallivan**
7 **COSMIC VEGA (IRE)**, 4, b g Lope de Vega (IRE)—Pivotal Era **Long Inch Ltd**
8 **ELZAAMSAN (IRE)**, 4, b c Elzaam (AUS)—Lady Conway (USA) **Mr P Rooney**
9 **FINANS BAY (IRE)**, 5, b h Kodiac—Wrood (USA) **Mr N Hartery**
10 **GOLDEN TWILIGHT (IRE)**, 5, b g Dawn Approach (IRE)—Great Hope (IRE) **Mr F W Lynch**
11 **HODD'S GIRL (IRE)**, 5, gr m Zebedee—Ms Inkonia Hodd (IRE) **Rocky Horror Partnership**
12 **JE T'AI PORTE (IRE)**, 4, b f Footstepsinthesand—Hasanza (USA) **Mrs L Halford**
13 **LADY DE VESCI (IRE)**, 9, ch m Approve (IRE)—La Bandola (GER) **Anita Soros**
14 **NOVA ORCHID (IRE)**, 4, b f Mount Nelson—Slipper Orchid (IRE) **Mrs Caroline Roper**
15 **REGINALDS TOWER (IRE)**, 5, b g Canford Cliffs (IRE)—La Femme (IRE) **Mr N Hartery**
16 **SAMEASITEVERWAS (IRE)**, 5, br g Sageburg (IRE)—Print It On Lips (IRE) **Mrs L Halford**
17 **SLIEVE BEARNAGH (IRE)**, 5, b h Zoffany (IRE)—Angels Story (IRE) **Mr P Rooney**
18 **SURROUNDING (IRE)**, 9, b m Lilbourne Lad (IRE)—Roundabout Girl (IRE) **Mr P E I Newell**
19 **WYCHWOOD WHISPER (IRE)**, 4, b f Belardo (IRE)—Paimpolaise (IRE) **Mr M Enright**
20 **ZILEO**, 4, b g Galileo (IRE)—Lady Zuzu (USA) **Mr P Rooney**

THREE-YEAR-OLDS
21 **ALOOQAAL (IRE)**, b c Zoffany (IRE)—Natural Bloom (IRE) **Mr Mohamad Ibn Ghayam Almutairi**
22 **CEALLACH (IRE)**, ch c Lope de Vega (IRE)—Alvee (IRE) **Mr P Rooney**
23 **ENDLESS SEASON (IRE)**, b f War Command (USA)—Kabaw (IRE) **Mr Nasir Askar**
24 **GUESS (IRE)**, b br c Elzaam (AUS)—Singapore Secret (IRE) **Ms Leah Halford**
25 **HAVANA PEARL (IRE)**, b f Camelot—Golden Pearl **Mr M Enright**
26 **INCHTURK (IRE)**, bl c Le Havre (IRE)—Pirita (IRE) **Mr N Hartery & Mr J McGee**
27 **KAMPALA BEACH (IRE)**, b c Belardo (IRE)—Translator (IRE) **Mr M Phelan**
28 **LORD ABAMA (IRE)**, ch c Profitable (IRE)—Dancing Years (IRE) **Castle Beech Partnership**
29 **MILLIE'S STREET (IRE)**, b f Belardo (IRE)—Coincidently **Mr Thomas Radley**
30 **PINEHURST (IRE)**, gr g Clodovil (IRE)—Grand Oir (USA) **Mr N Hartery**
31 **RICCARDI MEDIDI (IRE)**, ch c No Nay Never (USA)—Duchessofflorence **Mr M Enright**
32 **RIHANI (IRE)**, b c Churchill (IRE)—Raydiya (IRE) **H. H. The Aga Khan**
33 **RIYAMI (IRE)**, b c Fastnet Rock (AUS)—Riyaba (IRE) **H. H. The Aga Khan**
34 **SIWANI (IRE)**, b c Harzand (IRE)—Sichilla (IRE) **H. H. The Aga Khan**
35 **START LINE (IRE)**, b c Rock of Gibraltar (IRE)—Elmaam **Mr Nasir Askar**
36 **TURBO TWO (IRE)**, b c Holy Roman Emperor—Swish (GER) **Mr Sammy Hon Kit Ma**
37 **UNCONQUERABLE KEEN (IRE)**, b c Clodovil (IRE)—Queenie Keen (IRE) **Mr N Hartery**

TWO-YEAR-OLDS
38 B c 18/04 Siyouni (FR)—Alwaysandforever (IRE) (Teofilo (IRE)) **Mr M Enright**
39 B c 03/05 Bungle Inthejungle—Ayr Missile (Cadeaux Genereux) (52721) **Mr Sammy Hon Kit Ma**
40 B c 18/02 U S Navy Flag (USA)—Boca Raton (Approve (IRE)) (44218) **Mrs G. Freyne**
41 B f 18/04 Acclamation—Broadway Duchess (IRE) (New Approach (IRE)) (72279) **Mr Ahmed Aldubaili**
42 Ch f 21/03 Australia—Diylawa (IRE) (Mastercraftsman (IRE)) **H. H. The Aga Khan**
43 B f 16/03 Elzaam (AUS)—Esmaggie (Muhtathir) (21259)
44 B f 30/03 Buratino (IRE)—Firecrown (IRE) (Iffraaj) **Dundalk Racing Club**
45 B c 10/04 Elzaam (AUS)—Happy Wedding (IRE) (Green Tune (USA)) **Cornate Ltd**
46 **IMADPOUR (IRE)**, gr c 15/02 Le Havre (IRE)—Imrana (Azamour (IRE)) **H. H. The Aga Khan**
47 Gr c 22/03 Gutaifan (IRE)—Jeremy's Girl (IRE) (Jeremy) **Cornate Ltd**
48 **KADEEN (IRE)**, b c 13/05 New Approach (IRE)—Kadra (IRE) (Holy Roman Emperor) **H. H. The Aga Khan**
49 B f 08/04 Holy Roman Emperor (IRE)—Karamaya (IRE) (Invincible Spirit (IRE)) **H. H. The Aga Khan**
50 Ch c 19/04 Cotai Glory—Kocna (IRE) (Aussie Rules (USA)) (33000) **Castle Beech Partnership**
51 B c 23/02 Elzaam (AUS)—Lady Tyne (Halling (USA)) (34014) **Castle Beech Partnership**

MR MICHAEL HALFORD - continued

52 B c 23/02 Holy Roman Emperor (IRE)—Lake Louise (IRE) (Haatef (USA)) (26361) **Castle Beech Partnership**
53 Ch f 13/04 Australia—Nourah (IRE) (Shamardal (USA)) (93537) **Mr Isa Bin Haider**
54 B f 11/04 Elzaam (AUS)—Playamongthestars (AUS) (Galileo (IRE))
                                                Mr. O.B.P. Carroll, Mr. Dermot Kelly and Mr. Tony Vaughan
55 B c 10/05 U S Navy Flag (USA)—Queensberry (GER) (Tertullian (USA)) (30000) **Castle Beech Partnership**
56 **RAUZAN (IRE),** b c 08/02 Australia—Rayisa (IRE) (Holy Roman Emperor (IRE)) **H. H. The Aga Khan**
57 B f 25/04 No Nay Never (USA)—Sendmylovetorose (Bahamian Bounty) **Mr M Enright**
58 **SLIEVE BINNIAN (IRE),** gr c 24/04 Awtaad (IRE)—Qertaas (IRE) (Linamix (FR)) (34014) **Mr P Rooney**
59 B c 05/03 Footstepsinthesand—Victorious Secret (IRE) (Holy Roman Emperor (IRE)) (28912) **Mr Sammy Hon Kit Ma**
60 Ch c 12/02 Exceed And Excel (AUS)—Zayn Zen (Singspiel (IRE)) (45000) **Mr Sammy Hon Kit Ma**

Flat Jockey: Niall McCullagh, Ronan Whelan. **Conditional Jockey:** Eamonn Fitzgerald. **Apprentice Jockey:** Ciaran Moody.
Amateur Jockey: Mr Joshua Halford.

| **234** | **MRS DEBRA HAMER, Carmarthen**
Postal: **Bryngors Uchaf, Nantycaws, Carmarthen, Dyfed, SA32 8EY**
Contacts: **HOME 01267 234585 MOBILE 07980 665274**
EMAIL **hamerracing@hotmail.com** |
|---|---|

1 **DEAL EM HIGH,** 5, ch g Mountain High (IRE)—Dirty Deal **Mr I. R. Goatson**
2 **DEAL EM LUCKY,** 6, b m Yorgunnabelucky (USA)—Dirty Deal **Mr I. R. Goatson**
3 **LAYERTHORPE (IRE),** 10, b bl g Vale of York (IRE)—Strobinia (IRE) **Mr C. A. Hanbury**
4 **LOOKS LIKE POWER (IRE),** 12, ch g Spadoun (FR)—Martovic (IRE) **Mr C. A. Hanbury**
5 **MEECHLANDS MAGIC,** 6, b br g Multiplex—Do It On Dani **Mrs J. M. Edmonds**
6 **PENNANT EMPRESS,** 6, b m Lucarno (USA)—Pennant Princess **Mr P. J. Woolley**
7 **SADDLERS QUEST,** 8, b m Dr Massini (IRE)—Lady Maranzi **Mrs D. A. Hamer**
8 **TOBEFAIR,** 12, b br g Central Park (IRE)—Nan **Down The Quay Club**

Assistant Trainer: Mr M. P. Hamer.

| **235** | **MRS ALISON HAMILTON, Denholm**
Postal: **Dykes Farm House, Denholm, Hawick, Roxburghshire, TD9 8TB**
Contacts: **PHONE 01450 870323 MOBILE 07885 477349**
EMAIL **Alisonhamilton53@yahoo.com** |
|---|---|

1 **BALRANALD (FR),** 6, b gr g Mastercraftsman (IRE)—Shining Glory (GER) **J. P. G. Hamilton**
2 **BUTTEVANT LADY (IRE),** 9, b m Presenting—Off She Goes (IRE) **J. P. G. Hamilton**
3 **CHOIX DES ARMES (FR),** 10, b g Saint des Saints (FR)—Kicka **J. P. G. Hamilton**
4 **GUN MERCHANT,** 9, b g Kayf Tara—Pearly Legend **Mr & Mrs D S Byers & Jpg Hamilton**
5 **MOUNT MELLERAY (IRE),** 7, ch g Flemensfirth (USA)—Prowler (IRE) **J. P. G. Hamilton**
6 **PAINTERS LAD (IRE),** 11, b g Fruits of Love (USA)—Great Cullen (IRE) **J. P. G. Hamilton**
7 **SHAUGHNESSY,** 9, b g Shantou (USA)—Sudden Beat **J. P. G. Hamilton**
8 **SKYHILL (IRE),** 9, b g Gold Well—Classic Mari (IRE) **Mr & Mrs D S Byers & Jpg Hamilton**
9 **STAND STAUNCH (IRE),** 4, b g Camelot—Takawiri (IRE) **J. P. G. Hamilton**
10 **TOWERBURN (IRE),** 13, b g Cloudings (IRE)—Lady Newmill (IRE) **J. P. G. Hamilton**
11 **TURBO COMMAND (IRE),** 5, gr g War Command (USA)—The Tempest **J. P. G. Hamilton**

Assistant Trainer: Mr G. Hamilton.

236 MR ANDREW HAMILTON, Carluke
Postal: **Nellfield House, Braidwood, Carluke, Lanarkshire, ML8 4PP**
Contacts: **PHONE 01555 771502**

1 **EL JEFE (IRE)**, 5, b g Born To Sea (IRE)—Ros Mountain (IRE) **Mr A. B. Hamilton**
2 **FLASH MORIVIERE (FR)**, 7, b g Maresca Sorrento (FR)—Fleur de Princesse (FR) **Mr A. B. Hamilton**
3 **IF NOT FOR DYLAN (IRE)**, 7, b g Doyen (IRE)—Exit Stage Left (IRE) **Mr A. B. Hamilton**

237 MRS ANN HAMILTON, Newcastle Upon Tyne
Postal: **Claywalls Farm, Capheaton, Newcastle Upon Tyne, Tyne and Wear, NE19 2BP**
Contacts: **PHONE 01830 530219 MOBILE 07704 670704**
EMAIL annhamilton1952@hotmail.com

1 **BAVINGTON BOB (IRE)**, 7, br g Court Cave (IRE)—Chocolate Silk (IRE) **Mr I. Hamilton**
2 **HELLO JUDGE**, 6, b g Martaline—Oeuvre Vive (FR) **Mr I. Hamilton**
3 **NOTTELLINYA (IRE)**, 5, br m Kalanisi (IRE)—Crofton Trail (IRE) **Mr I. Hamilton**
4 **NUTS WELL**, 11, b g Dylan Thomas (IRE)—Renada **Mr I. Hamilton**
5 **PAY THE PIPER (IRE)**, 7, b g Court Cave (IRE)—Regal Holly **Mr I. Hamilton**
6 **TOMMY'S OSCAR (IRE)**, 7, b g Oscar (IRE)—Glibin (IRE) **Mr I. Hamilton**

Assistant Trainer: Ian Hamilton.

238 MR MICKY HAMMOND, Middleham
Postal: **Oakwood Stables, East Witton Road, Middleham, Leyburn, North Yorkshire, DL8 4PT**
Contacts: **PHONE 01969 625223 MOBILE 07808 572777**
EMAIL micky@mickyhammondracing.co.uk WEBSITE www.mickyhammondracing.co.uk

1 **ADMIRAL HORATIO (IRE)**, 4, b g Mount Nelson—Kerry's Girl (IRE) **Mrs B. M. Lofthouse**
2 **AIR OF APPROVAL (IRE)**, 4, gr f Mastercraftsman (IRE)—Rhiannon (IRE) **Mrs A. King**
3 **AMBER RUN (IRE)**, 7, b g Arcadio (GER)—Dorcet'slast Stand (IRE) **Lady S Toomes, Mrs J Hill & Partners**
4 **APPLAUS (GER)**, 10, b g Tiger Hill (IRE)—All About Love (GER) **Mrs G. Hogg**
5 **BALKOTIC (FR)**, 6, b g Balko (FR)—Aurore Celtique (FR) **Raypasha**
6 **BANDIT D'AINAY (FR)**, 8, b g Crossharbour—Ne M'Oubliez Pas (FR) **The Golden Cuckoo**
7 **BONNE VITESSE (IRE)**, 4, b f Fast Company (IRE)—Mirabile Dictu (IRE) **The Golden Cuckoo**
8 **BRICKADANK (IRE)**, 6, b g Cape Cross (IRE)—Tralanza (IRE) **A & S Associates**
9 **BULLDOZE (IRE)**, 7, gr g Notnowcato—Cap The Rose (IRE) **M. D. Hammond**
10 **BURDIGALA (FR)**, 9, b g Way of Light (USA)—Tiara **Rosemary Hetherington & Partner**
11 **BURNAGE BOY (IRE)**, 6, b g Footstepsinthesand—Speedi Mouse **JFW Properties Limited**
12 **CARNIVAL ZAIN**, 5, b g Youmzain (IRE)—Lady Fashion **Newroc & Partner**
13 **COCKNEY BEAU (FR)**, 7, gr g Cockney Rebel (IRE)—Salsa Melody (FR) **Cheerleader Racing**
14 **CORNERSTONE LAD**, 8, b g Delegator—Chapel Corner (IRE) **Mrs B. M. Lofthouse**
15 **COUNTESS OLIVIA (IRE)**, 5, ch m Ruler of The World (IRE)—Twelfth Night (IRE) **John & Kate Sidebottom**
16 **DADDYJACKS SPECIAL (FR)**, 6, gr g Spirit One (FR)—Great Way (FR) **Mr S. Nicols**
17 **DESARAY GIRL (FR)**, 7, gr m Montmartre (FR)—Feria To Bitch (FR) **Resdev Ltd**
18 **DIS DONC (FR)**, 9, b g Kingsalsa (USA)—Skarina (FR) **Ursa Major & Partners**
19 **DRAGONS WILL RISE (IRE)**, 6, b g Dragon Pulse (IRE)—Jaldini (IRE) **The Golden Cuckoo**
20 **ELENA DE LA VEGA**, 5, b m Toronado (IRE)—Haiti Dancer
21 **ENFIN PHIL (FR)**, 8, ch g No Risk At All (FR)—Nheyranne (FR) **Randall Orchard & Partners**
22 **ERAGONE (FR)**, 8, gr g Martaline—Sharonne (FR) **Mr S. Sutton**
23 **FOSTER'SISLAND**, 7, b g Trans Island—Mrs Eff **The Oakwood Nobels**
24 **FRANKELIO (FR)**, 7, b g Frankel—Restiadargent (FR) **Forty Forty Twenty**
25 **FREDDIE'S FRONTIER (IRE)**, 6, b g Sans Frontieres (IRE)—Supreme Style (IRE) **Mrs J. E. Newett**

MR MICKY HAMMOND - continued

26 **FURAX (FR)**, 7, gr g Martaline—Veleha (FR) **Ursa Major & Partners**
27 **GERYVILLE (FR)**, 6, b g Rail Link—Rosaville (FR) **Mr R. M. Howard**
28 **GETAWAY JEWEL (IRE)**, 8, b g Getaway (GER)—Fada's Jewel (IRE) **Mr P. Ellerby**
29 **GRAND DU NORD (FR)**, 6, b g Montmartre (FR)—Vanille d'Ainay (FR) **Middleham Park Racing & Mr S Nicols**
30 **GRANGE RANGER (IRE)**, 10, b g Kalanisi (IRE)—Grangeclare Flight (IRE) **Oakwood Rainbow**
31 **GREAT BALLINBORIS (FR)**, 6, b g Ballingarry (IRE)—Rotswana (FR) **Mr J. W. Burnett**
32 **GREAT RAFFLES (FR)**, 6, b g Kapgarde (FR)—Une Artiste (FR) **The Golden Cuckoo**
33 **HERESMAX (IRE)**, 4, b g Gutaifan (IRE)—Euroceleb (IRE) **Mr M. Andrews**
34 **HIDEO (FR)**, 5, b g Cokoriko (FR)—Saora (FR) **Two Nicks & A Mick**
35 **HIGH NOON (IRE)**, 10, b g Westerner—Seymourswift **Mr Nick Pietrzyk & Partner**
36 **HOWZAT HIRIS (FR)**, 5, gr m Al Namix (FR)—Une Dame d'Or (FR) **Sticky Wicket Racing**
37 **ILAYA (FR)**, 8, gr m Kapgarde (FR)—Tour Magic (FR) **The Golden Cuckoo**
38 **IRV (IRE)**, 6, ch g Zoffany (IRE)—Marion Antoinette (IRE) **I. M. Lynch**
39 **JUST PADDY'S BAND (IRE)**, 6, b g Sholokhov (IRE)—Tweedledrum **Chapman, Tennant & Turnbull**
40 **JUSTFORJAMES (IRE)**, 13, b g Dr Massini (IRE)—Over The Road (IRE) **J4J Partnership**
41 **KAYF ADVENTURE**, 11, b g Kayf Tara—My Adventure (IRE) **Cheltenham Trail & Cleeve Racing Club**
42 **KILDRUM (IRE)**, 9, b g Milan—Close Flame (IRE) **Mr T. M. Clarke**
43 **KING OF UNICORNS**, 5, b g Night of Thunder (IRE)—Aviacion (BRZ) **J. Buzzeo**
44 **KNOCKNAMONA (IRE)**, 11, b g Trans Island—Faraday Lady (IRE) **The Rat Pack Racing Club**
45 **LATE DATE (IRE)**, 11, b g Oscar (IRE)—Regents Ballerina (IRE) **County Set Six & Partner**
46 , B f Garswood—Laughing Water (FR) **Mr S. Lockyer**
47 , Ch g Shirocco (GER)—Libby Mae (IRE)
48 **MASTER GUSTAV**, 6, b g Mahler—Annaghbrack (IRE) **Mrs B. M. Lofthouse**
49 **MIRRIE DANCERS (IRE)**, 4, b g Harzand (IRE)—Beatrice Aurore (IRE) **Miss R. Dennis**
50 **MONAGHAN BOY (IRE)**, 5, b g Court Cave (IRE)—Ferrestown Lady (IRE) **The Golden Cuckoo**
51 **MR LOMBARDI (IRE)**, 7, b g Milan—The Real Athlete (IRE) **Mr J. N. Swinbank**
52 **MUSICALITY**, 5, b g Kyllachy—Allegro Viva (USA) **Mrs G. Hogg**
53 **MYBOYMAX (FR)**, 4, b g Myboycharlie (IRE)—Plebeya (IRE) **Mr A. Bithell**
54 **MYGIRLMEL**, 4, gr f Bobby's Kitten (USA)—Albacocca **Mr A. Bithell**
55 **NOT WHAT IT SEEMS (IRE)**, 6, b g Robin des Pres—Kyle Ruby (IRE) **Mr R. Sugden**
56 **ONENIGHTINTOWN (IRE)**, 8, b g Robin des Pres (FR)—Snug Bunch (IRE) **The Rat Pack Racing Club**
57 **PENPAL (FR)**, 7, ch g Muhtathir—Penkinella (FR) **The Golden Cuckoo**
58 **PERFECT MAN (IRE)**, 11, b g Morozov (USA)—Garrisker (IRE) **The Rat Pack Racing Club**
59 **PIECEDERESISTANCE (IRE)**, 4, b g Gleneagles (IRE)—Positive Step (IRE) **Mr R. Sugden**
60 **PROFILES MIX (FR)**, 4, b g Gemix (FR)—Eolia (FR) **Ms Dianne Morley & Mr Stewart Dobson**
61 **QUOTELINE DIRECT**, 9, ch g Sir Percy—Queen's Pudding (IRE) **JFW Properties Limited**
62 **RADDLE AND HUM (IRE)**, 8, b m Milan—Gaybric (IRE) **Miss R. Dennis**
63 **RED AMAPOLA**, 4, b f Marcel (IRE)—Si Belle (IRE) **Miss R. Dennis**
64 **RED SKYE DELIGHT (IRE)**, 6, gr m Clodovil (IRE)—Sole Bay **Miss R. Dennis**
65 **RORY AND ME (IRE)**, 7, b g Shamardal (USA)—Rosawa (FR) **Mr Richard Howard & Mr Ben Howard**
66 **ROXYFET (FR)**, 12, b g Califet (FR)—Roxalamour (FR) **Mr Samuel Sutton & Partners**
67 **ROYAL VILLAGE (IRE)**, 10, b g Scorpion (IRE)—Etoile Margot (FR) **Cheltenham Trail & Cleeve Racing Club**
68 **ROYLE STEEL (FR)**, 4, b g Spanish Moon (USA)—Suffisante (FR) **Mr A. E. Tasker**
69 **SCHIEHALLION MUNRO**, 9, ch g Schiaparelli (GER)—Mrs Fawlty **Tennant, Lynch,Sharpe and Boston**
70 **SHAWS BRIDGE (IRE)**, 9, b g Kalanisi (IRE)—Zaffarella (IRE) **Newroc & Co**
71 **SHIGHNESS**, 5, b m Passing Glance—Sharwakom (IRE) **Keep The Faith Partnership**
72 **SINCERELY RESDEV**, 7, br g Rock of Gibraltar (IRE)—Sincerely **Resdev Ltd**
73 **SPARKLE IN HIS EYE**, 6, ch g Sea The Stars (IRE)—Nyarhini **Mr S. Sutton**
74 **SQUARE VIVIANI (FR)**, 11, b g Satri (IRE)—Idria (GER) **Mr R. Sugden**
75 **STRIKE WEST (IRE)**, 10, b g Westerner—Fuel Queen (IRE) **The Multi-Taskers**
76 **THE FUNDANCE KID (IRE)**, 6, ch g Getaway (GER)—Hardy Star (IRE) **Mr S. Nicols**
77 **THE PINE MARTIN (IRE)**, 12, br g Kalanisi (IRE)—Regal Holly **The Rat Pack Racing Club**
78 **THE RESDEV WAY**, 9, b g Multiplex—Lady Duxyana **Resdev Ltd**
79 **THE RETRIEVER (IRE)**, 7, ch g Shamardal (USA)—Silent Secret (IRE) **R M & T Holdings Limited & Partners**
80 **THE RUTLAND REBEL (IRE)**, 6, b g Delegator—Do Disturb (IRE) **Mr R. Sugden**
81 **THE VERY THING (IRE)**, 8, b g Getaway (GER)—Katie Quinn (IRE) **Mr D. Walpole**
82 **TRAC (FR)**, 5, b g Kingsalsa (USA)—Belobaka (FR) **Randall Orchard & Partners**
83 **TREVELYN'S CORN (IRE)**, 9, b g Oscar (IRE)—Present Venture (IRE) **Mr D. Lees**
84 **TRIMMERS LANE (IRE)**, 12, b g Publisher (USA)—Kilcormac Glow (IRE) **Mr I. Ender**
85 **TROUBLE SHOOTER (IRE)**, 6, b g Delegator—Khibraat **Mr T. M. Clarke**

MR MICKY HAMMOND - continued

86 **UCCELLO (IRE)**, 4, b g Frankel—Apsara (FR) **Red & Whites**
87 **WADACRE MONIKA**, 5, b m Yeats (IRE)—Marilyn (GER) **Wadacre Stud**
88 **WALKONBY (IRE)**, 5, ch m Sixties Icon—Shadows Ofthenight (IRE) **Cheltenham Trail & Cleeve Racing Club**
89 **WESTERN MELODY (IRE)**, 5, b m Sir Prancealot (IRE)—Western Tune (IRE) **Mrs G. Hogg**
90 **WHO'S THE GUV'NOR (IRE)**, 8, b g Gold Well—Clamit Brook (IRE) **Mr & Mrs I P Earnshaw**
91 **WISTERIAROSE**, 6, b m Leading Light (IRE)—Mille Et Une (FR) **Mrs J. E. Newett**

THREE-YEAR-OLDS

92 **ARMOURED (IRE)**, b g Lope de Vega (IRE)—Rayisa (IRE) **Miss R. Dennis**
93 **FIFTYSHADESARESDEV (FR)**, gr g Johnny Barnes (IRE)—Tina Nova (FR) **Resdev Ltd**
94 **MERLIN'S GOLD (IRE)**, b g Mastercraftsman (IRE)—Strumming (IRE) **Mr S. Nicols**
95 **RESDEV THUNDER**, b g Night of Thunder (IRE)—Winner's Wish **Resdev Ltd**

TWO-YEAR-OLDS

96 Br f 02/03 Footstepsinthesand—Kofariti (IRE) (Kodiac) (1429)

Other Owners: R. P. E. Berry, Mr J. Cain, Mr P. W. Chapman, Mr S. J. M. Cobb, Mr R. Doak, Mr S. Dobson, Mr I. P. Earnshaw, Mrs J. Earnshaw, G. Godsman, M. D. Hammond, Mr D. A. Harrison, Mrs R. Hetherington, Mr T. Heywood, Mrs J. Hill, Mr J. A. Hill, Mrs J. Hill, Mr B. R. Howard, Mr R. M. Howard, Mr M. Kent, Mr R. Manners, Ms J. Matthews-Griffiths, Middleham Park Racing XXIII, Ms D. Morley, Mr G. Newton, Mr S. Nicols, G. R. Orchard, T. S. Palin, Mr N. Pietrzyk, M. Prince, R M & T Holdings Limited, Mr J. Reid, Resdev Ltd, Mr A. Savage, Mr J. Sidebottom, Mrs K. Sidebottom, A. W. Sinclair, Mr S. Sutton, Mrs G. M. Swinglehurst, Mr C. Talbot, Mr J. E. Tennant, Lady S. Toomes, Mrs B. Turnbull, O. R. Weeks.

Assistant Trainer: Mrs G. Hogg.

NH Jockey: Alain Cawley, Joe Colliver. **Conditional Jockey:** Billy Garritty, Aidan Macdonald, Emma Smith-Chaston. **Apprentice Jockey:** Aiden Brookes. **Amateur Jockey:** Miss R. Smith, James Waggott.

---

239 | MR GARY HANMER, Tattenhall
Postal: **Church Farm, Harthill Lane, Harthill, Tattenhall, Chester, Cheshire, CH3 9LQ**
Contacts: **MOBILE 07737 181165**

1 **BALLYRATH (IRE)**, 12, b g Flemensfirth (USA)—Rose Wee (IRE) **Mr C. F. Moore**
2 **COSTLY DIAMOND (IRE)**, 8, ch m Mahler—Sweet Ouzel (IRE) **TGK Construction Co. Ltd**
3 **DAWN RAIDER (IRE)**, 10, b g Mahler—Woodview Dawn (IRE) **Mr T. G. Kelly**
4 **DEE EIRE**, 5, bl m Gentlewave (IRE)—Kahipiroska (FR) **The Deeside Partnership**
5 **DEE LANE (IRE)**, 9, br g Oscar (IRE)—Royal Robin (IRE) **The Deeside Partnership**
6 **DEE STAR (IRE)**, 9, b g Shantou (USA)—Alicias Lady (IRE) **The Deeside Partnership**
7 **FANDABIDOZI (IRE)**, 4, ch g Mastercraftsman (IRE)—Cranky Spanky (IRE) **Mr G. Evans**
8 **FLAMING AMBITION (IRE)**, 5, b g Fame And Glory—Gran Chis (IRE)
9 **FUSIONFORCE (IRE)**, 15, b g Overbury (IRE)—Seviot **Mr S. P. Edkins**
10 **HIGH COUNSEL (IRE)**, 13, br g Presenting—The Bench (IRE) **Herongate Racers**
11 **HILLVIEW (IRE)**, 6, b g Fruits of Love (USA)—Da Das Delight (IRE) **Mr D. O. Pickering**
12 **IBERIA (IRE)**, 5, b g Galileo (IRE)—Beauty Bright (IRE)
13 **INISHBIGGLE (IRE)**, 7, b g Asian Heights—Leahs Joy (IRE) **Miss G. Davies**
14 **ISTHEBAROPEN (IRE)**, 9, b m Grape Tree Road—Seviot **Mr G. Evans**
15 **KNOCKNAGOSHEL (IRE)**, 9, b g Kalanisi (IRE)—Granny Clark (IRE) **Knock Knock Syndicate**
16 **LEDHAM (IRE)**, 7, b g Shamardal (USA)—Pioneer Bride (USA) **Mr G. Evans**
17 **LOCH GARMAN ARIS (IRE)**, 12, b g Jammaal—See Em Aime (IRE) **The Brookes Family**
18 **LOCKDOWN LASS**, 4, b f Albaasil (IRE)—Littlemoor Lass **Lockdown Racing**
19 **LOU TREK (IRE)**, 8, b g Linda's Lad—Nara Eria (FR) **Mr T. G. Kelly**
20 **MAGHEROARTY STAR (IRE)**, 6, b m Watar (IRE)—Cailin Aoibhinn (IRE) **Mr D. O. Pickering**
21 **MALINA OCARINA**, 7, b m Malinas (GER)—Ocarina Davis (FR) **M.H. Racing Malina**
22 **O'GRADY'S BOY (IRE)**, 11, b g Kalanisi (IRE)—Jemima Jay (IRE) **The Deeside Partnership**
23 **OSCAR NOMINATION (IRE)**, 10, b g Getaway (GER)—Nightofthe Oscars (IRE) **The Deeside Partnership**

MR GARY HANMER - continued

24 **SIR TIVO (FR)**, 8, b g Deportivo—Miss Possibility (USA) **Mrs J. A. Ashley**
25 **STEEL WAVE (IRE)**, 12, br g Craigsteel—Musical Waves (IRE) **Mr S. Walker**
26 **STONY MAN (IRE)**, 6, b g Getaway (GER)—Answer My Question (IRE) **Lockdown Racing**
27 **SUPERIOR GLANCE**, 7, br m Passing Glance—Qualitee **The Ed-chester Partnership**
28 **WBEE (IRE)**, 7, b g Yeats (IRE)—Consultation (IRE) **Mrs M. D. Ritson**
29 **WHAT A TIME (IRE)**, 6, b g Fame And Glory—Baden's Firth (IRE) **Moorland Racing & Mark Hammond**
30 **WHITE WALKER**, 7, gr g Dream Eater (IRE)—Soleil Sauvage **The Ed-chester Partnership**

Other Owners: Mr S. P. Edkins, Mr M. J. Hammond, Mrs A. M. Mace, S. A. Mace, Moorland Racing, Mr G. J. Winchester.

240	**MR RICHARD HANNON, Marlborough**

Postal: **Herridge Racing Stables, Herridge, Collingbourne Ducis, Wiltshire, SN8 3EG**
Contacts: **PHONE 01264 850254 FAX 01264 850076**
EMAIL kevin@richardhannonracing.co.uk WEBSITE www.richardhannonracing.co.uk

1 **ALWAYS FEARLESS (IRE)**, 5, ch g Camacho—Zenella
2 **BIG WING (IRE)**, 5, b g Free Eagle (IRE)—Orafinitis (IRE)
3 **CHINDIT (IRE)**, 4, b c Wootton Bassett—Always A Dream
4 **CUBAN CIGAR**, 4, b g Havana Gold (IRE)—Semayyel (IRE)
5 **DEWEY ROAD (IRE)**, 4, b c No Nay Never (USA)—Celestial Dream (IRE)
6 **DILLYDINGDILLYDONG**, 4, b g Territories (IRE)—Cephalonie (USA)
7 **DINGLE (IRE)**, 4, b g Footstepsinthesand—Beal Ban (IRE)
8 **ETONIAN (IRE)**, 4, b c Olympic Glory (IRE)—Naan (IRE)
9 **FANCY MAN (IRE)**, 4, b c Pride of Dubai (AUS)—Fancy (IRE)
10 **GRAND SCHEME (IRE)**, 4, b g Territories (IRE)—Antillia
11 **GUSTAV HOLST (IRE)**, 4, b g Sea The Stars (IRE)—Scarlet And Gold (IRE)
12 **HAPPY ROMANCE (IRE)**, 4, b f Dandy Man (IRE)—Rugged Up (IRE)
13 **KEEP RIGHT ON (IRE)**, 4, b c Acclamation—Khalice
14 **KOOL MOE DEE (IRE)**, 4, b g Mehmas (IRE)—Senadora (GER)
15 **LAFAN (IRE)**, 4, b g Dandy Man (IRE)—Light Glass (IRE)
16 **LEXINGTON KNIGHT (IRE)**, 4, ch g Night of Thunder (IRE)—Petit Adagio (IRE)
17 **MAFIA POWER**, 5, b g Gleneagles (IRE)—Rivara
18 **MAMMASAIDKNOCKUOUT (IRE)**, 4, b f Vadamos (FR)—Open Verse (USA)
19 **MOJO STAR (IRE)**, 4, b c Sea The Stars (IRE)—Galley
20 **MR TYRRELL (IRE)**, 8, b g Helmet (AUS)—Rocking
21 **MUMS TIPPLE (IRE)**, 5, ch g Footstepsinthesand—Colomone Cross (IRE)
22 **OH THIS IS US (IRE)**, 9, b h Acclamation—Shamwari Lodge (IRE)
23 **PURE DREAMER**, 4, b c Oasis Dream—Pure Line
24 **REVEREND HUBERT (IRE)**, 4, ch g Zoffany (IRE)—Bright Sapphire (IRE)
25 **ROYAL EVENT (IRE)**, 4, b f Golden Horn—Salacia (IRE)
26 **SIAM FOX (IRE)**, 4, b g Prince of Lir (IRE)—Folegandros Island (FR)
27 **SIR RUMI (IRE)**, 4, ch g Gleneagles (IRE)—Reine des Plages (IRE)
28 **STATE SECRETARY (IRE)**, 4, b g Muhaarar—Danetime Out (IRE)
29 **TAHITIAN PRINCE (FR)**, 5, b g Siyouni (FR)—Tehamana (IRE)
30 **TEODOLINA (IRE)**, 4, b f Kodiac—Teodelight (IRE)
31 **TYPHOON TEN (IRE)**, 6, b g Slade Power (IRE)—Cake (IRE)
32 **VENTURA TORMENTA (IRE)**, 4, b c Acclamation—Midnight Oasis
33 **VICTORIOUS NIGHT (IRE)**, 4, b c Night of Thunder (IRE)—Akuna Magic (IRE)

THREE-YEAR-OLDS

34 **AMERICAN KESTREL (IRE)**, b f Starspangledbanner (AUS)—Marsh Hawk
35 **AMIGA MEU**, b f Cable Bay (IRE)—Todber
36 **AN ANGEL'S DREAM (FR)**, ch f Dream Ahead (USA)—Sandy's Charm (FR)
37 **ARDBRACCAN (IRE)**, b f Lawman (FR)—Bosphorus Queen (IRE)
38 **ARMOR**, b br c No Nay Never (USA)—Hestia (FR)

MR RICHARD HANNON - continued

39 **BALLET OF DUBAI (IRE),** b f Dubawi (IRE)—Lilian Baylis (IRE)
40 **BATTLE POINT (IRE),** b c Dandy Man (IRE)—Paddy Again (IRE)
41 **BETSHOOF,** b c Night of Thunder (IRE)—Surprise (IRE)
42 **BOSH (IRE),** b c Profitable (IRE)—Tropical Mist (IRE)
43 **BYKER (IRE),** b c Le Havre (IRE)—Bridge of Peace
44 **CABRAKAN (IRE),** b c Divine Prophet (AUS)—Ready's Legend (USA)
45 **CHEF D'ETAT (IRE),** ch g Ribchester (IRE)—Fluvial (IRE)
46 **CLASE AZUL ULTRA (IRE),** b c Mehmas (IRE)—Ashtown Girl (IRE)
47 **CONDUCIVE (IRE),** b c Profitable (IRE)—Amalina
48 B f The Gurkha (IRE)—Couragetocontinue (IRE)
49 **DAWN OF LIBERATION (IRE),** b c Churchill (IRE)—Danetime Out (IRE)
50 **DESERT ANGEL (IRE),** b gr c Dark Angel (IRE)—Slieve Mish (IRE)
51 **DUELIST,** b c Dubawi (IRE)—Coplow
52 **ELLADE,** b f Showcasing—Entree
53 **EXCELING (IRE),** b f Exceed And Excel (AUS)—Jadaayil
54 **FARHH NORTH,** b f Farhh—Heading North
55 B c Shalaa (IRE)—Fazendera (IRE)
56 **FLINTSTONE (IRE),** ch c Starspangledbanner (AUS)—Madame Cherie (USA)
57 **FODEN,** b g Garswood—Allegramente
58 **GARGLE,** b f Bated Breath—Gravitation
59 **GEOPOLITIC (IRE),** b c Mehmas (IRE)—Nina Bonita (IRE)
60 **GISBURN (IRE),** ch c Ribchester (IRE)—Disclose
61 **GOD OF THUNDER (IRE),** b c Tagula (IRE)—Tawjeeh
62 **GUBBASS (IRE),** b c Mehmas (IRE)—Vida Amorosa (IRE)
63 **GUITAR,** b g Mayson—Clapperboard
64 **HELENE,** b f Olympic Glory (IRE)—Travel Writer (IRE)
65 **HEREDIA,** br gr f Dark Angel (IRE)—Nakuti (IRE)
66 **HOLIDAY,** b c Time Test—Precious Angel (IRE)
67 **INTERNAL CONFLICT (IRE),** b c Highland Reel (IRE)—Swift Action (IRE)
68 **ISEMEL (IRE),** b f Camacho—Mia Madonna
69 **KODIAS SANGARIUS (IRE),** b f Kodiac—Oui Say Oui (IRE)
70 **LAASUDOOD (USA),** b c War Front (USA)—Lahudood
71 **LIFE'S A BEACH (IRE),** b c Footstepsinthesand—Acca Laurentia (IRE)
72 **LOOE BEACH (IRE),** br c Footstepsinthesand—Ruxleys Star (USA)
73 **LOQUACE (IRE),** b f Exceed And Excel (AUS)—Parle Moi (USA)
74 **LUSAIL (IRE),** b c Mehmas (IRE)—Diaminda (IRE)
75 **MAGICAL DIAS,** b f Havana Gold (IRE)—Maremmadiavola (IRE)
76 **MARITIME RULES (IRE),** b g Mehmas (IRE)—Beauty of The Sea
77 **MEKBAT (FR),** b c Zelzal (FR)—Al Markhiya (IRE)
78 B f No Nay Never (USA)—Miss Understood (IRE)
79 **MONET'S SUNRISE,** b g Le Havre (IRE)—Distant (USA)
80 **MONITOR,** b c Dabirsim (FR)—Discipline
81 **MUGADER (FR),** ch c Olympic Glory (IRE)—Al Anqa
82 **MUNDANA LILY,** b f Fast Company (IRE)—Mundana (IRE)
83 **NIGHT ARC,** b c Twilight Son—Gymnaste (IRE)
84 **OH HERBERTS REIGN (IRE),** b c Acclamation—Western Safari (IRE)
85 **OWER INDEPENDENCE,** b f Adaay (IRE)—Mary's Pet
86 B f Ribchester (IRE)—Pavillon
87 **PRIDE ASIDE,** b f Pride of Dubai (AUS)—Arabda
88 **PYRRHIC DANCER (IRE),** b c Holy Roman Emperor (IRE)—Kirk's Dancer (USA)
89 **RATTLING,** b f Acclamation—Westadora (IRE)
90 **RAZZLE DAZZLE,** b c Muhaarar—Bint Almukhtar (IRE)
91 **RIVER PRIDE,** b f Oasis Dream—Highest
92 **ROBJON,** b g Mukhadram—Barnezet (GR)
93 **ROUSAY (IRE),** gr ro f Muhaarar—Ronaldsay
94 **SALITEH,** b f Ardad (IRE)—Poesy
95 **SANDY PARADISE (IRE),** ch c Footstepsinthesand—Duljanah (IRE)
96 **SAY GOODNIGHT (IRE),** b f Ribchester (IRE)—Galley
97 **SEA THE SUNSET,** b c Sea The Moon (GER)—Dubai Cyclone (USA)
98 **SEVERN STOKE,** b f Swiss Spirit—Amber Lane

MR RICHARD HANNON - continued

  99 SHABBAB (FR), b c Zelzal (FR)—One River (FR)
100 SHARVARA, b g Kingman—Tendency (IRE)
101 SIAMSA (IRE), b f Starspangledbanner (AUS)—Sliabh Luachra (IRE)
102 SIXTH STREET (FR), b f Toronado (IRE)—La Undecima (FR)
103 SKY SILK (IRE), ch f The Gurkha (IRE)—Inez
104 SPACE ODYSSEY (IRE), b c Sea The Stars (IRE)—Lady Of Dubai
105 SUNAINA (IRE), ch f Farhh—Petite Nymphe
106 SYMPHONY PERFECT (IRE), b f Fast Company (IRE)—Irish Romance (IRE)
107 SYSTEM (IRE), b f Galileo Gold—Spiritual Air
108 TACARIB BAY, b c Night of Thunder (IRE)—Bassmah
109 TASHKENT (IRE), b c Acclamation—Colour Blue (IRE)
110 THUNDER MAX, ch c Night of Thunder (IRE)—Tuolumne Meadows
111 THUNDER QUEEN, b f Night of Thunder (IRE)—Muzhil (IRE)
112 TROPEZ POWER (IRE), b g Cotai Glory—Warm Welcome
113 WHIRLWIND, b c Night of Thunder (IRE)—Hokkaido
114 WINDSEEKER, b c Aclaim (IRE)—Itsinthestars
115 WITCH HUNTER (FR), b c Siyouni (FR)—Sorciere (IRE)
116 B c Olympic Glory (IRE)—Ysandre
117 ZOOM, b c Adaay (IRE)—The Giving Tree (IRE)

TWO-YEAR-OLDS

118 B c 11/02 Starspangledbanner (AUS)—Aja (IRE) (Excellent Art) (115000)
119 AL HARGAH (IRE), b f 18/03 Muhaarar—Platinum Pearl (Shamardal (USA))
120 AL NOAAMAN, b c 23/03 Dubawi (IRE)—Great And Small (Galileo (IRE)) (50000)
121 Ch c 09/02 Dandy Man (IRE)—Alhawdaj (USA) (Speightstown (USA)) (36190)
122 B c 24/04 Sea The Moon (GER)—Aliyfa (IRE) (Spinning World (USA)) (63776)
123 Br c 18/01 No Nay Never (USA)—All To Do With It (IRE) (Canford Cliffs (IRE)) (59524)
124 B c 17/02 Kingman—Alsindi (IRE) (Acclamation)
125 B f 03/04 Dubawi (IRE)—Aqlaam Vision (Aqlaam)
126 ARMOUR PROPRE (IRE), ch f 15/03 Profitable (IRE)—Foot of Pride (IRE) (Footstepsinthesand) (45714)
127 Br c 02/01 Caravaggio (USA)—Aurora Spring (IRE) (Power) (150000)
128 B f 06/03 Poet's Word (IRE)—Barnezet (GR) (Invincible Spirit (IRE))
129 Gr f 19/02 Havana Grey—Bassmah (Harbour Watch (IRE))
130 B c 07/02 Starspangledbanner (AUS)—Beach Wedding (IRE) (Footstepsinthesand) (85714)
131 Ch f 24/03 Mastercraftsman (IRE)—Bright Eyed (IRE) (Galileo (IRE))
132 BRILLIANT COLOURS (IRE), b c 23/02 Exceed And Excel (AUS)—Indigo Butterfly (FR) (Le Havre (IRE)) (135000)
133 B c 30/03 Gustav Klimt (IRE)—Caramel Sundae (Oratorio (IRE)) (49524)
134 Ch c 20/04 Shamardal (USA)—Castleacre (Exceed And Excel (AUS))
135 CLASSIC, b c 31/03 Dubawi (IRE)—Date With Destiny (IRE) (George Washington (IRE)) (260000)
136 DAYYAN (IRE), b c 18/03 Kodiac—Dutch Destiny (Dutch Art) (38095)
137 DELLAROC QUEEN (IRE), b f 05/03 Le Havre (IRE)—Vrai (IRE) (Dark Angel (IRE)) (76531)
138 Br gr f 28/04 Clodovil (IRE)—Deora De (Night Shift (USA)) (11000)
139 DHI QAR, b c 07/04 Night of Thunder (IRE)—Sefaat (Haatef (USA)) (470000)
140 B f 11/03 Kodiac—Diaminda (IRE) (Diamond Green (FR)) (470000)
141 B f 13/01 Churchill (IRE)—Divisimo (Dansili)
142 Ch f 23/04 Sea The Stars (IRE)—Dorcas Lane (Norse Dancer (IRE)) (400000)
143 B f 23/04 Profitable (IRE)—Dylan Alexander (IRE) (Dylan Thomas (IRE)) (28571)
144 B c 02/03 Unfortunately (IRE)—Eleventh Hour (IRE) (Invincible Spirit (IRE)) (28571)
145 Br f 21/02 Zoustar (AUS)—Felissa (GER) (Soldier Hollow) (185000)
146 B c 13/02 Kodi Bear (IRE)—Final Treat (IRE) (Acclamation) (175000)
147 B c 15/04 Footstepsinthesand—Fine Judgment (Compton Place) (59048)
148 B c 28/04 Profitable (IRE)—Flick Show (IRE) (Fastnet Rock (AUS)) (47619)
149 B f 27/02 Acclamation—Free To Roam (IRE) (Bushranger (IRE)) (51429)
150 B f 11/05 Zoustar (AUS)—Full Mandate (IRE) (Acclamation) (60000)
151 GAALLIB, b c 21/02 Territories (IRE)—Flighty Clarets (IRE) (Bahamian Bounty) (28571)
152 GALEXIA, b f 04/01 Galileo—Illuminate (IRE) (Zoffany (IRE))
153 GALORE (IRE), b f 23/04 Profitable (IRE)—Dylan Alexander (IRE) (Dylan Thomas (IRE))
154 Ch f 09/04 Dubawi (IRE)—Geisha Girl (IRE) (Galileo (IRE))
155 GLORY SKY (IRE), ch f 12/03 Cotai Glory—Artax Hope (IRE) (Kyllachy) (26667)

MR RICHARD HANNON - continued

156 GREAT BEDWYN, b c 08/02 Showcasing—Mistress Quickly (IRE) (Mastercraftsman (IRE)) (150000)
157 HECTIC, b c 04/05 Massaat (IRE)—Ceedwell (Exceed And Excel (AUS)) (41905)
158 B f 11/03 Zoffany (IRE)—Hells Babe (Hellvelyn)
159 Ch f 19/03 Farhh—Imasumaq (IRE) (Teofilo (IRE)) (85714)
160 B f 10/02 Cotai Glory—Invincible Me (IRE) (Invincible Spirit (IRE)) (130000)
161 B c 03/03 Sioux Nation (USA)—Jewel In The Sand (IRE) (Bluebird (USA)) (66667)
162 JILTED, b f 27/03 Brazen Beau (AUS)—Sleepy Dust (IRE) (Rip Van Winkle (IRE)) (22000)
163 B c 08/03 Acclamation—Kassandra (IRE) (Dandy Man (IRE)) (155000)
164 KING SHARJA, b c 14/03 Kingman—Sharja Queen (Pivotal)
165 B c 13/04 Havana Grey—Lady Estella (IRE) (Equiano (FR)) (38095)
166 B f 09/04 Golden Horn—Lady Heidi (High Chaparral (IRE)) (25000)
167 LIGHTNING ELIZA, ch c 31/03 Night of Thunder (IRE)—Elis Eliz (IRE) (Lord Shanakill (USA)) (300000)
168 Gr f 18/03 Dark Angel (IRE)—Liwa Palace (Oasis Dream) (125000)
169 B f 31/03 Dandy Man (IRE)—Looks Great (New Approach (IRE)) (30000)
170 B c 01/02 Saxon Warrior (JPN)—Loved So Much (Dansili) (82000)
171 B f 05/04 Acclamation—Lucina (Machiavellian (USA))
172 B f 29/04 U S Navy Flag (USA)—Lumiere Noire (FR) (Dashing Blade) (62000)
173 Ch f 11/03 Cracksman—Mademoiselle Marie (FR) (Evasive) (26000)
174 MALHUMORADA (IRE), b f 10/02 Fast Company (IRE)—Miss Moody (IRE) (Frozen Power (IRE)) (11905)
175 Ch f 22/04 Havana Grey—Mamma Morton (IRE) (Elnadim (USA)) (33333)
176 B c 03/04 Cotai Glory—Masai Queen (IRE) (Mujadil (USA)) (52381)
177 B f 10/03 Showcasing—Midnightly (Acclamation) (38095)
178 MISS HELEN (IRE), b f 11/04 U S Navy Flag (USA)—Fluvial (IRE) (Exceed And Excel (AUS)) (38095)
179 B c 18/01 Kessaar (IRE)—Miss Purity Pinker (IRE) (One Cool Cat (USA)) (47619)
180 B c 22/02 Camacho—Mots Croises (Cape Cross (IRE)) (43810)
181 B c 14/04 Awtaad (IRE)—My Henrietta (IRE) (Henrythenavigator (USA)) (28000)
182 B c 15/03 Kingman—Nashmiah (IRE) (Elusive City (USA))
183 NIGHT LIFE, b f 31/01 Nathaniel (IRE)—Singing Sky (Oasis Dream)
184 ODIBIL (IRE), b f 24/03 Camacho—Lido Lady (IRE) (Danehill Dancer (IRE)) (10629)
185 OH SWEET TABU (IRE), b f 27/03 Zoustar (AUS)—Threetimesalady (Royal Applause) (93537)
186 B f 20/04 Le Havre (IRE)—Onceuponastar (IRE) (Sea The Stars (IRE)) (40000)
187 ONSLOW GARDENS (IRE), br c 21/04 Footstepsinthesand—Just Darcy (Danehill Dancer (IRE)) (60000)
188 OPTIVA STAR (IRE), b c 22/02 U S Navy Flag (USA)—Leaf (IRE) (Montjeu (IRE)) (59524)
189 OUTRACE (IRE), ch c 17/01 Camacho—Trace of Scent (IRE) (Acclamation) (33333)
190 PALAMON (IRE), ch c 24/02 Decorated Knight—Seschat (IRE) (Sinndar (IRE)) (47619)
191 B c 26/02 Kodiac—Pashmina (IRE) (Barathea (IRE)) (30000)
192 B f 20/03 Kingman—Perfect Angel (IRE) (Dark Angel (IRE))
193 B gr c 27/03 Kitten's Joy (USA)—Picco Uno (USA) (Macho Uno (USA))
194 PINK LILY, ch f 03/03 Sixties Icon—Mellow (Bahamian Bounty)
195 PLAYACTOR, b c 25/02 Make Believe—Say To Me (FR) (Redoute's Choice (AUS)) (58000)
196 PLAYBACK, b f 26/01 Recorder—Make Fast (Makfi)
197 B c 29/03 Saxon Warrior (JPN)—Polygon (Dynaformer (USA))
198 POWERDRESS (IRE), b f 24/03 Dandy Man (IRE)—Nuclear Option (IRE) (Frozen Power (IRE)) (123810)
199 PRETTY PEG (IRE), b f 30/01 Awtaad (IRE)—Letizia (IRE) (Tamayuz) (46769)
200 PRIDE OF SPAIN (IRE), ch c 20/04 Lope de Vega (IRE)—Pride (IRE) (Peintre Celebre (USA)) (320000)
201 B f 23/03 Ardad (IRE)—Pryers Princess (Medicean) (32000)
202 B f 12/03 Camelot—Quixotic (Pivotal)
203 RED FORT (FR), b c 25/01 Zoustar (AUS)—Fortitude (IRE) (Oasis Dream) (42517)
204 REFINE (IRE), b f 25/04 Starspangledbanner (AUS)—Divert (IRE) (Averti (IRE)) (80952)
205 B f 20/04 Dark Angel (IRE)—Ripalong (IRE) (Revoque (IRE))
206 Gr 09/03 Profitable (IRE)—Rochitta (USA) (Arch (USA)) (65000)
207 B f 12/04 Sea The Moon (GER)—Rock Follies (Rock of Gibraltar (IRE)) (33333)
208 SALOMON PICO (FR), b c 04/04 Almanzor (FR)—Alta Stima (IRE) (Raven's Pass (USA)) (114796)
209 SAM'S HOPE, b f 15/03 Awtaad (IRE)—Delightful Belle (USA) (Elusive Quality (USA)) (40000)
210 B c 27/03 Harry Angel (IRE)—Samaah (IRE) (Cape Cross (IRE)) (150000)
211 B gr c 10/02 Gutaifan (IRE)—Senadora (GER) (Tertullian (USA)) (30000)
212 SHOT, b f 02/03 Acclamation—Gladiatrix (Compton Place) (76190)
213 B f 11/02 Recorder—Sightseeing (New Approach (IRE)) (7000)
214 SIGNCASTLE CITY (IRE), gr c 15/04 Dark Angel (IRE)—Uae Queen (Oasis Dream)
215 B f 02/02 Profitable (IRE)—Singapore Lilly (IRE) (Mujadil (USA)) (72279)

MR RICHARD HANNON - continued

216 B f 03/02 Galileo Gold—Sketching (Nathaniel (IRE)) (57143)
217 Ch c 04/03 Sea The Stars (IRE)—Soltada (IRE) (Dawn Approach (IRE)) (160000)
218 B c 19/01 Iffraaj—Spinaminnie (IRE) (Moss Vale (IRE)) (72000)
219 SPRING CHORUS, b f 23/04 New Approach (IRE)—Joys of Spring (IRE) (Invincible Spirit (IRE))
220 STAMFORD BLUE (IRE), b c 30/01 Fast Company (IRE)—Chelsea Corsage (IRE) (Teofilo (IRE)) (33333)
221 STARMAS (IRE), b f 22/01 Mehmas (IRE)—Startori (Vettori (IRE)) (50000)
222 B f 03/03 Acclamation—Subtle Affair (IRE) (Barathea (IRE)) (26667)
223 SUDOOL (IRE), b f 14/01 Galileo Gold—Savannah Poppy (IRE) (Statue of Liberty (USA)) (65000)
224 SWEAR (IRE), b f 21/03 Camacho—Very Honest (IRE) (Poet's Voice) (28000)
225 B c 07/02 Cracksman—Tamaanee (AUS) (Teofilo (IRE)) (20000)
226 TAMANGO SANDS (IRE), b c 04/05 Footstepsinthesand—Couragetocontinue (IRE) (Canford Cliffs (IRE)) (21259)
227 B c 24/02 No Nay Never (USA)—Teofilo's Princess (IRE) (Teofilo (IRE))
228 TESSA, ch f 29/02 Havana Gold (IRE)—Lovely Memory (IRE) (Shamardal (USA)) (26000)
229 THE PARENT, b c 14/02 Frankel—Sophie P (Bushranger (IRE)) (280000)
230 THREEBARS (IRE), ch f 01/02 Cotai Glory—Lady Mega (IRE) (Kodiac) (83810)
231 UNCLE, b c 29/02 Harry Angel (IRE)—Heliograph (Ishiguru (USA)) (85714)
232 B f 27/03 Night of Thunder (IRE)—Wadaa (USA) (Dynaformer (USA))
233 B f 04/04 Charm Spirit (IRE)—Washington Blue (Rip Van Winkle (IRE)) (952)
234 B c 12/02 Mehmas (IRE)—Would It Matter (IRE) (Morpheus) (65000)
235 B f 13/03 Invincible Spirit (IRE)—You're Back (USA) (Street Cry (USA))

Head Man: Colin Bolger, Tony Gorman.

Flat Jockey: Pat Dobbs, Thore Hammer Hansen, Sean Levey, Rossa Ryan. **Apprentice Jockey:** Liam Browne.

---

241   MR GEOFFREY HARKER, Thirsk
Postal: **Stockhill Green, York Rd, Thirkelby, Thirsk, North Yorkshire, YO7 3AS**
Contacts: **PHONE 01845 501117 MOBILE 07803 116412, 07930 125544**
EMAIL gandjhome@aol.com WEBSITE www.geoffharkerracing.com

1 ELDELBAR (SPA), 8, ch g Footstepsinthesand—Malinche **The Twelve Minimum Racing Club**
2 HAIL SEZER, 5, b g Intrinsic—Nice One **The Twelve Minimum Racing Club**
3 KEY LOOK (IRE), 5, ch m Dawn Approach—Fashion Line (IRE) **Holmfirth Racing**
4 ROCKET ROD (IRE), 5, b g Australia—Tessa Reef (IRE) **The Twelve Minimum Racing Club**
5 RUM RUNNER, 7, b g Havana Gold (IRE)—Thermopylae **The Twelve Minimum Racing Club**
6 SAVALAS (IRE), 7, gr g Zebedee—Tap The Dot (IRE) **The Twelve Minimum Racing Club**
7 SCOTTISH SUMMIT (IRE), 9, b g Shamardal (USA)—Scottish Stage (IRE) **Banerjee,N & Harker**
8 WENTWORTH FALLS, 10, gr g Dansili—Strawberry Morn (CAN) **The Fall Guys Club**

THREE-YEAR-OLDS
9 GOLDEN RAINBOW, b c Havana Gold (IRE)—Stereophonic (IRE) **Holmfirth Racing**

Assistant Trainer: Jenny Harker.

NH Jockey: W. T. Kennedy.

242 **MR RICHARD HARPER, Kings Sutton**
Postal: **Home Farm, Kings Sutton, Banbury, Oxfordshire, OX17 3RS**
Contacts: **PHONE 01295 810997 MOBILE 07970 223481**
EMAIL richard@harpersfarm.co.uk

1 **STORM RISING (IRE)**, 9, b g Canford Cliffs (IRE)—Before The Storm **R. C. Harper**
2 **THOMAS BLOSSOM (IRE)**, 12, b g Dylan Thomas (IRE)—Woman Secret (IRE) **R. C. Harper**

Assistant Trainer: C. Harper.

243 **MRS JESSICA HARRINGTON, Kildare**
Postal: **Commonstown Stud, Moone, Co. Kildare, Ireland**
Contacts: **PHONE +353 59 862 4153 MOBILE +353 87 256 6129**
EMAIL jessica@jessicaharringtonracing.com WEBSITE www.jessicaharringtonracing.com

1 **ACE AUSSIE (IRE)**, 4, b c Australia—Queenscliff (IRE)
2 **ANNER CASTLE (IRE)**, 4, b c Fastnet Rock (AUS)—Marigold Hotel (IRE)
3 **ARAGON (IRE)**, 7, b g Yeats (IRE)—Dancera (GER)
4 **ASHDALE BOB (IRE)**, 7, b g Shantou (USA)—Ceol Rua (IRE)
5 **AURORA PRINCESS (IRE)**, 4, b f The Gurkha (IRE)—Rub A Dub Dub
6 **AUTUMN EVENING**, 5, ch g Tamayuz—Martagon Lily
7 **BARBADOS (IRE)**, 6, b g Galileo (IRE)—Sumora (IRE)
8 **BARRINGTON COURT**, 8, ch m Mastercraftsman—Arabian Hideaway
9, B c Walk In The Park (IRE)—Beau Bridget (IRE)
10 **BOOLA BOOLA (IRE)**, 5, b g Invincible Spirit (IRE)—We Can Say It Now (AUS)
11 **BOPEDRO (FR)**, 6, b g Pedro The Great (USA)—Breizh Touch (FR)
12 **CADILLAC (IRE)**, 4, b c Lope de Vega (IRE)—Seas of Wells (IRE)
13 **CAN'T IMAGINE (IRE)**, 5, ch m Shantou (USA)—Madame des Champs (IRE)
14 **CHANGING THE RULES (IRE)**, 5, b g Walk In The Park (IRE)—Blooming Quick (IRE)
15 **CLIMATE (IRE)**, 4, b f Australia—Frappe (IRE)
16 **CROSSHILL (IRE)**, 7, b g Sholokhov (IRE)—Rathvawn Belle (IRE)
17 **CYCLADIC (IRE)**, 4, b f Fastnet Rock (AUS)—Peloponnese (FR)
18 **DERRINLAUR (IRE)**, 4, b f Fastnet Rock (AUS)—Lady Bones (IRE)
19 **DISCORDANTLY (IRE)**, 8, b g Salutino (GER)—Collinstown Queen (IRE)
20 **EDISON KENT (IRE)**, 6, b g Leading Light (IRE)—Kentish Town (IRE)
21 **EVER PRESENT**, 6, br g Elusive Pimpernel—Persian Memories
22 **EXIT POLL (IRE)**, 8, b g Elusive Pimpernel (USA)—Carolobrian (IRE)
23 **FAME AND JOY (IRE)**, 6, b m Fame And Glory—Coonagh Cross (IRE)
24 **FLOR DE LA LUNA**, 5, b m Sea The Moon—Fresa
25 **FORBEARANCE (IRE)**, 5, b m Galileo (IRE)—Nechita (AUS)
26 **GIULIANA (GER)**, 4, b f Muhaarar—Golden Whip
27 **GOLDEN LYRIC**, 4, b br f Lope de Vega (IRE)—As Good As Gold (IRE)
28 **GUIRI (GER)**, 7, ch g Motivator—Guardia (GER)
29 **HELL BENT (IRE)**, 4, ch c Mastercraftsman (IRE)—Fikrah
30 **ILMIG (IRE)**, 5, b g Galileo (IRE)—Acoma (USA)
31 **INSTANT RETURN**, 6, b g Elzaam—Instant Memories
32, B f Soldier of Fortune (IRE)—Jeree (IRE)
33 **JESINA (IRE)**, 6, b m Milan—Jeree (IRE)
34 **JETARA (IRE)**, 4, b f Walk In The Park (IRE)—Jelan (IRE)
35 **JUNGLE COVE (IRE)**, 5, gr g Mastercraftsman (IRE)—Purple Glow (IRE)
36 **JUNGLE JUNCTION (IRE)**, 7, br g Elusive Pimpernel (USA)—Consignia (IRE)
37 **LADY ANNER (IRE)**, 5, b m Fastnet Rock (AUS)—Lady Bones (IRE)
38 **LAELAPS (IRE)**, 4, b c Exceed And Excel (AUS)—Magen's Star (IRE)
39 **LEO DE FURY (IRE)**, 6, ch h Australia—Attire
40 **LIFETIME AMBITION**, 7, b g Kapgarde—Jeanquiri
41 **MAC'S XPRESS (IRE)**, 4, ch g Mount Nelson—Snob's Supreme (IRE)

MRS JESSICA HARRINGTON - continued

42 4, B f Robin des Champs (FR)—Manhattan Babe (IRE)
43 **MAUD GONNE SPIRIT (IRE)**, 5, ch m Intello—Bari
44 **MIGHTY MEGGSIE (IRE)**, 6, b m Arakan—Angel Loez
45 **MOROSINI (FR)**, 7, b g Martaline—Iris du Berlais (FR)
46 **MRS GRIMLEY (IRE)**, 4, b f Australia—Yakshini (IRE)
47 **MY HOLY FOX (IRE)**, 4, br f Holy Roman Emperor (IRE)—My Renee (USA)
48 **MY MINERVINA (IRE)**, 4, b f Holy Roman Emperor (IRE)—Are You Mine (IRE)
49 **NEVERUSHACON (IRE)**, 11, b g Echo of Light—Lily Beth (IRE)
50 **NJORD (IRE)**, 6, b g Roderic O'Connor—Rosalind Franklin
51 **O'REILLY (FR)**, 4, b c Frankel—Fann (USA)
52 **ONLY SKY (IRE)**, 4, b f Sea The Stars (IRE)—Star Mon Amie (IRE)
53 **ONLYHUMAN (IRE)**, 9, b g Invincible Spirit (IRE)—Liscune (IRE)
54 **PAHLAVI (IRE)**, 5, b g Palavicini (USA)—Persian Memories (IRE)
55 **PORT STANLEY (IRE)**, 8, b g Papal Bull—Prairie Moonlight (GER)
56 **RAPID RESPONSE (FR)**, 8, br m Network (GER)—La Grande Villez (FR)
57 **REAL APPEAL (GER)**, 5, b g Sidestep (AUS)—Runaway Sparkle
58 **SANDYMOUNT BABY (IRE)**, 5, b m Elusive Pimpernel (USA)—Joleah (IRE)
59 **SCOPELLO (IRE)**, 4, b f Elusive Pimpernel (USA)—Madame des Champs (IRE)
60 **SHONA MEA (IRE)**, 5, b m Dragon Pulse (IRE)—Weekend Getaway (IRE)
61 **SIGN FROM ABOVE (IRE)**, 4, b c Sea The Stars (IRE)—Martine's Spirit (IRE)
62 **SILVER SHEEN (IRE)**, 8, b g Sulamani—Silver Gypsy
63 **SIZING MAURITIUS (IRE)**, 5, b g Martaline—Beau Bridget (IRE)
64 **SIZING POTTSIE (FR)**, 8, b g Kapgarde (FR)—Line Salsa (FR)
65 **STRIKING (FR)**, 4, b g Equiano (FR)—Distinctive Look (IRE)
66 **SUMMER GALE (IRE)**, 4, b g Camelot—Luas Line (IRE)
67 **TAIPAN (FR)**, 4, b c Frankel—Kenzadargent (FR)
68 **TAURAN SHAMAN (IRE)**, 6, b h Shamardal—Danelissima
69 **THAT'S JUST DANDY (IRE)**, 4, b g Dandy Man (IRE)—Union City Blues (IRE)
70 **THE BLUE BRILLIANT (IRE)**, 4, b f Fastnet Rock (AUS)—Butterfly Blue (IRE)
71 **THE VERY MAN (IRE)**, 8, b g Jeremy (USA)—Mill Meadow (IRE)
72 **TORREADOR**, 6, b h Toronado (IRE)—Pompey Girl
73 **VALLE DE LA LUNA**, 4, b f Galileo (IRE)—Fiesolana (IRE)
74 **WINGIN A PRAYER (IRE)**, 7, b g Winged Love—Toubliss

THREE-YEAR-OLDS

75 **ADONIS (IRE)**, ch c Siyouni (FR)—Rajaratna (IRE)
76 **AIRGLOW (USA)**, b f Kitten's Joy (USA)—Absolute Crackers (IRE)
77 **ALIZARINE**, b f Sea The Moon (GER)—Alea Iacta
78 **ASTELIA (IRE)**, ch f Sea The Stars (IRE)—Agapantha (USA)
79 **BEGINISH**, ch c New Approach (IRE)—La Superba (IRE)
80 **BENITOITE (IRE)**, b f Pivotal—Crystal Diamond
81 **CAROLINE HERSCHEL (IRE)**, ch f Zoffany (IRE)—Compostela
82 **CAROMIL**, b f Sea The Stars (IRE)—Greenisland (IRE)
83 **CONFIDENT STAR (IRE)**, b c Lope de Vega (IRE)—Freedom March
84 **COWBOY JUSTICE**, b c Lope de Vega (IRE)—Starflower
85 **DARK VEGA (IRE)**, b f Lope de Vega (IRE)—Dream Club
86 **DISCOVERIES (IRE)**, b f Mastercraftsman (IRE)—Alpha Lupi (IRE)
87 **DOMESTIC GODDESS**, b gr f Caravaggio (USA)—Jasmine Blue (IRE)
88 **ECOUTEZ (IRE)**, b f Exceed And Excel (AUS)—Ecoutila (USA)
89 **EUROCRAT**, b g Holy Roman Emperor (IRE)—Apparatchika
90 **EXQUISITE ACCLAIM (IRE)**, b c Acclamation—Exquisite Ruby
91 **FAIR JOE (IRE)**, b g Bated Breath—Boragh Jamal (IRE)
92 **FENNELA (IRE)**, b f Sea The Stars (IRE)—Green Room (USA)
93 **FUMATA (IRE)**, gr c Fastnet Rock (AUS)—Marigold Hotel (IRE)
94 **HA HA HA (IRE)**, b f Dark Angel (IRE)—Fashionable
95 **IRISH LULLABY**, gr f Nathaniel (IRE)—Victoria Regina (IRE)
96 **IT'S SNOWING (IRE)**, b ro f Kodiac—Snow Pixie (USA)
97 **KOMEDY KICKS (IRE)**, b f Churchill (IRE)—Komedy (IRE)
98 **LOPES GOLD (IRE)**, ch f Lope de Vega (IRE)—Perfect Alchemy (IRE)

MRS JESSICA HARRINGTON - continued

  99 B f Fastnet Rock (AUS)—Love Charm
100 LUCKY KUNA (FR), ch c Lope de Vega (IRE)—Kuna Yala (GER)
101 LUCKY SAN JORE, gr c Lope de Vega (IRE)—Claba di San Jore (IRE)
102 MAGICAL LAGOON (IRE), b f Galileo (IRE)—Night Lagoon (GER)
103 MAGNIFICENT LADY (IRE), b f Galileo (IRE)—Night Visit
104 B f Wootton Bassett—Maria Letizia
105 MIGHTY MO MISSOURI (IRE), b g Zoffany (IRE)—What Say You (IRE)
106 NECTARIS, b f Sea The Moon (GER)—Angelic Air
107 NOT UNCERTAIN (JPN), b f Deep Impact (JPN)—Unbelievable (IRE)
108 PAPA K, b c Kodiac—Alonsoa (IRE)
109 PARIS LIGHTS (IRE), b c Siyouni (FR)—Cabaret (IRE)
110 PARIS PEACOCK (IRE), b f Muhaarar—Weekend Fling (USA)
111 POPPY PETAL (IRE), b f Fast Company (IRE)—Rare Ransom
112 PRINCESS AZURE, ch f Air Force Blue (USA)—Princess Sinead (IRE)
113 PRINCESS RAJJ, b f Rajj (IRE)—Princess Aloof (IRE)
114 ROCK OF CANDY, b f Fastnet Rock (AUS)—Affability (IRE)
115 SABLONNE, b f Dark Angel (IRE)—Starlit Sands
116 SHAKY OPERATOR, b c Street Sense (USA)—Accusation (USA)
117 SHORT N SWEET (IRE), b f Exceed And Excel (AUS)—Carte de Visite (USA)
118 SIERRA NEVADA (USA), b f American Pharoah (USA)—Visions of Clarity (IRE)
119 STELLAROCK (IRE), b f Fastnet Rock (AUS)—Wild Child (IRE)
120 SUPAGIRL, ch f Pride of Dubai (AUS)—Mighty Girl (IRE)
121 THREE LAWS (IRE), b f Wootton Bassett—Gravitee (FR)
122 TOURING PRODUCTION, ch f Australia—Evita
123 TREVAUNANCE (IRE), b f Muhaarar—Liber Nauticus (IRE)
124 TUT TUT, b f Kodi Bear (IRE)—Tut (IRE)
125 VERLINGA (IRE), b f Dubawi (IRE)—Bocca Baciata (IRE)
126 VIAREGGIO, b f Caravaggio (USA)—Just Joan (IRE)
127 VILLANOVA QUEEN (IRE), ch f Mastercraftsman (IRE)—Quads (IRE)
128 VINTAGE FAME (IRE), b c Frankel—Vintage Folly
129 WILLAMETTE VALLEY (IRE), b f Galileo (IRE)—Fire Lily (IRE)
130 WILLESEE, b f Gleneagles (IRE)—Sandstone
131 YASHIN (IRE), b c Churchill (IRE)—Mirdhak
132 B c Champs Elysees—Zaafran

TWO-YEAR-OLDS

133 ALALCANCE, gr f 19/02 Mastercraftsman (IRE)—Alamara (Galileo (IRE))
134 Ch c 25/03 Pivotal—Allegretto (IRE) (Galileo (IRE)) (62000)
135 Ch c 24/01 Galileo (IRE)—Alpha Centauri (IRE) (Mastercraftsman (IRE))
136 B c 15/05 Mastercraftsman (IRE)—Alpha Lupi (IRE) (Rahy (USA))
137 Ch f 18/04 Bobby's Kitten (USA)—Apparatchika (Archipenko (USA))
138 B c 13/04 Dubawi (IRE)—Attraction (Efisio) (425000)
139 B c 02/02 Lope de Vega (IRE)—Bella Estrella (IRE) (High Chaparral (IRE)) (123299)
140 B c 23/03 Profitable (IRE)—Bellechance (Acclamation) (19558)
141 B c 07/03 Showcasing—Blanc de Chine (IRE) (Dark Angel (IRE)) (110000)
142 B c 03/03 Kodi Bear (IRE)—Blue Marmalade (IRE) (Duke of Marmalade (IRE)) (23810)
143 B f 07/05 Galileo (IRE)—Bocca Baciata (IRE) (Big Bad Bob (IRE))
144 B f 13/02 No Nay Never (USA)—Cash In The Hand (USA) (Exchange Rate (USA))
145 Ch c 04/05 Pivotal—Chocolate Hills (FR) (Exceed And Excel (AUS)) (52721)
146 B f 12/04 Dark Angel (IRE)—Choose Me (IRE) (Choisir (AUS)) (195578)
147 B f 24/04 Belardo (IRE)—Combination (FR) (Dashing Blade) (52721)
148 Ch f 30/03 Australia—Countryside (Motivator)
149 B f 17/05 Churchill (IRE)—Crazy Volume (IRE) (Machiavellian (USA)) (85034)
150 B c 10/03 Footstepsinthesand—Desert's Queen (IRE) (Desert Prince (IRE)) (18095)
151 B f 29/02 Daiwa Major (JPN)—Diaphora (GER) (Pivotal)
152 B f 16/02 Frankel—Dream of Tara (IRE) (Invincible Spirit (IRE)) (85034)
153 B c 13/04 Holy Roman Emperor (IRE)—Elaysa (Shamardal (USA)) (76531)
154 B f 03/03 Saxon Warrior (JPN)—Encore L'Amour (Azamour (IRE)) (50000)
155 Gr f 15/01 Mastercraftsman (IRE)—Etoile Filante (So You Think (NZ))

MRS JESSICA HARRINGTON - continued

156 B f 23/01 Siyouni (FR)—Gabrielle (FR) (Dark Angel (IRE)) (80000)
157 Gr f 10/03 Dark Angel (IRE)—Ghazawaat (FR) (Siyouni (FR)) (119048)
158 B f 31/03 Exceed And Excel (AUS)—Immediate (Oasis Dream) (165000)
159 B c 10/03 Kodiac—Jadanna (IRE) (Mujadil (USA))
160 B c 16/05 Galileo (IRE)—Lady Lara (IRE) (Excellent Art) (212585)
161 Ch gr f 29/02 Mastercraftsman (IRE)—Lady of The Lamp (IRE) (Invincible Spirit (IRE))
162 Ch f 13/04 Gleneagles (IRE)—Lamyaa (Arcano (IRE)) (57000)
163 B c 07/05 Kodiac—Liber Nauticus (IRE) (Azamour (IRE))
164 B f 03/03 Showcasing—Minoria (Harbour Watch (IRE)) (52000)
165 **MISS YVONNE (IRE)**, ch f 05/04 Churchill (IRE)—Bright Snow (USA) (Gulch (USA))
166 Gr f 04/05 Galileo (IRE)—Mrs Danvers (Hellvelyn) (320000)
167 B f 29/02 Australia—Mt of Beatitudes (IRE) (Fastnet Rock (AUS)) (27211)
168 Br c 06/02 Zoustar (AUS)—My Aquarian (IRE) (Dubawi (IRE))
169 B c 11/04 Exceed And Excel (AUS)—Mzyoon (IRE) (Galileo (IRE)) (42517)
170 **NEOWISE (USA)**, b f 20/02 Recoletos (FR)—Ode To Psyche (IRE) (Dansili)
171 Ch c 15/03 Saxon Warrior (JPN)—Nick's Nikita (IRE) (Pivotal) (61224)
172 **OCEAN QUEST (IRE)**, ch f 24/03 Sioux Nation (USA)—Gold Zain (Aqlaam)
173 B c 30/03 Invincible Spirit (IRE)—Prima Luce (IRE) (Galileo (IRE)) (89286)
174 B c 08/03 War Front (USA)—Princess Highway (USA) (Street Cry (IRE))
175 B c 24/03 No Nay Never (USA)—Princess Sinead (IRE) (Jeremy (USA)) (85034)
176 Ch c 13/04 Shamardal (USA)—Quariana (GER) (Lomitas) (115000)
177 B c 08/03 Footstepsinthesand—Queen of Carthage (USA) (Cape Cross (IRE)) (535714)
178 B f 01/05 Churchill (IRE)—Queenscliff (IRE) (Danehill Dancer (IRE)) (106293)
179 Ch c 13/03 Night of Thunder (IRE)—Royal Whisper (Royal Applause) (75000)
180 B f 28/04 Le Havre (IRE)—Sandsnow (IRE) (Verglas (IRE))
181 B c 07/05 Oasis Dream—Sandstone (Dansili)
182 B c 24/03 Lope de Vega (IRE)—Saraha (Dansili) (66327)
183 B c 15/04 Sioux Nation (USA)—Scripture (IRE) (Sadler's Wells (USA))
184 B f 02/04 Dark Angel (IRE)—She's Complete (IRE) (Oratorio (IRE))
185 **SOUNDS OF HEAVEN**, b f 14/02 Kingman—Ring The Bell (IRE) (Galileo (IRE)) (650000)
186 B c 19/04 Dubawi (IRE)—Spectre (FR) (Siyouni (FR)) (410000)
187 **STARIAM (IRE)**, ch f 21/03 Sea The Stars (IRE)—I Am (IRE) (Galileo (IRE))
188 B c 06/03 Invincible Spirit (IRE)—Tamadhor (IRE) (Arcano (IRE)) (78231)
189 Br c 30/03 Kuroshio (AUS)—Thraya Queen (Shamardal (USA)) (17143)
190 Ro gr c 30/04 Pivotal—Tigrilla (IRE) (Clodovil (IRE)) (38265)
191 Ch c 09/02 Postponed (IRE)—Tropicana Bay (Oasis Dream) (5000)
192 B c 22/02 Zoustar (AUS)—Wingingit (IRE) (Helmet (AUS)) (50000)
193 B f 21/04 Saxon Warrior (JPN)—Yellowhammer (Raven's Pass (USA)) (80782)
194 **YOUCRACKMEUP**, b f 20/04 Cracksman—Epic Emirates (Dubawi (IRE)) (17857)
195 Ch f 20/04 Zoustar (AUS)—Ysper (FR) (Orpen (USA)) (45000)
196 Ch c 18/03 Saxon Warrior (JPN)—Zaitana (IRE) (Zoffany (IRE)) (57823)

Assistant Trainer: Miss Kate Harrington, Eamonn Leigh.

---

244 **MISS CLAIRE LOUISE HARRIS, Umberleigh**
Postal: **Langridge Farm, Atherington , Barnstaple , Devon, EX37 9HP**
Contacts: **PHONE** 07458 381716
EMAIL clharris1986@hotmail.co.uk

1 **FLUTISTE (FR)**, 7, b g Secret Singer (FR)—Nanny (FR) **Mr M. G. Tucker**
2 **GETALEAD (IRE)**, 6, b g Getaway (GER)—Site-Leader (IRE) **Mr K. Pickard**
3 4, B gr f Gutaifan (IRE)—Hattie Jacques **Mr K. Pickard**
4 **WHATABOUTWALT (IRE)**, 6, ch g Salutino (GER)—Cyclone Lorraine (IRE) **Langridge Farm Racing**

245 MISS GRACE HARRIS, Shirenewton

Postal: **White House, Shirenewton, Chepstow, Gwent, NP16 6AQ**
Contacts: **MOBILE 07912 359425**
EMAIL **graceharris90@gmail.com** WEBSITE **www.graceharrisracing.com**

1 AIR OF YORK (IRE), 10, b g Vale of York (IRE)—State Secret **Mrs L. A. Cullimore**
2 FAINT HOPE, 10, ch g Midnight Legend—Rhinestone Ruby **Mrs Elaine Tate & Partner**
3 FINAL LIST (IRE), 8, ch g Doyen (IRE)—Lady Goldilocks (IRE) **Foxhills Racing Limited**
4 FIRST FURLOUGH, 5, b g Phenomena—Madam Molly **Mr R. C. Williams**
5 HALF NELSON, 7, ch g Mount Nelson—Maria Antonia (IRE) **Jonathan Thomas & Partner**
6 JUSTSHORTOFABUBBLE, 5, b g Midnight Legend—Auld Fyffee (IRE) **Michelle Harris & Deberah Lawton**
7 KARAKORAM, 7, b g Exceleration (IRE)—Portrait **Grace Harris Racing**
8 LE FIGARO FAOUDEL (FR), 7, b g Nicobar—Lectrice (FR) **Grace Harris Racing**
9 LORD BILL (IRE), 5, ch g Touch of Land (FR)—Hayward's Heath **Andrew & James Colthart**
10 LUXY LOU (IRE), 4, ch f The Last Lion (IRE)—Dutch Courage **Mr Ronald Davies & Mrs Candida Davies**
11 ON CALL (IRE), 9, b g Flemensfirth (USA)—Oscar's Reprieve (IRE) **Red & Black Racing**
12 PASSING KATE, 5, b m Passing Glance—Another Kate (IRE) **D. M. Richards**
13 PERFECT SIGN (IRE), 4, b f Charm Spirit (IRE)—Exceedingly Rare (IRE) **Mr J. Thomas**
14 SEARCHING (IRE), 10, gr g Mastercraftsman (IRE)—Miracolia (IRE) **Mr B. Poacher**
15 SECRET SECRET (IRE), 6, b g Born To Sea (IRE)—Maughami **Mr C. Johnston**
16 SHANROE TIC TEC (IRE), 10, b g Flemensfirth (USA)—Bonny Hall (IRE) **Brendon Sabin & Partner**
17 SOLDIER'S SON, 6, b g Epaulette (AUS)—Elsie's Orphan **Grace Harris Racing**
18 SYMBOL OF HOPE, 4, b g Dandy Man (IRE)—Catalina Bay (IRE) **2 Counties Racing**
19 TALLY'S SON, 8, b g Assertive—Talamahana **Paul & Ann de Weck**
20 WISE GLORY (IRE), 5, b g Muhaarar—Bint Almukhtar (IRE) **Foxhills Racing Limited**

THREE-YEAR-OLDS

21 TOPOFTHETRIFLE (IRE), b f Galileo Gold—Pretty Pebble (IRE) **Mrs S. M. Maine**

Other Owners: Mr A. Clancy, Mr J. Colthart, Mrs C. M. Davies, Mr R. I. D. Davies, Mrs A. De Weck, Grace Harris Racing, Miss G. Harris, Ms M. Harris, Mrs D. L. S. Lawton, Mr B. Sabin, Mrs E. Tate, Mr J. Thomas, P. L. de Weck.

Assistant Trainer: Michelle Harris. **Head Girl:** Christina Berry.

246 MR MILTON HARRIS, Warminster

Postal: **The Beeches, Deverill Road, Sutton Veny, Warminster, Wiltshire, BA12 7BY**
Contacts: **MOBILE 07879 634308**

1 ACHY BREAKY HEART (IRE), 8, b m Milan—Hazy Outlook (IRE) **Mr C. J. Harding**
2 ALIOMAANA, 4, ch f Raven's Pass (USA)—Taqdees (USA) **Aliomaana Partnership**
3 APPRECIATE (IRE), 4, ch g Australia—Became (USA) **Mr M. Harris**
4 AWAY FOR SLATES (IRE), 12, b g Arcadio (GER)—Rumi **Mrs Anthea Williams & Partner**
5 BARI BREEZE (IRE), 7, b g Shirocco (GER)—Byerley Sophie (IRE) **C Harding & M Harris**
6 BILL AND BARN (IRE), 11, br g Presenting—Forgotten Star (IRE) **Mrs S. E. Brown**
7 CHECKITSME, 5, b m Telescope—Sweet Charlie **M Harris & Pegasus Bloodstock Ltd**
8 CIRRUS, 4, ch f Starspangledbanner (AUS)—Callendula **Mr G. Wells**
9 DANNY WHIZZBANG (IRE), 9, b g Getaway (IRE)—Lakil Princess (IRE) **Danny Whizzbang Partnership**
10 ESCOBEDO, 4, b c Nathaniel (IRE)—Notary **The Sophisticates**
11 FIRE LAKE (IRE), 5, ch m Mustajeeb—Saiddaa (USA) **Mr A. Badri**
12 FOOTSTEPSINTHERYE (IRE), 4, b g Footstepsinthesand—Maontri (IRE) **Mr M. Harris**
13 GALAH, 4, b f Australia—Lunar Spirit **Mr A. Badri**
14 GENUFLEX, 4, b g Holy Roman Emperor (IRE)—Gravitation **Mr J. F. Pearl**
15 GLOBAL AGREEMENT, 5, ch g Mayson—Amicable Terms **Global Partnership**
16 HASTY PARISIAN (IRE), 4, ch g Champs Elysees—Va'vite (IRE) **The Hasty Parisian Partnership**
17 IF KARL'S BERG DID, 7, b g Fame And Glory—Mayberry **Air-water Treatments Ltd**
18 JACAMAR (GER), 7, b g Maxios—Juvena (GER) **Mark & Maria Adams**
19 JACKSON HILL (IRE), 8, b g Jeremy (USA)—Definite Leader (IRE) **The Jackson 8**
20 JANUS (IRE), 7, br g Rock of Gibraltar (IRE)—Jardina (GER) **Mr M. Harris**
21 KHAN (GER), 8, b h Santiago (GER)—Kapitol (GER) **Mark & Maria Adams**
22 KING'S PROCTOR (IRE), 7, b g Cape Cross (IRE)—Alimony (IRE) **Air-water Treatments Ltd**

MR MILTON HARRIS - continued

23 **KNIGHT SALUTE**, 4, b g Sir Percy—Shadow Dancing **Four Candles Partnership**
24 **KNOWWHENTOHOLDEM (IRE)**, 7, b br g Flemensfirth (USA)—Definite Design (IRE)
Sutton Veny Racing Syndicate
25 **LEGIONAR (GER)**, 4, ch g Protectionist (GER)—Lomitas Dream **Four Candles Partnership**
26 **LITTLE HERCULES (IRE)**, 4, b c Buratino (IRE)—Dubai In Bloom (IRE) **Mr M. Harris**
27 **MARINE (IRE)**, 4, b g Sea The Stars (IRE)—Ignis Away (FR) **Four Candles**
28 **MASTEROFTHEHEIGHTS (IRE)**, 6, b g Masterofthehorse (IRE)—Martha's Way **Mr A. Harrison**
29 **MI LADDO (IRE)**, 6, gr g Lilbourne Lad (IRE)—Fritta Mista (IRE) **Emdells Limited**
30 **MORDRED (IRE)**, 6, b g Camelot—Endure (IRE) **Middleham Park Racing XCV**
31 **MR YEATS (IRE)**, 5, b g Yeats (IRE)—Va'vite (IRE) **Emdells Limited**
32 **MULLENBEG (IRE)**, 5, b m Walk In The Park (IRE)—Oscars Joy (IRE) **Mr M. Harris**
33 **PANDA SEVEN (FR)**, 5, b g Wootton Bassett—Hermanville (IRE) **Mr M. Harris**
34 **PHILLIPSTOWN ELLEN (IRE)**, 5, b m Xtension (IRE)—Royal Bean (USA) **Mr C. J. Harding**
35 **PRESENTING YEATS (IRE)**, 6, b g Yeats (IRE)—Va'vite (IRE) **Mrs D. Dewbery**
36 **PYRAMID PLACE (IRE)**, 5, b g Authorized (IRE)—Attima **PP & R Syndicate**
37 **RAASED (IRE)**, 5, b g Teofilo (IRE)—Yanabeeaa (USA) **PP & R Syndicate**
38 **ROMEO'S BOND**, 4, gr g Monsieur Bond (IRE)—Choral Singer **Mark & Maria Adams**
39 **ROSY REDRUM (IRE)**, 4, ch f Pride of Dubai (AUS)—Diamond Duchess (IRE) **Mark & Maria Adams**
40 **SERGEANT (FR)**, 5, b g Nutan (IRE)—Stella Marina (IRE) **Mr D. K. Tye**
41 **SILVER SHADE (FR)**, 4, gr g Kendargent (FR)—Lady's Secret (IRE) **Mr C. J. Baldwin**
42 **SLEEPYSAURUS (GER)**, 7, b g Authorized (IRE)—Saloon Rum (USA) **Superior Enterprises LTD**
43 **SONGO (IRE)**, 6, b g Most Improved (IRE)—Sacre Fleur (IRE) **Mr M. Harris**
44 **STIMULATING SONG**, 7, ch g Stimulation (IRE)—Choral Singer **A & & Adam**
45 **SUFI**, 8, ch g Pivotal—Basanti (USA) **WLT Racing Syndicate**
46 **TECHNOLOGICAL**, 7, gr g Universal (IRE)—Qeethaara (USA) **Air-water Treatments Ltd**
47 **VICTORIAS PEAK (IRE)**, 7, b m Fame And Glory—Rosin de Beau (IRE) **Superior Enterprises LTD**
48 **WETANWINDY**, 7, br g Watar (IRE)—Tinkwood (IRE) **Mr M. Harris**

THREE-YEAR-OLDS

49 Ch g El Kabeir (USA)—Diamond Duchess (IRE)
50 **MITIGATION**, b g Nathaniel (IRE)—Maskunah (IRE)
51 **MUCUNA (GER)**, b f Guiliani (IRE)—Monaway (IRE) **Mr D. K. Tye**
52 Gr f Universal (IRE)—Qeethaara (USA)
53 **TRACEYS JOINT (IRE)**, b f Dragon Pulse (IRE)—Blas Ceoil (USA) **Mr C. J. Harding**

TWO-YEAR-OLDS

54 **STAFF SERGEANT LEN (GER)**, b g 12/03 Nutan (IRE)—Stella Marina (IRE) (Dylan Thomas (IRE)) **Mr D. K. Tye**

Other Owners: Mr M. Adams, Mrs M. E. Adams, Mrs S. E. Brown, Mr P.S. Campbell, Mr P. Connolly, Mr R. H. Davies, Mrs D. Dewbery, Emdells Limited, Mr P. Fitzpatrick, Four Candles Partnership, Mr R. Garner, Mr J. G. Giddings, Mr C. J. Harding, Mr M. Harris, Mr A. Harrison, Mr A. T. Howard, Mr B. Jagger, Mr D. M. Jenkins, Mr D. Lyons, Mark & Maria Adams, Mr E. McCarthy, Mr J. P. Naylor, Mrs R. E. Nelmes, Mr M. O'Mahony, Pegasus Bloodstock Limited, Miss L. Whitham, Mr M. Whitham, Mr N. D. Whitham, Mrs A. M. Williams.

247

MR RONALD HARRIS, Chepstow
Postal: **Ridge House Stables, Earlswood, Chepstow, Monmouthshire, NP16 6AN**
Contacts: PHONE **01291 641689** MOBILE **07831 770899** FAX **01291 641258**
EMAIL **ridgehousestables.ltd@btinternet.com** WEBSITE **www.ronharrisracing.co.uk**

1 **BARE GRILS (IRE)**, 4, b g Kodi Bear (IRE)—By The Edge (IRE) **H. M. W. Clifford**
2 **DIAMOND VINE (IRE)**, 14, b g Diamond Green (FR)—Glasnas Giant **Ridge House Stables Ltd**
3 **EAGLE ONE**, 4, b g Gleneagles (IRE)—Gloryette **The Rising Sun Racing**
4 **ELZAAM'S DREAM (IRE)**, 6, b m Elzaam (AUS)—Alinda (IRE) **Ridge House Stables Ltd**
5 **EQUALLY FAST**, 10, b g Equiano (FR)—Fabulously Fast (USA) **Mr S. Bell**

MR RONALD HARRIS - continued

6 **EYE OF THE WATER (IRE)**, 6, b g Lilbourne Lad (IRE)—Desert Location **Mr M. E. Wright**
7 **GLAMOROUS FORCE**, 5, b g Lethal Force (IRE)—Glamorous Spirit (IRE) **M Doocey, S Doocey & P J Doocey**
8 **I'M WATCHING YOU**, 5, ch g Harbour Watch (IRE)—Victrix Ludorum (IRE) **Ridge House Stables Ltd**
9 **LIGHT OF ATHENA (IRE)**, 8, b m Doyen (IRE)—Reflecting (IRE) **Mrs D. Titmus**
10 **LUSCIFER**, 5, b g Heeraat (IRE)—Nut (IRE) **Mr Tony K Singh & Mr S Doocey**
11 **MERWEB (IRE)**, 7, gr g Shamardal (USA)—Ashley Hall (USA) **J. A. Gent**
12 **POWERFUL DREAM (IRE)**, 9, b m Frozen Power (IRE)—Noble View (USA) **Ridge House Stables Ltd**
13 **SARAH'S VERSE**, 5, b m Poet's Voice—Sancai (USA) **Ridge House Stables Ltd**
14 **SECRET POTION**, 8, b g Stimulation (IRE)—Fiancee (IRE) **Ridge House Stables Ltd**
15 **TEXAN NOMAD**, 10, ch g Nomadic Way (USA)—Texas Belle (IRE) **Mr J. W. Miles**
16 **THE DALEY EXPRESS (IRE)**, 8, b g Elzaam (AUS)—Seraphina (IRE) **The W.H.O. Society**
17 **THEGREYVTRAIN**, 6, gr m Coach House (IRE)—Debutante Blues (USA) **Ridge House Stables Ltd**
18 **WE'RE REUNITED (IRE)**, 5, b g Kodiac—Caelis **H. M. W. Clifford**

THREE-YEAR-OLDS

19 **FAIR AND SQUARE**, b g Kodiac—Slatey Hen (IRE) **Mr Malcolm Wright & Ridgehouse Stables Ltd**
20 **GLAMOROUS EXPRESS (IRE)**, b c Gutaifan (IRE)—Glamorous Air (IRE) **M Doocey, S Doocey & P J Doocey**
21 **MY NAME'S HOWARD**, gr g Outstrip—Whirlwind Romance (IRE) **Mr Wayne Clifford &ridgehousestables Ltd**
22 **SUGARSNAP**, gr f Farhh—Serena Grae

TWO-YEAR-OLDS

23 **GLAMOROUS STAR (IRE)**, b f 08/04 Gutaifan (IRE)—Glamorous Air (IRE) (Air Express (IRE)) (40000)
M Doocey, S Doocey & P J Doocey

Other Owners: H. M. W. Clifford, Mr M. A. Doocey, Mr P. J. Doocey, Mr S. Doocey, Ridge House Stables Ltd, Mr K. Singh, Mr M. E. Wright.

Flat Jockey: Luke Morris.

|248| **MR SHAUN HARRIS, Worksop**
Postal: **Pinewood Stables, Carburton, Worksop, Nottinghamshire, S80 3BT**
Contacts: **PHONE 01909 470936 MOBILE 07761 395596**
EMAIL shaunharrisracing@yahoo.com WEBSITE www.shaunharrisracing.co.uk

1 **AL SUIL EILE (FR)**, 6, gr g Alhebayeb (IRE)—Visual Element (USA) **J. Morris**
2 **ALI STAR BERT**, 6, b g Phoenix Reach (IRE)—Clumber Pursuits **Notts Racing, S A Harris & Miss H Ward**
3 **BALLYVIL (IRE)**, 5, b g Clodovil (IRE)—Welsh Diva **Notts Racing, S A Harris & Miss H Ward**
4 **ORBIT OF IOLITE**, 6, ch g Sun Central (IRE)—Blue Clumber **Miss G. H. Ward**
5 **TOMMYTWOHOOTS**, 4, b g Bated Breath—Lady Lube Rye (IRE) **J. Morris**
6 **UNCLE HENRY (IRE)**, 8, b g Henrythenavigator (USA)—Shebelia (GER) **S. A. Harris**

THREE-YEAR-OLDS

7 **GAAZOOO (IRE)**, ch g Cotai Glory—Gaazaal (IRE) **J. Morris**

TWO-YEAR-OLDS

8 **DARAMOUNT SUNLIGHT**, ch f 11/03 Sun Central (IRE)—Delphyne (Mount Nelson) **Miss G. H. Ward**

Assistant Trainer: Miss G. H. Ward.

249 MR GARY HARRISON, Lanark
Postal: **Highacre, New Trows Road, Lesmahagow, Lanark, Lanarkshire, ML11 0JS**
Contacts: **PHONE 07717 757162**
EMAIL garyharrison1968@gmail.com

1 **BELLA FEVER (URU)**, 6, b m Texas Fever (USA)—Passionbabypassion (USA) **Miss E. Johnston**
2 **BUILDING YEAR (IRE)**, 8, b g Intikhab (USA)—The Oldladysays No (IRE) **Miss S. K. Harrison**
3 **DAIJOOR**, 6, br g Cape Cross (IRE)—Angel Oak **Miss S. K. Harrison**
4 **FAIRYWORLD (USA)**, 5, b m City Zip (USA)—Looking Glass (USA) **The Fairyworld Partnership**
5 **MAJOR PUSEY**, 10, ch g Major Cadeaux—Pusey Street Lady **Miss S. K. Harrison**
6 **NIGHT MOON**, 8, b g Dubawi (IRE)—Scatina (IRE) **Miss S. K. Harrison**
7 **ORIENTAL RELATION (IRE)**, 11, gr g Tagula (IRE)—Rofan (USA) **Miss E. Johnston**
8 **SILVERBOOK**, 7, b g New Approach (IRE)—Sahraah (USA) **Miss E. Johnston**
9 **VENUSTA (IRE)**, 6, b m Medicean—Grevillea (IRE) **Miss S. K. Harrison**

250 MISS LISA HARRISON, Aldoth
Postal: **Cobble Hall, Aldoth, Nr Silloth, Cumbria, CA7 4NE**
Contacts: **PHONE 016973 61753 MOBILE 07725 535554 FAX 016973 42250**
EMAIL lisa@daharrison.co.uk

1 **A PLACE APART (IRE)**, 8, b g Power—Simadartha (USA) **D A Harrison Racing**
2 **GREEN ZONE (IRE)**, 11, b g Bushranger (IRE)—Incense **T Hunter & D A Harrison Racing**
3 **HATTAAB**, 9, b g Intikhab (USA)—Sundus (USA) **D A Harrison Racing**
4 **INSTINGTIVE (IRE)**, 11, b g Scorpion (IRE)—Fully Focused (IRE) **D A Harrison & Abbadis Racing & Thompson**
5 **LIZZY'S GIRL**, 7, b m Multiplex—Might Do
6 **MALANGEN (IRE)**, 7, b g Born To Sea (IRE)—Lady's Locket (IRE) **T Hunter & D A Harrison Racing**
7 **MILEVA ROLLER**, 10, b m Multiplex—Alikat (IRE) **D A Harrison Racing**
8 **MUWALLA**, 15, b g Bahri (USA)—Easy Sunshine (IRE) **Bell Bridge Racing**
9 **SOLWAY HONEY**, 7, b m Multiplex—Solway Brook (IRE) **D A Harrison Racing**
10 **SOLWAY MOLLY**, 7, b m Trans Island—Solway Sunset **D A Harrison Racing**
11 **SOLWAY PRIMROSE**, 8, b m Overbury (IRE)—Solway Rose **D A Harrison Racing**
12 **WILLY NILLY (IRE)**, 5, b g Morpheus—Subtle Shimmer **Abbadis Racing & D A Harrison Racing**

Other Owners: Abbadis Racing Club, Mrs F. H. Crone, D A Harrison Racing, Mr D. Gillespie, Mr J. D. Graves, Miss L. Harrison, Mr R. A. Harrison, Mr W. H. Harrison, Mr T. Hunter, R. E. Jackson, Mr K. V. Thompson.

251 MR BEN HASLAM, Middleham
Postal: **Castle Hill Stables, Castle Hill, Middleham, Leyburn, North Yorkshire, DL8 4QW**
Contacts: **PHONE 01969 624351 MOBILE 07764 411660**
EMAIL office@benhaslamracing.com WEBSITE www.benhaslamracing.com

1 **BLAZER (FR)**, 11, ch g Network (GER)—Juppelongue (FR) **Mr J. P. McManus**
2 4, Br f Nayef (USA)—Bond's Gift **South Yorkshire Racing**
3 **BRELAN D'AS (FR)**, 11, b g Crillon (FR)—Las de La Croix (FR) **Mr J. P. McManus**
4 **CALEVADE (IRE)**, 6, gr g Gregorian (IRE)—Avoidance (USA) **D Shapiro, Mrs Anne Haslam & Partners**
5 **CASH AGAIN (FR)**, 10, b g Great Pretender (IRE)—Jeu de Lune (FR) **Mr P Adams & Mrs C Barclay**
6 **COUNTISTER (FR)**, 10, b m Smadoun (FR)—Tistairly (FR) **Mr J. P. McManus**
7 **DR SANDERSON (IRE)**, 8, b g Jeremy (USA)—Guydus (IRE) **Mr J. P. McManus**
8 **FIGHTFORTHEROSES (IRE)**, 7, b g Galileo (IRE)—Gwynn (IRE) **Mr J. P. McManus**
9 **FORTAMOUR (IRE)**, 6, b g Es Que Love (IRE)—Kathy Sun (IRE) **Chris Cleevely & Racing Knights**
10 **GAMEFACE (IRE)**, 8, b g Oscar (IRE)—Queensland Bay **Mr J. P. McManus**

MR BEN HASLAM - continued

11 **GELBOE DE CHANAY (FR)**, 6, b m Rail Link—Rose Celebre (FR) **Mr J. P. McManus**
12 **LADY SHANAWELL (IRE)**, 6, ch m Lord Shanakill (USA)—Lukes Well (IRE) **Blue Lion Racing IX**
13 **LASKADINE (FR)**, 7, b m Martaline—Laskadoun (FR) **Mr J. P. McManus**
14 **LIGHTENING COMPANY (IRE)**, 4, b g Fast Company (IRE)—Shama's Song (IRE) **Cxv, Widdup**
15 **LIGHTNING ATTACK (IRE)**, 6, b g Lethal Force (IRE)—Afrodita (IRE) **Mr S. J. Robinson**
16 **LORD CAPRIO (IRE)**, 7, b g Lord Shanakill (USA)—Azzurra du Caprio (IRE) **Blue Lion Racing IX**
17 **MACHO PRIDE (IRE)**, 4, b g Camacho—Proud Maria (IRE) **The Auckland Lodge Partnership**
18 **MILLIONAIRE WALTZ (IRE)**, 5, b g Heeraat (IRE)—Radio Gaga **Mr S. J. Robinson**
19 **NATALEENA (IRE)**, 6, b m Nathaniel (IRE)—Hayyona **Shapiro,Milner,Rees,Nicol,Feeney & Adams**
20 **OUR LAURA B (IRE)**, 4, b f Sans Frontieres (IRE)—Dear Bach (IRE) **Dave Barry**
21 **PHOENIX STRIKE**, 5, b g Casamento (IRE)—Promise You **Mr D. Shapiro**
22 **PINKIE BROWN (FR)**, 10, gr g Gentlewave (IRE)—Natt Musik (FR) **Mr S. J. Robinson**
23 **PROTEK DES FLOS (FR)**, 10, b g Protektor (GER)—Flore de Chantenay (FR) **Mr J. P. McManus**
24 **RITCHIE STAR (IRE)**, 6, b g Lilbourne Lad (IRE)—Array of Stars (IRE) **Mr R. Tocher**
25 **ROXBORO ROAD (IRE)**, 9, b g Oscar (IRE)—Pretty Neat (IRE) **Mr J. P. McManus**
26 **SANDRET (IRE)**, 6, b g Zebedee—Sava Sunset (IRE) **Mr B. M. R. Haslam**
27 **SASSOON**, 6, ch g Poet's Voice—Seradim **Mr S. J. Robinson**
28 **SCOOP THE POT (IRE)**, 12, b g Mahler—Miss Brecknell (IRE) **Mr J. P. McManus**
29 **SOLO SAXOPHONE (IRE)**, 8, b g Frankel—Society Hostess (USA) **Golden Equinox Racing**
30 **SPIDER PIG (IRE)**, 6, b br g Yeats (IRE)—Beaus Polly (IRE) **More Turf Racing**
31 **THATBEATSBANAGHER (IRE)**, 8, b g Flemensfirth (USA)—Katie's Jem (IRE) **Mr J. P. McManus**
32 **WE STILL BELIEVE (IRE)**, 4, b br g Lawman (FR)—Curious Lashes (IRE)

Sam Farthing, Linda McGarry & Ken Nicol

33 **WILLIE JOHN**, 7, b g Dansili—Izzi Top **Mr F. Ibragimov**

THREE-YEAR-OLDS

34 **AGONYCLITE**, b c Dabirsim (FR)—Hoku (IRE) **Daniel Shapiro & David Clifford**
35 **BIYARIQ (IRE)**, b f Cotai Glory—Baltic Belle (IRE) **Mr M. R. H. Al Saadi**
36 **CALLSIGN PHOENIX (IRE)**, ch f Air Force Blue (USA)—Rocktique (USA) **Sam Farthing & Ben Haslam**
37 **COBRA KAI (IRE)**, b g Holy Roman Emperor (IRE)—Hala Hala (IRE) **Daniel Shapiro & David Clifford**
38 **CODE PURPLE**, b c Ribchester (IRE)—Sugar Free (GER) **Daniel Shapiro & David Clifford**
39 **DO I DREAM (IRE)**, b f Mondialiste (IRE)—Novita (FR) **Racing Knights**
40 **ON THE RIVER**, b g Heeraat (IRE)—Lady Lekki (IRE) **The Multifruit Syndicate**
41 **ORIGINTRAIL (IRE)**, b f Profitable (IRE)—Miss Azeza **Daniel Shapiro & David Clifford**
42 **SWEETEST COMPANY (IRE)**, b f Fast Company (IRE)—Florida City (IRE) **Racing Knights & Partner**

TWO-YEAR-OLDS

43 B f 14/04 Kodiac—Capriole (Noverre (USA)) (80782) **Daniel Shapiro & David Clifford**
44 B c 02/04 Kodiac—Chatham Islands (USA) (Elusive Quality (USA)) (71429) **Daniel Shapiro & David Clifford**
45 B f 29/04 Mayson—Lady Lekki (IRE) (Champs Elysees) **Mr B. M. R. Haslam, Mr D. Shapiro**
46 B c 02/03 Mehmas (IRE)—Luminous Gold (Fantastic Light (USA)) (71429) **Daniel Shapiro & David Clifford**
47 B c 17/04 Sioux Nation (USA)—Two Pass (IRE) (Mtoto) (28571) **Mr B. M. R. Haslam**
48 B f 11/02 Kodiac—Welsh Anthem (Singspiel (IRE)) (106293) **Daniel Shapiro & David Clifford**

Other Owners: Mr P. Adams, Mrs C. Barclay, Mr C. R. Cleevely, Mr D. Clifford, Mr S. Farthing, Mrs J. M. Feeney, Mr J. S. Feeney, Mrs A. M. C. Haslam, Mr B. M. R. Haslam, Mrs L. McGarry, Middleham Park Racing CXV, Mrs S. V. Milner, Mr K. Nicol, T. S. Palin, M. Prince, Racing Knights, Mr M. Rees, Mr D. Shapiro, Mr D. P. Widdup, Mr P. G. Wood.

252	**MR NIGEL HAWKE, Tiverton** Postal: **Thorne Farm, Stoodleigh, Tiverton, Devon, EX16 9QG** Contacts: **PHONE 01884 881666 MOBILE 07769 295839** EMAIL nigel@thornefarmracingltd.co.uk WEBSITE www.nigelhawkethornefarmracing.co.uk

1 **A NEW SIEGE (IRE)**, 7, ch m New Approach (IRE)—Arminta (USA) **Atlantic Friends Racing**
2 **ALMINAR (IRE)**, 9, b g Arakan (USA)—Classic Magic (IRE) **Mr M. J. Phillips**
3 **BALLYMAGROARTY BOY (IRE)**, 9, b g Milan—Glazed Storm (IRE) **Nigel Hawke Racing Club & Partners**
4 **BELLA BEAU (IRE)**, 7, b m Jeremy (USA)—Bella Patrice (IRE) **Mr M. J. Phillips**

MR NIGEL HAWKE - continued

5 **BERT WILSON (IRE)**, 5, b g Canford Cliffs (IRE)—Inishkea (USA) **Kapinhand, Surefire Racing & Partner**
6 **BOULETTE (IRE)**, 4, b g Epaulette (AUS)—Tiz The Whiz (USA)
7 **BRING THE ACTION (IRE)**, 6, b g Jet Away—Lady Firefly (IRE) **Exors of the Late C. Holmes-Elliott**
8 **CALL ME SAINTE (FR)**, 5, b m Saint des Saints (FR)—Call Me Blue (FR) **Hawke, Simms, Browne, Capps**
9 **CATCH ME NOT**, 7, b m Flemensfirth (USA)—Dorabelle (IRE) **Dare To Dream Racing**
10 **DAWN TROUPER (IRE)**, 7, b g Dawn Approach (IRE)—Dance Troupe **Mr R. Lane**
11 **DONNACHA (IRE)**, 4, br g Jet Away—Archdale Ambush (IRE) **Mrs M. J. Martin**
12 **EUROWORK (FR)**, 8, bl g Network (GER)—Nandina (FR) **R. J. & Mrs J. A. Peake**
13 **GALORE DESASSENCES (FR)**, 6, b g Rail Link—Villezbelle (FR) **Mr M. J. Phillips**
14 **GEORDIE WASHINGTON (IRE)**, 6, b br g Sageburg (IRE)—Rathturtin Brief (IRE) **Atlantic Friends Racing**
15 **GUARDIA TOP (FR)**, 6, b m Top Trip—Jour de Chance (FR) **Terence Wood, Samuel Jefford & Partners**
16 **HARTLAND QUAY (IRE)**, 7, b gr g Arcadio (GER)—Regents Ballerina (IRE) **Mr Richard Weeks & Partner**
17 **HOBSONS BAY (IRE)**, 4, b g Camelot—Emirates Joy (USA) **Mr S. Jefford**
18 **INFERNO SACREE (FR)**, 4, b g Saint des Saints (FR)—Altesse Sacree (FR) **Mr R. Lane**
19 **INSTANT DE BONHEUR (FR)**, 4, b f Karaktar (IRE)—Par Bonheur (FR)
Mr Mike Izaby White & Mrs Denise E Smith
20 **IRON WINGS (FR)**, 4, gr g Lord du Sud (FR)—Vive La Reine (FR) **Mr M. J. Phillips**
21 **KENDELU (IRE)**, 7, b g Yeats (IRE)—Supreme Baloo (IRE) **Ken & Della Neilson & Partners**
22 **LE MUSEE (FR)**, 9, b g Galileo (IRE)—Delicieuse Lady **Mrs K Hawke,W Simms & Dragonfly Racing**
23 **LIL CODEY (IRE)**, 6, b m Dandy Man (IRE)—Blue Reema (IRE) **Michael Phillips/ Samuel Quigley**
24 4, Ch g Doyen (IRE)—Medimli (IRE)
25 **MY GRANNY LILY**, 4, b f Pether's Moon (IRE)—Pont Royal (FR) **Mr Samuel Quigley Thornefarmracingltd**
26 **NACHI FALLS**, 9, ch g New Approach (IRE)—Lakuta (IRE) **Nigel Hawke Racing Club & Associate**
27 **NOVUS ADITUS (IRE)**, 6, b g Teofilo (IRE)—Novel Approach (IRE) **Atlantic Friends Racing**
28 **ONNAROLL (FR)**, 4, b g Kapgarde (FR)—Sainte Borgue (FR) **Mrs K. Hawke & Mr W. Simms**
29 **OURO BRANCO (FR)**, 9, b g Kapgarde (FR)—Dolce Vita Yug **Pearce Bros & Partner**
30 **POLA CHANCE (FR)**, 6, gr m Boris de Deauville (FR)—Take A Chance (FR) **Smithbevanbrowneridleymeadvale**
31 **PROFESSOR CALCULUS**, 4, b g Twilight Son—Roslea Lady (IRE) **Nigel Hawke Racing Club & Associate**
32 **SHIELDED (IRE)**, 4, b g Buratino (IRE)—Shambolique **Mrs K. Hawke & Mr W. Simms**
33 **SINDABELLA (FR)**, 6, b m Sinndar (IRE)—Figarella Gaugain (FR) **Surefire Racing 1**
34 **SOME DETAIL (IRE)**, 8, b g Getaway (GER)—You Should Know Me (IRE) **Milltown Racing**
35 **THE IMPOSTER (FR)**, 5, b g Authorized (IRE)—Miss Dixie **Mark Philips & J H Gumbley**
36 **THEOCRAT (IRE)**, 5, b g Teofilo (IRE)—Novel Approach (IRE) **Atlantic Friends Racing**
37 **UNFINISHED BUSINES**, 4, gr f Clovis du Berlais (FR)—A Cappella Lido (FR) **Paul Stacey & Friends**
38 **WAVECREST**, 7, gr g Carlotamix (FR)—Go Girl (IRE) **Mr M. J. Phillips**
39 **YAAZAAIN**, 6, b g Iffraaj—Tamazirte (IRE) **Mead Vale S.Quigley R.Dennis Partnership**

THREE-YEAR-OLDS
40 **MY ROSA'S GOLD**, ch f Havana Gold—Louya (IRE) **Mr J. H. Gumbley & Partners**
41 **TIMELESS CLASSIC**, b gr f Outstrip—Timeless **The Time Enough Stud Partnership**

Assistant Trainer: Edward Buckley, Katherine Hawke.

---

253 MR MICHAEL HAWKER, Chippenham
Postal: **Battens Farm, Allington, Chippenham, Wiltshire, SN14 6LT**

1 **FAMA ET GLORIA (IRE)**, 6, b g Fame And Glory—Clonogan (IRE) **Mr M. R. E. Hawker**
2 **MORTENS LEAM**, 10, b g Sulamani (IRE)—Bonnet's Pieces **Mr M. R. E. Hawker**
3 **MR JORROCKS**, 7, b g Scorpion (IRE)—Sheknowsyouknow **Mr M. R. E. Hawker**
4 **SPOTTY DOG**, 7, ch g Sixties Icon—Where's My Slave (IRE) **Mr M. R. E. Hawker**

254 MR RICHARD HAWKER, Rode
Postal: **Rode Farm, Rode, Bath, Somerset, BA11 6QQ**
Contacts: **PHONE 01373 831479**

1 **BABY MOONBEAM**, 7, bl gr m Passing Glance—Charliebob **R. G. B. Hawker**
2 **BLACKTHORN WINTER**, 8, b g Morozov (USA)—Presenting Gayle (IRE) **Mr D. J. Adams**
3 **FARCEUR DE MAULNE (FR)**, 7, b g Doctor Dino (FR)—Alize de La Prise (FR) **Landowners, Penwill, Skuse**
4 **GASTARA**, 7, b g Kayf Tara—Gaspaisie (FR) **Ms Gillian Metherell**
5 **JACK SNIPE**, 13, b g Kirkwall—Sea Snipe **Mrs P. J. Pengelly**
6 **JANESLITTLEVOICE**, 8, ch m Jelani (IRE)—Janes Allweather **Miss J. Nicholls**
7 **LAKE SHORE DRIVE (IRE)**, 10, b g Thewayyouare (USA)—Labrusca **Mr J. Kennedy**
8 **PRINCE OF BAD LINS (GER)**, 4, ch g Nutan (IRE)—Pastellrosa (IRE) **Ms J. Bennett**
9 **SASTRUGA (IRE)**, 9, b g Masterofthehorse (IRE)—Crimson Blue (IRE) **Mr B. A. Hawker**
10 **SPARKLING DAWN**, 10, gr m Sulamani (IRE)—Clotted Cream (USA) **Mr P. M. Tosh**
11 **THIRSTY FARMER**, 8, b g Sulamani (IRE)—Sweet Shooter **Rolling Aces**

Other Owners: J. F. Baldwin, Mr N. Penwill, Mr B. Skuse, The Lansdowners, R. T. Wilkins.

255 MISS ALICE HAYNES, Newmarket
Postal: **11 Park Cottages, Park Lane, Newmarket, Suffolk, CB8 8BB**
Contacts: **PHONE 07585 558717**
EMAIL alice@alicehaynesracing.co.uk

1 **AMASOVA**, 4, ch f Pivotal—Russian Heroine **Garrad Brothers Equine**
2 **ARLO'S SUNSHINE**, 5, b g Cable Bay (IRE)—Touching (IRE) **Miss A. Haynes**
3 **MAYSONG**, 5, ch g Mayson—Aldeburgh Music (IRE) **Mr A. York**
4 **MIGHTY POWER (IRE)**, 4, gr g Markaz (IRE)—Tooley Woods (IRE) **Work Hard Play Hard Partnership**
5 **MUHALHEL (IRE)**, 4, b g Lope de Vega (IRE)—Abbagnato **Mr A. Harris**
6 **SMART CONNECTION (IRE)**, 5, b g Dutch Art—Endless Love (IRE) **Burton Lodge Racing Club & A Haynes**
7 **STRONG POWER (IRE)**, 5, b g Kodiac—Soft Power (IRE) **One Day Soon**
8 **THE COLA KID**, 5, gr g Lethal Force (IRE)—George's Gift **The Bruiser Boyz**
9 **UNIQUE CUT (IRE)**, 4, b f Kodiac—Intaglia **Nick Bradley Racing 41 & A Haynes**
10 **YOU MISSED HER (IRE)**, 4, b f Camacho—Woolstone **Miss H. McMurdo**

THREE-YEAR-OLDS

11 **AWAY WIT DA FAIRYS (IRE)**, b g Camacho—Disco Lights **Miss A. Haynes**
12 **BLACK ECHO (FR)**, b f Olympic Glory (IRE)—Big Monologue (IRE) **Nick Bradley Racing 18**
13 **BOUDICA WARRIOR (IRE)**, b f War Command (USA)—Miss Estrada (IRE) **Aviatica Bloodstock Limited**
14 **CHANSON D'AMOUR**, gr f Dark Angel (IRE)—Coral Mist **Mr A. Harris**
15 **DEFINITIVE FORCE (IRE)**, b c Dandy Man (IRE)—Harvest Joy (IRE) **Burton Lodge Racing Club & A Haynes**
16 **FREYABELLA**, b f Kodiac—Crecy **The Secret Service**
17 **HOLLOW STEEL (IRE)**, b f Cotai Glory—Sunny Hollow **Mr A. Harris**
18 **INDIEANGELINA**, b f Acclamation—Sulaalaat **The Hidden Brace**
19 **ISOBEL MOORE**, gr f Spill The Beans (AUS)—Zia (GER) **Mrs E. Haynes**
20 **JOSIES KID (IRE)**, b g Ardad (IRE)—Low Cut Affair (IRE) **The Bruiser Boyz & Partner**
21 **LADY HONORE**, b f Dartmouth—Saint Honore **Mr P. Bocking**
22 **LET EM HAVE IT (IRE)**, b c Ribchester—Genuine Quality (USA) **Middleham Park Racing LXVIII**
23 **MR PROFESSOR (IRE)**, b g Profitable (IRE)—Law of The Range **Amo Racing Limited**
24 **NURSECLAIRE (FR)**, b f Ribchester—Nymeria (GER) **Nick Bradley Racing 19 & Sohi**
25 **STEEL DUCHESS (IRE)**, b f Mehmas (IRE)—Lawman's Lady (IRE) **Mr A. Harris**
26 **U A E FIFTY (IRE)**, b g Dandy Man (IRE)—Bounty'S Spirit **Middleham Park Racing, A Haynes**

TWO-YEAR-OLDS

27 Gr f 06/02 Gregorian (IRE)—Apple Anni (IRE) (Fast Company (IRE)) (4500)
28 B f 02/03 Havana Grey—Blithe Spirit (Byron) (24000) **Amo Racing Limited**
29 **CHAMPAGNE STEEL (IRE)**, gr c 19/04 Kodiac—Angelic Guest (IRE) (Dark Angel (IRE)) (15238) **Mr A. Harris**

MISS ALICE ELIZABETH HAYNES - continued

30 B c 24/03 Kessaar (IRE)—Classic Image (Exceed And Excel (AUS)) (29524) **Amo Racing Limited**
31 B f 08/02 Havana Gold (IRE)—First Secretary (Nayef (USA)) (8095)
32 GEMINI STAR (IRE), b f 24/02 Starspangledbanner (AUS)—Star Fire (Dark Angel (IRE)) (28000) **Mr G. P. Budd**
33 B c 17/03 Kodi Bear (IRE)—Irish Cliff (IRE) (Marju (IRE)) (30000) **Amo Racing Limited**
34 B f 27/03 Aclaim (IRE)—Last Frontier (FR) (Kendargent (FR)) (1905)
35 STEEL LOOKING, b c 19/02 Expert Eye—On The Stage (Swiss Spirit) (25000)

Other Owners: Mr D. Abraham, Aviatica Bloodstock Limited, Mr W. Boyle, Mr N. Bradley, Burton Lodge Racing Club, China Racing Club, Mr A. Emery, Foxtrot Racing Management Ltd, Mr G. Hatcher, Miss A. Haynes, Mrs E. Haynes, Miss S. Holden, Mr J. Liang, Middleham Park Racing CXXIII, Nick Bradley Racing 41, Mr A. C. O Sullivan, T. S. Palin, M. Prince, Mr F. Sonny, Mr P. Young.

Racing Secretary: Miss Holly Hall.

MR JONATHAN HAYNES, Brampton
256
Postal: **Cleugh Head, Low Row, Brampton, Cumbria, CA8 2JB**
Contacts: **PHONE 016977 46253 MOBILE 07771 511471**

1 BERTIELICIOUS, 14, b g And Beyond (IRE)—Pennepoint **J. C. Haynes**
2 COMEONRITA, 4, ch f Black Sam Bellamy (IRE)—Pennepoint **J. C. Haynes**
3 DOROTHY'S FLAME, 10, ch m Black Sam Bellamy (IRE)—Flame of Zara **J. C. Haynes**
4 HIDDEN CARGO (IRE), 10, b g Stowaway—All Heart **J. C. Haynes**
5 MR JV, 6, ch g And Beyond (IRE)—Flame of Zara **J. C. Haynes**

MISS GAIL HAYWOOD, Moretonhampstead
257
Postal: **Stacombe Farm, Doccombe, Moretonhampstead, Newton Abbot, Devon, TQ13 8SS**
Contacts: **PHONE 01647 440826**
EMAIL gail@gghracing.com **WEBSITE** www.gghracing.com

1 LADY WOLF, 6, b m Kuroshio (AUS)—Angry Bark (USA) **Devrain Partners**
2 MINELLA MOJO (IRE), 10, b g King's Theatre (IRE)—On The Horizon (IRE) **Miss G. G. Haywood**
3 PIDDIES REFLECTION, 4, br f Geordieland (FR)—Piddie's Power **Jan Mead and Sally Paton**
4 POL MA CREE, 7, b g Arvico (FR)—Mere Salome (IRE) **Phillip & Mary Creese & Nicky Dunford**
5 SCOFFSMAN, 7, b g Dansili—Purissima (USA) **Mr D. Mead**
6 4, B g Arvico (FR)—Torridge Lily **Miss G. G. Haywood**
7 VINNIE THE HODDIE (IRE), 8, b g Vinnie Roe (IRE)—Blackwater Babe (IRE) **The Nascent Partnership**
8 ZULU, 8, b g Cockney Rebel (IRE)—Pantita **Haywood's Heroes**

Other Owners: Mr P. V. Creese, Mrs S. M. Creese, Ms N. J. Dunford, Miss G. G. Haywood.

NH Jockey: David Noonan, Ben Poste.

258 MR NICKY HENDERSON, Lambourn

Postal: **Seven Barrows, Lambourn, Hungerford, Berkshire, RG17 8UH**
Contacts: **PHONE 01488 72259 MOBILE 07774 608168**
EMAIL njh@njhenderson.com

1 **AHORSEWITHNONAME,** 7, b m Cacique (IRE)—Sea of Galilee **Mr D. J. Burke & Mr P Alderson**
2 **ANOTHER BROWN BEAR (IRE),** 6, b g Shirocco (GER)—Full of Spirit (IRE) **G. B. Barlow**
3 **ANOTHER VENTURE (IRE),** 11, ch g Stowaway—Hard Luck (IRE) **Mrs L. Daly**
4 **ATTACCA (IRE),** 4, b g Mahler—Listening (IRE) **Mrs P. J. Pugh**
5 **BALCO COASTAL (FR),** 6, b g Coastal Path—Fliugika (FR) **Mr M. R. Blandford**
6 **BALKEO (FR),** 5, b g Galiway—Hukba (IRE) **Mrs M. Donnelly**
7 **BALLYCROSS,** 11, b g King's Theatre (IRE)—Ninna Nanna (FR) **Mr Oscar Singh & Miss Priya Purewal**
8 **BALLYHIGH (IRE),** 5, b g Canford Cliffs (IRE)—Storm Run (IRE) **Unique Financial Racing Partnership**
9 **BENEFACT (IRE),** 4, gr g Sholokhov (IRE)—Sagarich (FR) **Mr J. Palmer-Brown**
10 **BLAIRGOWRIE (IRE),** 4, b g Yeats (IRE)—Gaye Preskina (IRE) **Highclere T'Bred Racing - Blairgowrie**
11 **BLUE HEAVEN,** 5, b m Blue Bresil (FR)—Spring Flight **Her Majesty The Queen**
12 **BLUE STELLO (FR),** 6, b g Spider Flight (FR)—Benina (FR) **Owners Group 081**
13 **BOLD REACTION (IRE),** 5, ch g Waldpark (GER)—Queen Dream (FR) **Andy Bell & Fergus Lyons**
14 **BOOM BOOM (IRE),** 4, b g Califet (FR)—She Is A Cracker (FR) **Unique Financial Racing Partnership**
15 **BOTHWELL BRIDGE (IRE),** 7, b g Stowaway—Raise The Issue (IRE) **Victoria Dunn & Nicholas Mustoe**
16 **BRAVE EAGLE,** 10, b g Yeats (IRE)—Sinful Pleasure (IRE) **R. M. Kirkland**
17 **BRAVE JEN,** 4, b f Kayf Tara—Fenney Spring **Unique Financial Racing Partnership**
18 **BRIDAL KNOT (IRE),** 5, b m Walk In The Park (IRE)—Knotted Midge (IRE) **The Knot Again Partnership**
19 **BRILLIANT PRESENT (IRE),** 6, br m Presenting—Ouro Preto **Mr & Mrs J. D. Cotton**
20 **BROOMFIELD BURG (IRE),** 6, br g Sageburg (IRE)—Somedaysomewhere (IRE) **Mr J. P. McManus**
21 **BURROWS EDGE (FR),** 9, b g Martaline—La Vie de Boitron (FR) **M. A. C. Buckley**
22 **BUTTSBURY LADY,** 7, b m Great Pretender (IRE)—Ceilidh Royal **Mrs R. H. Brown**
23 **BUVEUR D'AIR (FR),** 11, b g Crillon (FR)—History (FR) **Mr J. P. McManus**
24 **BUZZ (FR),** 8, gr g Motivator—Tiysha (IRE) **Thurloe for Royal Marsden Cancer Charity**
25 **CALL ME LORD (FR),** 9, b br g Slickly (FR)—Sosa (GER) **Mr Simon Munir & Mr Isaac Souede**
26 **CAPTAIN MORGS (IRE),** 6, b g Milan—Gold Donn (IRE) **The Albatross Club**
27 **CARIBEAN BOY (FR),** 8, gr g Myboycharlie (IRE)—Caribena (FR) **Mr Simon Munir & Mr Isaac Souede**
28 **CHAMP (IRE),** 10, b g King's Theatre (IRE)—China Sky (IRE) **Mr J. P. McManus**
29 **CHANTRY HOUSE (IRE),** 8, br g Yeats (IRE)—The Last Bank (IRE) **Mr J. P. McManus**
30 **CHASAMAX (IRE),** 7, b g Jeremy (USA)—Peratus (IRE) **International Plywood (Importers) Ltd**
31 **CITY CHIEF (IRE),** 5, b g Soldier of Fortune (IRE)—Galant Ferns (IRE) **Mrs M. Donnelly**
32 **COLONIAL DREAMS (IRE),** 10, b g Westerner—Dochas Supreme (IRE) **C. N. Barnes**
33 **COMMODORE MILLER,** 5, b g Blue Bresil (FR)—Milliegait **HP Racing Commodore Miller**
34 **CONSTITUTION HILL,** 5, b g Blue Bresil (FR)—Queen of The Stage (IRE) **M. A. C. Buckley**
35 **CRAIGNEICHE (IRE),** 8, br g Flemensfirth (USA)—Itsalark (IRE) **R. M. Kirkland**
36 **DIAMOND RIVER (IRE),** 7, ch g Imperial Monarch (IRE)—River Clyde (IRE)

Jockey Club Ownership (SW 2020) Limited

37 **DICKIE DIVER (IRE),** 9, b g Gold Well—Merry Excuse (IRE) **Mr J. P. McManus**
38 **DOCTE DINA (FR),** 8, ch m Doctor Dino (FR)—Artofmen (FR) **James and Jean Potter Ltd**
39 **DODDIETHEGREAT (FR),** 6, b g Fame And Glory—Asturienne **Mr K. Alexander**
40 **DUSART (IRE),** 7, b g Flemensfirth (USA)—Dusty Too **R. A. Bartlett**
41 **ELUSIVE BELLE (IRE),** 8, b m Elusive Pimpernel (USA)—Soviet Belle (IRE) **Annabel Waley-cohen & Family**
42 **EMIR SACREE (FR),** 8, b g Network (GER)—Altesse Sacree (FR) **G. L. Porter**
43 **EPATANTE (FR),** 8, b m No Risk At All (FR)—Kadjara (FR) **Mr J. P. McManus**
44 **FABLE (FR),** 7, b m Coastal Path—Toscane des Fleurs (FR) **Owners Group 078**
45 **FALCO BLITZ (IRE),** 8, b g Falco (USA)—Ignited **Axom LXXVII**
46 **FANTASTIC LADY (IRE),** 7, b m Network (GER)—Latitude (FR) **E. R. Hanbury**
47 **FAROUK DE CHENEAU (FR),** 7, b g Day Flight—Kardamone (FR) **Owners Group 049**
48 **FATHER JOHN (FR),** 7, b g Secret Singer (FR)—Oudette (FR) **Middleham Park Racing XI**
49 **FILS D'OUDAIRIES (FR),** 7, b g Saint des Saints (FR)—Pythie d'Oudairies (FR) **Mr C. M. Grech**
50 **FIRESTEP (IRE),** 6, b g Mahler—Springinherstep (IRE) **Charles Dingwall & the Infamous Five**
51 **FIRST STREET,** 5, b g Golden Horn—Ladys First **Lady C. Bamford & Miss A. Bamford**
52 **FISHCAKE (IRE),** 5, ch m Mahler—Martovic (IRE) **FB Racing Club**
53 **FIX SUN (FR),** 7, b g Al Namix (FR)—Quelly Bruere (FR) **Mr Simon Munir & Mr Isaac Souede**
54 **FRED (FR),** 7, b br g Cokoriko (FR)—Veribelle (FR) **Mr Simon Munir & Mr Isaac Souede**
55 **FUGITIVES DRIFT (IRE),** 7, b g Yeats (IRE)—Shebeganit (IRE) **HP Racing Fugitives Drift**

MR NICKY HENDERSON - continued

56 **FULL OF LIGHT (IRE)**, 6, gr g Leading Light (IRE)—Scartara (FR) **Deva Racing Full of Light**
57 **FUSIL RAFFLES (FR)**, 7, b g Saint des Saints (FR)—Tali des Obeaux (FR) **Mr Simon Munir & Mr Isaac Souede**
58 **GALLYHILL (IRE)**, 7, b g Getaway (GER)—Tanit **Mr C. M. Grech**
59 **GIPSY DE CHOISEL (FR)**, 6, b br g Great Pretender (IRE)—Beautiful Choisel (FR)
　　　　　　　　　　　　　　　　　　　　　　　　　　　　　　Mr Simon Munir & Mr Isaac Souede
60 **GLYNN (IRE)**, 8, b g Winged Love (IRE)—Barnish River (IRE) **Owners Group 039**
61 **GO CHIQUE (FR)**, 8, b m Crillon (FR)—Similaresisoldofa (FR) **Middleham Park Racing CX**
62 **GO SACRE GO (FR)**, 6, b g Network (GER)—Altesse Sacree (FR) **G. L. Porter**
63 **GRAN LUNA (FR)**, 6, b m Spanish Moon (USA)—Coppena (FR) **Surrey Racing (GL)**
64 **GRAND MOGUL (IRE)**, 8, b g Presenting—Oligarch Society (IRE) **Mrs B. A. Hanbury**
65 **HANDS OFF (IRE)**, 4, ch g Getaway (GER)—Gaye Lady (IRE) **Seven Barrows Limited**
66 **HAUL AWAY (IRE)**, 9, b g Stowaway—Lisacul Queen (IRE) **R. M. Kirkland**
67 **HEROSS DU SEUIL (FR)**, 5, b g Rail Link—Tulipe du Seuil (FR) **Mrs M. Donnelly**
68 **HOOPER**, 6, b g Rip Van Winkle (IRE)—Earth Amber **Pump & Plant Services Ltd**
69 **HORN CAPE (FR)**, 5, gr g Fame And Glory—Capstone (USA) **Mr J. P. McManus**
70 **HURLING MAGIC (IRE)**, 8, b g Doyen—Distelle (IRE) **Owners Group 035**
71 **HURRICANE LE DUN (FR)**, 5, b g Doctor Dino (FR)—Heviz (FR) **Dingwall, Draper, Higginson, Stirling**
72 **HYLAND (FR)**, 5, gr g Turgeon (USA)—Medine (FR) **The Ten From Seven**
73 **I AM MAXIMUS (IRE)**, 6, b g Authorized (IRE)—Polysheba (FR) **Mr C. M. Grech**
74 **I AM ROCCO**, 5, br g Kayf Tara—Isabello (IRE) **Mr C. M. Grech**
75 **ILE DE JERSEY (FR)**, 4, b f Night Wish (GER)—Zenita des Brosses (FR) **Owners Group 094**
76 **IMPULSIVE ONE (USA)**, 4, b g Union Rags (USA)—Hokey Okey (USA) **Mr Simon Munir & Mr Isaac Souede**
77 **IOLAOS DU MOU (FR)**, 4, b g Coastal Path—Thelemise du Mou (FR)
78 **ISSUING AUTHORITY (IRE)**, 5, ch g Flemensfirth (USA)—Mini's Last (IRE) **Owners Group 101**
79 **JANIKA (FR)**, 9, b g Saddler Maker (IRE)—Majaka (FR) **Mr Simon Munir & Mr Isaac Souede**
80 **JONBON (FR)**, 6, b g Walk In The Park (IRE)—Star Face (FR) **Mr J. P. McManus**
81 **KINCARDINE**, 5, b g Kayf Tara—Side Step **Her Majesty The Queen**
82 **KING OTTOKAR (FR)**, 6, b g Motivator—Treasure (FR) **Mrs S. M. Roy**
83 **KINGSAND BAY**, 5, b g Blue Bresil (FR)—Crystal Princess (IRE) **Middleham Park Racing LIV**
84 **LADY D'ARBANVILLE**, 4, bl f Authorized (IRE)—Miracle Maid **Mr D. J. Burke**
85 **LELANTOS (IRE)**, 6, br g Presenting—Western Focus (IRE) **Middleham Park Racing XCI**
86 **LUCCIA**, 4, ch f The Gurkha (IRE)—Earth Amber **Pump & Plant Services Ltd**
87 4, B f Blue Bresil (FR)—Madam Fontaine (FR) **Seven Barrows Limited**
88 **MAJOR STING (IRE)**, 6, b g Scorpion (IRE)—Suzababe (IRE) **The SMBs**
89 **MARIE'S ROCK (IRE)**, 7, b br m Milan—By The Hour (IRE) **Middleham Park Racing XLII**
90 **MARMALAID**, 5, gr m Martaline—Miracle Maid **Mr D. J. Burke & Mr P Alderson**
91 **MEADOWSUITE (IRE)**, 4, b f Spanish Moon (USA)—La Premiere Dame (FR) **Lady Tennant**
92 **MENGLI KHAN (IRE)**, 9, b g Lope de Vega (IRE)—Danielli (IRE) **Mr M. A. R. Blencowe**
93 **MILL GREEN**, 10, b g Black Sam Bellamy (IRE)—Ceilidh Royal **Mrs R. H. Brown**
94 **MIND SUNDAY (IRE)**, 6, gr m Never On Sunday (FR)—Mind Master (USA) **Walters Plant Hire Ltd**
95 **MISTER COFFEY (FR)**, 7, b g Authorized (IRE)—Mamitador **Lady C. Bamford & Miss A. Bamford**
96 **MISTER FISHER (IRE)**, 8, b g Jeremy (USA)—That's Amazing (IRE) **James and Jean Potter Ltd**
97 **MONTE CRISTO (FR)**, 6, b g Montmartre (FR)—Rylara des Brosses (FR) **Mr Simon Munir & Mr Isaac Souede**
98 **MOONLIGHT FLIT (IRE)**, 6, b g Getaway (GER)—Dreaming On (IRE) **Thurloe 57**
99 **MORNING VICAR (IRE)**, 9, b g Beneficial—Mary's Little Vic (IRE) **The Parishioners**
100 **MOT A MOT (FR)**, 6, gr g Martaline—Gaily Zest (USA) **Walters Plant Hire & Potter Group**
101 **MOUNT PLEASANT**, 5, b g Mount Nelson—Polish Belle **Mr M. A. R. Blencowe**
102 **NEIL THE LEGEND**, 8, b g Passing Glance—Call Me A Legend **Mr D. White**
103 4, B g Milan—Niamh's Away (IRE)
104 **NO ORDINARY JOE (IRE)**, 6, b g Getaway (GER)—Shadow Dearg (IRE) **Mr J. P. McManus**
105 **ON THE BLIND SIDE (IRE)**, 10, b g Stowaway—Such A Set Up (IRE) **Mr Alan Spence**
106 **OVERPRICED MIXER**, 5, b g Harbour Watch (IRE)—Chincoteague (IRE) **Owners Group 051**
107 **PARISIAN BLUE**, 6, b br m Getaway (GER)—Another Evening (IRE) **Crimbourne Bloodstock**
108 **PAROS (FR)**, 5, ch g Masterstroke (USA)—Soft Blue (FR) **Middleham Park Racing CXXV**
109 **PATROCLUS (IRE)**, 6, b g Shirocco (GER)—King'sandqueen's (IRE) **Walters Plant Hire & Potter Group**
110 **PEACE OF ROME (GER)**, 4, gr g Jukebox Jury (IRE)—Peace Flower (IRE) **Mr Alan Spence**
111 **PENTLAND HILLS (IRE)**, 7, b g Motivator—Elle Galante (GER) **Owners Group 031**
112 **PISTOL WHIPPED (IRE)**, 8, b g Beneficial—Holiday Time (IRE) **Mr A. Speelman & Mr M. Speelman**
113 **PROGRESSIVE**, 5, b m Nathaniel (IRE)—Graduation **A D Spence & John Connolly**
114 **PROPELLED**, 5, b g Kapgarde (FR)—Polly Peachum (IRE) **Middleham Park Racing LXI & Peter Lamb**

MR NICKY HENDERSON - continued

115 QUEENS CAVE (IRE), 9, b m Court Cave (IRE)—Shuilan (IRE) **Mr K. Alexander**
116 QUEENS ROCK (IRE), 5, b m Shirocco (GER)—Lohort Castle (IRE) **Seven Barrows Limited**
117 QUICKBUCK (IRE), 5, b g Walk In The Park (IRE)—Buck's Blue (FR) **Mr M. A. R. Blencowe**
118 RATHER BE (IRE), 11, b g Oscar (IRE)—Irish Wedding (IRE) **Eventmasters Racing**
119 ROCCSTAR BAY, 4, b f Telescope (IRE)—Miss Rocco **E. R. Hanbury**
120 4, B g Sixties Icon—Rose Row **Mrs S. M. Roy**
121 ROYAL MAX (FR), 4, b g Maxios—Rahada (GER) **Lady M. B. Dulverton**
122 ROYAL RUBY, 10, b g Yeats (IRE)—Close Harmony **Mrs R. H. Brown**
123 RUDY CAPRICE (FR), 5, gr g Sholokhov (IRE)—Mega Sister (FR) **Loose Ends**
124 RUSSIAN RULER (IRE), 5, b br g Sholokhov (IRE)—Hot Choice **Unique Financial Racing Partnership**
125 SCARPERED (IRE), 5, b g Getaway (GER)—Finola's Gift (IRE) **The Steeple Chasers**
126 SCARPIA (IRE), 8, ch g Sans Frontieres (IRE)—Bunglasha Lady (IRE) **Mrs T. J. Stone-Brown**
127 SHISHKIN (IRE), 8, b g Sholokhov (IRE)—Labarynth (IRE) **Mrs M. Donnelly**
128 SON OF CAMAS (FR), 7, ch g Creachadoir (IRE)—Camas (FR) **Loose Ends**
129 4, Ch f Mahler—Spring Baloo (IRE) **Canter Banter Racing**
130 5, B m Leading Light (IRE)—Springinherstep (IRE)
131 STEAL A MARCH, 7, b g Mount Nelson—Side Step **Her Majesty The Queen**
132 STORM OF INTRIGUE (IRE), 10, b g Oscar (IRE)—Storminoora (IRE) **Mr Oscar Singh & Miss Priya Purewal**
133 SURFMAN, 6, b g Kingman—Shimmering Surf (IRE) **P. L. Winkworth**
134 SURREY QUEST (IRE), 5, b g Milan—Roztoc (IRE) **Surrey Racing (SQ)**
135 SWAPPED (FR), 5, b g Sinndar (IRE)—La Bezizais (FR) **Mr A. Speelman & Mr M. Speelman**
136 4, B f Mount Nelson—Tatispout (FR) **Seven Barrows Limited**
137 THE BOMBER LISTON (IRE), 6, b g Yeats (IRE)—True Britannia **Mr J. P. McManus**
138 THE BREW MASTER (IRE), 5, b g Mahler—Raphuca (IRE) **R. M. Kirkland**
139 THE CARPENTER (IRE), 6, gr g Shantaram—Just Another Penny (IRE) **Owners Group 086**
140 THEATRE GLORY (IRE), 5, b m Fame And Glory—Native Beauty (IRE) **Canter Banter Racing 2**
141 TIME FLIES BY (IRE), 7, ch g Getaway (GER)—What A Mewsment (IRE) **Mr J. P. McManus**
142 TOUCHY FEELY, 5, b m Kayf Tara—Liberthine (FR) **Mr R. B. Waley-Cohen**
143 TWEED SKIRT, 5, b m Martaline—Theatre Girl **Just Four Men With Rose Tinted Glasses**
144 VALSHEDA, 7, b g Milan—Candy Creek (IRE) **Mr & Mrs R. G. Kelvin-Hughes**
145 WALKING ON AIR (IRE), 5, b g Walk In The Park (IRE)—Refinement (IRE) **Mrs D. A. Tabor**
146 WAVE THE WAND, 5, b g Gentlewave (IRE)—Magic Score **Her Majesty The Queen**
147 WESTWOOD RYDER (IRE), 5, b g Flemensfirth (USA)—Beeverstown Girl (IRE) **The Albatross Club**
148 WILL CARVER (IRE), 7, b g Califet (FR)—Rock Angel (IRE) **Owners Group 064**
149 WIND OF FORTUNE (IRE), 4, b g Shirocco (GER)—Tara Rocks **HP Racing Wind Of Fortune**
150 WISEGUY (IRE), 6, b g Fame And Glory—Sunset Queen (IRE) **Mrs John Magnier & Mrs Paul Shanahan**

Other Owners: P. S. Alderson, Miss J. K. Allison, Mr C. M. A. Aston, R. K. Aston, Miss A. C. Bamford, Lady Bamford, R. A. Bartlett, Mr A. J. Bell, Mrs T. Bell, Blythe Stables LLP, Mr D. J. Burke, Business Moves Group Ltd, J. P. Connolly, Mr C. B. J. Dingwall, Miss V. C. Dunn, Mr M. Gummerson, N. J. Henderson, Just Four Men, Mrs S. A. J. Kinsella, Mrs C. Lyons, Mr F. Lyons, Fergus & Caroline Lyons, Mrs S. Magnier, Mr P. Martin, S. E. Munir, N. Mustoe, Mr C. M. Parker, Mrs M. Parker, Mr S. R. C. Philip, Miss P. Purewal, Rose Tinted Glasses, Mrs L. M. Shanahan, Mr A. Singh, Mr I. Souede, Anthony Speelman, Mr M. Speelman, Mr Alan Spence, Sundorne Products (Llanidloes) Ltd, The Infamous Five, Mrs A. Waley-Cohen, Mr R. B. Waley-Cohen, Mr S. B. Waley-Cohen, Walters Plant Hire Ltd, Mr D. White, Mr S. Williams.

NH Jockey: James Bowen, Aidan Coleman, Nico De Boinville, Daryl Jacob.

Conditional Jockey: Nathan Brennan, Ben Ffrench Davis.

259 MR PAUL HENDERSON, Whitsbury
Postal: **1 Manor Farm Cottage, Whitsbury, Fordingbridge, Hampshire, SP6 3QP**
Contacts: **PHONE 01725 518113 MOBILE 07958 482213 FAX 01725 518113**
EMAIL phendersonracing@gmail.com

1 **ABBEY STREET (IRE)**, 11, b g Asian Heights—Cnocbui Cailin (IRE) **Mr and Mrs J Baigent**
2 **ALLARDYCE**, 10, b g Black Sam Bellamy (IRE)—Woore Lass (IRE) **Jockey Club Ownership (SW 2020) Limited**
3 **BALLYEGAN HERO (IRE)**, 11, b g Oscar (IRE)—Kelly Gales (IRE) **Table 8 & Mr J Duffy**
4 **DOITFORTHEVILLAGE (IRE)**, 13, b g Turtle Island (IRE)—Last Chance Lady (IRE) **The Rockbourne Partnership**
5 **DOUBLE FUN**, 5, b m Dunaden (FR)—Gowithdflo (IRE) **Blackwood Partners**
6 **DOYEN QUEEN (IRE)**, 8, b m Doyen (IRE)—Panoora Queen (IRE) **NHRE Racing Club**
7 **DUARIGLE (IRE)**, 10, ch g Dubai Destination (USA)—Silver Valley (IRE) **A Pearson E Hawkings M Jenner P Scope**
8 **ENTRE DEUX (FR)**, 8, b g Khalkevi (IRE)—Evitta (FR) **Mr S. Tulk**
9 **GOOD MAN VINNIE (IRE)**, 11, ch g Vinnie Roe (IRE)—Pellerossa (IRE) **Sarah Habib & Ed Hawkings**
10 **GREAT KHAN (IRE)**, 11, b g Kalanisi (IRE)—Can't Stop (GER) **J. P. Duffy**
11 **HATCHET JACK (IRE)**, 10, b g Black Sam Bellamy (IRE)—Identity Parade (IRE)
                                                   A J Pearson, Mark Jenner, Ed Hawkings
12 **KYLENOE DANCER**, 4, ch f Norse Dancer (IRE)—Kylenoe Fairy (IRE) **Mr E. J. Hawkings**
13 **LARCADIO (IRE)**, 9, b g Arcadio (GER)—Le Ciel (IRE) **Mr C. Clark**
14 **MAASAI WARRIOR (IRE)**, 7, b g Lovelace—No Case (IRE) **A Pearson E Hawkings M Jenner P Scope**
15 **MR STUBBS (IRE)**, 11, b g Robin des Pres (FR)—Crystal Stream (IRE) **Mrs J. L. Chappell**
16 **NO DRAMA (IRE)**, 7, ch g Mahler—Calimesa (IRE) **The Sundowners**
17 **POLAR LIGHT**, 7, b m Norse Dancer (IRE)—Dimelight **J. P. Duffy**
18 **ROCK ON BARNEY (IRE)**, 11, b g Fracas (IRE)—Monthly Sessions (IRE) **Mr R. G. Henderson**
19 **SAN PEDRO**, 5, b g Gleneagles (IRE)—Elle Woods (IRE) **The Rockbourne Partnership**
20 **SHAW'S CROSS (IRE)**, 10, b g Mr Dinos (IRE)—Capparoe Cross (IRE) **Mareildar Racing Part 1**
21 **SMALL BAD BOB (IRE)**, 7, b g Big Bad Bob (IRE)—Baileys Gleam **John H W Finch & Rockbourne Partnership**
22 **STORM HILL (IRE)**, 7, gr g Mahler—Midnight Pleasure (IRE) **Mr E. J. Hawkings**
23 **THEBELLSOFSHANDON (IRE)**, 7, b g Fame And Glory—Western Cowgirl (IRE) **Table 8 & Mr J Duffy**

Other Owners: Mr C. P. Bennett, J. P. Duffy, Mr J. H. W. Finch, Mr R. J. Galpin, Mrs S. J. Habib, Mr E. J. Hawkings, Mr P. F. Henderson, Mr M. E. Jenner, Mr A. Pearson, Mr P. T. Scope, Table 8, The Rockbourne Partnership.

260 MR MICHAEL HERRINGTON, Thirsk
Postal: **Garbutt Farm, Cold Kirby, Thirsk, North Yorkshire, YO7 2HJ**
Contacts: **MOBILE 07855 396858**
EMAIL info@michaelherringtonracing.co.uk WEBSITE www.michaelherringtonracing.co.uk

1 **ANIF (IRE)**, 8, b g Cape Cross (IRE)—Cadenza (FR) **Stuart Herrington & Peter Forster**
2 **BAY OF NAPLES (IRE)**, 6, b g Exceed And Excel (AUS)—Copperbeech (IRE) **Mrs S. E. Lloyd**
3 **BEYOND INFINITY**, 5, ch g Bated Breath—Lady Gloria **Tara Moon Partnership**
4 4, B f Harzand (IRE)—Cailin Meidhreach (IRE) **Mr M. Sharpe**
5 **COPAKE (IRE)**, 4, b g Kodiac—Allegation (FR) **Michael Herrington Racing Club**
6 **DUBAI JEANIUS (IRE)**, 4, b g Pride of Dubai (AUS)—Tempura (GER) **Mrs H. J. Lloyd-Herrington**
7 **EDESSANN (IRE)**, 6, ch g Lope de Vega (IRE)—Edelmira (IRE) **Away Days Racing Club**
8 **GLORIOUS CHARMER**, 6, b g Charm Spirit (IRE)—Fantacise **Mrs H. J. Lloyd-Herrington**
9 **GOOD EARTH (IRE)**, 5, b g Acclamation—Madhatten (IRE) **Mrs H. J. Lloyd-Herrington**
10 **KNOCKABOUT QUEEN**, 6, b m Sixties Icon—Rough Courte (IRE) **Mrs Shelley Tucker Partnership**
11 **LADY ALAVESA**, 7, b m Westlake—Matilda Peace **Mrs S. E. Lloyd**
12 **LOVE DESTINY**, 5, b g Lethal Force (IRE)—Danehill Destiny **S Herrington, P Forster & Team Given 5**
13 **MAHARASHTRA**, 6, ch g Schiaparelli (GER)—Khandala (IRE) **Nicholas Baines & Mrs H Lloyd-herrington**
14 **QUIET PRIDE**, 6, b m Sholokhov (IRE)—Flemens Pride **David Frame & Mrs H Lloyd-herrington**
15 **RATAFIA**, 4, b g Iffraaj—Aetna **Ingram Racing**
16 **STEELRIVER (IRE)**, 12, b g Iffraaj—Numerus Clausus (FR) **Away Days Racing Club**
17 **STREET POET (IRE)**, 9, b g Poet's Voice—Street Star (USA) **Nicholas Baines & Mrs H Lloyd-herrington**
18 **THAAYER**, 7, b g Helmet (AUS)—Sakhya (IRE) **Mrs H. Lloyd-herrington & S. Herrington**

MR MICHAEL HERRINGTON - continued

19 **THE GAME OF LIFE**, 7, b g Oasis Dream—Velvet Star (IRE) **Mrs H. J. Lloyd-Herrington**
20 **TIGER SPIRIT (IRE)**, 5, b m Charm Spirit (IRE)—Tiger Lilly (IRE) **K & L Fitzsimons**
21 **YOSHIMI (IRE)**, 5, gr g Dream Ahead (USA)—Dawn Dew (GER) **Mrs S. E. Lloyd**

THREE-YEAR-OLDS

22 **BY MOONLIGHT**, b f Twilight Son—Cecily **C. G. Rowles Nicholson**
23 B g Koropick (IRE)—Melodize **Michael Marsh & Griffiths**

TWO-YEAR-OLDS

24 B f 02/03 Charm Spirit (IRE)—Roxy Star (IRE) (Fastnet Rock (AUS)) (7619) **Mr M. Sharpe**
25 B c 01/04 Roaring Lion (USA)—Sea Chorus (Singspiel (IRE)) (21000) **Mr M. Sharpe**
26 B c 11/02 Fountain of Youth (IRE)—Tawaasul (Haafhd) (8095) **Michael Herrington Racing Club**

Other Owners: Mr N. J. Baines, K. Fitzsimons, Mrs L. Fitzsimons, Mr P. D. Forster, Mr D. Frame, Mr D. C. Griffiths, Mr J. S. Herrington, Mr I. Jackson, Mrs H. J. Lloyd-Herrington, Mr M. Marsh, Team Given 5, Mr K. Tucker, Mrs S. M. Tucker.

Assistant Trainer: Helen Lloyd-Herrington.

261
MRS LAWNEY HILL, Aston Rowant
Trainer did not wish details of their string to appear

262
MR CHARLES HILLS, Lambourn
Postal: **Wetherdown House, Lambourn, Hungerford, Berkshire, RG17 8UB**
Contacts: **PHONE 01488 71548**
EMAIL info@charleshills.co.uk WEBSITE www.charleshills.co.uk

1 **CAESONIA**, 6, ch m Garswood—Agrippina **Mrs Fiona Williams**
2 **CARAUSIUS**, 5, b g Cacique (IRE)—Domitia **Mrs Fiona Williams**
3 **DARK SHIFT**, 4, gr c Dark Angel (IRE)—Mosuo (IRE) **Mr H. Frost**
4 **EQUALITY**, 4, b g Equiano (FR)—Penny Drops **Kennet Valley Thoroughbreds II**
5 **EQUILATERAL**, 7, b g Equiano (FR)—Tarentaise **Mrs Fitri Hay**
6 **GARRUS (IRE)**, 6, gr g Acclamation—Queen of Power (IRE) **Mrs Susan Roy**
7 **IBIZA ROCKS**, 4, gr g Dark Angel (IRE)—The Thrill Is Gone **Mr Christopher Wright**
8 **KHAADEM (IRE)**, 6, br g Dark Angel (IRE)—White Daffodil (IRE) **Mrs Fitri Hay**
9 **KING'S KNIGHT (IRE)**, 5, b h Dark Angel (IRE)—Oatcake **Mr Ziad A Galadari**
10 **MAY SONIC**, 6, b g Mayson—Aromatherapy **Hills Angels**
11 **MENAI BRIDGE**, 4, b g Cable Bay (IRE)—Sonnellino **N. N. Browne, K. P. McNamara**
12 **MUMMY'S BOY**, 4, br g Footstepsinthesand—Dance On The Hill (IRE) **Mr C. I. Johnston**
13 **MUTASAABEQ**, 4, br c Invincible Spirit (IRE)—Ghanaati (USA) **Shadwell Estate Company Ltd**
14 **POGO (IRE)**, 6, b h Zebedee—Cute **Gary & Linnet Woodward**
15 **ROYAL COMMANDO (IRE)**, 5, b h No Nay Never (USA)—Online Alexander (IRE) **Mr Ziad A Galadari**
16 **SARATOGA GOLD**, 4, ch c Mayson—Lady Sylvia **Mr David J. Keast**
17 **SHOBIZ**, 4, b g Showcasing—Royal Confidence **Mr D. M. James**
18 **SPOOF**, 7, b g Poet's Voice—Filona (IRE) **Gary & Linnet Woodward**
19 **THE ATTORNEY (IRE)**, 4, b c Kodiac—Next Trial (IRE) **Mr Ziad A Galadari**
20 **TOMMY DE VITO**, 5, b g Dandy Man (IRE)—Rohlindi **Chelsea Thoroughbreds - Goodfellas**
21 **TOUCHWOOD (IRE)**, 4, b g Invincible Spirit (IRE)—Aaraamm (USA) **Mr H. Frost**
22 **VINDOLANDA**, 6, ch m Nathaniel (IRE)—Cartimandua **Mrs Fiona Williams**

THREE-YEAR-OLDS

23 **ALDHAJA (USA)**, b c War Front (USA)—Aqsaam (USA) **Faringdon Place 1 Partnership**

MR CHARLES HILLS - continued

24 **ALLAYAALI (IRE)**, b f Dark Angel (IRE)—Faraday Light (IRE) **Shadwell Estate Company Ltd**
25 **BEACHES**, b c Churchill (IRE)—Know Me Love Me (IRE) **Julie Martin & David R. Martin & Partner**
26 **BELL SHOT (IRE)**, b g Dark Angel (IRE)—Merry Me (IRE) **Mrs Fitri Hay**
27 **CAESAR NERO**, b c Territories (IRE)—Publilia **Chelsea T'Breds, J. Lindop & M. Murphy**
28 **CEPHALUS**, b c Cable Bay (IRE)—Angels Wings (IRE) **Jerry Hinds & Philip Herbert**
29 **CHEPCHIK**, b f Helmet (AUS)—Mystique **Jeremy Gompertz & Partner**
30 **DILIGENTLY DONE**, b f Due Diligence (USA)—Quite A Story **Mildmay Racing & D. H. Caslon**
31 **DREAM SHOW**, b c Tamayuz—Got To Dream **Galloping On The South Downs Partnership**
32 **HERSILIA**, b f Adaay (IRE)—Vespasia **Mrs Fiona Williams**
33 **IBN ALDAR**, br c Twilight Son—Bint Aldar **Mr Ziad A Galadari**
34 **IMPERATIVE**, b c Sea The Stars (IRE)—Kelly Nicole (IRE) **Mrs Fitri Hay**
35 **INVERNESS (IRE)**, b c Highland Reel (IRE)—Four Eleven (CAN) **Steven Rocco & Partners**
36 **KILLEARN (IRE)**, b c Footstepsinthesand—Virginia Celeste (IRE) **Mr R A Bartlett & Partner**
37 **LADY MADONNA**, b f Muhaarar—The Thrill Is Gone **Christopher Wright & Richard Davies**
38 **LOVES ME LIKEAROCK**, gr f Lethal Force (IRE)—Love On The Rocks (IRE) **The Chriselliam Partnership**
39 **MAGHLAAK**, b c Muhaarar—Ghanaati (USA) **Shadwell Estate Company Ltd**
40 **MAIDEN'S GREEN**, b f Oasis Dream—Inyordreams **Mr H. Frost**
41 **MARSH BENHAM (IRE)**, ch g Galileo Gold—Zelie Martin (IRE) **The Red House Racing Club**
42 **MAYFAIR STROLL (IRE)**, b f Gleneagles (IRE)—Zadalla **Chelsea T'Breds, J. Lindop & M. Murphy**
43 **NICKLEBY (IRE)**, b g Kodi Bear (IRE)—Laheen (IRE) **Owners Group 088**
44 **NO MORE TIERS**, b f Hot Streak (IRE)—Aromatherapy **PJL Racing**
45 **OFFICER ON PARADE**, b g Nathaniel (IRE)—Sandy Shores **J. H. Widdows**
46 **ORAZIO**, br gr c Caravaggio (USA)—Lady Fashion **Mrs Susan Roy**
47 **PAPA DON'T PREACH (IRE)**, b c Kodiac—Paella (IRE) **Mr H. Frost**
48 **PHINOW (IRE)**, b c Mehmas (IRE)—Patience A Plenty (IRE) **John & Jessica Dance**
49 **ROXZOFF (IRE)**, b g Zoffany (IRE)—Aljumar (IRE) **Jerry Hinds & Philip Herbert**
50 **RUSHED (IRE)**, b c Cotai Glory—Hasty (IRE) **Mrs Fitri Hay**
51 **SONNY LISTON (IRE)**, b c Lawman (FR)—Stars In Your Eyes **Chelsea Thoroughbreds - The Big Bear**
52 **STORYTIME**, b f Time Test—Perfect Story (IRE) **Dr Bridget Drew & Partners**
53 **TAMARAMA**, b f Muhaarar—Kalsa (IRE) **Mr James A. Oldham**
54 **TUSCAN (IRE)**, b c Churchill (IRE)—Orcia (IRE) **John & Jessica Dance**
55 **VAYNOR (IRE)**, ro g Mastercraftsman (IRE)—Sanaya (IRE) **Mrs Fitri Hay**
56 **WANEES**, b c Le Havre (IRE)—Waldnah **Shadwell Estate Company Ltd**
57 **WILLOUGHBY BAY (IRE)**, b f Profitable (IRE)—Emperors Pearl (IRE) **Guards Club Racing Limited**

TWO-YEAR-OLDS

58 **AL MUQDAD**, ch c 26/02 Zoustar (AUS)—Miss Work of Art (Dutch Art) (100000)
59 Gr c 04/03 Wootton Bassett—Amaranthe (FR) (Mastercraftsman (IRE)) (72279)
60 B f 12/01 Awtaad (IRE)—Angevine (Sir Percy) (23810)
61 Gr f 11/03 Caravaggio (USA)—Anyone Special (IRE) (Invincible Spirit (IRE)) (80000)
62 B f 28/02 Acclamation—Beatify (IRE) (Big Bad Bob (IRE)) (40000)
63 B c 23/03 Territories (IRE)—Bereka (Firebreak) (40000)
64 **BODORGAN (IRE)**, gr c 17/01 El Kabeir (USA)—Silver Rose (IRE) (Dark Angel (IRE)) (52381)
65 B c 12/03 Zoustar (AUS)—Brevity (Street Cry (IRE)) (40000)
66 B f 17/04 Oasis Dream—Cartimandua (Medicean)
67 B f 04/04 Oasis Dream—Cloud's End (Dubawi (IRE))
68 B c 03/05 Caravaggio (USA)—Crazyforlovingyou (USA) (Arch (USA)) (25000)
69 B c 29/04 Gustav Klimt (IRE)—Cuilaphuca (IRE) (Danetime (IRE)) (14000)
70 **DIVINE LIBRA (IRE)**, gr c 18/04 Dark Angel (IRE)—Rakiza (IRE) (Elnadim (USA)) (75000)
71 B c 23/02 Acclamation—Dukinta (IRE) (Dubawi (IRE)) (95238)
72 B c 16/02 Bated Breath—Enfijaar (IRE) (Invincible Spirit (IRE)) (63776)
73 B c 09/02 Havana Grey—Fashion Trade (Dansili) (50000)
74 B c 10/05 Gleneagles (IRE)—Fauran (IRE) (Shamardal (USA))
75 **GALERON (IRE)**, b c 02/03 Camacho—Society Gal (IRE) (Galileo (IRE)) (38265)
76 B f 20/02 Expert Eye—Garraun (IRE) (Tamayuz) (38095)
77 **GERALT OF RIVIA (IRE)**, ch c 23/04 El Kabeir (USA)—Wojha (IRE) (Pivotal) (49320)
78 B c 20/02 Harry Angel (IRE)—Music And Dance (Galileo (IRE)) (125000)
79 B f 13/03 Sioux Nation (USA)—Iffraaj Pink (IRE) (Iffraaj)
80 Ch c 07/03 Saxon Warrior (JPN)—Imtiyaaz (IRE) (Starspangledbanner (AUS)) (42000)

MR CHARLES HILLS - continued

81 B c 26/04 Cityscape—In Your Time (Dalakhani (IRE)) (22000)
82 B f 18/03 Lawman (FR)—Influent (IRE) (Shamardal (USA)) (26000)
83 B f 07/04 Exceed And Excel (AUS)—Kaks Roosid (FR) (Youmzain (IRE)) (46769)
84 LABIQA (IRE), b f 14/04 Muhaarar—Inez (Dai Jin) (65000)
85 LADY ALARA (IRE), b f 16/04 Invincible Spirit (IRE)—Red Halo (IRE) (Galileo (IRE)) (110000)
86 LAKE ELOISE (IRE), b f 29/03 Kodiac—Bronze Baby (USA) (Silver Charm (USA)) (85714)
87 B c 22/02 Havana Grey—Light of Love (Dylan Thomas (IRE)) (23810)
88 B c 10/05 Oasis Dream—Love On The Rocks (IRE) (Exceed And Excel (AUS)) (19000)
89 LUDDEN LASS (IRE), b f 09/05 Dandy Man—Xinji (IRE) (Xaar) (28000)
90 B c 26/04 Invincible Spirit (IRE)—Madany (IRE) (Acclamation)
91 MINKA (IRE), b f 04/04 Kodiac—Queen's Code (IRE) (Shamardal (USA)) (140000)
92 B c 15/03 Muhaarar—Mission Secrete (IRE) (Galileo (IRE)) (75000)
93 MOUNTAIN FLOWER (IRE), b f 13/03 Iffraaj—Moonlife (IRE) (Invincible Spirit (IRE)) (130000)
94 B f 11/02 Sea The Stars (IRE)—Neshmeya (Lawman (FR))
95 B c 14/02 Tasleet—Orange Pip (Bold Edge) (75000)
96 PADDY'S DAY (IRE), b c 17/03 Starspangledbanner (AUS)—Elusive Gold (IRE) (Elusive City (USA)) (57823)
97 B c 29/04 Dandy Man (IRE)—Parakopi (IRE) (Green Desert (USA)) (30000)
98 B f 02/02 Muhaarar—Perfect Star (Act One)
99 B c 13/05 Dubawi (IRE)—Rufoof (Zamindar (USA))
100 B c 17/02 Invincible Spirit (IRE)—Safeenah (Oasis Dream)
101 SARATOGA SPIRIT, ch f 01/03 Tasleet—Lady Sylvia (Haafhd)
102 Gr c 12/04 Tasleet—Servilia (Lethal Force (IRE)) (12000)
103 SHOGUN'S KATANA, br c 25/03 Territories (IRE)—Rock Ace (IRE) (Verglas (IRE)) (35238)
104 Ch c 17/03 Zoustar (AUS)—Shumoos (USA) (Distorted Humor (USA))
105 B c 26/03 Churchill (IRE)—Stage Queen (IRE) (Oasis Dream) (75000)
106 B c 25/03 Muhaarar—Terentia (Diktat) (32000)
107 B f 10/02 Sioux Nation (USA)—Wedding Dress (Tamayuz)

Assistant Trainer: Nicola Dowell, Jamie Insole.

<table><tr><td>**263**</td><td>**MRS CLAIRE WENDY HITCH, Watchet**
Postal: **Higher Sminhays Farm, Brendon Hill, Watchet, Somerset, TA23 0LG**
EMAIL barnlane@btinternet.com</td></tr></table>

1 BALLYATTY, 7, b g Kayf Tara—Charmaine Wood **Mrs C. W. Hitch**
2 BOTHIE LADY (IRE), 5, b m Kalanisi (IRE)—Lackagh Lass (IRE) **Mrs C. W. Hitch**
3 6, B gr m Sulamani (IRE)—Clotted Cream (USA) **Mrs C. W. Hitch**
4 EVERY BREAKIN WAVE (IRE), 12, b g Double Eclipse (IRE)—Striking Gold (USA) **Mrs C. W. Hitch**
5 HOLERDAY RIDGE (IRE), 7, b g Mahler—Deep Lilly **Mrs C. W. Hitch**
6 HOT SMOKED, 9, br m Eastern Anthem (IRE)—Waheeba **Mrs C. W. Hitch**
7 SAMBURU SHUJAA (FR), 9, b g Poliglote—Girelle (FR) **Mrs C. W. Hitch**
8 SMARTMANDARCY (IRE), 7, b g Arakan (USA)—Queens Quay **Mrs C. W. Hitch**
9 WINTER GETAWAY (IRE), 9, b m Getaway (GER)—Galzig (IRE) **Mr R. M. E. Wright**

<table><tr><td>**264**</td><td>**MR MARK HOAD, Lewes**
Postal: **Windmill Lodge Stables, Spital Road, Lewes, East Sussex, BN7 1LS**
Contacts: PHONE 01273 480691, 01273 477124 MOBILE 07742 446168 FAX 01273 477124
EMAIL markhoad@aol.com</td></tr></table>

1 HEY HO LET'S GO, 6, b g Dream Ahead (USA)—Lookslikeanangel **Mrs K. B. Tester**
2 HISTORY WRITER (IRE), 7, b g Canford Cliffs (IRE)—Abhasana (IRE) **Mrs K. B. Tester**

MR MARK HOAD - continued

THREE-YEAR-OLDS

3 Ch c Ruler of The World (IRE)—Bit Windy **Mr K. W. Sneath**
4 **OUTTATHEBLUE**, gr g Charming Thought—Debutante Blues (USA) **I Am Wild Syndicate**

---

265 **MR PHILIP HOBBS, Minehead**
Postal: **Sandhill, Bilbrook, Minehead, Somerset, TA24 6HA**
Contacts: **PHONE 01984 640366 MOBILE 07860 729795 FAX 01984 641124**
EMAIL pjhobbs@pjhobbs.com WEBSITE www.pjhobbs.com

1 **A LITTLE FAITH**, 5, b m Garswood—Highland Stardust **The Juwireya Partnership**
2 **ACROSS THE CHANNEL (FR)**, 7, b g Dunkerque (FR)—Aulne River (FR) **Mr A. L. Cohen**
3 **ADVANTURA (IRE)**, 5, b g Watar (IRE)—Keys Hope (IRE) **A. P. Staple**
4 **ALBERIC (FR)**, 5, b g Poliglote—Khayance (FR) **Corrina LTD**
5 **ARC RYDER**, 4, b g Kayf Tara—Ryde Back **Mrs J. A. S. Luff**
6 **ARIAN (IRE)**, 10, b m King's Theatre (IRE)—Brave Betsy (IRE) **Mr D. M. Mathias**
7 4, B g Milan—Aroka (FR) **P. J. Hobbs**
8 **AUBA ME YANG (IRE)**, 6, b g Fame And Glory—No Bodys Flame (IRE) **Salvo & Alex Giannini, N.Farrell**
9 **BREFFNIBOY (FR)**, 8, b g Sageburg (IRE)—Dawn Cat (USA) **F. A. Clegg**
10 **CAMPROND (FR)**, 6, b g Lope de Vega (IRE)—Bernieres (IRE) **Mr J. P. McManus**
11 **CANASTERO (IRE)**, 6, b g Getaway (IRE)—Lucky Pigeon (IRE) **Mrs C. Skan**
12 **CELEBRE D'ALLEN (FR)**, 10, ch g Network (GER)—Revoltee (FR) **A. Stennett**
13 **CHABICHOU DUPOITOU**, 6, gr m Martaline—Tidara Angel (IRE) **Hot To Trot Racing & Robert Waley-cohen**
14 **CHALGROVE (FR)**, 6, b g Le Havre (IRE)—Exit To Derawlin (IRE) **Snowdrop Stud Company Ltd**
15 **CHEF D'EQUIPE (FR)**, 10, b g Presenting—Millesimee (FR) **D. Maxwell**
16 **CHILLABELLA**, 6, ch m Black Sam Bellamy (IRE)—Miss Chinchilla **The Philip Hobbs Racing Partnership II**
17 **COOLNAUGH HAZE (IRE)**, 4, b g Lawman—Midas Haze **Highclere Thoroughbred Racing - Cool**
18 **CROSSING THE BAR (IRE)**, 5, b g Poet's Voice—Ship's Biscuit **Mr S. Giannini & Mrs A. Giannini**
19 **DAN'S CHOSEN (IRE)**, 7, b g Well Chosen—Miss Audacious (IRE) **The Philip Hobbs Racing Partnership II**
20 **DEFI DU SEUIL (FR)**, 9, b g Voix du Nord (FR)—Quarvine du Seuil (FR) **Mr J. P. McManus**
21 **DEISE ABA (FR)**, 9, b g Mahler—Kit Massini (IRE) **Exors of the Late Mr T. J. Hemmings**
22 **DEMOPOLIS (FR)**, 8, b g Poliglote—Princess Demut (GER) **Mr J. P. McManus**
23 4, B g Cannock Chase (USA)—Desirable Rhythm (IRE) **P. J. Hobbs**
24 **DOLLY DELIGHTFUL**, 4, b f Soldier of Fortune (IRE)—Dolores Delightful (FR) **My Racing Manager Friends**
25 **DOLPHIN SQUARE (IRE)**, 8, b g Shantou (USA)—Carrig Eden Lass (IRE) **D. Maxwell**
26 **EARTH COMPANY (IRE)**, 6, b br g Arcadio (GER)—Lady Rhinestone (IRE) **R. M. Penny**
27 **EARTH LORD (IRE)**, 6, ch g Mahler—Glebe Beauty (IRE) **R. M. Penny**
28 **ECU DE LA NOVERIE (FR)**, 8, b g Linda's Lad—Quat'sous d'Or (FR) **D. Maxwell**
29 **ENERGY ONE**, 4, b f Kayf Tara—One For Joules (IRE) **Mr D. M. Mathias**
30 **FANCY YOUR CHANCES (IRE)**, 5, br m Presenting—May's June (IRE) **Mr J. P. McManus**
31 **FOR LANGY (FR)**, 7, b g Day Flight—Jubilee II (FR) **D. Maxwell**
32 **FOREVER DES LONG (FR)**, 7, b g Blue Bresil (FR)—Fetuque Du Moulin (FR)
                                                                           Noel Fehily Racing Syndicates-Forever De
33 4, B g Milan—Gales Queen (IRE) **P. J. Hobbs**
34 **GLASHA'S PEAK**, 8, b m Flemensfirth (USA)—Peggies Run **Sir Christopher & Lady Wates**
35 **GOLDEN SOVEREIGN (IRE)**, 8, b g Gold Well—Fugal Maid (IRE) **Mr L. Quinn**
36 **GOSHEVEN (IRE)**, 9, b g Presenting—Fair Choice (IRE) **The Grocer Syndicate**
37 **GREAT OCEAN (IRE)**, 6, b g Great Pretender (IRE)—Diamond of Diana (FR) **Mr S. Giannini & Mrs A. Giannini**
38 **GUERNESEY (FR)**, 6, gr g Martaline—Myrtille Jersey (FR) **J. T. Warner**
39 **HEAD AND HEART**, 5, b m Mount Nelson—Don't Stop Me Now (FR) **Mr L. Quinn**
40 **HONESTLYNTRUFULLY (IRE)**, 6, b g Getaway (GER)—Sixty Forty (IRE) **Clifford & Janet Gibbs**
41 **HONORARY COLONEL (IRE)**, 6, b g Ocovango—Mushagak (IRE) **Mr A. E. Peterson**
42 **HOPE YOU DO (FR)**, 5, b g Boris de Deauville (IRE)—Une Tournee (FR) **Mr J. P. McManus**
43 **IBERIO (GER)**, 5, b g Kamsin (GER)—Imogen (GER) **Brocade Racing**
44 **ICEBURGH BAY (IRE)**, 6, b g Sageburg (IRE)—Aspelenie (IRE) **The Philip Hobbs Racing Partnership**

MR PHILIP HOBBS - continued

45 **ISLAND RUN**, 5, b g Blue Bresil (FR)—Penneyrose Bay **Sir Christopher & Lady Wates**
46 **JATILUWIH (FR)**, 8, ch g Linda's Lad—Jaune de Beaufai (FR) **D. Maxwell**
47 **JERRYSBACK (IRE)**, 10, b g Jeremy (USA)—Get A Few Bob Back (IRE) **Mr J. P. McManus**
48 **KABUKI**, 6, b m Kayf Tara—Violet Express (FR) **Annabel Waley-cohen & Family**
49 **KALOOKI (GER)**, 8, gr g Martaline—Karuma (GER) **Mr A. L. Cohen**
50 **KANUKANKAN (IRE)**, 7, ch g Arakan (USA)—Blow A Gasket (IRE) **Mrs L. R. Lovell**
51 5, B h Malinas (GER)—Keelans Choice (IRE) **P. J. Hobbs**
52 **KEEP MOVING (FR)**, 10, b g Linda's Lad—Keeping Gold (FR) **The Country Side**
53 **KEEP ROLLING (IRE)**, 9, ch g Mahler—Kayles Castle (IRE) **Mick Fitzgerald Racing Club**
54 **KEEP WONDERING (IRE)**, 8, b g Scorpion (IRE)—Supreme Touch (IRE) **Andy Bell & Fergus Lyons**
55 **KEPY BLANC (FR)**, 7, ch g Kapgarde (FR)—Villemanzie (FR) **D. Maxwell**
56 **KIMARELLI**, 5, b m Schiaparelli (GER)—Kim Tian Road (IRE) **Knaves Ash Racing**
57 **LANGLEY HUNDRED (IRE)**, 5, b g Sholokhov (IRE)—Theregoesthetruth (IRE) **The Englands and Heywoods**
58 **LARKBARROW LAD**, 9, b g Kayf Tara—Follow My Leader (IRE) **The Englands and Heywoods**
59 **LE LIGERIEN (FR)**, 9, b g Turgeon (USA)—Etoile de Loir (FR) **D. R. Churches**
60 **LITTLE RIVER BAY (IRE)**, 7, b m Shirocco (GER)—Penneyrose Bay **Sir Christopher & Lady Wates**
61 **LONGSHANKS (IRE)**, 8, b g Scorpion (IRE)—Cash A Lawn (IRE) **Unity Farm Holiday Centre Ltd**
62 **LUTTRELL LAD (IRE)**, 6, b g Beat Hollow—Fairly Definite (IRE) **Owners for Owners Luttrell Lad**
63 **MAD MIKE (IRE)**, 4, b g Soldier of Fortune (IRE)—Manorville (IRE) **The Macaroni Beach Society**
64 **MAJESTIC MERLIN**, 7, b g Midnight Legend—Posh Emily **J.L & P Frampton A.M Midgley R.J Hodges**
65 **MAN OF LIGHT (FR)**, 5, ch g Manduro (GER)—Pilgrim of Grace (FR) **My Racing Manager Friends**
66 **MASTER WORK (FR)**, 9, b g Network (GER)—Mascarpone (FR) **Mr B K Peppiatt & Mr D R Peppiatt**
67 **MASTERS LEGACY (IRE)**, 7, br g Getaway (GER)—Gently Go (IRE) **Mrs P. M. Bosley**
68 **MISTER MARBLES (IRE)**, 6, br g Doyen (IRE)—Presenting Marble (IRE) **Mr A. E. Peterson**
69 **MISTRAL LADY**, 4, b f Shirocco (GER)—Peggies Run **Sir Christopher & Lady Wates**
70 **MONEY SPINNER (IRE)**, 5, b g Soldier of Fortune (IRE)—Floral Spinner **Mr A. E. Peterson**
71 **MONVIEL (IRE)**, 5, gr g Montmartre (FR)—Mont Doree (FR) **Dr V. M. G. Ferguson**
72 **MUSICAL SLAVE (IRE)**, 9, b g Getaway (GER)—Inghwung **Mr J. P. McManus**
73 **MY KEEPSAKE**, 6, br m Kalanisi (IRE)—Dudeen (IRE) **The Vintage Hunters**
74 **NO COMMENT**, 11, br g Kayf Tara—Dizzy Frizzy **Mr J. P. McManus**
75 **OFF THE PLANET (IRE)**, 7, ch g Presenting—Kings Diva (IRE) **The Brushmakers**
76 **ONE FOR YOU (IRE)**, 7, b g Yeats (IRE)—Tempest Belle (IRE) **Martin St. Quinton & Tim Syder**
77 **ORBYS LEGEND (IRE)**, 6, b g Milan—Morning Legend (IRE) **Highclere Thoroughbred Racing - Milan**
78 **PILEON (IRE)**, 8, b g Yeats (IRE)—Heath Heaven **Mr Tim Syder & Martin St Quinton**
79 **PIPER (IRE)**, 5, b g Soldier of Fortune (IRE)—Nia (IRE) **R. A. Bartlett**
80 **POL CROCAN (IRE)**, 7, br g Shirocco (GER)—She's All That (IRE) **Mrs C. Skan**
81 **POTTERS VENTURE (IRE)**, 8, b g Arcadio (GER)—Starventure (IRE) **Mr A. E. Peterson**
82 **PULLING STUMPS (IRE)**, 5, b g Soldier of Fortune (IRE)—Pride of The Braid (IRE) **Highclere T'Bred Racing**
   - Pulling Stumps
83 5, B m Arctic Cosmos (USA)—Redunderthebed (IRE) **F. R. Jarvey**
84 **ROLLING DYLAN (IRE)**, 11, ch g Indian River (FR)—Easter Saturday (IRE) **Mrs S. Hobbs**
85 **SANDY BOY (IRE)**, 8, b g Tajraasi (USA)—Annienoora (IRE) **Mrs B. A. Hitchcock**
86 **SASSIFIED (IRE)**, 4, ch g Excelebration (IRE)—Satwa Pearl **Mr J. P. McManus**
87 5, Ch m Midnight Legend—Semi Colon (FR) **P. J. Hobbs**
88 **SHANTOU SUNSET**, 8, ch m Shantou (USA)—Kingara **The Philip Hobbs Racing Partnership**
89 **SHARP SHADOW (IRE)**, 6, br m Fame And Glory—Sharps Express (IRE) **Mrs J. J. Peppiatt**
90 4, B g Kayf Tara—She Ranks Me (IRE) **Louisville Syndicate**
91 **SMARTY WILD**, 8, b g Fair Mix (IRE)—Blaeberry **Mr Michael & Mrs Norma Tuckey**
92 **SPORTING JOHN (IRE)**, 7, b br g Getaway (GER)—Wild Spell (IRE) **Mr J. P. McManus**
93 **ST BARTS (IRE)**, 8, b g High Chaparral (IRE)—Lindeman (IRE) **A. Stennett**
94 4, B g Blue Bresil (FR)—Sting In The Gale **Louisville Syndicate**
95 **STELLAR MAGIC (IRE)**, 7, b g Arctic Cosmos (USA)—Inter Alia (IRE) **A. Stennett**
96 **STORM FORCE BEN (IRE)**, 8, b g Fame And Glory—Torduff Storm (IRE) **Dr V. M. G. Ferguson**
97 5, B m Kayf Tara—Supreme Gem (IRE) **I. K. Johnson**
98 **THYME HILL**, 8, b g Kayf Tara—Rosita Bay **The Englands and Heywoods**
99 **TRUCKIN AWAY (IRE)**, 8, br g Getaway (GER)—Simons Girl (IRE) **Brocade Racing**
100 **UMNDENI (FR)**, 8, b br g Balko (FR)—Marie Royale (FR) **& Giannini**
101 **WILDFIRE WARRIOR (IRE)**, 7, b g Flemensfirth (USA)—Lady of Fortune (IRE) **Mrs D. L. Whateley**
102 **WOTASTUNNER**, 5, b g Passing Glance—Posh Emily **R.J.H. Unity Farm Partnership**
103 **ZANZA (IRE)**, 8, b g Arcadio (GER)—What A Bleu (IRE) **Louisville Syndicate Elite**

MR PHILIP HOBBS - continued

Other Owners: Mr A. J. Bell, Mrs T. Bell, Blythe Stables LLP, Mrs A. E. M. Broom, Mr G. R. Broom, Mr C. Bull, C. J. Butler, Mr J. P. Cooper, Miss I. D. Du Pre, Mr A. D. England, Mrs E. England, J. L. Frampton, Mr P. S. Frampton, John Frampton & Paul Frampton, Mrs A. Giannini, Mr S. Giannini, Mrs J. E. Gibbs, Mr A. H. Heywood, Mr A. S. Heywood, R. J. Hodges, Mr R. S. Hoskins, Hot To Trot Jumping, Mrs C. Lyons, Mr F. Lyons, Fergus & Caroline Lyons, A. M. Midgley, B. K. Peppiatt, D. R. Peppiatt, D. A. Rees, N. C. Savery, Mr M. G. St Quinton, Mr T. D. J. Syder, M. J. Tuckey, Mrs N. Tuckey, Unity Farm Holiday Centre Ltd, Mrs A. Waley-Cohen, Mr R. B. Waley-Cohen, Mr S. B. Waley-Cohen, C. J. M. Walker, Sir Christopher Wates, Lady G. F. Wates.

Assistant Trainer: Ben Robarts, Johnson White.

NH Jockey: Micheal Nolan, Tom O'Brien. **Conditional Jockey:** Sean Houlihan, Ben Jones.

Amateur Jockey: Mr Isaac Buncle, Mr Tom Dixon, Mr Jack Martin, Mr David Maxwell.

---

266 MISS CLARE HOBSON, Royston
Postal: **Upper Coombe Farm, Coombe Road, Kelshall, Royston, Hertfordshire, SG8 9SA**
Contacts: **MOBILE 07966 734889**
EMAIL clarehobsonracing@gmail.com

1 ASCOT JUNGLE (IRE), 5, ch m Bungle Inthejungle—Red Red Rose **Mr I. G. Titmuss**
2 AYDA (FR), 5, b m War Command (USA)—Rampoldina **The Win Or Booze Racing Syndicate**
3 BRIGHT SAFFRON, 7, ch m Champs Elysees—Mercy Pecksniff **Smith's Wapping Partnership**
4 EMBOLDEN (IRE), 5, b g Kodiac—Sassy Gal (IRE) **Molen, Ball, Judd, Dunne & White**
5 INFINITE BEAUTY (IRE), 4, gr ro f Dark Angel (IRE)—Natural Beauty **The Pink House Partnership**
6 5, B g Universal (IRE)—Jump To The Beat **Mr H. R. Hobson**
7 KING CNUT (FR), 8, ch g Kentucky Dynamite (USA)—Makadane **Mr H. R. Hobson**
8 LUNA WISH, 5, b m Sea The Moon (GER)—Crystal Wish **Mrs C. D. Taylor**
9 MR NICE GUY (IRE), 6, b g Nathaniel (IRE)—Three Choirs (IRE) **Mr L. Brooks**
10 NOBOOKWORK (IRE), 6, ch g Shantaram—Glenbrook Memories (IRE) **Mr H. R. Hobson**
11 PERCY'S PRINCE, 6, b g Sir Percy—Attainable **Mrs S. Westerhuis**
12 RUSSIAN VIRTUE, 5, b g Toronado (IRE)—Russian Rhapsody **Mr L. Brooks**
13 SEVERUS ALEXANDER (IRE), 6, b g Zoffany (IRE)—Sacrosanct (IRE) **Mrs C. D. Taylor**
14 SPOTTED DICK, 6, b g Dick Turpin (IRE)—Ice Apple **Mr H. R. Hobson**
15 THE TURFACCOUNTANT (IRE), 6, b g Ask—Kayfs Fancy (IRE) **Greg, Greg, Harry & Parsley**
16 UNCLE O, 8, gr g Fair Mix (IRE)—Clever Liz **Mr H. R. Hobson**
17 VINNIE'S GETAWAY (IRE), 8, b g Getaway (GER)—Trixskin (IRE) **The Fox and Duck syndicate**
18 WOODFORD BRIDGE, 6, b m Champs Elysees—A Lulu Ofa Menifee (USA) **Mr G. Molen**

TWO-YEAR-OLDS

19 B c 19/03 Tagula (IRE)—Alphaba (IRE) (Zebedee) **Mr L. Brooks**
20 ITS COMING HOME, b c 11/02 Outstrip—Scarlet Ribbons (Zoffany (IRE)) (1200) **Mr L. Brooks**

---

267 MR RICHARD HOBSON, Little Rissington
Postal: **Bobble Barn Farm, Little Rissington, Cheltenham, Gloucestershire, GL54 2NE**
Contacts: **PHONE 01451 820535 MOBILE 07939 155843**
EMAIL hobson.r1@sky.com WEBSITE www.richardhobsonracing.co.uk

1 CHIC NAME (FR), 10, b g Nickname (FR)—Vuelta Al Ruedo (FR) **The Boom Syndicate**
2 DEFI SACRE (FR), 9, b g Network (GER)—Iowa Sacree (FR) **Mr R. I. H. Wills**
3 DISCKO DES PLAGES (FR), 9, b g Balko (FR)—Lady des Plages (FR) **Gordon Farr & Gerry M Ward**
4 ECHO WATT (FR), 8, gr g Fragrant Mix (IRE)—Roxane du Bois (FR) **The Boom Syndicate**
5 EUREU DU BOULAY (FR), 8, b g Della Francesca (USA)—Idole du Boulay (FR) **J. & R. Hobson**
6 FAMILY BUSINESS (FR), 5, b g Kitkou (FR)—Santa Senam (FR) **Stoneleigh Racing**
7 FANZIO (FR), 7, b g Day Flight—Tu L'As Eu (FR) **Ms S. A. Fox**

MR RICHARD HOBSON - continued

  8 **FUGITIF (FR)**, 7, b g Ballingarry (IRE)—Turiane (FR) **Carl & E. Hussain**
  9 **HI RIKO (FR)**, 5, b g Cokoriko (FR)—Vanille d'Ex (FR) **Mr D. W. Brookes**
10 **HUSSARD BRUN (FR)**, 5, b g Coastal Path—Ausone d'Alienor (FR) **Mr R. H. Hobson**
11 **INGENNIO (FR)**, 4, b g Lauro (GER)—Casbah Rose (FR) **Ms S. A. Fox**
12 **LORD DU MESNIL (FR)**, 9, b g Saint des Saints (FR)—Ladies Choice (FR) **Mr Paul Porter & Mike & Mandy Smith**
13 **PARISIENNE GOLD (FR)**, 5, b m Network (GER)—Parthenia (IRE) **The Boom Syndicate**
14 **PETIT PALAIS**, 7, ch g Champs Elysees—Galicuix **Mr R. H. Hobson**
15 **RAMONEX (GER)**, 11, b g Saddex—Ramondia (GER) **Mr R. H. Hobson**
16 **RIDERS ONTHE STORM (IRE)**, 9, br g Scorpion (IRE)—Endless Moments (IRE) **Carl Hinchy & Mark Scott**
17 **SAINT XAVIER (FR)**, 10, b g Saint des Saints (FR)—Princesse Lucie (FR) **Mr R. H. Hobson**
18 **VALADOM (FR)**, 13, gr g Dadarissime (FR)—Laurana (FR) **Mr R. H. Hobson**
19 **WILD BREEZE (IRE)**, 6, b g Pour Moi (IRE)—Nerissa (IRE) **Stoneleigh Racing**

Other Owners: Mr G. C. Farr, Mr C. S. Hinchy, Mr R. H. Hobson, Dr E. Hussain, Mr M. S. Scott, Mr J. Sheppard, Mr G. M. Ward.

Assistant Trainer: Shirley Jane Becker, **Head Lad:** Dawson Lees.

Conditional Jockey: Jordan Nailor, Paul O'Brien.

---

268 MR SIMON HODGSON, Ludgershall
Postal: **12 Hei - Lin Way, Ludgershall, Andover, Hampshire, SP11 9QH**
Contacts: PHONE 07786 730853
EMAIL hodgsters@hotmail.co.uk

  1 **C'EST NO MOUR (GER)**, 9, b g Champs Elysees—C'Est L'Amour (GER) **Mr P. R. Hedger & P C F Racing Ltd**
  2 **CHARLIE ARTHUR (IRE)**, 6, b g Slade Power (IRE)—Musical Bar (IRE) **The 19th Hole Syndicate**
  3 **DELAGATE THIS LORD**, 8, b g Delegator—Lady Filly **Mrs M. S. Teversham**
  4 **FINAIR**, 5, b m Finjaan—Afro **P C F Racing Ltd**
  5 **FOLLOW YOUR HEART (IRE)**, 4, b g Estidhkaar (IRE)—Al Gharrafa **Mr K. Sohi**
  6 **HELETA**, 5, b m Helmet (AUS)—Juno Moneta (IRE) **P C F Racing Ltd**
  7 **JUST THAT LORD**, 9, ch g Avonbridge—Lady Filly **Mrs M. S. Teversham**
  8 **MR MAC**, 8, b g Makfi—Veronica Franco **P C F Racing Ltd**
  9 **THE CRUISING LORD**, 6, b g Coach House (IRE)—Lady Filly **Mrs M. S. Teversham**
10 **TOTAL COMMITMENT (IRE)**, 6, b g Exceed And Excel (AUS)—Crysdal **P C F Racing Ltd**
11 **TRALEE HILLS**, 8, gr ro g Mount Nelson—Distant Waters **P C F Racing Ltd**
12 **TWILIGHT MADNESS**, 4, ch c Twilight Son—Rhal (IRE) **Mr P. R. Hedger & P C F Racing Ltd**

THREE-YEAR-OLDS

13 **APACHE STAR (IRE)**, br g No Nay Never (USA)—Instinctively (IRE) **Mr K. Sohi**
14 **NATURAL IMPULSE**, b c Intrinsic—Kodi da Capo (IRE) **Results Racing**
15 **PAY FOR ADAAY**, b g Adaay (IRE)—Gracilia (FR) **P C F Racing Ltd**
16 **PEARL REEF**, b f Havana Gold (IRE)—Cockney Dancer **Mr K. Sohi**
17 **QEYAAM (IRE)**, gr f Oasis Dream—Aghaany **Mr K. Sohi**
18 **WINDSONG (IRE)**, b f Kodi Bear (IRE)—Notte Illuminata (IRE) **Mr K. Sohi**

Other Owners: P. R. Hedger, P C F Racing Ltd.

269   MR HENRY HOGARTH, Stillington
Postal: **New Grange Farm, Stillington, York**
Contacts: **PHONE 01347 811168 MOBILE 07788 777044 FAX 01347 811168**
EMAIL harryhogarth@ymail.com

1 **ARCHIE BROWN (IRE)**, 8, b g Aizavoski (IRE)—Pure Beautiful (IRE) **Hogarth Racing**
2 **GEMINI FIRE (IRE)**, 5, ch g Mahler—Verde Goodwood **Hogarth Racing**
3 **GOLDRAPPER (IRE)**, 9, b g Gold Well—Mrs Bukay (IRE) **Hogarth Racing**
4 **LANDACRE BRIDGE**, 6, b g Kayf Tara—Wee Dinns (IRE) **Hogarth Racing**
5 **MANCE RAYDER (IRE)**, 9, b g Flemensfirth (USA)—J'Y Viens (FR) **Hogarth Racing**
6 **STONEY STREET**, 6, b g Gentlewave (IRE)—Flemengo (IRE) **Hogarth Racing**
7 **THE BLACK SQUIRREL (IRE)**, 9, br g Craigsteel—Terra Lucida (IRE) **Hogarth Racing**

Other Owners: Mr H. P. Hogarth, J. Hogarth, J. L. Hogarth, P. H. Hogarth.

NH Jockey: Jamie Hamilton. **Conditional Jockey:** Billy Garritty.

270   MR SAM HOLDSWORTH, Ivybridge
Postal: **Quarry Farm, Modbury, Ivybridge, Devon, PL21 0SF**
EMAIL sam.holdsworth@sky.com

1 **AIRTON**, 9, b g Champs Elysees—Fly In Style **A. S. T. Holdsworth**
2 **ALWAYS TEA TIME**, 6, b m Indian Haven—Magical Wonderland **A. S. T. Holdsworth**
3 **MISSYLADIE (FR)**, 8, b m Born King (JPN)—Ladie de Briandais (FR) **A. S. T. Holdsworth**
4 **PORTENTOSO (GER)**, 7, b g Santiago (GER)—Piccola (GER) **A. S. T. Holdsworth**
5 **PWLL CARN MAGGIE**, 4, b ro f Proclamation (IRE)—Scarlett O'Tara **A. S. T. Holdsworth**
6 **THE DEVON DUMPLING**, 9, b m Fair Mix (IRE)—Star of Magic **A. S. T. Holdsworth**

271   MR DARRYLL HOLLAND, Newmarket
Postal: **The Cottage, Harraton Court Stables, Chapel Street, Exning, Newmarket, Suffolk, CB8 7HA**
Contacts: **PHONE 07901 550909**
EMAIL info@harratoncourtstables.com

1 7, B g Air Chief Marshal (IRE)—Baraaya (IRE) **Harraton Court Stables Ltd**
2 **I'M MABLE**, 4, b f Cable Bay (IRE)—Triskel **Ms S. V. Hattersley**
3 **LILKIAN**, 5, ch g Sepoy (AUS)—Janie Runaway (IRE) **Harraton Court Stables Ltd**
4 **YORKSHIRE PIRLO (IRE)**, 4, b g Mehmas (IRE)—Suffer Her (IRE) **Move In Corner Forward Syndicate**

THREE-YEAR-OLDS
5 **DREAM LOFTY DREAMS**, b g Lawman (FR)—Saskia's Dream **Rob Nugent & Harraton Court Stables Ltd**
6 **DYNAMIC TALENT**, b g Aclaim (IRE)—Burnt Fingers (IRE) **Harraton Court Stables Ltd**
7 **MESBAR**, b g Markaz (IRE)—Baqqa (IRE)
8 **SILKS DREAM (IRE)**, b c Mehmas (IRE)—Tajbell (IRE) **Barry Silkman & Gary Pascoe**
9 **SILKS PASS**, b c Excelebration (IRE)—Jadwiga **Barry Silkman & Gary Pascoe**
10 **SUANNI**, gr c Lethal Force (IRE)—Glee Club **Silkman Pascoe & Harraton Court Stables**
11 **THEY DON'T KNOW (IRE)**, b c Vocalised (USA)—Fields of May (IRE) **Mr A. Mekni**

TWO-YEAR-OLDS
12 **GRACE ANGEL**, b f 22/02 Harry Angel (IRE)—Sparkle (Oasis Dream) (12000) **Mr R. Nugent**
13 B f 17/03 Cityscape—Meet Me Halfway (Exceed And Excel (AUS)) (2000) **Mr S. Bissix**
14 **PEARL EYE**, b c 24/04 Expert Eye—Treat Gently (Cape Cross (IRE)) (22000) **Mr R. Nugent**
15 **PRIMROSE RIDGE**, b f 03/04 Aclaim (IRE)—Primrose Place (Compton Place) (8000) **Harraton Court Stables Ltd**
16 Gr c 01/04 Brazen Beau (AUS)—Zia (GER) (Grand Lodge (USA)) (12000) **Mr S. Bissix**

Other Owners: Harraton Court Stables Ltd, Mr R. Nugent, G. J. Pascoe, B. Silkman.

272 **MISS SARAH HOLLINSHEAD, Upper Longdon**
Postal: **Lodge Farm, Upper Longdon, Rugeley, Staffordshire, WS15 1QF**
Contacts: PHONE **01543 490298**

1 **BUT YOU SAID (IRE)**, 5, b m No Nay Never (USA)—San Macchia **Dallas Racing & Partner**
2 **CASTLEREA TESS**, 9, ch m Pastoral Pursuits—Zartwyda (IRE) **Mr John Graham & Sarah Hollinshead**
3 4, B f Telescope (IRE)—Cherished Love (IRE) **Mr J. Gould**
4 **DIAMOND JILL (IRE)**, 5, b m Footstepsinthesand—Sindiyma (IRE) **Mr J. Gould**
5 **DIAMOND JOEL**, 10, b g Youmzain (IRE)—Miss Lacroix **Mrs N. S. Harris**
6 **DREAMS OF GOLD**, 7, b g Goldmark (USA)—Song of Kenda **L & A Holland**
7 **FINAL ATTACK (IRE)**, 11, b g Cape Cross (IRE)—Northern Melody (IRE) **N. Chapman**
8 **FLORA PAGET**, 6, b m Kayf Tara—Lysways **Miss S. A. Hollinshead**
9 **GEALACH GHORM (IRE)**, 8, b g Finsceal Fíor (IRE)—Saintly Wish (USA) **Miss S. A. Hollinshead**
10 **GMS PRINCE**, 7, b g Kayf Tara—Zartwyda (IRE) **Graham Brothers Racing Partnership**
11 **HEAD HIGH (IRE)**, 9, gr g Mastercraftsman (IRE)—Elisium **Mrs M Moore & Sarah Hollinshead**
12 **JENNY REN**, 7, b m Multiplex—Cherished Love (IRE) **Mr J. Gould**
13 **LOOKFORARAINBOW**, 9, b g Rainbow High—Look Here's May **The Giddy Gang**
14 5, B m Kayf Tara—Norma Hill **Mr G. Lloyd**
15 **QUELLE VITESSE (GER)**, 4, b f Golden Horn—Queensberry (GER) **Stellar Racing**
16 **QUIET THUNDER (IRE)**, 4, b f Night of Thunder (IRE)—Elevator Action (IRE) **Mr J. Gould & Mr R. Gould**
17 **SINNDARELLA (IRE)**, 6, b m Fast Company (IRE)—Alafzara (IRE) **R & M Moseley, Slater, Gould & Laughland**
18 **SUREWECAN**, 10, b g Royal Applause—Edge of Light **The Giddy Gang**
19 **UNCLE BERNIE (IRE)**, 12, gr g Aussie Rules (USA)—Alwiyda (USA) **Miss S. A. Hollinshead**

THREE-YEAR-OLDS
20 B f Adaay (IRE)—Look Here's Dee **S. L. Edwards**
21 **SNOOZE LANE (IRE)**, b g Free Eagle (IRE)—Sindiyma (IRE)

Other Owners: Mr M. A. Glassett, Mr J. Gould, Mr R. Gould, Mr J. R. Graham, Mr A. L. Holland, Miss S. A. Hollinshead,
Mr A. Lawrence, Mrs M. A. Moore, Mrs L. J. Pickard.

---

273 **MRS STEPH HOLLINSHEAD, Rugeley**
Postal: **Catmint Lodge, Bardy Lane, Upper Longdon, Rugeley, Staffordshire, WS15 4LJ**
Contacts: HOME **01543 327609** PHONE **07554 008405** MOBILE **07791 385335**
EMAIL **steph_hollinshead@hotmail.co.uk** WEBSITE **www.stephhollinsheadracing.com**

1 **AL SIMMO**, 5, b m Al Kazeem—Magic Destiny **R. Bailey**
2 **ALCHEMYSTIQUE (IRE)**, 5, b m Authorized (IRE)—Nice To Know (FR) **Lysways Racing**
3 **ALICE KAZEEM**, 4, ch f Al Kazeem—Kawartha **Mrs F. Leyland**
4 **HOTCITY**, 5, b m Cityscape—Even Hotter **Mrs V. C. Gilbert**
5 **LADY MANDER**, 4, b f Albaasil (IRE)—Goldeva **Hollinshead & Pyle**
6 **LOCALLINK (IRE)**, 8, b g Sandmason—Suny House **The Captain On the Bridge Partnership**
7 **MISS MOCKTAIL (IRE)**, 7, b m Getaway (GER)—Identity Parade (IRE) **Lysways Racing**
8 **MISS TRIXIE**, 4, b f Bated Breath—Epiphany **Mr N. Mence**
9 **PUSHOVER**, 5, gr m Hellvelyn—Soft Touch (IRE) **Chapel Stud Ltd & Loughshore Racing Synd**
10 **RACY STACEY**, 5, ch m Fast Company (IRE)—Stilettoesinthemud (IRE) **Andrew & S Hawkins**
11 **RED ALLURE**, 7, ch m Mayson—Lark In The Park (IRE) **Mia Racing**
12 **THE GOLDEN CUE**, 7, ch g Zebedee—Khafayif (USA) **The Golden Cue Partnership**
13 **VELOCISTAR (IRE)**, 4, b f Starspangledbanner (AUS)—Mahsooba (USA) **Sleeve It Ltd**

THREE-YEAR-OLDS
14 **EPICENTRE**, b gr f Heeraat (IRE)—Richter Scale (IRE) **Mr A. C. Gray**
15 **MADASAHATTER**, b f Mattmu—Makindi **Abacus Bloodstock & Veronica Gilbert**
16 **MALHAM TARN COVE**, gr ro c Heeraat (IRE)—Spirit of Rosanna **Mr J. Holcombe**
17 **NATTY MEDDLER (IRE)**, b c Dandy Man (IRE)—Interlope (IRE) **M. A. N. Johnson**
18 **PEPSI CAT (IRE)**, b f Tamayuz—Music Pearl (IRE) **Mrs D. A. Hodson**
19 **ROSIE RED**, b f Twilight Son—Merletta **Mrs D. A. Hodson**

MRS STEPH HOLLINSHEAD - continued

Other Owners: Abacus Bloodstock Racing Club, Bucklands Farm & Stud Ltd, Mr K. Close, Mrs V. C. Gilbert, Mr A. C. Gray, Mrs S. C. Hawkins, Mrs L. A. Hollinshead, Loughshore Racing Syndicate, Mr S. J. Matheson, M. J. F. Pyle, Mr G. T. Rowley, A. Tickle, Mrs I. M. Tickle, M. A. Tickle.

Assistant Trainer: Adam Hawkins.

---

274   MR ANTHONY HONEYBALL, Beaminster
Postal: **Potwell Farm, Mosterton, Beaminster, Dorset, DT8 3HG**
Contacts: **PHONE 01308 867452 MOBILE 07815 898569**
EMAIL anthony@ajhoneyballracing.co.uk WEBSITE www.ajhoneyballracing.co.uk

1 **ACEY MILAN (IRE)**, 8, b g Milan—Strong Wishes (IRE) **Owners For Owners: Acey Milan**
2 4, B br f Soldier of Fortune (IRE)—Aventia (IRE)
3 **BELLE DE MANECH (FR)**, 6, gr m Vision d'Etat (FR)—Noor Forever (FR) **Mr M. R. Chapman**
4 **BLEUE AWAY (IRE)**, 8, b m Getaway (GER)—Majorite Bleue (FR) **Potwell Racing Syndicate I**
5 **BOB BACKUS (IRE)**, 7, b g Milan—Boro Bee (IRE) **Decimus Racing IV**
6 **BOHEMIAN LAD (IRE)**, 4, b g Mahler—Rehill Lass (IRE) **Decimus Racing IX**
7 **CAPE VIDAL**, 5, b h Kayf Tara—Midnight Minx **Potwell Racing Syndicate III**
8 **CAPTAIN CLAUDE (IRE)**, 5, b g Soldier of Fortune (IRE)—Princess Supreme (IRE) **Decimus Racing V**
9 4, B f Doyen (IRE)—Carrigeen Queen (IRE) **Wessex Racing Club**
10 **COQUELICOT (FR)**, 6, b br m Soldier of Fortune (IRE)—Moscow Nights (FR) **Geegeez.co.uk PA**
11 **CREDO (IRE)**, 7, b m Fame And Glory—Tasmani (FR) **Potwell Racing Syndicate II**
12 **DEAR RALPHY (IRE)**, 6, b g Westerner—Letterwoman (IRE) **Mr J. M. Pike**
13 **DEJA VUE (IRE)**, 8, b m Fame And Glory—Westgrove Berry (IRE) **Axom LXXVI**
14 **DREAMING BLUE**, 5, b g Showcasing—Got To Dream **R. W. Devlin**
15 **EMZARA (IRE)**, 6, b m Califet (FR)—Strike An Ark (IRE) **Hancock, Rowe & Wright**
16 **FANFARON DINO (FR)**, 7, gr g Doctor Dino (FR)—Kadjara (FR) **Mr J. P. McManus**
17 **FIRESTREAM**, 5, b g Yeats (IRE)—Swincombe Flame **Buckingham, Chapman, Langford & Ritzema**
18 **FORTUITOUS FAVOUR (IRE)**, 4, b f Soldier of Fortune (IRE)—Northwood Milan (IRE) **Mr A. Honeyball**
19 **FORTUNA LIGNA (IRE)**, 5, br m Soldier of Fortune (IRE)—Quiet Thought (IRE) **Owners for Owners Fortuna Ligna**
20 **FORWARD PLAN (IRE)**, 6, b g Valirann (FR)—Culmore Native (IRE) **The Steeple Chasers**
21 **GABRIEL'S GETAWAY (IRE)**, 5, b g Getaway (GER)—Chosen Destiny (IRE)
Buckingham, Chapman, Kingston &Langford
22 **GLORIOUS ISOLATION (IRE)**, 6, gr m Fame And Glory—Stay At Home Mum (IRE) **Mr M. W. Pendarves**
23 **GOOD LOOK CHARM (FR)**, 6, b m Cokoriko (FR)—Une d'Ex (FR) **The Isle of Blue and White**
24 **GUSTAVIAN (IRE)**, 7, b g Mahler—Grange Oscar (IRE) **Decimus Racing I**
25 **HATOS (FR)**, 5, b g Diamond Boy (FR)—Santalisa (FR) **Hats off to Hatos**
26 **HOWLINGMADMURDOCK (IRE)**, 5, b g Soldier of Fortune (IRE)—Bell Storm (IRE) **The Soldiers of Fortune**
27 **IL MAGNIFICO (FR)**, 4, b g Spanish Moon (USA)—Unique Star (FR) **Ms G. S. Langford**
28 **JAIL NO BAIL (IRE)**, 5, b g Mahler—Kittys Oscar (IRE) **Bryan Drew & Friends, Chapman & Kingston**
29 **JEPECK (IRE)**, 13, b g Westerner—Jenny's Jewel (IRE) **Mr J. M. Pike**
30 **KHALINA STAR**, 5, b m Kayf Tara—Alina Rheinberg (IRE) **Geegeez.co.uk PA**
31 **KILBEG KING (IRE)**, 7, b g Doyen (IRE)—Prayuwin Drummer (IRE) **M.R.Chapman, E.Jones & H.Kingston**
32 **KONIGIN ISABELLA (GER)**, 4, b f Isfahan (GER)—Konigin Cala (GER) **geegeez.co.uk KI**
33 **LE COEUR NET (FR)**, 10, ch g Network (GER)—Silverwood (FR) **Wessex Racing Club**
34 **LILITH (IRE)**, 7, b m Stowaway—Flirthing Around (IRE) **Decimus Racing VI**
35 **MARCO ISLAND (IRE)**, 5, b g Mahler—Florida Belle (IRE) **Buckingham, Chapman, Langford & Ritzema**
36 **MARILYN MONROE (IRE)**, 9, b m Scorpion (IRE)—Go On Eileen (IRE) **Some Like It Hot**
37 **MIDNIGHT CALLISTO**, 7, br m Midnight Legend—Carrigeen Queen (IRE) **Ms G. S. Langford**
38 **MISTER ALLEGRO**, 4, b g Bernardini (USA)—Joyful Hope **Mr S. C. Browning**
39 **MOBHI DICK**, 5, b g Recharge (IRE)—Mobhi Boreen (IRE)
40 **MONTEPLEX**, 5, b m Multiplex—Montelfolene (IRE) **Mickley Stud & Mr D. Mossop**
41 **NOTBITTERBUTBETTER**, 5, b m Champs Elysees—Purely By Chance **D. G. Pryde**
42 **POUR ME ANOTHER**, 5, b g Pour Moi (IRE)—Karliysha (IRE) **Potwell Racing Syndicate II**
43 **PRECIOUS**, 6, b m Midnight Legend—Carrigeen Queen (IRE) **Cartwright & Callaway**

MR ANTHONY HONEYBALL - continued

44 **PURE VISION (IRE)**, 11, b g Milan—Distillery Lane (IRE) **Mr J. P. McManus**
45 **REGAL ENCORE (IRE)**, 14, b g King's Theatre (IRE)—Go On Eileen (IRE) **Mr J. P. McManus**
46 4, B g Black Sam Bellamy (IRE)—Rouquine Sauvage **Mr J. P. McManus**
47 **RUBYS REWARD**, 6, b m Dr Massini (IRE)—Cresswell Ruby (IRE) **The Brambles**
48 **SAM BROWN**, 10, b g Black Sam Bellamy (IRE)—Cream Cracker **Mr T. C. Frost**
49 **SERIOUS CHARGES (IRE)**, 5, b g Soldier of Fortune (IRE)—South West Nine (IRE) **Potwell Racing Syndicate III**
50 **STARSHIP MONA**, 4, b f Telescope (IRE)—Lifeboat Mona **The Lifeboat Crew**
51 **SULLY D'OC AA (FR)**, 8, b g Konig Turf (GER)—Samarra d'Oc (FR) **Mr J. P. McManus**
52 **SWINCOMBE FLEAT**, 6, b m Yeats (IRE)—Swincombe Flame **Yeo Racing Partnership**
53 **UCANAVER**, 6, bl m Maxios—Purely By Chance **Ifuwonner Partnership**
54 **WHYNOTNOWKEN (IRE)**, 5, ch g Notnowcato—Midnight Lira **B. A. Derrick**
55 **WINDANCE (IRE)**, 7, b g Shirocco (GER)—Maca Rince (IRE) **Decimus Racing III**
56 **WORLD OF DREAMS (IRE)**, 6, b g Kayf Tara—Rose of The World (IRE) **R. Huggins, Bisogno P Williams**

THREE-YEAR-OLDS

57 **A WISH AWAY (IRE)**, gr f Mastercraftsman (IRE)—First Love (IRE) **The Wish Away Partnership**
58 **MATTHIAS**, b g Black Sam Bellamy (IRE)—Rouquine Sauvage **Mrs J. L. Buckingham**

Other Owners: Mr M. Bisogno, Bryan Drew and Friends, Mrs J. L. Buckingham, Mrs D. M. Callaway, Mr P. R. Cartwright, Mr M. R. Chapman, Mr B. J. C. Drew, Mr N. Hancock, Mr R. W. Huggins, Mr E. Jones, R. Kent, Mr H. Kingston, Ms G. S. Langford, Dr B. Mayoh, D. Mossop, Mrs D. J. Ritzema, Mr M. W. Rowe, Step By Step Supporting Independence Ltd, The Lifeboat Crew Syndicate, Mr P. Williams, Mr B. J. C. Wright.

Assistant Trainer: Rachael Honeyball.

NH Jockey: Aidan Coleman, David Noonan, Rex Dingle. **Conditional Jockey:** Ben Godfrey.

---

275 **MR CHRISTOPHER HONOUR, Ashburton**
Postal: Higher Whiddon Farm, Ashburton Down, Newton Abbot, Devon, TQ13 7EY
Contacts: HOME 01364 652500 MOBILE 07771 861219
EMAIL tojohonour@aol.com

1 **DOLLY BIRD**, 4, b f Shantou (USA)—Sparron Hawk (FR) **The Dolly Bird Syndicate**
2 **GAELIC DREAMER**, 5, gr g Dream Eater (IRE)—Gaelic Lime **Mrs J. Elliott**
3 **GAELIC THUNDER**, 7, b g Arvico (FR)—Gaelic Lime **Mrs J. Elliott**
4 **GRUMPY CHARLEY**, 7, gr g Shirocco (GER)—Whisky Rose (IRE) **G. D. Thompson**
5 **GRUMPY FREYA**, 7, ch m Malinas (GER)—Thedeboftheyear **G. D. Thompson**
6 **LEGEND OF ZORRO (IRE)**, 9, ch g Touch of Land (FR)—Wotaglen (IRE) **G. D. Thompson**
7 **MAYHEM MYA**, 5, b m Authorized (IRE)—Thedeboftheyear **G. D. Thompson**
8 **SHORTCROSS STORM (IRE)**, 7, b g September Storm (GER)—Lady Leila (IRE) **Cotswold Stone Supplies Ltd**
9 **TILE TAPPER**, 8, b g Malinas (GER)—Darn Hot **Cotswold Stone Supplies Ltd**
10 **TROED Y MELIN (IRE)**, 10, b g Craigsteel—Kissangel (IRE) **No Illusions Partnership**
11 **WITH POISE**, 4, b f Telescope (IRE)—With Grace **No Illusions Partnership**

Assistant Trainer: Rebekah Honour.

---

276 **MISS LAURA HORSFALL, Towcester**
Postal: Glebe Barn Stables, Blakesley Road, Maidford, Towcester, Northamptonshire, NN12 8HN
EMAIL horsfalllaura@hotmail.co.uk

1 **CITY ROLLER (IRE)**, 4, b g Scorpion (IRE)—Pearl's A Singer (IRE) **Miss L. Horsfall**
2 **ERNIE BILKO (IRE)**, 5, ch g Shirocco (GER)—Molly's Case (IRE) **Miss L. Horsfall**
3 4, B g Soldier of Fortune (IRE)—Fille d'Honfleur
4 **JUST A WHIM**, 8, b m Gold Well—Redunderthebed (IRE) **Mr M. W. Redman**
5 **KATIES ESCAPE (IRE)**, 7, ch m Getaway (GER)—Katies Pet (IRE) **F. R. Jarvey**
6 **LASTORDERSPLEASE (IRE)**, 5, b m Arctic Cosmos (USA)—The Bar Maid **F. R. Jarvey**

MISS LAURA HORSFALL - continued

7 **LONG SYMPHONY (IRE)**, 5, b g Mahler—Ashlings Princess (IRE) **Miss L. Horsfall**
8 **MUCH TOO DEAR (IRE)**, 4, ch g Getaway (GER)—Redunderthebed (IRE)
                                             Mr M Redman F Jarvey M Thomas N Allen
9 **MYSPACENOTYOURS**, 7, b m Dr Massini (IRE)—Home By Midnight **Martin Redman & Maurice Thomas**
10 **STORM ARCADIO (IRE)**, 6, b g Arcadio (GER)—Site Missy (IRE) **Mick White & Steve Horsfall**

Other Owners: Mr N. G. Allen, Mr G. Horsfall, Miss L. Horsfall, Mr S. Horsfall, F. R. Jarvey, Mr M. W. Redman, Mr M. H. Thomas, Mr M. E. White.

277	**MR JAMES HORTON, Middleham** Postal: **Garden View, Brecongill, Coverham, Leyburn, Yorkshire, DL8 4TJ** Contacts: **WORK 07810 872778 HOME 01969 640416** EMAIL jameshorton56.jh@gmail.com

1 **ASJAD**, 4, b g Iffraaj—Riskit Fora Biskit (IRE) **John & Jessica Dance**
2 **GHOST RIDER (IRE)**, 4, b c Dark Angel (IRE)—Priceless Jewel **John & Jessica Dance**
3 **IL BANDITO (IRE)**, 4, b g Acclamation—Molly Dolly (IRE) **John & Jessica Dance**

THREE-YEAR-OLDS

4 **ENCOURAGEABLE (IRE)**, b c Profitable (IRE)—Dutch Courage **John & Jessica Dance**
5 B c Kingman—Hasten (IRE) **John & Jessica Dance**
6 **PHANTOM FLIGHT**, b c Siyouni (FR)—Qushchi **John & Jessica Dance**
7 **SAM MAXIMUS**, b c Showcasing—Daring Day **John & Jessica Dance**
8 **TOPOMANIA**, b c Siyouni (FR)—Aristocratic Lady (USA) **John & Jessica Dance**

TWO-YEAR-OLDS

9 B f 12/02 Ardad (IRE)—Be My Angel (Dark Angel (IRE)) (190000) **John & Jessica Dance**
10 B c 08/04 Oasis Dream—Beychella (USA) (Scat Daddy (USA)) (140000) **John & Jessica Dance**
11 B f 15/01 No Nay Never (USA)—Broderie Anglaise (IRE) (Galileo (IRE)) (140000) **John & Jessica Dance**
12 B f 24/03 Showcasing—Chibola (ARG) (Roy (USA)) (105000) **John & Jessica Dance**
13 B c 04/05 Cotai Glory—Diamond Finesse (IRE) (Red Clubs (IRE)) (40000) **John & Jessica Dance**
14 B c 19/02 Dark Angel (IRE)—Elusive Beauty (IRE) (Elusive Pimpernel (USA)) (114286) **John & Jessica Dance**
15 B c 14/04 Havana Gold (IRE)—Epatha (IRE) (Highest Honor (FR)) (38095) **John & Jessica Dance**
16 B c 29/02 Showcasing—Flower Fashion (FR) (Flower Alley (USA)) (130000) **John & Jessica Dance**
17 B c 12/04 Siyouni (FR)—Fusion (IRE) (Cape Cross (IRE)) (200000) **John & Jessica Dance**
18 B c 26/02 Invincible Spirit (IRE)—Jolyne (Makfi) (85000) **John & Jessica Dance**
19 Ch f 06/03 Sea The Stars (IRE)—Mambo Light (USA) (Kingmambo (USA)) (300000) **John & Jessica Dance**
20 B c 04/04 Kodiac—Milana (FR) (Mark of Esteem (IRE)) (120000) **John & Jessica Dance**
21 Br c 26/03 Sea The Stars (IRE)—My Spirit (IRE) (Invincible Spirit (IRE)) (178571) **John & Jessica Dance**
22 B br f 06/03 Dubawi (IRE)—Peace In Motion (USA) (Hat Trick (JPN)) (400000) **John & Jessica Dance**
23 B c 17/02 Dark Angel (IRE)—Relation Alexander (IRE) (Dandy Man (IRE)) (78095) **John & Jessica Dance**
24 B c 08/03 Churchill (IRE)—Rose Blossom (Pastoral Pursuits) (95000) **John & Jessica Dance**
25 B f 18/01 Starspangledbanner (AUS)—Shannow (IRE) (Pivotal) (57143) **John & Jessica Dance**
26 B c 29/01 Gleneagles (IRE)—Simmie (IRE) (Fast Company (IRE)) (40000) **John & Jessica Dance**
27 B f 27/03 Sea The Stars (IRE)—Sindjara (USA) (Include (USA)) (76531) **John & Jessica Dance**
28 B f 14/02 Bated Breath—Susan Stroman (Monsun (GER)) **John & Jessica Dance**
29 **TOO MUCH**, br f 11/01 Showcasing—Girls Talk (IRE) (Shamardal (USA)) (90476) **John & Jessica Dance**

---

278 MS GEORGIE HOWELL, Tenbury Wells
Postal: **Woodstock bower farm, Broadheath, Tenbury Wells, Worcestershire, WR15 8QN**
Contacts: PHONE 07968 864433
EMAIL georgie@drill-service.co.uk

1 **BLACK LIGHTNING (IRE)**, 9, br g Whitmore's Conn (USA)—Annie May (IRE) **Ms G. P. C. Howell**
2 **CHAIN SMOKER**, 9, ch g Shantou (USA)—Handmemy Moneydown (IRE) **Ms G. P. C. Howell**
3 **MAWLOOD (IRE)**, 6, b g Dawn Approach (IRE)—Kalaatah (USA) **Ms G. P. C. Howell**
4 **MESSAGE TO MARTHA**, 7, b m Milan—Message Personnel (FR) **Ms G. P. C. Howell**
5 **ORNUA (IRE)**, 11, ch g Mahler—Merry Heart (IRE) **Ms G. P. C. Howell**
6 **POLLARDS FEN (IRE)**, 7, ch g Sans Frontieres (IRE)—Shy Sheila (IRE) **Ms G. P. C. Howell**
7 **PUPPET WARRIOR**, 10, ch g Black Sam Bellamy (IRE)—Rakajack **Ms G. P. C. Howell**
8 4, B c Lucarno (USA)—Shropshirelass **Ms G. P. C. Howell**
9 **SUB LIEUTENANT (IRE)**, 13, b g Brian Boru—Satellite Dancer (IRE) **Ms G. P. C. Howell**
10 **TIS BUT A SCRATCH**, 6, br g Passing Glance—Shropshirelass **Ms G. P. C. Howell**
11 **TOAD**, 9, b g Shirocco (GER)—One Gulp **Ms G. P. C. Howell**
12 **YOURHOLIDAYISOVER (IRE)**, 15, ch g Sulamani (IRE)—Whitehaven **Ms G. P. C. Howell**

279 MRS DEBBIE HUGHES, Tonyrefail
Postal: **Tyr Heol Farm, Pantybrad, Tonyrefail, Rhondda, Mid Glamorgan, CF39 8HX**
EMAIL dimots@btinternet.com

1 **BORN TO FROLIC (IRE)**, 7, b g Born To Sea (IRE)—Desert Frolic (IRE) **Mrs D. J. Hughes**
2 **DANCING LILLY**, 7, ch m Sir Percy—Bhima **Mrs D. J. Hughes**
3 9, B m Mount Nelson—Focosa (ITY) **Mrs D. J. Hughes**
4 **GIVEN (IRE)**, 5, b m Ivawood (IRE)—Annacurra (IRE) **Mrs D. J. Hughes**
5 4, Ch f Indian Haven—Jinks And Co **Mrs D. J. Hughes**
6 **LESS OF THAT (IRE)**, 8, b m Canford Cliffs (IRE)—Night Glimmer (IRE) **Mrs D. J. Hughes**
7 **LOVELY ACCLAMATION (IRE)**, 8, b m Acclamation—Titova **Mrs D. J. Hughes**
8 **MAJOR ASSAULT**, 9, b g Kyllachy—Night Premiere (IRE) **Mrs D. J. Hughes**
9 **NATTY DRESSER (IRE)**, 7, b g Dandy Man (IRE)—Parlour **Mrs D. J. Hughes**
10 **PICC AN ANGEL**, 6, b m Piccolo—Bhima **Mrs D. J. Hughes**
11 4, B c Moohaajim (IRE)—Somerset Falls (UAE) **Mrs D. J. Hughes**
12 **STOP N START**, 10, ch m Piccolo—Dim Ots **Mrs D. J. Hughes**
13 **TIME HAS WINGS (IRE)**, 4, b f Moohaajim (IRE)—Rozene (IRE)
14 **WIRRAWAY (USA)**, 6, ch g Australia—Fly Past **Mrs D. J. Hughes**

THREE-YEAR-OLDS

15 B c Mayson—Elysee (IRE) **Mrs D. J. Hughes**
16 B f Mayson—Royal Assent

280 MR RICHARD HUGHES, Upper Lambourn
Postal: **Weathercock House, Upper Lambourn, Hungerford, Berkshire, RG17 8QT**
Contacts: PHONE 01488 71198 MOBILE 07768 894828
EMAIL office@richardhughesracing.co.uk WEBSITE www.richardhughesracing.co.uk

1 **BASCULE (FR)**, 4, ch g Kendargent (FR)—New River (IRE) **The New River Partnership**
2 **BONNIE LAD**, 4, ch c Havana Gold (IRE)—Bonnie Grey **BPC, Taylor & Young**
3 **BRENTFORD HOPE**, 5, b g Camelot—Miss Raven (IRE) **Bernardine & Sean Mulryan**
4 **BRUNEL CHARM**, 5, b g Charm Spirit (IRE)—Manyara **R & S Needham**
5 **BUGLE MAJOR (USA)**, 7, gr g Mizzen Mast (USA)—Conference Call **The Golfers**

MR RICHARD HUGHES - continued

6 **CALLING THE WIND (IRE)**, 6, b g Authorized (IRE)—Al Jasrah (IRE) Mrs J. A. Wakefield
7 **CRIMSON SAND (IRE)**, 4, b g Footstepsinthesand—Crimson Sunrise (IRE) Mrs J. A. Wakefield
8 **KARIBANA (IRE)**, 5, b g Hallowed Crown (AUS)—Queen Wasp (IRE) M Clarke, P Munnelly & D Waters
9 **KATH'S LUSTRE**, 7, b m Dick Turpin (IRE)—It's Dubai Dolly Mr M. M. Cox
10 **KATH'S TOYBOY**, 4, gr g Gregorian (IRE)—It's Dubai Dolly Mr M. M. Cox
11 **MERLIN'S BEARD**, 4, b br g Dark Angel (IRE)—Welsh Cake M. J. Caddy
12 **MISS TIKI**, 4, ch f Zoffany (IRE)—Teeky The Lakota Partnership & Mrs Janie Blake
13 **NELSON GAY (IRE)**, 4, b g Mehmas (IRE)—Rublevka Star (USA) Mr R Gander & Partner
14 **ONE LAST DANCE (IRE)**, 4, b f Camelot—Controversy Mr B. Bailey
15 **PRINCE IMPERIAL (USA)**, 5, b g Frankel—Proportional Highclere T'Bred Racing-Prince Imperial
16 **SCHWARTZ (IRE)**, 4, b g Kodiac—Easy Times Mr A. G. Smith
17 **SUNSET IN PARIS (IRE)**, 4, b g Camelot—Trail of Tears (IRE) Bernardine & Sean Mulryan
18 **TO THE BAR (IRE)**, 4, ch g Tamayuz—Coachhouse Lady (USA) J. Alharbi
19 **TOP BREEZE (IRE)**, 6, b g Gale Force Ten—Shamarlane Life's A Breeze
20 **TYNWALD**, 4, b g Toronado (IRE)—Queen's Prize Mr Richard Hughes

THREE-YEAR-OLDS

21 **APACHE GREY (IRE)**, gr g El Kabeir (USA)—Laurelita (IRE) K Lawrence, P Merritt & Mrs J Blake
22 **AUSSIE BANKER**, b c Muhaarar—Aristotelicienne (IRE) Mr P. Cook
23 **BENY NAHAR ROAD (IRE)**, b c Nathaniel (IRE)—Wonder Why (GER) J. Alharbi
24 **BETHERSDEN BOY (IRE)**, b g Excelebration (IRE)—Doctor's Note Rj Rexton & Cd Dickens
26 **BONDI MAN**, ch c Australia—Honorine (IRE) Mr A. Al Mansoori
27 **BRIDES BAY (IRE)**, b f Cable Bay (IRE)—State Anthem Highclere Thoroughbred Racing - Lavender
27 **BRIGANTES WARRIOR**, b c Ribchester (IRE)—Saphira's Fire (IRE) M. J. Caddy
28 **BRILLIANT NEWS (IRE)**, b c Camacho—Belle of The Blues (IRE) The Queens
29 **CAREWELL COVER (IRE)**, b g Footstepsinthesand—Golden Easter (USA) WKH (Hinksey Lane) Ltd
30 **CAVALLUCCIO (IRE)**, br g Caravaggio (USA)—Gale Song Cognition Land & Water & M Clarke
31 **CHIEF WHITE FACE**, ch g Showcasing—Martha Watson (IRE) J. Alharbi
32 **COPPERPLATE**, ch c Nathaniel (IRE)—Rosika Mr J. W. Reed
33 **CRUSH AND RUN (IRE)**, b g Zoffany (IRE)—Mooching Along (IRE) Thames Boys
34 **DASH FOR IT (IRE)**, b g Camacho—Jeewana Mrs Philip Snow & Partners
35 **GOLD MEDAL**, b g Olympic Glory (IRE)—Velvet Revolver (IRE) Chris Kelly Developments Ltd
36 **HAMMOCK**, b f Showcasing—Surcingle (USA) Ms H N Pinniger & Mrs S King
37 **HIGHLAND OBSESSION (IRE)**, b f Highland Reel (IRE)—Infatuation Clarke, Devine, Munnelly A Regan
38 **INCOME (IRE)**, b f Profitable (IRE)—Coolnagree (IRE) Mr Martin Clarke & Partner
39 **INTELLIGENTSIA (IRE)**, ch f Exceed And Excel (AUS)—Discernable Her Majesty The Queen
40 **KIMNGRACE (IRE)**, b f Profitable (IRE)—Estonia P Cook & A Whelan
41 **LADYPACKSAPUNCH**, b f Time Test—Punchy Lady Clarke, Devine, Munnelly A Regan
42 **LION'S DREAM (FR)**, b c Dabirsim (FR)—Full Rose J. Alharbi
43 **LOST OF LOVE**, b c Australia—Nur Jahan (IRE) Mr I. Sze
44 **MARION'S STAR (IRE)**, b f Starspangledbanner (AUS)—Allou Yialou (IRE) Mr R. H. Flower
45 **MEYDAN ROSE (IRE)**, b f Pride of Dubai (AUS)—Gentle Breeze (IRE) J. Alharbi
46 **MORE DIAMONDS (IRE)**, b f Zoffany (IRE)—Pellinore (USA) J. Alharbi
47 **MYRIAD (IRE)**, ch c Cotai Glory—Superabundance (IRE) Mr John Henwood & Partner
48 **MYTHICAL STAR**, b g Starspangledbanner (AUS)—Timeless Gift (IRE) Mrs L. Bailey
49 **NAMJONG BOYS**, b g Kingman—Lacarolina (FR) Mr I. Sze
50 **OLYMPIC DREAM**, b c New Approach (IRE)—Mazuna (IRE) Mr A. Al Mansoori
51 **ONE MORE DREAM**, br c Bated Breath—Gracefilly Mr B. Bailey
52 **RING OF BEARA (FR)**, b c Wootton Bassett—Harem Mistress (IRE) Bernardine & Sean Mulryan
53 **ROSA MYSTICA (IRE)**, b f Mehmas (IRE)—Champagne Aerial (IRE) Gallaghers
54 **SPACE TRACKER (IRE)**, b g Havana Gold (IRE)—Never In (IRE) K. A. Dasmal
55 **TESSY LAD (IRE)**, b g Australia—Maracuja M&O Construction & Civil Engineering Ltd
56 **VILLALOBOS (IRE)**, b g Footstepsinthesand—Swift Acclaim (IRE) L Turland and A Smith
57 **WHOLEOFTHEMOON (IRE)**, b g Zoffany (IRE)—Shared Experience Bernardine & Sean Mulryan
58 **ZERO CARBON (IRE)**, b c Acclamation—Clotilde Cognition Land & Water & M Clarke

TWO-YEAR-OLDS

59 B c 02/04 Holy Roman Emperor (IRE)—Camisole (IRE) (Teofilo (IRE)) (19048) Mr D. A. Thorpe
60 **CANDLE OF HOPE**, br f 08/03 Cable Bay (IRE)—Good Hope (Cape Cross (IRE)) Her Majesty The Queen

MR RICHARD HUGHES - continued

61 B c 01/03 Zoffany (IRE)—Capella's Song (IRE) (Oratorio (IRE)) (55000) **R & K Lawrence**
62 B f 10/04 Havana Gold (IRE)—Chicas Amigas (IRE) (Dragon Pulse (IRE)) (47619) **Mr P. Cook**
63 CINNODIN, b c 03/05 Anodin (IRE)—Cinnilla (Authorized (IRE)) (26000) **Ellipsis li-cinnodin**
64 EDGE OF EMBER, br gr c 15/04 Cracksman—White Wedding (IRE) (Green Desert (USA)) (55000)
Graham Doyle & Hazel Lawrence
65 FICTIONAL (IRE), b c 10/02 Make Believe—Hidden Girl (IRE) (Tamayuz) (80952) **The Dakota Partnership**
66 Ch f 31/03 Fast Company (IRE)—Gaazaal (IRE) (Iffraaj) (19048) **Clay, Gadd & Fleming**
67 Ch c 25/03 Ribchester (IRE)—Joyce Compton (IRE) (Tamayuz) (26667)
68 B c 10/03 Prince of Lir (IRE)—Lost Highway (IRE) (Danehill Dancer (IRE)) (22109)
69 Ch c 24/04 Night of Thunder (IRE)—Mia San Triple (Invincible Spirit (IRE)) (20000) **Sir David Seale**
70 B c 18/03 Kodiac—Millevini (IRE) (Hawk Wing (USA)) (19048) **M. J. Caddy**
71 Ch c 09/02 Ribchester (IRE)—Mirabile Dictu (IRE) (King's Best (USA)) (119048) **Bernardine & Sean Mulryan**
72 NOGO'S DREAM, b c 05/03 Oasis Dream—Morning Chimes (IRE) (Shamardal (USA)) (90000)
Rj Rexton & Cd Dickens
73 Ch f 21/03 Ulysses (IRE)—Piano (Azamour (IRE)) (59048) **The Heffer Syndicate**
74 B c 21/03 Churchill (IRE)—Polly Perkins (IRE) (Pivotal) (85000)
75 REAL GAIN (IRE), b c 27/02 Profitable (IRE)—Real Me (Mark of Esteem (IRE)) (110000)
Clarke, Jeffries, Lawrence & Cox
76 B f 13/03 Havana Gold (IRE)—Rio's Cliffs (Canford Cliffs (IRE)) (35000) **Mr A. Al Mansoori**
77 SATURNALIA (GER), b c 02/04 Holy Roman Emperor (IRE)—Soprana (GER) (Cadeaux Genereux) (15000)
Ms H. N. Pinniger
78 SCHUMANN (IRE), b c 29/04 Dandy Man (IRE)—Bibliotheca (JPN) (Harbinger) (64626)
Highclere T'Bred Racing - Louise Gluck
79 B c 24/02 Tamayuz—Shakdara (USA) (Street Cry (IRE)) (28571) **John McGarry & Richard Hughes**
80 B c 08/03 Awtaad (IRE)—Stereophonic (IRE) (Acclamation) (26667)
81 THE THAMES BOATMAN, b c 19/03 Havana Grey—Gilt Linked (Compton Place) (15000)
The Thames Boatman Racing Partnership

Other Owners: Mr P. W. Bedford, Mrs J. A. Blake, Mr S. Blight, Mr S. Buy, Mr M. Clarke, Miss J. P. Clay, Mr P. Cook, Mr M. M. Cox, Mr R. J. Dellar, J. T. Devine, Mr C. Dickens, Mr G. J. Doyle, Ellipsis II, Mrs D. J. Fleming, Mrs J. Gadd, R. A. Gander, Mr S. A. Geraghty, Mr J. Goddard, Mrs A. J. Hamilton-Fairley, Mr R. Hannon, Mr J. P. Henwood, Mr R. Hosking, Mr Richard Hughes, Mr J. Jeffries, Mrs S. King, Mr R. Lane, Miss H. M. Lawrence, Mr K. Lawrence, Mr E. Malone, Mr J. J. McGarry, Mr P. D. Merritt, Mr M. J. Mitchell, Mrs B. Mulryan, Mr S. Mulryan, Mr P. A. Munnelly, Mr S. Needham, Ms H. N. Pinniger, Mr J. Ramsden, Mr A. Regan, Mr R. J. Rexton, Mr D. W. Rogers, Ms F. E. Rogers, Mr N. S. Scandrett, Mr A. G. Smith, Mr N. Taylor, Mr G. P. Triefus, L. R. Turland, Mr D. S. Waters, Mr A. Whelan, Mrs F. P. Young.

Apprentice Jockey: Tyler Heard, Finley Marsh, George Rooke.

MRS SARAH HUMPHREY, West Wratting
281
Postal: **Yen Hall Farm, West Wratting, Cambridge, Cambridgeshire, CB21 5LP**
Contacts: **PHONE 01223 291445 MOBILE 07798 702484**
EMAIL sarah@yenhallfarm.com WEBSITE www.sarahhumphrey.co.uk

1 BLUE WHISPER, 7, ch g Bated Breath—Vivid Blue **Mrs S. J. Humphrey**
2 4, B f Clovis Du Berlais—Call At Midnight
3 GLIMPSE OF GOLD, 11, b g Passing Glance—Tizzy Blue (IRE) **Yen Hall Farm Racing**
4 GLOIRE D'ATHON (FR), 6, b g Doctor Dino (FR)—Aster d'Athon (FR) **Mrs J. Pitman**
5 GO ON GAL (IRE), 9, b m Approve (IRE)—Jeritza **Yen Hall Farm Racing**
6 IRISH SOVEREIGN (IRE), 7, b g Getaway (GER)—Magdoodle (IRE) **Yen Hall Farm Racing**
7 ITS GONNAHAPPEN (IRE), 6, b g Flemensfirth (USA)—Royal Choice (IRE) **Liz Reid, Mark Howard & Partners**
8 JACKS TOUCH (IRE), 7, b m Jeremy (USA)—Jennys Gem (USA) **The Jack's Touch Partnership**
9 JUST AT MIDNIGHT, 5, b m Pether's Moon (IRE)—Call At Midnight **Mrs S. J. Humphrey**
10 KIERAN'S ANGEL, 4, gr f Nayef (USA)—Silver Lily (IRE) **Silver Lily Bloodstock**

MRS SARAH HUMPHREY - continued

11 **NICKLE BACK (IRE)**, 6, b g Mustameet (USA)—Mill House Girl (IRE) **The Friday Lunch Club**
12 **RAILWAY MUICE (IRE)**, 9, b g Yeats (IRE)—Ar Muin Na Muice (IRE) **Mrs S. J. Humphrey**
13 **REDBRIDGE ROSIE (IRE)**, 5, b m Soldier of Fortune (IRE)—Miss Island (IRE)
14 **VALENCIA BORGET (FR)**, 5, ch m Masked Marvel—Feuille de Route (FR) **Humphreys and Brown Racing**

THREE-YEAR-OLDS

15 Ch f Nayef (USA)—Silver Lily (IRE) **Silver Lily Bloodstock**

Other Owners: Ms L Bell, Dr R. C. Britton, Mr S. Brown, Mrs S. H. Greenlees, Mr M. Howard, Mrs S. J. Humphrey, Mr N. Humphreys, Mr D. F. Nott, Mrs E. Reid, Mrs S. Scobie, Mr G. A. Thomas, Mr J Thomas, Mrs L Thomas.

Assistant Trainer: Mr A. R. Humphrey.

NH Jockey: Sean Bowen, Aidan Coleman, Nick Scholfield. **Conditional Jockey:** Alexander Thorne.

Apprentice Jockey: William Humphrey. **Amateur Jockey:** Jack Wilmot.

---

282   MR MITCHELL HUNT, Bridgwater
Postal: **Barford Stables, Spaxton, Bridgwater, Somerset, TA5 1AF**
Contacts: **PHONE 07540 732460**
EMAIL mitchell.hunt@rocketmail.com

1 **ARMY OF ONE (GER)**, 5, b m Kingston Hill—Auctorita (GER) **Mr L. Robins**
2 **BARFORD DIVA**, 5, b m Kingston Hill—Jaja de Jau **Barford Racing**
3 **CHANKAYA**, 5, ch g Dubawi (IRE)—Splashdown **Barry Silkman & Gary Pascoe**
4 5, B m Ocovango—Derella (IRE) **Familia Venari Syndicate**
5 **IRISH ED**, 4, b g Norse Dancer (IRE)—Dancing Hill
6 **JUST GO FOR IT**, 9, b m Passing Glance—Just Jasmine **Mr S. G. Atkinson**
7 **LETS GO DUTCHESS**, 12, b m Helissio (FR)—Lets Go Dutch **K. Bishop**
8 **MARDOOF (IRE)**, 4, b g Awtaad (IRE)—Yanabeeaa (USA) **Barford Premier**
9 **MINI YEATS (IRE)**, 5, br gr g Yeats (IRE)—Rocapella **Mrs P. A. Hunt**
10 **OPTICALITY**, 4, b f Coach House (IRE)—Panoptic **Mr P. Simmons**
11 **RAYS RABBLE**, 5, b br m Blue Bresil (FR)—Queens Grove **Slabs & Lucan**

Other Owners: G. J. Pascoe, B. Silkman.

---

283   MR KEVIN HUNTER, Natland
Postal: **Larkrigg, Natland, Cumbria, LA9 7QS**
Contacts: **PHONE 015395 60245**

1 **DAVID JOHN**, 11, b g Overbury (IRE)—Molly's Secret **J. K. Hunter**
2 **KINGOFTHECOTSWOLDS (IRE)**, 8, b g Arcadio (GER)—Damoiselle **J. K. Hunter**
3 **RIP ROCKS PADDY OK (IRE)**, 7, b g Rip Van Winkle (IRE)—Marula (IRE) **J. K. Hunter**
4 **THAT'S MY DUBAI (IRE)**, 9, b m Dubai Destination (USA)—Musical Accord (IRE) **J. K. Hunter**

284 MISS LAURA HURLEY, Tiverton
Postal: **Ringstone Stables, Oakford, Tiverton, Devon, EX16 9EU**
Contacts: **MOBILE 07999 693322**
EMAIL **lauramhurley@hotmail.com**

1 **BANG ON (IRE)**, 9, ch g Fracas (IRE)—Carramanagh Lady (IRE) **Mrs R. E. Hurley**
2 **BRIGHT FOCUS**, 4, b g Telescope (IRE)—Azione **Mrs R. E. Hurley**
3 **BROUGHTONS RHYTHM**, 13, b g Araafa (IRE)—Broughton Singer (IRE) **Mrs R. E. Hurley**
4 **CANDYMAN CAN (IRE)**, 12, b g Holy Roman Emperor (IRE)—Palwina (FR) **Mrs R. E. Hurley**
5 **CAPTAIN PUGWASH (IRE)**, 8, b g Sir Prancealot (IRE)—Liscoa (IRE) **Mrs R. E. Hurley**
6 **CATCHIN TIME (IRE)**, 14, b g Chineur (FR)—Lady Dane (IRE) **Mrs R. E. Hurley**
7 **DEEP INFERNO (IRE)**, 6, b br g Flemensfirth (USA)—Waist Deep (IRE) **Mr M. Tucker**
8 **HEY BUD**, 9, b g Fair Mix (IRE)—Azione **Forever Gold Syndicate**
9 **LADY AMY**, 5, b m Telescope (IRE)—Azione **Mr M. P. P. Brend**
10 **LIGHTNING GOLD**, 7, ch m Black Sam Bellamy (IRE)—Santera (IRE) **Mr P. W. Gillbard**
11 **STANS THE MAN (IRE)**, 5, b g Milan—Strong Roe (IRE) **Having the craic**
12 4, Gr g Kingston Hill—Wednesday Girl (IRE) **Miss E. M. G. Pickard**

285 MR ROGER INGRAM, Epsom
Postal: **Wendover Stables, Burgh Heath Road, Epsom, Surrey, KT17 4LX**
Contacts: **PHONE 01372 749157, 01372 748505**
MOBILE 07773 665980, 07715 993911 FAX 01372 748505
EMAIL **roger.ingram.racing@virgin.net** WEBSITE **www.rogeringramhorseracing.com**

1 **DOUBLE LEGEND (IRE)**, 7, b g Finsceal Fior (IRE)—Damask Rose (IRE) **Mrs Cathy Hallam & Wendover Racing**
2 **FINAL CHOICE**, 9, b g Makfi—Anasazi (IRE) **Mrs S. Ingram**
3 **GIOVANNI TIEPOLO**, 5, b g Lawman (FR)—Leopard Creek **Mr M. F. Cruse**
4 **MISS POLLYANNA (IRE)**, 6, ch m Helmet (AUS)—Ivy Batty (IRE) **Mrs Cathy Hallam & Wendover Racing**
5 **NO SUCH LUCK (IRE)**, 5, b g Tamayuz—Laftah (IRE) **Mr M. F. Cruse**
6 **ONE STEP BEYOND (IRE)**, 5, b g Exceed And Excel (AUS)—Yours Truly (IRE) **Mrs S. Ingram**
7 **SUN FESTIVAL**, 4, b g Toronado (IRE)—Raymi Coya (CAN) **Mrs S. Ingram**

THREE-YEAR-OLDS
8 **IVY ROSIE (IRE)**, b f Iffraaj—Free To Roam (IRE) **Maximum Racing**

Assistant Trainer: Sharon Ingram.

Apprentice Jockey: Rhiain Ingram.

286 MR ANDY IRVINE, East Grinstead
Postal: **Shovelstrode Racing Stables, Homestall Road, Ashurst Wood, East Grinstead, West Sussex, RH19 3PN**
Contacts: **PHONE 07970 839357**
EMAIL **andy01031976@yahoo.co.uk**

1 **BACKINFORGLORY (IRE)**, 6, b m Fame And Glory—Backinthere (IRE) **The Lump Oclock the Secret Circle**
2 **BEAUFORT WEST (IRE)**, 8, b g Getaway (GER)—Blessingindisguise (IRE) **Mr D. Shaw**
3 **BLARNEY BATELEUR (IRE)**, 9, b m Flemensfirth (USA)—Blarney Kestrel (IRE) **Miss S. Searle**
4 **BRANDY CROSS (IRE)**, 8, b g Le Fou (IRE)—Glenquin (IRE) **Surefire Racing**
5 **BROWN BULLET (IRE)**, 7, b m Arcadio (GER)—Barrack Buster **Dan Shaw Simon Clare Andy Irvine**
6 **CLONDAW ROBIN (IRE)**, 9, ch g Robin des Champs (FR)—Old Town Queen (IRE) **The Plum Merchants**
7 **COILLTE EILE (IRE)**, 9, b m Stowaway—Aughwilliam Lady (IRE) **Mr P K & Mrs A J Adams**
8 **DEVIOUS DICKS DAME**, 7, b m Dick Turpin (IRE)—Bridal White **The Secret Circle Racing Club**
9 **ESCAPEFROMALCATRAZ (FR)**, 5, b g Youmzain (IRE)—Waajida **Taylor & O'Dwyer**
10 **FINNEGAN'S GARDEN (IRE)**, 13, b g Definite Article—Tri Folene (FR) **Mr K. Corke**

MR ANDY IRVINE - continued

11 **GODOT (IRE),** 5, ch g Getaway (GER)—La Cerisaie **Taylor & O'Dwyer**
12 **GUSTAV (IRE),** 12, b g Mahler—Pakaradyssa (FR) **The Plum Merchants**
13 **HARRY HAZARD,** 8, b g Schiaparelli (GER)—Eveon (IRE) **Mr A. Lewers**
14 **HESBEHINDYOU (IRE),** 6, b g Curtain Time (IRE)—Veronica's Gift (IRE) **The Plum Merchants**
15 **HONEST OSCAR (IRE),** 7, b m Oscar (IRE)—Honest Chance (FR) **Adrian Lewers the Lump Oclock Syndicate**
16 **KALAKAWA ENKI (FR),** 8, b g Buck's Boum (FR)—Baba San Siro (FR) **Five Star Racing Group**
17 **KING OF THE SHARKS (IRE),** 9, b g Flemensfirth (USA)—Kings Rose (IRE) **Go Faster Syndicate**
18 **MISS GET THE VEUVE,** 4, b f Getaway (GER)—Miss Milborne **Miss S. Searle**
19 **MONTY'S AWARD (IRE),** 10, b g Oscar (IRE)—Montys Miss (IRE) **Jokulhlaup Syndicate**
20 **MR JACK (IRE),** 10, ch g Papal Bull—Miss Barbados (IRE) **Mr R. Dean**
21 **O'RAHILLY (IRE),** 10, b g Aristotle (IRE)—Linoora (IRE) **The Lump Oclock the Secret Circle**
22 **OSCAR ASCHE (IRE),** 8, b g Oscar (IRE)—Boro Supreme (IRE) **Dare To Dream Racing**
23 **SCRUTINISE,** 10, b g Intense Focus (USA)—Tetravella (IRE) **Mrs L. Bowtell**
24 **SILENT PARTNER,** 5, b g Fast Company (IRE)—Peace Lily **Mr A. Dean**
25 **THE REAL JET (IRE),** 6, ch m Jet Away—Stonehouse (IRE) **Bowtell, Shinton, Clare V Lewis**
26 **TRIBESMANS GLORY (IRE),** 8, b g Jeremy (USA)—Benecash (IRE) **Dare To Dream Racing**
27 **WHITLOCK,** 7, ch g Dutch Art—Barynya **Eventmasters Racing**

Other Owners: Mr J. P. M. Bowtell, S. J. Clare, Mrs A. J. Gardiner, Mr P. K. Gardiner, Mr A. J. Irvine, Mr A. Lewers, Mr V. Lewis, Mr D. Shaw, Mr J. D. Shinton, The Lump O'Clock Syndicate, The Secret Circle, Mr A. N. Waters.

---

287 **MR DEAN IVORY, Radlett**
Postal: **Harper Lodge Farm, Harper Lane, Radlett, Hertfordshire, WD7 7HU**
Contacts: **PHONE 01923 855337 MOBILE 07785 118658 FAX 01923 852470**
EMAIL deanivoryracing@gmail.com WEBSITE www.deanivoryracing.co.uk

1 **ADACE,** 4, b f Adaay (IRE)—Marjong **Mr J. L. Marsden**
2 **ADMIRAL'S LAUNCH (IRE),** 4, b g Fastnet Rock (AUS)—Reflective (USA) **Martyn McGuinness & Radlett Racing**
3 **BADENSCOTH,** 8, b g Foxwedge (AUS)—Twice Upon A Time **P. J. Skinner**
4 **BROXI (IRE),** 4, b br g Kodi Bear (IRE)—Own Gift **Heather Yarrow & Lesley Ivory**
5 **CHARMING KID,** 6, b g Charm Spirit (IRE)—Child Bride (USA) **The Cool Silk Partnership**
6 **DANCINGINTHEWOODS,** 5, b g Garswood—Pachanga **Solario Racing (Ashridge)**
7 **DOR'S DIAMOND,** 6, gr g Gregorian (IRE)—Primavera **Mrs D. A. Carter**
8 **DORS TOYBOY (IRE),** 5, gr g Dark Angel (IRE)—Rathaath (IRE) **Mrs D. A. Carter**
9 **FIGHTING TEMERAIRE (IRE),** 9, b g Invincible Spirit (IRE)—Hot Ticket (IRE) **Michael & Heather Yarrow**
10 **HOT CHESNUT,** 4, ch f Camacho—Hot Ticket (IRE) **Heather & Michael Yarrow**
11 **KERRERA,** 9, ch m Champs Elysees—Questa Nova **Mrs G. Thomas**
12 **LAURENTIA (IRE),** 6, b m Iffraaj—Brynica (FR) **B.Edwards & M.Hayes**
13 **LIBRISA BREEZE,** 10, gr g Mount Nelson—Bruxcalina (FR) **Mr A. G. Bloom**
14 **MAMUNIA,** 4, b g Swiss Spirit—Shahrazad (IRE) **Mr L. J. Doolan**
15 **MAZZORBO,** 4, b g Cable Bay (IRE)—Pink Diamond **Dr A. J. F. Gillespie**
16 **MOONLIT CLOUD,** 4, b f Sea The Moon (GER)—Apple Blossom (IRE) **Dr A. J. F. Gillespie**
17 **NEZAR (IRE),** 11, ch g Mastercraftsman (IRE)—Teddy Bears Picnic **Mrs D. A. Carter**
18 **NICKY BABY (IRE),** 8, gr g Dark Angel (IRE)—Moon Club (IRE) **Mrs D. A. Carter**
19 **PLEDGE OF HONOUR,** 6, b g Shamardal (USA)—Lura (USA) **Mr D. K. Ivory**
20 **SOARING SPIRITS (IRE),** 12, ch g Tamayuz—Follow My Lead **Mrs D. A. Carter**
21 **STAKE ACCLAIM (IRE),** 10, b g Acclamation—Golden Legacy (IRE) **Mr M. J. Yarrow**
22 **TROPICS (USA),** 14, ch g Speightstown (USA)—Taj Aire (USA) **Mr D. K. Ivory**
23 **YIMOU (IRE),** 7, b g Kodiac—Heroine Chic (IRE) **K. T. Ivory**

THREE-YEAR-OLDS

24 **LUNA LIGHT (IRE),** b f Highland Reel (IRE)—Moonwise (IRE) **Martyn McGuinness & Radlett Racing**
25 **SHARP DISTINCTION,** ch g Tamayuz—Pin Cushion **Solario Racing (Berkhamsted)**
26 **THE SPOTLIGHT KID,** b g Mayson—Marjong **Mr J. L. Marsden**
27 **THOMAS EQUINAS,** ch g Mayson—Hot Ticket (IRE) **Michael & Heather Yarrow**
28 **TWILIGHT BAY,** b f Twilight Son—Winifred Jo **Solario Racing (Childwickbury)**

MR DEAN IVORY - continued

TWO-YEAR-OLDS
29 B f 02/05 Frankel—Bruxcalina (FR) (Linamix (FR)) (180000) **Michael & Heather Yarrow**
30 B c 13/03 Camacho—Forgotten Wish (IRE) (Lilbourne Lad (IRE))
31 **HAVECHATMA,** b f 21/04 Havana Grey—Marjong (Mount Nelson) **Mr J. L. Marsden**
32 Ch f 14/03 Cracksman—Hot Ticket (IRE) (Selkirk (USA)) **Mr B. & Heather Yarrow**
33 **MOLLY VALENTINE (IRE),** b f 14/02 Tamayuz—Molly Dolly (IRE) (Exceed And Excel (AUS)) (75000)
Heather & Michael Yarrow
34 Ch f 12/02 Bated Breath—Nigh (IRE) (Galileo (IRE)) (52000) **Heather & Michael Yarrow**
35 B f 05/03 Kodiac—Sanna Bay (IRE) (Refuse To Bend (IRE)) (38000) **Michael & Heather Yarrow**

Other Owners: Dean Ivory Racing Ltd, Mr B. S. F. Edwards, Mr M. Hayes, Mr D. K. Ivory, Mrs L. A. Ivory, Mr M. McGuinness, Radlett Racing, Mrs H. Yarrow, Mr M. J. Yarrow.

Assistant Trainer: Chris Scally.

---

288 **MISS TINA JACKSON, Loftus**
Postal: **Tick Hill Farm, Liverton, Loftus, Saltburn, Cleveland, TS13 4TG**
Contacts: **PHONE 01287 644952 MOBILE 07774 106906**

1 **BLACK OPIUM,** 8, b m Black Sam Bellamy (IRE)—Fragrant Rose **Mr H. L. Thompson**
2 **CUSTODIAN (IRE),** 5, b h Muhaarar—Zuhoor Baynoona (IRE) **Mr H. L. Thompson**
3 **ELISHEVA (IRE),** 4, ch f Camacho—Smoken Rosa (USA) **Mr H. L. Thompson**
4 **ENAMAY,** 4, b f Lethal Force (IRE)—Postulant **Mr H. L. Thompson**
5 **IVORS INVOLVEMENT (IRE),** 10, b g Amadeus Wolf—Summer Spice (IRE) **Mr H. L. Thompson**
6 **JAMIH,** 7, ch g Intello (GER)—Hannda (IRE) **Mr H. L. Thompson**
7 **JAMIL (IRE),** 7, b g Dansili—Havant **Mr H. L. Thompson**
8 **JAN DE HEEM,** 12, ch g Dutch Art—Shasta **Miss T. Jackson**
9 **MADAM SCULLY,** 9, ch m Flying Legend (USA)—Sally Scally **Mr H. L. Thompson**
10 **MISTER SMARTY,** 5, ch g Black Sam Bellamy (IRE)—Miss Sunflower **Mr H. L. Thompson**
11 **POINT OF WOODS,** 9, b g Showcasing—Romantic Myth **Mr H. L. Thompson**
12 **PURPLE HARRY,** 14, gr g Sir Harry Lewis (USA)—Ellfiedick **Mr H. L. Thompson**
13 **ROSY RYAN (IRE),** 12, b m Tagula (IRE)—Khaydariya (IRE) **Mr H. L. Thompson**
14 **SNITCH (IRE),** 8, b g Witness Box (USA)—Kind Oscar (IRE) **Mr H. L. Thompson**
15 **THOMAS CRANMER (USA),** 8, b g Hard Spun (USA)—House of Grace (USA) **Mr H. L. Thompson**
16 **WALLACE,** 9, gr m Fair Mix (IRE)—Winnie Wild **Miss T. Jackson**
17 **WESTERN WOLF,** 6, b g Westerner—Winnie Wild **Miss T. Jackson**
18 **YOUNOSO,** 11, b g Alflora (IRE)—Teeno Nell **Mr H. L. Thompson**

TWO-YEAR-OLDS
19 B f 28/02 Equiano (FR)—Bendis (GER) (Danehill (USA)) (13000) **Mr H. L. Thompson**

---

289 **MR BEN JAMES, Whitcombe**
Postal: **Whitcombe Monymusk Racing Stables, Whitcombe, Dorchester, Dorset, DT2 8NY**
Contacts: **PHONE 07707 748528**
EMAIL bendavidjames@outlook.com

1 **STILETTO,** 4, b g Frankel—High Heeled (IRE) **Mrs M. A. Crook**
2 **VITALLINE,** 4, b g Due Diligence (USA)—Vitta's Touch (USA) **Mrs M. A. Crook**

THREE-YEAR-OLDS
3 **PETITE JOE,** b g Champs Elysees—Pilcomayo (IRE) **Mrs M. A. Crook**
4 **WHITCOMBE ROCKSTAR,** b g Footstepsinthesand—Roshina (IRE) **Mrs M. A. Crook**

290	**MISS HANNAH JAMES, Malvern**

Postal: **The Merries Farm, Rye Street, Birtsmorton, Malvern, Worcestershire, WR13 6AS**

1 **BATCH ME**, 6, b m Native Ruler—Bach Me (IRE) **Miss H. L. James**
2 **EMMAS DILEMMA (IRE)**, 10, b m Gold Well—Emmas Island (IRE) **Miss H. L. James**
3 **JUNIOR MASSINI**, 7, b g Dr Massini (IRE)—Bach Me (IRE) **Miss H. L. James**
4 **MEGASCOPE**, 5, b g Telescope (IRE)—Megan Mint **Miss H. L. James**
5 **MINNEIGH MOZZE (FR)**, 6, gr m Phoenix Reach (IRE)—Mickie **Miss H. L. James**
6 **POLYPUTTHEKETTLEON**, 8, b m Arvico (FR)—Sainte Kadette (FR) **Miss H. L. James**
7 **SPROGZILLA**, 13, gr m Fair Mix (IRE)—Gentle Approach **Miss H. L. James**

291	**MR LEE JAMES, Malton**

Postal: **Cheesecake Hill Stables, Norton, Malton, North Yorkshire, YO17 9PJ**
Contacts: **PHONE 01653 699466 MOBILE 07732 556322**

1 **JACKMAN**, 8, gr g Aussie Rules (USA)—Fit To Burst **Mr Ian Johnson & Partner**

Other Owners: Mr I Johnson, Mrs C. Lloyd James.

Assistant Trainer: Carol James.

292	**MR IAIN JARDINE, Carrutherstown**

Postal: **Hetlandhill Farms, Carrutherstown, Dumfries, Dumfriesshire, DG1 4JX**
Contacts: **PHONE 01387 840347 MOBILE 07738 351232**
WORK EMAIL office@iainjardineracing.com WEBSITE www.iainjardineracing.com

1 **ABOLISH**, 6, b g Sepoy (AUS)—Striking Choice (USA) **Lycett Racing Ltd**
2 **AFTER JOHN**, 6, b g Dutch Art—Rosacara **Lady Jouse Partnership**
3 **ANIMORE**, 9, b m Sulamani (IRE)—More Likely **Mrs A. F. Tullie**
4 **BLOW BY BLOW (IRE)**, 11, ch g Robin des Champs (FR)—Shean Rose (IRE) **The Strattonites**
5 **BULLS AYE (IRE)**, 4, ch g Intello (GER)—Wo de Xin **Mr G. R. McGladery**
6 **CALL ME HARRY (IRE)**, 5, b g Make Believe—Lake Moon **D & D Armstrong Ltd & Mr L Westwood**
7 **COOL MIX**, 10, gr g Fair Mix (IRE)—Lucylou (IRE) **D&D Armstrong Limited**
8 **CRYSTAL GUARD (IRE)**, 4, b g Lope de Vega (IRE)—Crystal Melody **R. A. Green**
9 **DINO BOY (FR)**, 9, b g Diamond Boy (FR)—Odeline (FR) **R. A. Green**
10 **DUNGEON BROOK**, 6, b g Black Sam Bellamy (IRE)—Millie N Aire **M. R. Johnson**
11 **DUNNET HEAD (IRE)**, 4, b g Sholokhov (IRE)—Champagne Ruby (IRE) **R. A. Green**
12 **EQUIDAE**, 7, ch h Equiano (FR)—Dularame (IRE) **Mr I. Jardine**
13 **EXCELCIUS (USA)**, 6, b g Exceed And Excel (AUS)—Crying Shame (USA) **Mr G. R. McGladery**
14 **EXIT TO WHERE (FR)**, 8, b r Kapgarde (FR)—Rapsodie Sea (FR) **R. A. Green**
15 **GOLD DES BOIS (FR)**, 8, ch g Full of Gold (FR)—Equatoriale (FR) **R. A. Green**
16 **HAVANA PARTY**, 4, ch g Havana Gold (FR)—Ferayha (IRE) **Let's Be Lucky Racing 27**
17 **HAVEYOUMISSEDME**, 4, b g Helmet (AUS)—Haydn's Lass **Lycett Racing Ltd & Mr I Jardine**
18 **INNSE GALL**, 4, b g Toronado (IRE)—Reaf **C. H. McGhie**
19 **JUMP THE GUN (IRE)**, 5, b g Make Believe—Sound of Guns **Let's Be Lucky Racing 26**
20 **KATS BOB**, 4, ch g Bobby's Kitten (USA)—Dreaming of Stella (IRE) **Colin Dorman & Tommy Dorman**
21 **KAVANAGHS CROSS (IRE)**, 7, b g Califet (FR)—Mugs In Milan (IRE) **K Jardine R Griffiths**
22 **LASTOFTHECOSMICS**, 7, b g Shirocco (GER)—Cosmic Case **The Cosmic Cases**
23 **LITTLE BY LITTLE**, 4, ch f Sixties Icon—Steppe By Steppe **The Duchess of Sutherland**
24 **MERRICOURT (IRE)**, 6, gr g Mizzen Mast (USA)—Elite **Mr A. McLuckie**
25 **MUTAWAARID**, 4, br g Dawn Approach (IRE)—Murahana (IRE) **Mr Kenneth MacPherson**
26 **NEW DELHI EXPRESS (IRE)**, 6, ch g Leading Light (IRE)—O What A Girl (IRE) **Jardine & Shannon**
27 **OOT MA WAY (FR)**, 4, b f Power—Olivia (IRE) **Iain Jardine Racing Club**
28 **PARAMARIBO (IRE)**, 4, b g Sea The Moon (GER)—Homepage **C. H. McGhie**
29 **PEARL WARRIOR**, 6, ch g Dunaden (FR)—Pure Speculation **Owners Group 079**

MR IAIN JARDINE - continued

30 **PURE SURF (IRE),** 6, ch m Frammassone (IRE)—Eventide **Mr I. Jardine**
31 **PUSH FOR SIXTY,** 4, bl g Sixties Icon—Push Me (IRE) **Alex & Janet Card**
32 **RAINS OF CASTAMERE,** 5, ch g Harbour Watch (IRE)—Shrimpton **Mrs W. Duffus**
33 **RAVENSCRAIG CASTLE,** 4, gr g Nathaniel (IRE)—In The Soup (USA) **Castle Racing Scotland**
34 **ROAN,** 6, gr ro g Black Sam Bellamy (IRE)—I Got Rhythm **D&D Armstrong Limited**
35 5, B g Dylan Thomas (IRE)—See More Marbles
36 **SHE'SASUPERMACK (IRE),** 9, b m Arakan (USA)—Castleknock (IRE) **Mrs C Brown & Mr Michael Wares**
37 **SIMPLE STAR (IRE),** 4, b g Sea The Stars (IRE)—Simple Elegance (USA) **Mrs D. M. Monteith**
38 **SIR CHESTER (IRE),** 5, ch g Frammassone (IRE)—Knotty Ash Girl (IRE) **Twenty To One**
39 **SLEIGHT,** 4, b g Showcasing—Magic (IRE) **Bruce & Susan Jones**
40 **SMART LASS (IRE),** 7, b m Casamento (IRE)—Smart Ass (IRE) **Mr G. R. McGladery**
41 **STAR,** 6, ch g Black Sam Bellamy (IRE)—Ballinargh Girl (IRE) **M. R. Johnson**
42 **THE DELRAY MUNKY,** 10, b m Overbury (IRE)—Delray Beach (FR) **The Twelve Munkys**
43 **THE GLOAMING (IRE),** 4, gr f Gutaifan (IRE)—On High **The Strattonites**
44 **TOKARAMORE,** 10, b m Sulamani (IRE)—More Likely **Mr F. McClung**
45 **TOSHACK (IRE),** 4, b gr f Dark Angel (IRE)—Lady Katanga **Iain Jardine Racing Club**
46 **TRICORN (IRE),** 8, b g Helmet (AUS)—Special Dancer **Lady O'Reilly, J P Hames & T Dorman**
47 **VOIX DU REVE (FR),** 10, br g Voix du Nord (FR)—Pommbelle (FR) **D & D Armstrong Ltd & Mr L Westwood**
48 **WEATHER FRONT (USA),** 9, ch g Stormy Atlantic (USA)—Kiswahili **Mr Ken Eales & Self Preservation Society**
49 **WOTSMYNAME (IRE),** 5, ch g Famous Name—Nadeems Stella (IRE) **K Jardine R Griffiths S Greig**
50 **ZUMAATY (IRE),** 4, b g Tamayuz—Blackangelheart (IRE) **Let's Be Lucky Racing 34**
51 **ZURAIG,** 4, gr g Teofilo (IRE)—Dakatari (FR) **The Cricketers**

THREE-YEAR-OLDS

52 **ABBIE POWER (IRE),** b f Bungle Inthejungle—Lady's Locket (IRE) **Mr S. Fyffe**
53 **BEST CHECKER,** b g Due Diligence (USA)—Porthgwidden Beach (USA) **Mr G. R. McGladery**
54 **CARNIVAL TIMES,** ch f Time Test—Gypsy Carnival **The Duchess of Sutherland**
55 **DAJARUS,** b f Holy Roman Emperor (IRE)—Music Lesson **The Strattonites**
56 B g The Last Lion (IRE)—Duchess Dora (IRE) **Mr J. Fyffe**
57 B c Swiss Spirit—Flylowflylong (IRE) **The Strattonites**
58 **GURKHALI GIRL (IRE),** b f The Gurkha (IRE)—Ardbrae Lady **The Duchess of Sutherland**
59 **HOPEDALE,** b f Vadamos (FR)—Milldale **The Duchess of Sutherland**
60 Gr f Mastercraftsman (IRE)—In The Soup (USA)
61 **JKR COBBLER (IRE),** b c Awtaad (IRE)—Lady Vyrnwy (IRE) **Mr I. Jardine**
62 Ch f Highland Reel (IRE)—Marilyn (GER)
63 **MATTI (IRE),** b f Dragon Pulse (IRE)—Paradwys (IRE) **Mrs J. M. MacPherson**
64 **MINTNTHAT,** b g Lawman (FR)—Dream Dancing (IRE) **Mr I. Jardine**
65 **MONICA,** b f Havana Gold (IRE)—Littlemisssunshine (IRE) **Mrs J. M. MacPherson**
66 **NOVAK,** gr g Mastercraftsman (IRE)—Parknasilla (IRE) **Mrs F. E. Mitchell**
67 **SHOWMEDEMONEY (IRE),** b g Divine Prophet (AUS)—Escapism (IRE) **Cool Jazz**
68 **ST ANDREW'S CASTLE,** b c Iffraaj—Age of Chivalry (IRE) **Iain Jardine Racing Club**
69 Ch g Mastercraftsman (IRE)—Steal The Show (AU)
70 **THE GAY BLADE,** b g Mazameer (IRE)—Big Mystery (IRE) **Musselburgh Lunch Club**
71 **VAMOS CHICA (IRE),** b f Vadamos (FR)—Krynica (USA) **Let's Be Lucky Racing 32**

TWO-YEAR-OLDS

72 B f 10/01 Sioux Nation (USA)—Cmonbabylitemyfire (IRE) (Piccolo) (23810)
73 **SUTUE ALSHAMS (IRE),** b c 31/03 Golden Horn—Gile Na Greine (IRE) (Galileo (IRE)) **Mr I. C. Jones**

Other Owners: Mrs C. Brown, D&D Armstrong Limited, Mr M. Dolder, Mr C. Dorman, Mr T. M. Dorman, Mr K. F. Eales, K. R. Elliott, Mr G. G. Friel, Mr R. J. Goodfellow, Mr S. Greig, Mr R. M. Griffiths, J. P. Hames, Mr A. Hynd, Mr I. Jardine, Mr K. Jardine, Mr B. Jones, Mr I. C. Jones, Mrs S. Jones, K Jardine R Griffiths, Lycett Racing Ltd, Mr G. R. McGladery, Mr B. Melrose, Lady C. J. O'Reilly, Mr N. Shannon, The Self Preservation Society, Mr G. T. Wallace, Mr M. P. Wares, Mr L. J. Westwood, Mr T. J. Whiting.

Head Man: Robert Stevenson.

Flat Jockey: Jamie Gormley. **NH Jockey:** Conor O'Farrell. **Apprentice Jockey:** Shannon Watts.

293 MR WILLIAM JARVIS, Newmarket
Postal: **Phantom House Stables, Fordham Road, Newmarket, Suffolk, CB8 7AA**
Contacts: **HOME 01638 662677 PHONE 01638 669873 MOBILE 07836 261884 FAX 01638 667328**
EMAIL **mail@williamjarvis.com** WEBSITE **www.williamjarvis.com**

1. **ARQOOB (IRE)**, 4, b g Estidhkaar (IRE)—Via Ballycroy (IRE) **Little Staughton Farms Ltd**
2. **BEAUTY CHOICE**, 5, b g Bated Breath—Modesty's Way (USA) **Mr D. H. Batten**
3. **DUKE OF VERONA (IRE)**, 4, gr g Belardo (IRE)—Somewhere (IRE) **R. C. C. Villers**
4. **FLAGGED**, 4, ch f Starspangledbanner (AUS)—Grasped **Rathordan Partnership**
5. **NATALIE ROSE**, 5, b m Zoffany (IRE)—Gala Rose **M. G. H. Heald**
6. **SENDACARD**, 5, br m Showcasing—Valentine Glory **The Raceology Partnership**
7. **SERAPHINITE (IRE)**, 5, gr m Gutaifan (IRE)—Ellasha **The Raceology Partnership**

THREE-YEAR-OLDS
8. **BULLEIT**, ch g Helmet (AUS)—Flora Medici **The Raceology Partnership**
9. **CONNIE'S ROSE**, b f Adaay (IRE)—Sing So Sweetly **The Phantom House Partnership**
10. **DR BRERETON (IRE)**, ch f Dawn Approach (IRE)—Back In The Frame **The Raceology Partnership**
11. **GLEN ETIVE**, b g Exceed And Excel (AUS)—Betty Loch **P. C. J. Dalby & R. D. Schuster**
12. **GLOBEMASTER (IRE)**, b c Acclamation—Katchy Lady **The Phantom House Partnership**
13. **HUMAAM (USA)**, b c Kitten's Joy (USA)—Uniformly Yours (CAN) **Little Staughton Farms Ltd**
14. **LEAPING LENA**, b f Caravaggio (USA)—Lauren Louise **Hot To Trot Racing 2**
15. B f Camelot—Lucht Na Gaeilge (IRE) **Ms E. L. Banks**
16. **SPY GAME (IRE)**, b br f Awtaad (IRE)—Soul Mountain (IRE) **The Raceology Partnership**
17. **WEDDING PLANNER**, ch f Cityscape—Speech **The Raceology Partnership**

TWO-YEAR-OLDS
18. B f 02/03 Oasis Dream—Anzac (IRE) (Shamardal (USA)) (28000) **Partnership 2**
19. B c 28/03 Nathaniel (IRE)—Lanita (GER) (Anabaa (USA)) (45000) **Partnership 1**
20. **LAWMAKER**, gr c 04/02 Mastercraftsman (IRE)—Zacchera (Zamindar (USA)) (52000) **The Raceology Partnership**
21. B f 02/02 Dark Angel (IRE)—Mrs Gallagher (Oasis Dream) **Ms E. L. Banks**
22. **OUT RULE (IRE)**, br c 14/04 Karakontie (JPN)—Leaf Blower (USA) (Hat Trick (JPN)) (32000)
   The Raceology Partnership
23. **PEMBROKESHIRE**, b c 30/01 Iffraaj—Gwerrann (Dansili) (28000) **P. C. J. Dalby & R. D. Schuster**
24. B f 09/04 Roaring Lion (USA)—Purr Along (Mount Nelson) (80000) **Ms E. L. Banks**
25. B f 08/04 Bobby's Kitten (USA)—Salome (FR) (Fuisse (FR)) (11000) **Mr Paul Malone**
26. B f 21/04 Cotai Glory—Stylish One (IRE) (Invincible Spirit (IRE)) (20000) **Dr J. Walker**

Other Owners: Mr Colin Bryce, Mr William Davies, Mr Alastair Donald, Mr Tony Foster, Miss Sally E Hall, Mr Diamaid Kelly, Mr Jonathan Law, Mrs Elizabeth Maybury, Mrs Paula Moody, Mr Andrew Muddyman, Mrs Alison Reed, Mr Danny Robinson, Mr Martin Shenfield, Mr James Slade.

Assistant Trainer: James Toller.

---

294 MISS RUTH JEFFERSON, Malton
Postal: **Newstead Stables, Beverley Road, Norton, Malton, North Yorkshire, YO17 9PJ**
Contacts: **PHONE 01653 697225 MOBILE 07976 568152**
WEBSITE **www.ruthjefferson.co.uk**

1. **BALLYWHATSIT (IRE)**, 4, b g Kalanisi (IRE)—Silver Charmer **Drew & Ailsa Russell**
2. **CYRUS KEEP (IRE)**, 9, b g Doyen (IRE)—Overbranch **Ruth Jefferson Racing Club**
3. **EDMOND DANTES (FR)**, 6, b g Walk In The Park (IRE)—Divine Surprise (IRE) **Drew & Ailsa Russell**
4. **FLINT HILL**, 6, ch g Excelebration (IRE)—Modify **Whitelock, Clemitson R Jefferson**
5. **INCA PRINCE (IRE)**, 4, b g Fast Company (IRE)—Angel Stevens (IRE) **Whitelock, Clemitson R Jefferson**
6. **LEMON T**, 9, gr g Sulamani (IRE)—Altogether Now (IRE) **Newstead Racing Partnership**
7. **LUNAR CHIEF**, 4, b g Pether's Moon (IRE)—Oleohneh (IRE) **The Steeple Chasers**
8. **MASTER ALAN**, 7, b g Norse Dancer (IRE)—Overbranch **Mrs I C Straker & Steven Key**
9. **MAURITIAN BOLT (IRE)**, 7, ch g Le Fou (IRE)—Fleeting Arrow (IRE) **Miss N. R. Jefferson**
10. 4, B c Norse Dancer (IRE)—Our Ethel **Miss N. R. Jefferson**
11. **RETRIEVE THE STICK**, 13, b m Revoque (IRE)—Anabranch **Miss N. R. Jefferson**

MISS RUTH JEFFERSON - continued

12 4, B f Mount Nelson—Retrieve The Stick **Miss N. R. Jefferson**
13 ROBYN PUD (IRE), 8, b m Kalanisi (IRE)—Quit The Noise (IRE) **Derek Gennard & Gillian Gennard**
14 SECRET EAGLE, 4, ch g Pearl Secret—Piste **Miss N. R. Jefferson**
15 SIR JIM (IRE), 7, b g Shirocco (GER)—Stick Together **Derek Gennard & Gillian Gennard**
16 SOUNDS RUSSIAN (IRE), 7, b g Sholokhov (IRE)—Reevolesa (IRE) **Claxby & Co**
17 SWITCH PARTNER (IRE), 5, b m Presenting—Almada (FR) **The Switched On Club**
18 TEMPLE MAN, 10, b g Sulamani (IRE)—Altogether Now (IRE) **Mrs I C Straker & Steven Key**

THREE-YEAR-OLDS
19 ROEBUCK BAY, ch f Beat Hollow—Down Ace (IRE) **Miss N. R. Jefferson**
20 SAGONIGE, b f Blue Bresil (FR)—Oleohneh (IRE) **Miss N. R. Jefferson**

TWO-YEAR-OLDS
21 B g 23/04 Norse Dancer (IRE)—Ethelwyn (Alflora (IRE))
22 B g 08/05 Yeats (IRE)—Oleohneh (IRE) (Flemensfirth (USA))

Other Owners: Mrs L. M. Clemitson, D. Gennard, Mrs G. Gennard, Miss N. R. Jefferson, Mr S. Key, Mrs A. Russell, A. J. R. Russell, Mrs R. A. Straker, R. C. Whitelock.

295

MR D. J. JEFFREYS, Evesham
Postal: **Ballards Farm, Hinton-on-the-Green, Evesham, Worcestershire, WR11 2QU**
Contacts: **PHONE 07917 714687**
EMAIL djjeffreys15@hotmail.co.uk

1 AL MUFFRIH (IRE), 7, b g Sea The Stars (IRE)—Scarlet And Gold (IRE) **Mr M. E. Smith**
2 AUGHNACURRA KING (IRE), 9, ch g Tajraasi (USA)—Cracking Kate (IRE) **Mark E Smith & Jaykayjay Pals Ak**
3 AYR OF ELEGANCE, 10, b m Motivator—Gaelic Swan (IRE) **Mrs A. Landale**
4 BEN BRODY (IRE), 12, b g Beneficial—Thethirstyscholars (IRE) **Mark E Smith & the Bb Pony Gang 5**
5 BLOOD EAGLE, 6, b g Sea The Stars (IRE)—Directa Princess (GER) **Mr M. E. Smith**
6 CARDBOARD GANGSTER, 7, gr g Norse Dancer (IRE)—Hiho Silver Lining **Mr M. E. Smith**
7 EMOTIONAL MEMORIES (IRE), 5, b g Arctic Cosmos (USA)—Emotional Melody (IRE)
8 ENEMENEMYNEMO (IRE), 7, b g Lakeshore Road (USA)—Portobello Sunrise (IRE) **Mr M. E. Smith**
9 FLIGHTY BRIDE, 7, b h Bahri (USA)—Flighty Mist **J. R. Jeffreys**
10 GEROLAMO CARDANO, 6, b g Motivator—Dark Quest **Mr M. E. Smith**
11 GETAMAN (IRE), 9, b g Getaway (GER)—Zingarella's Joy (IRE) **Mrs A. Landale**
12 KAYLEN'S MISCHIEF, 9, ch g Doyen (IRE)—Pusey Street Girl **Mr M. E. Smith**
13 KILDIMO (IRE), 7, b br g Stowaway—Beananti (IRE) **Mr M. E. Smith**
14 LAND OF MY DELIGHT (IRE), 6, b g Shantou (USA)—Gurteen Flyer (IRE) **Mr D. Jeffreys**
15 LIVELY CITIZEN (IRE), 7, b g Frammassone (IRE)—Acinorev (IRE) **Mark E Smith,Brake Horse Power Syndicate**
16 LOXLEY LANE, 5, b m Black Sam Bellamy (IRE)—Java Rose
17 MR MANTILLA (IRE), 8, b g Publisher (USA)—Mantilla Madam (IRE) **No Gimmes Partnership**
18 MUSTANG ALPHA (IRE), 7, b g Stowaway—Tupia (FR) **Mrs C. Kendrick**
19 ORDER OF ST JOHN, 5, b g Coach House (IRE)—Gospel Music **Rupert Frost & Ed Shaw**
20 PETRASTAR, 7, b g Passing Glance—Petrarchick (USA) **Mr M. E. Smith**
21 RAKHINE STATE (IRE), 9, b g Arakan (USA)—Oiselina (FR) **Mr Stuart Stanley & Mr Adam Lucock**
22 SIMPLY TRUE (IRE), 5, ch g Camacho—Faussement Simple (IRE) **Mr M. E. Smith**
23 THE GOLD BUG (IRE), 7, b g Shantou (USA)—Eva La Diva (IRE) **Mrs M. Fleming**
24 TOE JEFFREY, 9, b g Sulamani (IRE)—Minouchka (FR) **Mrs P. M. Shirley-Beavan**

Other Owners: Mr A. T. Chatwin, Sr B. J. Collins, Mr R. E. Frost, Mr A. W. Lucock, Mr E. C. F. Shaw, Mr M. E. Smith, Mr S. Stanley, The BB Pony Gang 5, The Brake Horse Power Syndicate, The JayKayJay PALS AK Syndicate.

296 MR J. R. JENKINS, Royston
Postal: **Kings Ride, Therfield Heath, Royston, Hertfordshire, SG8 9NN**
Contacts: **PHONE 01763 241141, 01763 246611 MOBILE 07802 750855 FAX 01763 248223**
EMAIL john@johnjenkinsracing.co.uk WEBSITE www.johnjenkinsracing.co.uk

1 **ACE TIME**, 8, b g Sinndar (IRE)—Desert Run (IRE) **B. S. P. Dowling**
2 **AMAL (IRE)**, 4, b f No Nay Never (USA)—Lundy Island **Crofters Racing Syndicate**
3 **BASHARAT**, 4, br g Bated Breath—Nos Da **Ms A. Juskaite**
4 **BUNGLEDUPINBLUE (IRE)**, 4, b f Bungle Inthejungle—Generous Heart **Mr Q. Khan**
5 **CARMELA SOPRANO**, 4, gr f Hellvelyn—Caramelita **Golden Equinox Racing**
6 **CHARLIE MY BOY (IRE)**, 5, gr g Leading Light (IRE)—Theionlady (IRE) **Mr A. J. Taylor**
7 **CHLOELLIE**, 7, b m Delegator—Caramelita **Mrs V. Bullard**
8 **COMPANY MINX (IRE)**, 5, gr m Fast Company (IRE)—Ice Haven (IRE) **Mrs C. Goddard**
9 **JOE PROUD**, 4, b g Sepoy (AUS)—Irrational **Mrs I. C. Hampson**
10 **MAYKIR**, 6, b g Mayson—Kiruna **Mrs C. Goddard**
11 **PARTY PLANNER**, 5, gr m Mastercraftsman (IRE)—Sweet Sixteen (IRE) **Mrs W. A. Jenkins**
12 **SHERELLA**, 5, b m Delegator—Mediterranean Sea (IRE) **Mrs W. A. Jenkins**
13 **SIR RODNEYREDBLOOD**, 5, ch g Roderic O'Connor (IRE)—Red Blooded Woman (USA) **Mrs C. Goddard**
14 **TELL ELL**, 4, b f Proconsul—Ellcon (IRE) **Mr M. Turner**
15 **TILSWORTH LUKEY**, 9, b g Sixties Icon—Chara **Michael Ng**
16 **TILSWORTH ROSE**, 8, b m Pastoral Pursuits—Pallas **Michael Ng**
17 **TILSWORTH SAMMY**, 7, b g Mount Nelson—Chara **Michael Ng**
18 **TILSWORTH TAIBO**, 5, ch m Coach House (IRE)—Cavallo da Corsa **Michael Ng**
19 **TILSWORTH VALERIE**, 4, b f Cable Bay (IRE)—Cavallo da Corsa **Michael Ng & Valerie Rumley**
20 **ZAHIRAH**, 8, b m Mullionmileanhour (IRE)—Numanthia (IRE) **Mr Humphry Solomons**

THREE-YEAR-OLDS
21 **ARTEMISIA GENTILE (IRE)**, gr f Caravaggio (USA)—Horse Sense (IRE) **Mr T. C. Lines**
22 **BANG ON THE BELL**, b g Heeraat (IRE)—Bella Beguine **Mr M. Turner**
23 **ELF RISING**, ch g Hot Streak (IRE)—Rise **Elf Rising Partnership**
24 **GOOD TO GO**, b g Heeraat (IRE)—Ellcon (IRE) **Mr M. Turner**
25 **ILONA TAMARA (FR)**, b f Pedro The Great (USA)—La Houssay (FR) **Mr T. C. Lines**
26 **TEASYWEASY**, gr g Outstrip—Dangerous Moonlite (IRE) **& Henderson, Mr N. Henderson, Mr J. Henderson**
27 **TILSWORTH JADE**, b f Ardad (IRE)—Ashwell Rose **Michael Ng**
28 **TILSWORTH ONYA TA**, b g Ardad (IRE)—Pallas **Michael Ng**
29 **UPPA TOWEN**, ch g Proconsul—Gib (IRE) **Golden Equinox Racing**

Other Owners: Mrs Veronica Bullard & Mrs Wendy Jenkins, B. S. P. Dowling, Mr M. D. Goldstein, Mrs I. C. Hampson, Mrs W. A. Jenkins, Michael Ng, Mrs V. Rumley, Mr R. Stevens.

297 MR BRETT JOHNSON, Epsom
Postal: **The Durdans Stables, Chalk Lane, Epsom, Surrey, KT18 7AX**
Contacts: **MOBILE 07768 697141**
EMAIL thedurdansstables@googlemail.com WEBSITE www.brjohnsonracing.co.uk

1 **ANISOPTERA (IRE)**, 5, ch m Casamento (IRE)—Dragonera **Tann & Mr N Jarvis**
2 **BEAUTIFUL CROWN**, 4, b g Helmet (AUS)—Bright Halo (IRE) **Mr C. Westley**
3 **DEMBE**, 4, b g Garswood—Disco Ball **Mr A. Gorman**
4 **HERON (USA)**, 8, b g Quality Road—Dreamt **01 Racing Partnership**
5 **KINDERFRAU**, 4, b f Sea The Stars (IRE)—Prussian **Mr R. E. Pain**
6 **MOEL ARTHUR (USA)**, 4, b g Flintshire—Quest To Peak (USA) **Kestonracingclub**
7 **MUSTANG KODI (IRE)**, 4, b g Kodi Bear (IRE)—Modello (IRE) **Kestonracingclub**
8 **RAKEMATIZ**, 8, ch g Pivotal—Regal Velvet **Mr C. Westley**
9 **STOPNSEARCH**, 5, b g War Command (USA)—Secret Suspect **Mr R. E. Pain**
10 **TREPIDATION**, 5, b g Bated Breath—True Pleasure (IRE) **Tann & Mr N Jarvis**
11 **TRUE BELIEF (IRE)**, 6, b g Excelebration (IRE)—It's True (IRE) **Mr C. Westley**

MR BRETT JOHNSON - continued

12 **VIOLET'S LADS (IRE)**, 8, b m Myboycharlie (IRE)—Cape Violet (IRE) **The Savy Group**

THREE-YEAR-OLDS
13 **DAMASCUS FINISH (IRE)**, gr g Markaz (IRE)—Impressive Victory (USA) **Tann & Mr N Jarvis**
14 **FOZZIE BEAR (IRE)**, b g Kodiac—Dabtiyra (IRE) **J. Daniels**
15 **JOANIE'S GIRL**, b f Pearl Secret—Jackline **Only Fools Have Horses**
16 **SURREY TERRITORIES (IRE)**, b g Territories (IRE)—Fasten Up **Mr G. Dixon**

Other Owners: Mr M. Cumins, Mr N. Hale, Mr S. Hills, Mr N. A. Jarvis, Mr G. Peck, Mrs S. Rutherford, Mr G. Tann, Mr B. D. Townsend, Miss L. Wilde.

Assistant Trainer: Vanessa Johnson.

---

298 **MR KENNY JOHNSON, Newcastle Upon Tyne**
Postal: **Grange Farm, Newburn, Newcastle Upon Tyne, Tyne and Wear, NE15 8QA**
Contacts: **PHONE 01388 721813, 0191 267 4464 MOBILE 07774 131121**
EMAIL kennyjohnson68@hotmail.co.uk WEBSITE www.johnsonracing.co.uk

1 **BIG BOLD GOLD (IRE)**, 8, b g Gold Well—Coole Assembly (IRE) **Mr K. Johnson**
2 **BLUEFORTYTWO**, 9, gr g Overbury (IRE)—Celine Message **Mr K. Johnson**
3 **BOBBIE THE DAZZLER (IRE)**, 8, b m Lawman (FR)—Fashion Statement **Johnson Racing /Paul O'Mara**
4 **HIGH SHERIFF (IRE)**, 8, b g Fame And Glory—Morning Legend (IRE) **Kenny Johnson & Mrs K Elliott**
5 **ON WE GO (IRE)**, 9, b m Robin des Pres (FR)—Clan Music (IRE) **Kenny Johnson & Mrs K Elliott**
6 **ONE YEAR OUT**, 5, b g Intrinsic—Politelysed **J. & Kenny Johnson**
7 4, Ch g Intrinsic—Politelysed
8 **SWEET FLORA (IRE)**, 8, b m Arcadio (GER)—Country Flora **Johnson Racing /Paul O'Mara**

Other Owners: Mrs K. Elliott, Mr K. Johnson, Mr J. Lund, Mr P. O'Mara.

Conditional Jockey: Callum Bewley, Tommy Dowson, Kane Yeoman.

---

299 **MISS EVE JOHNSON HOUGHTON, Blewbury**
Postal: **Woodway, Blewbury, Didcot, Oxfordshire, OX11 9EZ**
Contacts: **PHONE 01235 850480 MOBILE 07721 622700 FAX 01235 851045**
EMAIL Eve@JohnsonHoughton.com WEBSITE www.JohnsonHoughton.com

1 **A SHINING MOON (IRE)**, 4, ch g Sea The Moon (GER)—Aliana (GER) **Mrs C. L. Bonner**
2 **ACCIDENTAL AGENT**, 8, b g Delegator—Roodle **Mrs F. M. Johnson Houghton**
3 **ALEZAN**, 5, ch m Dawn Approach (IRE)—Sarinda **Mr M. Middleton-Heath**
4 **DANVILLE**, 4, b g Muhaarar—Faustinatheyounger (IRE) **Viscount Astor**
5 **ENDURING**, 4, b g Coulsty (IRE)—Yearbook **Mr M. Middleton-Heath**
6 **ET TU BRUTE (IRE)**, 4, b g Holy Roman Emperor (IRE)—Xinji (IRE) **G C Stevens & Partner**
7 **FLAME OF FREEDOM (IRE)**, 4, b f Dragon Pulse (IRE)—Catalan (IRE) **Miss E. A. Johnson Houghton**
8 **GRANARY QUEEN (IRE)**, 4, ch f Dragon Pulse (IRE)—Multi Grain **Mrs S Gray, Ian Gray & Mr J Whitworth**
9 **HMS PRESIDENT (IRE)**, 5, b g Excelebration (IRE)—Dance Hall Girl (IRE) **HP Racing HMS President**
10 **HYANNA**, 7, b m Champs Elysees—Highly Spiced **Mr G. C. Vibert**
11 **JUMBY (IRE)**, 4, b c New Bay—Sound of Guns **Anthony Pye-Jeary & David Ian**
12 **KARUOKA**, 4, br f Awtaad (IRE)—Dubai Fashion (IRE) **G. C. Stevens**
13 **LADY ELYSIA**, 6, ch m Champs Elysees—Lost In Lucca **The Nigel Bennett Partnership**
14 **MOUNT OLYMPUS**, 4, b g Olympic Glory (IRE)—Ile Rouge **HP Racing Mount Olympus**
15 **NOBLE MASQUERADE**, 5, b g Sir Percy—Moi Aussi (USA) **HP Racing Noble Masquerade**

MISS EVE JOHNSON HOUGHTON - continued

16 **PERSUASIVE POWERS**, 4, b f Medicean—Antebellum (FR) **Bloomsbury Stud**
17 **PUNCHBOWL FLYER (IRE)**, 5, b g Dream Ahead (USA)—All On Red (IRE) **The Punch Bunch**
18 **SCARLET DRAGON**, 9, b g Sir Percy—Welsh Angel
19 **THE PRINCES POET**, 4, b g Brazen Beau (AUS)—Poesy **HP Racing The Princes Poet**
20 **TIPSY LAIRD**, 4, b g Gleneagles (IRE)—Lady Eclair (IRE) **Mr & Mrs Nicholas Johnston**
21 **UNCLE DICK**, 4, b g Toronado (IRE)—Golden Waters **Eden Racing Club**

THREE-YEAR-OLDS

22 **BASCINET**, ch g Helmet (AUS)—Finale **Miss E. A. Johnson Houghton**
23 **CABINET OF CLOWNS (IRE)**, gr ro g Tamayuz—Silver Games (IRE) **Hon Mrs J. M. The Corbett & Mr Chris Wright**
24 **DOOLILY**, b f Due Diligence (USA)—Peace Lily **Mrs F. M. Johnson Houghton**
25 **DREAMING**, b g Territories (IRE)—Kerry's Dream **Anthony Pye-Jeary & David Ian**
26 **DUE A RUM**, b g Due Diligence (USA)—Rum Swizzle **The Nigel Bennett Partnership**
27 **FLYING SECRET**, b g Showcasing—Secret Sense (USA) **Jacobsconstructionholdings& Mr E Kelly**
28 **GREEK PHILOSOPHER**, b g Gutaifan (IRE)—Edessa (IRE) **The Woodway 20**
29 **GREG THE GREAT**, gr g Gregorian (IRE)—Fantasy Queen **Mrs Z. C. Campbell-Harris**
30 **JADE COUNTRY**, b c Territories (IRE)—Oasis Jade **D. J. Deer**
31 **KING OF THE DANCE (IRE)**, b g Havana Gold (IRE)—Figurante (IRE) **HP Racing King Of The Dance**
32 **LAGUNA VENETA (IRE)**, ch f New Bay—Laviniad (IRE) **Ballylinch Stud**
33 **LOCKSMITH (IRE)**, gr g Mastercraftsman (IRE)—Notion of Beauty **Eden Racing**
34 **MISS METROPOLITAN**, ch f Cityscape—Support Fund (IRE) **The Ascot Colts & Fillies Club**
35 **MONACELLA (IRE)**, b f Churchill (IRE)—Bezique **Aston House Stud**
36 **MYSTERY MONARCH**, b g Aclaim (IRE)—King's Miracle (IRE) **McNamee Hewitt Harding Rice**
37 **NUVOLARI**, b c Time Test—Luang Prabang (IRE) **Mick and Janice Mariscotti**
38 **READYFORANYTHING**, b g Dabirsim (FR)—Lucky Lucrecia (IRE) **Overbury Stallions Ltd**
39 **SHEER ROCKS**, ch c Iffraaj—Paradise Cove **Anthony Pye-Jeary & David Ian**
40 **SUZY'S SHOES**, ch f Nathaniel (IRE)—Wittgenstein (IRE) **Mr M. Middleton-Heath**
41 **TARATARI**, gr c Caravaggio (USA)—Premiere Danseuse **Mr G. J. Owen**

TWO-YEAR-OLDS

42 **ARUMADAAY**, b f 24/04 Adaay (IRE)—Rum Swizzle (Mawatheeq (USA))
43 **BARLEYBROWN**, b c 24/04 Zoustar (AUS)—Shozita (Showcasing) (40000) **Mr S. Barley**
44 **BAULAC**, b c 07/03 Fulbright—Nuptials (USA) (Broken Vow (USA)) **Boanas & Raw**
45 **BELLAZZO (IRE)**, ch c 15/03 Belardo (IRE)—Mujadil Jane (Lethal Force (IRE)) (15238) **Eden Racing IV**
46 **BIG R**, b c 15/02 Cotai Glory—Turugaat (Fantastic Light (USA)) (16000) **The Nigel Bennett Partnership**
47 **BLATANT**, b c 15/02 Brazen Beau (AUS)—Savanne Sauvage (IRE) (Lope de Vega (IRE)) (20000) **The Woodway 20**
48 **BLUELIGHT BAY (IRE)**, b c 08/05 Exceed And Excel (AUS)—Siren's Cove (Sir Percy) (82000)
  Jacobs Construction (Holdings) Limited, & E Harley
49 **BODEGA NIGHTS**, b br f 22/04 Tasleet—Robbie Roo Roo (Kheleyf (USA)) (14000)
  Neil Simpson & Tom Crookenden
50 **BOY BROWNING**, b c 21/01 Brazen Beau (AUS)—Rahaaba (IRE) (Dubawi (IRE)) (15000) **HP Racing Boy Browning**
51 **BUCCABAY (IRE)**, b c 07/04 Saxon Warrior (JPN)—Fifth Commandment (IRE) (Holy Roman Emperor (IRE)) (33333)
  The Buckingham Partnership
52 **BUSSENTO**, b c 27/03 Oasis Dream—Super Saturday (IRE) (Pivotal) (30000) **Mick and Janice Mariscotti**
53 **GOLSPIE**, b c 20/03 Ribchester—Surrey Storm (Montjeu (IRE)) (50000) **Mick and Janice Mariscotti**
54 **GREASED LIGHTNING**, ch c 25/03 Lightning Spear—How High The Sky (IRE) (Danehill Dancer (IRE)) (26000)
  Anthony Pye-Jeary & David Ian
55 **JACKALOPE**, b c 24/04 Sea The Moon (GER)—Nezhenka (With Approval (CAN)) (18000) **T. C. Stewart**
56 B c 02/05 Havana Gold (IRE)—Jalela (Canford Cliffs (IRE)) (30000)
57 **KANOHI BREEZE**, b f 22/03 Expert Eye—Sommesnil (IRE) (King's Best (USA)) (19048) **The Kimber Family**
58 **KINGS PAGEANT**, b c 25/02 Massaat (IRE)—Queens Revenge (Multiplex) (4762) **HP Racing Kings Pageant**
59 Ch c 04/04 Outstrip—Lady Marigold (IRE) (Intense Focus (USA))
60 **LAST CHANCE SALOON (IRE)**, b f 11/04 Mukhadram—Comfort In Sound (USA) (War Front (USA)) **Mr C. N. Wright**
61 B c 09/04 Twilight Son—Light Hearted (Green Desert (USA))
62 Ch f 03/04 Farhh—Lulani (IRE) (Royal Applause) **Mr & Mrs James Blyth Currie**
63 **LUNARSCAPE**, gr f 16/02 Cityscape—Moon Song (Lethal Force (IRE)) **Hunscote Stud Limited**
64 B c 02/04 Lope de Vega (IRE)—Lunesque (IRE) (Azamour (IRE)) (44000) **Anthony Pye-Jeary & David Ian**
65 **PERCY BLAKENEY**, b c 03/03 Sir Percy—Angel's Quest (FR) (Dark Angel) **HP Racing Percy Blakeney**
66 **POPPY FIELD (IRE)**, b f 22/01 James Garfield (IRE)—Coup de Main (IRE) (Oasis Dream) (6000) **The Woodway 20**

MISS EVE JOHNSON HOUGHTON - continued

67 RAGE OF BAMBY (IRE), b f 27/02 Saxon Warrior (JPN)—Rabiosa Fiore (Sakhee's Secret) (29762)
Hot To Trot Racing 1 & Kildaragh Stud

68 Bl ro f 23/04 Charming Thought—Reprieval (FR) (Kendargent (FR))
69 SAILING ON, ch c 02/03 New Approach (IRE)—Prowess (IRE) (Peintre Celebre (USA)) **Mr M H Dixon**
70 STREETS OF GOLD (IRE), b c 19/01 Havana Gold (IRE)—Truly Honoured (Frankel) (25714)
J Allison & G C Stevens

71 WHISTLE AND FLUTE, b c 31/03 Dandy Man (IRE)—Maria Ormani (IRE) (Roderic O'Connor (IRE)) (12381)
The Woodway 20

Other Owners: Mr J. Allison, Mr P. Bentley, Bloomsbury Stud, Mrs A. M. Boanas, Mr P. A. Buckley, Mr H. M. Butler, The Hon Mrs C. Corbett, Mr T. Crookenden, Mr I. J. B. Gray, Mrs S. Gray, Mr R. Harding, J. E. Harley, Mr L. N. Hewitt, Mr D. Ian, Jacobs Construction (Holdings) Limited, Miss E. A. Johnson Houghton, R. F. Johnson Houghton, Mr N. Johnston, Mrs S. Johnston, Mr C. Jones, Mr H. F. Kearns, Mr E. Kelly, Mrs J. M. Mariscotti, Mr M. G. Mariscotti, Mr B. P. McNamee, Mrs J. A. McWilliam, Mr A. J. Pye-Jeary, Mrs H. B. Raw, Mrs E. R. Rice, HP Racing Scarlet Dragon, Mr N. Simpson, G. C. Stevens, Mr J. Whitworth, Mr C. N. Wright.

Assistant Trainer: Georgina Scott.

Apprentice Jockey: Georgia Dobie.

CHARLIE AND MARK JOHNSTON, Middleham
Postal: Johnston Racing Ltd, Kingsley House Racing Stables,
Middleham, Leyburn, Yorkshire, DL8 4PH
Contacts: PHONE 01969 622237
EMAIL info@johnston.racing WEBSITE johnston.racing

1 ALBA ROSE, 4, b f Muhaarar—Reckoning (IRE) **Dr J. Walker**
2 BAILEYS DERBYDAY, 4, b g New Approach (IRE)—Posteritas (USA) **G R Bailey Ltd (Baileys Horse Feeds)**
3 DARK COMPANY (IRE), 4, b g Fast Company (IRE)—Roseraie (IRE) **Johnston Racing Ltd**
4 DUTCH DECOY, 5, ch g Dutch Art—The Terrier **Owners Group 052**
5 ENFRANCHISE (IRE), 4, br f Invincible Spirit (IRE)—Saoirse Abu (USA)
Sheikh Hamdan Bin Mohammed Al Maktoum
6 FAIRMAC, 4, gr g Lethal Force (IRE)—Kenyan Cat **Middleham Park Racing VI**
7 FIRE DANCING, 4, b f Iffraaj—Street Fire (IRE) **Mr Alan Spence**
8 FOREST FALCON (IRE), 4, b g Raven's Pass (USA)—Malmoosa (IRE)
Sheikh Hamdan Bin Mohammed Al Maktoum
9 GOLDEN FLAME (IRE), 4, b c Golden Horn—Flame of Gibraltar (IRE)
Sheikh Hamdan Bin Mohammed Al Maktoum
10 IF YOU DARE, 4, b c Equiano (FR)—Love Action (IRE) **Middleham Park Racing LXXIX**
11 KING'S ADVICE, 8, ch g Frankel—Queen's Logic (IRE) **Kingsley Park 27 - Ready To Run**
12 KINGS PRINCE, 4, b c Kingman—Dynaforce (USA) **Crone Stud Farms Ltd, Johnston Racing Ltd**
13 LIVING GLANCE, 6, b g Camelot—Jazz Girl (IRE) **Barbara & Alick Richmond**
14 LOVE IS GOLDEN (IRE), 4, b c Golden Horn—Holy Moon (IRE) **Crone Stud Farms Ltd**
15 MARCH LAW (IRE), 4, b g Lawman (FR)—Dookus (IRE) **Susan & John Waterworth**
16 MILITARY TWO STEP (FR), 4, gr f Jukebox Jury (IRE)—Step This Way (USA) **Mr C. R. Hirst, D. C. Livingston**
17 NAYEF ROAD (IRE), 6, ch h Galileo (IRE)—Rose Bonheur **M. Obaida**
18 NO FLIES ON ME (FR), 4, b f Bow Creek (IRE)—Cosquillas (IRE) **Johnston Racing Ltd**
19 PILLAR OF HOPE, 4, b g Awtaad (IRE)—Great Hope (IRE) **C. C. Buckley**
20 ROSE OF KILDARE (IRE), 5, b m Make Believe—Cruck Realta **Qatar Racing Limited**
21 SHE GOT THE LOOK (IRE), 4, b f Camelot—Jessie Jane (IRE) **M. W. Graff**
22 SHEM (IRE), 4, b g Kodiac—Noahs Ark (IRE) **Mr R. Walker**
23 SKY DEFENDER, 6, b h Farhh—Al Mahmeyah **Mr H. R. Bin Ghedayer**
24 SOAPY STEVENS, 4, b g Harzand (IRE)—Zubova **Mr J. M. Duggan & Mr S. Brown**
25 STATE OF BLISS (IRE), 4, b g Gleneagles (IRE)—Crystal Valkyrie (IRE) **Barbara & Alick Richmond**
26 SUBJECTIVIST (IRE), 5, b h Teofilo (IRE)—Reckoning (IRE) **Dr J. Walker**
27 THE LAST LION (IRE), 8, b g Choisir (AUS)—Mala Mala (IRE) **John Brown, Megan Dennis & Partner**

CHARLIE AND MARK JOHNSTON - continued

28 **THEMAXWECAN (IRE)**, 6, b g Maxios—Psychometry (FR) **D. C. Livingston**
29 **THUNDEROUS (IRE)**, 5, b g Night of Thunder (IRE)—Souviens Toi **Highclere T'Bred Racing - George Stubbs**
30 **TOP OF THE POPS**, 4, b g Kingman—Whirly Bird **Mr Alan Spence**
31 **TOUSSAROK**, 4, b g Iffraaj—Frangipanni (IRE) **Titanium Racing Club**
32 **TRIBAL ART (IRE)**, 4, b c Farhh—Chaquiras (USA) **Sheikh Hamdan Bin Mohammed Al Maktoum**
33 **VICTORY STAR**, 5, ch g Night of Thunder (IRE)—Oud Metha **Johnston Racing Ltd**
34 **WADACRE GOGO**, 4, b f The Gurkha (IRE)—Glenreef **Wadacre Stud**
35 **WEST END CHARMER (IRE)**, 6, b g Nathaniel (IRE)—Solar Midnight (USA) **Mr M. McHale**

THREE-YEAR-OLDS

36 **ACHNAMARA**, b c Kodiac—Albamara **Johnston Racing Ltd**
37 **AGREEABILITY**, b f Bobby's Kitten (USA)—Moi Aussi (USA) **Miss K. Rausing**
38 **ALLARMISTA**, b f National Defense—Alta Moda **Miss K. Rausing**
39 Ch c Gleneagles (IRE)—Ange Bleu (USA) **Mr N. Y. O. Askar**
40 **APPROACHABILITY**, ch c New Approach (IRE)—Posterity (IRE) **Brian Yeardley & Partner**
41 **ASK PETER (FR)**, b f Jukebox Jury (IRE)—Attima **Johnston Racing Ltd**
42 **AUNTIE MARGARET (FR)**, b f Kendargent (FR)—Dommyah **Mr & Mrs Paul & Clare Rooney**
43 **AUSTRIAN THEORY (IRE)**, b c Awtaad (IRE)—Cedar Sea (IRE) **Dr J. Walker**
44 **BAILEYS ACCOLADE**, b f Aclaim (IRE)—Missisipi Star (IRE) **G R Bailey Ltd (Baileys Horse Feeds)**
45 **BAILEYS LIBERTY**, b f Iffraaj—Baileys Jubilee **G R Bailey Ltd (Baileys Horse Feeds)**
46 **BETTER HALF**, b f Bobby's Kitten (USA)—Beta **Miss K. Rausing**
47 **BIRDIE PUTT (IRE)**, b f Gleneagles (IRE)—Inch Perfect (USA) **N Browne, I Boyce & Partner**
48 **BLOOD ORANGE (IRE)**, ch c New Approach (IRE)—Rosewater (IRE) **Sheikh Hamdan Bin Mohammed Al Maktoum**
49 **BOY ABOUT TOWN**, b c Frankel—Miss Marjurie (IRE) **Susan & John Waterworth**
50 **CABINET MAKER (IRE)**, gr g Mastercraftsman (IRE)—Elegant Peace (IRE) **Kennet Valley Thoroughbreds XII**
51 **CAMPESE**, b g Australia—Dubka **Kingsley Park 21**
52 **CAPITAL THEORY**, b g Muhaarar—Montalcino (IRE) **Dr J. Walker**
53 **CASI CRUDO**, b g Authorized (IRE)—Adalawa (IRE) **M. W. Graff**
54 **CAVENDISH**, ch g Iffraaj—Bess of Hardwick **Kingsley Park 21**
55 **CHOIRMASTER**, ch g Iffraaj—Lamentation **Kingsley Park 20**
56 **DEVASBOY**, gr c Ectot—Belliflore (FR) **Deva Racing (DB)**
57 **DUBAI LEADER**, b c Golden Horn—Zaeema **Sheikh Hamdan Bin Mohammed Al Maktoum**
58 **ENKINDLE**, b g New Approach (IRE)—Enlace **Sheikh Hamdan Bin Mohammed Al Maktoum**
59 **ESPRESSOO**, gr f Dark Angel (IRE)—Elas Diamond **Newsells Park Stud Limited**
60 **ETERNAL GLORY (IRE)**, b f Cotai Glory—Carry On Katie (USA) **Kingsley Park 20**
61 **EXCLUSIVE TIMES**, b f The Gurkha (IRE)—Al Janadeirya **Times Of Wigan Ltd**
62 **FIVE STARS**, b f Sea The Stars (IRE)—Kissable (IRE) **M. W. Graff**
63 **FLAMBOROUGH**, ch g Farhh—Strictly Lambda **The Kingsley Park 25 - The Originals**
64 **FLASH MOB**, b c Siyouni (FR)—Beach Belle **Qatar Racing Ltd & Lady O'Reilly**
65 **GANGWAY (IRE)**, b g Gleneagles (IRE)—An Saincheann (IRE) **Kingsley Park 27 - Ready To Run**
66 **GOLDEN DISC (IRE)**, b c Golden Horn—Mamonta **Crone Stud Farms Ltd**
67 **GOLDEN SANDS (IRE)**, ch g Footstepsinthesand—Varna **HJW Partnership**
68 **GREAT EMPRESS (IRE)**, ch f Teofilo (IRE)—Cite Veron (FR) **AlMohamediya Racing**
69 **HIGHLAND PREMIERE**, b g Highland Reel (IRE)—Forthefirstime **Kingsley Park 26**
70 **I'M A GAMBLER**, b g No Nay Never (USA)—We Are Ninety (USA) **John Brown & Megan Dennis**
71 **INTRIGUING LADY (IRE)**, b f Fascinating Rock (IRE)—Anam Allta (IRE) **Kingsley Park 22**
72 **KNIGHTSWOOD (IRE)**, ch c Decorated Knight—Neuquen (IRE)
73 **LEVITATE (IRE)**, ch c Australia—Aoife Alainn (IRE) **Kingsley Park 20**
74 **LIV LUCKY (IRE)**, b f Profitable (IRE)—Living Art (USA) **Jane Newett & Dougie Livingston**
75 **LOVE DE VEGA (IRE)**, ch c Lope de Vega (IRE)—Ribble (FR) **Crone Stud Farms Ltd**
76 **LUMINOUS LIGHT**, ch c Iffraaj—Perfect Light (IRE) **Sheikh Hamdan Bin Mohammed Al Maktoum**
77 **MACKENZIE ROSE (IRE)**, b f Dark Angel (IRE)—Kelsey Rose **Mrs S. E. Rowett**
78 **MADAME AMBASSADOR**, ch f Churchill (IRE)—Lady Jane Digby **Miss K. Rausing**
79 **MADAME BONBON (FR)**, ch f Iffraaj—Apres Midi (IRE) **C. Bryce**
80 **MAGGIE'S DELIGHT**, gr f Mastercraftsman (IRE)—Motheeba (USA) **Mr & Mrs Paul & Clare Rooney**
81 **MAGNETIC FIELD**, ch f Postponed—Luminous **Sheikh Hamdan Bin Mohammed Al Maktoum**
82 **MARCELO'S WAY (IRE)**, b g War Command (USA)—Assault On Rome (IRE) **Mrs Christine E Budden & Partners**
83 **MISS CONSTRUED (IRE)**, b f Fast Company (IRE)—Fork Handles **Kingsley Park 21**
84 **MY DUBAWI (IRE)**, b g Dubawi (IRE)—Cape Dollar (IRE) **Mr S. Suhail**

CHARLIE AND MARK JOHNSTON - continued

85 **NORDHALLA (IRE)**, ch f Divine Prophet (AUS)—Chellalla **Susan & John Waterworth**
86 **OUTBREAK**, b c Dark Angel (IRE)—Purr Along **Qatar Racing Limited**
87 **OUTSIDE WORLD**, gr f Iffraaj—Nahoodh (IRE) **Sheikh Hamdan Bin Mohammed Al Maktoum**
88 **PONS AELIUS (IRE)**, b c Galileo (IRE)—Laugh Out Loud **Susan & John Waterworth**
89 **QIPAO**, b f Muhaarar—The Gold Cheongsam (IRE) **Chasemore Farm LLP**
90 **RAINBOW COLOURS (IRE)**, b f Dark Angel (IRE)—Rachelle (IRE) **Sheikh Hamdan Bin Mohammed Al Maktoum**
91 **RED KITE (IRE)**, b c Gleneagles (IRE)—Vive Les Rouges **Kingsley Park 22**
92 **ROYAL PATRONAGE (FR)**, b c Wootton Bassett—Shaloushka (IRE) **Highclere T'Bred Racing - Woodland Walk**
93 **RUBY RUBY**, b f Invincible Spirit (IRE)—Elas Ruby **3 Batterhams and a Reay**
94 **SATANIC MOON**, b c Sea The Moon (GER)—Diablerette **The Kingsley Park 25 - The Originals**
95 **SHARP COMBO (IRE)**, b g Bated Breath—Combination (FR) **Kingsley Park 26**
96 **SILVER KITTEN**, ch f Bobby's Kitten (USA)—Argenterie **Kingsley Park 26**
97 **SPIRIT CATCHER (IRE)**, ch c New Bay—Lidanski (IRE) **Titanium Racing Club**
98 **SPY**, b g Muhaarar—Confidential Lady **Kingsley Park 22**
99 **STEPPES (IRE)**, b f Bow Creek (IRE)—Step This Way (USA) **Johnston Racing Ltd**
100 **SUBJECTIVE VALUE**, br g Cable Bay (IRE)—Triton Dance (IRE) **Dr J. Walker**
101 **SUFFRAJET (IRE)**, b f Golden Horn—Liberating **Miss D Finkler, A Herd, Dr P Holloway 1**
102 **SUPER STARS (IRE)**, b c Sea The Stars (IRE)—Valais Girl **Mr M. Doyle**
103 Gr f Showcasing—Sweet Alabama **Middleham Park Racing LIII**
104 **TEMPORIZE**, b g Postponed (IRE)—Party Line **S. R. Counsell**
105 **THE GATEKEEPER (IRE)**, b g Excelebration (IRE)—Cherry Creek (IRE) **Middleham Park Racing XIV**
106 **TIPPY TOES**, b f Havana Gold (IRE)—Mullein **C. Bryce**
107 **TOGAI**, b c Dubawi (IRE)—Danedream (GER) **Mr H. R. Bin Ghedayer**
108 **TROJAN HORSE (IRE)**, ch c Ulysses (IRE)—Guardia (GER) **Mr R. W. Huggins**
109 **TURN BACK TIME**, b f Time Test—Diamond Run **Mascalls Stud**
110 **VALUE THEORY (IRE)**, ch f Gleneagles (IRE)—Venetian Beauty (USA) **Dr J. Walker**
111 **VINTAGE FASHION (IRE)**, b f Iffraaj—Pleasemetoo (IRE) **Sheikh Hamdan Bin Mohammed Al Maktoum**
112 **WADACRE GRACE**, b f Brazen Beau (AUS)—Glenreef **Wadacre Stud**
113 **WADACRE TIR**, ro c Churchill (IRE)—Trip To Glory (FR) **Wadacre Stud**
114 **WHITCLIFFE (IRE)**, gr g Kendargent (FR)—Lady Slippers (IRE) **L. M. Zetland**
115 **WHITEFEATHERSFALL (IRE)**, ch c Zoffany (IRE)—Naomh Geileis (USA) **Mrs Christine E Budden & Partners**
116 B g Exceed And Excel (AUS)—Windsor County (USA) **Sheikh Hamdan Bin Mohammed Al Maktoum**
117 **WORLD WITHOUT LOVE**, ch f Ulysses (IRE)—Reckoning (IRE) **Mascalls Stud**
118 **YORKINDNESS**, b f Nathaniel (IRE)—Yorkidding **Mr P. R. York**
119 **ZESTFUL**, b f Postponed (IRE)—Heart's Content (IRE) **Sheikh Hamdan Bin Mohammed Al Maktoum**

TWO-YEAR-OLDS

120 **A LITTLE RESPECT (IRE)**, ch f 17/02 Sea The Stars (IRE)—Simannka (IRE) (Mastercraftsman (IRE)) (20000)
Susan & John Waterworth
121 Gr c 01/03 Kendargent (FR)—Alma Mater (Sadler's Wells (USA)) (68027) **Kingsley Park 29 - Gold**
122 **ALTA COMEDIA**, b f 09/04 Bobby's Kitten (USA)—Alta Moda (Sadler's Wells (USA)) **Miss K. Rausing**
123 Ch c 28/03 Footstepsinthesand—Antebellum (FR) (Anabaa (USA)) (20000)
Mr George Houghton, Johnston Racing Ltd
124 **ARTISAN DANCER (FR)**, b c 14/05 Mastercraftsman (IRE)—Russiana (IRE) (Red Ransom (USA)) (22109)
The Makyowners
125 B f 05/04 Gustav Klimt (IRE)—Assault On Rome (IRE) (Holy Roman Emperor (IRE))
Mrs Christine E Budden & Partners
126 B f 08/04 Postponed (IRE)—Aviacion (BRZ) (Know Heights (IRE)) (9354) **J. Alharbi**
127 B br f 28/03 No Nay Never (USA)—Belle Isle (Pastoral Pursuits) (127551) **M. C. Sweeney & Partners**
128 **BENACRE (IRE)**, b c 16/04 Australia—Sent From Heaven (IRE) (Footstepsinthesand) (52000)
Susan & John Waterworth
129 **BERWICK LAW (IRE)**, ch f 26/04 Zoffany (IRE)—Standing Rock (IRE) (Fastnet Rock (AUS)) (57823) **Dr J. Walker**
130 **BULLDOG SPIRIT (IRE)**, b c 19/05 Churchill (IRE)—Banimpire (IRE) (Holy Roman Emperor (IRE)) (6667)
Gallop Racing
131 **CAPTAIN POTTER**, b c 28/03 Almanzor (FR)—Astroglia (USA) (Montjeu (IRE)) (32000) **C Team Syndicate**
132 Gr c 15/04 Roaring Lion (USA)—Cascading (Teofilo (IRE)) (56973) **Susan & John Waterworth**
133 Ch c 20/04 Iffraaj—City Glam (ARG) (Grand Reward (USA)) **Sheikh Hamdan Bin Mohammed Al Maktoum**
134 Ch f 15/04 New Approach (IRE)—Concordia (Pivotal) **Sheikh Hamdan Bin Mohammed Al Maktoum**
135 B f 25/03 Zoffany (IRE)—Cornakill (USA) (Stormin Fever (USA)) (9524) **Kingsley Park 30**

CHARLIE AND MARK JOHNSTON - continued

136 B c 03/04 Nathaniel (IRE)—Coyote (Indian Ridge) (60000) **Mr H. Dalmook Al Maktoum**
137 B f 08/03 Roaring Lion (USA)—Dame d'Honneur (IRE) (Teofilo (IRE)) (25510) **J. Alharbi**
138 Ch f 17/02 Cracksman—Dance The Dream (Sir Percy) (57000) **J. Alharbi**
139 Gr c 25/03 Mastercraftsman (IRE)—Desert Haze (New Approach (IRE)) (14456) **Kingsley Park 31**
140 B c 31/03 No Nay Never (USA)—Devoted To You (IRE) (Danehill Dancer (IRE)) (100000) **J. Alharbi**
141 B c 27/04 Starspangledbanner (AUS)—Dingle View (IRE) (Mujadil (USA)) (18707) **Kingsley Park 30**
142 DORNOCH CASTLE (IRE), ch c 27/02 Gleneagles (IRE)—Crown Light (Zamindar (USA)) (25510)
                                                                         John Brown & Megan Dennis
143 B c 04/02 Ribchester (IRE)—Dream Book (Sea The Stars (IRE)) **Sheikh Hamdan Bin Mohammed Al Maktoum**
144 DUBAI MILE (IRE), ch c 20/03 Roaring Lion (USA)—Beach Bunny (IRE) (High Chaparral (IRE)) (17007) **A. Al Shaikh**
145 Ch c 07/05 Pivotal—Dusty Red (Teofilo (IRE)) (38095) **Middleham Park Racing**
146 B f 04/03 Cracksman—Dynaforce (USA) (Dynaformer (USA)) (78000) **Mrs J. E. Newett**
147 Br f 20/04 Shamardal (USA)—Elshaadin (Dalakhani (IRE)) (144558) **Mr C. R. Hirst**
148 B f 15/02 Massaat (IRE)—Endless Night (GER) (Tiger Hill (IRE)) (11429) **J. Alharbi**
149 Ch f 08/03 Postponed (IRE)—Entertainment (Halling (USA)) **Sheikh Hamdan Bin Mohammed Al Maktoum**
150 B f 19/04 Sioux Nation (USA)—Fancy (IRE) (Galileo (IRE)) (34014) **J. Alharbi**
151 B f 10/04 Kingman—Ferevia (Motivator) (51020) **Deva Racing (KM)**
152 FINN'S CHARM, b c 28/03 Kingman—Annabelle's Charm (IRE) (Indian Ridge) (42000) **Dr J. Walker**
153 Gr c 23/01 Sea The Stars (IRE)—Five Fifteen (FR) (Zafeen (FR)) (12755) **Kingsley Park 31**
154 Ch c 01/05 Australia (IRE)—Forces of Darkness (IRE) (Lawman (FR)) (21259) **Kingsley Park 30**
155 B c 29/04 Belardo (IRE)—Fork Handles (Doyen (IRE)) (5102) **J. Alharbi**
156 Ch f 03/05 Bobby's Kitten (USA)—Forthefirstime (Dr Fong (USA)) (9524)
                                                  Around The World Partnership, Johnston Racing Ltd
157 FOX FLAME, b f 19/01 Iffraaj—Street Fire (IRE) (Street Cry (IRE)) **Mr A.D. Spence & Mr & Mrs P.Hargreaves**
158 FRAGRANCE, b f 20/02 Oasis Dream—Bahamadam (Bahamian Bounty) (105000)
                                                  Highclere T'Bred Racing -Albert Einstein
159 B f 11/02 Showcasing—Game Zone (IRE) (Hurricane Run (IRE)) (34014) **Kingsley Park 28 - Gold**
160 B c 19/04 Kingman—Gemstone (IRE) (Galileo (IRE)) (55000) **J. Alharbi**
161 GET STUCK IN (IRE), gr c 26/02 Dark Angel (IRE)—Ultra Appeal (Lawman (FR)) (75000)
                                                  Barbara & Alick Richmond
162 B c 30/04 Siyouni (FR)—Giants Play (USA) (Giant's Causeway (USA)) (90000) **Newsells Park Stud Limited**
163 B f 20/04 Roaring Lion (USA)—Golden Lilac (IRE) (Galileo (IRE)) (72279) **Qatar Racing Limited**
164 GRAIN OF HOPE, b f 10/02 Anodin (IRE)—Grain Only (Machiavellian (USA)) **Miss K. Rausing**
165 Ch f 20/04 Farhh—Great Virtues (IRE) (Teofilo (IRE)) **Sheikh Hamdan Bin Mohammed Al Maktoum**
166 B f 17/04 Oasis Dream—Green Swallow (IRE) (Green Tune (USA)) (30612) **J. Alharbi**
167 HADRIANUS (IRE), b c 08/06 Galileo (IRE)—Laugh Out Loud (Clodovil (IRE)) (62000) **Susan & John Waterworth**
168 HOPE YOU CAN RUN (IRE), ch c 12/04 Lope de Vega (IRE)—Shelbysmile (USA) (Smart Strike (CAN)) (97789)
                                                  Crone Stud Farms Ltd
169 B f 20/04 Hawkbill (USA)—In The Soup (USA) (Alphabet Soup (USA)) **Wadacre Stud**
170 IN THESE SHOES (IRE), ch f 13/03 Starspangledbanner (AUS)—Majenta (IRE) (Marju (IRE)) (20000)
                                                  Barbara & Alick Richmond
171 B c 25/02 Le Havre (IRE)—Jumooh (Monsun (GER)) (55000) **Mr S. Suhail**
172 Gr f 13/02 Decorated Knight—Katch Me Katie (Danehill (USA)) (15306) **J. Alharbi**
173 KHAL (IRE), b c 26/03 Roaring Lion (USA)—Penny Pepper (IRE) (Fast Company (IRE)) (42517)
                                                  Arn Capital & S Counsell
174 KILLYBEGS WARRIOR (IRE), b c 05/02 Saxon Warrior (JPN)—Alltherightmoves (IRE) (Namid) (42517)
                                                  Mr M. Doyle
175 KRONA, b f 20/04 Sea The Moon (GER)—Kwanza (Exchange Rate (USA)) **Miss K. Rausing**
176 Br c 18/01 Acclamation—Lamya (USA) (Choisir (AUS)) **Mr H. A. Lootah**
177 B f 16/03 Churchill (IRE)—Lincoln Rocks (Rock of Gibraltar (IRE)) (30000) **G.P.S. Heart of Racing (Bloodstock) Ltd**
178 Ch c 03/04 Ulysses (IRE)—Local Spirit (USA) (Lion Cavern (USA)) (12000) **Kingsley Park 32 - The Originals**
179 B f 11/02 Oasis Dream—Lomapamar (Nashwan (USA)) **Mascalls Stud**
180 LUDO'S LANDING (IRE), b c 26/03 Kodiac—Most Beautiful (Canford Cliffs (IRE)) (52000)
                                                  Mrs J. Jones, Mr P. Jones
181 MADAM MACHO, ch f 30/04 Camacho—Madam President (Royal Applause) (220000) **Chasemore Farm LLP**
182 B f 20/03 Dark Angel (IRE)—Majestic Jasmine (IRE) (New Approach (IRE)) (68000) **Kingsley Park 29 - Gold**
183 MICKEY MONGOOSE, bc 21/03 Lope de Vega (IRE)—Midnight Crossing (IRE) (Dark Angel (IRE)) (150000) **P. Dean**
184 B c 06/04 Footstepsinthesand—Miss Buckshot (IRE) (Tamayuz) (35000) **Mrs J. E. Newett**
185 Ch c 22/01 Sea The Stars (IRE)—Model (FR) (Mastercraftsman (IRE)) **Mr H. A. Lootah**
186 B c 18/04 Roaring Lion (USA)—Momentus (IRE) (Montjeu (IRE)) (7000) **Qatar Racing Limited**

CHARLIE AND MARK JOHNSTON - continued

187 **MONTEVIDEO (IRE)**, b f 15/04 Teofilo (IRE)—Cherry Creek (IRE) (Montjeu (IRE)) (44218) **Dr J. Walker**
188 **MUIR WOOD**, b c 05/03 Teofilo (IRE)—St Francis Wood (USA) (Irish River (FR)) (60000) **Dr J. Walker**
189 B f 08/02 Golden Horn—My Call (Shamardal (USA)) (20952) **Blue Candi Lab London Ltd**
190 B c 12/04 Caravaggio (USA)—Night Fever (IRE) (Galileo (IRE)) (67000) **S. Ali**
191 Ch f 17/03 Cracksman—Olvia (IRE) (Giant's Causeway (USA)) (25510) **Jane Newett & Dougie Livingston**
192 B f 13/02 New Approach (IRE)—Ouja (Sea The Stars (IRE)) (20000) **Kingsley Park 31**
193 B c 28/01 Exceed And Excel (AUS)—Pabouche (FR) (Dubawi (IRE)) **Sheikh Hamdan Bin Mohammed Al Maktoum**
194 B c 25/04 Postponed (IRE)—Party Line (Montjeu (IRE)) **S. R. Counsell**
195 B c 18/02 Expert Eye—Pontenuovo (FR) (Green Tune (USA)) (30000) **Mr Alan Spence**
196 Ch c 14/02 Ulysses (IRE)—Prominence (Pivotal) **Iain Services & Co Ltd**
197 B f 23/02 Kodiac—Ridge Ranger (IRE) (Bushranger (IRE)) (75000) **Mr C. R. Hirst**
198 Ch c 07/02 Frankel—Scarlett Rose (Royal Applause) (170000) **Mr P. Fitzsimons**
199 B f 15/03 Sioux Nation (USA)—Shemiyla (FR) (Dalakhani (IRE)) (14286) **Gallop Racing**
200 **SIR JOCK BENNETT (IRE)**, b c 03/04 Almanzor (FR)—Biswa (USA) (Kafwain (USA)) (115000) **P. Dean**
201 **SIRONA (GER)**, b f 28/04 Soldier Hollow—Si Luna (GER) (Kallisto (GER)) (44218) **Ms J. E. McGivern**
202 **SMOOTH RYDER (IRE)**, b c 16/02 Smooth Daddy (USA)—Silesie (USA) (Magician (IRE)) (114286) **Mr C. Johnston**
203 Gr c 08/02 U S Navy Flag (USA)—Snowflakes (IRE) (Galileo (IRE)) (51020)

> **Fine Claret Racing, More Turf Racing & Partner**

204 B f 25/03 Kingman—Souvenir Delondres (FR) (Siyouni (FR)) **Christopher Wright**
205 B c 03/02 Dark Angel (IRE)—Spesialta (Indian Ridge) (72279) **J. Alharbi**
206 Gr f 29/03 Dark Angel (IRE)—Spinola (FR) (Spinning World (USA)) (37000)

> **Miss D Finkler, A Herd, Dr P Holloway 1**

207 **STRUTH (IRE)**, ch c 12/03 Australia—Portrait of A Lady (IRE) (Peintre Celebre (USA)) (16190)

> **Mrs S Russell & A M Russell**

208 Gr f 23/01 Showcasing—Syann (IRE) (Daylami (IRE)) (34014) **J. Alharbi**
209 Ch f 25/03 Saxon Warrior (JPN)—Take A Deep Breath (Bated Breath) (40000) **Ahmad Bintooq, Wendy O'Leary**
210 **TENERIFE SUNSHINE**, ch c 07/04 Lope de Vega (IRE)—Yarrow (Sea The Stars (IRE)) (75000)

> **Crone Stud Farms Ltd**

211 B c 29/04 Bungle Inthejungle—Titian Saga (IRE) (Titus Livius (FR)) (72279) **Kingsley Park 28 - Gold**
212 **TROJAN LEGEND**, ch c 22/01 Ulysses (IRE)—Intimation (Dubawi (IRE)) (62000) **Mr R. W. Huggins**
213 B br c 09/02 Churchill (IRE)—True Verdict (IRE) (Danehill Dancer (IRE)) (25000) **Jane Newett & Dougie Livingston**
214 **VENETIAN (IRE)**, b c 29/04 Awtaad (IRE)—Venetian Beauty (Lear Fan (USA)) (30000) **Dr J. Walker**
215 Ch c 26/02 Siyouni (FR)—Vue Fantastique (FR) (Motivator) **Kingsley Park 29 - Gold**
216 Br gr c 21/02 Roaring Lion (USA)—Whirly Bird (Nashwan (USA)) (70000) **Kingsley Park 28 - Gold**
217 Br gr c 13/02 Galileo (IRE)—Wind Chimes (Mastercraftsman (IRE)) (76531) **Mrs J. E. Newett**
218 B c 18/02 Outstrip—Yorkindred Spirit (Sea The Stars (IRE)) **Jane Newett & Dougie Livingston**
219 B c 10/04 Exceed And Excel (AUS)—Zabeel Park (USA) (Medicean) **Sheikh Hamdan Bin Mohammed Al Maktoum**
220 B c 10/03 Iffraaj—Zara (BRZ) (Redattore (BRZ)) **Sheikh Hamdan Bin Mohammed Al Maktoum**

Flat Jockey: Joe Fanning, Franny Norton. **Apprentice Jockey:** Andrew Breslin, Jonny Peate, Oliver Stammers.

---

301 **MR ALAN JONES, Timberscombe**
Postal: **East Harwood Farm, Timberscombe, Minehead, Somerset, TA24 7UE**
Contacts: **MOBILE 07901 505064 FAX 01633 680232**
EMAIL heritageracing@btconnect.com WEBSITE www.alanjonesracing.co.uk

1 **COCARDIER (FR)**, 5, b g My Risk (FR)—Tamaline (FR) **Mr A. E. Jones**
2 4, B g Clovis du Berlais (FR)—Dancing Emily (IRE)
3 **DUHALLOW LAD (IRE)**, 10, b g Papal Bull—Macca Luna (IRE) **Mr A. E. Jones**
4 **GOOD BYE (GER)**, 7, ch g Tertullian (USA)—Guantana (GER) **Some Girls Have All The Luck**
5 **I'M NOTAPARTYGIRL**, 9, b m Arvico (FR)—Lady Shirley Hunt **Mr A. E. Jones**
6 **INGENUITY**, 7, b g Slickly (FR)—Onlyyouknowme (IRE) **Mrs S. D. Barnes**
7 **JACK'S A LEGEND**, 7, b g Midnight Legend—Dancing Emily (IRE) **Burnham Plastering & Drylining Ltd**
8 **LADY AVERY (IRE)**, 10, b m Westerner—Bobs Article (IRE) **Mr A. E. Jones**
9 **LADY EXCALIBUR (IRE)**, 5, b m Camelot—Market Forces **Burnham Plastering & Drylining Ltd**

MR ALAN JONES - continued

10 **MISSMEBUTLETMEGO**, 12, b g With The Flow (USA)—Bay Bianca (IRE)
11 **POKARI (FR)**, 10, ch g Bonbon Rose (FR)—Pokara (FR) **Mr A. E. Jones**
12 5, B h Bollin Eric—Rest And Be (IRE)
13 **STAND BY ME (FR)**, 12, b g Dream Well (FR)—In Love New (FR) **Mr A. E. Jones**
14 **THEHARDERYOUWORK (IRE)**, 5, b m Fame And Glory—Toile d'Auteuil (FR)
15 **US AND THEM (IRE)**, 9, b g Stowaway—Manorville (IRE) **Burnham Plastering & Drylining Ltd**
16 **VETONCALL (IRE)**, 10, b g Well Chosen—Miss Audacious (IRE) **Mr A. E. Jones**

Assistant Trainer: Miss A. Bartelink.

NH Jockey: Paddy Brennan, Tom O'Brien.

MR ADRIAN PAUL KEATLEY, Malton
Postal: **36 The Gallops, Norton, Malton, North Yorkshire, YO17 9JU**
Contacts: **PHONE 07934 903387**

1 **BELVEDERE BLAST (IRE)**, 4, ch g Buratino (IRE)—Zelie Martin (IRE) **Swanland Partnership**
2 **CHAMPAGNE TERRI (IRE)**, 6, b m Elzaam (AUS)—Cresta Rise **Ontoawinner & B Keatley**
3 **DASH OF SPICE (IRE)**, 8, br g Teofilo (IRE)—Dashiba **Ontoawinner, Bainbridge, Bolingbroke**
4 **DRUMCONNOR LAD (IRE)**, 12, b g Winged Love (IRE)—Drumconnor Lady (IRE)
                                                       Mr David Keys & Mrs Breda Keatley
5 **GRANNIE ANNIE (IRE)**, 5, b m Battle of Marengo (IRE)—Cresta Rise **Ontoawinner, Andy Finneran**
6 **KIHAVAH**, 5, ch g Harbour Watch (IRE)—Roheryn (IRE) **JAB**
7 **MONSIEUR POM POM (FR)**, 4, b br g Pomellato (GER)—Mischka (IRE) **Ontoawinner & B Keatley**
8 **ONE PUNCH TERRI**, 4, ch f Mukhadram—Engaging **Ontoawinner & B Keatley**
9 **SHALAA ASKER**, 4, b g Shalaa (IRE)—Miracle Seeker **Ontoawinner, Andy Finneran**
10 **THE MOUSE DOCTOR (IRE)**, 9, b g Lord Shanakill (USA)—Afilla **Here For The Craic**
11 **WOBWOBWOB (IRE)**, 4, b g Prince of Lir (IRE)—Ishimagic **Ontoawinner, Andy Finneran**

THREE-YEAR-OLDS

12 **ALASKAN JEWEL (IRE)**, b f Kodiac—Dutch Destiny **Ontoawinner, Mr&Mrs Bainbridge**
13 **ALLEGHANY (IRE)**, b f Fast Company (IRE)—Virtudes (IRE) **Keatley Racing Owners Group**
14 **ARDAT**, b f Ardad (IRE)—Polly Floyer **Ontoawinner, Andy Finneran**
15 **AYLING**, b g Adaay (IRE)—Loughtownlady (IRE) **Ontoawinner & B Keatley**
16 **BUNGLE BAY (IRE)**, b g Bungle Inthejungle—Jenny's Dancer **Ontoawinner & B Keatley**
17 **CHELSEA ANNIE (IRE)**, b f Mehmas (IRE)—Miss Sally (IRE) **Ontoawinner & B Keatley**
18 **DUNGAR GLORY (IRE)**, ch f Cotai Glory—Independent Girl (IRE) **Ontoawinner & B Keatley**
19 **HA LONG BAY (IRE)**, ch g Mastercraftsman (IRE)—Sou Anguillarina (IRE) **H. M. Hurst**
20 **HAYLEY B (IRE)**, ch f Decorated Knight—Negotiate **Ontoawinner & B Keatley**
21 **ISLADAAY (IRE)**, b f Adaay (IRE)—Sun Angel (IRE) **Ontoawinner & B Keatley**
22 **JEWEL OF KABEIR (IRE)**, b f El Kabeir (USA)—Apple Spirit (USA) **Ontoawinner, Mr&Mrs Bainbridge**
23 **KYBER CRYSTAL (IRE)**, gr f El Kabeir (USA)—Lapis Blue (IRE) **Ontoawinner and O Loughlin**
24 **LOCHSIDE LASS (IRE)**, b f Ribchester (IRE)—Santermete (IRE) **Ontoawinner & B Keatley**
25 **MOONLIGHT DAWN (IRE)**, ch g Dawn Approach (IRE)—Mymoonlightdancer (IRE) **Mr A. Conneally**
26 **OCTOPHOBIA (IRE)**, b f Acclamation—Billie Eria (IRE) **Ontoawinner & B Keatley**
27 **PENELOPEBLUEYES (IRE)**, b f National Defense—City Vaults Girl (IRE) **The Cosy At Home Family And Friends**
28 **TWO SUMMERS (IRE)**, b f Acclamation—Phalaborwa **Ontoawinner & B Keatley**

Other Owners: Mr L. A. Bolingbroke, Mr S. Bridge, Mr J. Doherty, Mr D. Gavigan, Mrs B. Keatley, Mr D. Keys, Mr A. Manson, Mr N. J. O'Brien, Ontoawinner, Mr & Mrs Bainbridge, Mr N. Reilly, Mr A. Sheils.

303 MRS FIONA KEHOE, Leighton Buzzard
Postal: **The Croft Farm, Wing Road, Stewkley, Leighton Buzzard, Bedfordshire, LU7 0JB**
Contacts: **PHONE 07795 096908**
EMAIL f.kehoe@btinternet.com

1 **LADI CHALA (FR)**, 5, b m Golden Horn—Rock Me Baby **M. Kehoe**
2 **SAILED AWAY (GER)**, 4, b g Sea The Moon (GER)—Sail (IRE) **M. Kehoe**

304 MR MARTIN KEIGHLEY, Moreton-In-Marsh
Postal: **Condicote Stables, Luckley, Longborough, Moreton-In-Marsh, Gloucestershire, GL56 0RD**
Contacts: **MOBILE 07767 472547**
EMAIL keighleyracing@btinternet.com WEBSITE www.martinkeighley.com

1 **AMBASSADOR (IRE)**, 5, b g Invincible Spirit (IRE)—Natural Bloom (IRE) **Mr D. Parry**
2 **BACK ON THE LASH**, 8, b g Malinas (GER)—Giovanna **M. Boothright**
3 **BE THANKFUL**, 7, ch m Helmet (AUS)—Be Joyful (IRE) **Martin Keighley Racing Club**
4 **BEN BUIE (IRE)**, 8, br g Presenting—Change of Plan (IRE) **Martin Keighley Racing Partnership 10**
5 **BIG NASTY**, 9, b g Black Sam Bellamy (IRE)—Hello My Lovely **Peel Racing Syndicate**
6 **BLACK PANTHER (IRE)**, 6, br g Nayef (USA)—Amjaad **Mr D. A. Maughan**
7 **BORDERLINE (IRE)**, 4, b g Sans Frontieres (IRE)—Seana Ghael (IRE) **The Four Sages**
8 **BREIZH ALKO (FR)**, 11, ch g Balko (FR)—Quisiera (FR) **Mr D. Parry**
9 **BRIANNA ROSE (IRE)**, 5, ch m Ocovango—Coco Milan (IRE) **Mr M. P. Baker**
10 4, B g Court Cave (IRE)—Bright Blaze (IRE) **Mr D. Parry**
11 **BRORSON (IRE)**, 6, b g Getaway (GER)—Artic Vic (IRE) **Mr D. A. Maughan**
12 **CAPRICIA (IRE)**, 7, b m Mahler—Bobset Leader (IRE) **Martin Keighley Racing Partnership 5**
13 **CARUMBA (IRE)**, 12, b g Gold Well—Sarah Marshall (IRE) **The Stars & Diamonds Racing Club**
14 **CULVERWELL**, 11, b g Midnight Legend—Give Me Strength (IRE) **The Stars & Diamonds Racing Club**
15 **CUT AND RUN**, 9, b m Getaway (GER)—Somethinaboutmolly (IRE) **Martin Keighley Racing Club**
16 **DEBDEN BANK**, 8, b g Cacique (IRE)—Rose Row **Martin Keighley Racing Partnership 6**
17 **DREAMSUNDERMYFEET (IRE)**, 7, br g Yeats (IRE)—Change of Plan (IRE) **Owners for Owners Dreamers**
18 **DUKE OF LUCKLEY (IRE)**, 5, b g Mahler—Emily's Princess (IRE) **Owners for Owners Duke Of Luckley**
19 **ENFORCEMENT (IRE)**, 7, b g Lawman (FR)—Elodie **Martin Keighley Racing Club**
20 **FINESCOPE**, 4, b f Telescope (IRE)—Fine Moment
21 **FORECAST**, 10, ch g Observatory (USA)—New Orchid (USA)
22 **FOUND ON (IRE)**, 7, b m Mahler—Court Gamble (IRE) **Mr O. F. Ryan**
23 **GENOVESE (IRE)**, 4, b g Sans Frontieres (IRE)—Killoughey Babe (IRE) **Martin Keighley Racing Partnership 9**
24 **HERECOMESHOGAN (IRE)**, 5, b g Sageburg (IRE)—Constant Approach (IRE) **The Cotswold Lockdowners**
25 **KALIBRATE (IRE)**, 4, br g Califet (FR)—Clondalee (IRE) **Mkrp8 & O For O Kalibrate**
26 **KAZONTHERAZZ**, 6, b m Kayf Tara—Giovanna **The Meagher Family**
27 4, Ch f Gentlewave (IRE)—Love of Tara
28 **MOZZARO (IRE)**, 7, b g Morozov (USA)—Baraza (IRE) **Owners for Owners Mozzaro**
29 **PAY THE WOMAN (IRE)**, 8, b m Doyen (IRE)—Mono Dame (IRE) **Foxtrot Racing Pay The Woman**
30 **PINNACLE PEAK**, 7, b g Passing Glance—Giovanna **M. Boothright**
31 5, B m Blue Bresil (FR)—Play With Fire
32 **REVE**, 8, b g Nathaniel (IRE)—Rouge (FR) **Mr O. F. Ryan**
33 **ROBSAM (IRE)**, 7, b g Mahler—Silver Set (IRE) **Mr M. Capp**
34 **SAMTARA**, 8, b g Kayf Tara—Aunt Harriet **Mr & Mrs R. Allsop**
35 **SARASOTA STAR (IRE)**, 6, gr ro g Zebedee—Riviera Rose (IRE) **Bishop, Bowkley, Davis, Hughes & Hughes**
36 **SHE HAS NOTIONS (IRE)**, 5, b g Soldier of Fortune (IRE)—Moscow Mo Chuisle (IRE)
                                               Martin Keighley Racing Partnership 11
37 **SOJOURN (IRE)**, 9, b g Getaway (GER)—Toscar (IRE) **Jon & Jacqueline Hughes**
38 **SPANISH PRESENT (IRE)**, 6, b g Presenting—Sesenta (IRE) **Mr D. A. Maughan**
39 **TEN PAST MIDNIGHT**, 6, b g Midnight Legend—Thornton Alice **Serendipity Syndicate 2006**
40 **WITNESS PROTECTION (IRE)**, 9, b g Witness Box (USA)—Queen's Exit **Foxtrot Racing Witness Protection**

MR MARTIN KEIGHLEY - continued

THREE-YEAR-OLDS
41 B c Black Sam Bellamy (IRE)—Karmest
42 B c Ocovango—Minoras Return (IRE)

TWO-YEAR-OLDS
43 B c 08/03 Idaho (IRE)—Seana Ghael (IRE) (Oscar (IRE))

Other Owners: Mr D. Abraham, Mrs J. Abraham, Mr R. Allsop, Mrs Y. E. Allsop, Mr P. K. Davis, Mr J. M. Gibbs, Mr E. J. Hughes, Mrs J. Hughes, MKRP8, Owners for Owners Kalibrate, The The Tenovus Partnership.

Assistant Trainer: Mrs Belinda Keighley, **Yard Sponsor:** Mr Neil Lloyd FBC Manby Bowdler.

NH Jockey: James Best, Sean Bowen. **Conditional Jockey:** James Robottom. **Amateur Jockey:** Mr Harry Atkins.

305

MR SHAUN KEIGHTLEY, Newmarket
Postal: Flat 1, Harraton Court Stables, Church Lane, Exning, Newmarket, Suffolk, CB8 7HF

1 **CANIMAR,** 7, b m Havana Gold (IRE)—Acquifer **Miss J. V. Pahlman**
2 **CATAPULT,** 7, b g Equiano (FR)—Alectrona (FR) **Mr S. L. Keightley**
3 **JOHN JOINER,** 10, b g Captain Gerrard (IRE)—Nigella **Mr S. L. Keightley**
4 **SAN JUAN (IRE),** 5, b g Tagula (IRE)—Bigasiwannabe (IRE) **Mr S. L. Keightley**
5 **SECRATARIO (FR),** 7, ch g Kendargent (FR)—Amoa (USA) **D. S. Lovatt**
6 **SILVER NEMO (IRE),** 4, gr g Markaz (IRE)—Jealous Beauty (IRE) **Ms C. J. White**
7 **SOUND OF U A E (IRE),** 4, b g Champs Elysees—Sandbox Two (IRE)

THREE-YEAR-OLDS
8 B g Intrinsic—Cthulhu (USA)
9 **QUEEN PREMPEH,** ch f Equiano (FR)—Dignify (IRE)
10 **ROGSKI,** b g Swiss Spirit—Faience **Ms C. J. White**
11 Gr f El Kabeir (USA)—Yin

306

MR CHRISTOPHER KELLETT, Lathom
Postal: 6 Canal Cottages, Ring O Bells Lane, Lathom, Ormskirk, Lancashire, L40 5TF
Contacts: PHONE 01704 643775 MOBILE 07966 097989
EMAIL CNKellett@outlook.com WEBSITE www.chriskellettracing.co.uk

1 **BEGOODTOYOURSELF (IRE),** 7, b g Getaway (GER)—Loreley (IRE) **Blythe Stables LLP**
2 **BLISTERING BARNEY (IRE),** 6, b g Sir Prancealot (IRE)—Eternal View (IRE) **Andy Bell & Fergus Lyons**
3 **CHANCE FINALE (FR),** 8, br g Blue Bresil (FR)—Ballade Nordique (FR) **Tracey Bell & Caroline Lyons**
4 **CLONDAW STORM (IRE),** 8, gr g September Storm (GER)—Oh So Smart (IRE) **Blythe Stables LLP**
5 **DECONSO,** 6, b g Dandy Man (IRE)—Tranquil Flight **Andy Bell & Fergus Lyons**
6 **DORETTE (FR),** 9, b m Kingsalsa (USA)—Ombrelle (FR) **Blythe Stables LLP**
7 **KILFILUM CROSS (IRE),** 11, gr g Beneficial (IRE)—Singh Street (IRE) **Andy Bell & Fergus Lyons**
8 **SOLAR IMPULSE (FR),** 12, b g Westerner—Moon Glow (FR) **Andy Bell & Fergus Lyons**
9 **SOMTHINGPHENOMENAL,** 5, b g Phenomena—Quite Something **Mrs J. S. Roscoe-Casey**
10 **THE GRAND VISIR,** 8, b g Frankel—Piping (IRE) **Andy Bell & Fergus Lyons**

THREE-YEAR-OLDS
11 **ARRIANNIE,** b gr f Lethal Force (IRE)—Bithynia (IRE) **Blythe Stables LLP**
12 **DARBUCKS (IRE),** ch c Profitable (IRE)—By Jupiter **Mr W. Buckley & Mr S. Darby**

Other Owners: Mr A. J. Bell, Mrs T. Bell, Blythe Stables LLP, Mr W. Buckley, Mr S. Darby, Mrs C. Lyons, Mr F. Lyons, Fergus & Caroline Lyons.

---

307 MISS GAY KELLEWAY, Newmarket

Postal: **Queen Alexandra Stables, 2 Chapel Street, Exning, Newmarket, Suffolk, CB8 7HA**
Contacts: **PHONE 01638 577778 MOBILE 07974 948768**
EMAIL gaykellewayracing@hotmail.co.uk WEBSITE www.gaykellewayracing.com

1 **BOLT N BROWN**, 6, b m Phoenix Reach (IRE)—Beat Seven **Logistics Terminal LLP**
2 **BORO LASS**, 4, b f Phoenix Reach (IRE)—Comtesse Noire (CAN) **Mrs Kay Deveney & Winterbeck Stud**
3 **CAPLA SPIRIT**, 5, b g Cable Bay (IRE)—Warden Rose **Capla Developments & Partners**
4 **CENTRAL CITY (IRE)**, 7, b g Kodiac—She Basic (IRE) **Moorgate Racing Limited**
5 **CRUNCHIE (IRE)**, 4, ch g Showcasing—Porthilly (IRE) **Moorgateracingltd&strictlyfunracingclub**
6 **CUBAN HOPE (IRE)**, 6, b g Teofilo (IRE)—Dochas Is Gra (IRE) **Chill Out Syndicate & Mr W.A. Robinson**
7 **HABANERO STAR**, 5, b m Mayson—Highly Spiced **Premier Thoroughbred Racing Ltd**
8 **MOVEONUP (IRE)**, 6, gr g Zebedee—Emma Dora (IRE) **B. C. Oakley**
9 **MUKHA MAGIC**, 6, b g Mukhadram—Sweet Lemon (IRE) **J Moynihan,R Mortlock & Exors of P Crook**
10 **PERONI**, 4, b g Pastoral Pursuits—Piddies Pride (IRE)
11 **PROFESSOR GALANT**, 4, b f Coach House (IRE)—Calypso Music **Mr M. Wolkind**
12 **SCALE FORCE**, 6, gr g Lethal Force (IRE)—Alectrona (IRE) **William Robinson & Moorgate Racing Ltd**
13 **SILVER BUBBLE**, 4, b gr f Mayson—Skyrider (IRE) **W Robinson, G Kelleway & Partners**
14 **THEYAZIN (FR)**, 4, b g Siyouni (FR)—Dalamar **Mr H. A. Almarri**
15 **THOMAS KERSHAW (IRE)**, 7, b g Shirocco (GER)—Our Girl Lucy (IRE) **Strictly Fun Racing Club**

THREE-YEAR-OLDS

16 **ANIFICAS BEAUTY (IRE)**, b f Exceed And Excel (AUS)—Khajool (IRE) **Mr K. Rummun**
17 **CAPLA BLUE**, ch f Phoenix Reach (IRE)—Yojojo (IRE) **Capla Developments&winterbeck Manor Stud**
18 **CAPLA PHOENIX**, b f Phoenix Reach (IRE)—Chocolada **Capla Developments&winterbeck Manor Stud**
19 **NOOO MORE (IRE)**, b g Ribchester (IRE)—Lyric of Fife (IRE) **Miss G. M. Kelleway**
20 **SECRET BEAR**, ch g Pearl Secret—Ceilidh Band **B. C. Oakley**

TWO-YEAR-OLDS

21 **HAALAND (IRE)**, ch g 26/03 Buratino (IRE)—Khajool (IRE) (Haafhd) (3401) **Miss G. M. Kelleway**
22 **MARGARET'S FUCHSIA**, ch f 07/04 Dandy Man (IRE)—Quintessenz (GER) (Soldier Hollow) (12381)
Under The Hammer
23 B c 18/02 Tasleet—Midnight Fantasy (Oasis Dream) (5238) **Moorgate Racing Limited**
24 **NATIVE MELODY (IRE)**, b f 23/02 Bungle Inthejungle—Native Picture (IRE) (Kodiac) (14286)
Premier Thoroughbred Racing Ltd
25 **OCEAN CLOUD (IRE)**, b f 23/01 Camacho—Sea of Knowledge (IRE) (Sea The Stars (IRE)) **Under The Hammer**
26 **SILVER NIGHTFALL**, b f 26/03 Adaay (IRE)—Godzilla's Girl (Mastercraftsman (IRE)) **Miss G. M. Kelleway**
27 **TWINKLE TWILIGHT**, ch f 01/04 Twilight Son—Miami Sunset (Archipenko (USA)) (2000) **Under The Hammer**

Other Owners: Miss V. L. Allan, Mr M. R. Brown, Mr K. S. Chambers, Chill Out Syndicate, Mr J. B. Cohen, Exors of the Late P. F. Crook, Mrs K. M. Deveney, Mr T. V. Edwards, Miss G. M. Kelleway, Miss V. Macmahon, Moorgate Racing Limited, Mr R. Mortlock, Mr J. Moynihan, Mr R. A. Newbold, A. B. Parr, Mr W. A. Robinson, Mr M. J. Short, Strictly Fun Racing Club, Mr P. Stubbins, Winterbeck Manor Stud Ltd, Mr M. Wolkind.

Assistant Trainer: Anne-Sophie Crombez, **Head Girl:** Liz Mullin.

308 MRS STEF KENIRY, Middleham

Postal: **Barry Keniry Racing, Warwick Lodge, North Road, Middleham, North Yorkshire, DL8 4PB**

1 **HERMANUS (IRE)**, 10, ch m Golan (IRE)—Almost Trumps **Mrs S. J. Keniry**
2 **MACS BLESSINGS (IRE)**, 6, b g Society Rock (IRE)—Lear's Crown (USA) **Mrs S. J. Keniry**
3 **OLD SALT (IRE)**, 10, b g Craigsteel—Andrea Gale (IRE) **Mrs J. Keys**

THREE-YEAR-OLDS

4 **BUKELA**, b g Mondialiste (IRE)—Lady Amakhala **Mr & Mrs G. Turnbull**
5 **MISS WORLD**, b f Mondialiste (IRE)—Miss Marvellous (USA) **Mr & Mrs G. Turnbull**
6 **RAINBOW BISCUIT**, b c Outstrip—Rainbow Dancing
7 **SOUTH OF WINTER**, ch f Mondialiste (IRE)—Renaissant **Mr & Mrs G. Turnbull**

309 MR NICK KENT, Brigg
Postal: **Newstead House, Newstead Priory, Cadney Road, Brigg, Lincolnshire, DN20 9HP**
Contacts: **PHONE 01652 650628 MOBILE 07710 644428**
EMAIL nick@nickkent.co.uk WEBSITE www.nickkent.co.uk

1 **BAGHDAD CENTRAL (IRE)**, 6, br g Mores Wells—Katowice (IRE) **Ms V. M. Cottingham**
2 **BALLYCALLAN FAME (IRE)**, 7, b m Fame And Glory—Sallie's Secret (IRE)

Wendy & Teresa Wesley & Mr Nick Kent

3 **CATLIN**, 7, b m Bollin Eric—Linen Line **Cynthia Commons, Nick Kent**
4 **DOCTOR DEX (IRE)**, 9, b g Oscar (IRE)—Larnalee (IRE) **Crossed Fingers Partnership**
5 **ERNE RIVER (IRE)**, 7, b g Califet (FR)—Lusty Beg (IRE) **Crossed Fingers Partnership**
6 **GILBERTINA**, 5, b m Universal (IRE)—Saaboog **Mrs M. E. Kent**
7 **HARRY DU BERLAIS (IRE)**, 5, b g Shirocco (GER)—Theatre Mole (IRE) **Crossed Fingers Partnership**
8 **KEEL OVER**, 11, b g Gamut (IRE)—Kayf Keel **Miss L. M. Haywood**
9 **MICK MAESTRO (FR)**, 9, b g Air Chief Marshal (IRE)—Mick Maya (FR) **Crossed Fingers Partnership**
10 **MOORE ON TOUR (IRE)**, 6, gr g Cloudings (IRE)—Really Royale (FR) **Crossed Fingers Partnership**
11 **QUEEN OF FAME (IRE)**, 8, b m Fame And Glory—Ballerina Queen (IRE) **Mr R. M. Evans**
12 4, B f Gentlewave (IRE)—Saaboog
13 **SAYAR (IRE)**, 9, b g Azamour (IRE)—Seraya (FR) **Nick Kent Racing Club II**
14 **WHO'S IN THE BOX (IRE)**, 8, b g Witness Box (USA)—See The Clouds **Mr Andy Parkin, Nick Kent**

Other Owners: Miss C. Commons, Mr J. M. Fawbert, Mr J. N. Kent, Mr A. R. P. Parkin, Ms T. L. Wesley, Mrs W. M. Wesley, Mr N. Williamson.

Assistant Trainer: Mrs Jane Kent.

310 MR T J KENT, Newmarket
Postal: **Providence Gate Stables, Hamilton Road, Newmarket, Suffolk, CB8 0NY**
Contacts: **PHONE 07880 234291**
EMAIL terry@tjkentracing.co.uk

1 **ATASER**, 4, b g Sayif (IRE)—Psychic's Dream **Guaymas**
2 **COCO'S DREAM**, 4, b f Pearl Secret—Yali (IRE) **Mr T. Kent**
3 **DIFFIDENT SPIRIT**, 4, b g Sayif (IRE)—Abbotsfield (IRE) **Guaymas**
4 **GRAPHITE (FR)**, 8, gr g Shamardal (USA)—Fairly Grey (FR) **T J Kent 1 (Graphite)**
5 **MR MARVLOS (IRE)**, 4, b g Vadamos (FR)—Petite Boulangere (IRE) **Mr S. Decani**
6 **OBSIDIAN KNIGHT (IRE)**, 4, br g Awtaad (IRE)—Holda (IRE) **Mr T. Kent**
7 **ROBERT FROST (USA)**, 5, ch g Munnings (USA)—Sorenstam (USA) **Mr T. Kent**
8 **SUPER DEN**, 5, b g Dutch Art—Loch Jipp (USA) **Guaymas**

THREE-YEAR-OLDS

9 B f Havana Gold (IRE)—Calm Attitude (IRE) **Mr T. Kent**
10 **CLIFFS OF FURY**, b g Time Test—Inner Sea (USA) **Mrs Fiona Shaw**
11 **INDIAN TERRITORIES**, b c Territories (IRE)—Indian Story (IRE)

Mr & Mrs R. W. Reed, R. W. Reed, Mrs E. J. Reed

12 **NEMORUM**, b c Stimulation (IRE)—Thicket **Mr T. Kent**
13 **WARRIOR SQUARE**, b c Adaay (IRE)—Ziefhd **Mr T. Kent**

TWO-YEAR-OLDS

14 B c 22/04 Oasis Dream—Indian Story (IRE) (Indian Ridge) **Mr & Mrs R. W. Reed, R. W. Reed, Mrs E. J. Reed**
15 B c 28/04 Elzaam (AUS)—Sugarformyhoney (IRE) (Dutch Art) (2000)
16 B f 17/03 Buratino (IRE)—Ziefhd (Haafhd) (2200) **Mr T. Kent**

Assistant Trainer: Lewis Kent. **Apprentice Jockey:** Lewis Kent.

311 MR LEONARD KERR, Irvine
Postal: **Annick Lodge, Irvine, Ayrshire, KA11 2AN**

1 **ALIEN ENCOUNTER**, 6, gr gr m Black Sam Bellamy (IRE)—Inthesettlement **Mr A Kerr Mr L Kerr**
2 **NEW ZEALANDER**, 5, b g Australia—Dalasyla (IRE) **Mr A Kerr Mr L Kerr**
3 **REETAZEETAJONES**, 4, b f Pether's Moon (IRE)—Scotland Act (FR) **Mr A Kerr Mr L Kerr**
4 **SWORD OF FATE (IRE)**, 9, b g Beneficial—Beann Ard (IRE) **Mr A Kerr Mr L Kerr**

312 MR ALAN KING, Barbury Castle
Postal: **Barbury Castle Stables, Wroughton, Wiltshire, SN4 0QZ**
Contacts: **PHONE 01793 815009 MOBILE 07973 461233 FAX 01793 845080**
EMAIL alan@alanking.biz WEBSITE www.alankingracing.co.uk

1 **ALDSWORTH**, 4, b g Pether's Moon (IRE)—Handmaid **David J S Sewell & Burling Family**
2 **ALTERNATIVE FACT**, 7, b g Dalakhani (IRE)—O Fourlunda **The Alternative Lot**
3 **BERINGER**, 7, b g Sea The Stars (IRE)—Edaraat (USA) **L Field, B Cognet, N Farrell, J Spack**
4 **BETTERFOREVERYONE**, 5, b g Cokoriko (FR)—Lady Emily **Mr J. R. D. Anton**
5 **BIG BOY BOBBY (IRE)**, 4, b g Vadamos (FR)—Duchess of Foxland (IRE) **Incipe Partnership**
6 **BLAME IT ON SALLY (IRE)**, 6, b g Canford Cliffs (IRE)—Sliding Scale **Owners Group 053**
7 4, B f Passing Glance—Call Me A Star **Pitchall Stud Partnership**
8 **CALL OF THE WILD (IRE)**, 5, b g Fame And Glory—Glory Days (GER) **Mr J. P. McManus**
9 **CANELO (IRE)**, 9, ch g Mahler—Nobody's Darling (IRE) **Mr J. P. McManus**
10 **CARAMELISED**, 4, b g Dansili—Caster Sugar (USA) **Jastar Ltd & Harry Wigan**
11 **CATBIRD SEAT (IRE)**, 5, b g Kingston Hill—Celestial Dream (IRE) **Dan Gilbert & Andrew Bruce**
12 **CHOSEN PATH (IRE)**, 9, b g Well Chosen—Karsulu (FR) **McNeill Family and Prodec Networks Ltd**
13 **CLIFTON BRIDGE (IRE)**, 5, b g Ask—Queen Sophie (IRE) **McNeill Family & Stone Family**
14 **COEUR DE LION**, 9, b g Pour Moi (IRE)—Hora **The Barbury Boys**
15 **COOL STONE**, 6, b m Kayf Tara—Stoney Path **Mrs Sue Welch & Alan King**
16 **CRYSTAL MOON (IRE)**, 5, ch g Shirocco (GER)—Liscannor (IRE) **Mrs J. A. Watts**
17 **DANCE WITH FIRE**, 6, ch g Norse Dancer (IRE)—Ruby Kew (IRE) **Mrs S. C. Welch**
18 **DEYRANN DE CARJAC (FR)**, 9, b g Balko (FR)—Queyrann (FR) **Mr J. A. Law**
19 **DICKENS (IRE)**, 4, b g Excelebration (IRE)—Open Book **McNeill Family & Niall Farrell**
20 **DIDONATO (IRE)**, 7, b m Milan—Dream Lass (IRE) **Mr S. Smith**
21 **DINO VELVET (FR)**, 9, b g Naaqoos—Matgil (FR) **McNeill Family & Niall Farrell**
22 **EDWARDSTONE**, 8, b g Kayf Tara—Nothingtoloose (IRE) **Robert Abrey & Ian Thurtle**
23 **ERNEST GRAY**, 5, b g Walk In The Park (IRE)—Emily Gray (IRE) **Mr A. J. Peake**
24 **ES PERFECTO (IRE)**, 7, ch g Shirocco (GER)—Shadow Dearg (IRE) **Mrs E. A. Prowting**
25 4, B g Clovis du Berlais (FR)—Fabrika **Alan King**
26 **FIDUX (FR)**, 9, b g Fine Grain (JPN)—Folle Tempete (FR) **AXOM LXVIII**
27 **FINEST VIEW**, 5, b m Passing Glance—Call Me A Legend **Pitchall Stud Partnership**
28 **FOREVER WILLIAM**, 4, ch g Sea The Moon (GER)—Archina (IRE) **The Barbury Lions 6**
29 **FORGET THE WAY**, 5, b g Getaway (GER)—Forget The Ref (IRE) **Robert Abrey & Ian Thurtle**
30 **FOUNTAIN CROSS**, 4, b g Muhaarar—Infamous Angel **Mr D. J. Barry**
31 **FRATERNEL (FR)**, 7, b g Kap Rock (FR)—Valence (FR) **Mr T. D. J. Syder**
32 **FUTURE INVESTMENT**, 6, b g Mount Nelson—Shenir **Mrs E. A. Prowting**
33 **GAVI DI GAVI (IRE)**, 7, b g Camacho—Blossom Deary (IRE) **Alan King & Niall Farrell**
34 **GLIDE DOWN (USA)**, 4, b g Point of Entry (USA)—On A Cloud (USA) **James Wigan & Alan King**
35 **GRANDEUR D'AME (FR)**, 6, b g Desir d'Un Soir (FR)—Sourya d'Airy (FR) **Tim Syder & Dominic Burke**
36 **GREEN PLANET (IRE)**, 5, b g Australia—Maleha (IRE) **The Unlikely Lads**
37 **GREYSTOKE**, 6, b g Sixties Icon—Siri **Robert & Lucy Dickinson**
38 **GRISBI DE BERCE (FR)**, 6, b g Tin Horse (IRE)—Volupia de Berce (FR) **Charles Dingwall & Alan King**
39 **GROSVENOR COURT**, 6, b g Shirocco (GER)—Hurricane Milly (IRE) **Farrell, Gallagher, Gressier & Murray**
40 **HALL LANE (IRE)**, 4, ch g Mount Nelson—Cashalass (IRE) **Jerry Wright & the Lee Family**
41 **HARBOUR LAKE (IRE)**, 6, br g Shantou (USA)—Aibrean (IRE) **Exors of the Late Mr T. J. Hemmings**
42 **HASEEFAH**, 5, b m Teofilo (IRE)—Halaqa (IRE) **Michael Rembaum & Michael Tuckey**
43 **HAZARD COLLONGES (FR)**, 5, b g Coastal Path—Prouesse Collonges (FR) **Mr Simon Munir & Mr Isaac Souede**

MR ALAN KING - continued

44 **HEART OF A LION (IRE)**, 7, b g Yeats (IRE)—Lady Secret (FR) **Mr J. P. McManus**
45 **HER INDOORS (IRE)**, 5, b m Raven's Pass (USA)—Superfonic (FR) **McNeill Family & Niall Farrell**
46 **HOSTILE**, 8, ch g Malinas (GER)—Skew **Alan King & C & H Barrett**
47 **HOTTER THAN HELL (FR)**, 8, ch m No Risk At All (FR)—Ombrelle (FR) **The Devil's Advocates**
48 **INCHICORE (IRE)**, 5, b m Galileo (IRE)—Luas Line (IRE) **Apple Tree Stud**
49 **ISOLATE (FR)**, 6, b g Maxios—Unaided **Noel Fehily Racing - Isolate**
50 **JABOTICABA (IRE)**, 8, ch g Muhtathir—Janiceinwonderland (FR) **Owners Group 025**
51 **JAY BEE WHY (IRE)**, 7, b g Yeats (IRE)—Lady Bernie (IRE) **David J S Sewell & Tim Leadbeater**
52 **JEREMIAH**, 7, ch g Kheleyf (USA)—Tessie **M. L. Ayers**
53 **JERMINNIE GREEN (IRE)**, 8, b m Jeremy (USA)—Minnie Maguire (IRE) **Coupland, Farrell, I Wheeler**
54 **JUST IN TIME**, 8, b g Excelebration (IRE)—Flying Finish (FR) **HP Racing Just In Time**
55 **KALMA**, 4, b f Mukhadram—Peters Spirit (IRE) **Elysees Partnership**
56 5, B g Pether's Moon (IRE)—Karla June **James and Jean Potter Ltd**
57 **KOZIER (GER)**, 8, ch g Muhtathir—Kasumi (GER) **Loose Cannon Racing**
58 **LETMELIVEMYLIFE**, 4, b g Oasis Dream—Itiqad **Ms L. Judah**
59 **LIVERPOOL KNIGHT**, 4, b g Golden Horn—Nouriya **Ms L. Judah**
60 **LUNAR SHADOW**, 4, b f Sea The Moon (GER)—The Pirate's Queen (IRE) **Apple Tree Stud**
61 **MADIBA PASSION (FR)**, 8, b g Al Namix (FR)—Birsheba (FR) **M Deeley, J Dale & A King**
62 **MAID ON THE MOON**, 5, b m Pether's Moon (IRE)—Handmaid **The Burling Family Ltd**
63 **MAJOR DUNDEE (IRE)**, 7, b g Scorpion (IRE)—Be My Granny **Exors of the Late Mr T. J. Hemmings**
64 **MASACCIO (IRE)**, 5, gr g Mastercraftsman (IRE)—Ange Bleu (USA) **McNeill Family & Niall Farrell**
65 **MESSIRE DES OBEAUX (FR)**, 10, b g Saddler Maker (IRE)—Madame Lys (FR)
                                                          Mr Simon Munir & Mr Isaac Souede
66 **METHUSALAR (IRE)**, 6, b g Sholokhov (IRE)—Pixie Dust (IRE) **Top Brass Partnership**
67 **MIDNIGHT GLANCE**, 7, b g Passing Glance—Magical Legend **R. H. Kerswell**
68 **MIDNIGHTREFERENDUM**, 9, b m Midnight Legend—Forget The Ref (IRE)
                                                          Robert Abrey, Ian Thurtle & David Gibbon
69 **MIDNIGHTS LEGACY**, 5, b h Midnight Legend—Giving **Pitchall Stud Partnership**
70 **MOONAMACAROONA**, 6, b m Flemensfirth (USA)—Forever Present (IRE) **Netherfield House Stud**
71 **MR G**, 5, b g Galileo (IRE)—Giofra **Ian Gosden & Richard & Stephen House**
72 **MR PUMBLECHOOK**, 8, b g Midnight Legend—Definitely Pip (IRE) **Mr D. J. S. Sewell**
73 **NEBUCHADNEZZAR**, 7, b g Planteur (IRE)—Trexana **Top Brass 2**
74 **NINA THE TERRIER (IRE)**, 6, b m Milan—Shees A Dante (IRE) **Mr C. B. J. Dingwall**
75 **NO RECOLLECTION**, 4, br g Dansili—Talawat **M. Kerr-Dineen**
76 **NOBBY (IRE)**, 8, b g Authorized (IRE)—Magic Music (IRE) **R. Bailey**
77 **NORTH LODGE (IRE)**, 5, b g Presenting—Saddleeruppat (IRE) **McNeill Family & Niall Farrell**
78 **NOTACHANCE (IRE)**, 8, b g Mahler—Ballybrowney Hall (IRE) **David J S Sewell & Tim Leadbeater**
79 **NOTHINGTOCHANCE**, 5, b m Kayf Tara—Nothingtoloose (IRE) **Robert Abrey & Ian Thurtle**
80 **OCEANLINE (IRE)**, 4, b g Adaay (IRE)—Ocean Bluff (IRE) **Million in Mind Partnership**
81 **ON TO VICTORY**, 8, b g Rock of Gibraltar (IRE)—Clouds of Magellan (USA) **HP Racing On To Victory**
82 5, B g Black Sam Bellamy (IRE)—One Wild Night **Mrs J. A. Watts**
83 **OUTONPATROL (IRE)**, 8, gr m Stowaway—Burnt Oil Babe (IRE) **McNeill Family & Niall Farrell**
84 **PAINLESS POTTER (IRE)**, 4, b g Camacho—Wider World (IRE) **Mr R. Gilbert**
85 **PASS THE LOVE ON**, 5, b m Passing Glance—Call Me A Star **Pitchall Stud Partnership**
86 **PEACE RIVER**, 6, b g Yeats (IRE)—Takotna (IRE) **Ian Payne & Kim Franklin**
87 **PECKINPAH (IRE)**, 6, ch g Excelebration (IRE)—Melodrama (IRE) **Coupland, Gemmell, Hues & Sullivan**
88 **PERFECT HARMONY**, 10, b g Definite Article—Brandam Supreme (IRE) **Mrs E. A. Prowting**
89 **PICCADILLY LILLY**, 5, b m Authorized (IRE)—Hora **Trull House Stud & R. Waley-cohen**
90 **POTTERMAN**, 9, b g Sulamani (IRE)—Polly Potter **James and Jean Potter Ltd**
91 **PRESENTING PETE (IRE)**, 5, b g Presenting—Ciandarragh (IRE) **Mr & Mrs R. Scott**
92 **PUMPKIN'S PRIDE**, 6, b g Malinas (GER)—Peel Me A Grape **Mrs E. A. Prowting**
93 **RAFIKI (FR)**, 4, b g The Last Lion (IRE)—Adalawa (IRE) **Alan King & Niall Farrell**
94 **RAINBOW DREAMER**, 9, b g Aqlaam—Zamhrear **The Maple Street Partnership**
95 **RAYMOND TUSK (IRE)**, 7, b g High Chaparral (IRE)—Dancing Shoes (IRE) **The Unlikely Lads**
96 **RESTITUTION (FR)**, 4, b g Frankel—Restiana (FR) **Highclere T'Bred Racing - Restitution**
97 **RIDEAU CANAL (IRE)**, 7, b g Robin des Champs (FR)—Miss Vinnie (IRE) **Farrell Field Sigler**
98 **ROBIOLA (IRE)**, 4, b g Harzand (IRE)—Weeping Wind **Mr Simon Munir & Mr Isaac Souede**
99 **ROSCOE TARA**, 7, b g Kayf Tara—Aunt Harriet **Mr & Mrs R. Allsop**
100 **ROYAL PRETENDER (FR)**, 6, br g Great Pretender (IRE)—Robinia Directa (GER) **Mrs C. Skan**
101 **SARSEN (USA)**, 4, gr ro g Noble Mission—Kelley Marie (USA) **Elite Racing 002**

MR ALAN KING - continued

102 **SATURDAY SONG**, 6, b g Kayf Tara—Fernello **Mr S. Doyle**
103 **SCEAU ROYAL (FR)**, 10, b g Doctor Dino (FR)—Sandside (FR) **Mr Simon Munir & Mr Isaac Souede**
104 **SENIOR CITIZEN**, 9, b g Tobougg (FR)—Mothers Help **McNeill Family Ltd**
105 **SON OF RED (IRE)**, 5, b g French Navy—Tarziyma (IRE) **Ian Gosden & Richard House**
106 **SONNING (IRE)**, 4, gr g The Gurkha (IRE)—Moon Empress (FR) **McNeill Family & Patrick&scott Bryceland**
107 **SWORD BEACH (IRE)**, 5, ch g Ivawood (IRE)—Sleeping Princess (IRE) **Hp Racing Sword Beach & Ptnr**
108 **TECHNOLOGY (IRE)**, 5, b g Yeats (IRE)—Little Fashionista (IRE) **McNeill Family Ltd**
109 **TERRAFIRMA LADY (IRE)**, 7, b m Court Cave (IRE)—Didn't You Know (FR) **WKH (Hinksey Lane) Ltd**
110 **THE DEVILS DROP (IRE)**, 9, b g Court Cave (IRE)—Concernforkillen (IRE) **Mr D. M. Mason**
111 **THE GLANCING QUEEN (IRE)**, 8, b m Jeremy (USA)—Glancing (IRE) **Dingwall, Farrell, Hornsey & Murray**
112 **THE HOOD (IRE)**, 4, b g Invincible Spirit (IRE)—Reclamation (IRE) **Mr J. A. Law**
113 **THE KICKING QUEEN (IRE)**, 6, b m Beat Hollow—Shivermetimber (IRE) **Mr & Mrs C. Harris**
114 **THE OLYMPIAN (IRE)**, 6, ch g Olympic Glory (IRE)—Basira (FR) **Alan King**
115 **THE UNIT (IRE)**, 11, b g Gold Well—Sovana (FR) **International Plywood (Importers) Ltd**
116 **THEONLYWAYISWESSEX (FR)**, 4, b br g Maxios—Terra Fina **Marsh, Kelly, Meacham, Davies & Mordaunt**
117 **THIS ONES FOR FRED (IRE)**, 4, b br g Markaz (IRE)—Green Chorus (IRE) **Mr P. Coombs**
118 **THUNDER AHEAD**, 4, b g Dark Angel (IRE)—Champagne Time (IRE) **Maybe Only Fools Have Horses**
119 **TINCHOO**, 4, b f Adaay (IRE)—Tinshu (IRE) **Llewelyn,Runeckles**
120 **TREMWEDGE**, 6, b g Foxwedge (AUS)—Tremolo Pointe (IRE) **Ljp Racing**
121 **TRITONIC**, 5, ch g Sea The Moon (GER)—Selenography **McNeill Family & Mr Ian Dale**
122 **TRUESHAN (FR)**, 6, b g Planteur (IRE)—Shao Line (FR) **Singula Partnership**
123 **TWILIGHT TWIST**, 4, b g Twilight Son—Fiftyshadesofpink (IRE) **Magee Bickerton Monaghan Farrell & King**
124 **UNIVERSAL DAVE**, 6, b g Universal (IRE)—Nant Y Mynydd **Noel Fehily Racing Syndicates Universal**
125 **VALDEZ**, 15, ch g Doyen (IRE)—Skew **Alan King**
126 **VALLERES (FR)**, 7, b g Coastal Path—Duchesse Pierji (FR) **Mr Simon Munir & Mr Isaac Souede**
127 **VAZIR (FR)**, 4, b g Siyouni (FR)—Vazira (FR) **The Unlikely Lads**
128   5, B g Flemensfirth (USA)—W Six Times **Judy & Jamie Magee**
129 **WHO CARES WINS (IRE)**, 4, b f Hallowed Crown (AUS)—Savignano **L. Lillingston**
130 **WHO DARES WINS (IRE)**, 10, b g Jeremy (USA)—Savignano **HP Racing Who Dares Wins**
131 **WURLITZER**, 4, b g Adaay (IRE)—Olympic Medal **Owners Group 067**
132 **WYNN HOUSE**, 7, ch m Presenting—Glorious Twelfth (IRE) **Mr J. R. D. Anton**
133 **Y FYN DUW A FYDD**, 7, b m Nathaniel (IRE)—Dignify (IRE) **R. Mathew**

THREE-YEAR-OLDS

134 **ADMIRALTY HOUSE**, ch g Sea The Stars (IRE)—Akrivi (IRE) **Alan King & Niall Farrell**
135 **ALHABOR**, b c Intello (GER)—Eternally **M. Kerr-Dineen**
136 **BENJAMIN BEAR (IRE)**, b c Kodiac—Mrs Robinson **Simon Ellen & Partners**
137 **BIT HARSH (IRE)**, b c Australia—Shortmile Lady (IRE) **Alan King & Anthony Bromley**
138 **CHICAGO GAL**, ch f Cityscape—Crooked Wood (USA) **Hunscote Stud Limited**
139 **DAL MALLART**, b f Muhaarar—Dalvina **St Albans Bloodstock Limited**
140 **FAST FORWARD (FR)**, b g Recorder—Forward Feline (FR) **Kennet Valley Thoroughbreds IX**
141 **FORWARD FLIGHT (IRE)**, b g Declaration of War (USA)—On A Cloud (USA) **James Wigan & Alan King**
142 **FOUR NOTES**, b f Night of Thunder (IRE)—Dolcetto (IRE) **Mrs Lesley Field & Mr Aiden Murphy**
143 **GIVE A LITTLE BACK (FR)**, b c Zelzal (FR)—Boyarynya (USA) **Ms L. Judah**
144 **HEROIC HOLLY (IRE)**, ch f Australia—Happy Holly (IRE) **Hunscote Stud Limited**
145 **JAD MAHAL (FR)**, b c Dabirsim (FR)—Cheveley (IRE) **Simon Munir & Isaac Souede**
146 **KASAI RIVER (IRE)**, b g Wootton Bassett—Nianga (GER) **Mr J. A. Law**
147 **MR RUMBALICIOUS (IRE)**, b c Kodiac—Intaglia **Let's Get Ready To Rumble Partnership**
148 **PANGLOSS**, b c Havana Gold (IRE)—Fantastic Santanyi **R. Mathew**
149 **PARADIAS (GER)**, b c Kodiac—Paraisa **Dodds-Smith, Farrell, Hodgson & Coupland**
150 **RAMPOLDI PLAN (USA)**, ch c Hard Spun (USA)—Coal and Ice (USA) **Mr Simon Munir & Mr Isaac Souede**
151 **REVERSION (IRE)**, b c Adaay (IRE)—Dutch Desire **Mr Simon Munir & Mr Isaac Souede**
152 **SOUS SURVEILLANCE**, b g Passing Glance—Liddle Dwiggs **Martyn Butler & Four Point Racing**
153 **SUPER LOVER**, b c Zoffany (IRE)—Love Your Looks **Frederickellis,Thorstenfeddern&alan King**
154 **TUDDENHAM GREEN**, b g Nathaniel (IRE)—Social Media **Simon Munir, Isaac Souede & Partners**
155 **TYING THE KNOT (USA)**, b c Noble Mission—Hope's Diamond (USA) **Mr A. J. Peake**
156 **VICTORY (IRE)**, b c Churchill (IRE)—Mill Point **Barry, Trowbridge A King**

MR ALAN KING - continued

Mr D. R. Chennells, Mr B. R. Cognet, Mr A. P. Coupland, Mr W. I. C. Dale, Mrs R. L. J. Dickinson, Mr R. R. Dickinson, Mr C. B. J. Dingwall, Mr I. Dodds-Smith, Mr F. J. Ellis, Mr N. Farrell, Dr T. A. Feddern, Mrs L. H. Field, Four Point Racing, Miss K. M. Franklin, Mr A. Gemmell, D. H. Gibbon, Mr D. R. Gilbert, Mr I. F. Gosden, HP Racing Sword Beach, Mrs C. A. Harris, Mr C. I. K. Harris, Mr D. F. Hill, Mrs M. A. Hornsey, Mr R. House, Mr S. J. House, Mr D. Hues, Jastar Capital Limited, R. G. Kelvin-Hughes, Alan King, Mr E. T. D. Leadbeater, Exors of the Late W. P. Ledward, Mr R. D. Lee, Mr R. M. Levitt, Mr S. Macauley, Mrs J Magee, Mr J. Magee, Mr A. R. W. Marsh, McNeill Family Ltd, Mr J. Monaghan, S. E. Munir, H. A. Murphy, Mr J. J. Murray, Ms L. A. Nolan, Mr P Nolan, Mr I. T. Payne, Mr A. J. Peake, W. H. Ponsonby, Prodec Networks Ltd, Mr M. J. Rembaum, Richard House & Stephen House, Mr S. J. Rogers, Mr D. J. S. Sewell, Mr J. Sigler, Mr I. Souede, Mrs J. A. Spack, Stone Family, Mr R. T. Sullivan, Mr T. D. J. Syder, Mr A. L. Tappin, The Burling Family Ltd, The Lee Family, Mr I. R. Thurtle, K. P. Trowbridge, M. J. Tuckey, Mr R. B. Waley-Cohen, Mrs S. C. Welch, Mr I. T. Wheeler, Mr H. E. Wigan, J. Wigan, Mrs L. J. Williams, J. Wright.

Assistant Trainer: Dan Horsford, **Pupil Assistant:** Robin Smith, **Yard Sponsor:** HARE.

NH Jockey: Tom Bellamy, Tom Cannon, Gavin Sheehan. **Conditional Jockey:** Alexander Thorne.

Apprentice Jockey: Georgia King.

---

313 MR NEIL KING, Barbury Castle
Postal: Upper Herdswick Farm, Burderop, Wroughton, Swindon, Wiltshire, SN4 0QH
Contacts: PHONE 01793 845011 MOBILE 07880 702325 FAX 01793 845011
EMAIL neil@neil-king.co.uk WEBSITE www.neil-king.co.uk

```
 1  AIDE MEMOIRE (IRE), 6, b m Rip Van Winkle (IRE)—Bessichka  The Ridgeway Racing For Fun Partnership
 2  BALAGAN, 7, b g Great Pretender (IRE)—Lovely Origny (FR)  Mr A. L. Cohen
 3  BALLYHAWKISH, 6, b g Kayf Tara—Massannie (IRE)  Ken Lawrence & Roy Mousley
 4  BOULTING FOR GLORY (IRE), 7, b g Fame And Glory—Westgrove Berry (IRE)  Mr C. Boultbee-Brooks
 5  CANYON CITY, 9, b g Authorized (IRE)—Colorado Dawn  A Whyte, J Bone, D Nott & B Smith
 6  CHENG GONG, 6, b g Archipenko (USA)—Kinetica  Three Kingdoms Racing
 7  CUBAN COURT (IRE), 4, b g Court Cave—Havana Dancer (IRE)
 8  CUBSWIN (IRE), 8, b m Zamindar (USA)—Moonlight Rhapsody (IRE)  Mr D Caldwell & Mr K Lawrence
 9  FUNWAY MONARCH (IRE), 7, b g Imperial Monarch (IRE)—Mount Radhwa (IRE)  Mr R. N. Bothway
10  GAME IN THE PARK (FR), 9, b g Walk In The Park (IRE)—Learning Game (USA)  N. King
11  GIVE ME A CUDDLE (IRE), 6, b g Court Cave (IRE)—Social Society (IRE)  Mr A. L. Cohen
12  4, B f Blue Bresil (FR)—Hope Royal
13  I HOPE STAR (IRE), 6, b g Casamento (IRE)—Bint Nayef (IRE)  Sal's Pals
14  JAN MAAT (GER), 9, gr g Electric Beat—Jeanine (GER)  N. King
15  JUSTIFIED, 5, br g Authorized (IRE)—Caribbean Dancer (USA)  Mr B Bell, Mr M Harrod & Mr G Sainsbury
16  KENYAN COWBOY (IRE), 6, b g Sholokhov (IRE)—Joleen (IRE)  Mrs C. Kendrick
17  KEY INSTINCT, 5, b m Intrinsic—Tellmethings  Mr M. H. Wood
18  LIFETIME LEGEND (IRE), 4, b g Pride of Dubai (AUS)—Livia Galilei (IRE)  Ken Lawrence & Roy Mousley
19  LOOKAWAY (IRE), 5, ch g Ask—Barrack's Choice (IRE)  Mr P. M. H. Beadles
20  MALINA JAMILA, 6, b m Malinas (GER)—Haveyoubeen (IRE)  Maundrell, Sawyer & Andrews
21  NEARLY PERFECT, 8, b g Malinas (GER)—The Lyme Volunteer (IRE)  Mr P. M. H. Beadles
22  NORDANO (GER), 6, ch g Jukebox Jury (IRE)—Navajo Queen (GER)  A Whyte, T Messom & D Nott
23  ONEMOREFORTHEROAD, 7, b g Yorgunnabelucky (USA)—Vinomore  Rupert Dubai Racing
24  PERFECT MYTH, 8, b m Midnight Legend—Perfect Silence  R. J. Vines
25  POET'S CORNER, 6, b g Poet's Voice—Helter Helter (USA)  Sal's Pals
26  7, B g Mount Nelson—Razor Sharp  J. C. S. Wilson
27  REMEMBER THE MAN (IRE), 9, b g Dalakhani (IRE)—Perfect Hedge  Poynton Harrod Smith & Darlington
28  SACKETT, 11, b g Midnight Legend—Gloriana  The Ridgeway Racing For Fun Partnership
29  SIR TAWEEL (IRE), 4, b g Sir Prancealot (IRE)—Qualia (IRE)  Kevin O'Donnell & David Fremel
30  SPORTING ACE (IRE), 6, b g Shantou (USA)—Knockbounce View (IRE)  Ken Lawrence & Roy Mousley
31  SWIFT CRUSADOR, 11, b g Kayf Tara—Goldenswift (IRE)  N. King
32  THE BANDIT (IRE), 7, br g Stowaway—Highly Presentable (IRE)  Mr P. M. H. Beadles
33  THE KNOT IS TIED (IRE), 7, b g Casamento (IRE)—Really Polish (USA)  Ken Lawrence & Roy Mousley
```

MR NEIL KING - continued

34 **TIKI FIRE (IRE)**, 4, b f Awtaad (IRE)—Debutantin **Mrs H. M. Buckle**
35 **UNDOUBTEDLY**, 5, b m Authorized (IRE)—Lovely Origny (FR) **Mr A. L. Cohen**

Other Owners: Mr T. P. Andrews, Mr B. Bell, Mr J. Bone, Mr D. R. Caldwell, Mr N. J. Catterwell, Mr P. J. Darlington, D. P. Fremel, Mr M. Harrod, N. King, Mr K. Lawrence, Mrs A. E. Maundrell, Mr T. J. Messom, Mr R. Mousley, Mr D. F. Nott, Mr K. O'Donnell, Mr B. Poynton, Mr G. T. Sainsbury, Mr A. F. Sawyer, Mr D. P. Smith, Mr R. W. Smith, Mr A. A. Whyte.

Racing Secretary: Oriana-Jane Baines.

Flat Jockey: Ben Curtis, Luke Morris. **NH Jockey:** Bryony Frost.

---

314 **MR PHILIP KIRBY, Richmond**
Postal: **Green Oaks Farm, East Appleton, Richmond, North Yorkshire, DL10 7QE**
Contacts: **PHONE 01748 517337 MOBILE 07984 403558**
EMAIL pkirbyracing@gmail.com WEBSITE www.philipkirbyracing.co.uk

1 **ADELPHI SPRITE**, 6, b g Cityscape—Cailin Na Ri (IRE) **Barry and Virginia Brown**
2 **ALOISA**, 4, b f Kayf Tara—Alina Rheinberg (GER)
3 **ANOTHER THEATRE (IRE)**, 9, b m Shantou (USA)—Whats Another One (IRE) **Zoe Hassall & George Hassall**
4 **ARTHUR MAC (IRE)**, 9, ch g Getaway (GER)—Orchardstown Moss (IRE) **The Vacuum Pouch Company Limited**
5 **AUTONOMY**, 6, b g Dansili—Funsie (FR) **Hambleton Racing XXXIV & Partner**
6 **BAMBOO BAY (IRE)**, 4, b g Camelot—Anna Karenina (USA) **Harbour Rose Partnership**
7 **BARLEY BREEZE**, 5, gr g Kapgarde (FR)—Attene de Sivola (FR) **Tor Side Racing**
8 **BE THE DIFFERENCE (IRE)**, 6, b g Califet (FR)—Rinroe Flyer (IRE) **The Vacuum Pouch Company Limited**
9 **BIG EARS (IRE)**, 6, b m Yeats (IRE)—Theleze (FR) **Mrs J. A. Darling**
10 **BILLIAN (IRE)**, 4, b g Mehmas (IRE)—Truly Magnificent (USA) **Bill Fraser & Adrian Pritchard**
11 **BLACK EBONY**, 8, br g Malinas (GER)—Our Ethel **The Mount Fawcus Partnership**
12 **BURROWS SEESIDE (FR)**, 5, b g Sidestep (AUS)—See Your Dream
13 **BUSBY (IRE)**, 7, b g Kodiac—Arabian Pearl (IRE) **The Busby Partnership**
14 **BUSHYPARK (IRE)**, 8, b g Le Fou (IRE)—Aztec Pearl **Mr P. A. Kirby**
15 **CARLOS FELIX (IRE)**, 5, ch g Lope de Vega (IRE)—Quad's Melody (IRE) **Mr & Mrs D. Yates**
16 **CLASSIC ESCAPE (IRE)**, 9, b g Golan (IRE)—Seana Ghael (IRE) **Hold My Beer Syndicate**
17 **DEFINING BATTLE (IRE)**, 6, gr g Lope de Vega (IRE)—Royal Fortune (IRE) **Mr & Mrs D. Yates**
18 **DIAKOSAINT (FR)**, 7, b g Saint des Saints (FR)—Diananisse (FR) **The Vacuum Pouch Company Limited**
19 **EN MEME TEMPS (FR)**, 8, b g Saddler Maker (IRE)—Lady Reine (FR) **Hope Eden Racing Limited**
20 **FILLE D'AVIGNON (IRE)**, 7, br m Getaway (GER)—Site-Leader (IRE) **The Topspec II Partnership**
21 **FIRCOMBE HALL**, 4, ch c Charming Thought—Marmot Bay (IRE) **RedHotGardogs**
22 **FIRST ILLUSION (IRE)**, 6, b g Westerner—No Manners Molly (IRE) **The Vacuum Pouch Company Limited**
23 **GALAXY DANCER**, 5, b m Telescope (IRE)—La Doelenaise **TopSpeed Thoroughbreds**
24 **GANDHI MAKER (FR)**, 6, b g Policy Maker (IRE)—Thellya d'Arc (FR) **Mr A. McCormack**
25 **GLAMOROUS ICON (IRE)**, 4, ch f Presenting—Vic Chic (IRE)
26 **GOLFE CLAIR (FR)**, 6, b g Masked Marvel—Ocean Beach (FR) **Mr P. R. Rawcliffe**
27 **GOWANLAD**, 5, b g Mayson—Aahgowangowan (IRE) **Gowan Racing**
28 **GREEN OAKS TOP CAT**, 5, ch m Soldier of Fortune (IRE)—Molly Cat **The Philip Kirby Racing Club**
29 **GREY MATTER (FR)**, 4, gr g Intello (GER)—Aifa **The French Connection**
30 **HAPPY GO LOTTIE**, 4, b f Camelot—Get Happy (IRE) **The Philip Kirby Racing Club**
31 **HIDDEN COMMANDER (IRE)**, 7, b g Shirocco (GER)—Gift of Freedom (IRE)
The Vacuum Pouch Company Limited
32 **ICE PYRAMID (IRE)**, 7, ch g New Approach (IRE)—Coolnagree (IRE) **Bill Fraser & Adrian Pritchard**
33 **ICONIC BELLE**, 8, ch m Sixties Icon—Five Bells (IRE) **Bainbridge, Cornforth**
34 **INTERCONNECTED**, 8, br g Network (GER)—R de Rien Sivola (FR) **Mr & Mrs D. Yates**
35 **LADY'S PRESENT (IRE)**, 5, b m Presenting—Lady Chloe **The Team Kirby Partnership**
36 **LEOPOLDS ROCK (IRE)**, 6, ch g Rock of Gibraltar (IRE)—Trianon **Tor Side Racing**
37 **LETHAL STEPS**, 7, gr g Lethal Force (IRE)—Tanda Tula (IRE) **Hope Eden Racing Limited**
38 **LITTLE INDIA (FR)**, 6, ch m Manduro (GER)—Jolie Laide (IRE) **Hope Eden Racing Limited**
39 **LONG TO BE (FR)**, 6, gr ro g Montmartre (FR)—Tobetall **John Matthews & Hambleton Xxxiv**

MR PHILIP KIRBY - continued

40 **LORD BUTTONS,** 6, b g Presenting—Lady Chapp (IRE) **Mrs J. Sivills**
41 **LORD TORRANAGA (FR),** 7, b g Planteur (IRE)—Marie Cuddy (IRE) **Lord Torranaga Partnership**
42 **LOUIS' VAC POUCH (IRE),** 10, b g Oscar (IRE)—Coming Home (FR) **Cornforth,Stephenson, Barlow & Rutherford**
43 **LUCKY ICON (IRE),** 8, b g Sixties Icon—Sauterelle (IRE) **Mrs J. Sivills**
44 **MADEEH,** 6, b g Oasis Dream—Ashaaqah (IRE) **Harbour Rose Partnership**
45 **MAGELLAN,** 8, b g Sea The Stars (IRE)—Hector's Girl **Mr P. A. Kirby**
46 **MARTALINDY,** 5, b m Martaline—Helen Wood **The Philip Kirby Racing Club**
47 **MASTER NEWTON (IRE),** 7, gr g Mastercraftsman (IRE)—French Friend (IRE) **Master Newton Partnership**
48 **MAYWAY,** 4, b f Mayson—Lighted Way **The Yorbus Syndicate**
49 **MCGARRY (IRE),** 8, b g Mahler—Little Pearl (IRE) **The Vacuum Pouch Company Limited**
50 **MIDNIGHT LEGACY (IRE),** 8, b m Getaway (GER)—Lady of The Hall (IRE) **Hambleton Racing Ltd XXXIV**
51 **MISSCARLETT (IRE),** 8, b m Red Rocks (IRE)—Coimbra (USA) **Mrs J. Porter**
52 **MOSAAWAAH (IRE),** 4, b g Fast Company (IRE)—Alternanthera **Hambleton Racing Ltd XXXIV**
53 **MOUNTAIN GLORY,** 5, b g Fame And Glory—Pickworth (IRE) **Mrs J. Sivills**
54 **MR CARBONATOR,** 7, b g Bated Breath—Diamond Lass (IRE) **Alan Fairhurst & David Fairhurst**
55 **MR MCCALL,** 4, b g Farhh—Naayla (IRE) **Mrs W. Burdett**
56 **MY STRONG MAN (IRE),** 6, b g Authorized (IRE)—Lady Chloe **The Platinum Partnership**
57 **NIVEN (IRE),** 9, b g Elusive Pimpernel (USA)—Ginger Lily (IRE) **John Birtles & Bill Allan**
58 **RAFFLES REBEL,** 4, ch g Al Kazeem—Go Between **Hope Eden Racing Limited**
59 **RAIFF (IRE),** 8, b g Shamardal (USA)—Estigaama (USA) **Mr D. R. Platt**
60 **RAVENSCAR (IRE),** 6, b m Helmet (AUS)—Cry Pearl (USA) **Mr J. A. Hall**
61 **RED FORCE ONE,** 7, ro g Lethal Force (IRE)—Dusty Red **The Yorkshire Puddings**
62 **ROBERT JOHNSON,** 4, ch g Helmet (AUS)—Sensationally **Mr M. V. Coglan**
63 **SAN MIGUEL (IRE),** 6, b g El Salvador (IRE)—Majestic Benbulben (IRE) **Mr A. McCormack**
64 **SCALLOWAY CASTLE (IRE),** 4, b br g Ocovango—Ashlings Princess (IRE) **The Earl of R. L. Ronaldshay**
65 **SENTIMENTAL LADY (IRE),** 4, b f Doyen (IRE)—Lady Chloe **Mr P. A. Kirby**
66 **SEXY BEAST,** 7, b g Teofilo (IRE)—Wadaat **The Good Looking Partnership**
67 **SHOW PROMISE,** 8, b g Josr Algarhoud (IRE)—Show Potential (IRE) **The Busby Partnership**
68 **SIR JIMMY ALLEN (FR),** 5, gr g Spanish Moon (USA)—Uranus Le Dun (FR) **FDC Holdings Ltd**
69 **SKYCUTTER (FR),** 4, b g Scissor Kick (AUS)—Skysweeper (FR) **The French Connection**
70 **SMART BOYO,** 4, b g War Command (USA)—Luluti (IRE) **smartwater utilities**
71 **SOARING STAR (IRE),** 5, b g Starspangledbanner (AUS)—Peig (IRE) **Hambleton Racing Ltd XXV**
72 **STARGAZER (IRE),** 9, b g Canford Cliffs (IRE)—Star Ruby (IRE) **Zoe Hassall & George Hassall & P Kirby**
73 **STITCH UP (IRE),** 6, b g Milan—Be My Granny **Mr D. Carter**
74 4, B g Sholokhov (IRE)—Sunlight (IRE) **Mr D. Carter**
75 **SUNSET WEST (IRE),** 7, b g Westerner—Sunshine Haven (IRE) **The Vacuum Pouch Company Limited**
76 **TELHIMLISTEN (IRE),** 6, b g Fame And Glory—Hiwaitilitellu (IRE) **Mr P. A. Kirby**
77 **TOMMASO (IRE),** 4, b g Bobby's Kitten (USA)—Aseela (IRE) **Mrs J. Porter**
78 **TOP VILLE BEN (IRE),** 10, b g Beneficial—Great Decision (IRE) **Harbour Rose Partnership**
79 **TOP VILLE BOBBY (IRE),** 5, b g Yeats (IRE)—Great Decision (IRE) **Harbour Rose Partnership**
80 **WADMAL,** 4, ch g Free Eagle (IRE)—Camlet **Mr & Mrs G. Turnbull**
81 **WEMYSS POINT,** 10, b g Champs Elysees—Wemyss Bay **The Green Oaks Partnership**
82 **WHOSHOTTHESHERIFF (IRE),** 8, b g Dylan Thomas (IRE)—Dame Foraine (FR) **Hambleton Racing Ltd XXXIV**
83 **WILLING TO PLEASE,** 5, b m Iffraaj—Tebee's Oasis **& & Fairhurst**
84 **WINFOLA (FR),** 8, gr m Motivator—Romance Bere (FR) **The Silver Linings Partnership**
85 **WYE AYE,** 7, b g Shirocco (GER)—A Media Luz (FR) **The Well Oiled Partnership**
86 **ZWICKY,** 5, b g Sixties Icon—Emma Lee **Mr P. A. Kirby**

THREE-YEAR-OLDS

87 **BARNEYS GIFT (FR),** b g Johnny Barnes (IRE)—Diamond Surprise **Mr & Mrs D. Yates**
88 **CARACRISTI,** b f Mondialiste (IRE)—Jen Jos Enigma (IRE) **Ace Bloodstock & P Kirby**
89 **JASEY (IRE),** b g Holy Roman Emperor (IRE)—Euroceleb (IRE) **Hope Eden Racing Ltd & Mrs C Barclay**
90 B c Milan—Lady Chloe
91 **LUCRUM (IRE),** b f Profitable (IRE)—Ebtisama (USA) **Hope Eden Racing Ltd & Mrs C Barclay**
92 **MARILLA (IRE),** b g f Ribchester (IRE)—Fresh Mint (IRE) **Hope Eden Racing Ltd & Mrs C Barclay**
93 Br g Mondialiste (IRE)—Musikhani **Mr P. A. Kirby**
94 **PERFECT GLORY (IRE),** b g Cotai Glory—Perfect Venture **Syps & Mrs Wendy Burdett**
95 **ROSIE'S THUNDER,** b g Night of Thunder (IRE)—Skid (IRE) **Mr P. A. Kirby**
96 **SPANISH BUTTONS (FR),** b g Spanish Moon (USA)—Lady Westerner **The Spanish Buttons Partnership**

MR PHILIP KIRBY - continued

TWO-YEAR-OLDS

97 Ch f 05/05 Sea The Moon (GER)—Best Side (IRE) (King's Best (USA)) (26361) **FDC Holdings Ltd**
98 Ch f 06/04 Mayson—Dazakhee (Sakhee (USA))
99 B f 15/03 Free Eagle (IRE)—Etesian (IRE) (Shirocco (GER)) (2551)
100 B c 20/04 Yeats (IRE)—Lady Chloe (Noverre (USA))
101 B c 26/01 Brazen Beau (AUS)—Marmot Bay (IRE) (Kodiac)
102 Ch c 29/04 Order of St George (IRE)—Miss Cilla (IRE) (Shernazar) (17007)
103 SMART BUCKS, b c 27/04 Buck's Boum (FR)—Lady Westerner (Westerner) **Mr P. A. Kirby**
104 Ch c 05/04 Fast Company (IRE)—Village Fete (Singspiel (IRE)) (34014) **FDC Holdings Ltd**
105 WOODCHIP, ch c 26/04 Getaway (GER)—Helen Wood (Lahib (USA)) **Mr P. A. Kirby**

Other Owners: Ace Bloodstock Ltd, Mr W. Allan, Mrs R. A. Bainbridge, Mrs C. Barclay, Mr D. Barlow, Mr J. Birtles, Mrs W. Burdett, R. G. Capstick, Mr A. Cartledge, Mrs C. J. Casterton, Mr A. G. Clark, Mrs S. M. Clark, Mr J. Cornforth, Mr B. H. Dolan, Mr H. Doyle, Mr A. Fairhurst, Mr D. H. Fairhurst, Alan Fairhurst & David Fairhurst, Mrs R. Fitzgerald, Mr M. D. Foden, Mrs E. C. Fraser, W. R. Fraser, Mrs R. M. E. Gibbon, Mrs G. L. Halder, Hambleton Racing Ltd, Hambleton Racing Ltd XXXIV, Mr G. A. Hassall, Mr N. A. D. Hassall, Mrs Z. L. Hassall, Hope Eden Racing Limited, Mr A. Jowsey, Mr P. A. Kirby, Mrs P. R. Kirby, Mrs S. Knowles, Mrs E. M. Lloyd, Mr J. Matthews, Mr J. McInerney, Mrs J. Morgan, Mr A. Pritchard, RedHotGardogs, Hugh T. Redhead, Mrs D. J. Ritzema, L. M. Rutherford, SYPS (UK) Ltd, Mr H. Stephenson, The Vacuum Pouch Company Limited, Mr S. R. H. Turner, Mr L. Waugh, Mrs V. M. Waugh, Mr S. J. Wyatt, Mrs A. V. Yates, Mr D. Yates.

Assistant Trainer: Simon Olley.

NH Jockey: Tommy Dowson, Joe Williamson. **Amateur Jockey:** Mr Henry Newcombe.

---

315 MR SYLVESTER KIRK, Upper Lambourn
Postal: **Cedar Lodge Stables, Upper Lambourn, Hungerford, Berkshire, RG17 8QT**
Contacts: **PHONE 01488 73215 MOBILE 07768 855261**
EMAIL info@sylvesterkirkracing.co.uk WEBSITE www.sylvesterkirkracing.co.uk

1 ALICESTAR, 4, b f Charming Thought—Atheera (IRE) **Marchwood Recycling Ltd**
2 BENNY AND THE JETS (IRE), 6, ch g Showcasing—Orange Pip **Deauville Daze Partnership**
3 DIVA DANCER, 4, b f Twilight Son—Lead A Merry Dance **Miss A. J. Rawding**
4 FURTHER MEASURE (USA), 5, b g English Channel (USA)—Price Tag **Marchwood Aggregates**
5 INDEED, 7, b g Showcasing—Argumentative **Marchwood Aggregates**
6 KODIAK ATTACK (IRE), 6, b g Kodiac—Good Clodora (IRE) **Mrs J. A. Fowler**
7 RANIA (IRE), 4, b f Estidhkaar (IRE)—Little Oz (IRE) **Mr R. Clothier & Miss J. Gray**
8 SALOUEN (IRE), 8, b g Canford Cliffs (IRE)—Gali Gal (IRE) **Mr K. Balasuriya**
9 SEATTLE ROCK, 4, b f Fastnet Rock (AUS)—Snoqualmie Girl (IRE) **J. C. Smith**
10 STRAIGHT TALKING, 4, gr f Frankel—Straight Thinking (USA) **Miss Alison Jones**
11 STUDY THE STARS, 4, b g Due Diligence—Celestial Bay

THREE-YEAR-OLDS

12 CICELY (IRE), b f The Gurkha (IRE)—Wingspan (USA) **Neil Simpson & Partners**
13 B f Mastercraftsman (IRE)—Density **N. Pickett**
14 EVERYBODY DANCE (IRE), b f No Nay Never (USA)—Inca Wood (UAE) **Mrs J. A. Fowler**
15 B f Profitable (IRE)—Logique (FR)
16 RESILIENCE, b g Aclaim (IRE)—Calypso Choir **J. C. Smith**
17 SAINT PETER (IRE), b c Holy Roman Emperor (IRE)—Dirtybirdie **Mr N Pickett & Partner**
18 SHE'S THE BOSS, b f El Kabeir (USA)—Fantastic Spring (USA) **Miss Alison Jones**
19 THELADYMISSMAISIE (IRE), b f Es Que Love (IRE)—Balqaa (USA)
20 TOSCA TIME, b f Time Test—Opera Glass **J. C. Smith**
21 URNEYMAN (IRE), b g Belardo (IRE)—Marmalade Cat
22 B f Muhaarar—Veiled Intrigue

MR SYLVESTER KIRK - continued

TWO-YEAR-OLDS

23 B c 11/03 National Defense—Attracted To You (IRE) (Hurricane Run (IRE)) (17007)
24 **CHINDWIN,** b c 09/02 Saxon Warrior (JPN)—Cay Dancer (Danehill Dancer (IRE)) (205000) **Mr K. Balasuriya**
25 Gr c 23/03 Acclamation—Chiringuita (USA) (Hard Spun (USA)) (22000)
26 B f 17/04 Kodiac—City Girl (IRE) (Elusive City (USA)) **J. C. Smith**
27 B g 03/04 Territories (IRE)—Finale (Holy Roman Emperor (IRE)) (3000)
28 B f 05/05 Australia—Loch Mirage (Elusive City (USA)) **J. C. Smith**
29 **MANUHA (IRE),** b c 25/03 U S Navy Flag (USA)—Araajmh (USA) (Street Cry (IRE)) (80000) **Mr K. Balasuriya**
30 **MELLOW MOOD,** b f 29/03 Bated Breath—Going For Gold (Baratthea (IRE)) (2500) **Neil Simpson & Partners**
31 B f 29/01 Acclamation—She Believes (IRE) (Arcano (IRE)) (60000) **Marchwood Recycling Ltd**
32 B c 30/03 Time Test—Snoqualmie Girl (IRE) (Montjeu (IRE)) **J. C. Smith**
33 B c 14/06 Galileo (IRE)—Timbuktu (IRE) (Fastnet Rock (AUS)) **J. C. Smith**

Other Owners: Mr R. W. Clothier, Miss J. F. Gray, S. A. Kirk, N. Pickett, Mrs L. M. Shanahan, Mr N. Simpson.

Assistant Trainer: Fanny Kirk.

---

316 MR STUART KITTOW, Cullompton
Postal: **Orchard House, Blackborough, Cullompton, Devon, EX15 2JD**
Contacts: **HOME 01823 680183 MOBILE 07714 218921**
EMAIL stuartkittowracing@hotmail.com WEBSITE www.stuartkittowracing.com

1 **BEYOND EQUAL,** 7, b g Kheleyf (USA)—Samasana (IRE) **Stuart Wood & Partner**
2 **FREDDY FANATAPAN,** 7, b g Nathaniel (IRE)—Pan Galactic (USA) **Dr G. S. Plastow**
3 **GHERKIN,** 5, b g Coach House (IRE)—Our Piccadilly (IRE) **Mrs G. R. Shire**
4 **MONTERIA (IRE),** 4, b g Mehmas (IRE)—Rip Van Music (IRE) **Reg Gifford & Bernice Walter**
5 **MR CHILL,** 5, b g Gentlewave (IRE)—Arctic Magic (IRE) **Mrs G. R. Shire**
6 **NEWTON JACK,** 5, b g Fast Company (IRE)—Jackline **Newton Barn Racing**
7 **ORIENTAL SPIRIT,** 4, b g Swiss Spirit—Yat Ding Yau (FR) **The Oriental Spirit Partnership**
8 **PRODUCTIVE (IRE),** 5, b g Dark Angel (IRE)—Thawrah (IRE) **Mrs P. E. Hawkings**
9 **THE DENHOLM BANDIT,** 8, b g Kayf Tara—Black Annie (IRE) **Alastair and Rachel Bell**
10 **TIBBIE DUNBAR,** 6, b m Poet's Voice—Gold Approach **Mr J. R. Urquhart**

THREE-YEAR-OLDS

11 **CORNISH STORM,** b g Coach House (IRE)—Dancing Storm **M. E. Harris**
12 **COUP DE FORCE,** b f Lethal Force (IRE)—Dilgura **The Coup de Force Partnership**
13 **FAWN AT PLAY,** ch f Recorder—Raymi Coya (CAN) **R. S. E. Gifford**
14 **NOTRE MAISON,** b f Coach House (IRE)—Our Piccadilly (IRE) **Mrs G. R. Shire**

TWO-YEAR-OLDS

15 **CHALK MOUNTAIN,** gr gr g 15/02 Outstrip—Perfect Muse (Oasis Dream)
16 B g 06/04 Brazen Beau (AUS)—Dilgura (Ishiguru (USA))
17 B c 31/01 Intrinsic—Kodi da Capo (IRE) (Kodiac)
18 **PAPABELLA,** b f 12/02 Ardad (IRE)—Plauseabella (Royal Applause) **Mrs G. R. Shire**

Other Owners: Mr A. R. Bell, Mrs R. Bell, R. S. E. Gifford, W. S. Kittow, Mrs B. Walter, Mr S. C. Wood.

Assistant Trainer: Mrs Judy Kittow.

Flat Jockey: Rob Hornby. **NH Jockey:** David Noonan, Tom Scudamore.

317 **MR WILLIAM KNIGHT, Newmarket**
Postal: **Rathmoy Stables, Hamilton Road, Newmarket, Suffolk, CB8 0GU**
Contacts: PHONE **01638 664063** MOBILE **07770 720828**
EMAIL **william@wknightracing.co.uk** WEBSITE **www.wknightracing.co.uk**
TWITTER **@WKnightRacing**

1 **AJRAD**, 4, ch g New Approach (IRE)—Princess Cammie (IRE) **Canisbay Bloodstock**
2 **AUTHOR'S DREAM**, 9, gr g Authorized (IRE)—Spring Dream (IRE) **Mr & Mrs Conroy**
3 **DUAL IDENTITY (IRE)**, 4, b g Belardo (IRE)—Teide Lady **Kennet Valley Thoroughbreds IV**
4 **GAUNTLET (IRE)**, 5, b g Galileo (IRE)—Danedrop (IRE) **J & P Seabrook & Tim Fisher**
5 **KING OF THE SOUTH (IRE)**, 5, b g Kingman—South Atlantic (USA) **S. Ali**
6 **LORDSBRIDGE BOY**, 6, b g Equiano (FR)—Fontaine House **Mr Roger & Mrs Suzie Beadle**
7 **MARY LOU (GER)**, 4, b f Protectionist (GER)—Mindemoya River (FR) **Mrs R. Baenziger-Gisi**
8 **MOKTASAAB**, 4, ch g Lope de Vega (IRE)—Dash To The Front **Mr H. Redknapp**
9 **PEARL BEACH**, 5, b m Footstepsinthesand—Western Pearl **Mr & Mrs N. Welby**
10 **PERCY'S PRIDE (IRE)**, 4, b f Sir Percy—Cartoon **S. Ali**
11 **SIR BUSKER (IRE)**, 6, b g Sir Prancealot (IRE)—Street Kitty (IRE) **Kennet Valley Thoroughbreds Xi Racing**
12 **SUNDAYINMAY (GER)**, 4, b f Pastorius (GER)—Simply Noble (GER) **Mrs R. Baenziger-Gisi**
13 **YEAR OF THE DRAGON (IRE)**, 4, b g Dragon Pulse (IRE)—Poplar Close (IRE) **Mr J. I. Barnett**

THREE-YEAR-OLDS

14 **AMZAAN (IRE)**, b f Dubawi (IRE)—Meeznah (USA) **Saif Ali & Saeed H. Altayer**
15 **ASHURA**, b f Muhaarar—Al Fareej (IRE) **S. Ali**
16 **ASTRAL BEAT (IRE)**, ch g Cotai Glory—Beat The Stars (IRE) **Racing & G. Stevens**
17 **ATLANNA**, b f Sea The Moon (GER)—Banana Split **Wardley Bloodstock**
18 **BRAZILIAN LORD**, b g Muhaarar—Brazilian Style **P. L. Winkworth**
19 **BUNKER BAY (IRE)**, b g Australia—Alf Guineas (IRE) **Kennet Valley Thoroughbreds X**
20 **CHECKANDCHALLENGE**, b br c Fast Company (IRE)—Likeable **Mr A. Hetherton**
21 B f New Approach (IRE)—Dance Awhile (IRE) **Mr A. Al Mansoori**
22 **FELLOWSHIP (IRE)**, b g Fulbright—Street Kitty (IRE) **Badger's Set**
23 **GATECRASHER GIRL**, ch f Lope de Vega (IRE)—Parsnip (IRE) **Chasemore Farm LLP**
24 **GOLD CHARM (IRE)**, b f Golden Horn—Deveron (USA) **S. Ali**
25 **GREYART**, gr g Caravaggio (USA)—Chiffonade (IRE) **S. Ali**
26 **HARB**, b g Muhaarar—Maid For Winning (USA) **Gallagher Bloodstock Limited**
27 **KINGDOM GIRL**, b f Kingman—Oshiponga **S. Ali**
28 **LELABAD**, b g Invincible Spirit (IRE)—Lanansaak (IRE) **& Seabrook**
29 **LORDSBRIDGE GIRL**, b f Adaay (IRE)—Tempting **Mr Roger & Mrs Suzie Beadle**
30 **OUR BOY SAM**, ch g Mazameer (IRE)—Bobby Vee **Mr Roger & Mrs Suzie Beadle**
31 **QUEL KAIMA (GER)**, b f Exceed And Excel (AUS)—Queensberry (GER) **Badger's Set II**
32 **ROYAL THUNDER**, b g Night of Thunder (IRE)—Spinning Melody (USA) **Saif Ali & Saeed H. Altayer**
33 **SECRET TRYST**, b f Brazen Beau (AUS)—Keep The Secret **Mr & Mrs N. Welby**
34 **SHARE THE PROFITS (IRE)**, b f Profitable (IRE)—Muhadathat **Rathmoy Racing**
35 **SUNSET AND VINE**, b g Muhaarar—Sunset Avenue (USA) **S. Ali**
36 **TIMESOFTHEESSENCE (IRE)**, b g Time Test—Alys Love **Susie & A. Hetherton**
37 Ch f Teofilo (IRE)—Tunkwa (FR) **Mr A. Al Mansoori**

TWO-YEAR-OLDS

38 **BEACH KITTY (IRE)**, b f 25/02 Gustav Klimt (IRE)—Street Kitty (IRE) (Tiger Hill (IRE)) (35000)
John & Peter Seabrook & Mrs Ann Foley
39 B c 16/04 Lope de Vega (IRE)—Dansky (IRE) (Dansili) (100000) **Gallagher Bloodstock & Ballylinch Stud**
40 **GOLDEN MOON**, b c 18/02 Havana Gold—Sorella Bella (IRE) (Clodovil (IRE)) (72000) **S. Ali**
41 Ch c 07/03 New Approach (IRE)—Halima Hatun (USA) (Algorithms (USA)) **Mr A. Menahi**
42 **HOLKHAM BAY**, b c 04/03 Aclaim (IRE)—Tumblewind (Captain Rio) (12500) **Norfolk Thoroughbreds**
43 Gr c 22/04 Kodiac—Natheer (USA) (Exchange Rate (USA)) (40000) **Mr J. I. Barnett**
44 B f 18/03 Zoffany (IRE)—Poplar Close (IRE) (Canford Cliffs (IRE)) (11429) **J.I. Barnett & Rathmoy Racing**
45 Br f 24/03 Golden Horn—Qaafeya (IRE) (New Approach (IRE)) (58000) **Mr J. I. Barnett**
46 B c 06/04 Gleneagles (IRE)—Sabaweeya (Street Cry (IRE)) (45000) **Pmg Partnership**
47 **STORY HORSE**, b c 23/02 Bated Breath—Salutare (IRE) (Sadler's Wells (USA)) (65000) **Badger's Set III**
48 B c 08/03 Hawkbill (USA)—Zacheta (Polish Precedent (USA)) **S. Ali**

MR WILLIAM KNIGHT - continued

Other Owners: Ballylinch Stud, Mr J. I. Barnett, Mr R. Beadle, Mrs S. Beadle, Mr G. Burchell, Mr T. J. Fisher, Mrs A. Foley, Gallagher Bloodstock Limited, Mrs E. J. Gregson-Williams, Mr R. W. Gregson-Williams, Mrs S. K. Hartley, Mr A. Hetherton, Mr R. S. Hoskins, Kennet Valley Thoroughbreds XI, R. F. Kilby, Mr J. D. M. King, Mrs E. J. J. Knight, W. J. Knight, Rathmoy Racing, Rathmoy Racing II, Mr J. F. Seabrook, Mr P. Seabrook, G. C. Stevens, Miss M. E. Stopher.

Assistant Trainer: Kayleigh Flower.

318
MR HILAL KOBEISSI, Newmarket
Postal: **8 Tom Jennings Close, Newmarket, Suffolk, CB8 0DU**
Contacts: **PHONE 07856 067990**
EMAIL hilalkob@live.com

1 **ALJASRA UNITED (FR)**, 4, b g Olympic Glory (IRE)—La Seine (USA) **Al Jasra Racing**

THREE-YEAR-OLDS

2 **ALJASRAPRINCESS (FR)**, ch f Olympic Glory (IRE)—La Seine (USA) **Al Jasra Racing**
3 **ALNOOD (IRE)**, b f Profitable (IRE)—Maramba (USA) **D. P. Fremel**
4 **GURKHALI WARRIOR (IRE)**, b g The Gurkha (IRE)—Quiet Down (USA) **Al Rashed Racing**
5 **MADE OF GOLD**, ch c Highland Reel (IRE)—Chapel Choir **Mr H. A. A. M. Al-Abdulmalik**
6 **PIMLICO (IRE)**, b br c No Nay Never (USA)—Gems **Al Jasra Racing**
7 **ROLLING THE DICE (IRE)**, b f Mehmas (IRE)—Padma **Mr H. A. A. M. Al-Abdulmalik**
8 **THUNDER VALLEY**, ch g Night of Thunder (IRE)—Moonstone Rock **Mr A. A. A. Almulla**

TWO-YEAR-OLDS

9 B c 02/03 James Garfield (IRE)—Hi Milady (IRE) (Sir Prancealot (IRE)) (9779) **Al Jasra Racing**
10 **UNIVERSAL GRACE**, b f 20/01 Brazen Beau (AUS)—Spritzig (Exceed And Excel (AUS)) (15000) **D. P. Fremel**

319
DANIEL AND CLAIRE KUBLER, Lambourn
Postal: **Sarsen Farm, Upper Lambourn, Hungerford, Berkshire, RG17 8RG**
Contacts: **PHONE 07984 287254**

1 **ABBEY HEIGHTS**, 4, b g Dark Angel (IRE)—Ducissa **Mr & Mrs G. Middlebrook**
2 **BOWLAND PARK**, 4, b g New Bay—Distinctive **Mr & Mrs G. Middlebrook**
3 **DON'T TELL CLAIRE**, 5, ro m Gutaifan (IRE)—Avenbury **Mr A. Stonehill**
4 **HELM ROCK**, 4, b g Pivotal—Nibbling (IRE) **Capture the Moment VII**
5 **L'ENCLUME**, 4, ch f Gleneagles (IRE)—Mama Quilla (USA) **Mr & Mrs G. Middlebrook**
6 **NANTOSUELTA (IRE)**, 4, b f Kodiac—Dearest Daisy **Crowd, New Image Contracts & Partners**
7 **OUTRAGE**, 10, ch g Exceed And Excel (AUS)—Ludynosa (USA) **Capture the Moment & Crowd Racing**
8 **PERCY'S LAD**, 4, ch g Sir Percy—Victory Garden **Mr A. Kerr**
9 **PLEASANT CHARM**, 4, b f Charming Thought—Albertine Rose **Mr & Mrs G. Middlebrook**
10 **SENECA CHIEF**, 8, b g Invincible Spirit (IRE)—Albertine Rose **Mr & Mrs G. Middlebrook**
11 **ZULU GIRL**, 5, b m Lethal Force (IRE)—Upskittled **Trish and Colin Fletcher-Hall**

THREE-YEAR-OLDS

12 **ATLANTIC HEART (IRE)**, b f Twilight Son—Heaven's Sake **Mr P. O'Connor**
13 **CONTESSA VERDE**, b f Intello (GER)—Ducissa **Mr & Mrs G. Middlebrook**
14 B g Invincible Spirit (IRE)—Distinctive **Mr & Mrs G. Middlebrook**
15 **ELLEN CLACY**, b f Havana Gold (IRE)—Melbourne Memories **Diskovery Partnership IX**
16 **EMINENT ANGEL**, b gr f Dark Angel (IRE)—Eminently **Mr & Mrs G. Middlebrook**

DANIEL AND CLAIRE KUBLER - continued

17 **FISCAL POLICY (IRE)**, ch c Profitable (IRE)—Penny's Gift **Mr & Mrs G. Middlebrook**
18 **FROM LITTLE ACORNS**, ch g Postponed (IRE)—Rue Cambon (IRE) **Oakmere Racing**
19 **GHYLL MANOR (IRE)**, b g Gleneagles (IRE)—Jubilant Lady (USA) **Mr & Mrs G. Middlebrook**
20 **HELM PRINCESS (IRE)**, b f Prince of Lir (IRE)—Tartufo Dolce (IRE) **Bell, Thompson Mr Middlebrook**
21 **LIL GUFF**, b f Twilight Son—Lady McGuffy (IRE) **H. M. W. Clifford**
22 Ch g Australia—Mama Quilla (USA) **Mr & Mrs G. Middlebrook**
23 **OUTGATE**, br c Outstrip—Penny Drops **Mr & Mrs G. Middlebrook**
24 **POET'S REALM**, b g Territories (IRE)—Poetic Queen (IRE) **Mr & Mrs G. Middlebrook**
25 **PRESENTLY**, b f Time Test—Rosaceous **Mr & Mrs G. Middlebrook**
26 **PROMOTION**, b g Fast Company (IRE)—Quiet Elegance **J Lukas, T Aspinall & Partners**
27 **RAMPAGE (IRE)**, b g New Bay—Hall Hee (IRE) **D Blunt & G Middlebrook**
28 **SOUTHWOLD (IRE)**, b c Gleneagles (IRE)—Intrigue **Mr & Mrs G. Middlebrook**
29 Ch f Almanzor (FR)—Sweet Cecily (IRE) **H. M. W. Clifford**

TWO-YEAR-OLDS

30 B f 09/02 Camelot—Acquainted (Shamardal (USA)) **Mr & Mrs G. Middlebrook**
31 Gr f 25/02 Ribchester (IRE)—Albertine Rose (Namid) **Mr & Mrs G. Middlebrook**
32 B c 01/03 Gustav Klimt (IRE)—Black Meyeden (FR) (Black Minnaloushe (USA)) (57143)
33 B f 25/03 Cityscape—Break Time (Dansili) (22000)
34 Gr ro f 09/02 The Factor (USA)—Chime Hope (USA) (Street Cry (IRE)) **Mr & Mrs G. Middlebrook**
35 **CIARA PEARL**, b f 14/02 Twilight Son—Upskittled (Diktat) (20000) **Mr A. Stonehill**
36 B br f 26/02 New Approach (IRE)—Dalasyla (IRE) (Marju (IRE)) (30000)
37 B f 09/02 Oasis Dream—Dubai Affair (Dubawi (IRE)) (85000)
38 B c 01/02 Cityscape—Dubai Cyclone (USA) (Bernardini (USA))
39 B c 23/04 Bobby's Kitten (USA)—Elation (IRE) (Invincible Spirit (IRE)) **Mr & Mrs G. Middlebrook**
40 B c 18/02 Zoffany (IRE)—Future Energy (Frankel) (25000)
41 B c 04/02 Poet's Word (IRE)—Kelamita (IRE) (Pivotal) (15000)
42 B c 29/02 Cracksman—Penny Drops (Invincible Spirit (IRE)) (57000)
43 B f 24/02 New Bay—Penny Rose (Danehill Dancer (IRE)) (20000) **Mr & Mrs G. Middlebrook**
44 B f 15/03 Time Test—Quiet Elegance (Fantastic Light (USA)) (20000)

Other Owners: Mr A. G. Bell, Mr D. Blunt, David & Yvonne Blunt, Mrs Y. Blunt, Capture Syndicate II, Crowd Racing Partnership, Mr C. M. Fletcher, Mrs P. A. Hall, Mrs C. E. Kubler, Mr C. McKenna, Mr G. Middlebrook, Mr & Mrs G. Middlebrook, Mrs L. A. Middlebrook, Miss M. A. Thompson.

---

320 MR TOM LACEY, Woolhope
Postal: **Sapness Farm, Woolhope, Herefordshire, HR1 4RG**
Contacts: **MOBILE 07768 398604**
EMAIL tom@cottagefield.co.uk WEBSITE www.cottagefield.co.uk

1 **ADRIMEL (FR)**, 7, b br g Tirwanako (FR)—Irise De Gene (FR) **Lady C. Bamford & Miss A. Bamford**
2 **ARGONAUTA (IRE)**, 6, b g Getaway (GER)—Oscar Ladensa (IRE) **Mr Jerry Hinds & Mr Ashley Head**
3 **BEAN NORTY**, 6, gr m Malinas (GER)—Bouncing Bean **Miss I. H. Pickard**
4 **BENITO (FR)**, 5, b g Rail Link—Aspolina (IRE) **Mrs C. Brooks**
5 **BLOW YOUR WAD (IRE)**, 4, b g Walk In The Park (IRE)—Molly's Mate (IRE) **Mr Jerry Hinds & Mr Ashley Head**
6 **CAMEMBERT ELECTRIC (IRE)**, 6, ch m Sholokhov (IRE)—On The Horizon (IRE) **Mr J. Thomas**
7 **CARN A CHLAMAIN (USA)**, 4, b g Fed Biz (USA)—Chalonitka (USA) **ValueRacingClub.co.uk**
8 **CRUZ CONTROL (FR)**, 5, b g Saint des Saints (FR)—En La Cruz (FR) **Mr F Green & Mr J Chinn**
9 **DIBBLE DECKER (IRE)**, 6, b g Jet Away—Bella Minna (IRE) **ValueRacingClub.co.uk**
10 **DORKING BOY**, 8, ch g Schiaparelli (GER)—Megasue **Galloping On The South Downs Partnership**
11 **FLASHING GLANCE**, 9, b g Passing Glance—Don And Gerry (IRE) **Barrett, Meredith, Panniers, Wilde**
12 **GINNY'S DESTINY (IRE)**, 6, b g Yeats (IRE)—Dantes Term (IRE) **Gordon & Su Hall**
13 **GLORY AND FORTUNE (IRE)**, 7, b g Fame And Glory—Night Heron (IRE) **Mr J. Hinds**
14 **GLORY AND HONOUR (IRE)**, 6, b g Elusive Pimpernel (USA)—On Khee **Mr Jerry Hinds & Mr Ashley Head**
15 **GOLD CLERMONT (FR)**, 6, b m Balko (FR)—Une Dame d'Or (FR) **Doyoufollow Partnership**

MR TOM LACEY - continued

16 **HESQUE DE L'ISLE (FR)**, 5, b g Saddler Maker (IRE)—Naiade de L'Isle (FR) **Mr J. Hinds**
17 **HIGHEST SUN (FR)**, 8, b g Sunday Break (JPN)—Highest Price (FR) **Mr A. J. Head**
18 **HIGHSTAKESPLAYER (IRE)**, 6, b g Ocovango—Elivette (FR) **Mr Jerry Hinds & Mr Ashley Head**
19 **HUNTING PERCIVAL**, 7, b g Sir Percy—Motcombe (IRE) **Lady N. F. Cobham**
20 **IMMORTAL FAME (IRE)**, 6, b g Fame And Glory—Calverleigh Court (IRE) **Mr F. J. Allen**
21 **KIMBERLITE CANDY (IRE)**, 10, b g Flemensfirth (USA)—Mandys Native (IRE) **Mr J. P. McManus**
22 **KING FERDINAND (IRE)**, 6, b g Milan—Nobody's Darling (IRE) **Mr J. Hinds**
23 **KISHORN**, 5, b m Kayf Tara—Apple Town **Mr P. J. H. Wills**
24 4, B g Getaway (GER)—La Scala Diva (IRE) **Mr Jerry Hinds & Mr Ashley Head**
25 **LAMANVER STORM**, 7, b g Geordieland (FR)—Lamanver Homerun **Dr D. Christensen**
26 **LOSSIEMOUTH**, 7, b g Makfi—First Bloom (USA) **Lady N. F. Cobham**
27 **MACFIN (IRE)**, 6, br g Dylan Thomas (IRE)—Justfour (IRE) **Mr T. F. Lacey**
28 **MARTY TIME (FR)**, 6, gr g Martaline—Shahwarda (FR) **Mr Jerry Hinds & Mr Ashley Head**
29 **NEVILLE'S CROSS (IRE)**, 7, b g Stowaway—Dancing Bird (IRE) **Mr F Green & Mr J Chinn**
30 **NOCTE VOLATUS**, 7, b g Midnight Legend—Aeronautica (IRE) **Lady Cobham & Dauntsey Park**
31 **OPERATION MANNA**, 6, b g Champs Elysees—Vickers Vimy **Lady N. F. Cobham**
32 4, B g Getaway (GER)—Party Belle
33 **PIAFF BUBBLES (IRE)**, 6, b br g Fame And Glory—Liss Na Tintri (IRE) **Mr Jerry Hinds & Mr Ashley Head**
34 **POUNDING POET (IRE)**, 6, b g Yeats (IRE)—Pestal And Mortar (IRE) **Mrs T. P. James**
35 **PRIMITIC (FR)**, 4, b g Creachadoir (IRE)—Sistadenn (FR)
36 **QUICK DRAW (IRE)**, 6, b g Getaway (GER)—Sept Verites (FR) **Alice Bamford, Cpe Brooks & Mr C Palmer**
37 **RED NIKA (FR)**, 7, br g Denham Red (FR)—Nika Glitters (FR) **Mr D. Kellett**
38 **ROGER RAREBIT**, 5, b g Black Sam Bellamy (IRE)—Rebekah Rabbit (IRE) **Mr P. J. H. Wills**
39 **ROSMUC RELAY (IRE)**, 10, b g Presenting—Aughrim Vic (IRE) **Mr J. F. Perriss**
40 **SAN AGUSTIN (IRE)**, 6, b g Ocovango—Presentingmissoats (IRE) **P J King & Son**
41 **SCIPION (IRE)**, 6, b g Shantou (USA)—Morning Calm **Mr T. F. Lacey**
42 **SEBASTOPOL (IRE)**, 8, b g Fame And Glory—Knockcroghery (IRE) **Mr C. Boultbee-Brooks**
43 **SWEET SPIRIT (FR)**, 8, b m Linda's Lad—Childermas (IRE) **John Priday, Mike Mifflin & Wyn Owen**
44 **TEA CLIPPER (IRE)**, 7, b g Stowaway—A Plus Ma Puce (FR) **Mr Jerry Hinds & Mr Ashley Head**
45 **TERRIERMAN (IRE)**, 8, br g Getaway (GER)—Dibella (IRE) **Mr L. R. Attrill**
46 **THOMAS PATRICK (IRE)**, 10, b g Winged Love (IRE)—Huncheon Siss (IRE) **Mr D. Kellett**
47 **TOKARA (IRE)**, 6, b m Flemensfirth (USA)—Maple Lady (IRE) **John Nicholls Racing**
48 **TOUCAN SAM**, 4, b g Frankel—Ridafa (IRE) **Lady Bamford**
49 **VELASCO (IRE)**, 6, b g Sholokhov (IRE)—Bilboa (FR) **Mr D. Kellett**
50 **VENGEANCE**, 4, b g Schiaparelli (GER)—Titch Strider (IRE) **Mr J. F. Panvert**
51 **YOU NAME HIM**, 6, b g Proclamation—Scarlett O'Tara **HFT Forklifts Limited**

Other Owners: Miss A. C. Bamford, Lady Bamford, Mr P. L. Barrett, Mr C. P. E. Brooks, Mr W. J. Chinn, Lady N. F. Cobham, Mr N. D. Cox, Mr G. S. M. Day, F. M. Green, Mr G. A. Hall, Mrs S. L. Hall, Mr A. J. Head, Mr J. Hinds, Mr J. J. King, Mrs V. C. King, Mr G. J. Meredith, Mr T. M. Mifflin, Mr J. A. M. Nicholls, Mrs J. J. Nicholls, Mr D. W. Owen, Mr C. Palmer, Mr N. J. Panniers, J. Priday, Miss V. C. Sturgis, Mr W. E. Wilde.

NH Jockey: Stan Sheppard. **Conditional Jockey:** Dylan Kitts.

	MR NICK LAMPARD, Marlborough
321	Postal: **South Cottage, 2 The Crossroads, Clatford, Marlborough, Wiltshire, SN8 4EA** Contacts: **PHONE 01672 861420**

1 4, B f Eastern Anthem (IRE)—Goochypoochyprader **The Ivy**
2 **HOOCHYGOOCHYMAN**, 6, b g Gentlewave (IRE)—Goochypoochyprader **The Ivy**
3 **LOGAN'S CHOICE**, 7, b g Redoute's Choice (AUS)—Bright Morning (USA) **The Ivy**

322 MR JUSTIN LANDY, Leyburn
Postal: **2 Beckwood, Spennithorne, Leyburn, North Yorkshire, DL8 5FB**
EMAIL jlandyracing@hotmail.com

1 DO NO WRONG (IRE), 6, br g Sageburg (IRE)—Uncommited (IRE) **Mrs P. Southerington**
2 LALOCHEZIA (IRE), 7, ch g Shirocco (GER)—Flemens Pride **Mrs P. Southerington**
3 MOONLIGHT BEAM (IRE), 7, b g Kalanisi (IRE)—Assidua (IRE) **Mrs P. Southerington**
4 RUMBLE B (IRE), 8, b g Presenting—John's Eliza (IRE) **Mr J. P. G. Landy**

323 MISS EMMA LAVELLE, Marlborough
Postal: **Bonita Racing Stables, Ogbourne Maizey, Marlborough, Wiltshire, SN8 1RY**
Contacts: PHONE 01672 511544 MOBILE 07774 993998 FAX 01672 511544
EMAIL info@emmalavelle.com WEBSITE www.emmalavelle.com

1 AHEAD OF THE FIELD (IRE), 7, ch g Flemensfirth (USA)—Last of The Bunch **Andy & The Frisky Fillies**
2 AVALANCHE PEAK (IRE), 5, ch g Soldier of Fortune (IRE)—Rossadare (IRE) **Mr D. Donoghue**
3 BERTIE BLUE, 5, b g Blue Bresil (FR)—Madame Allsorts **Biltmore Syndicate**
4 BIG FISH (IRE), 4, b g Flemensfirth (USA)—Tweedledrum **N. Mustoe**
5 BOREHAM BILL (IRE), 10, b g Tikkanen (USA)—Crimond (IRE) **Mrs S. P. Foran**
6 BUSTER THOMAS (IRE), 11, b g Westerner—Awesome Miracle (IRE) **Axom LXVII**
7 CANTY BAY (IRE), 5, b g Shantou (USA)—Afairs (IRE) **Mr G. P. MacIntosh**
8 CAPTAIN BROOMFIELD (IRE), 6, b g Arakan (USA)—Presenting d'Azy (IRE) **Mr A. Gemmell**
9 CLASSIC KING (IRE), 4, b g Champs Elysees—Hangar Six (IRE) **Mr & Mrs W & Dr T Davies & Mrs T Grundy**
10 CONNOLLY (IRE), 4, b g Califet (FR)—Bartlemy Bell (IRE) **Mr T. D. J. Syder**
11 DAGUENEAU (IRE), 7, b g Champs Elysees—Bright Enough **Mr A. Gemmell**
12 DE RASHER COUNTER, 10, b g Yeats (IRE)—Dedrunknmunky (IRE) **Makin' Bacon Partnership**
13 DO YOU THINK, 6, b m So You Think (NZ)—Leblon (IRE) **Bonita Racing Club**
14 DREAM IN THE PARK (IRE), 5, b g Walk In The Park (IRE)—Old Dreams (IRE) **P. G. Jacobs**
15 EASTERLY, 6, b m Shirocco (GER)—Easter Dancer **Easter Racing Club**
16 ECLAIR GURY (FR), 8, b g Califet (FR)—Matasurf (FR) **Dominic Burke & Tim Syder**
17 EUREKA CREEK (IRE), 6, b m Jet Away—Copper River (IRE) **Sailing to Byzantium**
18 FEDELTA (IRE), 8, b g Flemensfirth (USA)—Old Moon (IRE) **Exors of the Late Mr T. J. Hemmings**
19 FLEMCARA (IRE), 10, b g Flemensfirth (USA)—Cara Mara (IRE) **Andy & The Frisky Fillies**
20 FLYING NUN (IRE), 7, b m Robin des Champs (FR)—Mystic Masie (IRE) **N. Mustoe & A. Gemmell**
21 GENERAL MEDRANO (IRE), 5, b g Ocovango—Talween **Elite Racing 003**
22 GOLD LINK (FR), 6, b g Rail Link—Une de Montot (FR) **Owners Group 057**
23 GREY FOX (IRE), 5, gr g Gutaifan (IRE)—Boucheron **Mrs Jennifer Simpson Racing**
24 GUARD DUTY, 5, b g Kapgarde (FR)—Ile de See (FR) **Owners Group 074**
25 HANG IN THERE (IRE), 8, b g Yeats (IRE)—Jaldemosa (FR) **Tim Syder & Andrew Gemmell**
26 HAWK'S WELL (IRE), 8, b g Yeats (IRE)—Our Song **Mrs N. Turner & Mrs E. Fenton**
27 HIGHLY PRIZED, 9, b br g Manduro (GER)—Razzle (USA) **H.Pridham & D.Donoghue**
28 HUNTING BROOK (IRE), 5, b g Presenting—Fleur d'Ainay (IRE) **Bryan & Philippa Burrough**
29 IRISH PROPHECY (IRE), 9, b g Azamour (IRE)—Prophets Honor (FR) **N. Mustoe**
30 JEMIMA P (IRE), 8, b m Jeremy (USA)—Peig Alainn (IRE) **The Three A's Syndicate**
31 JUBILYMPICS, 10, b m Kapgarde (FR)—Pepite de Soleil (FR) **Hoe Racing**
32 KILLER CLOWN (IRE), 8, b g Getaway—Our Soiree (IRE) **Mr T. D. J. Syder**
33 KING'S THRESHOLD (IRE), 5, b g Yeats (IRE)—Pearl Buttons **Sailing to Byzantium**
34 LADY CARO (IRE), 4, b f Soldier of Fortune (IRE)—Springinherstep (IRE)
Alison & Tony Millett & Charles Dingwall
35 LIGHT N STRIKE (IRE), 6, b g Leading Light (IRE)—One Rose **Salvo & Alex Giannini, N.Farrell**
36 MANOFTHEMOUNTAIN (IRE), 9, b g Mahler—Womanofthemountain (IRE) **P. G. Jacobs**
37 MASTER MILLINER (IRE), 6, ch g Helmet (AUS)—Aqualina (IRE) **Mrs Jennifer Simpson Racing**
38 MIKHAILA (IRE), 4, b f Sholokhov (IRE)—Turica (IRE) **Alison & Tony Millett & Emma Fenton**
39 MINELLA BUSTER (IRE), 6, br g Beat Hollow—Itsallaracket (IRE) **The Pick 'N' Mix Partnership**
40 MISTY BLOOM (IRE), 9, b m Yeats (IRE)—Misty Mountain (IRE) **Bonita Racing Club**
41 MUMBO JUMBO (IRE), 6, b g Califet (FR)—Touched By Angels (IRE) **N. Mustoe**
42 MUSKOKA (IRE), 4, b g Milan—Fine Fortune (IRE) **Mrs P. J. Travis**
43 MY SILVER LINING (IRE), 6, gr m Cloudings (IRE)—Welsh Connection (IRE) **Mrs C. J. Djivanovic**

MISS EMMA LAVELLE - continued

44 **NOLLYADOR (FR)**, 5, b g No Risk At All (FR)—Playa du Charmil (FR) **Highclere Thoroughbred Racing -Nollyador**
45 **ONEANDAHALFDEGREES (IRE)**, 4, ch f Flemensfirth (USA)—Leading Lady **The High Altitude Partnership**
46 **PAISLEY PARK (IRE)**, 10, b g Oscar (IRE)—Presenting Shares (IRE) **Mr A. Gemmell**
47 **PEMBERLEY (IRE)**, 9, b g Darsi (FR)—Eyebright (IRE) **Laurie Kimber & Partners**
48 **PITCH IT UP**, 6, b g Black Sam Bellamy (IRE)—Mtilly **Mrs S. Metcalfe**
49 **POINT HIM OUT (USA)**, 5, b g Point of Entry (USA)—Rahy's Colors (USA) **H.Pridham & D.Donoghue**
50 **RAJARAN (FR)**, 5, gr g Martaline—Ravna (FR) **The High Altitude Partnership**
51 **REBEL INTENTIONS (IRE)**, 5, b g Aiken—Robin's Solo (IRE) **The Hon J. R. Drummond**
52 **RED ROOKIE**, 7, ch g Black Sam Bellamy (IRE)—Auction Belle **The Hawk Inn Syndicate 3**
53 **ROCKY LAKE (IRE)**, 6, b g Presenting—Cool Quest (IRE) **Exors of the Late Mr T. J. Hemmings**
54 **RUNSWICK BAY**, 7, b g Arvico (FR)—Chantal **The Hon J. R. Drummond**
55 **SAM BARTON**, 7, b g Black Sam Bellamy (IRE)—Bartons Bride (IRE) **Exors of the Late Mr T. J. Hemmings**
56 **SHANG TANG (IRE)**, 8, b g Shantou (USA)—Ballyguider Bridge (IRE) **T. Syder & N. Mustoe**
57 **SHIROCCAN ROLL**, 8, b g Shirocco (GER)—Folie Dancer **Lavelle, Major D Ryan**
58 **SHIROCCY ROAD**, 6, b m Shirocco (GER)—Folie Dancer **J. R. Lavelle & Dr Mark Scott**
59 **SILENT ASSISTANT (IRE)**, 8, b g Sans Frontieres (IRE)—Monanig Lass (IRE) **Lavelle, Awdry & Williams**
60 **STORM LORD (IRE)**, 6, br gr g Yeats (IRE)—Lady Sagamix (FR) **Kevin Lloyd & Nicky Turner**
61 **TABLE THIRTY FOUR**, 5, br g Blue Bresil (FR)—Whoops A Daisy **D.Burke, T.Syder & Mrs D.L.Whateley**
62 **TARA NIECE**, 9, b m Kayf Tara—Pepite de Soleil (FR) **Hoe Racing**
63 **TARAHUMARA**, 6, b g Kayf Tara—My World (FR) **N. Turner & C. Schicht**
64 **TEDWIN HILLS (IRE)**, 5, b g Getaway (GER)—Ashwell Lady (IRE) **Mr S. W. Turner**
65 **THE STREET (IRE)**, 6, b g Fame And Glory—Baileys Partytime **Exors of the Late Mr T. J. Hemmings**
66 **THE SWEENEY (IRE)**, 10, b g Oscar (IRE)—Banningham Blaze **N. Mustoe**
67 **THUNDER SURF**, 9, ch g Helmet (AUS)—Quiquillo (USA) **Bonita Racing Club**
68 **THUNDERSTRUCK (IRE)**, 8, b g Fame And Glory—Go Sandy Go (IRE) **Gemmell, Lavelle & Williams**
69 **TOP DOG (IRE)**, 5, b g Leading Light (IRE)—Princess Leya (IRE) **N. Mustoe**
70 **TWO TO TANGO**, 4, b g Kayf Tara—Folie Dancer **J.R. Lavelle & Paul G. Jacobs**
71 **VOICE OF CALM**, 6, b m Poet's Voice—Marliana (IRE) **Tim Syder & Hungerford Park Partnership**
72 **WATER WAGTAIL**, 15, b g Kahyasi—Kentford Grebe **D. I. Bare**
73 **WESTERN VICTORY (IRE)**, 9, b m Westerner—Zara's Victory (IRE) **Swanbridge Bloodstock Limited**
74 **WILD WILBUR (IRE)**, 6, ch g Presenting—Kon Tiky (FR) **Mr & Mrs W & Dr T Davies & Mrs T Grundy**
75 **WOULDUBEWELL (IRE)**, 8, b m Gold Well—Howrwedoin (IRE) **Owners Group 063**
76 **YOUNG BUTLER (IRE)**, 6, b g Yeats (IRE)—Name For Fame (USA) **Mr T. D. J. Syder**
77 **ZARAFSHAN (IRE)**, 6, b g Shamardal (USA)—Zarshana (IRE) **Mr R. J. Lavelle**

THREE-YEAR-OLDS

78 **JESUILA DES MOTTES (FR)**, b f Voiladenuo (FR)—Ouheta des Mottes (FR) **Mrs C. J. Djivanovic**

Other Owners: Mr C. V. Awdry, Miss C. E. Babey, Mr D. M. Bradshaw, Mr D. J. Burke, B. R. H. Burrough, Mrs P. J. Burrough, Mrs S. C. Davies, Dr T. J. W. Davies, Mr W. P. L. Davies, Mr C. B. J. Dingwall, Mr D. Donoghue, Mr J. B. Duffy, Mr N. Farrell, Mr A. Gemmell, Mrs A. Giannini, Mr S. Giannini, Mrs T. A. Grundy, Hungerford Park Limited, P.G. Jacobs, Mr R. S. Keck, Mr L. G. Kimber, Miss I. G. Langton, Miss E. C. Lavelle, Mr J. R. Lavelle, Mr R. J. Lavelle, Mr K. A. Lloyd, Mrs L. N. Major, Mrs S. Metcalfe, Mr & Mrs A Millett, Mr A. J. Millett, Mrs A. M. Millett, N. Mustoe, Ms H. A. Pridham, Mr D. J. Ryan, K. P. Ryan, Miss C. Schicht, Dr M. J. Scott, Mrs J. I. Simpson, Mr W. H. Simpson, Mr J. Smee, Mr T. D. J. Syder, Mrs N. C. Turner, Mrs V. A. Villers, Mr A. G. Weston, Exors of the Late Mr P. R. Weston, Mrs D. L. Whateley, Mrs P. H. Williams, Mr I. P. Wixon, Mr B. J. Wren.

Assistant Trainer: Barry Fenton.

---

324   **MR TOBY LAWES, Beare Green**
Postal: **Henfold House Cottage, Henfold Lane, Beare Green, Dorking, Surrey, RH5 4RW**
EMAIL **toby@tobylawesracing.com**

1 **ALKOPOP (GER)**, 8, gr g Jukebox Jury (IRE)—Alkeste (GER) **Mr Andrew & Sarah Wates**
2 **BALLYGLASS (IRE)**, 5, b g Montmartre (FR)—Wite Lioness **R. M. Kirkland**
3 **EYE OF AN EAGLE (FR)**, 9, b g Linda's Lad—Vie des Aigles (FR) **Mr Andrew & Sarah Wates**
4 **FRENCH CRUSADER (FR)**, 9, b g Kapgarde (FR)—Largesse (FR) **R. M. Kirkland**
5 **GEOMETRICAL (IRE)**, 5, ch g Dawn Approach (IRE)—Symmetrical (USA)
6 **GO FORRIT (IRE)**, 8, b g Jeremy (USA)—Ben Roseler (IRE) **Mr Andrew & Sarah Wates**

MR TOBY LAWES - continued

7 **GONE WALKABOUT (IRE)**, 4, b g Walk In The Park (IRE)—Money Boat (IRE) **Mr Andrew & Sarah Wates**
8 **JOYFUL KIT (IRE)**, 6, b m Getaway (GER)—Kitara (GER) **National Hunt Racing Club**
9 **KANNAPOLIS (IRE)**, 7, b g Makfi—Alta Definizione (IRE) **Henfold Harriers**
10 **KAP AUTEUIL (FR)**, 7, b g Kapgarde (FR)—Turboka (FR) **Mr Andrew & Sarah Wates**
11 **NASHVILLE NIPPER (IRE)**, 8, b g Millenary—Benfrasea (IRE) **Beare With Us Wheeler, Hawkins & Copley**
12 **NICKOBOY (FR)**, 7, b g Full of Gold (FR)—Dikanika (FR) **Mr Andrew & Sarah Wates**
13 **ONEWAYORTOTHER (IRE)**, 4, b g Great Pretender (IRE)—Betwixt (IRE) **Mr Andrew & Sarah Wates**
14 **REALTA ROYALE**, 4, b f Pether's Moon (IRE)—Sky Calling **Mr M. J. Allen**
15 **SAYO**, 8, gr g Dalakhani (IRE)—Tiyi (FR) **Eventmasters Racing**
16 **SUBLIME HEIGHTS (IRE)**, 6, b g Arcadio (GER)—Corrag Lass (IRE) **Mr Andrew & Sarah Wates**
17 **VOCAL DUKE (IRE)**, 6, b g Vocalised (USA)—Heir Today (IRE) **Mr B. L. M. Barnett**
18 **VOYAGE DE RETOUR (IRE)**, 10, b g Craigsteel—Taipers (IRE) **Mrs E. A. Bingley**
19 **ZACONY REBEL (IRE)**, 7, b g Getaway (GER)—Bay Rebel (IRE) **Mr Andrew & Sarah Wates**

Other Owners: Mrs C. V. Copley, Mrs A. Hawkins, Mr T. Lawes, Miss E. Scott, The Beare With Us Partnership, A. T. A. Wates, Mrs S. M. Wates, Mr N. J. Wheeler.

---

325 MISS KERRY LEE, Presteigne
Postal: **Bell House, Byton, Presteigne, Powys, LD8 2HS**
Contacts: MOBILE **07968 242663**
EMAIL kerry@kerrylee.co.uk WEBSITE www.kerrylee.co.uk

1 **BALLYBEGG (IRE)**, 7, b g Mahler—Rebel Flyer (IRE) **Glass Half Full**
2 **BLACK POPPY**, 6, b g Kayf Tara—Poppy Come Running (IRE) **West Coast Haulage Limited**
3 **DEMACHINE**, 8, b g Flemensfirth (USA)—Dancingonthemoon (IRE) **West Coast Haulage Limited**
4 **DESTINED TO SHINE (IRE)**, 10, b g Dubai Destination (USA)—Good Shine (IRE) **Campbell-mizen**
5 **DO IT FOR THY SEN (IRE)**, 8, ch g Mountain High (IRE)—Ashlings Princess (IRE) **L & Lee**
6 **EATON COLLINA (IRE)**, 7, b g Milan—Flowers On Sunday (IRE) **Mrs H. Watson**
7 **EATON HILL (IRE)**, 10, b g Yeats (IRE)—Guilt Less (FR) **Mrs H. Watson**
8 **FAY CE QUE VOUDRAS (IRE)**, 6, b m Getaway (GER)—Buck's Blue (FR) **W. Roseff**
9 **FINANCIER**, 9, ch g Dubawi (IRE)—Desired **W. Roseff**
10 **GREENROCK ABBEY (IRE)**, 6, ch g El Salvador (IRE)—Aos Dana (IRE) **L & Lee**
11 **HELLFIRE PRINCESS**, 5, ch m Dunaden (FR)—Ryde Back **W. Roseff**
12 **HENRI LE BON (IRE)**, 7, b g Sea The Stars (IRE)—Speed Song **W. Roseff**
13 **KRAQUELINE (FR)**, 5, gr m Martaline—Free Sky (FR) **West Coast Haulage Limited**
14 **LICIA ST GOUSTAN (FR)**, 5, b m Great Pretender (IRE)—Saint Goustan (FR) **W. Roseff**
15 **MAGIC DANCER**, 10, b g Norse Dancer (IRE)—King's Siren (IRE) **The Magic Partnership**
16 **NEMEAN LION (GER)**, 5, b g Golden Horn—Ninfea (GER) **W. Roseff**
17 **NEW FOUND FAME (IRE)**, 6, b g Fame And Glory—Coco Opera (IRE) **West Coast Haulage Limited**
18 **NOT SURE (IRE)**, 6, br g Presenting—Pink Mist (IRE) **W. Roseff**
19 **ORCHARD GROVE (IRE)**, 6, b g Valirann (FR)—Little Vinnie (IRE) **Mr D. M. Morgan**
20 **PIMLICO POINT (IRE)**, 5, ch g Flemensfirth (USA)—Royale Flag (FR) **W. Roseff**
21 **SHAMAN DU BERLAIS (FR)**, 9, b g Saint des Saints (FR)—Shinca (FR) **Mrs C. M. Marles**
22 **STORM CONTROL (IRE)**, 9, b g September Storm (GER)—Double Dream (IRE) **W. Roseff**
23 **TOP GAMBLE (IRE)**, 14, ch g Presenting—Zeferina (IRE) **Miss K. Lee**
24 **TOWN PARKS (IRE)**, 11, b g Morozov (USA)—Outdoor Heather (IRE) **Mrs J. A. Beavan**

Other Owners: Mr R. L Baker, Mr G. T. Gilbert, R. A. Lee, Mr P. T. G. Phillips, W. Roseff.

Assistant Trainer: Richard Lee.

NH Jockey: Jamie Moore, Richard Patrick. **Conditional Jockey:** Daire McConville.

326 MR PATRICK LEECH, Newmarket
Postal: **41 High Street, Cheveley, Newmarket, Suffolk, CB8 9DQ**
Contacts: **PHONE 01638 731513**
EMAIL shortyleech@btinternet.com

1 **ANNAKONDA (IRE)**, 6, b m Morpheus—Royal Esteem **Mr W. J. S. Prosser**
2 4, B c Starspangledbanner (AUS)—Buttonhole **Mr W. J. S. Prosser**
3 **CHATEAU PEAPOD**, 5, b m Coach House (IRE)—Dash of Lime **Mr W. J. S. Prosser**
4 **ECOLOGICALLY KIND**, 4, b f Charm Spirit (IRE)—Whatizzit **Mr W. J. S. Prosser**
5 **INDIAN PEARL**, 4, b c Pearl Secret—Faldal **Mr W. J. S. Prosser**
6 4, B f Kendargent (FR)—L'Addition **Mr W. J. S. Prosser**
7 **LYNCHPIN (IRE)**, 6, b h Camacho—River Bounty **Mr W. J. S. Prosser**
8 **MAXIMIZE**, 5, b m Garswood—Dazzling View (USA) **Mr W. J. S. Prosser**
9 **MITIGATOR**, 6, b g Delegator—Snake Skin **Mr W. J. S. Prosser**
10 4, B c Zoffany (IRE)—Promise Me (IRE) **Mr W. J. S. Prosser**
11 **RED DWARF (IRE)**, 4, ch f Belardo (IRE)—Bureau (IRE) **Mr W. J. S. Prosser**
12 **REFORMED CHARACTER**, 6, b h Zoffany (IRE)—Sallysaysso (IRE) **Mr W. J. S. Prosser**
13 **SILVEEANNA**, 4, b f Equiano (FR)—Silvee **Mr W. J. S. Prosser**
14 **TAYANNA**, 4, ch f Sepoy (AUS)—Isla Azul (IRE) **Mr W. J. S. Prosser**

THREE-YEAR-OLDS

15 Ch f Belardo (IRE)—Berry Baby (IRE) **Mr W. J. S. Prosser**
16 B f Sir Percy—Faldal **Mr W. J. S. Prosser**
17 **LOUISIANA BAY (IRE)**, b f Profitable (IRE)—Becuille (IRE) **Mr W. J. S. Prosser**
18 Ch c Bungle Inthejungle—Potternello (IRE) **Mr W. J. S. Prosser**
19 **THOUGHTFUL GIFT**, b f Charming Thought—Millsini **Mr W. J. S. Prosser**

TWO-YEAR-OLDS

20 B f 27/04 Camacho—Buttonhole (Montjeu (IRE)) (6500) **Mr W. J. S. Prosser**
21 B f 23/04 Mayson—Lulea (Authorized (IRE)) **Mr W. J. S. Prosser**
22 B f 15/05 Garswood—Rhythmical (Halling (USA)) **Mr W. J. S. Prosser**
23 Ch f 09/02 Hot Streak (IRE)—Wotnot (IRE) (Exceed And Excel (AUS)) (7000) **Mr W. J. S. Prosser**

327 MRS SOPHIE LEECH, Newnham
Postal: **Leech Racing Limited, Tudor Racing Stables, Elton Road, Elton, Newnham, Gloucestershire, GL14 1JN**
Contacts: **PHONE 01452 760691 MOBILE 07775 874630**
EMAIL info@leechracing.co.uk WEBSITE www.leechracing.co.uk

1 **ADJALI (GER)**, 7, b g Kamsin (GER)—Anabasis (GER) **The Has Been's**
2 **ANDALEEP (IRE)**, 6, b g Siyouni (FR)—Oriental Magic (GER) **Dark Blue Bloodstock**
3 **APPLESANDPIERRES (IRE)**, 14, b g Pierre—Cluain Chaoin (IRE) **Exors of the Late C. J. Leech**
4 **ASHUTOR (FR)**, 8, gr g Redoute's Choice (AUS)—Ashalanda (FR) **Dark Blue Bloodstock**
5 **BOLTISSIME (FR)**, 7, b g Dawn Approach (IRE)—Be Yourself (FR) **Stephane Huteau & Leech Racing**
6 **BONBON AU MIEL (FR)**, 11, b g Khalkevi (IRE)—Friandise II (FR) **Mr J. T. Finch**
7 **BRAINSTORM (FR)**, 4, b g No Risk At All (FR)—She Hates Me (IRE) **Mr J. T. Finch**
8 **CHESTNUT PETE**, 7, ch g Native Ruler—Rabbit **Mike Harris Racing Club**
9 **CLONDAW CIAN (IRE)**, 12, br g Gold Well—Cocktail Bar (IRE) **G. D. Thompson**
10 **CRACKING SMART (FR)**, 10, b g Great Pretender (IRE)—Maya du Frene (FR) **Mike Harris Racing Club & Partner**
11 **DEFILADE**, 6, b g Bated Breath—Zulema **Mike Harris Racing Club**
12 **DOUX PRETENDER (FR)**, 9, b g Great Pretender (IRE)—Lynnka (FR) **Mr J. T. Finch**
13 **ENFANT ROI (FR)**, 8, b g Saint des Saints (FR)—Super Maman (FR) **Mr J. T. Finch**
14 **FINNISTON FARM**, 7, b g Helmet (AUS)—Logic **Mr J. T. Finch**
15 **GARO DE JUILLEY (FR)**, 10, b g Ungaro—Lucy de Juilley (FR) **G. D. Thompson**
16 **HUGSY (IRE)**, 4, b g Dandy Man (IRE)—Hugs 'n Kisses (IRE) **Mr C. R. Leech**
17 **LIFESJUSTAFLICKER**, 4, b g Hot Streak (IRE)—Pitter Patter **Riddle Me Ree**
18 **LYGON ROCK (IRE)**, 9, b g Robin des Champs (FR)—Cute Lass (IRE) **Exors of the Late C. J. Leech**
19 **MAGNA SAM**, 8, b g Black Sam Bellamy (IRE)—Angie Marinie **Mr S. Price**
20 **MAN OF PLENTY**, 13, ch g Manduro (GER)—Credit-A-Plenty **G. D. Thompson**

MRS SOPHIE LEECH - continued

21 MCGROARTY (IRE), 11, b g Brian Boru—Uffizi (IRE) **The Has Been's**
22 MILROW (IRE), 9, b g Tamayuz—Cannikin (IRE) **Mr J. J. Cocks**
23 MUSICAL, 6, b g Eastern Anthem (IRE)—Magical Legend **R. H. Kerswell**
24 OLD HARRY ROCKS (IRE), 10, b g Milan—Miss Baden (IRE) **G. D. Thompson**
25 RASANGO (FR), 11, b g Astarabad (USA)—Ravna (FR) **Mr J. T. Finch**
26 SPES ENERGICAL (FR), 5, b m No Risk At All (FR)—Energica (FR) **Mr S. Sutton**
27 TAMARILLO GROVE (IRE), 15, b g Cape Cross (IRE)—Tamarillo **Cheltenham Racing Club**
28 THE LONGEST DAY (IRE), 6, b g Milan—Court Leader (IRE) **Exors of the Late C. J. Leech**
29 THESE HAPPY DAZE, 5, ch g Sholokhov (IRE)—Gaspaie (FR) **Happy Daze Racing Syndicate**
30 TIGER TAP TAP (GER), 7, ch g Jukebox Jury—Tomato Finish (GER) **Mr S. Sutton**
31 TWO TAFFS (IRE), 12, b g Flemensfirth (USA)—Richs Mermaid (IRE) **The Has Been's**
32 UTILITY (GER), 11, b g Yeats (IRE)—Ungarin (GER) **Dark Blue Bloodstock**
33 VANITEUX (FR), 13, br g Voix du Nord (FR)—Expoville (FR) **Mr C. R. Leech**
34 WE'VE GOT PAYET, 8, b g Authorized (IRE)—Missoula (USA) **Mr Steve Ashley & Mr Gary Pettit**
35 WEST WIZARD (FR), 13, b br g King's Theatre (IRE)—Queen's Diamond (GER) **J. O'Brien**
36 YANKEE STADIUM (IRE), 5, b g Galileo (IRE)—Switch (USA) **Mr J. T. Finch**
37 ZUREKIN (IRE), 6, b g Martaline—Fleur d'Ainay (FR) **Mr J. T. Finch**

THREE-YEAR-OLDS

38 LORD STANLEY (IRE), br g Decorated Knight—Babberina (IRE) **Dark Blue Bloodstock**
39 MAGNA BELLA, b f Due Diligence (USA)—Sugar Beet **Mrs S. Price**
40 VINCE LOMBARDI, b c Sea The Moon (GER)—First Destinity (FR) **Dark Blue Bloodstock**

Other Owners: Mr S. A. Ashley, Mr M. Casey, A. D. I. Harris, Mr M. E. Harris, Mr S. Huteau, Exors of the Late C. J. Leech, Mr C. R. Leech, Mr G. Pettit, G. D. Thompson, Mr M. Walshe.

Assistant Trainer: Christian Leech.

328
MISS TRACEY LEESON, Maidford
Postal: Glebe Stables, Blakesley Heath Farm, Maidford, Northants, NN12 8HN
Contacts: MOBILE 07761 537672
EMAIL traceyl31@hotmail.co.uk WEBSITE www.traceyleesonracing.co.uk

1 DELLBOY TROTTER (IRE), 6, b g Dylan Thomas (IRE)—Super Daisy (IRE) **Mr P. A. Long**
2 GODIVA'S BAY (IRE), 8, b g Tobougg (IRE)—Ivy Lane (IRE) **The Blakesley Racing Club**
3 HUNSBURY, 4, b g Fast Company (IRE)—Nouvelle Lune **Mr P. A. Long**
4 MOROVAL (IRE), 11, b g Morozov (USA)—Valerie Ellen (IRE) **The Blakesley Racing Club**
5 NORTH SOUTH ROSIE (IRE), 6, bl m Ocovango—South Street (IRE) **The Blakesley Racing Club**
6 SLEVE DONARD (IRE), 8, b g Mountain High (IRE)—Ceart Go Leor (IRE) **The Blakesley Racing Club**
7 TOP DRAWER (IRE), 8, b g Doyen (IRE)—Merry Gladness (IRE) **The Peter Partnership**

329
MRS SHEILA LEWIS, Brecon
Postal: Mill Service Station, Three Cocks, Brecon, Powys, LD3 0SL
Contacts: PHONE 01497 847081
EMAIL sheilalewisracing1@gmail.com

1 BALZAC, 5, b g Lope de Vega (IRE)—Miss You Too **Mr G. Wilson**
2 COTTON END (IRE), 8, gr m Scorpion (IRE)—Scartara (FR) **Mr G. Wilson**
3 FAMILY POT (FR), 7, gr g Monitor Closely (IRE)—Nikitries (FR) **W. B. R. Davies**
4 FASHION'S MODEL (IRE), 6, gr m Flemensfirth (USA)—Fashion's Worth (IRE) **W. B. R. Davies**
5 GRIS MAJEUR (FR), 5, gr g Gris de Gris (IRE)—Partie Majeure (FR) **W. B. R. Davies**
6 INGEBORG ZILLING (IRE), 6, ch m Mahler—Lindy Lou **Mr R. M. O. Lloyd**
7 KNIGHT COMMANDER, 9, br g Sir Percy—Jardin **Foxhunters In Mind**

MRS SHEILA LEWIS - continued

  8 **MITCHELL STREET**, 5, br g Dunaden (FR)—Laurens Ruby (IRE) **HSWHO Syndicate**
  9 **PORT LOCKROY (FR)**, 5, b g Australia—Synchronic (IRE) **Mr T. Lewis**
10 **SINISTER MINISTER**, 7, bl gr g Malinas (GER)—Champagne Lil **Foxhunters In Mind**
11 **STRAW FAN JACK**, 7, gr g Geordieland (FR)—Callerlilly **Mr G. Wilson**
12 **TOM O'ROUGHLEY (IRE)**, 7, b g Yeats (IRE)—Thegoodwans Sister (IRE) **Mrs S. W. Lewis**
13 **VOLCANO (FR)**, 8, gr g Martaline—Lyli Rose (FR) **W. B. R. Davies**
14 **WELL BRIEFED (IRE)**, 7, b m Mahler—The Irish Whip **Mr R. M. O. Lloyd**

330	**MR CRAIG LIDSTER, Malton**
	Postal: **11 Spring Beck Avenue, Norton, Malton, Yorkshire, YO17 9FL**
	Contacts: **PHONE 07892 714425**

1 **DIVINE CONNECTION**, 5, b m Cable Bay (IRE)—Divine Power **Newgen Racing Group**
2 **MARTA BOY**, 4, ch g Sepoy (AUS)—Perfect Story (IRE) **Newgen Racing Group**
3 **MASQUE OF ANARCHY (IRE)**, 6, b g Sir Percy—Charming (IRE) **Newgen Racing Group**
4 , Ch f Bated Breath—Merriment **Mr G. Wragg**
5 **STEP TO THE TOP (IRE)**, 7, b m Doyen (IRE)—Step On My Soul (IRE) **Mr G. Wragg**
6 **THE LAST POSH**, 7, b m Sulamani (IRE)—Posh Bird (IRE) **Mr G. Wragg**

THREE-YEAR-OLDS

7 **RUNSHAW LANE**, b g Mayson—Skipton (IRE) **Newgen Racing Group**

TWO-YEAR-OLDS

  8 B c 31/03 Mondialiste (IRE)—Bondesire (Misu Bond (IRE)) **Mr & Mrs G. Turnbull**
  9 B c 16/03 Mondialiste (IRE)—Craic Agus Spraoi (IRE) (Intense Focus (USA))
10 B f 08/02 Exceed And Excel (AUS)—Delia Eria (IRE) (Zamindar (USA))
11 **GOLDEN ALBA (IRE)**, b f 11/03 Galileo Gold—Albatraa (IRE) (Nayef (USA)) (1905) **Newgen Racing Group**
12 B f 27/02 Pearl Secret—Indigo Beat (Tamayuz) (2500) **Newgen Racing Group**
13 Ch f 22/03 Mondialiste (IRE)—Sibaya (Exceed And Excel (AUS))
14 **SILK HILL**, ch c 12/04 Mukhadram—Merriment (Makfi) **Mr G. Wragg**
15 **SKY'S THE LIMIT**, b f 10/04 Mukhadram—Fly To The Top (Mastercraftsman (IRE)) **Mr G. Wragg**

331	**MR BERNARD LLEWELLYN, Bargoed**
	Postal: **Ffynonau Duon Farm, Pentwyn, Fochriw, Bargoed, Mid Glamorgan, CF81 9NP**
	Contacts: **PHONE 01685 841259 MOBILE 07960 151083, 07971 233473 FAX 01685 843838**
	EMAIL bernard.llewellyn@btopenworld.com

  1 **ADRIAN (GER)**, 5, gr h Reliable Man—Anna Desta (GER) **B. J. Llewellyn**
  2 **ARTY CAMPBELL (IRE)**, 12, b g Dylan Thomas (IRE)—Kincob (USA) **B. J. Llewellyn**
  3 **ASCOT DAY (FR)**, 8, ch g Soave (GER)—Allez Hongkong (GER)
  4 **BRYANWOOD (IRE)**, 4, b g Garswood—Amary (IRE) **B. J. Llewellyn & Mr S. James**
  5 **CANAL ROCKS**, 6, gr g Aussie Rules (USA)—In Secret **Mr D Maddocks & Partner**
  6 **COGITAL**, 7, b g Invincible Spirit (IRE)—Galaxy Highflyer **Mr Alex James & Mr B. J. Llewellyn**
  7 **INDIGO TIMES (IRE)**, 5, gr g Alhebayeb (IRE)—Easy Times **Mr Gethyn Mills & Mr B. J. Llewellyn**
  8 **KING CHARLES (USA)**, 5, b g Lemon Drop Kid (USA)—La Reine Lionne (USA) **B. J. Llewellyn**
  9 **MIND HUNTER**, 4, b g Gleneagles (IRE)—Gadwa **Mr Alex James & Mr B. J. Llewellyn**
10 **NABHAN**, 10, b g Youmzain (IRE)—Danidh Dubai (IRE) **Mr Gethyn Mills & Mr B. J. Llewellyn**
11 **PAPAS BOY (IRE)**, 5, ch g Mukhadram—Lovely Dancer (IRE) **PC Bloodstock**
12 **PORT OR STARBOARD (IRE)**, 5, b g Epaulette (AUS)—Galley **Lland Af Cwrw**
13 **REMEDIUM**, 4, b g Adaay (IRE)—Lamentation **B. J. Llewellyn**
14 **TRIPLE NICKLE (IRE)**, 6, b m So You Think (NZ)—Secret Shine (IRE) **Mr Alex James & Mr B. J. Llewellyn**
15 **ZAMBEZI FIX (FR)**, 7, gr g Zambezi Sun—Lady Fix (FR) **Mr Gethyn Mills & Mr B. J. Llewellyn**

MR BERNARD LLEWELLYN - continued

16 **ZAMBEZI MAGIC**, 5, b g Zoffany (IRE)—Millestan (IRE) **B. J. Llewellyn**

Other Owners: Mr A. James, Mr S. James, B. J. Llewellyn, Mr D. P. Maddocks, G. Mills, Mr J. Thorney.

Assistant Trainer: J L Llewellyn.

Flat Jockey: Daniel Muscutt, David Probert. **Conditional Jockey:** Jordan Williams, Robert Williams.

Amateur Jockey: Miss Jessica Llewellyn.

---

332 **MR JOHN E. LONG, Brighton**
Postal: Southdown Stables, Bear Road, Brighton, East Sussex, BN2 6AB
Contacts: MOBILE 07815 186085, 07958 296945
EMAIL winalot@aol.com

1 5, Ch g Mazameer (IRE)—Bermacha **M. J. Gibbs**
2 **CAPE GRECO (USA)**, 7, b g Cape Blanco (IRE)—High Walden (USA) **R Blyth & S Colville**
3 **CATIVO RAGAZZO**, 7, ch g Multiplex—Sea Isle **M. J. Gibbs**
4 **DECORA (IRE)**, 5, ch m Conduit (IRE)—Grevillea (IRE) **R Blyth & S Colville**
5 **KINGMON'S BOY**, 7, b g Denounce—Ela d'Argent (IRE) **J. King**
6 **KNOCKOUT BLOW**, 7, b g Lethal Force (IRE)—Elidore **R Blyth & S Colville**
7 **LIBBRETTA**, 7, ch m Libranno—Dispol Katie **Mrs A. M. Sturges**
8 **MAGICINTHEMAKING (USA)**, 8, br m Wildcat Heir (USA)—Love in Bloom (USA) **M. J. Gibbs**

Assistant Trainer: Miss S Cassidy.

Flat Jockey: Hollie Doyle.

---

333 **MR CHARLIE LONGSDON, Chipping Norton**
Postal: Hull Farm Stables, Stratford Road, Chipping Norton, Oxfordshire, OX7 5QF
Contacts: WORK 01608 645556 MOBILE 07775 993263
EMAIL info@charlielongsdonracing.com WEBSITE www.charlielongsdonracing.com

1 **ALGHAZAAL**, 5, ch g Teofilo (IRE)—Tanfidh **Mr B. Bailey**
2 **ALIEN STORM (IRE)**, 4, b g Getaway (GER)—Missusan (IRE) **Ian Brown & Philip Donnison**
3 **ALMAZHAR GARDE (FR)**, 7, ch g Kapgarde (FR)—Loin de Moi (FR) **Kate & Andrew Brooks**
4 **BEYOND THE CLOUDS**, 9, ch g Peintre Celebre (USA)—Evening **Mr R. J. Aplin**
5 **BYZANTIUM LAD (IRE)**, 8, b g Yeats (IRE)—Socialite Girl **Stormy Syndicate**
6 **CARLOW FARMER (IRE)**, 9, b g Stowaway—Supreme Fivestar (IRE) **The Harlequins Racing**
7 **CASTLE ROBIN (IRE)**, 7, ch g Robin des Champs (FR)—Coco Opera (IRE) **Bradley Partnership**
8 **CHAMPAGNE NOIR (IRE)**, 8, br g Stowaway—Prayuwin Drummer (IRE) **Gavin MacEchern**
9 **DO WANNA KNOW (IRE)**, 8, b g Frammassone (IRE)—Mille Et Une Nuits (FR) **Girls Allowed**
10 **DUE REWARD (IRE)**, 9, b g Westerner—Long Acre **Mr D. A. Halsall**
11 **ECLAIR ON LINE (FR)**, 8, gr g Dream Well (FR)—Odeline (FR) **Eclair On Line Syndicate**
12 5, B g Telescope (IRE)—Elflora **Mr K Merry**
13 **EVERYONESGAME (IRE)**, 5, ch g Jet Away—Rose Vic (IRE) **Mr M. Olden**
14 **FREETHINKER (IRE)**, 6, b g Libertarian—Supreme Magical **The Free Thinkers**
15 **GAELIC PARK (IRE)**, 6, br g Ocovango—The Last Bank (IRE)
16 **GEORGE BANCROFT**, 4, ch g Australia—Extensive **Mr J. P. McManus**
17 **GLEBE ROAD (IRE)**, 6, b g Fame And Glory—Poppy Baloo (IRE) **Cracker Syndicate**
18 **GLEN FORSA (IRE)**, 10, b g Mahler—Outback Ivy (IRE) **Merriebelle Irish Farm Limited**
19 **GLENCASSLEY (IRE)**, 7, b g Yeats (IRE)—Reseda (GER) **Mr G. Leon**
20 **GLIMPSE OF GALA**, 6, b m Passing Glance—Apple Days **The Tweed Clad Fossils**
21 **GUETAPAN COLLONGES (FR)**, 6, b g Saddler Maker (IRE)—Saturne Collonges (FR) **Mr J. P. McManus**

MR CHARLIE LONGSDON - continued

22 **HAAS BOY (FR)**, 5, b g Diamond Boy (FR)—Naker Mome (FR) **Mr M. Olden**
23 **HECTOR JAVILEX (FR)**, 5, b g Saddler Maker (IRE)—Peps Jarzeene (FR) **Mr D. M. Mason**
24 **HIGH YIELD**, 5, b g Yeats (IRE)—Midsummer Magic **Her Majesty The Queen**
25 **HOOT AT MIDNIGHT**, 7, b m Midnight Legend—Kahooting **Mr & Mrs N. F. Maltby**
26 **HORUS DU CERISIER (FR)**, 5, ch g Coastal Path—Tyrmix Qana (FR)
27 **IF I SAY (IRE)**, 5, b m Free Eagle (IRE)—Wandering Star (IRE) **Merriebelle Irish Farm Limited**
28 **ILLEGAL MODEL (IRE)**, 8, b g Stowaway—She's So Beautiful (IRE) **Mr D. A. Halsall**
29 **JAMACHO**, 8, ch g Camacho—Obsessive Secret (IRE) **The Stratford-On-Avon Racecourse Company, Ltd**
30 **JUST YOUR TYPE (IRE)**, 10, br g Morozov (USA)—Enistar (IRE) **Mr T. Hanlon**
31 **LARGY NIGHTS (IRE)**, 8, b g Jeremy (USA)—Rowdy Nights (IRE) **Mrs J. A. Wakefield**
32 **LITTLE BRUCE (IRE)**, 10, b g Yeats (IRE)—Lady Rolfe (IRE) **The Gps Partnership**
33 **LYRICAL GENIUS (IRE)**, 5, b g Milan—Rheinland (IRE) **Thackray, Ogilvy, King & Williams**
34 **MANINSANE (IRE)**, 7, ch g Salutino (GER)—Don't Fall (IRE) **Barrels Of Courage**
35 **MIDNIGHT JEWEL**, 6, b g Midnight Legend—Follow The Dream **Ms G. E. Morgan**
36 **MOON KING (FR)**, 6, br g Sea The Moon (GER)—Maraba (IRE) **Merriebelle Irish Farm Limited**
37 **NIGHTFLY**, 11, br m Midnight Legend—Whichway Girl **Mrs D. P. G. Flory**
38 **NO NO TANGO**, 5, ch g Sixties Icon—Until Forever (IRE) **Don Sebastiao Partnership**
39 **NO WORD (IRE)**, 6, b m Shantaram—Pip 'n Pop (IRE)
40 **OSCAR MONTEL (IRE)**, 8, b g Oscar (IRE)—Montel Girl (IRE) **Robert Aplin & Stratford Racecourse 2**
41 **PARRAMOUNT**, 6, b g Mount Nelson—Queen Soraya **Mr A. Fox-Pitt**
42 **PETER'S PORTRAIT (IRE)**, 9, b g Portrait Gallery (IRE)—Fancyfacia (IRE) **Four Nags and a Horse**
43 **PRESENT STORM**, 6, b m Presenting—Sunami Storm (IRE) **Mr R. J. Aplin**
44 **RARE EDITION (IRE)**, 5, b g Califet (FR)—Quaspia (FR)
45 **RIVARROS (FR)**, 7, b g Agent Secret (IRE)—Rive Sarthe (FR) **100 Not Out**
46 **SAINT DALINA (FR)**, 8, b m Saint des Saints (FR)—Dalina (FR) **Mr D. A. Halsall**
47 **SCENE NOT HERD (IRE)**, 7, b g Aizavoski (IRE)—Jessaway (IRE) **Swanee River Partnership**
48 **SHAH AN SHAH**, 8, ch g Shirocco (GER)—Queen Soraya **Mr A. Fox-Pitt**
49 **SNOW LEOPARDESS**, 10, gr m Martaline—Queen Soraya **Mr A. Fox-Pitt**
50 5, B m Carlotamix—Spin The Wheel **The Charlie Longsdon Racing Club**
51 **STROLL ON BY (IRE)**, 5, b g Walk In The Park (IRE)—Liss Croga (IRE) **Old Gold Racing 9**
52 **TEA FOR FREE (IRE)**, 7, b g Court Cave (IRE)—Golan Gale (IRE) **Mrs S. M. Monkland**
53 **THE MIGHTY ARC (IRE)**, 7, b g Arcadio (GER)—Funcheon Lady (IRE) **Leon & Thornton Families**
54 **THE WISE TRAVELLER (IRE)**, 6, b g Getaway (GER)—Butterfly Betty (IRE) **The Endeavour Racing Syndicate**
55 **TRAIN HILL (IRE)**, 6, b g Subtle Power (IRE)—Aljapip (IRE) **Old Gold Racing 11**
56 **VIVAS (FR)**, 11, b br g Davidoff (GER)—Lavircas (FR) **Mr N. Davies**
57 **WESTERN MILLER (IRE)**, 11, b g Westerner—Definite Miller (IRE) **The Pantechnicons IV**
58 **WESTERN ZEPHYR (IRE)**, 5, b g Westerner—Beneficial Breeze (IRE) **Swanee River Partnership**
59 **WHAT ABOUT TIME (FR)**, 8, br g Oscar (IRE)—Fennor Rose (IRE) **What About Time Syndicate**
60 **ZESTFUL HOPE (FR)**, 5, b g Zanzibari (USA)—Chamdespoir (FR) **Ms G. E. Morgan**

Other Owners: Mr R. J. Aplin, Mr A. L. Brooks, Mrs K. L. Brooks, Kate & Andrew Brooks, Mr I. M. Brown, P.J. Donnison, Mr D. P. King, Mr C. E. Longsdon, Mrs S. Longsdon, Mrs J. Maltby, Mr N. F. Maltby, Ms G. E. Morgan, Dr M. M. Ogilvy, Ramscove Ltd, Mr W. G. Rolfe, Stratford Racecourse 2, Mrs M. A. Thackray, The Charlie Longsdon Racing Club, Mr M. V. Williams.

NH Jockey: Paul O'Brien.

---

334 **MR DAVID LOUGHNANE, Tern Hill**
Postal: Helshaw Grange, Warrant Road, Tern Hill, Shropshire
Contacts: MOBILE 07527 173197
EMAIL info@daveloughnaneracing.com WEBSITE www.daveloughnaneracing.com

1 **AMBER ISLAND (IRE)**, 5, b m Exceed And Excel (AUS)—Raphinae **Mr D. J. Lowe**
2 **APEX KING (IRE)**, 8, b g Kodiac—Rainbowskia (FR) **Mr N. I. Willis**
3 **BABY STEPS**, 6, b g Paco Boy (IRE)—Stepping Out (IRE) **Mr D. J. Lowe**
4 **CAROLINE DALE**, 4, b f Lethal Force (IRE)—Stepping Out (IRE) **Janet Lowe 1**
5 **CHASE THE DOLLAR**, 4, b g Frankel—Cape Dollar (IRE) **Lydonford Ltd**
6 **CHICA BELLA (IRE)**, 4, gr f Gutaifan (IRE)—Maracuja **A&b Air Systems Ltd & Partner**
7 **CITY STORM**, 4, ch g Cityscape—Spate Rise **Mr P. Onslow**

MR DAVID LOUGHNANE - continued

8 **CRITICAL THINKING (IRE)**, 8, b g Art Connoisseur (IRE)—Cookie Cutter (IRE) **Mr J. Rocke**
9 **DARK PINE (IRE)**, 5, b g Dandy Man (IRE)—Suitably Discreet (USA) **Mr G. Dewhurst**
10 **DUBAI WARRIOR**, 6, b g Dansili—Mahbooba (AUS) **Sheikh M. B. K. Al Maktoum**
11 **FAR FROM A RUBY**, 5, b m Farhh—Pretty Miss **Miss S. L. Hoyland**
12 **FFION**, 5, b m Sepoy (AUS)—Exceedingly **Mr A. Gray**
13 **FIZZY FEET (IRE)**, 6, b m Footstepsinthesand—Champagne Mistress **Mr D. J. Lowe**
14 **HAZEL (IRE)**, 4, b f No Nay Never (USA)—Asteya (IRE) **Mrs C. C. Regalado-Gonzalez**
15 **INEVITABLE OUTCOME (IRE)**, 5, b m Ivawood (IRE)—Foreplay (IRE) **Mr D. J. Lowe**
16 **KAAHIRA**, 4, b f Kingman—Mahbooba (AUS) **Sheikh M. B. K. Al Maktoum**
17 **KIM WEXLER (IRE)**, 4, b f Mehmas (IRE)—Foreplay (IRE) **Mr D. J. Lowe**
18 **LAMMAS**, 5, b g Heeraat (IRE)—Spate Rise **Mr P. Onslow**
19 **LOLA SHOWGIRL (IRE)**, 5, gr m Night of Thunder (IRE)—Exempt **Mr K. A. Lloyd**
20 **MONSARAZ**, 5, b g Cityscape—Rattleyurjewellery **Mr P. Onslow**
21 **MR SENSIBLE (USA)**, 4, b br g Street Sense (USA)—Laura's Pleasure (USA) **Amo Racing Limited**
22 **PLUMETTE**, 6, b m Compton Place—Belatorio (IRE) **Mr J. Rocke**
23 **RICHARD R H B (IRE)**, 5, b g Fulbright—Royal Interlude (IRE) **Peter R Ball & Gentech Products Ltd**
24 **ROCKETS RED GLARE**, 4, ch g Starspangledbanner (AUS)—Spirit of Paris (IRE) **Mr D. J. Lowe**
25 **SCREAMING PETRUS**, 4, b g Kingman—Putyball (USA) **Amo Racing Limited**
26 **SPIRIT OF SISRA (IRE)**, 4, b f Zoffany (IRE)—Tadris (USA) **Mr T. Graham**
27 **TIO MIO (IRE)**, 4, b c Teofilo (IRE)—Celeste de La Mer (IRE) **Mr A. C. Waney**
28 **TRUMBLE (IRE)**, 4, b g Power—Picabo (IRE) **T. E. Ford**

THREE-YEAR-OLDS

29 **ART EXPERT**, b g Exceed And Excel (AUS)—Private Advisor **Mr T. R. Hartley**
30 **AUGMENTARIUM (IRE)**, ch f New Bay—Scatina (IRE) **David Lowe & Mrs M Cantillon**
31 **BABABOBO (IRE)**, b g Australia—Sweet Temptation (IRE) **A&b Air Systems Ltd & Partner**
32 **CLARE BEAR BUNCH**, b f Helmet (AUS)—Clara Schumann **Mr N. I. Willis**
33 **DAYMAN (GER)**, b c Oasis Dream—Daytona (GER) **Amo Racing Limited**
34 **DERRYMORE BOY (IRE)**, b g Dawn Approach (IRE)—Timeless Whisper (IRE) **BR-2 Racing Club**
35 **DON'T TELL GARY**, b g Danon Ballade (JPN)—Whistleberry (IRE) **Mrs K. L. Morgan**
36 **EL MAXIMO (IRE)**, gr g Mastercraftsman (IRE)—Impressionist Art (USA) **A&b Air Systems Ltd & Partner**
37 **FEARLESS ANGEL (IRE)**, b f Belardo (IRE)—Oddysey (IRE) **Amo Racing Limited**
38 **FOREVER BRIGHT (IRE)**, b g Fulbright—Dazzling Light (UAE) **Lewis, Willis, Dewhurst & Gentech**
39 **FORTUNA DUFFLECOAT**, ch c National Defense—Almamia **Mr N. I. Willis**
40 **GO BEARS GO (IRE)**, b br c Kodi Bear (IRE)—In Dubai (USA) **Amo Racing Limited & P Waney**
41 **GORGEOUS STAR (FR)**, b f Dabirsim (FR)—Ironique (USA) **Amo Racing Limited**
42 **HELLO YOU (IRE)**, b f Invincible Spirit (IRE)—Lucrece **Amo Racing Limited**
43 **KAPE MOSS**, b f Equiano (FR)—Chrissycross (IRE) **Eclipse First Racing**
44 **LEOPOLD BLOOM**, b c Ulysses (IRE)—Zuhoor Baynoona (IRE) **Dewhurst, Batters & Jch Bloodstock**
45 **LOLA AUGUSTUS (IRE)**, b g Dabirsim (FR)—Kazaroza (FR) **Mr K. A. Lloyd**
46 **MITSY MOP**, b f Coulsty (IRE)—Ringarooma **Mr N. I. Willis**
47 **MOJOMAKER (IRE)**, b c Mehmas (IRE)—Ajla (IRE) **Mr D. J. Lowe**
48 **PROVINCE**, b f Territories (IRE)—Breve **Bearstone Stud Limited**
49 **RITEASRAIN**, b f Fountain of Youth (IRE)—Right Answer **Bearstone Stud Limited**
50 **ROBASTA (IRE)**, ch g Mehmas (IRE)—Gilded Truffle (IRE) **Mr D. J. Lowe**
51 **RUBY JULES**, b f The Gurkha (IRE)—Frances Stuart (IRE) **Mr R. A. Sankey**
52 **SHARRON MACREADY (IRE)**, b f Mehmas (IRE)—Foreplay (IRE) **Mr D. J. Lowe**
53 **SPACER (IRE)**, br gr c Starspangledbanner (AUS)—First Party **Mr D. J. Lowe**
54 **THE RANTER**, ch c Brametot (IRE)—Money Note **Mr P. Brookes**
55 **TILLYMINT (IRE)**, ch f Galileo Gold—Singora Lady (IRE) **Mr A. Owen**
56 **UMAX (IRE)**, b c Kingman—Bella Nostalgia (IRE) **Amo Racing Limited & Arjun Waney**
57 **WAR BRAVE (IRE)**, b g Due Diligence (USA)—Compass Rose (IRE) **Mr P. Clifton**

TWO-YEAR-OLDS

58 B c 20/04 Holy Roman Emperor (IRE)—Atamana (IRE) (Lahib (USA)) (25714)
  Ontoawinner, Mrs M Cantillon & Partner
59 **CARMELA (IRE)**, br f 10/03 Tasleet—Jayla (New Approach (IRE)) (35238) **The Many Saints**
60 **DEGUELLO (IRE)**, b c 09/04 Dark Angel (IRE)—Lady Springbank (IRE) (Choisir (AUS)) (38095) **Mr T. R. Hartley**
61 B f 14/02 Oasis Dream—Inshiraah (FR) (Holy Roman Emperor (IRE))

MR DAVID LOUGHNANE - continued

62 B f 15/03 Ribchester (IRE)—Key Light (IRE) (Acclamation) (78000) **Mr D. J. Lowe**
63 B c 17/02 Highland Reel (IRE)—Marah Dubai (FR) (Dubawi (IRE)) (11905) **The Many Saints**
64 B f 09/04 Kuroshio (AUS)—Midnight Destiny (IRE) (Dark Angel (IRE)) (38095) **Mr A. Owen**
65 B f 14/04 Camacho—Miracolia (IRE) (Montjeu (IRE)) (25510) **Mr K. A. Lloyd**
66 **PORTRAITIST (IRE),** b f 19/02 Awtaad (IRE)—Lyric Piece (Dutch Art) (19048) **Mr T. R. Hartley**
67 B c 03/03 Profitable (IRE)—Rasan (Dansili) (22857) **Mr R. A. Sankey**
68 B c 27/03 Kodi Bear (IRE)—Slovak (IRE) (Iffraaj) (64762) **Mr D. J. Lowe**

Other Owners: A&B Air Systems Ltd, Amo Racing Limited, Mr P. Ball, Mr M. Batters, Mr S. Bridge, Mrs M. Cantillon, Mr G. Dewhurst, Gentech Products Ltd, Mr G. S. Goss, Mr J. C. Hassett, Miss S. L. Hoyland, Mr A. Lewis, Mr D. J. Lowe, Mrs J. Lowe, Mr T. J. Moran, Mr S. N. Mound, Mr N. J. O'Brien, Ontoawinner, Mr R. A. Sankey, Mr M. Satchell, Mr A. C. Waney, Mr P. Waney, Mr N. I. Willis.

---

335 MR MARK LOUGHNANE, Kidderminster
Postal: Rock Farm, Rock Cross, Rock, Kidderminster, Worcestershire, DY14 9SA
Contacts: **MOBILE 07805 531021**

1 **AFKAAR (USA),** 4, b g Kitten's Joy (USA)—Celestial Woods (USA) **Over The Moon Racing**
2 **ALGHEED (IRE),** 4, b f Dark Angel (IRE)—Rathaath (IRE) **S. & A. Mares**
3 **ALWAYS DREAMING,** 4, b f Oasis Dream—Along Came Casey (IRE) **S. & A. Mares**
4 **ARCADIAN NIGHTS,** 4, b g Exceed And Excel (AUS)—Lady Lahar
5 **BARBILL (IRE),** 6, b g Zebedee—Fiuise (IRE) **Mr K. Sohi**
6 **BLUE MEDICI,** 8, b g Medicean—Bluebelle **Mr L. A. Bellman**
7 **BOOKMARK,** 4, b f New Approach (IRE)—Free Verse **Live In Hope Partnership**
8 **BROUGHTONS FLARE (IRE),** 6, ch g Rip Van Winkle (IRE)—Purple Glow (IRE) **Mrs C. M. Loughnane**
9 **BUY ME BACK,** 5, b m Lethal Force (IRE)—Delft **Mr B. M. Parish**
10 **CHOCOLATE BOX (IRE),** 8, b g Zoffany (IRE)—Chocolate Mauk (USA) **Racing Facades Syndicate**
11 **CIOTOG (IRE),** 4, ch g Dandy Man (IRE)—Cristal Fashion (IRE) **Precision Facades Ltd**
12 **CITY ESCAPE (IRE),** 5, b m Cityscape—Lady Gabrielle (IRE) **Out Of Bounds Racing Club**
13 **CRAFTER (IRE),** 4, b g Muhaarar—Boston Rocker (IRE) **Mr L. A. Bellman**
14 **DAHEER (USA),** 5, ch g Speightstown (USA)—Elraazy (USA) **The Likely Lads**
15 **DAYSAQ (IRE),** 5, b g Invincible Spirit (IRE)—Fawaayed (IRE) **Mrs C. M. Loughnane**
16 **EL HOMBRE,** 8, ch g Camacho—Nigella **Over The Moon Racing**
17 **EL PATRON (IRE),** 4, b g Kodiac—Smart Bounty **Mr K. Sohi**
18 **FAITHHOPEANDGLORY,** 4, b f Coach House (IRE)—Queen Hermione (IRE) **Mr D. A. Olver**
19 **FIRST CHARGE (IRE),** 5, b g Dansili—Melodramatic (IRE) **Mr L. A. Bellman**
20 **GOING BACK TO CALI,** 4, b g Pride of Dubai (AUS)—Chelsey Jayne (IRE) **Mr K. Sohi**
21 **GUSTAV GRAVES,** 4, b g Bobby's Kitten (USA)—Bondesire **Big Lachie Syndicate**
22 **IMPERIAL COMMAND (IRE),** 5, b g War Command (USA)—Acts Out Loud (USA) **M J Refrigeration Transport Ltd**
23 **INNER CIRCLE (IRE),** 8, b g Choisir (AUS)—Eternity Ring **Mrs C. M. Loughnane**
24 **JEDDEYD (IRE),** 5, b g Make Believe—Lady Shanghai (IRE) **Mrs C. M. Loughnane**
25 **MASKED IDENTITY,** 7, b g Intello (GER)—Red Bloom **D. S. Lovatt**
26 **MOXY MARES,** 7, ch g Motivator—Privalova (IRE) **S. & A. Mares**
27 **MR DIB DAB (FR),** 5, b g Dabirsim (FR)—Naan (IRE) **S. & A. Mares**
28 **NEVER SAID NOTHING (IRE),** 5, b g Hallowed Crown (AUS)—Semiquaver (IRE) **Precision Facades Ltd**
29 **PRECISION STORM,** 5, gr g Dragon Pulse (IRE)—Way To The Stars **Precision Facades Ltd**
30 **QASBAZ (IRE),** 5, b g Make Believe—Esuvia (IRE) **Mr L. A. Bellman**
31 **RED JASPER,** 5, ch g Showcasing—Spate (IRE) **Mr C. Bacon**
32 **RICKSEN,** 5, b g Acclamation—Quantum (IRE) **Tipton Hotshots Syndicate**
33 **ROCK BOY GREY (IRE),** 7, gr g Dark Angel (IRE)—Innocent Air (IRE) **The Likely Lads**
34 **ROYAL BORN (IRE),** 6, b g Born To Sea (IRE)—Albarouche **Mr N. A. Marks**
35 **SNOWBOMBER,** 4, ro g Lethal Force (IRE)—Colourfilly **Mr L. A. Bellman**
36 **SPIRIT OF JACOB,** 5, ch m Casamento (IRE)—Queen Hermione (IRE) **Dr D. Chapman-Jones**
37 **STARFIGHTER,** 6, b g Sea The Stars (IRE)—Starlit Sands **Mr L. A. Bellman**
38 **TAKEONEFORTHETEAM,** 7, b g Bahamian Bounty—Miss Bond (IRE) **S. & A. Mares**
39 **TRIGGERED (IRE),** 6, b g Dandy Man (IRE)—Triggers Broom (IRE) **L Bellman & S & A Mares**
40 **UNIVERSAL EFFECT,** 6, b m Universal (IRE)—Saaboog **S & A Mares & Precision Facades Ltd**
41 **WALDLOWE,** 4, b g Le Havre (IRE)—Waldnah **Newsells Park Stud Limited**
42 **WELL PREPARED,** 5, b g Due Diligence (USA)—Amazed **Mr L. A. Bellman**

MR MARK LOUGHNANE - continued

43 **WHATZUPWITHME**, 4, gr g Lethal Force (IRE)—Whatami **Mr R. W. Prince**

THREE-YEAR-OLDS
44 **BEARING BOB**, ch g Bobby's Kitten (USA)—Danlia (IRE) **Against All Odds Racing**
45 **D DAY HERO (IRE)**, b gr g Nayef (USA)—Natheer (USA) **Mr D. A. Olver**
46 **DELIGHTFILLY**, b f Adaay (IRE)—Colourfilly **Mr L. A. Bellman**
47 **EESHA MEESH**, b f Farhh—Nota Bene (GER) **Mr K. Sohi**
48 **FRANKLIN SAINT (IRE)**, b g Caravaggio (USA)—I Am (IRE) **Mr K. Sohi**
49 **FRISTEL (IRE)**, b g Holy Roman Emperor (IRE)—Kyanight (IRE) **Mrs C. M. Loughnane**
50 **JAM TART**, b f Gregorian (IRE)—Ettie Hart (IRE) **D. S. Lovatt**
51 **JANAAT (IRE)**, ch f Ribchester (IRE)—Lexi's Love (USA) **S. & A. Mares**
52 **KEEP ME HAPPY**, b f Stimulation (IRE)—Verus Delicia (IRE) **Mr R. M. Brilley**
53 **LEAVEITWITHME (IRE)**, b f War Command (USA)—Inca Husky (IRE) **M J Refrigeration Transport Ltd**
54 **MUMAYAZ (IRE)**, b g Tamayuz—Rashaaqa **Mrs C. M. Loughnane**
55 **NEAT AND DANDY (IRE)**, b g Dandy Man (IRE)—Isabella Vite (IRE) **Mr K. Sohi**
56 **RICKENBACKER (IRE)**, b g Requinto (IRE)—Mattinata **Alan & Sue Cronshaw**
57 **STYLISH WHISPA**, b f Bated Breath—Sighora (IRE) **Mr L. A. Bellman**
58 B f Oasis Dream—Whatami
59 **YOUNG WINSTON**, b g Churchill (IRE)—Come With Me **Mr C. Bacon**

TWO-YEAR-OLDS
60 B f 24/02 Poet's Word (IRE)—Arabian Music (IRE) (Kheleyf (USA)) (8571)
61 B f 22/04 Dandy Man (IRE)—Colourfilly (Compton Place) **Mr L. A. Bellman**
62 **IL CAMPEONE (IRE)**, b f 12/03 Expert Eye—Mrs Greeley (Mr Greeley (USA)) (16190) **Mr K. Sohi**
63 **LEONNA (IRE)**, b f 14/04 Expert Eye—Shy Audience (IRE) (Sir Prancealot (IRE)) (48000) **Mr K. Sohi**
64 **NINETYNINEPROBLEMS (IRE)**, b f 18/04 Sioux Nation (USA)—Worthington (IRE) (Kodiac) (30000) **Mr K. Sohi**
65 **TOP OF THE CLASS**, ch f 17/03 Zoustar (AUS)—The Gold Cheongsam (IRE) (Red Clubs (IRE)) (50000) **Mr K. Sohi**

Other Owners: Mr L. A. Bellman, Mrs A. Mares, Mr S. Mares, S. & A. Mares, Precision Facades Ltd.

---

336 MR ROBERT LUKE, Haverfordwest
Postal: Selvedge, Clarbeston Road, Dyfed, SA63 4QR
EMAIL robluke82@hotmail.com

1 **CIDER DRINKER**, 7, b m Apple Tree (FR)—Sniper Alley (IRE) **Mr R. E. Luke**
2 **GENERAL PICTON (IRE)**, 10, b g Beneficial—Back To Cloghoge (IRE) **Mr R. E. Luke**
3 **GOOD GREEF**, 7, gr m Geordieland (FR)—Red Reef **Mr R. E. Luke**

---

337 MR BENJAMIN LUND, Bridgwater
Postal: Smocombe Racing Stables, Enmore, Bridgwater, Somerset, TA5 2DY
EMAIL lundequine@gmail.com

1 **BLUE HEATHER (IRE)**, 8, b m Doyen (IRE)—Limavady (IRE) **Mr B. V. Lund**
2 **DARK HEATHER (IRE)**, 5, b m Laverock (IRE)—Grainne Delight (IRE) **Mr J. O. Smith**
3 **EXMOOR FOREST (IRE)**, 5, b g Sageburg (IRE)—Horner Vale (IRE) **West Country Racing**
4 **GLENGEEVER (IRE)**, 6, b g Scorpion (IRE)—Anns Island (IRE) **Mr B. V. Lund**
5 **JACK THE FARMER**, 6, br g Kalanisi (IRE)—Deploys Dream (IRE) **West Country Racing**
6 **KIND WITNESS**, 9, b m Witness Box (USA)—Kind Oscar (IRE) **Ben Lund Racing Club**
7 **LEXINGTON BULLET**, 4, b f Showcasing—Starbotton **Ben Lund Racing Club**
8 **PEGGYCLARE (IRE)**, 9, ch m Vertical Speed (FR)—Outdoor Heather (IRE) **Ben Lund Racing Club**
9 **PONTRESINA (IRE)**, 9, b g Milan—Gilt Benefit (IRE) **Ben Lund Racing Club**
10 **PRINCE MTM (IRE)**, 5, b g Hallowed Crown (AUS)—Magical Rose (IRE) **MTM PASSIVE FIRE PROTECTION LTD**

MR BENJAMIN LUND - continued

11 **ROSSERK ABBEY (IRE),** 9, ch g Fruits of Love (USA)—Here Comes Alli (IRE) **Mr B. V. Lund**
12 5, Ch h Tamayuz—Shaddeya (IRE) **Mr B. V. Lund**
13 4, B br f Elusive Pimpernel (USA)—Sister Slew (IRE) **Mr B. V. Lund**

THREE-YEAR-OLDS

14 **NATIONAL STAR (IRE),** b g National Defense—Starbright (IRE) **Mr B. V. Lund**
15 **Gr f El Kabeir (USA)—Purple Velvet (IRE) Mr B. V. Lund**
16 **SCUTI (IRE),** b f Dragon Pulse (IRE)—Highly Exclusive (IRE)
17 B f Buratino (IRE)—Square Pants (USA) **Mr B. V. Lund**

338

MR SHAUN LYCETT, Witney
Postal: **Fairspear Racing Stables, Fairspear Road, Leafield, Witney, Oxfordshire, OX29 9NT**
Contacts: **PHONE 01451 824143 MOBILE 07788 100894**
EMAIL trainer@bourtonhillracing.co.uk WEBSITE www.bourtonhillracing.co.uk

1 **IDOAPOLOGISE,** 5, b g Havana Gold (IRE)—Shiba (FR) **Dan Gilbert & Andrew Bruce**
2 **JENSON BENSON (IRE),** 4, b g Kodi Bear (IRE)—Star Fire **L & M Atkins**
3 **LIVA (IRE),** 7, ch g Champs Elysees—Resistance Heroine **L & M Atkins**
4 **PARK PADDOCKS (IRE),** 8, b g Sea The Stars (IRE)—Dream of The Hill (IRE) **Mr D. R. Gilbert**
5 **RELATIVE EASE,** 6, b m Sayif (IRE)—Shohrah (IRE) **L & M Atkins**
6 **RICK BLAINE (IRE),** 5, b g Ruler of The World (IRE)—Saturday Girl **Mr D. R. Gilbert**
7 **RUBY LILY,** 4, b f Nayef (USA)—Lily Lenor (IRE) **Mr D. R. Gilbert**
8 **SPEECH ROOM (IRE),** 5, b g Sea The Stars (IRE)—Dream of The Hill (IRE) **L & M Atkins**
9 **STATELY HOME (IRE),** 5, gr g Clodovil (IRE)—Lady Spangles (IRE) **Mr D. R. Gilbert**
10 **THE KING'S STEED,** 9, b g Equiano (FR)—King's Siren (IRE) **D Gilbert, J Lancaster, G Wills**
11 **TORCELLO (IRE),** 8, ch g Born To Sea (IRE)—Islandagore (IRE) **Mr D. R. Gilbert**
12 **WEEKLY GOSSIP (IRE),** 11, br g Kalanisi (IRE)—Mary's Little Vic (IRE) **L & M Atkins**

Other Owners: Mr L. Atkins, Mrs M. Atkins, Mr A. Bruce, Mr D. R. Gilbert.

339

MISS JESSICA MACEY, Doncaster
Postal: **Mayflower Stables, Saracens Lane, Scrooby, Doncaster, South Yorkshire, DN10 6AS**
Contacts: **PHONE 07588 374797**
EMAIL macey.jess@gmail.com

1 **BLOOD MOON,** 9, b g Equiano (FR)—First Eclipse (IRE) **Sheikh K. A. I. S. Al Khalifa**
2 **BLUELLA,** 7, b m Equiano (FR)—Mata Hari Blue **Mr M. J. Golding**
3 **DARK SIDE PRINCE,** 5, b g Equiano (FR)—Dark Side Princess **Mr M. M. Foulger**
4 **EYES (IRE),** 4, b f Dandy Man (IRE)—Ebony Street (USA) **Not Now Partnership**
5 **HARDY,** 4, bl g Heeraat (IRE)—Miss Lesley **Wentdale Limited**
6 **HARRY HAAFHD,** 4, b g Haafhd—Rhostal (IRE) **Goldfox Racing**
7 **MISS FERNANDA (IRE),** 4, b f Prince of Lir (IRE)—Livadream (IRE) **Mr M. M. Foulger**
8 **PHOENIX STAR (IRE),** 6, b g Alhebayeb (IRE)—Volcanic Lady (IRE) **Flying High Syndicate**
9 **SWEET ANGEL,** 5, b m Heeraat (IRE)—Sweet Lily Pea (USA) **Supreme Bloodstock**
10 **TRINITY GIRL,** 5, b m Teofilo (IRE)—Micaela's Moon (USA) **G Mr Fowler, S Dwyer**

THREE-YEAR-OLDS

11 **BALLISTIC BERRY,** b f Brazen Beau (AUS)—Chevise (IRE) **Strawberry Fields Stud**
12 **BERRY QUICK,** b g Fast Company (IRE)—Quick Thought (IRE) **Strawberry Fields Stud**
13 **DARK SIDE THUNDER,** b g Night of Thunder (IRE)—Dark Side Princess **Mr M. M. Foulger**
14 B c Swiss Spirit—Dutch Mistress **Goldrush Racing**
15 **HE'S SO BRAZEN,** b g Brazen Beau (AUS)—Sweet Lily Pea (USA) **Mr C. Harris**
16 B f Territories (IRE)—Precious Secret (IRE)

---

340 MR JOHN MACKIE, Church Broughton
Postal: The Bungalow, Barton Blount, Church Broughton, Derby
Contacts: PHONE 01283 585603, 01283 585604 MOBILE 07799 145283 FAX 01283 585603
EMAIL jmackieracing@gmail.com

1 AVAILABLE ANGEL, 4, b f Heeraat (IRE)—Available (IRE) **Derbyshire Racing II**
2 BALADIO (IRE), 6, ch m Iffraaj—Balamana (FR) **Derbyshire Racing III**
3 BARTON KNOLL, 10, b g Midnight Legend—Barton Flower **Mr S. W. Clarke**
4 BERTOG, 7, ch g Sepoy (AUS)—Lucky Token (IRE) **Mr S. Goodwin**
5 CUBANO (IRE), 4, ch g Havana Gold (IRE)—Special Miss **Mr N. I. Willis**
6 CUSTARD THE DRAGON, 9, b g Kyllachy—Autumn Pearl **Derbyshire Racing**
7 ELHAFEI (USA), 7, br g Speightstown (USA)—Albamara **Mr N. I. Willis**
8 ELLAND ROAD BOY (IRE), 4, b g Dandy Man (IRE)—Red Ivy (IRE) **Mr N. I. Willis**
9 GOOD LISTENER (IRE), 4, b g Mehmas (IRE)—Looks Great **& Yardley**
10 HURRICANE ALI (IRE), 6, b g Alhebayeb (IRE)—Hurricane Irene (IRE) **Mr M. J. Fruhwald**
11 MISS BAMBY, 7, b m Kayf Tara—Bamby (IRE) **Mrs S. P. Granger**
12 MR TG (IRE), 8, b g Flemensfirth (USA)—Bollin Jasmine **Mrs S. P. Granger**
13 MUST BE AN ANGEL (IRE), 5, gr m Dark Angel (IRE)—Lapis Blue (IRE) **Mr N. I. Willis**
14 NASHY (IRE), 5, br g Camelot—Venus de Milo (IRE) **The Derbyshire Optimists**
15 NAT LOVE (IRE), 5, b g Gregorian (IRE)—Chaguaramas (IRE) **Mr J. Kearns**
16 OFF TO ALABAMA, 4, b g Telescope (IRE)—Off By Heart **Mrs E. M. Mackie**
17 RAINBOW JET (IRE), 5, b m Dream Ahead (USA)—Star Jet (IRE) **NSU Leisure & Mrs Carolyn Seymour**
18 SHARPCLIFF, 5, b g Farhh—Avonrose **Moorland Racing**
19 STELLA MARIS, 4, b f Sea The Stars (IRE)—Zeb Un Nisa **Mr N. I. Willis**
20 TILIA CORDATA (IRE), 4, b f Zoffany (IRE)—Limetree Lady **Mr N. A. Hayward**
21 VIVENCY (USA), 5, b m Noble Mission—Hint of Joy (USA) **Derbyshire Racing IV**

THREE-YEAR-OLDS
22 ALASKAN WIND (IRE), b f Kodiac—Parasail **Mr N. I. Willis**
23 AMAZING MOLLIE, b f Brazen Beau (AUS)—Avonrose **Moorland Racing**
24 ITSY BITSY BEAR, b f Intrinsic—Rosealee (IRE) **Mr N. I. Willis**
25 LUCKY SHAKE (FR), b f Zelzal (FR)—Lucky Lot **David & Ros Chapman**
26 VON DER LEYEN (IRE), b f Gleneagles (IRE)—Wild Idle (USA) **David & Ros Chapman**
27 WILLOW PILLOW (IRE), gr f Zoffany (IRE)—Divine Promesse (FR) **Mr N. I. Willis**

TWO-YEAR-OLDS
28 B f 19/04 Sioux Nation (USA)—Double High (High Chaparral (IRE)) (952)
29 B f 15/05 Telescope (IRE)—Just Milly (Milan)
30 Br f 11/03 Massaat (IRE)—Magical Daze (Showcasing) (2857)

Other Owners: Mr D. O. Chapman, Mrs R. M. H. Chapman, NSU Leisure Ltd, Mrs C. Seymour, Mr M. Yardley, Mrs W. J. Yardley.

341 MR MICHAEL MADGWICK, Denmead
Postal: Forest Farm, Forest Road, Denmead, Waterlooville, Hampshire, PO7 6UA
Contacts: PHONE 023 9225 8313 MOBILE 07835 964969

1 BIG 'N BETTER, 10, b g Revoque (IRE)—Donastrela (IRE) **W. M. Smith**
2 DONO DI DIO, 7, b m Nathaniel (IRE)—Sweet Cecily (IRE) **Mr O. Lodge**
3 FAMILY FORTUNES, 8, ch g Paco Boy (IRE)—Barawin (IRE) **Los Leader**
4 FORESHORE, 5, b g Footstepsinthesand—Skinny Love
5 LARGO BAY (USA), 4, ch g Flintshire—No Panic (USA) **Mr J. Lane**
6 MISS RECYCLED, 7, b m Royal Applause—Steel Free (IRE) **Recycled Products Limited**
7 RESPLENDENT ROSE, 5, b m Havana Gold (IRE)—Attlongglast **Mrs L. N. Harmes**
8 STORMBOMBER (CAN), 6, ch g Stormy Atlantic (USA)—Swanky Bubbles (CAN) **Los Leader**
9 TARNEEMAT, 4, b f War Command (USA)—Sounds of April (IRE) **Mr K. Tyre**
10 TIME TO BREEZE, 5, b f Mullionmileanhour (IRE)—Shantou Breeze (IRE) **M. J. Madgwick**
11 VLANNON, 7, b g Captain Gerrard (IRE)—Attlongglast **M Gannon, H Vlatas, M Willis, L N Harmes**
12 WHAT'S MY LINE, 5, b g Sixties Icon—Leading Star **M. J. Madgwick**
13 WHERE'S TOM, 7, b g Cape Cross (IRE)—Where's Susie **Recycled Products Limited**

MR MICHAEL MADGWICK - continued

THREE-YEAR-OLDS

14 **MISS MALOU**, b f War Command (USA)—Nawaashi **M. J. Madgwick**

Other Owners: Mr M. Gannon, Mrs L. N. Harmes, M. J. Madgwick, Mr W. R. Oliver, Mr T. Smith, Mr H. Vlatas, Mr M. Willis.

Assistant Trainer: David Madgwick.

Flat Jockey: Adam Kirby. **NH Jockey:** Marc Goldstein. **Amateur Jockey:** Mr Lance Madgwick.

---

342   **MRS HEATHER MAIN, Wantage**
Postal: Kingston Common Farm, Kingston Lisle, Wantage, Oxfordshire, OX12 9QT
Contacts: WORK 01367 820124 MOBILE 07920 558860
EMAIL heather.main@hotmail.com WEBSITE www.heathermainracing.com

1 **ACTAEA**, 4, b f Adaay (IRE)—Aqaba **Mr J. P. Repard**
2 **AL KOUT**, 8, gr g Oasis Dream—Honorlina (FR) **Wetumpka Racing**
3 **CAPTAIN HADDOCK (IRE)**, 5, b g Make Believe—Kayd Kodaun (IRE) **Good & Main**
4 **CELTIC EMPRESS**, 4, b f Golden Horn—Cartimandua **Llewelyn,Runeckles**
5 **CLOUD THUNDER**, 5, gr g Poet's Voice—Cloud Illusions (USA) **Coxwell Partnership**
6 **COLONEL WHITEHEAD (IRE)**, 5, b g Showcasing—Lady Brigid (IRE) **Mr. Andrew Tuck & Wetumpka Racing**
7 **DANITA**, 4, br f Fountain of Youth (IRE)—Anya **Mrs L. M. Alexander**
8 **ENGLISH SPIRIT**, 4, ch g Swiss Spirit—Cloud Illusions (USA) **Wetumpka Racing**
9 **ISLAND BRAVE (IRE)**, 8, b h Zebedee—Tip the Scale (USA) **D. M. Kerr**
10 **MARSHAL DAN (IRE)**, 7, b g Lawman (FR)—Aunt Nicola **Coxwell Partnership**
11 **MISTER BLUEBIRD**, 4, b g Outstrip—Childesplay **Dawn Aldham & Wetumpka Racing**
12 **MOSTAWAA**, 6, ch g Poet's Voice—Mumtaza **The Haroldians**
13 **NIGELLA SATIVA**, 6, gr m Gentlewave (IRE)—Just Popsy **Wetumpka Racing**
14 **NUMITOR**, 8, gr g Schiaparelli (GER)—Just Popsy **Mr Paul G. Jacobs & Wetumpka Racing**
15 **POLAR CLOUD**, 6, gr g Mount Nelson—Cloud Illusions (USA) **Wetumpka Racing**
16 **SECRET GLOW (IRE)**, 4, ch g Sepoy (AUS)—Moon Sister (IRE) **The Desk Till Dawn Partnership**
17 **SONG OF THE ISLES (IRE)**, 6, ch m Tagula (IRE)—Musicology (USA) **Wetumpka Racing**

THREE-YEAR-OLDS

18 **AGAPANTHER**, b f Outstrip—Byroness **A & Racing**
19 **BERRYGAR**, ch g Garswood—Front Page News **Mr & Mrs D. R. Guest**
20 B g Nayef (USA)—Blue Zealot (IRE) **Mr J. S. M. Fill**
21 **DARK ISLAND**, b c Night of Thunder (IRE)—Western Pearl **D. M. Kerr**
22 **DARK ISLAND STAR (IRE)**, b f Caravaggio (USA)—Saturn Girl (IRE) **D. M. Kerr**
23 **DIAMOND GIRL**, b f Profitable (IRE)—Lady Brigid (IRE) **D. M. Kerr**
24 **HERMONIE**, gr f Alhebayeb (IRE)—Zeehan **Mondial Racing**
25 **ILEACH MATHAN (IRE)**, gr g Kodi Bear (IRE)—Juliette Fair (IRE) **Coxwell Partnership**
26 **ISLAND BANDIT (IRE)**, ch c Zarak (FR)—Lady of The Court (IRE) **D. M. Kerr**
27 **KADIMA IMPERIAL**, gr f Outstrip—Tibibit **D. Cohen**
28 **LA BELLE VIE**, b f Iffraaj—Belle Dauphine **Andrew Knott & Wetumpka Racing**
29 **MASTERMINDING (IRE)**, ch g Mastercraftsman (IRE)—Enjoy Life (IRE) **Beccle, Moss and Wetumpka Racing**
30 **MOSTLY SUNNY (IRE)**, ch g Zarak (FR)—Belle Above All
31 **SIR RANDOLPH**, b g Churchill (IRE)—Esteemable **Llewelyn,Runeckles**
32 **STONKING**, b g Farhh—Vizinga (FR) **Mr Paul G. Jacobs & Wetumpka Racing**
33 **UNSUNG HERO (IRE)**, b c Iffraaj—Red Avis **Mr Donald Kerr & Wetumpka Racing**
34 **WIZARDING**, b g Showcasing—Dutch S **Mondial Racing & Robert Haim**

Other Owners: Ms D. C. Aldham, Mr S. E. Beccle, Mr J. Bernstein, Mr F. C. Durbin, Feel Good Racing Club, Miss C. A. Green, Mr D. R. Guest, Mr R. Haim, P.G. Jacobs, D. M. Kerr, Mr A. Knott, Sir J. A. Mactaggart, Mr C. M. T. Main, Mrs H. S. Main, J. P. M. Main, Mondial Racing, Mr M. J. Moss, Mr J. Ross, Share A Winner, Mr M. R. Telfer, Mr A. Tuck, Wetumpka Racing.

343 MRS JANE VICTORIA MAKIN, Monk Fryston
Postal: **Fryston Lodge Farm, Off A63, South Milford, Leeds, North Yorkshire, LS25 5JE**
Contacts: **PHONE 07836 763979**
EMAIL regmakin@gmail.com

1 5, B m Getaway (GER)—Rose's Emma (IRE) **Mr R. G. Makin**
2 **SCHIAPARANNIE**, 10, b m Schiaparelli (GER)—Annie's Answer (IRE) **Mr R. G. Makin**

344 MR PHILLIP MAKIN, Easingwold
Postal: **Well Close Farm, York Road, Easingwold, York, North Yorkshire, YO61 3EN**
Contacts: **PHONE 07968 045436**
EMAIL philmakin.21@hotmail.co.uk

1 **BIG DUTCHIE (IRE)**, 4, b g Dutch Art—Exceedingly **Mr Alan Gray & Partner**
2 **CAPTAIN VALLO (IRE)**, 4, ch g Mehmas (IRE)—Top Dollar **J. Binks**
3 **DEBATED**, 4, ch g Bated Breath—Lady Sledmere (IRE) **Ryedale Racing**
4 **EXCHEQUER (IRE)**, 11, ch g Exceed And Excel (AUS)—Tara's Force (IRE) **Mr J Toes & Mr J O'Loan**
5 **IMPRESSOR (IRE)**, 5, b g Footstepsinthesand—Little Empress (IRE) **Aidan O'Ryan & Partner**
6 **JUNGLE INTHEBUNGLE (IRE)**, 6, ch g Bungle Inthejungle—Princess Banu **Mr John Hanbury & Partner**
7 **POLITICS (IRE)**, 4, b g Muhaarar—Wrong Answer **Wolf Pack 4 & Dj's Roofing Ltd**
8 **STORM OVER (IRE)**, 8, b g Elnadim (USA)—Stormy View (USA) **P. J. Makin**
9 **TOMMY R (IRE)**, 4, b g Holy Roman Emperor (IRE)—Serafina's Flight **Mr P. S. Riley**
10 **TRUE MASON**, 6, b g Mayson—Marysienka **Mr J. T. Hanbury**

THREE-YEAR-OLDS
11 **BRAZEN AKOYA**, b f Brazen Beau (AUS)—Broughtons Jewel (IRE) **White Rose Bloodstock**
12 **COTAI CLASS (IRE)**, ch g Cotai Glory—Classy Lassy (IRE) **Mr J. T. Hanbury**
13 **THE MENSTONE GEM (IRE)**, ch g Galileo Gold—Masela (IRE) **JP Racing Club Limited**
14 Gr f Hot Streak (IRE)—The River Wild **J. Binks**
15 **THUNDERHILL (IRE)**, b g Zoffany (IRE)—Leniency (IRE) **Mr W. Dennison**
16 **TINKERSTAR (IRE)**, b c Fast Company (IRE)—Zebgrey (IRE) **Exors of the Late W. Pooleman**

TWO-YEAR-OLDS
17 B f 29/04 Sioux Nation (USA)—Cabelo (IRE) (Azamour (IRE)) (10204)
18 B c 13/04 Massaat (IRE)—High Speed (IRE) (Kodiac) (20952)
19 Ch f 24/01 Camacho—Lady Heart (Kyllachy) (9354) **Mr J. T. Hanbury**
20 B f 25/02 Kodiac—Lumi (IRE) (Canford Cliffs (IRE)) (15306) **Mr P. S. Riley**
21 Br c 03/03 Footstepsinthesand—Nu Couche (FR) (Sunday Break (JPN)) (14286) **Mr J Toes & Mr J O'Loan**
22 Gr c 08/04 Gutaifan (IRE)—Ragtime Dancer (Medicean) (7653) **J. Binks**
23 B c 25/03 Estidhkaar (IRE)—Xerxes (IRE) (Key of Luck (USA)) (3401)

345 MRS ALYSON MALZARD, Jersey
Postal: **Les Etabl'yes, Grosnez Farm, St Ouen, JE3 2AD, Jersey**
Contacts: MOBILE **+44 7797 738128**
EMAIL malzardracing@gmail.com

1 **ALLEGRO JETE (FR)**, 5, gr ro g Style Vendome—Neuilly **Sheik A'leg Racing**
2 **BAL AMIE (FR)**, 8, b g Ballingarry—Amie Roli **Mr Anthony Taylor**
3 **BRING THE MONEY (IRE)**, 5, b g Anjaal—Princess Banu **Mr R J Vibert**
4 **DARK MOONLIGHT (IRE)**, 5, b g Kodiac—On Location **Mr & Mrs Simon Harrison-White**
5 **FOURNI (IRE)**, 13, b m Rakti—Eckbeag **Miss Joan Lowery**
6 **HARD TO HANDEL**, 10, b g Stimulation—Melody Maker **The Baroque Partnership, Mr Matt Watkinson**
7 **HONCHO (IRE)**, 10, b g Dark Angel (IRE)—Discolights **Sheik A'leg Racing**
8 **ISAAC D'AUBRELLE (FR)**, 4, b g Rail Link—Etoile D'Aubrelle **Mr P G Somers**
9 **ISLAND SONG (IRE)**, 8, b m Equiano—Fortuna Limit **Mr P G Somers**
10 **MENDACIOUS HARPY (IRE)**, 11, b m Dark Angel (IRE)—Idesia **Malzard Racing**

MRS ALYSON MALZARD - continued

11 **NEVER SAID NOTHING (IRE)**, 5, b g Hollowed Crown—Semiquaver **Mr R J Vibert**
12 **NOVEMBER RAIN (FR)**, 4, b f Sidestep (AUS)—Candidasa **Mr P G Somers**
13 **RELAXED BOY (FR)**, 9, b g Le Havre (IRE)—Joyce **Mr P G Somers**
14 **RUBEUS (IRE)**, 5, b g Alhebayeb—Peaceful Kingdom **Mr & Mrs Dominic Thatcher**
15 **TIMETODOCK**, 6, b g Harbour Watch (IRE)—Unwrapit **Mr Anthony Taylor**

Amateur Jockey: Miss Victoria Malzard, Mr Freddie Tett.

---

346 | MANOR HOUSE STABLES, Malpas
Postal: **Manor House Stables, Malpas, Cheshire, SY14 8AD**
Contacts: **PHONE 01948 820485 FAX 01948 820495**
WEBSITE www.manorhousestables.com

Awaiting appointment for Tom Dascombe at time of going to press

1 **BAKERSBOY**, 4, b g Oasis Dream—Dubai Bounty
2 **BREATHALYZE (FR)**, 5, b g Bated Breath—Laber Ildut (IRE)
3 **COMMONSENSICAL**, 4, b g Bated Breath—Critical Path (IRE)
4 **FIRST LOTT**, 4, b f Harbour Watch (IRE)—Don't Tell Mary (IRE)
5 **FOOLS RUSH IN (IRE)**, 4, br g Mehmas (IRE)—Faddwa (IRE)
6 **GIFTED RULER**, 5, b g Muhaarar—Dubai Bounty
7 **HE'S A KEEPER (IRE)**, 5, gr g Brazen Beau (AUS)—Silver Grey (IRE)
8 **MIRAMICHI (IRE)**, 4, gr g Markaz (IRE)—Mattinata
9 **MISTY GREY (IRE)**, 5, gr g Dark Angel (IRE)—Chinese White (IRE)
10 **PAWS FOR THOUGHT (IRE)**, 4, b g Requinto (IRE)—Kitty Softpaws (IRE)
11 **RAJINSKY (IRE)**, 6, b g Zoffany (IRE)—Pink Moon (IRE)
12 **SOLENT GATEWAY (IRE)**, 4, b g Awtaad (IRE)—Aoife Alainn (IRE)
13 **THE NU FORM WAY (FR)**, 4, b g Le Havre (IRE)—Jamboree (IRE)
14 **ZOFFEE**, 6, b g Zoffany (IRE)—Mount Crystal (IRE)

THREE-YEAR-OLDS

15 **AMOR VINCIT OMNIA (IRE)**, b c Caravaggio (USA)—Dress Rehearsal (IRE)
16 **AMPLE POWER (FR)**, b c New Bay—Olma (SAF)
17 **BOX TO BOX (IRE)**, b c Kodiac—Alyaafel
18 **CEI CONNAH (IRE)**, gr g El Kabeir (USA)—Areyaam Rose (IRE)
19 **COSTA ADEJE (IRE)**, b g Cotai Glory—Penny Rouge (IRE)
20 B f Kingman—Cut Short (USA)
21 **DEDENNE**, b f Kingman—Roedean (IRE)
22 **EVER GIVEN (IRE)**, b c Kodi Bear (IRE)—Lil's Joy (IRE)
23 **FLAMING RIB (IRE)**, b c Ribchester (IRE)—Suddenly (GER)
24 **FOCUS ON GOLD (IRE)**, b g Galileo Gold—Race In Focus (IRE)
25 **GLITTERING CHOICE**, b f Havana Gold (IRE)—Adorable Choice (IRE)
26 **HE'S A GENTLEMAN (IRE)**, gr c Dark Angel (IRE)—Cut No Ice (IRE)
27 **HYPERSONICAL (IRE)**, b g Kingman—Flying Fairies (IRE)
28 **LADY VALENTINE**, b f No Nay Never (USA)—Mais Si
29 **LARKIN (IRE)**, gr c Dark Angel (IRE)—Plagiarism (USA)
30 **LITTLE MISS DYNAMO (IRE)**, b f Starspangledbanner (AUS)—Frankly So (IRE)
31 **LORDMAN (IRE)**, b c El Kabeir (USA)—Lady Marita (IRE)
32 **MR MCCANN (IRE)**, b c Kodiac—Copperbeech (IRE)
33 **NOTEABLE (IRE)**, ch f Profitable (IRE)—Jenny Lind
34 **OCIOS (IRE)**, b f Kodiac—Easy Times
35 **PRINCE OF PERSIA (IRE)**, b c Holy Roman Emperor (IRE)—Lisa Gherardini (IRE)
36 **ROMAN DRAGON**, b c Heeraat (IRE)—Trixie Malone
37 **ROUDEMENTAL (IRE)**, b c Footstepsinthesand—Nonetheless (IRE)
38 **SKITTLEBOMBZ**, b c Starspangledbanner (AUS)—Joquina (IRE)
39 **SO SMART (IRE)**, b g Dandy Man (IRE)—Model Looks (IRE)
40 **VICTORIA FALLS (IRE)**, b f Heeraat (IRE)—Lady Red Oak

MANOR HOUSE STABLES - continued

TWO-YEAR-OLDS

41 B c 02/05 Tasleet—All On Red (IRE) (Red Clubs (IRE)) (48000)
42 B c 03/02 Twilight Son—Allegramente (Dansili) (37000)
43 B c 19/04 Lope de Vega (IRE)—Along Came Casey (IRE) (Oratorio (IRE)) (120000)
44 Ch c 26/02 Iffraaj—Anticipation (FR) (Muhtathir) (46000)
45 **AUSDAISIA (IRE),** b c 05/05 Australia—Young Daisy Miller (IRE) (Azamour (IRE)) (20952)
46 Br c 26/03 Sea The Stars (IRE)—Chachamaidee (IRE) (Footstepsinthesand) (160000)
47 B f 10/04 Night of Thunder (IRE)—Coillte Cailin (IRE) (Oratorio (IRE)) (61905)
48 Ch c 04/01 No Nay Never (USA)—Coral Shell (IRE) (High Chaparral (IRE)) (80000)
49 B c 21/04 Camacho—Dame Judi (IRE) (Shamardal (USA)) (30476)
50 **DOUBLE OBAN,** b c 30/03 Territories (IRE)—Zaaneh (IRE) (Aqlaam) (19048)
51 B c 30/04 Dandy Man (IRE)—Dutch Courage (Dutch Art) (43810)
52 **GLORIOUS ANGEL (IRE),** b f 14/04 Cotai Glory—Angel Meadow (Mayson) (23810)
53 B c 27/04 Expert Eye—Gold Again (USA) (Touch Gold (USA)) (38095)
54 B f 26/03 U S Navy Flag (USA)—Ibiza Dream (Night Shift (USA)) (33333)
55 B c 25/04 Camacho—Imelda Mayhem (Byron) (30476)
56 B c 11/03 Dragon Pulse (IRE)—Island Odyssey (Dansili) (7619)
57 B f 22/04 Sioux Nation (USA)—Kristal Xenia (IRE) (Xaar) (72000)
58 Gr c 17/03 Gutaifan (IRE)—Lava Light (Sixties Icon) (16000)
59 **LUXURIOUS NATION (IRE),** b f 20/04 Sioux Nation (USA)—Luxuria (IRE) (Kheleyf (USA)) (27211)
60 **MACHITO (IRE),** b c 21/04 Dandy Man (IRE)—Naadrah (Muhtathir) (30476)
61 B c 18/03 Showcasing—Maelia (USA) (Redoute's Choice (AUS)) (70000)
62 **MELWOOD BOY,** b c 29/04 Massaat (IRE)—Kirrin Island (Arch (USA))
63 **MONKMOOR PIP,** b c 18/01 Fast Company (IRE)—Jal Mahal (Sepoy (AUS)) (2857)
64 B f 16/04 Starspangledbanner (AUS)—Parisian Chic (IRE) (Kodiac) (18000)
65 B c 17/03 Gustav Klimt (IRE)—Poetic Queen (IRE) (Dylan Thomas (IRE)) (18000)
66 Ch c 17/02 Dragon Pulse (IRE)—Proud Maria (IRE) (Medicean) (32381)
67 B c 29/04 No Nay Never (USA)—Ravish (Efisio) (63776)
68 Ch f 15/04 El Kabeir (USA)—Rural Celebration (Pastoral Pursuits) (40000)
69 **SAMAGON,** b c 09/02 Lightning Spear—Velvet Revolver (IRE) (Mujahid (USA)) (47619)
70 B c 24/01 Aclaim (IRE)—Selfara (Oasis Dream) (54286)
71 Ch c 28/03 Havana Grey—Seven Magicians (USA) (Silver Hawk (USA)) (52381)
72 Ch c 06/05 Zoffany (IRE)—Shake The Moon (GER) (Loup Solitaire (USA)) (55000)
73 B f 08/03 Washington DC (IRE)—Show Willing (USA) (Sir Prancealot (IRE))
74 **SIR RAJ (IRE),** b c 24/03 Holy Roman Emperor (IRE)—Pink Moon (IRE) (Namid) (7619)
75 B c 25/04 Fountain of Youth (IRE)—Siren Song (Poet's Voice)
76 Ch c 24/02 Cotai Glory—Special Chocolate (IRE) (Canford Cliffs (IRE)) (28000)
77 **STENTON GLIDER (IRE),** b f 18/03 Dandy Man (IRE)—Crystal Malt (IRE) (Intikhab (USA)) (33333)
78 B f 15/02 Dawn Approach (IRE)—Suddenly (GER) (Excelebration (IRE)) (14286)
79 B c 13/03 Showcasing—Tahiti (Royal Applause) (35000)
80 B f 07/04 Ribchester (IRE)—Tara Celeb (Excelebration (IRE)) (34000)
81 B f 06/05 Massaat (IRE)—Trixie Malone (Ishiguru (USA))
82 B c 02/02 Kodiac—Usra (IRE) (Requinto (IRE))
83 **WOLF OF KINGSTREET (IRE),** b c 24/02 Dandy Man (IRE)—Moonline Dancer (FR) (Royal Academy (USA)) (30476)
84 **ZIVANIYA,** ch c 19/03 Cityscape—Rosie Royce (Acclamation) (42857)

347	**MR GEORGE MARGARSON,** Newmarket

Postal: **Graham Lodge, Birdcage Walk, Newmarket, Suffolk, CB8 0NE**
Contacts: **PHONE** 01638 668043 **MOBILE** 07860 198303
EMAIL george@georgemargarson.co.uk **WEBSITE** www.georgemargarson.co.uk

1 **BLAME CULTURE (USA),** 7, b g Blame (USA)—Pearl In The Sand (IRE) **The Bean Club**
2 **CARIBBEAN SPRING (IRE),** 9, b g Dark Angel (IRE)—Bogini (IRE) **The Bean Club**
3 **FARRH TO SHY,** 4, b f Farhh—Coconut Shy **Mr F. G. Butler**
4 **FLIBBERTIGIBBET (IRE),** 4, ch f Prince of Lir (IRE)—Mairead Anne (USA) **Graham Lodge Partnership**
5 **MEDIA GUEST (FR),** 4, b br g Belardo (IRE)—Media Day (IRE) **John Guest Racing Ltd**
6 **PROTECTED GUEST,** 7, b g Helmet (AUS)—Reem Star **John Guest Racing Ltd**

MR GEORGE MARGARSON - continued

    7 **ROPEY GUEST**, 5, b g Cable Bay (IRE)—Hadeeya **John Guest Racing Ltd**
    8 **SPIRITED GUEST**, 6, b g Swiss Spirit—Choisette **John Guest Racing Ltd**

THREE-YEAR-OLDS

    9 **GOLDEN SPICE (USA)**, b f Golden Horn—Punita (USA) **Mr A. Al Mansoori**
  10 **IDEAL GUEST (FR)**, b g Shalaa (IRE)—Rue Renan (IRE) **John Guest Racing Ltd**

TWO-YEAR-OLDS

  11 **MYTHICAL GUEST (IRE)**, b c 18/03 Make Believe—Fonda (USA) (Quiet American (USA)) (58000)

                                                 John Guest Racing Ltd
  12 **ZINA COLADA**, b br f 26/02 Brazen Beau (AUS)—Coconut Shy (Bahamian Bounty) **Mr F. G. Butler**

Assistant Trainer: Katie Margarson.

Apprentice Jockey: Miss Abbie Pierce. **Amateur Jockey:** Miss Rosie Margarson.

---

348   **MR ANDREW J. MARTIN, Chipping Norton**
        Postal: Yew Tree Barn, Hook Norton Road, Swerford, Chipping Norton, Oxfordshire, OX7 4BF
        Contacts: **MOBILE 07815 698359**

    1 **CASSOWARY (IRE)**, 4, ch f Australia—Arose **Farrier Jump Jets**
    2 **CHARLIE'S GLANCE**, 6, b g Passing Glance—Call Me A Legend **A. J. Martin**
    3 **GLANCE AT ME**, 4, b f Passing Glance—Marys Legend
    4 **MIDNIGHT GINGER**, 6, ch m Midnight Legend—Calamintha **Mr A. V. John**
    5 **MIDNIGHT POPSTAR**, 8, b m Midnight Legend—It's Missy Imp **Andy Martin Racing Club**
    6 **MILITARIAN**, 12, b g Kayf Tara—Mille Et Une (FR) **Andy Martin Racing Club**
    7 **SCHIAPARELLI TEDDY**, 6, ch g Schiaparelli (GER)—Trifollet **A. J. Martin**

---

349   **MISS NICKY MARTIN, Minehead**
        Postal: **Great Bradley, Withypool, Minehead, Somerset, TA24 7RS**
        Contacts: **PHONE 01643 831175 MOBILE 07980 269510**
        EMAIL nickymartin3@hotmail.co.uk

    1 **ALMOST GOTAWAY (IRE)**, 5, b g Getaway (GER)—Isles of Icane (IRE) **Bradley Partnership**
    2 **BEAR GHYLLS (IRE)**, 7, br g Arcadio (GER)—Inch Princess (IRE) **Bradley Partnership**
    3 **CALL SIMON (IRE)**, 7, b g Fame And Glory—All My Judges **Bradley Partnership**
    4 **CAN YOU BELIEVE IT (IRE)**, 9, br g Oscar (IRE)—Cassilis (IRE) **Bradley Partnership**
    5 **CRAIC MAGIC (IRE)**, 7, b g Oscar (IRE)—Chantoue Royale (FR) **Bradley Partnership**
    6 **FEVERTRE (IRE)**, 7, ch g Sans Frontieres (IRE)—Avoca Star (IRE) **Bradley Partnership**
    7 **HILL COUNTRY (FR)**, 4, b g Masterstroke (USA)—Barbarasse (FR) **Bradley Partnership**
    8 4, Br g Famous Name—Inch Princess (IRE)
    9 **JUST LOOSE CHANGE**, 5, gr g Yorgunnabelucky (USA)—Ovilia (IRE) **Bradley Partnership**
  10 **LEADING CHOICE (IRE)**, 5, b g Leading Light (IRE)—Rachel's Choice (IRE) **Bradley Partnership**
  11 **LIGHT EM UP NIGEL (IRE)**, 6, b g Leading Light (IRE)—Hushed Up (IRE) **Bradley Partnership**
  12 **LUCKY SO AND SO (IRE)**, 5, b g Lucky Speed (IRE)—Limerick Rose (IRE) **Bradley Partnership**
  13 **MAGIC MARMALADE (IRE)**, 19, ch g Mohaajir (USA)—Kylogue's Delight
  14 **MOLE TRAP**, 11, b m Kayf Tara—Fairly High (IRE) **Bradley Partnership**
  15 4, B c Shirocco (GER)—Monks Charm (IRE) **Bradley Partnership**
  16 4, B g Ito (GER)—Morning Moon **Bradley Partnership**
  17 **MY LAST OSCAR (IRE)**, 7, b g Oscar (IRE)—Power Again (GER) **Bradley Partnership**

MISS NICKY MARTIN - continued

18 PENCIL (IRE), 5, ch g Retirement Plan—Maggie From Dunlo (IRE)
19 STEADY AWAY (IRE), 8, b g Fame And Glory—Inch Pride (IRE) **Bradley Partnership**
20 SYKES (IRE), 13, b g Mountain High (IRE)—Our Trick (IRE) **Bradley Partnership**
21 THE TWO AMIGOS, 10, b g Midnight Legend—As Was **Bradley Partnership**
22 VODKA ALL THE WAY (IRE), 10, b g Oscar (IRE)—Fully Focused (IRE) **Bradley Partnership**
23 WRONG SHAPE BALL (IRE), 6, b g Mahler—Ask June (IRE) **Bradley Partnership**

---

350 MR CHRISTOPHER MASON, Caerwent
Postal: **Whitehall Barn, Five Lanes, Caerwent, Newport, Monmouthshire, Np26 5pe**
Contacts: **HOME 01291 422172 PHONE 07767 808082 MOBILE 07970 202050**
WORK EMAIL cjmasonracing@yahoo.co.uk

1 ATTY'S EDGE, 6, b g Coach House (IRE)—Belle's Edge **International Plywood (Importers) Ltd**
2 EASTERN DELIGHT (IRE), 4, b c Camacho—Glamorous Air (IRE) **Robert and Nina Bailey**
3 EDGE OF THE BAY, 5, b m Cable Bay (IRE)—Sharpened Edge **Mr S Bishop & Mr C Mason**
4 GILT EDGE, 6, b m Havana Gold (IRE)—Bright Edge **Mr S Bishop & Mr C Mason**
5 GLAMOROUS BREEZE, 4, b c Cable Bay (IRE)—Go Glamorous (IRE) **Robert and Nina Bailey**
6 HAGIA SOPHIA, 4, b f Territories (IRE)—Aarti (IRE) **Mr K. B. Hodges**
7 JUST GLAMOROUS (IRE), 9, b h Arcano (IRE)—Glamorous Air (IRE) **Robert and Nina Bailey**
8 ON EDGE, 4, b g Mayson—Edge of Light **Chris Mason Racing**
9 5, B g Harbour Watch (IRE)—Superior Edge **Chris Mason Racing**

THREE-YEAR-OLDS
10 OCEAN EDGE, b f Aclaim (IRE)—Bright Edge **Chris Mason Racing**

TWO-YEAR-OLDS
11 B f 30/04 Cable Bay (IRE)—Bright Edge (Danehill Dancer (IRE)) **International Plywood (Importers) Ltd**
12 B f 28/04 Cable Bay (IRE)—Edge of Light (Xaar)
13 B f 25/04 Cable Bay (IRE)—Superior Edge (Exceed And Excel (AUS))

Assistant Trainer: Miss Evie Young.

Amateur Jockey: Miss Evie Young.

---

351 MRS JENNIFER MASON, Cirencester
Postal: **Manor Farm, Ablington, Bibury, Cirencester, Gloucestershire, GL7 5NY**
Contacts: **PHONE 01285 740445 MOBILE 07974 262438**
EMAIL pwmason2002@yahoo.co.uk WEBSITE www.jennifermasonracing.com

1 FRILLY FROCK (IRE), 8, b m Mahler—Killoughey Baby (IRE) **Mason Racing Club**
2 MADAM DELUXE, 7, b m Malinas (GER)—Easibrook Jane **Mason Racing Club**
3 WICK GREEN, 9, b g Sagamix (FR)—Jolly Dancer **Shy John Partnership**

Assistant Trainer: Mr Peter W. Mason.

Amateur Jockey: Mr Peter Mason.

---

352 MISS JANE MATHIAS, Llancarfan
Postal: **Crosstown, Llancarfan, Vale of Glamorgan, CF62 3AD**
Contacts: **MOBILE 07779 382727**

1 **DEFINATELY VINNIE**, 12, ch g Vinnie Roe (IRE)—Sohapara **Mrs S. E. Mathias**
2 **SISTER SOPHIE**, 6, b m Dr Massini (IRE)—Sohapara **Miss J. E. Mathias**

353 MR PHILIP MCBRIDE, Newmarket
Postal: **Exeter House Stables, 33 Exeter Road, Newmarket, Suffolk, CB8 8LP**
Contacts: **PHONE 01638 667841 MOBILE 07929 265711**

1 **BROUGHTONS PEACE**, 4, b f Adaay (IRE)—Broughtons Secret **P. J. McBride**
2 **CAMACHESS (IRE)**, 6, b m Camacho—Heeby Jeeby **The Narc Partnership**
3 **POKER MASTER (IRE)**, 5, b g Sepoy (AUS)—Three Cards **Mr Ian Pattle & P J Mcbride**
4 **PRISCILLA'S WISH**, 4, b f Adaay (IRE)—Ghedi (IRE) **Mr C Massie & Mr Pj McBride**

THREE-YEAR-OLDS

5 B g Brazen Beau (AUS)—Camelopardalis **P. J. McBride**
6 **HOPEMAN HARBOUR**, b g Lethal Force (IRE)—Falling Angel **Mr C Massie & Mr Pj McBride**
7 **SILKEN PETALS**, b f Pastoral Pursuits—Super Midge **The PMRacing Partnership**

TWO-YEAR-OLDS

8 **CARRY ON AITCH (IRE)**, b f 16/02 Fast Company (IRE)—Blue Willow (Exceed And Excel (AUS)) (32000)
Mr Howard J. Cooke & Mr P. J. Mcbride
9 **EQUIAMI**, b c 15/04 Equiano (FR)—Handsome Molly (Halling (USA)) (8000) **The Ten Fools & A Horse Partnership**

Other Owners: Mr C. M. Budgett, Mr A. D. Bunce, Mr H. J. Cooke, N. L. Davies, Mr C. Massie, P. J. McBride, Mr I. J. Pattle, Pmracing (Uk) Ltd, Mrs M. F. Taylor, Mr R. Wilson.

354 MR DONALD MCCAIN, Cholmondeley
Postal: **D McCain Racing Ltd, Bankhouse, Cholmondeley, Cheshire, SY14 8AL**
Contacts: **PHONE 01829 720351, 01829 720352 MOBILE 07903 066194**
EMAIL info@donaldmccain.co.uk **WEBSITE** www.donaldmccain.co.uk

1 **A DIFFERENT KIND (IRE)**, 5, b g Doyen (IRE)—Ma Minx (IRE) **Mr D. Rowe**
2 **AKENTRICK**, 6, b g Champs Elysees—Torcross **Donald McCain Racing Club**
3 **ARMATTIEKAN (IRE)**, 8, b g Arakan (USA)—Serpentine Mine (IRE) **Clwydian International**
4 **AWAY AT DAWN (IRE)**, 7, b g Getaway (GER)—Wings At Dawn (IRE) **Mr G. E. Fitzpatrick**
5 **BAREBACK JACK (IRE)**, 6, b g Getaway (GER)—Dubh Go Leir (IRE) **Mr T. G. Leslie**
6 **BARNABAS COLLINS (IRE)**, 7, b g Shantou (USA)—G Day Sile (IRE) **Mr T. G. Leslie**
7 **BARRICHELLO**, 6, b g Gentlewave (IRE)—Tambourine Ridge (IRE) **Owners Group 066**
8 **BARROWDALE (IRE)**, 7, b g Cloudings (IRE)—Tanya Thyne (IRE) **Exors of the Late Mr T. J. Hemmings**
9 **BARRULE PARK**, 6, b g Kayf Tara—Rare Vintage (IRE) **Exors of the Late Mr T. J. Hemmings**
10 **BEACH BREAK**, 8, b g Cacique (IRE)—Wemyss Bay **Mr G. E. Fitzpatrick**
11 **BIRD ON THE WIRE (FR)**, 7, ch g Martaline—Titi Jolie (FR) **Donald McCain Racing Club**
12 **BLAKENEY POINT**, 9, b g Sir Percy—Cartoon **T W Johnson & G Maxwell**
13 **BLUEBERRY WINE (IRE)**, 6, b g Dylan Thomas (IRE)—Buttonhole Rose (IRE) **Red Rum Racing 2**
14 **BOB'S BAR (IRE)**, 6, b g Darsi (FR)—Kilcoltrim Society (IRE) **Cheshire Bloodstock Racing**
15 **BROTHER PAT**, 7, b g Muhtathir—Comtesse du Sud (FR) **Birkdale Bloodstock**
16 **CALZA NERA (IRE)**, 5, b m Milan—Gazzas Dream (IRE) **Pbp Racing**
17 **CARTONNE (FR)**, 5, b g Balko (FR)—Nuance Tartare (FR) **Dave & Matt Slater**

MR DONALD MCCAIN - continued

18 **CENOTICE**, 8, b g Phoenix Reach (IRE)—Kenny's Dream **Mr D. McMahon**
19 **CHASE OUTLAW**, 6, b g Gentlewave (IRE)—Asola Blue (FR) **Four Counties**
20 5, B m Midnight Legend—Chocca Wocca **James & Jean Potter Ltd 1**
21 **CHTI BALKO (FR)**, 10, br g Balko (FR)—Ina Scoop (FR) **Tim & Miranda Johnson**
22 **CHUVELO (IRE)**, 7, b g Milan—Bargante (IRE) **Mr T. G. Leslie**
23 **COLLINGHAM (GER)**, 4, b g Samum (GER)—Chandos Rose (IRE) **Mr J. Fyffe**
24 **CONSTANCIO (IRE)**, 9, b g Authorized (IRE)—Senora Galilei (IRE) **Elite Racing Club**
25 **COULD BE TROUBLE (IRE)**, 7, b m Yeats (IRE)—She's No Trouble (IRE) **KC Sofas Ltd**
26 **COURT JURADO (IRE)**, 8, b g Court Cave (IRE)—Glen Eile (IRE) **David & Carol Shaw**
27 **COUSIN OSCAR (IRE)**, 10, b g Oscar (IRE)—On The Jetty (IRE) **Mr T. G. Leslie**
28 **CREATIVE CONTROL (IRE)**, 6, b g Battle of Marengo (IRE)—Intricate Dance (USA) **Clwydian Connections**
29 **DANGER MONEY**, 5, ch g Nayef (USA)—Generous Diana **Colin Taylor & Kay Wilding**
30 **DEDANSER (IRE)**, 6, b g Frammassone (IRE)—Courtown Bowe VII **Sarah & Wayne Dale**
31 **DONLADD (IRE)**, 8, b g Cloudings (IRE)—Kentford Serotina **Mr A Lake & Partners**
32 **DREAMS OF HOME (IRE)**, 6, b g Jet Away—Knocktartan (IRE) **Colin Taylor & Kay Wilding**
33 **DURRAGH (IRE)**, 5, b m Camelot—Laylati (IRE) **Mr Robert Aplin**
34 **ESME SHELBY (IRE)**, 7, b m Arctic Cosmos (USA)—Kyle Again (IRE) **Red Rum Racing 1**
35 **FALANGHINA**, 5, gr m Ocovango—Whisky Rose (IRE) **Mrs C. A. Shaw**
36 **FINISK RIVER**, 9, gr g Red Rocks (IRE)—Scopa d'Assi (IRE) **Mr Les Buckley**
37 **FIVEANDTWENTY**, 5, br m Farhh—Fen Guest **Middleham Park Racing XCVI**
38 **FORPADDYTHEPLUMBER (IRE)**, 6, b g Ask—Doneraile Parke (IRE) **Mr G. E. Fitzpatrick**
39 **FRUIT N NUT (IRE)**, 6, b g Carlotamix (FR)—Perilously (USA) **Mr Les Buckley**
40 **GAELIK COAST (FR)**, 8, br g Coastal Path—Gaelika (IRE) **Mr T. G. Leslie**
41 **GALUNGGUNG (FR)**, 6, gr g Khalkevi (IRE)—Unibelle (FR) **Nigel Dunnington & David Shaw**
42 **GARRIX DE LA SEE (FR)**, 6, gr g Al Namix (FR)—Janita de La See (FR) **Miss C. McCracken**
43 4, Ch g Doyen—Gaye Flora
44 **GENEVER DRAGON (IRE)**, 5, b g Dragon Pulse (IRE)—Glen Ginnie (IRE) **Middleham Park Racing C**
45 **GEROMINO (FR)**, 6, b g Masked Marvel—Romane Place (FR) **Mr G. E. Fitzpatrick**
46 **GLORY BRIDGE (IRE)**, 6, b g Fame And Glory—Youngborogal (IRE) **Exors of the Late Mr T. J. Hemmings**
47 **GOLD EMERY (FR)**, 6, gr g Doctor Dino—Queissa (FR) **Tim & Miranda Johnson**
48 **GOOBINATOR (USA)**, 6, ch g Noble Mission—Lilac Lilly (USA) **Mr T. G. Leslie**
49 **GRAIN D'OUDAIRIES (FR)**, 6, b g Kapgarde (FR)—Miss d'Estruval (FR) **Mr J. P. McManus**
50 **GREDIN (FR)**, 6, ch g Masked Marvel—Valbrune (FR) **N.Y.P.D Racing**
51 **GREY SKIES (IRE)**, 6, gr g Cloudings (IRE)—Garden Heaven (IRE) **Mr Thomas Fearn**
52 **HART OF STEEL (IRE)**, 7, gr g Ask—Boberelle (IRE) **Mr N. Hartley**
53 **HEARTBREAK KID (IRE)**, 7, b g Getaway (GER)—Bella's Bury **Mr T. G. Leslie**
54 **HIDALGO DE L'ISLE (FR)**, 5, b g Coastal Path—Agence de L'Isle (FR) **Mr T. G. Leslie**
55 **HONNOLD**, 5, br g Sea The Moon (GER)—Aloha **Hale Racing Limited**
56 **ICEMAN DENNIS (FR)**, 4, gr g Spanish Moon (USA)—Queissa (FR) **Mr Jon Glews**
57 **ISLEBRIAND (FR)**, 4, b g On Est Bien (IRE)—Bloane (FR)
58 **JOMIG DES BOIS (FR)**, 5, b g Great Pretender (IRE)—Norma Jean (IRE) **Greener Day Racing**
59 **JUNGLE JACK**, 6, ch g Doyen (IRE)—Skew **Mr T. G. Leslie**
60 **KAYFAST WARRIOR (IRE)**, 4, b g No Nay Never (USA)—Stranded **Middleham Park Racing XXXVI**
61 **KENSINGTON ART**, 6, b g Dutch Art—Lady Luachmhar (IRE) **Mark Kelly Racing Syndicate**
62 **KHAMSIN MOOR**, 7, b g Shirocco (GER)—Holme Rose **D. R. McCain**
63 **KILLANE (IRE)**, 7, b g Cloudings (IRE)—Kilkylane (IRE) **The Horses Mouth Racing Club**
64 **LADY TREMAINE (IRE)**, 7, b m Kalanisi (IRE)—Lough Lein Leader (IRE) **Duncan, Dunnington, Nicholls & Shaw**
65 **LARGY REACH**, 6, b g Phoenix Reach (IRE)—Kallithea (IRE) **Red Rum Racing 3**
66 **LATINO FLING (IRE)**, 7, b m Milan—Five of Spades (IRE) **Colin Taylor & Kay Wilding**
67 **LINDWALL (IRE)**, 4, ch g Australia—Cochabamba (IRE) **The Shinton Family**
68 **LOST IN TRANSIT (IRE)**, 5, gr g Libertarian—Rosafi (IRE) **David & Carol Shaw**
69 **LOVIN JUKEBOX (IRE)**, 4, b g Jukebox Jury (IRE)—Lovin Desert (GER)
70 **LUCKIE MONEY (IRE)**, 6, b m Most Improved (IRE)—Indian Bounty **Barry McGleenon & Thomas McAlister**
71 **MACKENBERG (GER)**, 7, b g Jukebox Jury (IRE)—Mountain Melody (GER) **Mr T. G. Leslie**
72 **MALPAS (IRE)**, 7, b g Milan—Skipping Along (IRE) **Mr N. Hartley**
73 **MASKED CRUSADER (FR)**, 6, gr g Masked Marvel—Textos (FR) **The Good Stock Syndicate**
74 **MASTER MALACHY (IRE)**, 6, b g Mastercraftsman (IRE)—Stroke of Six (IRE) **Mr T. G. Leslie**
75 **MAXIMILIAN (GER)**, 6, ch g Adlerflug—Maxima (GER) **Owners Group 099**
76 **MAYLAH (IRE)**, 4, b g Mayson—Mahlah (IRE) **Mrs Carol Shaw 1**
77 **MILANS EDGE (IRE)**, 7, b m Milan—The Keane Edge (IRE) **James and Jean Potter Ltd**

MR DONALD MCCAIN - continued

78   **MINELLA DRAMA (IRE)**, 7, b g Flemensfirth (USA)—Midsummer Drama (IRE) **Green Day Racing**
79   **MINELLA PLUS (IRE)**, 5, b g Walk In The Park (IRE)—Violin Davis (FR) **C McCracken & B Ryan-Beswick**
80   **MINELLA TRUMP (IRE)**, 8, b g Shantou (USA)—One Theatre (IRE) **Mr T. G. Leslie**
81   **MINELLADESTINATION (IRE)**, 5, b m Flemensfirth (USA)—Tweedledrum **Penketh & Sankey Jech Racing Club**
82   **MISTER WHITAKER (IRE)**, 10, b g Court Cave (IRE)—Benbradagh Vard (IRE) **Mr T. G. Leslie**
83   **MOONLIT PARK (IRE)**, 5, b m Walk In The Park (IRE)—Lakil Princess (IRE) **Mr T. G. Leslie, Mr Richard Kent**
84   **MR GOLD (IRE)**, 5, b g Milan—Assistance **Sarah & Wayne Dale**
85   **NACHO (IRE)**, 4, b g Camacho—Equinette (IRE) **Mrs Carol Shaw 1**
86   **NAVAJO PASS (IRE)**, 6, b g Nathaniel (IRE)—Navajo Charm **Mr T. G. Leslie**
87   **NAYATI (FR)**, 8, b g Spirit One (FR)—Smadouce (FR) **C P Racing**
88   **NEFYN POINT**, 8, gr g Overbury (IRE)—So Cloudy **Tim & Miranda Johnson**
89   **NELL'S BELLS (IRE)**, 6, b m Milan—Miss Cilla (IRE) **Mrs S. C. Leslie**
90   **NOBLE NORMAN**, 4, b g Norse Dancer (IRE)—Grande Terre (IRE) **Mr & Mrs G Calder**
91   **NORA THE XPLORER**, 7, b m Norse Dancer (IRE)—Bijou Love (IRE) **Mr D. Sherlock**
92   **OBEY THE RULES (IRE)**, 7, br g Rule of Law (USA)—Mamie Buggles (USA) **Mr Jon Glews**
93   **OCTOBER STORM**, 9, br g Shirocco (GER)—Cyber Star **Donald McCain Racing Club**
94   **ONTHEFRONTFOOT (IRE)**, 8, b g Shantou (USA)—On The Backfoot (IRE) **Duncan, Dunnington, Nicholls, & Shaw**
95   **OTTONIAN**, 8, ch g Dubawi (IRE)—Evil Empire **Nigel Dunnington & David Shaw**
96   **POGUE (IRE)**, 9, gr g Stowaway—Night Palm (IRE) **Mr J. Turner**
97   **PRESENTANDCOUNTING (IRE)**, 8, b g Presenting—Count On Me (IRE) **Mr J. Turner**
98   **PUNTA PRIMA (IRE)**, 5, br g Mahler—Ballinahow Ann (IRE) **Mrs J. L. Edwards**
99   **RALF DES NOES (FR)**, 5, b g Balko (FR)—Summer Cider (IRE) **Tim & Miranda Johnson**
100 **RED VISION (FR)**, 7, b g Vision d'Etat (FR)—Petale Rouge (FR)
101 **REGGAE DE BAUNE (FR)**, 4, ch g Spanish Moon (USA)—Sofia de Baune (FR)
102 **RICHMOND LAKE (IRE)**, 6, b g Westerner—Chic Milan (IRE) **Exors of the Late Mr T. J. Hemmings**
103 **RIVER WALK (IRE)**, 6, b g Scorpion (IRE)—Lucy Rouge (IRE) **Exors of the Late Mr T. J. Hemmings**
104 **ROC OF DUNDEE (IRE)**, 5, b m Shirocco (GER)—Miss Dundee (IRE) **Miss C. McCracken**
105 **RUSSCO (IRE)**, 4, b g Coulsty (IRE)—Russian Spirit **Colin Taylor & Kay Wilding**
106 **SACRE PIERRE (FR)**, 4, b g On Est Bien (IRE)—Goldance (FR) **Cheshire Bloodstock Racing 1**
107 **SCHMIDT (IRE)**, 10, b g Beneficial—Doyle's Pride (IRE) **Hale Racing & Partners**
108 **SEE THE SEA (IRE)**, 8, b m Born To Sea (IRE)—Shahmina (IRE) **The Shinton Family 1**
109 **SILVER FLYER**, 6, b g Malinas (GER)—Silver Gypsy (IRE) **Nigel Dunnington & David Shaw**
110 **SINCE DAY ONE (IRE)**, 6, b g Fame And Glory—Collou (IRE) **Mrs A. E. Strang Steel**
111 **SOMEWHAT CLOUDY (IRE)**, 6, b m Presenting—Clara Mc Cloud (IRE) **Miss C. McCracken**
112 5, B g Arctic Cosmos (USA)—South Queen Lady (IRE) **TopSpeed Thoroughbreds**
113 **SPECTACULAR GENIUS (IRE)**, 5, ch g Doyen (IRE)—Present Line (IRE) **Mr T. G. Leslie**
114 **SPIRIT OF REGULUS (IRE)**, 4, gr g Walk In The Park (IRE)—La Segnora (FR) **Colin Taylor & Kay Wilding**
115 4, B f Doyen (IRE)—Stateable Case (IRE)
116 **STEINKRAUS (IRE)**, 7, b g Jeremy (USA)—Red Fern (IRE) **Mr M. Pryde**
117 **SULLIVAN'S BROW (IRE)**, 7, b g Flemensfirth (USA)—Beths Bell (IRE) **KC Sofas Ltd**
118 **SWEET AUBURN (IRE)**, 6, b m Ask—Snug Bunch (IRE) **The Lyle Family & Hale Racing Ltd**
119 **TAKE ME TO THE SKY (IRE)**, 5, b g Tamayuz—Nassaakh **Birkdale Bloodstock**
120 **TARAGRACE (IRE)**, 6, b m Presenting—Seekayclaire (IRE) **Mr W. Ryan-Beswick**
121 **TEASING GEORGIA (IRE)**, 6, b m New Approach (IRE)—Hallowed Park (IRE) **Mr J. Turner**
122 **THE BIG JETAWAY (IRE)**, 6, b g Jet Away—Shady Pines (IRE) **Mr B. Ryan-Beswick**
123 **THE CON MAN (IRE)**, 9, b g Oscar (IRE)—Phillis Hill **Mr T. G. Leslie**
124 **THE SOME DANCE KID (IRE)**, 9, b g Shantou (USA)—River Rouge (IRE) **The Blue Nuns**
125 **TIM PAT (IRE)**, 6, b g Mahler—April Thyne (IRE) **Beswick Brothers Bloodstock**
126 **TIMETOROE (IRE)**, 8, b m Vinnie Roe (IRE)—Shokalocka Baby (IRE) **Donald McCain Racing Club**
127 **TRICK OF THE TAIL (IRE)**, 4, ch g Shantou (USA)—Nova Cyngi (USA) **David & Carol Shaw**
128 **UPAGAINSTIT (IRE)**, 5, b g Presenting—Sunami Storm (IRE) **Miss C. McCracken**
129 **WINDING ROE (IRE)**, 8, ch g Vinnie Roe (IRE)—Brown Sheila (IRE) **Mr Thomas Fearn**
130 **WORD HAS IT (IRE)**, 8, b g Jeremy (USA)—Rathfeigh (IRE) **Mr T. G. Leslie**
131 **YELLOW JACKET**, 5, b g Blue Bresil (FR)—Cent Prime
132 **ZAFAR (GER)**, 7, b g Kamsin (GER)—Zambuka (FR) **Mrs S. K. McCain**
133 **ZAMOND (FR)**, 6, b g Diamond Green (FR)—Cosavita (FR) **Birkdale Bloodstock**

THREE-YEAR-OLDS

134 B f Australia—Applause (IRE) **Mr T. G. Leslie & Mr David Redvers**

MR DONALD MCCAIN - continued

135 ECLAIRANT LE MONDE, b f Champs Elysees—Clemency **David, Ben & Thomas Lockwood 1**

Other Owners: David Ben & Thomas Lockwood, Cheshire Bloodstock Racing, Mr D. Duncan, Mr N. C. Dunnington, Hale Racing Limited, Mr P. Haughey, James and Jean Potter Ltd, Mr T. Johnson, Mr A. Lake, Mr T. G. Leslie, Mr D. J. Lockwood, Mrs A. Lyle, Mr J. R. Lyle, Mr G. Maxwell, Mr T. McAlister, D. R. McCain, Mr P. McCourt, Miss C. McCracken, Mr B. McGleenon, Mr B. L. McQuaid, Mr M. G. Meagher, Mr D. Moyes, Mr C. Nicholls, Mr D. Redvers, Mr B. Ryan-Beswick, Mr W. Ryan-Beswick, Mrs C. A. Shaw, Mr D. M. Shaw, Mr A. P. Shinton, Mr M. H. Shinton, Mr J. M. Smart, Mr C. Taylor, The Lyle Family, The Shinton Family, Mr N. Watt.

Assistant Trainer: Adrian Lane.

NH Jockey: Brian Hughes. **Conditional Jockey:** Theo Gillard, Peter Kavanagh, Abbie McCain.

Amateur Jockey: Charlie Maggs, Will Maggs, Toby McCain-Mitchell.

---

355 MR TIM MCCARTHY, Godstone
Postal: **Nags Hall Farm, Oxted Road, Godstone, Surrey, RH9 8DB**
Contacts: **PHONE 01883 740379 MOBILE 07887 763062**
EMAIL tim@tdmccarthy.com

1 **SOLDIER IN ACTION (FR),** 9, ch g Soldier of Fortune (IRE)—Ripley (GER) **Surrey Racing Club**
2 **W G GRACE (IRE),** 7, b g Exceed And Excel (AUS)—Ownwan (USA) **Homecroft Wealth Racing & T D McCarthy**
3 **WATER THIEF (USA),** 10, b g Bellamy Road (USA)—Sometime (IRE) **Surrey Racing Club**
4 **WHITE TOWER (IRE),** 8, b g Cape Cross (IRE)—Star Blossom (USA) **Surrey Racing Club**

Other Owners: Mr J. A. Collins, Homecroft Wealth Racing, Homecroft Wealth Racing & T D McCarthy, T. D. McCarthy, Mr S. J. Piper.

Assistant Trainer: Mrs C.V. McCarthy.

---

356 MR PHIL MCENTEE, Newmarket
Postal: **Racefield Stables, Carriageway, Hamilton Road, Newmarket, Suffolk, CB8 7JQ**
Contacts: **PHONE 01638 662092 MOBILE 07802 663256**
WORK EMAIL mcenteephil@yahoo.com

1 **ALAFDHAL (IRE),** 4, ch g Lope de Vega (IRE)—Afdhaad **Miss M. Hancox**
2 **BOBBY ON THE BEAT (IRE),** 4, b g Bobby's Kitten (USA)—Late Night Movie (IRE) **Ruby Red Racing**
3 **CONTINGENCY FEE,** 7, b g Helmet (AUS)—Hearsay **Miss R. B. McEntee**
4 **MY JEANIE RAI,** 4, b f Golden Horn—Blue Beacon **Miss M. Hancox**
5 **PORFIN (IRE),** 4, b g Belardo (IRE)—Tropical Mist (IRE) **T. D. Johnson**
6 **RIVER CHORUS (IRE),** 4, b f Mehmas (IRE)—Scarlet Pimpernel **Carol & David Whymark**
7 **ROCKESBURY,** 7, b g Foxwedge (AUS)—Nellie Ellis (IRE) **Mrs R. L. Baker**
8 **SANTA FLORENTINA,** 4, b f Oasis Dream—Entree **Mr J. M. Paxton**
9 **SEALED OFFER,** 4, b f Lethal Force (IRE)—Royal Seal **Carol & David Whymark**
10 **SECOND KINGDOM,** 4, b g Make Believe—Simple Magic (IRE) **Miss R. B. McEntee**
11 **SECRET TO SUCCESS,** 4, b f Iffraaj—Secret Hint **Miss M. Hancox**
12 **SMART QIBILI (USA),** 4, ch g Speightster (USA)—Allerton (USA) **T. D. Johnson**
13 **SPLIT DOWN SOUTH,** 6, gr g Dark Angel (IRE)—Brown Eyed Honey **T. D. Johnson**
14 **TELL'EM NOWT,** 4, b g Belardo (IRE)—Taleteller (USA) **Miss M. Hancox**

THREE-YEAR-OLDS

15 **BILL PLUMB (IRE),** b g Footstepsinthesand—Provence **Miss M. Hancox**
16 **BRACE FOR IMPACT (IRE),** b f Cotai Glory—Just A Runaway **T. D. Johnson**
17 **DIRTY BARRY (USA),** b g Blame (USA)—Cheer For Foxes (USA) **Miss M. Hancox**
18 B g Swiss Spirit—Hearsay **Miss R. B. McEntee**
19 **TOM HAZELGROVE (IRE),** gr g Alhebayeb (IRE)—With A Twist **Miss M. Hancox**
20 Ch f The Gurkha (IRE)—Weekend Lady (IRE) **T. D. Johnson**

Other Owners: Mrs C. Whymark, Mr D. Whymark.

357 MR MURTY MCGRATH, Maidstone
Postal: **Galway Barn, Kiln Barn Road, East Malling, Kent, ME19 6BG**
Contacts: **PHONE 01732 840173 MOBILE 07818 098073**
EMAIL mjmcgrath@hotmail.com

1 **BALLYBAY (IRE)**, 5, b g Walk In The Park (IRE)—Maple Lady (IRE) **Gallagher Bloodstock Limited**
2 **BALLYBAYMOONSHINER (FR)**, 4, b g Dandy Man (IRE)—Haven's Wave (IRE) **Gallaghers**
3 5, B g Beat All (USA)—Dizzy Whizz **M. McGrath**
4 **SEI BELLA**, 8, b m Crosspeace (IRE)—Dizzy Whizz **M. McGrath**
5 **WHO WHAT WHEN**, 7, b m Champs Elysees—Freya Tricks **Gallaghers**

THREE-YEAR-OLDS

6 **NOVA VIDA**, b f Pride of Dubai (AUS)—Umneeyatee (AUS) **Gallaghers**

Assistant Trainer: Heidi McGrath.

358 MRS JEAN MCGREGOR, Milnathort
Postal: **Wester Tillyrie Steading, Milnathort, Kinross, KY13 0RW**
Contacts: **PHONE 01577 861792 MOBILE 07764 464299**
EMAIL purebred68@hotmail.co.uk

1 **DIAMOND ROAD (IRE)**, 8, b g Tikkanen (USA)—Silver Tassie (FR) **Off and Running**
2 **GIAMAS**, 9, b g Bollin Eric—Ginger Brandy **Mrs D. Thomson**
3 6, B m Bollin Eric—Ginger Brandy **Mrs D. Thomson**
4 **JACKOFHEARTS**, 14, b g Beat Hollow—Boutique **Mrs J. C. McGregor**
5 **OSCAR BLUE (IRE)**, 12, gr g Oscar (IRE)—Blossom Rose (IRE) **Tillyrie Racing Club**

NH Jockey: Henry Brooke, Sean Quinlan.

359 MR CHRISTOPHER MCSHARRY, Sheriff Hutton
Postal: **Dudley Hill Farm, Sheriff Hutton, York, North Yorkshire, YO60 6RU**
Contacts: **PHONE 01347 868156**
EMAIL chris.mcsharry@dudleyhillfarm.co.uk

1 **CEOLWULF**, 6, gr g Fame And Glory—Spieta (IRE) **Mr C. P. McSharry**
2 **TIGERPOMP**, 7, b m Fame And Glory—Saltbarrow **Mr C. P. McSharry**
3 **TIMETOTALK (IRE)**, 6, b g Milan—Zalda **Mr C. P. McSharry**
4 **VIN DE PAIL (FR)**, 6, b g Silver Frost (IRE)—Dame de Pail (FR) **Mr C. P. McSharry**
5 **WELLFLEET WITCH**, 6, b m Black Sam Bellamy (IRE)—Indeed To Goodness (IRE) **Mr C. P. McSharry**

TWO-YEAR-OLDS

6 B f 21/02 Tasleet—Dora's Sister (IRE) (Dark Angel (IRE)) (15238) **Mr C. P. McSharry**
7 Gr f 03/01 Dark Angel (IRE)—Edge of The World (IRE) (Fastnet Rock (AUS)) (17143) **Mr C. P. McSharry**

360 MR MARTYN MEADE, Manton
Postal: **Manton Park, Marlborough, Wiltshire, SN8 4HB**
Contacts: **PHONE 01672 555000 MOBILE 07879 891811**
EMAIL mmeade@martynmeaderacing.com WEBSITE www.martynmeaderacing.com

1 **BAKE (IRE)**, 4, b g Toronado (IRE)—Rock Cake (IRE)
2 **HOVER (IRE)**, 5, ch g Free Eagle (IRE)—Badr Al Badoor (IRE)
3 **INFRASTRUCTURE**, 7, ch g Raven's Pass (USA)—Foundation Filly
4 **LONE EAGLE (IRE)**, 4, b c Galileo (IRE)—Modernstone
5 **METHOD (IRE)**, 4, ch c Mehmas (IRE)—Darsan (IRE)
6 **TECHNIQUE**, 4, b gr f Mastercraftsman (IRE)—Lifting Me Higher (IRE)

MR MARTYN MEADE - continued

   7 VARIYANN (FR), 6, b g Shamardal (USA)—Vazira (FR)

THREE-YEAR-OLDS

   8 ADELAISE (IRE), b f Lawman (FR)—Adelasia (IRE)
   9 AUDITOR, b c Profitable (IRE)—Crown (IRE)
 10 BARLEY (IRE), b c Mehmas (IRE)—Cornakill (USA)
 11 CHAIRMAN (FR), b c Almanzor (FR)—Nimbin
 12 CITYJET (IRE), b g Air Force Blue (USA)—Pellucid
 13 CONSERVATIVE (IRE), b g Churchill (IRE)—Fairy Dancer (IRE)
 14 CORSINI (IRE), ch f Mastercraftsman (IRE)—Il Palazzo (USA)
 15 CRESTA (FR), ch c New Bay—La Negra (IRE)
 16 DAIQUIRI (IRE), br c Lope de Vega (IRE)—Pale Mimosa (IRE)
 17 KANAKAM, ch c Galileo Gold—Bukhoor (IRE)
 18 NEPTUNIAN (IRE), b c Prince of Lir (IRE)—Empress Theodora
 19 OBJECT, b c Aclaim (IRE)—Quiet Protest (USA)
 20 SIKORSKY, b c Dubawi (IRE)—Hoyam
 21 TIMELINE (IRE), b f Ribchester (IRE)—Guajira (FR)
 22 ZECHARIAH (IRE), b c Nathaniel (IRE)—Nancy O (IRE)

TWO-YEAR-OLDS

 23 B f 09/02 Nathaniel (IRE)—Francisca (USA) (Mizzen Mast (USA))
 24 B c 25/03 Fastnet Rock (AUS)—Heroic Heart (FR) (Invincible Spirit (IRE)) (63810)
 25 B c 14/02 Dubawi (IRE)—I Am Beautiful (IRE) (Rip Van Winkle (IRE)) (106293)
 26 Ch c 09/05 Teofilo (IRE)—Ilulisset (FR) (Rock of Gibraltar (IRE)) (17143)
 27 B f 06/03 New Bay—Jamboree Girl (Bahamian Bounty) (19048)
 28 Ch c 15/03 Tamayuz—Mikandy (IRE) (Arcano (IRE)) (66667)
 29 B f 25/02 Harry Angel (IRE)—Patent Joy (IRE) (Pivotal) (16190)
 30 B c 23/03 Caravaggio (USA)—Private Paradise (IRE) (Galileo (IRE)) (35000)
 31 Gr c 07/02 Mastercraftsman (IRE)—Sequester (Selkirk (USA)) (61224)
 32 B c 14/02 Aclaim (IRE)—Simballina (IRE) (Azamour (IRE))
 33 B c 07/04 Dabirsim (FR)—Twilight Mystery (Acclamation) (36000)
 34 B f 16/03 Iffraaj—Wilamina (IRE) (Zoffany (IRE))
 35 B f 10/02 Nathaniel (IRE)—Yoga (IRE) (Monsun (GER)) (34014)

Other Owners: Aquis Hong Kong Pty Ltd, Ballylinch Stud, Canning Downs, Mr D. A. Farrington, Highclere T'Bred Racing - Cutting Garden, Manton Park Racing, Mantonbury Stud, Mr C. J. Murfitt, Mr J. P. M. O'Connor, Mrs M. P. O'Rourke, Mrs B.V. Sangster, Sefton Syndicate.

Assistant Trainer: Charlotte Hutchinson.

---

361 **MR NOEL MEADE, Navan**
Postal: **Tu Va Stables, Castletown KP, Navan, Co Meath, C15 F384, Ireland**
Contacts: **PHONE +353 46 905 4197 MOBILE +353 87 256 6039**
EMAIL tuvastables@gmail.com WEBSITE www.noelmeade.com

   1 ANOTHER STAR (IRE), 5, b m Rule Of Law—Lady Rosetta
   2 BARBARY MASTER, 7, br g Presenting—Daisies Adventure
   3 BEACON EDGE (IRE), 8, b g Doyen—Laurel Gift (IRE)
   4 BEN SIEGEL, 4, b c Tamayuz—Spring Crocus
   5 BEN THOMSON (IRE), 6, b g Famous Name—Essaoira Jewel
   6 BILL DOOLIN, 5, b g Australia—Star Waves (IRE)
   7 BLACK HAWK EAGLE (IRE), 4, b g Awtaad—Nimboo
   8 BRACE YOURSELF (IRE), 9, ch g Mahler—Angelica Garnett
   9 BUGS MORAN (IRE), 5, b g Pour Moi—Vivachi
 10 CASK MATE (IRE), 9, b g Kalanisi (IRE)—Littleton Liberty
 11 CHARLIE BASSETT (IRE), 5, b g Lawman (FR)—Xinji (IRE)
 12 CONOR HOGAN (IRE), 6, b g Camelot—La Sylvia
 13 CRASSUS (IRE), 5, b h War Command—Buck Aspen

MR NOEL MEADE - continued

14 **CROSSGUNS**, 5, b g Epaulette (AUS)—Maoin Dor (IRE)
15 **DALY TIGER (FR)**, 9, b g Tiger Groom—Reine Tresor (FR)
16 **DE NAME ESCAPES ME (IRE)**, 12, ch g Vinnie Roe (IRE)—Heartlight (IRE)
17 **DIOL KER (FR)**, 8, b g Martaline—Stiren Bleue (FR)
18 **EUROBOT**, 8, ch g Malinas (GER)—L'Aventure (FR)
19 **EVERGLOW**, 7, b g Presenting—Cent Prime
20 **EVERGREEN AND RED**, 4, b g Requinto—Lukes Well
21 **FANTASIA ROQUE (FR)**, 7, b m Blue Bresil—Bible Gun
22 **FARCEUR DU LARGE (FR)**, 7, b g Turgeon (USA)—Antagua (FR)
23 **FERMOYLE**, 4, b g Fast Company—Mindy
24 **FUOCO**, 4, b f Requinto—Buck Aspen
25 **GLOBAL BRIEF (IRE)**, 4, b f Aizavoski—Grand Diem
26 **GOING IN STYLE**, 4, b g Dream Ahead—Loutka
27 **HARALD HARDRAD (IRE)**, 7, b g Jeremy—Highland Dani
28 **HARRY ALONZO (IRE)**, 6, ch g Montmartre—Patrola
29 **HEISENBERG (IRE)**, 6, b g Milan—Native Idea
30 **HELVIC DREAM**, 5, b h Power—Rachevie (IRE)
31 **HELVIC PRINCESS**, 4, b f Marcel—Jersey Cream
32 **HENRY BROWN (IRE)**, 7, b g Mahler—Blackeyedsue (IRE)
33 **HES A HARDY BLOKE (IRE)**, 7, b g Aizavoski—Talk Of Rain
34 **HIGHLAND CHARGE (IRE)**, 7, b g Fame And Glory—Full Of Birds
35 **HYMIE WEISS**, 6, ch g Ocovango—Had To Be Done
36 **IDAS BOY (IRE)**, 8, ch g Dubai Destination—Witness Express
37 **IN YOUR SHADOW (IRE)**, 8, gr g Stowaway—Classic Lin (FR)
38 **JEFF KIDDER (IRE)**, 5, b g Hallowed Crown (AUS)—Alpine
39 **JERANDME (IRE)**, 8, b g Azamour—Estrelle
40 **JESSE EVANS (IRE)**, 6, b g So You Think—American Princess
41 **JOSHUA WEBB**, 7, b g Flemensfirth (USA)—Lady of Appeal (IRE)
42 **KILLER MODE (IRE)**, 7, b g Doyen—Cantou
43 **LAYFAYETTE (IRE)**, 5, b h French Navy—Scala Romana
44 **LIEUTENANT COMMAND (FR)**, 8, gr g Kendargent (FR)—Maternelle (FR)
45 **LUKE SHORT**, 5, b g Sayif (IRE)—Acclamare (IRE)
46 **LUNAR POWER (IRE)**, 4, ch g Power—Dusty Moon
47 **MAKINGACHAMP (IRE)**, 4, b g Champs Elysees—Maka
48 **MARE QUIMBY**, 6, b m Presenting—Kings Artist
49 **MOMENTS PAST (IRE)**, 5, b m Fame And Glory—Endless Moments
50 **MOUNT BROWN (IRE)**, 5, b g Fulbright—Creese
51 **NUCKY JOHNSON (IRE)**, 4, b g Vadamos—Sinful Pleasure
52 **PINKERTON**, 6, br g Ocovango—Mistress Pope
53 **POWERFUL TED (IRE)**, 7, b g Power—Haaf OK
54 4, B g Famous Name—Queen Commander
55 **SCHOOL BOY HOURS (IRE)**, 9, b g Presenting—Trinity Alley (IRE)
56 **SCRUM HALF**, 4, b g Dawn Approach—My Henrietta
57 **SHEISBYBRID (IRE)**, 4, gr f Mastercraftsman—Empowermentofwomen
58 **SIBERIAN PRINCE (IRE)**, 6, ch g Shirocco—Sue N Win
59 **SKOL**, 6, ch g Presenting—Larkbarrow
60 **STEEL CABLE**, 7, b g Well Chosen—Apache Rose (IRE)
61 **THE MODEL KINGDOM (IRE)**, 5, b m Aizavoski—Fickle Fortune
62 **THEDEVILSCOACHMAN (IRE)**, 6, br g Elusive Pimpernel—Hagawi
63 **TOO BRIGHT (IRE)**, 4, b g Fulbright—Galeaza
64 **TOUT EST PERMIS (FR)**, 9, gr g Linda's Lad—Kadalbleue (FR)
65 **ULTRAPOWER (IRE)**, 5, b g Power—Caresse
66 **WITH A START (IRE)**, 7, b g See The Stars—Sudden Blaze
67 **WONDER SPIRIT**, 4, b g Charm Spirit—Cloud Line

THREE-YEAR-OLDS

68 **ALICE DIAMOND (IRE)**, ch f Dawn Approach—Elouges
69 **BEESCATTY (IRE)**, gr g El Kabeir—Bee Eater
70 **BRIDGEHEAD (IRE)**, b g Belardo—Creese

MR NOEL MEADE - continued

71 **CHESTNUTTER (IRE)**, ch f Anjaal—Sapporo
72 B g Gleneagles—Elltaaf
73 B g Morpheus—Felix Gold
74 **FOREIGN POLICY (IRE)**, gr g Outstrip—Seschat
75 **GANDERSTOWN (IRE)**, b g Vadamos—Celestial Fable
76 **HOTEL WREN (IRE)**, b g Dragon Pulse—Ruby Girl
77 **JAMES HENRY (IRE)**, b g Kodiac—Refuse To Give Up
78 **JOE MASSERIA (IRE)**, b g Fast Company—Island Home
79 **LADY OF INISHFREE (IRE)**, br f Farhh—Bittern
80 **MARM (IRE)**, b f Cotai Glory—Most Radiant
81 **MIGHT AND MERCY**, ch g Pearl Secret—Rocknahardplace
82 **POETS COTTAGE (IRE)**, b g Zoffany—Pearl Sea
83 **THE REBEL BREEN (IRE)**, b g Bated Breath—Style And Grace
84 **ZOFFMAN (IRE)**, b g Zoffany—Empowermentofwomen

TWO-YEAR-OLDS

85 B f 04/05 American Pharoah—Ana Luna (Dream Well)
86 Ch c 21/04 Dragon Pulse—Catch Light (Shirocco)
87 B c 05/02 Dragon Pulse—Chizzler (Baltic King)
88 B c 05/05 Starspangledbanner—Destalink (Rail Link)
89 Ch f 24/04 Churchill—Duljanah (Dream Ahead)
90 **DUTCH GOLD (IRE)**, b c 01/02 Galileo Gold—Dutch Monarch (Dutch Arg)
91 B c 10/02 Adaay—Firoza (King's Best)
92 B c 02/05 Sea The Stars—Furia Cruzada (Newfoundland)
93 B c 29/03 Churchill—Glass Slipper (Danehill)
94 B f 13/02 Kessaar—Hope Against Hope (Dark Angel)
95 B c 05/03 Muhaarar—Kasayid (Pivotal)
96 Gr f 16/03 El Kabeir—Light Laughter (Distorted Humor)
97 B c 11/02 Raven's Pass—Maarit (Harbour Watch)
98 B f 06/02 Mukhadram—Maraaseem (Invincible Spirit)
99 B f 06/03 Fast Company—Marmalade Cat (Duke Of Marmalade)
100 B c 06/03 Galileo Gold—Miss Sally (Danetime)
101 Ch c 18/04 Australia—Myrica (Dansili)
102 B c 30/04 Nigh Of Thunder—Nefetari (Kodiac)
103 Ch c 03/04 Noble Mission—Pick And Choose (Street Cry)
104 B c 13/02 Dragon Pulse—Princesse Savoie (Tamayuz)
105 Ch c 24/02 National Defense—Rarement (Monsun)
106 B f 15/04 Profitable—Rockahoolababy (Kalanisi)
107 B c 10/04 Anjaal—Sharp Applause (Royal Applause)
108 B br f 11/04 Churchill—Special Assignment (Lemon Drop Kid)
109 Ch f 22/04 Belardo—Spectacular Show (Spectrum)
110 B c 17/03 Elusive Pimpernel—Summer Spice (Key Of Luck)
111 B f 01/01 Mukhadram—Wahgah (Distorted Humor)
112 B f 25/03 Bungle Inthejungle—Zalanga (Azamour)

Assistant Trainer: Damien McGillick. **Head Man:** Paul Cullen. **Travelling Head:** Emma Connolly.

Racing Secretary: Katie Daly. **NH Jockey:** Sean Flanagan. **Conditional Jockey:** Eoin Walsh.

362	**MR NEIL MECHIE, Leyburn** Postal: 55 The Springs, Middleham, Leyburn, North Yorkshire, DL8 4RB

1 **BEAUTIFUL MIX**, 10, b m Fair Mix (IRE)—Just Beautiful (FR) **The Kerr and Mechie Families**
2 **BILLY WEDGE**, 7, b g Arabian Gleam—Misu Billy **Mr D. Tate**
3 **CHARLEMAINE (IRE)**, 5, b g War Command (USA)—Newyearresolution (USA) **N. Mechie**
4 **MEDICINE WHEEL**, 6, b g Multiplex—Blushing Heart **Mrs S. M. Pearson**
5 **MONTICELLO (IRE)**, 8, b g Teofilo (IRE)—Towards (USA) **Mrs L. E. Mechie**

---

363 **MR BRIAN MEEHAN, Manton**
Trainer did not wish details of their string to appear

---

364 **MR DAVID MENUISIER, Pulborough**
Postal: Shinco Racing Limited, Coombelands Racing Stables,
Coombelands Lane, Pulborough, West Sussex, RH20 1BP
Contacts: MOBILE 07876 674095
WORK EMAIL david@dmhorseracing.com WEBSITE www.dmhorseracing.com
TWITTER @DavidMenuisier

1 **ATALANTA'S BOY**, 7, b g Paco Boy (IRE)—Affirmatively **Mrs Monica Josefina Borton & Partner**
2 **BELLOCCIO (FR)**, 4, ro g Belardo (IRE)—Three Cards **All for One Racing**
3 **DIAMOND CUTTER**, 4, b g Harzand (IRE)—Djumama (IRE) **The Diamond Cutters**
4 **FINDONO (FR)**, 4, b br g Wootton Bassett—Sapore di Roma (IRE) **Mr R. J. Scott**
5 **FLYIN' SOLO**, 5, br g Roderic O'Connor (IRE)—Fille Good **Mrs H. Ringrose & Mrs D. Thompson**
6 **FOR LOVE OF LOUISE**, 4, b f Nathaniel (IRE)—A Legacy of Love (IRE) **Mrs B. A. Karn-Smith**
7 **FOXTROT SIZZLER (GER)**, 4, b g Pride of Dubai (AUS)—Firedance (GER) **I. J. Heseltine**
8 **KENAHOPE (FR)**, 4, b f Kendargent (FR)—Make Up (FR) **Mr P. D. Wells**
9 **MIGRATION (IRE)**, 6, b g Alhebayeb (IRE)—Caribbean Ace (IRE) **Gail Brown Racing (IX)**
10 **ROBERT HOOKE**, 4, ch g French Fifteen (FR)—Wightgold **The Island Hero Syndicate**
11 **SOTO SIZZLER**, 7, b g Mastercraftsman (IRE)—Jalousie (IRE) **I. J. Heseltine**
12 **TWISTED REALITY**, 4, b f Fastnet Rock—Lady Dragon **Twisted Reality Partners**
13 **WANNABE BETSY (IRE)**, 5, b m Siyouni (FR)—Wannabe Special **Ms E. L. Banks**
14 **WINTER REPRISE (FR)**, 5, b g Intello (GER)—Winter Fashion (FR) **Mr C. A. Washbourn**

THREE-YEAR-OLDS

15 **ADELA OF CHAMPAGNE (FR)**, b f Kingman—Havre de Paix (FR) **Clive Washbourn & Peter Fagan**
16 **AR EL BEE (FR)**, b g Le Havre (IRE)—Gregoraci (FR) **Ms E L Banks & Mr G Augustin-normand**
17 **ATLANTIS BLUE**, ch f Cityscape—Deep Blue Sea **Atlantis Blue Partnership**
18 **BAEZ**, b f Sixties Icon—Sinndarina (FR) **Mr C. N. Wright**
19 **BERMUDIANA (FR)**, b f Johnny Barnes (IRE)—Kenzahope (FR) **Bermuda Racing Ltd**
20 **BOBBY'S BLESSING**, b c Bobby's Kitten (USA)—Affirmatively **Mrs Monica Josefina Borton & Partner**
21 **CAIUS CHORISTER (FR)**, b f Golden Horn—Corpus Chorister (FR) **Mr C. A. Washbourn**
22 **CANDY SHACK (FR)**, b f Almanzor (FR)—Dilbar (IRE) **Mr C. N. Wright**
23 **DARISANA (FR)**, b f Dariyan (FR)—Sanada (IRE) **About A Girl Racing**
24 **DEFFERELLA**, b f Postponed (IRE)—Cradle of Life (IRE) **Chasemore Farm LLP**
25 **EGOISTE (USA)**, b g Flintshire—Denomination (USA) **Shinco Racing Limited**
26 **FALLEN FROM HEAVEN**, b f Postponed (IRE)—Fallen Star **Normandie Stud Ltd**
27 **FLAMENCO FAN**, b f Dark Angel (IRE)—Annabelle's Charm (FR) **Merry Fox Stud Limited**
28 **FLORENT**, b c Kingman—Fleurissimo **Normandie Stud Ltd**
29 **GOLDSMITH (IRE)**, b g Shalaa (IRE)—Ingot of Gold **Gail Brown Racing (XIII)**
30 **GONNETOT (FR)**, b g Recorder—Gondole **Gerard Augustin-normand & Partner**
31 **HEY BAILS**, b g Muhaarar—White Dress (IRE) **Mr M. R. Francis**
32 **LA BELLE AURORE (FR)**, b f Motivator—Radiation (FR) **The Glow Worms**
33 **LIBRA TIGER**, ch g Territories (IRE)—Show Aya (IRE) **S. Al Ansari**
34 **LIONEL**, ch c Lope de Vega (IRE)—Gretchen **Normandie Stud Ltd**
35 **MISSY'S HOBBS**, ch f Australia—Swain's Gold (USA) **W. F. H. Carson**
36 **MOGILEVICH (FR)**, b g Recorder—Starsic (FR) **Mr K Sohi & Partner**
37 **NORTH ROCK (FR)**, b c Johnny Barnes (IRE)—Noble Manners (IRE) **Bermuda Racing Ltd**
38 **OTTILIEN (FR)**, b f Holy Roman Emperor (IRE)—Vezina (FR) **Quantum Leap Racing XVI**
39 **SECRET ARMY**, ch g Territories (IRE)—Secret Insider (USA) **Gail Brown Racing (D)**
40 **SIR BOB PARKER (FR)**, b c Siyouni (FR)—Pacifique (IRE) **M. H. Watt**
41 **SOAMES FORSYTE**, b c Siyouni (FR)—Fleur Forsyte **Normandie Stud Ltd**
42 **SPYFALL (FR)**, b f Iffraaj—Gallifrey **Chasemore Farm LLP**

TWO-YEAR-OLDS

43 B c 26/01 Le Havre (IRE)—Arendelle (Camelot) **Chasemore Farm LLP, Nick Mustoe**

MR DAVID MENUISIER - continued

44 **ASHMORE (IRE)**, b c 30/04 More Than Ready (USA)—Revolutionintheair (USA) (Declaration of War (USA)) (58000)
                                                         Gail Brown Racing/Shooting
45 B f 03/03 Expert Eye—Bizzarria (Lemon Drop Kid (USA)) (38000) **Guy Watkins**
46 B c 14/03 Cityscape—Buxlow Belle (FR) (Authorized (IRE)) **Mrs A. K. Oldfield**
47 **GEM**, b f 08/03 Frankel—Keertana (Johar) **Prime Equestrian Racing**
48 **GOODWOOD VISION**, b f 10/02 Oasis Dream—Redskin Dancer (IRE) (Namid) (52000)
                                                Goodwood Racehorse Owners Group Limited
49 B f 13/03 Camelot—High Fidelity (Peintre Celebre) **Quantum Leap Racing IV**
50 **KEHLANI (FR)**, b f 08/03 Cracksman—Beautiful Heroine (High Chaparral) **Prime Equestrian Racing**
51 B f 09/04 Bated Breath—Kekova (Montjeu) **Gordon Roddick**
52 B f 08/04 Dark Angel (IRE)—Ma Cherie (Galileo (IRE)) (72279) **Ms E. L. Banks**
53 **METAVERSE (IRE)**, ch c 09/03 Starspangledbanner (AUS)—Golden Song (Singspiel (IRE)) (70000) **Mr K. Sohi**
54 **MUNCH (FR)**, ch f 31/01 New Bay—Madernia (Duke Of Marmalade) **Prime Equestrian Racing**
55 **ON THE CARDS (FR)**, b br c 15/04 Attendu (FR)—Radiation (FR) (Anabaa (USA))
                                                  Mrs S. J. Davis, Mr P. Mitchell
56 Ch c 14/03 Zoustar—Pertinence (Fasliyev) **Prime Equestrian Racing**
57 **PRAIRIE CHIEF (IRE)**, ch c 30/03 Sioux Nation (USA)—Obama Rule (IRE) (Danehill Dancer (IRE)) (60000)
                                                  Gail Brown Racing (XIV)
58 **PURE GOLD**, b f 31/01 Golden Horn—Nathalie (Nathaniel (IRE)) (32000) **Hurst-brown, Ham, Needham**
59 **RULE OF THUMB (FR)**, ch c 22/04 Highland Reel—Lockup (Inchinor) **Prime Equestrian Racing**
60 **SAKURA STAR**, b f 11/05 Awtaad—Shamakiya (Intikhab) **Mr S. A. Ashley, James Rowsell**
61 B f 24/03 Recorder—Salvation (Montjeu) **Mr C. N. Wright, Andy MacDonald**
62 **SURGE (FR)**, b f 22/03 Churchill—Kapitale (Dubawi) **Prime Equestrian Racing**
63 B f 14/04 Sioux Nation—Tahilla (Holy Roman Emperor) **M. H. Watt**
64 B c 23/03 Recoletos—Vezina (Bering) **Quantum Leap Racing**
65 **WAXING GIBBOUS**, b f 05/02 Sea The Moon (GER)—Mary Boleyn (IRE) (King's Best (USA)) **Chasemore Farm LLP**

Other Owners: Mr R. V. Alberto, Miss J. K. Allison, Mr L. Arstall, Mr S. A. Ashley, Miss Emily Charlotte Asprey, Mr G. L. R. Augustin-Normand, Ms E. L. Banks, Mr J. J. Brummitt, Mr D. J. Burke, W. F. H. Carson, Mrs H. G. Clinch, P & S Davis, Mrs S. J. Davis, Mr M. Edwards, Mr P. M. Fagan, Mr C. D. Ham, Mrs S. Holtby, Mrs J. Hurst-Brown, Mr J. J. Lancaster, Mrs M. J. Martinez-Borton, Mr D. J. Merson, Mr P. Mitchell, Mr J. Needham, Mr J. P. M. O'Connor, Mrs H. J. Ringrose, Shinco Racing Limited, Mr K. Sohi, Mrs D. Thompson, Mr C. A. Washbourn, Mr C. N. Wright, Mr R. J. Wright.

Assistant Trainer: James Johnson, **Head Lad:** Joe Herbert, Philippe Mercier, **Travelling Head:** Christophe Aebi,

Secretary: Anne Grzywacz.

---

365   MISS REBECCA MENZIES, Sedgefield
Postal: Howe Hills Farm, Sedgefield, Stockton-On-Tees, Cleveland, TS21 2HG
Contacts: **MOBILE 07843 169217**
WORK EMAIL Rebecca@rebeccamenziesracing.co.uk **WEBSITE** www.rebeccamenziesracing.com
TWITTER @Rebeccaemenzies

1 **AMMA LORD (IRE)**, 6, b g Arcadio (GER)—Emma Jane (IRE) **J. Wade**
2 **ARCANJA (IRE)**, 8, gr g Arcadio (GER)—Nanja Monja (IRE) **J. Wade**
3 **AREYOUWITHUS (IRE)**, 7, b g Watar (IRE)—Miss Sinnott (IRE) **J. Wade**
4 **ASK PADDINGTON (IRE)**, 8, ch g Ask—Dual Obsession **The Mag & the Mackem**
5 **BATMAN FOR EVER (GER)**, 5, gr g Jukebox Jury (IRE)—Bear Nora (GER) **Mr A. McCormack**
6 **BATOCCHI**, 4, b g Bated Breath—Tarocchi (USA) **Team Given 4**
7 **BOLTON**, 4, ch g Eagle Top—Another Paris **Mr J. D. Spensley & Mrs M. A. Spensley**
8 **BOOT 'N' SHOE (IRE)**, 4, b g Ask—Phecda (FR) **Mr D. Parry**
9 **BOURBON BORDERLINE (IRE)**, 8, b g Milan—Daraheen Diamond (IRE) **Mike and Eileen Newbould**
10 **BOWLAND BELLE**, 5, b m Black Sam Bellamy (IRE)—Samrana (FR) **Graham & Christine Seward**
11 **BRAVANTINA**, 7, b m Trans Island—Falbrina (IRE) **Nunstainton Racing Club**
12 **BROOMHILL DAISY**, 6, b m Arcadio (GER)—Ballcrina Girl (IRE)
13 **CHECK MY PULSE (IRE)**, 6, b g Dragon Pulse (IRE)—Little Luxury (IRE) **Miss M. D. Myco**

MISS REBECCA MENZIES - continued

14 **CHESTERVILLE (IRE)**, 8, ch g Stowaway—Macville (IRE) **Rebecca Menzies Racing Partnerships**
15 **COURT CASE (IRE)**, 4, b g Court Cave (IRE)—Dark Sari (IRE) **J. Wade**
16 **DALYOTIN (FR)**, 6, b g Poliglote—Dalyonne (FR) **Gay & Peter Hartley**
17 **DARE THE BEAR (IRE)**, 5, br g Milan—Dancing Baloo (IRE) **J. Wade**
18 **DARK AGENT (IRE)**, 4, gr g Dark Angel (IRE)—Lethal Lena (IRE) **Mr G. R. McGladery**
19 **DOGGED**, 5, b g Due Diligence (USA)—Bling Bling (IRE) **Saddle Your Dreams**
20 **FEVER ROQUE (FR)**, 7, gr g Diamond Boy (FR)—Belle Saga (FR) **Graham & Christine Seward**
21 **FONZERELLI (IRE)**, 6, b m Schiaparelli (GER)—Cadoutene (FR) **Graham & Christine Seward**
22 **FOXWOOD (IRE)**, 4, b g Milan—She Took A Tree (FR) **J. Wade**
23 **GETAREASON (IRE)**, 9, ch g Getaway (GER)—Simple Reason (IRE) **Titanium Racing Club**
24 **GRUMPY MCGRUMPFACE (IRE)**, 7, b g Arctic Cosmos (USA)—Celestial Spirit (IRE) **Love To Race Partnership**
25 **HALCYON DAYS**, 13, b g Generous (IRE)—Indian Empress **Centaur Racing Club**
26 **HIGH MOON**, 7, b g Midnight Legend—Dizzy Frizzy **Miss M. D. Myco**
27 **HUNTSMAN'S CALL (IRE)**, 5, b g Golden Horn—Fragrancy (IRE) **Sapphire Print Solutions Rcj Associates**
28 **INGLEBY HOLLOW (IRE)**, 10, ch g Beat Hollow—Mistress Twister **Dave Scott & The Fallen Angels**
29 **JOHNNY ESTELLA (IRE)**, 4, b g No Nay Never (USA)—Sapphire Diva (IRE) **Mr J. Soiza**
30 **KOPA KILANA (IRE)**, 5, ch g Milan—Kophinou (FR) **J. Wade**
31 **LOUIS TREIZE (IRE)**, 6, ch g Slade Power—Black Rodded **Peter Clarke Racing Partners**
32 **LOVE YOUR WORK (IRE)**, 6, ch g Helmet (AUS)—Little Italy (USA) **Flash Figs Racing**
33 **MAHANAKHON POWER**, 5, b g Gleneagles (IRE)—Lady Eclair (IRE) **Stoneleigh Racing II**
34 **MAJOR SNUGFIT**, 6, ch g Ruler of The World (IRE)—Bridle Belle **Mr A Greenwood & Mr S Windle**
35 **MALIN DAZE (IRE)**, 4, b g Milan—Daisy's Sister **J. Wade**
36 4, B g Kingman—Mary Boleyn (IRE) **Mr G. R. McGladery**
37 **METAL MAN (IRE)**, 6, ch g Australia—Nick's Nikita (IRE) **Breath Of Fresh Air Racing**
38 **MIDNIGHT CHIEF (IRE)**, 4, b g Conduit (IRE)—Presentingatdawn (IRE) **J. Wade**
39 **MR SHADY (IRE)**, 5, gr g Elzaam (AUS)—Whitershadeofpale (IRE) **Ursa Major Racing Club & Partner 1**
40 **NATIVE CHOICE (IRE)**, 6, ch g Well Chosen—Native Kin (IRE) **J. Wade**
41 **NORTONTHORPEBANKER**, 4, b br g Charming Thought—Scented Garden **E. A. Brook**
42 **ODD SOCKS HAVANA (IRE)**, 4, b g Havana Gold (IRE)—Hamloola **Breath Of Fresh Air Racing**
43 **ONWARD ROUTE (IRE)**, 8, b g Yeats (IRE)—Just Stunning (IRE) **J. Wade**
44 **RAECIUS FELIX (IRE)**, 8, ch g Stowaway—Dances With Waves (IRE) **J. Wade**
45 **RAFFERTY'S RETURN (IRE)**, 7, b g Schiaparelli (GER)—Duchess Theatre (IRE) **J. Wade**
46 **RANGER BOB (IRE)**, 5, ch g Camacho—Mavis Davis (IRE) **Love To Race Partnership**
47 **RETURN TICKET (IRE)**, 9, b g Getaway (GER)—Capelvenere (IRE) **J. Wade**
48 **RITSON (IRE)**, 7, b g Jeremy (USA)—Ellen's Choice (IRE) **Mr P R Walker & Mr R Walker**
49 **ROAD WARRIOR**, 8, gr g Fair Mix (IRE)—Mimi Equal **Mr N. Taylor**
50 **SAO (FR)**, 8, b br g Great Pretender (IRE)—Miss Country (FR) **Gary Eves & Partner**
51 **SCHALKE**, 7, b g Malinas (GER)—Prospero's Belle (IRE) **Sapphire Print Solutions Ltd**
52 **SCHEGGI (IRE)**, 4, b c Holy Roman Emperor (IRE)—Shomus (USA) **Mr J. Adams**
53 **SCORCHED BREATH**, 6, b g Bated Breath—Danvers **Breath Of Fresh Air Racing**
54 **SCOTTISH ACCENT (IRE)**, 9, b g Golan (IRE)—Onthelongfinger (IRE) **Blacklock Simpson & Partner**
55 **SCOTTISH KING (IRE)**, 6, ch g Imperial Monarch (IRE)—Thanks Bobby (IRE) **Mr J. W. F. Veitch**
56 **SECRETINTHEPARK**, 12, ch g Sakhee's Secret—Lark In The Park (IRE) **Mia Racing**
57 **SET IN STONE (IRE)**, 8, b m Famous Name—Storminateacup (IRE) **Weight, Howe & Oliver**
58 **SIGNORE PICCOLO**, 11, b g Piccolo—Piccolo Cativo **Mike and Eileen Newbould**
59 **SNOWY BURROWS (FR)**, 6, gr m Montmartre (FR)—Condoleezza (FR) **4Racing Owners Club**
60 **SO SAVVY**, 4, ch g Sepoy (AUS)—How Fortunate **E. A. Brook**
61 **SOMEWHERE SECRET**, 8, ch g Sakhee's Secret—Lark In The Park (IRE) **Mia Racing**
62 **STORM LORENZO (IRE)**, 7, ch g Doyen (IRE)—Gallant Express (IRE) **Miss M. D. Myco**
63 **STRAIGHT ASH (IRE)**, 7, gr g Zebedee—Blackangelheart (IRE) **NP Racing Syndicate**
64 **TABOU BEACH BOY**, 6, b g Mukhadram—Illandrane (IRE) **J. Wade**
65 **TAKE CENTRE STAGE (IRE)**, 5, b g Fame And Glory—Glibin (IRE) **Mr C. M. Scholey**
66 **THORNABY EXCEED**, 4, ch g Eagle Top—Ingleby Exceed (IRE) **Ingleby Bloodstock Limited**
67 **THREE PLATOON**, 4, b c Kingman—Brevity (USA) **J Soiza & D Lovatt**
68 **TOI STOREY (IRE)**, 9, b g Winged Love (IRE)—Where's Herself (IRE) **Liz Dixon & Shelagh Fagen**
69 **TRAVEL LIGHTLY**, 7, b m Showcasing—Upton Seas **E. A. Brook**
70 **TWISTED DREAMS (USA)**, 5, b br g Twirling Candy (USA)—Sweet Promises (USA) **Titanium Racing Club**
71 **TWOSHOTSOFTEQUILA (IRE)**, 5, b g Snow Sky—Inouette (IRE) **Hetton Boys**
72 **UKNOWMYMEANING (IRE)**, 8, ch g Touch of Land (FR)—Lucy Lodge (IRE) **The Extra Time Partnership**
73 **VINTAGE POLLY (IRE)**, 5, br m Gutaifan (IRE)—Payphone **Club Racing Vintage Partnership**

MISS REBECCA MENZIES - continued

74 **WATER OF LEITH (IRE),** 4, b g Kodiac—Zakhrafa (IRE) **Flash Figs Racing**
75 **WYNFORD (IRE),** 9, ch g Dylan Thomas (IRE)—Wishing Chair (USA) **Stoneleigh Racing II**
76 **YOU SOME BOY (IRE),** 7, b g Dylan Thomas (IRE)—You Some Massini (IRE) **J. Wade**

THREE-YEAR-OLDS

77 **BLACK MAMBA,** ch f Helmet (AUS)—Handsome Molly **J Soiza & D Lovatt**
78 **FLURRY HEART,** ch f Sea The Moon (GER)—Twilight Sparkle (IRE) **Mr G. R. McGladery**
79 **HARWOOD LADY (IRE),** ch f Cotai Glory—Magh Meall **McIntosh & Blacklock**
80 **HOI AN BEACH,** gr g Outstrip—Pryers Princess **H. M. Hurst**
81 **MISS CALCULATION (IRE),** b f Profitable (IRE)—Maria Kristina (FR) **Liz Dixon & Shelagh Fagen**
82 B f My Dream Boat (IRE)—Royal Blossom (IRE) **He Who Dares Partnership**
83 **STANLEY SNUGFIT,** b g Adaay (IRE)—Magical Daze **Mr A. G. Greenwood**

Other Owners: Mr P. I. Baker, Mr I. M. Blacklock, Mrs A. B. M. Cuddigan, Mrs E. M. Dixon, Mr M. Dunn, Mr G. Eves, Miss S. Fagen, Mrs S. H. Fawcett, Ms D. Fields, Mr A. G. Greenwood, Mr P. J. Howe, Mr D. A. Knowles, Mr P. Lawrenson, D. S. Lovatt, Mrs J. O. E. Mangles, Mrs E. McIntosh, Dr I. McIntosh, Miss R. E. A. Menzies, Mrs E. E. Newbould, Mr J. M. Newbould, Mr R. G. Oliver, RCJ Associates Ltd, Sapphire Print Solutions Ltd, Mr D. Scott, Mrs C. Seward, Mr G. Seward, Mr I. Simpson, Mr J. Soiza, Mr J. D. Spensley, Mrs M. A. Spensley, Major P. H. K. Steveney, Mr B. Stevens, Mr C. Talbot, The Fallen Angels, A. Tickle, Mrs I. M. Tickle, M. A. Tickle, URSA Major Racing, Mrs G. B. Walford, Mr P. R. Walker, Mr R. Walker, Mr A. C. Weight, Dr P. M. Weight, Mr S. A. Windle.

Secretary: Mrs Emma Ramsden, **Business & Racing Manager:** Philip Lawrenson, **Yard Sponsor:** Bluegrass Horse Feeds.

Flat Jockey: Cam Hardie, PJ McDonald, Megan Nicholls. **NH Jockey:** Nathan Moscrop, Conor O'Farrell.

Amateur Jockey: Miss Leah Cooper.

---

366 **MR PAUL MIDGLEY,** Westow
Postal: **The View, Sandfield Farm, Westow, York, North Yorkshire, YO60 7LS**
Contacts: **PHONE 07971 048550 MOBILE 07976 965220 FAX 01653 658790**
EMAIL ptmidgley@aol.com WEBSITE www.ptmidgley.com

1 **BALLINTOY HARBOUR (IRE),** 4, b f Vadamos (FR)—Fingal Nights (IRE) **Mr H. Thornton & Mr P. T. Midgley**
2 **BIRKENHEAD,** 5, b g Captain Gerrard (IRE)—Vilnius **Chris Priestley & Partner**
3 **BUNIANN (IRE),** 6, b g Tamayuz—Darajaat (USA) **Chapman Hammond & Stephenson**
4 **BURNING CASH (IRE),** 4, b g Strath Burn—Passified Lady (USA) **Mr C. Priestley & Mr M. Hammond**
5 **DISCOMATIC (IRE),** 4, b g Estidhkaar (IRE)—Alltherightmoves (IRE)
6 **DR RIO (FR),** 6, b g Rio de La Plata (USA)—Dr Wintringham (IRE) **Mrs Jayne M. Gollings**
7 **ELEGANT ERIN (IRE),** 5, b m Dandy Man (IRE)—Eriniya (IRE) **R J Bloodstock**
8 **ELZAAL (IRE),** 4, b g Elzaam (AUS)—Alice Liddel (IRE) **The Blackburn Family**
9 **ENDERMAN,** 4, b g Bated Breath—Wish You Luck **Mr Colin Alton & Mr P. T. Midgley**
10 **EXCUISITE,** 4, gr f Gregorian (IRE)—Amour Fou (IRE)
11 **GLORY FIGHTER,** 6, b g Kyllachy—Isola Verde **Mr R. Bradley**
12 **GOOD LUCK FOX (IRE),** 6, b g Society Rock (IRE)—Violet Ballerina (IRE) **Sheila Bradley & P. T. Midgley**
13 **HARROGATE (IRE),** 7, br g Society Rock (IRE)—Invincible Me (IRE) **Zacava Racing**
14 **INDIAN SOUNDS (IRE),** 6, b g Exceed And Excel (AUS)—Sarinda **Robert Bradley & P T Midgley**
15 **J R CAVAGIN (IRE),** 6, b g Oasis Dream—International Love (IRE) **A Bell & M Hammond**
16 **JAMES WATT (IRE),** 6, b g Morpheus—Tomintoul Singer (IRE) **Mr C. Priestley & Mr M. Hammond**
17 **LAHORE (USA),** 8, br g Elusive Quality (USA)—Nayarra (IRE) **Mrs W. Burdett**
18 **LATIN FIVE (IRE),** 5, b g Camacho—Penolva (IRE) **R Wardlaw & Partners**
19 **LEODIS DREAM (IRE),** 6, b g Dandy Man (IRE)—Paddy Again (IRE) **Mr R. Bradley**
20 **MACMERRY JIM,** 4, b g The Last Lion (IRE)—Life Is Golden (USA) **Mad 4 Fun Paul Williamson & Partners**
21 **MARSELAN (IRE),** 4, b g Awtaad (IRE)—Monclaire (GER)
22 **MID WINSTER,** 6, b m Burwaaz—Cayman Fox **John Blackburn & Alan Bell**
23 **MILITIA,** 7, b g Equiano (FR)—Sweet As Honey **Mr A. Bell & Mr P. T. Midgley**
24 **MR ORANGE (IRE),** 9, b g Paco Boy (IRE)—Shirley Blake (IRE) **Mr J Blackburn & Mr A Turton**

MR PAUL MIDGLEY - continued

25 **NIBRAS AGAIN,** 8, b g Kyllachy—Regina **Peedeetee Syndicate, Ta Stephenson & Twm**
26 **PROSPECT,** 4, b g Shalaa (IRE)—Souville **Slaters Arms Racing & Partner**
27 **REGULAR INCOME (IRE),** 7, b g Fast Company (IRE)—Max Almabrouka (USA) **Mr M. K. Hammond**
28 **RUN THIS WAY,** 4, b f Cannock Chase (USA)—Prime Run **Mr A. Bell & Mr P. T. Midgley**
29 **SALUTI (IRE),** 8, b g Acclamation—Greek Easter (IRE) **R Bradley & M Hammond**
30 **THE BELL CONDUCTOR (IRE),** 5, b g Dandy Man (IRE)—Saffian **Mrs W. Burdett**
31 **THRILLA IN MANILA,** 6, b g Iffraaj—Tesary **Ian Massheder & Sandfield Racing**
32 **VAN GERWEN,** 9, ch g Bahamian Bounty—Disco Ball **Ryan Chapman & Partner**
33 **VENTURA EXPRESS,** 5, ch g Mayson—Mail Express (IRE) **Double Espresso & Partners**

THREE-YEAR-OLDS

34 **CHANT FOR MORE (IRE),** b g Alhebayeb (IRE)—Golden Anthem (USA) **Mr K Everitt & Partner**
35 **DARBY SABINI,** b g Hot Streak (IRE)—Holder's Hill (IRE) **Ryan Chapman & Partner**
36 **LIVELIFETOTHEFULL,** b g Havana Gold (IRE)—Walk On Bye (IRE) **J Blackburn, Imperial Racing & Sandfield**
37 **MAKE A PROPHET (IRE),** b g Divine Prophet (AUS)—Miss Mirabeau **Northern Sealants Ltd & Mr R Wardlaw**
38 Br f No Nay Never (USA)—Miss Lacey (IRE) **Mr C. Priestley & Mr M. Hammond**
39 B f Battle of Marengo (IRE)—Nufooth (IRE) **Mr I. Mason, Mr M. Mason**
40 **ORIENT JEWEL,** b g Orientor—Ss Vega **The Brady Girls**
41 **SUNSET OVER LOULE,** b g Twilight Son—Pride of Kinloch **Mr G. J. Paver**
42 **TEXAS MAN (IRE),** ch g Dandy Man—Texas Queen **Syps & Mrs Wendy Burdett**
43 **VADAMIAH (IRE),** b f Vadamos (FR)—Ghanimah **The Blackburn Family**

TWO-YEAR-OLDS

44 B g 22/04 Aclaim (IRE)—Beau Strata (IRE) (Dandy Man (IRE))
45 B c 28/03 Bated Breath—Commence (Oasis Dream) (24762) **Mrs W. Burdett**
46 **CRUZ DA ASSUMADA,** b f 19/02 Fountain of Youth (IRE)—Kinloch Pride (Kyllachy) **Mr G. J. Paver**
47 **FRANK THE SPARK,** ch c 09/04 Orientor—Annie Gee (Primo Valentino (IRE)) **Mr F. Brady**
48 B f 22/02 Kessaar (IRE)—Opinionated Lady (IRE) (Society Rock (IRE)) (12755) **D. Mann, Mr D. J. Poulter**

Other Owners: Mr C. Alton, Mr J. M. Barker, Mr P. Bateson, Mr J. Batty, A. Bell, Mr A. B. Blackburn, Mrs G. I. Blackburn, Mr J. N. Blackburn, Blackburn Family, Mr R. Bradley, Mrs S. Bradley, Robert Bradley & P T Midgley, Mrs A. Brady, Miss H. Brady, Miss R. Brady, Mrs W. Burdett, Mr R. Chapman, Mr A. Denham, Mr K. M. Everitt, Mr M. K. Hammond, & Mason, Mr I. R. Massheder, Mr P.T. Midgley, Mr T. W. Midgley, Mrs W. Midgley, Northern sealants Ltd, Peedeetee Syndicate, D & D Poulter, Mr C. Priestley, R J Bloodstock, Mr I. Robinson, Mrs R. Robinson, SYPS (UK) Ltd, Sandfield Racing, T. A. Stephenson, Mr H. Thornton, Mr A. Turton, Mr A. D. Ward, M & R Wardlaw, Mr R. Wardlaw, Mr P. Williamson.

Assistant Trainer: Mrs W. E. Midgley.

367
MR ROD MILLMAN, Cullompton
Postal: **The Paddocks, Dulford, Cullompton, Devon, EX15 2DX**
Contacts: **PHONE 01884 266620 MOBILE 07885 168447**
EMAIL rod.millman@ic24.net

1 **ABLE KANE,** 5, b g Due Diligence (USA)—Sugar Beet **Mr T. H. Chadney**
2 **AIRSHOW,** 7, ch g Showcasing—Belle des Airs (IRE) **Middleham Park Racing XXXIV**
3 **BAMA LAMA,** 4, ch f Equiano (FR)—Kindia (IRE) **Canisbay Bloodstock**
4 **BILLY MILL,** 4, b g Adaay (IRE)—Phantom Spirit **Canisbay Bloodstock**
5 **COPPERKIN,** 4, ch g Helmet (AUS)—Loulou (USA) **Mr M J Watson & Deborah Collett**
6 **CRAZY LUCK,** 4, b f Twilight Son—Suerte Loca (IRE) **Crown Connoisseurs**
7 **CRYSTAL CASQUE,** 7, ch m Helmet (AUS)—Crystal Moments **The Dirham Partnership**
8 **EXUDING,** 4, br f Showcasing—Exceptionelle **D. J. Deer**
9 **FAST STEPS (IRE),** 4, b g Footstepsinthesand—Inis Boffin **E. J. S. Gadsden**
10 **FOUR ADAAY,** 4, b f Adaay (IRE)—Sonko (IRE) **The Four Adaay Syndicate**
11 **HANDYTALK (IRE),** 9, b g Lilbourne Lad (IRE)—Dancing With Stars (IRE) **Cantay Racing**
12 **HAWRIDGE FLYER,** 8, b g Sir Percy—Strictly Lambada **E. J. S. Gadsden**
13 **HURRICANE HELEN,** 4, br gr f Gutaifan (IRE)—Dame Helen **JPM Racing I**
14 **MASTER GREY (IRE),** 7, gr g Mastercraftsman (IRE)—Market Day **The Links Partnership**

MR ROD MILLMAN - continued

15 **MOUNTAIN ASH (IRE)**, 4, gr g Sir Prancealot (IRE)—El Morocco (USA) **Always Hopeful Partnership 2**
16 **PRIDE OF HAWRIDGE (IRE)**, 4, b g Vadamos (FR)—Face The Storm (IRE) **E. J. S. Gadsden**
17 **PRINCE OF HARTS**, 6, br g Dalakhani (IRE)—Reaf **Mr T. W. Morley**
18 **ROCKINOVERTHEWORLD**, 5, b m Ruler of The World (IRE)—Maramkova (IRE) **Mrs S. Y. Thomas**
19 **SILENT FLAME**, 4, b f Al Kazeem—Burnt Fingers (IRE) **Miss Gloria Abbey**
20 **SINGING THE BLUES (IRE)**, 7, b g Sir Prancealot (IRE)—Atishoo (IRE) **Crown Connoisseurs**
21 **SIR PLATO (IRE)**, 8, b g Sir Prancealot (IRE)—Dessert Flower (IRE) **M.J. Tidball & B.R. Millman**
22 **SWEET PURSUIT**, 8, b m Pastoral Pursuits—Sugar Beet **Always Hopeful Partnership**
23 **TIGHTEN UP**, 4, b f Garswood—Royal Ivy **Canisbay Bloodstock**

THREE-YEAR-OLDS

24 **AMAZONIAN DREAM (IRE)**, b c Bungle Inthejungle—Grandmas Dream **Great Western Racing**
25 **FOREVER DREAMING (IRE)**, ch f Dream Ahead (USA)—Melrose Abbey (IRE) **JPM Racing II**
26 **MISS ANACO**, b f Adaay (IRE)—Sonko (IRE) **Anaco Racing Partnership**
27 **ON THE BORDER**, b f Territories (IRE)—Plover **Canisbay Bloodstock**
28 B f Nathaniel (IRE)—Seaham Hall **Mrs S. A. J. Kinsella**
29 **SOI DAO (IRE)**, b f Twilight Son—Home Cummins (IRE) **Daddies Girl Partnership**
30 **THE PRINCE (IRE)**, b g Prince of Lir (IRE)—Eliza Snow (IRE) **Mr D. A. Klein**
31 **THE RESIDENCIES (IRE)**, ch g Slade Power (IRE)—Snowdrops **Mrs S. A. J. Kinsella**
32 **TWILIGHT TONE**, b br g Twilight Son—Bikini **Crown Connoisseurs**

TWO-YEAR-OLDS

33 B c 09/04 Dandy Man (IRE)—Bratislava (Dr Fong (USA)) (35000) **Crown Connoisseurs**
34 B f 11/03 Outstrip—Cajun Moon (Showcasing) **Canisbay Bloodstock**
35 B f 04/04 Anjaal—Clifton Dancer (Fraam) (5500)
36 B f 18/03 Camacho—Dame Helen (Royal Applause) (17000)
37 **DAVID'S GIFT**, ch f 12/04 Master Carpenter (IRE)—Ladybird Blue (Captain Gerrard (IRE)) **Kittymore Racing**
38 **GENEPI (IRE)**, b f 29/01 Galileo Gold—Last Hooray (Royal Applause) (35000) **Mr M. J. Watson**
39 **JUST A SPARK**, b f 01/02 Bungle Inthejungle—One Kiss (Sayif (IRE)) (13000) **Next Ones A Grey Partnership**
40 B f 20/04 Camacho—Mary Thomas (IRE) (Zoffany (IRE)) (27000) **Mr D. A. Klein**
41 B f 21/01 Territories (IRE)—Plover (Oasis Dream) **Canisbay Bloodstock**
42 **PRINCESS NAOMI**, ch f 13/04 Master Carpenter (IRE)—Achianna (USA) (Gemologist (USA)) **Mr C. Demetriou**
43 **RADUCANU**, b f 13/05 Massaat (IRE)—Limegrove (Captain Gerrard (IRE)) (9524) **Tom Chadney's Flat Mates**
44 **SAFARI DREAM (IRE)**, b c 03/05 Bungle Inthejungle—Grandmas Dream (Kyllachy) (35000)
Great Western Racing Ii
45 B f 18/04 Havana Grey—Secret Romance (Sakhee's Secret)
46 **TAGLINE**, ch f 30/04 Havana Grey—Terse (Dansili) (14000) **Mainline Racing**

Other Owners: Mr J. F. A. Berry, Mr S. J. Brown, Mr T. H. Chadney, Miss D. Collett, Mrs J. A. Daly, Mr R. W. Daly, Mr R. D. Gamlin, Mr A. H. Hornby, Horniwinks Racing Syndicate, R. F. Kilby, Mrs S. M. Langridge, B. R. Millman, Mr A. M. Nolan, Mr S. M. Perry, Ms Z. L. Pinchbeck, Mr C. H. Saunders, Miss M. E. Stopher, Mr M. J. Tidball, Mr T. Tompkins, Mr M. J. Watson, Mr R. C. Watts.

Assistant Trainer: Mr James Millman, Louise Millman, Pat Millman.

Flat Jockey: Oisin Murphy. **Apprentice Jockey:** Oliver Searle. **Amateur Jockey:** Mr Pat Millman.

---

368 **MR RICHARD MITCHELL, Dorchester**
Postal: **East Hill Stables, Piddletrenthide, Dorchester, Dorset, DT2 7QY**
Contacts: PHONE **01300 348739** MOBILE **07775 843136**
EMAIL **easthillstables@tiscali.co.uk**

1 **COTTON CLUB (IRE)**, 11, b g Amadeus Wolf—Slow Jazz (USA) **Mr J. Boughey**
2 **POUR UNE RAISON (FR)**, 7, b br g Kapgarde (FR)—Got Aba (FR) **Mrs S. H. May**

Assistant Trainer: Mrs E. Mitchell.

369 | MR RICHARD MITFORD-SLADE, Norton Fitzwarren

Postal: Pontispool Farm, Allerford, Norton Fitzwarren, Taunton, Somerset, TA4 1BG
Contacts: PHONE 01823 461196 MOBILE 07899 994420 FAX 01823 461508
EMAIL rms@pontispool.com

1 BELLA LAZANIA, 6, b m Milan—Allerford Lily **R Mitford-Slade & Lucy Johnson**
2 LAZY SUNDAY, 8, b m Schiaparelli (GER)—Sari Rose (FR) **Pontispool Racing Club**
3 MAGGIE GREY, 6, gr m Geordieland (FR)—Westbourne (IRE) **R Mitford-Slade & Lucy Johnson**
4 MASTER TRADESMAN (IRE), 11, ch g Marienbard (IRE)—Tobeornotobe (IRE) **Pontispool Racing Club**
5 MOJITO ROYALE (FR), 6, ch g Champs Elysees—Sister Agnes (IRE) **Withyslade**
6 NORMANDY SOLDIER, 8, b g Apple Tree (FR)—Primitive Quest **Pontispool Racing Club**
7 SAMUEL JACKSON, 10, b g Alflora (IRE)—Primitive Quest **R Mitford-Slade & Lucy Johnson**
8 START POINT, 6, b m Getaway (GER)—Allerford Annie (IRE) **Pontispool 1**

Other Owners: Mrs L. Fielding-Johnson, R. C. Mitford-Slade.

Assistant Trainer: Lucy Fielding-Johnson.

---

370 | MR JAMES MOFFATT, Cartmel

Postal: Pit Farm Racing Stables, Cartmel, Grange-Over-Sands, Cumbria, LA11 6PJ
Contacts: PHONE 015395 33808 MOBILE 07767 367282 FAX 015395 36236
EMAIL jamesmoffatt@hotmail.co.uk WEBSITE www.jamesmoffatt.co.uk

1 ALQAMAR, 8, b g Dubawi (IRE)—Moonsail **Varlien Vyner-Brooks, Dave&Yvonne Simpson**
2 ALTRUISM (IRE), 12, b g Authorized (IRE)—Bold Assumption **Mr V R Vyner-Brooks, Mr K Bowron**
3 BATTLE OF TORO (IRE), 6, gr g New Approach (IRE)—Galician **Mr J. T. Hanbury**
4 BINGO, 6, b g Eastern Anthem (IRE)—It's A Discovery (IRE) **Kevin & Anne Glastonbury**
5 BURBANK (IRE), 10, b g Yeats (IRE)—Spring Swoon (FR) **D&y Simpson,D.Blyth,B.B Syndicate**
6 CAPTAIN MOIRETTE (FR), 10, gr g Kap Rock (FR)—Rahana Moirette (FR) **Ladsdoracing**
7 GOLDEN TOWN (IRE), 11, b g Invincible Spirit (IRE)—Princesse Dansante (IRE) **STM Racing**
8 JELSKI (GER), 8, b g Kallisto (GER)—Just Zoud **The Running In Rail Partnership**
9 LADY BOWES, 8, b m Malinas (GER)—Blazing Bay (IRE) **Bowes Lodge Stables**
10 MINELLA CHARMER (IRE), 11, b g King's Theatre (IRE)—Kim Hong (IRE)
Varlien Vyner-Brooks,Dave&Yvonne Simpson
11 MOONLIGHT SPIRIT (IRE), 6, b g Dubawi (IRE)—Moonsail **D&y Simpson,D Blyth,MLS Syndicate**
12 NATIVE FIGHTER (IRE), 8, b g Lawman (FR)—Night of Magic (IRE) **D&y Simpson & N.F Syndicate**
13 NO HIDING PLACE (IRE), 9, b g Stowaway—Subtle Gem (IRE) **Racing in Furness**
14 OAKMONT (FR), 9, ch g Turtle Bowl (IRE)—Onega Lake (IRE) **The Sheroot Partnership**
15 ONE FINE MAN (IRE), 7, br g Jeremy (USA)—American Jennie (IRE) **Mr J. T. Hanbury**
16 OUR SAM, 6, b g Black Sam Bellamy (IRE)—Arisea (IRE) **Geordie & Taffy**
17 SAINT PATRIC, 6, b g Universal (IRE)—Blazing Bay (IRE) **Bowes Lodge Stables**
18 THE STEWARD (USA), 11, b g Street Cry (IRE)—Candlelight (USA) **Jim Bracken, Keith Hadwin & DJM**
19 TOKYO GETAWAY (IRE), 8, ch m Getaway (GER)—Golden Blossom (IRE) **Mr R. Finnegan**
20 YUKON (IRE), 5, ro g Lope de Vega (IRE)—Alegra **The Vilprano Partnership**

Other Owners: Mr P. Bartlett, Mr D. Blyth, Mr K. Bowron, Mr S. Jones, Mr D. J. Simpson, Dave & Yvonne Simpson, Mrs Y. Simpson, The Burbank Syndicate, The Moonlight Spirit syndicate, The Native Fighter Syndicate, Mr V. R. Vyner-Brooks, Mr B. Walton, Mrs J. C. Wilson, Mr S. Wilson.

Assistant Trainer: Nadine Moffatt.

NH Jockey: Henry Brooke, Brian Hughes. **Conditional Jockey:** Charlotte Jones.

371 MR ISMAIL MOHAMMED, Newmarket
Postal: **Grange House Stables, Hamilton Road, Newmarket, Suffolk, CB8 0TE**
Contacts: **PHONE 01638 669074 MOBILE 07747 191606, 07766 570271**
EMAIL justina.stone@dubairacingclub.com

1 **AWAY HE GOES (IRE)**, 6, b g Farhh—Island Babe (USA) **Mr K. S. Sulaiman**
2 **CORAZONADA (IRE)**, 5, ch m Camacho—Giant Dancer (USA) **Mr M. Al Suboosi**
3 **EXCEEDINGLY REGAL (IRE)**, 4, b g Exceed And Excel (AUS)—Aquatinta (GER) **Mr A. Al Mansoori**
4 **GOOD EFFORT (IRE)**, 7, b h Shamardal (USA)—Magical Crown (USA) **Mr A. Al Mansoori**
5 **GOOD REGAL**, 4, ch f Universal (IRE)—Regal Sultana **Mr A. Al Mansoori**
6 **MAGICAL MILE (IRE)**, 4, ch g Sepoy (AUS)—Magical Crown (USA) **Mr A. Al Mansoori**
7 **NIBRAS SHADOW (IRE)**, 5, gr m Dark Angel (IRE)—Althea Rose (IRE) **S. H. Altayer**
8 4, B c Golden Horn—Tunkwa (FR) **Mr A. Al Mansoori**

THREE-YEAR-OLDS
9 **ALSAMYAH**, ch f Farhh—Chasing Rubies (IRE) **Mr I. Mohammed**
10 **BARQ AL EMARAT (IRE)**, b c Mehmas (IRE)—Green Briar **Mr I. Mohammed**
11 B f New Approach (IRE)—Bumptious **Mr I. Mohammed**
12 B f Sea The Stars (IRE)—Chachamaidee (IRE) **S. H. Altayer**
13 **CRAFT IN SILK (IRE)**, b f Mastercraftsman (IRE)—Silkwood **S. H. Altayer**
14 **EAGLE PATH (IRE)**, gr f Gleneagles (IRE)—Shirin of Persia (IRE) **Mr A. Al Mansoori**
15 B f Ribchester (IRE)—Fading Light **Mr A. Al Mansoori**
16 **GLIDING BAY**, b c Muhaarar—Regal Hawk **Mr I. Mohammed**
17 **MANSHOODAH (USA)**, b f Union Rags (USA)—Smart Seattle (USA) **Mr I. Mohammed**
18 **NABOO (IRE)**, ch c Profitable (IRE)—Starletina (IRE) **S. H. Altayer**
19 **RAMDON ROCKS**, b c Iffraaj—Panova **S. H. Altayer**
20 **REBEL LOVE (IRE)**, ch f Dandy Man (IRE)—Illuminating Dream (IRE) **S. H. Altayer**
21 **SEA STONE (IRE)**, b c Sea The Stars (IRE)—White Moonstone (USA) **Mr A. Al Mansoori**
22 **SHOW MAKER (USA)**, b c Empire Maker (USA)—Belle Ete (USA) **S. H. Altayer**
23 Gr f Caravaggio (USA)—Tassina (GER) **S. H. Altayer**
24 **TOTAL MASTER**, ch c Mastercraftsman (IRE)—Totally Lost (IRE) **Mr A. Al Mansoori**
25 **WINNING EMPRESS**, b f Bobby's Kitten (USA)—Flashing Colour (GER) **S. H. Altayer**
26 **ZAIN CLAUDETTE (IRE)**, ch f No Nay Never (USA)—Claudette (USA) **S. H. Altayer**

TWO-YEAR-OLDS
27 B c 03/04 Kodiac—Alkhawarah (USA) (Intidab (USA)) (55000) **Mr A. Al Mansoori**
28 B f 09/04 Harry Angel (IRE)—Always Thankful (Showcasing) **S. H. Altayer**
29 B c 11/03 Havana Grey—Chasing Rubies (IRE) (Tamayuz) (19048) **Mr I. Mohammed**
30 Ch f 02/04 Exceed And Excel (AUS)—Claudette (USA) (Speightstown) (190476) **S. H. Altayer**
31 B f 05/03 Kodi Bear (IRE)—Colour Blue (IRE) (Holy Roman Emperor (IRE)) (30476) **S. Ali**
32 Ch c 14/03 Mondialiste (IRE)—Dream Child (IRE) (Pivotal) (25714) **S. Ali**
33 B f 30/04 Galileo Gold—Home Cummins (USA) (Rip Van Winkle (IRE)) (40000) **Mr I. Mohammed**
34 B c 26/01 Mastercraftsman (IRE)—Madeira Moon (IRE) (Invincible Spirit (IRE)) (28571) **Mr A. Al Mansoori**
35 B c 01/05 Shamardal (USA)—Meeznah (USA) (Dynaformer (USA)) **Saif Ali & Saeed H. Altayer**
36 B f 24/04 Jungle Cat (IRE)—Muhadathat (Showcasing) **Mr A. Al Mansoori**
37 B c 18/04 Dandy Man (IRE)—Nancy Astor (Shamardal (USA)) (22857) **Mr K. S. Sulaiman**
38 B c 28/01 Ribchester (IRE)—Natalisa (IRE) (Green Desert (USA)) (23810) **Mr K. S. Sulaiman**
39 B f 06/03 Jungle Cat (IRE)—One Minute (IRE) (Kodiac) **Mr A. Al Mansoori**
40 B c 16/01 Lope de Vega (IRE)—Pacific Angel (IRE) (Dalakhani (IRE)) (55000) **Mr I. Mohammed**
41 Ch c 21/03 No Nay Never (USA)—Poetic Imagination (Exceed And Excel (AUS)) (90476) **S. H. Altayer**
42 B c 19/04 Kodiac—Say No Now (IRE) (Refuse To Bend (IRE)) (125000) **Mr A. Al Mansoori**
43 B c 26/03 U S Navy Flag (USA)—Show Rainbow (Haafhd) (57143) **S. H. Altayer**
44 B f 11/04 Bobby's Kitten (USA)—Skinny Love (Holy Roman Emperor (IRE)) (12000) **Mr I. Mohammed**
45 B f 01/04 Lope de Vega (IRE)—Stellar Glow (IRE) (Sea The Stars (IRE)) (125000) **S. H. Altayer**
46 Ch f 29/04 Washington DC (IRE)—Symphonic Dancer (USA) (Smart Strike (CAN)) (11429) **Mr A. Al Mansoori**
47 Ch f 01/02 Footstepsinthesand—Yasmeena (USA) (Mr Greeley (USA)) (12000) **Mr I. Mohammed**
48 Ch f 02/02 Dandy Man (IRE)—Zebgrey (IRE) (Zebedee) (14000) **Mr I. Mohammed**

Assistant Trainer: Mike Marshall.

372 **MRS LAURA MONGAN, Epsom**
Postal: **Condover Stables, Langley Vale Road, Epsom, Surrey, KT18 6AP**
Contacts: **PHONE 01372 271494 MOBILE 07788 122942 FAX 01372 271494**
EMAIL ljmongan@hotmail.co.uk WEBSITE www.lauramongan.co.uk

1 **ASCRAEUS,** 5, b m Poet's Voice—Sciacca (IRE) **Mrs P. J. Sheen**
2 **BLAIRLOGIE,** 5, b g Roderic O'Connor (IRE)—Desert Morning (IRE) **Mrs L. J. Mongan**
3 **BOWMAN (IRE),** 4, b g Lawman (FR)—Jo Bo Bo (IRE) **Mrs P. J. Sheen**
4 **FIRST AVENUE,** 17, b g Montjeu (IRE)—Marciala (IRE) **Mrs L. J. Mongan**
5 **IMPART,** 8, b g Oasis Dream—Disclose
6 **MADAM MAY,** 4, b f Telescope (IRE)—Madame de Guise (FR) **Mrs P. J. Sheen**
7 **MILLIONS MEMORIES,** 6, b g Zoffany (IRE)—Millestan (IRE) **Mrs P. J. Sheen**
8 **MOUNT MOGAN,** 5, b g Helmet (AUS)—Super Midge **Mrs P. J. Sheen**
9 **MY BOY JAMES (IRE),** 10, br g Getaway (GER)—Parkality (IRE) **Mrs P. J. Sheen**
10 **ONE DAY,** 4, b f Adaay (IRE)—Pelican Key (IRE) **Mrs P. J. Sheen**
11 **PATRIOCTIC (IRE),** 4, b g Vadamos (FR)—Height of Vanity (IRE) **Mrs P. J. Sheen**
12 **PATSY'S NUMBER ONE,** 4, br g Avonbridge—Blaise For Me **Mrs L. J. Mongan**
13 **PICKYOUROWN (IRE),** 5, ch g Cityscape—Mildoura (FR) **Mrs P. J. Sheen**
14 **PLEDGE OF PEACE (IRE),** 5, b g New Approach (IRE)—Hoodna (IRE) **Mrs P. J. Sheen**
15 **POP YA COLLAR (IRE),** 4, b g Pride of Dubai (AUS)—Yeah Baby (IRE) **Mrs P. J. Sheen**
16 **SEA TIDE,** 8, b m Champs Elysees—Change Course **Mrs P. J. Sheen**

THREE-YEAR-OLDS

17 **DAZZERLING (IRE),** ch c Starspangledbanner (AUS)—Chances Are (IRE) **Mrs P. J. Sheen**
18 **KANUHURA,** b f Kodiac—Gameday **Mrs L. J. Mongan**
19 **LAST ROAR (IRE),** b g The Last Lion (IRE)—Western Tune (IRE) **Mrs P. J. Sheen**
20 **NEWS GIRL (IRE),** b f New Bay—Lady Correspondent (USA) **Mrs P. J. Sheen**

Assistant Trainer: Ian Mongan.

NH Jockey: Tom Cannon.

---

373 **MR GARY MOORE, Horsham**
Postal: **Cisswood Racing Stables, Sandygate Lane, Lower Beeding,
Horsham, West Sussex, RH13 6LR**
Contacts: **PHONE 01403 891912**
EMAIL info@garymooreracing.com

1 **A TOI PHIL (FR),** 12, b g Day Flight—Lucidrile (FR) **Teme Valley**
2 **ABINGWORTH,** 4, b g Kapgarde (FR)—Flute Bowl **Mr C. E. Stedman**
3 **AGE OF WISDOM (IRE),** 9, ch g Pivotal—Learned Friend (GER) **The 1901 Partnership**
4 **AGGAGIO (FR),** 4, b g Born To Sea (IRE)—Ravage **Aura (Gas) Holdings Ltd**
5 **AIGUILLETTE,** 6, b g Epaulette (AUS)—Lucky Dice **Heart of the South Racing 108**
6 **ALBERT VAN ORNUM (FR),** 5, b g Authorized (IRE)—Diena (FR) **Mr P. T. Mott**
7 **ANTONY (FR),** 12, b g Walk In The Park (IRE)—Melanie du Chenet (FR) **The Winning Hand**
8 **AUTHORISED SPEED (FR),** 5, b g Authorized (IRE)—Tangaspeed (FR) **Gallagher Bloodstock Limited**
9 **BARN OWL,** 4, b c Frankel—Thistle Bird **Mr S. Packham**
10 **BEALACH (IRE),** 5, b g New Approach (IRE)—Samya **Naarn Breds**
11 **BEAU FRENCH (FR),** 4, ch g French Fifteen (FR)—Beau Fete (ARG) **D. & M. Channon**
12 **BENEVOLENTDICTATOR,** 8, ch g Schiaparelli (GER)—Kim Fontenail (FR) **The Knights Of Pleasure**
13 **BIG BARD,** 4, b g Poet's Voice—Big Moza **Mr A Watson & Mr B Malyon**
14 **BLACK GERRY (IRE),** 7, b g Westerner—Triptoshan (IRE) **Mrs M. Devine**
15 **BOTOX HAS (FR),** 6, b g Dream Well (FR)—Bournie (FR) **Mr J. K. Stone, Mrs Y. M. Stone**
16 **BRAMBLEDOWN,** 6, b g Canford Cliffs (IRE)—Pretty Flemingo (IRE) **E. A. Condon**
17 **BROUGHTONS COMPASS,** 5, b g Henrythenavigator (USA)—Sayrianna **Mr B Pay**
18 **CALL OFF THE DOGS (IRE),** 7, ch g Bienamado (USA)—Lady Charmere (IRE) **G. L. Moore**
19 **CAPRICORN PRINCE,** 6, ch g Garswood—Sakhee's Pearl **Mrs A. P. Wilkinson**
20 **CASA LOUPI,** 5, ch g Casamento (IRE)—Kameruka **Mrs V. Pritchard-Gordon**
21 **CELESTIAL POINT (IRE),** 4, b f Pivotal—Hestia (FR) **Mr C. E. Stedman**

MR GARY MOORE - continued

22 **CHAMPAGNE PIAFF (FR)**, 4, b br g Le Havre (IRE)—Galaxe (FR) **Mr A. J. Head**
23 **CHEQUE EN BLANC (FR)**, 10, b br g Bernebeau (FR)—Necossaise (FR) **Mrs E. A. Kiernan**
24 **DAREBIN (GER)**, 10, ch g It's Gino (GER)—Delightful Sofie (GER) **Chris Stedman & Mark Albon**
25 **DIRHAM EMIRATI (FR)**, 4, b g Vadamos (FR)—Allez Y (IRE) **Ashley, Carr, Duncan, Ives, Moorhead**
26 **DONALD LLEWELLYN**, 5, b g Pivotal—Rose Law **Mr C. E. Stedman**
27 **DORKING LAD**, 7, b g Sholokhov (IRE)—Brookville (IRE) **Galloping On The South Downs Partnership**
28 **DURDLE DOOR**, 4, ch f Sepoy (AUS)—Dubai Media (CAN) **Mr C. E. Stedman**
29 **EARLY DU LEMO (FR)**, 9, gr g Early March—Kiswa (FR) **Mr A. J. Head**
30 **EDITEUR DU GITE (FR)**, 8, b g Saddex—Malaga de St Sulpice (FR) **The Preston Family, Friends & T Jacobs**
31 **EIRICK**, 4, gr g Geordieland (FR)—Viking Treasure **Miss L. J. Wallens**
32 **EL HAGEB ROSE (FR)**, 8, b g Coastal Path—Ile Rose (FR) **G. L. Moore**
33 **ELISEZMOI (FR)**, 8, gr g Lord du Sud (FR)—Diva de La Borie (FR) **The Knights Of Pleasure**
34 **ERAGON DE CHANAY (FR)**, 8, b g Racinger (FR)—Rose Celebre (FR) **Five Star Racing Group**
35 **ESSENTIAL JACO (GER)**, 5, b g Pastorius (GER)—Echo Mountain **Arnold, Wood, Jacobs, L Moore**
36 **FASCINATING LIPS (IRE)**, 5, b g Canford Cliffs (IRE)—Fantastic Lips (GER) **Mr H. Redknapp**
37 **FIFTY BALL (FR)**, 7, b g Cokoriko (FR)—Voix de Montot (FR) **Mr S. Packham**
38 **FLAMINGER (FR)**, 7, gr g Racinger (FR)—Landalouse (FR) **Mrs E. H. Avery**
39 **FRENCH BUMPER (IRE)**, 6, b g Court Cave (IRE)—Tatispout (FR)
40 **FULL BACK (FR)**, 7, b g Sinndar (IRE)—Quatre Bleue (FR) **Mr A. J. Head**
41 **GENTLEMAN'S DREAM (IRE)**, 10, b g Flemensfirth (USA)—Fair And Aisey (IRE) **Dedman Properties Limited**
42 **GIVEGA (FR)**, 6, b g Authorized (IRE)—Sivega (FR) **Mr A. J. Head**
43 **GLENO (IRE)**, 10, ch g Ask—Lwitikila **Crystal Racing Syndicate**
44 **GOLDEN BOY GREY (FR)**, 6, ch g Diamond Boy (FR)—Betwixt (IRE) **Mrs R. A. Arnold**
45 **GORHAM'S CAVE**, 8, b g Rock of Gibraltar (IRE)—Moiava (FR) **Mrs A. L. Lofts**
46 **GOSHEN (FR)**, 6, b g Authorized (IRE)—Hyde (FR) **Mr S. Packham**
47 **GUGUSS COLLONGES (FR)**, 6, b g Secret Singer (FR)—Une Collonges (FR)

Mr David Gilmour & Mr James Dellaway

48 **HADDEX DES OBEAUX (FR)**, 5, b g Saddex—Shifra (FR) **Mr O. S. Harris**
49 **HAYEDO (GER)**, 4, b g Sea The Moon (GER)—Hello Honey (GER) **Mr H. Redknapp**
50 **HE'S A LATCHICO (IRE)**, 4, b g Fast Company (IRE)—Daliana **G. L. Moore, Mr D. Oneill**
51 **HECOULDBETHEONE (IRE)**, 5, b g Shirocco (GER)—Shecouldbetheone (IRE) **Mr & Mrs R Sage**
52 **HENLEY PARK**, 5, ch g Paco Boy (IRE)—Sunny Afternoon **Mrs S. A. Windus**
53 **HERMINO AA (FR)**, 5, b g Sinndar (IRE)—Acqua Luna (FR) **Galloping On The South Downs Partnership**
54 **HIGH UP IN THE AIR (FR)**, 8, ch g Famous Name—You Got The Love **Mr P. T. Mott**
55 **HIT THE ROCKS (IRE)**, 7, br g Fast Company (IRE)—Skerries (IRE) **P Moorhead, H Moorhead, J Collins 1**
56 **HOUKA D'OUDAIRIES (FR)**, 5, gr m Gris de Gris (FR)—Quinine (FR) **B. Noakes & Baroness S. Noakes**
57 **HUDSON DE GRUGY (FR)**, 5, b g Falco (USA)—Queen de Grugy (FR) **Alan Jamieson Site Services Ltd**
58 **ICONIC MUDDLE**, 9, gr g Sixties Icon—Spatham Rose **Saloop**
59 **IL RE DI NESSUNO (FR)**, 7, b g Sinndar (IRE)—Lady Elgar (IRE) **Mr A. J. Head**
60 **IMPHAL**, 8, b g Nathaniel (IRE)—Navajo Rainbow **Anthony Carr**
61 **IN THE AIR (FR)**, 4, b c Coastal Path—Sably (FR) **Mr O. S. Harris**
62 **ISAYALITTLEPRAYER**, 5, b m Nathaniel (IRE)—I Say (IRE) **Heart of the South Racing 117**
63 **JERRASH**, 5, b g Kayf Tara—Sudden Light (IRE) **Mr Jerry Hinds & Mr Ashley Head**
64 **JUMPING CATS**, 7, ch g Champs Elysees—Pivotal Drive (IRE) **Heart of the South Racing 128**
65 **JUMPING FOR JOY (FR)**, 4, b f Authorized (IRE)—Soft Pleasure (USA) **Mr R. Forster**
66 **JUNKANOO**, 5, b g Epaulette (AUS)—Bahamian Music (IRE) **Jacobs Construction & Mr J Harley**
67 **KOTMASK (FR)**, 4, ch g Masked Marvel—Kotkiline (FR) **Aura (Gas) Holdings Ltd**
68 **LANGAFEL (IRE)**, 4, b g Fast Company (IRE)—Miracle Steps (CAN) **Mrs Arnold & Partner**
69 **LARRY**, 9, b g Midnight Legend—Gaspaisie (FR) **Galloping On The South Downs Partnership**
70 **LAVORANTE (IRE)**, 6, br g Milan—Pinkeen Lady (IRE) **Mrs M. Devine**
71 **LEGAL RIGHTS (GER)**, 5, ch g Hunter's Light (IRE)—Lutindi (GER) **Heart of the South Racing 126**
72 **LETSCRACKON (IRE)**, 5, b m Camacho—Laetoli (ITY) **Exors of the late Mrs C. Reed**
73 **MADAA (IRE)**, 4, ch g Le Havre (IRE)—Elraazy **G. L. Moore**
74 **MAKE MY DAY (IRE)**, 6, b g Galileo (IRE)—Posset **Mr S. Packham**
75 **MANUCCI (IRE)**, 6, b g Nathaniel (IRE)—American Spirit (IRE) **Mr O. S. Harris**
76 **MARKS BEAR (IRE)**, 4, b g Kodi Bear (IRE)—Elizabeth Swann **Exors of the late Mrs C. Reed**
77 **MISTER TICKLE (IRE)**, 8, b g Morozov (USA)—Tatiana (IRE) **Sunville Rail Limited**
78 **MOULINS CLERMONT (FR)**, 4, b g Free Port Lux—Ania de Clermont (FR) **Alan Jamieson Site Services Ltd**
79 **MOVETHECHAINS (IRE)**, 8, b g Robin des Champs (FR)—Clash Artist (IRE) **Mr O. S. Harris**
80 **NASSALAM (FR)**, 5, ch g Dream Well (FR)—Ramina (GER) **Mr J. K. Stone**

MR GARY MOORE - continued

81 **NATURAL HISTORY**, 7, b g Nathaniel (IRE)—Film Script **Hail Sargent Evans**
82 **NATURALLY HIGH (FR)**, 7, b g Camelot—Just Little (FR) **Hail Sargent Evans**
83 **NEMINOS (FR)**, 4, ch g Showcasing—An Riocht (IRE) **Mr N. J. Grayston, Mrs S. Grayston**
84 **NEXT LEFT (IRE)**, 6, b g Sans Frontieres (IRE)—Mountainviewqueen (IRE) **Mr T. C. McKeever**
85 **NIGHT EAGLE (IRE)**, 4, b g Free Eagle (IRE)—Life At Night (IRE) **Mr S. Chambers**
86 **ODIN'S QUEST**, 4, b g Gentlewave (IRE)—Sablonne (USA) **Mr C. E. Stedman**
87 **OH CRUMBS**, 5, b g Roderic O'Connor (IRE)—Just Josie **Saloop**
88 **ON THE NOSE**, 4, b f Brazen Beau (AUS)—Little Annie **Shine & Pay**
89 **OZZIE MAN (IRE)**, 6, b g Ask—Pardkota (IRE) **Mr P. Hunt**
90 **PLATINUM PRINCE**, 5, gr g Harbour Watch (IRE)—Sakhee's Pearl **Mrs A. P. Wilkinson**
91 **PONCHO (FR)**, 4, b g Motivator—Strelkita (IRE) **G. L. Moore, Mr S. Packham**
92 **PORTICELLO (FR)**, 4, b g Sholokhov (IRE)—Chinawood (FR) **Mr O. S. Harris**
93 **PURE BUBBLES (GER)**, 4, b g Protectionist (GER)—Peace Society (USA) **Mr J. G. Jones**
94 **QUIANA**, 7, b g Pour Moi (IRE)—Quisitor (IRE) **Shark Bay Racing & Mr G L Moore**
95 **QULOOB**, 8, b g New Approach (IRE)—Jadhwah **Heart of the South Racing 120**
96 **RAFIOT (USA)**, 6, b g Elusive Quality (USA)—Viva Rafaela (BRZ) **Mr B. Hepburn**
97 **RAIHAAN (IRE)**, 6, ch g Intello (GER)—Masaafat **Mr J. G. Jones**
98 **RAY'S THE ONE**, 5, b g Mount Nelson—Tenpence **Past The Post Racing**
99 **REINATOR (FR)**, 6, b g Motivator—Vie de Reine (FR) **Mr C. E. Stedman**
100 **RICHIDISH (FR)**, 7, b g Spanish Moon (USA)—Briere (FR) **Galloping On the South Downs & G L Moore**
101 **RIOHACHA (FR)**, 5, b g Sea The Moon (GER)—Beyond The Dream (USA) **Heart of the South Racing 125**
102 **ROBIN'S DREAM**, 6, b g Kayf Tara—Sudden Light (IRE) **Mr Jerry Hinds & Mr Ashley Head**
103 **ROYAUME UNI (IRE)**, 5, b br g Galileo (IRE)—Night Lagoon (GER) **Mrs E. H. Avery**
104 **RUBY YEATS**, 11, b m Yeats (IRE)—Newbay Lady **Heart of the South Racing 122**
105 **SALIGO BAY (IRE)**, 4, b g New Bay—Glorification **Alan Jamieson Site Services Ltd**
106 **SAN PEDRO DE SENAM (FR)**, 9, br g Saint des Saints (FR)—Tetiaroa (FR)

Mrs Jane George & Mrs Helen Shelton

107 **SCHELEM (FR)**, 5, b g Orpen (USA)—Sol Schwarz **Mr P. Hunt**
108 **SEABORN (IRE)**, 8, b g Born To Sea (IRE)—Next To The Top **Mr I. Beach**
109 **SEMSER**, 5, b g Siyouni (FR)—Serres (IRE) **Mr M. Warner**
110 **SHALLWEHAVEONEMORE (FR)**, 5, b g Authorized (IRE)—Princess Roseburg (USA) **Mr S. Packham**
111 **SHANTOU MASTER (IRE)**, 7, b g Shantou (USA)—Brown Bess (IRE) **Mr D. Channon**
112 **SILASTAR**, 5, b g Sea The Stars (IRE)—Silasol (IRE) **Silastar Racing Syndicate**
113 **SOPRAN THOR (FR)**, 7, b g Authorized (IRE)—Sopran Slam (IRE) **Galloping On the South Downs Partnership**
114 **STORMINGIN (IRE)**, 9, gr g Clodovil (IRE)—Magadar (USA) **Catherine Reed & Gary Moore**
115 **SUSSEX RANGER (USA)**, 8, b g Hat Trick (JPN)—Purple (USA) **The The Tongdean Partnership**
116 **SYMPHORINE (FR)**, 4, gr f Spanish Moon (USA)—Snow Berry (FR) **Galloping On the South Downs Partnership**
117 **SYSTEMIC**, 5, b g Toronado—Saskia's Dream **P Moorhead, H Moorhead & J Collins**
118 **TAMARIS (IRE)**, 5, br g Dansili—Fleur de Cactus (IRE) **Team Tasker**
119 **TARA ITI**, 4, ch g Sixties Icon—Royal Warranty **Mark Albon & Gary Moore**
120 **TAZKA (FR)**, 7, b m Network (GER)—Tazminya **B. Noakes & Baroness S. Noakes**
121 **TEDDY BLUE (GER)**, 4, b g Sea The Moon (GER)—Tickle Me Blue (GER)
122 **TENFOLD (IRE)**, 5, b g Born To Sea (IRE)—Dear Dream (IRE) **G. L. Moore**
123 **THE FLYING SOFA (FR)**, 9, b g Sholokhov (IRE)—La Julie (IRE) **Galloping On the South Downs Partnership**
124 **THE WHIPMASTER (IRE)**, 4, ch g Mastercraftsman (IRE)—Birdie Queen **The Golf Partnership**
125 **THINK TRIGGER (IRE)**, 4, b g Epaulette (AUS)—Khibraat **Mr S. Lockyer**
126 **TIME TO BURN (IRE)**, 4, b f Bobby's Kitten (USA)—Wholesome (USA) **Lech Racing Ltd**
127 **TORONADO GREY**, 4, gr g Toronado—Debutante Blues (IRE) **Jacobs Construction (Holdings) Limited**
128 **TRANSATLANTIC (FR)**, 5, b g Le Havre (IRE)—Aquamerica (USA)
129 **TWENTY TWENTY (IRE)**, 7, b g Henrythenavigator (USA)—Distinctive Look (IRE) **Mark Albon & Gary Moore**
130 **VISION CLEAR (GER)**, 7, b g Soldier Hollow—Vive Madame (GER) **Anthony Head**
131 **VORASHANN (FR)**, 6, b g Sinndar (IRE)—Visorama (IRE) **T. Jacobs, J.E. Harley & Mr G.L. Moore**
132 **WAIKIKI WAVES**, 9, b g Alexandros—Lulabelle Spar (IRE) **Heart of the South Racing 119**
133 **WARRANTY (FR)**, 5, b g Authorized (IRE)—Ballymena Lassie
134 **WEST ON SUNSET (FR)**, 5, b m Westerner—Flute Bowl **Mr C. E. Stedman**
135 **YORKSEA (FR)**, 4, ch g Sea The Stars (IRE)—Queen's Jewel **Aura (Gas) Holdings Ltd**
136 **ZHIGULI (IRE)**, 7, b g Flemensfirth (USA)—Grangeclare Flight (IRE) **Druzhba Racing Partnership**

MR GARY MOORE - continued

THREE-YEAR-OLDS
137 **ASENSE**, b f Equiano (FR)—Atwix **The Calculated Speculators**
138 **BRILLIANT BLUE (IRE)**, b c Ribchester (IRE)—Sea of Knowledge (IRE) **Mr T Jacobs & Mr J E Harley**
139 **COPPERKNOB (IRE)**, ch c Churchill (IRE)—Mironica (IRE) **Mr S. Packham**
140 **EXECUTIVE POOL**, b g Churchill (IRE)—She's So Flawless (IRE) **The Dubai Five**
141 **HILL STATION (FR)**, b c Born To Sea (IRE)—Fulani's (IRE) **Mr J. B. Robinson**
142 **KLIP KLOPP**, ch c Night of Thunder (IRE)—Wakeup Little Suzy (IRE) **Mrs E Avery & Mr G L Moore**
143 **PROUD FAIRY**, b f Garswood—Wish You Luck **Mrs S. L. Cross**
144 **RECKON I'M HOT**, b g Hot Streak (IRE)—Dark Reckoning **Heart of the South Racing 127**
145 **ROBS SECRET**, b g Garswood—Snow Globe **Vicki & Sallyann Cross**
146 **STARSPANGLEDJAMA (IRE)**, b g Starspangledbanner (AUS)—Retinal (IRE)
Alan Jamieson Site Services & G L Moore
147 **VOODOO RAY (IRE)**, ch g Ribchester (IRE)—Midget **Sunville Rail Limited**

TWO-YEAR-OLDS
148 **NOVUS (IRE)**, b f 21/02 Dandy Man (IRE)—Fleur de Nuit (IRE) (Montjeu (IRE)) (17143) **Mr O. Jackson**
149 **OJ LIFESTYLE (IRE)**, b c 10/04 Gleneagles (IRE)—Vetlana (IRE) (Vale of York (IRE)) (52000) **Mr O. Jackson**

Other Owners: Alan Jamieson Site Services Ltd, Mr M. L. Albon, Mrs R. A. Arnold, Mrs S. A. Ashley, Mrs E. H. Avery, Anthony Carr, Mr D. Channon, Mrs M. Channon, Mr J. A. Collins, Mrs S. L. Cross, Mr A. J. A. Dellaway, J. T. Devine, Mr G. C. Dreher, Mr M. Duncan, Mr D. L. Evans, G L Moore Racing, Galloping On The South Downs Partnership, Mrs J. George, Mr D. S. Gilmour, & Grayston, Mr J. E. Hale, J. E. Harley, Mr A. J. Head, Mr P. A. Herbert, Mr J. Hinds, Mr D. L. Ives, T. Jacobs, Jacobs Construction (Holdings) Limited, D. Leon, Mr D. Llambias, Danny & Gary Moore, G. L. Moore, Steven & Gary Moore, Mr P. B. Moorhead, Mr J. Muir, C. B. Noakes, Baroness S. Noakes, P Moorhead, H Moorhead & J Collins, Mr B Pay, Mrs V. K. Phelan, Exors of the late Mrs C. Reed, SSLS LTD, Mr R. J. Sage, Mrs T. J. Sage, Mr R. D. Sargent, Mrs H. J. Shelton, Mr C. E. Stedman, & Stone, Mrs Y. M. Stone, The Preston Family & Friends Ltd, Mrs S. Voikhanskaya, Dr M. Voikhansky, Miss C. A. Webb, Mr M. K. Webb, Mr T. Wood.

Assistant Trainer: David Wilson, **Racing Secretary:** Maria Workman.

Flat Jockey: Hector Crouch, Ryan Moore, Tom Queally. **NH Jockey:** Jamie Moore, Joshua Moore.

Conditional Jockey: Niall Houlihan. **Apprentice Jockey:** Rhys Clutterbuck, Anna Gibson, Aidan Keely.

Amateur Jockey: Mr George Gorman, Mr Robert Hargreaves.

---

374 MR J. S. MOORE, Upper Lambourn
Postal: Berkeley House Stables, Upper Lambourn, Hungerford, Berkshire, RG17 8QP
Contacts: PHONE 01488 73887 MOBILE 07860 871127, 07900 402856 FAX 01488 73997
EMAIL jsmoore.racing@btopenworld.com WEBSITE www.stanmooreracing.co.uk

1 **ALALA (IRE)**, 4, gr f Alhebayeb (IRE)—Rumuz (IRE) **D. G. Iceton**
2 **BOMB SQUAD (IRE)**, 4, gr g Lethal Force (IRE)—Dutch Destiny **Eventmasters Racing & J S Moore**
3 **BROCKAGH CAILIN**, 7, b m Helmet (AUS)—Step Softly **Gridline Racing**
4 **EASY EQUATION (FR)**, 4, b g Rajsaman (FR)—Simple Solution (USA) **Roy Humphrey & J S Moore**
5 **FACT OR FABLE (IRE)**, 5, gr g Alhebayeb (IRE)—Unreal **Mrs Wendy Jarrett & J S Moore**
6 **HOT DAY**, 4, b g Adaay (IRE)—Sunny York (IRE) **Mr T. G. Vaughan**
7 **MAGICAL WISH (IRE)**, 6, br g Heeraat (IRE)—Tomintoul Magic (IRE) **Mr M. Khalid Abdul Rahim**
8 **PAPAS GIRL (IRE)**, 4, b f Mehmas (IRE)—Sunny Harbor (IRE) **Pc Bloodstock & J S Moore**
9 **UTHER PENDRAGON (IRE)**, 7, b g Dragon Pulse (IRE)—Unreal **Mrs Wendy Jarrett & J S Moore**
10 **WHOLELOTAFUN (IRE)**, 4, b c Sir Prancealot (IRE)—Gatamalata (IRE) **Mrs Wendy Jarrett & J S Moore**
11 **WONDER ELMOSSMAN (IRE)**, 4, b c Elzaam (AUS)—Karenka (IRE) **Paul Kwok & Ms Angel Li**
12 **WONDER ELZAAM (IRE)**, 5, b h Elzaam (AUS)—Artful Panda (IRE) **Kwok, A & Racing Group**

THREE-YEAR-OLDS
13 **ALREADY GONE (IRE)**, b g Zoffany (IRE)—Whatelseaboutyou (IRE) **Mr Kieron Badger & J S Moore**
14 **BIRKIE GIRL**, b f Buratino (IRE)—Noble Nova **Mrs S Gray, Mr Ian Gray & Sara Moore**
15 **HAVANA GOLDRUSH**, b c Havana Gold (IRE)—Riot of Colour **S & Galloway**
16 B c Estidhkaar (IRE)—Joy For Life **J. S. Moore & Partner**

MR J. S. MOORE - continued

17 **LANDSHIP (IRE)**, b g Estidhkaar (IRE)—Shamiya (IRE) **J. S. Moore**
18 **ROYSTAN GIRL**, ch f Outstrip—Pose (IRE) **Roy & S Moore**
19 **RUITH LE TU**, b g Aclaim (IRE)—Let's Dance (IRE) **Mrs Wendy Jarrett & J S Moore**
20 **THE WIZARD OF EYE (IRE)**, ch c Galileo Gold—Prom Dress **O Humphrey A Favell R Humphrey J S Moore**
21 **VAXHOLM (IRE)**, b g Estidhkaar (IRE)—Lovely Dancer (IRE) **Eventmasters Racing & J S Moore**
22 **VLAD THE IMPALER (IRE)**, b g Vadamos (FR)—Catamaran (IRE) **J. S. Moore**

TWO-YEAR-OLDS

23 **FOOTSTEPS**, b f 26/03 Footstepsinthesand—Ruxleys Star (USA) (Artie Schiller (USA)) **Pineapple Stud & J S Moore**
24 **HOW LONG**, gr c 29/01 Mastercraftsman (IRE)—Dinvar Diva (Dalakhani (IRE)) (5000)

Mr Kieron Badger & J S Moore
25 **MIRABELLO BAY (IRE)**, ch g 24/04 Belardo (IRE)—Stone Roses (IRE) (Zebedee) (2857) **Caroline & S Moore**
26 B f 28/04 Washington DC (IRE)—Sitting Pritty (IRE) (Compton Place) (952) **Eventmasters Racing & J S Moore**

Other Owners: Mr M. J. Ablett, Mrs R. Ablett, Mr K. P. Badger, Eventmasters Racing, Mrs A. Favell, Mr B. S. Galloway, Mr I. J. B. Gray, Mrs S. Gray, Mr P.J. Grimes, Mr O. Humphrey, Mr R. V. Humphrey, Ms C. Instone, Mr A. James, Mrs W. J. Jarrett, Mr P. Kwok, Ms A. LI, Mr E. McGlinchey, Mr N. J. McGlinchey, J. S. Moore, Mrs S. J. Moore, Mr J. Nunn, Orbital Racing Group, PC Bloodstock, Mrs D. Sheasby, Mr E. J. N. Sheasby, R. C. Smith, The Pineapple Stud.

Assistant Trainer: Mrs S. Moore. **Racing Secretary:** Miss Cathy Holding.

Apprentice Jockey: Miss Sophie Reed.

375	**MISS LAURA MORGAN, Waltham On The Wolds** Postal: Foxfield Stud, Goadby Road, Waltham On The Wolds, Melton Mowbray, Leicestershire, LE14 4AG Contacts: **PHONE 01664 464571 MOBILE 07817 616622** EMAIL lauramorg@hotmail.co.uk

1 **ADAMHILL (IRE)**, 7, b g Oscar (IRE)—Benefit of Porter (IRE) **Mr F. K. Baxter**
2 **AGAINST ALL ODDS (FR)**, 7, b m Saint des Saints (FR)—Cue To Cue **Mr & Mrs W. J. Williams**
3 **ANGEL'S ENVY**, 10, b m Yeats (IRE)—Caoba **A. Lyons**
4 **BEAUTIFUL BEN (IRE)**, 12, b g Beneficial—Almnadia (IRE) **A. Lyons**
5 **BOLD ENDEAVOUR**, 6, b g Fame And Glory—Araucaria (IRE) **Countrywide Park Homes Ltd**
6 **CABALGATA**, 7, gr m Mastercraftsman (IRE)—Winning Sequence (FR) **Miss L. Morgan**
7 **CHAMP IS REAL**, 6, b g Kayf Tara—The Prime Viper (IRE) **Mr A. Rogers**
8 **CLEAR THE RUNWAY (IRE)**, 6, b g Jet Away—Minish Yeats (IRE) **Mr A. Rogers**
9 **CUDDLY DUDLEY (FR)**, 5, b g Kapgarde (FR)—Cue To Cue **Mr & Mrs W. J. Williams**
10 **DIVA'S MIX**, 7, b m Fair Mix (IRE)—Divisa (GER) **Miss L. Morgan**
11 **DOM PERRY**, 6, b g Doyen (IRE)—Aphrodisias (FR) **Rushmoor Stud**
12 **DREAM POINT (IRE)**, 7, b m Iffraaj—Dream Club **Mr T. H. A. Barton**
13 **FIRE AWAY (IRE)**, 9, b g Getaway (GER)—Joan's Girl (IRE) **The Stagger Inn**
14 **FIRST ANGEL (FR)**, 6, b g Anabaa Blue—Fontaine de Mars (FR) **Mr S. Sugden**
15 **FISHING FOR LIKES (IRE)**, 6, b g Arcadio (GER)—Status Update (IRE) **Hanbury & Read**
16 **FOR FITZ SAKE (IRE)**, 6, b g Califet (FR)—Hollygrove (IRE) **Mrs A. M. Williams**
17 **FRIARY ROCK (FR)**, 7, b g Spanish Moon (USA)—Zenita des Brosses (FR) **The 1759 Syndicate**
18 **GENTLE JOLIE**, 6, b m Gentlewave (IRE)—Madam Jolie (IRE) **Mr A. Rogers**
19 **GOOD MAN PAT (IRE)**, 9, b g Gold Well—Basically Supreme (IRE) **Mr S. Sugden**
20 **HAASAB (IRE)**, 9, b g Sakhee (USA)—Badweia (USA) **Miss L. Morgan**
21 **HASANKEY (IRE)**, 6, gr g Mastercraftsman (IRE)—Haziyna (IRE) **The Hanky Panky Partnership**
22 **HERE COMES MR TEE**, 5, b g Telescope (IRE)—Owlesbury Dream (IRE)
23 **HERE WE HAVE IT (IRE)**, 7, b g Mahler—Islands Sister (IRE) **Hanbury & Fretwell**
24 **ILLUSION OF TIME (IRE)**, 4, b g Sea The Stars (IRE)—Dolce Strega (IRE) **J. C. Fretwell**
25 **INSIDE INFORMANT (USA)**, 4, b g Flintshire—Endless Light **Brandt, Burdett, Bloy**
26 **J'AI FROID (IRE)**, 9, b g Flemensfirth (USA)—Park Wave (IRE) **Mrs K. Bromley**
27 **LICKLIGHTER (IRE)**, 11, b g Brian Boru (IRE)—Daranado (IRE) **Mr P. L. Read**

MISS LAURA MORGAN - continued

28 **LION FACE (IRE)**, 4, b g Animal Kingdom (USA)—Blue Enzian (USA)
29 **LOFTY**, 6, b g Harbour Watch (IRE)—Curly Come Home **Mr T. H. A. Barton**
30 **LOUGHDERG ROCCO (IRE)**, 6, br g Shirocco (GER)—Banaltra (GER) **Newark Castle Partnership**
31 **LUNAR BOUNTY**, 5, b m Sea The Moon (GER)—The Pirate's Queen (IRE) **Miss L. Morgan**
32 **MUYAM SPIRIT (FR)**, 8, ch g Muhaymin (USA)—The Cat Eater (FR)
33 **NOW THEN WENDY**, 5, bl m Mukhadram—Dusting (IRE) **Evans & Britnell**
34 **PERCUSSION**, 7, b g Malinas (GER)—Tambourine Ridge (IRE) **E. R. Hanbury**
35 **RADETZKY MARCH (IRE)**, 7, b g Imperial Monarch (IRE)—Madgehil (IRE) **Mrs M. J. Pepperdine**
36 **RAFFERTY (IRE)**, 8, b g Arcadio (GER)—Mighty Star (IRE) **Triumph In Mind**
37 **ROCKET ROBBO**, 5, b g Multiplex—Sphere (IRE) **Mr S. Smithurst**
38 **SCALLYWAGS**, 5, br m Kayf Tara—Lakaam **Mr T. P. Radford**
39 **SCATTERCASH (IRE)**, 6, ch m Mahler—Casiana (GER) **Mr J. Britnell**
40 **SEA POEM (IRE)**, 5, b m Fame And Glory—Gentle Alice (IRE)
41 **SEEMINGLY SO (IRE)**, 9, br g Dubai Destination (USA)—Jane Hall (IRE) **S. Townshend & P. Read**
42 **SERIOUS MOOD (IRE)**, 9, b g Scorpion (IRE)—Criaire Nouveau (IRE) **Miss L. Morgan**
43 **SOCIALIST AGENDA**, 6, ch g Sir Percy—Mercy Pecksniff **Mr James Fyffe & Mr Scott Fyffe**
44 **STOPPERS SISTA (IRE)**, 7, b m Arcadio (GER)—Avenging Angel (IRE) **The Arcadians**
45 **SUPREME YEATS (IRE)**, 6, b g Yeats (IRE)—Supreme Bailerina (IRE) **Racecrowd W.M.G Racing Club**
46 **TAQWAA (IRE)**, 9, ch g Iffraaj—Hallowed Park (IRE) **R. A. Jenkinson**
47 **TARDREE (IRE)**, 8, ch g Mahler—Brownie Points (IRE) **Bennett & O'Brien**
48 **THE SUMBA ISLAND (GER)**, 5, b m Authorized (IRE)—Tricoteuse **The Welly Wobblers Club**
49 **THE VOLLAN (IRE)**, 8, b g Scorpion (IRE)—Print It On Lips (IRE) **Mrs E. Holmes**
50 **THE WILD WESTERNER (IRE)**, 7, b g Westerner—Nosey Oscar (IRE) **Mrs J. Hanson**
51 **THOMAS TODD**, 12, b g Passing Glance—Miss Danbys **Burton, Copley & Todd**
52 **TOM CREEN (IRE)**, 7, b g Yeats (IRE)—Casiana (GER) **J. W. Hardy**
53 **UISCE UR (IRE)**, 10, b m City Honours (USA)—Luna Fairy (IRE) **Launde Park Farm Partnership**
54 **WHERES MAUD GONE (IRE)**, 6, b m Yeats (IRE)—Barchetta (IRE) **Countrywide Park Homes Ltd**
55 **ZAKHAROVA**, 8, ch m Beat Hollow—Tcherina (IRE) **Mr & Mrs W. J. Williams**

Other Owners: Mr D. E. Balfe, Mr S. J. Bennett, Mr J. S. Birch, D. Bloy, Mr W. R. Bowler, Mr J. Britnell, Mr A. Brooks, Mr P. Burdett, Mr R. J. Burton, Mr T. A. Caswell, Mr M. Collie, Mr M. Copley, Mr A. I. Derry, Mr J. I. Derry, Mr M. Evans, J. C. Fretwell, Mr J. Fyffe, Mr S. Fyffe, Mr W. Hanbury, Harlequin Direct Ltd, Mr L. J. Heaver, Miss L. Morgan, Mr M. P. Obrien, Mr I. K. Pardy, Mr P. L. Read, Mr B. Ryan-Beswick, Mr W. Ryan-Beswick, Miss L. Todd, Mr S. Townshend, Mrs M. Williams, W. J. Williams.

Assistant Trainer: Tom Morgan.

Amateur Jockey: Miss A. Peck.

376

MR MOUSE MORRIS, Fethard
Postal: **Everardsgrange, Fethard, Co. Tipperary, Ireland**
Contacts: **PHONE +353 52 613 1474 MOBILE +353 86 854 3010 FAX +353 52 613 1654**
EMAIL mouse@eircom.net

1 **CAESAR ROCK (IRE)**, 6, b g Mahler—Supreme Von Pres (IRE) **M. O'Flynn, J. O'Flynn**
2 **CAMINO ROCK (IRE)**, 5, b g Blue Bresil (FR)—Cresswell Ruby (IRE) **M. O'Flynn, J. O'Flynn**
3 **FOXY JACKS (IRE)**, 8, b g Fame And Glory (IRE)—Benefit Ball (IRE) **D. Desmond**
4 **FRANCISCIAN ROCK (IRE)**, 5, b g Fame And Glory—Mrs Dempsey (IRE) **M. O'Flynn, J. O'Flynn**
5 **FRENCH DYNAMITE (FR)**, 7, b g Kentucky Dynamite (USA)—Matnie (FR) **Robcour**
6 **GANDY MAN (IRE)**, 6, b g Arcadio (GER)—Topsham Belle (IRE) **Mr R. A. Scott**
7 **GENTLEMANSGAME (IRE)**, 6, b g Gentlewave (IRE)—Grainne Ni Maille **Robcour**
8 **GET MY DRIFT (FR)**, 6, b g Spanish Moon (USA)—Voila (FR) **J. P. McManus**
9 5, B m Walk In The Park (IRE)—In The Waves (IRE) **S. Casey**
10 **JOE BLOM (IRE)**, 5, b g Mahler—Gorgeousreach (IRE) **Mrs A. Daly**
11 **LIMEKILN ROCK (IRE)**, 5, b g Doyen (IRE)—Distelle (IRE) **M. O'Flynn, J. O'Flynn**
12 5, B m Walk In The Park (IRE)—Papion Lady (IRE) **S. Walsh**
13 4, B g Mahler—Pop Princess **M. F. Morris**
14 **ROBIN SCHERBATSKY (IRE)**, 6, b m Milan—Benefit Ball (IRE) **Robcour**
15 **SAMS PROFILE (IRE)**, 8, b g Black Sam Bellamy (IRE)—Lucylou (IRE) **M. O'Flynn, J. O'Flynn**
16 **SEAN HOGAN (IRE)**, 7, b g Tear Drops (IRE)—Flemensfirth (USA) **Maura Ryan**

MR MOUSE MORRIS - continued

17 **SMOKE AND MIRRORS (IRE)**, 6, b g Leading Light (IRE)—Liss Ui Riain (IRE) **Mrs John Magnier**
18 **WHATSITABOUT (FR)**, 4, gr g Morandi (FR)—Top Crystal (IRE) **Mr R. A. Scott**
19 **WHATSNOTOKNOW (IRE)**, 7, b g Mahler—Whos To Know (IRE) **Mr R. A. Scott**

Other Owners: L.F Curtin, Mrs Trish Hyde, Sean O'Driscoll, Room For One More Syndicate.

---

377 **MR PATRICK MORRIS, Prescot**
Postal: **Avenue House, George Hale Avenue, Knowsley Park, Prescot, Merseyside, L34 4AJ**
Contacts: **MOBILE 07545 425235**
EMAIL Patrickmorris76@yahoo.com

1 **ALJARDAA (IRE)**, 4, b f Muhaarar—Yasmeen **Dr S. Lane**
2 **ARABIST**, 6, b g Invincible Spirit (IRE)—Highest **Dr M. B. Q. S. Koukash**
3 **BELL HEATHER (IRE)**, 9, b m Iffraaj—Burren Rose (USA) **Dr M. B. Q. S. Koukash**
4 **BRIAN THE SNAIL (IRE)**, 8, gr g Zebedee—Sweet Irish **H. Morrison**
5 **GABRIAL (IRE)**, 13, b g Dark Angel (IRE)—Guajira (FR) **Dr M. B. Q. S. Koukash**
6 **GABRIAL THE DEVIL (IRE)**, 7, b g Epaulette (AUS)—Grasshoppergreen (IRE) **Dr M. B. Q. S. Koukash**
7 **GABRIAL THE ONE (IRE)**, 6, b g Zoffany (IRE)—Guilia **Dr M. B. Q. S. Koukash**
8 **GABRIAL THE WIRE**, 6, b g Garswood—Nightunderthestars **Dr M. B. Q. S. Koukash**
9 **GABRIALS BOY**, 6, b g Paco Boy (IRE)—Statua (IRE) **Dr M. B. Q. S. Koukash**
10 **HEART OF SOUL (IRE)**, 7, b g Makfi—Hadrian's Waltz (IRE) **Dr M. B. Q. S. Koukash**
11 **HOCHFELD (IRE)**, 8, b g Cape Cross (IRE)—What A Charm (IRE) **Dr M. B. Q. S. Koukash**
12 **HOT TEAM (IRE)**, 6, b g Zoffany (IRE)—Ahd (USA) **Dr M. B. Q. S. Koukash**
13 **LEXI THE ONE (IRE)**, 5, b m Dandy Man (IRE)—Garter Star **Dr M. B. Q. S. Koukash**
14 **MANCINI**, 8, ch g Nathaniel (IRE)—Muscovado (USA) **Dr M. B. Q. S. Koukash**
15 **PACINO**, 6, b g Heeraat (IRE)—Ringtail (USA) **Dr M. B. Q. S. Koukash**
16 **POWERALLIED (IRE)**, 9, b g Camacho—Kaplinsky (IRE) **Dr M. B. Q. S. Koukash**
17 **RESHOUN (FR)**, 8, b g Shamardal (USA)—Radiyya (IRE) **Dr M. B. Q. S. Koukash**
18 **STREET LIFE**, 5, ch g Hot Streak (IRE)—Atheera (IRE) **Dr M. B. Q. S. Koukash**
19 **ZAMJAR**, 8, b g Exceed And Excel (AUS)—Cloud's End **Dr M. B. Q. S. Koukash**

---

378 **MR HUGHIE MORRISON, East Ilsley**
Postal: **Summerdown, East Ilsley, Newbury, Berkshire, RG20 7LB**
Contacts: **PHONE 01635 281678 MOBILE 07836 687799 FAX 01635 281746**
EMAIL hughie@hughiemorrison.co.uk WEBSITE www.hughiemorrison.co.uk

1 **AFFAIR**, 8, b m Sakhee's Secret—Supatov (USA) **H. Morrison**
2 **AMERICAN GERRY (IRE)**, 6, b g Americain (USA)—Hurricane Society (IRE) **Mrs M. R. Geake**
3 **AURORA STAR (FR)**, 4, b g Harzand (IRE)—Maleficent **Mr S. B. S. Ronaldson**
4 **BEARAWAY (IRE)**, 4, b g Kodiac—Fair Sailing (IRE) **H. Morrison**
5 **BEGGARMAN**, 5, ch g Toronado (IRE)—Let's Dance (IRE) **Howses Stud**
6 **CHARMING PARADISE**, 4, b g Charming Thought—Amanjena **M. E. Wates**
7 **CURTIZ**, 5, b g Stimulation (IRE)—Supatov (USA) **Mrs J. Parkes**
8 **DELTA BAY**, 4, b f Nathaniel (IRE)—Tropicana Bay **Helena Springfield Ltd**
9 **FILANDERER**, 6, b g Kayf Tara—Flirtatious **Mrs M. D. W. Morrison**
10 **FINAL ENCORE**, 5, b g Dunaden (FR)—Act Three **One More Moment of Madness**
11 5, B m Kayf Tara—Flirtatious **Mrs M. D. W. Morrison**
12 **HUDDLETON MAC (IRE)**, 4, b g Awtaad (IRE)—Melodique (FR) **Mr A McAlpine & Ms M Lund**
13 **LADY PERCIVAL**, 4, b f Sir Percy—Daffydowndilly **Lady Blyth**
14 **LEGENDARY DAY**, 4, b g Adaay (IRE)—Dubai Legend **A. N. Solomons**

MR HUGHIE MORRISON - continued

15 **MARIDADI**, 6, b m Beat Hollow—Mighty Splash **Mr D. H. Low**
16 **MISS FAIRFAX (IRE)**, 6, ch m Imperial Monarch (IRE)—Stein Castle (IRE) **The Hill Stud**
17 **MRS FITZHERBERT (IRE)**, 4, b f Kingman—Stupendous Miss (USA) **Sonia M. Rogers & Anthony Rogers**
18 **NOT SO SLEEPY**, 10, ch g Beat Hollow—Papillon de Bronze (IRE) **Lady Blyth**
19 **OUR JESTER**, 6, b g Garswood—Cill Rialaig **Pangfield Racing V**
20 **QUICKTHORN**, 5, b g Nathaniel (IRE)—Daffydowndilly **Lady Blyth**
21 **RAVENS ARK**, 5, ch g Raven's Pass (USA)—Wonderful Desert **Beachview Corporation Ltd**
22 **ROSEMARY AND THYME**, 4, b f Camelot—Scarborough Fair **Mr P. Brocklehurst**
23 **STAY WELL**, 4, b g Iffraaj—Sweeping Up **Ben & Sir Martyn Arbib**
24 **SULOCHANA (IRE)**, 5, br m Lope de Vega (IRE)—Yakshini (IRE) **Mr P. Brocklehurst**
25 **SURREY GOLD (IRE)**, 4, b g Golden Horn—Shemiyla (FR) **Surrey Racing (SG)**
26 **THIRD WIND**, 8, b bg g Shirocco (GER)—Act Three **Mrs A. J. Hamilton-Fairley**
27 **THUNDERCLAP (IRE)**, 4, b g Night of Thunder (IRE)—Former Drama (USA) **T. Pilkington & Mr R. A. Pilkington**
28 **URBAN ARTIST**, 7, ch m Cityscape—Cill Rialaig **Pangfield Racing V**
29 **VINO VICTRIX**, 4, b g Sir Percy—Valeria Victrix (IRE) **Mr S. B. S. Ronaldson**
30 **WHITEHAVEN (FR)**, 5, bl g Le Havre (USA)—Passion Blanche **P. C. J. Dalby & R. D. Schuster**

THREE-YEAR-OLDS

31 **ALYTH**, b c Muhaarar—Permission **Mrs J. Scott, Mr J. F. Dean & Lady Trenchard**
32 **BANNED**, b f Ulysses (IRE)—Clarietta **Martin Hughes & Michael Kerr-Dineen**
33 **BUSHFIRE**, ch c Australia—Aflame **Michael Kerr-dineen & Martin Hughes**
34 **CANTATA**, b f Oasis Dream—Summer's Eve **Wardley Bloodstock**
35 **COCONUT BAY**, b f Bated Breath—Tropicana Bay **Helena Springfield Ltd**
36 **HAYMAKER**, b g Muhaarar—Squash **Collett, Morrison & Partners**
37 **JULIUS**, ch g Ruler of The World (IRE)—Seramirabar **The Fairy Story Partnership**
38 **LYRICAL LADY**, gr f Lethal Force (IRE)—Faery Song (IRE) **M Dhillon, C Nixon, M Pierce, M Poe**
39 **MAKSUD**, b g Golden Horn—Althania (USA) **Thurloe Thoroughbreds LIV**
40 **MUMMA MAC**, gr f Ulysses (IRE)—White Wedding (IRE) **Mr & Mrs A McAlpine & Partners**
41 **NAZIMOVA**, b f Time Test—Nadeszhda **Miss K. Rausing**
42 **NUSA DUA**, b f Australia—Come Touch The Sun **St Albans Bloodstock Ltd & Partner**
43 **OP IT (IRE)**, b g Belardo (IRE)—Lexington Sky (IRE) **Sir Thomas Pilkington**
44 **PERCY JONES**, b g Sir Percy—Luisa Calderon **Mr A. Kheir**
45 **PLAGIARISE**, b f Showcasing—Copy-Cat **Hot To Trot Racing Vi**
46 **PRENUP (IRE)**, b f Profitable (IRE)—Intimacy (IRE) **Jastar Ltd, Murt Khan & Harry Wigan**
47 **PROMOTING (IRE)**, b c Showcasing—Aqualis **P. C. J. Dalby & R. D. Schuster**
48 **REELEMIN**, ch c Highland Reel (IRE)—Rainbow's Arch (IRE) **Mrs M. T. Bevan**
49 **SELKIRK GRACE**, ch f Cityscape—Jasmeno **MNC Racing**
50 **SHOCKWAVES**, gr c Sea The Moon (GER)—Having A Blast (USA) **M Kerr-Dineen, M Hughes & W Eason**
51 **SHOWMAN**, b c Kingman—Peinture Abstraite **Mr A. Kheir**
52 **STAY ALERT**, b f Fastnet Rock (AUS)—Starfala **Ben & Sir Martyn Arbib**
53 **SUGAR CANDIE**, b f Highland Reel (IRE)—Sweet Selection **Paul & Catriona Brocklehurst Bloodstock**
54 **TANGO TONIGHT**, ch f Pivotal—Last Tango Inparis **Helena Springfield Ltd**
55 **WAGGA WAGGA (IRE)**, ch c Australia—Quiz Mistress **The Fairy Story Partnership**

TWO-YEAR-OLDS

56 B c 14/03 Roaring Lion (USA)—African Plains (Oasis Dream) (32000)
        Alasdair Simpson, W. D. Eason, M. Kerr-Dineen
57 B c 25/03 Sea The Moon (GER)—Alvarita (Selkirk (USA)) (72000) **Martin Hughes & Michael Kerr-Dineen**
58 B c 27/03 Ribchester (IRE)—Art Institute (USA) (Arch (USA))
59 **ASPARTE**, b c 02/05 Time Test—Soinlovewithyou (USA) (Sadler's Wells (USA)) (45000) **Dr J. Wilson**
60 B f 04/04 Adaay (IRE)—Broadlands (Kheleyf (USA)) **The End-R-Ways Partnership & Partners**
61 **CEILIDH KING**, ch c 11/01 Highland Reel (IRE)—Poet's Princess (Poet's Voice)
        Paul & Catriona Brocklehurst Bloodstock
62 **CLEVER RELATION**, b c 21/03 Intello (GER)—Sweet Selection (Stimulation (IRE)) (70000) **Bruton Street**
63 B f 12/02 Showcasing—Coquet (Sir Percy) **Lord Margadale & Mrs Belinda Scott**
64 **FLEET FEET**, ch c 24/02 Footstepsinthesand—Seramirabar (Zamindar (USA)) **The Fairy Story Partnership**
65 **HELIANTHUS**, b c 26/03 Aclaim (IRE)—Sunflower (Dutch Art) **N. M. H. Jones**
66 B f 26/01 Stimulation (IRE)—Inya Lake (Whittingham (IRE))
67 B f 22/01 Adaay (IRE)—Josefa Goya (Saakhee's Secret) **The TOD Partnership**

MR HUGHIE MORRISON - continued

68 **KYLE OF LOCHALSH**, b c 03/04 Highland Reel (IRE)—Quiz Mistress (Doyen (IRE)) **The Fairy Story Partnership**
69 **MISTRAL STAR**, b f 14/02 Frankel—Shirocco Star (Shirocco (GER)) **Helena Springfield Ltd**
70 B c 14/02 Invincible Spirit (IRE)—Monzza (Montjeu (IRE)) (50000) **Michael Kerr-dineen & Martin Hughes**
71 **MR MISTOFFELEES (IRE)**, b c 24/02 Siyouni (FR)—Jellicle Ball (IRE) (Invincible Spirit (IRE))
                                                                    One More Moment of Madness
72 B f 10/04 Adaay (IRE)—Noble Nova (Fraan) **The Hon Miss M. A. Morrison & Partners**
73 Ch c 30/01 Highland Reel (IRE)—Rainbow's Arch (IRE) (Dubawi (IRE)) (20000)
                                                    Alasdair Simpson, W. D. Eason, M. Kerr-Dineen
74 **ROYAL CAPE (IRE)**, b c 08/03 Gleneagles (IRE)—Kikonga (Danehill Dancer (IRE)) (50000)
                                                                    P. C. J. Dalby & R. D. Schuster
75 Ch c 28/04 Bobbys Kitten (USA)—Songerie (Hernando (FR))
                                        The Hon. Miss M. Morrison, Mr T. Pickford, Mr R. Angliss & Partners
76 B f 24/02 Stimulation (IRE)—Supatov (USA) (Johannesburg (USA)) (952) **H. Morrison**
77 **SURREY BELLE**, b f 03/04 Golden Horn—Al Reem (Raven's Pass (USA)) (51871) **Surrey Racing Limited**
78 B c 02/05 Pivotal—Sweeping Up (Sea The Stars (IRE)) **Ben & Sir Martyn Arbib**
79 B c 02/02 Massaat (IRE)—Tranquil Flight (Oasis Dream) **The Hon Miss M. A. Morrison & Partners**
80 B c 02/05 Profitable (IRE)—Ugnegya (IRE) (Teofilo (IRE)) **Mr H. E. Wigan**

Other Owners: Mr G Ball, Mr C. M. Budgett, Mrs A Chapple, Miss D. Collett, Mrs A. M. Garfield, L. A. Garfield, Mrs S. Hamilton, Mr H Hampson, C. J. Harper, Mr R. S. Hoskins, Mrs J. C. Lascelles, Mr A. R. Macdonald-Buchanan, Mr A Parker, Mrs L. O. Sangster, Mrs A Usher.

Assistant Trainer: Mr Charles Harris.

---

379 **WILLIAM MUIR AND CHRIS GRASSICK, Lambourn**
Postal: **Linkslade, Wantage Road, Lambourn, Hungerford, Berkshire, RG17 8UG**
Contacts: PHONE **01488 73748**
EMAIL **william@williammuir.com**

1 **COUNTRY PYLE**, 4, b f New Approach (IRE)—La Pyle (FR) **K & W Bloodstock Limited & Mr R W Devlin**
2 **FIREPOWER (FR)**, 5, b g Starspangledbanner (AUS)—Torentosa (FR) **Mrs M. E. Morgan**
3 **GENERAL ZOFF**, 7, b g Zoffany (IRE)—Aunt Julia **Purple & Lilac Racing X**
4 **GIUSEPPE CASSIOLI**, 5, b h Bated Breath—Olympic Medal **J O'Mulloy & W R Muir**
5 **HAMMY END (IRE)**, 6, b g Mount Nelson—Northern Affair (IRE) **Mr J. M. O'Mulloy**
6 **JUST HUBERT (IRE)**, 6, b g Dunaden (FR)—La Tulipe (FR) **Foursome Thoroughbreds**
7 **MITROSONFIRE**, 4, gr g Lethal Force (IRE)—Blaugrana (IRE) **Mr J. M. O'Mulloy**
8 **NEWYORKSTATEOFMIND**, 5, b g Brazen Beau (AUS)—Albany Rose (IRE)
                                                    Purple & Lilac Racing-Spotted Dog P'ship
9 **PERFECT MATCH (IRE)**, 4, b f Dubawi (IRE)—Purr Along **Mr C. L. A. Edginton & Mr W. R. Muir**
10 **PYLEDRIVER**, 5, b h Harbour Watch (IRE)—La Pyle (FR) **K & W Bloodstock Limited & Mr R W Devlin**
11 **RADIANT LIGHT**, 4, b g Fastnet Rock (AUS)—Gertrude Gray (IRE) **Mr M. T. Grassick**
12 **SHUV H'PENNY KING**, 4, b g Twilight Son—Cardrona **Mr M. P. Graham**

THREE-YEAR-OLDS

13 **CONFUNDO**, ch g Charming Thought—Bertie's Best **Mr R. Haim & Partner**
14 **CONQUERING**, b br g Dabirsim (FR)—Faustinatheyounger (FR) **Muir Racing Partnership - Leicester**
15 **DANZA DELLA LUNA**, ch f Phoenix Reach (IRE)—Sister Moonshine **Mr K. R. E. Rhatigan**
16 **EDDIE THE BEAGLE**, gr g Lawman (FR)—Moonlight Silver **Foursome Thoroughbreds**
17 B f Danon Ballade (JPN)—Franny Nisbet
18 **GALIAC**, b c Kodiac—Gallipot **Perspicacious Punters Racing Club**
19 **HAAFMOON**, ch c Haafhd—Maimoona (IRE) **Batsford Stud Racing Club**
20 **KING'S COURSE (IRE)**, b br c Gleneagles (IRE)—Desert Run (IRE) **C. L. A. Edginton**
21 **MAKING MUSIC (IRE)**, b f Mastercraftsman (IRE)—Rapacity Alexander (IRE) **Foursome Thoroughbreds**
22 **MAYTREE RESPITE (IRE)**, b c Mehmas (IRE)—Loveisreckless (IRE) **Mr J. M. O'Mulloy**

WILLIAM MUIR AND CHRIS GRASSICK - continued

23 **MIGHTY AFRA (IRE)**, b f Zoffany (IRE)—Sweet Coconut **K. A. Dasmal**
24 **PROFOUND ALEXANDER (IRE)**, gr f Kodiac—Smokey Quartz (IRE) **W. R. Muir**
25 **RED VINEYARD (IRE)**, ch c Slade Power (IRE)—Artisia (IRE) **Foursome Thoroughbreds**
26 **RENEGADE ROSE (IRE)**, b f Slade Power (IRE)—Three D Alexander (IRE) **Purple & Lilac Racing**
27 **SALT TREATY (IRE)**, ch g National Defense—Salty Sugar **Muir Racing Partnership - Flemington**
28 **SEVEN SPRINGS**, b f Lethal Force (IRE)—Blacke Forest **M. J. Caddy**
29 **SNAPCRACKLEPOP**, b g Acclamation—Sweet Secret **W. R. Muir**
30 **STOCKPYLE**, b c Oasis Dream—La Pyle (FR) **K & W Bloodstock Limited & Mr R W Devlin**
31 **SWAYZE**, b c Showcasing—Dream Dreamer **Baker, d'Arcy, Grassick**

TWO-YEAR-OLDS

32 **BAGGY POINT (IRE)**, b c 14/04 New Bay—All Time (Dansili) (28000) **C. L. A. Edginton**
33 Gr f 24/02 Mastercraftsman (IRE)—Desert Run (IRE) (Desert Prince (IRE)) (25000)
34 B f 30/03 Camacho—Dufoof (IRE) (Shamardal (USA)) (35000) **Muir Racing Partnership - Newbury**
35 Br f 01/05 Frankel—La Pyle (FR) (Le Havre (IRE)) **K & W Bloodstock Limited & Mr R W Devlin**
36 B br c 26/02 Tasleet—Likeable (Dalakhani (IRE)) (45000) **K. A. Dasmal**
37 Bl f 08/04 Lethal Force (IRE)—Loveisreckless (IRE) (Mount Nelson) **Mr J. M. O'Mulloy**
38 B f 28/03 Mastercraftsman (IRE)—Meetyouatthemoon (IRE) (Excelebration (IRE)) (8000)
Mr C.L.A.Edginton & Mr K.Jeffery

39 B c 05/04 Tasleet—Midnight Sky (Desert Prince (IRE)) (45000)
40 **OVERNIGHT OATS**, b c 19/03 Muhaarar—Integral (Dalakhani (IRE)) (45000) **Wedgwell Partners**
41 **SAXON SCENE (IRE)**, b c 11/03 Saxon Warrior (JPN)—Crystal Morning (IRE) (Cape Cross (IRE)) (25000)
Clarke, Edginton, Niven

42 **SO SLEEPY**, b f 03/02 Oasis Dream—If So (Iffraaj) (95000) **Foursome Thoroughbreds**
43 B c 18/03 New Approach (IRE)—Srda (USA) (Kingmambo (USA)) (35000)
44 B c 23/03 Camacho—Sweet Secret (Singspiel (IRE)) (40000) **Carmel Stud**

Other Owners: Mr M. J. Baker, Mr J. Bernstein, Mr G. Caldwell, Mr N. Clark, Mr D. G. Clarke, Mr M. D'Arcy, R. W. Devlin, C. L. A. Edginton, Mr M. P. Graham, Mr C. Grassick, Mr R. Haim, Mr A. Harman, Mr K. Jeffery, K & W Bloodstock Limited, Mr C. Moore, W. R. Muir, Mr A. J. Niven, Mr J. M. O'Mulloy, Mr D. L. Quaintance, Mr P. D. Quaintance, Mr R. M. Webb, Mr P. J. Wheatley.

---

380 **MR CLIVE MULHALL, Scarcroft**
Postal: **Scarcroft Hall Farm, Thorner Lane, Scarcroft, Leeds, Yorkshire, LS14 3AQ**
Contacts: **HOME 0113 289 3095 MOBILE 07979 527675**
EMAIL clivemulhallracing@gmail.com, clive@scarcrofthallracing.co.uk

1 **ANEEDH**, 12, b g Lucky Story (USA)—Seed Al Maha (USA) **Mrs C. M. Mulhall**
2 **BIGBADBOY (IRE)**, 9, b g Big Bad Bob (IRE)—Elegantly (IRE) **Ms Y Featherstone & Mrs M Mulhall**
3 **LORD SERENDIPITY (IRE)**, 10, gr g Lord Shanakill (USA)—Elitista (FR)
4 **SHE IS WHAT SHE IS**, 7, b m Desideratum—Alimure

Assistant Trainer: Mrs Martina Mulhall.

Amateur Jockey: Miss Charlotte Mulhall.

381 MR NEIL MULHOLLAND, Limpley Stoke
Postal: Conkwell Grange Stables, Conkwell, Limpley Stoke, Bath, Avon, BA2 7FD
Contacts: MOBILE 07739 258607
EMAIL neil@neilmulhollandracing.com WEBSITE www.neilmulhollandracing.com

1 AGENT SAONOIS (FR), 6, gr g Saonois (FR)—Agosta (FR) The Affordable (3) Partnership
2 ANY NEWS (IRE), 7, ch g Stowaway—Kisskiss Bang Bang (IRE) Mrs J. N. Cartwright
3 BALLYMILAN, 7, b m Milan—Ballyhoo (IRE) Heart Racing HR2
4 BARNARDS GREEN (IRE), 6, ch g Getaway (GER)—Strawberry Lane (IRE) Mr M. C. Creed
5 BE EASY (GER), 5, b m Samum (GER)—Bandeira (GER) Be Easy Partnership
6 BELLE NA BANN (IRE), 6, b m Califet (FR)—Cut 'n' Run (IRE) Neil Mulholland Racing Ltd
7 BLAKEY BEAR, 6, b g Trans Island—La Vie Est Belle Neil Mulholland Racing Ltd
8 BLUMEN GLORY (IRE), 6, b g Fame And Glory—Blume (IRE) Colony Stable Llc
9 BRIEF TIMES (IRE), 6, b g Doyen (IRE)—Dali's Theatre Ms S. M. Exell
10 CANADA KID, 10, ch g Apple Tree—Island of Memories (IRE) P. C. Tory
11 CAROLINES CHARM (IRE), 8, b g Masterofthehorse (IRE)—Truckers Princess (IRE) The Affordable Partnership
12 CASTLE FROME (IRE), 5, b m Walk In The Park (IRE)—Clear Riposte (IRE) Mrs P. L. Bridel
13 CASTLE QUARTER (IRE), 6, b g Zoffany (IRE)—Queen's Pudding (IRE) Mr G. Teversham
14 CELTIC FORTUNE (IRE), 5, b g Soldier of Fortune (IRE)—Rhinestone Cowgirl (IRE) D. M. Bell
15 CHINWAG, 7, b g Trans Island—Clohamon Gossip (IRE) The Boot Inn Partnership
16 CHIRICO VALLIS (FR), 10, b g Poliglote—Quora Vallis (FR) Mr J. P. McManus
17 CONCRETE KING (IRE), 8, b g Morozov (USA)—Mags Millar (IRE) Mr O. S. Harris
18 CONKWELL ROSIE, 6, b m Sulamani (IRE)—Maori Legend Mrs H. R. Cross
19 CREMANT (IRE), 8, b g Getaway (GER)—Opera Season (IRE) Mr P. M. Simmonds
20 CRYSTAL TIMES (IRE), 5, b m Ocovango—Funny Times Crystal Times Racing Syndicate
21 DEAD RIGHT, 10, b g Alflora (IRE)—April Queen Mr J. P. McManus
22 DONCESAR DE PRETOT (FR), 9, gr g Saddler Maker (IRE)—Kobila (FR)
23 DYNAMIC KATE (IRE), 6, br m Yeats (IRE)—Alverstone BG Racing Partnership
24 EAGLE'S FIRST, 5, b m Free Eagle (IRE)—Al Kahina Stephen & Gloria Seymour
25 EMANATE, 4, b g Coach House (IRE)—Emerald Girl (IRE) Mr J. Heaney
26 EXELERATOR EXPRESS (FR), 8, b g Poliglote—Reine de Lestrade (FR) Walters Plant Hire & Potter Group
27 5, B br ar Sir Percy—Fairy Slipper Dajam Ltd
28 FINGERONTHESWITCH (IRE), 12, b g Beneficial—Houseoftherisinsun (IRE) Cahill, Atwell & Crofts
29 FIRST QUEST (USA), 8, b g First Defence (USA)—Dixie Quest (USA) The Affordable (2) Partnership
30 FRAU GEORGIA (IRE), 8, b m Germany (USA)—Sumability (USA) Mr J. Henderson
31 FULL AUX ROIS (FR), 7, b g Diamond Boy (FR)—Jouable (FR) Mr J. Hobbs
32 FULL OF SURPRISES (FR), 7, b m No Risk At All (FR)—Fontaine Riant (FR) Mr J. P. McManus
33 GARINCHA (IRE), 6, b g Ask—Mandy Winger Mr R Flower & Dajam
34 GLENDRUID (IRE), 8, b g Beneficial—Carrigeen Diamond (IRE) Murphys Law (Ireland) Syndicate
35 GLENVIEW BEAUTY (IRE), 5, b m Shirocco (GER)—Calverleigh Court (IRE) The Affordable Partnership
36 GOLDEN EMBLEM (IRE), 8, ch m Presenting—Merry Excuse (IRE) Diamond Racing Ltd
37 GREAT SNOW (FR), 5, b m Great Pretender (IRE)—Snow Berry (FR) Walters Plant Hire Ltd
38 HAPPY RETURNS, 5, b m Recharge (IRE)—Bonne Anniversaire Wincanton Race Club
39 HASHTAG VAL (FR), 5, b m Cokoriko (FR)—Altesse Premiere (FR) Mr J. P. McManus
40 HAWAII DU MESTIVEL (FR), 5, ch g No Risk At All (FR)—Pensee du Mestivel (FR) Mrs J. Gerard-Pearse
41 HEAVEY, 8, b g Trans Island—Clohamon Gossip (IRE) Qdos Racing
42 HIDDEN DEPTHS (IRE), 7, b g Dark Angel (IRE)—Liber Nauticus (IRE) Mr A. J. Russell
43 HOBB'S DELIGHT, 6, b g Milan—Hobb's Dream (IRE) Mr J. Hobbs
44 HOBBS JOY, 5, b g Norse Dancer (IRE)—Hobb's Dream (IRE)
45 ICONE D'AUBRELLE (FR), 4, b g Cokoriko (FR)—Tiree A Part (FR) Mr R. B. Waley-Cohen
46 INDIAN BRAVE (IRE), 11, b g Definite Article—Fridays Folly (IRE) J. J. Maguire
47 INOUI MACHIN (FR), 4, b g Honolulu (IRE)—Firmini (FR) Walters Plant Hire Ltd
48 INSPECTOR LYNLEY, 5, b g Nathaniel (IRE)—Duchess of Seville Mrs H. R. Cross
49 IRISH ODYSSEY (IRE), 9, gr g Yeats (IRE)—Ma Furie (FR) Mr A. G. Bloom
50 JAUNTY SORIA, 9, ch m Malinas (GER)—Jaunty Spirit Miss J. A. Goddard
51 JUMP OVER THE MOON (IRE), 5, b g Yeats (IRE)—Moon Over Monaloo (IRE) G. P. and Miss S. J. Hayes
52 JUST HENNY, 8, b m Midnight Legend—Exchanging Glances Abbott & Bunch
53 KAHINA RULES, 7, b m Aussie Rules (USA)—Al Kahina Stephen & Gloria Seymour
54 KANSAS CITY CHIEF (IRE), 13, b g Westerner—Badawi Street Jersey Racing Friends
55 LA CAVSA NOSTRA (IRE), 10, b g Flemensfirth (USA)—Pharenna (IRE) Neil Mulholland Racing Ltd
56 LA PAGERIE (FR), 5, b m Khalkevi (IRE)—Belle Yepa (FR) Walters Plant Hire Ltd

MR NEIL MULHOLLAND - continued

57 **LORD ACCORD (IRE)**, 7, b g Yeats (IRE)—Cush Jewel (IRE) **Lynne & Angus Maclennan**
58 **MAGNIFICENT BEN (IRE)**, 7, b g Sans Frontieres (IRE)—Lakeshore Lodge (IRE) **Mr O. S. Harris**
59 **MALIBOO (IRE)**, 9, b m Mahler—Aboo Lala (IRE) **Premier Care Management**
60 **MALINAS ISLAND**, 7, ch g Malinas (GER)—Island of Memories (IRE) **P. C. Tory**
61 **MAN OF THE SEA (IRE)**, 6, ch g Born To Sea (IRE)—Hurricane Lily (IRE) **Dajam Ltd**
62 **MASTERDREAM (FR)**, 5, b g Sea The Stars (IRE)—Santa Christiana (FR) **Mr D. B. Harris**
63 **MILANESE ROSE (IRE)**, 6, gr m Milan—Ma Furie (FR) **Proudley & Whymark Partnership**
64 **MILKWOOD (IRE)**, 8, b g Dylan Thomas (IRE)—Tropical Lake (IRE) **Ms J. Bridel**
65 **MILREU HAS (FR)**, 7, b g Kapgarde (FR)—Miss Benedicte (FR) **Mr J. P. McManus**
66 **MISS JEANNE MOON (IRE)**, 8, b m Getaway (GER)—Moon Approach (IRE) **Mrs H. R. Cross & Mrs S. A. Keys**
67 **MISTER SWEETS (IRE)**, 7, b g Scorpion (IRE)—Fast Finisher (IRE) **Equi ex Incertis Partners**
68 **MOLLIANA**, 7, b m Olden Times—The Screamer (IRE) **Dajam Ltd**
69 **MOLLY CAREW**, 10, b m Midnight Legend—Moyliscar **Mrs S. A. Keys**
70 **MONGOL EMPEROR (IRE)**, 7, b g Imperial Monarch (IRE)—Hurricane Bella (IRE) **Equi ex Incertis Partners**
71 **MONT SAINT VINCENT (FR)**, 6, gr g Montmartre (FR)—Chamanka (FR) **Walters Plant Hire Ltd**
71 **MOTHILL (IRE)**, 4, b g Golden Horn—Jilnaar (IRE) **Mr J. Gray**
73 **NEACHELLS BRIDGE (IRE)**, 10, ch g Getaway (GER)—Strawberry Lane (IRE) **Mr M. C. Creed**
74 **NINA'S FIELD**, 4, ch f Cannock Chase (USA)—Art Critic (USA) **Dajam Ltd**
75 **NO FIXED CHARGES (IRE)**, 7, b g Scorpion (IRE)—Soniadoir (IRE) **Neil Mulholland Racing Club**
76 **NO WORRIES**, 8, b g Passing Glance—Silver Sequel **Dajam Ltd**
77 **NORMAN KINDU**, 4, b g Lawman (FR)—Kindu **Diamond Racing Ltd**
78 **NOVIS ADVENTUS (IRE)**, 10, b g New Approach (IRE)—Tiffed (USA) **F&M Bloodstock Limited**
79 **OF COURSE YOU CAN**, 4, b f Yeats (IRE)—Free Thinking
80 **PADDY HUSSEYS TAXI (IRE)**, 6, gr g Carlotamix (FR)—Wensum Dancer **Neil Mulholland Racing Ltd**
81 **PELTWELL (IRE)**, 9, b m Milan—Fast Finisher (IRE) **Mrs P. L. Bridel**
82 **PLANNED PARADISE (IRE)**, 6, b g Westerner—Quel Bleu (IRE) **Neil Mulholland Racing Ltd**
83 **PRINCESS T**, 7, gr m Aussie Rules (USA)—Fairy Slipper **Harte Investments Ltd & Dajam Ltd**
84 **QUARTER BLUE**, 4, b f Equiano (FR)—Royal Obsession (IRE) **Fighting Chance Syndicate**
85 **RAGAMUFFIN (IRE)**, 7, b g Arcadio (GER)—Mill Race Annie (IRE) **Mrs J. N. Cartwright**
86 **RENEGADE ARROW (FR)**, 6, ch g Motivator—Cinders' Prize **F&M Bloodstock Limited**
87 **ROCK ON RITA (IRE)**, 6, b m Shirocco (GER)—Gilt Free (IRE) **Mr J. P. McManus**
88 **ROOKIE TRAINER (IRE)**, 8, b g Gold Well—Crazy Falcon (IRE) **Noel Fehily Racing Syndicates-Rookie Tra**
89 **RUNASIMI RIVER**, 9, ch m Generous (IRE)—Zaffaranni (IRE) **Mrs G. A. Davies**
90 **SAINTE DOCTOR (FR)**, 6, gr m Doctor Dino (FR)—Pakoonah **Mr J. P. McManus**
91 **SCARDURA (IRE)**, 8, b g Stowaway—Sosua (IRE) **Mrs J. N. Cartwright**
92 **SEVENOFUS (IRE)**, 6, b m Yeats (IRE)—Gortnagowna (IRE) **Tim & Liz Heal**
93 **SIMPLY SIN (IRE)**, 7, b g Footstepsinthesand—Miss Sally (IRE) **Neil Mulholland Racing Ltd**
94 **SOLWARA ONE (IRE)**, 8, b g Gold Well—Turquoise Green (IRE) **Mrs J. Gerard-Pearse**
95 **SUPER DUPER SAM**, 6, ch g Black Sam Bellamy (IRE)—With Grace **D. V. Stevens**
96 **TANGO BOY (IRE)**, 9, ch g Flemensfirth (USA)—Hello Kitty (IRE) **Mr A. G. Bloom**
97 **THE BOLD THADY (IRE)**, 5, b g Milan—Princesse Rooney (FR)
98 **THE TURTLE SAID**, 5, b g Manduro (GER)—Goslar **Mrs P. M. Bunch**
99 **THE TWISLER**, 10, b g Motivator—Panna **Neil Mulholland Racing Club**
100 **TRANSLINK**, 7, b g Rail Link—Ocean Transit (IRE) **Mr B. F. Mulholland**
101 **TRUE ROMANCE (IRE)**, 8, gr g Mastercraftsman (IRE)—Full of Love (IRE) **Mr K. S. Ward**
102 **VIKING RUBY**, 9, ch m Sulamani (IRE)—Viking Torch **Ms S. M. Exell**
103 **VIS A VIS**, 8, b g Dansili—Pretty Face **Ashley Carr, Eismark & Packham**
104 **VOCAL RING (IRE)**, 4, b g Vocalised (USA)—Fainne (IRE) **The Southstand Syndicate**
105 **WATERGRANGE JACK (IRE)**, 6, b g Sintarajan (IRE)—Prestissimo **Mrs J. N. Cartwright**
106 **WINGED ISLE**, 7, b g Winged Love (IRE)—Zaffaranni (IRE) **Mrs G. A. Davies**
107 **WOOD GROVE**, 6, ch m Malinas (GER)—Queens Grove

Other Owners: Mr T. J. Abbott, Mrs L. Atwell, Mr J. J. Brummitt, Mrs P. M. Bunch, Mr M. G. Cahill, A. Carr, Mr H. Carr, Mrs A. C. Crofts, Mrs H. R. Cross, Dajam Ltd, Mr M. Edwards, Mr E. Eismark, Mr R. H. Flower, Mr S. Harbour, Harte Investments Limited, Mr G. P. Hayes, Miss S. J. Hayes, Mrs E. A. Heal, Mr T. Heal, Mrs S. A. Keys, Mr A. Maclennan, Mrs L. Maclennan, Mr S. Packham, Mr P. J. Proudley, Mrs G. P. Seymour, Mr S. G. Seymour, Sundorne Products (Llanidloes) Ltd, Mr J. N. Trueman, Mrs R. A. Turner, Mr R. F. Turner, Walters Plant Hire Ltd, Mr J. K. Whymark.

Assistant Trainer: Andrew Doyle.

MR NEIL MULHOLLAND - continued

NH Jockey: James Best, Robbie Dunne, Tom Scudamore, Sam Twiston-Davies.

Conditional Jockey: Philip Donovan, Harry Reed. **Amateur Jockey:** Millie Wonnacott.

---

382 MR LAWRENCE MULLANEY, Malton
Postal: **Raikes Farm, Great Habton, Malton, North Yorkshire, YO17 6RX**
Contacts: **PHONE 01653 668595 MOBILE 07899 902565**
EMAIL nicolamullaney@yahoo.co.uk

1 **FIRE EYES (FR)**, 4, b f Toronado (IRE)—Aldayha (IRE) **Ian Buckley & Ben Buckley**
2 **GORGEOUS GENERAL**, 7, ch g Captain Gerrard (IRE)—Gorgeous Goblin (IRE) **Mr S. Humphries**
3 **MERRY SECRET (IRE)**, 4, b g Elzaam (AUS)—Secret Liaison (IRE) **Mr S Rimmer & Partners**
4 **OUR LITTLE PONY**, 7, b m Bated Breath—Cracking Lass (IRE) **L. A. Mullaney**
5 **ROYAL PROSPECT (IRE)**, 7, b g Thewayyouare (USA)—Jillian (USA) **Mr Shaun Humphries & Partner**
6 **SNAZZY JAZZY (IRE)**, 7, b g Red Jazz (USA)—Bulrushes **Ian Buckley & Ben Buckley**

THREE-YEAR-OLDS

7 **CAPTAINHUGHJAMPTON**, ch g Mondialiste (IRE)—Sibaya **Ian Buckley & Ben Buckley**
8 **CONTACTLESS (IRE)**, ch g Dandy Man (IRE)—She's A Queen (IRE) **Mr L. Ryan**
9 **FERGUSSINGSDABLUES**, b g Heeraat (IRE)—Evocative **Ian Buckley James Lomas**
10 B g Mondialiste (IRE)—File And Paint (IRE) **L. A. Mullaney**
11 **LS ELEVEN**, b g Mondialiste (IRE)—Shuttlecock **Ian Buckley & Ben Buckley**

TWO-YEAR-OLDS

12 Ch c 16/02 Mondialiste (IRE)—Turin (IRE) (Raven's Pass (USA)) **Mr S. J. Rimmer**

---

383 MR MICHAEL MULLINEAUX, Tarporley
Postal: **Southley Farm, Alpraham, Tarporley, Cheshire, CW6 9JD**
Contacts: **PHONE 01829 261440 MOBILE 07753 650263 FAX 01829 261440**
EMAIL southlearacing@btinternet.com WEBSITE www.southleyfarm.co.uk

1 **BABYDUKE**, 5, b g Heeraat (IRE)—Baby Queen (IRE) **Mr G. B. Hignett**
2 **BOB'S GIRL**, 7, b m Big Bad Bob (IRE)—Linda (FR) **S. A. Pritchard**
3 **DAVID'S BEAUTY (IRE)**, 9, b m Kodiac—Thaisy (USA) **Mr G. B. Hignett**
4 **DODGY BOB**, 9, b g Royal Applause—Rustam **M. Mullineaux**
5 **DOVES DELIGHT**, 4, b g Recharge (IRE)—Two Turtle Doves (IRE) **Mr K. Mottershead**
6 **INMEMORYOFMILLY (IRE)**, 5, b m Fruits of Love (USA)—Lake Wakatipu **Mr G. Cornes**
7 **LUCKY MONARCH (IRE)**, 6, b m Imperial Monarch (IRE)—County Gate (IRE) **Mr L. Tomlinson**
8 **LUCKYANGEL**, 5, gr m Yorgunnabelucky (USA)—Ya Halla (IRE) **Mr G. Cornes**
9 **LUNAR JET**, 8, ch g Ask—Lightning Jet **County Charm Windows & Conservatories**
10 **OVERCHURCH**, 11, b m Overbury (IRE)—Namoi **Mr R. A. Royle**
11 **PEACHEY CARNEHAN**, 8, ch g Foxwedge (AUS)—Zubova **Mr K. Jones**
12 **PRINCE OF ROME (IRE)**, 6, gr g Lethal Force (IRE)—Garraun (IRE) **Mrs A. Turner**
13 **ROBEAM (IRE)**, 6, b g Helmet (AUS)—Secret Flame **Mr K. Jones**
14 **ROCK WARBLER (IRE)**, 9, ch g Raven's Pass (USA)—Rare Tern (IRE) **Mr R. A. Royle**
15 **SCREECHING DRAGON (IRE)**, 5, b g Tagula (IRE)—Array of Stars (IRE)
County Charm Windows & Conservatories
16 **SHESADABBER**, 6, b m Heeraat (IRE)—Saorocain (IRE) **Mrs A. Turner**
17 10, Ch m Sulamani (IRE)—Sunny Parkes **M. Mullineaux**
18 **SWISS SANCERRE**, 4, b f Swiss Spirit—Adele Blanc Sec (FR) **Mr G. B. Hignett**

Assistant Trainer: Susan Mullineaux, Stuart Ross.

Amateur Jockey: Miss M. J. L. Mullineaux.

384 MR SEAMUS MULLINS, Amesbury

Postal: Wilsford Stables, Wilsford-Cum-Lake, Amesbury, Salisbury, Wiltshire, SP4 7BL
Contacts: PHONE 01980 626344 MOBILE 07702 559634
EMAIL info@seamusmullins.co.uk WEBSITE www.seamusmullins.co.uk

1 BABY SHAM, 4, b f Sir Percy—Zamzama (IRE) **Simon & Christine Prout**
2 BAGAN, 8, ch g Sulamani (IRE)—Aunt Rita (IRE) **Simon & Christine Prout**
3 BARROWMOUNT (IRE), 6, b g Mountain High (IRE)—Nans Mare (IRE) **Geoff Barnett & Brian Edgeley**
4 EN COEUR (FR), 8, b g Kap Rock (FR)—Fairyleap (IRE) **Woodford Valley Racing**
5 HEDYCHIUM (IRE), 4, b f Battle of Marengo (IRE)—Crystal Belle (IRE) **S Mullins Racing Club**
6 HUMANISTE (IRE), 7, b g Intello (GER)—Wingspan (USA) **Simon & Christine Prout**
7 I SEE YOU WELL (FR), 9, b g Air Chief Marshal (IRE)—Bonne Mere (FR)
Philippa Downing, Clive Dunning & S Pitt
8 4, B g Mahler—Jenny's Jewel (IRE) **Old Avenue Racing**
9 KENTFORD DRAKE, 6, b g Norse Dancer (IRE)—Kentford Dabchick **D. I. Bare**
10 KENTFORD MALLARD, 9, b m Sulamani (IRE)—Kentford Grebe **D. I. Bare**
11 KENTFORD SWANSONG, 5, b m Sulamani (IRE)—Kentford Grebe **D. I. Bare**
12 LAKESIDE LAD, 7, b g Alkaased (USA)—Kimmeridge Bay **Simon & Christine Prout**
13 MAHLER'S PROMISE (IRE), 7, b g Mahler—Loadsapromise (IRE) **The One More Sleep Racing Syndicate**
14 MISS CURIOSITY, 4, b f Life Force (IRE)—Lady Contessa (IRE) **Mr M. S. Rose**
15 MISTER SOUL (FR), 4, b g Planteur (IRE)—Mick Toscane (FR) **Old Avenue Racing**
16 MORFEE (IRE), 6, b g Dylan Thomas (IRE)—Ma Baker (IRE) **Ann & Morfee**
17 MORODER (IRE), 8, b g Morozov (USA)—Another Tonto (IRE) **Ann & Morfee**
18 MOUNTAIN GREY (IRE), 4, gr ro g Mount Nelson—Lady Friend **Mrs P. de W. Johnson**
19 OBORNE LADY (IRE), 9, b m Watar (IRE)—Lady Shackleton (IRE) **Simon & Christine Prout**
20 POSTMAN (FR), 9, ch g American Post—Pepperjuice (GER) **Dr & Mrs John Millar**
21 ROKO GEORGE (IRE), 6, b g Shirocco (GER)—Needed The Run (IRE) **The St Georges Hill Racing Syndicate**
22 ROMANOR, 8, b g Holy Roman Emperor (IRE)—Salinia (IRE) **Four Hens & A Cock**
23 SCUD (IRE), 4, b g Doyen (IRE)—Bahri Sugar (IRE) **Lord N. Monson**
24 SHELDON (IRE), 6, ch g Shantou (USA)—Feabhra (IRE) **Mrs D. H. Potter**
25 SILVER NICKEL (IRE), 8, gr g Gold Well—Cooper's Rose (IRE) **S Mullins Racing Club**
26 SPRINGAR, 4, b f Norse Dancer (IRE)—Samba Sound (IRE) **Mrs R. A. Jowett**
27 THE BIG RED ONE, 5, ch g Indian Haven—Brunette'sonly (IRE) **Mr J. R. Gerrelli**
28 THE CATHAL DON (IRE), 6, b br g Westerner—Flying Answer (IRE) **The Rumble Racing Club**
29 THE PINK'N, 6, gr g Dunaden (FR)—Lady Friend **Mrs P. de W. Johnson**
30 THINK FOR A MINIT, 6, b g Sixties Icon—Time To Think **Mrs V. F. Hewett**
31 TOMMIE BEAU (IRE), 7, b g Brian Boru—Bajan Girl (FR) **Simon & Christine Prout**
32 4, B g Mahler—Vicky Milan (IRE) **Andrew Cocks & Tara Johnson**
33 VIN ROUGE (IRE), 4, ch g Zoffany (IRE)—Adventure Seeker (FR) **Star in Sky Racing**
34 WHATCOLORISTHEWIND (IRE), 5, b m Shirocco (GER)—Needed The Run (IRE) **J. W. Mullins**
35 WILDERNESS, 7, b m Cityscape—Moonlight Applause **Mrs R Jowett, C R Dunning & Up the Glens**

THREE-YEAR-OLDS

36 B f Doyen (IRE)—Bahri Sugar (IRE) **J. W. Mullins**
37 Ch f Jack Hobbs—Ballinlina **Mrs R. A. Jowett**
38 CLONSILLA ROSE (IRE), b f Elzaam (AUS)—Crozet Islands (USA) **Gervin Creaner & Charlie Creaner**
39 Gr g Mount Nelson—Lady Friend **Mrs P. de W. Johnson**
40 SPARKLING AFFAIR (IRE), b c Profitable (IRE)—Exclusive Diamond **J. W. Mullins**

TWO-YEAR-OLDS

41 B c 21/05 Haafhd—Take A Drop (IRE) (Bushranger (IRE)) **J. W. Mullins**

Other Owners: Mr G. Barnett, Mr C. G. Creaner, Mr G. Creaner, Miss P. M. Downing, Mr C. R. Dunning, B. R. Edgeley, Mr D. J. Erwin, Miss S. Gorman, Mrs R. A. Jowett, Mrs A. Leftley, Mrs J. D. Millar, Dr J. W. Millar, Mr D. Morfee, J. W. Mullins, C. I. C. Munro, Ms S. Pitt, Mrs C. A. Prout, Mr S. P. Prout, Mr A. Randle, Mrs S. J. Rawlins, The Up The Glens Partnership, Miss R. Toppin, Mr P. M. Weston.

Assistant Trainer: James Mullins, **Yard Sponsor:** Simon Prout/We Do Vans.

NH Jockey: James Best, Sean Houlihan, Micheal Nolan, Daniel Sansom.

MR WILLIAM P. MULLINS, Carlow

385

Postal: Closutton, Bagenalstown, Co. Carlow, Ireland
Contacts: PHONE +353 59 972 1786 MOBILE +353 87 256 4940 FAX +353 59 972 2709
EMAIL wpmullins@eircom.net WEBSITE www.wpmullins.com

1 **ADAMANTLY CHOSEN (IRE)**, 5, b g Well Chosen—Sher's Adamant (IRE)
2 **AGUSTA GOLD (IRE)**, 9, b m Gold Well—Chloes Choice (IRE)
3 **AIONE (FR)**, 9, b g Coastal Path—La Horquela (IRE) **Mrs S Ricci**
4 **AL BOUM PHOTO (FR)**, 10, b g Buck's Boum (FR)—Al Gane (FR) **Mrs J Donnelly**
5 **ALLAHO (FR)**, 8, b g No Risk At All (FR)—Idaho Falls (FR) **Cheveley Park Stud**
6 **ALLEGORIE DE VASSY (FR)**, 5, b m No Risk At All (FR)—Autignac (FR)
7 **ANNAMIX (FR)**, 9, gr g Martaline—Tashtiyana (IRE) **Mrs S Ricci**
8 **APPRECIATE IT (IRE)**, 8, b g Jeremy (USA)—Sainte Baronne (FR) **Miss M A Masterson**
9 **ARAMON (GER)**, 9, b g Monsun (GER)—Aramina (GER) **Aramon Syndicate**
10 **ARCTIC WARRIOR (GER)**, 6, b g Pastorius (GER)—Adelma (GER) **J. P. McManus**
11 **ASLUKWOODHAVIT (FR)**, 6, b g Yorgunnabelucky (USA)—She's The Lady **Roger Brookhouse**
12 **ASTERION FORLONGE (FR)**, 8, gr g Coastal Path—Belle du Brizais (FR) **Mrs J Donnelly**
13 **AUTHORIZED ART (FR)**, 7, b g Authorized (IRE)—Rock Art (IRE) **Nicholas Peacock**
14 **BACARDYS (FR)**, 11, b br g Coastal Path—Oasice (FR) **Shanakiel Racing Syndicate**
15 **BACHASSON (FR)**, 11, gr g Voix du Nord (FR)—Belledonne (FR) **Edward O'Connell**
16 **BELLE METAL (IRE)**, 5, b m Soldier of Fortune (IRE)—Elphis Supreme (IRE) **Leinster Partnership**
17 **BERET ROUGE (IRE)**, 7, b m Big Bad Bob (IRE)—Pink Hat (IRE) **Mrs J M Mullins**
18 **BERKSHIRE ROYAL (IRE)**, 7, b g Sir Percy—Forest Express (AUS) **Mrs J M Mullins**
19 **BILLAWAY (IRE)**, 10, b g Well Chosen—Taipans Girl (IRE) **J Turner**
20 **BLACKBOW (IRE)**, 9, b g Stowaway—Rinnce Moll (IRE) **Roaringwater Syndicate**
21 **BLEU BERRY (FR)**, 11, b g Special Kaldoun (FR)—Somosierra (FR) **Luke McMahon**
22 **BLUE LORD (FR)**, 7, b g Blue Bresil (FR)—Lorette (FR) **Simon Munir & Isaac Souede**
23 **BLUE SARI (FR)**, 7, b g Saddex—Blue Aster (FR) **John P. McManus**
24 **BRAHMA BULL (IRE)**, 11, ch g Presenting—Oligarch Society (IRE) **Mrs S. Ricci**
25 **BRANDY LOVE (IRE)**, 6, b m Jet Away—Bambootcha (IRE) **C M Grech**
26 **BRING ON THE NIGHT (IRE)**, 5, ch h Gleneagles (IRE)—Brasileira
27 **BRONN (FR)**, 5, b g Notnowcato—Cluain Easa (IRE)
28 **BROOKLYNN GLORY (IRE)**, 7, b m Fame And Glory—Clamit Brook (IRE) **Swords Bloodstock**
29 **BURNING VICTORY (FR)**, 6, b m Nathaniel (IRE)—M'Oubliez Pas (USA) **Mrs Audrey Turley**
30 **BURROWS SAINT (FR)**, 9, b g Saint des Saints (FR)—La Bombonera (FR) **Mrs S. Ricci**
31 **CAPODANNO (FR)**, 6, ch g Manduro (GER)—Day Gets Up (FR) **J. P. McManus**
32 **CAPTAIN KANGAROO (IRE)**, 7, ch h Mastercraftsman (IRE)—We Can Say It Now (AUS)
    Kanga Racing & Brett Graham Syndicate
33 **CAREFULLY SELECTED (IRE)**, 10, b g Well Chosen—Knockamullen Girl (IRE) **Miss M. A. Masterson**
34 **CASH BACK (FR)**, 9, b g Linda's Lad—Holding (FR) **Watch This Space Syndicate**
35 **CASTLEBAWN WEST (IRE)**, 9, b g Westerner—Cooksgrove Lady (IRE) **Mrs Rose Boyd Partnership**
36 **CAVALLINO (IRE)**, 7, ch g Presenting—Roque de Cyborg (IRE) **Malcolm C. Denmark**
37 **CHACUN POUR SOI (FR)**, 10, b g Policy Maker (IRE)—Kruscyna (FR) **Mrs S Ricci**
38 **CIEL DE NEIGE (FR)**, 7, b g Authorized (IRE)—In Caso di Neve (FR) **John P. McManus**
39 **CILAOS EMERY (FR)**, 10, b g Califet (FR)—Queissa (FR) **Luke McMahon**
40 **CLASS CONTI (FR)**, 10, b g Poliglote—Gazelle Lulu (FR) **Simon Munir & Isaac Souede**
41 **CLASSIC GETAWAY (IRE)**, 6, br g Getaway (GER)—Classic Magic (IRE)
42 **CONCERTISTA (FR)**, 8, ch m Nathaniel (IRE)—Zagzig **Simon Munir & Isaac Souede Partnership**
43 **DANDY MAG (FR)**, 9, br g Special Kaldoun (FR)—Naiade Mag (FR) **G Mercer/D Mercer/Mrs Caren Walsh**
44 **DARK VOYAGER (IRE)**, 5, b g Raven's Pass (USA)—Je T'Adore (IRE) **Mrs J Donnelly**
45 **DATA BREACH (FR)**, 5, b g Pether's Moon (IRE)—Bochafina (FR) **McNeill Family**
46 **DEPLOY THE GETAWAY (IRE)**, 7, b g Getaway (GER)—Gaelic River (IRE) **Cheveley Park Stud**
47 **DINOBLUE (FR)**, 5, ch m Doctor Dino (FR)—Blue Aster (FR)
48 **DINOLAND (FR)**, 4, b g Doctor Dino (FR)—Acland Street (FR)
49 **DOLCITA (FR)**, 7, b m Saint des Saints (FR)—Orcantara (FR) **Sullivan Bloodstock Limited**
50 **DYSART DASHER (IRE)**, 5, b g Flemensfirth (USA)—Dysart Dancer (IRE)
51 **DYSART DIAMOND (IRE)**, 7, ch m Shirocco (GER)—Dysart Dancer (IRE) **Eleanor Manning**
52 **DYSART DYNAMO (IRE)**, 6, b g Westerner—Dysart Dancer (IRE)
53 **EASY GAME (FR)**, 8, b g Barastraight—Rule of The Game (FR) **Nicholas Peacock**
54 **ECHOES IN RAIN (FR)**, 6, b m Authorized (IRE)—Amarantine (FR) **Barnane Stud**
55 **ECHOES IN RAIN (FR)**, 6, b m Authorized (IRE)—Amarantine (FR)

MR WILLIAM P. MULLINS - continued

56 **EGALITY MANS (FR)**, 8, bl g Network (GER)—Quissisia Mans (FR) **Mrs J Donnelly**
57 **EL BARRA (FR)**, 8, br g Racinger (FR)—Oasaka (FR) **Mrs S Ricci**
58 **EL FABIOLO (FR)**, 5, b g Spanish Moon (USA)—Sainte Mante (FR)
59 **ELIMAY (FR)**, 8, gr m Montmartre (FR)—Hyde (FR) **John P. McManus**
60 **ELIXIR D'AINAY (FR)**, 8, ch g Muhtathir—Perle du Bocage (FR) **John P. McManus**
61 **EN BETON (FR)**, 8, br g Network (GER)—Nee A Saint Voir (FR) **Cheveley Park Stud**
62 **ENERGUMENE (FR)**, 8, b g Denham Red (FR)—Olinight (FR) **Anthony Bloom**
63 **FACILE VEGA (FR)**, 5, b g Walk In The Park (IRE)—Quevega (FR)
64 **FAKIR RODINO (FR)**, 7, gr g Gris de Gris (IRE)—Riviere Normande (FR)
65 **FAN DE BLUES (FR)**, 7, b g Poliglote—Tire En Touche (FR) **Simon Munir & Isaac Souede**
66 **FAROUT (IRE)**, 5, gr g Dark Angel (IRE)—Transhumance (IRE)
67 **FEIGH (IRE)**, 4, ch f Well Chosen—Greatartist (IRE)
68 **FERNY HOLLOW (IRE)**, 7, b br g Westerner—Mirazur (IRE) **Cheveley Park Stud**
69 **FIGHTER ALLEN (FR)**, 7, b g Vision d'Etat (FR)—Reaction (FR) **Chris Jones**
70 **FILS SPIRITUEL (FR)**, 7, b g Presenting—Toque Rouge (FR) **Mrs J Donnelly**
71 **FINEST EVERMORE (IRE)**, 6, b m Yeats (IRE)—St Helans Bay (IRE) **J. Turner**
72 **FIVE O'CLOCK (FR)**, 7, b g Cokoriko (FR)—Rodika (FR) **Mrs S Ricci**
73 **FOLLOW THE BRAVE (FR)**, 5, b g Motivator—Finella (FR)
74 **FOVEROS (FR)**, 7, b g Authorized (IRE)—Fanurio's Angel (FR) **Luke McMahon**
75 **FRANCO DE PORT (FR)**, 7, b h Coastal Path—Ruth (FR) **Bruton Street IV Partnership**
76 **GAELIC WARRIOR (GER)**, 4, b g Maxios—Game of Legs (FR)
77 **GAILLARD DU MESNIL (FR)**, 6, gr g Saint des Saints (FR)—Athena du Mesnil (FR) **Mrs J. Donnelly**
78 **GALOPIN DES CHAMPS (FR)**, 6, bl g Timos (GER)—Manon des Champs (FR) **Mrs Audrey Turley**
79 **GANAPATHI (FR)**, 6, b g Samum (GER)—Une Dame d'Avril (FR) **Mrs J. Donnelly**
80 **GARS EN NOIR (FR)**, 6, b g Masked Marvel—Touche Noire (FR) **Mrs J. Donnelly**
81 **GAULOISE (FR)**, 6, ch m Samum (GER)—Sans Histoire (FR) **Kenneth Alexander**
82 **GELEE BLANCHE (FR)**, 6, b m Samum (GER)—Voix du Coeur (FR) **Tiger Tail Again Syndicate**
83 **GENTLEMAN DE MEE (FR)**, 6, b g Saint des Saints (FR)—Koeur de Mee (FR)
84 **GIBRALTAR (IRE)**, 5, b g Tamayuz—Red Halo (IRE)
85 **GJOUMI (FR)**, 6, ch m Maresca Sorrento (FR)—Onvavoir (FR) **S McManus**
86 **GLENGOULY (FR)**, 6, b g Coastal Path—Roulmapoule (FR)
87 **GLENS OF ANTRIM (IRE)**, 7, b m Flemensfirth (USA)—Cottage Theatre (IRE) **J. P. McManus**
88 **GORKI D'AIRY (FR)**, 6, b g Legolas (JPN)—Norsa d'Airy (FR) **Mrs J. M. Mullins**
89 **GOVEN (FR)**, 6, b g Poliglote—Sweeny (FR)
90 **GRAND BORNAND (FR)**, 6, gr g Montmartre (FR)—Ubriska (FR) **Mrs S Ricci**
91 **GRANGEE (FR)**, 6, br m Great Pretender (IRE)—Quelle Mome (FR) **Syndicates.Racing**
92 **GRIVEI (FR)**, 5, ch g Muhtathir—Stourza (FR)
93 **HA D'OR (FR)**, 5, b g Nidor (FR)—Rosewort (FR) **Mrs S Ricci**
94 **HAUT EN COULEURS (FR)**, 5, b g Saint des Saints (FR)—Sanouva (FR) **Mrs J. Donnelly**
95 **HAUTURIERE (FR)**, 5, ch m No Risk At All (FR)—Ocean Beach (FR)
96 **HAWAI GAME (FR)**, 5, b g Diamond Boy (FR)—Rule of The Game (FR)
97 **HEIA (FR)**, 5, b m No Risk At All (FR)—Ulla de Montot (FR)
98 **HENN SEE (FR)**, 5, br g Slickly Royal (FR)—Onvavoir (FR)
99 **HERCULE DU SEUIL (FR)**, 5, br g Saddler Maker (IRE)—Cibelle du Seuil (FR)
100 **HI HO PHOENIX**, 6, gr g Phoenix Reach (IRE)—Silverlined **Mrs A.M & RJD Varmen**
101 **HONKY TONK (IRE)**, 5, b g Walk In The Park (IRE)—Arctic Lady (GER)
102 **HORANTZAU D'AIRY (FR)**, 5, b g Legolas (JPN)—Panzara d'Airy (FR)
103 **HORS PISTE (FR)**, 5, b m Kapgarde (FR)—Valgardena (FR)
104 **HUBRISKO (FR)**, 5, b g Doctor Dino (FR)—Ubriska (FR)
105 **HUNTERS YARN (IRE)**, 5, b g Fame And Glory—Full of Birds (FR)
106 **HYBERY (FR)**, 8, b g Centennial (IRE)—Zalagarry (FR) **Hybery Racing Syndicate**
107 **HYBRIS (FR)**, 5, ch g Martaline—Oasice (FR)
108 **ICARE ALLEN (FR)**, 4, b g Cokoriko (FR)—Coeur d'Allen (FR)
109 **IDOLES DES JEUNES (FR)**, 6, b m Helmet (AUS)—Akka
110 **IL ETAIT TEMPS (FR)**, 4, ch g Jukebox Jury (IRE)—Une des Sources (FR)
111 **IMPULSIVE DANCER (IRE)**, 4, br g Dragon Pulse (IRE)—Viennese Whirl
112 **IN EXCESS (FR)**, 4, b g Walzertakt (GER)—Bouee En Mer (FR)
113 **JAMES DU BERLAIS (FR)**, 6, ch g Muhtathir—King's Daughter (FR) **Simon Munir & Isaac Souede**
114 **JAMES GATE (IRE)**, 5, b g Shantou (USA)—Annie May (IRE)
115 **JANIDIL (FR)**, 8, b g Indian Daffodil (IRE)—Janidouce (FR) **John P. McManus**

MR WILLIAM P. MULLINS - continued

116 **JON SNOW (FR)**, 7, br g Le Havre (IRE)—Saroushka (FR) **Mrs S Ricci**
117 **JUNGLE BOOGIE (IRE)**, 8, b g Gold Well—A Better Excuse (IRE) **Malcolm C. Denmark**
118 **KEMBOY (FR)**, 10, b g Voix du Nord (FR)—Vitora (FR) **Kemboy/Brett Graham/Ken Sharp Syndicate**
119 **KILCRUIT (IRE)**, 7, b g Stowaway—Not Broke Yet (IRE) **Miss M A Masterson**
120 **KLARC KENT (FR)**, 6, b g Spanish Moon (USA)—Kryptonie (FR)
121 **KLASSICAL DREAM (FR)**, 8, b g Dream Well (FR)—Klassical Way (FR) **Mrs Joanne Coleman**
122 **KOTAYA (FR)**, 6, gr m Mastercraftsman (IRE)—Kozaka (FR)
123 **LA PRIMA DONNA (FR)**, 5, b m Saint des Saints (FR)—Princesse d'Anjou (FR)
124 **LARGY HILL (IRE)**, 5, b g Flemensfirth (USA)—Rowansgift (IRE)
125 **LIVELOVELAUGH (IRE)**, 12, b g Beneficial—Another Evening (IRE) **Mrs S. Ricci**
126 **LORD ROYAL (FR)**, 7, gr g Lord du Sud (FR)—Tinoroyale **Paul Connell & Alan McGonnell**
127 **M C MULDOON (IRE)**, 7, gr g Mastercraftsman (IRE)—Alizaya (FR) **Mrs J M Mullins**
128 **MADMANSGAME**, 5, bl g Blue Bresil (FR)—Grainne Ni Maille
129 **MANITOPARK AA (FR)**, 6, b m Walk In The Park (IRE)—Manitoba (FR) **Simon Munir & Isaac Souede**
130 **MAZE RUNNER (IRE)**, 7, b g Authorized (IRE)—Alice Rose (FR) **Mrs J. M. Mullins**
131 **MELON**, 10, ch g Medicean—Night Teeny **Mrs J. Donnelly**
132 **MICRO MANAGE (IRE)**, 6, ch h Rip Van Winkle (IRE)—Lillebonne (FR) **Merriebelle Irish Farm Limited**
133 **MINELLA COCOONER (IRE)**, 6, b g Flemensfirth (USA)—Askanna (IRE)
134 **MONKFISH (IRE)**, 8, ch g Stowaway—Martovic (IRE) **Mrs S Ricci**
135 **MR ADJUDICATOR**, 8, b g Camacho—Attlongglast **David Bobbett**
136 **MR COLDSTONE (IRE)**, 6, b g Tamayuz—Dance Lively (USA) **David Bobbett**
137 **MT LEINSTER (IRE)**, 8, ch g Beat Hollow—Sixhills (FR) **Roaringwater Syndicate**
138 **MY SISTER SARAH (IRE)**, 8, ch m Martaline—Reste Ren Or (IRE) **Barnane Stud**
139 **ONTHEROPES (IRE)**, 8, b g Presenting—Dushion (IRE) **Cheveley Park Stud**
140 **PARMENION**, 4, b g Soldier Hollow—Pearls Or Passion (FR)
141 **PAUL MARVEL (FR)**, 5, gr g Masked Marvel—Paulmie (FR)
142 **PINK IN THE PARK (IRE)**, 5, b m Walk In The Park (IRE)—Pink Hat (IRE)
143 **PONT AVAL (FR)**, 9, b m Soldier of Fortune (IRE)—Panzella (FR) **N G King**
144 **POWER OF PAUSE (IRE)**, 7, ch g Doyen (IRE)—Shady Pines (IRE) **Miss M A Masterson**
145 **PROTEKTING (FR)**, 4, b g Saddex—Protektion (FR)
146 **RAMILLIES (IRE)**, 7, gr g Shantou (USA)—Mrs Wallensky (IRE) **Mrs J Donnelly**
147 **RECITE A PRAYER (IRE)**, 7, b g Recital (FR)—Old Madam (IRE)
148 **REDEMPTION DAY**, 5, b g Blue Bresil (FR)—Cutielilou (FR)
149 **ROBINNIA (IRE)**, 7, b m Robin des Champs (FR)—Dreams And Songs **Closutton Racing Club**
150 **ROYAL RENDEZVOUS (IRE)**, 10, b g King's Theatre (IRE)—Novacella (FR) **Dr S P Fitzgerald**
151 **SAINT ROI (FR)**, 7, b g Coastal Path—Sainte Vigne (FR) **John P. McManus**
152 **SAINT SAM (FR)**, 5, b g Saint des Saints (FR)—Ladeka (FR) **Edward J Ware**
153 **SALDIER (FR)**, 8, b g Soldier Hollow—Salve Evita **Mrs S Ricci**
154 **SHADOW RIDER (IRE)**, 8, ch g Martaline—Samansonnienne (FR) **J. P. McManus**
155 **SHARJAH (FR)**, 9, b g Doctor Dino (FR)—Saaryeh **Mrs S. Ricci**
156 **SHEWEARSITWELL (IRE)**, 7, b m Shirocco (GER)—Ware It Vic (IRE) **Closutton Racing Club**
157 **SIR ARGUS**, 5, b g Soldier of Fortune (IRE)—Oligarch Society (IRE)
158 **SIR GERHARD (IRE)**, 7, b g Jeremy (USA)—Faanan Aldaar (IRE)
159 **SKY SPRINTER (IRE)**, 5, b g Shantou (USA)—Levmoss Lady (IRE)
160 **STATE MAN (FR)**, 5, ch g Doctor Dino (FR)—Arret Station (FR) **Mrs J. Donnelly**
161 **STATTLER (IRE)**, 7, br g Stowaway—Our Honey (IRE) **R. A. Bartlett**
162 **STATUAIRE (FR)**, 7, b m Muhtathir—Arret Station (FR)
163 **STONES AND ROSES (IRE)**, 8, b g Shantou (USA)—Compelled (IRE) **P. Reilly & C. Reilly**
164 **STORMY IRELAND (FR)**, 8, b m Motivator—Like A Storm (IRE) **Sullivan Bloodstock Limited**
165 **STRATUM**, 9, b g Dansili—Lunar Phase (IRE) **Anthony Bloom**
166 **TAKE TEA (IRE)**, 7, b m Flemensfirth (USA)—Saine d'Esprit (FR)
167 **TASITEASAI (IRE)**, 5, b m Sageburg (IRE)—Tasitiocht (IRE)
168 **TAX FOR MAX (GER)**, 5, b h Maxios—Tomato Finish (GER) **Simon Munir & Isaac Souede**
169 **THE BIG GETAWAY (IRE)**, 8, b g Getaway (GER)—Saddlers Dawn (IRE) **Mrs J Donnelly**
170 **THE NICE GUY (IRE)**, 7, b g Fame And Glory—Kilbarry Beauty (IRE) **Malcolm C. Denmark**
171 **TORNADO FLYER (IRE)**, 9, b g Flemensfirth (USA)—Mucho Macabi (IRE) **TFP Partnership**
172 **UNCLE PHIL (IRE)**, 5, b g Walk In The Park (IRE)—Synthe Davis (FR)
173 **VADALY (FR)**, 4, b f Vadamos (FR)—Formerly (FR)
174 **VALLEY BREEZE (FR)**, 8, b g Sunday Break (JPN)—Valdemossa (FR) **Luke McMahon**
175 **VALLEY BREEZE (FR)**, 8, b g Sunday Break (JPN)—Valdemossa (FR)

MR WILLIAM P. MULLINS - continued

176 **VAUBAN (FR)**, 4, ch g Galiway—Waldfest
177 **VIVA DEVITO (IRE)**, 5, br g Malinas (GER)—Red Cattiva
178 **WHAT PATH (FR)**, 5, b g Coastal Path—Quoi d'Autre (FR)
179 **WHATDEAWANT (IRE)**, 6, b g Aizavoski (IRE)—Hidden Reserve (IRE) **Sean & Bernadine Mulryan**
180 **WHISKEY LULLABY (IRE)**, 7, b m Stowaway—Joie de Cotte (FR)
181 **WHISKEY SOUR (IRE)**, 9, b h Jeremy (USA)—Swizzle Stick (IRE) **Luke McMahon**
182 **YOUMDOR (FR)**, 5, b g Youmzain (IRE)—Decize (FR) **McNeill Family**
183 **ZENON (IRE)**, 8, b g Galileo (IRE)—Jacqueline (IND) **Dreaming Cups Syndicate**

386
MISS AMY MURPHY, Newmarket
Postal: Southgate Stables, Hamilton Road, Newmarket, Suffolk, CB8 0NQ
Contacts: PHONE 01638 484907 MOBILE 07711 992500
EMAIL info@amymurphyracing.com WEBSITE www.amymurphyracing.com

1 **ALBORKAN (FR)**, 5, b g Joshua Tree (IRE)—Plaine Monceau (FR) **Alan & Sally Coney, Mr J. Hambro**
2 **BAILEYS EXCELERATE (FR)**, 7, gr g Excelebration (IRE)—Cruel Sea (USA) **Baileys Horse Feeds & Partner**
3 4, B f Authorized (IRE)—Carole's Spirit **Mr P. Murphy**
4 **CHATEAU D'IF (FR)**, 4, b g Intello (GER)—Moonlight Cass (IRE) **Chasing Euros Racing Club**
5 **DANIEL DERONDA**, 5, b g Siyouni (FR)—Madonna Dell'orto **A White & Partner**
6 **DEPOSIT (IRE)**, 5, b g Sea The Stars (IRE)—Interim Payment (USA) **Empress Racing & Partner**
7 **EHRMANN (IRE)**, 4, b g Dragon Pulse (IRE)—Desiderada (IRE) **D. L. de Souza**
8 **HAWTHORN COTTAGE (IRE)**, 9, b m Gold Well—Miss Kilkeel (IRE) **Melbourne 10 Racing**
9 **IRONHILL (IRE)**, 6, b g Leading Light (IRE)—Azaban (IRE)
10 **KALASHNIKOV (IRE)**, 9, br g Kalanisi (IRE)—Fairy Lane (IRE) **Mr P. Murphy**
11 **KALEB (IRE)**, 4, b g Sir Percy—Kalane (IRE) **Mr P. Murphy**
12 **KALMOOR (IRE)**, 5, b g Kalanisi (IRE)—Fairy On The Moor (IRE) **Mr P. Murphy**
13 **LOGAN ROCKS (IRE)**, 7, b g Yeats (IRE)—Countess Comet (IRE) **The Rann Family**
14 5, B m Getaway (GER)—Luna Nuova (IRE) **The Rann Family**
15 4, B f Black Sam Bellamy (IRE)—Mariah Rollins (IRE) **Mr P. Murphy**
16 **MARIE PARADIS (IRE)**, 4, b f Belardo (IRE)—Snowy Peak **Amy Murphy Racing Club**
17 **MARLBOROUGH SOUNDS**, 7, b g Camelot—Wind Surf (USA) **Vitality Cbd Partners & Mr Julian Taylor**
18 **MERCIAN PRINCE (IRE)**, 11, b g Midnight Legend—Bongo Fury (FR) **Mr P. Murphy**
19 **PRIDE OF AMERICA (FR)**, 5, b g American Post—Atarfe (IRE) **Haven't A Pot, D. Macauliffe & Anoj Don**
20 **PROUD MARI**, 5, b m Shirocco (GER)—Mariah Rollins (IRE) **Racing To Profit Syndicate & Partner**
21 **PURE JADE**, 4, b f Blue Bresil (FR)—Countess Comet (IRE) **The Rann Family**
22 **RAQISA**, 4, b f Mukhadram—Hazy Dancer **A White & Partner**
23 **SAMILLE (IRE)**, 5, b m Kodiac—Monicalew **Mick Jaselsky & Partner**
24 **SOLDIER ON PARADE**, 5, b g Dunaden—Litewska (IRE) **Hostages To Fortune**
25 **SYMBOLIC SPIRIT (FR)**, 5, b m Westerner—Carole's Spirit **Hot To Trot Jumping**
26 **THEGREATESTSHOWMAN**, 6, ch g Equiano (FR)—Conversational (IRE) **Amy Murphy Racing Club**
27 **TONYX**, 6, b m Nathaniel (IRE)—Kadoma **The Rann Family**
28 **URBAN WAR (IRE)**, 4, b g Mehmas (IRE)—Urban Beauty (IRE) **Constellation Syndicate & Partner**
29 **WEST SIDE GLORY (IRE)**, 4, ch f Dutch Art—Finishingthehat **D. L. de Souza**

THREE-YEAR-OLDS

30 **BAILEYS BLING**, ch f Profitable (IRE)—Ring For Baileys **G R Bailey Ltd (Baileys Horse Feeds)**
31 **BAILEYS EMINENCE (FR)**, b br g Holy Roman Emperor (IRE)—Baileys Mirage (FR)
G R Bailey Ltd (Baileys Horse Feeds)
32 **GEE EIGHT (IRE)**, ch g Tamayuz—Peace Summit **Miss A. L. Murphy**
33 **GOLDEN MAYFLOWER**, b f Golden Horn—Pelerin (IRE) **Syndicates.Racing I & Partner**
34 **KIT GABRIEL (IRE)**, b c Kodiac—Maleha (IRE) **Mr C. Johnston**
35 **MOONLIGHT FROLIC**, b f Bated Breath—Chicita Banana **Mr C.E. Dale & Mrs V Knight & Partners**
36 **OASIS IRLANDES**, b c Gutaifan (IRE)—Midst **D. L. de Souza**
37 **RINGO STARLIGHT**, b g Twilight Son—Ring of Love **Mr P. Venner**
38 **TARBAAN (IRE)**, ch g Tamayuz—Rocana **Constellation Syndicate & Partner**
39 **TWILIGHT STEEL**, b f Twilight Son—Sally (FR) **Andrew Harris & Partner**

MISS AMY MURPHY - continued

TWO-YEAR-OLDS

40 B g 25/02 Buratino (IRE)—Archange (FR) (Arcano (IRE)) (25000) **Solario Racing**
41 Ch c 21/04 Showcasing—Baileys Showgirl (FR) (Sepoy (AUS)) **G R Bailey Ltd (Baileys Horse Feeds)**
42 B f 31/03 Australia—Lemon Rock (Green Desert (USA)) (25000) **Rathdown Bloodstock**
43 B f 13/04 Cityscape—Shes Queen (IRE) (Baltic King) (1000) **Miss A. L. Murphy**

Other Owners: Mr S. J. Armstrong, Mr J. Cantillon, Mr A. R. Culumbarapitiyage Don, Mr C.E. Dale & Mrs V. Knight, Mr M. S. J. Dyer, Mr G. Freeman, Mr K. C. Freeman, G R Bailey Ltd (Baileys Horse Feeds), James Ortega Bloodstock Ltd, Mr M. Jaselsky, Daniel MacAuliffe & Anoj Don, Miss A. L. Murphy, Mr N. Nathwani, P. A. Oppenheimer, Miss N. K. Rajani, Mr G. P. D. Rann, Mrs L. E. Rann, Mr J. P. Ryan, Mr A. J. Taylor, Mr A. J. White, Mr J. Wright.

---

387 **MR MIKE MURPHY, Westoning**
Postal: **Broadlands, Manor Park Stud, Westoning, Bedfordshire, MK45 5LA**
Contacts: **PHONE 01525 717305 MOBILE 07770 496103 FAX 01525 717305**
EMAIL mmurphy@globalnet.co.uk WEBSITE www.mikemurphyracing.com

1 **ARIA ROSE**, 7, b g Cityscape—Leelu **P. Banfield**
2 **BAMO MC**, 8, gr g Hellvelyn—Soft Touch (IRE) **Mr M. Murphy**
3 **BREEZYANDBRIGHT (IRE)**, 4, b g Epaulette (AUS)—Tranquil Sky **Moir & Murphy**
4 **CITYZEN SERG (IRE)**, 5, b g Raven's Pass (USA)—Summer Dream (IRE) **URSA Major Racing**
5 **DUSTY DAMSEL**, 6, ch m Toronado (IRE)—Dusty Answer **The Calm Partnership**
6 **GARTH ROCKETT**, 8, b g Delegator—Leelu **P. Banfield**
7 **GENERAL SAGO (IRE)**, 4, b g Fascinating Rock (IRE)—Why Now **New Vision Bloodstock**
8 **LE REVEUR (IRE)**, 5, b g Dream Ahead (USA)—Don't Be **Sarabex**
9 **MULZIM**, 8, b g Exceed And Excel (AUS)—Samaah (IRE) **Victoria Taylor & Family**
10 **MY BOY FRANKIE**, 4, b g Fountain of Youth (IRE)—Lady Moscou (IRE) **Mr C. D. J. O'Dowd**
11 **SPACESUIT**, 5, b g Sea The Moon (GER)—Casaca **Ms A. D. Tibbett**
12 **VELVET VISTA**, 6, b m Sea The Moon (GER)—Battery Power **Sarabex**
13 **WORKING MANS BOY**, 4, b g Heeraat (IRE)—High Will (FR) **BR-2 Racing Club**

THREE-YEAR-OLDS

14 **BOLD AND LOYAL**, b g Frankel—Birdwood **Mrs E. A. P. Haynes**
15 **ENLIGHTENMENT (IRE)**, ch f Mehmas (IRE)—So Easy (IRE) **The Adams, Laws & Murphy**
16 **GOLDEN ROMANCE (IRE)**, ch f Profitable (IRE)—Calipatria **Miss S. J. Ballinger**
17 **HOPEFORTHEBEST**, ch c Helmet (AUS)—Bestfootforward **Moir & Murphy**
18 **LA EQUINATA**, b f Equiano (FR)—La Fortunata
19 **PARK FARM PRINCE**, b c Pearl Secret—Frozen Princess
20 **POWEREDBYLIGHTNING**, b g Cable Bay (IRE)—Hypnology (USA) **Mr R. J. Moore**
21 **SOVEREIGN BELLE (IRE)**, ch f No Nay Never (USA)—Impressible
22 **THE CHARMER (IRE)**, ch g Dandy Man (IRE)—Charmgoer (USA) **Moir & Murphy**
23 **VELVET VULCAN**, b g Nathaniel (IRE)—Battery Power **Sarabex**

TWO-YEAR-OLDS

24 B f 22/03 Massaat (IRE)—Aruan (Equiano (FR))
25 **HEDENHAM**, b f 07/03 Heeraat (IRE)—Denham (Denounce)
26 **JESSE LUC**, b c 21/04 Brazen Beau (AUS)—Be Amazing (IRE) (Refuse To Bend (IRE)) (8000) **P. Banfield**
27 Ch c 16/04 Garswood—La Fortunata (Lucky Story (USA)) (6000)
28 Ch f 21/03 Mehmas (IRE)—Melodize (Iceman) (28000)
29 B gr c 14/04 Caravaggio (USA)—Out of Time (IRE) (Anabaa (USA)) (32000) **Apollo Horses I**
30 **VELVET VOGUE**, b f 10/03 Intello (GER)—Battery Power (Royal Applause) **Sarabex**

Other Owners: Mr S. Moir, Mr M. Murphy.

Assistant Trainer: Michael Keady.

---

388 MR OLLY MURPHY, Wilmcote

Postal: **Warren Chase Stables, Wilmcote, Stratford-Upon-Avon, Warwickshire, CV37 9XG**
Contacts: **PHONE 01789 613347**
EMAIL office@ollymurphyracing.com WEBSITE www.ollymurphyracing.com

1 **ABEGUDSAM (IRE)**, 5, ch g Doyen (IRE)—Pleasetellmeittrue (IRE) **Mr C. J. Haughey**
2 **AFRICAN DANCE (IRE)**, 7, br g Shirocco (GER)—Dani California **Bective Stud**
3 **ALLAVINA (IRE)**, 7, b m Getaway (GER)—One Cool Kate (IRE) **Mr C. Boultbee-Brooks**
4 **ALPHA CARINAE (IRE)**, 7, ch m Robin des Champs (FR)—Annas Present (IRE) **Mr M. Fennessy**
5 **AM I WRONG (IRE)**, 5, gr g Soldier of Fortune (IRE)—Medimli (IRE) **Mr A. L. Cohen**
6 **ANGEL OF HARLEM**, 9, b m Presenting—Whoops A Daisy **Patrick & Scott Bryceland**
7 **AUDITORIA**, 5, b m Gleneagles (IRE)—Authora (IRE) **Nick Brown Racing**
8 **BARONY LEGENDS (IRE)**, 6, b g Yeats (IRE)—Monty's Sister (IRE) **Bective Stud**
9 **BARRICANE**, 7, b g Kayf Tara—Alina Rheinberg (GER) **Premier Thoroughbred Racing Ltd&partner**
10 **BELIEVE JACK (FR)**, 5, b g Make Believe—Sandslide **Five Saints Racing**
11 **BENIGN DICTATOR (IRE)**, 5, b g Getaway (GER)—Canto Creek **The Wayward Pilgrims**
12 **BEST TRITON (IRE)**, 7, b g Mustameet (USA)—Ad Astra (IRE) **Foxtrot Racing Syndicate 1**
13 **BEYOND EVERYTHING (FR)**, 6, gr g Cima de Triomphe (IRE)—Dear Valentine (FR) **Mr C. J. Haughey**
14 **BLAZER'S MILL (IRE)**, 8, b g Westerner—Creation (IRE) **Mrs J. A. Wakefield**
15 **BOBBY SOCKS**, 5, b g Kayf Tara—Bobs Present **H. A. Murphy**
16 **BOREEN BOY (IRE)**, 6, b g Valirann (FR)—Annas Back (IRE) **Owners Group 095**
17 **BREWIN'UPASTORM (IRE)**, 9, b g Milan—Daraheen Diamond (IRE) **Ms B. J. Abt**
18 **BUBBLES OF GOLD (IRE)**, 9, b g Gold Well—Bubble Bann (IRE) **Bective Stud**
19 **BUTCH**, 5, b g Kayf Tara—Leading On **McNeill Family Ltd**
20 **CALIPSO COLLONGES (FR)**, 10, b g Crossharbour—Ivresse Collonges (FR) **The Black Horse Hotel Bridgnorth**
21 **CAPTAIN BIGGLES (IRE)**, 7, gr g Milan—Timon's Present **Mrs D. L. Whateley**
22 **CAPTAIN FANTASTIC (IRE)**, 5, b g Soldier of Fortune (IRE)—Chapel Queen (IRE) **A. J. Wall**
23 **CELTIC TARA**, 8, b m Kayf Tara—Valdas Queen (GER) **A. P. Racing**
24 **CHAMPAGNESUPEROVER (IRE)**, 7, b g Jeremy (USA)—Meldrum Hall (IRE)
    McNeill Family & Patrick&scott Bryceland
25 **CHASING FIRE**, 5, b g Maxios—Kahara **Mrs D. L. Whateley**
26 **CHESTNUT ROSE (IRE)**, 6, ch m Ocovango—Last of The Bunch **Bective Stud**
27 **CHIPPING AWAY (IRE)**, 4, b g Gutaifan (IRE)—Smashing (IRE) **Apollo Horse Racing Hassall McCarthy**
28 **CHOSEN PORT (IRE)**, 6, b m Well Chosen—Despute (IRE) **Bective Stud**
29 **CLAY ROGERS (IRE)**, 7, b g Imperial Monarch (IRE)—Fly Bid (IRE) **Future Champions Racing Syndicate**
30 **COLLOONEY (IRE)**, 8, b g Yeats (IRE)—Amber Trix (IRE) **Mr J. P. McManus**
31 **CONTEMPLATEMYFAITH (IRE)**, 6, b g Califet (FR)—Liss A Chroi (IRE) **Owners Group 087**
32 **COPPERLESS**, 7, b g Kayf Tara—Presenting Copper (IRE) **Aiden Murphy & Alan Peterson**
33 **COREY'S COURAGE**, 6, b m Dunaden (FR)—Valdas Queen (GER) **A. P. Racing**
34 **DEL DUQUE (IRE)**, 7, b g Fame And Glory—Chirouble (IRE) **Deva Racing Del Duque**
35 **DOCTOR KEN (FR)**, 6, b g Doctor Dino (FR)—Kendoretta (FR) **Mrs D. L. Whateley**
36 **DOMINIC'S FAULT**, 9, b g Camelot—Midnight Angel (GER) **Mrs D. L. Whateley**
37 **DR SEB (FR)**, 5, ch g Doctor Dino (FR)—Gareduhavre (FR) **Mrs D. L. Whateley**
38 **DR T J ECKLEBURG (IRE)**, 4, b g Lawman (FR)—Imtidaad (USA) **Dominic Burke & Tim Syder**
39 **DUBAI GUEST (IRE)**, 7, b g Dubai Destination (USA)—Formidable Guest **Oceana Racing**
40 **DUKE OF ROCKINGHAM**, 6, b g Kayf Tara—Our Jess (IRE) **Mrs D. L. Whateley**
41 **EAGLEHILL (FR)**, 8, gr g Blue Bresil (FR)—Ratina de Vaige (FR) **Mr J. P. McManus**
42 **EAVESDROPPING**, 6, b m Kayf Tara—Leading On **Deva Racing Eavesdropping, M Muldoon**
43 **ENEMY COAST AHEAD**, 8, br g Malinas (GER)—Penang Princess **McNeill Family Ltd**
44 **EWOOD PARK (IRE)**, 7, b g Shirocco (GER)—Windfola (FR) **McNeill Family Ltd**
45 **FABRIQUE EN FRANCE (FR)**, 7, b g Yeats (IRE)—Knar Mardy **Bective Stud**
46 **FAIRLY FAMOUS (IRE)**, 5, b g Fame And Glory—Fairly Definite (IRE) **H. A. Murphy**
47 **FEARLESS (IRE)**, 7, b g Arakan (USA)—La Spezia (IRE) **Dominic Burke & Tim Syder**
48 **FINAWN BAWN (IRE)**, 9, b g Robin des Champs (FR)—Kayanti (IRE) **Ready Steady Go**
49 **FIRST CLASS RETURN (IRE)**, 9, b g Let The Lion Roar—Chitty Bang Bang (IRE) **Mr O. J. Murphy**
50 **FLETCH (FR)**, 7, b g Kayf Tara—Oeuvre Vive (FR) **Ms B. J. Abt**
51 **FLEURMAN (IRE)**, 4, b g Marmerchstman (USA)—Fleur de Nuit (IRE) **Bective Stud**
52 **FOLLOW THAT**, 8, b m Malinas (GER)—Leading On **B. Hawkins**
53 **FOXEY**, 7, b g Foxwedge (AUS)—Blue Lyric **Mr M. J. James**
54 **FOXINTHEBOX (IRE)**, 6, b g Presenting—Forces of Destiny (IRE) **A. Butler**
55 **FRANKLY MR SHANKLY (GER)**, 5, b g Maxios—Four Roses (IRE) **Patrick & Scott Bryceland**

MR OLLY MURPHY - continued

56 **FRESH NEW DAWN (IRE)**, 10, ch g Flemensfirth (USA)—Star Shuil (IRE) **The Dream Big Syndicate**
57 **GETAWAY LILY BEAR (IRE)**, 6, b m Getaway (GER)—Jemima Jones (IRE) **Owners Group 082**
58 **GETAWAY LUV (IRE)**, 7, b g Getaway (GER)—Ut Love (FR) **Emily Boultbee Brooks Racing**
59 **GINISTRELLI (IRE)**, 6, b g Frankel—Guaranda **Mrs J. A. Wakefield**
60 **GO DANTE**, 6, b g Kayf Tara—Whoops A Daisy **Ms B. J. Abt**
61 **GOLEIRIHEM (IRE)**, 6, b g Shirocco (GER)—Corona Moon (IRE) **Touchwood Racing**
62 **GRACES ORDER (IRE)**, 7, b m Mahler—Janebailey **Peaky Blinders**
63 **GRANDADS COTTAGE (IRE)**, 7, ch g Shantou (USA)—Sarah's Cottage (IRE) **Mr J. Hales**
64 **GREY SPIRIT (IRE)**, 7, gr g Dark Angel (IRE)—Buttonhole **A J Wall & Briton International**
65 **GUNSIGHT RIDGE**, 7, b g Midnight Legend—Grandma Griffiths **Mrs D. L. Whateley**
66 **HALONDO (FR)**, 5, b g Cokoriko (FR)—Rive Gauche (FR) **Mrs D. L. Whateley**
67 **HARDI DU MESNIL (FR)**, 5, b g Masterstroke (USA)—Athena du Mesnil (FR) **Mr R. B. Waley-Cohen**
68 **HERE COMES MCCOY (IRE)**, 7, br g Dylan Thomas (IRE)—Is It Here (IRE) **Mr C. J. Haughey**
69 **HERO (FR)**, 5, b g Saddler Maker (IRE)—Burma (FR) **Mrs D. L. Whateley**
70 **HEY BOB (IRE)**, 10, br g Big Bad Bob (IRE)—Bounty Star (IRE) **Theblackhorsehotelbridgnorth & Partner**
71 **HIGHATE HILL (IRE)**, 8, b g Presenting—Lisrenny Lady **Patrick & Scott Bryceland**
72 **HOGAN (IRE)**, 6, b g Fame And Glory—Don't Be Upset (IRE) **Farrell Field Cognet Sigler**
73 **HOKELAMI (FR)**, 5, b br g Coastal Path—Une Brik (FR) **A. Butler**
74 **HOURVARI (FR)**, 5, b g My Risk (FR)—Ty Perrine (FR) **Mrs D. L. Whateley**
75 **HUNTERS CALL (IRE)**, 12, b g Medaaly—Accordiontogelica (IRE) **Holloway,Clarke,Black**
76 **I K BRUNEL**, 6, b g Midnight Legend—Somethinaboutmolly (IRE) **McNeill Family and Prodec Networks Ltd**
77 **ITALIAN SPIRIT (IRE)**, 6, b g Fame And Glory—Coco Milan (IRE) **Mrs J. A. Wakefield**
78 **ITCHY FEET (FR)**, 8, b g Cima de Triomphe—Maeva Candas (FR) **Kate & Andrew Brooks**
79 **JAMES FORT (IRE)**, 5, b g Fame And Glory—Well Clad (IRE) **Foxtrot Racing**
80 **JETAWAY JOEY (IRE)**, 7, b g Getaway (GER)—Present Your Own (IRE) **Ms B. J. Abt**
81 **JETT (IRE)**, 11, b g Flemensfirth (USA)—La Noire (IRE) **Mr R. B. Waley-Cohen**
82 **KEEPYOURDREAMSBIG (FR)**, 4, b g Vision d'Etat (FR)—Take This Waltz (FR) **Mr C. J. Haughey**
83 **KRAZY PAVING**, 10, b g Kyllachy—Critical Path (IRE) **All The Kings Horses & Mr Aiden Murphy**
84 **LAURA BULLION (IRE)**, 6, b m Canford Cliffs (IRE)—Vivachi (IRE) **Mrs J. A. Wakefield**
85 **LE BON VIVANT (FR)**, 4, ch g Doctor Dino (FR)—School of Thought (FR) **Mr A. L. Cohen**
86 **LEARNTALOT (IRE)**, 6, ch g Ask—Lady Alacoque (IRE) **Mr A. L. Cohen**
87 **LET'S HAVE ANOTHER (IRE)**, 6, b g Fame And Glory—Rocella Lago (IRE) **Harry Redknapp & Aiden Murphy**
88 **LINELEE KING (IRE)**, 7, gr g Martaline—Queen Lee (FR) **Mrs D. L. Whateley**
89 **LITTLE MISS DANTE**, 4, b f Kayf Tara—Whoops A Daisy **Ms B. J. Abt**
90 **LORD OF KERAK**, 7, b g Martaline—Mille Et Une (FR) **Mrs D. L. Whateley**
91 **LUCKELLO**, 6, b m Yorgunnabelucky (USA)—Timarello (IRE) **Skylark Racing**
92 **LUPUS REGEM**, 6, b g Iffraaj—Miss Villefranche **Mrs D. L. Whateley**
93 **MACHO MOVER (IRE)**, 7, b g Camacho—Fanciful Dancer **Jacques Law P'ship & M Lyons**
94 **MACKELDUFF (FR)**, 6, gr g Martaline—Evitta (FR) **Tommy Elphick & Mary Shalvey**
95 **MADE FOR YOU**, 7, b g Cape Cross (IRE)—Edallora (IRE) **H. A. Murphy**
96 **MAKTHECAT (FR)**, 6, b g Makfi—Troiecat (FR) **geegeez.co.uk OM**
97 **MASADA KNIGHT (IRE)**, 6, b g Fame And Glory—Rematch (IRE) **Mrs D. L. Whateley**
98 **MEXICAN BOY (IRE)**, 6, gr g Kayf Tara—J'Y Viens (FR) **The Four Timers**
99 **MINI CREST (IRE)**, 7, b m Flemensfirth (USA)—Cooper's Crest (IRE) **Non League Racing & Partner**
100 **MONEYKENNY**, 4, gr ro g Kendargent (FR)—Divine Touch **Deva Racing Moneykenny**
101 **MOORE MARGAUX (IRE)**, 7, b g Flemensfirth (USA)—Omas Glen (IRE) **Graeme Moore, Kate & Andrew Brooks**
102 **NICKOLSON (FR)**, 8, b g No Risk At All (FR)—Incorrigible (FR) **Mr T. D. J. Syder**
103 **NO RISK DES FLOS (FR)**, 7, gr g No Risk At All (FR)—Marie Royale (FR) **Mrs D. L. Whateley**
104 **NOTRE PARI (IRE)**, 8, br g Jeremy (USA)—Glynn Approach (IRE) **Mr J. P. McManus**
105 **OUT THE GLEN (IRE)**, 9, b g Millenary—Dicera (IRE) **Sky's The Limit**
106 **OVERTHETOP (IRE)**, 8, br g Flemensfirth (USA)—Dawn Bid (IRE) **What the Elle**
107 **PARLIAMENT HILL**, 4, ch g Sir Percy—Fauran (IRE) **Mrs D. L. Whateley**
108 **PORT OF MARS (IRE)**, 8, b g Westerner—Sarahall (IRE) **Bective Stud**
109 **RACY LACEY (IRE)**, 4, b f No Nay Never (USA)—Lace (IRE) **The UTV Syndicate**
110 **RAMBO T (IRE)**, 5, b g Ocovango—Biddy's Boru (IRE) **MPB Contractors Limited**
111 **RAMMING SPEED (IRE)**, 5, b br g Califet (FR)—Omas Glen (IRE) **Graeme Moore, Kate & Andrew Brooks**
112 **RESTANDBETHANKFUL**, 6, br g Califet (FR)—Persian Forest **McNeill Family & Patrick&scott Bryceland**
113 **RIGHT TURN (IRE)**, 4, b g Kodiac—Miss Topsy Turvy (IRE) **Ladies In Racing**
114 **RIO SILVA**, 5, gr m Blue Bresil (FR)—A Cappella Lido (FR) **A. J. Wall**
115 **RIPPER ROO (FR)**, 7, gr g Smadoun (FR)—Sninfia (IRE) **Deva Racing Ripper Roo,Shalvey&Partners**

MR OLLY MURPHY - continued

116 **ROCK ON TOMMY**, 7, gr g Fair Mix (IRE)—Little Carmela **Premier Thoroughbred Racing Ltd**
117 **ROCK THE HOUSE (IRE)**, 7, b g Scorpion (IRE)—Holiday Time (IRE) **FGD Limited**
118 **SALLEY GARDENS (IRE)**, 6, b g Yeats (IRE)—Glenlogan (IRE) **Touchwood Racing**
119 **SAN FERMIN (IRE)**, 6, b g Sans Frontieres (IRE)—Taipans Girl (IRE) **Mr A. E. Peterson**
120 **SECRET TRIX**, 5, b g Kayf Tara—Box of Trix (IRE) **H. A. Murphy**
121 **SHOAL BAY (IRE)**, 9, b g Gold Well—Ring Hill **Mrs C. Skan**
122 **SMACKWATER JACK (IRE)**, 8, b g Flemensfirth (USA)—Malachy's Attic (IRE) **Par Four**
123 **SPORTY JIM (IRE)**, 5, ch g Flemensfirth (USA)—Ma Belle Amie **Mr Terry Warner & the McNeill Family**
124 **STORM OF LIGHT (IRE)**, 6, b g Fame And Glory—Blazing Moon (IRE) **Mrs D. L. Whateley**
125 **STRONG GLANCE**, 9, bl g Passing Glance—Strong Westerner (IRE) **Welfordgolf syndicate**
126 **SURE TOUCH**, 6, b g Yeats (IRE)—Liberthine (FR) **Mr R. B. Waley-Cohen**
127 **SWINGING LONDON (IRE)**, 4, b g Dark Angel (IRE)—Malka (FR) **A. Butler**
128 **TAMAR BRIDGE (IRE)**, 7, b g Jeremy (USA)—Mise En Place **McNeill Family and Prodec Networks Ltd**
129 **TEASE AND SEIZE (FR)**, 4, b g Motivator—Serenada (FR) **Stephen R Hodgkinson & Partner**
130 **THE WOLF (FR)**, 8, ch g Kapgarde (FR)—Ges (FR) **McNeill Family and Prodec Networks Ltd**
131 **THOMAS DARBY (IRE)**, 9, b g Beneficial—Silaoce (FR) **Mrs D. L. Whateley**
132 **THUNDER ROCK (IRE)**, 6, b g Shirocco (GER)—La Belle Sauvage **McNeill Family & Mr Ian Dale**
133 **TIGERBYTHETAIL (IRE)**, 6, b g Yeats (IRE)—Talktothetail (IRE) **Ms B. J. Abt**
134 **TINNAHALLA (IRE)**, 5, b g Starspangledbanner (AUS)—Bright Bank (IRE) **Mrs J. A. Wakefield**
135 **UKANTANGO (IRE)**, 5, ch g Ocovango—Molly Be **Mr A. E. Peterson**
136 **URBAN GRIT (IRE)**, 5, b g Cityscape—Lady Azamour (IRE) **TopSpeed Thoroughbreds**
137 **VALUPO (IRE)**, 6, b g Valirann (FR)—Sameaway (IRE) **Foxtrot NH Racing Partnership**
138 **VOCALISER (IRE)**, 10, b g Vocalised (USA)—Bring Back Matron (IRE) **The Songsters**
139 **VOKOLOHS (IRE)**, 6, ch g Sholokhov (IRE)—Quarry Thyne (IRE) **Mr O. J. Murphy**
140 **WALKONTHEWILDSIDE (FR)**, 6, b g Walk In The Park (IRE)—My Lady Link (FR)
Mrs Diana L. Whateley & Mr Aiden Murphy

141 **WASHINGTON**, 6, br g Westerner—Present Leader **Mr T. D. J. Syder**
142 **WEEBILL**, 10, b g Schiaparelli (GER)—Wee Dinns (IRE) **Mrs C. Skan**
143 **WHAT WILL BE (IRE)**, 6, b g Thewayyouare (USA)—Gali Gal (IRE) **The Dream Big Syndicate**
144 **WOLFSPEAR (IRE)**, 6, b g Fame And Glory—Espresso Lady (IRE) **Mrs D. L. Whateley**
145 **WORLD TRIP**, 7, b m Universal (IRE)—Maiden Voyage **Foxtrot Nh Racing Partnership & Partner**

Other Owners: Mr D. Abraham, All The Kings Horses, Mr N. W. Bailey, Mr S. T. Black, Boultbee Brooks Ltd, Miss E. Boultbee-Brooks, Briton International, Mr A. L. Brooks, Mrs K. L. Brooks, Mr P. Bryceland, Mrs S. Bryceland, Mr D. J. Burke, Mr A. Carr, Miss E. J. Clarke, Mr B. R. Cognet, Mr W. I. C. Dale, Deva Racing Eavesdropping, Deva Racing Ripper Roo, Mr T. Elphick, Mr N. Farrell, Mrs L. H. Field, Foxtrot NH Racing Partnership, B. H. Goldswain, Exors of the Late Mrs J. B. H. Goldswain, Mr J. R. Hales, Miss L. J. Hales, Mr P. Henchoz, Mr S. R. Hodgkinson, Mr J. R. Holloway, Mr D. Jacques, Jacques Law Partnership, Mr M. J. E. Lyons, Mr J. A. J. Martin, Mr L. Martin, McNeill Family Ltd, Mr G. Moore, Mr M. Muldoon, Mrs A. L. M. Murphy, H. A. Murphy, Mr O. J. Murphy, Non League Racing, Mr A. E. Peterson, Mr S. Powell, Premier Thoroughbred Racing Ltd, Prodec Networks Ltd, Mr H. Redknapp, Mr B. Reynolds, Ms M. Shalvey, Mr J. Sigler, Mr G. N. Spurway, Mr T. D. J. Syder, The Black Horse Hotel Bridgnorth, Mr R. Tongue, A. J. Wall, J. T. Warner, Mrs D. L. Whateley, Mrs M. G. Whittaker.

Assistant Trainer: Gerard Tumelty.

NH Jockey: Aidan Coleman, David England. **Conditional Jockey:** Fergus Gregory, Callum McKinnes, Lewis Stones.

Amateur Jockey: Mr James King, Mr Luke Scott.

---

389 MR PAT MURPHY, Hungerford

Postal: Glebe House, School Lane, East Garston, Hungerford, Berkshire, RG17 7HR
Contacts: PHONE 01488 648473
EMAIL patgmurphy13@gmail.com

1 **GALTEE MOUNTAIN (IRE)**, 7, br g Mountain High (IRE)—Kings Queen (IRE) **P. G. Murphy**
2 **MINELLA HUB (IRE)**, 7, b g Shirocco (GER)—Fedaia (IRE) **P. G. Murphy**
3 **NESSFIELD BLUE**, 8, b g Kayf Tara—Bella Medici **Murphy & Chantler**
4 **NEVERBEEN TO PARIS (IRE)**, 7, b g Champs Elysees—Island Paradise (IRE) **Mr P. M. Claydon**
5 **OHNODONTTAKEMEHOME (FR)**, 5, gr g Cima de Triomphe (IRE)—Koyotte d'Agrostis (FR)
Graeme Moore, Kate & Andrew Brooks

MR PAT MURPHY - continued

  6 **REALLYRADICAL (IRE)**, 9, b g Insatiable (IRE)—Glenogra Cailin (IRE) **Mrs B. I. Chantler**
  7 **TRUCKIN WITH PADDY (IRE)**, 7, b g Imperial Monarch (IRE)—Our Alma (IRE) **Adam Tucker & Chris Aubrey**
  8 **VIGNONI**, 4, b g Helmet (AUS)—Mondovi **P. G. Jacobs**

THREE-YEAR-OLDS
  9 **AMALFI GEM (IRE)**, b f Cotai Glory—Diamond Circle **The Limoncello's**

Other Owners: Mr C. Aubrey, Mr A. L. Brooks, Mrs K. L. Brooks, Mrs B. I. Chantler, Mr G. Moore, P. G. Murphy, Mr A. J. Tucker.

390	**MR BARRY MURTAGH, Carlisle**
	Postal: **Hurst Farm, Ivegill, Carlisle, Cumbria, CA4 0NL**
	Contacts: **PHONE** 017684 84649 **MOBILE** 07714 026741 **FAX** 017684 84744
	EMAIL suemurtagh7@gmail.com

  1 **BARABOY (IRE)**, 12, b g Barathea (IRE)—Irina (IRE) **A. R. White**
  2 **BORDER VICTOR**, 10, b g Beat All (USA)—Sambara (IRE) **Mrs A. Stamper**
  3 **CAPTAIN COURAGEOUS (IRE)**, 9, b g Canford Cliffs (IRE)—Annacloy Pearl (IRE) **Mrs S. A. Murtagh**
  4 **CURTANA**, 5, b m Saddler's Rock (IRE)—Lady Blade (IRE) **Mrs A. Stamper**
  5 **DERRACRIN**, 5, ch g Mustajeeb—Transvaal Sky **Mrs S. A. Murtagh**
  6 **ELIXER (IRE)**, 9, b g Oscar (IRE)—Sunny Native (IRE) **Hurst Farm Racing**
  7 **ELUSIVE RED (IRE)**, 8, b g Elusive Pimpernel (USA)—Spin In The Wind (IRE) **Mrs S. A. Murtagh**
  8 **GEYSER**, 6, b g Gale Force Ten—Popocatepetl (FR) **Mrs A. Stamper**
  9 **NAKADAM (FR)**, 12, b g Nickname (FR)—Cadoudame (FR) **Mrs S. A. Murtagh**
10 **RITA R (IRE)**, 4, b f Tagula (IRE)—Ashtaroute (USA) **A. R. White**
11 **SHE'S A GEM**, 5, b m Dapper—Tara Springs **Mrs A. Stamper**
12 **SORBONNE**, 6, ch g Cityscape—Sorcellerie **Mike Proudfoot & Sue Murtagh**

Assistant Trainer: S. A. Murtagh.

Conditional Jockey: Lorcan Murtagh. **Apprentice Jockey:** Connor Murtagh.

391	**DR JEREMY NAYLOR, Shrewton**
	Postal: **The Cleeve Stables, Elston, Shrewton, Salisbury, Wiltshire, SP3 4HL**
	Contacts: **PHONE** 01980 620804 **MOBILE** 07771 740126
	EMAIL info@jeremynaylor.com **WEBSITE** www.jeremynaylor.com

  1 **CROSSPOINT**, 9, b g Crosspeace (IRE)—Lile Na Casca (IRE) **Mrs C. Hobbs**
  2 **CROUCHING HARRY (IRE)**, 13, b g Tiger Hill (IRE)—Catwalk Dreamer (IRE) **Mrs S. P. Elphick**
  3 **FEARSOME FRED**, 13, b g Emperor Fountain—Ryewater Dream **Mrs S. P. Elphick**
  4 **SEERAJ**, 7, b g Fastnet Rock (AUS)—Star On High (USA) **Dr J. R. J. Naylor**

392	**MRS FIONA NEEDHAM, Thirsk**
	Postal: **Moor View, Knayton, Thirsk, Yorkshire, YO7 4AZ**
	Contacts: **PHONE** 07831 688625
	EMAIL fiona@catterickbridge.co.uk

  1 **DOUBLE COGNAC**, 7, b m Grape Tree Road—Chummy's Double **R. Tate**
  2 **SINE NOMINE**, 6, gr m Saint des Saints (FR)—Hymn To Love (FR) **R. Tate**
  3 **TEESCOMPONENTS BOY (IRE)**, 8, b g Midnight Legend—Northern Native (IRE) **R. Tate**

393 MRS HELEN NELMES, Dorchester
Postal: **Warmwell Stables, 2 Church Cottages, Warmwell, Dorchester, Dorset, DT2 8HQ**
Contacts: **PHONE 01305 852254 MOBILE 07977 510318**
EMAIL warmwellstud@tiscali.co.uk WEBSITE www.warmwellstables.co.uk

1 ITSABOUTIME (IRE), 12, gr g Whitmore's Conn (USA)—Blazing Love (IRE) **K. A. Nelmes**
2 KALMBEFORETHESTORM, 14, ch g Storming Home—Miss Honeypenny (IRE) **Warmwellcome Partnership**
3 LAOCH BEAG (IRE), 11, gr g King's Theatre (IRE)—Innocentines (FR) **Mr L. J. Burden**
4 MENAPIAN (IRE), 11, b br g Touch of Land (FR)—Mannequin (IRE) **T M W Partnership**
5 MERCHANT IN MILAN (IRE), 10, b g Milan—Azaban (IRE) **Mr L. J. Burden**
6 OVER THE RIVER, 6, b m Avonbridge—First Among Equals **Mr J. R. Dyer**
7 SERVEONTIME (IRE), 11, b g Echo of Light—Little Lovely (IRE) **K. A. Nelmes**
8 UNIVERSAL SECRET (IRE), 5, ch g Universal (IRE)—Quiet Beauty **Mr M. J. Hoskins**
9 WELLWILLYA, 4, gr grg g Universal (IRE)—Mons Meg **Mr L. J. Burden**

Assistant Trainer: K. Nelmes.

Conditional Jockey: Conor Ring.

394 MR TONY NEWCOMBE, Barnstaple
Postal: **Lower Delworthy, Yarnscombe, Barnstaple, Devon, EX31 3LT**
Contacts: **PHONE 01271 858554 MOBILE 07785 297210**
EMAIL huntshawequineforest@talktalk.net

1 AMAZON PRINCESS, 5, b m War Command (USA)—Last Lahar **Joli Racing**
2 BUG BOY (IRE), 6, b g Big Bad Bob (IRE)—Velvetina (IRE) **Dr S. P. Hargreaves**
3 IN PARADISE, 4, ch f Twilight Son—Resort **Joli Racing**
4 JOLI'S LEGACY (IRE), 4, b f Elzaam (AUS)—Joli Elegant (IRE) **Joli Racing**
5 JOYFUL SONG (IRE), 5, b m Teofilo (IRE)—Good Friend (IRE) **A. G. Newcombe**
6 KNOW NO LIMITS (IRE), 5, b m Outstrip—Singing Field (IRE) **A. G. Newcombe**
7 LIIMARI, 9, b m Authorized (IRE)—Snow Polina (USA) **A. G. Newcombe**
8 LIPPY LADY (IRE), 6, b m Bungle Inthejungle—Sayrah **A. G. Newcombe**
9 ROSE WHISPER, 5, gr m Dark Angel (IRE)—Warshah (IRE) **A. G. Newcombe**
10 SOVEREIGN STATE, 7, b g Compton Place—One Night In May (IRE) **R. Eagle**

THREE-YEAR-OLDS

11 TARKA COUNTRY, gr c Outstrip—Turaathy (IRE) **A. G. Newcombe**

Assistant Trainer: John Lovejoy.

395 DR RICHARD NEWLAND, Droitwich
Postal: **Urloxhey Farm, Elmbridge lane, Droitwich, Worcestershire, WR9 0NQ**
Contacts: **MOBILE 07956 196535**
EMAIL richard.newland1@btopenworld.com

1 ARISTOCRATE (FR), 5, b h Elusive City (USA)—Mitzi Blue (IRE) **Vfg Partnership**
2 ART OF DIPLOMACY, 6, b g Archipenko (USA)—Rowlestone Express **Three Pears Racing**
3 ASTROMACHIA, 7, b g Sea The Stars (IRE)—Fontley **Dr R. D. P. Newland**
4 BAASEM (USA), 6, ch g New Approach (IRE)—Ausus (USA) **Mr C. E. Stedman**
5 BALI BODY, 7, b g Doyen (IRE)—Burnt Oil Babe (IRE) **Foxtrot Racing Bali Body**
6 BBOLD (IRE), 8, b g Aizavoski (IRE)—Molly Be **BAA Management Ltd**
7 BENSON, 7, b g Beat Hollow—Karla June **Pump & Plant Services Ltd**
8 BOLINTLEA (IRE), 7, b m Le Fou (IRE)—Lady Boulea (IRE) **Foxtrot Racing Bolintlea**
9 CALL THE FAIRIES (IRE), 7, b m Westerner—Knockowen (IRE) **Mr C. N. Nightingale**
10 CAPTAIN BLACKPEARL, 8, ch g Black Sam Bellamy (IRE)—Bonne Anniversaire
                                                      R Foden T Keelan J Moynihan I Woodward
11 CAPTAIN COBAJAY (IRE), 9, b g Captain Rio—Brandam Supreme (IRE) **Mr J. P. G. Landy**

DR RICHARD NEWLAND - continued

12 **DASHING PERK**, 11, b g Kayf Tara—Dashing Executive (IRE) **Mr P. Jenkins**
13 **DAVITT ROAD GLORY (IRE)**, 7, b m Fame And Glory—Ballydunne Present (IRE) **P Jenkins & Partner**
14 **DREAMWEAVER (IRE)**, 6, b g Mastercraftsman (IRE)—Livia's Dream (IRE) **The Leicester Lads**
15 **DYNAMITE KENTUCKY (FR)**, 7, ch g Kentucky Dynamite (USA)—Madonna Incognito (USA)
                             Off The Clock Partners & Dr RDP Newland
16 **ENQARDE (FR)**, 8, b g Kapgarde (FR)—Usachaqa (FR) **Off The Clock Partners & Dr RDP Newland**
17 **FEIVEL (IRE)**, 7, b br g Le Fou (IRE)—Much Appreciated (IRE) **The Boondogglers**
18 **FIRST SOLDIER (FR)**, 6, ch g Soldier of Fortune (IRE)—First Choice (IRE) **Mr C. E. Stedman**
19 **FOILLAN (IRE)**, 7, b g Le Fou (IRE)—Castlevennon (IRE) **Hold My Beer Syndicate**
20 **FORTYFIVE WEST (IRE)**, 7, b g Le Fou (IRE)—Lucky Sorceress (IRE) **Foxtrot Racing Fortyfive West**
21 **FULGURIX (FR)**, 7, b g Maresca Sorrento (FR)—Union de Sevres (FR) **The The Tenovus Partnership**
22 **GALATA BRIDGE**, 5, b g Golden Horn—Infallible **Dr R. D. P. Newland**
23 **GAME SOCKS (IRE)**, 6, ch g Leading Light (IRE)—Late Night Deed **Chris Stedman & Mark Albon**
24 **GOSPELUS (FR)**, 6, b g Rail Link—Precieuze (FR) **The Choirboys**
25 **HERON CREEK (IRE)**, 5, b g Leading Light (IRE)—Campanella (GER) **M Albon & M P Tudor**
26 **HIGH TECH (FR)**, 5, b g Intello (GER)—Highborne (FR) **Mr P. C. W. Green**
27 **HYPNOTIK (FR)**, 5, b g Cokoriko (FR)—Advantime (FR)
28 **I'M SO BUSY**, 7, gr g Carlotamix (FR)—Ballcrina Girl (IRE) **Foxtrot Racing I'm So Busy**
29 **INDIGO LAKE**, 5, b g Frankel—Responsible **Imperium Syndicate**
30 **JESUITIQUE (FR)**, 7, b g Saint des Saints (FR)—Jaune de Beaufai (FR) **The Three Amigos**
31 **KATPOLI (FR)**, 7, b g Poliglote (FR)—Katkogarie (FR) **Mr C. E. Stedman**
32 **KING ARISE (IRE)**, 5, gr g Kingston Hill—Aries Ballerina (IRE) **Foxtrot Racing King Arise**
33 **LA RENOMMEE (FR)**, 4, b f Doctor Dino (FR)—Grande Cavale (FR) **Mrs L. J. Newland**
34 **LE PATRIOTE (FR)**, 10, b g Poliglote—Sentosa (FR) **Canard Vert Racing Club**
35 **LET ME BE (IRE)**, 6, b g Gale Force Ten—Peryzat (IRE) **Mr P. Drinkwater**
36 **MASON JAR (FR)**, 8, ch g No Risk At All (FR)—Queen's Theatre (FR) **Foxtrot Racing Mason Jar**
37 **MINELLA ENCORE (IRE)**, 10, b g King's Theatre (IRE)—Stashedaway (IRE) **Foxtrot Racing Minella Encore**
38 **MOTION IN LIMINE (IRE)**, 7, b g Court Cave (IRE)—My Memory (IRE) **Mr J. H. Graham**
39 **MR HAILSTONE (IRE)**, 6, b g Sageburg (IRE)—Gaye Steel (IRE) **Formulated Polymer Products Ltd**
40 **MR MULDOON (IRE)**, 9, ch g Rajj (IRE)—Miss Muldoon (IRE) **Foxtrot Racing Mr Muldoon**
41 **MR WOODY (IRE)**, 8, b g Shantou (USA)—She's On The Case (IRE) **Mr A. B. Leyshon**
42 **OLYMPIC CONQUEROR (IRE)**, 6, b g Olympic Glory (IRE)—Queen's Conquer **Mr T. A. Lee**
43 **ON THE WILD SIDE (IRE)**, 9, b g Robin des Champs (FR)—Clear Riposte (IRE) **M Albon & M P Tudor**
44 **ORCHESTRAL RAIN (IRE)**, 5, b g Born To Sea (IRE)—Musical Rain (IRE) **Mark Albon & Chris Stedman**
45 **PURPLE KING (IRE)**, 8, ch g Lope de Vega (IRE)—Dixie Dance (IRE) **Foxtrot Racing Purple King**
46 **REBEL LEADER (IRE)**, 8, b g Milan—Chicharito's Gem (IRE) **Celtic New Bees**
47 **RETROSPECT (IRE)**, 5, b g Frankel—Looking Back (IRE)
48 **REWIRED**, 4, ch g Power—Kekova **Opulence Thoroughbreds NH**
49 **RIKOBOY (FR)**, 5, b g Enrique—Dikanika (FR) **Mr D. J. Smith**
50 **ROSE SEA HAS (FR)**, 7, gr g Kapgarde (FR)—Vaibuscar Has (FR) **The Berrow Hill Partnership**
51 **ROSTELLO (FR)**, 7, ch g Fuisse (FR)—Rose d'Ete (FR) **Dr R. D. P. Newland**
52 **SAGE ADVICE (IRE)**, 5, b g Make Believe—Purple Sage (IRE) **Imperium Syndicate**
53 **SAQUON (IRE)**, 6, b g Arcadio (GER)—Seana Ghael (IRE) **Foxtrot Racing Saquon**
54 **SEINESATIONAL**, 7, b g Champs Elysees—Kibara **Mr C. E. Stedman**
55 **SHUIL DONN (IRE)**, 8, b g Arctic Cosmos (USA)—Shuil Dubh (IRE) **Mrs D. W. Davenport**
56 **SINGASONGSAM**, 5, b g Black Sam Bellamy (IRE)—Vin Rose **Mr P. Drinkwater**
57 **SIR CANFORD (IRE)**, 6, b g Canford Cliffs (IRE)—Alexander Divine
58 **SOUTH TERRACE (IRE)**, 7, b g Fame And Glory—Supreme Sales (IRE) **South Terrace Partnership**
59 **SUMMER MOON**, 6, ch g Sea The Moon (GER)—Songerie **Dr R. D. P. Newland**
60 **TANGO ECHO CHARLIE (IRE)**, 8, b g Stowaway—Wining N Okanagan (IRE) **Briton International & Partner**
61 **TASTE THE FEAR (IRE)**, 7, b g Mores Wells—No Complaints But (IRE) **In It For Fun Partnership & Dr R Newland**
62 **TCHOUPINMINZAC (FR)**, 5, b g Falco (USA)—Ninive (FR) **Marie's Dream Team**
63 **THE TEXAN (FR)**, 6, ch g Ocovango—Buzy Lizzie (IRE) **Murcotts Ltd**
64 **THIRTYFOURSTITCHES (IRE)**, 7, b g Fairly Ransom (USA)—Blue Berlais (IRE) **Doom Bar Beach Club**
65 **TIGER ORCHID (IRE)**, 7, b g Mores Wells—Akarita (IRE) **Foxtrot Racing The Red Caps**
66 **TIP TOP TONTO (IRE)**, 6, b g Milan—Sarahs Quay (IRE)
67 **WHATSDASTORY (IRE)**, 9, b m Beneficial—Supreme Contender (IRE) **Plan B**
68 **WHIZZ KID (GER)**, 6, ch g Teofilo (IRE)—Wurfspiel (FR) **Foxtrot Racing Whizz Kid**
69 **WHOSHOTWHO (IRE)**, 11, br g Beneficial—Inishbeg House (IRE) **Foxtrot Racing Whoshotwho & Partner**
70 **WICKED WEST (IRE)**, 6, b g Westerner—Wilde Sapphire (IRE) **Mr M. P. Tudor**

DR RICHARD NEWLAND - continued

71 **WIGGLESWORTH (IRE)**, 7, b g Doyen (IRE)—Arctic Aunt (IRE) **Rioja Raiders 04**
72 **WILL VICTORY (FR)**, 6, br m Willywell (FR)—Gesa Mixa (FR) **David's Partnership**
73 **YCCS PORTOCERVO (FR)**, 7, gr g Martaline—Griva (FR) **Mrs M C Litton&mrs F D McInnes Skinner**

Other Owners: Mr D. Abraham, Mrs J. Abraham, Mr M. L. Albon, Mr M. P. Ansell, Mr L. A. Bolingbroke, Briton International, Mr N. A. Clark, Mr A. M. Clarke, Mr A. S. P. Drake, Mr J. M. O. Evans, Foxtrot Racing Management Ltd, **Foxtrot Racing:** Whoshotwho, Mr A. S. A. Garden, Mr J. M. Gibbs, B. H. Goldswain, Exors of the Late Mrs J. B. H. Goldswain, Mr P. C. W. Green, Mr R. Gudge, Hold My Beer Syndicate, Mr T. Hughes, In It For Fun, Mr P. Jenkins, Mrs P. J. Litton, Mr J. Lloyd-Townshend, Mr J. D. Mayo, Mrs F. D. McInnes Skinner, Dr R. D. P. Newland, C. G. Nicholl, Mr C. Obank, Off The Clock Partners, Mr A. J. Ramsden, Spur of the Moment, Mr C. E. Stedman, Mr M. P. Tudor, Mrs M. Twomey.

Assistant Trainer: Rod Trow.

NH Jockey: Charlie Hammond. **Conditional Jockey:** Cillin Leonard.

---

396 MISS ANNA NEWTON-SMITH, Jevington
Postal: **Bull Pen Cottage, Jevington, Polegate, East Sussex, BN26 5QB**
Contacts: PHONE **01323 488354** MOBILE **07970 914124**
EMAIL **annanewtonsmith@gmail.com** WEBSITE **www.annanewtonsmith.co.uk**

1 **DASHING SPIRIT (IRE)**, 5, b g Sir Prancealot (IRE)—Gwyllion (USA) **The Hamptons Racing Partnership**
2 **FORGOT ONE (IRE)**, 7, b g Le Fou (IRE)—Ready For Ballett (IRE) **The Hamptons Racing Partnership**
3 **MIS CASEY (IRE)**, 6, b m Sageburg (IRE)—The Real Casey (IRE) **The Hamptons Racing Partnership**
4 **SHIROCCO'S DELIGHT (IRE)**, 5, ch g Shirocco (GER)—Far Rock (IRE) **The Beano Partnership**

Other Owners: Mr I. S. Berger, Mr M. J. Dolan, Mr S. K. Dolan, Mr N. Lambert.

Assistant Trainer: Nicola Worley.

---

397 MR ADRIAN NICHOLLS, Sessay
Postal: **The Ranch, Sessay, Thirsk, North Yorkshire, YO7 3ND**
Contacts: PHONE **01845 597428**

1 **ABATE**, 6, br g Bated Breath—Red Kyte **The Never Say No Racing Club**
2 **BURJ MALINKA (IRE)**, 4, ch g Pride of Dubai (AUS)—Malinka (IRE) **Dubelem (Racing) Limited**
3 **LLEYTON (IRE)**, 10, b br g Kalanisi (IRE)—Bonnie Parker (IRE) **& Southerington**
4 **MO CELITA (IRE)**, 4, b f Camacho—Asterism **Mr David Howden & Mr David Redvers**
5 **TEES SPIRIT**, 4, br g Swiss Spirit—Mistress Twister **Ingleby Bloodstock Ltd & The Ivy League**
6 **THE BIG HOUSE (IRE)**, 6, b g Coach House (IRE)—Tekhania (IRE) **Mr A. Nicholls**
7 **THORNABY PEARL**, 4, b g Pearl Secret—Juncea **Ingleby Bloodstock Limited**
8 **TWICE ADAAY**, 4, b f Adaay (IRE)—Amber Heights **Mr A. Nicholls**

THREE-YEAR-OLDS

9 **BUILD ME UP (IRE)**, ch f Speightstown (USA)—Moon River (IRE) **Mr D. P. Howden**
10 **CAPALL MEAR (IRE)**, b f Zoffany (IRE)—Jowana (IRE) **Mr A. Nicholls**
11 **DRILL TO DREAM**, b f Australia—Mascarene (USA) **Mr D. Hazelwood**
12 **HIPPO (IRE)**, gr f Gutaifan (IRE)—Fairy Cloak (IRE) **Mr A. Nicholls**
13 **HOT FLUSH (IRE)**, b f Siyouni (FR)—Cheering (USA) **Mr A. Nicholls**
14 **HURT YOU NEVER (IRE)**, b f Dandy Man (IRE)—Kyllarney **Mr D. Stone**
15 **NEPALESIAN (IRE)**, ch g The Gurkha (IRE)—Way of Light (IRE) **Middleham Park Racing XV**
16 **NEVER NO TROUBLE**, b f Time Test—Kitba **Mr A. N. Brooke Rankin**

MR ADRIAN NICHOLLS - continued

17 **NO GUTS NO GLORY (IRE)**, b br f Cotai Glory—Rublevka Star (USA) **Middleham Park Racing XLIX**
18 **PEPPER STREAK (IRE)**, b f Hot Streak (IRE)—Rohesia **Roscourt**
19 **POETIKEL PIECE**, b f Mayson—Nardin **Mr A. Nicholls**
20 **RIBTIDE**, b g Ribchester (IRE)—Tarando **Mr A. Nicholls**

Other Owners: Mr P. I. Baker, Mr M. Dunn, Mr G. C. J. Haffenden, Mr J. Hilden, Mr C. M. Hills, Mr D. P. Howden, Ingleby Bloodstock Limited, Mr D. Redvers, Ms C. Southerington, Mrs P. Southerington, The Ivy League.

398

MR PAUL NICHOLLS, Ditcheat
Postal: **Manor Farm Stables, Ditcheat, Shepton Mallet, Somerset, BA4 6RD**
Contacts: **PHONE 01749 860656 MOBILE 07977 270706**
EMAIL info@paulnichollsracing.com WEBSITE www.paulnichollsracing.com

1 **ACCOMPLICE (FR)**, 8, gr g Network (GER)—Miss Vitoria (FR) **Mrs Kathy Stuart**
2 **ADRIEN DU PONT (FR)**, 10, b g Califet (FR)—Santariyka (FR) **Mrs Johnny De La Hey**
3 **ALCALA (FR)**, 12, gr g Turgeon (USA)—Pail Mel (FR) **Owners Group 016**
4 **ALL DANCER (FR)**, 5, ch g No Risk At All (FR)—Maia Dancer (FR) **Kate & Andrew Brooks**
5 **AMENON (FR)**, 7, b g Saint des Saints (FR)—La Couetrie (FR) **Mr & Mrs J. D. Cotton**
6 **AMOUR DE NUIT (IRE)**, 10, b g Azamour (IRE)—Umthoulah (IRE) **Mr Andrew Williams**
7 **ASK FOR GLORY (IRE)**, 8, b g Fame And Glory—Ask Helen (IRE) **Mr Colm Donlon & Mr & Mrs P. K. Barber**
8 **ATHOLL STREET (IRE)**, 7, b g Jeremy (USA)—Allthewhile (IRE) **Exors of the Late Mr T. J. Hemmings**
9 **BARBADOS BUCK'S (IRE)**, 7, b g Getaway (GER)—Buck's Blue (FR) **The Stewart Family**
10 **BATHSHEBA BAY (IRE)**, 7, br g Footstepsinthesand—Valamareha (IRE) **Mr M. F. Geoghegan**
11 **BELL EX ONE (IRE)**, 4, b g Excelebration (IRE)—Bonnie Bluebell (IRE) **Mr Alexander McGregor**
12 4, B g Soldier of Fortune (IRE)—Bell Walks Day (IRE) **Gordon & Su Hall**
13 **BIRDS OF PREY (IRE)**, 8, b g Sir Prancealot (IRE)—Cute **Mrs Kathy Stuart**
14 **BOB AND CO (FR)**, 11, b g Dom Alco (FR)—Outre Mer (FR) **D. Maxwell**
15 **BRAVE KINGDOM (FR)**, 6, b g Brave Mansonnien (FR)—New Foundation (IRE)
                                                    Graeme Moore, Kate & Andrew Brooks
16 **BRAVEMANSGAME (FR)**, 7, b g Brave Mansonnien (FR)—Genifique (FR) **John Dance & Bryan Drew**
17 **BREWERS PROJECT (IRE)**, 8, b g Aizavoski (IRE)—Shaylee Wilde (IRE) **The Hon Mrs C. A. Townshend**
18 **BROKEN HALO**, 7, b g Kayf Tara—Miss Invincible **Giraffa Racing - BH**
19 **CALVA D'AUGE (FR)**, 7, b g Air Chief Marshal (IRE)—Hill Ou Elle (FR) **Owners Group 040**
20 **CAMMY BEAR (IRE)**, 5, b g Norse Dancer (IRE)—Alegralil **Stuart & Shelly Parkin**
21 **CAP DU MATHAN (FR)**, 7, b g Kapgarde (FR)—Nounjya du Mathan (FR) **The Stewart Family**
22 **CAPTAIN DESTINY**, 5, b g Kapgarde (FR)—New Destiny (FR) **Diana Whateley & Dominic Burke**
23 **CARRY ON THE MAGIC (IRE)**, 8, b br g Jeremy (USA)—Bisoguet (FR) **Highclere Thoroughbred Racing - Magic**
24 **CAT TIGER (FR)**, 8, b g Diamond Boy (FR)—Miss Canon (FR) **D. Maxwell**
25 **CHAVEZ (IRE)**, 6, b g Yeats (IRE)—Rock The Baby (IRE) **M. C. Denmark**
26 **CLAN DES OBEAUX (FR)**, 10, b g Kapgarde (FR)—Nausicaa des Obeaux (FR)
                                                    Mr & Mrs P.K.Barber, G.Mason, Sir A Ferguson
27 **COMPLETE UNKNOWN (IRE)**, 6, b g Dylan Thomas (IRE)—Silver Stream (IRE) **Mr C. K. Ong & Mr I. Warwick**
28 **CONFIRMATION BIAS (IRE)**, 7, b g Presenting—Bonnie Parker (IRE) **Mr Colm Donlon**
29 **COUNTRY LADY**, 4, b f Kapgarde (FR)—Miss Country (FR) **The Brooks Family & P.J. Vogt**
30 **CUT THE MUSTARD (FR)**, 10, br m Al Namix (FR)—Tadorna (FR) **The Unlikely Lads**
31 **CYRNAME (FR)**, 10, b g Nickname (FR)—Narquille (FR) **Mrs Johnny De La Hey**
32 **DANCINGONTHEEDGE (FR)**, 5, b m Kapgarde (FR)—Solarize (FR) **Old Gold Racing 4**
33 **DANNY KIRWAN (IRE)**, 9, b g Scorpion (IRE)—Sainte Baronne (FR) **Mrs Johnny De La Hey**
34 **DARGIANNINI (FR)**, 7, b g Fame And Glory—You Take Care (IRE) **Dominic Burke & Kate & Andrew Brooks**
35 5, Br g Sageburg (IRE)—Davids Delight (IRE) **M. C. Denmark**
36 **DIEGO DU CHARMIL (FR)**, 10, b g Ballingarry (IRE)—Daramour (FR) **Mrs Johnny De La Hey**
37 **DOLOS (FR)**, 9, b g Kapgarde (FR)—Redowa (FR) **Mrs Johnny De La Hey**
38 **DON ALVARO (FR)**, 6, b g Muhtathir—New Destiny (FR) **Diana Whateley & Dominic Burke**
39 **DUC DE BOURBON (FR)**, 6, b g Buck's Boum (FR)—Astre Eria (FR) **Mr J. P. McManus**
40 **ECCO (FR)**, 7, b g Maxios—Enjoy The Life **Mr Colm Donlon**

MR PAUL NICHOLLS - continued

41 EGLANTINE DU SEUIL (FR), 8, b m Saddler Maker (IRE)—Rixia du Seuil (FR) **The Unlikely Lads**
42 ENRILO (FR), 8, bl g Buck's Boum (FR)—Rock Treasure (FR) **Martin Broughton & Friends 4**
43 4, B g Mount Nelson—Eoz (IRE) **The Stewart Family**
44 ERITAGE (FR), 8, b g Martaline—Sauves La Reine (FR) **Mrs A. Tincknell**
45 FAME AND FUN (IRE), 5, b g Fame And Glory—Tabachines (FR) **Mrs J. Hitchings**
46 FIRE FLYER (IRE), 4, b g Shantou (USA)—Eva La Diva (IRE) **Mr M. F. Geoghegan**
47 FLASH COLLONGES (FR), 7, b g Saddler Maker (IRE)—Prouesse Collonges (FR) **The Gi Gi Syndicate**
48 FLEMENSTIDE (IRE), 7, b g Flemensfirth (USA)—Keep Face (FR) **Mr P K Barber & Mr P J Vogt**
49 FLIC OU VOYOU (FR), 8, b g Kapgarde (FR)—Hillflower (FR) **Mr Colm Donlon**
50 FRIEND OR FOE (FR), 7, b g Walk In The Park (IRE)—Mandchou (FR) **Gordon & Su Hall**
51 FRODON (FR), 10, b g Nickname (FR)—Miss Country (FR) **Mr P. J. Vogt**
52 FROSTY LADY (FR), 5, gr m Silver Frost (IRE)—Beautiful Gem (FR) **Mr & Mrs J. D. Cotton**
53 GAME WINNER (FR), 6, br g Diamond Boy (FR)—Quelle Eria (FR) **Mr Noel Fehily**
54 GAULOIS (FR), 6, b g Samum (GER)—Pail Mel (FR) **Owners Group 085**
55 4, B g Kayf Tara—Gaye Sophie **The Stewart Family, Mr P. J. Vogt**
56 GELINO BELLO (FR), 6, b g Saint des Saints (FR)—Parade (FR) **Mr & Mrs J. D. Cotton**
57 GET THE APPEAL (IRE), 8, b m Getaway (GER)—Lady Appeal (IRE) **Middleham Park Racing IX**
58 GETAWAY TRUMP (IRE), 9, b g Getaway (GER)—Acinorev (IRE) **Owners Group 023**
59 GLAJOU (FR), 6, b g Network (GER)—Toscane (FR) **Middleham Park Racing XLVVIII & Peter Lamb**
60 GOLD BULLION (FR), 6, b g Fame And Glory—Tornade d'Ainay (FR) **M. C. Denmark**
61 GRACE A VOUS ENKI (FR), 6, b g Dream Well (FR)—Cadiane (FR) **Mrs J. Hitchings**
62 GRAND SANCY (FR), 8, b g Diamond Boy (FR)—La Courtille (FR) **Martin Broughton Racing Partners**
63 GRANGE ROAD (IRE), 7, b g Oscar (IRE)—Niamh's Away (IRE) **Deva Racing Grange Road**
64 GREANETEEN (FR), 8, b g Great Pretender (IRE)—Manson Teene (FR) **Mr Chris Giles**
65 GRIVETANA (FR), 4, ch f No Risk At All (FR)—Stourza (FR) **Mr D. J. Burke, Mr Tim Syder**
66 HACKER DES PLACES (FR), 5, b g Great Pretender (IRE)—Plaisance (FR) **Owners Group 068**
67 HALF DOZEN (IRE), 5, b g Sageburg (IRE)—Sixofone (IRE) **John & Jessica Dance**
68 HALO DES OBEAUX (FR), 5, gr g Al Namix (FR)—Almeria des Obeaux (FR) **Mr P. J. Vogt**
69 HARD FROST (FR), 5, b g Silver Frost (IRE)—Lottie Belle (FR) **Mr & Mrs J. D. Cotton**
70 HASHTAG BOUM (FR), 5, b m Al Namix (FR)—Engagee (FR) **Mr Colm Donlon**
71 HELL RED (FR), 5, gr g Martaline—Queen Margot (FR) **Sir Martin Broughton & Friends 6**
72 HENRI THE SECOND (FR), 5, b g Saddler Maker (IRE)—Rock Treasure (FR) **Martin Broughton & Friends 7**
73 HERMES ALLEN (FR), 5, b g Poliglote—Une Destine (FR)
              G. A. Mason, Sir A. Ferguson, Mr J. R. Hales, Mr J. Diver
74 HIGHLAND HUNTER (IRE), 9, gr g Subtle Power (IRE)—Loughine Sparkle (IRE) **T. Barr**
75 HITMAN (FR), 6, b g Falco (USA)—Tercah Girl (FR) **Mason, Hogarth, Ferguson & Done**
76 HOLETOWN HERO (FR), 5, br g Buck's Boum (FR)—Voix du Coeur (FR) **Mr M. F. Geoghegan**
77 HUELGOAT (FR), 5, b g Voiladenuo (FR)—Cavadee (FR) **Owners Group 080**
78 HUFLOWER (FR), 5, b g Saddex—Send Me Flower (FR) **Mr Chris Giles**
79 HUGOS NEW HORSE (FR), 5, b g Coastal Path—Pour Le Meilleur (FR) **The Stewart Family**
80 HUGOS OTHER HORSE, 8, b g Gold Well—Wicked Crack (IRE) **The Stewart Family**
81 HURRICANE DANNY (FR), 4, ch g No Risk At All (FR)—Tornade d'Ainay (FR) **Martin Broughton & Friends 2**
82 ICEO (FR), 4, b g Coastal Path—Rocroi (FR) **Mr Chris Giles**
83 IFAILALOI (FR), 4, b g Jeu St Eloi (FR)—Vared (FR) **McNeill Family Ltd**
84 IL RIDOTO (FR), 5, b g Kapgarde (FR)—L'Exploratrice (FR) **Giles, Hogarth, Mason & McGoff**
85 IMPREVU DU LARGE (FR), 4, b g Kapgarde (FR)—Emy Chope (FR) **D. G. Staddon**
86 INCA DE LAFAYETTE (FR), 4, gr g Gris de Gris (IRE)—Queen de Lafayette (FR) **Owners Group 100**
87 INDIVIDUALISTE (FR), 4, ro g Cima de Triomphe (IRE)—Intellingencia (FR) **Elite Owners Ireland**
88 IRISH HILL (GER), 4, gr g Kingston Hill—Irresistable (GER) **Sir Martin Broughton & Friends 8**
89 ISAAC DES OBEAUX (FR), 4, b g Kapgarde (FR)—Varda des Obeaux (FR)
              G Mason, Sir A Ferguson, Mr&Mrs P K Barber
90 JEREMY PASS (IRE), 7, b g Jeremy (USA)—Toulon Pass (IRE) **John & Jessica Dance**
91 KANDOO KID (FR), 6, gr g Kapgarde (FR)—Scarlett du Mesnil (IRE) **Mr M. F. Geoghegan**
92 KAPCORSE (FR), 9, br g Kapgarde (FR)—Angesse (FR) **Mr J. P. McManus**
93 KAYF TAOI, 6, b g Kayf Tara—Patsie Magern **Mr Colm Donlon**
94 KICK UP A STORM (IRE), 4, b g Shantou (USA)—Erins Stage (IRE) **Mrs C. H. Moger**
95 KILLALOAN (IRE), 4, b g Fastnet Rock (AUS)—Farranjordan **Owners Group 093**
96 KILMINGTON ROSE (IRE), 7, ch m Presenting—Robyn's Rose (IRE) **Mr Charles Pelham & Mr Henry Pelham**
97 KNAPPERS HILL (IRE), 6, b g Valirann (FR)—Brogella (IRE) **Mr P K Barber & Mr P J Vogt**

MR PAUL NICHOLLS - continued

98 **KNOWSLEY ROAD (IRE)**, 5, b g Flemensfirth (USA)—Rowanville Lady (IRE)

Mr Charles Pelham & Mr Henry Pelham

99 **KRUGER PARK (FR)**, 4, ch g Kapgarde (FR)—Fleur De Sel De Re (FR) **Mr B. J. McManus, Mr D. J. Coles**

100 **LE CHIFFRE D'OR (FR)**, b g Montmartre (FR)—Lady Denisa **Mr Chris Giles**

101 **LALLYGAG (GER)**, 5, b g It's Gino (GER)—Laviola (GER) **D. G. Staddon**

102 **LALOR (GER)**, 10, b g It's Gino (GER)—Laviola (GER) **D. G. Staddon**

103 **LARCHMONT LASS (IRE)**, 4, b f Walk In The Park (IRE)—Tocororo (IRE) **Mr M. F. Geoghegan**

104 **LARGY TRAIN**, 5, b g Yorgunnabelucky (USA)—Snow Train **Million in Mind Partnership**

105 **LE CHIFFRE D'OR (FR)**, 6, gr g No Risk At All (FR)—Miss Vitoria (FR) **Gordon & Su Hall**

106 4, B g Mount Nelson—Letherbelucky (IRE) **McNeill Family & Mr G Mason**

107 **MAGIC SAINT (FR)**, 8, b g Saint des Saints (FR)—Magic Poline (FR) **Mr & Mrs J. D. Cotton**

108 **MAGISTRATO (FR)**, 4, b g Kapgarde (FR)—Franche Alliance (FR) **Mrs Johnny De La Hey**

109 **MAKIN'YOURMINDUP**, 5, b g Kayf Tara—Subtilty **Owners Group 090**

110 **MANORBANK (IRE)**, 7, b g Arcadio (GER)—Kind Word (IRE) **Owners Group 065**

111 6, B g Blue Bresil (FR)—Maralypha (FR) **The Stewart Family**

112 **MARVELLOUS MICK**, 4, b g Blue Bresil (FR)—Mickie **Mr M. F. Geoghegan**

113 **MATTERHORN (FR)**, 4, b g Martaline—Sacarine (FR) **Mrs Johnny De La Hey**

114 **MCFABULOUS (IRE)**, 8, b g Milan—Rossavon (IRE) **Giraffa Racing**

115 **MICK PASTOR (FR)**, 6, b g Meshaheer (USA)—Mick Oceane (FR) **Mr J. P. McManus**

116 **MILAN BRIDGE (IRE)**, 6, b g Milan—Ice Princess (IRE) **Exors of the Late Mr T. J. Hemmings**

117 **MIRANDA (IRE)**, 7, b m Camelot—Great Artist (FR) **Owners Group 034**

118 **MON FRERE (IRE)**, 6, b g Pour Moi (IRE)—Sistine **Elite Racing Club**

119 **MONMIRAL (FR)**, 5, bl g Saint des Saints (FR)—Achere (FR) **Sir A Ferguson G Mason J Hales & L Hales**

120 **MONT DES AVALOIRS (FR)**, 9, b g Blue Bresil (FR)—Abu Dhabi (FR) **Mrs Johnny De La Hey**

121 **MONTYS MEDOC (IRE)**, 6, b g Westerner—Kilbarry Medoc (IRE) **Insurance Friends**

122 **MR GLASS (IRE)**, 6, b g Sholokhov (IRE)—Maryota (FR) **John & Jessica Dance**

123 **OLD GOLD**, 4, b g Blue Bresil (FR)—She's da One (IRE) **Old Gold Racing**

124 **ONETHREEFIVENOTOUT (IRE)**, 6, b g Milan—Back To Loughadera (IRE) **The Stewart Family**

125 **OSCARS MOONSHINE (IRE)**, 7, b g Oscar (IRE)—Scrapper Jack (IRE) **Mrs E. Lane**

126 **OUTLAW PETER (IRE)**, 6, b g Mustameet (USA)—My Katie (IRE) **The Stewart Family, Dench, Ferguson & Mason**

127 **PASO DOBLE (IRE)**, 5, br g Dawn Approach (IRE)—Baila Me (GER) **Mr G. F. Brooks**

128 **PENTIRE HEAD (IRE)**, 4, ch g Presenting—Kneeland Lass (IRE) **Mr Paul K. Barber & Mr Roger Eddy**

129 **PETROSSIAN (IRE)**, 6, br g Sageburg (IRE)—Innisfree Dawn (FR) **M. C. Denmark**

130 **PIC D'ORHY (FR)**, 7, b g Turgeon (USA)—Rose Candy (FR) **Mrs Johnny De La Hey**

131 **PLEASANT MAN**, 4, b g Galileo (IRE)—Melito (AUS) **McNeill Family & Patrick & Scott Bryceland**

132 **POLITOLOGUE (FR)**, 11, gr g Poliglote—Scarlet Row (FR) **Mr J. Hales**

133 **POZO EMERY (FR)**, 5, b g Le Havre (IRE)—Chic Et Zen (FR) **The Stewart Family**

134 5, B g Fame And Glory—Princess Mairead (IRE) **M. C. Denmark**

135 **QUEL DESTIN (FR)**, 7, ch g Muhtathir—High Destiny (FR) **Martin Broughton & Friends**

136 **RAINYDAY WOMAN**, 7, b m Kayf Tara—Wistow **Mr S. White**

137 **REAL STEEL (FR)**, 9, b g Loup Breton (IRE)—Kalimina (FR) **Mrs Kathy Stuart & Sullivan Bloodstock Ltd**

138 **RED RISK (FR)**, 7, b g No Risk At All (FR)—Rolie de Vindecy (FR) **Middleham Park Racing XLIV & A&j Ryan**

139 **ROQUE IT (IRE)**, 8, b g Presenting—Roque de Cyborg (IRE) **Gordon & Su Hall**

140 **ROUGE VIF (FR)**, 8, b g Sageburg (IRE)—Rouge Amour (FR) **Kate & Andrew Brooks**

141 **RUBAUD (FR)**, 4, b g Air Chief Marshal (USA)—Fulgence (FR) **Chris Giles & Brendan McManus**

142 **SABRINA (IRE)**, 7, b m Yeats (IRE)—En Vedette (FR) **Owners Group 030**

143 **SAINT CALVADOS (FR)**, 9, b g Saint des Saints (FR)—Lamorrese (FR) **Kate & Andrew Brooks**

144 **SAINT SONNET (FR)**, 7, b g Saint des Saints (FR)—Leprechaun Lady (FR) **Mr Colm Donlon**

145 **SAMARRIVE (FR)**, 5, b g Coastal Path—Sambirane (FR) **Mrs Johnny De La Hey**

146 **SANDALWOOD (IRE)**, 5, ch g Martaline—Balli Flight (FR) **Owners Group 072**

147 **SCARAMANGA (IRE)**, 7, b g Mastercraftsman (IRE)—Herboriste **M. C. Denmark**

148 **SEASIDE LEGEND (IRE)**, 4, b g Adlerflug (GER)—It Gorl (GER) **Jackson & Monk**

149 **SECRET INVESTOR**, 10, b g Kayf Tara—Silver Charmer **Hills of Ledbury Ltd**

150 **SECRET SCRIPTURE**, 6, ch g Mount Nelson—Kauto Shiny (FR) **Old Gold Racing 8**

151 **SENDING LOVE (IRE)**, 9, b g Scorpion (IRE)—Dato Vic (IRE) **The Unlikely Lads**

152 **SHANTOU FLYER (IRE)**, 12, b g Shantou (USA)—Carrigmorna Flyer (IRE) **D. Maxwell**

153 **SHEARER (IRE)**, 6, b g Flemensfirth (USA)—The Crown Jewel (IRE) **McNeill Family Ltd**

154 **SILENT REVOLUTION (IRE)**, 6, b g Sholokhov (IRE)—Watson River (IRE) **Mr Colm Donlon**

155 **SILVER FOREVER (IRE)**, 8, gr m Jeremy (USA)—Silver Prayer (IRE) **Mr Colm Donlon**

156 **SIMPLY THE BETTS (IRE)**, 9, b g Arcadio (GER)—Crimson Flower (IRE) **Kate & Andrew Brooks**

MR PAUL NICHOLLS - continued

157 **SIR PSYCHO (IRE)**, 6, b g Zoffany (IRE)—Open Book **Martin Broughton & Friends 3**
158 **SIROCO JO (FR)**, 5, ch g Hurricane Cat (USA)—Diana Vertica (FR) **Mr P. J. Vogt**
159 **SISTER SAINT (FR)**, 5, gr m Martaline—Minirose (FR) **Mrs Johnny De La Hey**
160 **SKATMAN (IRE)**, 7, br g Mustameet (USA)—Maid For Action (IRE) **Mr Chris Giles**
161 **SOLDIER OF LOVE**, 9, b g Yeats (IRE)—Monsignorita (IRE) **M. C. Denmark**
162 **SOLO (FR)**, 6, b g Kapgarde (FR)—Flameche (FR) **Mrs Johnny De La Hey**
163 **SONIGINO (FR)**, 5, b g It's Gino (GER)—Soniador (FR) **Sir A Ferguson G Mason J Hales & L Hales**
164 **SONNY CROCKETT (IRE)**, 7, b g Robin des Champs (FR)—Onewayortheother (IRE) **M. C. Denmark**
165 **SOUTHFIELD SCOPE**, 4, b g Telescope (IRE)—Chamoss Royale (FR) **Mrs Angela Yeoman**
166 **STAGE STAR (IRE)**, 6, b g Fame And Glory—Sparky May **Owners Group 044**
167 **STAY AWAY FAY (IRE)**, 5, b g Shantou (USA)—Augusta Bay **Mr Chris Giles**
168 **STORM ARISING (IRE)**, 8, b g Yeats (IRE)—Ceol Rua (IRE) **Barry Fulton & Mrs Angela Hart**
169 **STRATAGEM (FR)**, 6, gr g Sunday Break (JPN)—Our Ziga (FR) **D. Maxwell**
170 **SWITCH HITTER (IRE)**, 7, b g Scorpion (IRE)—Country Time (IRE) **Hills of Ledbury Ltd**
171 **TAHMURAS (FR)**, 5, b g Falco (USA)—Alinga's Lass (IRE) **Noel Fehily Racing Syndicates Tahmuras**
172 **TAKE YOUR TIME (IRE)**, 7, b g Dubai Destination (USA)—Don't Be Bleu (IRE) **Owners Group 060**
173 **TAMAROC DU MATHAN (FR)**, 7, b g Poliglote—Thisbee du Mathan (FR) **Mrs Johnny De La Hey**
174 **TANGO TARA**, 6, b g Kayf Tara—Bling Noir (FR) **Middleham Park Racing XXXIX & Peter Lamb**
175 **TARRAS WOOD (IRE)**, 4, b g Kayf Tara—Wood Lily (IRE) **The Gi Gi Syndicate**
176 **THAMES WATER (IRE)**, 5, ch g Flemensfirth (USA)—Cottage Theatre (IRE) **McNeill Family & Mr Tim Murphy**
177 **THREEUNDERTHRUFIVE (IRE)**, 7, b g Shantou (USA)—Didinas (FR) **McNeill Family Ltd**
178 **THYME WHITE (IRE)**, 6, b g Anodin (IRE)—Jane (GER) **The Stewart Family & Michael Blencowe**
179 **TIME TO TINKER (IRE)**, 7, br g Stowaway—Zuzka (IRE) **Mrs A. Tincknell**
180 **TIMEFORATUNE**, 6, b g Yorgunnabelucky (USA)—Timeforagin **Mr J. Hales**
181 **TINKLERS HILL (IRE)**, 4, b g Milan—Beautiful War (IRE) **The Hon Mrs C. A. Townshend**
182 **TOPOFTHEGAME (IRE)**, 10, ch g Flemensfirth (USA)—Derry Vale (IRE) **Mr Chris Giles & Mr & Mrs P K Barber**
183 **TRUCKERS LODGE (IRE)**, 10, b g Westerner—Galeacord (IRE) **Gordon & Su Hall**
184 **TULIN**, 5, b g Gleneagles (USA)—Talawat **Elite Racing 001**
185 **TWIN POWER (IRE)**, 5, b g Milan—Knockfierna (IRE) **McNeill Family & M & A Wainwright**
186 **UBETYA (IRE)**, 7, b g Le Fou (IRE)—Valentina Gaye (IRE) **Mr A. J. Peake**
187 **URBAN SOLDIER (IRE)**, 5, br g Soldier of Fortune (IRE)—She's No Pet (IRE) **Middleham Park Racing CXI**
188 **VIROFLAY (FR)**, 5, b g Air Chief Marshal (IRE)—Red Vixen (FR) **The Stewart Family**
189 **WILD MAX (GER)**, 7, b g Maxios—Wildfahrte (GER) **Owners Group 036**
190 **YALA ENKI (FR)**, 12, b br g Nickname (FR)—Cadiane (FR) **Hills of Ledbury Ltd**
191 **YOUNG BUCK (IRE)**, 8, b g Yeats (IRE)—Pepsi Starlet (IRE) **The Stewart Family**

THREE-YEAR-OLDS

192 Ch g Kapgarde (FR)—Buck's Babe (FR) **P. F. Nicholls**
193 Ch g Doctor Dino (FR)—Jane (GER) **G. A. Mason, The Stewart Family**

Other Owners: Mrs M. G. Barber, P. K. Barber, Mr J. Barnard, Mr M. A. R. Blencowe, Mr N. Brand, Mr A. L. Brooks, Mr G. F. Brooks, Mrs K. L. Brooks, Lady J. M. Broughton, Sir M. F. Broughton, Mr S. W. Broughton, Mr A. P. Brown, Mr P. Bryceland, Mr S. Bryceland, Mr D. J. Burke, Mr D. J. Coles, Mrs J. Dance, Mr J. E. Dance, A G J & Diver, Mr P. E. Done, Mr Colm Donlon, Mr B. J. C. Drew, Mr R. G. Eddy, Sir A. Ferguson, B. N. Fulton, Mr Chris Giles, Mrs D. M. Gregory, Mr J. R. Hales, Miss L. J. Hales, Mr G. A. Hall, Mrs S. L. Hall, Mr M. P. Hammond, Mrs A. R. Hart, P. H. Hogarth, Mr M. J. Holman, Mr A. Jackson, Mr P. Jackson, Mrs N. Jones, Mr S. Macauley, G. A. Mason, Mr J. M. McGoff, Mr B. J. McManus, McNeill Family Ltd, Mr K. Monk, Mrs M. E. Moody, Mr G. Moore, Mr T. P. Murphy, Mr F. Ong, Mrs S. Parkin, Mr S. J. Parkin, Mr A. J. Peake, Mr C. T. Pelham, Mr H. T. Pelham, Mr J. W. Randall, Miss Claire Simmonds, Mr B. D. Smith, Mr D. Smithyes, Mr D. D. Stevenson, Exor of the late A. Stewart, Mrs J. A. Stewart, Mrs Kathy Stuart, Sullivan Bloodstock Limited, The Stewart Family, Mr P. J. Vogt, Mr M. J. Wainwright, Mr I. Warwick, Mrs D. L. Whateley.

Assistant Trainer: Charlie Davies, Harry Derham, Natalie Parker.

Flat Jockey: Megan Nicholls. **NH Jockey:** Sean Bowen, Harry Cobden, Bryony Frost, Lorcan Williams.

Conditional Jockey: Tom Buckley, Bryan Carver, Angus Cheleda. **Amateur Jockey:** Mr Will Biddick, Miss Natalie Parker.

399 MR ADAM NICOL, Seahouses
Postal: **Springwood, South Lane, North Sunderland, Seahouses, Northumberland, NE68 7UL**
Contacts: **PHONE 01665 720320**
EMAIL adamnicol89@hotmail.co.uk

1 BARNEY STINSON (IRE), 6, b g Fame And Glory—Which Thistle (IRE) **The Risk Takers Partnership**
2 BELLELOISE, 4, b f Blue Bresil (FR)—Sabreflight **Mr D. Coates**
3 ECONOMIC EDITOR (IRE), 6, b g Jet Away—How Provincial (IRE) **UP4B**
4 FARNE ISLAND, 5, gr m Trans Island—Tigerific (IRE) **Ian Nicol Racing**
5 SPIDER'S BITE (IRE), 10, b g Scorpion (IRE)—Model Girl **The Risk Takers Partnership**
6 VELKERA (IRE), 8, br m Sholokhov (IRE)—April Gale (IRE) **The Seahouses Syndicate**
7 WISE EAGLE (IRE), 5, ch g Free Eagle (IRE)—Best Be Careful (IRE) **The Seahouses Syndicate**

400 MR PETER NIVEN, Malton
Postal: **Clovafield, Barton-Le-Street, Malton, North Yorkshire, YO17 6PN**
Contacts: **PHONE 01653 628176 MOBILE 07860 260999 FAX 01653 627295**
EMAIL pruniven@btinternet.com WEBSITE www.peterniven.co.uk

1 BRIAN BORANHA (IRE), 11, b g Brian Boru—Tapneiram (IRE) **Mrs K. J. Young**
2 CLOVA HOTEL, 4, b g Sixties Icon—Simply Mystic **Mrs J. A. Niven**
3 EARLY MORNING DEW (FR), 6, ch g Muhtathir—Rosee Matinale (FR) **Hard Held Partnership & Mr R J Marley**
4 GRAND MARIO (FR), 5, ch g Nom de d'La (FR)—Nina La Belle (FR) **Mr P. D. Niven & Mr M. Niven**
5 HURSTWOOD, 5, br gr g Dark Angel (IRE)—Haigh Hall **Hard Held Partnership & Angus Racing**
6 MALYSTIC, 8, b g Malinas (GER)—Mystic Glen **Clova Syndicate & Mrs J A Niven**
7 MINUTE WALTZ, 5, b m Sixties Icon—Mystic Glen **K & J Niven**
8 MISTY MANI, 7, b m Sulamani (IRE)—Mystic Glen **Mrs K Young & Mrs J A Niven**
9 5, Bl m Turgeon (USA)—Nicknack (FR) **Mr P. D. Niven & Mr M. Niven**
10 ONTHEROUGE, 4, b g Sixties Icon—Simply Rouge **Mrs Ja Niven Angus Racing Club Rumpole P**
11 SIMPLY MANI, 10, ch g Sulamani (IRE)—Simply Mystic **Mrs J A Niven & Angus Racing Club**
12 STORM FORCE ONE, 8, b m Schiaparelli (GER)—Force In The Wings (IRE) **Hedley, Little, Sharkey & Tomkins**
13 SUGAR BABY, 4, b g Monsieur Bond (IRE)—Sugar Town **Angus Racing Club & Mr P. D. Niven**
14 WICKLOW WARRIOR, 7, b g Sleeping Indian—Vale of Clara (IRE) **Mr P. D. Niven**

Other Owners: Angus Racing Club, Clova Syndicate, Mr B. W. Ewart, Miss C. Foster, Hard Held Partnership, Mr C. R. Hedley, Mr K. J. Little, Mr R. J. Marley, Mrs J. A. Niven, Mr M. W. G. Niven, Mr P. D. Niven, Mrs K. M. Richardson, M. A. Scaife, Mr W. K. D. Sharkey, The Rumpole Partnership, Ms L. P. Tomkins, Mrs K. J. Young.

401 MR JOHN NORTON, Barnsley
Postal: **Globe Farm, High Hoyland, Barnsley, South Yorkshire, S75 4BE**
Contacts: **HOME 01226 387633 MOBILE 07970 212707**
HOME EMAIL johnrnorton@hotmail.com FACEBOOK JRNorton

1 BLACK MARKET (IRE), 8, b g Yeats (IRE)—Aneda Dubh (IRE) **Fellowship Of The Rose Partnership 2**
2 DAKOTA BEAT (IRE), 7, ch g Beat Hollow—Rushmore Rose (IRE)

    Mrs E. Woodcock-Jones, Mr P. R. Woodcock-Jones
3 LANTANA DANCER (IRE), 4, b g Zoffany (IRE)—Dewdrop (IRE) **Bardsley, Barlow, Campbell & Tattersall**
4 MONJULES (FR), 4, b g Rajsaman (FR)—Equilibriste (FR) **Mr J. D. Mayo**
5 MUFTAKKER, 8, gr g Tamayuz—Qertaas (IRE) **J.R. Norton Ltd**
6 NAASIK, 9, b g Poet's Voice—Shemriyna (IRE) **Fellowship Of The Rose Partnership 2**
7 OLD DURHAM TOWN, 6, b g Fame And Glory—Oleohneh (IRE) **Jaffa Racing Syndicate**
8 WILLIAMWILBERFORCE, 5, b g Dream Ahead (USA)—Isabella Bird **Mrs D. Widdowson, A Tattersall**

Other Owners: Fellowship Of The Rose Partnership.

MR A. P. O'BRIEN, Ballydoyle
402 Postal: Ballydoyle Stables, Cashel, Co. Tipperary, Ireland
Contacts: **PHONE +353 62 62615**
EMAIL racingoffice@ballydoyle.com

1 **BOLSHOI BALLET (IRE)**, 4, b c Galileo (IRE)—Alta Anna (FR)
2 **BROOME (IRE)**, 6, b h Australia—Sweepstake (IRE)
3 **CLEVELAND (IRE)**, 4, b c Camelot—Venus de Milo (IRE)
4 **HIGH DEFINITION (IRE)**, 4, b c Galileo (IRE)—Palace (IRE)
5 **JEROBOAM (USA)**, 4, b c War Front (USA)—Outstanding (IRE)
6 **KYPRIOS (IRE)**, 4, ch c Galileo (IRE)—Polished Gem (IRE)
7 **MACQUARIE (IRE)**, 6, ch h Australia—Beyond Brilliance (IRE)
8 **MOTHER EARTH (IRE)**, 4, b f Zoffany (IRE)—Many Colours
9 **ORDER OF AUSTRALIA (IRE)**, 5, b h Australia—Senta's Dream
10 **WEMBLEY (IRE)**, 4, b c Galileo (IRE)—Inca Princess (IRE)
11 **WORDSWORTH (IRE)**, 4, ch c Galileo (IRE)—Chelsea Rose (IRE)

THREE-YEAR-OLDS

12 **AIKHAL (IRE)**, b c Galileo (IRE)—Diamond Fields (IRE)
13 **ANCHORAGE (IRE)**, b c Galileo (IRE)—Vanzara (FR)
14 **ARBUTUS (IRE)**, b c Galileo (IRE)—Sea Siren (AUS)
15 **ARK (IRE)**, b f Galileo (IRE)—Charlotte Bronte
16 **BLUEGRASS (IRE)**, b c Galileo (IRE)—Quiet Reflection
17 **BUTTERFLY ROSE (IRE)**, b f Galileo (IRE)—Awesome Maria (USA)
18 **CADAMOSTO (IRE)**, b c No Nay Never (USA)—Saucy Spirit
19 **CADOGAN SQUARE**, b c Churchill (IRE)—Madame Hoi (IRE)
20 **CADOGAN SQUARE**, b c Churchill (IRE)—Madame Hoi (IRE)
21 **CHAMPAGNE (IRE)**, b f Galileo (IRE)—Red Evie (IRE)
22 **CHANGINGOFTHEGUARD (IRE)**, b c Galileo (IRE)—Lady Lara (IRE)
23 **CHERUB (IRE)**, b f Galileo (IRE)—Race For The Stars (USA)
24 **COLOGNE (IRE)**, b c Galileo (IRE)—Life Happened (USA)
25 **CONCERT HALL (IRE)**, b f Dubawi (IRE)—Was (IRE)
26 **CONTARELLI CHAPEL (IRE)**, gr f Caravaggio (USA)—Chenchikova (IRE)
27 **COUGAR (JPN)**, b c Deep Impact (JPN)—Promise To Be True (IRE)
28 **CYCLAMEN (IRE)**, b f Mastercraftsman (IRE)—Simkana (IRE)
29 **DALMATIAN COAST (IRE)**, b c Galileo (IRE)—Keenes Royale
30 **DENVER (IRE)**, ch c Galileo (IRE)—Halfway To Heaven (IRE)
31 **DOWNING STREET (IRE)**, ch c Galileo (IRE)—Remember When (IRE)
32 **EMILY DICKINSON (IRE)**, b f Dubawi (IRE)—Chicquita (IRE)
33 **ENGAGEMENT RING (IRE)**, gr f Galileo (IRE)—Dialafara (FR)
34 **FLEET COMMANDER (IRE)**, b c Galileo (IRE)—Atlantic Jewel (AUS)
35 **FOREVER AND ALWAYS (IRE)**, ch f Galileo (IRE)—Chintz (IRE)
36 **GALLERIA BORGHESE (IRE)**, gr f Caravaggio (USA)—On Ice (IRE)
37 **GLOUNTHANE (IRE)**, b c Kodiac—Khaimah
38 **GULLIVER'S TRAVELS (IRE)**, b c Galileo (IRE)—Prudenzia (IRE)
39 **HARLEY STREET (IRE)**, b c Galileo (IRE)—Chanting (USA)
40 **HEART TO HEART (IRE)**, b f Zoffany (IRE)—Entreat
41 **HISTORY (IRE)**, b f Galileo (IRE)—Prize Exhibit
42 **HMS ENDEAVOUR (USA)**, b c War Front (USA)—Lady Eli (USA)
43 **HONEYCOMB (IRE)**, ch f Galileo (IRE)—Emerald Ring (IRE)
44 **HOPE DIAMOND (IRE)**, b f Galileo (IRE)—Danedrop (IRE)
45 **HOWTH (IRE)**, b c Churchill (IRE)—Muwakaba (USA)
46 **INSTRUMENTAL**, ch c No Nay Never (USA)—Strut
47 **IVY LEAGUE (IRE)**, b c Galileo (IRE)—Timbuktu (IRE)
48 **KING OF BAVARIA (IRE)**, b br c No Nay Never (USA)—Enharmonic (USA)
49 **KISS YOU LATER (IRE)**, b f Galileo (IRE)—Switch (USA)
50 **LEINSTER HOUSE (USA)**, b br c War Front (USA)—Ballydoyle (IRE)
51 **LILY POND (IRE)**, b f Galileo (IRE)—Alluringly (USA)
52 **LOCH NESS (IRE)**, b c Churchill (IRE)—Empowering (IRE)
53 **LOST (IRE)**, b f Frankel—Queen Cleopatra (IRE)
54 **LULLABY (IRE)**, ch f Galileo (IRE)—Holy Alliance (IRE)

MR A. P. O'BRIEN - continued

55 **LUXEMBOURG (IRE),** b c Camelot—Attire (IRE)
56 **MADONNADELROSARIO (IRE),** br gr f Caravaggio (USA)—Muravka (IRE)
57 **MARTINSTOWN (IRE),** b c Galileo (IRE)—Alive Alive Oh
58 **MIDDLEMARCH (IRE),** b c Caravaggio (USA)—Jigsaw (IRE)
59 **MINISTER OF WAR (IRE),** b c Churchill (IRE)—Regency Girl (IRE)
60 **MONTENEGRO (IRE),** b c Camelot—War Goddess (IRE)
61 **NAVAJO WARRIOR (JPN),** b c Deep Impact (JPN)—Fluff (IRE)
62 **NEVERLAND (USA),** b f Quality Road (USA)—Marvellous (IRE)
63 **NEW YORK CITY (IRE),** b c Invincible Spirit (IRE)—Rajeem
64 **NEWFOUNDLAND (IRE),** b c Deep Impact (JPN)—Best In The World (IRE)
65 **NINJA (IRE),** b c Galileo (IRE)—Kheleyf's Silver (USA)
66 **OH SO LOVELY (IRE),** b f Galileo (IRE)—Magic Tree (UAE)
67 **OLYMPIC FLAME (IRE),** br c Camelot—Crazy Volume (IRE)
68 **ONLY (JPN),** b f Deep Impact (JPN)—Winter (IRE)
69 **OVER THE RAINBOW (IRE),** b f Dubawi (IRE)—Seventh Heaven (IRE)
70 **PEACH BLOSSOM (IRE),** b f Galileo (IRE)—Amicus (AUS)
71 **PEROTAN (IRE),** b f Churchill (IRE)—Tanaghum
72 **POINT LONSDALE (IRE),** b c Australia—Sweepstake (IRE)
73 **PORTO CERVO (USA),** b f American Pharoah (USA)—Cherry Hinton
74 **PRETTIEST (USA),** ch f Dubawi (IRE)—Alice Springs (IRE)
75 **REALISM (IRE),** b c Galileo (IRE)—Where (IRE)
76 **RIVER THAMES (IRE),** b c Churchill (IRE)—Where's Sue (IRE)
77 **SAMUEL PEPYS (IRE),** b c Galileo (IRE)—Tiggy Wiggy (IRE)
78 **SCRIPTWRITER (IRE),** b c Churchill (IRE)—Pivotalia (IRE)
79 **SHARK BAY (IRE),** ch c Australia—Defrost My Heart (IRE)
80 **SKYLARK,** b f Galileo (IRE)—Shastye (IRE)
81 **SO BEAUTIFUL (IRE),** b f Galileo (IRE)—Acapulco (USA)
82 **STAR OF INDIA (IRE),** b c Galileo (IRE)—Shermeen (IRE)
83 **STONE AGE (IRE),** b c Galileo (IRE)—Bonanza Creek (IRE)
84 **SUN KING (IRE),** b c Galileo (IRE)—Song of My Heart (IRE)
85 **SUNDIAL (IRE),** b c Galileo (IRE)—Naples Bay (USA)
86 **SUSSEX (USA),** b c Dubawi (IRE)—Kissed (IRE)
87 **SWEDEN (IRE),** ch c Galileo (IRE)—Even Song (IRE)
88 **SWIRL (IRE),** b f Galileo (IRE)—Tepin (USA)
89 **TEMPLE OF ARTEMIS (IRE),** b c Galileo (IRE)—Mystical Lady (IRE)
90 **TENEBRISM (USA),** b f Caravaggio (USA)—Immortal Verse (IRE)
91 **THE ACROPOLIS (IRE),** b c Churchill (IRE)—Hairy Rocket
92 **THE ALGARVE (USA),** br f American Pharoah (USA)—Imagine (IRE)
93 **THE LUTE PLAYER (IRE),** gr c Caravaggio (USA)—Sparrow (IRE)
94 **THOUGHTS OF JUNE (IRE),** b f Galileo (IRE)—Discreet Marq (USA)
95 **TOY (IRE),** ch f Galileo (IRE)—You'resothrilling (USA)
96 **TUESDAY (IRE),** b f Galileo (IRE)—Lillie Langtry (IRE)
97 **TWINKLE (IRE),** b f Galileo (IRE)—Believe'n'succeed (AUS)
98 **UNITED NATIONS (IRE),** b c Galileo (IRE)—Christmas Kid (USA)
99 **WATERVILLE (IRE),** b c Camelot—Holy Moon (IRE)
100 **WEST COAST (IRE),** br gr f Dark Angel (IRE)—Wading (IRE)

TWO-YEAR-OLDS

101 B f 11/05 No Nay Never (USA)—Actress (IRE) (Declaration of War (USA))
102 B c 15/01 No Nay Never (USA)—Adventure Seeker (FR) (Bering) (272109)
103 B c 28/02 Galileo (IRE)—Again (IRE) (Danehill Dancer (IRE))
104 B c 15/02 Saxon Warrior (JPN)—Aktoria (FR) (Canford Cliffs (IRE)) (300000)
105 B c 25/02 No Nay Never (USA)—Alexandrova (IRE) (Sadler's Wells (USA))
106 B br c 09/02 Quality Road (USA)—Alice Springs (IRE) (Galileo (IRE))
107 B c 13/05 Galileo (IRE)—Anthem Alexander (Starspangledbanner (AUS)) (1100000)
108 B f 06/02 Dubawi (IRE)—Athena (IRE) (Camelot)
109 B c 29/03 Camelot—Attire (IRE) (Danehill Dancer (IRE)) (1020408)
110 Ch f 05/03 Justify (USA)—Ballydoyle (IRE) (Galileo (IRE))
111 B c 13/05 Dubawi (IRE)—Best In The World (IRE) (Galileo (IRE))

MR A. P. O'BRIEN - continued

112 B c 09/02 Camelot—Board Meeting (IRE) (Anabaa (USA)) (374150)
113 Ch c 24/04 No Nay Never (USA)—Bracelet (IRE) (Montjeu (IRE))
114 Br c 05/01 No Nay Never (USA)—Bridal Dance (IRE) (Danehill Dancer (IRE))
115 B c 11/04 Quality Road (USA)—Butterflies (IRE) (Galileo (IRE))
116 B c 10/05 Saxon Warrior (JPN)—Cassandra Go (IRE) (Indian Ridge) (459184)
117 B f 28/03 Saxon Warrior (JPN)—Chenchikova (IRE) (Sadler's Wells (USA))
118 B c 19/01 Camelot—Clear Skies (Sea The Stars (IRE))
119 Ch f 01/03 Justify (USA)—Clemmie (IRE) (Galileo (IRE))
120 B c 11/03 Australia—Could It Be Love (USA) (War Front (USA))
121 B c 03/03 No Nay Never (USA)—Crystal Diamond (Teofilo (IRE))
122 Ch f 15/02 Justify (USA)—Curvy (Galileo (IRE))
123 Ch f 02/03 Galileo (IRE)—Daddys Lil Darling (USA) (Scat Daddy (USA))
124 B c 15/05 Galileo (IRE)—Dialafara (FR) (Anabaa (USA))
125 B c 16/04 Galileo (IRE)—Different League (FR) (Dabirsim (FR))
126 B c 08/01 Justify (USA)—Dramatically (USA) (War Front (USA))
127 Br c 23/01 Camelot—Elbasana (IRE) (Indian Ridge) (340000)
128 B c 31/03 Camelot—Empowering (IRE) (Encosta de Lago (AUS))
129 B c 28/01 Dubawi (IRE)—Forever Together (IRE) (Galileo (IRE))
130 Br c 30/04 No Nay Never (USA)—Fork Lightning (USA) (Storm Cat (USA))
131 B f 07/02 Camelot—Frequential (Dansili) (340000)
132 B c 05/03 Justify (USA)—Gagnoa (IRE) (Sadler's Wells (USA))
133 Ch c 03/04 Saxon Warrior (JPN)—Gilt Edge Girl (Monsieur Bond (IRE)) (229592)
134 B br c 15/03 Lord Kanaloa (JPN)—Happily (IRE) (Galileo (IRE))
135 B f 24/02 Galileo (IRE)—Hazariya (IRE) (Xaar)
136 B c 11/05 Galileo (IRE)—Heartache (Kyllachy)
137 Ch f 12/02 Justify (USA)—Hence (IRE) (Galileo (IRE))
138 Ch f 23/03 Dubawi (IRE)—Highest Ever (IRE) (Galileo (IRE))
139 B f 18/04 Frankel—How High The Moon (IRE) (Fastnet Rock (AUS))
140 B c 15/02 No Nay Never (USA)—How's She Cuttin' (IRE) (Shinko Forest (IRE))
141 Ch f 08/03 Justify (USA)—Immortal Verse (IRE) (Pivotal)
142 B c 09/03 Galileo (IRE)—Inca Princess (IRE) (Holy Roman Emperor (IRE))
143 B c 20/04 Australia—Itqaan (USA) (Danzig (USA))
144 JACKIE OH (IRE), ch f 20/05 Galileo (IRE)—Jacqueline Quest (IRE) (Rock of Gibraltar (IRE))
145 B c 01/02 Camelot—Jazz Cat (IRE) (Tamayuz) (240000)
146 B c 03/03 Sioux Nation (USA)—Knock Stars (USA) (Soviet Star (USA)) (215000)
147 B f 16/01 Galileo (IRE)—Legatissimo (IRE) (Danehill Dancer (IRE))
148 B c 16/02 Galileo (IRE)—Lightning Thunder (Dutch Art) (650000)
149 B f 31/05 Galileo (IRE)—Lillie Langtry (IRE) (Danehill Dancer (IRE))
150 B f 15/01 Galileo (IRE)—Marsha (IRE) (Acclamation)
151 B c 27/01 Deep Impact (JPN)—Maybe (IRE) (Galileo (IRE))
152 B f 26/03 Galileo (IRE)—Meow (IRE) (Storm Cat (USA))
153 B f 21/01 Deep Impact (JPN)—Minding (IRE) (Galileo (IRE))
154 B f 24/01 Galileo (IRE)—Miss France (IRE) (Dansili) (625000)
155 Ch c 15/02 Justify (USA)—Moth (IRE) (Galileo (IRE))
156 B c 06/02 No Nay Never (USA)—Muirin (IRE) (Born To Sea (IRE))
157 Ch c 02/04 Australia—Muwakaba (USA) (Elusive Quality (USA))
158 B c 04/04 Justify (USA)—My Sister Sandy (USA) (Montbrook (USA))
159 Br f 08/05 Galileo (IRE)—Mystical Lady (IRE) (Halling (USA))
160 B f 30/03 Galileo (IRE)—Nickname (USA) (Scat Daddy (USA)) (1275510)
161 Ch f 08/01 Galileo (IRE)—One Moment In Time (IRE) (Danehill (USA))
162 Br gr f 03/01 No Nay Never (USA)—Pembina (IRE) (Dalakhani (IRE)) (306122)
163 B c 31/01 Galileo (IRE)—Penchant (Kyllachy)
164 B c 18/02 Galileo (IRE)—Prize Exhibit (Showcasing)
165 B f 19/03 Lord Kanaloa (JPN)—Promise To Be True (IRE) (Galileo (IRE))
166 B f 30/01 Galileo (IRE)—Quiet Reflection (Showcasing)
167 B c 09/04 Frankel—Qushchi (Encosta de Lago (AUS)) (925000)
168 B c 27/01 Dubawi (IRE)—Rain Goddess (IRE) (Galileo (IRE))
169 B c 06/03 Sioux Nation (USA)—Rhiannon (IRE) (High Chaparral (IRE)) (136054)
170 B br c 26/01 Deep Impact (JPN)—Rhododendron (IRE) (Galileo (IRE))
171 B c 23/04 No Nay Never (USA)—Seatone (USA) (Mizzen Mast (USA)) (450000)

MR A. P. O'BRIEN - continued

172 B f 06/03 Dubawi (IRE)—Seventh Heaven (IRE) (Galileo (IRE))
173 B c 31/01 Frankel—Shadow Hunter (IRE) (Arcano (IRE)) (450000)
174 B c 08/02 No Nay Never (USA)—Sweet Charity (FR) (Myboycharlie (IRE)) (527211)
175 B c 08/02 Mendelssohn (USA)—Tessie Flip (USA) (Grand Slam (USA)) (278067)
176 B c 07/05 Saxon Warrior (JPN)—Tickled Pink (IRE) (Invincible Spirit (IRE)) (115000)
177 Ch f 22/03 Galileo (IRE)—Tiggy Wiggy (IRE) (Kodiac)
178 B c 08/03 Justify (USA)—Together Forever (IRE) (Galileo (IRE)) (521376)
179 B f 30/04 Dubawi (IRE)—Wading (IRE) (Montjeu (IRE))
180 B c 08/05 Dubawi (IRE)—Was (IRE) (Galileo (IRE))
181 B c 04/04 Galileo (IRE)—Where (IRE) (Danehill Dancer (IRE))
182 B f 19/03 Lord Kanaloa (JPN)—Winter (IRE) (Galileo (IRE)) (163365)
183 B f 27/02 Galileo (IRE)—Words (IRE) (Dansili)

403	**MR DONNACHA O'BRIEN, Cashel** Postal: **Bawnmore Racing Stables, Ballyroe, Cashel, Tipperary, Ireland** EMAIL donnachaobrien50@gmail.com

1 EMPORIO (IRE), 4, ch c Zoffany (IRE)—Eirnin (IRE)
2 MOON DAISY (IRE), 4, b f Australia—Holy Alliance (IRE)

THREE-YEAR-OLDS

3 ABSOLUTE RULER (USA), b c War Front (USA)—Together Forever (IRE)
4 ARTISTIC CHOICE (IRE), br c Caravaggio (USA)—Chicago Girl (IRE)
5 ATLANTIC BREEZE (IRE), ch c No Nay Never (USA)—Flashy Wings
6 ELLIPTIC (IRE), b f Caravaggio (USA)—Aqua de Vida (IRE)
7 FIRST EMPEROR, b c Galileo (IRE)—Sky Lantern (IRE)
8 FLAGSHIP (JPN), b c Caravaggio (USA)—Peeping Fawn (USA)
9 I'M FEELIN FINE, b f Almanzor (FR)—Mujabaha
10 IMPERO (IRE), b c Zoffany (IRE)—On A Pedestal (IRE)
11 LUSTRE (IRE), b f Galileo (IRE)—Wave (IRE)
12 ONE WAY (IRE), b f Galileo (IRE)—Butterfly Cove (USA)
13 PIZ BADILE (IRE), b br c Ulysses (IRE)—That Which Is Not (USA)
14 PODIUM (IRE), b f Galileo (IRE)—Missvinski (USA)
15 PORTHOS (IRE), b c Galileo (IRE)—Sun Shower (IRE)
16 PUNTA DI PIEDI (IRE), b f Caravaggio (USA)—Queen Titi (IRE)
17 RED AZALEA (IRE), b f Galileo (IRE)—Music Box (IRE)
18 SIMPLY GLORIOUS (USA), b f War Front (USA)—Misty For Me (IRE)
19 SWEET AND LOVELY (IRE), b f Galileo (IRE)—La Traviata (USA)
20 TEA PARTY (IRE), br gr f Caravaggio (USA)—Airwave
21 TRUSTWORTHY (IRE), br f Caravaggio (USA)—All For Glory (USA)

TWO-YEAR-OLDS

22 B f 12/06 Galileo (IRE)—Alluringly (USA) (Fastnet Rock (AUS))
23 Ch c 08/04 Churchill (IRE)—Amjaad (Dansili) (150000)
24 Gr f 24/01 Caravaggio (USA)—Ask Me Nicely (IRE) (Fastnet Rock (AUS))
25 B f 23/02 Footstepsinthesand—Belong (IRE) (Fastnet Rock (AUS))
26 B f 13/05 Galileo (IRE)—Butterfly Cove (USA) (Storm Cat (USA))
27 Ch c 17/03 Mehmas (IRE)—C'Est Ma Souer (IRE) (Oratorio (IRE)) (250000)
28 CALLING ALL ANGELS (IRE), b br f 21/04 Dark Angel (IRE)—Single (FR) (Singspiel (IRE)) (76531)
29 B c 30/01 Footstepsinthesand—Caped Lady (IRE) (Cape Cross) (90476)
30 B c 22/03 Starspangledbanner (AUS)—Chamber Maid (Nathaniel (IRE)) (80000)
31 B f 26/05 Dubawi (IRE)—Chicquita (IRE) (Montjeu (IRE))
32 B f 15/04 No Nay Never (USA)—Cocoon (IRE) (Galileo (IRE))
33 Ch c 03/03 Showcasing—Dadao (Intello (GER)) (221088)

MR DONNACHA O'BRIEN - continued

34 B f 31/01 Churchill (IRE)—Deira Dubai (Green Desert (USA))
35 B c 01/03 No Nay Never (USA)—Detailed (IRE) (Motivator) (100000)
36 Ch c 21/03 Australia—Eccentricity (USA) (Kingmambo (USA))
37 B f 03/03 Fastnet Rock (AUS)—Eloquent (IRE) (Galileo (IRE))
38 B c 15/02 Wootton Bassett—Eneza (IRE) (Holy Roman Emperor (IRE)) (127551)
39 B f 07/01 Churchill (IRE)—Eos (IRE) (Declaration of War (USA))
40 B c 13/04 Churchill (IRE)—Euphrasia (IRE) (Windsor Knot (IRE)) (63776)
41 B c 09/05 Galileo (IRE)—Holy Alliance (IRE) (Holy Roman Emperor (IRE))
42 B c 24/04 Showcasing—Horse Sense (IRE) (Canford Cliffs (IRE)) (58000)
43 B c 24/02 Zoffany (IRE)—Inchikhan (Dalakhani (IRE)) (45000)
44 B c 17/03 Australia—Jamrah (IRE) (Danehill (USA))
45 B f 29/04 Galileo (IRE)—Life Happened (USA) (Stravinsky (USA))
46 Ch f 18/02 Australia—Madam Baroque (Royal Applause) (150000)
47 B f 09/02 Deep Impact (JPN)—Malicieuse (IRE) (Galileo (IRE))
48 B f 02/03 Mastercraftsman (IRE)—Masandra (IRE) (Desert Prince (IRE)) (32000)
49 **NUNCA (IRE)**, B f 25/03 No Nay Never (USA)—Inca Wood (UAE) (Timber Country (USA)) (89286)
50 B f 29/02 Churchill (IRE)—Perplexity (IRE) (Mastercraftsman (IRE))
51 B c 06/05 Galileo (IRE)—Rock Orchid (IRE) (Fastnet Rock (AUS)) (540000)
52 B f 24/02 Zoffany (IRE)—Sacrament (IRE) (Acclamation) (43810)
53 B f 13/04 Australia—Shannon Spree (Royal Applause) (40000)
54 Ch c 07/05 Galileo (IRE)—Simply Perfect (Danehill (USA))
55 Ch f 02/05 Galileo (IRE)—Stellar Wind (USA) (Curlin (USA))
56 B f 22/02 Zoustar (AUS)—Street Marie (USA) (Street Cry (IRE)) (42857)
57 B c 09/03 Profitable (IRE)—Tender Is Thenight (IRE) (Barathea (IRE)) (27000)
58 B c 04/04 Shamardal (USA)—That Which Is Not (USA) (Elusive Quality (USA))
59 B c 11/03 Kodiac (IRE)—Violet's Gift (IRE) (Cadeaux Genereux) (100000)
60 B c 04/03 Churchill (IRE)—War Goddess (IRE) (Champs Elysees)
61 Gr f 03/03 Galileo (IRE)—Ysoldina (FR) (Kendor (FR)) (425170)
62 Ch f 15/05 No Nay Never (USA)—Zagitova (IRE) (Galileo (IRE))

404	**MR FERGAL O'BRIEN, Cheltenham**

Postal: **Ravenswell Farm, Withington, Cheltenham, Gloucestershire, GL54 4DD**
Contacts: **MOBILE 07771 702829**
EMAIL **admin@fergalobrienracing.com**

1 **ACCIDENTAL LEGEND (IRE)**, 5, b g Shirocco (GER)—Cloth Fair (IRE) **Mr N. Brereton**
2 **AJAY'S WAYS (IRE)**, 8, b g Stowaway—Beechfield Queen (IRE) **BDRSyndicates**
3 **ALAPHILIPPE (IRE)**, 8, b g Morozov (USA)—Oscar Bird (IRE) **Mr N. Brereton**
4 **AMADORIO (FR)**, 7, b g Authorized (IRE)—Carolles (FR) **F&M Bloodstock Limited**
5 **AMI DESBOIS (FR)**, 12, b g Dream Well (FR)—Baroya (FR) **The Reserved Judgment Partnership**
6 **ANNUAL REVIEW (IRE)**, 7, b g Yeats (IRE)—Crafty Fancy (IRE) **Chris Graham & Graeme McPherson**
7 **ANOTHER FURLOUGH (IRE)**, 5, b g Shirocco (GER)—Rebel Warrior (IRE) **Mr David Leon & James Devine**
8 5, B m Telescope—Any Pearl
9 **ARMCHAIR FARMER (IRE)**, 6, b g Brian Boru—Cobajay Lady (IRE) **P J King & Son**
10 **ART APPROVAL (FR)**, 6, b g Authorized (IRE)—Rock Art (IRE) **Mr R. J. G. Lowe**
11 **ART MAN (FR)**, 5, ch g Manduro (GER)—Oscar Bird (IRE) **Mr P. Lowe, Mr R. J. G. Lowe**
12 **ASK A HONEY BEE (IRE)**, 8, b g Ask—Pure Honey (IRE) **Lewis, Lawson and Hope**
13 **ASK DILLON (IRE)**, 9, b g Ask—Mum's Miracle (IRE) **4 The Fun Partnership**
14 **ASK HENRY (IRE)**, 9, b g Ask—Miss Muppet (IRE) **Turf Club 2020 & Graeme McPherson**
15 5, B m Soldier of Fortune (IRE)—At The Pound Cross (IRE)
16 **AUTONOMOUS CLOUD (IRE)**, 6, b g Flemensfirth (USA)—August Hill (IRE)
Mr Terry Warner & the McNeill Family
17 **AVIEWTOSEA (IRE)**, 7, b g Where Or When (IRE)—Final Run (IRE) **The O'Brien McPherson Syndicate 1**
18 **BABY BEN (IRE)**, 6, b g Ask—Decheekymonkey (IRE) **BDRSyndicates**
19 5, Ch g Malinas (GER)—Ballygambon Girl (IRE)

MR FERGAL O'BRIEN - continued

20 **BARRAKHOV (IRE)**, 6, b g Sholokhov (IRE)—Barrack Buster **DI Adams, Ja Adams & G McPherson**
21 **BATHIVA (FR)**, 8, b g Spanish Moon (USA)—Thithia (FR) **Mrs J. Rees**
22 **BAY OF INTRIGUE**, 7, b g Sulamani (IRE)—Kahlua Cove **Mr Oscar Singh & Miss Priya Purewal**
23 **BECKY THE BOO**, 6, b m Schiaparelli (GER)—Sunnyland **The FOB Racing Partnership 10**
24 **BEYOND THE PALE (IRE)**, 7, b g Shirocco (GER)—Miss Mary Mac (IRE) **The FOB Racing Partnership 7**
25 **BHALOO (IRE)**, 4, br g Sageburg (IRE)—Feldaline (IRE) **Ms J. E. McGivern**
26 **BILLAMS LEGACY**, 7, b m Black Sam Bellamy (IRE)—Liqueur Rose **The Cod and Chips Twice Racing Syndicate**
27 **BILLY BOI BLUE**, 5, b g Blue Bresil (FR)—Kentucky Sky **BDRSyndicates**
28 **BLACK KALANISI (IRE)**, 9, b g Kalanisi (IRE)—Blackthorne Winter (IRE) **The Harefield Racing Club**
29 **BLUE BIKINI**, 6, b m Winged Love (IRE)—Bleu d'Avril (FR) **Nick Brown Racing**
30 **BLUE CLOVER**, 4, b f Clovis du Berlais (FR)—Asola Blue (FR) **F&M Bloodstock Limited**
31 **BLUE LUNA**, 6, b m Lucarno (USA)—Mighty Merlin **Mrs J. A. Watts**
32 **BLUE SANS (IRE)**, 7, b m Sans Frontieres (IRE)—California Blue (FR) **The FOB Racing Partnership 12**
33 **BONTTAY (IRE)**, 5, b m Westerner—Ben's Turn (IRE) **Mr C. B Brookes & Fergal O'Brien**
34 **BRIEF AMBITION**, 8, b g Yeats (IRE)—Kentucky Sky **C Coley, D Porter, H Redknapp, P Smith**
35 **BURRISTO (IRE)**, 4, ch g Buratino (IRE)—Gin Twist **P G Lowe & Friends**
36 **BYZANTINE EMPIRE**, 5, b g Golden Horn—Mainstay **Always Smiling**
37 **CALL ME TARA**, 5, b m Kayf Tara—Call Me Emma (IRE) **Upthorpe Racing**
38 **CAMPDEN LAD (IRE)**, 6, b g Doyen—Eckbeag (USA) **Mr F. M. O'Brien**
39 **CAP ST VINCENT (FR)**, 9, b g Muhtathir—Criquetot (FR) **The Yes No Wait Sorries & Mr Chris Coley**
40 **CAPE TOWN ERIN (IRE)**, 5, b m Arcadio (GER)—Emeranna (IRE) **Mr S. Conway**
41 **CAPTAIN CATTISTOCK**, 9, b g Black Sam Bellamy (IRE)—Pearl Buttons **Mr N. Brereton**
42 **CARLO DU BERLAIS (IRE)**, 5, gr g Carlotamix (FR)—Dark Ebony (IRE) **Owners Group 089**
43 **CASTEL GANDOLFO (IRE)**, 5, gr g Dark Angel (IRE)—Capulet Monteque (IRE) **Mr N. Brereton**
44 **CHAMPAGNE WELL (IRE)**, 9, b g Gold Well—Perkanod (IRE) **The Bolly Champagne Crew**
45 **CHANCYCOURT (IRE)**, 6, b g Court Cave (IRE)—She Saval (IRE) **O'Brien & Porter**
46 5, B g Shirocco (GER)—Chicago Vic (IRE)
47 **CITY DERBY (IRE)**, 6, ch g Ask—Reine d'Or (IRE) **Mr R. D. A. Hames**
48 **COOL TARA**, 7, b m Kayf Tara—Cool Spice **Mr W. Jones**
49 **COOLDINE BOG (IRE)**, 9, b g Court Cave (IRE)—Express Mail (IRE) **Mr N. D. Wellington**
50 **CORAL (FR)**, 7, gr g Martaline—Clipsy (FR) **Against All Odds Racing**
51 **CORDEY DANCER (FR)**, 5, b m Authorized (IRE)—Avoca Dancer (IRE) **Mr R. J. G. Lowe**
52 **COURTANDBOULD (IRE)**, 8, b g Court Cave (IRE)—Seaneen Mac Ri (IRE) **Craig & Laura Buckingham**
53 **CRAMBO**, 5, b g Saddler Maker (IRE)—Cardline (FR) **Sullivan Bloodstock Ltd & Chris Giles**
54 **CREGGAN WHITE HARE (IRE)**, 7, b br g Arcadio (GER)—Mia Zia (FR) **Mr S. Conway**
55 **CROSSRAIL**, 7, b m Rail Link—Get Me Home (IRE) **M. C. Denmark**
56 **DANDY MAG (FR)**, 9, b g Special Kaldoun (FR)—Naiade Mag (FR) **Mr G. L. Mercer**
57 **DE NAME EVADES ME (IRE)**, 10, b g Vinnie Roe (IRE)—Sound of The Crowd (IRE) **Brown Campbell James Foylan**
58 **DEHRADUN**, 6, b g Australia—Ridkata (IRE) **Mrs L.Day, Mr H.Burdett & Mr G.McPherson**
59 **DIV INE TARA**, 7, b m Kayf Tara—Mid Div And Creep **Mrs R Exall & Mr G Molen**
60 **DOC EL (IRE)**, 5, ch g Fracas (IRE)—Magpie (USA) **BDRSyndicates**
61 **DON'T STOP NOW**, 5, b g Champs Elysees—Trapeze **East India Racing**
62 **DREAM CHASER (FR)**, 4, b g Dream Ahead (USA)—Avodale (IRE) **Mr P Green & Partners**
63 **DREAMING OF GLORY (IRE)**, 6, b m Fame And Glory—Dream Function (IRE) **C. B. Brookes**
64 **DUBLIN FOUR (IRE)**, 8, ch g Arakan (USA)—Eluna **DI Adams, Ja Adams & G McPherson**
65 **EAGLE'S REALM**, 4, b g Free Eagle (IRE)—Regal Realm **Mr G. P. McPherson**
66 **EBONY WARRIOR (IRE)**, 4, br g Sholokhov (IRE)—Three Wood (IRE) **DI Adams, Ja Adams & G McPherson**
67 **ELHAM VALLEY (IRE)**, 5, gr g Tin Horse (IRE)—Dame du Floc (IRE) **Caveat Emptor Partnership**
68 **EYEOFTHESCORPION (IRE)**, 8, b g Scorpion (IRE)—Shuil Sharp (IRE) **With DI & Adams Adams**
69 **FASHION NOVA (IRE)**, 7, gr m Flemensfirth (USA)—Fashion's Worth (IRE) **A & K Ecofilm Ltd**
70 **FEAST (IRE)**, 5, b g Walk In The Park (IRE)—Lolli (IRE) **Sullivan Bloodstock Ltd & Chris Giles**
71 **FEEL THE PINCH**, 8, b g Librettist (USA)—Liqueur Rose **Mr B Jones & Son**
72 **FESTIVE GLORY (IRE)**, 6, b g Fame And Glory—Rose of Clare **Mrs J. Rees**
73 **FINAL NUDGE (IRE)**, 13, b g Kayf Tara—Another Shot (IRE) **Mrs J. Rees**
74 4, B g Gamut (IRE)—Final Run (IRE)
75 **FLANN**, 7, b g Brian Boru—Lady Karinga **Flann's Fans**
76 4, Ch f Soldier of Fortune (IRE)—Forever Young (IRE) **The Ravenstone Partnership**
77 **FORTHEGREATERGOOD (IRE)**, 8, b m Yeats (IRE)—Feast Or Famine (IRE) **Mrs J. A. Watts**
78 **FUJI ROCKS (IRE)**, 5, b g Jet Away—Star of The Season (IRE) **Guy Henriques & Michael Henriques**
79 **GENTLE LIFE**, 5, b m Gentlewave (IRE)—Luz de La Vida **Mr D. A. Thorpe**

MR FERGAL O'BRIEN - continued

80 **GET THE GAME (IRE)**, 7, b m Getaway (GER)—Sam Shuil (IRE) **Shaw Racing & Graeme McPherson**
81 **GETTHEPOT (IRE)**, 7, b g Getaway (GER)—Raheen Lady (IRE) **Shaw Racing & Graeme McPherson**
82 **GIGI'S BEACH**, 5, b g Oasis Dream—Clenor (IRE) **Miss S. Randell**
83 **GLOBAL FAME (IRE)**, 8, b g Fame And Glory—Kinard True (IRE) **C.Coley,Exors of Lord Vestey & ROA Arkle**
84 **GO TO WAR (IRE)**, 4, b g Soldier of Fortune (IRE)—Rate of Knots (IRE) **Mr G. Leon**
85 4, Br g Malinas (GER)—Golan Road (IRE)
86 **GOLDEN TAIPAN (IRE)**, 8, b g Golden Lariat (USA)—Rose of Taipan (IRE) **Double Barrels Of Courage**
87 **GOOD AND HARDY (IRE)**, 9, b g Westerner—Kilganey Maid (IRE) **The Groovy Gang**
88 **GORTROE JOE (IRE)**, 10, b g Beneficial—Rowlands Star (IRE) **J. T. Warner**
89 **GRAGEELAGH GIRL (IRE)**, 11, b m Craigsteel—Smiths Lady (IRE) **Mr F. M. O'Brien**
90 **GREAT HEART'JAC (FR)**, 7, br g Blue Bresil (FR)—Aqua Fontana (FR) **Mr L. D. Craze**
91 **GUMBALL (FR)**, 8, gr g No Risk At All (FR)—Good Time Girl (FR) **J. T. Warner**
92 **HARD AS NAILS**, 4, b f Black Sam Bellamy (IRE)—Cream Cracker **Mr R. Treacy**
93 **HEREWEGOHONEY (IRE)**, 6, b m Sageburg (IRE)—Knappogue Honey (IRE)

Middleham Park Racing & C and J Hobkirk
94 **HIDDEN BEAUTY**, 5, b m Kapgarde (FR)—Ma Councha (FR) **Nick Brown Racing**
95 **HIGH WELLS**, 8, b g High Chaparral (IRE)—Valencha **Mrs Jill Phillips & Graeme McPherson**
96 **HORIZON DOVE (FR)**, 5, b m Walk In The Park (IRE)—Fairytale Theatre (IRE) **Craig & Laura Buckingham**
97 **HORSE POWER (FR)**, 5, b g Coastal Path—Valle d'Ossau (FR) **Actionclad 2001 Ltd**
98 **HULLNBACK**, 5, b g Schiaparelli (GER)—Freydis (IRE) **We're Having A Mare (WHAM)**
99 **HUNNY MOON**, 8, ch m Flemensfirth (USA)—No More Money **C. B. Brookes**
100 **HUNTSMANS JOG (IRE)**, 8, b g Milan—Faucon **The Box 8 Partnership**
101 **HURRICANE HARVEY**, 8, b g Doyen (IRE)—Camp Fire (IRE) **Walid Marzouk & Richard Rowland**
102 **I'M WISER NOW (IRE)**, 8, b g Presenting—Reine Angevine (FR) **Mr J. C. Collett**
103 **IELLOW STAR (FR)**, 4, ch g Spanish Moon (USA)—Rose Star (FR) **DI Adams, Ja Adams & G McPherson**
104 **IMPERIAL ALCAZAR (IRE)**, 8, b g Vinnie Roe (IRE)—Maddy's Supreme (IRE) **Imperial Racing Partnership 2016**
105 **IMPERIAL ELYSIAN (IRE)**, 8, br g Kalanisi (IRE)—Diva Antonia (IRE) **Imperial Racing Partnership**
106 **IMPERIAL HURLEY (FR)**, 5, gr g Planteur (IRE)—Thalie Hurley (FR) **C & M Baker, K Ibberson, H Pearman**
107 **IMPERIAL LIGHTNING (IRE)**, 5, ch g Shantou (USA)—Vindonissa (IRE) **Imperial Racing Partnership 2016**
108 **IMPERIAL STORM (IRE)**, 6, ch g Shantou (USA)—Vindonissa (IRE) **Imperial Racing Partnership 2016**
109 **INCE (AUT)**, 5, gr m Reliable Man—Intricate Talent (USA) **Mr P. Loftus**
110 **JARVEYS PLATE (FR)**, 9, ch g Getaway (GER)—She's Got To Go (IRE)

The Yes No Wait Sorries & Mr Chris Coley
111 **JEREMY THE JINN (IRE)**, 7, br g Jeremy (USA)—Phantom Waters **Mrs J. Rees**
112 **JESSICA RABBIT**, 8, b m Mawatheeq (USA)—Intersky High (USA) **The Ladies Of Martins Hill**
113 **JOSIE ABBING (IRE)**, 8, b m Fame And Glory—Bella Venezia (IRE) **BDRSyndicates**
114 5, Ch g Mahler—Jumpingjude (IRE)
115 5, B m Universal (IRE)—Kahlua Cove **The FOB Racing Partnership 6**
116 **KALELULA**, 5, br m Kalanisi (IRE)—Akdara (IRE) **Craig & Laura Buckingham**
117 **KARL PHILIPPE (FR)**, 7, ch g Kentucky Dynamite (USA)—Kaer Gwell (FR)

C Coley, D Porter, H Redknapp, P Smith
118 **KINGSTON SUNFLOWER (FR)**, 5, bl m Authorized (IRE)—Kingston Acacia
119 **LADY JANE P (IRE)**, 6, b m Walk In The Park (IRE)—Rosee des Bieffes (FR) **The Shortlandoyle Syndicate**
120 **LANDEN CALLING (IRE)**, 6, gr g Watar (IRE)—Gill Hall Lady **The B Lucky Partnership**
121 **LASSUE**, 6, b m Geordieland (FR)—Annie Fleetwood **Mr W. Marzouk**
122 **LE MUR (FR)**, 5, b m Al Namix (FR)—Djafullime (FR) **The Humpty Dumpties**
123 **LEADING THEATRE (IRE)**, 6, b m Leading Light (IRE)—Theatre Days (IRE) **Mrs C. Kendrick**
124 **LEAVE HER TO ME**, 4, b f Kayf Tara—Marie Deja La (FR)
125 **LOCKDOWN DREAM**, 5, b g Cityscape—Makindi **Mr L. B. Carenza**
126 **LONG STAY**, 7, b g Nathaniel (IRE)—Mainstay **Mr R. Treacy**
127 **LORD P**, 5, b g Brazen Beau (AUS)—Netta (IRE) **Mr M. R. Breeze**
128 **LUNAR SOVEREIGN (IRE)**, 6, b g Dubawi (IRE)—Surprise Moment (IRE) **Craig & Laura Buckingham**
129 **LUTINEBELLA**, 6, b m Kayf Tara—West River (USA) **Blue StaRR Racing FOB**
130 **MAHON POINT**, 7, b g Kayf Tara—Freydis (IRE) **The Gud Times Partnership**
131 **MAMOON STAR (IRE)**, 4, b g Mamool (IRE)—Mariah Mooney (IRE) **The Sharnbrook Partnership**
132 **MANOTHEPEOPLE (IRE)**, 7, b g Mahler—Midnight Insanity (IRE) **The FOB Racing Partnership 2**
133 **MARBLE SANDS (FR)**, 6, gr g Martaline—Sans Rien (FR) **DI Adams, Ja Adams & G McPherson**
134 **MARQUIS OF CARABAS (IRE)**, 12, b br g Hurricane Run (IRE)—Miss Otis Regrets (IRE) **Mrs J. Rees**
135 **MAYBE DARK**, 6, b g Malinas (GER)—Nearly Dark **Miss S. Pilkington**
136 **MERRY BERRY**, 6, b m Malinas (GER)—Mayberry **Keeping The Dream Alive**

MR FERGAL O'BRIEN - continued

137 **MOON CHIME**, 4, b g Pether's Moon (IRE)—Bella (FR) **Dl Adams, Ja Adams & G McPherson**
138 **MOONSHINE SPIRIT**, 5, b g Telescope (IRE)—Liqueur Rose **The FOB Racing Partnership 5**
139 **MOOT COURT (IRE)**, 7, b g Court Cave (IRE)—Leney Dancer (IRE) **Ravenswell Renegades**
140 **MULBERRY HILL (IRE)**, 6, br m Califet (FR)—Massini Rose (IRE) **Dark Horse Racing Partnership Nine**
141 **NAIZAGAI (IRE)**, 5, b g Dark Angel (IRE)—Nazym (IRE) **Mr C. Kendrick**
142 **NIGHT DUTY (IRE)**, 6, br g Kalanisi (IRE)—Lerichi (IRE) **Dr Richard & Anne Rowland**
143 **NO NO JULIET (IRE)**, 9, br m Scorpion (IRE)—Full Imperatrice (FR) **Don Sebastiao Partnership**
144 **NO NO MAESTRO (IRE)**, 7, b g Mahler—Maisey Down **Don Sebastiao Partnership**
145 **NOTHIN TO ASK (IRE)**, 7, b g Ask—Nothin To Say (IRE) **The FOB Racing Partnership 11**
146 **ONAGATHERINGSTORM (IRE)**, 7, b g Imperial Monarch (IRE)—Springfield Mary (IRE) **Craig & Laura Buckingham**
147 **ONE HUNDRED NOTOUT (IRE)**, 6, b m Getaway (GER)—Roxtown **Glos Gipsies CC**
148 **ORDERED LIVES (IRE)**, 7, b m Shirocco (GER)—Count On Me (IRE) **Mr M. G. St Quinton**
149 **OSLO**, 5, b g Gleneagles (IRE)—Intercontinental **Mr N. Brereton**
150 **OUR COLOSSUS (IRE)**, 7, b g Yeats (IRE)—Itsalark (IRE) **Ray Treacy & Shaun Staplehurst**
151 **PAINT THE DREAM**, 8, b g Brian Boru—Vineuil (FR) **Mr D. Brace**
152 **PEERLESS BEAUTY**, 6, b m Phoenix Reach (IRE)—Sudden Beat **Smell The Flowers**
153 **PEKING ROSE**, 7, br g Passing Glance—Miniature Rose **The Coln Valley Partnership**
154 **PERCULATOR**, 5, b m Telescope (IRE)—Ancora (IRE)
155 **PETITE POWER (IRE)**, 13, b g Subtle Power (IRE)—Little Serena **P J King & Son**
156 **PHILLAPA SUE (IRE)**, 7, b m Scorpion (IRE)—Shuil Sharp (IRE) **Adams, Burdett & Graham**
157 **POETIC MUSIC**, 4, ch f Poet's Voice—Mofeyda (IRE) **Mr I. El Magdoub**
158 **POLISH**, 7, b g Teofilo (IRE)—Polygon (USA) **Caveat Emptor Partnership**
159 **POP THE CHAMPAGNE (FR)**, 6, b m Spanish Moon (USA)—Six Pack (FR) **Mrs Jill Phillips & Graeme McPherson**
160 **PRELUDE TO GLORY (IRE)**, 6, b m Fame And Glory—Prelude **Dl Adams, Ja Adams & G McPherson**
161 **PRIDE OF LECALE**, 11, b g Multiplex—Rock Gossip (IRE) **Noel Fehily Racing Syndicate 01**
162 **PRINCESS PRIYA (IRE)**, 5, b m Flemensfirth (USA)—Rosa Rugosa (IRE) **Mr Oscar Singh & Miss Priya Purewal**
163 **PULL AGAIN GREEN (IRE)**, 5, b g Kalanisi (IRE)—Clogher Valley (IRE) **Roy & Sally Green Tony & Karen Exall**
164 **PUNCTUATION**, 5, b g Dansili—Key Point (IRE) **Mr G. Leon**
165 **RATFACEMCDOUGALL (IRE)**, 9, b g Robin des Champs (FR)—Milano Bay (IRE) **Mrs C. Kendrick**
166 **REBEL ROXY (IRE)**, 6, ch m Sholokhov (IRE)—Sorivera **Mr I. Slatter**
167 **RED RIVER VALLEY (IRE)**, 6, b g Imperial Monarch (IRE)—Sunset View (IRE)
168 **REVE DE NIAMH**, 5, b m Telescope (IRE)—En Reve
169 **RIGHT DESTINATION (IRE)**, 8, b g Dubai Destination (USA)—Sainte Careigne (FR)
          The Yes No Wait Sorries & Mr Chris Coley
170 **ROBYNDZONE (IRE)**, 8, b g Frammassone (IRE)—Rebecca Susan **East India Racing**
171 **ROYAL MOGUL (IRE)**, 6, b g Doyen (IRE)—Tearaway Queen (IRE) **Craig & Laura Buckingham**
172 **ROYAL PRACTITIONER (IRE)**, 9, b m Dr Massini (IRE)—Valdas Queen (IRE) **A. P. Racing**
173 **SAMBA DANCER (FR)**, 7, b g Zambezi Sun—Dancing Amber (GER) **KHDRP**
174 **SAMMYLOU (IRE)**, 9, b g Beneficial—Carrigeen Diamond (IRE) **Dl Adams, Ja Adams & G McPherson**
175 4, B f Epaulette (AUS)—Santacus (IRE) **Mr J. C. Collett**
176 **SAVASTANO (FR)**, 4, b g Martaline—Frivolite (FR) **Dl Adams, Ja Adams & G McPherson**
177 **SCARLETT CLIPPER (IRE)**, 5, b m Milan—Crimson Flower (IRE) **Blue StaRR Racing FOB**
178 **SEISMIC WAVE**, 5, b g Gentlewave (IRE)—Sunnyland **Anne West and Pete James, Bill Foylan**
179 **SHALLOW RIVER (IRE)**, 6, b br g Ocovango—Nicola's Girl (IRE) **Mick Fitzgerald Racing Club**
180 **SHE'S A NOVELTY (IRE)**, 7, b m Approve (IRE)—Novel Fun (IRE) **Sally's Angels**
181 **SILVER HALLMARK**, 8, br gr g Shirocco (GER)—Gaye Sophie **Mr & Mrs William Rucker**
182 **SISTER MICHAEL (IRE)**, 6, b g Fame And Glory—Derriana (IRE) **The Odd Lot**
183 **SMOKING PIGEON**, 8, b g Midnight Legend—Velvet Dove **Kilkenny Racing Partnership**
184 **SORCERESS MEDEA (IRE)**, 5, b m Walk In The Park (IRE)—Nuit des Chartreux (FR) **The ARB Partnership**
185 **STACKS MOUNTAIN**, 9, b g Black Sam Bellamy (IRE)—Well Maid **Mr F. M. O'Brien**
186 **STONER'S CHOICE**, 7, br g Great Pretender (IRE)—High Benefit (IRE) **Mrs C. Kendrick**
187 **STUDENT CHAP (IRE)**, 6, br g Presenting—Prowler (IRE) **Shaw Racing & Graeme McPherson**
188 **SUNSET MELODY (IRE)**, 5, b m Westerner—Bobset Leader (IRE) **Nick Brown Racing**
189 **SURTITLE (IRE)**, 6, b g Presenting—Annabaloo (IRE) **Mrs V. F. Burke**
190 **SWORDSMAN (IRE)**, 8, br g Doyen (IRE)—Battle Over (FR) **Ms J. E. McGivern**
191 **TASHUNKA (IRE)**, 9, b m Flemensfirth (USA)—Las Palmlas (IRE) **The FOB Racing Partnership 3**
192 **TED DA TITAN**, 6, b g Kayf Tara—Aeronautica (IRE) **Mrs C. Kendrick**
193 **TED'S FRIEND (IRE)**, 6, b g Dylan Thomas (IRE)—Water Rock **Mrs C. Kendrick**
194 **TEETOTALLER**, 4, b g Black Sam Bellamy (IRE)—One Wild Night **Mennell, Logan and Coneyworths**
195 **TEQANY (IRE)**, 8, gr g Dark Angel (IRE)—Capulet Monteque (IRE) **Mrs J. A. Watts**

MR FERGAL O'BRIEN - continued

196 **TEQUILA BLAZE**, 8, b m Sakhee (USA)—Miss Sassi **The Tequila Tipplers**
197 **THE BEES KNEES (IRE)**, 7, b g Oscar (IRE)—Dolphins View (IRE) **Mrs C. Kendrick**
198 **THE BOGMANS BALL**, 5, b g Kayf Tara—Gaspaisie (FR) **Mrs M. Devine**
199 **THE GIRL THAT SANG (IRE)**, 8, b m Flemensfirth (USA)—Soul Mate (IRE) **Mr S. Conway**
200 **THE TOOJUMPA**, 9, b m Midnight Legend—Sunnyland **The FOB Racing Partnership 9**
201 **THEGALLANTWAY (IRE)**, 9, b g Stowaway—Imogens Fancy (IRE) **Caveat Emptor Partnership**
202 **THESETHINGSHAPPEN**, 4, b g Siyouni (FR)—National Day (IRE) **Ray Treacy & Jason Reed**
203 **THUNDERSOCKSSUNDAE (IRE)**, 7, b g Yeats (IRE)—Roseabel (IRE) **4 Left Footers & A Blewnose**
204 , B f Beat Hollow—Tickity Bleue **BDRSyndicates**
205 **TIMBERMAN (IRE)**, 7, b g Califet (FR)—Millrock Lady (IRE) **Mr J. Turner**
206 **TIMELESS BEAUTY (IRE)**, 7, b m Yeats (IRE)—Love Divided (IRE) **McNeill Family & Patrick&scott Bryceland**
207 **TIP TOP CAT (IRE)**, 7, b g Milan—Pilgara (IRE) **Ms J. E. McGivern**
208 **TRIOPAS (IRE)**, 10, b g Stowaway—Aine Dubh (IRE) **Mr F. M. O'Brien**
209 **ULTIMATE FAME (IRE)**, 6, b m Fame And Glory—Ultimate Echo (IRE) **Foxtrot Racing Syndicate 1**
210 **ULTIMATE GETAWAY (IRE)**, 8, b g Getaway (GER)—Ultimate Echo (IRE) **Foxtrot Racing: Ultimate Getaway**
211 **UNE DE LA SENIERE (FR)**, 7, ch m Noroit (GER)—Smabelle (FR) **Millennium Racing Club**
212 **VALENTINO DANCER**, 7, ch g Mastercraftsman (IRE)—Bertie's Best **Richard Hames & Alex Govorusa**
213 **VOLKOVKA (FR)**, 5, b m Camelot—Drole de Dame (IRE) **The Tyringham Partnership**
214 **WE GOTTA GETAWAY (IRE)**, 5, b g Getaway (GER)—Clooney Eile (IRE) **With DI & Adams Adams**
215 **YAUTHYM (GER)**, 6, b g Authorized (IRE)—Ymlaen (IRE) **The Oakley Partnership**
216 **YOUNG BUSTER (IRE)**, 6, b g Yeats (IRE)—Shatani (IRE) **The Good Stock Syndicate**
217 **ZALVADOS (FR)**, 9, ch g Soldier of Fortune (IRE)—Zariyana (IRE) **Mr D. C. Mercer**
218 **ZUCAYAN (FR)**, 5, b g Lucayan (FR)—John Quatz (FR) **Mr I. Slatter**
219 **ZULU DAWN (IRE)**, 8, b g Fame And Glory—Maslam (IRE) **Turf Club 2020 & Graeme McPherson**

THREE-YEAR-OLDS

220 **AILISH T**, b f Bated Breath—Meddling **Mr R. Treacy**
221 **JE FEEL AU POTEAU (FR)**, ch g Feel Like Dancing—Six Pack (FR)

Other Owners: Mr D. L. Adams, Mrs J. A. Adams, Mrs C. A. M. Baker, Mr M. J. Baker, Mr R. H. Beevor, C. B. Brookes, Sir M. F. Broughton, Mr P. Bryceland, Mr S. Bryceland, Mr P. J. Buist, Mr H. Burdett, Mr C. Buckingham, Mrs L. K. Buckingham, Mrs P. J. Buist, Mr H. Burdett, Mr D. J. Burke, Mr A. N. Cheyne, C. S. J. Coley, J. T. Devine, Mrs K. G. Exall, First With Mortgages Limited, Mr C. M. Giles, Mr A. Govorusa, Mr C. M. Graham, Mr P. T. Green, Mr R. D. A. Hames, Mr G. M. Q. Henriques, M. Henriques, Miss K. J. Ibberson, Mr B. M. Jones, Mrs N. Jones, Mr W. Jones, Mr J. J. King, Mrs V. C. King, D. Leon, & Lowe, Mrs C. Mackness, Col A. J. E. Malcolm, Mr W. Marzouk, McNeill Family Ltd, Mr G. P. McPherson, Mr G. Molen, Mr F. M. O'Brien, Mr I. M. O'Doherty, Mr M. P. Obrien, Mr H. J. Pearman, Mrs J. D. Phillips, Miss D. C. Porter, Miss P. Purewal, Mr J. Reed, Mrs A. Rowland, Dr R. N. Rowland, Shaw Racing Partnership 2, Mr A. Singh, Ms D. J. Spencer, Ms C. L. Spencer-Herbert, Mr S. Staplehurst, Sullivan Bloodstock Limited, The Yes No Wait Sorries, Mr R. Treacy, Turf Club 2020, J. T. Warner, Mrs R. B. Weaver, Mr P. Whitehead, T. C. Wilson.

Assistant Trainer: Sally Randell.

NH Jockey: Connor Brace, Paddy Brennan.

---

405 **MR JEDD O'KEEFFE**, Leyburn
Postal: **Highbeck Lodge, Brecongill, Coverham, Leyburn, North Yorkshire, DL8 4TJ**
Contacts: PHONE **01969 640330** MOBILE **07710 476705**
EMAIL **jedd@jeddokeefferacing.co.uk** WEBSITE **www.jeddokeefferacing.co.uk**

1 **ABUNDANT MOON (IRE)**, 4, b f Galileo (IRE)—Replete **John & Jessica Dance**
2 **AIR RAID**, 7, b g Raven's Pass (USA)—Siren Sound **Caron & Paul Chapman**
3 **BURROW SEVEN**, 5, gr g Kayf Tara—Gaye Sophie **Burrow Seven Racing Club**
4 **DEVIL'S ANGEL**, 6, gr g Dark Angel (IRE)—Rocking The Boat (IRE) **Titanium Racing Club**
5 **DREAM TOGETHER (IRE)**, 5, ch g Dream Ahead (USA)—Shamsalmaidan (IRE) **The Fatalists**
6 **FAIRFIELD FERRATA**, 6, b m Kayf Tara—Via Ferrata (FR) **Mrs J. A. Darling**
7 **FRINGILL DIKE (IRE)**, 5, ch g Mahler—Credo Star (IRE) **Caron & Paul Chapman**
8 , 4, Ch g Proconsul—Lucinda Lamb **Miss S.E. Hall & Mr C. Platts**
9 **MARTHA WILLOW**, 5, b m Martaline—Urticaire (FR) **Caron & Paul Chapman**

MR JEDD O'KEEFFE - continued

10 **MIAH GRACE,** 7, b m Malinas (GER)—Silver Gypsy (IRE) **Caron & Paul Chapman**
11 **MIRACLE EAGLE (IRE),** 5, b m Free Eagle (IRE)—Tartessian (IRE) **Yorkshire Owners Racing Club 2**
12 **MISS LAMB,** 6, b m Passing Glance—Lucinda Lamb **Miss S. E. Hall**
13 **MR BRAMLEY,** 4, ch g Schiaparelli (GER)—Apple Days **Mr H. M. Posner**
14 **MR SCRUMPY,** 8, b g Passing Glance—Apple Days **Mr H. M. Posner**
15 **PERCY WILLIS,** 4, b g Sir Percy—Peace Lily **The Unlikely Lads**
16 **RAINBOW'S GIFT,** 4, b g Nathaniel (IRE)—Riot of Colour **Highbeck Racing 1**
17 **RARE GROOVE (IRE),** 7, ch g Lope de Vega (IRE)—Ascot Lady (IRE) **John & Jessica Dance**
18 **RATTLE OWL,** 6, b g Kayf Tara—Rattlin **Racing4Business Ltd**
19 **SAISONS D'OR (IRE),** 7, ro g Havana Gold (IRE)—Deux Saisons **The Fatalists**
20 **VINTAGE FIZZ,** 5, ch g Sulamani (IRE)—Milan Athlete (IRE) **Manor House Racing**

THREE-YEAR-OLDS

21 **BRASINGAMAN BELLA,** b f Black Sam Bellamy (IRE)—Brasingaman Hifive **Mr R. J. Morgan**
22 **COEUR DE COEURS,** b f Mondialiste (IRE)—Blushing Heart **Mrs Sarah Pearson**
23 **COTAI GREY (IRE),** gr g Cotai Glory—Docklands Grace (USA) **Mr A. J. Peake**
24 B g Highland Reel (IRE)—Destalink **Highbeck Racing 5**
25 **GLOBAL PEACE,** b g Mondialiste (IRE)—La Arcadia (FR) **Mr & Mrs G. Turnbull**
26 **GOLDEN VINTAGE,** b f Golden Horn—Millevini (IRE) **Titanium Racing Club**
27 **HILTS (IRE),** b g New Bay—Creme Anglaise **Ellipsis**
28 **KENDRED FIRE (IRE),** ch g Anjaal—Champion Place **Yorkshire Owners Racing Club 1**
29 **KINCADE (IRE),** ch g Nathaniel (IRE)—Topaze Blanche (IRE) **Ellipsis**
30 **MISCHIEF MADE (IRE),** b c Invincible Spirit (IRE)—More Mischief **Caron & Paul Chapman**
31 **MYSTIC MOONSHADOW,** b f Showcasing—Dream of Joy (IRE) **Mystic Moonshadow Racing Club**
32 **NIKHI,** ch f Nathaniel (IRE)—Elysian Fields (GR) **Ellipsis**
33 Ch g Churchill (IRE)—Organza **Caron & Paul Chapman**
34 **PRINCE ACHILLE,** b g Reliable Man—Halle Bop **J. E. D. O'Keeffe**
35 **PUNTASTIC (IRE),** b g Dark Angel (IRE)—Tarakala (IRE) **John & Jessica Dance**
36 **ROLLAJAM (IRE),** ch g Belardo (IRE)—Papaya (IRE) **John & Jessica Dance**

TWO-YEAR-OLDS

37 **EVERYTHINGSHEWANTS,** b f 12/03 Muhaarar—Stella Point (IRE) (Pivotal) (26000) **Ellipsis II**
38 B f 02/03 Acclamation—Fanta Dielo (USA) (Bernardini (USA)) **Caron & Paul Chapman**
39 Ch f 27/03 Mondialiste (IRE)—Moghrama (IRE) (Harbour Watch (IRE)) **Mr & Mrs G. Turnbull**
40 **NOBODY TOLD ME,** b c 25/03 Intello (GER)—Dubka (Dubawi (IRE)) (42000) **Ellipsis II**
41 B f 13/04 Free Eagle (IRE)—Organza (Pour Moi) **Caron & Paul Chapman**
42 **OUT OF MISCHIEF,** b f 17/03 Invincible Spirit (IRE)—More Mischief (Azamour (IRE)) **Caron & Paul Chapman**

Assistant Trainer: Tim Hogg, Leanne Kershaw.

Amateur Jockey: Bailey Burns-Lewis.

406
MR DAVID O'MEARA, Upper Helmsley
Postal: **Willow Farm, Upper Helmsley, York, Yorkshire, YO41 1JX**
Contacts: PHONE **01759 372427** MOBILE **07747 352418**
EMAIL **info@davidomeara.co.uk** WEBSITE **www.davidomeara.co.uk**

1 **AL QAASIM (IRE),** 5, ch g Free Eagle (IRE)—Nebraas
2 **ALLIGATOR ALLEY,** 5, b g Kingman—Overturned
3 **ALPHA CRU (IRE),** 4, ch f Australia—Solfege
4 **ARRANMORE,** 5, b g Oasis Dream—Ceisteach (IRE)
5 **AZANO,** 6, b g Oasis Dream—Aznara (IRE)
6 **BLUE FOR YOU (IRE),** 4, ch g New Approach (IRE)—Love In The Sun (IRE)
7 **COLD STARE (IRE),** 7, b g Intense Focus (USA)—Ziria (IRE)
8 **COSMOS RAJ,** 4, b g Iffraaj—Cosmos Pink

MR DAVID O'MEARA - continued

9 **DARKNESS (FR)**, 4, b g Siyouni (FR)—Kerila (FR)
10 **DARWELL LION (IRE)**, 4, b c The Last Lion (IRE)—Darwell (IRE)
11 **EEETEE (IRE)**, 4, b g Fast Company (IRE)—Chiquita Picosa (USA)
12 **ESCOBAR (IRE)**, 8, b g Famous Name—Saying Grace (IRE)
13 **FIRMAMENT**, 10, b g Cape Cross (IRE)—Heaven Sent
14 **FROG AND TOAD (IRE)**, 4, b g Mehmas (IRE)—Fast Pick (IRE)
15 **GET SHIRTY (IRE)**, 6, b g Teofilo (IRE)—Soccer Mom (GER)
16 **GULLIVER**, 8, b g Sayif (IRE)—Sweet Coincidence
17 **HARD SOLUTION**, 6, ch g Showcasing—Copy-Cat
18 **HEADINGLEY (IRE)**, 4, b g Dawn Approach (IRE)—Gold Bubbles (USA)
19 **HORTZADAR**, 7, b g Sepoy (AUS)—Clouds of Magellan (USA)
20 **IMPROVISED (IRE)**, 4, ch f Raven's Pass (USA)—Kirouna (FR)
21 **KING'S COMMANDER (FR)**, 4, b g Authorized (IRE)—Millionaia (IRE)
22 **LOCAL BAY**, 4, b c Cable Bay (IRE)—Local Fancy
23 4, B f Kingman—Loch Jipp (USA)
24 **LORD GLITTERS (FR)**, 9, gr ro g Whipper (USA)—Lady Glitters (FR)
25 **MALTBY RAIDER (FR)**, 4, b g Fast Company (IRE)—Maundays Bay (IRE)
26 **MUSCIKA**, 8, b g Kyllachy—Miss Villefranche
27 **MYTHICAL MADNESS**, 11, b g Dubawi (IRE)—Miss Delila (USA)
28 **NAVAL CAPTAIN (IRE)**, 4, b g No Nay Never (USA)—Van de Cappelle (IRE)
29 **NOMADIC EMPIRE (IRE)**, 4, b g Kodiac—Beatify (IRE)
30 **ORBAAN**, 7, b g Invincible Spirit (IRE)—Contradict
31 **PATONTHEBACK (IRE)**, 4, b g Kodi Bear (IRE)—Miss Brief (IRE)
32 **PISANELLO (IRE)**, 5, b g Raven's Pass (USA)—Painting (IRE)
33 **QUEEN'S FAIR**, 4, b f Dansili—Queen's Best
34 **RHOSCOLYN**, 4, b g Territories (IRE)—Zeyran (IRE)
35 **SAFRAN (FR)**, 5, b g Dabirsim (FR)—Sosquaw (FR)
36 **SAGAUTEUR (FR)**, 6, b g Literato (FR)—Saga d'Ouilly (FR)
37 **SCHABANG (GER)**, 4, b f Pastorius (GER)—Staying Alive (GER)
38 **SHELIR (IRE)**, 6, b gr g Dark Angel (IRE)—Shelina (IRE)
39 **SOUL SEEKER (IRE)**, 5, b g Oasis Dream—Mad About You (IRE)
40 **STAR SHIELD**, 7, ch g Helmet (AUS)—Perfect Star
41 **STARSHIBA**, 5, b g Acclamation—Dashiba
42 **STAY SMART**, 4, b c Brazen Beau (AUS)—Absolutely Right (IRE)
43 **STONIFIC (IRE)**, 9, b g Sea The Stars (IRE)—Sapphire Pendant (IRE)
44 **SUDONA**, 4, b m Zoffany (IRE)—Vickers Vimy
45 **SUMMERGHAND (IRE)**, 8, b g Lope de Vega (IRE)—Kate The Great
46 **SURPRISE PICTURE (IRE)**, 4, b g Kodiac—Lovely Surprise (IRE)
47 **TAMASKA**, 4, ch g Starspangledbanner (AUS)—Premiere Danseuse
48 **TAMMANI**, 5, b g Make Believe—Gentle On My Mind (IRE)
49 **TENDENTIOUS**, 4, b g Intello (GER)—Capacious
50 **THUNDER BEAUTY (IRE)**, 4, b f Night of Thunder (IRE)—Quiania (IRE)
51 **TIGER TOUCH (USA)**, 5, b g American Pharoah (USA)—Osaila (IRE)
52 **YOUNG FIRE (FR)**, 7, b g Fuisse (FR)—Young Majesty (USA)
53 **ZENZERO (IRE)**, 4, ch g Twilight Son—Evangelical

THREE-YEAR-OLDS

54 **ALL ABOUT FREEDOM**, b f Muhaarar—All About Time
55 **ANIMATO**, ch c Ulysses (IRE)—Blithe
56 **AUTUMN FESTIVAL**, b c Poet's Voice—Kammaan
57 **BEAUZON**, b g Brazen Beau (AUS)—Pepper Lane
58 **BENZEMA**, b c Invincible Spirit (IRE)—Al Mahmeyah
59 **BIN HAYYAN (IRE)**, gr c Dark Angel (IRE)—Anahita (FR)
60 **CATHY'S GIRL (IRE)**, b f Belardo (IRE)—Chanter
61 **CITY VAULTS**, gr g Dark Angel (IRE)—Priceless Jewel
62 **COOLMEEN ROYAL (FR)**, b c Invincible Spirit (IRE)—Naissance Royale (IRE)
63 **COOLMEEN VEGA (IRE)**, ch c Lope de Vega (IRE)—Power's Dream (IRE)
64 **DARKER**, b g Twilight Son—Spinatrix
65 Ch c Exceed And Excel (AUS)—Dear Dancer (IRE)

MR DAVID O'MEARA - continued

66 **DEBIT CARD,** b f Adaay (IRE)—Starbotton
67 **DEPART A MINUIT,** b c Twilight Son—Grand Depart
68 **FLAME TALON (IRE),** b c Profitable (IRE)—Caldy Dancer (IRE)
69 **FORTUNE TOLD,** b f Mondialiste (IRE)—Reachforthestars (IRE)
70 **HEAD CHEF (IRE),** b g Awtaad (IRE)—Always A Dream
71 **HOTTER IN TIME,** ch f Hot Streak (IRE)—Sciarra
72 **ICONICDAAY,** b f Adaay (IRE)—Bond Bombshell
73 **IMPERIAL KHAN (IRE),** b c Kodiac—Beatify (IRE)
74 **IRISH APPROACH (IRE),** b g New Approach (IRE)—Gimasha
75 **IUR CINN TRA (IRE),** ch c Starspangledbanner (AUS)—Appreciating
76 **KARDINYA (IRE),** b c Mehmas—Sapphire Diva (IRE)
77 **KING'S CRUSADER,** b c New Approach (IRE)—Thousandkissesdeep (IRE)
78 **LACONIC,** b g Oasis Dream—Brevity (USA)
79 **LOVE INTEREST,** b f Time Test—Wild Mimosa (IRE)
80 **MAY BLOSSOM,** b f Mayson—Almond Branches
81 **MICK MCHUGH,** b c Caravaggio (USA)—Tanouma (USA)
82 **MIDHEAVEN (IRE),** b f Elzaam (AUS)—Moonstone Magic
83 **PHRYNE (IRE),** b f Mehmas—Doctrine
84 **REEL PROSPECT (IRE),** b g Highland Reel (IRE)—Candy Ride (IRE)
85 **SAMUEL SPADE (GER),** b g Myboycharlie (IRE)—Summarily (IRE)
86 **SCOTCH MISTRESS,** br f Twilight Son—La Rosiere (USA)
87 **SMILING JAYNE (IRE),** b br f Farhh—Limber Up (IRE)
88 B g Belardo (IRE)—Snowtime (IRE)
89 B f Australia—Solfege
90 B f Camelot—Spiritual Praise (IRE)
91 **STROMBOLI (IRE),** b g Acclamation—Shanooan (USA)
92 **TIME QUEST,** b g Time Test—Rainbow's Edge
93 **UNCLE JOHN,** b g Twilight Son—Nickels And Dimes (IRE)
94 **ZWIFT,** b f Kodiac—Yukon Girl (IRE)

TWO-YEAR-OLDS

95 B f 14/04 Harry Angel (IRE)—Absolutely Right (IRE) (Teofilo (IRE)) (20000)
96 **ADVANTAGE (IRE),** ch c 26/01 Profitable (IRE)—Dutch Rose (IRE) (Dutch Art) (57143)
97 Gr c 25/03 El Kabeir (USA)—Amurra (Oasis Dream) (29762)
98 B f 30/01 Mondialiste (IRE)—Barefoot Contessa (FR) (Dansili)
99 B c 19/03 Mondialiste (IRE)—Bogside Theatre (IRE) (Fruits of Love (USA))
100 **CARING,** b f 08/05 Dark Angel (IRE)—Ardent (Pivotal)
101 B f 06/04 Harry Angel (IRE)—Dear Dancer (IRE) (Teofilo (IRE)) (10000)
102 B c 18/04 Sioux Nation (USA)—Dutch Lilly (Dutch Art)
103 B f 20/04 Churchill (IRE)—Elizabelle (IRE) (Westerner) (51020)
104 **EPIC EFFECT,** b f 10/03 Ulysses (IRE)—Oasis Mirage (Oasis Dream)
105 B c 02/05 U S Navy Flag (USA)—Fresh Strike (Smart Strike (CAN)) (75000)
106 Gr f 02/05 Caravaggio (USA)—Grey Sky Blue (IRE) (Dylan Thomas (IRE))
107 B c 05/04 Ribchester (IRE)—Hoyamy (Dark Angel (IRE)) (38000)
108 B f 14/03 Mondialiste (IRE)—Indrahar (IRE) (Raven's Pass (USA))
109 **JUST JANET,** b f 09/01 Zoustar (AUS)—Coral Sea (Excelebration (IRE)) (55000)
110 B c 26/02 Mayson—Mary Stewart (IRE) (Dawn Approach (IRE))
111 B c 29/02 Massaat (IRE)—Matron (Bahamian Bounty)
112 Gr c 06/04 Markaz (IRE)—Mattinata (Tiger Hill (IRE)) (19048)
113 B f 09/02 Kodi Bear (IRE)—Midnight Martini (Night Shift (USA)) (60000)
114 B f 14/02 Zoustar (AUS)—Moons of Jupiter (USA) (War Front (USA)) (175000)
115 **NEXA BAY (IRE),** b f 05/04 New Bay (IRE)—Nexxia (FR) (Maxios) (10000)
116 B c 01/04 Ribchester (IRE)—Patterned (Dansili) (35000)
117 Ch c 22/04 The Gurkha (IRE)—Percy's Bird (IRE) (Sir Percy)
118 B c 23/04 Kodiac—Perfect Fun (Marju (IRE)) (125000)
119 B c 27/03 Profitable (IRE)—Poole Belle (IRE) (Canford Cliffs (IRE)) (22000)
120 Ch f 08/04 Sioux Nation (USA)—Queen Grace (Choisir (AUS)) (17007)
121 **RAINCLOUD,** ch f 07/03 Ulysses (IRE)—Flood Warning (Pivotal)
122 B c 30/03 Requinto (IRE)—Snowtime (IRE) (Galileo (IRE))

MR DAVID O'MEARA - continued

123 B f 10/05 Zoffany (IRE)—Solfege (Shamardal (USA))
124 B c 03/04 Highland Reel (IRE)—Spiritual Praise (IRE) (Acclamation)
125 **STAR OF LADY M,** gr f 31/03 Havana Grey—Abraj Dubai (USA) (Street Cry (IRE)) (15000)
126 Gr c 09/02 Roaring Lion (USA)—Stream Song (Mastercraftsman (IRE)) (120000)
127 B c 25/03 Muhaarar—Symposium (Exceed And Excel (AUS)) (15306)
128 **THE ANGELUS BELLE (IRE),** b f 11/04 Dandy Man (IRE)—Annamanamoux (USA) (Leroidesanimaux (BRZ)) (33333)
129 Ch f 09/03 Teofilo (IRE)—Trapeze (Pivotal) (22000)
130 **TWILIGHT TRYST (IRE),** b f 20/02 Twilight Son—Eleganza (IRE) (Balmont (USA)) (35000)
131 **VALE DOLOBO DANCER (IRE),** ch c 07/05 Mastercraftsman (IRE)—Tolzey (USA) (Rahy (USA)) (23000)
132 **ZEBADAAY,** b c 07/04 Adaay (IRE)—Springing Baroness (Bertolini (USA)) (49524)

Assistant Trainer: Jason Kelly.

Flat Jockey: Daniel Tudhope, Jason Watson. **Apprentice Jockey:** Mark Winn.

407

MRS DANIELLE O'NEILL, North Fawley
Postal: **The Old Granary, North Fawley, Wantage, Oxfordshire, OX12 9NJ**
Contacts: **PHONE 01488 639350 MOBILE 07931 193790**
EMAIL danni@fawleyhousestud.com

1 **BARDD (IRE),** 10, b g Dylan Thomas (IRE)—Zarawa (IRE) **Fawley House Stud**
2 **COMMANDER MILLER,** 8, b g Shirocco (GER)—Milliegait **Fawley House Stud**
3 **DEER HUNTER (IRE),** 6, b g Fame And Glory—Subtle Gem (IRE) **Fawley House Stud**
4 **GOAHEADWITHTHEPLAN (IRE),** 7, b g Stowaway—Backandillo (IRE) **Fawley House Stud**
5 **VERSATILITY,** 8, b g Yeats (IRE)—Stravinsky Dance **Fawley House Stud**

Assistant Trainer: Stephen O'Neill.

408

MR JOHN O'NEILL, Bicester
Postal: **Hall Farm, Stratton Audley, Nr Bicester, Oxfordshire, OX27 9BT**
Contacts: **PHONE 01869 277202 MOBILE 07785 394128**
EMAIL jgoneill4@gmail.com

1 **CAPPARATTIN,** 7, b g Universal (IRE)—Little Miss Prim **J. G. O'Neill**
2 **ONURBIKE,** 14, b g Exit To Nowhere (USA)—Lay It Off (IRE) **J. G. O'Neill**
3 **SLEPTWITHMEBOOTSON,** 7, b m Universal (IRE)—Temple Heather **Ms L. M. Keane**
4 **SONGDANCE,** 5, b m Norse Dancer (IRE)—Overlay **Ms L. M. Keane**
5 **W S GILBERT,** 8, b g Librettist (USA)—Little Miss Prim **Ms L. M. Keane**

409

MR JONJO O'NEILL, Cheltenham
Postal: **Jackdaws Castle, Temple Guiting, Cheltenham, Gloucestershire, GL54 5XU**
Contacts: **PHONE 01386 584209**
EMAIL racingoffice@jonjooneillracing.com WEBSITE www.jonjooneillracing.com

1 **A DISTANT PLACE (IRE),** 7, b g Sunday Break (JPN)—South Africa (FR) **The Four Bosses**
2 **ALL THE GLORY,** 5, b m Fame And Glory—Glorybe (GER) **TopSpeed Thoroughbreds**
3 **AN TAILLIUR (FR),** 6, gr g Authorized (IRE)—Dirama (FR) **Mr Pat Hickey**
4 **ANNIE MC (IRE),** 8, b m Mahler—Classic Mari (IRE) **Coral Champions Club**
5 **ANY SUNDAY SUNDAY (IRE),** 6, b g Califet (FR)—My Valley (IRE) **Mrs Fitri Hay**
6 **ANYHARMINASKING (IRE),** 5, b g Getaway (GER)—Collen Beag (IRE) **Mrs Gay Smith**
7 **ANYWAYYOULOOKATIT (IRE),** 9, b g Presenting—Whyalla (IRE) **Mr J. P. McManus**
8 **APACHE CREEK (IRE),** 7, ch g Shantou (USA)—Galshan (IRE) **Team Tuff**
9 **ARRIVEDERCI (FR),** 7, gr g Martaline—Etoile d'Ainay (FR) **Martin Broughton & Friends 1**

MR JONJO O'NEILL - continued

10 **ASHFIELD PADDY (IRE)**, 8, b g Publisher (USA)—Thats Grace (IRE) **The Hon Mrs E. J. Wills**
11 **BAISE MON TCHU (IRE)**, 4, b g Shirocco (GER)—Lady Elite (IRE) **Mr Danny Walker**
12 **BEAN IN TROUBLE (IRE)**, 8, gr g Sulamani (IRE)—Bouncing Bean **The Piranha Partnership**
13 **BERTIE'S BANDANA (IRE)**, 5, b g Notnowcato—Alright Kitty (IRE) **DYDB Marketing Limited**
14 **BETHKA (IRE)**, 4, b br f Walk In The Park (IRE)—Lakil Princess (IRE) **Mr Steve Killalea**
15 **BETTY'S BANJO (IRE)**, 5, b m Fame And Glory—Betty's The Best (IRE) **Mrs Fitri Hay**
16 **BIOWAVEGO (IRE)**, 5, b g Presenting—Clara Bel La (IRE) **P14 Medical Ltd & Dydb Marketing Ltd.**
17 **BLUE SHARK (IRE)**, 5, b g Shirocco (GER)—Meara Trasna (IRE) **The Ocean Partnership**
18 **BOB BOB RICARD (IRE)**, 4, b g Bathyrhon (GER)—Russian Memories (FR) **Mr Paul Downing**
19 **CAME FROM NOTHING (IRE)**, 4, b g Beat Hollow—By The Hour (IRE) **Mr Danny Walker**
20 **CARRIGDOUN BOY (IRE)**, 5, b g Valirann (FR)—Coosan Belle (IRE) **Ms Anna Baldwin**
21 **CARYS' COMMODITY (IRE)**, 7, b g Fame And Glory—Native Sunrise (IRE) **Mrs Fitri Hay**
22 **CAWTHORNE LAD (IRE)**, 6, ch g Coach House (IRE)—Upton Seas **Mr Nigel Wilks**
23 **CLONDAW PROMISE (IRE)**, 8, b g Gold Well—Present Promise (IRE) **Highfields Farm Partnership**
24 **CLOTH CAP (IRE)**, 10, b g Beneficial—Cloth Fair (IRE) **Exors of the Late Mr Trevor Hemmings**
25 **COBOLOBO (FR)**, 10, br g Maresca Sorrento (FR)—Nanou des Brosses (FR) **Anne, Harriet & Lucinda Bond**
26 **COEUR SEREIN (IRE)**, 8, b g Fame And Glory—Balvenie (IRE) **Mr Andrew Ralph**
27 **COLLECTORS ITEM (IRE)**, 5, b g Flemensfirth (USA)—Leading Lady **Jackdaws Antiques**
28 **COPPER COVE (IRE)**, 5, b g Jet Away—Cherry Island (IRE) **The Hon Mrs E. J. Wills**
29 **DANA'S GEM (IRE)**, 4, b f Milan—At Present (IRE) **Mr Graham Freeman**
30 **DESTIN D'AJONC (IRE)**, 9, b g Martaline—Fleur d'Ajonc (FR) **Mr J. P. McManus**
31 **DJANGO DJANGO (FR)**, 9, br g Voix du Nord (FR)—Lady Jannina **Martin Broughton & Friends 5**
32 **DOLLAR BAE (IRE)**, 5, b m Sageburg (IRE)—Molly Hound (IRE) **The Perfect Partnership**
33 **DR HEGARTY (IRE)**, 5, b g Califet (FR)—Millrock Lady (IRE) **P14 Medical Ltd & Dydb Marketing Ltd.**
34 **EASYSLAND (FR)**, 8, b br g Gentlewave (IRE)—Island du Frene (FR) **Mr J. P. McManus**
35 **FAME AND CONCRETE (IRE)**, 6, b g Fame And Glory—Masiana (IRE) **Mr Pat Hickey**
36 **FILE ILLICO (IRE)**, 7, b g Cokoriko (FR)—Noryane (FR) **The Hon Mrs E. J. Wills**
37 **FLAMES OF PASSION (IRE)**, 6, b m Flemensfirth (USA)—Night of Passion (IRE) **Deva Racing Champagne Wilde**
38 **FLEMINPORT (IRE)**, 9, b g Flemensfirth (USA)—Geek Chic (IRE) **Mr J. P. McManus**
39 **FLIGHT DECK (IRE)**, 8, b g Getaway (GER)—Rate of Knots (IRE) **Mr J. P. McManus**
40 **FOLKS ON THE HILL**, 7, b g Black Sam Bellamy (IRE)—Any Pearl **Mr Robin Stanton-Gleaves**
41 **FRISCO BAY (IRE)**, 7, b g Yeats (IRE)—Heath Heaven **Bassaire Cleanrooms Ltd.**
42 **GARRY CLERMONT (FR)**, 7, b g Maresca Sorrento (FR)—Kalidria Beauchene (FR) **Mrs C. M. Walsh**
43 **GENERATION GAP (IRE)**, 8, b g Olden Times—Kerso (IRE) **The Hon Mrs E. J. Wills**
44 **GWENNIE MAY BOY (IRE)**, 4, b g Mahler—Samsha (IRE) **Ms Gwendoline M. Clarke**
45 **HALF THE FREEDOM**, 6, ch g Haafhd—Free At Last **The Free At Last Partnership**
46 **HALIFAX (FR)**, 5, b g Saddler Maker (IRE)—Oudette (FR) **Mrs Katya Banks**
47 **HANG TOUGH**, 8, b g Geordieland (FR)—Allerford Lily **Tough Troop Partnership**
48 **HEAD LAW (FR)**, 5, b g Network (GER)—Law (FR) **Mr J. P. McManus**
49 **HENRY GONDOFF**, 7, b g Great Pretender (IRE)—Mi Money **The Sting Partnership**
50 **HEY JOE (IRE)**, 7, b g Oscar (IRE)—Jordrell (IRE) **J. C. & S. R. Hitchins**
51 **HIGHLAND GETAWAY (IRE)**, 4, b g Getaway (GER)—Hollygrove Rumba (IRE) **The Hon Mrs E. J. Wills**
52 **HOLLY (FR)**, 5, b m Voiladenuo (FR)—Righty Malta (FR) **Mr J. P. McManus**
53 **HUNGRY HILL (IRE)**, 5, b g Fame And Glory—Echo Queen (IRE) **Martin Tedham & Wasdell Properties Ltd.**
54 **ILESTDANCINGSPIRIT (FR)**, 4, ch g Coastal Path—Une d'Ex (FR) **The Magic Circle Partnership**
55 **IRON BRIDGE (IRE)**, 6, b g Milan—Chit Chat **Exors of the Late Mr Trevor Hemmings**
56 **ITSO FURY (IRE)**, 5, b g Fame And Glory—Qui Plus Est (FR) **Mrs Gay Smith**
57 **JUDICIAL LAW (IRE)**, 5, b g Fame And Glory—Miss Overdrive **Mrs Gay Smith**
58 **KENTANDDOVER (IRE)**, 5, b g Sir Percy—Kristalette (IRE) **Graeme Moore, Kate & Andrew Brooks**
59 **KILBROOK (IRE)**, 7, b g Watar (IRE)—Daly Lady (IRE) **Delancey, Mrs Jonjo O'Neill**
60 **KIOTO SUN (GER)**, 4, b g Pastorius (GER)—Kurfurstin (GER) **The Hon Mrs E. J. Wills**
61 **KNOWN (IRE)**, 8, b g Fame And Glory—Aasleagh Lady (IRE) **DYDB & Wilks Partnership**
62 **LAND GENIE**, 4, b g Flemensfirth (USA)—Queen of The Stage (IRE) **Mr Terry McKeever**
63 **LETMETELLUSOMETHIN**, 4, b g Shirocco (GER)—Early Dawne **Letmetellusomethin Partnership**
64 **LIMETREE BOY (IRE)**, 6, b g Shirocco (GER)—Bells Glory (IRE) **Mr Mike Gaskell**
65 **LOCK'S CORNER (IRE)**, 8, b g Gold Well—Last Century (IRE) **Mr J. P. McManus**
66 **MAGIC SEVEN (IRE)**, 4, b g Doyen (IRE)—Magic Maze (IRE) **Mr C. Johnston**
67 **MAMMIES BOY (IRE)**, 4, b g Getaway (GER)—Tonaphuca Girl (IRE) **What's The Craic Syndicate**
68 **MANINTHESHADOWS (IRE)**, 7, ch g Well Chosen—Grannys Kitchen (IRE) **Mr Andrew Riley**
69 **MAYPOLE CLASS (IRE)**, 8, b g Gold Well—Maypole Queen (IRE) **Delancey**

MR JONJO O'NEILL - continued

70 **MERCUTIO ROCK (FR)**, 6, b g Maresca Sorrento (FR)—Mondovi (FR) **Mr Michael O'Flynn & Delancey**
71 **MINELLA TILL DAWN (IRE)**, 10, br g Shantou (USA)—Have At It (IRE) **Mr J. P. McManus**
72 **MONBEG GENIUS (IRE)**, 6, b g Shantou (USA)—Ella Watson (IRE) **Barrowman Racing Limited**
73 **MORNING SPIRIT (IRE)**, 7, b g Milan—Morning Legend (IRE) **Mr Pat Hickey**
74 **MOSCOW SPY (IRE)**, 5, gr g Jet Away—Regents Ballerina (IRE) **Mrs Katya Banks**
75 **MR BIGGS**, 5, b g Telescope (IRE)—Linagram **P14 Medical Ltd T/A Platform 14**
76 **ON THE BANDWAGON (IRE)**, 7, b g Oscar (IRE)—Deep Supreme (IRE) **Mr Alan Nolan**
77 **ORRISDALE (IRE)**, 8, b g Oscar (IRE)—Back To Loughadera (IRE) **Miss Katharine Holland**
78 **PALMERS HILL (IRE)**, 9, b g Gold Well—Tosca Shine (IRE) **Mr J. P. McManus**
79 **PAPA TANGO CHARLY**, 7, ch g No Risk At All (FR)—Chere Elenn (FR)

        Martin Tedham & Wasdell Properties Ltd.
80 **PENS MAN (IRE)**, 7, ch g Sholokhov (IRE)—Dudeen (IRE) **Girls on Lockdown**
81 **PETIT TONNERRE (FR)**, 4, b g Waldpark (GER)—Perpette (FR) **Mr J. P. McManus**
82 **PHIL THE THRILL (FR)**, 6, gr g Dabirsim (FR)—Parirou (GER) **Miss Berys Connop**
83 **POWERFUL HERO (AUS)**, 5, br g Better Than Ready (AUS)—Glennie West (AUS) **Creative Earth Productions**
84 **PRESENT CHIEF (IRE)**, 8, b g Presenting—Daizinni **Mr Pat Hickey**
85 **PRIDE ROCK (IRE)**, 6, b g Westerner—Byerley Beauty (IRE) **Roel Hill Farm & Mr Michael O'Flynn**
86 **PRINCE ESCALUS (IRE)**, 7, b g Jeremy—So You Said (IRE) **The As You Like It Syndicate**
87 **PRIORY WOOD (IRE)**, 7, b g Shirocco (GER)—Passlands (IRE) **Jackdaws Racing**
88 **PYFFO (IRE)**, 4, b g Shantou (USA)—Maryota (FR) **Mr Andrew Ralph**
89 **QUARENTA (FR)**, 10, b br g Voix du Nord (FR)—Negresse de Cuta (FR) **Martin, Jocelyn & Steve Broughton**
90 **QUARTZ DU RHEU (FR)**, 7, b g Konig Turf (GER)—Lady Akara (FR) **Mr J. P. McManus**
91 **RABSKI (IRE)**, 6, b g Beat Hollow—Scarlet Feather (IRE) **Mrs Siobhan McAuley**
92 **RED DIRT ROAD (IRE)**, 5, b g Fame And Glory—Miss Otis Regrets (IRE) **Mr Danny Walker**
93 **RED MAPLE (IRE)**, 6, b g Sholokhov (IRE)—Champagne Ruby (IRE) **Mr Toby Cole**
94 **ROCK OF THE NATION (IRE)**, 4, b g Soldier of Fortune (IRE)—You Take Care (IRE)

        Mr Michael O'Flynn & Roel Hill Farm
95 **ROCKED UP (IRE)**, 6, b m Westerner—Rock Gossip (IRE) **Chick's Horseracing, Marks, Evans**
96 **SACRE COEUR (FR)**, 6, gr m Montmartre (FR)—Singaporette (FR) **David's Partnership**
97 **SAINT DAVY (FR)**, 5, b g Balko (FR)—Saintejoie (FR) **Mrs Gay Smith**
98 **SERMANDO (FR)**, 8, ch g Fuisse (FR)—Josephjuliusjodie (FR) **Creative Earth Productions**
99 **SHANTOU'S MELODY (IRE)**, 6, b g Shantou (USA)—Glens Melody (IRE) **Perfect Strangers Partnership**
100 4, B g Flemensfirth (USA)—Shees A Dante (IRE) **Mr Eric Brook**
101 **SIDESHIFT (FR)**, 5, b g Sidestep (AUS)—Shamazing **Mr Robin Stanton-Gleaves**
102 **SKY PIRATE**, 9, b g Midnight Legend—Dancingwithbubbles (IRE) **Martin Tedham & Wasdell Properties Ltd.**
103 **SKYLANNA BREEZE (IRE)**, 7, b g Primary (USA)—Waist Deep (IRE) **The Three Cabelleros**
104 **SOARING GLORY (IRE)**, 7, b g Fame And Glory—Hapeney (IRE) **Mr Pat Hickey**
105 **SOLDIEROFTHESTORM (IRE)**, 4, ch c Soldier of Fortune (IRE)—Fiddlededee (IRE) **Mrs Peter Bond**
106 **SPRINGWELL BAY**, 5, b g Kayf Tara—Winning Counsel (IRE) **Mrs Gay Smith**
107 **STEADY THE SHIP (IRE)**, 6, ch g Ocovango—Vinnie's Princess (IRE) **Pitch Racing**
108 **T'ARAISON (FR)**, 5, b g Buck's Boum (FR)—Al Gane (FR) **Mr J. P. McManus**
109 **TEDHAM**, 8, b g Shirocco (GER)—Alegralil **Martin Tedham & Wasdell Properties Ltd.**
110 **THE COMPOSEUR (IRE)**, 7, b g Mahler—Oscar's Reprieve (IRE) **Jonjo O'Neill Racing Club**
111 **THEME TUNE (IRE)**, 7, b g Fame And Glory—Supreme Melody (IRE) **Exors of the Late Mr Trevor Hemmings**
112 **TIME TO GET UP (IRE)**, 9, ch g Presenting—Gales Return (IRE) **Mr J. P. McManus**
113 **TRACK AND TRACE (IRE)**, 5, b g Mahler—Princess Bella (IRE) **Bruton St.**
114 **UNSINKABLE MOLLY B**, 4, br f Blue Bresil (FR)—Perfect Promise (USA) **Mr Danny Walker**
115 **UPTOWN LADY (IRE)**, 7, b m Milan—Lady Zephyr (IRE) **Mr Russell McAllister**
116 **VALENTINE GETAWAY (IRE)**, 4, b f Getaway (GER)—Awesome Miracle (IRE) **The Valentine Partnership**
117 **WALK IN MY SHOES (IRE)**, 6, b m Milan—Bonnies Island (IRE) **Creative Earth Productions**
118 **WALK OF NO SHAME (IRE)**, 5, b m Walk In The Park (IRE)—Ultimate Echo (IRE) **Hillary Peachey & Sharon Wilks**
119 **WASDELL DUNDALK (FR)**, 7, ch g Spirit One (FR)—Linda Queen (FR) **Martin Tedham & Wasdell Properties Ltd.**
120 **WHEN YOU'RE READY (IRE)**, 8, gr g Malinas (GER)—Royale Wheeler (FR) **Local Parking Security Limited**
121 **YES INDEED (FR)**, 5, b g Martaline—She Hates Me (IRE) **Mr Michael O'Flynn & Roel Hill Farm**
122 **YOUNG WOLF (IRE)**, 9, b g Vinnie Roe—Missy O'Brien (IRE) **Mrs Gay Smith**
123 **YULONG MAGICREEF (IRE)**, 5, b g Fastnet Rock (AUS)—Lindikhaya (IRE) **The Magic Circle Partnership**
124 **ZABEEL CHAMPION**, 5, b g Poet's Voice—Stars In Your Eyes **Martin Tedham & Wasdell Properties Ltd.**
125 **ZONDA (FR)**, 4, gr g Martaline—Tornada (FR) **Martin Broughton Racing Partners 2**

MR JONJO O'NEILL - continued

Other Owners: Mr N. J. Bate, Mrs J. D. Beslee, Miss H. Bond, Miss L. Bond, Mrs Peter Bond, Mr N. Brand, Mr A. Brookes, Mr A. L. Brooks, Mrs K. L. Brooks, Lady J. M. Broughton, Sir M. F. Broughton, Mr S. W. Broughton, Mr A. P. Brown, Chick's Horseracing Ltd, Mr D. J. Coles, Mr R. Collins, DYDB Marketing Limited, Delancey, Mr P. Evans, Mrs D. M. Gregory, Mrs S. Hall-Tinker, Mr M. P. Hammond, J. C. Hitchins, S. R. Hitchins, Mr T. Jackson, Mr D. Kehoe, Mr J. Lloyd-Townshend, Mr R. Marks, Mr J. D. Mayo, Mr G. Moore, Mr M. O'Flynn, P14 Medical Ltd T/A Platform 14, Ms H. Peachey, Mr C. J. Pearce, Mr S. P. Perryman, Roel Hill Farm limited, Mr P. G. Taiano, Mr M. J. Tedham, Mrs L. Vaines, Wasdall Properties Ltd, Mr Nigel Wilks, Mrs S. Wilks.

NH Jockey: Alain Cawley, Adrian Heskin, Will Kennedy, Richie McLernon, Jonjo O'Neill Jr, Nick Scholfield, Gavin Sheehan.
Conditional Jockey: Kevin Brogan, William Marshall. **Amateur Jockey:** Jamie Brace, AJ O'Neill.

---

410 **MR BRIAN O'ROURKE, Upper Lambourn**
Postal: **Maple Tree House, Newbury Road, Great Shefford, Hungerford, Berkshire, RG17 7DT**
Contacts: **PHONE 01488 670290**
EMAIL **brian@brianorourkebloodstock.com**

1 **AL GAIYA (FR),** 5, b m Olympic Glory (IRE)—Lathah (IRE) **Brian O'Rourke Bloodstock Ltd**
2 **FROSTED ANGEL (IRE),** 4, gr f Dark Angel (IRE)—Cut No Ice (IRE) **Sba Racing Limited**
3 **MAGNIFICENCE (FR),** 4, b f Kingman—Alamarie (FR) **Sba Racing Limited**
4 **MELLENCAMP (IRE),** 4, b g Kodi Bear (IRE)—Tiggy Two (IRE) **Mr D. Ward**

THREE-YEAR-OLDS

5 **ANCIENT CAPITAL,** b c Frankel—Spirit of Xian (IRE) **Rockcliffe Stud**
6 **BANSHEE (IRE),** b f Iffraaj—Reflective (USA) **B. E. Nielsen**
7 **DELAHOUSSAYE (IRE),** ch g Footstepsinthesand—Brianna Bay (IRE) **Brian O'Rourke Bloodstock Ltd**
8 **GULICK (IRE),** b g Dragon Pulse (IRE)—Make A Dance (USA) **Brian O'Rourke Bloodstock Ltd**

Other Owners: Mr B. W. Keswick, Mr S. L. Keswick.

---

411 **MR JOHN O'SHEA, Newnham-on-Severn**
Postal: **The Stables, Bell House, Lumbars Lane, Newnham, Gloucestershire, GL14 1LH**
Contacts: **PHONE 01452 760835 MOBILE 07917 124717 FAX 01452 760233**
WEBSITE **www.johnoshearacing.co.uk**

1 **BOLLY BULLET (IRE),** 5, b g Helmet (AUS)—Champagne Aerial (IRE) **Pete Smith & Phil Hart Racing**
2 **DUNDORY (IRE),** 6, b g Holy Roman Emperor (IRE)—Lady Bones (IRE) **The Cross Racing Club**
3 **FIGHT FOR IT (IRE),** 4, b g Camelot—Dorothy B (IRE) **K. W. Bell**
4 **FLIP MODE,** 5, b g Lethal Force (IRE)—Canukeepasecret **Mr S. P. Price**
5 **FORTUNE TRAVELLER,** 5, b m Soldier of Fortune (IRE)—When In Roam (IRE) **Mr J. R. Salter**
6 **GET UP THEM STEPS,** 8, b g Excelebration (IRE)—Flag Day **K. W. Bell**
7 **GORDONONTHEORGAN (IRE),** 5, ch g Anjaal—Turban Bay (IRE) **Mr P. Smith**
8 **HARVIE WALLBANGER (IRE),** 6, b g Mahler—Initforthecrack (IRE) **K. W. Bell**
9 **JESSIE PYE,** 4, b f Heeraat—Under My Spell **Mr J. R. Salter**
10 **JIMMY BELL,** 11, b g Tiger Hill—Armada Grove **K. W. Bell**
11 **JUST THE MAN (FR),** 6, gr g Rajsaman—Yachtclubgenoa (IRE) **K. W. Bell**
12 **MACOCHA (IRE),** 5, b m Camacho—Book of Manners **The Cross Racing Club**
13 **MACS DILEMMA (IRE),** 4, b g Coulsty—Ohsosecret **Miss H. O. G. Jones**
14 **MAJOR VALENTINE,** 10, b g Major Cadeaux—Under My Spell **Mr P. Smith**
15 **MONSIEUR FANTAISIE,** 4, b g Make Believe—Rachel Tiffany (USA) **Phil Hart & the Cross Racing Club**
16 **OUTBACK FRONTIERS (IRE),** 6, ch g Sans Frontieres (IRE)—Bord de Loire (FR) **Mr S. P. Price**

MR JOHN O'SHEA - continued

17 **PIPS TUNE**, 4, ch g Helmet (AUS)—Paquerettza (FR) **The Cross Racing Club**
18 **POWER OF LAZARUS (IRE)**, 5, ch g Power—Agnista (IRE) **Miss H. O. G. Jones**
19 **RICHIE VALENTINE**, 8, b g Native Ruler—Karmest **Mr N. G. H. Ayliffe**
20 **SCARLET RUBY**, 5, b m Al Kazeem—Monisha (FR) **The Cross Racing Club**
21 **SOME NIGHTMARE (IRE)**, 5, b g Dream Ahead (USA)—Isolde's Return **The Cross Racing Club**
22 **SONIC GOLD**, 6, b g Schiaparelli (GER)—Sonic Weld **K. W. Bell**
23 **THE BELFRY BOY**, 7, ch g Black Sam Bellamy (IRE)—Lac Marmot (FR) **K. W. Bell**
24 4, B g Getaway (GER)—Valsugana (IRE) **The Cross Racing Club**

THREE-YEAR-OLDS

25 **MY OPINION (IRE)**, b g Pride of Dubai (AUS)—Trust Your Opinion (IRE) **The Cross Racing Club**
26 **THE EMBEZZLER**, b g Fast Company (IRE)—Steal The Curtain **The Cross Racing Club**

Other Owners: Mr N. G. H. Ayliffe, Mrs S. Guest, Mr P. G. Hart, The Cross Racing Club.

Flat Jockey: Robert Havlin, Luke Morris.

MR GEOFFREY OLDROYD, Pocklington
Postal: **Yapham Grange, Pocklington, York, Yorkshire, YO42 1PB**
Contacts: **PHONE 01653 668279**
EMAIL oldroydgeoff@gmail.com

1 **FOREVER'S LADY**, 4, b f Toronado (IRE)—Forever's Girl **Bond Thoroughbred Limited**
2 **HIGHEST WAVE**, 4, b f Muhaarar—Tibesti **Bond Thoroughbred Limited**
3 **NEVER SAY NEVER (IRE)**, 4, b f No Nay Never (USA)—Tahara (IRE) **Bond Thoroughbred Limited**
4 **RISE HALL**, 7, b g Frankel—Forever Bond **Bond Thoroughbred Limited**
5 **SEA STORM**, 6, ch m Monsieur Bond (IRE)—Chez Cherie

THREE-YEAR-OLDS

6 **DOCTOR KHAN JUNIOR**, b c Muhaarar—Ladies Are Forever **Bond Thoroughbred Limited**
7 B f Muhaarar—Forever's Girl **Bond Thoroughbred Limited**
8 **SKYEFALL**, b f Monsieur Bond (IRE)—Bond Artist (IRE) **Bond Thoroughbred Limited**

MR HENRY OLIVER, Abberley
Postal: **Stable End, Worsley Racing Stables, Bank Lane, Abberley, Worcester, Worcestershire, WR6 6BQ**
Contacts: **PHONE 01299 890143 MOBILE 07701 068759**
EMAIL henryoliverracing@hotmail.co.uk WEBSITE www.henryoliverracing.co.uk

1 **BALLYCORR (IRE)**, 7, b g Imperial Monarch (IRE)—Taras Child (IRE)
2 **BOYS OF WEXFORD**, 5, b g Millenary—Floradorado
3 **CAPTAIN ATTRIDGE (IRE)**, 4, b g Raven's Pass (USA)—High Queen (IRE)
4 **COASTGUARD STATION (IRE)**, 6, ch g Dylan Thomas (IRE)—Shuruwaat (IRE)
5 **COME ON GARY (IRE)**, 6, b g Milan—Cercle des Amis (FR)
6 **DAENERYS STORMBORN (IRE)**, 9, br m September Storm (GER)—Ceo Draiochta (IRE)
7 **DR OAKLEY (IRE)**, 8, ch g Le Fou (IRE)—Two Choices (IRE)
8 **GENEROUS DAY (IRE)**, 10, b g Daylami (IRE)—Our Pride
9 **GENTLE FRANK**, 6, ch g Gentlewave (IRE)—Himitas (FR)
10 **HARD TO FORGET (IRE)**, 9, b g Gold Well—Raheen Na Hoon (IRE)
11 **PATIENT OWNER (IRE)**, 7, b g Getaway (GER)—La Femme Blanche (IRE)
12 **REINE FEE (IRE)**, 9, b m Kalanisi (IRE)—Cave Woman (IRE)

MR HENRY OLIVER - continued

13 **SKINFLINT (IRE)**, 10, b g Scorpion (IRE)—Gales Hill (IRE)
14 **THE BIG BITE (IRE)**, 9, b g Scorpion (IRE)—Thanks Noel (IRE)

Owners: Andyfreight Holdings Limited, Best Foot Forward Two, Catch Twenty Two, Catchtwentytwo,Andyfreight Holdingsltd, Mrs S. A. Gent, Mr N. Griffith, Mr N T Griffith & H M Haddock, Mrs H. M. Haddock, Ms S. A. Howell, Mr H. J. Oliver, Mr K. Sohi, Talking Pictures TV Limited, R. G. Whitehead.

NH Jockey: James Davies.

414

MR JAMIE OSBORNE, Upper Lambourn
Postal: **The Old Malthouse, Upper Lambourn, Hungerford, Berkshire, RG17 8RG**
Contacts: **PHONE 01488 73139 MOBILE 07860 533422**
EMAIL info@jamieosborne.com WEBSITE www.jamieosborne.com

1 **ALIGNAK**, 6, gr h Sea The Moon (GER)—Albanova **R. J. Tufft**
2 **APPARATE**, 6, b g Dubawi (IRE)—Appearance **Gregg Ryan**
3 **BIG LITTLE LIE (FR)**, 4, b f Dark Angel (IRE)—Felcine (IRE) **Dargle Equine (uk) Ltd & Partner**
4 **BRAINS (IRE)**, 6, b g Dandy Man (IRE)—Pure Jazz (IRE) **The Judges & Partner**
5 **CHIEF LITTLE HAWK (USA)**, 4, ch g Air Force Blue (USA)—Marylebone (USA) **Barratt Racing**
6 **CLADDAGHDUFF (IRE)**, 4, b c Estidhkaar (IRE)—Attracted To You (IRE)
7 **CLIFFS OF CAPRI**, 8, b g Canford Cliffs (IRE)—Shannon Spree **Melbourne 10 Racing**
8 **CREMA INGLESA (IRE)**, 4, b f Lope de Vega (IRE)—Creme Anglaise **Hunscote Stud Ltd & John O'Connor**
9 4, B c Noble Mission—Dreamt **Mr Khalid bin Mishref**
10 **DUTY OF CARE**, 4, b g Kingman—Exemplify
11 **ETON COLLEGE (IRE)**, 5, b g Invincible Spirit (IRE)—Windsor County (USA)
12 **FIGHTING POET (IRE)**, 4, b g The Gurkha (IRE)—Inkling (USA)
13 **FREE SOLO (IRE)**, 5, ch g Showcasing—Amuser (IRE) **The Judges and Partner**
14 **GOLD MAZE**, 5, b g Golden Horn—Astonishing **London Design Group Limited**
15 **HASHTAGMETOO (USA)**, 5, b m Declaration of War (USA)—Caribbean Princess (USA) **The Other Club**
16 **IMPOSSIBLEPOSSIBLE (IRE)**, 4, b g Gutaifan (IRE)—Fanciful Dancer **Mr A Taylor & Partner**
17 **JERRIAIS**, 4, br g Geordieland (FR)—La Verte Rue (USA) **Mr A. Taylor**
18 **JERSEY GIFT (IRE)**, 4, b g Nathaniel (IRE)—Pharadelle (IRE) **Mr A Taylor & Partner**
19 **LIAM'S LEGEND (USA)**, 5, gr ro h Liam's Map (USA)—Indian Legend (USA) **Mr Khalid bin Mishref**
20 **LUNAR SPACE (IRE)**, 4, ch g Dawn Approach (IRE)—Luminaria (IRE) **The Judges & Partner**
21 **MEKONG**, 7, b g Frankel—Ship's Biscuit **Mr Khalid bin Mishref**
22 **MILLTOWN STAR**, 5, b g Roderic O'Connor—Hail Shower (IRE)
23 **MISS SLIGO (IRE)**, 5, b m New Approach (IRE)—Illandrane (IRE) **The Q Party**
24 **MR ALCHEMY**, 5, gr g Leroidesanimaux (BRZ)—Albaraka **The Q Party**
25 **NORTHERN (IRE)**, 4, b g Camelot—Myrica **V7 Recruitment Ltd & Partner**
26 **OUZO**, 6, b g Charm Spirit (IRE)—Miss Meltemi (IRE)
27 **PEERLESS (IRE)**, 4, b g Kodiac—Etesian Flow
28 **RAISING SAND**, 10, b g Oasis Dream—Balalaika **Nick Bradley Racing 22 & Partner**
29 **SEVENTH KINGDOM**, 4, b g Frankel—Nayarra (IRE) **Barratt Racing**

THREE-YEAR-OLDS

30 **AKA FLIPPER (IRE)**, b g Bungle Inthejungle—Convidada (IRE) **Rothstein & Held Racing Limited & Ptn**
31 **BOAFO BOY**, b c Lope de Vega (IRE)—Royal Empress (IRE) **Rothstein & Held Racing Limited & Ptn**
32 **BRYNTEG**, b g Ardad (IRE)—Across The Galaxy **Mrs J. M. T. Martin**
33 **CHORUS GIRL**, b f Showcasing—Lady Lockwood **The 10 For 10 Partnership**
34 **CHRISTOPHER**, b g Dabirsim (FR)—New Providence **The 10 For 10 Partnership**
35 **DEAC'S GIRL (IRE)**, ch f Churchill (IRE)—Kaabari (USA) **The 10 For 10 Partnership**
36 **DREAM HARDER (IRE)**, b g Muhaarar—Silent Thoughts (IRE) **The 10 For 10 Partnership**
37 B f Bated Breath—Enigmatique **The 10 For 10 Partnership**
38 **GAME NATION**, b g Le Havre (IRE)—Mt of Beatitudes (IRE) **Jacobs Construction Ltd&city Gaming Ltd**
39 **HUSCARI (IRE)**, gr f Caravaggio (USA)—Greatest Place (IRE) **Mrs H Allanson & Partners**

MR JAMIE OSBORNE - continued

40 **JACKMEISTER RUDI**, b c Churchill (IRE)—Beyond Desire **Rothstein & Held Racing Limited & Ptn**
41 **JELLY BABY (USA)**, b br f Twirling Candy (USA)—Opal Blue (IRE) **Mrs M. Slack, Mrs J. Slack Jell**
42 B f Geordieland (FR)—La Verte Rue (USA) **Mr A. Taylor**
43 B g Lawman (FR)—Luminata (IRE)
44 **NOTIONS (IRE)**, ch g Lope de Vega (IRE)—Golden Shadow (IRE) **Mr M C Morris & Partner**
45 **SHENZHEN SUBWAY (IRE)**, b c Kodi Bear (IRE)—Classic Legend **Rothstein & Held Racing Limited & Ptn**
46 **SHUT UP AND DANCE (IRE)**, b f Kodiac—Natural Blues **V7 Recruitment Ltd & Partner**
47 B g Dark Angel (IRE)—Thawrah (IRE)
48 **WROUGHT IRON**, gr g Dark Angel (IRE)—Swiss Kiss **The 10 For 10 Partnership**

TWO-YEAR-OLDS

49 **ALL DUNN**, b c 13/02 Oasis Dream—Bimbo (Iffraaj) (55000) **Alasdair Simpson,Victoria Dunn & Partner**
50 B f 29/01 Harry Angel (IRE)—Atlaal (Dansili) (37000) **Griffiths de Kock Racing Syndicate**
51 **BEN LOMOND (IRE)**, b c 11/03 Gleneagles (IRE)—Coquette Rouge (IRE) (Croco Rouge (IRE)) (32000)
                                   Mr J Palmer-Brown
52 B f 18/03 New Bay—Caterina di Cesi (Cape Town) (IRE) (30000) **Clipper Logistics**
53 B c 07/03 Harry Angel (IRE)—Dubai Bounty (Dubai Destination (USA)) (70000) **Seymour Bloodstock and Partners**
54 B c 05/04 Shalaa (IRE)—Love And Cherish (IRE) (Excellent Art) (25000) **Mr Denis J Barry & Partner**
55 Ch f 10/02 Zoustar (AUS)—Meeting Waters (Aqlaam) (20000)
56 B c 17/03 Acclamation—Nudge (Dansili) (15306)
57 Ch c 13/02 Equiano (FR)—Path of Peace (Rock of Gibraltar (IRE)) **Homecroft Wealth Racing**
58 B c 20/04 Mehmas (IRE)—Puttore (IRE) (High Chaparral (IRE))
59 B f 02/03 Muhaarar—Pyrenean Queen (IRE) (Zoffany (IRE)) (32000)
60 B c 19/04 Galileo Gold—Red Blanche (IRE) (Red Clubs (IRE)) (5714)
61 B f 13/04 Sir Percy—Six Cents (IRE) (Shirocco (GER)) **Hunscote Stud Limited**
62 B f 14/03 Expert Eye—Tanouma (USA) (Mr Greeley (USA)) (30000)
63 B f 27/03 Camacho—Va Pensiero (IRE) (High Chaparral (IRE))

Assistant Trainer: Jimmy McCarthy.

Flat Jockey: Nicola Currie. **Apprentice Jockey:** Saffie Osborne.

415
MISS EMMA OWEN, Nether Winchendon
Postal: **Muskhill Farm, Nether Winchendon, Aylesbury, Buckinghamshire, HP18 0EB**
Contacts: **PHONE 01844 290282 MOBILE 07718 984799**
EMAIL emma.l.owen@hotmail.com

1 **ANNAJEMIMA**, 8, b m Firebreak—Leaping Flame (USA) **Miss E. L. Owen**
2 **AUSTIN FRIARS**, 10, b g New Approach (IRE)—My Luigia (IRE) **Miss E. L. Owen**
3 **BAHAMIAN HEIGHTS**, 11, b g Bahamian Bounty—Tahirah **Miss E. L. Owen**
4 **DIVINE MESSENGER**, 8, b g Firebreak—Resentful Angel **Miss E. L. Owen**
5 **DUTIFUL SON (IRE)**, 12, b g Invincible Spirit (IRE)—Grecian Dancer **Miss E. L. Owen**
6 **FIREGUARD**, 9, b g Firebreak—Leaping Flame (USA) **Miss E. L. Owen**
7 **HIGHER COURT (USA)**, 14, b g Shamardal (USA)—Nawaiet (USA) **Miss E. L. Owen**
8 **HIGHPLAINS DRIFTER (IRE)**, 11, b g High Chaparral (IRE)—Ghazeenah **Miss E. L. Owen**
9 **JOSHLEE (IRE)**, 8, b m Dark Angel (IRE)—Kay Es Jay (FR) **Miss E. L. Owen**
10 **LEGAL MIND**, 9, ch h Firebreak—La Sorrela (IRE) **Miss E. L. Owen**
11 **MILLDEAN BILLY (IRE)**, b g Dandy Man (IRE)—Strawberriesncream (IRE) **Miss E. L. Owen**
12 **MILLDEAN PANTHER**, 6, b g Mayson—Silver Halo **Miss E. L. Owen**
13 **MUSICAL COMEDY**, 11, b g Royal Applause—Spinning Top **Miss E. L. Owen**
14 **PEDDERY**, 6, b g Pastoral Pursuits—Resentful Angel **Miss E. L. Owen**
15 **RED HANRAHAN (IRE)**, 11, b g Yeats (IRE)—Monty's Sister (IRE) **Miss E. L. Owen**
16 **REIGNITE**, 7, b g Firebreak—Resentful Angel **Miss E. L. Owen**
17 **SEA THE WAVES**, 9, b g Canford Cliffs (IRE)—April (IRE) **Mr L. F. Daly**
18 **THE ARISTOCAT (IRE)**, 7, b m Kitten's Joy (USA)—Letters (FR) **Miss E. L. Owen**
19 **VERETA (IRE)**, 6, b m Dick Turpin (IRE)—Vera Lou (IRE) **Mr L. F. Daly**

416 MR PATRICK OWENS, Newmarket
Postal: **Authorized Yard, St Gatien Stables, Vicarage Road, Newmarket, Suffolk, CB8 8HP**
Contacts: **PHONE 07796 036878**
EMAIL powens@patrickowens.co.uk

1 **ADAAY TO REMEMBER**, 4, b f Adaay (IRE)—Cross My Heart **GB Horseracing**
2 **MISS VELVETEEN (IRE)**, 5, b m Free Eagle (IRE)—Velvet Star (IRE) **Mr Patrick Owens**
3 **PRONTISSIMO**, 4, b g Toronado (IRE)—Eastern Glow **K. A. Dasmal**

THREE-YEAR-OLDS
4 **ADNAAN**, b c Ardad (IRE)—News Desk **K. A. Dasmal**
5 B f Moohaajim (IRE)—La Grande Elisa (IRE) **Paul Cairns Racing Limited**
6 **TOOMEVARA (IRE)**, b g Bated Breath—Kerrys Requiem (IRE) **Authorized Syndicate**
7 **WAJD**, b f Pearl Secret—Queen of The Tarts **Mr M. S. Al Shahi**

TWO-YEAR-OLDS
8 **ALMARIN (IRE)**, b c 13/04 Belardo (IRE)—Princess Severus (IRE) (Barathea (IRE)) (9524)
                                                                Mr R. E. Bamford, Mrs K. E. Bamford
9 B c 17/03 Gregorian (IRE)—La Belle Maison (IRE) (Titus Livius (FR)) (17007) **Mr M. S. Al Shahi**
10 **STRAWBERRY BELLE (IRE)**, b f 02/03 Adaay (IRE)—Strawberry Leaf (Unfuwain (USA)) (16000) **GB Horseracing**
11 **TABSHEER**, b c 23/04 Tasleet—Tan Tan (King's Best (USA)) (42000) **K. A. Dasmal**
12 B f 27/04 No Nay Never (USA)—Za'hara (IRE) (Raven's Pass (USA)) (21259) **Mr M. S. Al Shahi**

417 MR HUGO PALMER, Newmarket
Postal: **Kremlin Cottage Stables, Snailwell Road, Newmarket, Suffolk, CB8 7DP**
Contacts: **PHONE 01638 669880 MOBILE 07824 887886 FAX 01638 666383**
EMAIL info@hugopalmer.com WEBSITE www.hugopalmer.com

1 **BATTERED**, 8, b g Foxwedge (AUS)—Swan Wings **Mr Hugo Palmer**
2 **BRUNNERA**, 4, b f Dubawi (IRE)—Romantica **Juddmonte Farms Ltd**
3 **CHOCOYA**, 4, ch f Sepoy (AUS)—Silver Games (IRE) **Mr Christopher Wright**
4 **DANTORA**, 4, b c Dansili—Rostova (USA) **Juddmonte Farms Ltd**
5 **GOOD SOUL**, 4, gr f Mukhadram—Royal Dalakhani (IRE) **Kremlin Cottage IX**
6 **LOVELY BREEZE (IRE)**, 4, b f Sepoy (AUS)—Power of Light (IRE) **Dr A. Ridha**
7 **NEW FORCE**, 4, ch g New Approach (IRE)—Honky Tonk Sally **Sheikh I. S. Al Khalifa**
8 **NOMAN (IRE)**, 4, b g Shalaa (IRE)—Mathool (IRE) **Al Shaqab Racing UK Limited**
9 **POWER OF STATES (IRE)**, 6, b g Lope de Vega (IRE)—Allegation (FR) **Dr A. Ridha**
10 **QUENELLE D'OR**, 4, b f Golden Horn—Quenelle **Lady Derby & Lady Ritblat**
11 **RED OCTOBER (IRE)**, 6, ch g Dawn Approach (IRE)—Mamonta **Mrs Clodagh McStay & Partner**
12 **SET POINT (IRE)**, 4, b g Sea The Stars (IRE)—Hot Sauce (IRE) **John Livock & Nat Lacy**

THREE-YEAR-OLDS
13 **ARION**, b f Dubawi (IRE)—Filia Regina **Lady Derby & Lady Ritblat**
14 **ASEAN LEGEND (IRE)**, b c Australia—Queenscliff (IRE) **Mr K. K. B. Ho**
15 **BEAUTIFUL SURPRISE**, ch f Ribchester (IRE)—Lovely Surprise (IRE) **Dr A. Ridha**
16 B f Bated Breath—Chigun **Mr V. I. Araci**
17 **CUBAN BEAT**, b f Havana Gold (IRE)—Stroll Patrol **Qatar Racing Ltd**
18 **DANCE FLOOR DIVA (IRE)**, ch f Highland Reel (IRE)—Flawless Beauty **Mrs Vanessa Palmer**
19 **DIG TWO (IRE)**, b g Cotai Glory—Vulnicura (IRE) **Mr L. L. Lee**
20 **DUBAWI LEGEND (IRE)**, b c Dubawi (IRE)—Lovely Pass (IRE) **Dr A. Ridha**
21 **EBRO RIVER (IRE)**, ch c Galileo Gold—Soft Power (IRE) **Al Shaqab Racing UK Limited**
22 **EVOCATIVE SPARK (IRE)**, b c Frankel—Hyper Dream (IRE) **Mr V. I. Araci**
23 **GOVERNMENT (IRE)**, gr c Caravaggio (USA)—Love And Laughter (IRE) **Qatar Racing & David Howden**
24 **HERETIC (IRE)**, ch c Galileo Gold—Al Jawza **Highclere Tbred Racing, C Fahy & Partner**
25 **HIERARCHY (IRE)**, ch c Mehmas (IRE)—Cheworee **David Howden & Qatar Racing**

MR HUGO PALMER - continued

26 **HOW IMPRESSIVE (IRE)**, ch c Starspangledbanner (AUS)—Bright New Day (IRE) **Middleham Park Racing XCIX**
27 **JILMOD (IRE)**, b g Galileo Gold—Kuala Queen (IRE) **Al Shaqab Racing UK Limited**
28 **JOKING**, b f Time Test—Comic (IRE) **Floors Stud Ltd**
29 **NAGA EYE (IRE)**, b c Acclamation—Gianetta (SWI) **Mr L. L. Lee**
30 **NATIVE ANGEL**, b f Zoffany (IRE)—MI Angel **Mr V. I. Araci**
31 **NEPTUNE LEGEND (IRE)**, b g Invincible Spirit (IRE)—Kate The Great **Mr K. K. B. Ho**
32 **NOLTON CROSS (IRE)**, b c Dark Angel (IRE)—Pandora's Box (IRE) **Middleham Park Racing XCII**
33 **NOVA LEGEND (IRE)**, b c Galileo (IRE)—Ghurra (USA) **Mr K. K. B. Ho**
34 **NOVEL LEGEND (IRE)**, b c Nathaniel (IRE)—Majestic Dubawi **Mr K. K. B. Ho**
35 **OCHIL HOUSE (IRE)**, b c Gleneagles (IRE)—House Point **Mr V. I. Araci**
36 **PLANET LEGEND (IRE)**, ch c Galileo (IRE)—Zut Alors (IRE) **Mr K. K. B. Ho**
37 **POWER OF BEAUTY (IRE)**, b g Slade Power—Beautiful Filly **Dr A. Ridha**
38 **PYSANKA (FR)**, b c Holy Roman Emperor (IRE)—Ukraine (IRE) **Mr L. L. Lee**
39 **RISK AVERSE (IRE)**, b f Dark Angel (IRE)—Freedom Pass (USA) **Tony O'Connor & Reinsurance Partners**
40 **SALVE JAPAN**, b f Dabirsim (FR)—Salve Diana (GER) **Hunscote Stud Limited**
41 **SCOT'S GRACE (IRE)**, b f Mehmas (IRE)—Ms O'Malley (IRE) **Mr B. Havern**
42 **SKY LEGEND**, ch c Galileo (IRE)—Spectre (FR) **Mr K. K. B. Ho**
43 B f Le Havre (IRE)—Spinning Queen **Mr E. P. Babington**
44 **STAR LEGEND (IRE)**, b c Galileo (IRE)—Thai Haku (IRE) **Mr K. K. B. Ho**
45 **SYDNEY STREET**, b g Dark Angel (IRE)—Minnaloushe (IRE) **Chelsea Thoroughbreds - Girls Syndicate**
46 **THUNDER LEGEND (IRE)**, b c Night of Thunder (IRE)—Vitoria (IRE) **Mr K. K. B. Ho**
47 **UNILATERALISM (IRE)**, ch g Starspangledbanner (AUS)—Barnet **Mr L. L. Lee**

TWO-YEAR-OLDS

48 B c 23/02 Al Wukair (IRE)—Al Dweha (IRE) (Invincible Spirit (IRE)) **Al Shaqab Racing UK Limited**
49 Gr c 08/02 Mastercraftsman (IRE)—Belle Above All (New Approach (IRE)) (36190) **FOMO Syndicate**
50 B c 26/03 Free Eagle (IRE)—Candle Lit (IRE) (Duke of Marmalade (IRE)) (29762)
51 **CARVED IN STONE**, b c 17/04 Mastercraftsman (IRE)—Bride Unbridled (IRE) (Hurricane Run (IRE))
  Al Asayl Bloodstock Ltd
52 Ch c 22/02 Zoustar (AUS)—Castle Hill Cassie (IRE) (Casamento (IRE)) **Mr David Howden**
53 B c 20/03 Havana Grey—Chandresh (Holy Roman Emperor (IRE)) (70000) **Mr L. L. Lee**
54 **CHELSEA GREEN (IRE)**, b f 29/03 U S Navy Flag (USA)—Agapantha (USA) (Dynaformer (USA)) (80000)
  Chelsea Thoroughbreds - Girls Syndicate
55 **CHRONOGRAPH**, ch c 27/02 Recorder—Basque Beauty (Nayef (USA)) (35000) **Sheikh I. S. Al Khalifa**
56 B f 15/01 No Nay Never (USA)—Conniption (IRE) (Danehill Dancer (USA)) (110000) **Lady Mimi Manton**
57 B c 12/04 Lope de Vega (IRE)—Cottonmouth (IRE) (Noverre (USA)) (125000) **John O'Connor & Partners**
58 **COVERT LEGEND**, b c 17/03 Zoustar (AUS)—Miss You Too (Montjeu (IRE)) (61905) **Mr K. K. B. Ho**
59 B c 31/01 Lightning Spear—Dark Reckoning (Equiano (FR)) (17000)
60 B f 13/01 Territories (IRE)—Doobahdeedoo (USA) (Animal Kingdom (USA)) (55272)
  Al-Khail,Babington,Gallagher et al
61 B f 16/02 U S Navy Flag (USA)—Emirates Joy (USA) (Street Cry (IRE)) (28571)
62 B f 25/01 Zoustar (AUS)—Evil Spell (Dutch Art) (40000)
63 **FLEUR DE MER (IRE)**, b f 14/02 Dark Angel (IRE)—Hespera (Danehill (USA)) **Al Asayl Bloodstock Ltd**
64 Ch c 23/04 Footstepsinthesand—Gabardine (Pivotal) (92000) **Al Shaqab Racing UK Limited**
65 B f 11/05 Invincible Spirit (IRE)—Ghurra (USA) (War Chant (USA)) (150000) **Mr & Mrs R. Scott**
66 B c 17/02 Roaring Lion (USA)—Glories (USA) (Galileo (IRE)) **Qatar Racing Ltd**
67 B f 10/02 Camacho—Guthanna Gaoithe (Poet's Voice) (15000)
68 B f 27/04 Roaring Lion (USA)—Kiyoshi (Dubawi (IRE)) **Qatar Racing Ltd**
69 B f 24/02 Wootton Bassett—Kuna Yala (GER) (Manduro (GER)) (70000) **Mr C Wright & Miss E Asprey**
70 B c 30/01 Zoustar (AUS)—La Rioja (Hellvelyn) **Qatar Racing Ltd**
71 Br c 15/04 Invincible Spirit (IRE)—Lovely Pass (IRE) (Raven's Pass (USA)) **Dr A. Ridha**
72 Ch f 18/04 Roaring Lion (USA)—Maid To Dream (Oasis Dream) (62000) **Tony O'Connor & Reins Partners 2**
73 B f 23/04 Golden Horn—Mary's Choice (GER) (Redoute's Choice (AUS)) **HackettJohnPaulRickMike**
74 B c 20/04 Lope de Vega (IRE)—Maureen (IRE) (Holy Roman Emperor (IRE)) (140000) **Al Shaqab Racing UK Limited**
75 **NAVARRE EXPRESS**, gr f 14/02 Roaring Lion (USA)—Great Court (USA) (Mastercraftsman (IRE))
  Hunscote Stud & Mrs Lynne Maclennan
76 Br f 27/02 No Nay Never (USA)—Now You're Talking (IRE) (Zoffany (IRE)) (150000) **Sheikh I. S. Al Khalifa**
77 Ch c 08/04 Galileo Gold—Operissimo (Singspiel (IRE)) (65000) **Mr L. L. Lee**
78 B f 25/04 Galileo Gold—Pale Orchid (IRE) (Invincible Spirit (IRE)) (44218) **Mr E. D. Tynan**

MR HUGO PALMER - continued

79 B c 03/03 Golden Horn—Power of Light (IRE) (Echo of Light) **Dr A. Ridha**
80 Ch c 26/02 No Nay Never (USA)—Predawn (IRE) (Fastnet Rock (AUS)) **Mr V. I. Araci**
81 B c 01/03 Kingman—Priceless Jewel (Selkirk (USA)) (150000) **Middleham Park Racing**
82 B f 21/01 Saxon Warrior (JPN)—Silky (IRE) (Montjeu (IRE)) (85034) **Babington,Lacy,Shanahan,Tynan**
83 B f 01/04 Zoustar (AUS)—Stella Blue (FR) (Anabaa (USA)) **Qatar Racing Ltd**
84 B c 19/02 Unfortunately (IRE)—The Chemist (Dutch Art) (62000) **Al Shaqab Racing UK Limited**
85 B f 19/03 Dubawi (IRE)—Unforgetable Filly (Sepoy (AUS)) **Dr A. Ridha**

418	**MR JOSEPH PARR, Newmarket** Postal: **5 Greenfields, Newmarket, Suffolk, CB8 8DR** Contacts: **PHONE 07876 262169** EMAIL josephparr@hotmail.com

1 **ALJARYAAL (FR)**, 4, b g Siyouni (FR)—Jane Eyre **Mr J. E. Parr**
2 **ARTHUR'S VICTORY (IRE)**, 4, b f Buratino (IRE)—Impressive Victory (USA) **Mr M. Downey**
3 **BEDFORD BLAZE (IRE)**, 4, b g Dandy Man (IRE)—Hawaajib (FR) **Superlative Racing**
4 **CRESTWOOD**, 4, b g Garswood—Cresta Gold **Team Lodge Racing**
5 **ENIGMATIC (IRE)**, 8, b g Elnadim (USA)—Meanwhile (IRE) **Trevor & Ruth Milner**
6 **ENTHUSED (IRE)**, 5, b g Zoffany (IRE)—Question Times **Mr O. S. Harris**
7 **G'DAAY**, 4, b g Adaay (IRE)—Gilt Linked **Trevor & Ruth Milner**
8 **HALIC**, 4, b g Golden Horn—Pavlosk (USA) **Mr O. S. Harris**
9 **HELLO ME (IRE)**, 4, b f Mehmas (IRE)—Safe Place (USA) **Martley Hall Stud Ltd.**
10 **LUCAYAN**, 4, gr f Belardo (IRE)—Sandy Cay (USA) **Trevor & Ruth Milner**
11 **MC'TED**, 4, b g Garswood—Granny McPhee **A J McNamee & L C McNamee**
12 **ONLY DEBRIS (IRE)**, 4, b g Exceed And Excel (AUS)—Shapoura (FR) **Martley Hall Stud Ltd.**
13 **PRINCE OF BEL LIR (IRE)**, 4, b g Prince of Lir (IRE)—Harvest Joy (IRE) **The Skills People Group Ltd**
14 **QUEEN OF BURGUNDY**, 6, b m Lethal Force (IRE)—Empress Adelaide **Trevor & Ruth Milner**
15 **RECTORY ROAD**, 6, b g Paco Boy (IRE)—Caerlonore (IRE) **Mr S. Bond**
16 **ROMAN DYNASTY (IRE)**, 4, b g Mehmas (IRE)—Empress Ella (IRE) **Trevor & Ruth Milner**
17 **YAGOOD (IRE)**, 6, ch g Teofilo (IRE)—Tabassum (IRE) **Mr O. S. Harris**
18 **ZULU HOURS**, 4, b f Sakhee (USA)—Majuba Lady (IRE) **Mr J. E. Parr**

THREE-YEAR-OLDS

19 B f Australia—Artwork Genie (IRE)
20 **CONNIE R (IRE)**, b f Gutaifan (IRE)—Amurra **Mr P. S. Riley**
21 **GALILEO GLASS (IRE)**, b c Galileo Gold—Tahoo (IRE) **New Frontiers Ventures Limited**
22 **GIOVANNI BAGLIONE (IRE)**, gr c Caravaggio (USA)—Like A Star (IRE) **Trevor & Ruth Milner**
23 B f Garswood—Granny McPhee **A J McNamee & L C McNamee**
24 **KELAPA**, b f Aclaim (IRE)—Keriyka (IRE) **Away Days & Saxstead**
25 **LETHAL TOUCH**, gr f Lethal Force (IRE)—Loving Touch **Trevor & Ruth Milner**
26 **STORM KODI**, b f Kodiac—Myth **Mr N. A. Marks**
27 **THE GREEN MAN (IRE)**, b c Acclamation—Lydia Becker **Mr J. F. Stocker**
28 **TOKEN TRADER (IRE)**, b f Mehmas (IRE)—Evie Be Kool (IRE) **New Frontiers Ventures Limited**

TWO-YEAR-OLDS

29 Gr c 07/02 Mastercraftsman (IRE)—Aspasi (Dalakhani (IRE)) (10000)
30 B f 09/03 Bungle Inthejungle—Avizare (Lawman (FR)) (24762) **Mr O. S. Harris**
31 Gr f 20/04 Havana Grey—Conversational (IRE) (Thousand Words) (15000) **Mr J. E. Parr**
32 B c 23/01 Profitable (IRE)—Invernata (FR) (Holy Roman Emperor (USA)) (33333) **Trevor & Ruth Milner**
33 **KALAMUNDA**, b c 07/02 Zoustar (AUS)—Karen's Caper (USA) (War Chant (USA)) (85000) **Trevor & Ruth Milner**
34 B c 29/03 Expert Eye—Shamandar (FR) (Exceed And Excel (AUS)) (66667) **Mr O. S. Harris**

Other Owners: Away Days Racing Club, A. J. McNamee, Mr L. McNamee, Mrs R. L. Milner, Mr T. Milner, Mr J. Riley, Mr P. S. Riley, Saxtead Livestock Ltd.

419 **MR MARK PATTINSON, Epsom**
Postal: **Flat 3, White House Stables, Tattenham Corner Road, Epsom, Surrey, KT18 5PP**
Contacts: **MOBILE 07961 835401**

1 HAVERGATE ISLAND, 4, b g Coach House (IRE)—Jethou Island **Mrs F A Veasey & G. B. Partnership**
2 NUBOUGH (IRE), 6, b g Kodiac—Qawaasem (IRE) **M I Pattinson Racing**
3 PERFECT SYMPHONY (IRE), 8, b g Dandy Man (IRE)—Fields of Joy (GER) **Mr M. Pattinson**
4 RAINBOW SIGN, 4, b g Adaay (IRE)—Pax Aeterna (USA) **M. G. H. Heald**
5 VITESSE DU SON, 5, b g Fast Company (IRE)—Sister Guru **Scuderia Di Vincitori**

THREE-YEAR-OLDS

6 SHEARWATER, b c Coach House (IRE)—The Lady Mandarin **M I Pattinson Racing**

Other Owners: Mr A. M. H. Heald, M. G. H. Heald, Mrs F. A. Veasey.

---

420 **MR BEN PAULING, Bourton-on-the-Water**
Postal: **Bourton Hill Farm, Bourton Hill, Bourton-On-The-Water,
Cheltenham, Gloucestershire, GL54 2LF**
Contacts: **PHONE 01451 821252 MOBILE 07825 232888**
EMAIL ben@benpaulingracing.com WEBSITE www.benpaulingracing.com

1 A DEFINITE GETAWAY (IRE), 4, b g Getaway (GER)—Def It Vic (IRE) **Bruton Street UK - III**
2 ANGE ENDORMI (IRE), 6, ch g Leading Light (IRE)—Maxford Lady (IRE) **Mrs G. Morgan**
3 ANIGHTINLAMBOURN (IRE), 8, b m Gold Well—Madgehil (IRE) **The Megsons**
4 APPLE ROCK (IRE), 8, b g Royal Anthem (USA)—Wayward Cove **Presumption in Favour Partnership**
5 ARTEMISION, 6, b g Gentlewave (IRE)—Miss Fahrenheit (IRE) **T K Racing Ltd**
6 AWAYTHELAD (IRE), 5, b g Getaway (GER)—Jennys Joy (IRE) **Geri and The Pacemakers**
7 BANGERS AND CASH (IRE), 6, b g Fame And Glory—Cash Customer (IRE) **OAP II**
8 BETTY'S BELLE, 5, b m Schiaparelli (GER)—Burgundy Betty (IRE) **Mrs B. M. Henley**
9 BIG DIFFERENCE (IRE), 9, b g Presenting—Roque de Cyborg (IRE) **Mr M. Waters**
10 BOBBY BOW (IRE), 8, b g Frammassone (IRE)—Bramble Cottage (IRE) **Mrs G. Morgan**
11 BOWTOGREATNESS (IRE), 6, br g Westerner—Miss Baden (IRE) **Harry Redknapp & Sophie Pauling**
12 CHADLINGTON LAD (IRE), 4, b g Estidhkaar (IRE)—Fuaigh Mor (IRE) **Mr R. J. Catling**
13 CHEATING JACK (FR), 5, gr g Montmartre (FR)—Headdress (FR) **Mrs S. Pauling**
14 CHESS PLAYER (IRE), 7, ch g No Risk At All (FR)—Merci Jandrer (FR) **Mrs Rachel Brodie & Mr John Brodie**
15 CLAPTON HILL, 4, b g Dunaden (FR)—Rosita Bay
16 COULDBEAWEAPON (IRE), 5, ch g Mahler—Wild Fuchsia (IRE)
17 DE BARLEY BASKET (IRE), 9, b g Alkaadhem—Lady Willmurt (IRE) **Mrs S N J Embiricos & Ms A Embiricos**
18 DEL LA MAR ROCKET (IRE), 6, b g Fame And Glory—Pipe Lady (IRE) **Les de La Haye & Martin Mundy**
19 DENSWORTH (IRE), 5, b g Kayf Tara—Mariah's Way **OAP Syndicate**
20 DOCK ROAD (IRE), 6, ch g Shirocco (GER)—Representing (IRE) **Mr J. P. McManus**
21 DOMINATEUR (FR), 9, b g Desir d'Un Soir (FR)—Sourya d'Airy (FR) **Mr D. R. M. Griffiths**
22 5, B g Shirocco (GER)—Easter Bonnie (IRE)
23 ENCASHMENT, 5, b m Casamento (IRE)—Burton Ash **Mrs S. Lee & Mr E. Lee**
24 FAWSLEY SPIRIT (IRE), 9, b g Stowaway—Apple Trix (IRE) **Mrs Rachel Brodie & Mr Clive Bush**
25 FINE CASTING (IRE), 6, b g Shantou (USA)—Fine Fortune (IRE) **Mrs S. P. Davis**
26 FOLLY HILL, 6, b m Mount Nelson—Burton Ash **Mrs S. Lee & Mr E. Lee**
27 GALAHAD THREEPWOOD, 5, b g Nathaniel (IRE)—Tesary **The Megsons**
28 GENTLEMAN VALLEY (FR), 6, b g Kapgarde (FR)—Richona (FR) **The Megsons**
29 GET PREPARED, 7, b g Black Sam Bellamy (IRE)—Star Ar Aghaidh (IRE) **The Aldaniti Partnership**
30 GIEVES (IRE), 4, ch g Shirocco (GER)—Lady of Appeal (IRE) **Pump & Plant Services Ltd**
31 GLOBAL CITIZEN (IRE), 10, b g Alkaadhem—Lady Willmurt (IRE) **The Megsons**
32 GLORIOUS OSCAR (IRE), 5, b g Fame And Glory—Flowers On Sunday (IRE) **Mr & Mrs J Tuttiett**
33 GUARDINO (FR), 6, br g Authorized (IRE)—Monicker **Merriebelle Irish Farm Limited**
34 HARDY BOY (FR), 5, gr g Diamond Boy (FR)—Alize du Berlais (FR) **Martin & Lynn Jones**
35 HARPER'S BROOK (IRE), 6, b g Ask—Un Jour D Ete (FR) **The Megsons**

MR BEN PAULING - continued

36 **HIRAC (FR)**, 5, b g Bernebeau (FR)—Nosika d'Airy (FR) **Mrs S. Pauling**
37 **HONOR GREY (IRE)**, 7, b g Flemensfirth (USA)—Rose Island **Mr & Mrs J Tuttiett**
38 **I'M SPELLBOUND (IRE)**, 6, b g Doyen (IRE)—Magic Park (IRE) **Mr Simon Munir & Mr Isaac Souede**
39 **IMPERIAL KNIGHT (IRE)**, 5, b g Mahler—And Whatever Else (IRE) **Middleham Park Racing LXXXIX**
40 4, B g Blue Bresil (FR)—Ishka Baha (IRE) **The Megsons**
41 **IVETWIGGEDIT**, 5, b m Schiaparelli (GER)—Southern Exit **Mr L. J. Strangman**
42 4, B g Milan—Jet Empress (IRE)
43 **KENNACK BAY (FR)**, 7, br g Balko (FR)—Nuance Tartare (FR) **The Kennack Bay Partnership**
44 **KILDISART (IRE)**, 10, b g Dubai Destination (USA)—Princess Mairead (IRE) **Mr Simon Munir & Mr Isaac Souede**
45 **LADY ROBINN**, 5, br m Robin des Champs (FR)—Friendly Craic (IRE) **Nicholas Piper & Claire E. Piper**
46 **LE BREUIL (FR)**, 10, ch g Anzillero (GER)—Slew Dancer **Mrs E. A. Palmer**
47 **LE GRAND LION (FR)**, 6, gr g Turgeon (FR)—Grande Cavale (FR) **The Lion Tamers**
48 **LIFEISAHIGHWAY (IRE)**, 8, b g Court Cave (IRE)—Miss Top (IRE) **The Rascal Flatts Partnership**
49 **MALINELLO**, 7, b g Malinas (GER)—Wyldello **Martin & Lynn Jones**
50 **MISTER WATSON**, 8, b g Mawatheeq (USA)—Island Odyssey **The Jp Girls**
51 **MOLE COURT (IRE)**, 5, b g Court Cave (IRE)—Running Wild (IRE) **Mr O. Troup**
52 **MUCHO MAS (IRE)**, 6, b g Fame And Glory—Ceart Go Leor (IRE) **Mrs J. A. Wakefield**
53 **NADAITAK**, 8, b g Teofilo (IRE)—Tanfidh **The Megsons**
54 4, B g Califet (FR)—Nechtan (IRE)
55 **NESTOR PARK (FR)**, 9, b g Walk In The Park (IRE)—Cila (FR) **Mrs S. P. Davis**
56 **NIVLAC (IRE)**, 8, b g Court Cave (IRE)—Marys Article (IRE) **The Ben Pauling Racing Club**
57 **NORLEY (IRE)**, 7, b g Yeats (IRE)—No Moore Bills **Mrs G. Morgan**
58 **NORTHERN BOUND (IRE)**, 6, b g Fruits of Love (USA)—Noble Choice **Mrs E. L. Kendall**
59 **NOT AT PRESENT (IRE)**, 7, br g Presenting—Anna Magdalena (IRE) **Mrs Rachel Brodie & Mr John Brodie**
60 **NOW IS THE WINTER (IRE)**, 8, b g Fame And Glory—Supreme Melody (IRE) **Brown & Reddin**
61 **ON SPRINGS (IRE)**, 7, b g Mahler—Wild Fuchsia (IRE) **Sophie Pauling & Les de La Haye**
62 **ONE TOUCH (IRE)**, 8, b g Court Cave (IRE)—Star Bui (IRE) **Martin & Lynn Jones**
63 **OPTIMISE PRIME (IRE)**, 6, b g Shantou (USA)—Wilde Ruby (IRE) **Mrs Rachel Brodie & Mr John Brodie**
64 **PENCREEK (FR)**, 9, ch g Konig Shuffle (GER)—Couture Fleurs (FR) **Mrs G. S. Worcester**
65 **PHIL THE SOCK (IRE)**, 5, b g Fame And Glory—Quinnsboro Native (IRE) **The Stewkley Shindiggers Partnership**
66 **POMEROL GEORGE (IRE)**, 6, b g Fame And Glory—My Native (IRE) **Mrs S. Pauling**
67 **QUINTA DO MAR (IRE)**, 7, b g Califet (FR)—Cara Mara (IRE) **The Bourtoneers**
68 **RAVEN'S TOWER (USA)**, 12, b g Raven's Pass (USA)—Tizdubai (USA) **Mrs S. Pauling**
69 4, B g Blue Bresil (FR)—Samandara (FR)
70 **SCOTCH ON DA ROCKS (IRE)**, 5, b g Fame And Glory—Final Episode (IRE) **Mrs S. Pauling**
71 **SEBASTIAN BEACH (IRE)**, 11, b g Yeats (IRE)—Night Club **The Megsons**
72 **SERJEANT PAINTER**, 7, b g Royal Applause—Szabo's Art **Mrs S. Pauling**
73 **SEVERANCE**, 6, b g Nathaniel (IRE)—Decorative (IRE) **The Megsons**
74 **SHAKEM UP'ARRY (IRE)**, 8, b g Flemensfirth (USA)—Nun Better (IRE) **Mr H. Redknapp**
75 **SILVER ATOM (IRE)**, 4, gr g Vadamos (FR)—Dalaway (IRE) **Mrs E. A. Palmer**
76 **SLIPWAY (IRE)**, 7, b g Stowaway—Little Sioux (IRE) **Mrs S. N. J. Embiricos**
77 **SMUGGLERS CLIFF (IRE)**, 5, br g Califet (FR)—Dontcallerthat (IRE) **Mrs S. Pauling**
78 4, Ch g Mount Nelson—South Africa (FR)
79 **SOUTH MOUNTAIN (IRE)**, 6, b g Westerner—Maryiver (IRE) **Bruton Street UK - III**
80 **SPECIAL BUDDY (IRE)**, 8, b g Robin des Pres (FR)—Annees d'Or (IRE) **Mr B. P. Pauling**
81 **SPORTING MIKE (IRE)**, 5, b g Walk In The Park (IRE)—Kates The Boss (IRE) **Mrs Rachel Brodie & Mr John Brodie**
82 **STOKES (IRE)**, 7, b g Califet (FR)—Iktitafs Sister (IRE) **The Ben Pauling Racing Club**
83 **THE COB (IRE)**, 8, b g Let The Lion Roar—Millenium Love (IRE) **The Cob Nuts**
84 **THE MACON LUGNATIC**, 8, b g Shirocco—Didbrook **Genesis Racing Partnership II**
85 **UNIT SIXTYFOUR (IRE)**, 7, b g Sholokhov (IRE)—Dixie Chick (IRE) **Owners Group 062**
86 **WEE TONY (IRE)**, 4, b g Califet (FR)—Afar Story (IRE) **Mr S. D. Reddin**
87 **WHATSUPWITHYOU (IRE)**, 8, b g Shantou (USA)—Whats Up Britta (IRE) **Co-Foundations Ltd**
88 **YOUR DARLING (IRE)**, 7, b g Shirocco (GER)—Carries Darling **Lord & Lady Vestey**

Other Owners: Mr I. N. Baillie, Mr J. W. Brodie, Mrs R. A. Brodie, Mr P Brown, Mr C. Bush, Mr L. De la Haye, Ms A. E. Embiricos, Mrs S. N. J. Embiricos, Mrs J. D. Farrant, Mr C. Fenwick, W. F. Frewen, Mr T. R. Gittins, Glassex Holdings Ltd, Mr M. D. Hankin, The Marquis of Headfort, J H & N J Foxon Ltd, Mrs L. Jones, Mr M. Jones, Mr E. Lee, Mrs S. M. Lee, Mr M. Mundy, S. E. Munir, Mr E. D. Nicolson, Mr C. Noell III, Mr B. P. Pauling, Mrs S. Pauling, Miss C. E. Piper, Mr N. Piper, Mr S. D. Reddin, Mr H. Redknapp, Mr I. Souede, Mrs A. J. Tuttiett, Mr J. E. Tuttiett, Exors of the Late Lord Vestey, Lady Vestey, Mrs C. A. Waters, Mrs N. J. White, Mrs G. S. Worcester.

MR BEN PAULING - continued

Assistant Trainer: Thomas David, **Head Girl:** Gill Tate, **Secretary:** Hannah Vowles.

NH Jockey: Kielan Woods. **Conditional Jockey:** Luca Morgan.

---

421   MR SIMON PEARCE, Newmarket
Postal: **1 Whitegates, Newmarket, Suffolk, CB8 8DS**
Contacts: **PHONE 01638 664669**
EMAIL spearceracing@hotmail.co.uk

1 **ABRAAJ (FR)**, 4, b g Shalaa (IRE)—Wonderous Light (IRE) **Conde, Hanger, Jones, Noone & Noone**
2 **BARTHOLOMEW J (IRE)**, 8, ch g Fast Company (IRE)—Mana (IRE) **Nigel Hanger, Eric Jones & Partners**
3 **CURVATIOUS**, 4, b f Telescope (IRE)—Tanwir **A Partnership**
4 **FULL INTENTION**, 8, b g Showcasing—My Delirium **Killarney Glen & Lydia Pearce**
5 **HANOVERIAN KING (GER)**, 4, b g Showcasing—Hasay **The Showstoppers**
6 **HIDING DAVE (IRE)**, 4, b g Ivawood (IRE)—Lady Lizabeth (IRE) **Deerfield Syndicate**
7 **MIGHTY MIND**, 5, b h Poet's Voice—Cool Catena **Mr A. Dal Pos**
8 **NOBLE PEACE**, 9, b g Kyllachy—Peace Concluded **Killarney Glen**
9 **RED EVELYN**, 4, ch f Garswood—Skara Brae **Deerfield Syndicate**
10 **STORM CATCHER (IRE)**, 4, b g Vadamos (FR)—Next Life **Nigel Hanger & Eric Jones**
11 **TARAVARA (IRE)**, 4, b g The Gurkha (IRE)—Red Blossom **Killarney Glen**
12 **VICTORY ROSE**, 6, b m Bated Breath—Albany Rose (IRE) **Deerfield Syndicate**
13 **WRENS ROSE (FR)**, 5, b m Zanzibari (USA)—Montoria (FR)

THREE-YEAR-OLDS

14 **KISSED BY ICE**, gr f El Kabeir (USA)—Nouveau Foret **Howard Duff Racing**
15 **STUBBLE FIELD**, b f Adaay (IRE)—Lady Estella (IRE) **Howard Duff Racing**
16 **THE POMO**, gr f El Kabeir (USA)—High Drama (IRE) **Audrey Lawham & Partners**

Other Owners: S. Andrews, Mr H. Crothers, N. M. Hanger, J. Harrison, Mr E. Jones, Killarney Glen, Mrs L. Matthews, Nigel Hanger & Eric Jones, Mrs L. S. Pearce, Simon Pearce.

---

422   MR OLLIE PEARS, Malton
Postal: **The Old Farmhouse, Beverley Road, Norton, Malton, North Yorkshire, YO17 9PJ**
Contacts: **PHONE 01653 690746 MOBILE 07760 197103**
EMAIL info@olliepearsracing.co.uk WEBSITE www.olliepearsracing.co.uk

1 **CROWN PRINCESS (IRE)**, 4, b f Mehmas (IRE)—Al Hanyora **Ownaracehorse Ltd, M Reay & K West**
2 **FLISS FLOSS**, 4, gr f Lethal Force (IRE)—Raggle Taggle (IRE) **Mr A. Caygill**
3 **HARRY LOVE (IRE)**, 5, b g Lawman (FR)—Gimmick (IRE) **Ownaracehorse Ltd & Mr Ollie Pears**
4 **KRYSTAL MAZE (IRE)**, 4, b f Kodiac—Escapism (IRE) **T. Elsey**
5 **READY FREDDIE GO (IRE)**, 4, b g Swiss Spirit—Barbieri (IRE) **Ownaracehorse Ltd, Keates & West**
6 **SUSIE JAVEA**, 5, b m Coach House (IRE)—Charlevoix (IRE) **Mr A. Caygill**

THREE-YEAR-OLDS

7 **ASHTEAD (IRE)**, br g Invincible Spirit (IRE)—Elphin **Mrs S. D. Pearson**
8 **COLIGONE KATE**, ch f Garswood—Dubai Walk (ITY) **H Bradshaws LTD Coligone**
9 **GOLDEN GAL (IRE)**, br f Galileo Gold—Dubai Princess (IRE) **Ownaracehorse Ltd & Mr Ollie Pears**
10 **MY BROTHER JACK (IRE)**, b g Decorated Knight—Bella Bella (IRE) **Jo-co Partnership**
11 **OUTSMART (IRE)**, gr g Outstrip—Mi Rubina (IRE) **Jo-co Partnership**
12 **QWELDRYK (IRE)**, b f Galileo Gold—Fainleog (IRE) **T. Elsey**

MR OLLIE PEARS - continued

13 **QWICKEN (IRE)**, gr f Gutaifan (IRE)—Miss Wicklow (IRE) **Ownaracehorse Ltd & K West**
14 B f Peace Envoy (FR)—Spanish Beauty **Mr R. S. Marshall**

TWO-YEAR-OLDS
15 **A DAY TO DREAM (IRE)**, b g 19/04 Adaay (IRE)—Tara Too (IRE) (Danetime (IRE)) (4500)
                                                                    Ownaracehorse Ltd & Mr Ollie Pears
16 B g 04/02 Brazen Beau (AUS)—Anushka Noo Noo (Makfi) **Mr A. Caygill**
17 **AURORA GLORY (IRE)**, b f 14/03 Cotai Glory—Al Hanyora (Teofilo (IRE)) (11429)
                                                          Pam Moll, Timothy O'Gram & Mike Reay
18 **BEAUTIFUL MUM**, b f 05/03 Charm Spirit (IRE)—Merton Matriarch (Cadeaux Genereux) (2000)
                                                                    Ownaracehorse Ltd & Mr Ollie Pears
19 **CHRISTMAS EVE (IRE)**, b f 26/03 Holy Roman Emperor (IRE)—Slieve (Selkirk (USA)) (4286)
                                                                    Ownaracehorse Ltd & Mr Ollie Pears
20 **GO BUNNY (IRE)**, ch f 18/01 National Defense—Typify (Shirocco (GER)) (3827) **Try As We May Partnership**
21 **HIDDEN CODE (IRE)**, b g 19/03 Kessaar (IRE)—Khibrah (Dark Angel (IRE)) (6667)
                                                                    Ownaracehorse Ltd & Mr Ollie Pears
22 B g 14/04 Buratino (IRE)—Impressive Victory (USA) (Street Cry (IRE)) **Michael Downey & Ollie Pears**
23 **LET'S GO HUGO (IRE)**, ch g 24/03 Unfortunately (IRE)—Barbieri (IRE) (Encosta de Lago (AUS)) (5905)
                                                                    Ownaracehorse & Dave Keates
24 **LOVELIEST**, br f 22/03 Unfortunately (IRE)—Harbour Siren (Harbour Watch (IRE)) (3333) **O. J. Pears**
25 B g 25/04 Cotai Glory—Miriam's Song (Royal Applause) (10000) **Mr A. Caygill**
26 B g 19/01 Camacho—Our Valkyrie (High Chaparral (IRE)) (2000) **O. J. Pears**

Other Owners: Mrs D. L. Cooney, Mr E. Cooney, Mr M. Downey, Mrs D. J. Humphrey, Mr D. Keates, Mrs P.E. Moll, T. J. O'Gram, Ownaracehorse Ltd, O. J. Pears, Mr I. Pritchard, Mr M. A. Reay, K. C. West.

Assistant Trainer: Vicky Pears.

---

423   MISS LINDA PERRATT, East Kilbride
Postal: **North Allerton Farm, East Kilbride, Glasgow, Lanarkshire, G75 8RR**
Contacts: **PHONE 01355 303425 MOBILE 07931 306147**
EMAIL linda.perratt@btinternet.com

1 **CHINESE SPIRIT (IRE)**, 8, gr g Clodovil (IRE)—In The Ribbons **Mr Sandy Jarvie & Miss L. Perratt**
2 **GRANDADS BEST GIRL**, 5, b m Intrinsic—Mitchelland **Miss L. A. Perratt**
3 **HARD NUT (IRE)**, 5, b g Gutaifan (IRE)—With A Twist **Mr W. F. Perratt**
4 **JUDGMENT CALL**, 4, br g Pivotal—Madonna Dell'orto **M. Sawers**
5 **KEEP COMING (IRE)**, 6, b g Leading Light (IRE)—Pretty Present (IRE) **M & L Perratt**
6 **LUCKY VIOLET (IRE)**, 10, b m Dandy Man (IRE)—Rashida **The Hon Miss H. Galbraith**
7 **MARAAKIZ (IRE)**, 4, b g Muhaarar—Entisaar (AUS) **Mr B. A. Jordan**
8 **MONHAMMER**, 4, b g Awtaad (IRE)—Soviet Terms **Peter Tsim & Linda Perratt**
9 **NODSASGOODASAWINK**, 4, ch f Sixties Icon—Winkaway **R. Winning & Partner**
10 **POCKLEY**, 4, b g Shalaa (IRE)—Wanting (IRE) **Mr R. Winning**
11 **RETIREMENT BECKONS**, 7, b g Epaulette (AUS)—Mystical Ayr (IRE) **R. Winning & Partner**
12 **SALTMARKET**, 7, b g Multiplex—Kiera Marie (IRE) **M & L Perratt**
13 **SIXCOR**, 4, b g Sixties Icon—Roccor **Linda Perratt Racing Club**
14 **STREAMLINE**, 5, b g Due Diligence (USA)—Ahwahnee **Mr R. Winning**

THREE-YEAR-OLDS
15 **PASHA BAY**, b g Cable Bay (IRE)—Cafe Express (IRE) **The Hon Miss H. Galbraith**

Other Owners: Mr A. Jarvie, Miss L. A. Perratt, M. Sawers, P. Tsim, Mr R. Winning.

Flat Jockey: Tom Eaves, P. J. McDonald. **Apprentice Jockey:** Leanne Ferguson.

424 MRS AMANDA PERRETT, Pulborough
Postal: **Coombelands Racing Stables, Pulborough, West Sussex, RH20 1BP**
Contacts: **PHONE 01798 873011 MOBILE 07803 088713**
EMAIL aperrett@coombelands-stables.com **WEBSITE** www.amandaperrett.com

1 **COUNT OTTO (IRE),** 7, b g Sir Prancealot (IRE)—Dessert Flower (IRE) **Count Otto Partnership**
2 **FRONTISPIECE,** 8, b g Shamardal (USA)—Free Verse **The Frontispiece Partnership**
3 **LAVENDER'S BLUE (IRE),** 6, b m Sea The Stars (IRE)—Beatrice Aurore (IRE) **B. Andersson**
4 **MAZZURI (IRE),** 7, ch m Raven's Pass (USA)—Essexford (IRE) **Mrs S. M. Conway**
5 **MOWALEDA (USA),** 4, b f Distorted Humor (USA)—Basaata (USA) **Mrs F Cotton, Mr & Mrs P Conway**
6 **NELLIE MOON,** 4, b br f Sea The Moon (GER)—Queen's Dream (IRE) **Nellie Moon Partnership**
7 **REBEL TERRITORY,** 4, b g Territories (IRE)—Saucy Minx (IRE) **Mrs F Cotton, Mr & Mrs P Conway**
8 **SAAHEQ,** 8, b g Invincible Spirit (IRE)—Brevity (USA) **Coombelands Racing Syndicate**
9 **SAYIFYOUWILL,** 4, b f Sayif (IRE)—Amirah (IRE) **Richard Cheadle & Partners**
10 **SIR JOSEPH SWAN,** 4, b g Paco Boy (IRE)—Candle **Mrs B. A. Karn-Smith**
11 **TAQSEEMAAT,** 4, b f Nayef (USA)—Mooakada (IRE) **Mrs A. J. Perrett**
12 **YOU'RE HIRED,** 9, b g Dalakhani (IRE)—Heaven Sent **G. D. P. Materna**
13 **ZIKANY,** 4, b g Zoffany (IRE)—Rosika **Mrs A. M. Lewis**

THREE-YEAR-OLDS
14 **BALLET BLANC,** ch f Highland Reel (IRE)—Bouvardia **Mrs A. J. Perrett**
15 Ch f Australia—Beatrice Aurore (IRE) **B. Andersson**
16 **BORNTOBEALEADER (IRE),** ch c Churchill (IRE)—Shake The Moon (GER) **The Borntobealeader Partnership**
17 **LATER DARLING,** b g Postponed (IRE)—Saucy Minx (IRE) **Mrs F Cotton, Mr & Mrs P Conway**
18 **LEVEL UP (IRE),** b g Hot Streak (IRE)—Kamarinskaya (USA) **James, Jenkins & Partners**
19 **MISS DOWN UNDER (IRE),** ch f Australia—Pocket of Stars (IRE) **Miss Down Under Partnership**
20 **SIR ALFRED M,** b c Equiano (FR)—Secret Sands (IRE) **J. H. Widdows**

TWO-YEAR-OLDS
21 **AUTOLYCUS,** ch c 08/03 Cracksman—Elysian Fields (GR) (Champs Elysees) (30000) **Mr John P Connolly**
22 **DOVENA,** ch f 25/02 Nathaniel (IRE)—Curtains (Dubawi (IRE)) (10000) **The Dovena Partnership**
23 **DREAM OF MISCHIEF,** b c 14/04 Oasis Dream—Saucy Minx (IRE) (Dylan Thomas (IRE))
Mrs F Cotton, Mr & Mrs P Conway
24 **FREETODREAM,** b c 08/02 Muhaarar—Twilight Spirit (Assertive) (17000) **Freetodream Partnership**
25 **IMPERIOUSITY,** ch c 10/02 Tasleet—Great Hope (Halling (USA)) (50000) **D & B James and Partners**
26 **SHOWGAL (IRE),** b br f 28/01 Showcasing—Fearn's Pippin (Dubawi (IRE)) (60000) **B & D James and Partners**
27 **TOUS LES GRIS,** gr f 07/02 Lethal Force (IRE)—Tiger Milly (Tiger Hill (IRE))

Assistant Trainer: Mark Perrett.

---

425 MR PAT PHELAN, Epsom
Postal: **Ermyn Lodge, Shepherds Walk, Epsom, Surrey, KT18 6DF**
Contacts: **PHONE 01372 229014 MOBILE 07917 762781 FAX 01372 229001**
EMAIL pat.phelan@ermynlodge.com **WEBSITE** www.ermynlodge.com

1 **DEVIZES (IRE),** 6, b g Dubawi (IRE)—Dalasyla (IRE) **Celtic Contractors Limited**
2 **EPSOM FAITHFULL,** 5, b m Coach House (IRE)—La Fortunata **Epsom Racegoers No.2**
3 **ERMYNS DOTTIE,** 4, br f Mayson—Young Dottie **Mr A. Smith**
4 **HACKBRIDGE,** 7, b g Archipenko (USA)—Famcred **Mr P. J. Wheatley**
5 **HAYKAL,** 4, b f Nathaniel (IRE)—Rhagori **P. P. Mclaughlin**
6 **HONORE,** 4, b g Telescope (IRE)—Saint Honore **Mr P. Bocking**
7 **ICONIC MOVER,** 4, ch g Sixties Icon—Run For Ede's **Mr A. Smith**
8 **LEGEND OF FRANCE,** 9, ch m Flying Legend (USA)—Bonne Anniversaire **Ermyn Lodge Stud Limited**
9 **OPTIMISTIC BELIEF (IRE),** 4, b g Make Believe—Panglossian (IRE) **Mr J. F. Lang**
10 **PRINCESSE ANIMALE,** 5, b m Leroidesanimaux (BRZ)—Isabella Beeton **Mr A. Smith**
11 **REECELTIC,** 7, b g Champs Elysees—Sense of Pride **Celtic Contractors Limited**

MR PAT PHELAN - continued

12 **SEPRANI**, 8, b m Sepoy (AUS)—King's Guest (IRE) **Book 3 Partnership**
13 **STAR OF EPSOM**, 4, b f Sir Percy—Isabella Beeton **Epsom Racegoers No.3**
14 **WEARDIDITALLGORONG**, 10, b m Fast Company (IRE)—Little Oz (IRE) **P. P. Mclaughlin**

THREE-YEAR-OLDS

15 **ABIE MY BOY**, ch g Equiano (FR)—Ellie In The Pink (IRE) **A. B. Pope**

Flat Jockey: J. F. Egan, Shane Kelly, Kieran O'Neill. **NH Jockey:** James Best, Josh Moore.

Conditional Jockey: Sean Houlihan. **Apprentice Jockey:** Paddy Bradley, Sophie Ralston.

---

426 **MR KEVIN PHILIPPART DE FOY, Newmarket**
Postal: **Machell Place Stables, Old Station Road, Newmarket, Suffolk, CB8 8DW**
Contacts: **PHONE 07551 498273**
EMAIL kevin@kpfracing.com

1 **ABU MALEK (IRE)**, 4, b g Acclamation—Brunch Bellini (FR) **Sheikh A. H. F. M. A. Al Sabah**
2 **ALREHB (USA)**, 5, gr g War Front (USA)—Tahrir (IRE) **KB Thoroughbreds**
3 **BERYL THE PERIL (IRE)**, 4, ch f Dandy Man (IRE)—Lady of Rohan **The Champagne Poppers**
4 **COVERT MISSION (FR)**, 4, b g Lope de Vega (IRE)—Beach Belle **Owners Group 092**
5 **EARTH GIANT (IRE)**, 4, b c Zoffany (IRE)—Snowgal (IRE) **The Zodiacs**
6 **JUAN DE MONTALBAN (IRE)**, 4, ch g Lope de Vega (IRE)—Abilene **Sheikh A. H. F. M. A. Al Sabah**
7 **LETMELIVEMYLIFE**, 4, b g Oasis Dream—Itiqad
8 **LIVERPOOL KNIGHT**, 4, b g Golden Horn—Nouriya
9 **MAIN TARGET**, 4, ch c Pivotal—Jazzi Top **Sheikh A. H. F. M. A. Al Sabah**
10 **MOBARHIN (IRE)**, 4, b c Muhaarar—Fadhayyil (IRE) **The Zodiacs**
11 **PEPITE DE AMOUR**, 4, b f Telescope (IRE)—Pepite de Soleil (FR)
12 **STREET KID (IRE)**, 4, ch g Street Boss (USA)—Brushed Gold (USA) **Run Away Racing Galtee More Syndicate**
13 **THE FIRST HURRAH (FR)**, 4, b f Muhaarar—Sweet Cecily (IRE) **Dr H. Crawford**
14 **TWENTYSHARESOFGREY**, 4, bl gr f Markaz—Carsulae (IRE) **The Champagne Poppers**
15 **VAFORTINO (IRE)**, 4, b g New Bay—Arbaab (USA) **Venice Consulting & Gambini**

THREE-YEAR-OLDS

16 **ADJUDICATOR (IRE)**, gr g Dark Angel (IRE)—African Moonlight (UAE) **The Adjudicators**
17 **ADORABLE YOU (IRE)**, b f Zarak (FR)—Embraceable You **Normandie Stud Ltd**
18 **ARGIRL**, b f Ardad (IRE)—Lassies Envoi **The Johnson Grundy Partnership**
19 **BAILEYSGUTFEELING (IRE)**, b c Gutaifan (IRE)—Baileys Pursuit **Miss D. E. Steed**
20 **BROWN MOUSE (IRE)**, b f Showcasing—Shemda (IRE) **Mr I. Dodds-Smith**
21 **CHASING LOVE**, b g Charming Thought—Royal Confidence **Mr P. Hancock**
22 **DESERT MIRACLE**, ch g Postponed (IRE)—Mia San Triple
23 **EDWARD JENNER (IRE)**, b g Vadamos (FR)—Zakyah
24 **ELSALS**, b c Havana Gold (IRE)—Ejaazah (IRE) **KB Thoroughbreds**
25 **FAN THE FLAMES (IRE)**, b c Lawman (FR)—True Crystal (IRE) **Sheikh A. H. F. M. A. Al Sabah**
26 **GIDWA (IRE)**, b g Ribchester (IRE)—Gheedaa (USA) **Midlands Racing Club**
27 **GIEWONT (IRE)**, b g Aclaim (IRE)—Short Shrift (IRE) **The Giewont Syndicate**
28 **GIVE A LITTLE BACK (FR)**, b c Zelzal (FR)—Boyarynya (USA)
29 **GLENDA'S SPIRIT (IRE)**, b f Gleneagles (IRE)—Martine's Spirit (IRE)
30 **KERENSA**, b f Territories (IRE)—Viola da Braccio (IRE) **Miss L. G. Robinson**
31 **NEW PURSUIT (IRE)**, ch g New Bay—Soliza (IRE) **Run Away Racing Quest Syndicate**
32 **NICHOLAS GEORGE**, ch c Reliable Man—Carisolo **Normandie Stud Ltd**
33 **OCTOPUS (IRE)**, gr c Kendargent (FR)—Mountain Melody (GER)
34 **PEARL GLORY (IRE)**, b f Cotai Glory—Oatmeal **Team Valor Llc & Gary Barber**
35 **POKHARA (IRE)**, b f The Gurkha (IRE)—Shagra (IRE) **Run Away Racing Himalayan Syndicate**
36 **ROCK MELODY (IRE)**, b f Fascinating Rock (IRE)—Legal Lyric (IRE) **The Across the Pond Partnership**
37 **ROSE BARTON (IRE)**, b f Caravaggio (USA)—Marie Celeste (IRE) **Mrs S. Rogers**

MR KEVIN PHILIPPART DE FOY - continued

38 ROYAL AVIATION (USA), ch g American Pharoah (USA)—Queen of The Sand (IRE) **Sheikh A. H. F. M. A. Al Sabah**
39 SHAMLAAN (IRE), ch c Mehmas (IRE)—Streisand (IRE) **Sheikh A. H. F. M. A. Al Sabah**
40 THE GANGES (IRE), gr c Markaz (IRE)—Heavenly River (FR) **Byerley Thoroughbreds LTD**
41 TIARE (FR), b f Ectot—Love On Top (FR) **Sheikh A. H. F. M. A. Al Sabah**
42 TORVI, b f Gutaifan (IRE)—Characterized

TWO-YEAR-OLDS

43 APOLLO'S ANGEL, gr f 01/02 Dark Angel (IRE)—Ebony Flyer (SAF) (Jet Master (SAF))
Team Valor, Cayton Park Stud, Mr A Singh
44 B c 24/02 Holy Roman Emperor (IRE)—Bagira (USA) (Giant's Causeway (USA)) (27619)
45 BE A GRIZZLY, b c 09/02 Kodiac—Bristol Fashion (Dansili) (150000) **KB Thoroughbreds & Partner**
46 BEAR ON THE LOOSE (IRE), b c 08/03 Footstepsinthesand—Ihtiraam (IRE) (Teofilo (IRE)) (85034)
KB Thoroughbreds
47 B c 11/05 Territories (IRE)—Broughtons Revival (Pivotal) (9000)
48 BYEFORNOW, b f 15/01 Charm Spirit (IRE)—Zumran (Rock of Gibraltar (IRE)) (11000) **Mrs C. E. Percival**
49 CLIPSHAM LA HABANA, gr c 18/04 Havana Grey—Vitta's Touch (USA) (Touch Gold (USA)) (16000) **Mr F Morley**
50 D DAY ARVALENREEVA (IRE), ch f 11/04 Mastercraftsman (IRE)—Eccellente Idea (IRE) (Excellent Art) (48000)
Mr D Olver
51 B f 30/04 Starspangledbanner (AUS)—Empress Ella (IRE) (Holy Roman Emperor (IRE)) (67000)
52 B f 01/02 Kessaar (IRE)—Esedra (IRE) (Hurricane Run (IRE)) (23000) **Clipper Logistics**
53 B c 24/04 Cracksman—Fashion Parade (Fastnet Rock (AUS)) (12000) **Sheikh A. H. F. M. A. Al Sabah**
54 B f 28/03 Kingman—Flower of Life (IRE) (Galileo (IRE)) **Clipper Logistics**
55 B c 12/02 Holy Roman Emperor (IRE)—French Bid (AUS) (Anabaa (USA)) (30476) **Sheikh A. H. F. M. A. Al Sabah**
56 KARADOW (IRE), ch c 27/04 Starspangledbanner (AUS)—Vera Lilley (IRE) (Verglas (IRE)) (70000)
Miss L. G. Robinson
57 KYNSA (IRE), b f 31/03 Make Believe—Fact Or Folklore (IRE) (Lope de Vega (IRE)) (60000) **Miss L. G. Robinson**
58 B c 30/01 Sea The Stars (IRE)—La Mortola (Dubawi (IRE)) (200000)
59 Gr f 24/03 Havana Grey—Livella Fella (IRE) (Strategic Prince) (15000) **Sheikh A. H. F. M. A. Al Sabah**
60 B f 13/03 Iffraaj—Magique (IRE) (Jeremy (USA)) (5000)
61 MIYAGI (IRE), b c 14/02 James Garfield (IRE)—Omanome (IRE) (Acclamation) (80952) **KB Thoroughbreds**
62 B f 05/02 Dandy Man (IRE)—Monaleen (IRE) (High Chaparral (IRE)) (38000) **Clipper Logistics**
63 B grc 19/03 Havana Grey—Naivasha (Captain Gerrard (IRE)) (30000) **Sheikh A. H. F. M. A. Al Sabah**
64 B c 14/04 Oasis Dream—Papaver (Dansili) (25000) **C J Murfitt and Partners**
65 QUICK FLING, ch f 21/04 Bungle Inthejungle—Promiscuous (Kingman) **Chris & Janice Wright, Richard Davies**
66 SCARLET, ch f 26/01 Sir Percy—Symbol (Nathaniel (IRE)) **Dr C. M. H. Wills**
67 B f 29/02 Awtaad (IRE)—Sharedah (IRE) (Pivotal) (34000)
68 Ch c 25/03 Zoffany (IRE)—Spicy (Footstepsinthesand) (50000) **Quantum Leap Racing Ltd**
69 B f 13/04 Mastercraftsman (IRE)—Starrylita (IRE) (Galileo (IRE)) (13180)
70 B f 20/04 Sioux Nation (USA)—Supreme Quest (Exceed And Excel (AUS)) **Brownsbarn Thoroughbreds**
71 B f 06/04 Territories (IRE)—Sweet Dream (Oasis Dream) (25000) **Runaway Racing Canderel Syndicate**
72 THE BLACK HOLE (IRE), gr c 04/05 Dark Angel (IRE)—Miranda Frost (IRE) (Cape Cross (IRE)) (13605) **A. Al Shaikh**
73 THIS IS OUR TIME, b c 21/03 Brazen Beau (AUS)—Meet Marhaba (IRE) (Marju (IRE)) **A. Al Shaikh**
74 B f 28/02 Awtaad (IRE)—Tutti Frutti (Teofilo (IRE)) (26000)

---

427 ## MR RICHARD PHILLIPS, Moreton-in-Marsh
Postal: **Adlestrop Stables, Adlestrop, Moreton-in-Marsh, Gloucestershire, GL56 0YN**
Contacts: WORK **01608 658710** MOBILE **07774 832715**
EMAIL **info@richardphillipsracing.com** WEBSITE **www.richardphillipsracing.com**

1 5, B g Sageburg (IRE)—Brown Arrow (IRE) **The Aspirationals**
2 CORRANY (IRE), 8, br g Court Cave (IRE)—Time For An Audit **Carbine Of London Racing 3**
3 5, Ch m Gentlewave (IRE)—Days Like These
4 ELFRIDE, 6, ch m Black Sam Bellamy (IRE)—Just Missie **Mr D. G. Redfern**
5 FINE THEATRE (IRE), 12, b g King's Theatre (IRE)—Finemar Lady (IRE) **Richard Phillips Racing Syndicate**
6 5, B g Pether's Moon (IRE)—Fleetstone **Richard Phillips Racing Syndicate**

MR RICHARD PHILLIPS - continued

7 **FLYING DRAGON (FR)**, 6, b g War Command (USA)—Histoire de Jouer (FR) **The Dreamers**
8 **GREAT STAR (IRE)**, 5, gr g Dylan Thomas (IRE)—Pandorama Lady (IRE) **Mrs J. A. Watts**
9 **IRON HORSE**, 11, b g Kayf Tara—What A Vintage (IRE) **The Someday's Here Racing Partnership**
10 **KEEP IT BRIEF**, 5, b g Muhaarar—Brevity (USA) **Mr E. J. Ware**
11 **LADY OF AUTHORITY**, 7, b m Kheleyf (USA)—Miss Authority **The Listeners**
12 **LESSER (IRE)**, 8, b g Stowaway—Aine Dubh (IRE) **The C Level Partnership**
13 **MATTIE ROSS**, 6, b m Champs Elysees—Ommadawn (IRE) **The Zara Syndicate**
14 5, B m Kingston Hill—Mayolynn (USA) **The Cavallo Syndicate**
15 **METHODTOTHEMAGIC (IRE)**, 7, b m Sans Frontieres (IRE)—Cindy's Fancy (IRE)
Dalziel Family, T White, J Inverdale
16 **MRS BARNES (IRE)**, 9, b m Ask—Jills Oscar (IRE) **Mr & Mrs R Scott**
17 **ORGANDI (FR)**, 10, br m Early March—Creme Pralinee (FR) **Beautiful People**
18 **PICANHA**, 8, br g Malinas (GER)—Royal Bride **Mrs E. A. Prowting**
19 **POP MISTRESS (IRE)**, 6, ch m Sixties Icon—Mayolynn (USA) **Goodwood Owners Drinks Session**
20 **ROBIN DES SMOKE (IRE)**, 7, b m Robin des Pres (FR)—Thanks For Smoking (IRE) **Mrs E. A. Prowting**
21 **ROSSBEIGH STRAND (IRE)**, 7, b g Mahler—Could Do **Nut Club Partnership**
22 **RUN ROSIE RUN**, 6, b m Native Ruler—No Compromise **Better Than Working**
23 **SHADOW WALKER (IRE)**, 8, b g Stowaway—Ilikeyou (IRE) **Mr C. Pocock**
24 **TOTTERDOWN**, 11, b g Pasternak—Yeldham Lady **The Adlestrop Club**
25 **TULANE (IRE)**, 7, br g Arcano (IRE)—Jeunesse Doree (IRE) **Mr R. T. Phillips**

THREE-YEAR-OLDS

26 Ch f Prince of Lir (IRE)—Shadow Mountain **Mr R. T. Phillips**

Yard Sponsor: Tori Global.

---

428 **MR DAVID PIPE, Wellington**
Postal: **Pond House, Nicholashayne, Wellington, Somerset, TA21 9QY**
Contacts: **PHONE 01884 840715 FAX 01884 841343**
EMAIL david@davidpipe.com WEBSITE www.davidpipe.com TWITTER @davidpiperacing

1 **ABAYA DU MATHAN (FR)**, 10, b g Al Namix (FR)—Swahilie du Mathan (FR) **Mrs J. E. Wilson**
2 **ADAGIO (GER)**, 5, b g Wiener Walzer (GER)—Aspidistra (GER) **Bryan Drew and Friends / Prof. C.Tisdall**
3 **AFFOBURG (FR)**, 8, b g Sageburg (IRE)—Affolante (USA) **Mrs J. E. Wilson**
4 **AL ROC (FR)**, 11, br g Great Pretender (FR)—Al Cov (FR) **Mrs J. E. Wilson**
5 **ANGLERS CRAG**, 7, bl g Multiplex—Overyou **D. Mossop**
6 **ASTIGAR (FR)**, 6, gr g No Risk At All (FR)—Sissi de Teille (FR) **The Angove Family**
7 **AWESOMEDUDE**, 6, ch g Australia—Millevini (IRE) **ValueRacingClub.co.uk**
8 **BARRIER PEAKS (FR)**, 6, b g Blue Bresil (FR)—La Balzane (FR) **The Angove Family**
9 **BASHFUL BOY (FR)**, 6, b g Magician (IRE)—Bacheliere (USA) **Milldean Racing Syndicate**
10 **BELGUARDO (FR)**, 5, b g Kapgarde (FR)—Bella Giaconda (GER) **Decimus Racing VII**
11 **BEN LILLY (IRE)**, 5, b g Gleneagles (IRE)—Aristocratic Lady (USA) **David Pipe Racing Club**
12 **BRINKLEY (FR)**, 7, gr g Martaline—Royale Majesty (FR) **Mrs A. E. M. Broom, Mr G. R. Broom**
13 **BUMPY JOHNSON (IRE)**, 6, ch g Imperial Monarch (IRE)—Country Flora **Mrs A. E. M. Broom, Mr G. R. Broom**
14 **CADEAU D'OR (FR)**, 5, b g Le Havre (IRE)—Hill of Grace
15 **COLONY QUEEN**, 6, b m Gregorian (IRE)—Queen Margrethe **The Angove Family**
16 **CROSSING LINES (IRE)**, 8, b g Jeremy (USA)—Coco Opera (IRE) **Middleham Park Racing CXVII**
17 **D'JANGO (IRE)**, 9, br g Balko (FR)—Quizas Jolie (FR) **Mrs J. E. Wilson**
18 **DELL' ARCA (IRE)**, 13, br g Sholokhov (IRE)—Daisy Belle (GER) **Prof. C. Tisdall**
19 **DELLAWAY (IRE)**, 5, b g Getaway (GER)—Dublin (IRE) **Prof C. Tisdall**
20 **DO YA FEEL LUCKY (IRE)**, 8, b m Aizavoski (IRE)—Carthanoora (IRE) **Somerset Racing**
21 **DOYEN LA LUTTE (IRE)**, 6, b m Doyen (IRE)—Castletown Girl **The Contractors**
22 **DRAG RACE (IRE)**, 4, ch f Zoffany (IRE)—Aja (IRE) **David Pipe Racing Club**

MR DAVID PIPE - continued

23 **DUC DE BEAUCHENE (FR)**, 9, b g Saddler Maker (IRE)—Quatia d'Angron (FR) **Mr J. P. McManus**

24 **EAMON AN CNOIC (IRE)**, 11, b g Westerner—Nutmeg Tune (IRE) **The Angove Family**

25 **EDEN DU HOUX (FR)**, 8, b g Irish Wells (FR)—Maralypha (FR) **Prof C. Tisdall**

26 **EL PASO WOOD (FR)**, 8, b g Anzillero (GER)—Wonder Wood (FR) **Mrs J. E. Wilson**

27 **FIRST LORD OF CUET (FR)**, 8, gr g Lord du Sud (FR)—Alyce (FR)
      M. C. Pipe, Mr J. E. Potter, Mrs M. J. Potter, Mr P. J. Green, James & Jean Potter

28 **FLAMMARION (GER)**, 6, b g Sea The Moon (GER)—Favorite (GER) **The Willpower Partnership**

29 **GERICAULT ROQUE (FR)**, 6, b g Montmartre (FR)—Nijinska Delaroque (FR) **Prof C. Tisdall & Mr B. Drew**

30 **GRANGECLARE GLORY (IRE)**, 7, b g Fame And Glory—Annies Joy (IRE) **Friends of Ebony Horse Club**

31 **GWENCILY BERBAS (FR)**, 11, b g Nickname (FR)—Lesorial (FR) **Mr A. J. Ryan**

32 **HEURE DE GLOIRE (FR)**, 5, b m Kapgarde (FR)—Lounoas (FR) **Mrs J P E Cunningham & Mr G M Cunningham**

33 **HOME FARM HOUSE (IRE)**, 7, bl m Winged Love (IRE)—Recession Lass (FR) **H. M. W. Clifford**

34 **INDUNO (IRE)**, 8, b g Flemensfirth (USA)—Vast Consumption (IRE) **R. A. Bartlett**

35 **IRON HEART**, 5, b g Muhaarar—Kiyoshi **Decimus Racing VIII**

36 **ISRAEL CHAMP (IRE)**, 7, b g Milan—La Dariska (FR) **John White & Anne Underhill**

37 **ITACARE (FR)**, 5, gr g Silver Frost (FR)—Steadfast (FR) **Somerset Racing**

38 **KALZARI (FR)**, 4, b br f Zanzibari (USA)—Kalianda (FR) **Gillards Transport Ltd & John White**

39 **KEPAGGE (IRE)**, 8, b g Getaway (GER)—Miracle Lady **Mrs S. J. Ling**

40 **KINGOFTHEWEST (FR)**, 6, b g Westerner—Other Salsa (FR) **Friends From The West**

41 **KOI DODVILLE (FR)**, 4, b g French Fifteen (FR)—Konkan (IRE) **Mr S. M. Mercer**

42 **KOLISI (IRE)**, 4, b g Harzand (IRE)—Wild Step (GER) **W. F. Frewen**

43 **KOTKI (FR)**, 5, gr g Montmartre (FR)—Kotkicha (FR) **David Pipe Racing Club**

44 **LADY RESET**, 6, ch m Yorgunnabelucky (USA)—Reset City **Mrs L. Webb**

45 **LADYKILLER (GER)**, 6, ch g Kamsin (GER)—Lady Jacamira (GER) **Prof C. Tisdall & Mr B. Drew**

46 **LAST QUARTER (FR)**, 5, b g Walk In The Park (IRE)—Lunar Path (FR) **Brocade Racing**

47 **LEONCAVALLO (IRE)**, 10, br g Cape Cross (IRE)—Nafura **ValueRacingClub.co.uk**

48 **LITTLE RED LION (IRE)**, 8, b g Sans Frontieres (IRE)—Rever Up (FR) **Prof C. Tisdall**

49 **MAIN FACT (USA)**, 9, b g Blame (USA)—Reflections **Mr M. A. Munrowd, Miss S. B. Munrowd**

50 **MAJOR ROBINSON (IRE)**, 6, b g Kalanisi (IRE)—Annalore (IRE) **W. F. Frewen, Mrs R. E. White, Odfloors Ltd**

51 **MAKE ME A BELIEVER (IRE)**, 7, br g Presenting—Kiltiernan Robin (IRE) **Prof C. Tisdall & Jane Gerard-Pearse**

52 **MARTINImL (IRE)**, 7, b g Westerner—Gweedara (IRE) **Mrs L. Maclennan**

53 **MASTER BLAZE (IRE)**, 4, b g Nicaron (GER)—Baltria (FR) **Bryan Drew and Friends / Prof. C.Tisdall**

54 **MEEP MEEP MAG (IRE)**, 8, b m Getaway (GER)—Deadly Pursuit (IRE) **Mr M. Lambert & Mrs R. White**

55 **MISS M (IRE)**, 8, b m Mastercraftsman (IRE)—Tintern **David Pipe Racing Club**

56 **MORGENSTERN (FR)**, 5, b g Sommerabend—Pink And Red (USA) **Mrs J. E. Wilson**

57 **MR TAMBOURINE MAN (IRE)**, 5, b g Galileo (IRE)—Snow Queen (IRE) **B. G. Middleton, A. J. Shire**

58 **NABVUTIKA (IRE)**, 6, b m Poet's Voice—Elope (GER) **D. E. Pipe**

59 **NEON MOON (IRE)**, 6, b g No Risk At All (FR)—Hidden Horizons (IRE) **Mrs A. E. M. Broom, Mr G. R. Broom**

60 **NEW AGE DAWNING (IRE)**, 6, ch g Stowaway—Captain Supreme (IRE) **Mrs A. E. M. Broom, Mr G. R. Broom**

61 **NOBEL JOSHUA (AUT)**, 6, b br g Joshua Tree (IRE)—Namat (IRE) **Avalon Surfacing & Construction Co Ltd**

62 **NORDIC COMBINED (IRE)**, 8, b g Haafhd—Chilly Filly (IRE) **David Pipe Racing Club**

63 **NOUS ESPERONS**, 4, gr f Schiaparelli (GER)—Cathodine Cayras (FR) **Mr S. Kemble, Mr G Peck**

64 **OCEAN HEIGHTS**, 5, ch g Dubawi (IRE)—Ethereal Sky (IRE) **Mr D. C. Manasseh, Mrs L. Webb**

65 **OFF MY ROCCO (IRE)**, 6, b g Shirocco (GER)—Croise Naofa (IRE) **Mrs J. Gerard-Pearse**

66 **OLYMPE DE GOUGES**, 4, b f Charming Thought—Regina Cordium (IRE) **ValueRacingClub.co.uk**

67 **PACHACUTI (IRE)**, 5, b g Walk In The Park (IRE)—Mrs Mac Veale (IRE) **The Arthur White Partnership**

68 **PANIC ATTACK (IRE)**, 6, b m Canford Cliffs (IRE)—Toto Corde Meo (IRE) **Mr B. J. C. Drew**

69 **PARADISE ISLAND (FR)**, 6, b g Poliglote—Sugar Paradise (FR) **Mrs J. E. Wilson**

70 **PARICOLOR (FR)**, 6, b g Orpen (USA)—Kadiana (IRE) **Mrs J P E Cunningham & Mr G M Cunningham**

71 **PASQUALITA**, 5, b m Tai Chi (GER)—Petite Duchesse (GER) **Pipe's Prospectors**

72 **POKER PLAY (FR)**, 9, ch g Martaline—Becquarette (FR) **The Angove Family**

73 **RAMSES DE TEILLEE (FR)**, 10, gr g Martaline—Princesse d'Orton (FR) **John White & Anne Underhill**

74 **RANCO (IRE)**, 5, b g Makfi—Guerande (IRE) **Mr M. J. D. Lambert**

75 **RED HAPPY (FR)**, 5, ch g Red Dubawi (IRE)—Happynees (FR) **Mrs J. E. Wilson**

76 **RED LION LAD (IRE)**, 6, b g Flemensfirth (USA)—Hotline (IRE) **Prof C. Tisdall, Ms H. Ibrahim**

77 **REMASTERED**, 9, ch g Network (GER)—Cathodine Cayras (FR) **Mrs A. E. M. Broom, Mr G. R. Broom**

78 **ROMAIN DE SENAM (FR)**, 10, b g Saint des Saints (FR)—Salvatrixe (FR) **Mrs J. E. Wilson**

79 **SETME STRAIGHTMATE**, 6, ch g Malinas (GER)—Karamel
      C & Angove Family, Mr D. B. Angove, Mr S. J. Angove

80 **SEVENTEEN O FOUR (IRE)**, 5, ro g Gutaifan (IRE)—Bali Breeze (IRE) **Mr Barry Wright & Mrs Rosemary White**

MR DAVID PIPE - continued

81 **SEXY LOT (GER)**, 6, b m Camelot—Saldennahe (GER) **Mr P. W. Garnsworthy**
82 **SHOT BOII (IRE)**, 5, b g Malinas (GER)—Moncherie (IRE) **W. F. Frewen**
83 **SIDI ISMAEL (FR)**, 8, b g Great Pretender (IRE)—Tetouane (FR) **The Show is Over Syndicate**
84 **SIRUH DU LAC (FR)**, 9, b g Turgeon (USA)—Margerie (FR) **John White & Anne Underhill**
85 **STAR MAX (GER)**, 7, b g Maxios—Startissima **Pipe's Prospectors**
86 **THANKSFORTHEHELP (FR)**, 5, gr g Martaline—Agathe du Berlais (FR) **Mr J. P. McManus**
87 **THINKING (IRE)**, 7, b g So You Think (NZ)—Laetoli (ITY) **N. Shutts**
88 **TITIAN (IRE)**, 4, b g Iffraaj—Lucelle (IRE) **W. F. Frewen**
89 **TRUSTY SCOUT (IRE)**, 4, ch g Gleneagles (IRE)—Dutch Lilly **Mrs L. Webb**
90 **UMBRIGADO (IRE)**, 8, br g Stowaway—Dame O'Neill (IRE) **John White & Anne Underhill**
91 **VIA DOLOROSA (FR)**, 10, b g Konig Shuffle (GER)—Millie Hurley (FR) **Mrs J. E. Wilson**
92 **VIEUX LION ROUGE (FR)**, 13, ch g Sabiango (GER)—Indecise (FR) **Prof C. Tisdall, J. A. Gent**

Other Owners: Brocade Racing, Mrs A. E. M. Broom, Mr G. R. Broom, Mr G. M. Cunningham, Mrs J. P. E. Cunningham, Mr B. J. C. Drew, Mrs J. Gerard-Pearse, Gillards Transport Limited, Mr M. J. D. Lambert, Midd Shire Racing, Mr W Frewen, Mrs R White & Drm, Mrs Lynne Webb & Partner, Munrowd's Partnership, Mr George Peck, Potter, Pipe and Pete, C & Star, The Angove Family, Prof C. Tisdall, Prof Caroline Tisdall & Mr John Gent, Mrs A. Underhill, Mr A. J. White, Mrs R. E. White, Mr B. Wright.

Assistant Trainer: Mr M. C. Pipe C.B.E.

NH Jockey: David Noonan, Tom Scudamore. **Conditional Jockey:** Philip Armson, Fergus Gillard.

Amateur Jockey: Martin McIntyre.

---

429 **CHARLES AND ADAM POGSON, Farnsfield**
Postal: **Allamoor Farm, Mansfield Road, Farnsfield, Nottinghamshire, NG22 8HZ**
Contacts: PHONE **07977 016155**
EMAIL **adampogson@hotmail.co.uk**

1 **A STRIP OF AMY**, 5, b m Outstrip—Absent Amy (IRE) **Mr S. Dorey**
2 **BARACALU (FR)**, 11, gr g Califet (FR)—Myragentry (FR) **C. T. Pogson**
3 **GEORGE MALLORY**, 6, b g Kingman—Rose Et Noire (IRE) **Pete Wordingham & Charles Pogson**
4 **GETAWAY NORTH**, 9, b g Getaway (GER)—Kings Equity (IRE) **C. T. Pogson**
5 **LARCH HILL (IRE)**, 9, ch g Presenting—Misty Move (IRE) **Robert & Marie Smith & Charles Pogson**
6 **MARAJMAN (FR)**, 8, gr g Rajsaman (FR)—Mascarpone (FR) **Stephanie Kaye and M.T Hughes**
7 **MOIDORE**, 13, b g Galileo (IRE)—Flash of Gold **C. T. Pogson**
8 **MONARCHOFTHEGRANGE (IRE)**, 7, ch g Imperial Monarch (IRE)—Saipan Storm (IRE) **Mrs S. Tucker**
9 **OVERTOUGEORGE**, 8, b g Overbury (IRE)—Captivating Tyna (IRE) **C. T. Pogson**
10 **SIANNES STAR (IRE)**, 9, b g Arakan (USA)—Musical Madam (IRE) **Stephanie Kaye and M.T Hughes**
11 **THE RAVEN'S RETURN**, 9, b g Scorpion (IRE)—Mimis Bonnet (FR) **Stephanie Kaye and M.T Hughes**
12 **THE SKIFFLE KING (IRE)**, 6, b g Dylan Thomas (IRE)—Joe's Dream Catch (IRE) **M. Tucker**

Other Owners: Mrs S. K. Bunch, M. T. Hughes, C. T. Pogson, Mrs M. Smith, Mr R. Smith, P. L. Wordingham.

---

430 **MR JOE PONTING, Wotton-Under-Edge**
Postal: **Woodmans Farm, Hawkesbury Road, Hillesley, Wotton-Under-Edge, Gloucestershire, GL12 7RD**
Contacts: PHONE **01454 294554**
EMAIL **joeponting02@gmail.com**

1 **ARSONIST (GER)**, 4, b c Sea The Moon (GER)—Amalie (GER) **Mr J. Ponting**
2 **BAY WATCH (IRE)**, 8, b g Harbour Watch (IRE)—Karuga **P. J. Ponting**
3 **CODEBOOK**, 4, ch g New Approach (IRE)—Safe House (IRE) **P. J. Ponting**
4 **COTAI BEAR (IRE)**, 4, b g Kodi Bear (IRE)—Solace (USA) **P. J. Ponting**
5 **DAWN TAPPER (IRE)**, 4, b g Dawn Approach (IRE)—Super Hoofer (IRE) **P. J. Ponting**

MR JOE PONTING - continued

6 **GAVIN,** 4, b g Bated Breath—Under Milk Wood **P. J. Ponting**
7 **HEREIA (IRE),** 6, b g Olympic Glory (IRE)—Rolled Gold (USA) **P. J. Ponting**
8 **LOST HISTORY (IRE),** 9, b g Strategic Prince—Prelude **P. J. Ponting**
9 **TIQUER (FR),** 14, b g Equerry (USA)—Tirenna (FR) **Mr J. Ponting**

THREE-YEAR-OLDS

10 B c Dartmouth—Tara Mactwo
11 Ch c Jack Hobbs—Ykikamoocow
12 **YOU GO GIRL,** b f Twilight Son—Hard Walnut (IRE) **P. J. Ponting**

---

431 **MR JONATHAN PORTMAN, Upper Lambourn**
Postal: Whitcoombe House Stables, Upper Lambourn, Hungerford, Berkshire, RG17 8RA
Contacts: PHONE 01488 73894 MOBILE 07798 824513
EMAIL jonathan@jonathanportmanracing.com WEBSITE www.jonathanportmanracing.com

1 **BROAD APPEAL,** 8, ch g Medicean—Shy Appeal (IRE) **J. G. B. Portman**
2 **FULL APPROVAL (IRE),** 4, b f Mehmas (IRE)—Drifting Spirit (IRE) **Mr L. A. Bellman**
3 **HEADORA,** 4, b g Charming Thought—Keladora (USA) **Mr J Laws & Partners**
4 **HELLAVAPACE,** 4, br gr f Hellvelyn—Hasten (USA) **Fillies First**
5 **LOWENA,** 4, ch f Equiano (FR)—Agony And Ecstasy **Fillies First**
6 **MARK OF RESPECT (IRE),** 4, b g Markaz (IRE)—Music Pearl (IRE) **Berkeley Dollar Powell**
7 **MR SUNDANCER,** 4, b g Paco Boy (IRE)—Trumpet Lily **Mr P. Goodwin**
8 **NEW HEIGHTS,** 4, b f Intello (GER)—How High The Sky (IRE) **Simon Skinner & Partner**
9 **ORIN SWIFT (IRE),** 8, b g Dragon Pulse (IRE)—Hollow Green (IRE) **Mr L. A. Bellman**
10 **QUICK BREATH,** 7, b g Bated Breath—Shy Appeal (IRE) **Turf Club 2020 & Partner 1**
11 **RUSSIAN RUMOUR (IRE),** 5, b m Make Believe—Russian Rave **Fillies First**
12 **STRIKE,** 4, gr g Lethal Force (IRE)—Midnight Fling **Mr S. Emmet & Miss R. Emmet**
13 **SWALLOWDALE,** 4, b f Mukhadram—Windermere Island **C.R. Lambourne, M. Forbes, D. Losse**
14 **SWEET REWARD (IRE),** 5, b g Acclamation—Dangle (IRE) **Old Stoic Racing Club & Partner**
15 **THE BLUE BOWER (IRE),** 5, b m Morpheus—Blue Holly (IRE) **Mr A. I. F. Sim**
16 **TOYBOX,** 6, ch m Paco Boy (IRE)—Play Street **J. G. B. Portman**
17 **WAY OF LIFE,** 4, b g Havana Gold (IRE)—Upskittled **Berkeley Racing**
18 **WISPER (IRE),** 4, ch f Belardo (IRE)—Whisp (GER) **The Reignmakers**

THREE-YEAR-OLDS

19 **BABY BAY,** ch f New Bay—Albertine Rose **Jaliza Partnership**
20 **BELISA DE VEGA (IRE),** b f Fascinating Rock (IRE)—Royal Razalma (IRE) **One More Moment of Madness**
21 **BROLLY,** b f Caravaggio (USA)—Rainfall Radar (USA) **Fillies First**
22 **ELITE ETOILE,** br g Vadamos (FR)—Way To The Stars **Portlee Bloodstock**
23 **FALESIA BEACH,** ch f Twilight Son—Retake **Mrs Suzanne Williams & Partner**
24 **ICKYTOO,** b f Heeraat (IRE)—Icky Woo **Cr Lambourn, M Forbes, D Losse & Partner**
25 **INFINITE APPEAL,** b f Equiano (FR)—Shy Appeal (IRE) **Wood Street Syndicate**
26 **MANYANA,** b f Postponed (IRE)—Tenerife Song **Rockville Pike Partnership**
27 **MILD REFLECTION,** b f Aclaim (IRE)—Drift And Dream **Berkeley Racing**
28 **MREMBO,** b f Albaasil (IRE)—Shesha Bear **RWH Partnership**
29 **ROMANTIC MEMORIES,** b f Time Test—Midnight Fling **Mr S. Emmet & Miss R. Emmet**
30 **SEA DART (IRE),** b c Dutch Art—Reiffa (IRE) **Sheikh A. B. I. Al Khalifa**
31 **SIENNA BONNIE (IRE),** b f Kodi Bear (IRE)—Cucuma (FR) **Mrs Suzanne Williams & Partner**
32 **SILVERDALE,** gr f Hellvelyn—Silvala Dance **Whitcoombe Park Racing**
33 **SUN EMPEROR (IRE),** b br g Twilight Son—Coronation Day **Sheikh A. B. I. Al Khalifa**
34 **TWO TEMPTING (IRE),** ch g New Bay—Dangle (IRE) **Berkeley Racing**

TWO-YEAR-OLDS

35 B f 01/04 Twilight Son—Accede **Mrs D Joly**

MR JONATHAN PORTMAN - continued

36 **BEAR FORCE**, b c 28/02 Kodi Bear—Dew (Whipper) **Berkeley Racing**
37 **BONNSIE (IRE)**, b f 01/04 Kodi Bear (IRE)—Nymfia (IRE) (Invincible Spirit (IRE)) (13333)

Mrs Suzanne Williams & Partner

38 B f 01/04 Time Test—Diamond Run **Mascalls Stud**
39 B c 22/03 Bated Breath—Elbow Beach
40 **ENOCHDHU**, b c 09/02 Muhaarar—Gloryette **Julia Scott**
41 **HIGHLAND FLYER**, b c 02/02 Highland Reel (IRE)—Tobruk (IRE) (Declaration of War (USA)) (32000)

Mr L. A. Bellman

42 B c 04/02 Equiano (FR)—Hindsight **Whitcombe Park Racing**
43 Gr f 24/02 Havana Grey—Izola **Mrs M A Parker**
44 B f 01/04 Mayson—Jessie's Spirit (IRE) **Faraday Partnership**
45 **KNIGHTS GAMBIT**, b g 01/04 Sir Percy—Play Street **Mr Anthony Boswood**
46 **LYNWOOD LAD**, b c 19/03 Mayson—Faithful Promise **Philip Simpson**
47 Ch c 25/04 Dragon Pulse (IRE)—Monteamiata (IRE)
48 **OKTOBERFEST**, b c 07/04 Sea The Moon (GER)—Snow Ballerina (Sadler's Wells (USA)) (35000)

Mr A. N. Brooke Rankin

49 **PUNTERELLE**, b f 28/01 Footstepsinthesand—Maybelater **Hot To Trot Racing**
50 Ch f 13/01 Raven's Pass (USA)—Rivercat
51 B c 02/04 The Last Lion (IRE)—Singuita (GER)
52 **SISTER OF THOR**, b f 13/04 Anodin—Helisa **Ruffles Racing Club**
53 B c 01/04 Havana Grey—Stellarta **Mr Vincent Ward**

Other Owners: Mr E Ankarcrona, Mr I Bath, Mr S Beccle, Berkeley Racing, Mr M Blanshard, Mr H Bloomfield, Mr D Bonet, Mr B Booker, Mr D Brocklehurst, J. W. M. Brownlee, Mr A. N. Cheyne, Mr G Clark, Emma Clarke, Mr G Davies, Mr S Dawes, R. C. Dollar, Mr R Eagle, Mr A Edwards, Mr P Edwards, Miss R. E. Emmet, M. I. Forbes, Mr R Franklin, Mr J Gale, Mr A Goodman, Mr A. M. Hales, Mr C Hawkins, B. M. W. Hearn, Mrs S. J. Hearn, Mrs L Hobson, Mr J Homan, Mr S Hoskins, Mr A Hunter, Mr H. Kimbell, Mr G Kinch, C.R. Lambourne, M. Forbes, D. Losse, Mr J. F. S. Laws, Mrs L. J. Losse, Col A. J. E. Malcolm, Mrs C Mordaunt, Mr H Nass, Mrs A Plummer, Portlee Bloodstock, J. G. B. Portman, Mrs S. J. Portman, D. F. Powell, Mr R Pritchard, Mr J Repard, Mr E Scher, Mrs A Tearne, Mr R Tearne, Mr G Thomas, Mr D Tierney, Miss R Tregaskes, Mr P Tye, Mr R White, Mr G Wickens, Anita Wigan.

Amateur Jockey: Mr J. Harding.

---

432 **MR RYAN POTTER, Sellack**
Postal: **The Coach House, Sellack, Ross-On-Wye, Herefordshire, HR9 6LS**
EMAIL rdpotter88@googlemail.com

1 **ANGUS DE BULL (IRE)**, 6, b g Papal Bull—Diskretion (GER) **Mr R. D. Potter**
2 **BIG BAD BUZZ (IRE)**, 6, b g Doyen (IRE)—Little Moscow (IRE) **Carl & Emma Pyne**
3 **BRUSHED UP**, 9, b m Doyen (IRE)—Definite Artist (IRE) **R. F. Bailey**
4 **D'EDGE OF GLORY (IRE)**, 6, b m Fame And Glory—D'Gigi **Mr R. D. Potter**
5 **DON BERSY (FR)**, 9, b g Califet (FR)—Tropulka God (FR) **Mr R. D. Potter**
6 **EATON MILLER (IRE)**, 10, b g Milan—Four Fields (IRE) **Mr R. D. Potter**
7 **FIRST DU CHARMIL (FR)**, 10, ch g Ballingarry (IRE)—Famous Member (FR) **Mr R. D. Potter**
8 **GOODWILLHUNTING (IRE)**, 7, b g Carlotamix (FR)—One Edge (IRE) **Mr S. A. B. Steel**
9 **GUATEMALA LE DUN (FR)**, 6, gr g Poliglote—Uranus Le Dun (FR) **Mrs L. P. Vaughan**
10 **HIGH GROUNDS (IRE)**, 9, b g High Chaparral (IRE)—Civility Cat (USA) **Mr R. D. Potter**
11 **JETOILE (IRE)**, 7, b g Jeremy (USA)—Accordingtoherself (IRE) **Ms J. Bennett**
12 **LIGHT FLICKER (IRE)**, 10, b g Royal Anthem (USA)—Five Cents More (IRE) **S & V Peets**
13 **LITTLE WINDMILL (IRE)**, 12, ch g Mahler—Ennismore Queen (IRE) **Mr R. D. Potter**
14 **LUCKY BOUNCE (IRE)**, 5, b g Milan—Gracie B (IRE) **Mr R. D. Potter**
15 **MARIAS LAD (FR)**, 6, b g Martaline—Marie Deja La (FR) **Ryan Potter Racing Club**
16 **MISTERTOMMYSHELBY (IRE)**, 6, b g Alkaadhem—Coolkenna Contact (IRE) **Mr R. D. Potter**
17 **MON RAY (IRE)**, 5, b m Montmartre (FR)—Seven Even (FR) **Carl & Emma Pyne**
18 **OUT BY SIX (FR)**, 8, b g Scalo—Sixty Six (IRE) **Mr R. D. Potter**

MR RYAN POTTER - continued

19 **PAULS HILL (IRE)**, 10, b g Marienbard (IRE)—Lunar Star (IRE) **Ryan Potter Racing Club**
20 **PICKAMIX**, 11, gr g Sagamix (FR)—Star of Wonder (FR) **Mr W. Fox**
21 **PITTSBURG (IRE)**, 6, b g Sageburg (IRE)—Constant Approach (IRE) **Mr R. D. Potter**
22 **POST NO BILLS (IRE)**, 7, b g Mahler—Shining Lights (IRE) **Mr N. Pyne**
23 **SHESUPINCOURT**, 5, b m Court Cave (IRE)—Supreme Cove **Ryan Potter Racing Club**
24 **SISSINGHURST (IRE)**, 12, b g Kalanisi (IRE)—Sissinghurst Storm (IRE) **Mr R. D. Potter**
25 **TRUMPS BENEFIT (IRE)**, 9, b g Beneficial—Balla Brack (IRE) **C P Civil Engineering UK Ltd**

Other Owners: Ms V. Peets, Mr C. Pyne, Mrs E. R. Pyne, Mr S. A. B. Steel.

---

433 MRS CAMILLA POULTON, Lewes
Postal: **White Cottage, Stud Farm, Telscombe Village, Lewes, BN7 3HZ**
Contacts: **PHONE 01273 300127**
EMAIL camilla.poulton67@outlook.com

1 **ACED IT (IRE)**, 6, b g Lope de Vega (IRE)—Farranjordan **Crowd Racing & R Christison**
2 **BORN TO FINISH (IRE)**, 9, b g Dark Angel (IRE)—Music Pearl (IRE) **Crowd Racing & R Christison**
3 **D'AMBONNAY (IRE)**, 4, b g Hallowed Crown (AUS)—Encore du Cristal (USA) **P. S. Wardle**
4 **GOKOTTA (IRE)**, 4, b f Pride of Dubai (AUS)—Sivensen (IRE) **Mrs L. G. Talbot**
5 **INTO DEBT**, 6, b g Paco Boy (IRE)—Katherine Parr **Mrs C. D. Poulton**
6 **KAZIMIERZ (IRE)**, 5, b g Shooting To Win (AUS)—Encore du Cristal (USA) **Mr L. Stevens**
7 **MILITRY DECORATION (IRE)**, 7, b g Epaulette (AUS)—Funcheon Vale (IRE) **Crowd Racing & R Christison**
8 **MILLIE MALOO (IRE)**, 5, b m Mustameet (USA)—Deploythetank (IRE) **Mr T. R. Richardson**
9 **MOROMAC (IRE)**, 8, b g Morozov (USA)—My Bay Lady **Mrs C. D. Poulton**
10 **RUNRIZED (FR)**, 7, b g Authorized (IRE)—Courseulles (FR) **Crowd Racing Partnership**
11 **TOUCH OF THUNDER (IRE)**, 4, b g Beat Hollow—Sweetheart **Crowd Racing Partnership**
12 **ZAMARKHAN (FR)**, 9, b g Great Journey (JPN)—Zannkiya **Racing, Christison, F Bocker**

THREE-YEAR-OLDS

13 B f Bobby's Kitten (USA)—Gotcha Good (USA) **Mrs C. D. Poulton**
14 B f Bobby's Kitten (USA)—Righteous Renee (USA) **Mrs C. D. Poulton**
15 B f Telescope (IRE)—Strawberry Spirit (IRE) **Mrs C. D. Poulton**

Other Owners: Mrs F. E. Bocker, Mr R. Christison, Crowd Racing Partnership, Mr C. McKenna.

---

434 SIR MARK PRESCOTT BT, Newmarket
Postal: **Heath House, Moulton Road, Newmarket, Suffolk, CB8 8DU**
Contacts: PHONE **01638 662117**
EMAIL **sirmark@heathhousestables.com** WEBSITE **www.heathhousestables.com**
TWITTER **@HeathHouseNkt**

1 **ALERTA ROJA**, 4, gr f Golden Horn—Albaraka **Miss K. Rausing**
2 **ALPHABETICAL**, 5, gr g Archipenko (USA)—Albanova **Tim Bunting - Osborne House III**
3 **ALPINISTA**, 5, gr m Frankel—Alwilda **Miss K. Rausing**
4 4, B g Sakhee (USA)—Florie **Strawberry Fields Stud**
5 **GALILEO IMPACT (JPN)**, 4, b f Deep Impact (JPN)—Galileo Always (IRE) **C. Fipke**
6 **GENESIUS (IRE)**, 5, ch g Teofilo (IRE)—Craic Agus Spraoi (IRE) **Owners Group 076**
7 **LONGSIDER (IRE)**, 5, b g Ruler of The World (IRE)—Lady Dettoria (FR) **Middleham Park Racing LXXVII**
8 **REVOLVER (IRE)**, 5, b g Slade Power (IRE)—Swizzle Stick (IRE) **Ne'er Do Wells VI**
9 **ROYAL PLEASURE (IRE)**, 4, b g Kingman—Merry Jaunt (USA) **Tim Bunting - Osborne House**
10 **SECRET BOX**, 4, b g Le Havre (IRE)—Red Box **Cheveley Park Stud Limited**

SIR MARK PRESCOTT BT - continued

11 **SUMMER'S KNIGHT**, 4, b g Camelot—Summer's Eve **P. J. McSwiney-Osborne House**
12 **YAGAN (IRE)**, 4, b g Australia—Navajo Moon (IRE) **Middleham Park Racing L**

THREE-YEAR-OLDS

13 **ABBADO**, ch c Almanzor (FR)—Allegretto (IRE) **Cheveley Park Stud Limited**
14 **ALDABRA**, b f Bobby's Kitten (USA)—Altitude **Miss K. Rausing**
15 **ALLONS DANSER**, gr f Bobby's Kitten (USA)—Alba Stella **Miss K. Rausing**
16 **ANATOMIC**, gr c Ulysses (IRE)—Diagnostic **Cheveley Park Stud Limited**
17 **ANGAH (FR)**, b f Muhaarar—Chanterelle (FR) **KHK Racing Ltd**
18 **ARCADIAN FRIEND**, b g Lope de Vega (IRE)—Best Friend (IRE) **John Pearce Racing Limited**
19 **ARCLIGHT**, b f Champs Elysees—Florentia **Neil Greig & Sir Mark Prescott**
20 **AT THE DOUBLE (FR)**, b br g Almanzor (FR)—Express American (FR) **Charlie Walker - Osborne House II**
21 **BUTTRESS**, b f Ulysses (IRE)—Vaulted **Cheveley Park Stud Limited**
22 **CANDYTUFT**, b f Sea The Moon (GER)—Macleya (GER) **Cheveley Park Stud Limited**
23 **CAPPOQUIN (IRE)**, b f Muhaarar—Tecla (IRE) **Sonia M. Rogers & Anthony Rogers**
24 **CAPTAIN HOWSE (IRE)**, b g Australia—Merritt Island **Mr & Mrs John Kelsey-Fry**
25 **DAWAHY (IRE)**, ch f Bated Breath—Rahaala (IRE) **H.H. Shaikh Nasser Al Khalifa & F. Nass**
26 **DENNING**, ch g Recorder—Undress (IRE) **J. B. Haggas**
27 **EAGLE'S WAY**, ch g Gleneagles (IRE)—Martlet **Tim Bunting - Osborne House II**
28 **FLYAWAYDREAM**, b g Farhh—Mockinbird (IRE) **Caroline Gregson & the Gd Partnership**
29 **GLENISTER (IRE)**, b c Gleneagles (IRE)—Sistine **Elite Racing Club**
30 **GOLDEN SHOT**, b g Golden Horn—Quenelle **W E Sturt - Osborne House**
31 **GORDONS AURA (IRE)**, b g Golden Horn—Sequined (USA) **John Brown & Megan Dennis**
32 **LOVE DOWN UNDER**, ch c Australia—Love Divine **Lordship Stud**
33 **NOBLE MARK (IRE)**, ch g Animal Kingdom (USA)—Above The Mark (USA) **Jones, Julian, Lee & Royle**
34 **NORTH LINCOLN (IRE)**, b c Acclamation—Molly Dolly (IRE) **T. J. Rooney**
35 **OMNISCIENT**, b g Mukhadram—Miss Dashwood **Ne'er Do Wells VII**
36 **PRETENDING (IRE)**, gr f Make Believe—Gala **Denford Stud Limited**
37 **RUSHFORD**, b g Danon Ballade (JPN)—Cushat Law (IRE) **M & M Franklin**
38 **SEA KING**, br c Sea The Stars (IRE)—Pamona (IRE) **Charlie Walker - Osborne House III**
39 **SNAP AMBUSH (FR)**, ch f Almanzor (FR)—Penny Lane (GER) **H.H. Shaikh Nasser Al Khalifa & F. Nass**
40 **SPECTATRICE**, b f Fast Company (IRE)—Songerie **Miss K. Rausing**
41 **WHISPERING SONG**, b f Danon Ballade (JPN)—Jewelled **M & M Franklin**

TWO-YEAR-OLDS

42 B f 23/02 Sea The Stars (IRE)—Affability (IRE) (Dalakhani (IRE)) (265000) **Mt. Brilliant Farm & Ranch, LLC**
43 **ALEXANDRETTA**, b f 26/03 Sea The Moon (GER)—Alinstante (Archipenko (USA)) **Miss K. Rausing**
44 B br c 24/02 Protectionist (GER)—Batya (IRE) (Whipper (USA)) (18707) **Middleham Park Racing XXXV**
45 **BORN RULER**, b c 22/04 Kingman—Filia Regina (Galileo (IRE)) (40000) **Charlie Walker - Osborne House**
46 **BRAVE KNIGHT**, b c 01/02 Sir Percy—Belladonna (Medicean) (120000) **Neil Greig - Osborne House**
47 **BRAVURA**, b c 14/04 Saxon Warrior (JPN)—Approach (Darshaan) **Denford Stud Limited**
48 **CATHAYA**, b f 13/02 Ulysses (IRE)—Tallow (IRE) (Kodiac) **Cheveley Park Stud Limited**
49 **DARK GOLD**, br c 19/03 Havana Gold (IRE)—Muscovado (Mr Greeley (USA)) (85000)
                                                               Philip Bamford - Osborne House
50 **DESERT FALCON (IRE)**, b c 22/03 Gleneagles (IRE)—Love Oasis (Oasis Dream) (28571)
                                                     Allison, Gregson, Matterson & Satchell
51 B f 03/02 Invincible Spirit (IRE)—Don't Be (Fasiliyev (USA)) **J. Fill**
52 **IMPERIAL DREAM (IRE)**, b c 02/03 Holy Roman Emperor (IRE)—Iffa Red (IRE) (Iffraaj) (31429)
                                                           Gregson, Jenkins, Lee & Warman
53 Ch c 13/04 Australia—Merritt Island (Exceed And Excel (AUS)) **Mr & Mrs John Kelsey-Fry**
54 **MISS CYNTHIA**, b f 07/02 Sea The Moon (GER)—Best Friend (IRE) (Galileo (IRE)) **John Pearce Racing Limited**
55 **MOON FLIGHT (IRE)**, b c 19/02 Sea The Moon (GER)—Miss Margarita (Scat Daddy (USA)) (38000)
                                                                              W. J. S. Prosser
56 **NATACATA**, gr f 17/03 Kitten's Joy (USA)—Na Balada (BRZ) (Forestry (USA)) **Miss K. Rausing**
57 **OTTOMAN PRINCE (IRE)**, ch c 26/02 Zoffany (IRE)—Byzantium (Dutch Art) (46769)
                                                         Baxter, Charnley, Jones & Prosser
58 **ROBUSTO (IRE)**, b c 17/02 Churchill (IRE)—Blackgold Fairy (USA) (More Than Ready (USA)) (34014)
                                                                        Heath House Optimists
59 **ROSE OF ITHACA**, ch f 28/02 Ulysses (IRE)—Tallulah Rose (Exceed And Excel (AUS)) **Cheveley Park Stud Limited**

SIR MARK PRESCOTT BT - continued

60 TIFFANY (IRE), b f 02/05 Farhh—Affinity (Sadler's Wells (USA)) **Elite Racing Club**
61 TRUE LEGEND (IRE), b c 13/02 Camelot—Scarlet And Gold (IRE) (Peintre Celebre (USA)) (60000)
Tim Bunting - Osborne House IV
62 B c 02/02 Sea The Stars (IRE)—Vow (Motivator) (450000) **H.H. Sheikh Nasser Al Khalifa**
63 WILPENA POUND (IRE), b c 05/02 Australia—Hyphaema (IRE) (Rock of Gibraltar (IRE)) (20000)
Budd,Greenwood,Gregson,Troubridge,Mailer

Other Owners: N. B. Attenborough, B. D. Burnet, Mrs C. J. Casterton, J. Christmas, M. Dabner, D. Ellis, J. E. Fishpool, R. P. Fry, A. Moore, G. Moore, Mr & Mrs Glyn-Davies, Mr & Mrs T. F. Harris, M. A. C. Rudd, Exors of the Late W. E. Sturt, M. J. Tracey, E. J. Williams.

Assistant Trainer: William Butler, **Pupil Assistant:** Thomas Humphries.

Flat Jockey: Luke Morris.

435

MISS KATY PRICE, Llanigon
Postal: Willow Croft, Llanigon, Hay-On-Wye, Herefordshire, HR3 5PN
Contacts: **PHONE 07976 820819**
EMAIL katyprice2005@aol.com WEBSITE www.facebook.com/katypriceracing

1 DORAN'S BRIDGE (IRE), 6, b g Imperial Monarch (IRE)—Molly Connors (IRE) **Mr N. Elliott**
2 GALLOW FORD (IRE), 7, b g Westerner—Magical Theatre (IRE) **Mr N. Elliott**
3 GARRISON COMMANDER (IRE), 6, b g Garswood—Malea (IRE) **Mike Harris Racing Club**
4 KING OF BRAZIL (IRE), 5, b g Blue Bresil (FR)—Blue Ride (IRE) **Nick Elliott & Heather Shane**
5 MINELLACELEBRATION (IRE), 12, b b g King's Theatre (IRE)—Knocktartan (IRE) **Mr N. Elliott**
6 OUT FOR JUSTICE (IRE), 9, b g Beneficial—Dustys Delight (IRE) **Alastair & Pippa McLeish**
7 PREMIER D'TROICE (FR), 8, b g Great Pretender (IRE)—Mick Bora (FR) **Nick Elliott & Heather Shane**
8 ROSEISAROSEISAROSE (IRE), 8, gr m Jeremy (USA)—Roses And Wine (IRE) **Alastair & Pippa McLeish**
9 SADIE HILL (IRE), 5, ch m Kingston Hill—Sadie Thompson (IRE) **Making Hay**
10 SAM'S THE MAN, 5, ch g Black Sam Bellamy (IRE)—Blurred Lines (IRE) **Mr N. Berbillion**
11 SIR EGBERT, 9, b g Kayf Tara—Little Miss Flora **Mr E. W. Lewis**

Other Owners: Mr S. T. Black, Miss E. J. Clarke, Mr N. Elliott, A. D. I. Harris, Mr M. E. Harris, Mr J. R. Holloway, Mr A. D. McLeish, Mrs P. J. McLeish, Mrs H. E. Shane.

436

MR RICHARD PRICE, Hereford
Postal: Criftage Farm, Ullingswick, Hereford, Herefordshire, HR1 3JG
Contacts: **PHONE 01432 820263 MOBILE 07929 200598**

1 BELLEVARDE (IRE), 8, b m Kodiac—Pearl Mountain (IRE) **B. Veasey**
2 BILBOA RIVER (IRE), 6, b g Milan—Terracotta Queen (IRE) **K. Reece**
3 GRANDSTAND (IRE), 6, b g Kodiac—Lady Shanghai (IRE) **B. Veasey**
4 LILI WEN FACH (IRE), 5, gr m Gregorian (IRE)—Zuzinia (IRE) **My Left Foot Racing Syndicate**
5 MAD BARRY, 7, ch g Norse Dancer (IRE)—River Beauty **Mrs V. J. Morse**
6 OCEAN REACH, 6, b m Phoenix Reach (IRE)—Ocean Transit (IRE) **Mr G E Amey & Mr D M Boddy**
7 RHUBARB, 5, b m Nayef (USA)—Cockney Fire **Ocean's Five**
8 5, B m Pether's Moon (IRE)—River Beauty **Mrs V. J. Morse**

Other Owners: Mr G. E. Amey, Mr D. Boddy.

Assistant Trainer: Jane Price.

---

437 MR PETER PRITCHARD, Shipston-on-Stour
Postal: **Upper Farm Lodge, Upper Farm, Whatcote, Shipston-On-Stour, Warwickshire, CV36 5EF**
Contacts: **MOBILE 07376 500499**
EMAIL **pennypritch55@hotmail.co.uk**

1 5, B m Passing Glance—Astral Affair (IRE)
2 **EARCOMESALI,** 9, b m Passing Glance—Earcomesannie (IRE) **R. W. Stowe & Marc Miller**
3 **EARCOMESBOB,** 7, ch g Yorgunnabelucky (USA)—Earcomesannie (IRE) **R. W. Stowe & Marc Miller**
4 **EARCOMESTHEDREAM (IRE),** 19, b g Marignan (USA)—Play It By Ear (IRE)
5 **FRANZ KLAMMER,** 10, b g Midnight Legend—Ski **Mr M. J. Miller**
6 4, B f Passing Glance—Tilinisi (IRE)

THREE-YEAR-OLDS

7 B c Passing Glance—Astral Affair (IRE)
8 Br f Passing Glance—Earcomesannie (IRE)
9 B c Passing Glance—Tilinisi (IRE)

Assistant Trainer: Mrs E. Gardner.

NH Jockey: Tom Bellamy. **Conditional Jockey:** Charlie Hammond. **Amateur Jockey:** Claire Hardwick, Jordan Nailor.

---

438 MR DENIS QUINN, Newmarket
Postal: **Stockbridge Stables, 192 High Street, Newmarket, Suffolk, CB8 9AP**
Contacts: **MOBILE 07435 340008**

1 **DANCING ZEBEDEE (IRE),** 5, gr g Zebedee—Yaqoot **Mr D. P. Quinn**
2 **DEVIOUS DREAMER (IRE),** 4, ch g Buratino (IRE)—Divas Dream (IRE) **Mr D. P. Quinn**
3 **GOSSAMER SILK,** 4, ch f Equiano (FR)—Gossamer Seed (IRE) **Mr A. F. Keane**
4 **LYNNS BOY,** 4, ch g Coach House (IRE)—La Fortunata **Mr M. Ricketts**
5 **ROCKY SEA (IRE),** 6, b h Born To Sea (IRE)—Ice Rock (IRE) **Miss C. McKernan**
6 **SEE THE CELEBRITY,** 4, b c Fountain of Youth (IRE)—So Discreet **Mr D. P. Quinn**
7 **STAR OF ST LOUIS (FR),** 5, b g Style Vendome (FR)—Momix **Miss C. McKernan**

THREE-YEAR-OLDS

8 **BEEBEE,** b f Outstrip—Shadow of The Sun **Mr M. Ricketts**
9 **ISLE OF HOPE,** bl g Due Diligence (USA)—Rip Van Suzy (IRE) **Mr D. P. Quinn**
10 **LETTER OF THE LAW (IRE),** b g Lawman (FR)—Lady Ravenna (IRE) **Mr D. P. Quinn**

---

439 MR JOHN QUINN, Malton
Trainer did not wish details of their string to appear

440 MR ALASTAIR RALPH, Bridgnorth

Postal: **Bynd Farm, Bynd Lane, Billingsley, Bridgnorth, Shropshire, WV16 6PQ**
Contacts: **WORK 01746 860807 PHONE 07912 184217**
WORK EMAIL info@alastairralphracing.co.uk **WEBSITE** www.alastairralphracing.co.uk

1 4, B g Westerner—Answer Ur Phone (IRE) **Jones, Spiers and Hartwell**
2 **BILLINGSLEY (IRE),** 10, b g Millenary—Retain That Magic (IRE) **Alastair Ralph Racing**
3 **BLACK SAM VICKI,** 4, b f Black Sam Bellamy (IRE)—Overthrow **Strutting Cockerels Syndicate**
4 **BUTLER'S BRIEF (IRE),** 7, b g Yeats (IRE)—She's On The Case (IRE) **You Can Be Sure**
5 4, B f Clovis du Berlais (FR)—Cedelor (FR) **Mr R. D. Ralph**
6 **CHANCEUX (IRE),** 6, b g Mahler—Granny Mc Cann (IRE) **RSKM Bloodstock**
7 **DAMUT I'M OUT (IRE),** 12, b g Gamut (IRE)—Five Cents More (IRE) **Costello/Ralph Racing Partnership**
8 **DANCING WITH DECO (IRE),** 6, br g Milan—Miss Toulon (IRE) **The Dancing With Deco Partnership**
9 **DRENAGH (IRE),** 7, b g Kalanisi (IRE)—Diva Antonia (IRE) **B. Hawkins**
10 **ENCOUNTER A GIANT (IRE),** 10, b g Kalanisi (IRE)—Sumability (IRE) **The Hawkins Partnership**
11 **FLORRIE KNOX (IRE),** 9, gr g Gold Well—Miss Orphan (FR) **The Fortune Hunters**
12 **GENTLE RIVER,** 6, b g Gentlewave (IRE)—Absalom's Girl **The Gentle River Partnership**
13 **GETAWAY TOTHEROCK (IRE),** 9, b m Getaway (GER)—Theft **James, Archer, Ralph & Gentech**
14 **GLANCE FROM CLOVER,** 7, b g Passing Glance—Allforclover (IRE) **Miss S. Troughton**
15 **GOVERNOR GREEN (IRE),** 5, b g Aiken—Little Green (IRE) **The Fortune Hunters**
16 **GROOVEUR (FR),** 6, b g Ballingarry (IRE)—Kelle Home (FR) **Prm Bloodstock**
17 **HEY MISTER DJ (IRE),** 4, gr g Jukebox Jury (IRE)—Margarita (GER) **Mr R. J. Simpson**
18 **HILL OF HOPE (IRE),** 8, b g Court Cave (IRE)—Taisilk (IRE) **Mr M. A. Fothergill**
19 **HOLLY HARTINGO (IRE),** 6, b m Well Chosen—Hazel Toi (IRE) **The HHH Partnership**
20 **IN OUR DREAMS (IRE),** 6, gr g Cloudings (IRE)—No Moore Bills **Spiers & Hartwell, Ralph & Black**
21 **INN THE BULL (GER),** 9, ch g Lope de Vega (IRE)—Ile Rousse **Loose Cannon Racing**
22 **IONTACH CHEVAL,** 6, b g Dunaden (FR)—Dancing Emily (IRE) **RSKM Bloodstock**
23 **JACK SHARP (IRE),** 7, b br g Scorpion (IRE)—That's Amazing (IRE) **Walters Plant Hire & Potter Group**
24 **KABRIT (IRE),** 4, b g Mastercraftsman (IRE)—Twinkling Ice (USA) **Alastair Ralph Racing**
25 **KATESON,** 9, gr g Black Sam Bellamy (IRE)—Silver Kate (IRE) **DavidMRichardsandRobertsCWhittalWilliams**
26 **KRACQUER,** 8, ch g Schiaparelli (GER)—Norma Hill **Mr G. Lloyd**
27 **LLANTARA,** 11, b m Kayf Tara—Lady Llancillo (IRE) **That's Racing**
28 **LOST IN MONTMARTRE (FR),** 6, gr m Montmartre (FR)—Lost Maiby (FR) **Mr Gary White & Mr Gary Wood**
29 **MAGICAL MAGGIE,** 5, gr m Geordieland (FR)—Bollin Across **Mrs N. S. Harris**
30 **METHOD MADNESS (IRE),** 7, b g Sans Frontieres (IRE)—Inishbeg House (IRE) **Fothergills Sparey and Lewis**
31 **MIX OF CLOVER,** 8, b g Fair Mix (IRE)—Allforclover (IRE) **Miss S. Troughton**
32 **OSPREY CALL (IRE),** 7, br g Winged Love (IRE)—Courting Whitney (IRE) **Gentech, Franklin, Archer & James**
33 4, B g Hillstar—Penny Lough (IRE) **B. Hawkins**
34 4, B c Dunaden (FR)—Pickersleigh (IRE) **Mr M. H. Jones**
35 **POLLYONESOCK (IRE),** 4, b f Mount Nelson—Kenzie (IRE) **Mrs P. Simpson**
36 **QUEENHILL,** 5, b m Mountain High (IRE)—Pickersleigh (IRE) **Mr M. H. Jones**
37 **RISK D'ARGENT (FR),** 6, gr g My Risk (FR)—Villebruyere (FR) **Prm Bloodstock**
38 **ROCKADENN (FR),** 6, b g High Rock (IRE)—Nijadenn (FR) **S W Racing**
39 **TAP TAP BOOM,** 8, ro g Foxwedge (AUS)—Exclusive Approval (USA) **Gentech,James,Franklin,Bickmore&ralph**
40 **THANKYOURLUCKYSTAR,** 6, b g Dunaden (FR)—Cloudy Spirit **Mrs N. S. Harris**
41 **THE GREY FALCO (FR),** 7, gr g Falco (USA)—Take A Chance (FR) **The Roaming Roosters**
42 **TINTERN ABBEY (IRE),** 5, b m Mahler—Portobello Sunrise (IRE) **The Tintern Abbey Partnership**
43 **WHEESHT (IRE),** 8, br m Scorpion (IRE)—Retain That Magic (IRE) **James and Jean Potter Ltd**
44 **WHITE TURF (IRE),** 7, gr g Clodovil (IRE)—Holda (IRE) **Only Fools Own Horses**
45 **YOUR BAND,** 7, b g Helmet (AUS)—Kampai **Only Fools & Cockerels**

Yard Sponsor: Planned Office Interiors Ltd.

NH Jockey: Jonathan Burke, Nick Schofield. **Conditional Jockey:** Jay Tidball.

441 MR TIM REED, Hexham
Postal: **Moss Kennels, Haydon Bridge, Hexham, Northumberland, NE47 6NL**
Contacts: **PHONE 01434 344016 MOBILE 07703 270408**
EMAIL timreedracing@gmail.com

1 **ALF 'N' DOR (IRE)**, 11, ch g Flemensfirth (USA)—Greenflag Princess (IRE) **Mr W. T. Reed**
2 **CHOCTAW BRAVE (IRE)**, 8, br g Frammassone (IRE)—Full Deck (IRE) **Beswick Brothers Bloodstock**
3 **FORCE DE FRAP (FR)**, 7, b g Desir d'Un Soir (FR)—Flaurella (FR) **Beswick Brothers Bloodstock**
4 **LARGY FIX (IRE)**, 7, ch g Notnowcato—Fix It Lady (IRE) **North Counties**
5 **LEVEROCK LASS (IRE)**, 9, b m Olden Times—Hazelhall Princess (IRE)
        Beswick Bloodstock,Tim Reed,Mrs P Balmer
6 **RUINOUS (IRE)**, 7, b br g Aizavoski (IRE)—Will She Smile (IRE) **Mothers & Daughters**
7 **SHE'S A STEAL (IRE)**, 5, b m Flemensfirth (USA)—Thanks Awfully (IRE) **Mr & Mrs J. Morrison-Bell**
8 **TIME LEADER (IRE)**, 8, b g Scorpion (IRE)—Dancing Matilda (IRE) **Beswick Brothers Bloodstock**
9 **WELSH REIGN (IRE)**, 7, b g Imperial Monarch (IRE)—Marians Gem (IRE) **Mr W. T. Reed**
10 **WHY NOT DREAM (IRE)**, 4, b f Ask—Marvellous Dream (FR) **Mr & Mrs J. Morrison-Bell**

Other Owners: Mr S. C. Allen, Mrs P. Balmer, Beswick Brothers Bloodstock, Mr P. S. Davies, Mr J. K. Huddleston, Mr J. Jackson-Stops, Mr J. Morrison-Bell, Mrs K. A. Morrison-Bell, Mr W. T. Reed, Mr B. Ryan-Beswick, Mr W. Ryan-Beswick, Mrs C. J. Todd.

Assistant Trainer: Mrs E. J. Reed.

Conditional Jockey: Harry Reed.

442 MR DAVID REES, Haverfordwest
Postal: **Knock Moor, Clarbeston Road, Haverfordwest, Pembrokeshire, SA63 4SL**
Contacts: **PHONE 01437 731308 MOBILE 07775 662463 FAX 01437 731308**
EMAIL accounts@davidreesfencing.co.uk

1 **DUNBAR (FR)**, 9, gr g Lord du Sud (FR)—Jiletta (FR) **D & J Rees**
2 **KARANNELLE (IRE)**, 7, b m Nathaniel (IRE)—Dance Lively (USA) **D. A. Rees**
3 **KIERA ROYALE (IRE)**, 11, ch m Beneficial—Llancillo Lady (IRE) **D. A. Rees**
4 **KINGSTON KING (IRE)**, 8, b g Morozov (USA)—Gra Mo Chroi **D. A. Rees**
5 **MISTY MAN (IRE)**, 12, b m Westerner—Arcanum (IRE) **D. A. Rees**
6 **ROBIN OF SHERWOOD (IRE)**, 9, b br g Robin des Pres (FR)—Galleta **West Is Best**
7 **STEEL NATIVE (IRE)**, 11, b g Craigsteel—Princess Gloria (IRE) **D. A. Rees**

Other Owners: D. A. Rees, Mr J. E. Rees.

443 MRS HELEN REES, Dorchester
Postal: **Distant Hills, Chalmington, Dorchester, Dorset, DT2 0HB**
Contacts: **PHONE 07715 558289**
EMAIL helen-rees@live.co.uk

1 **BEYOND SUPREMACY (IRE)**, 10, b g Beneficial—Slaney Athlete (IRE) **Mrs H. E. Rees**
2 **MY ROCKSTAR (IRE)**, 6, b g Valirann (FR)—All Notoriety (IRE) **Mrs H. E. Rees**

444 MRS LYDIA RICHARDS, Chichester
Postal: **Lynch Farm, Hares Lane, Funtington, Chichester, West Sussex, PO18 9LW**
Contacts: **PHONE 01243 574882 MOBILE 07803 199061**
EMAIL lydia.richards@sky.com

1 **CERTAINLY RED**, 8, ch g Midnight Legend—Venetian Lass **The Venetian Lad Partnership**
2 **CITY TOUR**, 6, b g Dutch Art—Privacy Order **Mrs E. F. J. Seal**
3 **FLORENCE STREET**, 4, b f Iffraaj—Queen's Dream (GER) **Mrs L. Richards**
4 **GOOD NEWS**, 10, b g Midnight Legend—Venetian Lass **The Good News Partnership**
5 **MURHIB (IRE)**, 10, b g Sea The Stars (IRE)—Mood Swings (IRE) **The Murhib Partnership**
6 **SMITH (IRE)**, 6, ch g Dawn Approach (IRE)—Alazeya (IRE) **Mrs L. Richards**
7 **TARA**, 4, b f Toronado (IRE)—Demoiselle Bond **The Demoiselle Bond Partnership**

445 MR NICKY RICHARDS, Greystoke
Postal: **Rectory Farm, Greystoke, Penrith, Cumbria, CA11 0UJ**
Contacts: **HOME 017684 83160 PHONE 017684 83392 MOBILE 07771 906609**
EMAIL office@nickyrichardsracing.com WEBSITE www.nickyrichardsracing.com

1 **AUBIS WALK (FR)**, 6, b m Walk In The Park (IRE)—Aubisquinette (FR) **Mr K. Alexander**
2 **BIG BAD BEAR (IRE)**, 8, br g Jeremy (USA)—Our Polly (IRE) **Tor Side Racing**
3 **BON RETOUR (IRE)**, 7, b m Fame And Glory—Rosy de Cyborg (FR) **J. T. Ennis**
4 **BULLION BOSS (IRE)**, 6, b g War Command (USA)—Gold Bubbles (USA) **Multiple Sclerosis Borders Racing Club**
5 **CAIUS MARCIUS (IRE)**, 11, b g King's Theatre (IRE)—Ain't Misbehavin (IRE)
                 Mr C P Norbury & Tarzan Bloodstock
6 **CASTLE RUSHEN (IRE)**, 7, b g Fame And Glory—Rosie Suspect (IRE) **Exors of the Late Mr T. J. Hemmings**
7 **CHAPEL STILE (IRE)**, 10, b g Scorpion (IRE)—Peggy Cullen (IRE) **Langdale Bloodstock**
8 **CHIDSWELL (IRE)**, 13, b g Gold Well—Manacured (IRE) **David & Nicky Robinson**
9 **CONISTON CLOUDS (IRE)**, 6, gr g Cloudings (IRE)—Lincon Lady (IRE) **Accurite Racing**
10 **COURT DREAMING (IRE)**, 9, b g Court Cave (IRE)—Louis's Teffia (IRE) **Dark Horse Racing Ltd**
11 **CRYSTAL GLORY**, 6, b g Fame And Glory—Nile Cristale (FR) **Charlie Doocey / Cathal Doocey**
12 **EVERYDAY CHAMPAGNE (IRE)**, 6, gr g Doyen (IRE)—Magie de Toulouse (FR) **Katie & Brian Castle**
13 **FAMOUS BRIDGE (IRE)**, 6, b g Fame And Glory—Wahiba Hall (IRE) **Exors of the Late Mr T. J. Hemmings**
14 **FERNEY GREEN**, 6, ch m Schiaparelli (GER)—Miss Nellie (IRE) **Langdale Bloodstock**
15 **FINDTHETIME (IRE)**, 6, b g Shantou (USA)—Bisoguet (IRE) **Tor Side Racing**
16 4, B g Doyen (IRE)—First Line (GER) **Mr J. Fyffe**
17 **FLY BY MILAN (IRE)**, 7, b g Milan—So Proper (IRE) **Langdale Bloodstock**
18 **GEGE VILLE (FR)**, 6, b g Protektor (GER)—Auvloo Ville (FR) **Mrs A. Starkie**
19 **GLINGER FLAME (IRE)**, 10, gr g Daylami (IRE)—Titian Flame (IRE) **Mr James Westoll**
20 **GLITTERING LOVE (IRE)**, 10, b g Winged Love (IRE)—Glittering Image (IRE) **The Fife Boys + 1**
21 **GLORIOUS SPIRIT (IRE)**, 6, b m Fame And Glory—Mrs Dempsey (IRE) **The Spirit Partnership**
22 **HARD IRON (IRE)**, 6, b g Milan—Novacella (FR)
23 **HEADSCARF LIL (IRE)**, 8, b m Getaway (GER)—Bleu Money (IRE) **Accurite Racing & Tarzan Bloodstock**
24 **HOLME ABBEY**, 9, gr g Fair Mix (IRE)—Brockwell Abbey **The Roper Family**
25 **HOME FIRE**, 6, b g Frankel—Hot Snap **Langdale Bloodstock**
26 **HOUSTON TEXAS (IRE)**, 8, b g Dylan Thomas (IRE)—Royal Robin (IRE) **Mr A. S. Crawford**
27 **KAJAKI (IRE)**, 9, gr g Mastercraftsman (IRE)—No Quest (IRE) **Mr P. Polly**
28 **LUCKIE SEVEN (IRE)**, 4, b g Soldier of Fortune (IRE)—Uimhir A Seacht (IRE)
              Mrs I. C. Sellars & Major & Mrs P. Arkwright
29 **MAROWN (IRE)**, 8, b g Milan—Rosie Suspect (IRE) **Exors of the Late Mr T. J. Hemmings**
30 **MAUGHOLD HEAD**, 5, b g Fame And Glory—Misty Lass (IRE) **Exors of the Late Mr T. J. Hemmings**
31 **MAYO STAR (IRE)**, 10, b g Stowaway—Western Whisper (IRE) **Charlie Doocey / Cathal Doocey**
32 **MISS MILANO (IRE)**, 7, b m Milan—Dewasentah (IRE) **Tor Side Racing**
33 **MURVAGH BEACH (IRE)**, 7, ch g Doyen (IRE)—Magic Park (IRE) **David & Nicky Robinson**
34 **NELLS SON**, 7, b g Trans Island—Miss Nellie (IRE) **Langdale Bloodstock**
35 **NO REGRETS (IRE)**, 8, b g Presenting—E Mac (IRE) **Jim Ennis & Tony Killoran**
36 **PADDOCK COTTAGE (IRE)**, 6, b g Pour Moi (IRE)—Blend **D. Wesley-Yates**

MR NICKY RICHARDS - continued

37 **PARISENCORE (FR)**, 6, b g Walk In The Park (IRE)—Folk Dancing (FR)
Mrs I. C. Sellars & Major & Mrs P. Arkwright
38 **RELEASE THE KRAKEN (IRE)**, 6, b g Shantou (USA)—Guydus (IRE) **Mr J. Fyffe**
39 **RIBBLE VALLEY (IRE)**, 9, b g Westerner—Miss Greinton (GER) **D. Wesley-Yates**
40 **RIVER MEADOW (IRE)**, 6, b g Fame And Glory—Undecided Hall (IRE) **Exors of the Late Mr T. J. Hemmings**
41 **ROSE OF SIENA (IRE)**, 5, b m Califet (FR)—The Tabster (IRE) **Mrs Pat Sloan**
42 **ROYAL ARCADE (IRE)**, 7, b br g Arcadio (GER)—Miss Excitable (IRE) **Mrs F. D. McInnes Skinner**
43 **RUBYTWO**, 10, b m Sulamani (IRE)—Miss Nellie (IRE) **Langdale Bloodstock**
44 **SAUCE OF LIFE (IRE)**, 7, b g Califet (FR)—Salsaparilla (FR) **Mrs I. C. Sellars & Major & Mrs P. Arkwright**
45 **SERIOUS EGO (GER)**, 9, b g Sholokhov (IRE)—Sunshine Story (IRE) **Greystoke Owners**
46 **SHE'S A ROCCA (IRE)**, 7, b m Shirocco (GER)—Hannigan's Lodger (IRE)
Mrs I. C. Sellars & Major & Mrs P. Arkwright
47 **SMOKEY THE BANDIT (IRE)**, 7, b g Fame And Glory—No Ice Or Lemon (IRE) **Mrs Pat Sloan**
48 **SNOWY CLOUDS (IRE)**, 6, gr g Cloudings (IRE)—Wednesday Girl (IRE)
Highclere T/bred Racing - Snowy Clouds 1
49 **SOFT RISK (FR)**, 6, b g My Risk (FR)—Douce Ambiance (FR) **Mr James Westoll**
50 **SUMMERGROUNDS**, 6, b g Phoenix Reach (IRE)—Hannah Jacques (IRE)
51 **TFOU (FR)**, 6, b g Authorized (IRE)—Fire Moon Julie (FR)
52 **THE BEST WAY (FR)**, 4, b g Thewayyouare (USA)—Valentine (FR) **Multiple Sclerosis Borders Racing Club**
53 **UNCLE ALASTAIR**, 10, b g Midnight Legend—Cyd Charisse **Mr Eddie Melville & Partners**
54 **UNIVERSAL FOLLY**, 7, b g Universal—Madam Jolie (IRE) **Tor Side Racing**

Other Owners: Accurite Racing, Major P W. F. Arkwright, Mrs Sandra G. E. Arkwright, Mr O. Brownlee, Mr A. Cartledge, J. A. Dudgeon, Mrs R. L. Elliot, J. T. Ennis, Hale Racing Limited, Mr K. Haughey, Mrs L. Haughey, Mr T. A. Killoran, Mrs E. M. Lloyd, E. Q. Melville, Multiple Sclerosis Borders Racing Club, C. P. Norbury, Mrs N. P. Sellars, Mr A. R. Sutcliffe.

Assistant Trainer: Miss Joey Richards, Mr Harry Haynes, **Racing Secretary:** Isla Cameron-McIntosh,

Secretary: Antonia Reid.

NH Jockey: Brian Hughes, Danny McMenamin, Sean Quinlan. **Conditional Jockey:** Mark Galligan, Conor Rabbitt.

Amateur Jockey: Mr Lyall Hodgins.

---

446 **MR JOHN DAVID RICHES, Pilling**
Postal: **Moss Side Farm, Off Lancaster Road, Scronkey, Pilling, Lancashire, PR3 6SR**
Contacts: **PHONE 01253 799190**
EMAIL jrracing@btinternet.com

1 **ANGEL EYES**, 7, b m Piccolo—Miacarla **J R Racing**
2 **ASTAPOR**, 4, b g Sixties Icon—Good Morning Lady **J R Racing**
3 **MR GAMBINO**, 5, b g Music Master—Snow Dancer (IRE) **J R Racing**
4 **RAIN CAP**, 5, b g Fountain of Youth (IRE)—Rough Courte (IRE) **J R Racing**
5 **STORM MASTER**, 5, b g Music Master—Miacarla **J R Racing**
6 **TRULOVE**, 9, b m Piccolo—Snow Dancer (IRE) **J R Racing**

Other Owners: J. D. Riches, Mrs L. Wohlers.

447 **MR MARK RIMELL, Witney**
Postal: **Fairspear Equestrian Centre, Fairspear Road, Leafield, Witney, Oxfordshire, OX29 9NT**
Contacts: **PHONE 01993 878551 MOBILE 07778 648303, 07973 627054**
EMAIL rimell@rimellracing.com WEBSITE www.rimellracing.com

1 **CLOSENESS**, 4, b f Iffraaj—Pack Together **Cotswold racing owners 1**
2 **ENDLESS ADVENTURE**, 7, b g And Beyond (IRE)—Gulshique **Mrs C. Mackness**
3 **HALLWOOD (FR)**, 5, gr g Martaline—Ball of Wood (FR) **Roel Hill Farm limited**
4 **I'M A STARMAN**, 9, ch g Schiaparelli (GER)—Strathtay **M. G. Rimell**
5 **LADY OF GRACE (IRE)**, 4, ch f Dawn Approach (IRE)—Gracefield (USA)
6 **RAINBOW MIRAGE**, 5, ch m Garswood—Oasis Mirage **Miss S. M. Howes**
7 **THAPA VC (IRE)**, 4, b g The Gurkha (IRE)—Merritt Island **The Circle of five**

Assistant Trainer: Anne Rimell.

448 **MR DAVE ROBERTS, Kenley**
Postal: **Leasowes Farm, Kenley, Shrewsbury, Shropshire, SY5 6NY**
Contacts: **PHONE 07854 550606**

1 4, Ch g Cannock Chase (USA)—Cat Six (USA) **D. B. Roberts**
2 6, B m Norse Dancer (IRE)—Cat Six (USA) **D. B. Roberts**
3 **CHEEKY RICCO**, 8, ch g Shirocco (GER)—Good Thinking **Miss M. Anderson**
4 **G'DAY AUSSIE**, 9, b g Aussie Rules (USA)—Moi Aussi (USA) **Mr D. Bradbury**
5 **QUICK OF THE NIGHT**, 5, b m Gentlewave (IRE)—Message Personnel (FR)
6 **RACHEL LOUISE**, 7, b m Shirocco (GER)—Avoine (IRE) **Shropshire Racing**
7 **RACING SPIRIT**, 10, ch g Sir Percy—Suertuda **D. B. Roberts**
8 **RAVEN'S RAFT (IRE)**, 7, gr m Raven's Pass (USA)—Sea Drift (FR) **D. B. Roberts**
9 **STAMINA CHOPE (FR)**, 6, ch m Muhaymin (USA)—My Virginia (FR) **Mr D. Bradbury**
10 **TAMPICO ROCCO (IRE)**, 5, b br g Shirocco (GER)—Opera Gale (IRE) **Carder & Roberts**
11 **TONGANUI (IRE)**, 11, ch g Stowaway—Murrosie (IRE) **Mr G. Andrews**
12 **B m Telescope (IRE)—With Grace **D. B. Roberts**

Other Owners: Mr J. S. Bain, Mr D. T. Carder, D. B. Roberts, Dr A. D. Rogers.

449 **MR MIKE ROBERTS, Hailsham**
Postal: **Summertree Farm, Bodle Street Green, Hailsham, East Sussex, BN27 4QT**
Contacts: **PHONE 01435 830231 MOBILE 07774 208040**
EMAIL mike@summertree-racing.com

1 **ANDAPA (FR)**, 8, br m Kapgarde (FR)—Daniety (FR) **M. J. Roberts**
2 **CAP D'ANTIBES (IRE)**, 5, b g Society Rock (IRE)—Miss Verdoyante **M. J. Roberts**
3 **CONCHITA (GER)**, 7, b m Zoffany (IRE)—Cross Check (IRE) **M. J. Roberts**
4 **FALCON SUN (FR)**, 8, b g Falco (USA)—Pray For Sun (IRE) **M. J. Roberts**
5 **FORT DE L'OCEAN (FR)**, 7, b g Racinger (FR)—Iconea (FR) **M. J. Roberts**
6 **KIRUNA PEAK (IRE)**, 8, ch m Arcano (IRE)—Kirunavaara (IRE) **M. J. Roberts**
7 **PERFECT MOMENT (IRE)**, 9, b m Milan—Faucon **M. J. Roberts**

Assistant Trainer: Marie Martin.

450 MISS SARAH ROBINSON, Bridgwater
Postal: **Newnham Farm, Shurton, Stogursey, Bridgwater, Somerset, TA5 1QG**
Contacts: **PHONE 01278 732357 MOBILE 07866 435197, 07518 785291 FAX 01278 732357**
EMAIL info@sarahrobinsonracing.co.uk WEBSITE www.sarahrobinsonracing.co.uk

1 **DONT CALL ME DORIS**, 12, b m Franklins Gardens—Grove Dancer **Mr M. L. J. Fooks**
2 **FAMILY MAN (IRE)**, 9, b g Gold Well—Greenacre Mandalay (IRE) **Mr A. Woodley-Milburn**
3 **GETAWAY TOTHE WOOD (IRE)**, 7, b g Getaway (GER)—Salty Wind Lady (IRE) **Mr B. Robinson**
4 9, Gr g Passing Glance—Magical Wonderland **Mr B. Robinson**
5 **MILLIE'S FLYING**, 9, b m Franklins Gardens—Grove Dancer **Mr M. L. J. Fooks**
6 **MY FOREVER FRIEND (IRE)**, 14, b g Dr Massini (IRE)—Stormy Rose (IRE) **Mr B. Robinson**
7 **TIME IS TIME (IRE)**, 13, ch g Golan (IRE)—Minnie Ray (IRE) **Mr A. Woodley-Milburn**

Assistant Trainer: Mr R. J. Bailey, Mr B. Robinson.

---

451 MR PAUL D. ROBSON, Hawick
Postal: **1 Spittal On Rule, Hawick, Roxburghshire, TD9 8TA**
EMAIL spittalonrule@gmail.com

1 **BEN ASKER (IRE)**, 4, b g Rock of Gibraltar (IRE)—Roskeen (IRE) **A. Robson**
2 **DIFFERENT BEAT (IRE)**, 7, b m Beat Hollow—Cherry Falls (IRE) **A. Robson**
3 **FLAMBOYANT JOYAUX (FR)**, 7, b g Crossharbour—Merka (FR) **A. Robson**
4 **FRANZ JOSEF (IRE)**, 6, b g Jet Away—Invisible Spirit (IRE) **Mr P. D. Robson**
5 **HIGHLANDER HILL (IRE)**, 5, ch g Mahler—Cherish The Pear (IRE) **A. Robson**
6 **INTO THE FIRE (FR)**, 4, ch g Intello (GER)—Roman Ridge (FR) **Mr G. F. Adam & Mrs E. Adam**
7 **JUST DON'T KNOW (IRE)**, 9, b g Kalanisi (IRE)—Desperado Queen (IRE) **Border Caravans Ltd**
8 **NAE BOTHER AT A' (IRE)**, 4, b g Yeats (IRE)—Daisies Adventure (IRE) **Mr G. F. Adam & Mrs E. Adam**
9 **PAVLIK (IRE)**, 5, b g Morozov (USA)—Longwhitejemmy (IRE) **Marchcleuch Bloodstock**
10 **WHATSGOINGON (FR)**, 6, b g Ballingarry—Califea (FR) **Marchcleuch Bloodstock**

Other Owners: Mrs C. B. Herbert, Mr I. J. Herbert.

---

452 MISS PAULINE ROBSON, Capheaton
Postal: **Kidlaw Farm, Capheaton, Newcastle Upon Tyne, NE19 2AW**
Contacts: **PHONE 01830 530241 MOBILE 07814 708725, 07721 887489**
EMAIL pauline@prracing.co.uk

1 **BALLIN BAY (IRE)**, 4, b br g Milan—Ballinahow Ann (IRE) **J. Wade**
2 **CASTLETOWN (FR)**, 10, gr g Poliglote—Message Personnel (FR) **R. A. Green**
3 **DOYEN DU BAR (IRE)**, 6, b g Doyen (IRE)—Hollygrove Native (IRE) **Mr E. A. Elliott**
4 **GEORDIES DREAM**, 7, gr g Geordieland (FR)—Dream Leader (IRE) **J. Wade**
5 **GINE SACRE (FR)**, 6, gr m Laverock—Sacree (FR) **Mr I. Kurdi**
6 **LEAD THE PACK (IRE)**, 6, b g Leading Light (IRE)—Rudi Tuesday (IRE) **D & D Armstrong Ltd & Mr L Westwood**
7 **NORTHERN FALCON**, 7, b g Kayf Tara—Special Trinket (IRE) **Mr I. Kurdi**
8 **SHEEPYSHEEPSHEEP (FR)**, 5, b g Great Pretender (IRE)—Essaouira (FR) **R. A. Green**
9 **THE GREAT HOUDINI (IRE)**, 6, b g Getaway (GER)—Rosangla (FR) **Mr E. A. Elliott**
10 **UPSILON BLEU (FR)**, 14, b g Panoramic—Glycine Bleue (FR) **Mr & Mrs Raymond Anderson Green**

Other Owners: D&D Armstrong Limited, Mr L. J. Westwood.

Assistant Trainer: David Parker.

NH Jockey: Brian Hughes, Craig Nichol.

453 **MR RUSSELL ROSS, Consett**
Postal: **Rock Cottage Farm, 79 Iveston Lane, Consett, County Durham, DH8 7TB**

1 **LISLORAN (IRE)**, 6, b g Imperial Monarch (IRE)—Now Were Broke (IRE) **R. A. Ross**
2 **MOYROSS**, 11, b g Kayf Tara—Dancing Dasi (IRE) **R. A. Ross**
3 **TINTERN THEATRE (IRE)**, 11, b g King's Theatre (IRE)—Rith Ar Aghaidh (IRE) **R. A. Ross**
4 **YORGUNNABEAMUNKY**, 6, b m Yorgunnabelucky (USA)—Delray Beach (FR) **R. A. Ross**

454 **MR BRIAN ROTHWELL, Oswaldkirk**
Postal: **Old Post Office, Oswaldkirk, York, North Yorkshire, YO62 5XT**
Contacts: **PHONE 01439 788859 MOBILE 07969 968241**
EMAIL **brian.rothwell1@googlemail.com**

1 **ALLERTHORPE**, 5, b g Casamento (IRE)—Shirocco Passion **S. P. Hudson**
2 4, B c Ruler of The World (IRE)—Artistic Dawn (IRE) **B. S. Rothwell**
3 **BRIGHT DAWN (IRE)**, 5, b g Helmet (AUS)—Skywards Miles (IRE) **B. S. Rothwell**
4 **GLORYELLA**, 6, b m Yorgunnabelucky (USA)—Ceiriog Valley **The Jelly Boys**
5 **MERCURIAN**, 4, gr g Gregorian (IRE)—Symphony Star (IRE) **The Jelly Boys & Brian Rothwell**
6 **OUTOFTHEGLOOM**, 5, b m Heeraat (IRE)—Srimenanti **Mr S. P. Hudson & Mr Brian Rothwell**
7 **ROTHSON**, 5, b g Pour Moi (IRE)—Yawail **Mr S. P. Hudson & Mr Brian Rothwell**
8 **TURBULENT POWER**, 4, b f Power—Skywards Miles (IRE) **Mr S. P. Hudson & Mr Brian Rothwell**

THREE-YEAR-OLDS

9 B f Time Test—Artistic Dawn (IRE) **B. S. Rothwell**
10 **BELL BOTTOM BLUES**, b f Time Test—Yawail **B. S. Rothwell**
11 **BYDAY**, b f Adaay (IRE)—Byton **S. P. Hudson**
12 B f Cityscape—Kodiac Lady (IRE) **B. S. Rothwell**
13 **NOAHS ABBEY**, gr g Gregorian (IRE)—Bertha Burnett (IRE) **Mrs Greta Sparks & Mr Andrew Sparks**
14 Gr g Peace Envoy (FR)—Rambling Queen (IRE) **B. S. Rothwell**
15 Gr g Gregorian (IRE)—Skywards Miles (IRE) **B. S. Rothwell**
16 **STONEGATE**, b g Proconsul—Bonnie Burnett (IRE) **Mrs Greta Sparks & Mr Andrew Sparks**
17 B f Peace Envoy (FR)—Valley of The Moon (IRE) **B. S. Rothwell**

TWO-YEAR-OLDS

18 Br f 24/03 Massaat (IRE)—Kodiac Lady (IRE) (Kodiac) **B. S. Rothwell**
19 B c 05/04 Massaat (IRE)—Thornton Mary (Mawatheeq (USA)) **B. S. Rothwell**
20 B f 14/04 Rajasinghe (IRE)—Yawail (Medicean) (952) **B. S. Rothwell**

Other Owners: Mr N. J. Brannan, S. P. Hudson, Mr A. R. Morgan, B. S. Rothwell, Mr A. J. Sparks, Mrs G. Sparks.

455 **MR RICHARD ROWE, Pulborough**
Postal: **Ashleigh House Stables, Sullington Lane, Storrington, Pulborough, West Sussex, RH20 4AE**
Contacts: **PHONE 01903 742871 MOBILE 07831 345636**
EMAIL **richard@richardroweracing.com** WEBSITE **www.richardroweracing.co.uk/horses**
FACEBOOK **RichardRoweRacehorseTrainer** TWITTER **@rowe_racing**

1 **AIKENBREAKINHEART (IRE)**, 7, b g Aiken—Stelobel **Any Port In a Storm**
2 **AZTEC DREAMS**, 9, b g Oasis Dream—Agathe Rare (IRE) **Captain Adrian Pratt & Lord Clinton**
3 **BANNIXTOWN BOY (IRE)**, 8, b g Oscar (IRE)—Lucky Loch (IRE) **Any Port In a Storm**
4 **CELMA DES BOIS (FR)**, 10, b g Ballingarry (IRE)—Palafixe (FR) **Encore Partnership V**
5 **COLONEL KEATING (IRE)**, 10, b g Yeats (IRE)—Jabroot (IRE) **Capt Adrian Pratt & Friends**
6 **CONSTANT FRIDAY (IRE)**, 7, gr g Mahler—Mattys Joy (IRE) **Pink Birds**
7 **DANCE TO FAME (IRE)**, 7, b g Fame And Glory—Cooline Jana (IRE) **The Winterlee Partnership**
8 **DANDYLYON (IRE)**, 5, b m Gamut—Agladora (FR) **Mr D. Scott**

MR RICHARD ROWE - continued

9 **DELGANY MONARCH (IRE)**, 7, ch g Imperial Monarch (IRE)—Naughty Marietta (IRE) **Encore Partnership V11**
10 **EL PACO**, 6, b g Paco Boy (IRE)—Miss Marauder **The Blazing Partnership**
11 **FLASHDANZA**, 7, ch g Sepoy (AUS)—Photo Flash (IRE) **B. H. Page**
12 **KICKS AND ALE (IRE)**, 5, b g Pour Moi (IRE)—Spice Patrol (IRE)
13 **KNOWLEDGEABLE KING**, 5, ch g Schiaparelli (GER)—Encyclopedia **Scott Parnell Limited**
14 **MISTER MURCHAN (IRE)**, 9, b g Westerner—So Supreme (IRE) **The Winterlee Partnership**
15 **SET IN THE WEST (IRE)**, 6, b m Westerner—Set In Her Ways (IRE) **Mr D. Scott**
16 **SOARLIKEANEAGLE (IRE)**, 10, b g Scorpion (IRE)—Wayward Cove **B. H. Page**
17 **TATTLETALE (FR)**, 8, b g Linda's Lad—Barbarasse (FR) **Richard Rowe Racing Partnership**
18 **TOMMY DILLION (IRE)**, 6, b g Dylan Thomas (IRE)—Coolaghmore Yeats (IRE) **Winterfields Farm Ltd**
19 **TRUCKERS TIME (IRE)**, 10, b g Curtain Time (IRE)—Truckers Lady (IRE) **Mr J. L. J. Butcher**
20 **TZAR DE L'ELFE (FR)**, 12, b g Satri (IRE)—Rue Tournefort (FR) **Lord Clinton & Captain Adrian Pratt**
21 **UP THE STRAIGHT (IRE)**, 8, b g Arcadio (GER)—Kings Artist (IRE) **The Forever Partnership**
22 **VITAL SIGN (IRE)**, 9, b g Let The Lion Roar—Grace N' Favour (IRE) **Winterfields Farm Ltd**

Other Owners: Mr R. W. Baker, Mr D. M. Bradshaw, Mrs H. C. G. Butcher, Mrs J. Case, Lord Clinton, Mr C. S. Coombe-Tennant, Mrs S. K. Coombe-Tennant, Dr C. Cowell, Mrs J. E. Debenham, K. L. Hunter, Ms S. W. Jewell, Capt A. Pratt, R. Rowe, Mrs J. D. M. Sadler, Scott Parnell Limited, T. W. Wellard, Mr P. D. West, Mr P. R. Wilby, Winterfields Farm Ltd.

---

456   ## MISS MANDY ROWLAND, Lower Blidworth
Postal: Kirkfields, Calverton Road, Lower Blidworth, Nottingham, Nottinghamshire, NG21 0NW
Contacts: **PHONE** 01623 794831 **MOBILE** 07768 224666
EMAIL kirkfieldsriding@hotmail.co.uk

1 **CHINA EXCELS**, 15, b g Exceed And Excel (AUS)—China Beauty **Miss M. E. Rowland**
2 **EPIC CHALLENGE**, 7, b g Mastercraftsman (IRE)—Keep Dancing (IRE) **Miss M. E. Rowland**
3 **JAZZ LEGEND (USA)**, 9, b g Scat Daddy (USA)—Champion Ride (USA) **Miss M. E. Rowland**
4 **LET'S BE HAPPY (IRE)**, 8, gr m Mastercraftsman (IRE)—Corrozal (GER) **Miss M. E. Rowland**
5 **MABAADY**, 8, b g Bated Breath—Fifty (IRE) **Miss M. E. Rowland**
6 **MISS NORA ABU (IRE)**, 8, b m Gold Well—Miss Toulon (IRE) **Miss M. E. Rowland**

Assistant Trainer: Sarah Thomas.

Flat Jockey: Rob Hornby, Adam Kirby, Jimmy Quinn. **Apprentice Jockey:** William Cox.

---

457   ## MRS MELANIE ROWLEY, Bridgnorth
Postal: Bank Farm, The Smithies, Bridgnorth, Shropshire, WV16 4TE
Contacts: **PHONE** 01746 714025
EMAIL mel@mrpequestrian.co.uk

1 **BANANA JOE (IRE)**, 8, b g Getaway (GER)—Rosetiepy (FR) **Slater Stockwood Nicholson Partnership**
2 **BEWARE THE BEAR (IRE)**, 12, b g Shantou (USA)—Native Bid (IRE) **G. B. Barlow**
3 **BLUE BEACH**, 5, b m Kayf Tara—Flutter Bye (IRE) **Poplar Cottage Racing Club**
4 **BLUE BEAR**, 4, b g Blue Bresil (FR)—Kilronan High (IRE)
5 **CASTLE KEEP (IRE)**, 6, b g Leading Light—Castle Jane (IRE) **Mr P. Rowley**
6 4, Br g Scalo—Classic Angel (GER)
7 **DEERSTALKER (IRE)**, 4, b g Walk In The Park (IRE)—Pokerhuntress (IRE)
8 **DISKATEK (IRE)**, 4, b g Maxios—Diska (GER)
9 **ESPOIR DES FORGES (FR)**, 4, b g Doctor Dino (FR)—Ultratlantique (FR)
10 **FINALSHOT**, 9, b g Phoenix Reach (IRE)—Ryoshi **J. N. Dalton**
11 **HEAVENLY CLOUDS (IRE)**, 5, b m Milan—Bobbing Back (IRE) **Hot To Trot Jumping**

MISS MELANIE ROWLEY - continued

12 **I WILL FOLLOW HER,** 8, b m Schiaparelli (GER)—Katess (IRE) **Mrs M. C. Sweeney**
13 **IDAMIX (FR),** 4, b g Al Namix (FR)—Lonita d'Airy (FR)
14 **IDEALDES VILLERETS (FR),** 4, b g Maresca Sorrento (FR)—Qui L'Eut Cru (FR) **Mrs D. L. Whateley**
15 **KINDGIRL,** 4, b f Proconsul—Playful Girl (IRE) **J. N. Dalton**
16 **LATITUDE (IRE),** 6, b g Shirocco (GER)—Gift of Freedom (IRE) **Mrs A. D. Williams**
17 **LUCKY LUGGER,** 5, b g Yorgunnabelucky (USA)—Teme Trixie **A. E. Price**
18 **LUKE SAN,** 6, b g Excelebration (IRE)—Fantastisch (IRE) **Mrs M. C. Sweeney**
19 **MAHLAND (IRE),** 4, ch g Mahler—Ebaniya (IRE)
20 **MALAITA,** 6, b m Malinas (GER)—Aimela (IRE) **Fourgentsandalady**
21 **MARTALMIX'JAC (FR),** 5, gr g Lord du Sud (FR)—Andria (FR) **High and Low**
22 **MY BOBBY DAZZLER,** 7, b g Malinas (GER)—Ease And Grace **Mr R. Barrett**
23 **PERRYVILLE (IRE),** 5, b g Mahler—How Is Things (IRE) **Mrs C. J. Bibbey**
24 **PRIME TIME LADY,** 5, br m Westerner—Lady Everywhere **Poplar Cottage Racing Club**
25 **RAFFLE TICKET,** 8, b g Fair Mix (IRE)—Halo Flora **Countess V. C. Cathcart**
26 **SANDMARTIN,** 4, b g Martaline—Parthenia (IRE)
27 4, B br g Scalo—Shabady (FR)
28 **SULBRICK (IRE),** 7, b g Scorpion (IRE)—In Fact (IRE) **J. M. Nicholson**
29 **TIKITOV (IRE),** 6, b g Sholokhov (IRE)—Goodthyme Ticket (IRE) **Mr P. Rowley**
30 **TROOPER JONES,** 7, ch g Norse Dancer (IRE)—Grape Tree Bay **Mr P. A. Jones**
31 **UNCLE MAC (IRE),** 4, b g Maxios—Aigrette Garzette (IRE)
32 **VALTOR (FR),** 13, b g Nidor (FR)—Jossca (FR) **A. R. Bromley**
33 **WISHING AND HOPING (IRE),** 12, b g Beneficial—Desperately Hoping (IRE) **Mrs P. Andrews**

458

MS LUCINDA RUSSELL, Kinross
Postal: Arlary House Stables, Milnathort, Kinross, Tayside, KY13 9SJ
Contacts: PHONE 01577 865512 MOBILE 07970 645261 FAX 01577 861171
EMAIL lucindarussellracing@outlook.com WEBSITE www.lucindarussellracing.com

1 **AHOY SENOR (IRE),** 7, b g Dylan Thomas (IRE)—Dara Supreme (IRE) **Mrs C Wymer & Mr Pjs Russell**
2 **AIN'T MY FAULT (IRE),** 9, b g Beneficial—Coolnasneachta (IRE) **Foresight Racing**
3 **AONE ALLY,** 4, b g Mayson—Infatuate **Mrs H. Kelly**
4 **AURORA THUNDER,** 8, b m Malinas (GER)—Ninna Nanna (FR) **Allson Sparkle Ltd**
5 **BALLYARE,** 5, b g Hot Streak (IRE)—Saddlers Bend (IRE) **The Bristol Boys**
6 **BEAUTE NOIRE (IRE),** 6, br m Arcadio (GER)—Mrs Gordi **Ms L. V. Russell**
7 **BEHINDTHELINES (IRE),** 10, b g Milan—Sunset Leader (IRE) **London Scots for Doddie**
8 **BIG RIVER (IRE),** 12, b g Milan—Call Kate (IRE) **Two Black Labs**
9 **BIX BEIDERBECKE (FR),** 4, b gr g Mawatheeq (USA)—Like It Is (FR) **Mrs S Russell & A M Russell**
10 **BLOORIEDOTCOM (IRE),** 7, b g Holy Roman Emperor (IRE)—Peaceful Kingdom (USA) **Mutual Friends**
11 **BOLLINGERANDKRUG (IRE),** 7, b g Getaway (GER)—Out Performer (IRE) **Ms D. Thomson**
12 **BOY'S ON TOUR (IRE),** 10, b g Beneficial—Galant Tour (IRE) **Foresight Racing**
13 6, Ch g Universal (IRE)—Brockwell Park **Ms L. V. Russell**
14 **BUDDHA SCHEME (IRE),** 8, b g Milan—Benefit Scheme (IRE) **Mr G. R. McGladery**
15 **CABOY (FR),** 10, b g Nidor (FR)—Cadouya Girl (FR) **Goodtimes**
16 **CALLE MALVA (IRE),** 7, b m Getaway (GER)—Waydale Hill **Mrs C Wymer & Mr Pjs Russell**
17 **CAMP BELAN (IRE),** 6, b g Milan—Glencree Spirit (IRE) **Mrs S Russell & A M Russell**
18 **CELTIC FLAMES (IRE),** 12, gr g Celtic Swing—Don't Forget Shoka (IRE) **Mr W. T. Scott**
19 **CHAPEL GREEN (IRE),** 5, b g Dylan Thomas (IRE)—The Coolest Cat (IRE) **Ms L. V. Russell**
20 **CLEARLY CRAZY (IRE),** 6, b m Libertarian—Chika Boom (IRE) **Misses P & F Simpson**
21 **CORACH RAMBLER (IRE),** 8, b g Jeremy (USA)—Heart N Hope (IRE) **The Ramblers**
22 **CORRIGEEN ROCK (IRE),** 5, b g Westerner—Set In Her Ways (IRE) **The Caledonian Racing Society**
23 **DESTINY IS ALL (IRE),** 8, b g Prince Flori (GER)—Hearts Delight (IRE) **Mr J. R. Adam**
24 **DIAMOND STATE (FR),** 6, b g Vision d'Etat (FR)—Wonderful Diamond (FR) **Mr G. R. McGladery**
25 **DOMANDLOUIS (IRE),** 5, b g Getaway (GER)—Drive On Kate (IRE) **Two Black Labs**
26 **DON'T LOOK BACK,** 4, gr g Oasis Dream—Ronaldsay **Mrs H. Kelly**
27 **DOUGLAS TALKING (IRE),** 6, b g Dylan Thomas (IRE)—Look Who's Talking **The Bristol Boys & Peter J S Russell**

MS LUCINDA RUSSELL - continued

28 **ELMONO (FR)**, 11, ch g Epalo (GER)—Monareva (FR) **Gerry And The Pacemakers**
29 **EMIRAT DE CATANA (FR)**, 8, b g Linda's Lad—Kolada (FR) **Mr P. J. S. Russell**
30 **ENGLES ROCK (IRE)**, 6, b m Excelebration (IRE)—Lisa Gherardini (IRE) **Mrs H. Kelly**
31 **FETHARD GLORY (IRE)**, 6, b m Fame And Glory—Kilnockin Lady (IRE) **Kelso Lowflyers & Mr PJS Russell**
32 **FYFIN PATSY (IRE)**, 8, b m September Storm (GER)—Poshly Presented (IRE) **Fyfin Four**
33 **GEMOLOGIST (IRE)**, 7, b m Sir Percy—Tiffany Diamond (IRE) **Musselburgh Lunch Club**
34 **GRAND MORNING**, 10, b g Midnight Legend—Valentines Lady (IRE) **Mr J. P. McManus**
35 **GREEN VAULT (IRE)**, 6, b g Shirocco (GER)—Squeekaussie (IRE) **Mrs S Russell & A M Russell**
36 **HAUTE ESTIME (IRE)**, 5, b m Walk In The Park (IRE)—Terre Haute (IRE) **Brahms & Liszt**
37 **HECTOR MASTER (FR)**, 5, b g Masterstroke (USA)—Queen Maresca (FR) **Mrs S Russell & A M Russell**
38 **IDEM (FR)**, 4, b g Rail Link—Reflexion (FR) **The Boltons & Atholl Duncan**
39 **ITS A MIDNIGHT**, 5, ch m Midnight Legend—Just For Pleasure (IRE) **The Midnight Chasers**
40 **IZZY'S CHAMPION (IRE)**, 8, b g Gold Well—Native Crystal (IRE) **Mr & Mrs T. P. Winnell**
41 **LIFE MADE SIMPLE**, 5, b g Sulamani (IRE)—Swift Getaway (IRE) **The Crick Girls**
42 **LUCKY FLIGHT (FR)**, 8, b g Linda's Lad—Lili Flight (FR) **The Vikings**
43 **MAIFALKI (FR)**, 9, b g Falco (USA)—Makila (IRE) **Lamont Racing**
44 **METHODTOTHEMADNESS (IRE)**, 8, b m Gold Well—Odeeka (IRE) **Mrs S Russell & A M Russell**
45 **MIGHTY THUNDER**, 9, b g Malinas (GER)—Cool Island (IRE) **Allson Sparkle Ltd**
46 **MINT GOLD (IRE)**, 8, b g Gold Well—Lady Flyer (IRE) **Mrs S Russell & A M Russell**
47 **MONOCHROMIX (FR)**, 4, gr g Morandi (FR)—Lounamix (FR) **Mr Michael & Lady Jane Kaplan**
48 **NETYWELL (FR)**, 5, b g Willywell (FR)—Netova (FR) **Set K & Russell Russell**
49 4, B f Kayf Tara—Nonnetia (FR) **The Nostalgics**
50 **NOTNOWKATE'S (IRE)**, 5, ch m Notnowcato—Another Burden **Mr E. Burns**
51 **OPERATION OVERLORD (IRE)**, 7, b g Jeremy (USA)—Alfreeze **Mr J. P. McManus**
52 **OUR MARTY (FR)**, 4, b g Martinborough (JPN)—Dercia (FR) **Mrs S Russell & A M Russell**
53 **PASTURE SHADES (IRE)**, 5, ch m Sholokhov (IRE)—Maryota (FR) **R. A. Green**
54 **PETITE RHAPSODY (IRE)**, 7, b g Shirocco (GER)—Peggy Cullen (IRE) **Tay Valley Chasers Racing Club**
55 **PRAISE OF SHADOWS (IRE)**, 4, b g Exceed And Excel (AUS)—Moon Over Water (IRE) **Mrs H. Kelly**
56 **PRINCE DUNDEE (IRE)**, 9, b g Stowaway—Miss Dundee (IRE) **McNeill Racing & County Set Three**
57 **PRINCE OF PERTH (IRE)**, 4, b g Malinas (GER)—Emma Ami (IRE) **Set & J Russell**
58 **RAPID RAIDER (IRE)**, 4, ch g Golden Lariat (USA)—Golden Court (IRE) **Mrs S Russell & A M Russell**
59 **READYSTEADYBEAU (FR)**, 6, ch g Kapgarde (FR)—La Ville Aux Dames (FR) **Joanne & Peter Russell**
60 **RED MISSILE (IRE)**, 5, b g Battle of Marengo (IRE)—Plym **Mr Michael & Lady Jane Kaplan**
61 **RETURN FIRE (IRE)**, 6, b g Leading Light (IRE)—There On Time (IRE) **Tay Valley Chasers Racing Club**
62 **ROWDY RUSTLER (IRE)**, 7, b g Getaway (GER)—Posh Posy (IRE) **Mr J. R. Adam**
63 **ROYAL RESERVE (IRE)**, 9, b g Duke of Marmalade (IRE)—Lady Hawkfield (IRE) **Mr P. J. S. Russell**
64 **SCOTTISH WIND (FR)**, 4, b g Territories (IRE)—Isalou (FR) **Lamont Racing**
65 **SLAINTE MHOR (IRE)**, 8, b g Milan—Founding Daughter (IRE) **Mr P. J. S. Russell**
66 **SNOW JOEKING (IRE)**, 4, b g Snow Sky—Thereinimaygo (IRE) **Mr N. Hogan**
67 **SO THEY SAY**, 6, b m Malinas (GER)—Feisty Lass (IRE) **The Osprey Partnership**
68 **SONGOFTHELARK (IRE)**, 6, ch g Flemensfirth (USA)—Norabelle (IRE) **Mr G. R. McGladery**
69 **SPARK OF MADNESS (IRE)**, 6, b g Walk In The Park (IRE)—Prosopopee (IRE) **Mrs S Russell & A M Russell**
70 **SPEAK OF THE DEVIL (IRE)**, 9, ch g Mahler—A Fine Romance (IRE) **The County Set & Mr P Russell & Friends**
71 **SPRING PARK LADY (IRE)**, 7, b m Milan—Cuiloge Lady (IRE) **Mrs J. Bilsland**
72 **STYLISH MOMENT (IRE)**, 9, b g Milan—Up The Style (IRE) **The Crick Girls**
73 **SUTTON MANOR (IRE)**, 11, b g Gold Well—Nighty Bless (IRE) **County Set Five & the Red Shoes**
74 **TENBOBEACHWAY (IRE)**, 4, br g Malinas (GER)—Gift Wrapped (IRE) **Mrs C Wymer & Mr Pjs Russell**
75 **THEREISNODOUBT (IRE)**, 9, ch g Primary (USA)—Doubt (IRE) **Mrs H. Kelly**
76 **THUNDER IN MILAN (IRE)**, 6, b g Milan—Baby Briggs (IRE) **Allson Sparkle Ltd**
77 **TIKA TOO**, 5, b m Blue Bresil (FR)—Fabrika **D. P. Constable**
78 **TOROSAY (IRE)**, 4, b f Getaway (GER)—The Toft **Mr P. J. S. Russell**
79 **VENGEUR DE GUYE (FR)**, 13, b g Dom Alco (FR)—Mascotte de Guye (FR) **Brahms & Liszt**
80 **VINO'S CHOICE (IRE)**, 10, b g Kalanisi (IRE)—Ard's Pet (IRE) **Mr P. J. S. Russell**
81 **WELL ABOVE PAR (IRE)**, 10, b g Gold Well—Glynn Glory (IRE) **The Eagle Partnership**
82 **WEST END LADY (IRE)**, 7, b m Westerner—Nightofthe Oscars (IRE) **The Falcon Partnership**
83 **WITHOUT CONVICTION (IRE)**, 7, b m Aizavoski (IRE)—With Conviction (IRE) **Mrs C Wymer & Mr Pjs Russell**
84 **YOUR OWN STORY (IRE)**, 6, b g Shantaram—Forest Heiress (IRE) **Ms L. V. Russell**
85 **YOUR PLACE (IRE)**, 6, b m Scorpion (IRE)—Sheebadiva (IRE) **Dig In Racing**

MS LUCINDA RUSSELL - continued

THREE-YEAR-OLDS

86 **BOIS GUILLBERT (FR)**, ch g Ivanhowe (GER)—Ready Kap (FR) **Mr R. B. H. Young**
87 **CLOVIS BOY**, b g Clovis du Berlais (FR)—Denisette (FR) **Mrs S Russell & A M Russell**
88 **ESPRIT DU POTIER (FR)**, b gr g Montmartre (FR)—Absent Minded **Mr P. J. S. Russell**
89 B f Jack Hobbs—Gaye Flier (IRE) **Mr J. R. Adam**
90 **NORTHERN CARDINAL (FR)**, b br g Bathyrhon (GER)—Sagadoune (FR) **Ms L. V. Russell**
91 **OLD GREGORIAN**, b g Jack Hobbs—Thankyou Very Much **R. F. Gibbons**
92 B g Westerner—The Toft **Mr P. J. S. Russell**

TWO-YEAR-OLDS

93 B g 22/02 Garswood—Last Supper (Echo of Light) **R. F. Gibbons**

Other Owners: Mr J. A. Aitkenhead, Mr W. M. Allan, Mrs J. Bilsland, Mr G. Bolton, Mr G. R. Brown, A. Cadger, County Set Four, Mr N. A. Crofts, Mr A. B. Cuthill, Mr C. Dempster, Mr R. Doak, Mrs J. E. Dodd, Mr A. S. Duncan, Mr M. J. Fitzpatrick, Mr A. T. Galloway, Ms L. M. Gillies, G. Godsman, Mrs I. M. Grant, Mr J. Grant, E. D. Haggart, T. W. Hosier, K. L. Hunter, Mr D. R. James, Kelso Members Lowflyers Club, Mrs M Kennedy, Mr A. Kerr, Mrs C. J. Lamb, Mr R. M. Landale, Mrs Y. M. V. Learmonth, Ms A. M. MacInnes, Ms F. E. MacInnes, Ms S. C. Mackay, Mr G. R. McGladery, Mr J. C. McNeill, Mr R. McNeill, Mr M. G. Mellor, Mr Peter J Russell & Friends, Mr A. M. Russell, Ms L. V. Russell, Mr P. J. S. Russell, Mrs S. C. Russell, Miss F. I. Simpson, Miss P. A. Simpson, A. W. Sinclair, Miss M. M. Smith, Ms P. Spours, Mrs R. A. Stobart, The County Set, The County Set (Five), The County Set Three, The Red Shoes, Ms D. Thomson, Mr N. J. Turnbull, Mr G. T. Wallace, Mrs M. Winnell, Mr T. P. Winnell, Mrs C. E. Wymer.

Assistant Trainer: Blair Campbell, Jaimie Duff, Steven Kelly, Peter Scudamore, Cameron Wadge,

Head Girl: Vicky Haughton, Hannah Wilson, **Travelling Head:** Eleanor Warren.

NH Jockey: Derek Fox, Stephen Mulqueen. **Conditional Jockey:** Conner McCann, Patrick Wadge.

Amateur Jockey: Mr Gregor Walkingshaw.

---

459 MR JOHN RYAN, Newmarket
Postal: **Cadland Stables, Moulton Road, Newmarket, Suffolk, CB8 8DU**
Contacts: **PHONE 01638 664172 MOBILE 07739 801235**
EMAIL john.ryan@jryanracing.com WEBSITE www.jryanracing.com TWITTER @JohnRyanRacing

1 **ARTHUR'S ANGEL (IRE)**, 4, gr g Dark Angel (IRE)—Jellicle Ball (IRE) **Mr G. F. Smith-Bernal**
2 **BATTLE OF MARATHON (USA)**, 10, b g War Front (USA)—Sayedah (USA) **Emma Ryan & Partner**
3 **CATCH MY BREATH**, 6, gr g Bated Breath—Likeable **The Out of Puff Partnership**
4 4, B f Awtaad (IRE)—Flirty Thirty (IRE)
5 4, B f Mount Nelson—Glittering Image (IRE)
6 **GODDESS OF FIRE**, 5, b m Toronado (IRE)—Burnt Fingers (IRE) **Mr M. M. Foulger**
7 **HIROSHIMA**, 6, b g Nathaniel (IRE)—Lisiere (IRE) **Russell, Thompson, DAS Racing, Ryan**
8 **JACK RYAN (IRE)**, 5, b g Harbour Watch (IRE)—Anything (IRE) **Emma Ryan & Partner**
9 **OCEAN WILDE**, 4, b g Fountain of Youth (USA)—New Falcon (IRE) **John Ryan Racing Partnership**
10 **PISTOLETTO (USA)**, 5, b g War Front (USA)—Lerici (USA) **Mr J. A. Thompson, Mr S. D. Russell**

THREE-YEAR-OLDS

11 **ANGER MANAGEMENT**, b c Ribchester (IRE)—Despatch **BB Thoroughbreds**
12 **FOURSHADESOFSILVER**, gr c Ardad (IRE)—Reaching Ahead (USA)
   Mr J. B. Ryan, P. J. Donnison, Mr S. J. Lavallin, Mr J. A. Thompson
13 **LORD VADER**, ch c Ulysses (IRE)—Lysanda (GER) **Mr J. F. Stocker**
14 **MANACCAN**, ch c Exceed And Excel (AUS)—Shyrl **Mr G. F. Smith-Bernal**
15 **REEL OF FORTUNE (IRE)**, b f Highland Reel (IRE)—Romantic Stroll (IRE) **Das Racing & Mr J Ryan**
16 **SICILIAN VITO (IRE)**, b c Night of Thunder (IRE)—Pencarrow **Mr J. F. Stocker**

Other Owners: BB Thoroughbreds, DAS Racing Limited, A & Russell, Mr S. D. Russell, Donnison, Ryan, Mrs E. Ryan, Mr J. B. Ryan, Mr J. A. Thompson.

Amateur Jockey: Miss Tia Phillips.

460 **MR KEVIN RYAN, Hambleton**
Postal: Hambleton Lodge, Hambleton, Thirsk, North Yorkshire, YO7 2HA
Contacts: PHONE 01845 597010, 01845 597622 FAX 01845 597622
EMAIL office@kevinryanracing.com WEBSITE www.kevinryanracing.com

1 **ARROW OF GOLD (IRE)**, 5, ch g Galileo (IRE)—Fleche d'Or **Sheikh Mohammed Obaid Al Maktoum**
2 **BEN MACDUI (IRE)**, 4, b g Kodiac—Candiland (GER) **K&J Bloodstock Ltd**
3 **BERGERAC (IRE)**, 4, b g Kodi Bear (IRE)—Fancy Vivid (IRE) **Mrs Angie Bailey**
4 **BIELSA (IRE)**, 7, b g Invincible Spirit (IRE)—Bourbon Ball (USA) **King Power Racing Co Ltd**
5 **BROOMY LAW**, 4, b g Gleneagles (IRE)—Hooray **Sheikh Mohammed Obaid Al Maktoum**
6 **COTTAM LANE**, 4, b g Twilight Son—Alsium (IRE) **The Racing Emporium**
7 **DEXTER BELLE (IRE)**, 4, b f Ajaya—Thousandfold (USA) **Clipper Logistics**
8 **DIGITAL (IRE)**, 4, b g Kodi Bear (IRE)—Notte Illuminata (IRE) **Highclere T'bred Racing - Kodi Bear 1**
9 **EEH BAH GUM (IRE)**, 7, b g Dandy Man (IRE)—Moonline Dancer (FR) **Mr Nick Rhodes**
10 **EMARAATY ANA**, 6, b g Shamardal (USA)—Spirit of Dubai (IRE) **Sheikh Mohammed Obaid Al Maktoum**
11 **FORZA ORTA (IRE)**, 4, b g Fastnet Rock (AUS)—Follow A Star (IRE) **Highbank Stud**
12 **HELLO ZABEEL (IRE)**, 4, b g Frankel—Lady of The Desert (USA) **Mr Jaber Abdullah**
13 **JUAN ELCANO**, 5, ch g Frankel—Whatami **Sheikh Mohammed Obaid Al Maktoum**
14 **JUSTANOTHERBOTTLE (IRE)**, 8, ch g Intense Focus (USA)—Duchess K (IRE) **Mr Steve Ryan & Mr M J Tedham**
15 **MAGICAL SPIRIT (IRE)**, 6, ch g Zebedee—La Dame de Fer (IRE) **Hambleton Racing Ltd XXXII**
16 **RATHBONE**, 6, b g Foxwedge (AUS)—Frequent **Mrs Angie Bailey**
17 **SEVEN BROTHERS (IRE)**, 4, b g Slade Power (IRE)—Ihtifal **Mr Steve Ryan**
18 **SOUND REASON**, 4, ch g Hot Streak (IRE)—Brown Eyed Honey **Hambleton Racing Ltd XXIX**
19 **SPIRITOFTHENORTH (FR)**, 5, br g Bated Breath—Danlepordamsterdam (IRE) **Middleham Park Racing XLVI**
20 **VENTURA RASCAL**, 5, b g Fountain of Youth (FR)—Choisette **Middleham Park Racing CVII**

THREE-YEAR-OLDS

21 **ALEEZDANCER (IRE)**, b g Fast Company (IRE)—Clifton Dancer **Jack Berry & John Matthews**
22 **ALIA CHOICE**, b f Dark Angel (IRE)—Queen Kindly **Mr Jaber Abdullah**
23 **ANADORA**, b f Havana Gold (IRE)—Keladora (USA) **CHH Racing**
24 **ASAAYIL**, ch f Pride of Dubai (AUS)—Camargue **Emirates Park PTY Ltd**
25 **BADR (USA)**, ch c Kitten's Joy (USA)—Red Lodge (USA) **Emirates Park PTY Ltd**
26 **BAIKAL**, b g No Nay Never (USA)—Foreign Assignment (IRE) **Sheikh Mohammed Obaid Al Maktoum**
27 **BALLET STEPS**, b f Dabirsim (FR)—Savannah's Dream **Clipper Logistics**
28 **BINT ALSHARF**, b f Wootton Bassett—Star Lahib (IRE) **Mr Jaber Abdullah**
29 **BOONIE (IRE)**, b c Brazen Beau (AUS)—Dice Game **Seymour Bloodstock & Mark Balnaves**
30 **CATCH CUNNINGHAM (IRE)**, b g Kodiac—Faithful Duchess (IRE) **Mr Steve Ryan**
31 **CHRYSOS (USA)**, b br c Medaglia d'Oro (USA)—Crowley's Law **Chrysos Partners**
32 **CLARET CLUB**, ch g Hot Streak (IRE)—Greek Tragedy **Mr N. Dalgarno**
33 **COTAI WEST**, b f Cotai Glory—Capote West (USA)
34 **CRYPTO QUEST (IRE)**, b g Profitable (IRE)—Viking Fair **Mr T A Rahman**
35 **DARK MOON RISING (IRE)**, b c Night of Thunder (IRE)—Al Nassa (USA) **Mrs Angie Bailey**
36 **DIFFERENT LOOK (FR)**, br f Dabirsim (FR)—Danseuse Corse (FR) **Mrs Jill Ryan**
37 **DION BAKER (IRE)**, b g Ribchester (IRE)—Tiga Tuan (FR) **Mr T A Rahman**
38 **ESKEN ROSE (USA)**, b f Hootenanny (USA)—Eskenforandreya (USA) **Hambleton Racing Ltd XXXVIII**
39 **FAST AND LOOSE**, b g No Nay Never (USA)—Madam Valentine **Mr Steve Ryan**
40 **FONTEYN**, b f Farhh—Luzia **Sheikh Mohammed Obaid Al Maktoum**
41 **FRANZ**, b c Almanzor (FR)—Gemstone (IRE) **Haras d'Etreham & Cambridge Stud 1**
42 **GIS A SUB (IRE)**, b c Acclamation—Monclaire (GER) **Mr Steve Ryan**
43 **GREEN TEAM (FR)**, b c Wootton Bassett—On The Line (FR) **Ahmad Al Shaikh**
44 **GUEST LIST (IRE)**, gr f Ardad (IRE)—Heavenly Angel **Clipper Logistics**
45 **HALA HALA ATHMANI**, b f Dabirsim (FR)—Spasha **Mr Jaber Abdullah**
46 **KENTUCKY ROSE**, b f Adaay (IRE)—Flighty Clarets (IRE) **Mr Ahmed Jaber**
47 **KODEBREAKER (IRE)**, b g Kodi Bear (IRE)—Coachhouse Lady (USA) **Hambleton Racing Ltd XVI**
48 **LADY RAEBURN (IRE)**, b f Mehmas (IRE)—Smash (IRE) **Nick Bradley Racing 52**
49 **MANASLU (IRE)**, b g Starspangledbanner (AUS)—Dark Seductress (IRE) **K&J Bloodstock Ltd**
50 **MARHABA THE CHAMP**, ch c Galileo (IRE)—Lady of The Desert (USA) **Mr Jaber Abdullah**
51 **MAS PODER (IRE)**, b f Mehmas (IRE)—Ahdaath (IRE) **Nick Bradley Racing 21**
52 **MELAYU KINGDOM (IRE)**, ch g Mehmas (IRE)—Lauren's Girl (IRE) **Mr Michael Reilly**
53 **MERLIN'S LADY (IRE)**, b f Camelot—Mora Bai (IRE) **Sheikh Mohammed Obaid Al Maktoum**
54 **MICROBURST**, b c Night of Thunder (IRE)—Elis Eliz (IRE)

MR KEVIN RYAN - continued

55 **MILLION THANKS (IRE),** ch c Churchill (IRE)—Queen's Rose **Mr Jaber Abdullah**
56 **MONSIEUR JUMBO (FR),** gr g Caravaggio (USA)—Pretty Darling (IRE) **Mr T A Rahman**
57 **MORE THAN WELCOME (USA),** b br f More Than Ready (USA)—My Perfect Ten (USA)
More Than Welcome Partners

58 **MOTHER SHIPTON,** b f Showcasing—Pelican Key (IRE) **Clipper Logistics**
59 **MYKONOS (IRE),** b c Ribchester (IRE)—Dancing On Air (IRE) **Mykonos Partners**
60 **NAASMA (IRE),** b f Churchill (IRE)—Music Show (IRE) **Mr Jaber Abdullah**
61 **PEGGY SIOUX,** b f Oasis Dream—La Napoule **Guy Reed Racing**
62 **PENNYPEACE,** b f Postponed (IRE)—Friendlier **Highbank Stud**
63 **POSITIVE FORCE,** gr c El Kabeir (USA)—Clann Force **Sapphire Print Solutions Ltd**
64 **RAMBUSO CREEK (IRE),** b g Tagula (IRE)—Fine Prospect (IRE) **Hambleton Racing Ltd XXV**
65 **RAVENSWING (IRE),** gr c Dark Angel (IRE)—Future Generation (IRE) **Sheikh Mohammed Obaid Al Maktoum**
66 **ROCKPRINCESS,** b f Belardo (IRE)—Princess Rock **Bearstone Stud Limited**
67 **ROMANOVICH (IRE),** gr c Dark Angel (IRE)—My Favourite Thing **Sheikh Mohammed Obaid Al Maktoum**
68 **SADMAH,** b f Frankel—Mossfun (AUS) **Emirates Park PTY Ltd**
69 **SEQUEIRA LADY (IRE),** b f Mehmas (IRE)—Duchess of Foxland (IRE) **Martin McHale & Partner**
70 **SHALADAR (FR),** b g Shalaa (IRE)—Ultradargent (FR) **Hambleton Racing Ltd XLVII**
71 **SMULLEN (IRE),** ch g Camacho—Day By Day **Mrs Jill Ryan**
72 **SPITTING FEATHERS (IRE),** b g Iffraaj—Yellowhammer **Mr Steve Ryan**
73 B f Sea the Stars (IRE)—Stealth Missile (IRE) **Highbank Stud**
74 **SUN MAGIC (IRE),** b f Invincible Spirit (IRE)—Amplifier **Sheikh Mohammed Obaid Al Maktoum**
75 **SWEET GLANCE,** b f Ardad (IRE)—Brown Eyed Honey **Hambleton Racing Ltd XLVII**
76 **THE COOKSTOWN CAFU,** b c Invincible Spirit (IRE)—Miss Delila (USA) **Highbank Stud**
77 **THUNDER ROAR,** ch c Night of Thunder (IRE)—Dominike (ITY) **Thunder Roar Partners**
78 **THUNDERING,** b g Night of Thunder (IRE)—Cosmea **Mr Steve Ryan**
79 **TIME TO PARLEY,** b f Invincible Spirit (IRE)—Ashadihan **Mr T A Rahman**
80 **TRIPLE TIME (IRE),** b c Frankel—Reem Three **Sheikh Mohammed Obaid Al Maktoum**
81 **TRUE WARFARE,** br c Siyouni (FR)—Patronising **Clipper Logistics**
82 **TUDOR QUEEN (IRE),** b f Starspangledbanner (AUS)—Queen Elsa (IRE) **Highclere T'bred Racing - Cedar Tree 1**

TWO-YEAR-OLDS

83 B f 28/04 Kodiac—Clip Art (Acclamation) (47619)
84 Ch c 17/03 Camacho—Desert Way (IRE) (Giant's Causeway (USA)) (38095)
85 B c 03/03 Washington DC (IRE)—Epping Rose (IRE) (Kodiac) (22857) **Hambleton Racing Ltd XXVII**
86 Ro c 07/02 Dark Angel (IRE)—Eyes on Asha (IRE) **Mr T A Rahman**
87 B f 22/03 Harry Angel (IRE)—Fatal Attraction (Oasis Dream) (28000) **Mr S White**
88 **FLYING BARTY (IRE),** ch f 18/02 Starspangledbanner (AUS)—Dice Game (Shamardal (USA))
Chasemore Farm & Seymour Bloodstock
89 B c 17/03 Showcasing—Furbelow (Pivotal) (450000) **Sheikh Mohammed Obaid Al Maktoum**
90 Gr c 25/02 Dark Angel (IRE)—Jumira Princess (IRE) **Sheikh Mohammed Obaid Al Maktoum**
91 B f 31/03 Ardad (IRE)—Juncea (Elnadim (USA)) (31429) **Mr Roger Peel**
92 B c 02/02 Mehmas (IRE)—Juxtaposed (Three Valleys (USA)) (150000) **Sheikh Mohammed Obaid Al Maktoum**
93 B f 11/04 Havana Gold (IRE)—Keladora (Crafty Prospector (USA)) (27000) **Hambleton Racing Ltd XVI**
94 **LEAP YEAR LAD (IRE),** gr ro c 29/02 Havana Grey—Skeleton (IRE) (Tobougg (IRE)) (42857) **My Vein Clinic**
95 **MAGICDOLLAR,** b c 05/03 Washington DC (IRE)—She Mystifies (Indesatchel (IRE)) **Y&R Engineering Ltd**
96 Ch f 17/01 Prince of Lir (IRE)—Mairead Anne (USA) (Elusive Quality (USA)) (40000)
Sheikh Abdullah Almalek Alsabah
97 B c 03/03 Kodiac—Marian Halcombe (USA) (Bernardini (USA)) (57143)
98 B c 20/02 Cotai Glory—Miss Poppy (Averti (IRE)) (47000)
99 B f 16/04 Lope de Vega (IRE)—Nada (Teofilo (IRE)) **Sheikh Mohammed Obaid Al Maktoum**
100 B c 06/05 No Nay Never (USA)—Pandora's Box (IRE) (Galileo (IRE)) (80000) **Mr Steve Ryan**
101 Br f 06/03 Dark Angel (IRE)—Pixeleen (Pastoral Pursuits) (225000) **Sheikh Mohammed Obaid Al Maktoum**
102 B c 18/02 Kodiac—Ramone (IRE) (Marju (IRE)) (170000) **Sheikh Mohammed Obaid Al Maktoum**
103 Ch c 22/02 Almanzor (FR)—Rapid Transaction (USA) (A P Indy (USA)) (153061) **Haras d'Etreham & Al Shaqab**
104 B c 22/03 Lope de Vega (IRE)—Reem Three (Mark of Esteem (IRE)) **Sheikh Mohammed Obaid Al Maktoum**
105 B c 12/03 Ardad (IRE)—Relaxez Vous (IRE) (Raven's Pass (USA)) (57143)
106 Ch c 12/03 Night of Thunder (IRE)—Rosa Eglanteria (Nayef (USA)) (35000) **Mrs Janis MacPherson**
107 B f 17/03 Kodiac—Sahool **Mr Jaber Abdullah**
108 B c 27/02 Gleneagles (IRE)—Silken Soul (Dansili) (7619) **Riverside Racing Syndicate**

MR KEVIN RYAN - continued

109 B f 21/03 Night of Thunder (IRE)—Silver Clouds (IRE) (Oasis Dream) (61905)
110 **SNOW GIRL**, ch f 05/05 Washington DC (IRE)—Wether Girl (Major Cadeaux) (8000) **Bearstone Stud Limited**
111 B f 03/03 Havana Grey—Sonnellino (Singspiel (IRE)) (32000) **Sheikh Abdullah Almalek Alsabah**
112 B f 19/03 Night of Thunder (IRE)—Special Miss (Authorized (IRE)) (24762) **Mr Nick White**
113 B f 21/02 Monsieur Bond (IRE)—State Sovereignty **Mr JCG Chua**
114 **STELLA BLUE (IRE)**, b f 09/01 Bungle Inthejungle—Cliodhna (IRE) (Bahamian Bounty) (11000) **Mr Allan Kerr**
115 B f 06/04 Zoustar (AUS)—Sterling Sound (USA) (Street Cry (IRE)) (18000) **Hambleton Racing Ltd XXIX**
116 **U A E SPIRIT (IRE)**, ch c 03/04 Starspangledbanner (AUS)—Bequia (IRE) (Helmet (AUS)) (37000)
                                                                                              Ahmad Al Shaikh
117 Ch c 23/02 Zoustar (AUS)—Worship (IRE) (Havana Gold (IRE)) (57143) **Hambleton Racing Ltd XXVII**

Other Owners: Mr M. N. Balnaves, J. Berry, A. W. Black, Mrs J. E. Black, Chasemore Farm LLP, Mr B. N. Collier, J. Cullinan, Mr N. De Chambure, A. C. Henson, Highclere T'Bred Racing - Cedar Tree, Highclere Thoroughbred Racing Ltd, Highclere Thoroughbred Racing-Kodi Bear, Mrs R. G. Hillen, B. E. Holland, Mr A. Holmes, K&J Bloodstock Ltd, Mr B. J. Lindsay, Mr R. J. Marley, Mr J. Matthews, Mr M. McHale, Microburst Partners, Mrs Jill Ryan, Mr Steve Ryan, Seymour Bloodstock Pty Ltd, Mrs L. M. Shanahan, Mr M. J. Tedham.

Assistant Trainer: Adam Ryan.

Flat Jockey: Tom Eaves, Shane Gray, Kevin Stott. **Apprentice Jockey:** Oisin McSweeney.

---

461 MR AYTACH SADIK, Kidderminster
Postal: **Wolverley Court Coach House, Wolverley, Kidderminster, Worcestershire, DY10 3RP**
Contacts: PHONE **01562 852362** MOBILE **07803 040344**

1 **CELTIC CLASSIC (IRE)**, 6, b g Cacique (IRE)—Dabtiyra (IRE) **A. M. Sadik**
2 **NYOUFSEA**, 7, gr g Fair Mix (IRE)—Just Smokie **A. M. Sadik**
3 **SILVER STAR (FR)**, 9, gr g Silver Frost (IRE)—Suerte **A. M. Sadik**

---

462 MR MALCOLM SAUNDERS, Wells
Postal: **Blue Mountain Farm, Wells Hill Bottom, Haydon, Wells, Somerset, BA5 3EZ**
Contacts: PHONE **01749 841011** MOBILE **07771 601035**
EMAIL **malcolm@malcolmsaunders.co.uk** WEBSITE **www.malcolmsaunders.co.uk**

1 **BLUEBELL TIME (IRE)**, 6, br m Coach House (IRE)—Matterofact (IRE) **Mrs Ginny Nicholas & Mr M. S. Saunders**
2 **CORONATION COTTAGE**, 8, b m Pastoral Pursuits—Avrilo **Pat Hancock & Eric Jones**
3 **DIAMOND COTTAGE**, 5, ch m Cappella Sansevero—Avrilo **Pat Hancock & Eric Jones**
4 **JOY CHOI (IRE)**, 4, b f Territories (IRE)—Vintage Molly **Paul Nicholas / M S Saunders**
5 **PASTFACT**, 8, br g Pastoral Pursuits—Matterofact **Premier Conservatory Roofs**
6 **REDREDROBIN**, 5, b m Helmet (AUS)—Cape Rosie **M. S. Saunders**
7 **RUBY COTTAGE (IRE)**, 4, b f Coach House (IRE)—Avrilo **Pat Hancock & Eric Jones**
8 **SECRETFACT**, 9, br g Sakhee's Secret—Matterofact (IRE) **Premier Conservatory Roofs**

THREE-YEAR-OLDS

9 **DESERT (IRE)**, b f Havana Gold (IRE)—Jewel In The Sand (IRE)
10 **SOWS (IRE)**, b f Kodiac—Zvarkhova (FR) **M. S. Saunders**

Other Owners: D. J. Collier, Mr P. K. Hancock, Mr E. W. Jones, Mr P. S. G. Nicholas, Mrs V. L. Nicholas, M. S. Saunders.

463 MRS DIANNE SAYER, Penrith
Postal: **Town End Farm, Hackthorpe, Penrith, Cumbria, CA10 2HX**
Contacts: **PHONE 01931 712245 MOBILE 07980 295316**

1 **BALKING (FR)**, 4, ch g Balko (FR)—Anaqueen (FR) **Mr G. N. Critchley**
2 **BEENO (IRE)**, 13, b g Exit To Nowhere (USA)—Kay Theatre (IRE) **Mrs Margaret Coppola & Mrs Dianne Sayer**
3 **BERTIE'S BALLET**, 4, b g Albaasil (IRE)—More Ballet Money **Falcon's Line Ltd**
4 **CALLIOPE**, 9, b m Poet's Voice—Costa Brava (IRE) **Mr E. G. Tunstall**
5 **CHARLIE UBERALLES**, 6, ch g Geordieland (FR)—Sovereignoftheseas **Mr G. N. Critchley**
6 4, B g Shirocco (GER)—Cool Baranca (GER)
7 **DETECTIVE**, 6, b g Kingman—Promising Lead **A. Slack**
8 **FRIGHTENED RABBIT (USA)**, 10, b g Hard Spun (USA)—Champagne Ending (USA) **Mr R. A. Harrison**
9 **IDILICO (FR)**, 7, b g Lawman (FR)—Ydillique (IRE) **Mr Dennis J. Coppola & Mrs Dianne Sayer**
10 **IOLANI (GER)**, 10, b g Sholokhov (IRE)—Imogen (GER) **SJD Racing & Dianne Sayer**
11 **JACKHAMMER (IRE)**, 8, b g Thewayyouare (USA)—Ask Annie (IRE) **Margaret Coppola & Dianne Sayer**
12 **MILLIE THE MINX (IRE)**, 8, b m Medicean—Popocatepetl (FR) **A. R. White**
13 **PEPITE FLEURIE (IRE)**, 5, m Telescope (IRE)—Pepite Rose (FR) **Falcon's Line Ltd**
14 **PROPAGATION (IRE)**, 4, b g Acclamation—Thakerah (IRE) **A. R. White**
15 **REDARNA**, 8, ch g Aqlaam—Curtains **Graham Lund & Dianne Sayer**
16 **SAMS ROSEABELLE**, 6, b m Black Sam Bellamy (IRE)—Cashback Rose (IRE) **Mrs M. R. Lewis**
17 **SUMMER LIGHTENING**, 8, gr m Fair Mix (IRE)—Kristineau **Messrs A & R Lyle**
18 **THE NAVIGATOR**, 7, gr g Mastercraftsman (IRE)—Blessing (USA) **Mr G. H. Bell**
19 **TICO TIMES (IRE)**, 9, br g Arcadio (GER)—Roomier (IRE) **Mrs D. E. Slack**
20 **TONTO'S SPIRIT**, 10, b g Authorized (IRE)—Desert Royalty (IRE) **A. Slack**

Other Owners: Mr D. J. Coppola, Mrs M. Coppola, Mr G. Lund, Mrs A. Lyle, Mr J. R. Lyle, R. Lyle, Mr S. Nicholson, S J D Racing, Mrs H. D. Sayer.

Assistant Trainer: Miss Joanna Sayer.

Amateur Jockey: Miss Liz Butterworth, Miss Emma Sayer.

464 DR JON SCARGILL, Newmarket
Postal: **Red House Stables, Hamilton Road, Newmarket, Suffolk, CB8 0TE**
Contacts: **PHONE 01638 667767 MOBILE 07785 350705**
EMAIL jdscargill@gmail.com WEBSITE www.jonscargill.co.uk

1 **DISARMING (IRE)**, 5, b m War Command (USA)—Gloved Hand **Dr Edna Robson & Partner**
2 **IMAGEMAKER**, 4, b f Slade Power (IRE)—Publilia **Dr Edna Robson & Partner**
3 **LOVE POEMS (IRE)**, 5, b m Camelot—Dansable (IRE) **Theme Tune Partnership**
4 **MISTER SWIFT**, 4, ch g Eagle Top—Speedy Senorita (IRE) **J P T Partnership**
5 **MY PERFECT COUSIN**, 8, b g Showcasing—Torver **Silent Partners**
6 **PLACATED**, 4, b f Archipenko (USA)—Cosseted **Stuart Howard & Gb Horseracing**
7 **VERTICAL**, 4, ch f Al Kazeem—Greenery (IRE) **Dr Edna Robson & Partner**

Other Owners: GB Horseracing, Mr S. J. Howard, Dr E. M. Robson, Mr P.J. Scargill, Mrs S. M. Scargill.

465 MR DERRICK SCOTT, Minehead
Postal: **East Lynch, Minehead, Somerset, TA24 8SS**
Contacts: **PHONE 01643 702430 FAX 01643 702430**

1 **ACTONETAKETWO**, 12, b m Act One—Temple Dancer **Mrs R. Scott**
2 **ROYBUOY**, 15, b g Royal Applause—Wavy Up (IRE) **Mrs R. Scott**

NH Jockey: James Best.

466 **MR GEORGE SCOTT, Newmarket**
Postal: **Eve Lodge Stables, Hamilton Road, Hamilton Road, Newmarket, Suffolk, CB8 0NY**
Contacts: WORK **07833 461294**
EMAIL **george@georgescottracing.com** WEBSITE **www.georgescottracing.com**

1 **JACK THE TRUTH (IRE)**, 8, ch g Dandy Man (IRE)—Friendly Heart (CAN) **Mr J. Stephenson**
2 **MELLYS FLYER**, 4, b g Dandy Man (IRE)—Azhar **Investasurge Consulting Ltd**
3 **MISS MULLIGAN (IRE)**, 5, b m Gleneagles (IRE)—Banimpire (IRE) **Mr C. O. P. Hanbury**
4 **PRYDWEN (IRE)**, 4, b g Camelot—Honey Hunter (IRE) **Blue StaRR Racing**
5 **SIMULATION THEORY (IRE)**, 4, ch g Starspangledbanner (AUS)—Barawin (IRE) **Ms E. L. Banks**
6 **STRAWBERRY JACK**, 6, b g Foxwedge (AUS)—Strawberry Leaf **Mr J. Stephenson**
7 **TRIBUNA UFFIZI (IRE)**, 4, b g Zoffany (IRE)—Bunood (IRE) **Mr E Williams & Partner**

THREE-YEAR-OLDS

8 **ANOTHER ODYSSEY**, b g Ulysses (IRE)—Heho **Ms E Banks, Mr A Cooper & Mr M Lilley**
9 **BEDFORD HOUSE**, b g Dabirsim (FR)—Akhmatova **Offthebridle Podcast II**
10 **CAPTAIN KANE**, ch g Ulysses (IRE)—Foundation Filly **Bluestarr Racing & Partners**
11 **CLOCH NUA**, b g Exceed And Excel (AUS)—Lady Alienor (IRE) **Mr P. Trainor**
12 **EXCEEDINGLY SONIC**, ch f Exceed And Excel (AUS)—Modify **Mr M. Chan**
13 **HIGHLIGHTER (IRE)**, b g Australia—Cosmic Fire (FR) **Niarchos Family**
14 **KICK ON GIRL (IRE)**, b f Vadamos (FR)—Elkmait **Mr E. P. Babington**
15 **LOVE NEVER ENDING**, b f Siyouni (FR)—Encore L'Amour **Mr E. W. B. Williams**
16 **MISTRIX (IRE)**, b f Vadamos (FR)—Plus Ca Change (IRE) **Candour House & Partner Ii**
17 **RUBBELDIEKATZ**, b f Helmet (AUS)—For Henry (IRE) **Mr R. A. H. Evans**
18 B c No Nay Never (USA)—Sandglass
19 **T MAXIE (IRE)**, b f Swiss Spirit—Filatelia (IRE) **Mr D. Underwood**
20 **TIME LAPSE (IRE)**, b f Dark Angel (IRE)—Synchronic (IRE) **Niarchos Family**

TWO-YEAR-OLDS

21 Ch f 24/01 Starspangledbanner (AUS)—Abend (IRE) (Sea The Stars (IRE)) (19048)
22 B f 29/02 James Garfield (IRE)—Angel de La Gesse (FR) (Dark Angel (IRE)) (21905) **The Grey Racehorse**
23 **CARIAD**, b f 12/02 Cityscape—Edge of Love (Kyllachy) (5000) **Mr E. W. B. Williams**
24 **CHAPPY'S CAB (IRE)**, b c 12/02 Profitable (IRE)—Frabrika (IRE) (Intense Focus (USA)) (9000) **Mr D. Underwood**
25 **COCO JACK (IRE)**, b c 20/04 Wings of Eagles (FR)—Bright Morning (USA) (Storm Cat (USA)) (15238)
26 B c 01/02 Sioux Nation (USA)—Enliven (Dansili) (26000) **The Pals**
27 B c 03/05 Dandy Man (IRE)—Fashion Central (Dubawi (IRE)) (12381)
28 **GOOSE ROCK (IRE)**, b c 21/04 Mehmas (IRE)—Drifting Spirit (IRE) (Clodovil (IRE)) (100000)
29 Ch f 23/02 Decorated Knight—Happy Life (IRE) (Casamento (IRE)) (4000)
30 Gr f 18/03 El Kabeir (USA)—Little Audio (IRE) (Shamardal (USA)) (85714) **Ms E. L. Banks**
31 B c 10/03 Washington DC (IRE)—Minty Fox (Dalakhani (IRE)) (10000) **Mr M. J. Lilley**
32 B f 22/04 Caravaggio (USA)—Peloponnese (FR) (Montjeu (IRE)) **Niarchos Family**
33 Ch g 25/02 Iffraaj—Place de Moscou (IRE) (Rock of Gibraltar (IRE)) (20000)
34 Ch c 07/02 Buratino (IRE)—Ribbon Royale (Royal Applause) (27000) **Mr F. A. A. Nass**
35 B c 25/02 Buratino (IRE)—Rinaria (IRE) (Tamayuz) (15000) **Mr F. A. A. Nass**
36 **ROCKET RODNEY**, b c 30/01 Dandy Man (IRE)—Alushta (Royal Applause) (18000)
37 B c 30/03 Dawn Approach (IRE)—Silver Moon (Exceed And Excel (AUS)) (17143)
38 **SPARE RIB**, b c 26/04 Ribchester (IRE)—Fortune Hunter (IRE) (High Chaparral (IRE)) (9524)
39 B c 04/04 Adaay (IRE)—Tamaara (IRE) (Sepoy (AUS)) (25000) **Offthebridle Podcast**
40 **YAHTZEE (IRE)**, b f 08/04 Gregorian (IRE)—Rahanna (GER) (Azamour (IRE)) (16000) **The Yahtzee Partnership**

Other Owners: Ms E. L. Banks, Blue StaRR Racing, Mr K. J. Breen, Candour house, Mrs Catherine Cashman, Mr A. K. Cooper, Mr M. J. Lilley, Miss A. Mant, Mr A. P. Rogers, Mr G. O. Scott, The Grey Racehorse 1, Mr M. Walsh, Mr E. W. B. Williams.

467 MR JEREMY SCOTT, Dulverton

Postal: **Higher Holworthy Farm, Brompton Regis, Dulverton, Somerset, TA22 9NY**
Contacts: **WORK 01398 371414 MOBILE 07709 279483**
EMAIL holworthyfarm@yahoo.com WEBSITE Jeremyscottracing.net
INSTAGRAM @jeremyscottracing

1 **BALLYBLACK (IRE)**, 6, b g Shirocco (GER)—Papion Lady (IRE) **George & Glenda Giles**
2 **BAMPTON STAR**, 5, b g Kayf Tara—United (GER) **George & Glenda Giles**
3 **BONZA BOY**, 5, ch g Schiaparelli (GER)—Purple Patch **Mr G. T. Lever**
4 **CELTIC ART (FR)**, 5, ch g Mastercraftsman (IRE)—Irish Song (FR) **Mr J. P. Carrington**
5 **CHAMPAGNE COURT (IRE)**, 9, b g Court Cave (IRE)—Lady Taipan (IRE) **Coles, Smith, McManus & Broughton**
6 **CHAMPERSGALORE**, 5, b g Bollin Eric—Anomalous **Air Cdre Hallam & Mrs Martin Hallam**
7 **CHRISTOPHER CLIVE**, 4, b g Mountain High (IRE)—Badb Catha (IRE) **Mr G. F. Mugleston**
8 **CLONDAW DANCER (IRE)**, 8, b g Big Bad Bob (IRE)—Berocco (IRE) **Friends From Insurance**
9 **DASHEL DRASHER**, 9, b g Passing Glance—So Long **Mrs B Tully & Mr R Lock**
10 **DE YOUNG WARRIOR**, 9, b g Schiaparelli (GER)—Nobratinetta (FR) **Mrs H. L. Stoneman**
11 **DRASH ON RUBY**, 6, b m Passing Glance—So Long **Mrs B Tully & Mr R Lock**
12 **EMBERSCOMBE (IRE)**, 5, br m Califet (FR)—Market Niche (IRE) **The Exmoor Partners**
13 **KELTUS (FR)**, 12, gr g Keltos (FR)—Regina d'Orthe (FR) **Fistral Beach Ltd**
14 **KISSESFORKATIE (IRE)**, 8, b m Jeremy (USA)—Now Were Broke (IRE) **Derek Coles & Ian Gosden**
15 **KURAKA**, 8, b g Cacique (IRE)—Puzzling **Mrs S. A. Frost**
16 **LADY KK (IRE)**, 7, br m Shirocco (GER)—Lissard Lady (IRE) **Friends From Insurance**
17 **LEISSIERES EXPRESS**, 5, b g Telescope (IRE)—Maria Antonia (IRE) **Kit James & Matt James**
18 **MANOFMANYWORDS**, 10, b g Sulamani (IRE)—Spread The Word **Mrs P. J. Pengelly**
19 **MR MARS MAN**, 6, b g Schiaparelli (GER)—Arctic Magic (IRE) **Midd Shire Racing**
20 **NATIVE ROBIN (IRE)**, 12, br g Robin des Pres (FR)—Homebird (IRE) **Mr P. D. Moore**
21 **PETITEALFIE**, 6, b g Rocamadour—Rush House (IRE) **Mrs A. E. Baker**
22 **PETTICOAT LUCY (IRE)**, 6, b m Fame And Glory—Matties Isle (IRE) **Mr I F Gosden & Mr Dj Coles**
23 **PHOENIX RISEN**, 5, ch g Conduit (IRE)—Tchatchacoya (FR) **Mike & Maggie Horton**
24 **PILSDON PEN**, 5, b g Helmet (AUS)—Bisou **Mr D. E. Langley**
25 **PRIDE OF NEPAL**, 4, b g The Gurkha (IRE)—Best Regards (IRE) **The Punchestown Syndicate**
26 4, B g Kayf Tara—Shanxi Girl
27 **SIENNA ROYALE (IRE)**, 8, b m Sholokhov (IRE)—Dartmeet (IRE) **Air Cdre Hallam & Mrs Martin Hallam**
28 **SIZABLE SAM**, 7, ch g Black Sam Bellamy (IRE)—Halo Flora **The Hopefuls & Kelvin-hughes**
29 4, Ch f Dunaden—So Long **Mrs C. C. Scott**
30 4, B f Telescope (IRE)—Solid Land (FR)
31 **STORMY FLIGHT (IRE)**, 8, gr g Cloudings (IRE)—Help Yourself (IRE) **Mr Ian Murray & Mr Dave Smith**
32 5, B g Snow Sky—Suny House
33 **THAT OLE CHESTNUT (IRE)**, 7, ch g Fracas (IRE)—Minnie Turbo (IRE) **The Exmoor High Hopes**
34 **THE PLIMSOLL LINE**, 6, b g Dylan Thomas (IRE)—Patsy Choice (IRE) **Dave Smith & Mike Wright**
35 **THE RUSSIAN DOYEN (IRE)**, 9, b g Doyen (IRE)—Namloc (IRE) **Mr J. H. Frost**
36 **TIKKINTHEBOX (IRE)**, 10, b g Tikkanen (USA)—Surfing France (FR) **On A Mission**
37 **VILLANY (GER)**, 4, ch g Lord of England (GER)—Veligandu (GER)
38 **WAVERING DOWN (IRE)**, 7, b g Jeremy (USA)—Gortbofearna (IRE) **Mr J. H. Frost**

Other Owners: Mr S. W. Broughton, Mr D. J. Coles, Mrs G. D. Giles, Mr G. R. Giles, Mr I. F. Gosden, Mrs M. Hallam, Air Commodore M. R. Hallam, Mr M. Horton, Mrs M. Horton, Mr C. J. James, Mr M. J. James, Mrs E. A. Kelvin-Hughes, Mr & Mrs R. G. Kelvin-Hughes, R. G. Kelvin-Hughes, Mr R. J. Lock, Mr B. J. McManus, I. R. Murray, Mrs C. C. Scott, Mr J. R. M. Scott, Mr B. D. Smith, David H. Smith, The Hopefuls, Mrs B. J. Tully, Mr R. M. E. Wright.

Assistant Trainer: Camilla Scott, **Head Girl:** Laura Scott, **Racing Secretary:** Joe Scott,

Yard Sponsor: Chris Hendy Brendon Powerwashers.

NH Jockey: Rex Dingle, Matt Griffiths. **Conditional Jockey:** David Pritchard.

468 MISS KATIE SCOTT, Galashiels
Postal: **Stables Cottage, Millhaugh, Lindean, Galashiels, Scottish Borders**
Contacts: **MOBILE 07826 344577**

1 **4**, B br f Al Kazeem—Blaise Chorus (IRE) **Gallus Stud**
2 **BOLD LIGHT (IRE)**, 5, ch g Leading Light (IRE)—Turmoss (FR) **Mr J. Scott**
3 **COLINTON**, 4, b g Red Jazz (USA)—Magic Maisie **Star Racing**
4 **ELLADORA**, 4, b f Equiano (FR)—Somersault **Stevens Taylor Clark Raeburn Scott**
5 **FLAMING GLORY (IRE)**, 8, b g Gold Well—Pearlsforthegirls **Miss K. Scott**
6 **GETAWAY GERRY**, 8, b g Getaway (GER)—Loch Dhu (IRE) **Mark Boyd, Andrew Machray, Murray Scott**
7 **GREY TIKKANA**, 7, gr m Tikkanen (USA)—Think Green **Mr R. M. Boyd**
8 **GWEEDORE**, 5, b g Epaulette (AUS)—Ares Choix **Lamont Racing**
9 **NELLIE FRENCH (IRE)**, 5, b m Dragon Pulse (IRE)—Texas Ruby (USA) **Mrs S. Scott**
10 **ROCKLEY POINT**, 9, b g Canford Cliffs (IRE)—Statua (IRE) **The Vintage Flyers**
11 **SLAINTE MHATH**, 4, ch f Mayson—Ofelia (IRE) **Katie Scott Racing Syndicate**
12 **SPARTAKOS**, 4, b g Rajsaman (FR)—Medicean Bliss **Making Headway Racing**
13 **4**, B g Fast Company (IRE)—Tagtale (IRE) **Star Racing**
14 **THAT'S YOUR LOTTIE**, 7, b m Imperial Monarch (GER)—Caoba **The Jackson Partnership**
15 **THE MACKEM TORPEDO**, 6, b g Multiplex—Gagajulu **Ursa Major Racing & Partner**
16 **TOP MEDICI**, 6, b g Mr Medici (IRE)—Think Green **Mr R. M. Boyd**

THREE-YEAR-OLDS
17 **SAMURAI SNEDDZ**, b g Highland Reel (IRE)—Self Centred **Paddock Panners & Katie Scott**

TWO-YEAR-OLDS
18 Ch f 09/05 Dandy Man (IRE)—Tipperary Boutique (IRE) (Danehill Dancer (IRE)) (12000) **Making Headway Racing**
19 B f 13/04 Dawn Approach (IRE)—Whisp (GER) (Rainbow Quest (USA)) (12000) **Lamont Racing**

Other Owners: Dr F. A. Evans, Mr M. W. Hay, Mr A. Machray, Paddock Panners, Mrs A. M. Rhind, Miss K. Scott, Mr W. M. Scott, Mr F. Smith, Mr S. J. Sneddon, Mr C. Talbot, Mr S. A. Taylor, URSA Major Racing, Mrs G. B. Walford.

469 MR MICHAEL SCUDAMORE, Bromsash
Postal: **Eccleswall Court, Bromsash, Nr. Ross-on-Wye, Herefordshire, HR9 7PP**
Contacts: **PHONE 01989 750844 MOBILE 07901 853520**
EMAIL michael.scu@btconnect.com **WEBSITE** www.michaelscudamoreracing.co.uk

1 **BLAZER TWO**, 4, b g Cable Bay (IRE)—Tamara Moon (IRE) **Mrs B. V. Evans**
2 **BLOW THE BUDGET**, 4, b f Kayf Tara—Roche d'Or **Mr P. E. Truscott**
3 **CALDWELL**, 5, b g Dansili—Milford Sound **A & N Dower**
4 **CENTS IN THE CITY**, 4, b g Cityscape—Six Cents (IRE) **Hunscote Stud Limited**
5 **COMMANDER OF TEN (IRE)**, 5, b g Doyen (IRE)—Some Sport (IRE) **Mrs L. Maclennan**
6 **COPPER COIN**, 9, ch g Sulamani (IRE)—Silken Pearls **Mr P. E. Truscott**
7 **COURT MASTER (IRE)**, 9, b g Court Cave (IRE)—Lusos Wonder (IRE) **Mrs L. Maclennan**
8 **CZECH HER OUT (IRE)**, 8, b m Fame And Glory—Molly Hussey (IRE) **Having A Mare**
9 **DINSDALE**, 9, b g Cape Cross (IRE)—Emmy Award (IRE) **Gabby Gajova and Friends**
10 **DO YOUR JOB (IRE)**, 8, b g Fame And Glory—Full of Birds (FR) **Mr M. P. Dunphy**
11 **ELUSIVE POLLY**, 5, b m Kalanisi (IRE)—Parlez Vous
12 **ENVOL DE LA COUR (FR)**, 8, b g Maresca Sorrento (FR)—Reveuse de La Cour (FR) **Mr M. P. Dunphy**
13 **ESPECIALLY SO**, 7, br m So You Think (NZ)—Behra (IRE)
14 **FAITQUE DE L'ISLE (FR)**, 7, ch g Secret Singer (FR)—Naiade de L'Isle (FR)
DFA Racing (Donaldson, Currie, Edwards)
15 **FANCY SHAPES (IRE)**, 8, ch m Golden Lariat (USA)—Panglao Island (IRE) **Wink N' A Drink**
16 **FAR HORIZON (IRE)**, 4, b g Free Eagle (IRE)—Sparkling View (IRE) **Mr M. P. Dunphy**
17 **FIX AT ALL (FR)**, 6, b g No Risk At All (FR)—Lady Fix (FR) **Mrs L. Maclennan**
18 **GRIS GRIS TOP (FR)**, 6, gr g Gris de Gris (FR)—Tiptop Hugaux (FR) **Mrs L. Maclennan**
19 **HERECOMESFREDDIE**, 4, b g Gregorian (IRE)—Forever Loved **Racehorse Friends Partnership**

MR MICHAEL SCUDAMORE - continued

20 **HEY FRANKIE (IRE)**, 6, gr m Mahler—Flaming Poncho (IRE) **Mr M. P. Dunphy**
21 **HORIZON BLEU (FR)**, 5, b g Spanish Moon (USA)—Lili Bleue (FR) **Mrs L. Maclennan**
22 **ILLUSIVE APPEAL**, 6, b m Universal (IRE)—Eluding
23 **KARLIE**, 7, b m Schiaparelli (GER)—Deianira (IRE) **Mr M. P. Dunphy**
24 **LEBOWSKI (IRE)**, 7, b g Aizavoski (IRE)—Castle Supreme (IRE) **Mr M. P. Dunphy**
25 **LET IT SHINE**, 4, bl g Pether's Moon (IRE)—My Belle (FR) **Mr M. P. Dunphy**
26 **LET ME ENTERTAIN U**, 6, gr g Saint des Saints (FR)—My Belle (FR) **Mr M. P. Dunphy**
27 **MOFASA**, 6, b g Ocovango—Ninna Nanna (FR) **Mrs L. Maclennan**
28 **MR CHUA (IRE)**, 6, b g Cape Cross—Shama's Song (IRE) **Mr C. G. J. Chua**
29 **NADA TO PRADA**, 7, b m Kayf Tara—Ambrosia's Promise (IRE) **Mrs L. Maclennan**
30 **NORTHERN BEAU (IRE)**, 9, b m Canford Cliffs (IRE)—View (IRE) **Lynne & Angus Maclennan**
31 **PRINCESS OF MERCIA**, 5, b m Blue Bresil (FR)—Very Special One (IRE)
32 **ROBBIE DAZZLER**, 5, ch g Leading Light (IRE)—Mrs Roberts **Having A Mare**
33 **ROBIN DES THEATRE (IRE)**, 7, b br m Robin des Champs (FR)—Shannon Theatre (IRE) **Mr M. P. Dunphy**
34 **ROLFE REMBRANDT**, 4, ch g Dutch Art—Rebecca Rolfe **Hunscote Stud Limited**
35 **SASHENKA (GER)**, 6, b m Maxios—Sarabia (GER) **N. Pickett**
36 **SATURN 'N SILK**, 7, b m Universal (IRE)—Manaphy (FR) **Mr P. E. Truscott**
37 **SINURITA (IRE)**, 6, b m Yeats (IRE)—Hard To Please (IRE) **Mrs L. Maclennan**
38 **SOME CHAOS (IRE)**, 11, b g Brian Boru—Iruna Iris (IRE) **Mason Scudamore Racing**
39 **SON OF UHTRED (IRE)**, 5, b g Milan—Ballynarry (IRE)
40 **SUMELIA**, 7, ch m Sulamani (FR)—Aimela (FR) **Mr M. Scudamore, Mr P. E. Truscott**
41 **THE CRAZED MOON (IRE)**, 10, b m Yeats (IRE)—Rose Gallery (FR) **Mr M. P. Dunphy**
42 **THOR DE CERISY (FR)**, 8, b g Enrique—Midalisy (FR) **Mrs L. Maclennan**
43 **THYME 'N' TYDE (IRE)**, 4, b f Lucky Speed (IRE)—High Priestess (IRE) **Mr M. Scudamore, Mr P. E. Truscott**
44 **UPTON ROAD (IRE)**, 8, b g Jeremy (USA)—Reynard's Glen (IRE) **Mr M. R. Blandford**
45 **VINA BAY**, 4, b g New Bay—Danvina (IRE) **N. Pickett**

THREE-YEAR-OLDS

46 **IL GRUSCHEN (IRE)**, b g Free Eagle (IRE)—Topaz Clear (IRE) **Mr M. G. Savidge**

Other Owners: Mrs A. C. Dower, Mr N. Dower, Hunscote Stud Ltd & Michael Scudamore, Mr A. Maclennan, Mrs L. Maclennan, Mr A. Mason, Mr J. J. Murray, Mrs J. M. Murray, Mr John J Murray & Mrs Lynne MacLennan, Mr S. Robson, A & Scudamore, Mr M. Scudamore, Mrs M. L. Scudamore, Mark & Michael Scudamore, Mrs L. J. Sluman, Mr P. E. Truscott & Mr M. Scudamore.

Racing Secretary: Marilyn Scudamore.

NH Jockey: Richard Patrick, Ben Poste, Brendan Powell, Tom Scudamore.

---

470 ## MR DEREK SHAW, Sproxton
Postal: **The Sidings, Saltby Road, Sproxton, Melton Mowbray, Leicestershire, LE14 4RA**
Contacts: **PHONE** 01476 860578 **MOBILE** 07721 039645 **FAX** 01476 860578
EMAIL mail@derekshawracing.com **WEBSITE** www.derekshawracing.com

1 **AMAZING AMAYA**, 7, b m New Approach (IRE)—Faslen (USA) **P. E. Barrett**
2 **ANITA'S SPIRIT**, 5, b m Indian Haven—Sasheen **Mr J. Souster**
3 **CEDAR CAGE**, 5, b g Golden Horn—Faslen (USA) **P. E. Barrett**
4 **DAAFY (USA)**, 5, b g The Factor (USA)—Ishraak (USA) **Mr D. Shaw**
5 **DIAMOND MEMORIES**, 4, b f Due Diligence (USA)—Shaws Diamond (USA) **Mrs L. J. Shaw**
6 **DUBAI ELEGANCE**, 8, ch m Sepoy (AUS)—Some Sunny Day **Million Dreams Racing 1**
7 **FARHHSICAL**, 5, b g Farhh—Nabat Sultan **Mrs L. J. Shaw**
8 **HALA BE ZAIN (IRE)**, 4, b f Zoffany (IRE)—We Are Ninety (IRE) **Mr D. Shaw**
9 **JACK BEAN**, 4, b g Golden Horn—Faslen (USA) **P. E. Barrett**
10 **JAZZ MUSIC**, 5, b m Muhaarar—Propel (IRE) **Mrs L. J. Shaw**
11 **JUMIRA BRIDGE**, 8, b g Invincible Spirit (IRE)—Zykina **Mr N. P. Franklin**
12 **LADY IRIS**, 5, ch m Sepoy (AUS)—Button Moon (IRE) **P. E. Barrett**
13 **LITTLEMISSATTITUDE**, 5, b m Due Diligence (USA)—Lady Elalmadol (IRE) **Million Dreams Racing 1**

MR DEREK SHAW - continued

14 **PISELLI MOLLI (IRE)**, 4, ch f Dragon Pulse (IRE)—Dancing Duchess (IRE) P. E. Barrett
15 **PRINCE ABU (IRE)**, 5, gr g Dark Angel (IRE)—Saoirse Abu (USA) **Million Dreams Racing**
16 **SAMPHIRE COAST**, 9, b g Fastnet Rock (AUS)—Faslen (USA) P. E. Barrett
17 **SEABOROUGH (IRE)**, 7, b g Born To Sea (IRE)—Nobilissima (IRE) **Mr J. Souster**
18 **SIX STRINGS**, 8, b g Requinto (IRE)—Island Music (IRE) **Million Dreams Racing**
19 **SPIRIT OF HEAVEN**, 4, b g Swiss Spirit—Cool Image **Shawthing Racing Partnership & L Shaw**
20 **THE TRON**, 4, gr g Outstrip—Ming Meng (IRE) P. E. Barrett
21 **ULYSSES (GER)**, 8, b g Sinndar (IRE)—Ungarin (GER) **Million Dreams Racing**
22 **YOU'RE COOL**, 10, b g Exceed And Excel (AUS)—Ja One (IRE) **Mr D. Bichan**

THREE-YEAR-OLDS

23 **MADAME FENELLA**, b f Due Diligence (USA)—Fenella Fudge **Mrs L. J. Shaw**
24 **MISS BELLADONNA**, b f Brazen Beau (AUS)—Ming Meng (IRE) P. E. Barrett
25 **MR FUNKY MONKEY**, b g Hellvelyn—Nabat Sultan **Mrs L. J. Shaw**
26 **MR GINJA NINJA**, ch g Coach House (IRE)—Divasesque (IRE) **Mrs L. J. Shaw**
27 **TORSHI**, b f Muhaarar—Pickle P. E. Barrett

TWO-YEAR-OLDS

28 B c 17/03 Expert Eye—Faslen (USA) (Fasliyev (USA)) (30000)
29 B c 01/04 Bobby's Kitten (USA)—Kip (Rip Van Winkle (IRE))
30 B f 19/04 Hellvelyn—Naralsaif (IRE) (Arcano (IRE))
31 Gr f 19/04 Outstrip—Princess Heidi (IRE) (Intikhab (USA))

Other Owners: Million Dreams Racing, Mr I. D. Sellens, Mr D. Shaw, Mrs L. J. Shaw, Shawthing Racing Partnership.

Yard Sponsor: N & L Franklin Ltd.

---

471 **MRS FIONA SHAW, Dorchester**
Postal: **Skippet Cottage, Bradford Peverell, Dorchester, Dorset, DT2 9SE**
Contacts: **PHONE 01305 889350 MOBILE 07970 370444**
EMAIL fiona.shaw05@gmail.com

1 **BENVILLE BRIDGE**, 5, b g Bollin Eric—Kiwi Katie **John & Heather Snook**
2 **BROADOAK**, 7, b g Kayf Tara—Bird Without Wings (IRE) **John & Heather Snook**
3 **ETINCELLE ARTISTE (FR)**, 5, b g Great Pretender (IRE)—Forcat (FR) **Miss A. E. Fletcher**
4 **HYMN AND A PRAYER**, 9, br g Eastern Anthem (IRE)—Kryssa **Mrs F. M. Shaw**
5 **KIWI LING**, 7, br m Bollin Eric—Kiwi Katie **John & Heather Snook**
6 **MAX WOLF**, 5, ch g Schiaparelli (GER)—Cerise Sauvage
7 4, B g Arvico (FR)—Petite Pois
8 **SHOW ON THE ROAD**, 11, b g Flemensfirth (USA)—Roses of Picardy (IRE) **Mrs F. M. Shaw**
9 **SURE LISTEN (FR)**, 5, ch g Diamond Boy (FR)—Califea (FR) **Miss A. E. Fletcher**

Other Owners: Mrs H. A. Snook, J. W. Snook.

---

472 **MR MATT SHEPPARD, Ledbury**
Postal: **Home Farm Cottage, Eastnor, Ledbury, Herefordshire, HR8 1RD**
Contacts: **MOBILE 07770 625061 FAX 01531 634846**
EMAIL matthew.sheppard@cmail.co.uk

1 **ALWAYS ABLE (IRE)**, 7, b m Stowaway—Twotrailerparkgirl (IRE) **Veronica Silber & Marcus Jordan**
2 **BALIYAD (IRE)**, 7, gr g Sea The Stars (IRE)—Baliyana (IRE) **Mrs N. Sheppard**
3 **CAPTAIN GRINNAWAY (IRE)**, 5, b g Dylan Thomas (IRE)—Drumlynn Lass (IRE) **Miss M. Peterson**
4 **KESTREL VALLEY**, 8, b m Dr Massini (IRE)—Lady Karinga **Mrs J. M. Johnson**

MR MATT SHEPPARD - continued

    5 **NOT AVAILABLE (IRE)**, 7, b g Milan—Miss Arteea (IRE) **Mr A. J. Scrivin**
    6 **ONE FER MAMMA (IRE)**, 6, b g Dylan Thomas (IRE)—Miss Martel (IRE) **D. K. Yearsley**
    7 **POTTLERATH (IRE)**, 7, b g Yeats (IRE)—Truffle Fairy (IRE) **Lost In The Summer Wine**
    8 **WRONG WAY HARRY (IRE)**, 7, b g Carlotamix (FR)—Howrwelooking (IRE) **Cheltenhambuild Ltd**

Other Owners: Mr M. J. Jordan, Mrs H. V. Silber.

NH Jockey: Stan Sheppard.

---

473   **MR OLIVER SHERWOOD, Upper Lambourn**
Postal: **Neardown Stables, Upper Lambourn, Hungerford, Berkshire, RG17 8QP**
Contacts: **PHONE 01488 71411 MOBILE 07979 591867 FAX 01488 72786**
EMAIL oliver.sherwood@virgin.net WEBSITE www.oliversherwood.co.uk

    1 **A TIME TO SHINE (IRE)**, 7, b br g Malinas (GER)—Royal Bride **Tim Syder & Dominic Burke**
    2 **BABY SPICE**, 4, b f Kendargent (FR)—Blast Furnace (IRE) **Apiafi, Frost & Black**
    3 **BALLAQUANE (IRE)**, 7, b g Scorpion (IRE)—Barreenagh Beag (IRE) **Exors of the Late Mr T. J. Hemmings**
    4 **BEMBRIDGE (IRE)**, 6, b g Westerner—Brotenstown (IRE) **Mr J. Palmer-Brown**
    5 **BRUMMIE BOYS (IRE)**, 7, b g Flemensfirth (USA)—Bobs Article (IRE) **Mr Andrew Cohen & Mr Alan Kaplan**
    6 **CAPTAIN LARA (IRE)**, 4, b g Maxios—La Superba (IRE) **M. H. Dixon**
    7 **CILAOS GLACE (FR)**, 9, br g Voix du Nord (FR)—Miss Glacee (FR) **Heart of the South Racing 118**
    8 4, Br g Soldier of Fortune (IRE)—Coco des Champs (IRE) **Mr O. M. C. Sherwood**
    9 **COSSACK DANCER**, 6, br g Sholokhov (IRE)—Lecon Benefique (IRE) **Bryan & Philippa Burrough**
  10 **CRYPTO CURRENCY (IRE)**, 5, b g Yeats (IRE)—Jeunopse (IRE) **Mr T. D. J. Syder**
  11 **DEVONSHIRE ROCCO (IRE)**, 6, b g Shirocco (GER)—Duplicate Daughter (IRE) **Mrs S. A. White**
  12 **EAST BRIDGE (IRE)**, 6, b g Shirocco (GER)—Ballinahow Lady (IRE) **Exors of the Late Mr T. J. Hemmings**
  13 **FEODORA**, 7, b m Kayf Tara—La Harde (FR) **Mr R. Chugg**
  14 4, Ch f Getaway (GER)—Gambling Girl (IRE) **A & E Galvin**
  15 **GUERLAIN DE VAUX (FR)**, 6, b g Tiger Groom—Que du Charmil (FR) **Million in Mind Partnership**
  16 **HAVANELLA (IRE)**, 5, b m Saddler Maker (IRE)—Kavalle (FR) **The 4 Musketeers**
  17 **IMPERIAL MONARCH (IRE)**, 6, b g Imperial Monarch (IRE)—Ebony Hope (IRE) **Michael Fiddy & Richard Fleming**
  18 **JERSEY BEAN (IRE)**, 9, b g Court Cave (IRE)—Jennifers Diary (IRE) **Mr A. Taylor**
  19 **JERSEY LADY (FR)**, 6, ch m Martaline—La Bombonera (FR) **Mr A. Taylor**
  20 **JERSEY WONDER (IRE)**, 6, ch g Zoffany (IRE)—Magena (USA) **Mr A. Taylor**
  21 **LITTLE AWKWARD (FR)**, 6, gr g Montmartre (FR)—Seven Even (FR) **Michael Fiddy & Richard Fleming**
  22 **LOS HERMANOS (FR)**, 5, b g Sinndar (IRE)—La Dauvilla (FR) **The Neardowners**
  23 **MACLAINE**, 5, ch g Masked Marvel—Aisance (FR) **Mr T. D. J. Syder**
  24 **MAKETY**, 8, ch m Black Sam Bellamy (IRE)—Mi Money **Mrs S. A. White**
  25 **MANNING ESTATE (IRE)**, 8, b g Stowaway—Specifiedrisk (IRE) **Mr & Mrs Norman**
  26 **MILLY'S DAUGHTER**, 5, b m Geordieland (FR)—Mischievous Milly (IRE) **A Stewart & A Taylor**
  27 **MINELLA ROYALE**, 9, b g Shirocco (GER)—Lisa du Chenet (FR) **Minella Royale Partnership**
  28 **MISTERSISTER (FR)**, 5, gr g Wootton Bassett—Peace Mime (CAN) **Mr R. N. Frosell**
  29 4, B c Telescope (IRE)—Moonlight Music (IRE) **Mr M. A. Sherwood**
  30 **NAZWA (IRE)**, 4, b g Sepoy (AUS)—Kahalah Fantasy **Quicksilver Racing Partnership**
  31 **NEWTONIAN**, 5, b g Telescope (IRE)—Mi Money **Mr P. Mellett**
  32 **OCEAN DRIFTER (IRE)**, 7, b g Aizavoski (IRE)—Driftaway (IRE) **Mr T. D. J. Syder**
  33 **PEUR DE RIEN (FR)**, 9, b g Kapgarde (FR)—Tango Princess (FR) **Peur de Rien Syndicate**
  34 **PUFFIN BAY**, 5, b m Blue Bresil (FR)—Miss Rocco **E. R. Hanbury**
  35 **RAINBOW STORM (FR)**, 6, b g On Est Bien (IRE)—Rainbow Oceane (FR) **Our Racing Club**
  36 **REPUBLICAN**, 7, b g Kayf Tara—Noun de La Thinte (FR) **Mr E. J. Ware**
  37 **RHEBUS ROAD (IRE)**, 4, ch g Champs Elysees—Red Riddle (IRE) **Tim Syder & Dominic Burke**
  38 4, Gr g Malinas (GER)—Rosealainn (IRE) **Lady Thompson**
  39 **ROUGE ET BLANC (FR)**, 17, ch g Mansonnien (FR)—Fidelety (FR) **Mr O. M. C. Sherwood**
  40 **ROYAL LAKE (IRE)**, 6, b g Fame And Glory—Gran Chis (IRE) **Exors of the Late Mr T. J. Hemmings**

MR OLIVER SHERWOOD - continued

41 **SEASTON SPIRIT,** 9, b g Kayf Tara—Aphrodisias (FR) **Mr M. Fiddy**
42 **SPRINGTOWN LAKE (IRE),** 10, b g Gamut (IRE)—Sprightly Gal (IRE) **Mr T. D. J. Syder**
43 **TIMES ARE BLUE (IRE),** 4, b br g Champs Elysees—Times Are Grey (IRE) **Mr R. E. Kingston**
44 **TREVOR'S LAD (IRE),** 4, b g Milan—Jolie Landaise (FR) **Mr P. Mellett**
45 **VINTAGE RASCAL (FR),** 5, b g Nathaniel (IRE)—Irish Vintage (FR)
46 **WALK IN THE WILD (FR),** 6, b g Walk In The Park (IRE)—Sublimissime (FR) **Heart of the South Racing 121**
47 **WHAT'S OCCURRING (IRE),** 9, b g Rail Link—Lovely Origny (FR) **Mr Andrew Cohen & Mr Alan Kaplan**

Other Owners: Mr J. Apiafi, A. W. Black, Mr D. J. Burke, B. R. H. Burrough, Mrs P. J. Burrough, Mr A. L. Cohen, Mr M. Fiddy, Mr R. Fleming, Mr A. S. F. Frost, Mr E. Galvin, Alan Kaplan, Mr R. R. Norman, Mrs S. D. Norman, Mrs J. Rose, Mr O. M. C. Sherwood, Mr A. R. Stewart, Mr T. D. J. Syder, Mr A. Taylor.

Assistant Trainer: Andy Llewellyn, **Head Lad:** Stefan Namesansky, **Secretary:** Emma Chugg.

---

474 **MR OLIVER SIGNY, Lambourn**
Postal: **The Croft Stables, Upper Lambourn, Hungerford, Berkshire, RG17 8QH**
EMAIL oliver@oliversignyracing.com

1 **AGENT EMPIRE (GER),** 4, gr g Sidestep (AUS)—Adalea **Dunkley, Gumienny, Mackenzie & Signy**
2 **ANNUAL FLAVOUR (IRE),** 7, ch m Gamut (IRE)—Sprightly Gal (IRE) **Mrs F. Kempe**
3 **BE THE BEST (USA),** 6, b g Declaration of War (USA)—Memories For Us (USA) **Adam Signy and Ben Spiers**
4 **CHEF BOGO (FR),** 5, b g Balko (FR)—Ascella (FR) **Dunkley, Gumienny, Mackenzie & Signy**
5 **COACHMAN (FR),** 6, b g Maresca Sorrento (FR)—La Pelodette (FR) **Mrs S. McLean**
6 **COME DANCING (IRE),** 5, b g Fame And Glory—Minnie Ray (IRE) **Come Dancing Partnership**
7 **COURTLY LOVE,** 9, b m Kayf Tara—Tessanoora **Mrs S. McLean**
8 **DAVE AND BERNIE (IRE),** 7, b g Papal Bull—Iseult (IRE) **Oliver Signy Racing Club**
9 **DECORATED,** 4, ch g Nathaniel (IRE)—Trapeze **Mr O. Signy**
10 **ETAT MAJOR AULMES (FR),** 8, b g Della Francesca (USA)—River Gold Aulmes (FR) **Mr & Mrs A. Signy**
11 **FRENCH PARADOXE (FR),** 7, b g Day Flight—Sculture (FR) **Mick Fitzgerald Racing Club**
12 4, B f Vadamos (FR)—Isabella Glyn (IRE)
13 4, B g Ol' Man River (IRE)—Joan d'Arc (IRE)
14 **LAWD DYLAN (IRE),** 5, b g Dylan Thomas (IRE)—Vita Nuova (IRE) **The LSRFC SALVPS**
15 **MAD ABOUT SALLY (IRE),** 7, b br m Califet (FR)—Lou's Coole Girl (IRE) **Mr O. Signy**
16 **NO WORD OF A LIE,** 6, b g Milan—Agnese **Dunkley, Gumienny, Mackenzie & Signy**
17 **ROBIN DES FOX (IRE),** 6, b g Robin des Champs (FR)—Shesafoxylady (IRE) **I Barratt, A Signy & B Spiers**
18 **SAMBEZI (FR),** 6, b g Rajsaman (FR)—Tunis (FR) **Mrs S. McLean**
19 **SEA VILLAGE (IRE),** 4, b g Affinisea (IRE)—Etoile Margot (FR) **Mick Fitzgerald Racing Club**
20 **SOMETHING ROSIE (IRE),** 8, b m Gold Well—Pakaradyssa (FR) **Mrs F. Kempe**
21 **THE SCORPION KING,** 4, b g Scorpion (IRE)—Big Time Billy (IRE) **Mr & Mrs A. Signy**

Other Owners: Mrs C. J. Barratt, Mr I. J. Barratt, Mrs F. Kempe, Mr A. Signy, Mrs C. B. Signy, Mr O. Signy, Mr B. P. J. Spiers.

Head Lad: Albert Ennis, **Racing Secretary:** Mrs Katherine Signy.

475 **MR DAVID SIMCOCK, Newmarket**
Postal: **The Office, Trillium Place, Birdcage Walk, Newmarket, Suffolk, CB8 0NE**
Contacts: **PHONE 01638 662968 MOBILE 07808 954109, 07702 851561 FAX 01638 663888**
EMAIL david@davidsimcock.co.uk WEBSITE www.davidsimcock.co.uk

1 **AD INFINITUM**, 4, b f Golden Horn—Madame Hoi (IRE)
2 **APPROACH THE LAND**, 4, b g New Approach (IRE)—Royale Danehill (IRE)
3 **BLESS HIM (IRE)**, 8, b g Sea The Stars (IRE)—Happy Land (IRE)
4 **CLAP YOUR HANDS**, 6, b g Universal (IRE)—Woop Woop (IRE)
5 **DEAL A DOLLAR**, 6, b g Frankel—Cape Dollar (IRE)
6 **DEEP SIGH (FR)**, 4, b f Muhaarar—Sospira
7 **DUBAI EMPEROR (IRE)**, 4, b g Gleneagles (IRE)—Nateeja (IRE)
8 **FOLK DANCE**, 5, b m Golden Horn—Folk Opera (IRE)
9 **FORGE VALLEY LAD**, 5, b g Cityscape—Tamara
10 **HACKNESS HARRY**, 4, b g Swiss Spirit—Miss Fridaythorpe
11 **HEART OF THE SUN**, 4, b f Fastnet Rock (AUS)—Heartless
12 **HEATH RISE**, 4, b g Gleneagles (IRE)—Cubanita
13 **LOWER STREET**, 4, b f Kingman—Upper Street (IRE)
14 **MAGNETISED**, 4, b g Shamardal (USA)—Princess Nada
15 **MAN OF RIDDLES (USA)**, 4, b br g Temple City (USA)—Mien (USA)
16 **MINDSPIN**, 4, b g Shalaa (IRE)—Inner Sea (USA)
17 **MORLAIX**, 5, b g Mayson—Estemaala (IRE)
18 **OMNIVEGA (FR)**, 6, b g Siyouni (FR)—Vermentina (IRE)
19 **ORIENTAL ART**, 4, b g Archipenko (USA)—Robe Chinoise
20 **PREJUDICE**, 6, ch g Dubawi (IRE)—Ever Rigg
21 **RAAKIB ALHAWA (IRE)**, 6, b g Kingman—Starlet (IRE)
22 **RANI OF JHANSI**, 4, b f Invincible Spirit (IRE)—Madame Chiang
23 **REPERTOIRE**, 6, b g Bated Breath—Binche (USA)
24 **RODRIGO DIAZ**, 5, b g Golden Horn—Kitty Wells
25 **SCARBOROUGH CASTLE**, 5, b g Fastnet Rock (AUS)—Charlotte O Fraise (IRE)
26 **SMART CHAMPION**, 7, b g Teofilo (IRE)—Soryah (IRE)
27 **STARCZEWSKI (USA)**, 6, b g Magician (USA)—Lucifer's Stone (USA)
28 **TIGER CRUSADE (FR)**, 5, b g No Nay Never (USA)—Folle Allure (FR)
29 **UNIVERSAL ORDER**, 6, ch g Universal (IRE)—My Order

THREE-YEAR-OLDS

30 **ADJOURN**, ch g Postponed (IRE)—Micaela's Moon (USA)
31 **AIMING HIGH**, ch f Lope de Vega (IRE)—High Hopes
32 **ALBAYAADER (IRE)**, b f Kingman—Mubadarrat
33 **ALL ARE MINE (GER)**, ch c New Bay—Ardeola (GER)
34 B c Lemon Drop Kid (USA)—Bargain Blitz (USA)
35 **CASH (IRE)**, gr c Shamardal (USA)—Lady Rosamunde
36 B g Mastercraftsman (IRE)—Casila (IRE)
37 **CHING SHIH (IRE)**, b f Lope de Vega (IRE)—Madame Chiang
38 **CHOLA EMPIRE**, b c Territories (IRE)—Veena (FR)
39 **CLITHEROE**, ch f Ribchester (IRE)—Cheap Thrills
40 **CROMARTY (FR)**, b f Lope de Vega (IRE)—Carnachy (IRE)
41 **CUERNAVACA (FR)**, b f Lope de Vega (IRE)—Lady Darshaan (IRE)
42 **DALBY FOREST**, ch g Equiano (FR)—Primrose Valley
43 **FIRST DYNASTY (USA)**, b br c American Pharoah (USA)—Heavenly Thought (USA)
44 **FULFILLED**, b g Ulysses (IRE)—Zoella (USA)
45 **GLEN COVE (IRE)**, b g Ardad (IRE)—North East Bay (USA)
46 B g El Kabeir (USA)—Impasse
47 **KINGSTON JOY (IRE)**, b f Kingston Hill—Archetypal (IRE)
48 **KIWANO (FR)**, b c Dabirsim (FR)—Araca (FR)
49 B g Churchill (IRE)—La Corniche (FR)
50 **LIGHT INFANTRY (FR)**, ch c Fast Company (IRE)—Lights On Me
51 **MAKTOOB**, br g Awtaad (IRE)—Mudawanah
52 **MASTERCLASS**, gr g Lethal Force (IRE)—Kensington Gardens
53 B f Storm The Stars (USA)—Miss Carbonia (IRE)
54 **PINK HAZE (IRE)**, b f Lope de Vega (IRE)—Xaarienne

MR DAVID SIMCOCK - continued

55 B f Wootton Bassett—Reyamour
56 **THREE DIAMONDS**, b g Night of Thunder (IRE)—L'Eglise
57 **VIVE LA REINE**, b f Twilight Son—Aiming

TWO-YEAR-OLDS

58 **AIM STRAIGHT**, b c 06/05 Australia—High Hopes (Zamindar (USA))
59 B c 01/03 Lightning Spear—Aliyana (IRE) (Iffraaj)
60 **CITY OF YORK**, b c 24/02 Cityscape—Primrose Valley (Pastoral Pursuits)
61 **EMPRESS WU**, b f 01/02 Sea The Moon (GER)—Chinoiseries (Archipenko (USA))
62 **FOEDERATI (IRE)**, b f 18/02 Saxon Warrior (JPN)—Archangel Gabriel (USA) (Arch (USA)) (325000)
63 **FOLK STAR**, ch f 05/05 Le Havre (IRE)—Folk Opera (IRE) (Singspiel (IRE))
64 Ch gr f 15/02 Havana Grey—Frequent (Three Valleys (USA)) (82000)
65 **HARROGATE BETTY**, b f 10/03 Cityscape—Miss Fridaythorpe (Pastoral Pursuits)
66 B f 11/03 Dabirsim (FR)—Heliocentric (FR) (Galileo (IRE)) (27211)
67 B c 13/02 Cloth of Stars (IRE)—Ihsas (USA) (Rahy (USA)) (34014)
68 B f 24/02 Shamardal (USA)—Lady Rosamunde (Maria's Mon (USA))
69 B c 06/04 Wings of Eagles (FR)—Logjam (IRE) (Royal Academy (USA))
70 B c 07/04 Kingman—Longing (IRE) (Galileo (IRE)) (200000)
71 Ch c 21/03 Mastercraftsman (IRE)—Lyin Eyes (Equiano (FR)) (85000)
72 Ch f 09/03 Kitten's Joy (USA)—Miss Sugars (Harbour Watch (IRE))
73 B c 06/05 Mukhadram—Mooakada (Montjeu (IRE))
74 Gr c 21/01 Camelot—Moonrise Landing (IRE) (Dalakhani (IRE)) (150000)
75 **MS GREER**, b f 10/03 Bobby's Kitten (USA)—Ms Gillard (Aussie Rules (USA))
76 B c 06/05 Cotai Glory—Newlywed (IRE) (Authorized (IRE)) (50000)
77 **PFINGSTBERG (GER)**, ch c 07/04 Protectionist (GER)—Peace of Paradise (GER) (Sholokhov (IRE)) (27211)
78 B c 05/05 Air Force Blue (USA)—Purr And Prowl (USA) (Purim (USA))
79 B c 26/02 Kodiac—Recife (GER) (Giant's Causeway (USA)) (90000)
80 **ROSA CHINENSIS**, b f 23/05 Oasis Dream—Robe Chinoise (Robellino (USA))
81 B c 05/03 Harry Angel (IRE)—Sarshampla (IRE) (Elzaam (AUS))
82 B c 13/03 Roaring Lion (USA)—Secrete (FR) (Cape Cross (IRE)) (85034)
83 B f 31/01 Cracksman—Singyoursong (IRE) (Aqlaam)
84 B c 12/04 Expert Eye—Sliabh Luachra (IRE) (High Chaparral (IRE)) (80000)
85 Ch f 23/02 Lightning Spear—Starlit Sky (Galileo (IRE)) (30000)
86 B c 07/02 Churchill (IRE)—Strategy (Machiavellian (USA))
87 B c 27/03 Uncle Mo (USA)—Sweet Connie (USA) (Giant's Causeway (USA)) (28000)
88 B f 12/05 Iffraaj—Zubeida (Authorized (IRE))

Owners: Sheikh J. D. Al Maktoum, Mr A. Al Mansoori, Sultan Ali, Australian Bloodstock, Mr W. Baker, Abdulla Belhabb, Mr R. G. W. Brown, Mr C. L. Chen, Chola Dynasty, J. M. Cook, K. A. Dasmal, Khalifa Dasmal & Bryan Payne, Mr D. P Duffy, Mr R. El Youssef, The Future, Mrs F. H. Hay, Mr A. Howells, Mohammed Jaber, Mrs A. J. Jackson, Mr Jos & Mrs Jane Rodosthenous, Katherine Stewart & Alison Jackson, Mr J. Lovett, The Hon. Earle Mack, Millingbrook Racing, Never Say Die Partnership, A. F. O'Callaghan, Mr R. O'Callaghan, Mr E. M. O'Connor, Mr C. C. Payne, A. J. Perkins, A. M. Pickering, Quantum Leap Racing & Australian Bloodstock, Quantum Leap Racing XV, Amo Racing Ltd, Mr R. Rauscher, Miss K. Rausing, Dr A. Sivananthan, Mrs K. Sivananthan, St Albans Bloodstock Limited, Tick Tock Partnership, Tony Perkins & Partners, Twenty Stars Partnership, Major M. G. Wyatt.

Assistant Trainer: Sam Goldsmith.

Flat Jockey: Jamie Spencer. **Apprentice Jockey:** Olivia Haines.

476 **MR DAN SKELTON, Alcester**
Postal: **Lodge Hill, Shelfield Green, Shelfield, Alcester, Warwickshire, B49 6JR**
Contacts: **PHONE 01789 336339**
EMAIL **office@danskeltonracing.com** WEBSITE **www.danskeltonracing.com**
FACEBOOK **@DanSkeltonHorseracing** TWITTER **@DSkeltonRacing**
INSTAGRAM **@DanSkeltonRacing**

1 **ACROSS THE LINE (IRE)**, 7, b g Fame And Glory—La Protagonista (IRE) **Craig & Laura Buckingham**
2 **AGGY WITH IT (IRE)**, 8, b m Presenting—Agathe du Berlais (FR) **Andy & Sharon Measham**
3 **ALLMANKIND**, 6, b g Sea The Moon (GER)—Wemyss Bay **The Gredley Family**
4 **ALNADAM (FR)**, 9, b g Poliglote—Rosadame (FR) **Mr B. J. C. Drew**
5 **AMOOLA GOLD (GER)**, 9, b g Mamool (IRE)—Aughamore Beauty (IRE) **Mr & Mrs Gordon Pink**
6 **ANTUNES**, 8, b g Nathaniel (IRE)—Aigrette Garzette (IRE) **Mark & Maria Adams**
7 **APOTHICAIRE (FR)**, 6, b g Doctor Dino (FR)—Aqua Alta (FR) **Mr G. A. Carroll**
8 **ARTEMIS KIMBO**, 5, b m Saint des Saints (FR)—Early Dawne **Stuart & Shelly Parkin**
9 **ASHOKA (IRE)**, 10, gr g Azamour (IRE)—Jinskys Gift (IRE) **Mr Frank McAleavy & Mr Ian McAleavy**
10 **ASHTOWN LAD (IRE)**, 8, b g Flemensfirth (USA)—Blossom Trix (IRE) **Mr & Mrs D. Yates**
11 **BALLYGRIFINCOTTAGE (IRE)**, 7, b g Stowaway—Long Long Time (IRE) **Friends From Insurance**
12 **BEAKSTOWN (IRE)**, 9, b g Stowaway—Midnight Reel (IRE) **Mr B. J. C. Drew**
13 **BENNYS KING (IRE)**, 11, b g Beneficial—Hellofafaithful (IRE) **Mezzone Family**
14 **BERAZ (FR)**, 4, b c Zoffany (IRE)—Beshara (FR) **Owners Group 096**
15 **BLAKLION**, 13, b g Kayf Tara—Franciscaine (FR) **Mr & Mrs D. Yates**
16 **BLUE BUBBLES**, 5, b m Blue Bresil (FR)—Araucaria (IRE) **L & H Hales**
17 **BOOK OF SECRETS (IRE)**, 4, b g Free Eagle (IRE)—Alice Treasure (IRE) **Craig & Laura Buckingham**
18 **BOOMBAWN (IRE)**, 5, b g Dylan Thomas (IRE)—Well Clad (IRE) **Bullen-smith & Faulks**
19 **BOSS MAN FRED (IRE)**, 8, ch g Dubai Destination (USA)—Aboo Lala (IRE) **Masomo**
20 **CABOT CLIFFS (IRE)**, 5, ch g Gleneagles (IRE)—Hallouella **Craig & Laura Buckingham**
21 **CALICO (GER)**, 6, b g Soldier Hollow—Casanga (IRE) **Mr J. J. Reilly**
22 **CALLISTO'S KING (IRE)**, 5, b g Imperial Monarch (IRE)—Exit Bob (IRE) **Noel Fehily Racing Syndicates - C King**
23 **CAMDONIAN (IRE)**, 6, b g Shantou (USA)—Miss Garbo (IRE) **Masterson Holdings Limited**
24 **CAPTAIN CHAOS (IRE)**, 11, ch g Golan (IRE)—Times Have Changed (IRE) **Mike and Eileen Newbould**
25 **CH'TIBELLO (FR)**, 11, b g Sageburg (IRE)—Neicha (FR) **The Can't Say No Partnership**
26 **CHECKINFORSQUIRELS (IRE)**, 6, ch m Flemensfirth (USA)—Nivalt **Foxtrot Nh Racing Syndicate**
27 **CHILINLIKEAVILLAIN (IRE)**, 5, b g Imperial Monarch (IRE)—Witness Daughter (IRE) **Craig & Laura Buckingham**
28 **COLONEL MANDERSON (FR)**, 6, b g Kapgarde (FR)—Playact (IRE) **Babbitt Racing**
29 **COUSU MAIN (FR)**, 6, b g Buck's Boum (FR)—Just Pegasus (USA) **Lycett Racing Ltd**
30 **DAZZLING GLORY (IRE)**, 7, b g Califet (FR)—Market Niche (IRE) **Charles & Rachel Wilson**
31 **DEBECE**, 11, b g Kayf Tara—Dalamine (FR) **R. M. Kirkland**
32 **DESTRIER (FR)**, 9, b g Voix du Nord (FR)—Razia (FR) **Two Celts**
33 **DOCTOR PARNASSUS (IRE)**, 4, b g Make Believe—We'll Go Walking (IRE) **Mr D. W. Fox**
34 **DOG OF WAR (FR)**, 8, b g Soldier of Fortune (IRE)—Zainzana (FR) **Mr C. A. Donlon**
35 **DON HOLLOW (FR)**, 5, b g Soldier Hollow—Donna Philippa (GER) **Honestly Racing**
36 **DORISA QUEEN**, 6, b m Shirocco (GER)—Ellnando Queen **Mrs R. I. Vaughan**
37 **DOYOUKNOWWHATIMEAN**, 5, b g Martaline—Knar Mardy **R. M. Kirkland**
38 **DUKE OF BRONTE**, 8, b g Mount Nelson—Reaf **Harts Farm Stud 2**
39 **ECLAIR D'AINAY (FR)**, 8, b br g Network (GER)—Etoile d'Ainay (FR) **Mr J. Hales**
40 **ELLE EST BELLE**, 6, b m Fame And Glory—Katalina **Mrs S. Lawrence**
41 **EMILY'S STAR**, 5, b m Kayf Tara—Lisa du Chenet (FR) **1863 Racing**
42 **EMMAS JOY (IRE)**, 9, b m Gold Well—Emma Jane (IRE) **Julian Howl & Ian Tyrrell**
43 **ETALON (IRE)**, 5, b g Sholokhov (IRE)—So You Said (IRE) **Mrs S. Lawrence**
44 **FAIVOIR (FR)**, 7, b g Coastal Path—Qape Noir (FR) **Mrs S. Lawrence**
45 **FANCY STUFF (IRE)**, 5, br m Presenting—Deep Supreme (IRE) **Thirsty Thursday Syndicate**
46 **FAST BUCK (FR)**, 8, br g Kendargent (FR)—Juvenil Delinquent (USA) **Sullivan Bloodstock Limited**
47 **FIRAK (FR)**, 7, b g Fuisse (FR)—Nosika d'Airy (FR) **Charles & Rachel Wilson**
48 **FLASH THE STEEL (IRE)**, 10, b br g Craigsteel—Anna's Melody (IRE) **Mr J. J. Reilly**
49 **FLEGMATIK (FR)**, 7, ch g Fuisse (FR)—Crack d'Emble (FR) **N. W. Lake**
50 **FLOKI**, 8, b g Kalanisi (IRE)—La Dame Brune (FR) **Derek Coles & Langley's**
51 **FRERE D'ARMES (FR)**, 5, b g Bathyrhon (GER)—Ville Sainte (FR) **Belbroughton Racing Club**
52 **GAIA DU GOUET (FR)**, 6, b m Saddler Maker (IRE)—Newhaven (FR) **R. M. Kirkland**
53 **GALIA DES LITEAUX (FR)**, 6, b m Saddler Maker (IRE)—Serie Love (FR) **Mr M. Ariss**
54 **GENTLE CONNECTIONS**, 5, b m Gentlewave (IRE)—Well Connected **Yorton Racing**

MR DAN SKELTON - continued

55 **GET A TONIC (IRE)**, 6, b m Getaway (GER)—Atomic Winner (IRE) **Cherry Knoll Farm, M&t Ward & D Skelton**
56 **GET SKY HIGH (IRE)**, 7, ch m Getaway (GER)—Tell Me Emma (IRE) **Mr & Mrs Gordon Pink**
57 **GETAROUND (IRE)**, 7, gr g Getaway (GER)—Playing Around **Mr G. J. Wilson**
58 **GLOBAL FAMENGLORY (IRE)**, 6, b m Fame And Glory—Noble Pearl (GER) **Mrs S. Carsberg**
59 **GLOBAL HARMONY (IRE)**, 7, b m Flemensfirth (USA)—Violin Davis (FR) **Mrs S. Carsberg**
60 **GLORIOUS FUN (IRE)**, 5, b g Fame And Glory—Itsalark (IRE) **R. M. Kirkland**
61 **GO STEADY**, 10, b g Indian Danehill (IRE)—Pyleigh Lady **Popham, Rogers**
62 **GREATEST STAR (FR)**, 6, gr g Lord du Sud (FR)—Sacree Mome (FR) **Mrs J. A. Watts**
63 **GREGOR (FR)**, 6, gr g Montmartre (FR)—Agathe du Berlais (FR) **Coles, Langley D Skelton**
64 **GREY DAWNING (IRE)**, 5, gr g Flemensfirth (USA)—Lady Wagtail (IRE) **R. M. Kirkland**
65 **HATCHER (IRE)**, 9, b g Doyen (IRE)—African Keys (IRE) **P. H. Betts**
66 **HEEZER GEEZER (FR)**, 5, b g Cokoriko (FR)—Queen du Vallon (FR) **Mr S. M. Bough**
67 **HELTENHAM (FR)**, 5, ch g Masked Marvel—Souris Blanche (FR) **N. W. Lake**
68 **HIDDEN HEROICS (FR)**, 5, b g Coastal Path—Quine de Sivola (FR) **Mr I. Lawrence**
69 **HOMETOWN HERO (IRE)**, 7, b g Darsi (FR)—Kilcoltrim Society (IRE) **Estate Research Limited**
70 **HORIZON D'AINAY (FR)**, 5, ch g Network (GER)—Sirene d'Ainay (FR) **Simon & Lisa Hobson**
71 **IN THIS WORLD (FR)**, 4, b c Saint des Saints (FR)—Maia Royale (FR) **In This World Syndicate**
72 **JAY JAY REILLY (IRE)**, 6, b g Fame And Glory—Garden City (IRE) **Mr J. J. Reilly**
73 **JEFFERY'S CROSS (IRE)**, 6, b g Flemensfirth (USA)—Gleaming Spire
74 **JERSEY (IRE)**, 6, br g Presenting—Synthe Davis (FR) **M & E Boothright**
75 **JET PLANE (IRE)**, 6, b g Jet Away—Court Gamble (IRE) **Norman Lake & Susan Carsberg**
76 **JOHN LOCKE**, 5, ch g Mastercraftsman (IRE)—Sacred Shield **Sullivan Bloodstock Ltd & Chris Giles**
77 **KATEIRA**, 5, b m Kayf Tara—Raitera (FR)
78 **KAYF HERNANDO**, 6, b g Kayf Tara—Thrice Nice **Dick,Stevenson and Partners**
79 **KING D'ARGENT (FR)**, 7, ch g Kendargent (FR)—Ephigenie (IRE) **Andrew Dick & John Stevenson**
80 **KNICKERBOCKERGLORY (IRE)**, 6, b g Fame And Glory—The Brass Lady (IRE)
Chelsea Thoroughbreds - Knickerbocker
81 **KNIGHT IN DUBAI (IRE)**, 9, b g Dubai Destination (USA)—Bobbies Storm (IRE) **Mr & Mrs Ben Houghton**
82 **KNOCK EM BANDY**, 5, b m Presenting—Kerada (FR) **Mr N. Skelton**
83 **KOBRA (GER)**, 5, ch m Farhh—Kheshvar (IRE) **Chelsea Thoroughbreds & Partners**
84 **KRACKA NUT**, 5, b g Blue Bresil (FR)—More Like That (IRE) **Stonegrave Thoroughbreds**
85 **LAC DE CONSTANCE (FR)**, 6, gr g Martaline—Kendova (FR) **Mr A. L. Cohen**
86 **LAKOTA WARRIOR (IRE)**, 6, br g Valirann (FR)—Talkin Madam (IRE) **A G J & Diver**
87 **LANGER DAN (IRE)**, 8, b g Ocovango—What A Fashion (IRE) **Mr C. A. Donlon**
88 **LEYLAK (IRE)**, 5, b g Born To Sea (IRE)—Lidaya (USA) **Notalotterry**
89 **LONIMOSS BARELIERE (FR)**, 6, b g Palamoss (IRE)—Lonia Blue (FR) **Mr N. Skelton**
90 **LUCKY ONE (FR)**, 7, br g Authorized (IRE)—Lady Anouchka (IRE) **Sullivan Bloodstock & Hughes Crowley**
91 **LUSTLEIGH**, 5, b g Kayf Tara—My Petra
92 **LYDFORD**, 5, b g Fastnet Rock (AUS)—Miss Brown To You (IRE) **The Gredley Family**
93 **MARRACUDJA (FR)**, 11, b g Martaline—Memorial (FR) **Foxtrot Racing Marracudja**
94 **MARTHA BRAE**, 7, b m Shirocco (GER)—Harringay **Mrs R. I. Vaughan**
95 **MESSAGE PERSONNEL (FR)**, 4, b g Saint des Saints (FR)—Victoria Princess (FR) **Mr J. Hales**
96 **MIDNIGHT AURORA**, 9, ch m Midnight Legend—Bekkaria (FR) **Mr D. N. Skelton**
97 **MIDNIGHT RIVER**, 7, ch g Midnight Legend—Well Connected **Mr Frank McAleavy & Mr Ian McAleavy**
98 **MOCHACHOCACHINO (IRE)**, 5, b g Presenting—Ross Bay (IRE) **Mr A. L. Cohen**
99 **MOLLY OLLYS WISHES**, 8, b m Black Sam Bellamy (IRE)—September Moon **Mr D. Pugh**
100 **MOUNT TEMPEST (IRE)**, 5, b g Walk In The Park (IRE)—Tempest Missile (IRE)
Highclere Thoroughbred Racing Ltd
101 **MY DROGO**, 7, b g Milan—My Petra
102 **NIGHT IN MANHATTAN**, 6, b g Kayf Tara—One Gulp **Share My Dream**
103 **NO GETAWAY (IRE)**, 9, ch g Getaway (GER)—Nonnetia (FR) **Dick, Keenan, Sawer, Stevenson**
104 **NOT THAT FUISSE (FR)**, 9, b g Fuisse (FR)—Edelmira (FR) **Mr C. A. Donlon**
105 **NOTNOWLINDA (IRE)**, 5, br m Notnowcato—Moll Bawn (IRE) **Mr M. Ariss**
106 **NUBE NEGRA (SPA)**, 8, br g Dink (FR)—Manly Dream (FR) **Mr T. Spraggett**
107 **NURSE SUSAN (FR)**, 5, ch m Doctor Dino (FR)—Hembra (FR) **Mr C. A. Donlon**
108 **ONE FOR BILLY**, 10, b g Midnight Legend—Saxona (IRE) **Mr D. W. Fox**
109 **OUR JET (IRE)**, 8, ch g Jet Away—She's Bitting (IRE) **Mr C. Ohrstrom**
110 **PADLEYOUROWNCANOE**, 8, b g Nayef (USA)—Pooka's Daughter (IRE) **K.A.C. Bloodstock Limited**
111 **PARKIN FINE**, 5, b m Blue Bresil (FR)—Pumped Up Kicks (IRE) **Stuart & Shelly Parkin**
112 **PEMBROKE**, 5, b g Blue Bresil (FR)—Moyliscar

MR DAN SKELTON - continued

113 **PERCY'S WORD**, 8, b g Sir Percy—Laverre (IRE) **Mezzone Family**
114 **PIKAR (FR)**, 5, b g Masterstroke (USA)—Prairie Scilla (GER) **Yorton Racing**
115 **PLAYFUL SAINT (FR)**, 7, b g Saint des Saints (FR)—Playact (IRE) **Mr & Mrs J. D. Cotton**
116 **PRESENTING JEREMY (IRE)**, 7, b g Jeremy (USA)—Present Company (IRE) **Dick,Stevenson and Partners**
117 **PRESENTING NELLY**, 5, b m Kayf Tara—Forever Present (IRE) **Stuart & Shelly Parkin**
118 **PROSCHEMA (IRE)**, 7, ch g Declaration of War (USA)—Notable **Empire State Racing Partnership**
119 **PROTEKTORAT (FR)**, 7, b g Saint des Saints (FR)—Protektion (FR) **Sir A Ferguson G Mason J Hales & L Hales**
120 **QUIET FLOW**, 7, b g Sholokhov (IRE)—Sardagna (FR) **Mr C. A. Donlon**
121 **REDZOR (IRE)**, 9, b g Shantou (USA)—Knockara One (IRE) **Bryan Drew & Steve Roper**
122 **REILLY (IRE)**, 6, b g Milan—Flowers On Sunday (IRE) **Mr J. J. Reilly**
123 **RIDGEWAY (FR)**, 5, gr g Outstrip—Bocca Bianca (GER) **Foxtrot Racing Ridgeway**
124 **RIGGS (IRE)**, 7, b g Mahler—Cousin Kizzy (IRE) **Noel Fehily Racing Syndicates - Riggs**
125 **RISKINTHEGROUND (IRE)**, 5, b g Presenting—The Folkes Choice **3 Sons**
126 **RIVER LEGEND (IRE)**, 6, ch g Ocovango—China Reel (IRE) **R. M. Kirkland**
127 **ROCK LEGEND (IRE)**, 5, b g Maxios—Moraine **Owners Group 073**
128 **ROCKSTAR RONNIE (IRE)**, 7, b g Stowaway—Dimona (IRE) **Highclere Thoroughbred Racing - Rockstar**
129 **ROCKY MAN (FR)**, 4, b c Doctor Dino (FR)—Lady Speedy (IRE) **Colm Donlon & Alne Park Stud**
130 **RUNWITHTHETIDE (IRE)**, 5, b m Presenting—Don't Be Upset (IRE) **Highclere Thoroughbred Racing - Tide**
131 **SAIL AWAY (FR)**, 6, gr g Martaline—Baraka du Berlais (FR) **Mr & Mrs J. D. Cotton**
132 **SCOTS GOLD (IRE)**, 4, gr g Dark Angel (IRE)—Duchess Andorra (IRE) **Empire State Racing Partnership**
133 **SEVEN NO TRUMPS (IRE)**, 7, b g Milan—Ballyknock Present (IRE) **Mr Frank McAleavy & Mr Ian McAleavy**
134 **SHAN BLUE (IRE)**, 8, b g Shantou (USA)—Lady Roberta (IRE) **Mr C. A. Donlon**
135 **SHANNON BRIDGE (IRE)**, 9, ch g Flemensfirth (USA)—Bridgequarter Lady (IRE) **M. Boothright**
136 **SHE'S SO LOVELY (IRE)**, 6, b m Mahler—House-of-Hearts (IRE) **Winter Gold Racing 2**
137 **SHENTRI (FR)**, 5, b g Sri Putra—Shentala (FR) **Mr J. Lane**
138 **SHOLOKJACK (IRE)**, 6, b g Sholokhov (IRE)—Another Pet (IRE) **Sullivan Bloodstock & Hughes Crowley**
139 **SIGNAL POINT (IRE)**, 6, br m Fame And Glory—Derravaragh Native (IRE) **Nick Skelton & Enda Carroll**
140 **SMILING GETAWAY**, 5, ch m Getaway (GER)—One More Cookie (IRE) **James and Jean Potter Ltd**
141 **SOFIA'S ROCK (FR)**, 8, b g Rock of Gibraltar (IRE)—Princess Sofia (UAE) **Mezzone Family 1**
142 **SOYOUTHINKSOAGAIN (IRE)**, 7, b g So You Think (NZ)—Al Saqiya (USA) **Mr I. Lawrence**
143 **SPIRITOFTHEGAMES (IRE)**, 10, b g Darsi (FR)—Lucy Walters (IRE) **N. W. Lake**
144 **STARSKY (IRE)**, 8, b g Shantou (USA)—Lunar Star (IRE) **S Smith & S Campion**
145 **STEAL MY SUNSHINE**, 5, b g Black Sam Bellamy (IRE)—Amber Cloud **Mark & Maria Adams**
146 **STEPNEY CAUSEWAY**, 5, b g New Approach (IRE)—Wake Up Call **The Gredley Family**
147 **TARSEEM (IRE)**, 4, ch g Dawn Approach (IRE)—Saraha **Craig & Laura Buckingham**
148 **THIRD TIME LUCKI (IRE)**, 7, br g Arcadio (GER)—Definite Valley (IRE) **Mike and Eileen Newbould**
149 **TOKAY DOKEY (IRE)**, 8, b g Gold Well—Charming Present (IRE) **Mr C. A. Donlon**
150 **TOO FRIENDLY**, 4, b g Camelot—Chatline (IRE) **The Gredley Family**
151 **TURNAWAY (IRE)**, 5, ch g Getaway (GER)—Robins Turn (IRE) **Mr G. J. Wilson**
152 **UNEXPECTED PARTY (FR)**, 7, gr g Martaline—Reform Act (USA) **The Unexpected Party Syndicate**
153 **VIVA LAVILLA (IRE)**, 6, br g Getaway (GER)—Viva Forever (FR) **Mr & Mrs D. Yates**
154 **WALK IN CLOVER (IRE)**, 5, b m Walk In The Park (IRE)—Bridgequarter Girl (IRE) **The Blind Squirrels**
155 **WAR CALL (FR)**, 6, gr g Martaline—Bourbonnaise (FR) **Dick and Mandy Higgins**
156 **WATASHOCK (IRE)**, 5, ch g Sholokhov (IRE)—What A Princess (IRE) **P. H. Betts**
157 **WEST BALBOA (IRE)**, 6, b m Yeats—Rostellan (IRE) **Bullen-smith & Faulks**
158 **WEST CORK**, 8, b g Midnight Legend—Calaminta **Mike and Eileen Newbould**
159 **WEST TO THE BRIDGE (IRE)**, 9, b g Flemensfirth (USA)—Godlylady (IRE) **Mr P. J. Tierney**
160 **WHISPERING GYPSY (IRE)**, 7, ch m Beat Hollow—Thieving Gypsy (IRE) **Foxtrot Nh Racing Syndicate**
161 **WILD ROMANCE (IRE)**, 7, br m Kalanisi (IRE)—Aboo Lala (IRE) **Masomo**
162 **WILDE ABOUT OSCAR (IRE)**, 7, b g Oscar (IRE)—Baie Barbara (IRE) **Mike and Eileen Newbould**
163 **WILLIAM OF YORK**, 6, b g Kayf Tara—Shady Anne **Mike and Eileen Newbould**
164 **YVETTE GUILBERT (FR)**, 5, gr m Montmartre (FR)—La Bombonera (FR) **Mrs S. J. Faulks**

Other Owners: Mr D. Abraham, Alne Park Stud, Mr D. Balchin, Miss E. D. V. Boothright, M. Boothright, Mr S. M. Bough, Mr C. Buckingham, Mrs L. K. Buckingham, Mr P. P. J. Bullen-Smith, Ms J. S. Campion, Mr E. Carroll, Mrs S. Carsberg, Chelsea Thoroughbreds Ltd, Mr D. J. Coles, Miss J. Craymer, Judy Craymer & Nick Skelton, Mr A. D. Dick, Mr J. Diver, Mr C. A. Donlon, Mr B. J. C. Drew, Mrs M. H. Duprey, Mrs S. J. Faulks, Mrs L. Fellows, Sir A. Ferguson, Foxtrot Racing Management Ltd, Mr M. J. Freer, Mr C. M. Giles, Mr J. B. Gilruth, Mr H. R. Hales, Mr J. R. Hales, Miss L. J. Hales, Mrs A. J. Higgins, Mr R. S. Higgins, Mr P. B. R. Houghton, Mrs V. K. Houghton, Mr J. Howl, Mr N. Hughes, Johnston Racing Ltd, R. G. Kelvin-Hughes, N. W. Lake,

MR DAN SKELTON - continued

Mr D. E. Langley, Langley's, Mr K. MacLennan, Mrs E. Magnier, Mr J. P Magnier, Mrs S. Magnier, G. A. Mason, Mr F. McAleavy, Mr I. McAleavy, Mr A. R. Measham, Mrs S. M. Measham, Mr G. G. Mezzone, Mr L. M. Mezzone, Mrs S. M. Mezzone, Mezzone Family, Mrs E. E. Newbould, Mr J. M. Newbould, Mr H. J. O'Reilly, Mrs S. Parkin, Mr S. J. Parkin, Mr G. K. G. Pink, Mrs K. M. Pink, P.F. Popham, Mrs E. M. Pugh, Mr M. A. H. Rausing, Mr M. P Rogers, Mr S. R. Roper, Mr A. D. H. Salomon, Mrs K. Salters, Mrs L. M. Shanahan, Mr D. N. Skelton, Mr N. Skelton, Mrs S. Smith, Anthony Speelman, Mr M. Speelman, Srw Partnership, Mr J. M. Stevenson, Sullivan Bloodstock Limited, Mr E. D. Tynan, Mr I. Tyrrell, Mrs M. Ward, Mr T. Ward, C. M. Wilson, Mrs R. E. Wilson, Winter Gold Racing 2, Lord G. J. S. Worsley, Mrs A. V. Yates, Mr D. Yates.

Assistant Trainer: Tom Messenger,

Head Girl: Amber Blythe,

Head Lad: Tolley Dean, Joe Knox, Fin Mulrine, Nick Pearce, **Travelling Head:** Andy Gardner, Hannah Haywood, Phil Haywood,

Racing Secretary: Natalie Fisher, Ella Pearce, Tiggy Vale-Titterton.

NH Jockey: Bridget Andrews, Harry Skelton.

Amateur Jockey: Mr Murray Dodd, Mr Tristan Durrell, Miss Heidi Palin.

---

477 **MRS PAM SLY, Peterborough**
Postal: **Singlecote, Thorney, Peterborough, Cambridgeshire, PE6 0PB**
Contacts: **PHONE 01733 270212 MOBILE 07850 511267**

1 **ACERTAIN CIRCUS,** 12, ch g Definite Article—Circus Rose
2 **BELLICA,** 5, b m War Command (USA)—Asteroidea
3 **CHIC AVENUE,** 4, b f Champs Elysees—Chicklemix
4 **DARK SPEC,** 7, b g Dark Angel (IRE)—Speciosa (IRE)
5 **DAZZLING DAN (IRE),** 6, b g Dandy Man (IRE)—Scrumptious
6 **EILEENDOVER,** 5, b m Canford Cliffs (IRE)—Specialty (IRE)
7 **ELEANOR DUMONT,** 5, b m Westerner—Circus Rose
8 **FRANSHAM,** 8, b g Sulamani (IRE)—Circus Rose
9 **GENTLE ROSE,** 6, b m Gentlewave (IRE)—Iconic Rose
10 **GROUSEMAN,** 5, b g Kyllachy—Speciosa (IRE)
11 **HAAFAPIECE,** 9, ch g Haafhd—Bonnet's Pieces
12 **JOHN CLARE (IRE),** 6, b g Poet's Voice—Specialty (IRE)
13 **LIAM'S LASS (IRE),** 6, b m Dandy Man (IRE)—Rupa (IRE)
14 **MIXEDWAVE (IRE),** 5, b g Gentlewave (IRE)—Chicklemix
15 **PYRRHA LAGOON,** 5, ch g Universal (IRE)—Kaloni (IRE)
16 **SPECIAL MAYSON,** 4, b g Mayson—Specialty (IRE)
17 **TAKEIT EASY,** 7, b g Malinas (GER)—Circus Rose
18 **WILLIAM CODY,** 5, b g Westerner—Wistow
19 **XCITATIONS,** 7, b g Universal (IRE)—Bonnet's Pieces

THREE-YEAR-OLDS

20 **ANNIVERSARY BELLE (IRE),** b f No Nay Never (USA)—Annamanamoux (USA)
21 **ASHLEY GOLD,** b f Havana Gold (IRE)—Specialty (IRE)
22 **ASTRAL BEAU,** b f Brazen Beau (AUS)—Asteroidea
23 **CUBANISTA,** b g Havana Gold (IRE)—Multicultural (IRE)

TWO-YEAR-OLDS

24 **WINTERCRACK,** b f 17/03 Cracksman—Speciosa (IRE) (Danehill Dancer (IRE))

Owners: D. L. Bayliss, Mrs I. A. Coles, Dr T. J. W. Davies, Mr M. R. Davis, Family Sly, Mr S. R. T. Jones, Mr G. A. Libson, Pam's People, Miss L. Sly, M. H. S. Sly, Mrs P. M. Sly, Mr W. Sly, The Stablemates, The Stablemates II, Thorney Racing Partners.

NH Jockey: Kielan Woods. **Conditional Jockey:** Jack Andrews. **Amateur Jockey:** Miss Gina Andrews.

478 MR BRYAN SMART, Hambleton

Postal: Hambleton House, Sutton Bank, Thirsk, North Yorkshire, YO7 2HA
Contacts: PHONE 01845 597481 MOBILE 07748 634797 FAX 01845 597480
EMAIL office@bryansmart.plus.com WEBSITE www.bryansmart-racing.com FACEBOOK
Bryan-Smart-Racing TWITTER @BryanSmartRacin INSTAGRAM bryan_smart_racing

1 ANTAGONIZE, 6, b g Epaulette (AUS)—Hakuraa (IRE) **Crossfields Racing**
2 BLAZING SON, 4, ch g Mayson—Emblaze **The Smart Emblaze Partnership**
3 DEBAWTRY (IRE), 7, b m Camacho—Muluk (IRE) **Akebar Park Leisure Ltd**
4 DUE A WIN, 5, b g Due Diligence (USA)—Malelane (IRE) **D. Blake,C. Dinsdale,S.McCay & M.Beadle**
5 HEART THROB, 4, b f Brazen Beau (AUS)—Generously Gifted **Mr M. Barber Racing**
6 KENTUCKYCONNECTION (USA), 9, b g Include (USA)—Youcanringmybell (USA) **Woodcock Electrical Limited**
7 PALAZZO, 6, b g Morpheus—Sweet Power **Mr B. Smart**
8 PENOMBRE, 4, b g Twilight Son—Hayba **The Unscrupulous Judges**
9 REDZONE, 5, b g Sepoy (AUS)—Mythicism **Crossfields Racing**
10 REGIMENTO, 4, b g Casamento (IRE)—Last Dance **Mrs Freda Moody & Mr Bryan Smart**
11 SWISS CONNECTION, 6, b g Swiss Spirit—Sofonisba **Woodcock Electrical Ltd**
12 WRENTHORPE, 7, b g Hellvelyn—Milly-M **Dan Maltby Bloodstock Ltd & Mr B. Smart**
13 ZOOM STAR, 4, b f Mayson—Chinaconnection (IRE) **Woodcock Electrical Limited**

THREE-YEAR-OLDS

14 BOND CHAIRMAN, br g Kodiac—Wunders Dream (IRE) **Bond Thoroughbred Limited**
15 BOND POWER, b g War Command (USA)—Rhal (IRE) **Bond Thoroughbred & Christian Star Ptr**
16 DOOMSDAY, b g Lethal Force (IRE)—Ayasha **Crossfields Racing**
17 DRAWDOWN, b f Profitable (IRE)—Choisette **Crossfields Racing**
18 EMPEROR CARADOC (FR), b c Siyouni (FR)—Tribune Libre (IRE) **SDB Partnership**
19 FIREBOMB, b g Swiss Spirit—Emblaze **Crossfields Racing**
20 HIGH OPINION, b g Hellvelyn—Vanity (IRE) **The Smart Set**
21 HIGHLAND QUEEN (IRE), b f Acclamation—Medicean Queen (IRE) **Moody, Thompson & Powell**
22 INSTINCTION, b f Brazen Beau (AUS)—Spontaneity (IRE) **Crossfields Racing**
23 LADY OF YAPHAM (IRE), ch f Twilight Son—Danehill Destiny **Bond Thoroughbred Limited**
24 PARISIAC (IRE), b c Kodiac—Colgin **Spb Partnership**
25 PENWAY (IRE), b f Twilight Son—She's A Worldie (IRE) **Mr S. Chappell & Partner**
26 POLITICISM, b f Churchill (IRE)—Mythicism **Crossfields Racing**
27 PRINCESS KARINE, b f Aclaim (IRE)—Hakuraa (IRE) **Mr N. Derbyshire & Partner**
28 PROJECT DANTE, ch c Showcasing—Thatsallimsaying (IRE) **Bond Thoroughbred Limited**
29 SWEET MIST (USA), ch f Tonalist (USA)—Sweet Emma Rose (USA) **SDB Partnership**
30 TIERS OF JOY (FR), b br f Showcasing—Luna Moon **Rj Cornelius, G Godfrey & Partner**
31 TILLY THE FILLY (IRE), b f Caravaggio (USA)—Three Choirs (IRE) **SLB Partnership**
32 VENTURA TEASE, b f Fountain of Youth (IRE)—Finalize **Middleham Park Racing Lxxx & Partners**
33 WHEAL KITTY, b f Charming Thought—Katabatik Katie **Mrs P. A. Clark**
34 WHITEANDBLUE, b f Fountain of Youth (IRE)—Whiteandgold **Crossfields Racing**

TWO-YEAR-OLDS

35 Ch c 12/04 Charming Thought—Astley Park (Dutch Art) (10000) **Ceffyl Racing**
36 Ch f 25/03 Cotai Glory—Clef (Dutch Art) (65000)
37 KASINO, b f 27/03 Equiano (FR)—Katabatik Katie (Sir Percy)
38 MARGARET ELIZABETH (IRE), b f 23/01 Kodiac—Sagely (IRE) (Frozen Power (IRE)) (195578)
Bond Thoroughbred Limited
39 OPERATION GIMCRACK (IRE), ch c 07/04 Showcasing—Folk Melody (IRE) (Street Cry (IRE)) (160000)
Bond Thoroughbred Limited
40 PROJECT BLACK, b c 05/02 Showcasing—Dot Hill (Refuse To Bend (IRE)) (50000) **Bond Thoroughbred Limited**
41 REGINALD CHARLES, b c 16/03 Zoustar (AUS)—Melbourne Memories (Sleeping Indian) (90476)
Bond Thoroughbred Limited

Other Owners: M. Barber, Mr M. J. Beadle, Mr D. S. Blake, Mr G. R. Bond, Bond Thoroughbred Limited, Mr S. D. Bradley, Mr S. L. Bradley, Mr M. G. Bullock, Mrs T. Bullock, Mr S. E. Chappell, Mr S. Christian, Christian Star Partnership, R. J. Cornelius, Crossfields Racing, Dan Maltby Bloodstock Limited, Mr P. A. Darling, Mr N. V. Derbyshire, Mr J. C. Dinsdale, D. B. Elders, Mr G. Godfrey, Mrs A. C. Hudson, Mr S. McCay, Middleham Park Racing LXXX, Mrs F. B. Moody, R. A. Page, T. S. Palin, D. F. Powell, M. Prince, Mr B. Smart, Mr S. Thompson, Mr A. Welch, Woodcock Electrical Limited.

MR BRYAN SMART - continued

Assistant Trainer: Beth Smart, Victoria Smart.

Flat Jockey: Graham Lee. **Apprentice Jockey:** Gianluca Sanna.

---

479 MR JULIAN SMITH, Tirley
Postal: **Tirley Court, Tirley, Gloucester**
Contacts: **PHONE 01452 780461 MOBILE 07748 901175 FAX 01452 780461**
EMAIL **nicola.smith9156@o2.co.uk**

1 **CARO DES FLOS (FR)**, 10, b g Tiger Groom—Royale Marie (FR) **Mrs J.A. Benson & Miss S.N. Benson**
2 **DIAMOND ROSE**, 10, b m Sagamix (FR)—Swiss Rose **Grand Jury Partnership**
3 **FINE BY HER**, 6, b m Shirocco (GER)—High Benefit (IRE) **Mrs J.A. Benson & Miss S.N. Benson**
4 **GONE TO TEXAS (IRE)**, 6, b g Imperial Monarch (IRE)—Echo Falls (IRE) **Exors of the Late Mr D. E. S. Smith**
5 **SALLY'S GIRL**, 5, b m Black Sam Bellamy (IRE)—Shayana **Grand Jury Partnership**
6 **STAY OUT OF COURT (IRE)**, 11, b g Court Cave (IRE)—Lucky To Live (IRE) **Exors of the Late Mr D. E. S. Smith**
7 **THE RORY STORY (IRE)**, 11, b g Flemensfirth (USA)—Phardester (IRE) **Exors of the Late Mr D. E. S. Smith**

Other Owners: Mrs J. A. Benson, Miss S. N. Benson.

Assistant Trainer: Mrs Nicky Smith.

---

480 MR MARTIN SMITH, Newmarket
Postal: **Kremlin House Stables, Fordham Road, Newmarket, Suffolk, CB8 7AQ**
Contacts: **MOBILE 07712 493589**
WEBSITE **www.martinsmithracing.com**

1 **AFFLUENCE (IRE)**, 7, b g Thewayyouare (USA)—Castalian Spring (IRE) **The Affluence Partnership**
2 **ALEATORIC (IRE)**, 6, b g Dylan Thomas (IRE)—Castalian Spring (IRE) **Mr M. P. B. Smith**
3 **FRIENDS DON'T ASK**, 7, b g Champs Elysees—Kintyre **Mr Robert P Clarke & Partners**
4 **KENTUCKY HARDBOOT (IRE)**, 5, ch g Starspangledbanner (AUS)—Fanditha (IRE) **D. P. Fremel**
5 **LADY PENDRAGON**, 5, b m Camelot—Arthur's Girl **Sunville Rail Limited**
6 **MORANI KALI**, 4, ch g Charming Thought—Crystal Moments **Angela Stokes & Martin Smith Racing**

THREE-YEAR-OLDS

7 **ALL ABOUT ALICE (IRE)**, b f Excelebration (IRE)—Castalian Spring (IRE) **The Affluence Partnership**
8 B c Helmet (AUS)—Beyond Fashion **M B S Racing**
9 **ROCK ON TEDDY**, b g Scorpion (IRE)—Freedom Rock
10 **SHABS**, b c Aclaim (IRE)—Inagh River **Mr S. Rankine**
11 **THECOLOUROFMAGIC**, ch f Havana Gold (IRE)—Macnamara **Angela Stokes & Martin Smith Racing**

TWO-YEAR-OLDS

12 **TOXICOLOGIST**, b c 14/02 Expert Eye—Palais Glide (Proclamation (IRE)) (15000) **Mrs A. M. Stokes**

Other Owners: Mrs R. T. Rennie, Mr M. P. B. Smith, Mrs A. M. Stokes.

Pupil Assistant: Mr Paul-Ryan Clarke, **Racing Secretary:** Mrs Rachel Rennie.

Apprentice Jockey: Miss Georgia Lea.

481 **MISS PAULA SMITH, Malton**
Postal: **Woodyard Barn, Ruffin Lane, Eddlethorpe, Malton, North Yorkshire, YO17 9QU**
Contacts: **PHONE 07760 247207**
EMAIL Paulamsmith4@gmail.com

1 **DALLAS COWBOY (IRE)**, 12, b g Beneficial—Watson River (IRE) **Miss P. M. Smith**
2 **HALLOWED GROUND (IRE)**, 7, b g Mahler—Castlehaven (IRE) **Miss P. M. Smith**
3 **MAISON D'OR (IRE)**, 8, b g Galileo (IRE)—Thai Haku (IRE) **Miss P. M. Smith**
4 **MELROSE JACK**, 5, ch g Shirocco (GER)—Daisies Adventure (IRE) **Miss M. Chaston**
5 **PETRULER**, 5, b m Native Ruler—Petrarchick (USA) **Miss P. M. Smith**
6 **RYEDALE COWBOY (IRE)**, 5, b g Kalanisi (IRE)—Muscova Rose (IRE) **Miss P. M. Smith**
7 **SHANNON HILL**, 8, b g Kayf Tara—Shannon Native (IRE) **Miss P. M. Smith**
8 **SIMPLY LOVELEH**, 9, b m Beneficial—Pippedatthepost

482 **MR R. MIKE SMITH, Galston**
Postal: **West Loudoun Farm, Galston, Ayrshire, KA4 8PB**
Contacts: **PHONE 01563 822062 MOBILE 07711 692122**
EMAIL mike@mikesmithracing.co.uk WEBSITE www.mikesmithracing.co.uk

1 **AKAMANTO (IRE)**, 8, b g Cape Cross (IRE)—Allofus (IRE) **Reid Ross Smith**
2 **ASTUTE BOY (IRE)**, 8, b g Arcano (IRE)—Spa **Mr R. M. Smith**
3 **BLACK FRIDAY**, 7, b g Equiano (FR)—The Clan Macdonald **Riverside Racing**
4 **DESERT STRANGER**, 4, b g Helmet (AUS)—Jillanar (IRE) **Spittal Family**
5 **DON'T NEED TO KNOW (IRE)**, 8, b g Flemensfirth (USA)—Phardester (IRE) **Rms Racing**
6 4, Ch g Mount Nelson—Dromod Mour (IRE) **The Racing Suite**
7 **EARN YOUR STRIPES**, 4, b f Epaulette (AUS)—Midnight Bahia (IRE) **Burns Partnership**
8 **EAST HARLEM (IRE)**, 6, b g Leading Light (IRE)—Jill's Girl (IRE) **Spittal & Smith**
9 **EUCHAN FALLS (IRE)**, 5, ch g Poet's Voice—Miss Anneliese (IRE) **Blue Circle Racing**
10 **FATHERS ADVICE (IRE)**, 5, b g Aiken—I'll Have It (IRE) **The Racing Suite**
11 **FLYING MOON (GER)**, 6, b g Sea The Moon (GER)—Finity (USA) **West Loudoun Racing Club**
12 **FOUR KINGDOMS (IRE)**, 8, b g Lord Shanakill (USA)—Four Poorer (IRE) **The Covenanters**
13 **FOURTH OF JULY (IRE)**, 7, b g Salutino (GER)—Akasha (IRE) **Quigley & Smith**
14 **GLASSES UP (USA)**, 7, ch g English Channel (USA)—Hurricane Hallie (USA) **The Jolly Beggars**
15 **GO BOB GO (IRE)**, 5, b g Big Bad Bob (IRE)—Fire Up **Riverside Racing**
16 **GRANNY MAGS**, 6, b m Schiaparelli (GER)—Lady Racquet (IRE) **Bruce, Irving & Smith**
17 **HALLOW HALLIE (IRE)**, 4, b f Hallowed Crown (AUS)—Gold Tobougg **West Loudoun Racing Club**
18 4, B f Elusive Pimpernel (USA)—Hot On Her Heels (IRE)
19 4, Ch f Vendangeur (IRE)—I'll Have It (IRE)
20 **LAST GLANCE (IRE)**, 7, b g Shamardal (USA)—Linda Radlett (IRE)
21 **LIVELIFETOTHEMAX (IRE)**, 5, ch g Leading Light (IRE)—Maxford Lass **Miss P. A. Carnaby**
22 **MELANAMIX (IRE)**, 7, gr m Carlotamix (FR)—Melanjo (IRE) **Six In the Mix**
23 4, B g Golden Lariat (USA)—Miracle Millie (IRE)
24 4, B g Valirann (FR)—Monets Dream (IRE)
25 **ROYAL COUNTESS**, 6, b m Coach House (IRE)—Dont Tell Nan **Mr S. W. Dick**
26 **ROYAL PRINCESS**, 4, b f Fountain of Youth (IRE)—Royal Citadel (IRE) **Mr S. W. Dick**
27 **ROYAL REGENT**, 10, b g Urgent Request (IRE)—Royal Citadel (IRE) **Mr S. W. Dick**
28 4, B g Vendangeur (IRE)—Shady Pines (IRE)
29 4, B g Ol' Man River (IRE)—Sumability (IRE)
30 **THE ELECTRICIAN (IRE)**, 6, ch g Leading Light (IRE)—Spring Flower (IRE) **Quigley Smith & Spittal**
31 **THE JAD FACTOR (IRE)**, 6, b g Arcadio (GER)—Sumability (IRE) **Mr J. A. Dickson**
32 4, Ch g Rule of Law (USA)—Theatre Fool (IRE)
33 **TILSITT (FR)**, 5, b g Charm Spirit (IRE)—Azores (IRE) **Racing Connexions 10**
34 **WELL PLANTED (FR)**, 5, b g Planteur (IRE)—Next Dream (FR) **Drew & Ailsa Russell**
35 **WORLDLY APPROACH (IRE)**, 6, b m Dawn Approach (IRE)—Mundana (IRE) **Miss H. M. McMahon**
36 **WRECKED IT RALPH**, 4, b g Orientor—Rafta (IRE) **Toytown**

MR R. MIKE SMITH - continued

THREE-YEAR-OLDS
37 **CALDERBANK**, b gr g Bobby's Kitten (USA)—Outback Princess **Mr D. Orr**
38 **ROYAL EMPEROR**, b c Fountain of Youth (IRE)—Royal Citadel (IRE) **Mr S. W. Dick**
39 **SPORTY BILLY**, ch g Hot Streak (IRE)—Dolly Daydreamer **Mr A. D. Green**

Other Owners: Mr A. J. Bogle, Mr K. Bruce, Mr T. Clannachan, Mr R. Cooper, Mr R. Gibson, Mr A. D. Green, Mr K. Irving, Mr F. Milligan, Mr R. Quigley, Mr G. Reid, Mr I. Robertson, Mr A. C. Rodger, Mr A. M. Ross, Mrs A. Russell, A. J. R. Russell, Mr R. M. Smith, Mr A. H. Spittal, Miss B. Spittal, Mr I. Stewart.

483	**MRS SUE SMITH, Bingley**

Postal: **Craiglands Farm, High Eldwick, Bingley, West Yorkshire, BD16 3BE**
WORK EMAIL office@craiglandsracing.co.uk WEBSITE www.suesmithracing.co.uk

1 **ABSOLUTELY DYLAN (IRE)**, 9, b g Scorpion (IRE)—Cash Customer (IRE) **Beechfield**
2 **AIRE VALLEY LAD**, 8, b g Schiaparelli (GER)—Bonnie Rock (IRE) **Mrs S. J. Smith**
3 **ALGESIRAS**, 6, gr g Martaline—Message Personnel (FR) **Mrs S. J. Smith**
4 **AMERDALE**, 7, b g Schiaparelli (GER)—Bonnie Rock (IRE) **Mrs S. J. Smith**
5 **ANNAHARVEY LAD (IRE)**, 6, b g Famous Name—Annaharvey Pride (IRE) **Formulated Polymer Products Ltd**
6 4, B f Sageburg (IRE)—Arts Theater (IRE) **Mrs S. J. Smith**
7 **ASHOVER HILLS (IRE)**, 6, b g Yeats (IRE)—Bobnval (IRE) **Mr D. Sutherland**
8 **BURROWS DIAMOND (FR)**, 7, b m Diamond Boy (FR)—La Vie de Boitron (FR)
9 **BURROWS HALL (FR)**, 5, b g Hunter's Light (IRE)—La Vie de Boitron (FR)
10 **BURROWS LIGHT (FR)**, 4, ch g Hunter's Light (IRE)—Condoleezza (FR) **Mrs J. Morgan**
11 **CERENDIPITY (IRE)**, 5, b g Sageburg (IRE)—Check The Forecast (IRE) **Mrs A. Clarke**
12 **COPPER BEACH (IRE)**, 5, ch g Getaway (GER)—Lady McBride (IRE) **Mrs S. J. Smith**
13 **CRACKING FIND (IRE)**, 11, b g Robin des Pres (FR)—Crack The Kicker (IRE) **Mrs A. Ellis**
14 **DARSI'S DARLING (IRE)**, 6, b m Darsi (FR)—The Farmers Sister (IRE) **Mrs S. J. Smith**
15 **EAST STREET (IRE)**, 6, b g Mores Wells—Serpentine Mine (IRE) **Exors of the Late Mr T. J. Hemmings**
16 **EDDIE MUSH (IRE)**, 4, br g Sageburg (IRE)—So Proper (IRE) **Beechfield**
17 **EDGAR ALLAN POE (IRE)**, 8, b g Zoffany (IRE)—Swingsky (IRE) **McGoldrick Racing & I B Barker**
18 **FRIMEUR DE LANCRAY (FR)**, 7, b g Saddler Maker (IRE)—Jecyfly (FR) **Mrs A. Ellis**
19 **GETAWAY BAY (IRE)**, 10, b g Getaway (GER)—Wayward Star (IRE) **Mrs S. J. Smith**
20 **GOLDEN ROBIN (IRE)**, 8, br m Robin des Champs (FR)—Countess Eileen (IRE) **Mr G. J. Plimley**
21 **HEY BOY**, 7, b g Paco Boy (IRE)—Colourways (IRE) **Mrs S. J. Smith**
22 **INFORMATEUR (FR)**, 9, b g Maresca Sorrento (FR)—Isarella (GER) **Mrs J M Gray & Mr G R Orchard**
23 **ISKABEG LANE (IRE)**, 11, b g Westerner—Nosey Oscar (IRE) **Mrs S. J. Smith**
24 **JOKE DANCER**, 9, ch g Authorized (IRE)—Missy Dancer **D G Pryde & D Van Der Hoeven**
25 **JUST JESS (IRE)**, 6, b m Yeats (IRE)—She's On The Case (IRE) **Widdop Wanderers**
26 **KAPHUMOR (FR)**, 6, b g Kapgarde (FR)—Money Humor (IRE) **Mrs S. J. Smith**
27 **KAUTO D'AMOUR (FR)**, 7, b g Anabaa Blue—Kauto Luisa (FR) **Mrs S. J. Smith**
28 4, B g Sageburg (IRE)—Lightning Breeze (IRE) **Mrs S. J. Smith**
29 5, B h Multiplex—Linen Line **Mrs S. J. Smith**
30 **LOUGH DERG FARMER (IRE)**, 10, b g Presenting—Maryiver (IRE) **Mrs S. J. Smith**
31 **MIDNIGHT MYTH**, 6, b m Midnight Legend—Very Special One (IRE) **Mrs S. J. Smith**
32 4, B g Mahler—Miss Massini (IRE) **Mrs S. J. Smith**
33 **MYBURG (IRE)**, 6, br g Sageburg (IRE)—Prairie Call (IRE) **Mrs S. J. Smith**
34 **NORTH PARADE (IRE)**, 7, br g Dylan Thomas (IRE)—Retain That Magic (IRE) **Mrs S. J. Smith**
35 **PARELLIROC**, 6, b g Schiaparelli (GER)—Roc Mirage **Mrs S. J. Smith**
36 **PRAIRIE WOLF (IRE)**, 5, br g Sageburg (IRE)—Applause For Amy (IRE) **G. R. Orchard**
37 4, B g Workforce—Princess Oriane (IRE) **Mrs S. J. Smith**
38 **RAVENHILL ROAD (IRE)**, 11, ch g Exit To Nowhere (USA)—Zaffarella (IRE) **Phil & Julie Martin**
39 **RIGHT SAID TED (IRE)**, 5, b g Dylan Thomas (IRE)—Patsy Choice (IRE) **Mrs S. J. Smith**
40 **ROMEO BROWN**, 8, br g Yeats (IRE)—Santia **McGoldrick Racing**
41 **SCORCHIN**, 8, b g Multiplex—Lemon Queen (IRE) **Mrs S. J. Smith**
42 **SEVEN ARCHES**, 7, b g Yeats (IRE)—Santia **Mrs S. J. Smith**

MRS SUE SMITH - continued

43 **SHARP RESPONSE (IRE)**, 11, b g Oscar (IRE)—Lambourne Lace (IRE) **Formulated Polymer Products Ltd**
44 4, B g Iktibas—Silly Gilly (IRE) **Mrs S. J. Smith**
45 **SILVA ECLIPSE**, 9, gr g Multiplex—Linen Line **The Acre Bottom Syndicate**
46 **SMALL PRESENT (IRE)**, 7, b g Presenting—Serpentaria **Mrs A. Clarke**
47 4, Ch g Schiaparelli (GER)—Tahira (GER) **Mrs S. J. Smith**
48 **THE PADDY PIE (IRE)**, 9, b g Beneficial—Salsita (FR) **J. Wade**
49 **THELONGWAYAROUND (IRE)**, 9, b g Fruits of Love (USA)—Brass Neck (IRE) **Mrs J. Morgan**
50 **TREASURED COMPANY (IRE)**, 6, b g Fast Company (IRE)—Lady's Locket (IRE) **Mrs S. J. Smith**
51 **TRESHNISH (FR)**, 9, ch g Gold Away (IRE)—Didn't I Tell You (IRE) **D G Pryde & D Van Der Hoeven**
52 **TUMBLING DICE**, 7, b g Lucarno (USA)—Arctic Ring **Mrs S. J. Smith**
53 **VALENCE D'AUMONT (FR)**, 8, b g Sinndar (IRE)—Ice Ti (ITY) **Mrs J. Morgan**
54 **VINTAGE CLOUDS (IRE)**, 12, gr g Cloudings (IRE)—Rare Vintage (IRE) **Exors of the Late Mr T. J. Hemmings**
55 **WHAT'S THE SCOOP (IRE)**, 12, ch g Presenting—Dame d'Harvard (USA) **Mrs S. J. Smith**
56 **WOLF RUN (IRE)**, 7, b br g Presenting—Our Pride **Mr G. R. Orchard & Mrs J. M. Gray**

Other Owners: I. B. Barker, Mrs C. J. Casterton, Mrs J. M. Gray, Mr R. J. Longley, Mrs J. A. Martin, Mr P. J. Martin, McGoldrick Racing, Mrs J. Morgan, G. R. Orchard, D. G. Pryde, Mr D. P. van der Hoeven.

Assistant Trainer: Joel Parkinson, **Head Lad:** Reece Jarosiewicz, **Racing Secretary:** Rachel Swinden.

NH Jockey: Ryan Mania. **Conditional Jockey:** Sam Coltherd, Alexander Fielding, Thomas Willmott.

---

484 | **MISS SUZY SMITH, Lewes**
Postal: **Lower Coombe Stables, Angmering Park, Littlehampton, East Sussex, BN16 4EX**
Contacts: **MOBILE 07970 550828**
EMAIL suzy@suzysmithracing.co.uk **WEBSITE** www.suzysmithracing.co.uk
FACEBOOK @suzysmithracing

1 **ANIMAL (IRE)**, 6, b g Arcadio (GER)—Fantine (IRE) **James Rimmer & Chris Ames**
2 **CELESTIAL GAYLE (IRE)**, 5, b m Telescope (IRE)—Aimigayle **Everard Bloodstock & Suzy Smith**
3 **CLONDAW BISTO (IRE)**, 11, b g September Storm (GER)—Solo Venture (IRE) **The Palace Syndicate**
4 **COUNTERACT (IRE)**, 7, b g Dr Massini (IRE)—Aimigayle **Ms S. A. S. Palmer**
5 **DEBESTYMAN (IRE)**, 9, b g Mahler—Deise All Star (IRE) **The Plumpton Party**
6 **LIGHTNING BUG (IRE)**, 5, b m Starspangledbanner (AUS)—Redinha **The Bright Lights**
7 4, B f Arvico (FR)—Mad Moll (IRE)
8 **MARBLE PALACE**, 5, b m Sholokhov (IRE)—Easisbrook Jane **The Palace Syndicate**
9 5, B g Shirocco (GER)—Material World
10 **OSCARSMAN (IRE)**, 8, b g Oscar (IRE)—Ashwell Lady (IRE) **J Logan J Rimmer & S Smith**
11 **PILBARA**, 7, b g Tiger Groom—Golden Benefit (IRE) **Graham Jones, John Logan & Suzy Smith**
12 **RECORD HIGH (IRE)**, 5, b g Mahler—Leapy Lady (IRE) **Wallace Racing**
13 **ROSY WORLD**, 9, b m Shirocco (GER)—Material World **Mrs K. Allisat & Exors of the Late Mrs H. Ames**
14 **STRIKE THE FLINT**, 8, b m Shirocco (GER)—Material World **For & Smith**
15 **SUPERSTYLIN (IRE)**, 5, b g Califet (FR)—Bright Blaze (IRE) **Mrs V. Palmer**

THREE-YEAR-OLDS

16 B g Court Cave (IRE)—Aimigayle
17 B f September Storm (GER)—Material World **Miss S. Smith**
18 **SILVER HILL FLYER (IRE)**, b f Court Cave (IRE)—Jennifer Eccles **Mrs K. Allisat & Exors of the Late Mrs H. Ames**

TWO-YEAR-OLDS

19 B f 15/03 Linda's Lad—Mad Moll (IRE) (Heron Island (IRE))
20 Ch f 17/02 Jack Hobbs—Storm Patrol (Shirocco (GER)) **Miss S. Smith**

Other Owners: Mrs K. H. Allisat, Mr C. B. Ames, Mrs D. S. Everard, Mr S. M. Everard, Everard Bloodstock, Mr G. R. Jones, J. A. A. S. Logan, Mr J. Rimmer, Miss S. Smith, Table For Six, Ms C. Wallace, Mr D. Wallace, Mr J. Wallace, Mrs H. M. T. Woods.

Assistant Trainer: Mr S E Gordon-Watson.

Flat Jockey: Jane Elliott, Luke Morris, Jason Watson. **NH Jockey:** Micheal Nolan, Tom O'Brien, Gavin Sheehan.

485 MR JAMIE SNOWDEN, Lambourn

Postal: **Folly House, Upper Lambourn Road, Lambourn, Hungerford, Berkshire, RG17 8QG**
Contacts: **PHONE 01488 72800 MOBILE 07779 497563**
EMAIL info@jamiesnowdenracing.co.uk WEBSITE www.jamiesnowdenracing.co.uk
TWITTER @jamiesnowden INSTAGRAM jamie_snowden

1 **ALRIGHTJACK (IRE)**, 8, b g Stowaway—Brogella (IRE) **The GD Partnership**
2 **ANYTHINGFORLOVE**, 7, b m Black Sam Bellamy (IRE)—La Perrotine (FR) **Foxtrot Racing: Anythingforlove**
3 **ARBENNIG (IRE)**, 6, b br g Yeats (IRE)—Ultra Light (FR) **Awr Consultancy, Stacey, Kirk & Fields**
4 **BEHOLDEN**, 6, b g Cacique (IRE)—Pure Joy **Foxtrot Racing Beholden**
5 **BETWEEN THE WATERS (IRE)**, 11, ch g Indian River (FR)—Catch Ball **Mr J. E. Snowden**
6 **BRAVEHEART (IRE)**, 6, b g Westerner—Miss Knowall (IRE) **The Cherry Pickers**
7 **BUCKO'S BOY**, 7, b g Midnight Legend—Buxom (IRE) **A. J. & Mrs J. Ward**
8 **CHAPMANSHYPE (IRE)**, 8, b g Aizavoski (IRE)—Call Her Something (IRE) **The GD Partnership**
9 **CINDYSOX**, 4, b f Kayf Tara—Golden Gael **Mr E. J. M. Spurrier**
10 **COLLEGE OAK**, 7, ch g Norse Dancer (IRE)—Katmai (IRE) **Radleian Society, L Lovell & P Stacey**
11 **CORNICELLO (FR)**, 4, b g Penny's Picnic (IRE)—Breezy Hawk (GER) **ValueRacingClub.co.uk**
12 **DATSALRIGHTGINO (GER)**, 6, b g It's Gino (GER)—Delightful Sofie (GER) **The GD Partnership**
13 4, B f Flemensfirth (USA)—Day's Over
14 **DONNIE AZOFF (IRE)**, 6, ch g Dylan Thomas (IRE)—Bonny River (IRE) **The Footie Partnership**
15 **DUSKY DAYS (IRE)**, 5, ch g Flemensfirth (USA)—Day's Over **Mrs K. Gunn**
16 **EBONELLO (IRE)**, 5, b m Presenting—Ravello Bay **Friends of Ebony Horse Club**
17 **EXOD'ELA (FR)**, 8, b g Saddler Maker (IRE)—Queen'ela (FR) **Duck Jordan Wright Dellar Doel Woodward**
18 **EYE TO THE SKY**, 5, b g Telescope (IRE)—Somethinaboutmolly (IRE) **Mrs Z. A. E. Tindall**
19 **FACT OF THE MATTER (IRE)**, 12, b g Brian Boru—Womanofthemountain (IRE) **The Sandylini Racing Partnership**
20 **FORTUNATE FRED (FR)**, 7, b g Cokoriko (FR)—Rosalie Malta (FR) **Foxtrot Racing Fortunate Fred**
21 **GA LAW (FR)**, 6, b g Sinndar (IRE)—Law (FR) **The Footie Partnership**
22 **GIT MAKER (FR)**, 6, b g Saddler Maker (IRE)—Bamos (FR) **Sheep As A Lamb Syndicate**
23 **GREAT D'TROICE (FR)**, 4, b g Great Pretender (IRE)—Mick Bora (FR) **Buckett Flach Woodward Moran Sperling**
24 **GUINNESS AFFAIR (FR)**, 6, b g Fuisse (FR)—Ashkiyra (FR) **ValueRacingClub.co.uk**
25 **HARDY DU SEUIL (FR)**, 5, b g Coastal Path—Pervenche du Seuil (FR) **The Hardy Souls**
26 **HOGAN'S HEIGHT (IRE)**, 11, b g Indian River (FR)—Electre du Berlais (FR) **Foxtrot Racing: Hogan's Height**
27 **HOWDILYOUDO (IRE)**, 7, b g Presenting—Little Dil (IRE) **Chasing Gold Limited**
28 **JACK SPRAT**, 4, b g Walk In The Park (IRE)—Hell Cat Maggie (IRE) **Mr E. J. M. Spurrier**
29 **JANWORTH**, 5, b m Norse Dancer (IRE)—Buxom (IRE) **Jamie Snowden Racing Partnership**
30 **KILTEALY BRIGGS (IRE)**, 8, b g Fame And Glory—Baby Briggs (IRE) **McNeill Family Ltd**
31 **LEGENDS RYDE**, 7, ch m Midnight Legend—Ryde Back **AWTP Racing Partnership**
32 **MIDNIGHT CENTURION**, 6, b g Midnight Legend—Centoria (IRE) **The Wife Loves It Partnership**
33 **MILLDAM (FR)**, 4, gr g Martaline—Santa Dame (FR) **Goulden, & Hopgood**
34 **NIKOLAYEVA**, 5, b m Archipenko (USA)—Nezhenka **ValueRacingClub.co.uk**
35 **NO ANXIETY (IRE)**, 6, ch g Presenting—Joanne One (IRE) **Sir Chippendale Keswick**
36 **PARK THIS ONE (IRE)**, 5, b g Walk In The Park (IRE)—Soraya Pearl **Park This One Syndicate**
37 **PISGAH PIKE (IRE)**, 7, br g Famous Name—Music On D Waters (IRE) **ValueRacingClub.co.uk**
38 **PRESENT VALUE (IRE)**, 8, b g Gold Well—Presenting Shares (IRE) **ValueRacingClub.co.uk**
39 **REPRESENTING BOB (IRE)**, 6, ch g Presenting—Some Bob Back (IRE) **Beccle, Sperling, Allen & Hague**
40 **ROSE OHARA**, 6, b m Kayf Tara—Cinderella Rose **Jones Broughtons Wilson Weaver**
41 **SANDAROC**, 6, b m Shirocco (GER)—Shali San (FR) **The Sandaroc Syndicate**
42 **SEA THE CLOUDS (IRE)**, 5, b g Born To Sea (IRE)—Leo's Spirit (IRE) **ValueRacingClub.co.uk**
43 **SOLDIER OF DESTINY (IRE)**, 6, b g Presenting—Sagarich (FR) **Sir Chippendale Keswick**
44 **SOME DAY SOON (IRE)**, 9, b g Robin des Champs—Creative Approach (IRE)
   Ogilvy, Shaw, Morley&the Racegoers Club
45 **SPITFIRE GIRL (IRE)**, 5, b m Walk In The Park (IRE)—Calomeria **A Walk In The Park Partnership**
46 **STAREVITCH (FR)**, 6, b g Sinndar (IRE)—Folie Star Gate (FR) **ValueRacingClub.co.uk**
47 **STONEY MOUNTAIN (IRE)**, 9, ch g Mountain High (IRE)—Cherry Pie (FR) **Mrs A. Gillies**
48 **SUPER SURVIVOR (IRE)**, 6, b g Shantou (USA)—All The Best Mate (IRE) **Goulden, & Hopgood**
49 **TALLOW FOR COAL (IRE)**, 6, b g Arctic Cosmos (USA)—South Queen Lady (IRE) **Apache Star Racing**
50 **TEECEETHREE**, 4, b f Native Ruler—Tea Caddy **The Galloping Grannies/Teeceethree**
51 **THOMAS MACDONAGH**, 9, b g Black Sam Bellamy (IRE)—Taqreem (IRE)
   Sperling, Coomes, Davies, Hague, Collins
52 **TOP OF THE BAY (IRE)**, 5, b g Doyen (IRE)—Bay Dove **The Poised To Pounce Partnership**
53 **UP FOR PAROL (IRE)**, 6, b g Flemensfirth (USA)—Clarification (IRE) **Sir Chippendale Keswick**

MR JAMIE SNOWDEN - continued

54 **VALAMIX (IRE)**, 5, b g Valirann (FR)—Julimark (IRE) **The Poised To Pounce Partnership**
55 **VIVE DE CHARNIE (FR)**, 5, b m Zambezi Sun—Hecate (IRE) **Turf Club & Andrew Edwards**
56 **YOU WEAR IT WELL**, 5, b m Midnight Legend—Annie's Answer (IRE) **Normandie Stud Ltd**

Other Owners: AWR Consultancy Ltd, Miss B. Allen, Ms K. J. Austin, Mr S. E. Beccle, Mr A. L. Brooks, Mrs K. L. Brooks, Kate & Andrew Brooks, Sir M. F. Broughton, Mr S. W. Broughton, Mr A. N. Cheyne, Miss C. E. Davies, Mr G. Davison, Mr T. J. Dykes, Mr A. J. Edwards, Mr H. B. Fields, Mr N. Goulden, Mr B. H. Hague, Mr M. Hill, Mr K. Hopgood, Ms S. A. Hopgood, Mrs N. Jones, Mr J. C. Kirk, Mrs L. R. Lovell, Col A. J. E. Malcolm, Mr A. M. Morley, Dr M. M. Ogilvy, Mr A. M. Palk, Mr W. Palk, Racegoers Club Owners Group, Mr A. Rice, Mr N. R. Robinson, W. G. C. Shaw, Mr J. E. Snowden, Mrs J. Sperling, Mr P. A. Stacey, Stacey, Kirk & Fields, The Radleian Society Racing Syndicate, Turf Club 2020, Mr M. J. Wainwright, Mr A. J. Ward, Mrs J. Ward, Mrs R. B. Weaver, Mr D. P. Wiggin, T. C. Wilson.

Assistant Trainer: Emily Shepherd, **Head Girl:** Kate Robinson.

NH Jockey: Page Fuller, Gavin Sheehan.

---

486 **MR MIKE SOWERSBY, York**
Postal: **Southwold Farm, Goodmanham Wold, Market Weighton, York, East Yorkshire, YO43 3NA**
Contacts: **PHONE 01430 810534 MOBILE 07855 551056**

1 **FLEETING VISIT**, 9, b g Manduro (GER)—Short Affair
2 **GOOSEWOOD**, 5, b g Nathaniel (IRE)—Regina Cordium (IRE) **Mrs J. M. Plummer**
3 **HIDDEN GLEN (IRE)**, 9, ch g Stowaway—Gleanntan (IRE) **M. E. Sowersby**
4 **ISLA DIAMONDS**, 7, ch m Trans Island—Queen of Diamonds (IRE) **Miss E. C. Forman**
5 **JUPITER ROAD**, 6, b g Charm Spirit (IRE)—Thankful **Mr T J Stubbins & Mr M E Sowersby**
6 **LIQUIDISER**, 6, b g Monsieur Bond—Kaloni (IRE) **M. E. Sowersby**
7 **LUCY RULES (IRE)**, 4, b f Vadamos (FR)—Kodafine (IRE) **M. E. Sowersby**
8 **ONLY FOR PASCAL (IRE)**, 6, b m Arcadio (GER)—Emmas' House (IRE) **Mounted Gamess Assoc Syndicate**
9 **RANN OF KUTCH (IRE)**, 7, b m Dylan Thomas (IRE)—Scartara (FR) **Miss E. C. Forman**
10 **SIMPLY LUCKY (IRE)**, 13, b g Flemensfirth (USA)—Derrygowna Court (IRE) **The Southwold Set**
11 **SMASHING LASS (IRE)**, 6, ch m Sir Prancealot (IRE)—Gilded Truffle (IRE) **J. Payne**
12 **STRATEGIC (IRE)**, 7, b g Kodiac—Run To Jane (IRE) **R. D. Seldon**
13 **SUPREME STEEL (IRE)**, 11, b g Craigsteel—Tubber Gael Holly (IRE) **The Southwold Set**
14 **SWEETEST SMILE (IRE)**, 7, b m Champs Elysees—Scorn (USA) **Mrs Janet Cooper, Payne, Sowersby**
15 **WILLA**, 5, b m Dutch Art—Holberg Suite **M. E. Sowersby**
16 **ZEN MASTER (IRE)**, 10, b g Shantou (USA)—Back Log (IRE) **M. E. Sowersby**

THREE-YEAR-OLDS

17 **COMEONMEDUCK**, ch g Cityscape—Just Emma **M. E. Sowersby**

Other Owners: Mrs J. H. Cooper, J. Payne, M. E. Sowersby, T. J. Stubbins.

Assistant Trainer: Mary Sowersby.

Flat Jockey: Tom Eaves, James Sullivan.

NH Jockey: Brian Hughes.

Amateur Jockey: Mr Russell Lindsay.

487

MR JOHN SPEARING, Kinnersley
Postal: **Kinnersley Racing Limited, Kinnersley Racing Stables, Kinnersley, Severn Stoke, Worcestershire, WR8 9JR**
Contacts: **PHONE 01905 371054 MOBILE 07801 552922 FAX 01905 371054**
EMAIL jlspearing@aol.com

1 A SURE WELCOME, 8, b g Pastoral Pursuits—Croeso Bach **Kinnersley Partnership 3**
2 CAPTAIN SEDGWICK (IRE), 8, b m Approve (IRE)—Alinda (IRE) **Oakridge Racing**
3 DANNY BLEU (IRE), 4, gr g Clodovil (IRE)—Casual Remark (IRE)
4 HY EALES (IRE), 5, b m Passing Glance—Miss Conduct **Graham Eales & Kate Ive**
5 IT'S HOW WE ROLL (IRE), 8, b g Fastnet Rock (AUS)—Clodora (FR) **Kinnersley Partnership**
6 KINZ (IRE), 4, b f Footstepsinthesand—Talitha Kum (IRE) **Mr H. James**
7 4, B c Califet (FR)—Miss Conduct **Miss C. J. Ive**
8 PILLAR OF STEEL, 7, b m Shirocco (GER)—Miss Conduct **Miss C. J. Ive**
9 SHUTTHEGATE (IRE), 8, b g Milan—Miss Conduct **Kinnersley Partnership II**
10 SIXTY WEST, 4, ch g Helmet (AUS)—Deceived **Mr T. M. Hayes**
11 TOWER PRINCESS (IRE), 4, ch f Prince of Lir (IRE)—Malory Towers **Miss C. J. Ive**

THREE-YEAR-OLDS

12 CARAMELLO (IRE), ch f Ultra (IRE)—Putaringonit (IRE) **Oakridge Racing**

TWO-YEAR-OLDS

13 B f 28/04 Mayson—Malikayah (IRE) (Fasliyev (USA)) (18095) **Mr H. James**

Other Owners: G. M. Eales, Miss C. J. Ive.

Assistant Trainer: Miss C. Ive.

488

MR RICHARD SPENCER, Newmarket
Postal: **Sefton Lodge, 8 Bury Road, Newmarket, Suffolk, CB8 7BT**
Contacts: **PHONE 01638 675780 MOBILE 07720 064053**
WORK EMAIL richard.spencer@rebel-racing.co.uk

1 BERNARDO O'REILLY, 8, b g Intikhab (USA)—Baldovina **Rebel Racing (2)**
2 BIG NARSTIE (FR), 4, b br g Cable Bay (IRE)—Granadilla **Rebel Racing Premier III**
3 CAN'TSMILEWITHOUTU (IRE), 5, b g Shantou (IRE)—Maggies Oscar (IRE) **Mr P. M. Cunningham**
4 CHAMPAGNE SUPANOVA (IRE), 5, b g Camacho—Flawless Pink **Mr P. M. Cunningham**
5 CHIM CHIMNEY, 4, b g Cockney Rebel (IRE)—Wonderful Life (IRE) **Mr P. M. Cunningham**
6 CIGARETTESNALCOHOL (IRE), 6, ch g Ocovango—Moylisha Red (IRE) **Rebel Jumping II**
7 DANDY MAESTRO, 4, ch g Dandy Man (IRE)—Maids Causeway (IRE) **Mr J. Power**
8 DANNI CALIFORNIA (IRE), 4, gr f The Gurkha (IRE)—Satwa Ruby (FR) **Mr P. M. Cunningham**
9 GERTCHA (IRE), 5, b g Slade Power (IRE)—Elouges (IRE) **Team Dcl**
10 HAROLD SHAND (IRE), 4, b g Acclamation—Shy Audience (IRE) **Rebel Racing Premier III**
11 INSOMNIA, 4, b g Due Diligence (USA)—River Song (USA) **Rebel Racing Premier III**
12 KEYSER SOZE (IRE), 8, ch g Arcano (IRE)—Causeway Queen (IRE) **Rebel Racing (2)**
13 NIGHTBOAT TO CAIRO (IRE), 5, br g Soldier of Fortune (IRE)—Bobbina (IRE) **Mr P. M. Cunningham**
14 NO ESCAPE, 4, b g Cityscape—Elegant Annie **Mr Phil Cunningham & Mr Richard Spencer**
15 OCEAN EYES (IRE), 4, b f Mehmas (IRE)—Rise Up Lotus (IRE) **Mr P. M. Cunningham**
16 ODYSSEY GIRL (IRE), 5, gr m Gutaifan (IRE)—Lady Marita (IRE)
17 PEEJAYBEE (FR), 6, grey g Ballingarry (IRE)—Playa du Charmil (FR) **Martin Gowing & Paul Booker**
18 PROFESSIONAL WIDOW (IRE), 4, gr f Markaz (IRE)—Petite Cherie (IRE) **Mrs E. Cunningham**
19 PUMP IT UP, 4, ch f Charming Thought—Cherry Malotte **Mr P. M. Cunningham**
20 REVICH (IRE), 6, b g Requinto (IRE)—Kathleen Rafferty (IRE) **Middleham Park Lxvii & Phil Cunningham**
21 ROLL WITH IT (IRE), 6, b g Sholokhov (IRE)—Que Pasa (IRE) **Rebel Jumping II**
22 SIR JACK YEATS (IRE), 11, b g Yeats (IRE)—Quadrennial (IRE) **Gowing's Eleven**
23 STAY CLASSY (IRE), 6, ch m Camacho—Hollow Green (IRE) **Balasuriya,Cook,Cunningham,Gowing,Spencer**
24 THE CITY'S PHANTOM, 5, b g Free Eagle (IRE)—Meet Marhaba (IRE) **Mr P. M. Cunningham**

MR RICHARD SPENCER - continued

25 **THEFASTNTHECURIOUS,** 4, ch f Fast Company (IRE)—Dame Plume (IRE) **Mr P. M. Cunningham**
26 **TWISTEDFIRESTARTER (IRE),** 6, b g Sageburg (IRE)—Mercy Mission **Rebel Jumping II**
27 **TYSON FURY,** 5, ch g Iffraaj—Za Za Zoom (IRE) **Balasuriya,Cook,Cunningham,Gowing,Spencer**
28 **WINGS OF A DOVE (IRE),** 4, gr f Dark Angel (IRE)—Silk Bow **Mr P. M. Cunningham**
29 **WONDERWALL (IRE),** 6, b g Yeats (IRE)—Rock Me Gently **Rebel Jumping II**

THREE-YEAR-OLDS

30 **FUEGO,** b c Cityscape—La Pantera **Mr A. Cunningham**
31 **INTOXICATED,** b f Fountain of Youth (USA)—River Song (USA) **Mr P. M. Cunningham**
32 **LITTLE PRAYER (IRE),** b f Mehmas (IRE)—Nasimi **Mr P. M. Cunningham**
33 **LUCKY MAN (IRE),** b c Kodi Bear (IRE)—Vastitas (IRE) **Rebel Racing Premier IV**
34 **MR BIG STUFF,** b c Iffraaj—Groovejet **Mr P. M. Cunningham**
35 **SPACE COWBOY (IRE),** b c Kodi Bear (IRE)—Usem **Rebel Racing Premier IV**
36 **SUPERSTAR DJ,** b c Time Test—Excello **Mr P. M. Cunningham**
37 **THE MAD MONK (IRE),** gr g Gregorian (IRE)—Broadway Musical (IRE) **Rebel Racing Premier IV**
38 **TOO FUNKY,** b f Mayson—Instructress **Mr P. M. Cunningham**
39 **UNFINISHEDSYMPATHY (IRE),** b br f El Kabeir (USA)—Bella Ophelia (IRE) **Mrs E. Cunningham**

TWO-YEAR-OLDS

40 Ch c 02/03 Rajasinghe (IRE)—Bakoura (Green Desert (USA)) **Mr P. M. Cunningham**
41 Ch f 20/02 Rajasinghe (IRE)—Bronte Flyer (Nayef (USA)) **Mr P. M. Cunningham**
42 B f 29/04 Rajasinghe (IRE)—Caius College Girl (IRE) (Royal Applause) **Mr P. M. Cunningham**
43 B f 27/03 Rajasinghe (IRE)—Cherry Malotte (Pivotal) **Mr P. M. Cunningham**
44 B c 15/03 Muhaarar—Cockney Dancer (Cockney Rebel (IRE)) (44000) **Mr P. M. Cunningham**
45 B f 03/04 Rajasinghe (IRE)—Dame Plume (IRE) (Amadeus Wolf) **Mr P. M. Cunningham**
46 B c 25/03 Rajasinghe (IRE)—Encantar (Equiano (FR)) **Mr P. M. Cunningham**
47 B c 04/03 Rajasinghe (IRE)—Goodnightsuzy (IRE) (Azamour (IRE)) **Mr P. M. Cunningham**
48 B c 23/02 Iffraaj—Groovejet (Cockney Rebel (IRE)) **Mr P. M. Cunningham**
49 B c 09/03 Time Test—Heather Lark (IRE) (Shamardal (USA)) **Mr P. M. Cunningham**
50 Ch c 20/03 Rajasinghe (IRE)—Instructress (Diktat) **Mr P. M. Cunningham**
51 Ch c 09/04 Rajasinghe (IRE)—Lucia de Medici (Medicean) **Mr P. M. Cunningham**
52 B c 17/02 Rajasinghe (IRE)—Oneroa (IRE) (Dandy Man (IRE)) **Mr P. M. Cunningham**
53 B f 07/02 Rajasinghe (IRE)—Perfect Pose (IRE) (Amadeus Wolf) (4762) **Mr P. M. Cunningham**
54 B c 02/03 Rajasinghe (IRE)—Rebel Surge (IRE) (Kodiac) **Mr P. M. Cunningham**
55 B f 28/03 Rajasinghe (IRE)—Twizzell (Equiano (FR)) **Mr P. M. Cunningham**
56 B f 10/04 Rajasinghe (IRE)—Wonderful Life (IRE) (Canford Cliffs (IRE)) **Mr P. M. Cunningham**

Assistant Trainer: Mr Joe Akehurst, **Pupil Assistant:** Mr Jack Jones, **Travelling Head:** Miss Tegan Kerr.

Apprentice Jockey: Mr Angus Villiers.

---

489 **MR SEB SPENCER, Malton**
Postal: 79 Harvest Drive, Malton, North Yorkshire, YO17 7BF
Contacts: **MOBILE 07790 060050**
EMAIL sebspencerracing@gmail.com

1 **BANDSMAN RICE,** 5, b g Haafhd—Allashka (FR) **E.A. Moorey & E.G. Moorey**
2 **BIG MUDDY,** 5, b g Monsieur Bond (IRE)—Nine Red **Mac Racing**
3 **DESERT DREAM,** 8, b g Oasis Dream—Rosika **The Racing Emporium**
4 **JET SET GO,** 7, ch m Equiano (FR)—Golden Valley **D Bainbridge & N Bycroft**
5 **LITTLE MUDDY,** 6, b m Mr Medici (IRE)—Secret Oasis **Mac Racing**

THREE-YEAR-OLDS

6 **MUDDY LYNN,** b f Intrinsic—She's So Pretty (IRE) **N. Bycroft**

Other Owners: Mr D. R. Bainbridge, N. Bycroft, Mr D. Fogg, Mr E. A. Moorey, Mr E. G. Moorey.

490   **MR HENRY SPILLER, Newmarket**
Postal: Henry Spiller Racing, Sackville House Stables, Sackville Street, Newmarket, Suffolk, CB8 8DX
Contacts: MOBILE 07786 263997
WORK EMAIL henry@henryspiller.com EMAIL office@henryspiller.com
WEBSITE www.henryspiller.com

1 **ALMAAN (USA)**, 4, ch g Speightstown (USA)—Rosalind (USA) **Mr K. Clarke & Partner**
2 **CAMERATA (GER)**, 4, b f Kingman—Calyxa **Byerley Thoroughbreds Ltd**
3 **CLASSICAL MEMORIES (IRE)**, 4, b f Kodi Bear (IRE)—Lyric Piece **Dark Horse Partnership**
4 **CRACK REGIMENT (FR)**, 5, b g Siyouni (FR)—Coiffure **Mr R. P. A. Spiller**
5 **DARK DESIGN (IRE)**, 5, b g Gutaifan (IRE)—Divine Design (IRE) **Aj Racing**
6 **ETHEL C (IRE)**, 4, b f Zebedee—Lush (IRE) **Dethrone Racing**
7 **EXPERT OPINION**, 4, b g Worthadd (IRE)—Calypso Choir **Aj Racing**
8 **HUNTERS STEP**, 6, b g Mukhadram—Step Softly **Aj Racing**
9 **IRISH TIMES**, 7, b g Swiss Spirit—Amouage Royale (IRE) **Dark Horse Partnership**
10 **LAST TO BID (FR)**, 6, ch h Makfi—Last Song **Mr R. P. A. Spiller**
11 **LEGENDE D'ART (IRE)**, 5, b g Kingman—Legende Bleue **Dethrone Racing**
12 **MIDNIGHT LUCK**, 4, b gr f Gregorian (IRE)—Maybe Enough **Mr S. Davies**
13 **NAHAAB (FR)**, 4, b f Le Havre (IRE)—Desert Red (IRE) **& Noel**
14 **THE THIRD MAN**, 11, gr g Dalakhani (IRE)—Spinning Queen **Mrs D. Spiller**
15 **TRIPLE PEEL (FR)**, 4, b f Le Havre (IRE)—Scalambra **Mr R. P. A. Spiller**

THREE-YEAR-OLDS

16 B f Intello (GER)—Appointee (IRE) **Mr R. P. A. Spiller**
17 **BAKED ALASKA**, b f Iffraaj—Figment
18 **BENAD HASCHE (IRE)**, b f Estidhkaar (IRE)—Along The Shore (IRE) **Byerley Thoroughbreds Ltd**
19 **BINT ALSARAB (IRE)**, b f Zoffany (IRE)—Redmaven (IRE) **Byerley Thoroughbreds Ltd**
20 **BOADICEA BELLE (IRE)**, b f Holy Roman Emperor (IRE)—Belle des Airs (IRE) **Mr K. Clarke & Partner**
21 **BRAULIA**, b f Swiss Spirit—Faeroes (IRE) **G. B. Partnership**
22 B f Cityscape—Elegant Annie **Hunscote Stud Limited**
23 **ESTEFAN**, ch f Havana Gold (IRE)—L'Addition **Hunscote Stud Limited**
24 **MCQUEEN (IRE)**, ch c Zoffany (IRE)—Shahralasal (IRE) **Byerley Thoroughbreds Ltd**
25 **SIRIUS WHITE (IRE)**, gr g Markaz (IRE)—Piacere (IRE) **Dark Horse Partnership**
26 **TAHASUN (IRE)**, b f Tamayuz—Urjuwaan **Sarkar**
27 **TEEKANA**, b f Havana Gold (IRE)—Teeky **Moyns Park Estate and Stud Ltd**
28 **VICTORIA GROVE**, b f Siyouni (FR)—Baltic Best (IRE) **Mr R. P. A. Spiller**

TWO-YEAR-OLDS

29 B c 06/02 Aclaim (IRE)—Ulfah Dream (Oasis Dream) (17000) **Sarkar**

Other Owners: Mr K. Clarke, Mr A. M. H. Heald, M. G. H. Heald, Mrs D. Noel, Mr D. Sarkar, Mrs D. Sarkar, Mr J. Sarkar, Mr O. Sarkar, Mr H. Simcock, Mr H. C. Spiller, The Select Racing Club Limited.

---

491   **MR FOZZY STACK, Cashel**
Postal: Thomastown Castle Stud, Golden, Cashel, Co. Tipperary, Ireland
Contacts: PHONE +353 62 54129
EMAIL contact@stackracing.ie WEBSITE www.stackracing.ie

1 **AHANDFULOFSUMMERS**, 4, b f Galileo (IRE)—Scream Blue Murder (IRE)
2 **APOLLINAIRE**, 5, b g Poet's Voice—Affaire de Coeur
3 **CHEVAL BLANC**, 4, b gr c Dark Angel (IRE)—La Collina (IRE)
4 **FLYING ROCK**, 4, b f Air Force Blue (USA)—Cry Me A River (IRE)
5 **KING OF CASHEL (IRE)**, 5, b g Ruler of the World—pectin
6 **KONDO ISAMI (IRE)**, 4, b c Zouzou—galileo
7 **PITA PINTA (IRE)**, 4, b f Sir Percy—Bantam (IRE)
8 **TOOREEN ANGEL**, 5, b m Battle of Marengo (IRE)—Annmary Girl

MR FOZZY STACK - continued

THREE-YEAR-OLDS

- 9 **A SHIN UNDINE (IRE)**, b f Slade Power (IRE)—La Ina (GER)
- 10 **CASTLE STAR**, b c Starspangledbanner (AUS)—Awohaam
- 11 **DINGLE ROCK (IRE)**, b f No Nay Never (USA)—Dingle View (IRE)
- 12 **FIZZICAL**, ch f Starspangledbanner (AUS)—Medicean Star (IRE)
- 13 **HERMANA ESTRELLA**, b f Starspangledbanner (AUS)—The Last Sister
- 14 **JOHN THE BAPTIST**, b c Caravaggio—Scream Blue Murder (IRE)
- 15 **KEEP AN EYE OUT (IRE)**, b f Starspangledbanner (AUS)—Sunbird
- 16 **LECHRO**, ch f Highland Reel—Sirici
- 17 **MOODFORAMELODY**, b f Camelot—Polish Belle
- 18 **MY EYES ADORE YOU**, ch f Profitable—Crossanza
- 19 **PASO ROBLES**, ch f Ulysses—Fountain of Peace
- 20 B c Caravaggio (USA)—Queen Boudica
- 21 **RANCHO SANTA FE**, b f Frankel—Love is Blindless
- 22 **RED BUD**, b f Ribchester—Ghostflower
- 23 **RED LACEWING**, b f No Nay Never (USA)—Mala Mala
- 24 **RULER LEGEND (IRE)**, b c Camelot—Avenue Dargent
- 25 **STARSONG**, b f Starspangledbanner (AUS)—Meetyouatthemoon
- 26 **STARSONG (IRE)**, b f Starspangledbanner (AUS)—Meetyouatthemoon (IRE)
- 27 **TAWNY COSTER (IRE)**, b f Caravaggio—Briolette (IRE)
- 28 **THUNDER ECLIPSE**, b c Holy Roman Emperor (IRE)—Emirate Jewel
- 29 **WITCHOFTHEWOOD**, b f Lope de Vega—Elle Woods

TWO-YEAR-OLDS

- 30 B c 08/04 Zoustar (AUS)—Alexiade (IRE) (Montjeu (IRE)) (119048)
- 31 B f 16/02 Camelot—American Spirit (IRE) (Rock of Gibraltar (IRE)) (50000)
- 32 B br c 23/02 Night of Thunder (IRE)—Arabescatta (Monsun (GER)) (102041)
- 33 B f 28/04 Starspangledbanner (AUS)—Blue Dahlia (IRE) (Shamardal (USA))
- 34 B f 26/02 No Nay Never (USA)—Canada Water (Dansili) (200000)
- 35 B c 04/05 No Nay Never (USA)—Catch The Eye (IRE) (Oratorio (IRE)) (106293)
- 36 B f 14/03 Starspangledbanner (AUS)—Celestial Love (IRE) (Galileo (IRE)) (12381)
- 37 Ch f 29/03 Starspangledbanner (AUS)—Coco Rouge (IRE) (Shamardal (USA)) (100000)
- 38 Ch c 12/03 Sea The Stars (IRE)—Dame du Roi (IRE) (Dark Angel (IRE)) (297619)
- 39 B 30/01 Justify (USA)—Data Dependent (USA) (More Than Ready (USA))
- 40 B f 11/02 Mehmas (IRE)—Doris Marie (IRE) (Creachadoir (IRE)) (78095)
- 41 B c 09/01 No Nay Never (USA)—Dowager (Groom Dancer (USA)) (89286)
- 42 Ch f 23/02 Night of Thunder (IRE)—Elope (GER) (Tiger Hill (IRE)) (47000)
- 43 B f 09/05 Churchill (IRE)—Emirate Jewel (Pivotal)
- 44 B f 03/02 Camelot—Fastnet Mist (IRE) (Fastnet Rock (AUS)) (120000)
- 45 Ch c 26/04 Starspangledbanner (AUS)—Franzy (IRE) (Dragon Pulse (IRE)) (57143)
- 46 B c 12/04 Churchill—Gentle Breeze
- 47 B f 06/02 Starspangledbanner (AUS)—Glafyra (FR) (High Chaparral (IRE)) (51020)
- 48 B f 23/03 Starspangledbanner (AUS)—Hidden Charms (IRE) (Canford Cliffs (IRE))
- 49 Ch f 07/04 Footstepsinthesand—Inis Boffin (Danehill Dancer (IRE)) (110544)
- 50 Ch c 23/01 Starspangledbanner (AUS)—Keep Dancing (IRE) (Distant Music (USA)) (110000)
- 51 B c 05/05 Zoustar (AUS)—London Welsh (Cape Cross (IRE)) (76531)
- 52 Ch f 22/03 Churchill (IRE)—Many Hearts (USA) (Distorted Humor (USA)) (22109)
- 53 B f 15/05 Holy Roman Emperor (IRE)—Medicean Star (IRE) (Galileo (IRE))
- 54 B f 19/03 U S Navy Flag (USA)—Naahedh (Medicean) (34014)
- 55 B c 21/02 Hard Spun (USA)—Patti O'Rahy (USA) (Rahy (USA)) (111227)
- 56 Ch g 01/01 Night of Thunder (IRE)—Precious Dream (USA) (Mr Greeley (USA)) (157313)
- 57 Ch c 25/05 Starspangledbanner (AUS)—Pure Greed (IRE) (Galileo (IRE))
- 58 Ch f 12/04 Starspangledbanner (AUS)—Ravissante (IRE) (Galileo (IRE)) (29762)
- 59 **RUN RAN RUN (IRE)**, ch c 17/05 No Nay Never (USA)—Scream Blue Murder (IRE) (Oratorio (IRE))
- 60 Gr f 27/04 Starspangledbanner (AUS)—Serasana (Red Ransom (USA)) (55238)
- 61 Ch c 28/03 Starspangledbanner (AUS)—Virginia Celeste (IRE) (Galileo (IRE)) (69728)

Owners: Mr Rick Barnes, Mr Michael Begley, Craig Bernick, Peter Chiu, Iman Hartono, Mr T. Hyde Jnr, Mr D. Keoghan, Mrs J. Magnier, Mr Casey McLiney, Mr B. Parker, Mr P. Piller, Mrs Jane Rowlinson, Mary Slack, J. A. Stack, Mr Michael Tabor,

MR FOZZY STACK - continued

Genevieve Britton, Francis Brooke, Flaxman Stables, Mr Bon Ho, Mrs MV Magnier, Toshihiro Matsumoto, Mrs Eimear Mulhearne, R O'Callaghan, MR Michael O'Flynn, D Pearson, B Sangster, Mrs P Shanahan, Cayton Park Stud.

Flat Jockey: Mark Enright, Andrew Slattery. **Apprentice Jockey:** Olivia Shanahan.

---

492 **MR EUGENE STANFORD, Newmarket**
Postal: **2 Rous Memorial Cottages, Old Station Road, Newmarket, Suffolk, CB8 8DP**
Contacts: **PHONE 01638 665507 MOBILE 07761 223096**
EMAIL e.stanford077@btinternet.com WEBSITE www.eugenestanfordracing.com

1 **BELLA BLUR,** 10, ch m Showcasing—Ellablue **Miss C. R. Williams**
2 4, Ch f Equiano (FR)—Harpers Ruby **Mr J. A. Kay**
3 **Q CEE,** 9, b g Denounce—Gibraltar Lass (USA) **Mr M. W. Goodridge**

THREE-YEAR-OLDS

4 **ARCHIE HARPER,** b c Equiano (FR)—Harpers Ruby **Mr J. A. Kay**
5 B c Mondialiste (IRE)—La Havrese (FR) **Mr J. A. Kay**
6 **MEGANSEIGTHTEEN,** b f Ardad (IRE)—Mea Parvitas (IRE) **Jimmy Kay & Partner**

Other Owners: Mr J. A. Kay, Mr E. V. Stanford.

---

493 **MR DANIEL STEELE, Henfield**
Postal: **Blacklands House, Wheatsheaf Road, Wineham, Henfield, West Sussex, BN5 9BE**
Contacts: **PHONE 07809 405036**
EMAIL danielsteele14@hotmail.co.uk

1 **CHIVERS (IRE),** 11, b g Duke of Marmalade (IRE)—Thara (USA) **Mr D. R. Steele**
2 **CLONGOWES (IRE),** 8, b g New Approach (IRE)—Punctilious **Sam Tingey & Charlie Tingey**
3 4, B g Linda's Lad—Dainty Diva (IRE) **Vectis Racing**
4 **DELL ORO (FR),** 9, b g Walk In The Park (IRE)—Kallistea (FR) **D Steele S Tingey C Tingey**
5 **ELEVATED (IRE),** 5, b g Siyouni (FR)—Kahira (IRE) **Sam Tingey & Charlie Tingey**
6 **GABSTER (IRE),** 9, ch m Iffraaj—Mozie Cat (IRE) **Mr D. R. Steele**
7 **GOLD SOUK (IRE),** 5, b g Casamento (IRE)—Dubai Sunrise (USA) **Sam Tingey & Charlie Tingey**
8 **MINT JULEP,** 4, b f Helmet (AUS)—Ya Latif (IRE) **Vectis Racing**
9 **RACING COUNTRY (IRE),** 7, b g Dubawi (IRE)—Movin' Out (AUS) **Sam Tingey & Charlie Tingey**
10 **SAPPHIRE BOMBAY,** 5, b m Blue Bresil (FR)—Rosygo (IRE) **Mrs J. I. Phillips-Hill**
11 **THE DEFIANT,** 6, b g Morpheus—Killer Class **Mr D. R. Steele**

TWO-YEAR-OLDS

12 B f 02/04 Media Hype—Dainty Diva (IRE) (Indian Danehill (IRE)) **Mr D. R. Steele**

---

494 **MRS JACKIE STEPHEN, Inverurie**
Postal: **Conglass Farmhouse, Inverurie, Aberdeenshire, AB51 5DN**
Contacts: **PHONE 01467 621267 MOBILE 07980 785924 FAX 01467 620511**
EMAIL jackiestephen123@hotmail.com WEBSITE www.jackiestephenracing.com

1 **ANY JOB WILL DO (IRE),** 6, ch g Shirocco (GER)—Funcheon Lady (IRE) **Northern Lights Racing**
2 **CLEAR ABILITY (IRE),** 6, ch m Imperial Monarch (IRE)—Celtic Peace (IRE) **Lessells & Ritchie**
3 **DUNNOTTAR CASTLE,** 6, b g Kalanisi (IRE)—Sister Shannon (IRE) **Horn & Stephen**
4 **JOANNA I'M FINE (IRE),** 5, ch m Famous Name—Toye Native (IRE) **Mr G. Truscott**
5 **KILFINAN BAY (IRE),** 7, b g Mahler—Midnight Special (IRE) **Mrs J. S. Stephen**
6 **LOCK DOWN LUKE,** 6, b g Lucarno (USA)—La Grande Villez (FR) **P. & Mark Fleming**
7 **LOVELY SCHTUFF (IRE),** 10, b g Court Cave (IRE)—The Long Bill (IRE) **High Country Racing**

MRS JACKIE STEPHEN - continued

8 **SCULLYS FORGE (IRE)**, 8, ch g Doyen (IRE)—Queen of Questions (IRE) **Mrs J. S. Stephen**
9 **SPUTNIK (IRE)**, 7, b g Recital (FR)—Itlallendintears (IRE) **Neracehorses, Hamilton, Stephen&whyte**
10 **THE GREAT GEORGIE**, 7, b g Multiplex—For More (FR) **Mr P. G. Stephen**
11 **THE REAL RASCAL (IRE)**, 5, b g Sageburg (IRE)—Real Revival (IRE) **Mr P. G. Stephen**
12 **TOUGH OUT (IRE)**, 5, br g Tough As Nails (IRE)—Doutzen (IRE) **High Country Racing**
13 **WHOA BLACK BETTY (IRE)**, 7, br m Jeremy (USA)—Strong Lady (IRE) **Jackie Stephen Racing Club**
14 **WOLFCATCHER (IRE)**, 10, b g King's Best (USA)—Miss Particular (IRE) **Northern Lights Racing**

Other Owners: Mr D. L. Dunbar, Mr M. R. D. Fleming, Mr S. D. Hamilton, Mr C. Horn, Mr J. S. Lessells, North East Racehorses, Mr G. G. Ritchie, Mrs J. S. Stephen, Mr P. G. Stephen, Mr A. G. Whyte.

Assistant Trainer: Patrick Stephen.

495
MRS KATIE STEPHENS, Shaldon
Postal: **Sikymsa Meadow, Short Lane, Shaldon, Devon, TQ14 0HE**
EMAIL sikymsaracing@gmail.com

1 **ELLAS EREN**, 6, b m Norse Dancer (IRE)—Legion of Merit **Mrs K. J. Stephens**
2 **KING OF THE STORY (IRE)**, 6, b g Yeats (IRE)—Episodique (IRE) **Hollingsworth, Drewett, Fox & Porter**
3 **ROYAL PLAZA**, 11, b g King's Theatre (IRE)—Friendly Craic (IRE) **Friends Have Fun Racing**
4 **TEMPLIER (IRE)**, 9, b g Mastercraftsman (IRE)—Tigertail (FR) **Mr M. J. Langdell**

Other Owners: Mr D. H. Drewett, Mr M. J. T. Fox, Mr M. R. Hollingsworth, Mr M. J. Langdell, Mr P.B. Porter, Mrs K. J. Stephens.

496
MR ROBERT STEPHENS, Caldicot
Postal: **The Knoll, St. Brides Netherwent, Caldicot, Gwent, NP26 3AT**
Contacts: **MOBILE 07717 477177**
EMAIL robertdavidstephens@btinternet.com WEBSITE www.robertstephensracing.com

1 **BUMBLE BAY**, 12, b g Trade Fair—Amica **A Mossop & H Scale**
2 **ECHO DU LARGE (FR)**, 8, b g Blue Bresil (FR)—Gardagua (FR) **Castle Farm Racing**
3 **ESPRESSO FREDDO (IRE)**, 8, b g Fast Company (IRE)—Spring Bouquet (IRE) **Threes Company**
4 **FIRST DESTINATION**, 10, b m Rail Link—Hollow Quaill (IRE) **A. J. Mossop**
5 **GIRL FROM IPANEMA (IRE)**, 4, ch f Fast Company (IRE)—Siphon Melody (USA) **Mrs V. James**
6 **GOLDEN GLORY (IRE)**, 8, b m Fame And Glory—Howyakeepan (IRE) **Castle Farm Racing Golden Syndicate**
7 **HAVANA DAWN**, 5, gr m Havana Gold (IRE)—Rock Ace (IRE) **Mr R. D. Stephens**
8 **HEDGEINATOR (IRE)**, 12, ch g Beneficial—Annalecky (IRE) **Threes Company**
9 **KUMASI**, 5, ch g New Approach (IRE)—Ghanaian (IRE) **Mr R. D. Stephens**
10 **MELAKAZ (IRE)**, 4, br g Markaz (IRE)—Melatonina (IRE) **Mr T. J. Moynihan**
11 **MERE ANARCHY (IRE)**, 11, b g Yeats (IRE)—Maracana (IRE) **Les Oxley & R Stephens**
12 **PASSIN' THRU**, 6, b m Nathaniel (IRE)—Go Between **M Duthie & T Moynihan**
13 5, B m Arcadio (GER)—Pippedatthepost
14 **PORT NOIR**, 5, bl m Harbour Watch (IRE)—Cocabana **Cartwright Partnership**
15 **PUSH THE TEMPO (IRE)**, 9, b g Gold Well—Fairpark (IRE) **Castle Farm Racing**
16 **SON OF OZ**, 5, ch g Australia—Ambria (GER) **Threes Company**
17 **STREET JESTER**, 8, b g Avonbridge—Street Diva (USA) **Mr R. Miles**
18 **THE GARRISON (IRE)**, 8, b g Arakan (USA)—Kerry Lily (IRE) **Mrs V. James**
19 **TIFFANY ROSE**, 6, ch m Black Sam Bellamy (IRE)—Maria Antonia (IRE) **Threes Company**
20 **TUDORS TREASURE**, 11, b g Dr Massini (IRE)—Rude Health **Four Seasons Partnership**
21 **TURPIN GOLD**, 6, b g Dick Turpin (IRE)—Tamara **The Shinton Family**

MR ROBERT STEPHENS - continued

THREE-YEAR-OLDS
22 **ALYA'S GOLD AWARD (IRE)**, b f Starspangledbanner (AUS)—Quinta Verde (IRE) **Mrs V. James**

TWO-YEAR-OLDS
23 **BERAGON**, b g 09/04 Zoffany (IRE)—Got To Dream (Duke of Marmalade (IRE)) (5500) **A. J. Mossop**
24 B f 15/03 Free Eagle (IRE)—Grain de Beaute (IRE) (Lawman (FR)) (2857) **M Duthie & T Moynihan**
25 B g 07/02 Fast Company (IRE)—Hallouella (Halling (USA)) (10476) **Mrs V. James**
26 B c 18/04 Fast Company (IRE)—Starbright (IRE) (Duke of Marmalade (IRE)) (16190) **M Duthie & T Moynihan**

Other Owners: Mr L. Cartwright, Mr I. J. K. Croker, Mr M. Duthie, Mrs V. James, A. J. Mossop, Mr T. J. Moynihan, Mr L. T. Oxley, Mr W. B. H. Scale, D. T. Shorthouse, Mr K. Slade, Mr R. D. Stephens.

Assistant Trainer: Rosie Stephens.

NH Jockey: Ciaran Gethings, Micheal Nolan, Tom O'Brien. **Amateur Jockey:** Mr Craig Dowson, Mr Morgan Winstone.

---

497 | **MR JOHN STIMPSON, Newcastle-under-Lyme**
Postal: **Trainers Lodge, Park Road, Butterton, Newcastle-under-Lyme, Staffordshire, ST5 4DZ**
Contacts: **PHONE 01782 636020**
EMAIL john@redskyuk.com

1 **HURRICANE DYLAN (IRE)**, 11, b g Brian Boru—Definetly Sarah (IRE) **Mr J. Stimpson**
2 **LOBO DEL MAR**, 4, b g Fountain of Youth (USA)—Apache Glory (USA) **Mr J. Stimpson**
3 **MY BROTHER MIKE (IRE)**, 8, b g Bated Breath—Coming Back **Mr J. Stimpson**
4 **MY TOWN CHICAGO (USA)**, 7, b g Medaglia d'Oro (USA)—Say You Will (IRE) **Mr J. Stimpson**
5 **PERUVIAN SUMMER (IRE)**, 6, ch g Lope de Vega (IRE)—Need You Now (IRE) **Mr J. Stimpson**
6 **POPPOP (FR)**, 6, b g Great Pretender (IRE)—Bloody Sunday (FR) **Mr J. Stimpson**
7 **THE GREY BANDIT**, 5, bl g Gregorian (IRE)—Reel Cool **Mr J. Stimpson**
8 **VERONA SNOW**, 4, b g Fountain of Youth (USA)—Diletta Tommasa (IRE) **Mr J. Stimpson**

---

498 | **MR WILLIAM STONE, West Wickham**
Postal: **The Meadow, Streetly End, West Wickham, Cambridge, Cambridgeshire, CB21 4RP**
Contacts: **MOBILE 07788 971094**
EMAIL williamstone1@hotmail.co.uk

1 **DASHING DICK (IRE)**, 4, b g Cable Bay (IRE)—Raggiante (IRE) **Ron Spore & Dr C Scott**
2 **DASHING ROGER**, 5, b g Fast Company (IRE)—Croeso Cusan **R. C. Spore**
3 **JEANETTE MAY**, 6, b m Dick Turpin (IRE)—Clock Opera (IRE) **Mr Shane Fairweather & Dr C Scott**
4 **LALANIA**, 7, br m Kheleyf (USA)—George's Gift **Dr C. M. Scott**
5 **LITTLE BROWN TROUT**, 5, b g Casamento (IRE)—Clock Opera (IRE) **Dr C. M. Scott**
6 **LITTLE SUNFLOWER**, 4, ch f Pearl Secret—Dance In The Sun **Dr C. M. Scott**
7 **PILLARS OF EARTH**, 5, b g Nathaniel (IRE)—Aliena (IRE) **Four Winds Racing Partnership**

THREE-YEAR-OLDS
8 **DASHING PANTHER**, b c Slade Power (IRE)—Irrational **Ron Spore & Dr C Scott**
9 **DASHING RAT**, b c Adaay (IRE)—Hot Secret **R. C. Spore**
10 **DASHING TO YOU**, b g Olympic Glory (IRE)—Libre A Vous (FR) **Ron Spore & Dr C Scott**
11 **DE ROCKER**, ch g Equiano (FR)—Kawaii **Four Winds Racing Partnership**
12 B g Showcasing—Khaki (IRE) **R. C. Spore**
13 B c Gregorian (IRE)—Satin Waters **Ron Spore & P D West**

TWO-YEAR-OLDS
14 B f 01/03 Awtaad (IRE)—Georgie Hyde (Yeats (IRE)) (4000) **R. C. Spore**

MR WILLIAM STONE - continued

15 Br f 06/03 Zarak (FR)—Quandreviendrastu (IRE) (Dream Ahead (USA)) (9000) **R. C. Spore**
16 ROMANTIC SUNLIGHT, b f 12/04 Tasleet—Percy's Romance (Sir Percy) **Mrs E. A. P. Haynes**

499	**MR WILF STOREY, Consett**

Postal: **Grange Farm & Stud, Mugglewick, Consett, Consett, County Durham, DH8 9DW**
Contacts: **PHONE 01207 255259 MOBILE 07860 510441**
EMAIL wlstorey@metronet.co.uk WEBSITE www.wilfstorey.com

1 GOING UNDERGROUND, 5, ch g Lope de Vega (IRE)—Jam Jar
                                          H S Hutchinson and W Glass, H. S. Hutchinson, Mr W. D. Glass
2 PERFECT SOLDIER (IRE), 8, b g Kodiac—Independent Girl (IRE) **Gremlin Racing**
3 TARNHELM, 7, b m Helmet (AUS)—Anosti **wilfstoreyracingclub**

Assistant Trainer: Miss S. M. Doolan, Miss S. Storey.

500	**SIR MICHAEL STOUTE, Newmarket**

Postal: **Freemason Lodge, Bury Road, Newmarket, Suffolk, CB8 7BY**
Contacts: **PHONE 01638 663801 FAX 01638 667276**

1 AERION POWER (IRE), 4, b c Kingman—Applauded (IRE)
2 ASTRO KING (IRE), 5, b h Kingman—Astroglia (USA)
3 BAY BRIDGE, 4, b c New Bay—Hayyona
4 BOSS POWER (IRE), 5, b g Frankel—La Vinchina (GER)
5 CHAI YO POWER, 5, b g Le Havre (IRE)—Stella Bellissima (IRE)
6 DIAMONDS ARE KING (USA), 4, b c Air Force Blue (USA)—High Finance (IRE)
7 DREAM OF DREAMS (IRE), 8, ch g Dream Ahead (USA)—Vasilia
8 HASTY SAILOR (IRE), 5, b g Fastnet Rock (AUS)—Galileana (IRE)
9 HIGHEST GROUND (IRE), 5, b g Frankel—Celestial Lagoon (JPN)
10 INIGO JONES, 4, b g New Approach (IRE)—Spacious
11 JUST FINE (IRE), 4, b g Sea The Stars (IRE)—Bint Almatar (USA)
12 LIGHTS ON, 5, ch m Siyouni (FR)—In The Light
13 NOON STAR (USA), 4, b f Galileo (IRE)—Midday
14 POSSIBLE MAN, 4, b c Le Havre (IRE)—Baldovina
15 POTAPOVA, 4, b f Invincible Spirit (IRE)—Safina
16 REGAL REALITY, 7, b g Intello (GER)—Regal Realm
17 SATONO JAPAN (JPN), 5, b g Deep Impact (JPN)—Dubawi Heights
18 SOLID STONE (IRE), 6, br g Shamardal (USA)—Landmark (USA)
19 SUNRISE VALLEY (USA), 4, b f Karakontie (JPN)—Story (USA)
20 SWOON (FR), 4, b f Frankel—Marine Bleue (IRE)
21 TIGER BEETLE, 4, b g Camelot—Beach Frolic
22 TRAILA, 4, ch g Australia—Waila
23 TUCSON CLOUD (IRE), 4, b f Fastnet Rock (AUS)—Transhumance (IRE)
24 VILLE DE GRACE, 4, b f Le Havre (IRE)—Archangel Gabriel (USA)
25 WAHRAAN (FR), 4, ch g Le Havre (IRE)—Al Jassasiyah (IRE)

THREE-YEAR-OLDS

26 AEONIAN (IRE), b c Ulysses (IRE)—Ama (USA)
27 ALTJERINGA, b f Iffraaj—Altesse
28 ASSESSMENT, b c Kingman—Clinical
29 BALHAMBAR (FR), b c Almanzor (FR)—Moojeh (IRE)
30 BELIEVE IN STARS (IRE), b c Make Believe—Cruck Realta
31 CAPSTAN, b c Kingman—Arizona Jewel
32 CHICHEN ITZA, b f Fastnet Rock (AUS)—Phaenomena (IRE)
33 CHIMED, ch c Frankel—Timepiece
34 CRYSTAL CAPRICE (IRE), b f Frankel—Crystal Zvezda

SIR MICHAEL STOUTE - continued

35 **CRYSTAL DELIGHT,** ch c New Approach (IRE)—Crystal Capella
36 **CRYSTAL ESTRELLA,** b f Iffraaj—Crystal Etoile
37 **DESERT CROWN,** b c Nathaniel (IRE)—Desert Berry
38 Ch g Australia—Dubian To (IRE)
39 **DUNGEON,** b c Dubawi (IRE)—Dank
40 **EHTEYAT (GER),** b c Toronado (IRE)—Ella Ransom (GER)
41 **EQUAL SHARE (IRE),** b f Australia—Split Trois (FR)
42 **EVERY BLUE MOON (IRE),** ch f Lope de Vega (IRE)—Celestial Lagoon (JPN)
43 **FINE CHINA,** b f Mastercraftsman (IRE)—Chinoiseries
44 **GLORY NIGHTS (IRE),** b c Cotai Glory—Lady Lucia (IRE)
45 **HAVAILA (IRE),** ch c Le Havre (IRE)—Waila
46 **IKHTIRAAQ (IRE),** b c Invincible Spirit (IRE)—Mejala (IRE)
47 **IN PLAY,** b g Starspangledbanner (AUS)—Partitia
48 **INFINITIVE,** b f Ulysses (IRE)—Integral
49 **INVIGILATE,** b f Acclamation—Exemplify
50 **KIRILENKO,** b f Ulysses (IRE)—Marenko
51 **KITEFLYER,** b c Iffraaj—Star Value (IRE)
52 **KODIAC SIGN (IRE),** b c Kodiac—Querulous (USA)
53 **LEBSAYER (FR),** b c Shalaa (IRE)—Iltemas (USA)
54 **LOVE SOMEONE,** b f Sea The Stars (IRE)—Loveisallyouneed (IRE)
55 **LOVE YOU GRANDPA (IRE),** b f Frankel—Baldovina
56 B c Churchill (IRE)—Melodious
57 **MELODY CHER,** b f Siyouni (FR)—Carnoustie (FR)
58 **MIGDAM (FR),** b c Zelzal (FR)—Asyad (IRE)
59 **MORNING POST,** b c Time Test—Hayyona
60 **MORNING SUN (IRE),** b c Muhaarar—Jadanna (IRE)
61 **NAVAL COLLEGE,** b g Dartmouth—Sequence (IRE)
62 **NEW DIMENSION,** b c Ulysses (IRE)—Azhar
63 **PARAMETER,** b f Le Havre (IRE)—Criteria (IRE)
64 **PASTEL POWER (IRE),** b c Shalaa (IRE)—Lady Gorgeous
65 **PICUAL,** ch f Lope de Vega (IRE)—Spice Trail
66 **PROFESSION,** ch g Ulysses (IRE)—Echelon
67 **REAL DREAM (IRE),** b c Lope de Vega (IRE)—Laganore (IRE)
68 **RED RAMBLER,** ch c Iffraaj—Blushing Rose
69 **ROCK SIREN,** b f Ulysses (IRE)—Rock Choir
70 **SEE (USA),** br f War Front (USA)—Faufiler (IRE)
71 **SUNSTONE,** ch f Pivotal—Midsummer
72 **TABLES TURNED,** ch g Ulysses (IRE)—Mesa Fresca (USA)
73 **TERRA MITICA (IRE),** ch f Ulysses (IRE)—Mississippi Delta (USA)

Trainer did not supply details of their two-year-olds.

Owners: Her Majesty The Queen, Al Shaqab Racing UK Limited, Cheveley Park Stud Limited, Mr P. E. Done, Niarchos Family, Flaxman Stables Ireland Ltd, Mr T. Hirosaki, Mr C. M. Humber, Hunscote Stud Limited, Hunscote Stud Ltd & Mr Chris Humber, James Wigan & T. Hirosaki, Juddmonte Farms Ltd, King Power Racing Co Ltd, Newsells Park Stud Limited, Mr R. Ng, Niarchos Family & Airlie Stud, M. Obaida, Qatar Racing Limited, Miss K. Rausing, Mr A. P. Rogers, Mrs S. Rogers, Satomi Horse Company Ltd, Mr S. Suhail, Lord W. G. Vestey, J. Wigan, Sir Evelyn de Rothschild.

501

MRS ALI STRONGE, Eastbury
Postal: **Castle Piece Racing Stables, Eastbury, Hungerford, Berkshire, RG17 7JR**
Contacts: PHONE 01488 72818 MOBILE 07779 285205 FAX 01488 670378
EMAIL office@castlepiecestables.com WEBSITE www.castlepiecestables.com

1 **ARDMAYLE (IRE),** 10, ch g Whitmore's Conn (USA)—Welsh Connection (IRE) **The One and Only Partnership**
2 **EAIRSIDH (IRE),** 7, b g Arcadio (GER)—Inch Rose (IRE) **Select-Racing-Club Co Uk & Miss A Hyde**
3 **ESTRELA STAR (IRE),** 6, ch g Casamento (IRE)—Reem Star **Mrs A. J. Stronge**
4 **GATWICK KITTEN (USA),** 5, b g Kitten's Joy (USA)—Maibaby (IRE) **Mrs C. L. Smith**
5 **GLORY TIME,** 6, b g Olympic Glory (IRE)—Tunkwa (FR) **The Jury's Out Partnership**

MRS ALI STRONGE - continued

6 GRANDSCAPE, 7, b g Lemon Drop Kid (USA)—Unnatural (USA) **Mrs C. L. Smith**
7 HANNALITE, 5, ch m Nathaniel (IRE)—Bravia **Mr L. A. Bellman**
8 HELLUVABOY (IRE), 4, ch g Helmet (AUS)—Catbells (IRE) **Laurence Bellman & Keith Trowbridge**
9 LAKE SAND (IRE), 5, b g Footstepsinthesand—Lake Louise (IRE) **Mr L. A. Bellman**
10 PEERLESS PERCY (IRE), 5, b g Sir Percy—Victoria Montoya
11 RENARDEAU, 6, b g Foxwedge (AUS)—La Cucina (IRE) **Mr L. A. Bellman**
12 ROSEARELLI, 7, ch m Schiaparelli (GER)—Vin Rose **Select-Racing-Club Co Uk & Miss A Hyde**
13 SCORPION HAZE (IRE), 9, b g Scorpion (IRE)—Sea Maiden (IRE) **Shaw Racing Partnership 2**
14 SKY STORM, 5, ch m Night of Thunder (IRE)—Dinvar Diva
15 STORM MELODY, 9, b g Royal Applause—Plume **Shaw Racing Partnership 2 & Ali Stronge**
16 YORKTOWN (IRE), 5, b g Free Eagle (IRE)—Bryanstown (IRE) **Spencer-herbert, Herbert L Bellman**

THREE-YEAR-OLDS

17 JUST JOSH, b g Nathaniel (IRE)—Joshua's Princess **Spencer-Herbert,Herbert,Simmons&Kidger**
18 MUSICAL MYSTERY, b g Showcasing—Puzzled Look **G Bishop & A Kirkland**
19 NICOLAS ANDRY (IRE), b g Kodiac—Andry Brusselles **Mrs A. J. Stronge**
20 OUR NOBLE LORD, ch c Sir Percy—Lady Stardust **Mrs B. V. Evans**
21 SUNSETS DREAMERS (IRE), b f Awtaad (IRE)—Oasis Sunset (IRE) **Mrs A. J. Stronge**

TWO-YEAR-OLDS

22 B c 04/04 Zoffany (IRE)—Fantastic Account (Fantastic Light (USA)) (14286)
23 B f 30/01 Gregorian (IRE)—Greenery (Green Desert (USA))
24 Ch c 05/03 Mondialiste (IRE)—Just Jealous (Lope de Vega (IRE)) (8500)
25 B c 26/04 Churchill (IRE)—Rose of Africa (IRE) (Cape Cross (IRE)) (25000)

Other Owners: Mr L. A. Bellman, Mr G. S. Bishop, C Spencer-herbert & M Herbert, Mr M. R. Herbert, Miss A. B. Hyde, Dr A. I. Kirkland, Shaw Racing Partnership 2, Ms C. L. Spencer-Herbert, Mrs A. J. Stronge, The Select Racing Club Limited, K. P. Trowbridge, Mr P. Whitehead.

Assistant Trainer: Sam Stronge.

---

502 | MRS LINDA STUBBS, Malton
Postal: **Beverley House Stables, Beverley Road, Malton, North Yorkshire, YO17 9PJ**
Contacts: **HOME 01653 698731 MOBILE 07801 167707**
EMAIL l.stubbs@btconnect.com

1 CAREY STREET (IRE), 6, b g Bungle Inthejungle—Undulant Way **P.G.Shorrock & L.Stubbs**
2 OAKENSHIELD (IRE), 5, b g Invincible Spirit (IRE)—War Effort (USA) **Mr J. L. White**
3 OLD NEWS, 5, b g Dutch Art—Queen's Charter **Mr P. G. Shorrock**

THREE-YEAR-OLDS

4 LUNASA (IRE), b f Ivawood (IRE)—Royal Sateen **Mr M. Griffiths**

Other Owners: Mr P. G. Shorrock, Mrs L. Stubbs.

---

503 | MR ROB SUMMERS, Solihull
Postal: Summerhill Cottage, Danzey Green, Tanworth-in-Arden, Solihull
Contacts: **PHONE 01564 742667 MOBILE 07775 898327**

1 ATLANTIC STORM (IRE), 10, b g September Storm (GER)—Double Dream (IRE) **Mr A. R. Price**
2 HIGHLAND BOBBY, 7, b g Big Bad Bob (IRE)—Eolith **Mrs G. M. Summers**
3 RED ROLY, 6, b g Native Ruler—Photogenique (FR) **Mrs G. M. Summers**
4 SECRET MOSS, 7, ch m Schiaparelli (GER)—Secret Whisper **Mrs G. M. Summers**
5 ST MERRYN (IRE), 11, b g Oscar (IRE)—Kigali (IRE) **Mrs G. M. Summers**

Assistant Trainer: Mrs G. M. Summers.

504 MR TOM SYMONDS, Hentland

Postal: **Dason Court Cottage, Hentland, Ross-On-Wye, Herefordshire, HR9 6LW**
Contacts: **PHONE 01989 730869 MOBILE 07823 324649**
EMAIL dasoncourt@gmail.com WEBSITE www.thomassymonds.co.uk

1 BOBO MAC (IRE), 11, gr g Whitmore's Conn (USA)—Blazing Love (IRE) **C & M Baker, K Ibberson, H Pearman**
2 COBRA COMMANDER (IRE), 8, b g Beneficial—Run For Help (IRE) **Dean, Willetts & Vernon**
3 4, B f Milan—Crimson Flower (IRE)
4 FAZAYTE (FR), 7, b g Spider Flight (FR)—Vakina (FR) **Mrs C. M. Antcliff**
5 HIDOR DE BERSY (FR), 5, ch g Nidor (FR)—Tropulka God (FR) **The Hon Lady Gibbings**
6 HOLLYWOODIEN (FR), 11, gr g Martaline—Incorrigible (FR) **The Hon Lady Gibbings**
7 HYSTERY BERE (FR), 5, b g Pedro The Great (USA)—Mysteryonthebounty (USA) **The Hon Lady Gibbings**
8 ILLICO DES PLACES (FR), 4, b g Jeu St Eloi (FR)—Liliane Star (FR) **The Hon Lady Gibbings**
9 KELLAHEN (GER), 5, br g Wiesenpfad (FR)—Kurfurstin (GER)
10 LADY BERLAIS, 4, b f Clovis du Berlais (FR)—Lady of Llanarmon **The Nigel Jones & Roy Ovel Syndicate**
11 LEGENDARY RHYTHM, 6, b m Midnight Legend—Hot Rhythm **David Clark & Partner**
12 LEXI'S CHOICE (IRE), 6, b m Presenting—Gilt Ridden (IRE) **Palmer-Brown, Mason & Murphy**
13 LIBERTARIAN ROYALE (IRE), 4, b f Libertarian—Sheestown (IRE) **The Nigel Jones & Roy Ovel Syndicate**
14 LLANDINABO LAD, 7, ch g Malinas (GER)—Hot Rhythm **Celia & Michael Baker**
15 LOUD AS LIONS (IRE), 9, b g Flemensfirth (USA)—Misspublican (IRE) **C & M Baker, K Ibberson, H Pearman**
16 LUNA DORA, 5, gr m Pether's Moon (IRE)—Ixora (IRE) **Chase The Dream - Luna Dora**
17 MARTA DES MOTTES (FR), 5, b m Montmartre (FR)—Oktavia des Mottes (FR) **Mr S. Davies**
18 MASCARA PRINCESS (FR), 5, b m Charm Spirit (IRE)—Mascara (GER) **Mr S. Davies**
19 MINSTER (IRE), 5, ch g Mastercraftsman (IRE)—Mycenae **Mr T. R. Symonds**
20 MISTER BARCLAY, 4, b g Nathaniel (IRE)—Singapore Harbour (IRE) **C & M Baker, K Ibberson, H Pearman**
21 MORIKO DE VASSY (FR), 5, b g Cokoriko (FR)—Mona Vassy (FR) **Amis de Vassy**
22 MR WASHINGTON (IRE), 9, b g Vinnie Roe (IRE)—Anna Bird (IRE) **Mrs J. Hitchings**
23 NATURAL LOOK (IRE), 6, b m Ocovango—Honours Graduate (IRE) **Mr D. Needham**
24 NIGHT JET, 5, b g Telescope (IRE)—Midnight Belle **Mrs P. E. Holtorp**
25 OUT OF EXILE (IRE), 7, b g Mahler—Drama Chick **Mick Fitzgerald Racing Club**
26 RHIAN DE SIVOLA, 6, b m Kayf Tara—R de Rien Sivola (FR) **Mr S. Davies**
27 SONG FOR SOMEONE (GER), 7, ch g Medicean—Sweni Hill (IRE) **The Hon Lady Gibbings**
28 TABLE MOUNTAIN, 5, b m Phoenix Reach (IRE)—Cape Victoria **Mr S. Davies**

THREE-YEAR-OLDS

29 NAVAJO INDY, b g Nathaniel (IRE)—Navajo Charm **C & M Baker, K Ibberson, H Pearman**

Other Owners: Mrs C. A. M. Baker, Mr M. J. Baker, Mrs K. Casini, Chase The Dream, Mr D. J. Clark, Mr T. Dean, Miss K. J. Ibberson, Mr N. A. Jones, Mr G. J. F. Kimberley, Mr J. G. G. Mason, Mr R. M. Ovel, Mr J. Palmer-Brown, Mr H. J. Pearman, Mr T. R. Symonds, Miss J. Upton-Murphy, Miss S. J. Vernon, Mr P. J. Willetts.

---

505 MR JAMES TATE, Newmarket

Postal: **Jamesfield Place, Hamilton Road, Newmarket, Suffolk, CB8 7JQ**
Contacts: **PHONE 01638 669861 MOBILE 07703 601283 FAX 01638 676634**
EMAIL james@jamestateracing.com WEBSITE www.jamestateracing.com

1 GARDEN PARADISE (IRE), 5, b m Night of Thunder (IRE)—Coral Garden **S. Manana**
2 OCEAN WAVE, 4, ch f Le Havre (IRE)—Gold Sands (IRE) **S. Manana**
3 PRIORITISE (IRE), 4, b f Camelot—Penny Post (IRE) **S. Manana**
4 RAISE THE ROOF (IRE), 4, b f Free Eagle (IRE)—Starletina (IRE) **S. Manana**
5 SHOW YOURSELF, 4, b f Acclamation—Dare To Dream **S. Manana**
6 WALHAAN (IRE), 6, gr g Dark Angel (IRE)—Back In The Frame **Allwins Stables**

THREE-YEAR-OLDS

7 AUSSIE WARRIOR (IRE), b c Australia—Twilight Sky **S. Manana**
8 BRAVE THE STORM (IRE), ch c Night of Thunder (IRE)—Overtones **S. Manana**

MR JAMES TATE - continued

9 B c Dark Angel (IRE)—Ceaseless (IRE) **Sheikh R. D. Al Maktoum**
10 B f Exceed And Excel (AUS)—Cool Thunder (IRE) **Sheikh J. D. Al Maktoum**
11 COTAI BEAUTY (IRE), b f Cotai Glory—Petite Boulangere (IRE) **Sheikh J. D. Al Maktoum**
12 COUNTERATTACK, b c Frankel—Impala **S. Manana**
13 DIVINE RAPTURE, gr f Dark Angel (IRE)—Titivation **S. Manana**
14 EBTSAMA (IRE), b f Dark Angel (IRE)—Roseraie (IRE) **S. Ali**
15 EL HADEEYAH (IRE), b f Invincible Spirit (IRE)—Blhadawa (IRE) **Sheikh J. D. Al Maktoum**
16 FLAMING DAWN (IRE), b f Territories (IRE)—Pivotal's Princess (IRE) **S. Manana**
17 B f Mehmas (IRE)—Flat White (IRE) **Sheikh J. D. Al Maktoum**
18 B f Decorated Knight—Gadwa **S. Manana**
19 HIDDEN SANDS, ch f Dubawi (IRE)—Demurely (IRE) **S. Manana**
20 HIGH VELOCITY (IRE), gr c Gutaifan (IRE)—Reflect Alexander (IRE) **S. Manana**
21 B f Territories (IRE)—Itiqad **Houghton Bloodstock**
22 B f Shamardal (USA)—Jira **S. Manana**
23 LAKESIDE, b f Equiano (FR)—Three Ducks **S. Manana**
24 LIGHTNING APPROACH (IRE), b f Shamardal (USA)—Bright Approach (IRE) **S. Manana**
25 B f Frankel—Nashmiah (IRE) **S. Manana**
26 NAVAJO POET, b f Poet's Voice—Navajo Chant **S. Ali**
27 NEXT CHAPTER (IRE), b f Shamardal (USA)—Samdaniya **S. Manana**
28 OCEAN RULER, b c Shamardal (USA)—Saltanat (IRE) **S. Manana**
29 ON REFLECTION (IRE), gr c El Kabeir (USA)—Inourthoughts (IRE) **S. Manana**
30 B c Churchill (IRE)—Polygon (USA) **S. Manana**
31 RAVI ROAD (IRE), ch f Zoffany (IRE)—Crosstalk (IRE) **Mr I. Butt**
32 Br f Farhh—Red Tulip **Mr H. Dalmook Al Maktoum**
33 ROYAL ACLAIM (IRE), b f Aclaim (IRE)—Knock Stars (IRE) **Sheikh J. D. Al Maktoum**
34 SAHARA DESERT (IRE), b f Dubawi (IRE)—Asanta Sana (IRE) **S. Manana**
35 SCREENPLAY (IRE), b f Shamardal (USA)—Galactic Heroine **S. Manana**
36 SERIFOS, b f Kingman—Uleavemebreathless **Sheikh J. D. Al Maktoum**
37 SPECIAL FORCES, b c Holy Roman Emperor (IRE)—Affectionately **S. Manana**
38 STYLISH ICON (IRE), b f Starspangledbanner (AUS)—Refreshed (IRE) **S. Manana**
39 TAAQAT (FR), b f Pivotal—Taaqah (USA) **Sheikh J. D. Al Maktoum**
40 TAKE A STAND (IRE), b c Invincible Spirit (IRE)—You're Back (USA) **S. Manana**
41 B f Profitable (IRE)—Teodelight (IRE) **S. Manana**
42 TROIS VALLEES, b f New Bay—Bellwether **Sheikh J. D. Al Maktoum**
43 VIEWFINDER (IRE), ch c El Kabeir (USA)—Encore View **S. Manana**
44 VISION OF HOPE, b f Mastercraftsman (IRE)—Utopian Dream **S. Manana**
45 B br f Churchill (IRE)—Wadaa (IRE) **S. Manana**
46 WAIT TO EXCEL, b c Postponed (IRE)—Al Baidaa **S. Ali**

TWO-YEAR-OLDS

47 B br c 05/03 Aclaim (IRE)—Aloisi (Kalanisi (IRE)) (52000) **Sheikh J. D. Al Maktoum**
48 Ch f 19/02 Night of Thunder (IRE)—Ancestral (Bated Breath) **S. Manana**
49 B f 15/02 Kodiac—Arbitrary (Frankel) (19048) **Sheikh J. D. Al Maktoum**
50 B c 23/02 Oasis Dream—Beneventa (Most Welcome) (100000) **Sheikh J. D. Al Maktoum**
51 B c 26/03 Fastnet Rock (AUS)—Bright Approach (IRE) (New Approach (IRE)) (50000) **S. Manana**
52 B c 22/02 Siyouni (FR)—Coral Garden (Halling (USA)) **S. Manana**
53 B f 08/04 No Nay Never (USA)—Cry Me A River (IRE) (Danehill Dancer (IRE)) (130000) **Sheikh J. D. Al Maktoum**
54 Ch f 13/02 Saxon Warrior (JPN)—Doors To Manual (USA) (Royal Academy (USA)) **S. Manana**
55 DUBAI HARBOUR, b c 14/02 Invincible Spirit (IRE)—Asanta Sana (IRE) (Galileo (IRE)) **S. Manana**
56 Ch f 25/02 Ulysses (IRE)—Forever In Love (Dutch Art) **James Tate Racing Limited**
57 Ch c 10/03 Shamardal (USA)—Galactic Heroine (Galileo (IRE)) **S. Manana**
58 B c 12/04 Le Havre (IRE)—Gold Sands (IRE) (Cape Cross (IRE)) **S. Manana**
59 Ch f 16/04 Farhh—Heartsease (Pursuit of Love) (17000) **James Tate Racing Limited**
60 Ch c 06/02 Fastnet Rock (AUS)—Heaven's Angel (IRE) (Henrythenavigator (USA)) **S. Manana**
61 B f 25/03 Night of Thunder (IRE)—Hokkaido (Street Cry (IRE)) **S. Manana**
62 B f 27/03 Frankel—Impala (Oasis Dream) **S. Manana**
63 B c 04/03 Shamardal (USA)—Lamar (IRE) (Cape Cross (IRE)) (130000) **S. Ali**
64 B c 28/02 No Nay Never (USA)—Learza (IRE) (High Chaparral (IRE)) **S. Manana**
65 B c 17/04 Unfortunately (IRE)—Maybe Tomorrow (Zamindar (USA)) **S. Manana**

MR JAMES TATE - continued

66 Ch c 11/01 New Approach (IRE)—Morsian (Dubawi (IRE)) **S. Manana**
67 B c 04/04 Massaat (IRE)—Nippy (FR) (Anabaa (USA)) (28000) **S. Manana**
68 B c 06/04 Mehmas (IRE)—Olive Branch (IRE) (Arcano (IRE)) (120000) **Sheikh R. D. Al Maktoum**
69 B c 25/02 Oasis Dream—Populist (IRE) (Shamardal (USA)) **S. Manana**
70 B c 20/02 No Nay Never (USA)—Predicted (Dansili) **S. Manana**
71 B f 28/03 Dubawi (IRE)—Prefer (IRE) (Galileo (IRE)) **S. Manana**
72 B c 11/03 Harry Angel (IRE)—Purplest (Iffraaj) (41000) **S. Ali**
73 B f 22/04 James Garfield (IRE)—Qalahari (IRE) (Bahri (USA)) (18000) **S. Manana**
74 B c 02/03 New Approach (IRE)—Queen of The Stars (Sea The Stars (IRE)) **S. Ali**
75 B f 31/03 Dandy Man (IRE)—Refreshed (IRE) (Rip Van Winkle (IRE)) (9524) **S. Manana**
76 Br c 05/02 Showcasing—Regal Hawk (Singspiel (IRE)) **S. Manana**
77 Ch f 21/03 Night of Thunder (IRE)—Rekindle (Frankel) (40000) **S. Manana**
78 B f 21/03 Storm The Stars (USA)—Reroute (IRE) (Acclamation) **Sheikh R. D. Al Maktoum**
79 Ch f 27/04 Harry Angel (IRE)—Ring For Baileys (Kyllachy) (60000) **G R Bailey Ltd (Baileys Horse Feeds)**
80 Ch c 03/04 Farhh—Saltanat (IRE) (Duke of Marmalade (IRE)) **S. Manana**
81 B c 19/02 Invincible Spirit (IRE)—Second Generation (Dawn Approach (IRE)) **Sheikh R. D. Al Maktoum**
82 Ch f 02/03 Frankel—Shepherdia (IRE) (Pivotal) **S. Manana**
83 B f 15/02 Frankel—Souviens Toi (Dalakhani (IRE)) **S. Manana**
84 Ch c 15/02 Iffraaj—Spirit of Cuba (IRE) (Invincible Spirit (IRE)) (35000) **S. Manana**
85 B f 10/04 Iffraaj—Twinkle Twinkle (Exceed And Excel (AUS)) (23000) **S. Manana**
86 B f 24/03 Storm The Stars (USA)—Umneyati (Iffraaj) **Sheikh R. D. Al Maktoum**
87 B c 12/04 Kessaar—Willow Beck (Shamardal (USA)) (75000) **S. Ali**
88 Ch c 08/03 Churchill (IRE)—Zam Zoom (IRE) (Dalakhani (IRE)) **S. Manana**

Assistant Trainer: Mrs Lucinda Tate.

---

506 | **MR TOM TATE, Tadcaster**
Postal: **Castle Farm, Hazelwood, Tadcaster, North Yorkshire, LS24 9NJ**
Contacts: **PHONE 01937 836036 MOBILE 07970 122818**
EMAIL tomptate@zen.co.uk **WEBSITE** www.tomtate.co.uk

1 BAYRAAT, 6, b g Heeraat (IRE)—Baymist **T T Racing**
2 CRAGGAKNOCK, 11, b g Authorized (IRE)—Goodie Twosues **Mr C. Tremewan**
3 DESTROYER, 9, b g Royal Applause—Good Girl (IRE) **T T Racing**
4 EQUIANO SPRINGS, 8, b g Equiano (FR)—Spring Clean (FR) **T T Racing**
5 FIRST DANCE (IRE), 8, b m Cape Cross (IRE)—Happy Wedding (IRE) **T T Racing**
6 FREEWHEELIN, 4, b g Poet's Voice—Certral **T T Racing**
7 RELENTLESS SUN, 4, b g Twilight Son—Riccoche (IRE) **T T Racing**
8 THUNDER GAP, 5, b g Night of Thunder—Regal Hawk **T T Racing**
9 YOUNG TIGER, 9, b g Captain Gerrard (IRE)—Blades Princess **T T Racing**

THREE-YEAR-OLDS

10 BRUNELLO BREEZE, b g Bated Breath—Calima Breeze **T T Racing**

Assistant Trainer: Hazel Tate.

Flat Jockey: Tom Eaves, James Sullivan.

---

507 | **MR COLIN TEAGUE, Wingate**
Postal: **Bridgefield Farm, Trimdon Lane, Station Town, Wingate, County Durham, TS28 5NE**
Contacts: **PHONE 01429 837087 MOBILE 07967 330929**
EMAIL colin.teague@btopenworld.com

1 BRAZEN BELLE, 4, b f Brazen Beau (AUS)—Pepper Lane **Collins Chauffeur Driven Executive Cars**
2 INGLEBY COMMAND, 5, b g War Command (USA)—Mistress Twister **Collins Chauffeur Driven Executive Cars**
3 KOROPICK (IRE), 8, b g Kodiac—Kathoe (IRE) **Mr A. Rice**
4 LOLA REBEL (IRE), 4, b f Dandy Man (IRE)—Copperbeech (IRE) **Collins Chauffeur Driven Executive Cars**

MR COLIN TEAGUE - continued

5 **TAAMER**, 5, ch m Tamayuz—Abhajat (IRE) **Mr A. Rice**
6 **THORNABY NASH**, 11, br g Kheleyf (USA)—Mistress Twister **Mr N. Old**

 MR ROGER TEAL, Hungerford
Postal: **Windsor House Stables, Crowle Road, Lambourn, Hungerford, Berkshire, RG17 8NR**
Contacts: **PHONE 01488 491623 MOBILE 07710 325521**
EMAIL info@rogertealracing.com WEBSITE www.rogertealracing.co.uk

1 **ALCAZAN**, 4, b f Al Kazeem—Glorious Dreams (USA) **John O'Donnell & Noel Kelly**
2 **BEAR FORCE ONE**, 6, b g Swiss Spirit—Shesha Bear **Joe Bear Racing**
3 **BICKERSTAFFE**, 4, b c Mayson—Ocean Boulevard
4 **BLAZEON FIVE**, 4, b f Indian Haven—Precision Five **Calne Engineering Ltd**
5 **BRANSTON PIKKLE**, 4, b g Farhh—Triveni (FR) **Mr S. P. Barry**
6 **BRUTE FORCE**, 6, ch g Paco Boy (IRE)—Free Falling **A.C. Entertainment Technologies Limited**
7 **CHIPSTEAD**, 4, b c Mayson—Charlotte Rosina **Homecroft, Crampsie & Sullivan**
8 **CHORAL CLAN (IRE)**, 11, b g Oratorio (IRE)—Campbellite **Mrs P. A. Mitchell**
9 **CINZENTO (IRE)**, 6, gr g Lawman (FR)—Silver Samba **Mr G. Bhatti**
10 **CIVIL LAW (IRE)**, 5, gr g Dark Angel (IRE)—Tribune (FR) **D Bassom & P Cardosi**
11 **DANCING HARRY (IRE)**, 5, b g Camelot—Poisson d'Or **Fishdance Ltd**
12 **DANCING MASTER (IRE)**, 4, br gr g Mastercraftsman (IRE)—Poisson d'Or **Mr H. Teal**
13 **DARK ESTEEM (IRE)**, 4, b g Estidhkaar (IRE)—Poker Hospital **Windsor House Racing**
14 **FITWOOD STAR**, 6, b g Archipenko (USA)—Sasheen **Calne Engineering Ltd**
15 **GERT LUSH (IRE)**, 5, b m Bated Breath—Agent Allison **Mrs Muriel Forward & Dr G C Forward**
16 **GREY GALLEON (USA)**, 8, gr g Mizzen Mast (USA)—Floresta (USA) **BA Racing**
17 **GURKHA GIRL (IRE)**, 4, b f The Gurkha (IRE)—Freddie's Girl (USA) **Mrs A. Cowley**
18 **HUGOSTHERE**, 4, b g Cannock Chase (USA)—Ellablue **HOG Racing**
19 **JOHNNY REB**, 6, b g Showcasing—Specific Dream
20 **KAMAXOS (FR)**, 5, b g Maxios—Kamellata (FR) **Mr A. J. Edwards**
21 **KENZAI WARRIOR (USA)**, 5, b br g Karakontie (JPN)—Lemon Sakhee (CAN) **Rae & Carol Borras**
22 **KNOWWHENTORUN**, 4, b g Mayson—Josefa Goya **Homecroft Wealth Racing**
23 **MARION'S BOY (IRE)**, 5, ch g Mastercraftsman (IRE)—Freddie's Girl (USA) **Mrs A. Cowley**
24 **MICKS DREAM**, 4, b g Adaay (IRE)—Malelane (IRE) **M. F. Waghorn**
25 **OCEAN WIND**, 6, b h Teofilo (IRE)—Chan Tong (BRZ) **Rockingham Reins Limited**
26 **OXTED**, 6, b g Mayson—Charlotte Rosina **S Piper,T.Hirschfeld,D.Fish & J.Collins**
27 **PRINCELY**, 7, b h Compton Place—Royal Award **Mr G. Darling**
28 **ROCKING REG (IRE)**, 5, gr g Gutaifan (IRE)—Princess of Troy (IRE) **Mr T. J. Smith**
29 **SHARLA**, 4, b f Outstrip—Shersha (IRE) **Mrs M. Parker**
30 **SWISS PRIDE (IRE)**, 6, b g Swiss Spirit—Encore Encore (FR) **Idle B's & Sue Teal**
31 **WHENTHEDEALINSDONE**, 4, b g Dark Angel (IRE)—Maureen (IRE) **Mr A. Whelan**

THREE-YEAR-OLDS

32 B g Invincible Spirit—Bruno Heinke
33 **DAKOTA POWER**, b g Aclaim (IRE)—Vivid Blue **Dakota Racing**
34 **DANCING REEL (IRE)**, b c Highland Reel (IRE)—Poisson d'Or **Fishdance Ltd**
35 **DICKTATE**, b g Lawman (FR)—Gakku **Mr R. A. Teal**
36 **GRACEFULLALFIE**, ch c Night of Thunder (IRE)—Dularame (IRE) **P Cook & A Whelan**
37 **KANGAROO JACK (IRE)**, b c Galileo Gold—Joya Breeze (IRE) **Great Shefford Racing**
38 **MUMINAMILLION (IRE)**, ch f Galileo Gold—Lady Dettoria (FR) **Rockingham Reins Limited**
39 **MY MATE TED (IRE)**, gr c Caravaggio (USA)—Pop Art (IRE) **Mr M. J. Goggin**
40 **NEVER IN FOURTH**, ch g Coach House (IRE)—Bengers Lass (USA) **Mrs Muriel Forward & Dr G C Forward**
41 B c El Kabeir (USA)—Shes Ranger (IRE) **Mr M. J. Goggin**
42 **SILVERSCAPE**, gr c Cityscape—Miss Minuty **Miss J. S. Dorey**
43 **SISTERS IN THE SKY**, ch c Showcasing—Sunny York (IRE) **Mr David Gilmour & Mr James Dellaway**
44 **TRUE FORCE**, ch g Mayson—Light Hearted **Barry Kitcherside & Darren Waterer**
45 **VALUABLE ASSET**, b g Havana Gold (IRE)—Specific Dream **North Farm Stud Limited**

MR ROGER TEAL - continued

46 VIEWFROMTHESTARS (IRE), b g Starspangledbanner (AUS)—Condensed **A&G Bloodstock Ltd**
47 WHATS IN THE BAG (IRE), b c Dark Angel (IRE)—Kathoe (IRE) **A&G Bloodstock Ltd**

TWO-YEAR-OLDS
48 B c 08/04 Shalaa (IRE)—Alexander Queen (IRE) (King's Best (USA)) (60000) **Homecroft Wealth Racing**
49 HEART, b f 14/03 Fountain of Youth (IRE)—Al Hawa (USA) (Gulch (USA)) **Mrs D. F. Turner**
50 MIDSUMMER MUSIC (IRE), b f 07/02 Mendelssohn (USA)—Nabat Seif (USA) (Street Sense (USA)) (105000)
                                                                             Rae & Carol Borras
51 PANAMA, ch g 29/02 Havana Grey—Azure Amour (IRE) (Azamour (IRE)) (16000) **Mrs S. M. Teal**

Other Owners: Mr D. Bassom, Mrs C. A. Borras, Mr R. D. Borras, Mr P. Cardosi, A. J. Chambers, Mr J. A. Collins, Mr P. Cook, Mr D. Crampsie, Mr J. A. Dellaway, Fishdance Ltd, Dr G. C. Forward, Mrs M. E. Forward, Mr D. S. Gilmour, Homecroft Wealth Racing, Mr W. E. N Kelly, B. Kitcherside, Mr R. B. Kolien, Mr J. O'Donnell, Mr S. J. Piper, Mr M. A. Ransom, Mr S. M. Ransom, Mr J. A. Sullivan, Mrs S. M. Teal, The Idle B'S, Mr D. G. Waterer, Mr A. Whelan.

Assistant Trainer: Harry Teal.

---

509 **MR SAM THOMAS, Cardiff**
Postal: **Crossways, St Mellons Road, Lisvane, Cardiff, South Glamorgan, CF14 0SH**
Contacts: PHONE **07929 101751**
EMAIL samthomasracing@outlook.com, emma@samthomasracing.com
WEBSITE www.samthomasracing.com

1 AL DANCER (FR), 9, gr g Al Namix (FR)—Steel Dancer (FR) **Walters Plant Hire Ltd**
2 AMAZING TANGO (GER), 5, b g Tai Chi (GER)—Amazing Model (GER) **Walters Plant Hire Ltd**
3 4, B f Norse Dancer (IRE)—Another Kate (IRE) **Mr S. J. Thomas**
4 BALLYBEEN (IRE), 6, ch g Presenting—Dotchenka (FR) **Lightfoot, Mussell, Beswick Bloodstock**
5 BEFORE MIDNIGHT, 9, ch g Midnight Legend—Lady Samantha **Walters Plant Hire & Potter Group**
6 DEERE MARK, 5, b g Pether's Moon (IRE)—Henri Bella **Walters Plant Hire Ltd**
7 DOBRYN (FR), 6, b g No Risk At All (FR)—Brava (FR) **Walters Plant Hire Ltd**
8 ED KEEPER (FR), 4, b c Hunter's Light (IRE)—Charbelle (FR) **Walters Plant Hire Ltd**
9 GALILEO SILVER (IRE), 7, gr g Galileo (IRE)—Famous (IRE) **Walters Plant Hire & Potter Group**
10 GLENTROOL, 9, b g Passing Glance—Killala Bay (IRE) **Mr S. C. Appelbee**
11 GOOD RISK AT ALL (FR), 6, ch g No Risk At All (FR)—Sissi Land (FR) **Walters Plant Hire Ltd**
12 GREY DIAMOND (FR), 8, b g Gris de Gris (IRE)—Diamond of Diana (FR) **Walters Plant Hire Ltd**
13 4, B f Universal (IRE)—Haidees Reflection **Mr S. J. Thomas**
14 HURRICANE DEAL (FR), 5, gr g Hurricane Cat (USA)—Diluvienne (FR) **Walters Plant Hire Ltd**
15 INTEL DES BRUYERES (FR), 4, b g Spanish Moon (USA)—Innsbruck (FR) **Walters Plant Hire Ltd**
16 IVY'S SHADOW (IRE), 7, b m Jammaal—Red Chili (IRE) **Mr W. D. Morris**
17 IWILLDOIT, 9, b g Flying Legend (USA)—Lyricist's Dream **Diamond Racing Ltd**
18 JAZZ KING (FR), 6, gr g Kapgarde (FR)—Jaragua (FR) **Walters Plant Hire Ltd**
19 JUBILEE EXPRESS (FR), 5, b g No Risk At All (FR)—Bella Lawena (IRE) **Walters Plant Hire Ltd**
20 JUST NO RISK (FR), 6, ch g No Risk At All (FR)—Just Divine (FR) **Walters Plant,Spiers&hartwell,Egan Waste**
21 KALA NOIRE (IRE), 8, b g Kalanisi (IRE)—Lady Taipan (IRE) **Trolan, Evans**
22 KATATE DORI (FR), 4, b g Bathyrhon (GER)—Vavea (FR) **Walters Plant Hire Ltd**
23 LUMP SUM (FR), 4, b c Authorized (IRE)—Fleur Enchantee (FR) **Walters Plant Hire Ltd**
24 MARIO DE PAIL (FR), 7, gr g Blue Bresil (FR)—Sauveterre (FR) **Walters Plant Hire & Potter Group**
25 NOT A ROLE MODEL (IRE), 10, b g Helissio (FR)—Mille Et Une Nuits (FR) **St Mamadasado**
26 OLD TOWN ROAD (IRE), 9, b g Dylan Thomas (IRE)—Celtic House (IRE) **Mr S. J. Thomas**
27 OUR POWER (IRE), 7, b g Power—Scripture (IRE) **Walters Plant Hire & Potter Group**
28 PADDYS MOTORBIKE (IRE), 10, ch g Fast Company (IRE)—Saffa Garden (IRE)
                                                                 Walters Plant Hire Ltd Egan Waste Ltd
29 PALACIO (FR), 4, b g Khalkevi (IRE)—Belle Yepa (FR) **Walters Plant Hire Ltd**
30 POWERSTOWN PARK (IRE), 9, b g Craigsteel—Smiths Lady (IRE) **The Ipsden Invincibles**
31 PRINCE DES FICHAUX (FR), 5, b g No Risk At All (FR)—Princesse Kap (FR) **Walters Plant Hire Ltd**

MR SAM THOMAS - continued

32 **RANGE (IRE)**, 5, b g Shantou (USA)—Grapevine Sally (IRE) **Walters Plant Hire Ltd**
33 **REMEMBER ALLY (FR)**, 4, b g Sinndar (IRE)—Blue Lullaby (IRE) **Walters Plant Hire Ltd**
34 **ROYAL MAGIC (IRE)**, 10, b g Whitmore's Conn (USA)—Room To Room Magic (IRE) **Luke Harvey Racing Club**
35 **SHOMEN UCHI (FR)**, 5, b g Great Pretender (IRE)—Vavea (FR) **Walters Plant Hire Ltd**
36 **SKYTASTIC (FR)**, 6, b g Way of Light (USA)—Verzasca (IRE) **Walters Plant Hire Ltd**
37 **SLIP ROAD (IRE)**, 7, gr g Shantou (USA)—Agladora (FR) **Walters Plant Hire Ltd**
38 **SPONTHUS (FR)**, 7, b g Alianthus (GER)—Pavane du Kalon (FR) **Walters Plant Hire Ltd**
39 **STEEL ALLY (FR)**, 4, b g Doctor Dino (FR)—Poprock du Berlais (FR) **Walters Plant Hire Ltd**
40 **STOLEN SILVER (FR)**, 7, gr g Lord du Sud (FR)—Change Partner (FR) **Walters Plant Hire & Potter Group**
41 **SWEDISHHORSEMAFIA (IRE)**, 7, b g Shantou (USA)—Carrigmoorna Style (IRE) **Mr S. J. Thomas**
42 **THANK YOU BLUE**, 5, b g Blue Bresil (FR)—Tara Potter **Walters Plant Hire Ltd**
43 **TZARMIX (FR)**, 4, ch g Gemix (FR)—Tzarine de La Mone (FR) **Walters Plant Hire Ltd**
44 **VINCENZO (FR)**, 4, b g Doctor Dino (FR)—Sweet Nano (FR) **Walters Plant Hire Ltd**
45 **WE DONE IT (FR)**, 4, ro c Montmartre (FR)—Glicine (GER) **Walters Plant Hire Ltd**
46 **WELSH SAINT (FR)**, 8, b g Saint des Saints (FR)—Minirose (FR) **Walters Plant Hire Ltd**
47 **WILLIAM HENRY (IRE)**, 12, b g King's Theatre (IRE)—Cincuenta (IRE) **Walters Plant Hire Ltd**

THREE-YEAR-OLDS

48 **CELTIC DINO (FR)**, ch c Doctor Dino (FR)—Bal Celtique (FR) **Walters Plant Hire Ltd**
49 **JUST OVER LAND (FR)**, ch c No Risk At All (FR)—Sissi Land (FR) **Walters Plant Hire Ltd**
50 **MASTER AUSTRALIA (IRE)**, b c Australia—Mohican Princess **Walters Plant Hire Ltd**
51 **ROCKING MAN (FR)**, b c Manatee—Rockburn (FR) **Walters Plant Hire Ltd**

Other Owners: Beswick Brothers Bloodstock, Mrs P. L. Capper, Egan Waste Services Ltd, Miss E. Evans, Miss L. F. Evans, Mr A. P. G. Holmes, Mrs L. J. Lightfoot, Mr P. Lightfoot, Mr T. L. Llewellyn, Mr C. Mussell, Mrs J. C. Noel, Mr B. Ryan-Beswick, Mr W. Ryan-Beswick, Spiers & Hartwell Ltd, Mr W. D. Stovin, Sundorne Products (Llanidloes) Ltd, Mr J. Trolan, Walters Plant Hire Ltd.

NH Jockey: James Davies, Charlie Deutsch. **Conditional Jockey:** Harry Beswick, Richard Patrick.

510	**MRS JOANNE THOMASON-MURPHY, Chelmsford** Postal: Oakview, Leighams Road, Bicknacre, Chelmsford, Essex, CM3 4HF

1 **AFRICAN SUN (IRE)**, 5, b g Teofilo (IRE)—Castle Cross (IRE) **Mrs J. Thomason-Murphy**
2 **CANDY LOU**, 8, b m Schiaparelli (GER)—Candello **Mrs J. Thomason-Murphy**
3 **DARCYS HILL (IRE)**, 7, b m Milan—Royal Nora (IRE) **Mrs J. Thomason-Murphy**

511	**MR DAVID THOMPSON, Darlington** Postal: South View Racing, Ashley Cottage, South View, Bolam, Darlington, County Durham, DL2 2UP Contacts: PHONE 01388 832658, 01388 835806 MOBILE 07795 161657 FAX 01325 835806 EMAIL dwthompson61@hotmail.co.uk WEBSITE www.dwthompson.co.uk

1 **BAWAADER (IRE)**, 7, gr g Dark Angel (IRE)—Aspen Falls (IRE) **Mr N. Park**
2 **BELLEVUE LAD**, 4, ch g Hot Streak (IRE)—High Drama (IRE) **Mrs D. D. Jefferson**
3 **BIRDIE BOWERS (IRE)**, 5, b g Bungle Inthejungle—Shamiya (IRE) **K. Kirkup**
4 **BLAME THE FARRIER (IRE)**, 5, ch g Slade Power (IRE)—Silirisa (FR) **Mrs J. Snailum**
5 **CALUM GILHOOLEY (IRE)**, 8, br g Kalanisi (IRE)—Honeyed (IRE) **K. Kirkup**
6 **CIVIL JUSTICE GONE**, 4, b f Finjaan—Modern Lady **Mrs A. Kenny**
7 **COMBER MILL (FR)**, 10, ch g Le Fou (IRE)—Kalistina (FR) **Mick Martin Keith Boddy & Son**
8 **COUP DE GOLD (IRE)**, 6, br g Maxios—Astroglia (USA) **Mr N. Park**

MR DAVID THOMPSON - continued

9 **CUSACK,** 4, b g Heeraat (IRE)—Vera Richardson (IRE) **K. Kirkup**
10 **DIRCHILL (IRE),** 8, b g Power—Bawaakeer (USA) **Mr S. Murray**
11 **JEREJAK,** 5, b g Nathaniel (IRE)—Penang Power **J. A. Moore**
12 **KEEPER CHRIS (IRE),** 8, b g Ask—I'll See You Again (IRE) **Dial a Distance Racing**
13 **KHILWAFY,** 6, b g Mukhadram—Almass (IRE) **Park, Fleming & Souster**
14 **KHULU,** 6, ch g Burwaaz—Ingenti **D. A. J. Bartlett**
15 **KOLOSSUS,** 6, ch g Assertive—Bikini **Racing & Kevin Kirkup**
16 **LOSTNFOUND,** 9, b m Midnight Legend—La Cerisaie **Mr S. Murray**
17 **LUKOUTOLDMAKEZEBAK,** 9, b g Arabian Gleam—Angelofthenorth **NE1 Racing Club**
18 **MARTIN'S BRIG (IRE),** 5, b g Equiano (FR)—Weeza (IRE) **J. A. Moore**
19 **MOVIN'ON UP (IRE),** 7, b m Milan—Kalygarde (IRE) **J. A. Moore**
20 **POCO CONTANTE,** 5, b m Fast Company (IRE)—Littlemoor Lass **NE1 Racing Club**
21 **SPLASH OF VERVE (IRE),** 10, b g Fast Company (IRE)—Ellistown Lady (IRE) **Mrs A. Kenny**
22 **TRINITY STAR (IRE),** 11, gr g Kheleyf (USA)—Zamiyla (IRE) **Trinity Racing**
23 **VERTICE (IRE),** 5, ch m Toronado (IRE)—Asima (IRE) **Mick Martin Keith Boddy & Son**
24 **VISITANT,** 9, ch g Pivotal—Invitee **Mr N. Park**
25 **WHERES THE CRUMPET,** 4, ch f Mukhadram—Jivry **Mr S. Murray**

THREE-YEAR-OLDS

26 Ch f Assertive—Vera Richardson (IRE) **K. Kirkup**
27 B c Dragon Dancer—Zahara Joy

TWO-YEAR-OLDS

28 B f 13/01 Havana Grey—Anneani (IRE) (Bushranger (IRE)) **K. Kirkup**

Other Owners: Mr K. Boddy, Mr J. Cockcroft, Mr R. Cockcroft, Mr S. Cockcroft, Mr W. Cockcroft, Mr W. Fleming, K. Kirkup, Mr M. Martin, Mr A. N. J. McMahon, Mr P. J. McMahon, NE1 Racing Club, Mr N. Park.

Assistant Trainer: J. A. Moore.

Flat Jockey: Tony Hamilton.

---

512 **MR RONALD THOMPSON, Doncaster**
Postal: **No 2 Bungalow, Haggswood Racing Stable, Stainforth, Doncaster, South Yorkshire, DN7 5PS**
Contacts: **PHONE 01302 845904 MOBILE 07713 251141 FAX 01302 845904**
EMAIL ronracing@gmail.com

1 **FURNITURE FACTORS (IRE),** 4, b g Pride of Dubai (AUS)—I Hearyou Knocking (IRE) **B. Bruce & R. Thompson**
2 **LADY VALLETTA (IRE),** 5, ch m Ivawood (IRE)—Cesca (IRE) **Ronald Thompson**
3 **THECHILDREN'STRUST (IRE),** 7, br g Society Rock (IRE)—Estemaala (IRE) **B. Bruce & R. Thompson**

Other Owners: Mr B. Bruce, Ronald Thompson.

---

513 **MR VICTOR THOMPSON, Alnwick**
Postal: **Link House Farm, Newton By The Sea, Embleton, Alnwick, Northumberland, NE66 3ED**
Contacts: **PHONE 01665 576272 MOBILE 07739 626248**

1 **DE MAZZARO (IRE),** 8, b g So You Think (NZ)—Bolero Again (IRE) **V. Thompson**
2 **DEAUVILLE SOCIETY (IRE),** 7, b m Society Rock (IRE)—Dorothy Dene **V. Thompson**
3 **EX S'ELANCE (FR),** 8, b g Saddex—Pampa Brune (FR) **V. Thompson**
4 **GLORY,** 6, b g Olympic Glory (IRE)—Updated (FR) **V. Thompson**

MR VICTOR THOMPSON - continued

5 **JESS'S CORNER (IRE)**, 6, b g Footstepsinthesand—Hamalka (IRE) **V. Thompson**
6 **MUROOR (IRE)**, 9, ch g Nayef (USA)—Raaya (USA) **V. Thompson**
7 **PC DIXON**, 9, ch g Sixties Icon—Lakaam **V. Thompson**
8 **RAPID FRITZ (IRE)**, 13, ch g Kutub (IRE)—Another Pet (IRE) **V. Thompson**
9 **SWEET JUSTICE (IRE)**, 5, b m Lawman (FR)—Muluk (IRE) **V. Thompson**
10 **UP WITH THE PLAY (IRE)**, 5, b g Fracas (IRE)—Alertness (IRE) **V. Thompson**

Assistant Trainer: M Thompson.

---

514 MR SANDY THOMSON, Greenlaw
Postal: **Lambden, Greenlaw, Duns, Berwickshire, TD10 6UN**
Contacts: PHONE **01361 810211** MOBILE **07876 142787**
EMAIL **sandy@lambdenfarm.co.uk** WEBSITE **www.sandythomsonracing.co.uk**

1 **ALFSBOY (IRE)**, 7, b g Shirocco (GER)—Full of Spirit (IRE) **Carl Hinchy & Mark Scott**
2 **BAK ROCKY (IRE)**, 6, br g Shirocco (GER)—Leanne (IRE) **Mr A. M. Thomson**
3 4, B g Mahler—Ballybrowney Hall (IRE) **Mr S. Townshend**
4 **BARON BRIGGS (IRE)**, 5, b g Ocovango—Off She Goes (IRE) **R. A. Green**
5 **BASS ROCK (FR)**, 6, b g Martaline—Horta (IRE) **R. A. Green**
6 **BROTHERLY COMPANY (IRE)**, 10, b g Fast Company (IRE)—Good Lady (IRE) **The Reign It In Partnership**
7 **CARCACI CASTLE (IRE)**, 6, b g Getaway (GER)—Hakuna (IRE) **Mr M & Mrs M McPherson**
8 **CEDAR HILL (IRE)**, 8, b g Frammassone (IRE)—Dayamen **A & Manclark**
9 **COOLBANE BOY (IRE)**, 7, b g Mountain High (IRE)—Easter Saturday (IRE) **Michelle And Dan Macdonald**
10 **COOLKILL (IRE)**, 8, b g Arcadio (IRE)—Elisabetta (IRE) **Mr J. K. McGarrity**
11 **CROSSGALESFAMEGAME (IRE)**, 8, b m Mahler—Fame Forever (IRE) **J Fyffe & S Townshend**
12 **CURRAMORE (IRE)**, 8, b g Arcadio (IRE)—Beale Native (IRE) **Mrs F. E. Bocker**
13 4, B f Mahler—Dancing Baloo (IRE) **Mrs Q. R. Thomson**
14 **DELUXE RANGE (IRE)**, 7, b g Westerner—Kildea Cailin (IRE) **Watson & Lawrence**
15 **DEMOCRATIC OATH (IRE)**, 7, b g Stowaway—Reina Reed (IRE) **J Fyffe & S Townshend**
16 **DINGO DOLLAR (IRE)**, 10, ch g Golden Lariat (USA)—Social Society (IRE)
M Warren J Holmes R Kidner & J Wright
17 **DONNA'S DELIGHT (IRE)**, 11, b g Portrait Gallery (IRE)—Hot Lips (IRE) **D&D Armstrong Limited**
18 **DONNA'S DOUBLE**, 6, b g Fair Mix (IRE)—Elegant Accord (IRE) **D & D Armstrong Ltd & Mr L Westwood**
19 **DOYEN BREED (IRE)**, 7, ch g Doyen (IRE)—Sweet Empire (IRE) **The Explorers**
20 **DUC DE GRISSAY (FR)**, 9, b g Denham Red (FR)—Rhea de Grissay (FR) **Quona Thomson & Ken McGarrity**
21 **ELF DE RE (FR)**, 8, ch g Anabaa Blue—Ninon de Re (FR) **Mr J. K. McGarrity**
22 **EMPIRE STEEL (IRE)**, 8, gr g Aizavoski (IRE)—Talk of Rain (FR) **Mr A. J. Wight**
23 **FAIR MINX**, 8, gr m Fair Mix (IRE)—Blazing Diva (IRE) **Mr J. K. McGarrity**
24 **FANTASTIC ROCK (FR)**, 7, ch g Konig Turf (GER)—Rock Treasure (FR) **Mr W. D. Macdonald**
25 **FLOWER OF SCOTLAND (FR)**, 7, gr m Lord du Sud (FR)—Theme Song (FR) **R. A. Green**
26 5, B m Martaline—Gaspaisielle
27 **GERONIMO**, 11, b g Kadastrof (FR)—Triggers Ginger **Mr J. K. McGarrity**
28 **GET OUT THE GATE (IRE)**, 9, b g Mahler—Chartani (IRE) **J Fyffe & S Townshend**
29 **GOAST DANCER (FR)**, 6, b g Network (GER)—Verka de Thaix (FR) **The Potassium Partnership**
30 **GOODTIMES BADTIMES (IRE)**, 7, b g Doyen (IRE)—One Love (IRE) **Chicken Hutch Racers**
31 **GOT TRUMPED**, 7, ch g Thewayyouare (USA)—Madam President **Midnight Racing Club**
32 4, B f Nathaniel (IRE)—Helter Helter (USA) **Mrs Q. R. Thomson**
33 **HILL SIXTEEN**, 9, b g Court Cave (IRE)—Chasers Chic **J Fyffe & S Townshend**
34 **JIMMY'S JET**, 6, b g Jet Away—Southway Queen **Mr J. Fyffe**
35 **LARGY PERK (IRE)**, 8, b g Scorpion (IRE)—Ellens Perk (IRE) **Midnight Racing Club**
36 **MILVALE (IRE)**, 8, b g Ask—House-of-Hearts (IRE) **Trading Products Limited**
37 **MYMILAN (IRE)**, 9, b g Milan—Jill's Girl (IRE) **Tweed Valley Racing Club**
38 **NINETOFIVE (IRE)**, 5, b br g Malinas (GER)—Poulnasherry Dove (IRE) **Mr A. M. Thomson**
39 **OFF THE BEAT**, 8, ch g Black Sam Bellamy (IRE)—Off By Heart **Ken McGarrity & the Western Chasers**
40 **OVERCOURT**, 8, b g Court Cave (IRE)—Overlady **Mr W. F. Jeffrey**

MR SANDY THOMSON - continued

41 7, B m Getaway (GER)—Present Leader **Mrs Q. R. Thomson**
42 RIPPLET, 7, b m Rip Van Winkle (IRE)—Seradim **Mrs A. R. B. Mania**
43 ROB ROY MACGREGOR (IRE), 4, b g Walk In The Park (IRE)—Miss Baloo (IRE) **Quona Thomson & Ken McGarrity**
44 SALVINO (IRE), 6, b g Leading Light (IRE)—Sagabolley (IRE) **Mr A. J. Wight**
45 SARYSHAGANN (FR), 9, gr g Iffraaj—Serasana **Mr J. K. McGarrity**
46 SEEMORELIGHTS (IRE), 10, b g Echo of Light—Star Lodge **Watson & Lawrence**
47 SHAKA THE KING (IRE), 8, b g Yeats (IRE)—Kissantell (IRE) **D & D Armstrong Ltd & Mr L Westwood**
48 SILVER STAR MIX, 6, gr m Fair Mix (IRE)—Shady Olive **Six Star Racing**
49 SIRWILLIAMWALLACE (IRE), 9, b g Getaway (GER)—Mrs Milan (IRE) **Mr J. K. McGarrity**
50 SPACE SAFARI (FR), 9, b g Kapgarde (FR)—Prodiga (FR) **Mrs F. E. Bocker**
51 STONEY ROVER (IRE), 9, b g Scorpion (IRE)—Consultation (IRE) **Mr K. J. Telfer**
52 STORM NELSON (IRE), 9, b g Gold Well—Dabiyra (IRE) **Mr J. Fyffe**
53 THE FERRY MASTER (IRE), 9, b g Elusive Pimpernel (USA)—Dinghy (IRE) **The Potassium Partnership**
54 WAR SOLDIER (IRE), 5, b g Soldier of Fortune (IRE)—After Dark (IRE) **J Townson & P Thompson**

Other Owners: Mr N. Boyle, D&D Armstrong Limited, Mr J. Fyffe, A. Gilchrist, R. A. Green, Mr C. S. Hinchy, Mr A. J. W. Hogg, Mr S. A. Hollings, J. Holmes, Mr R. A. Kidner, Mrs P. A. Manclark, Mr J. K. McGarrity, Mr D. W. McIntyre, Mr M. H. McPherson, Mrs M. W. McPherson, Mr M. J. Roche, Mr M. S. Scott, The Western Chasers, Mr P. Thompson, Mrs Q. R. Thomson, Mr S. Townshend, J. Townson, Mr M. K. Warren, Mr L. J. Westwood, J. Wright.

Assistant Trainer: Mrs A. M. Thomson.

---

515 **MR JOE TICKLE, Tiverton**
Postal: **Lower Ford, Warbrightsley Hill, Stoodleigh, Tiverton, Devon, EX16 9QQ**
EMAIL **txi100@hotmail.com**

1 FALMOUTH QUEEN, 4, b f Cannock Chase (USA)—Queen's Ballerina (IRE) **Mr J. Tickle**
2 MARKMYWORD, 9, b m Resplendent Glory (IRE)—Spring Creek **Mr T. Floyd**
3 ROSE ABOVE IT (IRE), 6, b m Kalanisi (IRE)—West Hill Rose (IRE) **Mr K. Johns**
4 SCHOOL FOR SCANDAL (FR), 7, gr g Doctor Dino (FR)—School of Thought (FR)
5 SHANTOLIE (IRE), 8, b g Jeremy (USA)—Lady Elodie (IRE) **Joe Tickle Racing Club**
6 SWEARER (IRE), 6, br g Kalanisi (IRE)—Dance Cover (IRE) **Mr P. Emmins**
7 VENDANGE (IRE), 4, b g Le Havre (IRE)—Harvest Queen (IRE) **Mr K. Connors**

THREE-YEAR-OLDS
8 FALMOUTH BALLERINA, ch f Cannock Chase (USA)—Queen's Ballerina (IRE) **Mr J. Tickle**

---

516 **MR NIGEL TINKLER, Malton**
Postal: **Woodland Stables, Langton, Malton, North Yorkshire, YO17 9QR**
Contacts: HOME **01653 658245** MOBILE **07836 384225** FAX **01653 658542**
WORK EMAIL **nigel@nigeltinkler.com** EMAIL **sam@nigeltinkler.com**

1 ACKLAM EXPRESS (IRE), 4, b g Mehmas (IRE)—York Express **MPS Racing & M B Spence**
2 AS IF BY CHANCE, 4, b g Fountain of Youth (IRE)—Citron **Mrs Sara Hattersley & Miss Tracey Mann**
3 ATHOLLBLAIR BOY (IRE), 9, ch g Frozen Power (IRE)—Ellxell (IRE) **The Geezaaah Partnership**
4 BAKR, 4, b f Kodiac—Qawaasem (IRE) **Mr A. Chapman**
5 4, B c Cable Bay (IRE)—Bigger Picture (IRE) **R. S. Cockerill (Farms) Ltd**
6 COLEY'S KOKO (IRE), 4, b f Kodiac—Acclimatisation (IRE) **Mr J. R. Saville**
7 GINGER JAM, 7, ch g Major Cadeaux—Day By Day **Mr G. B. Davidson**
8 HIGH SECURITY, 4, b g Acclamation—Excelette (IRE) **Reliance Racing Partnership**
9 IMPERIUM BLUE, 4, gr g Lethal Force (IRE)—Exist **Mr & Mrs I. H. Bendelow**
10 ISLA KAI (IRE), 4, b g Awtaad (IRE)—Sidney Girl **Martin Webb Racing**
11 MEJTHAAM (IRE), 4, b f Exceed And Excel (AUS)—Adhwaa **Mr M. B. Spence, Mr A. D. Spence**

MR NIGEL TINKLER - continued

12 **NOT ON YOUR NELLIE (IRE)**, 5, b m Zebedee—Piccadilly Filly (IRE) **Exors of the Late J. D. Gordon**
13 **ROUNDHAY PARK**, 7, ch g Mayson—Brave Mave **Leeds Plywood & Doors Ltd**
14 **SHE'S A DEVA**, 4, b f Fountain of Youth (IRE)—Rosein **D M Caslin & Partner**
15 **SINGE ANGLAIS (IRE)**, 5, ch g Footstepsinthesand—Callanish **G Maidment Racing**
16 **STRANGERONTHESHORE**, 4, b f Cable Bay (IRE)—Stolen Glance **R. S. Cockerill (Farms) Ltd**
17 **TRUTH IN JEST**, 4, ch g Mayson—Where's Broughton **Dapper Partnership**
18 **VIOLETTE SZABO (IRE)**, 5, b m Excelebration (IRE)—Forthefirstime **Crawford Society 1**
19 **WHATWOULDYOUKNOW (IRE)**, 7, b g Lope de Vega (IRE)—Holamo (IRE) **Dearing Plastics Ltd & Mark Ingram**

THREE-YEAR-OLDS

20 **ANOTHER BERTIE (IRE)**, b g Acclamation—Temerity (IRE) **Mr J. R. Saville**
21 **ANOTHER INVESTMENT (IRE)**, b g Awtaad (IRE)—Mitzi Winks (USA) **J Glover R O'Donnell J Short N Skinner**
22 **BETTY BROWN**, b f Garswood—Where's Broughton **The Racing Emporium**
23 **COZICAN (IRE)**, b g Kodiac—Coconut Kisses **Martin Webb Racing**
24 **DANDY DINMONT (IRE)**, b g Dandy Man (IRE)—Coconut Kisses **MPS Racing Ltd, Mr M. A. Ollier, Mr S. Perkins**
25 **DOUGIES DREAM (IRE)**, b g Fast Company (IRE)—Sidney Girl **Martin Webb Racing**
26 **FORCE ELEVEN**, gr g Lethal Force—Grace Hull **Mr R. Hull**
27 **GLORY HALLELUJAH (IRE)**, ch g Cotai Glory—Island Vision (IRE) **Mr J Raybould & Mr S Perkins**
28 **GOLDEN DUKE (IRE)**, ch g Galileo Gold—Porta Portese **The Racing Emporium**
29 **LUCKY LUCKY LUCKY (IRE)**, b g Footstepsinthesand—Lovers Peace (IRE) **G Maidment Racing**
30 **LUCROSA (IRE)**, b f Profitable (IRE)—Opportuna
31 **MAYBE EVEN NEVER**, ch g Dream Ahead (USA)—Kashtan **D P Van Der Hoeven & D G Pryde**
32 **NOWTODOWITHME**, gr ro g Dark Angel (IRE)—Kodiva (IRE) **Dearing Plastics Ltd & Paul Burdett**
33 **PARADISE OF LOVE**, b f Iffraaj—Tropical Paradise (IRE) **Derrick Bloy & Harlequin Direct**
34 **PIASTRELLA (IRE)**, b f Awtaad (IRE)—Tingleo **Ceramic Tile Merchants Ltd**
35 **PRODIGIOUS BLUE (IRE)**, b g Bated Breath—Hellofahaste **Mr & Mrs I. H. Bendelow**
36 B f Ribchester—Spirit of Dubai (IRE) **Derrick Bloy & Harlequin Direct**
37 **TIBERIO SMILE**, b g Profitable (IRE)—Byrony (IRE) **J. R. Marshall**
38 **TRUST BERTIE (IRE)**, b g Mehmas (IRE)—Crystal Theatre (IRE) **Mr J. R. Saville**
39 **WOODLANDS CHARM (IRE)**, b f Kodiac—Causeway Charm (USA) **Woodlands Racing & Middleham Park Racing**

TWO-YEAR-OLDS

40 B c 26/04 Kessaar (IRE)—Applauding (IRE) (Royal Applause) (52381) **SYPS (UK) Ltd**
41 B c 08/02 Dandy Man (IRE)—Bahaarah (IRE) (Iffraaj) (10629) **The Dandymen**
42 **BELLA KOPELLA (IRE)**, b f 13/02 Awtaad (IRE)—Ajla (IRE) (Exceed And Excel (AUS)) (65000)

Martin Webb Racing

43 Br f 16/03 U S Navy Flag (USA)—Beylerbey (USA) (Street Cry (IRE)) (22109)
44 Br f 30/04 Wootton Bassett—Broken Applause (IRE) (Acclamation) (297619) **Martin Webb Racing**
45 B c 25/02 Awtaad (IRE)—Classic Legend (Galileo (IRE)) (11429) **The Flying Raconteurs**
46 Gr c 31/01 Make Believe—Danamight (IRE) (Danetime (IRE)) (35000)
47 Gr c 07/03 Roaring Lion (USA)—Every Time (Pivotal) (102041) **Harlequin Direct Ltd**
48 B f 16/02 Blame (USA)—Goodthingstaketime (IRE) (Canford Cliffs (IRE)) (30476) **D Balfe, M Ollier, N Skinner**
49 Ch c 22/04 Night of Thunder (USA)—Grace Hull (Piccolo) (36190) **Mr R. Hull**
50 **HEART OF ACKLAM**, b c 03/04 Zoffany (IRE)—Tingleo (Galileo (IRE)) (32000) **Amity Finance Ltd**
51 B g 12/03 Fountain of Youth (IRE)—Illusions (Toronado (IRE)) (2381) **Ms Sara Hattersley & Miss Tracey Mann**
52 B c 03/02 Showcasing—Impede (Bated Breath) (62000) **Mr Y. T. Szeto**
53 Ch c 29/02 Tamayuz—Into The Lane (IRE) (Excelebration (IRE)) (59048) **MPS Racing & Partners**
54 Ch f 22/02 Havana Grey—Jawaaneb (USA) (Kingmambo (USA)) (12755) **SYPS (UK) Ltd**
55 B c 25/03 Mondialiste (IRE)—Jeany (IRE) (Kodiac) **SYPS (UK) Ltd**
56 Ch c 15/04 Pearl Secret—Kashtan (Sakhee's Secret) **D. G. Pryde, Mr D. P. van der Hoeven**
57 B c 10/02 Cotai Glory—Kodafine (IRE) (Kodiac) (80000) **Harlequin Direct Ltd, SYPS (UK) Ltd, D. Bloy**
58 **LAKOTA BLUE**, br c 26/01 Sioux Nation (USA)—Thiel (Teofilo (IRE)) (42000) **Mr & Mrs I. H. Bendelow**
59 B c 07/03 New Bay—Luciole (High Chaparral (IRE)) (24762) **The Firefly Syndicate**
60 **MAJIL (IRE)**, b f 01/03 Mehmas (IRE)—Damask (IRE) (Red Clubs (IRE)) (45714) **Reliance Racing Partnership**
61 Ch c 14/04 Camacho—Midnight Oasis (Oasis Dream) (32313) **Woodlands Racing 2**
62 Bl c 10/03 Kuroshio (AUS)—Multamisa (USA) (Lonhro (AUS)) (19048) **Mr A. Chapman**
63 B c 11/05 Galileo Gold—Petite Boulangere (IRE) (Namid) (14286) **SYPS (UK) Ltd**
64 B br f 02/03 Awtaad (IRE)—Quenched (Dansili) (45000) **G Maidment Racing**
65 Gr ro f 29/03 Fast Company (IRE)—Saphira Silver (IRE) (Verglas (IRE)) (10476) **Harry Easterby**

MR NIGEL TINKLER - continued

66 B c 10/05 Dandy Man (IRE)—Sidney Girl (Azamour (IRE)) (25510)
67 B g 16/04 Exceed And Excel (AUS)—Silver Grey (IRE) (Chineur (FR)) (22857) **Ontoawinner**
68 B c 20/03 Monsieur Bond (IRE)—Stolen Glance (Mujahid (USA)) **R. S. Cockerill (Farms) Ltd**
69 B f 09/03 Ardad (IRE)—Talent Spotter (Exceed And Excel (AUS)) (75000) **Derrick Bloy & Harlequin Direct**
70 B c 14/04 Dandy Man (IRE)—Thought Is Free (Cadeaux Genereux) (6667)
71 B f 28/03 James Garfield (IRE)—Vulnicura (IRE) (Frozen Power (IRE)) (38265) **MPS Racing & Partners**
72 B c 13/04 Saxon Warrior (JPN)—War No More (USA) (War Front (USA)) (25000)

Mr M. B. Spence, Miss A Hodgson-Tuck
73 B c 27/03 Zoffany (IRE)—Wild Bloom (Exceed And Excel (AUS)) (34286) **Mr I Homer**

Other Owners: D. Bloy, Mr P. Burdett, Ms D. M. Caslin, Mr G. Darling, Dearing Plastics Ltd, Mr A. Denham, F. Drabble, Mr J. A. Glover, Harlequin Direct Ltd, Ms S. V. Hattersley, Mr M. Ingram, MPS Racing Ltd, Mr G. R. Maidment, Mr C. R. Marshall, Mr James Marshall & Mr Chris Marshall, Mrs T. L. McGowan, Middleham Park Racing XXIV, Mr L. Murray, Mr R. P. O'Donnell, T. S. Palin, Mrs J. J. Parvin, J. P. Parvin, Mr A. M. Pear, Racing, Olliers, Perkins, Mr S. Perkins, M. Prince, D. G. Pryde, J. Raybould, Mr J. A. B. Short, N. Skinner, Mr A. A. Smith, Mr M. B. Spence, The Crawford Society, Mr N. Tinkler, Mr M. Webb, Woodlands Racing, Mr D. P. van der Hoeven.

---

517 MR COLIN TIZZARD, Sherborne
Postal: **Venn Farm, Milborne Port, Sherborne, Dorset, DT9 5RA**
Contacts: PHONE 01963 250598 MOBILE 07976 778656 FAX 01963 250598
EMAIL info@colintizzard.co.uk WEBSITE www.colintizzard.co.uk

1 AKI BOMAYE (IRE), 7, gr g Stowaway—Line Grey (FR) **Mrs M. Middleton**
2 ALLSFINEANDANDY (IRE), 6, b g Dandy Man (IRE)—Swish Dancer (IRE) **Mr G. Kennington**
3 AMARILLO SKY (IRE), 6, b g Westerner—Bag of Tricks (IRE) **J P Romans & Taylor, O'Dwyer**
4 AMBION HILL (IRE), 7, b br g Getaway (GER)—Vertality (IRE) **Mr O. C. R. Wynne & Mrs S. J. Wynne**
5 ATAKAN (FR), 6, b g Sinndar (IRE)—Accusation (IRE) **The Reserve Tankers**
6 BERTIE WOOSTER (IRE), 4, b br g Beat Hollow—Fair Ina (IRE) **Mrs C. Knowles**
7 BIRDMAN BOB, 5, ch g Flemensfirth (USA)—Brijomi Queen (IRE) **Taylor & O'Dwyer**
8 BOLD CONDUCT (IRE), 8, b g Stowaway—Vics Miller (IRE) **J P Romans & Terry Warner**
9 BORN IN BORRIS (IRE), 8, b m Arcadio (GER)—Honour Own (IRE) **Mr R. M. Harvey-Bailey**
10 BOURBALI (FR), 5, b g Sinndar (IRE)—Saintheze (IRE) **Pope, Legg, Green T Swaffield**
11 BUCKHORN GEORGE, 7, gr g Geordieland (FR)—Waimea Bay

The Buckhorn Racing Team, Mr D. A. Mayes, M. M. Hooker
12 BUCKHORN ROCCO, 6, ch g Saddler's Rock (IRE)—Waimea Bay **The Buckhorn Racing Team**
13 BUTTERFLYCOLLECTOR (IRE), 4, ch f Flemensfirth (USA)—Jolivia (FR) **Susan & John Waterworth**
14 BUTTERWICK BROOK (IRE), 7, b g Getaway (GER)—Sheriussa (IRE) **The Butterwick Syndicate**
15 CATCH THE CUBAN, 6, b g Havana Gold (IRE)—Reyamour **C. L. Tizzard**
16 CHAMPAGNE MESDAMES (FR), 5, b g Diamond Boy (FR)—Olerone (FR) **The Wychwood Partnership**
17 CHAMPS HILL, 5, b g Champs Elysees—Grapes Hill **The Colin Tizzard Racing Club**
18 CHRISTMAS IN APRIL (FR), 10, b g Crillon (FR)—Similaresisoldofa (FR) **Swallowfield Racing**
19 COPPERHEAD, 8, ch g Sulamani (IRE)—How's Business **Mrs G. C. Pritchard**
20 COULD TALKABOUTIT (IRE), 5, b g Kayf Tara—Glen Countess (IRE) **Mr J. P. Romans**
21 DUC KAUTO (FR), 9, b g Ballingarry (IRE)—Kauto Lorette (FR) **Ann & Alan Potts Limited**
22 DYLAN'S DOUBLE (IRE), 5, b g Getaway (GER)—Summer Again (IRE) **Brocade Racing**
23 EARL OF WISDOM, 7, ch g Flemensfirth (USA)—Golden Sunbird (IRE) **The Wychwood Partnership**
24 EARTH BUSINESS (IRE), 6, b g Westerner—Shellys Creek (IRE) **Mrs C. E. Penny**
25 ELDORADO ALLEN (FR), 8, gr g Khalkevi (IRE)—Hesmeralda (FR) **J P Romans & Terry Warner**
26 ELEGANT ESCAPE (IRE), 10, b g Dubai Destination (USA)—Graineuaile (IRE) **Mr J. P. Romans**
27 ELIXIR DE NUTZ (FR), 8, gr g Al Namix (FR)—Nutz (FR) **J. T. Warner**
28 FAUSTINOVICK, 8, b g Black Sam Bellamy (IRE)—Cormorant Cove **The Faustinovick Syndicate**
29 FIDDLERONTHEROOF (IRE), 8, b g Stowaway—Inquisitive Look **Taylor, Burley & O'Dwyer**
30 FLOY JOY (IRE), 6, b g Arcadio (GER)—The Scorpion Queen (IRE) **Nigel Hanger & Eric Jones**
31 FURKASH (FR), 7, b g Al Namix (FR)—Meralda (FR) **Swallowfield Racing**
32 GETMEGOLD (IRE), 7, ch g Getaway (GER)—Sunset Gold (IRE) **Anne Broom & Wendy Carter**

MR COLIN TIZZARD - continued

33 **GOLDEN SUNRISE (IRE)**, 9, ch g Stowaway—Fairy Dawn (IRE) **Brocade Racing**
34 **HELFORD RIVER**, 8, b g Presenting—Lovely Origny (FR) **Brocade Racing**
35 **HOLNEST POUND**, 5, b g Arvico (FR)—Honey Tree **Mr E. R. Vickery**
36 **I SHUT THAT D'OR (FR)**, 4, b g Barastraight—Anicka d'Or (FR) **J. K. Powell Racing**
37 **ILOVETHENIGHTLIFE**, 4, b f Walk In The Park (IRE)—Belle De Londres (IRE)
38 **INVESTMENT MANAGER**, 6, b g Nathaniel (IRE)—Two Days In Paris (FR) **Brocade Racing**
39 **JPR ONE (IRE)**, 5, b br g Court Cave (IRE)—Lady Knightess (IRE) **Mr J. P. Romans**
40 **KAUTO THE KING (FR)**, 8, b g Ballingarry (IRE)—Kauto Luisa (FR) **Jenny Perry & Celia Goaman**
41 **KILLER KANE (IRE)**, 7, b g Oscar (IRE)—Native Idea (IRE) **J P Romans & Taylor, O'Dwyer**
42 **KING OF LOMBARDY (IRE)**, 4, b g Milan—Uranna (FR) **The Wychwood Partnership**
43 **L'AIR DU VENT (IRE)**, 8, b g Coastal Path—Bleu Perle (FR) **Brocade Racing**
44 **LAMANVER PIPPIN**, 9, b g Apple Tree (FR)—Lamanver Homerun **Dr D. Christensen**
45 **LANSPARK (IRE)**, 7, b g Milan—Sparky May **Ruxley Holdings Ltd**
46 **LOSTINTRANSLATION (IRE)**, 10, b g Flemensfirth (USA)—Falika (FR) **Taylor & O'Dwyer**
47 **MOLINEAUX (IRE)**, 11, b g King's Theatre (IRE)—Steel Grey Lady (IRE) **C. L. Tizzard**
48 **MY LADY GREY**, 8, gr m Presenting—Wassailing Queen **Mr J. Reed**
49 **NAME IN LIGHTS (IRE)**, 6, b g Fame And Glory—Chevalier Jet (IRE) **Mrs M. Middleton**
50 **NATIVE RIVER (IRE)**, 12, ch g Indian River (FR)—Native Mo (IRE) **Mrs A. E. M. Broom**
51 **NELSONS ROCK**, 7, b g Mount Nelson—Neardown Beauty (IRE) **Middleham Park Racing LXXXVIII**
52 **NO HUBS NO HOOBS (IRE)**, 6, b g Flemensfirth (USA)—Miss Brandywell (IRE) **Taylor & O'Dwyer**
53 **NUMBERS MAN (IRE)**, 6, b g Arctic Cosmos (USA)—Duchessofthehall (IRE) **The Reserve Tankers**
54 **OFALLTHEGINJOINTS (IRE)**, 8, b g Stowaway—Dinos Luso (IRE) **The Reserve Tankers**
55 **OFF TO A FLYER (IRE)**, 5, b g Shirocco (GER)—On The Up (IRE)
56 **OFTEN OVERLOOKED (IRE)**, 6, b br g Elusive Pimpernel (USA)—Alpinia (IRE) **Coral Champions Club**
57 **OSCAR ELITE (IRE)**, 7, b g Oscar (IRE)—Lady Elite (IRE) **Mrs M. Middleton**
58 **PER VINO VERITAS**, 7, b g Arvico (FR)—Countess Point **Mr D. S. Purdie**
59 **PREMIUMACCESS (IRE)**, 7, b g Milan—De Loose Mongoose (IRE) **Mr J. Reed**
60 **RECTORY OAK (IRE)**, 7, b br g Oscar (IRE)—Betty Roe (IRE) **Mrs G. C. Pritchard**
61 **RESERVE TANK (IRE)**, 8, b g Jeremy (USA)—Lady Bellamy (IRE) **The Reserve Tankers**
62 **ROBINSVILLE**, 5, b g Shirocco (GER)—This Town **John & Heather Snook**
63 **ROSE OF ARCADIA (IRE)**, 7, b m Arcadio (GER)—Rosie Lea (IRE) **Cheveley Park Stud Limited**
64 **SALCOMBE**, 6, b gr m Geordieland (FR)—Pems Gift **The FTC Syndicate**
65 **SCARFACE (IRE)**, 5, b g Milan—Consider Her Lucky (GER) **Taylor & O'Dwyer**
66 **SEYMOUR PROMISE (IRE)**, 6, b g Flemensfirth (USA)—Loadsapromise (IRE) **C. L. Tizzard**
67 **SHELIKESTHELIGHTS (IRE)**, 4, b f Kayf Tara—Unify **Taylor & O'Dwyer**
68 **SHERBORNE (IRE)**, 6, b g Getaway (GER)—Luck of The Deise (IRE) **Sharp, Nicholas & Kennington**
69 **SHIROCCO'S DREAM (IRE)**, 7, b m Shirocco (GER)—Dream Function (IRE) **J P Romans & Taylor, O'Dwyer**
70 **SIXTY DOLLARS MORE (FR)**, 6, b g Buck's Boum (FR)—Sacree City (FR) **Wendy & Malcolm Hezel**
71 **SIZING AT MIDNIGHT (IRE)**, 10, br g Midnight Legend—Issaquah (IRE) **Ann & Alan Potts Limited**
72 **SIZING CUSIMANO**, 9, b g Midnight Legend—Combe Florey **Ann & Alan Potts Limited**
73 **SIZING TARA**, 9, b g Kayf Tara—As Was **Ann & Alan Potts Limited**
74 **SLATE HOUSE (IRE)**, 10, b g Presenting—Bay Pearl (IRE) **Eric Jones, Geoff Nicholas, John Romans**
75 **SO SAID I**, 6, gr m Malinas (GER)—Wassailing Queen **And So Say All Of Us Partnership**
76 **SPIDER BILL**, 6, b g Arvico (FR)—The Final One
77 **STAR OF VALOUR (IRE)**, 7, b g Invincible Spirit (IRE)—Birthstone **Mr G. Kennington**
78 **STRIKING A POSE (IRE)**, 6, b g Getaway (GER)—Clonsingle Native (IRE)
                              Mr G. Kennington, Mr M. L. Sharp, Mr I. F. Gosden, Mrs E. C. Gosden
79 **SWEET CARYLINE**, 4, b f Blue Bresil (FR)—Mollasses **Mr J. P. Romans**
80 **THE BIG BREAKAWAY (IRE)**, 7, ch g Getaway (GER)—Princess Mairead (IRE)
                              Eric Jones, Geoff Nicholas, John Romans
81 **THE CHANGING MAN (IRE)**, 5, b g Walk In The Park (IRE)—Bitofapuzzle **Susan & John Waterworth**
82 **THE WHERRYMAN**, 4, b g Telescope (IRE)—La Perrotine (FR) **Susan & John Waterworth**
83 **THE WIDDOW MAKER**, 8, ch g Arvico (FR)—Countess Point **Mr D. S. Purdie**
84 **TRIPLE TRADE**, 6, b g Norse Dancer (IRE)—Doubly Gaspe **SJS Racing**
85 **VISION DES FLOS (FR)**, 9, b g Balko (FR)—Marie Royale (FR) **Ann & Alan Potts Limited**
86 **WALK AWAY NOW**, 7, b g Arvico (FR)—Dimpsy Time **Mr D. S. Purdie**
87 **WAR LORD (GER)**, 7, gr g Jukebox Jury (IRE)—Westalin (GER) **The Wychwood Partnership**
88 **WEST APPROACH**, 12, b g Westerner—Ardstown **C. L. Tizzard**
89 **WEST ORCHARD (IRE)**, 5, b g Westerner—Shellys Creek (IRE) **Orchard Racing**
90 **WESTERN BARON (IRE)**, 5, b g Westerner—Aylesbury Park (IRE) **The Alyasan Partnership**

MR COLIN TIZZARD - continued

91 **WETAKECAREOFOUROWN (IRE)**, 5, b g Mahler—Cooksgrove Lady (IRE) **Taylor & O'Dwyer**
92 **WHITE MOON (GER)**, 10, gr g Sholokhov (IRE)—Westalin (GER) **Brocade Racing**
93 **WHYDAH GALLY**, 6, b g Black Sam Bellamy (IRE)—Reverse Swing **Sam's Crew**

THREE-YEAR-OLDS
94 **MARLEY HEAD**, ch g Pride of Dubai (AUS)—Boast
95 **NON STOP (FR)**, b c Starspangledbanner (AUS)—Saint Hilary **Gavigan Kennedy Sharp**

Other Owners: Brocade Racing, Mrs A. E. M. Broom, Mr G. R. Broom, Mr N. Burley, Mrs W. Carter, Mr M. Gavigan, Mrs C. J. Goaman, Mr M. Green, Mr M. W. Hezel, Mrs W. M. Hezel, M. M. Hooker, Mr E. Jones, Mr R. Jones, Mr T. Kennedy, & Gosden, Sharp G Kennington, Mr G. Kennington, Miss B. E. Legg, Mr D. A. Mayes, Mr D. R. Mayes, Mrs S. A. Mayes, Mr G. Nicholas, Mr R. O'Dwyer, Mrs J. M. Perry, Mrs W. M. Pope, Mr J. P Romans, Mr D. J. Rushbrook, Mr M. L. Sharp, Mrs H. A. Snook, J. W. Snook, Mr T. J. Swaffield, Mr P. A. Taylor, Taylor & O'Dwyer, J. T. Warner, Mr J. A. Waterworth, Mrs S. Waterworth, O. C. R. Wynne, Mrs S. J. Wynne.

Assistant Trainer: Joe Tizzard, Chris Wald, **Racing Secretary:** Amanda Hibbs, **Secretary:** Deborah White,

Yard Sponsor: Coral.

NH Jockey: Brendan Powell. **Conditional Jockey:** Harry Kimber.

518	**SIR MARK TODD, Swindon** Postal: **Badgerstown, Foxhill, Swindon, Wiltshire, SN4 0DR** Contacts: **PHONE 01793 791228** **EMAIL mtoddracing@gmail.com**

1 **AMISI**, 6, ch m Nayef (USA)—Amicella
2 **DOUBLE TIME**, 4, b g Bated Breath—Darling Daisy
3 **MERCIAN HYMN**, 4, b g Siyouni (FR)—Astronomy Domine
4 **ROSE FANDANGO**, 4, ch f Exceed And Excel (AUS)—Mumtaza
5 **SEIXAS (IRE)**, 4, ch f Footstepsinthesand—Miss Brazil (IRE)
6 **TASMAN BAY (FR)**, 4, b c Le Havre (IRE)—Purely Priceless (IRE)
7 **WOW WILLIAM (FR)**, 4, b g The Wow Signal (IRE)—Naive (IRE)

THREE-YEAR-OLDS
8 **CAPE CORNWALL ROSE (IRE)**, b f Awtaad (IRE)—Alice Rose (IRE)
9 **PROPHET'S DREAM**, gr c Outstrip—Fool's Dream
10 **TIME STEP**, b c Time Test—Isostatic

TWO-YEAR-OLDS
11 B f 13/04 Night of Thunder (IRE)—Daintily Done (Cacique (IRE)) (32000)
12 B c 22/03 Time Test—Porthledden Flight (Kayf Tara)
13 Ch c 19/03 Tamayuz—Saving Grace (Mastercraftsman (IRE)) (16000)
14 B c 30/04 Footstepsinthesand—School Holidays (USA) (Harlan's Holiday (USA)) (27000)
15 Ch f 29/02 Zoustar (AUS)—Station House (IRE) (Galileo (IRE)) (35000)
16 **UNO GRANDE**, b c 24/01 Exceed And Excel (AUS)—Miss Chicane (Refuse To Bend (IRE)) (1000)
17 B f 17/02 Expert Eye—Upstanding (Pivotal)

Other Owners: Bloomsbury Stud, Mr. Martin Buick, Candour house, Mrs B. M. Cuthbert, Mr H. D. J. De Burgh, Mr T. Henderson, Mr B. J. Lindsay, Mrs J. E. A. Lindsay, Mrs T. L. Miller, Mrs S. O'Donnell, O.T.I. Racing, Rose Fandango Partnership, Mr J. Sarkar, Mrs P. A. Scott-Dunn, Mrs D. A. Sidebottom, Dr H. K. Tayton-Martin, The Mercian Partnership, The Seixas Partnership, Time Step Racing LLP, Lady C. Todd, Sir M. J. Todd, Sir P. J. Vela, Wow William Partnership.

519 MR MARTIN TODHUNTER, Penrith

Postal: **The Park, Orton, Penrith, Cumbria, CA10 3SD**
Contacts: PHONE **015396 24314** MOBILE **07976 440082** FAX **015396 24314**
WEBSITE **www.martintodhunter.co.uk**

1 **AFRICAN GLORY (IRE)**, 8, b m Fame And Glory—African Miss (IRE) **Coniston Old Men Syndicate**
2 **ARCTIC FOX**, 6, ch m Mastercraftsman (IRE)—Aurora Borealis (IRE) **Colin & Kay Wilding**
3 **ARRANGE (IRE)**, 4, gr f Mastercraftsman (IRE)—Watsdaplan (IRE) **Mr & Mrs Ian Hall**
4 **ASKING FOR ANSWERS (IRE)**, 9, ch g Ask—Equation (IRE) **Mrs Mrs Matthews & Mrs G Hazeldean**
5 **BOUNCING BOBBY (IRE)**, 5, b g Raven's Pass (USA)—Silicon Star (FR) **J. W. Hazeldean**
6 **COOL COUNTRY (IRE)**, 7, b g Dylan Thomas (IRE)—Mae's Choice (IRE) **Exors of the Late J. D. Gordon**
7 **FIRST REVOLUTION (IRE)**, 8, b g Jeremy (USA)—Shaigino (IRE) **Colin & Kay Wilding**
8 **JOIE DE VIVRE (IRE)**, 7, gr m Mastercraftsman (IRE)—Fragonard **Leeds Plywood & Doors Ltd**
9 **MOLINARI (IRE)**, 5, gr g Mastercraftsman (IRE)—Moon Empress (FR) **Mr & Mrs Ian Hall**
10 **SOUTHEAST ROSE (IRE)**, 9, b m Beat Hollow—Sunny South East (IRE) **The Surf & Turf Partnership**
11 **TEME SPIRIT (IRE)**, 8, b m Sans Frontieres (IRE)—Newtown Dancer (IRE) **Mr P. G. Airey**
12 **WELL CLICHE (IRE)**, 7, b m Milan—Thyngreesa **Murphy's Law Partnership**

Other Owners: P. W. Clement, Mr W. Downs, Mrs G. M. Hazeldean, Mrs S. J. Matthews, Mr C. Taylor, Miss K. M. Wilding.

520 MR MARCUS TREGONING, Whitsbury

Postal: **Whitsbury Manor Racing Stables, Whitsbury, Fordingbridge, Hampshire, SP6 3QQ**
Contacts: PHONE **01725 518889** MOBILE **07767 888100**
EMAIL **info@marcustregoningracing.co.uk** WEBSITE **www.marcustregoningracing.co.uk**

1 **ARTEMIS SKY**, 4, ch f Hunter's Light (IRE)—Starlit Sky **The Artemis Partnership.**
2 **ATALANTA BREEZE**, 6, b m Champs Elysees—Craighall **Miss S. M. Sharp**
3 **BARON SLICK (IRE)**, 6, b g Raven's Pass (USA)—Namely (IRE) **Mr M. P. Tregoning**
4 **BRONZE ANGEL (IRE)**, 13, b g Dark Angel (IRE)—Rihana (IRE) **Lady Tennant & Mr M P N Tregoning**
5 **CLOVELLY BAY (IRE)**, 11, b g Bushranger (IRE)—Crystalline Stream (FR) **Mr M. P. Tregoning**
6 **LA FORZA**, 4, b g Shalaa (IRE)—Seven Magicians (USA) **Mr M. P. Tregoning**
7 **MARGUB**, 7, ch g Bated Breath—Bahamian Babe **Mr M. P. Tregoning**
8 **MEADRAM**, 4, b g Mukhadram—Mea Parvitas (IRE) **Mrs M Wates**
9 **MUTASALLEM (IRE)**, 4, ch g Showcasing—Bright Glow **Mr M. P. Tregoning**
10 **ORIGINATOR (IRE)**, 4, ch g New Approach (IRE)—Gimasha **R. C. C. Villers**
11 **PEROTTO**, 4, ch g New Bay—Tschierschen (IRE) **Halcyon Thoroughbreds**
12 **POWER OF DARKNESS**, 7, b g Power—Summers Lease **R. C. C. Villers**
13 **STRATHSPEY STRETTO (IRE)**, 7, ch m Kyllachy—Rhythm And Rhyme (IRE)
Miss S Sharp & Mr M. P. N. Tregoning
14 **TRELINNEY (IRE)**, 6, b m Dandy Man (IRE)—Silvertine (IRE) **Mr M. P. Tregoning**
15 **VALPARAISO**, 4, b g Sir Percy—Entre Nous (IRE) **Halcyon Thoroughbreds**
16 **WISPER (IRE)**, 4, ch f Belardo (IRE)—Whisp (GER) **The Reignmakers**

THREE-YEAR-OLDS

17 **A LA FRANCAISE**, ch f Postponed (IRE)—Alamode **Miss K. Rausing**
18 **AL AZHAR (IRE)**, b g Invincible Spirit (IRE)—Arabian Comet (IRE) **John Wallis, Stephen Wallis, Nona Baker**
19 **LADYBIRD (IRE)**, b f Australia—Bessichka **Mr J. D. Manley**
20 **LANDING STRIP**, b f Outstrip—Quail Landing **Mr M. P. Tregoning**
21 **MISS BLUEBELLE (IRE)**, b f Awtaad (IRE)—Miss Bellbird (IRE) **T. & Rogers Family**
22 **MORGHOM**, ch c Dubawi (IRE)—Rifqah (USA) **Shadwell Estate Company Ltd**
23 **NAWRAS**, b c Sea The Stars (IRE)—Umniyah (IRE) **Shadwell Estate Company Ltd**
24 **OLIVETTI**, b g Showcasing—Tschierschen (IRE) **Halcyon Thoroughbreds**
25 **RIBHI (IRE)**, gr c Dark Angel (IRE)—Rihaam (IRE) **Shadwell Estate Company Ltd**

TWO-YEAR-OLDS

26 B c 20/03 Australia—Bessichka (Exceed And Excel (AUS)) **Mr J. D. Manley**

MR MARCUS TREGONING - continued

27 **COMMISSION,** ch c 10/04 Profitable (IRE)—Modify (New Approach (IRE)) (16000) **Longstock Thoroughbreds**
28 **GREEN SOLDIER,** b c 15/02 Cracksman—Kazeem (Darshaan) (22000) **A. Al Shaikh**
29 B c 10/04 Sea The Stars (IRE)—Intisaar (USA) (War Front (USA)) **Shadwell Estate Company Ltd**
30 **ISLAND STAR (IRE),** b c 13/04 New Approach (IRE)—My Fairy (IRE) (Sea The Stars (IRE)) (28000)
Matthew Family & Partner
31 **MARIE LAVEAU,** b f 22/02 Sir Percy—Mariee (Archipenko (USA)) **Miss K. Rausing**
32 B c 06/03 Cityscape—Milldale (Bushranger (IRE)) (5500) **Whitsbury II**
33 **SHAADEN (IRE),** b f 01/03 Invincible Spirit (IRE)—Rihaam (IRE) (Dansili) **Shadwell Estate Company Ltd**
34 **SKYSAIL,** ch c 20/03 Tasleet—Lady Marl (Duke of Marmalade (IRE)) (16000) **Whitsbury I**

Other Owners: Sir Thomas Pilkington, Mr A. P. Rogers, Mrs S. Rogers, Miss S. M. Sharp, Lady Tennant, Mr M. P. Tregoning.

Assistant Trainer: Angie Kennedy.

Flat Jockey: Martin Dwyer. **Amateur Jockey:** Mr George Tregoning.

---

521 MR GRANT TUER, Northallerton
Postal: **Home Farm, Great Smeaton, Northallerton, North Yorkshire, DL6 2EP**
Contacts: **PHONE 01609 881094 MOBILE 07879 698869 FAX 01609 881094**
EMAIL grant_tuer@btinternet.com

1 **ARABIC CULTURE (USA),** 8, b g Lonhro (AUS)—Kydd Gloves (USA) **Marjorie & Tuer**
2 **AWARD DANCER (IRE),** 4, b g Awtaad (IRE)—Music And Dance **Moment Of Madness**
3 **BLAZING HOT,** 5, ch g Hot Streak (IRE)—A Great Beauty **Flash Figs Racing**
4 **BUFORD,** 4, b g Lawman (FR)—Sibaya **T P & Tuer**
5 **CARIBBEAN SUNSET (IRE),** 4, b g Twilight Son—Guana (IRE) **Star Bloodstock Racing**
6 **CATHAYENSIS (IRE),** 4, b f Twilight Son—Chaenomeles (USA) **Allerton Racing & G Tuer**
7 **COWBOY SOLDIER,** 7, b g Kodiac—Urgele (FR) **Ebor Racing Club V111**
8 **CUSTARD,** 6, ch g Monsieur Bond (IRE)—Ailsa Craig (IRE) **Mr G. F. Tuer**
9 **DREAMCASING,** 4, br g Showcasing—Nandiga (USA) **Marjorie & Tuer**
10 **EMARATY HERO,** 5, b g Lope de Vega (IRE)—Valtina (IRE) **NG Racing**
11 **ETIKAAL,** 8, ch g Sepoy (AUS)—Hezmah **Moment Of Madness**
12 **GOLD TERMS,** 4, b f Havana Gold (IRE)—Easy Terms **Mr G. F. Tuer**
13 **GREAT RIDLEY,** 4, b g Garswood—Blue Maisey **Mr G. F. Tuer**
14 **GUNNERSIDE (IRE),** 5, gr g Gutaifan (IRE)—Suite (IRE) **Mr G. F. Tuer**
15 **GUSTAVE AITCH (FR),** 6, b g Maxios—Alyssandre (IRE) **Finch Moran Stone Smith Hooton Pearson-S**
16 **GUVENOR'S CHOICE (IRE),** 7, gr g Intikhab (USA)—Exempt **Royale Racing Syndicate**
17 **HART STOPPER,** 8, b g Compton Place—Angel Song **Mr G. F. Tuer**
18 **ILLUSIONIST (GER),** 5, b g Hot Streak (IRE)—Irishstone (IRE) **Miss M. A. Thompson**
19 **INDIAN VICEROY,** 6, b g Kodiac—Broadlands **Miss M. A. Thompson**
20 **KAAFY (IRE),** 6, b g Alhebayeb (IRE)—Serene Dream **Marjorie & Tuer**
21 **KING TRITON (IRE),** 4, b g Invincible Spirit (IRE)—Nada **Mr E. J. Ware**
22 **LEZARDRIEUX,** 5, b g Due Diligence (USA)—M'Selle (IRE) **Allerton Racing & G Tuer**
23 **LION TOWER (IRE),** 5, b g Exceed And Excel (AUS)—Memorial (AUS) **Hornby Hornets**
24 **MEWS HOUSE,** 5, ch g Coach House (IRE)—Beauty Pageant (IRE) **Flash Figs Racing**
25 **MILWAUKEE BLIZZARD (IRE),** 4, b f French Navy—Glyndebourne (IRE) **Mrs J. Keys**
26 **MOKAMAN,** 4, b g Dandy Man (IRE)—Percolator **Moment Of Madness 2**
27 **MYWAYISTHEONLYWAY (IRE),** 9, b g Tamayuz—Soul Custody (CAN) **Moment Of Madness**
28 **ONE HART,** 5, br g Gutaifan (IRE)—Crystal Morning (IRE) **Mr G. F. Tuer**
29 **REAL TERMS,** 5, b m Champs Elysees—Easy Terms **Mr G. F. Tuer**
30 **SKILLED WARRIOR (IRE),** 4, b g Holy Roman Emperor (IRE)—Sushi Tuna **Mr G. F. Tuer**
31 **STALINGRAD,** 5, b g War Front (USA)—I Am Beautiful (IRE) **Marjorie & Tuer**
32 **SUNSET GLOW (IRE),** 4, b g Pride of Dubai (AUS)—Golden Shine **Moment Of Madness**
33 **SWINGING EDDIE,** 6, b g Swiss Spirit—Bling Bling (IRE) **NG Racing**
34 **TASHGHEEL (IRE),** 4, b g Dark Angel (IRE)—Tawayna (IRE) **Ingham Racing Syndicate**
35 **TERMONATOR,** 6, ch g Monsieur Bond (IRE)—Easy Terms **Mr G. F. Tuer**

MR GRANT TUER - continued

36 **TOMMY TAYLOR (USA)**, 8, b g Mizzen Mast (USA)—Sharp Apple (USA) **Moment Of Madness**
37 **TWILIGHT SECRET**, 4, b g Twilight Son—Crinkle (IRE) **Mr G. F. Tuer**
38 **UCKERBY**, 4, ch g Hot Streak (IRE)—Pigeon Pie **Moment of Madness 3**
39 **UNASHAMED**, 4, b g Brazen Beau (AUS)—Glace (IRE) **Mr G. F. Tuer**
40 **WITHAM RIVER (IRE)**, 4, ch g Galileo (IRE)—Withorwithoutyou (IRE) **NG Racing**
41 **ZAGHAL (IRE)**, 4, b g Exceed And Excel (AUS)—Broadway Melody **Hornby Hornets**

THREE-YEAR-OLDS

42 **BARBARA'S INCHARGE**, b g Ardad (IRE)—Sleepy Dust (IRE) **The Muffed Punt Partnership**
43 **BICEP (IRE)**, b g Mehmas (IRE)—Crafty Notion (IRE) **Mr G. F. Tuer**
44 **DANDY'S DIVA (IRE)**, ch f Dandy Man (IRE)—Ai Chan (IRE) **Mr S. Laffan**
45 **DIRTYOLDTOWN (IRE)**, b c No Nay Never (USA)—Tadris (USA) **Mr C. J. Miller**
46 **LITUUS (IRE)**, b g Holy Roman Emperor (IRE)—Rip Van Music (IRE) **Racing, Blackburn G. Tuer**
47 **ROCADORA**, b f Havana Gold (IRE)—Birthstone **James Ortega Bloodstock Ltd**
48 **ROMANTIC THOUGHT**, ch g Charming Thought—Ermyn Express **Moment Of Madness**
49 B f Bated Breath—Rosehill Artist (IRE) **Mr G. F. Tuer**
50 **SHOWTIME MAHOMES**, b g Dabirsim (FR)—Magic Florence (IRE) **The Muffed Punt Partnership**
51 **SOCKBURN**, b g Garswood—Blue Maisey **Mr G. F. Tuer**
52 **WESTMORIAN**, b g Holy Roman Emperor (IRE)—Inca Trail (USA) **Miss M. A. Thompson**
53 **WOOBAY (IRE)**, b f Starspangledbanner (AUS)—Queenofthenorth (IRE) **Mr J. A. Swinbank**

Other Owners: Allerton Racing, Mr J. N. Blackburn, Mr M. Bland, Mr P. Brierley, Mr T. Brierley, Mr D. G. Colledge, Mr A. Franks, S. Franks, Imperial Racing & Mr John Blackburn, Mr T. S. Ingham, Mr A. G. Leggott, Mr M. D. Parker, Mr I. Robinson, Miss M. L. Taylor, Miss M. A. Thompson, Mrs V. Thompson, Mr G. F. Tuer.

---

522 MR JOSEPH TUITE, Lambourn
Postal: Felstead Stables, Folly Road, Lambourn, Hungerford, Berkshire, RG17 8QE
Contacts: MOBILE 07769 977351
EMAIL joe.tuite@tuiteracing.com WEBSITE www.tuiteracing.co.uk

1 **BYRON HILL (IRE)**, 5, b g Kingston Hill—Gwen Lady Byron (IRE) **David Thorpe & J Tuite**
2 4, B f Mastercraftsman (IRE)—Dynalosca (USA)
3 **KING'S CASTLE (IRE)**, 5, b g Camelot—Kikonga **Mr D. E. Langley**
4 **MICHIGAN STATE (FR)**, 4, b g Maxios—Ciacona (IRE) **B. E. Holland**
5 **SHADOW ANGEL (IRE)**, 4, b f Dark Angel (IRE)—Villanueva (IRE) **Mr J. Ward**
6 **TAHONTA (IRE)**, 4, b g Red Jazz (USA)—Jedward (IRE) **Mr J. M. Tuite**
7 **TIGA TUAN (FR)**, 9, b m Le Havre (IRE)—Ramita **Mr T. R. B. T. A. Shah**
8 **VIA SISTINA (IRE)**, 4, b f Fastnet Rock (AUS)—Nigh (IRE) **Mrs R. G. Hillen**
9 **WON LOVE (IRE)**, 4, b g Frankel—Blhadawa (IRE) **Mr D. A. Olver**
10 **ZEALOT**, 4, b g Pivotal—Devotion (IRE) **Mr J. M. Tuite**

THREE-YEAR-OLDS

11 **D DAY ODETTE**, br f Lawman (FR)—Morning Chimes (IRE) **Mr D. A. Olver**
12 **EVERLOVING (IRE)**, b gr f Acclamation—Chiringuita (USA) **Phillip Cove & Gb Horseracing**
13 **FAST DANSEUSE (IRE)**, b f Fast Company (IRE)—Zalanga (IRE) **Alan & Christine Bright**
14 **HEERS HARRY**, b g Heeraat (IRE)—Air Stricker (FR) **Mrs C. L. Dee**
15 **HOT LEGS LIL (IRE)**, ch f Hot Streak (IRE)—Flashy Queen (IRE) **Penny/Adrian Burton, Bob/Angela Lampard**
16 B f Lope de Vega (IRE)—Mrakeb (USA)
17 **THE ALCHEMIST (FR)**, ch g Havana Gold (IRE)—Zahrat Narjis **Mr J. M. Tuite**
18 **THE ORGANISER**, b g Coach House (IRE)—Poudretteite **Highclere T'bred Racing-the Organiser 1**

TWO-YEAR-OLDS

19 B f 09/04 Ardad (IRE)—Good Health (Magic Ring (IRE)) (12000) **GB Horseracing**
20 Br gr g 27/04 Sioux Nation (USA)—Gypsy Style (Desert Style (IRE))

MR JOSEPH TUITE - continued

21 B g 13/03 Sea The Moon (GER)—Kensington Gardens (Oasis Dream) (37000) **Primera Partnership**
22 Gr f 16/02 Gregorian (IRE)—Lady Kashaan (IRE) (Manduro (GER))
23 **LONG WEEKEND,** b f 17/04 Ardad (IRE)—Happy Escape (Delegator) (952) **Felstead Court Flyers**
24 B c 23/02 Gleneagles (IRE)—Sacred Harp (Oasis Dream) (27211) **Primera Partnership**
25 Ch f 05/03 Iffraaj—Yaa Mous (Farhh) (10000)

Other Owners: Mr A. D. Bright, Mrs C. Bright, Mr P. Cove, GB Horseracing, Highclere T'Bred Racing - The Organiser, Highclere Thoroughbred Racing Ltd, Mr P. J. Scargill, Mr D. A. Thorpe, Mr J. M. Tuite.

---

523   MR BILL TURNER, Sherborne
Postal: **Sigwells Farm, Sigwells, Corton Denham, Sherborne, Dorset, DT9 4LN**
Contacts: **PHONE 01963 220523 MOBILE 07932 100173 FAX 01963 220046**
EMAIL billturnerracing@gmail.com

1 **BORN AT MIDNIGHT,** 7, b g Midnight Legend—Wavet **Mr B. J. Goldsmith**
2 **CASSIS DE REINE,** 8, ch m Quatre Saisons—Reine de Violette **Mrs P. A. Turner**
3 **HILLBILLY,** 4, b g Coach House (IRE)—Dusty Dazzler (IRE) **Mrs P. A. Turner**
4 **HOLDENHURST,** 7, gr g Hellvelyn—Michelle Shift **Ansells Of Watford**
5 **KATHERINE PLACE,** 7, b m Showcasing—Folly Drove **Ansells Of Watford**
6 **LETSBE AVENUE (IRE),** 7, b g Lawman (FR)—Aguilas Perla (IRE) **Mr C. J. Sprake**
7 **LION'S VIGIL (USA),** 5, ch g Kitten's Joy (USA)—Keeping Watch (IRE) **Mr & Mrs Rj Manning**
8 **LITTLE BOY BLUE,** 7, gr g Hellvelyn—Dusty Dazzler (IRE) **Mrs P. A. Turner**
9 **MARETTIMO (IRE),** 8, b g Harbour Watch (IRE)—Renowned (IRE) **Mrs P. A. Turner**
10 **MIDNIGHT CALAMITY,** 8, ch m Malinas (GER)—Miss Calamity **The Floral Farmers**
11 **PACO LOCO,** 4, b g Heeraat (IRE)—Pack of Dreams (IRE) **Mr & Mrs Rj Manning**
12 **SCRAPPY JACK (IRE),** 4, b g Epaulette (AUS)—Jessie K **G A Haulage Ltd**
13 **SHAMADAAN,** 4, b g Invincible Spirit (IRE)—Rasmeyaa (IRE) **Mrs C. E. Peck**
14 **SIX FIVE SPECIAL,** 4, gr g Hellvelyn—Hound Music **Mrs P. A. Turner**

THREE-YEAR-OLDS

15 **LITTLE GIRL BLUE,** gr f Hellvelyn—Dusty Dazzler (IRE) **Mrs P. A. Turner**
16 **MAJOR GATSBY (IRE),** gr g The Grey Gatsby (IRE)—Monteamiata (IRE) **Mr & Mrs Rj Manning**
17 **MILLY MOLLY MANDY,** gr f Hellvelyn—Charlevoix (IRE) **Mrs P. A. Turner**

TWO-YEAR-OLDS

18 Ch c 06/02 Lightning Spear—Life Is Golden (USA) (Giant's Causeway (USA)) (46000) **Mrs P. A. Turner**
19 Gr c 14/04 Havana Grey—Snow Globe (Royal Applause) (3333) **Mrs P. A. Turner**
20 B f 12/02 Pearl Secret—Spanish Gold (Vettori (IRE))

Other Owners: Mr B. C. Ansell, Mrs B. C. Ansell, R. J. Manning, Mrs S. M. Manning.

Assistant Trainer: Kathy While.

---

524   MRS KAREN TUTTY, Northallerton
Postal: **Trenholme House Farm, Osmotherley, Northallerton, North Yorkshire, DL6 3QA**
Contacts: PHONE 01609 883624 MOBILE 07967 837406 FAX 01609 883624
EMAIL karentutty@btinternet.com WEBSITE www.karentuttyracing.co.uk

1 **ELIXSOFT (IRE),** 7, b m Elzaam (AUS)—Grandegrandegrande (IRE) **Thoroughbred Homes Ltd**
2 **FREAK OUT (IRE),** 4, b g Kodiac—Herridge (IRE) **Thoroughbred Homes Ltd**
3 **HER WAY,** 4, ch f Charming Thought—On Her Way **Thoroughbred Homes Ltd**
4 **LITTLE JO,** 8, b g Major Cadeaux—Discoed **Thoroughbred Homes Ltd**
5 **STRAWMAN (IRE),** 5, b g Starspangledbanner (AUS)—Youve Got A Friend (IRE) **Mr K. Till**
6 **TANGLED (IRE),** 7, b g Society Rock (IRE)—Open Verse (USA) **Grange Park Racing XIX**
7 **TWIN APPEAL (IRE),** 11, b g Oratorio (IRE)—Velvet Appeal (IRE) **Grange Park Racing**

MRS KAREN TUTTY - continued

THREE-YEAR-OLDS

8 **GHOSTED (IRE)**, ro g Kodiac—Loving **Thoroughbred Homes Ltd**
9 **MISS BRITAIN (IRE)**, b f Dandy Man (IRE)—Britain's Pride **Thoroughbred Homes Ltd**
10 **MOSTLY CLOUDY (IRE)**, b c Harzand (IRE)—Clarinda (FR) **Sd Velo**
11 **SHAHNAZ (IRE)**, b f Decorated Knight—Fol O'Yasmine **Maximum Racing & Thoroughbred Homes Ltd**
12 **SWEET MADNESS**, b f Galileo Gold—Windy Lane **Thoroughbred Homes Ltd**
13 **TREASURE TROUBE (IRE)**, br c Holy Roman Emperor (IRE)—Romantic View
Mrs Mary Winetroube & Thoroughbred Homes
14 **WHISPERING WINDS (IRE)**, ch f Buratino (IRE)—Guthanna Gaoithe **Thoroughbred Homes Ltd**

TWO-YEAR-OLDS

15 B c 26/03 Tagula (IRE)—Dat II Do (Bahamian Bounty) (8503)
16 B f 12/02 Fountain of Youth (IRE)—Shamrock Sheila (IRE) (Fast Company (IRE)) (7228)
17 B c 13/02 Profitable (IRE)—Tifawt (High Chaparral (IRE)) (7228)
18 B c 14/04 Harzand (IRE)—Vizean (IRE) (Medicean) (9500) **Mr E. Eismark**

Other Owners: Mr D. L. Chorlton, Mr E. Eismark, Maximum Racing, Thoroughbred Homes Ltd, Mrs K. J. Tutty, Mrs M. T. Winetroube.

Flat Jockey: Gemma Tutty.

---

525 | MR NIGEL TWISTON-DAVIES, Cheltenham
Postal: T/a Grange Hill Farm Limited, Grange Hill Farm, Naunton,
Cheltenham, Gloucestershire, GL54 3AY
Contacts: PHONE 01451 850278 MOBILE 07836 664440
EMAIL nigel@nigeltwistondavies.co.uk WEBSITE www.nigeltwistondavies.co.uk

1 **BALLINTUBBER BOY (IRE)**, 5, b g Robin des Champs (FR)—Manhattan Babe (IRE) **Mason and McGoff**
2 **BALLYANDY**, 11, b g Kayf Tara—Megalex **Options O Syndicate**
3 **BALLYBOUGH MARY (IRE)**, 6, b m Shirocco (GER)—In Sync (IRE) **Ms J. E. McGivern**
4 **BALLYCAMUS (IRE)**, 5, b g Presenting—Dotchenka (FR) **Mr N. A. Twiston-Davies**
5 **BALLYMILLSY**, 6, b g Lucarno (USA)—Brackenmoss (IRE) **Mrs M Mills & Mrs J Mills**
6 **BEAUPORT (IRE)**, 6, b g Califet (FR)—Byerley Beauty (IRE) **Bryan & Philippa Burrough**
7 **BEEP BEEP (IRE)**, 8, b g Presenting—Delgany Breese (IRE) **James & Jean Potter**
8 **BLACKCAUSEWAY**, 6, b g Robin des Champs (FR)—Bellino Spirit (IRE)
9 **BLENDED STEALTH**, 5, b g Walk In The Park (IRE)—Wyldello **Graham & Alison Jelley**
10 **BRISTOL DE MAI (FR)**, 11, gr g Saddler Maker (IRE)—La Bole Night (FR) **Mr Simon Munir & Mr Isaac Souede**
11 **CAFE PUSHKIN (FR)**, 6, b g Montmartre (FR)—Chausey (FR) **The Wasting Assets**
12 **CALL BLUE**, 5, b m Blue Bresil (FR)—Safari Run (IRE) **Walters Plant Hire Ltd**
13 **CHECKITOUT (IRE)**, 8, b g Salutino (GER)—Akasha (IRE) **Mills & Mason Partnership**
14 **EARLOFTHECOTSWOLDS (FR)**, 8, bl g Axxos (GER)—Sissi Land (FR) **Twiston-Davies, Mason, Greer & Kiely**
15 **ELMDALE (FR)**, 8, gr g Martaline—Victoire Jaguine (FR) **Mr R. J. Rexton**
16 **EMPHATIC QUALM (IRE)**, 7, b g Califet (FR)—Supreme Touch (IRE) **Graham & Alison Jelley**
17 **EQUINUS (FR)**, 4, b g Shantou (USA)—Merryisker (IRE) **Options O Syndicate**
18 **FANTASTIKAS (FR)**, 7, b g Davidoff (GER)—Negresse de Cuta (FR) **Imperial Racing Partnership 2016**
19 **FANTOMAS (FR)**, 6, b g Sinndar (IRE)—Trudente (FR) **Mr N. A. Twiston-Davies**
20 **FINE BY ME (IRE)**, 5, b g Kingston Hill—Ella Watson (IRE) **Twiston-Davies Equine**
21 **FORTYFOURFORTY**, 5, b g Pether's Moon (IRE)—Just A Whisper
22 **GOA LIL (IRE)**, 6, br g Samum (GER)—Unekaina (FR) **Mr N. A. Twiston-Davies**
23 **GOOD BOY BOBBY (IRE)**, 9, b g Flemensfirth (USA)—Princess Gaia (IRE) **Mr Simon Munir & Mr Isaac Souede**
24 **GOWEL ROAD (IRE)**, 6, b br g Flemensfirth (USA)—Hollygrove Samba (IRE) **Options O Syndicate**
25 **GUARD YOUR DREAMS**, 6, b g Fame And Glory—Native Sunrise (IRE) **Graham & Alison Jelley**
26 **GUY (IRE)**, 7, ch g Getaway (GER)—Sept Verites (FR) **The Hons W. G. & A. G. Vestey**
27 **HIGHER GROUND**, 5, b g Black Sam Bellamy (IRE)—Reverse Swing **Twiston-Davies Equine**
28 **I LIKE TO MOVE IT**, 5, b g Trans Island—Nobratinetta (FR) **Anne-Marie & Jamie Shepperd**
29 **IMPERIAL B G (IRE)**, 5, gr g Getaway (GER)—Milan Pride (IRE) **Imperial Racing Partnership**
30 **JASMIWA (FR)**, 4, b f Authorized (IRE)—Maikawa (FR) **Anne-Marie & Jamie Shepperd**
31 **JONJONTHEGINGESSON (IRE)**, 5, ch g Shirocco (GER)—Land of Pride (IRE) **Mr J. Neild**

MR NIGEL TWISTON-DAVIES - continued

32 **KING OF QUINTA (FR)**, 4, ch g Style Vendome (FR)—Dogaressa (IRE) **D. M. Proos**
33 **LEROY BROWN**, 7, b g Pasternak—Grenfell (IRE) **Mr N. A. Twiston-Davies**
34 **LORD OF CHESHIRE (FR)**, 5, b g Diamond Boy (FR)—Adelyta (FR) **Mason and McGoff**
35 **MADAM MALARKEY**, 4, br f Pether's Moon (IRE)—Grenfell (IRE) **Baker,Cooke,Dodd and Partners**
36 **MASTER CHEWY (IRE)**, 5, b g Walk In The Park (IRE)—Shake The Tree (IRE) **Anne-Marie & Jamie Shepperd**
37 **MOVEIT LIKE MINNIE (IRE)**, 5, b g Libertarian—Cassandrasway (IRE) **F. J. Mills**
38 **MR TRISTAR**, 5, b g Grand Finale (IRE)—Can't Remember **Team Tristar (UK) Ltd**
39 **MUCKAMORE (IRE)**, 8, b g Sholokhov (IRE)—Gales Return (IRE) **Noel Fehily Racing Syndicate- Muckamore**
40 **NAVEGAON GATE**, 4, b g Frankel—Cascata (IRE) **Mr N. A. Twiston-Davies**
41 **NINE NINE NINE**, 5, b g Soldier of Fortune (IRE)—Reves d'Amour (IRE) **Verdansk Racing**
42 **NOBLE SAVAGE (IRE)**, 7, b g Arcadio (GER)—Callerdiscallerdat (IRE) **C. C. Walker**
43 **ONCHAN (IRE)**, 7, b g Oscar (IRE)—Satellite Dancer (IRE) **Exors of the Late Mr T. J. Hemmings**
44 **ONE FORTY SEVEN (IRE)**, 10, b g Beneficial—Still Bubbly (IRE) **Graham & Alison Jelley**
45 **ONE TRUE KING (IRE)**, 7, ch g Getaway (GER)—Final Leave (IRE) **Teme Valley**
46 **POPPA POUTINE (IRE)**, 6, b g Sholokhov (IRE)—Sherchanceit (IRE) **Options O Syndicate**
47 **REDFORD ROAD**, 8, b g Trans Island—Maryscross (IRE) **Options O Syndicate**
48 **RIZZARDO**, 10, gr g Tikkanen (USA)—Last Spruce (USA) **Mr N. A. Twiston-Davies**
49 **ROBINSHILL (IRE)**, 11, ch g Robin des Champs (FR)—I Remember It Well (IRE) **Mr R. J. Rexton**
50 **ROCCO (IRE)**, 9, b g Shantou (USA)—Navaro (IRE) **Mr & Mrs P Carter**
51 **SEASON IN THE SUN**, 5, b g Blue Bresil (FR)—Kentford Dabchick **Anne-Marie & Jamie Shepperd**
52 **SPRING MEADOW (IRE)**, 5, b g Fame And Glory—Gales Present (IRE) **Walters Plant Hire & Potter Group**
53 **STREAM OF STARS**, 7, b g Sea The Stars (IRE)—Precious Gem (IRE) **Susie & Robert Frosell**
54 **SUMMIT LIKE HERBIE**, 10, ch g Sulamani—Colline de Fleurs **Friends Of Herbie**
55 **SUPAKALANISTIC (IRE)**, 9, b g Kalanisi (IRE)—Keys Hope (IRE) **Jump For Fun Racing**
56 **SUPASUNRISE (IRE)**, 6, b g Mores Wells—Sofia Aurora (USA) **Jump For Fun Racing**
57 **SUPER SIX**, 5, b gr g Montmartre (FR)—Hiho Silver Lining **Teme Valley**
58 **THE HOLLOW GINGE (IRE)**, 9, b g Oscar (IRE)—Some Gem (IRE) **The Ginge Army**
59 **THE MICK PRESTON (IRE)**, 6, gr g Shirocco (GER)—Izzy du Berlais (IRE) **The Preston Family Racing**
60 **THE NEWEST ONE (IRE)**, 7, b g Oscar (IRE)—Thuringe (FR) **S Such & CG Paletta**
61 **THE SILVER GINGE (FR)**, 5, gr g Full of Gold (FR)—La Nicoise (FR) **Mr J. Neild**
62 **THELASTHIGHKING (IRE)**, 6, ch g Roderic O'Connor (IRE)—End of The Affair (IRE) **Mr E. Whettam**
63 **THIRD STREET (IRE)**, 6, ch g Leading Light (IRE)—Oddly Presented (IRE) **Exors of the Late Mr T. J. Hemmings**
64 **TIGERS ROAR (IRE)**, 6, b g Leading Light (IRE)—Almnadia (IRE) **Million in Mind Partnership**
65 **TOP OF THE BILL (IRE)**, 6, b g Fame And Glory—Glory Days (GER) **C. C. Walker**
66 **TOPOFTHECOTSWOLDS (IRE)**, 8, b g Arcadio (GER)—Bambootcha (IRE) **Mr M. A. Reay**
67 **TORN AND FRAYED (FR)**, 8, b g Califet (FR)—Chic Et Zen (FR) **Mrs C. S. C. Beresford-Wylie**
68 **TORPILLO (FR)**, 7, ch g Alanadi (FR)—Astherate (FR) **Mr Simon Munir & Mr Isaac Souede**
69 **UNDERSUPERVISION (IRE)**, 6, ch g Doyen (IRE)—Dances With Waves (IRE) **Anne-Marie & Jamie Shepperd**
70 **VIENNA COURT (IRE)**, 7, br m Mahler—Gales Present (IRE) **James and Jean Potter Ltd**
71 **WHOLESTONE (IRE)**, 11, br g Craigsteel—Last Theatre (IRE) **Mr Simon Munir & Mr Isaac Souede**
72 **ZAMBELLA (FR)**, 7, b m Zambezi Sun—Visby (FR) **Mr Simon Munir & Mr Isaac Souede**

Other Owners: B. R. H. Burrough, Mrs P. J. Burrough, Mrs J. Carter, Mr P. A. Carter, Mr R. N. Frosell, Mrs S. P. B. Frosell, Mrs A. D. Jelley, G. S. Jelley, Mr D. M. Mason, G. a. Mason, Mr J. M. McGoff, F. J. Mills, Mrs J. M. Mills, Mrs M. Mills, W. R. Mills, S. E. Munir, Mr J. Neild, Mr P. Preston, Mr R. J. Rexton, Mrs A. Shepperd, Mr J. Shepperd, Mr I. Souede, Sundorne Products (Llanidloes) Ltd, The Hon A. G. Vestey, Lord W. G. Vestey, Walters Plant Hire Ltd.

Assistant Trainer: Carl LLewellyn, Jim Old.

NH Jockey: Tom Bellamy, Sam Twiston-Davies. **Conditional Jockey:** Eddie Edge, Finn Lambert, Jordan Nailor, Jack Savage.
Amateur Jockey: Zac Baker, Noah Brazg Carrell.

526 **MR JAMES UNETT, Wolverhampton**
Postal: 1 Dunstall Mews, Gorsebrook Road, Wolverhampton, West Midlands, WV6 0PE
Contacts: PHONE 01691 610001 MOBILE 07887 534753 FAX 01691 610001
EMAIL jamesunett1327@yahoo.co.uk WEBSITE www.jamesunettracing.com

1 **EBQAA (IRE)**, 8, b m Cape Cross (IRE)—Estedaama (IRE) **J. W. Unett**
2 **POPE GREGORY**, 5, gr g Gregorian (IRE)—La Gifted **The Dartmouth Racers**

MR JAMES UNETT - continued

3 **SENORITA EVA ROSE (IRE)**, 4, gr f Clodovil (IRE)—Spark Up **M. Watkinson & Partner**
4 **TOM TULLIVER**, 5, b g Hot Streak (IRE)—Belle Isle **M. Watkinson & Partner**

THREE-YEAR-OLDS

5 **ORO COSMICO**, ch g Universal (IRE)—Corsa All Oro (USA) **P. S. Burke**

Other Owners: J. W. Unett, Mr M. Watkinson.

Assistant Trainer: Miss C. H. Jones.

---

527 **MR MARK USHER, Lambourn**
Postal: **Rowdown House Stables, Upper Lambourn, Hungerford, Berkshire, RG17 8QP**
Contacts: **PHONE 01488 73630, 01488 72598 MOBILE 07831 873531**
EMAIL markusher.racing@btconnect.com WEBSITE www.markusherracing.co.uk

1 **BAGATELLE**, 5, ch m Kendargent (FR)—Blushing Beauty **Mrs T. J. Channing-Williams**
2 **BAYSTON HILL**, 8, br g Big Bad Bob (IRE)—Jessica Ennis (USA) **High Five Racing and Partners**
3 **BIRD FOR LIFE**, 8, b m Delegator—Birdolini **The Mark Usher Racing Club**
4 **BIRD TO LOVE**, 8, b m Delegator—Bird Over **The Mark Usher Racing Club**
5 **BLUE GALAXY**, 4, gr g Telescope (IRE)—Indigo **Ushers Court**
6 **BORN TO PLEASE**, 8, b m Stimulation (IRE)—Heart Felt **The Mark Usher Racing Club**
7 **DYLAN'S SEA SONG**, 8, b m Dylan Thomas (IRE)—Mary Sea (FR) **Ushers Court**
8 **FIRST VERSE (IRE)**, 4, b f Dandy Man (IRE)—Bronte Sister (IRE) **Twenty Four Carrot Racing**
9 **FREDDY MAC (IRE)**, 7, gr g Scorpion (IRE)—Pearlsforthegirls
10 **INTOXICATION**, 4, b f Havana Gold (IRE)—B Berry Brandy (USA) **Champagne And Shambles**
11 **LIBERTY BAY**, 4, b f Iffraaj—Light Fantastic **Rowdown Racing Partnership**
12 **MAKYON (IRE)**, 5, b g Make Believe—Mise (IRE) **The Mark Usher Racing Club**
13 **MEISTERZINGER (IRE)**, 4, br g Mastercraftsman (IRE)—Zingeeyah **The OAP Partnership (Mr J. Segust)**
14 **ON THE RIGHT TRACK**, 5, gr g Mukhadram—Jessica Ennis (USA) **Mrs T. J. Channing-Williams**
15 **PERTHSHIRE (IRE)**, 4, b g Gleneagles (IRE)—Destalink **Mr B. C. Rogan**
16 **Q TWENTY BOY (IRE)**, 7, ch g Dandy Man (IRE)—Judies Child (IRE) **The Mark Usher Racing Club**
17 **SKIBBEREEN**, 4, b g Harbour Watch (IRE)—Fruit Pastille **Champagne And Shambles**
18 **THE BAY WARRIOR (IRE)**, 4, b g The Gurkha (IRE)—Fraulein **Andy & Lizzie Cova**
19 **TIMEFORASPIN**, 8, b g Librettist (USA)—Timeforagin **The Unraceables**
20 **TIN FANDANGO**, 7, b g Steele Tango (USA)—Littlemoor Lass **Mr M. A. Humphreys**
21 **WILLINGLY**, 5, ch m Hot Streak (IRE)—Paradise Place **Miss J. Hynes**

THREE-YEAR-OLDS

22 **ADAAYINOURLIFE**, b g Adaay (IRE)—Sans Reward (IRE) **Andy & Lizzie Cova**
23 **ALCHEMIST'S DREAM**, b f Lawman (FR)—Royal Alchemist **The Ridgeway Alchemist's**
24 **ARLECCHINO'S GIFT**, b g Shalaa (IRE)—Represent (IRE) **Mr K. Senior**
25 **DULY AMAZED**, b g Due Diligence (USA)—Sweet Amazement **Amazing Times**
26 B f Adaay (IRE)—Golden Secret **The Mark Usher Racing Club**
27 **HEERATHETRACK**, b gr g Heeraat (IRE)—Jessica Ennis (USA) **High Five Racing and Partners**
28 B g Garswood—Nightunderthestars
29 **PEARL OF KUWAIT (IRE)**, ch f Pearl Secret—Anna Barkova (IRE) **A & N Dunn**
30 **SID'S ANNIE**, b f Farhh—Blushing Beauty **Twenty Four Carrot Racing**
31 **TWILIGHT REVENGE**, ch g Twilight Son—Sweetest Revenge (IRE) **The Ridgeway Partnership**

TWO-YEAR-OLDS

32 **ARLECCHINO'S STAR**, b f 11/04 Zoustar (AUS)—Sandy Cay (USA) (Mizzen Mast (USA)) (15000) **Mr K. Senior**

Other Owners: Mrs T. J. Channing-Williams, Mr A. Cova, Mrs E. Cova, Mr P. R. Doble, Mr D. P. Duffy, Mr N. Dunn, Mr T. Francis, High Five Racing, Mr P. R. Mattacks, P.DuffyD.SemmensVWilliamsRHarperMLoveday, Mr A. R. Pollard, Mr J. A. Segust, Mr D. M. Semmens, Mr J. A. Stansfield, Mr M. D. I. Usher.

Assistant Trainer: Michael Usher.

528 **MR ROGER VARIAN, Newmarket**
Postal: **Carlburg Stables, 49 Bury Road, Newmarket, Suffolk, CB8 7BY**
Contacts: **PHONE 01638 661702 FAX 01638 667018**
EMAIL office@varianstable.com WEBSITE www.varianstable.com

1 **ANGEL POWER**, 5, gr m Lope de Vega (IRE)—Burning Rules (IRE) **King Power Racing Co Ltd**
2 **BARADAR (IRE)**, 4, b br c Muhaarar—Go Lovely Rose (IRE) **Amo Racing Limited**
3 **BASHOSH (IRE)**, 4, ch c Dubawi (IRE)—Ferdoos **Sheikh Ahmed Al Maktoum**
4 **BELIEVE IN LOVE (IRE)**, 5, b m Make Believe—Topka (FR) **Mr K. Maeda**
5 **DINOO (IRE)**, 4, b g Starspangledbanner (AUS)—Shirley Blade (IRE) **Mr D. Vakilgilani**
6 **DRAGON SYMBOL**, 4, gr c Cable Bay (IRE)—Arcamist **Mr Y. Kubota**
7 **DUSKY LORD**, 4, b g Twilight Son—Petit Trianon **The Dusky Lord Partnership**
8 **EL DRAMA (IRE)**, 4, ch c Lope de Vega (IRE)—Victoire Finale **Sheikh Mohammed Obaid Al Maktoum**
9 **ENSEMBLE (IRE)**, 4, b f Nayef (USA)—Alqubbah (IRE) **Clipper Group Holdings Ltd**
10 **ESHAADA**, 4, b f Muhaarar—Muhawalah (IRE) **Shadwell Estate Company Ltd**
11 **FANTASTIC FOX**, 4, ch g Frankel—Vasilia **King Power Racing Co Ltd**
12 **FATHER OF JAZZ**, 4, b g Bahamian—Bark (IRE) **The Gredley Family**
13 **GREATGADIAN (GER)**, 4, b g Siyouni (FR)—Goathemala (GER) **King Power Racing Co Ltd**
14 **KRATOS**, 4, ch g Equiano (FR)—Miss Rimex (IRE) **Varian Racing V**
15 **LA TIHATY (IRE)**, 4, b c New Bay—Sister Dam's (IRE) **H.H. Shaikh Nasser Al Khalifa & F. Nass**
16 **LANEQASH**, 4, b g Cable Bay (IRE)—Bonhomie **Shadwell Estate Company Ltd**
17 **LEGEND OF DUBAI (IRE)**, 4, b c Dubawi (IRE)—Speedy Boarding **Sheikh Mohammed Obaid Al Maktoum**
18 **MOBADRA**, 4, b f Oasis Dream—Longing To Dance **Sheikh Ahmed Al Maktoum**
19 **MOVIN TIME**, 4, b g Fastnet Rock (AUS)—Time On **Sheikh Mohammed Obaid Al Maktoum**
20 **MYSTICAL AIR**, 4, b f Kingman—Dark Promise **Lordship Stud**
21 **NAGANO**, 4, b g Fastnet Rock (AUS)—Nazym (IRE) **N. Bizakov**
22 **NINE TALES (IRE)**, 4, b g Kingman—Sotka **King Power Racing Co Ltd**
23 **POSTILEO (IRE)**, 5, b h Galileo (IRE)—Posterity (IRE) **Sheikh Mohammed Obaid Al Maktoum**
24 **PRAIANO (GER)**, 4, b g Dubawi (IRE)—Praia (GER) **Sheikh Mohammed Obaid Al Maktoum**
25 **ROBERT WALPOLE**, 5, b g Golden Horn—Whazzat **The Gredley Family**
26 **ROYAL CHAMPION (IRE)**, 4, b c Shamardal (USA)—Emirates Queen **Sheikh Mohammed Obaid Al Maktoum**
27 **SAINT LAWRENCE (IRE)**, 4, b c Al Kazeem—Affluent **D. J. Deer**
28 **SAMMARR**, 4, b f Golden Horn—Ta Ammol **Sheikh Ahmed Al Maktoum**
29 **SAVE A FOREST (IRE)**, 4, b f Kingman—Bark (IRE) **The Gredley Family**
30 **SEVEN POCKETS (IRE)**, 5, b h Frankel—Vodka (JPN) **Mrs H. Varian**
31 **SHE DO**, 4, b f Siyouni (FR)—Minnaloushe (IRE) **The Gredley Family**
32 **STRAWBERRI**, 4, ch f Gleneagles (IRE)—Altesse Imperiale (IRE) **D. J. Deer**
33 **TEONA (IRE)**, 4, b f Sea The Stars (IRE)—Ambivalent (IRE) **A. Saeed**
34 **THIRD REALM**, 4, b c Sea The Stars (IRE)—Reem Three **Sheikh Mohammed Obaid Al Maktoum**
35 **TIMELESS SOUL (GER)**, 4, ch f Night of Thunder (IRE)—Tatienne (IRE) **Mr M. Almarzooqi**
36 **TINKER TOY**, 5, b g War Front (USA)—Cursory Glance (USA) **Merry Fox Stud Limited**
37 **TITLE (IRE)**, 4, b g Camelot—Danehill's Dream (IRE) **Highclere Tbred Racing-Charles Church**
38 **TYRRHENIAN SEA (IRE)**, 4, gr g Dark Angel (IRE)—Nocturne (GER) **Flaxman Stables Ireland Ltd**
39 **ZAAJEL**, 4, gr f Awtaad (IRE)—Elshaadin **Shadwell Estate Company Ltd**

THREE-YEAR-OLDS

40 **AIMERIC**, b c Frankel—Aris (IRE) **Sheikh Mohammed Obaid Al Maktoum**
41 **AKAARIM (IRE)**, b c Muhaarar—Nezwaah **Sheikh Ahmed Al Maktoum**
42 **AKHU NAJLA**, b c Kingman—Galicuix **KHK Racing Ltd**
43 **AL HUSN (IRE)**, b f Dubawi (IRE)—Hadaatha (IRE) **Shadwell Estate Company Ltd**
44 **ALWAYS LOVE YOU**, b f Siyouni (FR)—True Match **Amo Racing Limited**
45 **AMEYNAH (IRE)**, b f Exceed And Excel (AUS)—Tazffin (IRE) **Sheikh Ahmed Al Maktoum**
46 **ARAB CINDER (IRE)**, b f Zoffany (IRE)—Athreyaa **Mr F. A. Al Harthi**
47 **ASAASSI (FR)**, b c Sea The Moon (GER)—Octavine (IRE) **Sheikh Ahmed Al Maktoum**
48 **ASRAABB (IRE)**, b f Dark Angel (IRE)—Tantshi (IRE) **Sheikh Ahmed Al Maktoum**
49 **AUSTRALIAN HARBOUR**, b c Australia—Cashla Bay **Z. A. Galadari**
50 **BAYSIDE BOY (IRE)**, b c New Bay—Alava (IRE) **Teme Valley & Ballylinch Stud**
51 **BOLD RIBB**, b c Ribchester (IRE)—Bold Bidder **Teme Valley**
52 **BROADSPEAR**, b c Le Havre (IRE)—Flower of Life (IRE) **Highclere T'bred Racing - Broadspear**
53 **CANNY FETTLE (FR)**, ch g Distorted Humor (USA)—Liffey Dancer (IRE) **Merry Fox Stud Limited**
54 **CAPH STAR**, b c Siyouni (FR)—Caskelena (IRE) **N. Bizakov**

MR ROGER VARIAN - continued

55 **CASA LUNA (IRE),** b f Starspangledbanner (AUS)—Flowers of Spring (IRE) **Mr I. Alsagar**
56 **CLAIM THE CROWN (IRE),** b c Acclamation—Crown Light **Teme Valley**
57 **CONSENSUS DE VEGA (IRE),** b f Lope de Vega (IRE)—Ambassadrice **Opulence Thoroughbreds**
58 **CROACHILL (IRE),** b f Churchill (IRE)—Cronsa (GER) **Mr M. Saeed**
59 **DEFERRED,** ch c Postponed (IRE)—Platinum Pearl **Z. A. Galadari**
60 **DEVOTED POET,** b c Iffraaj—Devotion (IRE) **Teme Valley & Partner**
61 **DIVINE JEWEL,** b f Frankel—Agnes Stewart (IRE) **Mr K. Maeda**
62 **DOUX ESPRIT (IRE),** b c Invincible Spirit (IRE)—Sweet Acclaim (IRE) **Sheikh Mohammed Obaid Al Maktoum**
63 **DUBAI CLOVER (IRE),** b f Make Believe—Middlemist Red (USA) **Mr A. Bintouq**
64 **DUBAI POET,** b c Lope de Vega (IRE)—Hundi (IRE) **Sheikh Mohammed Obaid Al Maktoum**
65 **ELDAR ELDAROV,** b c Dubawi (IRE)—All At Sea **KHK Racing Ltd**
66 **ENFORCED (IRE),** b g Zoffany (IRE)—Llew Law **Sheikh Mohammed Obaid Al Maktoum**
67 **EXTRICATION,** ch c Iffraaj—Heavenly Scent **John Connolly & A D Spence**
68 **EYDON (IRE),** b c Olden Times—Moon Mountain **Prince A. A. Faisal**
69 **FAMILIAR DREAMS,** b f Postponed (IRE)—Familliarity **Helena Springfield Ltd**
70 **FAMILLE VERTE (IRE),** b f No Nay Never (USA)—Falling Rain (IRE) **Barnett, Fahy R S Marchant**
71 **FIRST NIGHTINGALE (IRE),** gr f Dark Angel (IRE)—Night Fever (IRE) **Mrs Barbara Facchino & Partner**
72 **FIRST OFFICER (IRE),** b c Galileo (IRE)—Weekend Strike (USA) **Westerberg, Magnier, Tabor & Smith**
73 **FLAG OF TRUTH (FR),** b c Starspangledbanner (AUS)—Dalakania (IRE) **Teme Valley**
74 Gr f Caravaggio (USA)—Flaming Sea (IRE) **Mr M. Khalid Abdul Rahim**
75 **FLORA FINCH,** b f Lawman (FR)—Madame Vestris (IRE) **Cheveley Park Stud Limited**
76 **FOXTROT,** b f Le Havre (IRE)—Russian Finale **Cheveley Park Stud Limited**
77 **FUTURE QUEEN,** b f Postponed (IRE)—Ajman Princess (IRE) **Sheikh Mohammed Obaid Al Maktoum**
78 **GASTRONOMY,** ch c Ulysses (IRE)—Cantal **Cheveley Park Stud Limited**
79 **GLAM DE VEGA (IRE),** ch c Lope de Vega (IRE)—Glamorous Approach (IRE)

Sheikh Mohammed Obaid Al Maktoum

80 **GLEN BUCK (IRE),** b c Lope de Vega (IRE)—Pecking Order (IRE) **Merry Fox Stud Limited**
81 **GOEMON,** gr c Dark Angel (IRE)—Spangled **Mr M. Khalid Abdul Rahim**
82 **HEXAMETER,** ch f Ulysses (IRE)—Rythmique (IRE) **Cheveley Park Stud Limited**
83 B c Galileo (IRE)—Homecoming Queen **Mr K. Yoshida**
84 **ILLUMINATED,** b c Muhaarar—Wowcha (IRE) **Mr M. Khalid Abdul Rahim**
85 **INDEMNIFY,** gr c Lope de Vega (IRE)—Karisma (IRE) **Miss Y. M. G. Jacques**
86 **IRISH FLAME,** b c Dark Angel (IRE)—Dream of Tara (IRE) **Teme Valley**
87 **ISLAY OF ANGLESEY (IRE),** b g Holy Roman Emperor (IRE)—Fiuise (IRE) **Opulence Thoroughbreds**
88 **IT IS NOW,** b g Time Test—Talent Spotter **A D Spence & John Connolly**
89 **JAZZ CLUB (IRE),** b c Starspangledbanner (AUS)—Princess Desire (IRE) **Smith, Magnier, Tabor & Westerberg**
90 **JULIA AUGUSTA,** b f Ulysses (IRE)—Empress Livia **Cheveley Park Stud Limited**
91 **KIND GESTURE,** ch f Decorated Knight—Dawn of Hope (IRE) **Prince A. A. Faisal**
92 **KINGMAX (IRE),** b c Kingman—Baino Hope (FR) **Amo Racing Limited**
93 **KITSUNE POWER (IRE),** b g Holy Roman Emperor (IRE)—Fire Heroine (USA) **King Power Racing Co Ltd**
94 **KODIAC BLUE,** b g Kodiac—Grande Bleue (IRE) **Brightwalton Bloodstock Two**
95 **LEUVEN POWER (IRE),** ch c Cotai Glory—Triggers Broom (IRE) **King Power Racing Co Ltd**
96 **LIR SPECIALE (IRE),** b c Prince of Lir (IRE)—Ma Bella Paola (FR) **Opulence Thoroughbreds**
97 **LORD PARAMOUNT,** b f Ribchester (IRE)—Affluent **D. J. Deer**
98 B c Al Rifai (IRE)—Los Ojitos (USA) **Mr M. Khalid Abdul Rahim**
99 **LOVE TROPHY POWER,** ch f Bated Breath—Desire **King Power Racing Co Ltd**
100 **MAANAFITH (USA),** b f Exceed And Excel (AUS)—Almashooqa (USA) **Shadwell Estate Company Ltd**
101 **MEDRARA,** b c Lope de Vega (IRE)—Moderah **Z. A. Galadari**
102 **MISS CAROL ANN (IRE),** b f Kingman—Miss Katie Mae (IRE) **Stag Hawk Stables**
103 **MITBAAHY (IRE),** b c Profitable (IRE)—Wrood (USA) **Mr Hasan Mefareh Alajmi & Fawzi Nass**
104 **MOOJDEE (IRE),** ch c Iffraaj—Goleta (IRE) **Sheikh Ahmed Al Maktoum**
105 **MOONIS (IRE),** b c Muhaarar—Muhawalah (IRE) **Shadwell Estate Company Ltd**
106 **MUKADDAMAH,** b f New Approach (IRE)—Craighall **Shadwell Estate Company Ltd**
107 **MYSTERY FOX (IRE),** b c Dark Angel (IRE)—Golden Rosie (IRE) **King Power Racing Co Ltd**
108 B f Dubawi (IRE)—Nahrain **Sheikh Ahmed Al Maktoum**
109 **NAHRI,** b c Sea The Stars (IRE)—Neamour **Shadwell Estate Company Ltd**
110 B g Muhaarar—Noozhah **Clipper Group Holdings Ltd**
111 **OBLONG SONG,** b f Nathaniel (IRE)—Our Queen of Kings **Newsells Park Stud Limited**
112 **OPEN CHAMPION (IRE),** b c Postponed (IRE)—Nargys (IRE) **Sheikh Mohammed Obaid Al Maktoum**
113 **PERIPATETIC,** b f Ulysses (IRE)—Dublino (USA) **Cheveley Park Stud Limited**

MR ROGER VARIAN - continued

114 **POET**, b g Kodiac—Swiss Diva **Lordship Stud**
115 **PRAKASA**, b f The Gurkha (IRE)—Khor Sheed **Sheikh Mohammed Obaid Al Maktoum**
116 **PRINCESS NIEVE (IRE)**, ch f Australia—Elektra Street **Opulence Thoroughbreds**
117 **PRISM (IRE)**, b f Fast Company (IRE)—Annee Lumiere (IRE) **Varian Racing VI**
118 **PURE DIGNITY**, ch f Dubawi (IRE)—Starlet's Sister (USA) **Hh Shaikh Nasser al Khalifa & Khk Racing**
119 **RIZG**, b c No Nay Never (USA)—Azenzar **Mr I. Alsagar**
120 **ROYAL DEBUT (IRE)**, b c Showcasing—Mathool (IRE) **Sheikh Mohammed Obaid Al Maktoum**
121 **SAKHEER**, b c Kingman—Deuce Again **KHK Racing Ltd**
122 B f Kitten's Joy (USA)—Search And Seizure (USA) **Sheikh Ahmed Al Maktoum**
123 **SEEOLA**, ch f Sea The Stars (IRE)—Golden Reign (IRE) **Ms A. Quinn**
124 **SHAMPION (IRE)**, b f Shamardal (USA)—Nada **Sheikh Mohammed Obaid Al Maktoum**
125 **SHARAC**, b f Kodiac—Al Sharood **A. Saeed**
126 **SHINJI (IRE)**, b g Kingston Hill—Albemarle **Mrs H. Varian**
127 **SILENCE IS GOLDEN**, b f Golden Horn—Mia Diletta **D J & B Spence**
128 **SILENT MONARCH (IRE)**, b f No Nay Never—Causeway Queen (IRE)

Sheikh Mohammed Obaid Al Maktoum

129 **SILVER VISION**, gr f Muhaarar—Surrealism **A. Saeed**
130 **SIR WINSTON (IRE)**, b c Churchill (IRE)—Boastful (IRE) **Mr Kevin A Quinn & Partner**
131 **SOCIAL CONTACT**, ch f Night of Thunder (IRE)—Operettist **Clipper Group Holdings Ltd**
132 **SOLAR ORBITER (IRE)**, b c Showcasing—Heliosphere (USA) **Flaxman Stables Ireland Ltd**
133 **SOLIDARITY (IRE)**, b g Zoffany (IRE)—Magena (USA) **The Bermuda Salman Morris Partnership**
134 **SONNERIE POWER (FR)**, ch c Almanzor (FR)—Nehalennia (USA) **King Power Racing Co Ltd**
135 **SOUND ANGELA**, b f Muhaarar—Instance **Mr Y. Masuda**
136 **SUBASTAR (IRE)**, b c Sea The Stars (IRE)—Suba (IRE) **Sheikh Mohammed Obaid Al Maktoum**
137 Ch c Nathaniel (IRE)—Ta Ammol **Sheikh Ahmed Al Maktoum**
138 **THREE PRIESTS (JPN)**, b f Deep Impact (JPN)—Guilty Twelve (USA) **Merry Fox Stud Limited**
139 **TOOPHAN (IRE)**, ch c New Approach (IRE)—Maoineach (USA) **Amo Racing Limited**
140 **TOP SPIRIT**, b c Invincible Spirit (IRE)—Ambivalent (IRE) **A. Saeed**
141 B c Bated Breath—Tremelo Pointe (IRE) **Sheikh Ahmed Al Maktoum**
142 **TSUBAKI**, b f Divine Prophet (AUS)—Simsimah (IRE) **Mrs S. Yoshimura**
143 **VOODOO QUEEN**, b f Frankel—Cursory Glance (USA) **Merry Fox Stud Limited**
144 **YAANAAS**, ch c Ulysses (USA)—Troarn (FR) **Shadwell Estate Company Ltd**
145 **ZAINALARAB**, b c Wootton Bassett—Zimira (IRE) **Shadwell Estate Company Ltd**
146 **ZAMEKA (IRE)**, b c No Nay Never (USA)—Al Ihsas (IRE) **GreenhalghTimmsSandersMcNameeTownbraccan**
147 **ZANBAQ (IRE)**, gr f Oasis Dream—Princess de Lune (IRE) **Shadwell Estate Company Ltd**
148 **ZENGA**, b f Lope de Vega—Blending **Toudo LLC**

TWO-YEAR-OLDS

149 **AL MUZN (IRE)**, b c 23/02 Oasis Dream—Queen's Pearl (IRE) (Exceed And Excel (AUS)) **Z. A. Galadari**
150 B c 05/05 Smooth Daddy (USA)—Anbella (FR) (Common Grounds) **Opulence Thoroughbreds**
151 B c 08/04 Kessaar (IRE)—Armum (IRE) (Society Rock) (90000) **Sheikh Ahmed Al Maktoum**
152 B f 23/01 Al Kazeem—Avessia (Averti (IRE)) **D. J. Deer**
153 B c 12/01 Showcasing—Awesome (Bahamian Bounty) (125000) **King Power Racing Co Ltd**
154 B c 25/01 Lope de Vega (IRE)—Bloomfield (Teofilo (IRE)) (260000) **Sheikh Mohammed Obaid Al Maktoum**
155 Ch f 19/01 Justify (USA)—Butterscotch (IRE) (Galileo (IRE)) (220000) **Mr K. Maeda**
156 B f 18/04 Saxon Warrior (JPN)—Cascella (IRE) (Iffraaj)
157 **CHARYN (IRE)**, gr c 09/04 Dark Angel (IRE)—Futoon (IRE) (Kodiac) **N. Bizakov**
158 **CLIMATE FRIENDLY**, ch f 20/02 Frankel—Unex Mona Lisa (Shamardal (USA)) **The Gredley Family**
159 **COBALT BLUE (IRE)**, ch c 01/05 Sioux Nation (USA)—Impressionist Art (USA) (Giant's Causeway (USA)) (59524)
160 **CREWE ALEXANDRA**, b f 16/03 Harry Angel (IRE)—Bark (IRE) (Galileo (IRE)) **The Gredley Family**
161 B f 09/03 Lope de Vega (IRE)—Crimson Rosette (IRE) (Teofilo (IRE))
162 B c 02/05 Dubawi (IRE)—Crown Queen (USA) (Smart Strike (CAN)) **Mr B. Leon**
163 B c 08/03 Muhaarar—Diamond Bangle (IRE) (Galileo (IRE)) **The Gredley Family**
164 **EXIMIOUS (IRE)**, b f 28/03 Exceed And Excel (AUS)—Estiqaama (USA) (Nayef (USA)) (100000)

Highclere T'Bred Racing - Marie Curie

165 Gr c 01/03 El Kabeir (USA)—Extricate (IRE) (Exceed And Excel (AUS)) (130000) **King Power Racing Co Ltd**
166 Ch f 26/01 New Bay—Farewell To You (Leroidesanimaux (BRZ)) **Sheikh Mohammed Obaid Al Maktoum**
167 B c 14/02 Sea The Stars (IRE)—Gumriyah (Shamardal (USA)) (260000) **Sheikh Mohammed Obaid Al Maktoum**

MR ROGER VARIAN - continued

168 INDEMNITY (IRE), b c 30/03 Lope de Vega (IRE)—Oriental Magic (GER) (Doyen (IRE)) (200000)
Highclere - George Bernard Shaw

169 KOLSAI, b c 01/05 Oasis Dream—Fizzi Top (Frankel) (160000) **N. Bizakov**

170 B c 05/04 Muhaarar—La Napoule (Piccolo) **Opulence Thoroughbreds**

171 Ch c 28/01 Dubawi (IRE)—Lady Momoka (IRE) (Shamardal (USA)) **Sheikh Mohammed Obaid Al Maktoum**

172 LITTLE HUG, b f 22/03 Invincible Spirit (IRE)—Another Charm (IRE) (Galileo (IRE))

173 B f 15/04 Galileo Gold—Love Intrigue (IRE) (Marju (IRE)) **Opulence Thoroughbreds**

174 MARAKESH, ch f 20/02 Decorated Knight—Turama (Pivotal) **Mr I. Alsagar**

175 B c 30/04 Lope de Vega (IRE)—Matauri Pearl (IRE) (Hurricane Run (IRE)) (360000) **Mr Y. Kubota**

176 B c 14/03 New Approach (IRE)—Melinoe (Sea The Stars (IRE)) (150000) **King Power Racing Co Ltd**

177 B f 21/02 Belardo (IRE)—Mojika (Redoute's Choice (AUS)) (6667) **Mrs H. Varian**

178 B c 31/01 Kingman—Nazym (IRE) (Galileo (IRE)) **N. Bizakov**

179 NEW ENDEAVOUR (IRE), b c 22/02 New Bay—Moody Blue (IRE) (Invincible Spirit (IRE)) (170068)
Teme Valley & Ballylinch Stud

180 PACO'S PRIDE, gr f 24/01 Roaring Lion (USA)—Paco's Angel (Paco Boy (IRE)) **Biddestone Racing XIII**

181 B c 03/05 Sea The Stars (IRE)—Potent Embrace (USA) (Street Cry (IRE)) (120000) **King Power Racing Co Ltd**

182 B c 17/02 Sea The Stars (IRE)—Pure Art (Dutch Art) (63776) **Varian Racing VII**

183 B c 12/02 Saxon Warrior (JPN)—Pure Symmetry (USA) (Storm Cat (USA)) (95000) **Mr F. A. Al Harthi**

184 RED DANIELLE, b f 09/02 Sea The Moon (GER)—Garabelle (IRE) (Galileo (IRE)) (45000) **Mr M. J. Power**

185 RUSSET GOLD, ch c 14/04 Al Kazeem—Affluent (Oasis Dream) **D. J. Deer**

186 SHIKHOVA, ch f 02/03 Starspangledbanner (AUS)—Frolova (Dutch Art) **Cheveley Park Stud Limited**

187 Ch f 19/04 Harry Angel (IRE)—Silken Skies (IRE) (Zoffany (IRE)) **Opulence Thoroughbreds**

188 B c 02/02 Bated Breath—Sleek (Oasis Dream) (130000) **Sheikh Ahmed Al Maktoum**

189 B c 14/03 Starspangledbanner (AUS)—Stranagone (IRE) (Motivator) (100000) **Mr Alan Spence**

190 B f 27/01 Lope de Vega (IRE)—Sunday Times (Holy Roman Emperor (IRE))

191 Ch f 16/02 Exceed And Excel (AUS)—Superego (Sepoy (AUS)) (160000)

192 Gr f 03/05 Muhaarar—Surrealism (Pivotal) **A. Saeed**

193 B f 22/04 Zoustar (AUS)—Time On (Sadler's Wells (USA)) **Mr R Barnett**

194 Ch c 26/02 Shamardal (USA)—Tranquil Star (Galileo (IRE)) **Sheikh Ahmed Al Maktoum**

195 B f 30/03 No Nay Never (USA)—Travel (USA) (Street Cry (IRE)) (100000)

196 B f 01/02 Australia—Tulipa Rosa (IRE) (Excelebration (IRE)) (40000)

197 B f 09/04 Justify (USA)—Virginia Waters (USA) (Kingmambo (USA))

198 Br c 11/03 Showcasing—Whispering Bell (IRE) (Galileo (IRE)) (45000) **Mr Hasan Mefareh Alajmi & Fawzi Nass**

199 WITCHING HOUR, b c 08/03 Frankel—Cursory Glance (IRE) (Distorted Humor (USA)) (320000)
Merry Fox Stud Limited

200 B f 18/04 Postponed (IRE)—Zeeba (IRE) (Barathea (IRE)) **Sheikh Mohammed Obaid Al Maktoum**

Other Owners: Mr R. Al Kamda, Sheikh I. S. Al Khalifa, H.H. Sheikh Nasser Al Khalifa, Mr H. M. H. A. Alajmi, Mrs J. A. Allen, Amo Racing Limited, Ballylinch Stud, Mr J. Barnett, Bermuda Racing Ltd, Brightwalton Bloodstock Limited, Mr M. J. S. Cockburn, J. P Connolly, Mr W. Crager, Mrs Barbara Faccinno, Mr C. J. Fahy, Mrs E. A. Harris, T. F. Harris, Mr P. Hondros, KHK Racing Ltd, Mrs S. Magnier, Mr R. P Marchant, Mr. S. Marchant, Mr M. Morris, Mr G. Moss, Mr F. A. A. Nass, Mr A. Pearson, Mr K. A. Quinn, A. Saeed, D. Smith, Mr Alan Spence, Mr M. B. Spence, M. Tabor, Teme Valley, Mrs H. Varian, Westerberg, Biddestone Racing XIII.

Assistant Trainer: Jo Fowles, George Hills. **Racing Secretary:** Jim Hiner.

---

529 | **MR TIM VAUGHAN, Cowbridge**
Postal: Pant Wilkin Stables, Aberthin, Cowbridge, CF71 7GX
Contacts: **PHONE** 01446 771626 **MOBILE** 07841 800081
EMAIL tim@timvaughanracing.com **WEBSITE** www.timvaughanracing.com

1 AIRTOTHETHRONE (IRE), 6, b g Yeats (IRE)—Sorcillera **Mrs C. S. Wilson**

2 ARINI, 5, b m Blue Bresil (FR)—Polly Potter **James and Jean Potter Ltd**

3 ARTISTIC ENDEAVOUR, 4, b g Kayf Tara—Dubh Eile (IRE) **Paul & Louise Bowtell**

4 BELLS OF PETERBORO (IRE), 7, gr g Carlotamix (FR)—Power of Future (GER) **Mr S. Grys & Mr M. O'Boyle**

5 BELLS OF RUTLAND (IRE), 5, gr g Kingston Hill—D'Gigi **Mr S. Grys & Mr M. O'Boyle**

6 BELLS OF STAMFORD, 5, b g Presenting—Passlands (IRE) **Mr S. Grys & Mr M. O'Boyle**

MR TIM VAUGHAN - continued

7 **BOBMAHLEY (IRE)**, 7, b g Mahler—Supreme Von Pres (IRE) **Mrs B. N. Ead**
8 **CALARULES**, 9, gr g Aussie Rules (USA)—Ailincala (IRE) **Oceans Racing**
9 **CAPE ROBIN (IRE)**, 8, ch g Robin des Champs (FR)—Our Pride **Optimumracing.Co.Uk & Mr Andrew P. Bell**
10 **CLEMENCIA (IRE)**, 6, b g Pour Moi (IRE)—Cleofila (IRE) **Mr D. W. Fox**
11 **COLONIAL EMPIRE**, 5, b g Zoffany (IRE)—Susan Stroman **Mr S. Grys & Mr M. O'Boyle**
12 **DALAMOI (IRE)**, 5, b g Pour Moi (IRE)—Dalamine (FR) **Mrs B. N. Ead**
13 **DESIGNER DESTINY (IRE)**, 8, b m Jeremy (IRE)—Gaye Steel (IRE) **Mr S. Grys & Mr M. O'Boyle**
14 **EVA'S OSKAR (IRE)**, 8, gr g Shirocco (GER)—Sardagna (FR) **Mrs Sally & Richard Prince**
15 **GYLLEN (USA)**, 7, b g Medaglia d'Oro (USA)—Miss Halory (USA) **Chepstow & Ffos Las Racing Club**
16 **HAWA BLADI (IRE)**, 6, ch g Sea The Stars (IRE)—Gentle On My Mind (IRE) **Pimlico Racing - Hawa Bladi**
17 **ISLE OF ARON**, 6, gr g Kayf Tara—Maggie Aron **Oceans Racing**
18 **JEAN GENIE (FR)**, 6, gr g Turgeon (USA)—Lady Koko **Oceans Racing**
19 **JUDEX LEFOU (IRE)**, 7, b g Le Fou (IRE)—Knockalaghan Maid (IRE) **Mr S. A. Clarke**
20 **LANDSMAN (IRE)**, 9, b g Canford Cliffs (IRE)—Mowaadah (IRE) **Graham & Lynne Handley**
21 **LAUGHARNE**, 11, b g Authorized (IRE)—Corsican Sunset (USA) **Oceans Racing**
22 **LE MILOS**, 7, b g Shirocco (GER)—Banjaxed Girl **Bovian Racing**
23 **LONDON (GER)**, 5, b m Lord of England (GER)—La Reine Noir (GER) **Joe Saumarez Smith & Partners**
24 **MADERA MIST (IRE)**, 8, ch m Stowaway—Odonimee (IRE) **Paul & Louise Bowtell**
25 **MOURZOUK (IRE)**, 5, b g Declaration of War (USA)—Mouraniya (IRE) **Pimlico Racing - Mourzouk**
26 **NORWEGIAN WOODS (IRE)**, 9, b g Arcadio (GER)—Water Ore (IRE) **David & Susan Luke & the Lucky Strats**
27 **ORIENTAL CROSS (IRE)**, 9, b m Cape Cross (IRE)—Orion Girl (GER) **Mr J Durston & Mr N Harris**
28 **OSCA LOCA (IRE)**, 9, b m Oscar (IRE)—Lohort Castle (IRE) **Paul & Louise Bowtell**
29 **POINT OF PRINCIPLE (IRE)**, 9, b g Rip Van Winkle (IRE)—L'Ancresse (IRE) **Oceans Racing**
30 **PRISON BREAK (IRE)**, 4, b g Muhaarar—World Class
31 **SILVER IN DISGUISE**, 8, gr g Sulamani (IRE)—Silver Spinner **Mr J Durston & Mr N Harris**
32 **TIGHT CALL (IRE)**, 8, ch g Mahler—Victory Anthem (IRE) **ER Newnham & JD Shinton**
33 **TIMELY GIFT (IRE)**, 9, b g Presenting—Give It Time **Carl, JJ, Chris, Mike, John & Hugh**
34 **TRIXSTER (IRE)**, 9, b g Beneficial—Our Trick (IRE) **The Pant Wilkin Partnership**
35 **TWILIGHT GLORY**, 6, b g Fame And Glory—Twilight Eclipse (IRE) **Tynewydd Investments Limited**
36 **WAX AND WANE**, 7, br g Maxios—Moonavvara (IRE) **ER Newnham & JD Shinton**
37 **WEAVER'S ANSWER**, 4, b g Dunaden (FR)—Oskar's Eva (IRE) **Mrs Sally & Richard Prince**
38 **YOUNG O'LEARY (IRE)**, 8, b g Scorpion (IRE)—Cantou (IRE) **Mr I. G. Prichard**

THREE-YEAR-OLDS

39 **BIELSA'S BUCKET**, b g Equiano (FR)—Friendship Is Love **& C Botham**

Other Owners: Fergus Anstock, Mr A. Bell, S. C. Botham, Mr J. P. M. Bowtell, Mrs L. Bowtell, Mr J. J. Brummitt, Mr P. G. Buist, Mr J. Durston, Mr M. Edwards, Mr S. Grys, Mr G. Handley, Mrs L. P Handley, Mr N. Harris, Mr B. Jagger, Mr D. M. Jenkins, Mr T. E. Kerfoot, A. D. Lowrie, Mrs D. J. Lowrie, Mr D. A. Luke, David & Susan Luke, Mrs S. Luke, Mr E. R. Newnham, Mr M. O'Boyle, R. J. Prince, Mrs S. Prince, A. Robinson, Mr J. W. Saumarez Smith, Mr J. D. Shinton, Mr M. A. Stratford, The Lucky Strats, Mr N. D. Whitham, optimumracing.co.uk.

Flat Jockey: David Probert. **NH Jockey:** Alan Johns. **Conditional Jockey:** Charlie Price.

---

530 **MR CHRISTIAN VON DER RECKE, Weilerswist**
Postal: Rennstall Recke GmbH, Hovener Hof 1, D-53919, Weilerswist, Germany
Contacts: PHONE +49 2254 845314 FAX +49 2254 845315
EMAIL recke@t-online.de WEBSITE www.rennstall-recke.de

1 **BARAKATLE**, 5, br g Poet's Voice—Baraket Fayrouz (FR)
2 **BLATTGOLD (GER)**, 7, ch h Alexandros—Bantiarna (GER)
3 **CHRISTOPH COLUMBUS (GER)**, 15, b g Noroit (GER)—Crying Love (GER)
4 **DOMSTURMER (GER)**, 4, ch c Lord of England (GER)—Diamond Ring (GER)

MR CHRISTIAN VON DER RECKE - continued

  5 DORMIO, 6, b g Equiano (FR)—Diska (GER)
  6 FAIR HURRICANE (GER), 7, b g Hurricane Run (IRE)—Fair Vision (GER)
  7 LARRY LOBSTER (GER), 4, ch g Lord of England (GER)—Lutindi (GER)
  8 MAYNE (IRE), 6, b g Dansili—Pink Damsel (IRE)
  9 MERESIDE PEARL (IRE), 4, ch f Pearl Secret—Setting Forth (IRE)
10 MISS CALACATTA (IRE), 4, ch f Frankel—Dulcet (IRE)
11 MODULATION, 4, b f Helmet (AUS)—Maybe Tomorrow
12 MORGENSTERN (GER), 5, b g Salut (GER)—Mangahla Love (GER)
13 NABLIRKA (GER), 7, b m Paolini (GER)—Niona (GER)
14 NOVELLINI (GER), 4, ch c Lord of England (GER)—Nightlight Angel (USA)
15 ORIHIME (IRE), 5, br m Canford Cliffs (IRE)—Rub A Dub Dub
16 OUTFIT, 5, gr g Outstrip—Hilden
17 POP ROCKSTAR (IRE), 10, b br g Flemensfirth (USA)—Special Ballot (IRE)
18 PRAETORIUS (GER), 5, gr h Novellist (IRE)—Ponte Tresa (FR)
19 PRETTY SOLDIER (GER), 5, b g Soldier Hollow—Pretty Smart (GER)
20 RED STORM (GER), 5, ch h Kamsin (GER)—Rustica (GER)
21 REDEMPTORIST (IRE), 7, b g Frozen Power (IRE)—Fly With Me (IRE)
22 RHODESIEN STAR (GER), 4, b c Arrigo (GER)—Rhodesien Sunshine (GER)
23 SEVEN O SEVEN (IRE), 4, br g Excelebration (IRE)—Sanadaat
24 SHERIN (GER), 5, b m Adlerflug (GER)—Shahil (GER)
25 SMUDO (IRE), 4, b g Canford Cliffs (IRE)—Sacre Fleur (IRE)
26 VIOLET RUN (IRE), 4, b f Heeraat (IRE)—Violet Ballerina (IRE)
27 WELAN (GER), 8, b h Mamool (IRE)—Weissagung (FR)

THREE-YEAR-OLDS

28 AMANDA ADVENTURE (GER), b f Poseidon Adventure (IRE)—Active Girl (GER)
29 AMELY ADVENTURE (GER), b f Poseidon Adventure (IRE)—Akatina (GER)
30 ARCHER (GER), b c Nutan (IRE)—Amora (IRE)
31 ARIELLA (GER), ch f Isfahan (GER)—Aspasionata (GER)
32 CASSIMERA (GER), b f Amaron—Cassilera (GER)
33 DOROTHY (FR), b f De Treville—Time Pressure
34 EARLY EIGHTIES (GER), ch f Recorder—Evie (FR)
35 JORDAN (GER), ch c Guiliani (IRE)—Juvena (GER)
36 KARLITO (FR), b c De Treville—Knightsbridge (BRZ)
37 LARIO (GER), b c Nutan (IRE)—Larmina (FR)
38 MELFIRE (GER), bl c Feuerblitz (GER)—Melody Fair (IRE)
39 NADIM (IRE), b c Highland Reel (IRE)—Nymphea (IRE)
40 SILIA (GER), b f Amarillo (IRE)—Saving Grace (GER)
41 TIRANA (GER), b f Nutan (IRE)—Turmalina (GER)

TWO-YEAR-OLDS

42 CHANDOS HOPE (GER), b f 20/04 Ito (GER)—Chandos Rose (IRE) (Mull of Kintyre (USA))
43 ILTIS (GER), b c 06/04 Nutan (IRE)—Invisible Flash (Invincible Spirit (IRE))
44 LIANE (GER), b f 18/02 Nutan (IRE)—Larmina (FR) (Thewayyouare (USA))
45 NACHTFALKE (GER), b c 22/03 Amarillo (IRE)—Navarra (IRE) (Invincible Spirit (IRE))
46 NEBRODI (GER), b c 21/03 Amarillo (IRE)—Niagara (GER) (High Chaparral (IRE))
47 RELY ON OLD SPORT (FR), gr c 21/02 The Grey Gatsby (IRE)—Carrigart Belle (GER) (Reliable Man) (34014)
48 TROOPER (GER), ch c 30/04 Hunter's Light (IRE)—Tipsy Tangerine (GER) (Soviet Star (USA)) (3401)

Flat Jockey: Liubov Grigorieva. **NH Jockey:** Sonja Daroszewski, Paul Johnson. **Conditional Jockey:** Amin Hajbabay.
Amateur Jockey: Miss Laura Giesgen.

531 MRS LUCY WADHAM, Newmarket

Postal: The Trainer's House, Moulton Paddocks, Newmarket, Suffolk, CB8 7PJ
Contacts: PHONE 01638 662411 MOBILE 07980 545776
EMAIL lucy@wadhamracing.com WEBSITE www.lucywadhamracing.co.uk

1 ABOUND, 5, b m Sir Percy—Atwix **The Considered Speculators**
2 ADMIRAL BARRATRY (FR), 9, b g Soldier of Fortune (IRE)—Haskilclara (FR) **Forster, Pepper & Summers**
3 ANOTHER MYSTERY, 5, b g Norse Dancer (IRE)—Misstree Pitcher **J & J McAndrew**
4 BOMBYX, 7, ch g Sir Percy—Bombazine (IRE) **The FOPS**
5 BRANDISOVA (IRE), 6, b m Shirocco (GER)—Gentle Alice (IRE) **Ms E. L. Banks**
6 CODE NAME LISE (IRE), 6, b m Fame And Glory—Firth of Five (IRE) **Ms E. L. Banks**
7 CONNIE WILDE (IRE), 7, b m Oscar (IRE)—Mandys Native (IRE) **The Sanguiners**
8 DANCE TO PARIS, 7, b m Champs Elysees—Riabouchinska **The Calculated Speculators**
9 DASH FULL OF CASH (IRE), 5, b g Milan—Cashalass (IRE) **P. H. Betts**
10 DOUBLETHETROUBLE, 4, ch g Pearl Secret—Kirunavaara (IRE) **R W Hayward & E R Wakelin**
11 EAST END GIRL, 5, b m Youmzain (IRE)—Bermondsey Girl **Mr & Mrs A E Pakenham & J J W Wadham**
12 ECLAIR DE GUYE (FR), 8, gr g Lord du Sud (FR)—Jouvence de Guye (FR)
                                                     E R Wakelin, R W Hayward & J J W Wadham
13 FLAT WHITE (FR), 5, ch m Olympic Glory (IRE)—Bolivia (GER) **Mr & Mrs A. E. Pakenham**
14 GAME ON FOR GLORY (IRE), 6, b m Fame And Glory—Jeunopse (IRE) **Mr J. Summers**
15 GLUTNFORPUNISHMENT, 6, b g Dawn Approach (IRE)—Oxsana **Mrs J. May**
16 GRAYSTONE (IRE), 4, gr ro g Dark Angel (IRE)—Crown of Diamonds (USA) **Mr J. Summers**
17 HURRICANE BAY, 6, b g Malinas (GER)—Another Storm **The Hanseatic League**
18 LITTLE LIGHT (FR), 8, b m Walk In The Park (IRE)—Luna Rossa (IRE) **Suiter Developments Limited**
19 MARTELLO SKY, 6, gr m Martaline—Kentucky Sky **The Sky Partnership**
20 MISS HERITAGE (IRE), 8, b m Pour Moi (IRE)—Haretha (IRE) **The Miss Heritage Partnership**
21 MISTRAL NELL, 5, b m Mount Nelson—Mistral Reine **Sara Dennis & Dominic Reilly**
22 O'CONNELL (IRE), 6, b g Westerner—Brixen (IRE) **R & T Ford**
23 PEARLY ISLAND, 6, b g Trans Island—Shinrock Pearl (IRE) **Mr S. C. McIntyre**
24 POTTERS HEDGER, 10, b g Midnight Legend—Loose Morals (IRE) **Mrs J. May**
25 POTTERS LEGEND, 12, b g Midnight Legend—Loose Morals (IRE) **Mrs J. May**
26 PRESENTING BELLE (IRE), 5, b m Valirann (FR)—Lace Parasol (IRE) **J & J McAndrew**
27 REGARDING RUTH (IRE), 8, b m Flemensfirth (USA)—May's June (IRE)
                                                     Suiter Developments Ltd & JJW Wadham
28 REVASSER (IRE), 5, b g Ask—Open Cry (IRE) **P. H. Betts**
29 SAMOURAI ONE (FR), 5, gr g Montmartre (FR)—Northern Ocean (FR) **Suiter Developments Limited**
30 SHANTUNG (IRE), 9, ch m Shantou (USA)—Sarah's Cottage (IRE) **Mrs G J Redman & Sons of Peter Philipps**
31 SIENNA BREEZE, 4, b f Camacho—Viking Rose (IRE) **Mr B. J. Painter**
32 SOMEKINDOFSTAR (IRE), 9, ch g Getaway (GER)—Katty Barry (IRE) **Mrs J. May**
33 SORBET, 7, b m Passing Glance—Fireburst **Mrs P. J. Toye**
34 TERRESITA (IRE), 5, b m Westerner—Brixen (IRE) **R & T Ford**
35 TINY TANTRUM (IRE), 6, b g Fame And Glory—Sara's Smile **Mrs N. C. Kappler**
36 TRINCOMALEE, 9, b g Malinas (GER)—Royal Tango **Hot to Trot Jumping&Mrs E Gordon Lennox**
37 WILL STING (IRE), 7, br g Scorpion (IRE)—Undecided Hall (IRE) **The Cyclones**

THREE-YEAR-OLDS

38 BADINAGE, b f Dabirsim (FR)—Pernickety **Mr & Mrs A. E. Pakenham**
39 KHAMSIN LADY, b f Bated Breath—Temple of Thebes (IRE) **Mr & Mrs A. E. Pakenham**
40 B c Black Sam Bellamy (IRE)—Mistral Reine **Mistral Sam Partnership**
41 ORIFLAMME, b f Awtaad (IRE)—Famusa **Mr & Mrs A. E. Pakenham**

Other Owners: Mrs S. Dennis, T. E. Ford, Mrs E. C. Gordon Lennox, Mr R. Forster, Mrs E. C. Gordon Lennox, Mr R. W. Hayward, Mr R. S. Hoskins, Hot To Trot Jumping, M. A. Kemp, Mr J. F. McAndrew, Mrs J. I. McAndrew, Mr A. E. Pakenham, Mr & Mrs A. E. Pakenham, Mrs V. H. Pakenham, M. L. Pepper, Mr R. Peters, Mr C. E. L. Philipps, Mr G. P. A. Philipps, Mr J. A. H. Philipps, Mrs G. J. Redman, Mr D. G. J. Reilly, Suiter Developments Limited, Mr J. Summers, J. J. W. Wadham, Mr E. R. Wakelin.

NH Jockey: Bryony Frost. Conditional Jockey: Corey McGivern.

532 **MISS TRACY WAGGOTT, Spennymoor**
Postal: **Awakening Stables, Merrington Road, Spennymoor, County Durham, DL16 7HD**
Contacts: **PHONE 01388 819012 MOBILE 07979 434498**
EMAIL tracywaggott@hotmail.com

1 GHATHANFAR (IRE), 6, br g Invincible Spirit (IRE)—Cuis Ghaire (IRE) **Mr W. J. Laws**
2 GOLD RING, 5, b g Golden Horn—La Dorotea (IRE) **Mr D. Tate**
3 GOOD NIGHT MR TOM (IRE), 5, b g Tagula (IRE)—Babylonian **Miss T. Waggott**
4 HAJEY, 5, ch g Raven's Pass (USA)—Almashooqa (USA) **Tracy Waggott & Sally Booth**
5 HENLEY, 10, b g Royal Applause—Making Waves (IRE) **Miss T. Waggott**
6 INTRINSIC BOND, 5, b g Intrinsic—Misu Billy **Mr D. Tate**
7 MRS BAGERRAN (IRE), 4, b f Kodiac—Habaayib **Mr S. W. Rain**

THREE-YEAR-OLDS

8 LILYWHITE, b f Hot Streak (IRE)—Broughtons Mystery **Mr W. J. Laws**
9 PREMIERSHIP, b g Mahsoob—Misu Billy **Mr D. Tate**
10 RAINBOW RAIN, b g Acclamation—Free Rein **Mr S. W. Rain**
11 RED COMMAND (IRE), b g War Command (USA)—Wajaha (IRE) **Tracy Waggott & W J Laws**
12 RIDE SALLY RIDE, b f Ruler of The World (IRE)—Noble Penny **Tracy Waggott & Sally Booth**
13 WITHOUT DELAY (IRE), ch f Decorated Knight—Apace (IRE) **Mr W. J. Laws**

---

533 **MR JOHN WAINWRIGHT, Malton**
Postal: **Granary House, Beverley Road, Norton, Malton, North Yorkshire, YO17 9PJ**
Contacts: **PHONE 01653 692993 MOBILE 07798 778070**
EMAIL jswainwright@googlemail.com

1 BIPLANE (USA), 4, b f Noble Mission—Aviate **J. S. Wainwright & Peter Clarke**
2 BOBBY SHAFT, 6, b g Garswood—She Mystifies **Wayne Bavill & John Wainwright**
3 CLAYTON HALL (IRE), 9, b g Lilbourne Lad (IRE)—Hawk Dance (IRE) **I. J. Barran**
4 DANDY'S ANGEL (IRE), 5, b m Dandy Man (IRE)—Party Pipit (IRE) **Anthony Ross & David Lumley**
5 DICK DATCHERY (IRE), 5, b g Make Believe—Bayja (IRE) **Mr W Bavill & Mr D. Bavill**
6 INTERNATIONAL LION, 5, ch g Kyllachy—Redskin Dancer (IRE) **Mr W Bavill & Mr D. Bavill**
7 LIVING'S BOY AN CO (FR), 7, b g Diamond Boy (FR)—Living Start (FR) **I. J. Barran**
8 MUATADEL, 9, b g Exceed And Excel (AUS)—Rose Blossom **Caballo Racing**
9 ONESTEPATATIME (IRE), 7, b m Jeremy (USA)—Good Thyne Lucy (IRE) **Mr A. J. Ross**
10 POWER POINT, 5, br g Cable Bay (IRE)—Frabjous **Mr W Bavill & Mr D. Bavill**
11 TANTASTIC, 4, b g Mayson—Love Island **Fast Track Racing**
12 TOSSAPENNY (IRE), 9, b g Presenting—Blueanna (IRE) **I. J. Barran**
13 WEARRAAH, 6, b g Heeraat (IRE)—Hoof's So Lucky **J. S. Wainwright**

TWO-YEAR-OLDS

14 MALINHEADSEAROVERS (IRE), b c 12/02 Zoffany (IRE)—Providencia (Oasis Dream) (17143) **D. R. & E. E. Brown**

Other Owners: Mr W. C. Bavill, D. R. Brown, Mrs E. E. Brown, Mr P. R. Clarke, Mr David John Lumley, Mr A. J. Ross, J. S. Wainwright.

Assistant Trainer: Mrs Fiona Wainwright.

Flat Jockey: Tom Eaves.

---

534 **MR ROBERT WALEY-COHEN, Banbury**
Postal: Upton Viva, Banbury, Oxfordshire, OX15 6HT
Contacts: **PHONE 01295 670538**

1 IGOR, 9, b g Presenting—Stravinsky Dance **Mr R. B. Waley-Cohen**
2 MAITREE EXPRESS, 8, br g Malinas (GER)—Shatabdi (IRE) **Mr R. B. Waley-Cohen**

535 MR MARK WALFORD, Sheriff Hutton
Postal: **Cornborough Manor, Cornborough Road, Sheriff Hutton, York, North Yorkshire, YO60 6QN**

1 **AMERICAN ANTHEM (IRE)**, 4, ch f Starspangledbanner (AUS)—Cloudy Girl (IRE) **Ursa Major Racing & Partner**
2 **AOIFE'S JOY (IRE)**, 5, b m Elzaam (AUS)—Spavento (IRE) **Mr K. Brown**
3 **BATTLE ANGEL (IRE)**, 4, gr f Iffraaj—Arabescatta **URSA Major Racing**
4 **BIT OF A QUIRKE**, 9, ch g Monsieur Bond (IRE)—Silk (IRE) **Mr A. Quirke & Mrs G. B. Walford**
5 **BOB MAHLER (IRE)**, 10, b g Mahler—Cooladurragh (IRE) **Bolingbroke, Howard, Molony & Sutton**
6 **BOBBA TEE**, 10, b g Rail Link—Trompette (USA) **David Furman & John Sugarman**
7 **BUSTER VALENTINE (IRE)**, 9, b g Ask—Femme du Noir (IRE) **The Mount Fawcus Partnership**
8 **CANDESCENCE**, 4, ch f Power—Bright Flash **Major & J Craggs**
9 **CASH TO ASH (IRE)**, 9, b g Westerner—Knocklayde Rose (IRE) **Amigos, Morrell, Johnson, Evans & Cowan**
10 **DIAMANT SUR CANAPE (FR)**, 4, b g Diamond Boy (FR)—Belledonne (FR) **Major, Holmes, & Wheeler**
11 **EVENT OF SIVOLA (FR)**, 8, ch g Noroit (GER)—Surprise de Sivola (FR) **Cw Racing Club & Ursa Major Racing**
12 **FLOATING ROCK (GER)**, 7, b g It's Gino (GER)—Fly Osoria (GER) **L & P Molony**
13 **GET GOING**, 5, b g Getaway (GER)—Bright Cloud (IRE) **Mrs M. Cooper**
14 **GHADBBAAN**, 6, ch g Intello (GER)—Rock Choir **URSA Major Racing**
15 **GIOVANNI CHANGE (FR)**, 7, gr g French Fifteen (FR)—Ask For Rain **Readers & Wiggy, the 8 Amigos & J Burns**
16 **GREEK KODIAC (IRE)**, 6, b g Kodiac—Greek Easter (IRE)
17 **INTO OVERDRIVE**, 7, b g Court Cave (IRE)—Lady Brig **Mrs W. Hamilton**
18 **IT JUST TAKES TIME (IRE)**, 4, br g Power—War Bride (GER) **Go Alfresco Racing Partners**
19 **JANTE LAW**, 6, gr g Gentlewave (IRE)—Ixora (IRE) **Grey Horse Syndicates & Mr P Drury**
20 **JOHNSON'S BLUE (IRE)**, 5, b g Westerner—Annimation (IRE)
21 **KINGS CREEK (IRE)**, 5, b g Elusive Quality (USA)—Nunavik (IRE) **New Vision Bloodstock**
22 **KODIMOOR (IRE)**, 9, b g Kodiac—Victoria Lodge (IRE) **Ursa Major Racing & Partner**
23 **LIVELY LIVVY**, 5, b m Passing Glance—All For Lily **Allott & Wordingham**
24 **MAGIC WAVE**, 6, b g Gentlewave (IRE)—Annie's Gift (IRE) **The Magic Circle**
25 **MAGICAL MAX**, 5, gr g Coach House (IRE)—Vellena **Mrs E Holmes, Mr M Johnson & Mrs Walford**
26 **MEGA YEATS (IRE)**, 8, br m Yeats (IRE)—Mega Mum (IRE) **The Mount Fawcus Partnership**
27 **MEHRAKI STAR (IRE)**, 4, b g Mehmas (IRE)—Aglette **Ursa Major Racing & Partner**
28 **MISS AMELIA**, 9, b m Midnight Legend—Miss Pross **Cambridge Racing**
29 **MISS CHARLTON**, 8, br m Passing Glance—Miss Pross **Mr J Cowan, Mr S Evans & Mr C Hogg**
30 **OASIS PRINCE**, 6, b g Oasis Dream—Demisemiquaver **Mr A. L. Bosomworth**
31 **ORKAN**, 8, b g Shirocco (GER)—Zefooha (FR) **Mr C J I & Mr J A Scarrow**
32 **PARIS PROTOCOL**, 9, b g Champs Elysees—Island Vista **Mrs G. B. Walford**
33 **POETRIA**, 4, b f Poet's Voice—Jozafeen **Mrs C. Steel**
34 **QUEST FOR LIRE**, 10, b g Dapper—Lewesdon Duchess **Mr A R. Douglas**
35 **ROCKMANN (FR)**, 7, b g Kap Rock (FR)—All Berry (FR) **Mr C. N. Herman**
36 **TEARAWAY TILLY**, 5, b m Passing Glance—Hopeand **Allott & Wordingham**
37 , B m Dick Turpin (IRE)—Trompette (USA) **David Furman & John Sugarman**
38 **WILLIAM OF ORANGE**, 11, b g Duke of Marmalade (IRE)—Critical Acclaim **Mr I. P. Drury**
39 **ZUMURUD (IRE)**, 7, gr g Zebedee—Thaisy (USA) **Ms M. Austerfield**

THREE-YEAR-OLDS

40 **HAVANA VISION**, ch g Havana Gold (IRE)—Swirling (IRE) **New Vision Bloodstock**
41 **HULTON RANGER (IRE)**, b g Slade Power (IRE)—City Dazzler (IRE) **Mrs G. B. Walford**
42 **ODAAT**, b f Equiano (FR)—Oilinda **Clayton Civil Engineering & Environmental Services Ltd**
43 B f Cannock Chase (USA)—Peal of Bells
44 **TINEGGIORI (FR)**, gr g Bated Breath—Validora (FR)
45 **WHO'S UR DANDY (IRE)**, ch f Dandy Man (IRE)—Fly By **Ursa Major Racing & Partner**

TWO-YEAR-OLDS

46 B g 28/02 Rajasinghe (IRE)—Broughtons Secret (Aqlaam) (3000)
47 B g 13/04 Bungle Inthejungle—Diablo Dancer (Zafeen (FR)) (18095)
48 **HAVANAWING**, b f 13/04 Havana Gold (IRE)—Sabrewing (IRE) (Fast Company (IRE)) (18000)
  Mrs M Austerfield, 8 Amigos, Mr J Burns
49 **KITTEN'S BAY**, b g 16/03 Kitten's Joy (USA)—Special Purpose (IRE) (Scat Daddy (USA)) (20952)
  Mrs M Austerfield, 8 Amigos, Mr J Burns
50 B c 22/03 Washington DC (IRE)—Natural Appeal (IRE) (Dark Angel (IRE)) (22857)

MR MARK WALFORD - continued

Other Owners: Mr J. Allott, Ms M. Austerfield, Mr L. A. Bolingbroke, Mr J. R. Burns, CW Racing Club, Cambridge Racing 1, Cambridge Racing Limited, Mr P. A. P. Clays, Mr James E. Cowan, Mr J. Craggs, D. J. Dickson, Mr I. P. Drury, Mr P. A. Emerson, Mr S. N. Evans, Mr D. I. Firth, Mr D. E. Furman, Grey Horse Syndicates, C. J. Grindal, Mr C. V. Hogg, Mrs E. Holmes, Mr G. P. Howard, Mr M. Johnson, Mrs S. V. Milner, Mr P. Molony, Mrs S. E. Morrell, Mr D. Percival, Mr A. K. Quirke, Mr J. N. Readman, Mr J. A. Scarrow, Mr J. B. Sugarman, Mr C. J. Sutton, Mr C. Talbot, The 8 Amigos, URSA Major Racing, Mrs G. B. Walford, Mr P. L. Welsby, Mrs A. M. Wheeler, Mr T. J. Wheeler, Mr T. J. Wigglesworth, Mr G. Wilson, P. L. Wordingham.

536
MR ROBERT WALFORD, Blandford
Postal: **Heart of Oak Stables, Okeford Fitzpane, Blandford, Dorset, DT11 0LW**
Contacts: **MOBILE 07815 116209**
EMAIL robertwalford1@gmail.com

1 AMELIA'S DANCE (IRE), 7, ch m Flemensfirth (USA)—Madame McGoldrick (IRE) **Major-Gen R. Keightley**
2 ART DECCO, 6, br g Dapper—Lewesdon Duchess **Buckingham, Chapman, Langford & Ritzema**
3 BLISTERING BOB, 7, b g Big Bad Bob (IRE)—Kristalette (IRE) **Mr R. Walford**
4 CASTCARRIE (IRE), 7, b m Yeats (IRE)—Turtle Lady (IRE) **Sue & Clive Cole & Ann & Tony Gale**
5 CHLOE'S COURT (IRE), 9, br m Court Cave (IRE)—Howaya Pet (IRE) **Cole, Gale, Levy & Mortimer**
6 EDE'IFFS ELTON, 8, b g Geordieland (FR)—Ede'iff **Mr A. Lees**
7 ELIOS D'OR (FR), 8, b g Puit d'Or (IRE)—Naker Mome (FR) **Lewis Nettley Racing**
8 FIRENZO (FR), 7, b g Network (GER)—Toscane (FR) **Mrs S. De Wilde**
9 FLAGRANT DELITIEP (FR), 7, gr g Fragrant Mix (IRE)—Naltiepy (FR) **Mrs C. M. Hinks**
10 FOXBORO (GER), 7, b g Maxios—Fair Breeze (GER) **Lewis Nettley Racing**
11 GAMBIE TIEP (FR), 6, b g Zambezi Sun—Uitiepy (FR) **KSB Bloodstock & Mrs Celia Djivanovic**
12 HIPOP DES ONGRAIS (FR), 5, gr g Voiladenuo (FR)—Pretty des Ongrais (FR) **Baroness D. M. Harding**
13 HITITI (FR), 5, b g Great Pretender (IRE)—Val'melodie (FR) **Dr & Mrs John Millar**
14 HOT IN THE CITY, 8, b m Eastern Anthem (IRE)—Kasamba **Heart of Oak Racing**
15 JUST STARDUST, 6, gr g Geordieland (FR)—Just Fee **A. J. M. Trowbridge**
16 LEADING SWOOP (IRE), 6, b g Leading Light (IRE)—One Swoop (IRE) **Gale Force One**
17 MANVERS HOUSE, 9, b g Schiaparelli (GER)—Freydis (IRE) **K S B, Mr M Doughty & Mrs Sarah Tizzard**
18 ONE FOR DUNSTAN (IRE), 7, b g Sholokhov (IRE)—Park Rose (IRE) **Gale Force Six**
19 OUR MERLIN, 10, b g Pasternak—Lorgnette **A. J. M. Trowbridge**
20 SHUTUPSHIRLEY, 5, b g Saddler's Rock (IRE)—Ede'iff **Chris Pugsley & Nigel Skinner**
21 TIP TOP MOUNTAIN (IRE), 7, b g Mountain High (IRE)—The Central Lady (IRE) **Mr R. J. Brown**
22 VAZIANI (FR), 8, b g Sinndar (IRE)—Visinova (FR) **Chris Pugsley & Acorn Builders Dorset**
23 WILLIAM PHILO, 5, ch g Black Sam Bellamy (IRE)—Jambles **Tony & Susan Brimble**

Other Owners: Acorn Builders Dorset LTD, Mrs S. J. Biggins, Mr A. F. G. Brimble, Mrs S. L. Brimble, Mr M. R. Chapman, Mr C. Cole, Mrs S. S. Cole, Mrs C. J. Djivanovic, Mr M. Doughty, Mrs A. G. Gale, Mr A. P. Gale, K S B Bloodstock, Ms G. S. Langford, Mr A. R. Levy, Mr A. Lewis, Mrs J. D. Millar, Dr J. W. Millar, Exors of the Late Mr B. Mortimer, Mr B. J. Nettley, C. C. Pugsley, Mrs D. J. Ritzema, N. Skinner, Step By Step Supporting Independence Ltd, Mrs S. L. Tizzard.

NH Jockey: James Best.

537
MR ED WALKER, Upper Lambourn
Postal: **Kingsdown Stables, Upper Lambourn, Hungerford, Berkshire, RG17 8QX**
Contacts: PHONE 01488 674148 MOBILE 07787 534145
EMAIL ed@edwalkerracing.com WEBSITE www.edwalkerracing.com

1 BELOVED (IRE), 4, b f Frankel—Love And Bubbles (USA) **Mr D. Ward**
2 CAME FROM THE DARK (IRE), 6, gr g Dark Angel (IRE)—Silver Shoon (IRE) **Mr P. K. Siu**
3 CANOODLED (IRE), 4, b f Mehmas (IRE)—Fondled **Mr L. A. Bellman**
4 CARADOC (IRE), 7, b g Camelot—Applause (IRE) **Mr P. K. Siu**
5 CLOSING BELL, 4, b f Siyouni (FR)—Wiener Valkyrie **Car Colston Hall Stud**
6 DESERT DOCTOR (IRE), 7, ch g Society Rock (IRE)—Dorn Hill **Mrs F. H. Hay**
7 DREAMLOPER (IRE), 5, b m Lope de Vega (IRE)—Livia's Dream (IRE) **Mr J. S. M. Fill**
8 FANTASY BELIEVER (IRE), 5, b g Make Believe—Avizare (IRE) **Chris & David Stam**

MR ED WALKER - continued

9 **GLENARTNEY**, 4, b f Le Havre (IRE)—Willoughby (IRE) **Cayton Park Stud Limited**
10 **GREAT AMBASSADOR**, 5, ch g Exceed And Excel (AUS)—Snoqualmie Girl (IRE) **Ebury Racing 6**
11 **HAFEET ALAIN (IRE)**, 6, b g Elzaam (AUS)—Batuta **Mr P. K. Siu**
12 **HASEEF (IRE)**, 4, gr g Dark Angel (IRE)—Silver Shoon (IRE) **Berkeley Greenwood & Partner**
13 **JONAH JONES (IRE)**, 6, b g No Nay Never (USA)—Conniption (IRE) **Mr D. Ward**
14 **JUAN SEGUIN (IRE)**, 4, b g Invincible Spirit (IRE)—Pretty Face **Mr Y. Alturaif**
15 **MOLLS MEMORY**, 7, ch m Helmet (AUS)—Bright Moll **Mr A. R. F. Buxton**
16 **MOUNTAIN PEAK**, 7, b g Swiss Spirit—Nolas Lolly (IRE) **Ebury Racing**
17 **MY MIRAGE (IRE)**, 4, b f Iffraaj—Interception (IRE) **B. E. Nielsen**
18 **NELL THE THIEF**, 4, b br f Zoffany (IRE)—Betty The Thief (IRE) **Mr D. Ward**
19 **PARACHUTE**, 4, ch g Sea The Stars (IRE)—Fly **Highclere Racing, T Vestey & P Silver**
20 **PEINTRE D'ETOILES (FR)**, 4, b f Sea The Stars (IRE)—Persian Sky **Mr D. Ward**
21 **POPMASTER (IRE)**, 4, gr g Gutaifan (IRE)—Best New Show (IRE) **Mr L. A. Bellman**
22 **PRIMO BACIO (IRE)**, 4, b f Awtaad (IRE)—Suvenna (IRE) **Mr D. Ward**
23 **RANDOM HARVEST (IRE)**, 4, b f War Front (USA)—Seta **Lady Bamford**
24 **RAY DAY**, 4, b f Adaay (IRE)—Rahyah **Mrs G. Walker**
25 **REINA DEL MAR (IRE)**, 4, b f Awtaad (IRE)—Star Approval (IRE) **Mr D. Ward**
26 **ROVANIEMI (IRE)**, 5, b g Oasis Dream—Landmark (USA) **Mr Y. Alturaif**
27 **ST GEORGE'S BAY**, 4, b g Cable Bay (IRE)—Basque Beauty **Lady Coventry & Partners**
28 **STORMY ANTARCTIC**, 9, ch g Stormy Atlantic (USA)—Bea Remembered **Mr P. K. Siu**
29 **SUNSET BAY**, 4, b f Cable Bay (IRE)—Light of Love **Brightwalton Bloodstock Limited**
30 **TENAYA CANYON**, 4, b f Due Diligence (USA)—Clouds Rest **Racegoers Club Owners Group**

THREE-YEAR-OLDS

31 **ABOVE IT ALL (IRE)**, b g Kodiac—Top Dollar **Ebury Racing 7**
32 **AMERICAN STAR (IRE)**, b g Starspangledbanner (AUS)—Signora Valentina (IRE) **Mr D. Ward**
33 **BLING ON THE MUSIC**, ch c Sea The Stars (IRE)—Crysdal **Lord A. Lloyd Webber**
34 **CAP DRAMONT**, ch g Iffraaj—Miss Cap Estel **John Pearce Racing Limited**
35 B f Frankel—Eartha Kitt **Chasemore Farm LLP**
36 **GLAM UP**, b f Showcasing—Complexion **Brightwalton Bloodstock Limited**
37 **KAWIDA**, b f Sir Percy—Kandahari **Miss K. Rausing**
38 **KINDNESS**, b f No Nay Never (USA)—Nancy Hart **Mr D. Ward**
39 **KING ALFRED (IRE)**, b c The Gurkha (IRE)—Vestavia (IRE) **Mr M. J. Cottis**
40 **KING OF JUNGLE (IRE)**, ch c Bungle Inthejungle—Ayr Missile **Mr P. K. Siu**
41 **KINGBOARD STAR (IRE)**, b g Cotai Glory—Jollification (IRE) **Mr K. W. Cheung**
42 **KINGOFHELL (IRE)**, b g Dark Angel (IRE)—Hay Chewed (IRE) **Mr P. K. Siu**
43 **LETUSGOTHENYOUANDI**, ch f Frankel—Cascata **Mr S. A. Stuckey**
44 **MAKAROVA**, b f Acclamation—Vesnina **Brightwalton Bloodstock Limited**
45 **MALCOLM**, b c Teofilo (IRE)—Interception (IRE) **B. E. Nielsen**
46 **MELEAGANT (FR)**, b g Camelot—Floating Away (USA) **Mr R Pegum, Mr B Greenwood & Mr C Dale**
47 **MIDNIGHT MOLL (IRE)**, b f Dark Angel (IRE)—Serena's Storm (IRE) **Rockcliffe Stud**
48 **PEGGOTY**, b f Hot Streak (IRE)—Semayyel (IRE) **Duchess of M. Beaufort**
49 **PIFFLE (IRE)**, b f Camacho—Siphon Melody (USA) **Mrs G. Walker**
50 **PRIMI ORDINIS (IRE)**, gr f Frankel—Real Smart (USA) **B. E. Nielsen**
51 **QUEEN OF COMEDY**, b f Kingman—Stage Presence (IRE) **Lady Bamford**
52 **SHABANO (GER)**, ch g Amaron—Summertime (GER) **B & I Dodds-smith**
53 **SHIBUYA SONG**, ch f New Approach (IRE)—Silent Music (IRE) **Mr C. E. Stedman**
54 **SPERANZOSO**, b g Siyouni (FR)—Joyful Hope **O.T.I. Racing**
55 **SPIRIT OF UAE**, b c Postponed (IRE)—Classic Code (IRE) **Green Team Racing**
56 **TIDAL STORM**, b g Sea The Moon (GER)—Kinetica **Mrs G. Austen-Smith**
57 **V TWELVE (IRE)**, br c Slade Power—Black Mascara (IRE) **Mr P. K. Siu**
58 **ZULU TRACKER (IRE)**, ch g Footstepsinthesand—Fligaz (FR) **Mrs F. H. Hay**

TWO-YEAR-OLDS

59 B c 03/05 Awtaad (IRE)—Arabian Pearl (IRE) (Refuse To Bend (IRE)) (32000) **Mr B. R. Halsall**
60 B f 09/03 Awtaad (IRE)—Bright New Day (IRE) (New Approach (IRE)) (23810)
61 **COCHIN**, b f 17/04 Churchill (IRE)—Slatey Hen (IRE) (Acclamation) **Bengough, Booth, Silver, Steed, Fittocks**
62 B c 17/02 Mayson—Dance East (Shamardal (USA)) (71429) **K. A. Dasmal**
63 B c 26/02 Dutch Art—Danehill Revival (Pivotal) **Mr D. Ward**

MR ED WALKER - continued

64 B c 07/02 Zoustar (AUS)—Dubai Media (CAN) (Songandaprayer (USA)) **Mr C. E. Stedman**
65 EMIRATES VOICE, b f 24/04 Brazen Beau (AUS)—Great Smile (IRE) (Galileo (IRE)) **Green Team Racing**
66 B c 05/03 Acclamation—Fast Lily (IRE) (Fastnet Rock (AUS)) (85000)
67 B c 03/02 Wootton Bassett—Forest Crown (Royal Applause) (200000) **Mr D. Ward**
68 B f 06/03 Lope de Vega (IRE)—Ghalyah (Frankel) (90000) **Mr D. Ward**
69 Ch f 28/04 Starspangledbanner (AUS)—Greenisland (IRE) (Fasliyev (USA)) (220000)
 Lord Lloyd Webber & Mr A Rosen
70 INCA QUEEN (IRE), b f 01/05 Oasis Dream—Inca Trail (USA) (Royal Academy (USA)) (70000) **Mr M. J. Cottis**
71 JUST A NOTION, b f 22/02 Le Havre (IRE)—Queen Cordelia (IRE) (Acclamation) (120000) **East Wind Racing Ltd**
72 KHINJANI, b f 09/03 Sir Percy—Kandahari (Archipenko (USA)) **Miss K. Rausing**
73 B c 20/03 Australia—London Plane (IRE) (Danehill Dancer (IRE)) **Mr P. K. Siu**
74 B c 06/03 Churchill (IRE)—Merry Me (IRE) (Invincible Spirit (IRE)) **Mrs F. H. Hay**
75 Br f 29/02 Sea The Stars (IRE)—Motivee (IRE) (Motivator) (60000)
76 B f 10/03 Churchill (IRE)—Nancy Hart (Sepoy (AUS)) **Mr D. Ward**
77 B c 07/03 Dandy Man (IRE)—Odyssee (FR) (Teofilo (IRE)) (47000)
78 Ch f 06/04 No Nay Never (USA)—Ornelia Ruee (FR) (Sea The Stars (IRE)) (127551) **Mr D. Ward**
79 Br f 27/02 Nathaniel (IRE)—Perfect Lady (Excelebration (IRE)) (20000)
80 PROSPERING (IRE), b c 25/04 Profitable (IRE)—Heavenly Angel (Dark Angel (IRE)) (40000)
 Greenwood, Dale, Silver, Homburg
81 Gr c 04/04 Gutaifan (IRE)—Shimmy Shoes (IRE) (Reckless Abandon) (15500) **Mr L. A. Bellman**
82 Bl c 30/04 Showcasing—Simply Me (New Approach (IRE)) **Mr L. A. Bellman**
83 B c 03/03 U S Navy Flag (USA)—Stor Mo Chroi (IRE) (Montjeu (USA)) (63776) **Mr D. Ward**
84 B f 20/02 Sea The Stars (IRE)—The Fairy (IRE) (Invincible Spirit (IRE)) (80782) **Mrs F. H. Hay**
85 Ch f 18/04 Cotai Glory—Triggers Broom (IRE) (Arcano (IRE)) **Kangyu International Racing (HK) Limited**
86 B c 16/02 Kingman—Twitch (IRE) (Azamour (IRE)) (190000) **Mrs F. H. Hay**
87 UNION COURT, b f 15/03 Havana Grey—Fyxenna (Foxwedge (AUS)) (18000) **Ebury Racing 3**
88 B f 19/04 Mehmas (IRE)—Warda (Pivotal) (190000) **Mr D. Ward**
89 B c 01/05 Dark Angel (IRE)—Warshah (IRE) (Shamardal (USA)) (60000) **Mr C. U. F. Ma**

Other Owners: Mr P. Afia, A. Al Shaikh, Mr A. A. Al Shaikh, Mr K. A. Alshaikh, Mr A. N. C. Bengough, Mr P. Booth, Mr M. J. Cottis, Mr L. Cowan, Mr C. E. Dale, Mr I. Dodds-Smith, Fittocks Stud, Mrs J. M. Forman Hardy. N. J. Forman Hardy, B. J. R. Greenwood, Highclere Thoroughbred Racing - Fly, Mrs E. A. Harris, T. F. Harris, Highclere Thoroughbred Racing Ltd, Mrs E. M. Hobson, Mr R. Homburg, Mr B. W. Keswick, Mr S. L. Keswick, Lord A. Lloyd Webber, Mr B Greenwood & Mr C Dale, Mr R. A. Pegum, Mr A. Rosen, Mr P. G. S. Silver, Dr C. Stam, Mr D. B. Stam, Mr G. Steed, Mr I. R. Twigden, T. R. G. Vestey, Mr E. C. D. Walker.

---

538 **MR CHRIS WALL, Newmarket**
Postal: Induna Stables, Fordham Road, Newmarket, Suffolk, CB8 7AQ
Contacts: HOME 01638 668896 MOBILE 07764 940255 FAX 01638 667279
EMAIL christianwall@btconnect.com WEBSITE www.chriswallracing.co.uk

1 ANGEL AMADEA, 4, gr f Dark Angel (IRE)—Keene Dancer **Wayman & Thomas**
2 BAGUE D'OR (IRE), 4, ch g Belardo (IRE)—Ravensburg **Mr S. Fustok**
3 CASTANA DIA (IRE), 4, ch f Dandy Man (IRE)—Day By Day **B. R. Westley**
4 DIVINE COMEDY (IRE), 4, b f Le Havre (IRE)—Epic Emirates **The Equema Partnership**
5 DOUBLE OR BUBBLE (IRE), 5, b m Exceed And Excel (AUS)—Mango Lady **Mr S. Fustok**
6 FLYING STANDARD (IRE), 5, ch g Starspangledbanner (AUS)—Snow Scene **Hintlesham Racing Ltd**
7 GLEN ESK, 5, b g Kyllachy—Ski Slope **Botham and Hutchinson**
8 GOLDIE HAWK, 5, b m Golden Horn—Always Remembered (IRE) **Mr S. Fustok**
9 HI HO SILVER, 8, gr g Camacho—Silver Spell **Mrs C. A. Wall**
10 KINGMANIA (IRE), 4, b f Kingman—Greek Goddess (IRE) **Mr S. Fustok**
11 MANGO BOY, 4, gr g New Bay—Mango Lady **Mr S. Fustok**
12 MUSTAZEED (IRE), 4, br g Territories (IRE)—Mejala (IRE) **Newmarket Racing Club HQiii**
13 OH IT'S SAUCEPOT, 8, b m Sir Percy—Oh So Saucy **The Eight of Diamonds**
14 THE THUNDERER (IRE), 4, b g Gleneagles (IRE)—Purple Sage (IRE) **The Clodhoppers**
15 TURNTABLE, 6, b g Pivotal—Masarah (IRE) **Induna Racing**
16 ZARNAVA (FR), 4, ch f Le Havre (IRE)—Zayva (FR) **Fram Racing Partners**

MR CHRIS WALL - continued

THREE-YEAR-OLDS

17 **CHIPS AND RICE**, b f Golden Horn—Semaral (IRE) **Mr D. M. Thurlby**
18 **COMMANDER HECTOR**, b g Postponed (IRE)—Hector's Girl **Mrs Doreen M Swinburn & Partner**
19 **FREE STEP (IRE)**, b f Muhaarar—Oriental Step (IRE) **Hughes & Scott**
20 **GLOBE PLAYER**, b g Nathaniel (IRE)—La Dorotea (IRE) **Mr S. Fustok**
21 **OH SO AUDACIOUS**, b f Mukhadram—Oh So Saucy **The Eight of Diamonds**
22 **RODOLFO**, b g Poet's Voice—Be Free **Hintlesham Racing Ltd**
23 **ROSE CAMIRA**, b f Camelot—Silent Act (USA) **Ms R. Grubmuller**
24 **SAVROLA (IRE)**, b g Churchill (IRE)—Toujours L'Amour **Mr S. Fustok**
25 **SPIT SPOT**, ch f Sir Percy—Taweyla (IRE) **Mr D. M. Thurlby**
26 **TOTAL JOY (IRE)**, b g Ribchester (IRE)—Ludi Lu (FR) **Mr S. Fustok**
27 **YOU'RE ON MUTE (FR)**, b f Olympic Glory (IRE)—Al Haffanah (IRE) **Mr D. M. Thurlby**

TWO-YEAR-OLDS

28 B f 17/03 Caravaggio (USA)—El Cuerpo E L'Alma (USA) (Harlan's Holiday (USA)) (52000) **Hughes & Scott**
29 B f 12/04 Sixties Icon—Esteemed Lady (Mark of Esteem) **Mrs Doreen M Swinburn & Partner**
30 **LOUAIZEH (IRE)**, b f 23/03 Ribchester (IRE)—Toujours L'Amour (Authorized (IRE)) **Mr S. Fustok**
31 **ROLLZ ROYZ**, ch c 13/02 Ribchester (IRE)—Greek Goddess (IRE) (Galileo (IRE)) **Mr S. Fustok**

Other Owners: P. J. W. Botham, C. J. A. Hughes, Mr D. A. Hutchinson, Mr K. D. Scott, P. Scott, Mrs D. M. Swinburn.

Apprentice Jockey: Kaiya Fraser, Seb Woods.

---

539 **MR TREVOR WALL, Ludlow**
Postal: **Gorsty Farm Flat, Whitcliffe, Ludlow, Shropshire, SY8 2HD**
Contacts: PHONE 01588 660219 MOBILE 07972 732080
EMAIL trevorwall56@outlook.com

1 4, B g Telescope (IRE)—Fairy Alisha
2 **HOT MADRAS (IRE)**, 14, b m Milan—Hot Fudge (IRE)
3 **LONGVILLE LILLY**, 7, b m Mawatheeq (USA)—Curtains **T. R. Wall**
4 **MAY MIST**, 10, b m Nayef (USA)—Midnight Mist (IRE) **A. H. Bennett**
5 **MY FOXY LADY**, 10, br m Sagamix (FR)—Marlbrook Fox **Miss J. C. L. Needham**
6 **PAT'S LIGHT**, 6, b m Black Sam Bellamy (IRE)—Kansas City (FR) **C. G. Johnson**
7 **RIGHT ROYALS DAY**, 13, b m Beneficial—Just For A Laugh **Miss J. C. L. Needham**

Assistant Trainer: Mrs J. A. Wall.

---

540 **MR CHARLIE WALLIS, Ardleigh**
Postal: **Benson Stud, Harts Lane, Ardleigh, Colchester, Essex, CO7 7QE**
Contacts: PHONE 01206 230779 MOBILE 07725 059355
EMAIL cwallis86@hotmail.com

1 **ABDUCTION (FR)**, 4, b g Acclamation—Perfect Day (IRE) **Dab Hand Racing**
2 **ACES (IRE)**, 10, b g Dark Angel (IRE)—Cute Ass (IRE) **Mrs H. Wallis**
3 **ALEEF (IRE)**, 9, b g Kodiac—Okba (USA) **Mrs H. Wallis**
4 **ARZAAK (IRE)**, 8, br g Casamento (IRE)—Dixieland Kiss (USA) **Mr M. M. Foulger**
5 **BERNARD SPIERPOINT**, 5, b g Harbour Watch (IRE)—Para Siempre **Mr R. A. Popely**
6 **BORN TO SIRE (IRE)**, 5, b g Born To Sea (IRE)—Sea of Wonders (IRE) **P. E. Axon**
7 **HIGHEST AMBITION (FR)**, 4, b g Siyouni (FR)—High Story (FR) **Mr E. Hayward**
8 **I AM A DREAMER**, 6, b g Dream Ahead (USA)—Alexander Ballet **Dab Hand Racing**
9 **IESHA**, 4, b f Cable Bay (IRE)—Royal Silk **J. M. Bradley**
10 **INDIAN AFFAIR**, 12, br g Sleeping Indian—Rare Fling (USA) **Mrs H. Wallis**
11 **IVAN DRAGO**, 4, br g Equiano (FR)—Tesary **Mr E. Hayward**
12 **LORNA COLE (IRE)**, 6, gr m Lethal Force (IRE)—Suedehead **P. E. Axon**
13 **SALSOUL (IRE)**, 4, b f Kodiac—Goldcrest **J.Titley & Jane Challen**

MR CHARLIE WALLIS - continued

14 **SIR HECTOR (IRE)**, 7, ch g Sir Prancealot (IRE)—Awwal Malika (USA) **J.Titley & Jane Challen**

THREE-YEAR-OLDS

15 **CHEESE THE ONE**, gr f Outstrip—Arabian Music (IRE) **Mr G. Bulloch**
16 **CWTCH (IRE)**, b f Kodiac—Vociferous Marina (IRE) **Mr E. Hayward**
17 B g Lethal Force (IRE)—Emulate **Mr R. A. Popely**
18 **HEMSBY PINE (IRE)**, b g Bated Breath—Pearl Diva (IRE) **Pine Developments Limited**
19 **LADY SPIRITUS (IRE)**, b f Bated Breath—Lady Glinka (IRE) **Strawberry Fields Stud**
20 B g Outstrip—Pompeia **Mr R. A. Popely**
21 **SHE'S GOT BOTTLE**, b f Lethal Force (IRE)—Lady Tabitha (IRE) **Gordon Bulloch & S Hardcastle D Szepler**
22 **TABEEB**, b g Bated Breath—Sparkle **Mr E. Hayward**
23 **VIENNA POPPY**, gr ro f Outstrip—La Adelita (IRE) **Mr R. A. Popely**

TWO-YEAR-OLDS

24 B c 15/04 Oasis Dream—Afternoon (IRE) (Rip Van Winkle (IRE)) (1500)
25 B g 16/02 Muhaarar—Alexis Carrington (IRE) (Mastercraftsman (IRE)) (1429) **Miss J. A. Challen**
26 B g 13/04 Unfortunately (IRE)—Enchanted Princess (Royal Applause) (1500) **P. E. Axon**

Other Owners: Mr G. Bulloch, Miss J. A. Challen, Mr S. Hardcastle, D. Pearson, A. D. Pirie, Mr D. Szepler, J. E. Titley.

Assistant Trainer: Hayley Wallis.

541

MRS JANE WALTON, Otterburn
Postal: **Dunns houses stables, Otterburn, Newcastle upon Tyne, Northumberland, NE19 1LB**
Contacts: **PHONE 01830 520677 MOBILE 07808 592701 FAX 01830 520677**
EMAIL dunnshouses@hotmail.com WEBSITE www.janewaltonhorseracing.co.uk

1 **EVEQUE (FR)**, 8, ch g Kotky Bleu (FR)—Gloria IV (FR) **Mrs J. M. Walton**
2 **PARELLI POWER**, 6, ch m Schiaparelli (GER)—Shankhouse Wells (IRE) **Jane Walton & George Charlton Partner**
3 **REAL ARMANI**, 10, ch g Sulamani (IRE)—Reel Charmer **Jane Walton & George Charlton Partner**
4 **REVERSE THE CHARGE (IRE)**, 15, b g Bishop of Cashel—Academy Jane (IRE) **Mrs J. M. Walton**
5 **UPTOWN HARRY (IRE)**, 8, b br g Morozov (USA)—Tudor Glyn (IRE) **Fresh Start Partnership**
6 **WESTEND THEATRE (IRE)**, 13, b g Darsi (FR)—Ballyvelig Lady (IRE) **Mrs J. M. Walton**

Other Owners: Mr G. A. G. Charlton, Miss D. M. Hall, Mrs M. R. Ridley, Miss J. Rutherford, Mrs J. M. Walton.

542

MR JIMMY WALTON, Morpeth
Postal: **Flotterton Hall, Thropton, Morpeth, Northumberland, NE65 7LF**
Contacts: **PHONE 01669 640253 MOBILE 07831 894120**

1 **BONNIE BANJO**, 4, b f Requinto (IRE)—Island Music (IRE) **J. B. Walton**
2 **CATCHAMAT**, 13, b m Overbury (IRE)—More Flair **Messrs F. T. Walton**
3 **CUDGEL**, 9, b g Sulamani (IRE)—Posh Stick **Messrs F. T. Walton**
4 **FRANKIES FIRE**, 9, b m Flying Legend (USA)—Watch The Wind **Messrs F. T. Walton**
5 **MATTHEW MAN**, 11, b g Bollin Eric—Garden Feature **Messrs F. T. Walton**
6 **ROLL OF THUNDER**, 13, b g Antonius Pius (USA)—Ischia **Messrs F. T. Walton**
7 **SUPER SUNDIAL**, 7, gr m Proclamation (IRE)—Garden Feature **Messrs F. T. Walton**
8 **WEST LAWN**, 6, b m Westlake—Garden Feature **Messrs F. T. Walton**

Other Owners: F. A. Walton, J. B. Walton.

543 MR TOM WARD, Upper Lambourn
Postal: **Whitehouse Stables, Upper Lambourn, Hungerford, Berkshire, RG17 8QP**
Contacts: **WORK EMAIL** tom@tomwardracing.com

1 **AFTA PARTY (IRE)**, 4, gr g Mastercraftsman (IRE)—Wood Fairy
2 **CAPOTE'S DREAM (IRE)**, 5, br g Dream Ahead (USA)—Capote West (USA)
3 **CHILLSEA (USA)**, 4, ch f Mshawish (USA)—Sandiva (IRE)
4 **CULTURE (FR)**, 6, b g Dream Ahead (USA)—Talon Bleu (FR)
5 **DEVIL'S CUB**, 4, b g Hellvelyn—Noor Al Haya (IRE)
6 **DIAMOND BAY**, 4, ch g New Bay—Amarillo Starlight (IRE)
7 **EAGLE COURT (IRE)**, 5, b g Free Eagle (IRE)—Classic Remark (IRE)
8 **FARASI LANE (IRE)**, 4, b g Belardo (IRE)—No Such Zone
9 **LUISA CASATI (IRE)**, 4, b f Vadamos (FR)—La Marchesa (IRE)
10 **MAJESTIC TEJAAN (IRE)**, 4, b f Zoffany (IRE)—Maybe So
11 **MISHAL STAR (IRE)**, 4, ch f Mehmas (IRE)—Ruzma (IRE)
12 **MOONSHINER (IRE)**, 4, ch f Mehmas (IRE)—Obsara
13 **MOURIYANI (USA)**, 4, b g City Zip (USA)—Mouraniya (IRE)
14 **RAGING RASCAL (IRE)**, 4, b g Coulsty (IRE)—Limousine
15 **ROMAN MIST (IRE)**, 4, gr f Holy Roman Emperor (IRE)—Drifting Mist
16 **THE TURPINATOR (IRE)**, 5, b g Canford Cliffs (IRE)—Bessichka
17 **TINTORETTO (IRE)**, 7, b g Lilbourne Lad (IRE)—Fanacanta (IRE)
18 **UNDER THE TWILIGHT**, 4, b f Twilight Son—Rococoa (IRE)
19 **ZHUI FENG (IRE)**, 9, b g Invincible Spirit (IRE)—Es Que

THREE-YEAR-OLDS
20 **BLENHEIM BELLE (IRE)**, b f Churchill (IRE)—Adja (IRE)
21 **DANGEROUS RASCAL (IRE)**, gr g Dark Angel (IRE)—Pastoral Girl
22 **DANSEMAI**, b f Twilight Son—The Dukkerer (IRE)
23 **DARK FLYER**, b c Gutaifan (IRE)—Light of Love
24 **DONNA ITALIANA**, b f Raven's Pass (USA)—Dry Your Eyes (ITY)
25 **DOUBLE CHERRY (IRE)**, b g Make Believe—My Uptown Girl
26 **PAOLO PANINI**, ch g Cityscape—Plume
27 **PAULO PANINI**, ch g Cityscape—Plume

TWO-YEAR-OLDS
28 **BE SASSY (IRE)**, b f 06/04 Starspangledbanner (AUS)—Hint of Glas (FR) (Silver Frost (IRE))
29 Ch f 06/04 Bungle Inthejungle—City Dazzler (IRE) (Elusive City (USA))
30 **FULL PRIME (IRE)**, ch f 23/03 Mehmas (IRE)—Mayorstone (IRE) (Exceed And Excel (AUS)) (80000)
31 B f 27/03 Showcasing—Iamfine (IRE) (Whipper (USA)) (28000)
32 Ch c 23/01 Hawkbill (USA)—La Pantera (Captain Rio) (8000)
33 **LADY DREAMER (IRE)**, b f 19/03 Dandy Man (IRE)—Weekend Getaway (IRE) (Acclamation) (59048)
34 Gr ro f 23/04 Dark Angel (IRE)—Light My Fire (IRE) (Dragon Pulse (IRE)) (76190)
35 B f 25/03 Profitable (IRE)—Magic Minor (IRE) (Montjeu (IRE)) (2857)
36 B f 01/02 Golden Horn—Neartica (FR) (Sadler's Wells (USA)) (5000)
37 Ch f 13/03 Gustav Klimt (IRE)—Peace Fonic (FR) (Zafonic (USA))
38 B f 20/02 Iffraaj—Perfect Spirit (IRE) (Invincible Spirit (IRE)) (25000)
39 Ch f 22/01 Sea The Stars (IRE)—Shahah (Motivator) (170000)
40 **SWEET IDEA**, b f 15/04 Charming Thought—Berkshire Honey (Sakhee's Secret) (20000)

Head Lad: Anthony James, Ciaran Jones.

Travelling Head: Joe Kirby.

Business & Racing Manager: Alex Lowe.

Yard Sponsor: The Pheasant Inn, Hungerford.

544 MR ARCHIE WATSON, Upper Lambourn

Postal: **Saxon Gate, Upper Lambourn, Hungerford, Berkshire, RG17 8QH**
Contacts: PHONE 01488 491247
EMAIL office@archiewatsonracing.com WEBSITE www.archiewatsonracing.com

1 **AL ZARAQAAN,** 5, br g Golden Horn—Asheerah
2 **ALAZWAR (IRE),** 4, b g Awtaad (IRE)—Venetian Beauty (USA)
3 **AMOR DE MI VIDA (FR),** 4, b f Dabirsim (FR)—Troiecat (FR)
4 **ARCTIC EMPEROR,** 4, b g Territories (IRE)—Selkirk Sky
5 **BOUNCE BACK,** 4, b f Territories (IRE)—Vereri Senes
6 **CLIFFTOP HEAVEN,** 5, b g Canford Cliffs (IRE)—Heaven's Sake
7 **CORINTHIA KNIGHT (IRE),** 7, ch g Society Rock (IRE)—Victoria Lodge (IRE)
8 **EXCEL POWER (IRE),** 4, b g Slade Power (IRE)—Rhythm Excel
9 **FIRST SNOWFALL,** 5, b m Dubawi (IRE)—Flying Cloud (IRE)
10 **GLEN SHIEL,** 8, ch g Pivotal—Gonfilia (GER)
11 **GROVE ROAD (IRE),** 6, ch g Mahler—Dear Frankie (IRE)
12 **IGOTATEXT (IRE),** 4, b g Ajaya—Tifawt
13 **IMPERIAL SANDS (IRE),** 4, b g Footstepsinthesand—Hadrienne
14 **LOUGH DERG LYRIC (IRE),** 10, b g Court Cave (IRE)—Fairy Swing (IRE)
15 **LUNA MAGIC,** 8, br m Mayson—Dayia (IRE)
16 **MEHMENTO (IRE),** 4, b g Mehmas (IRE)—Invincible Me (IRE)
17 **MENIN GATE (IRE),** 6, gr g Farhh—Telegraphy (USA)
18 **MIGHTY GURKHA (IRE),** 4, b c Sepoy (AUS)—Royal Debt
19 **NIFTY GETAWAY (IRE),** 6, b m Getaway (GER)—Buttonboard (IRE)
20 **NOTORIOUSLY RISKY,** 4, b f Starspangledbanner (AUS)—Precariously Good
21 **ONE TO GO,** 6, gr g Champs Elysees—Tina's Spirit (IRE)
22 **ONLY THE BRAVE (USA),** 6, b br m Exchange Rate (USA)—Contact (USA)
23 **OSTILIO,** 7, ch g New Approach (IRE)—Reem Three
24 **OUTBOX,** 7, b g Frankel—Emirates Queen
25 **PERCY PROSECCO,** 7, b g Sir Percy—Grapes Hill
26 **SON AND SANNIE (IRE),** 6, b g Es Que Love (IRE)—Anamundi
27 **SOUTHERN VOYAGE (FR),** 4, b g Wootton Bassett—Blue Blue Sea
28 **STAG HORN,** 5, b g Golden Horn—Starfala
29 **STONE SOLDIER,** 5, b g Mayson—La Adelita (IRE)
30 **STRIKE ME A POSE,** 4, b g Adaay (IRE)—Mookhlesa
31 **SURPRISE EXHIBIT,** 4, b g Showcasing—Astonishing (IRE)
32 **TABDEED,** 7, ch g Havana Gold (IRE)—Puzzled (IRE)
33 **TALABAAT,** 4, b f Shalaa (IRE)—Jufoon
34 **TEMPUS,** 6, b g Kingman—Passage of Time
35 **THE PERFECT CROWN (IRE),** 5, b g Hallowed Crown (AUS)—Perfect Fun
36 **THRONE HALL,** 5, b g Kingman—Appearance
37 **WISEACRE (IRE),** 4, gr g Dark Angel (IRE)—Bear Cheek (IRE)

THREE-YEAR-OLDS

38 **ALPINE LADY,** b f Postponed (IRE)—Mount Elbrus
39 **ARCHIANO,** b c Kodiac—Awe Struck
40 **ARWAAG (IRE),** b c Awtaad (IRE)—Bailonguera (ARG)
41 **AUNT BETHANY (IRE),** b f Cotai Glory—Lilac Mist
42 **BARGING THRU,** b g Profitable (IRE)—Rhythm Excel
43 **BLAAST,** b f Showcasing—Absolute Blast (IRE)
44 **BRUNO'S GOLD (IRE),** b c Galileo Gold—Please Me (IRE)
45 **CHIEF'S WILL (IRE),** ch c Slade Power (IRE)—Royal Debt
46 **COTAI STAR (IRE),** b c Cotai Glory—Star of Malta
47 **DUSKY PRINCE (IRE),** b g Prince of Lir (IRE)—Dusky Maid (IRE)
48 **FEDERAL STREET (IRE),** b g Kodiac—Lismore (USA)
49 **FLY TO GLORY (IRE),** ch g Cotai Glory—Kimbay (IRE)
50 **GOLDEN WHISPER,** ch f Helmet (AUS)—Golden Dirham
51 **LAST HOORAH,** ch g Bated Breath—Fibou (USA)
52 **MAGURO (FR),** b c Profitable (IRE)—Sushi Tuna
53 **MAHA DEWI (IRE),** b f Highland Reel (IRE)—Gold Lace (IRE)
54 **MISSCALL (IRE),** b f Kodiac—Payphone

MR ARCHIE WATSON - continued

55 **MOUNTBATTEN (IRE)**, bl g Dabirsim (FR)—Sapore di Roma (IRE)
56 **NAZANIN (USA)**, b br f Declaration of War (USA)—Woodland Scene (IRE)
57 **NOBLE ANTHEM (IRE)**, b c Starspangledbanner (AUS)—Queen Margherita
58 **PEPPERWORT (IRE)**, b g Mehmas (IRE)—Dittander
59 **PINK CARNATION**, b f Territories (IRE)—Dusty Red
60 **PRIME OBJECTIVE**, b c Churchill (IRE)—Darinza (FR)
61 **PURE CHARMER**, b f Charming Thought—Chandresh
62 **QUANTICO (IRE)**, b c Make Believe—Palladius
63 **RED SHOWGIRL**, ch f Showcasing—Red Fantasy (IRE)
64 **SHIN SAW GYI**, b f Ardad (IRE)—Posh Claret
65 **STORM DANCER (IRE)**, b f El Kabeir (USA)—Shamardyh (IRE)
66 **SUSANBEQUICK (IRE)**, b f Dabirsim (FR)—Brynica (FR)
67 **SWEEPING**, b g Siyouni (FR)—Sweeping Up
68 **TAHANI (IRE)**, ch f Profitable (IRE)—Bold Assumption
69 **TOP EXHIBIT**, b c Showcasing—Must Be Me
70 **TWELFTH KNIGHT (IRE)**, b c Haatef (USA)—Balm
71 **VERONA STAR (IRE)**, b c Gutaifan (IRE)—Julieta (IRE)
72 **WATERMELON SUGAR (IRE)**, gr g Gutaifan (IRE)—Looks Great
73 **WHERESTHEBARBIL (IRE)**, b gr f El Kabeir (USA)—Best New Show (IRE)

Trainer did not supply details of their two-year-olds.

Assistant Trainer: Stephanie Joannides.

Flat Jockey: Hollie Doyle, Adam McNamara. **Amateur Jockey:** Miss Brodie Hampson.

545

MR FRED WATSON, Sedgefield
Postal: Beacon Hill, Sedgefield, Stockton-On-Tees, Cleveland, TS21 3HN
Contacts: **PHONE** 01740 620582 **MOBILE** 07773 321472
EMAIL fredwatson@talktalk.net

1 **DARK ECLIPSE (IRE)**, 6, b g Slade Power (IRE)—Many Colours **F. Watson**
2 **GLEAMING ARCH**, 8, b g Arabian Gleam—Mrs Quince **F. Watson**
3 **JOYFUL STAR**, 12, b g Teofilo (IRE)—Extreme Beauty (USA) **F. Watson**
4 **NEWSPEAK (IRE)**, 10, b g New Approach (IRE)—Horatia (IRE) **F. Watson**
5 **ROYAL LEGEND**, 8, ch g New Approach (IRE)—Villarrica (USA) **F. Watson**
6 **STAR CITIZEN**, 10, b g New Approach (IRE)—Faslen (USA) **F. Watson**
7 **THE MONSIEUR MAN**, 5, b g Monsieur Bond (IRE)—Mad Jazz **F. Watson**

546

MR SIMON WAUGH, Morpeth
Postal: A G Waugh & Sons Limited, Molesden House, Molesden,
Morpeth, Northumberland, NE61 3QF
Contacts: **MOBILE** 07860 561445
EMAIL swaugh@dircon.co.uk

1 **COOLMOYNE**, 6, ch g Ocovango—High Life **Mrs S. A. York**
2 **DAN GUN (IRE)**, 8, b g Intikhab (USA)—Lady Magdalena (IRE) **Northumberland Racing Club**
3 **DARK AND DANGEROUS (IRE)**, 14, b g Cacique (IRE)—Gilah (IRE) **S. G. Waugh**
4 **HELLFIRE KODE**, 5, b g Helmet (AUS)—Secret Kode (IRE) **S. G. Waugh**
5 **INFINITE SUN**, 11, b g And Beyond (IRE)—Kingussie Flower **Mrs V. J. R. Ramm**
6 **KIDMAN (IRE)**, 6, b g Arcadio (GER)—Kilganey Maid (IRE) **Mr J. D. Thompson**

MR SIMON WAUGH - continued

7 **LITTLE ORANGE**, 8, ch g Trans Island—Falbrina (IRE) **Mrs S. A. York**
8 **LOUGHERMORE (IRE)**, 8, b g Milan—Seductive Dance **Mrs P. Waugh**
9 **PASSNOTALEGEND**, 9, b g Flying Legend (USA)—Passmenot **Miss D. M. M. Calder**
10 **SEGEDUNUM**, 4, ch g Cannock Chase (USA)—Arabian Sunset (IRE) **S. G. Waugh**
11 **SKY IS THE LINNET**, 8, ch m Native Ruler—Skybound **Miss D. M. M. Calder**
12 **THISTIMENEXTYEAR**, 8, gr g New Approach (IRE)—Scarlet Empire (IRE) **S. G. Waugh**

---

547 | **MR MARK WEATHERER, Leyburn**
Postal: **The Flat, Bolton Hall Racing Stables, Wensley, Leyburn, North Yorkshire, DL8 4UF**
Contacts: PHONE 01969 625735
EMAIL markweatherer@btinternet.com

1 **AMANI**, 4, b f Adaay (IRE)—Miss Wells (IRE) **M. Weatherer**
2 4, B f Garswood—Chasin' Rainbows **Mr B. Lapham**
3 **DEE DAY LANDING**, 5, b h Intrinsic—Heidenheim (IRE) **M. Weatherer**
4 **DIONYSIS (FR)**, 9, ch g Lucarno (USA)—Oasice (FR) **Mr B. Lapham**
5 **GLAN Y GORS (IRE)**, 10, b b g High Chaparral (IRE)—Trading Places **Mr B. Lapham**
6 **LITTLE MISS SASSY**, 4, b f Fast Company (IRE)—Laftah (IRE) **Jonathan Poulter & Ben Lapham**
7 **MAZZA ROCKS (IRE)**, 7, b m Red Rocks (IRE)—Sun City **Mr B. Lapham**
8 **MUZETTA'S WALTZ (IRE)**, 8, ch m Tobougg (IRE)—Brer Rabbit **M. Weatherer**
9 **SIR TAAJ**, 6, b h Sintarajan (IRE)—Brer Rabbit **M. Weatherer**
10 **SPIRITTAPPERGOODE**, 4, b g Eagle Top—Dutch Girl **M. Weatherer**
11 **UNIQUE COMPANY (IRE)**, 7, ch g Fast Company (IRE)—Unique Blanche **M. Weatherer**

TWO-YEAR-OLDS

12 **FIRE HEART**, b f 18/05 Pearl Secret—Winning Return (IRE) (Exceed And Excel (AUS)) **Mr B. Lapham**

Other Owners: Mr B. Lapham, Mr J. Poulter.

---

548 | **MR PAUL WEBBER, Banbury**
Postal: **Cropredy Lawn, Cropredy, Banbury, Oxfordshire, OX17 1DR**
Contacts: PHONE 01295 750226 MOBILE 07836 232465
EMAIL paul@paulwebberracing.com WEBSITE www.paulwebberracing.com

1 **BOUGHTBEFORELUNCH (IRE)**, 9, b g Dubai Destination (USA)—Anie (IRE) **The Let's Do Lunch Partnership**
2 **CECI WELLS**, 5, b m Orientor—Theatrical Dancer **Mr & Mrs Philip C. Smith**
3 **CHRONOS**, 5, b g Nayef (USA)—All Time **The Fitzdares Racing Syndicate**
4 **CLOUDY HILLS (IRE)**, 6, b g Cloudings (IRE)—Phillis Hill **Miss Sheena Pilkington**
5 **EEL PIE ISLAND**, 4, b f Sixties Icon—Ificaniwill (IRE) **Mr Paul Bowden**
6 **EURKASH (FR)**, 8, b g Irish Wells (FR)—Meralda (FR) **Cropredy Lawn Racing**
7 **EYED**, 5, b g Kayf Tara—One Gulp **Mr Martin Hughes**
8 **GETAWAY WITH YOU**, 4, ch g Getaway (GER)—Dizzy Frizzy **The Starjac Partnership**
9 **GO AS YOU PLEASE (IRE)**, 9, b g Jeremy (USA)—Aweebounce (IRE) **Mr J. P. McManus**
10 **GUMBO FLYER (FR)**, 6, b g Rail Link—Sariette de L'Isle (FR) **The Train Wreck Partnership**
11 **HAPPY INDEX**, 4, b f Blue Bresil (FR)—Alasi **Sir John Timpson**
12 **HARRY THE NORSEMAN**, 6, ch g Norse Dancer (IRE)—Titled Lady **Mr Julian Nettlefold**
13 **HE'S A KNOWALL (IRE)**, 7, b br g Oscar (IRE)—Miss Knowall (IRE) **Old Gold Racing 5**
14 **HELLO SUNSHINE (FR)**, 6, ch m Kapgarde (FR)—Louvisy (FR) **Nigel Jones & Paul Bowden**
15 **INDEFATIGABLE (IRE)**, 9, b m Schiaparelli (GER)—Spin The Wheel (IRE) **Mr Philip Rocher**
16 **KILFILUM WOODS (IRE)**, 6, b g Beat Hollow—Cheryls Island (IRE) **Mr Martin Hughes**

MR PAUL WEBBER - continued

17 **LADY DE VEGA**, 5, b m Lope de Vega (IRE)—Red Boots (IRE) **Old Gold Racing 3**
18 **LEADING MAN (IRE)**, 5, gr g Leading Light (IRE)—Nina Fontenail (FR) **Mr Philip Rocher**
19 **LITIGATE (IRE)**, 7, b g Shantaram—Spin The Wheel (IRE) **Mr Philip Rocher**
20 **LUNAR FLIGHT**, 5, br m Pether's Moon (IRE)—Vanilla Delight (IRE) **Miss Sheena Pilkington**
21 **MY GIFT TO YOU (IRE)**, 4, b g Kingston Hill—Ariels Serenade (IRE) **Mr Geoffrey Finlay**
22 **PAWPAW**, 5, b g Showcasing—Papaya (IRE) **Nigel Jones & Paul Bowden**
23 **SPECIAL ACCEPTANCE**, 9, b g Malinas (GER)—Doubly Guest **The Syndicators 2**
24 **TIKA MOON (IRE)**, 5, b g Casamento (IRE)—Trikala (IRE) **Mr Derek Mossop & Partners**
25 **TOMMY TRACEY (IRE)**, 6, br g Sholokhov (IRE)—Clash House (IRE) **Economic Security 1**
26 **UNDOMIEL**, 4, b f Nayef (USA)—Tindomiel **Cropredy Lawn Racing**
27 **WAY PAST MIDNIGHT**, 7, ch m Midnight Legend—Royale Performance **Swanbridge Bloodstock Limited**

THREE-YEAR-OLDS

28 **CRYSTAL MER**, b g Sea The Stars (IRE)—Yaazy (IRE) **Mr Martin Hughes**
29 **ELWING (IRE)**, b f Intello (GER)—Masandra (IRE) **Mr David Taylor**
30 B g Nathaniel (IRE)—Sparring Queen (USA) **Irish Partners**

TWO-YEAR-OLDS

31 Ch f 20/02 Cityscape—September Blaze **Bowden & Webber**

---

549 MR ADAM WEST, Epsom
Postal: **Flat 2, Lorretta Lodge, Tilley Lane, Headley, Epsom, Surrey, KT18 6EP**
Contacts: **MOBILE 07939 030046**
EMAIL westtraining@outlook.com

1 **ARTISAN BLEU (IRE)**, 4, b f Mastercraftsman (IRE)—Washington Blue **The Maverick Syndicate**
2 **BLACKTHIRTYONE**, 4, gr g Gregorian (IRE)—Morena Park **Mr R. C. P. Deacon**
3 **BRIAC (FR)**, 11, b g Kapgarde (FR)—Jarwin Do (FR) **Mr O. S. Harris**
4 **CAP'N (IRE)**, 11, b g Gamut (IRE)—Dawn Princess **Ishtar**
5 **CAPALA (IRE)**, 6, b g Swiss Spirit—Jezebel **Mr R. C. P. Deacon**
6 **CLASHANISKA (IRE)**, 6, b g Dark Angel (IRE)—Spirit Watch (IRE) **All Seasons Racing**
7 **COULDN'T COULD SHE**, 7, b m Sixties Icon—Emperatriz **Ross Deacon & Partners**
8 **DAANY (IRE)**, 5, b g Pivotal—Ejadah (IRE) **Mr T. J. Cusden**
9 **DAPHNE MAY**, 4, b f Mayson—Cambridge Duchess **Ownaracehorse & Partners Iii**
10 **FALINE**, 4, b f Hellvelyn—Lifetime Romance (IRE) **Mr R. C. P. Deacon**
11 **GLEN ROSA**, 4, b g Heeraat (IRE)—Aunt Minnie **Ownaracehorse & Partners Ii**
12 **KILGANER QUEEN (IRE)**, 12, b m Trans Island—La Prima Diva (IRE) **Ishtar**
13 **LAUGHING LUIS**, 8, b g Authorized (IRE)—Leitzu (IRE) **West Racing Partnership**
14 **LITTLE TIPSY**, 5, b m Harbour Watch (IRE)—B Berry Brandy (USA) **Mr A. J. Morton**
15 **LIVE IN THE MOMENT (IRE)**, 5, ch g Zebedee—Approaching Autumn **Steve & Jolene de'Lemos**
16 **MAID OF ARAGON (IRE)**, 4, b f Invincible Spirit (IRE)—Lily Passion **Mr S. K. McPhee**
17 **MICKYH (IRE)**, 6, b g Sageburg (IRE)—Anna's Melody (IRE) **Mike Hemmings & West Racing**
18 **MOHASSANA (USA)**, 4, b f More Than Ready (USA)—Safarjal (IRE) **Mr S. K. McPhee**
19 **MOUNTRATH**, 4, b f Helmet (AUS)—Malladore (IRE) **Mr D. Phelan**
20 **NIBLAWI (IRE)**, 10, b g Vale of York (IRE)—Finnmark **Fred Willson & Simon Heaney**
21 **NOAHTHIRTYTWORED (IRE)**, 6, b g Court Cave (IRE)—Royale Video (IRE) **Mrs J. M. West**
22 **ONE HANDSOME DUDE (IRE)**, 7, b g Canford Cliffs (IRE)—Allegrina (IRE) **Steve & Jolene de'Lemos**
23 **PRESUMING ED (IRE)**, 7, br g Westerner—Maracana (IRE) **All Seasons Racing**
24 **PRINCESS MAYSON (IRE)**, 5, b m Mayson—Queen Athena (IRE) **Mrs J. M. West**
25 **QUEEN OF THE ROAD**, 5, b m Kingston Hill—Lily Rules (IRE) **Mrs J. M. West**
26 **TELEFINA**, 4, b f Telescope (IRE)—Haatefina **Silver Lining Racing**
27 **THESPINNINGWHEEL (IRE)**, 7, b g Arakan (USA)—Dancing Jest (IRE)
28 **THIBAULT**, 9, b g Kayf Tara—Seemarye **Farm Fencing Limited**
29 **ZYON**, 8, gr g Martaline—Temptation (FR) **Mr S. W. Lang**

THREE-YEAR-OLDS

30 **BIG BEAR HUG**, b f Belardo (IRE)—Silkenveil (IRE) **Ownaracehorse & R Kent**

MR ADAM WEST - continued

31 **BYHOOKORBYCROOK,** b g Garswood—Broadlands **Ownaracehorse By Hook Or By Crook**
32 **CODSWALLOP,** gr g Outstrip—Lady Benedicte (IRE) **Sills, Colegate, Amass & West**
33 **COULDN'T COULD HE,** b g Alhebayeb (IRE)—Emperatriz **Mr R. C. P. Deacon**
34 **D'CRAICOFDAWN,** ch f Dawn Approach (IRE)—How Fortunate **Amass, Cusden & Allen**
35 Ro f Outstrip—Dame Plume (IRE) **Mr T. J. Cusden**
36 **DEN GRIMME AELLING (IRE),** b f Estidhkaar (IRE)—Veladiya (IRE) **Padraic O'Neill & Janice West**
37 **GILBERT,** b g Cityscape—Merry Diva **Ownaracehorse & Partners Ii**
38 B f Telescope (IRE)—Haatefina **Mr T. Francis**
39 **HINES,** ch g Spill The Beans (AUS)—Synaesthesia (FR) **Endless Acres ten**
40 **JAMES JUDE (IRE),** b g Kodiac—Tides Reach (IRE) **Padraic O'Neill & Janice West**
41 **LAND OF EAGLES,** ch g Havana Gold (IRE)—Disposition **Tom Cusden & Partner**
42 **LEYLA'S POWER (IRE),** b br f Adaay (IRE)—Gala Wedge **Tom Cusden & Partners**
43 **LIVE IN THE DREAM (IRE),** ch g Prince of Lir (IRE)—Approaching Autumn **Steve & Jolene de'Lemos**
44 **LOVE WHISPER (IRE),** b f Es Que Love (IRE)—Careless Whisper (IRE) **Stuart McPhee & Partners**
45 **RITA RANA (IRE),** b f The Gurkha (IRE)—Tureyth (USA) **Stuart McPhee & Paul Webster**
46 **ROLYPOLYMOLY,** b g Heeraat (IRE)—Elzebieta (IRE) **All Seasons Racing**
47 **TEMPUS FUGIT,** b g Heeraat (IRE)—Peace Lilly (USA) **John Heaney & Simon Heaney**
48 **TOOTS,** b f Outstrip—Inchberry **Star Pointe Ltd**
49 **VOLENTI (IRE),** b c Estidhkaar (IRE)—Izba (IRE) **West Racing Partnership**

TWO-YEAR-OLDS

50 B g 11/04 Fountain of Youth (IRE)—Bay Tree (IRE) (Daylami (IRE))
51 **BILLIE LOU,** b f 22/03 Intello (GER)—Silkenveil (IRE) (Indian Ridge) (7000) **Mr T. J. Cusden**
52 Ch c 18/02 Bated Breath—Haigh Hall (Kyllachy) (25000)
53 Ch g 26/03 Hawkbill (USA)—Hisaronu (IRE) (Stravinsky (USA)) (800)
54 B g 13/02 Hot Streak (IRE)—Hot Pursuits (Pastoral Pursuits) (800) **All Seasons Racing**
55 Ch f 03/05 Night of Thunder (IRE)—Moonstone Rock (Rock of Gibraltar (IRE))
56 **MR POSTMAN,** ch c 19/02 Bated Breath—Kitba (New Approach (IRE)) (10000) **Ownaracehorse & Partners Ii**
57 B f 09/04 Ardad (IRE)—Poppy Seed (Bold Edge) (21000)

Other Owners: Mr P. Allen, Mr D. Amass, Mr D. R. Botterill, Mr E. Boumans, Mrs L. R. Colegate, Mr T. J. Cusden, Mr S. De'Lemos-Pratt, Mr R. C. P. Deacon, D. Hassan, Mr J. Heaney, Mr S. Heaney, Mr M. J. Hemmings, R. Kent, Mr S. K. McPhee, Mr P. O'Neill, Ownaracehorse Ltd, Mr P. Sills, Mr J. Stevens, Mr J. Webb, Mr P. Webster, Mrs J. M. West, West Racing Partnership, Mr F. J. E. Willson, Mrs J. de'Lemos.

550	**MISS SHEENA WEST, Lewes**

Postal: **5 Balmer Farm Cottages, Brighton Road, Lewes, East Sussex, BN7 3JN**
Contacts: **MOBILE 07748 181804 FAX 01273 622189**
EMAIL sheenawest11@aol.com FACEBOOK @sheenawestracing

1 **AIR HAIR LAIR (IRE),** 6, ch g Zebedee—Blond Beauty (USA) **I Poysden,R Heal,B Beesley,D Harper-Jones**
2 **ALEXANDRA ROMANOV (IRE),** 5, ch m Sixties Icon—Russian Empress (IRE) **Balmer Farm Racing**
3 **ANYONEWHOHADAHEART,** 5, b m Sixties Icon—Bridie Ffrench **Miss S. West**
4 **BARD OF BRITTANY,** 8, b g Sayif (IRE)—Lily Le Braz **Mr M. Moriarty**
5 **CHERRY COLA,** 6, ch m Sixties Icon—Rose Cheval (USA) **Mr A. J. Head**
6 **COCHISE,** 6, b g Intello (GER)—Ship's Biscuit **Mr G. Box**
7 **CRYSTAL TIARA,** 6, gr m Gregorian (IRE)—Petaluma **Mark Albon & Sheena West**
8 **DECEPTION VALLEY (IRE),** 5, b g Slade Power (IRE)—Sahaayef (IRE) **Miss S. West**
9 **DING DING,** 11, ch m Winker Watson—Five Bells (IRE) **Mr I. E. Poysden**
10 **EVA ICON,** 4, gr f Sixties Icon—El Che **Mr S. K. Francis**
11 **EVIE MAY,** 6, b m Excelebration (IRE)—Visanilla (FR) **Miss M. M. Poulton**
12 **FRED BEAR (IRE),** 4, b g Kodi Bear (IRE)—Subtle Affair (IRE) **Mr M. Moriarty**
13 4, B f Sixties Icon—Hi Note
14 **JUSTANOTHER MUDDLE,** 13, gr g Kayf Tara—Spatham Rose **Saloop**
15 **KENNY GEORGE,** 7, b g Mawatheeq (USA)—One For Philip **Miss M. M. Poulton**

MISS SHEENA WEST - continued

16 **LAETOLI**, 4, b f Footstepsinthesand—Exentricity **Barry Walters Farms & Partner**
17 **LIMELIGHTER**, 6, b g Harbour Watch (IRE)—Steal The Curtain **Mr Ricki Vaughan & Partner**
18 **RALLY DRIVER**, 5, b g Gregorian (IRE)—Exentricity **Mr Ricki Vaughan & Partner**
19 **SIXTIES SECRET**, 7, b m Sixties Icon—Jollyhockeysticks **Miss S. West**
20 **SLY MADAM**, 4, b f Sixties Icon—Tanojin (IRE) **Miss S. West**
21 **STYLE COUNCIL (IRE)**, 6, b m Most Improved (IRE)—Open Your Heart (IRE) **The Shout to the Top Syndicate**
22 **SUNLINE**, 4, b f Cityscape—Symboline
23 **ZOLTAN VARGA**, 8, b g Sayif (IRE)—Mar Blue (FR) **Mr Ashley Head & Mr Garry Dreher**
24 **ZYRA'S LIONESS**, 4, b f Sixties Icon—Follow The Faith **Mr R. Vaughan**

Other Owners: Mr M. L. Albon, Barry Walters Farms, Mr B. R. D. Beesley, M. R. Channon, Mr G. C. Dreher, Mr D. T. Harper-Jones, Mr A. J. Head, Mr R. J. Heal, Mr I. E. Poysden, Mr R. Vaughan, Miss S. West.

Assistant Trainer: Megan Poulton.

NH Jockey: Marc Goldstein.

---

551   MR SIMON WEST, Middleham
Postal: **14A St Alkeldas Road, Middleham, Leyburn, North Yorkshire, DL8 4PW**
Contacts: **MOBILE 07855 924529**
EMAIL simonwest21@hotmail.co.uk WEBSITE www.mkmracing.co.uk

1 **AMOOD (IRE)**, 11, ch g Elnadim (USA)—Amanah (USA) **Mr S. G. West**
2 **CASAMARI ABBEY (IRE)**, 8, br g Jeremy (USA)—Sprightly Gal (IRE) **Mr P. C. Bryan**
3 **CRANK EM UP (IRE)**, 11, b g Royal Anthem (USA)—Carrawaystick (IRE) **Mr P. Hothersall**
4 **DORA DE JANEIRO (FR)**, 9, b m Ballingarry (IRE)—Katana (GER) **Mr P. Hothersall**
5 **ELLA NUTRARGILE (FR)**, 8, gr m Kapgarde (FR)—Odile de Neulliac (FR) **Mrs B. Hothersall**
6 **FABULEUX DU CLOS (FR)**, 7, b g Blue Bresil (FR)—Osmazome (FR) **Mr P. Hothersall**
7 **FILOU D'ANJOU (FR)**, 7, b g Maresca Sorrento (FR)—Miss d'Anjou (FR) **Mr P. Hothersall**
8 **GHOSTEEM FLECHOIS (FR)**, 6, gr g Smadoun (FR)—Lesteem (FR) **Exors of the Late J. D. Gordon**
9 **IT'S JUST TOMMY (IRE)**, 9, b g Tikkanen (USA)—Dusty Road (IRE) **Mr S. G. West**
10 **JIMINY CRICKET (IRE)**, 11, ch g Golden Lariat (USA)—Lady Smurfette (IRE) **Exors of the Late J. D. Gordon**
11 **KODI KOH (IRE)**, 7, b m Kodiac—Laywaan (USA) **Wild West Racing**
12 **LITTLE CHANCE**, 4, b f Milk It Mick—Slim Chance (IRE) **Mrs B. Hothersall**
13 **MIKE MCCANN (IRE)**, 14, b g Helissio (FR)—Inzamaam (IRE) **Wild West Racing**
14 **NELLIE DEEN (IRE)**, 9, b m Dream Ahead (USA)—Dorothy Dene **Mr S. G. West**
15 **QUERCUS SINUATA**, 4, ch f Garswood—Abonos (IRE) **Mr S. G. West**
16 **SHORT HEAD (GER)**, 7, b m Fastnet Rock (AUS)—Slight Advantage (IRE) **Wild West Racing**
17 **SO YOU THOUGHT (USA)**, 8, b g So You Think (NZ)—Lady of Akita (USA) **Exors of the Late J. D. Gordon**
18 **SUGARPIEHONEYBUNCH (IRE)**, 4, b f Fast Company (IRE)—Jeewana **Wild West Racing & Paul Bryan**
19 **TOUCH KICK (IRE)**, 11, b g Presenting—Bay Pearl (FR) **Hothersall & West**
20 **WESTY'S SUPER MARE (IRE)**, 7, ch m Golden Lariat (USA)—Lady Smurfette (IRE) **Mr S. G. West**

THREE-YEAR-OLDS

21 **FIGHTING CHANCE**, ch c Pastoral Pursuits—Slim Chance (IRE) **Mrs B. Hothersall**

Other Owners: Mr P. C. Bryan, Mrs B. Hothersall, Mr P. Hothersall, Mr D. Howarth, Mr S. G. West, Wild West Racing.

---

552   MR DAVID WESTON, West Overton
Postal: **c/o Flintstone Stud, West Overton, Marlborough, Wiltshire, SN8 4ER**
Contacts: **MOBILE 07966 641001**
EMAIL flintstone007@icloud.com

1 **ADMIRAL'S SUNSET**, 9, b m Mount Nelson—Early Evening **Miss E. Tanner**
2 **LADY PACIFICO**, 4, b f Sir Percy—Silken Ocean **Miss E. Tanner**
3 **SIX AND OUT**, 4, ch g Sixties Icon—Extremely Rare (IRE) **Miss E. Tanner**
4 **SOLSTALLA**, 10, b m Halling (USA)—Solstice **Miss E. Tanner**

553 MR TOM WESTON, Hindlip
Postal: **Offerton Farm, Offerton Lane, Hindlip, Worcester, Worcestershire, WR3 8SX**
Contacts: **MOBILE 07752 313698**

1 **HOLLOW STYLE (IRE)**, 6, b g Beat Hollow—Carrigmoorna Style (IRE) **Big Winners Big Dinners**
2 **STUMPS OR SLIPS (IRE)**, 5, ch g Getaway (GER)—Queeny's Princess (IRE) **Big Winners Big Dinners**
3 **THE LATE LEGEND**, 9, ch g Midnight Legend—Vin Rose **Mr G. J. Fisher**
4 **YEOMEN WARDER (IRE)**, 5, bl gr g Shirocco (GER)—Quarry Endeavour (IRE) **Mr T. H. Weston**

554 MR DONALD WHILLANS, Hawick
Postal: **Dodlands Steading, Hawick, Roxburghshire, TD9 8LG**
Contacts: **MOBILE 07565 609007**
EMAIL garrywhillans@gmail.com WEBSITE www.donaldwhillansracing.com

1 **BONNY HOUXTY**, 9, b m Native Ruler—Izons Croft **Mr W. M. Aitchison**
2 **BOTH BARRELS**, 4, ch g Saddler's Rock (IRE)—Red Legend
3 **COWBOY COOPER (IRE)**, 6, b g Frammassone (IRE)—Ball Park (IRE) **D. W. Whillans**
4 **EDEN MILL (IRE)**, 5, ch g Leading Light (IRE)—Mistress Pope (IRE) **J Fyffe & R Bewley**
5 **ELLISTRIN STAR**, 5, b m Passing Glance—Ellistrin Belle **Ellistrin Partnership**
6 **ENEMY AT THE GATE**, 6, b g Fame And Glory—Biondo (IRE) **D. W. Whillans**
7 **ETERNALLY YOURS**, 9, b m Sulamani (IRE)—Well Disguised (IRE) **D. W. Whillans**
8 **GIE IT LALDY**, 5, b gr g Multiplex—Celine Message **Simon & Angela Gillie**
9 5, B m Schiaparelli (GER)—Glenda Lough (IRE)
10 5, B m Black Sam Bellamy (IRE)—Izons Croft **Mr W. M. Aitchison**
11 **KINERTON HILL (IRE)**, 6, b g Kalanisi (IRE)—Gingerlina (IRE) **Simon & Angela Gillie**
12 4, Br gr f Hellvelyn—Lady Fiona
13 **LADY VILLANELLE (IRE)**, 7, b m Shantou (USA)—Definite Deploy (IRE) **Td9 Racing**
14 **MAID OF HOUXTY**, 7, b m Native Ruler—Izons Croft **Mr W. M. Aitchison**
15 **NEIGH BOTHA (IRE)**, 5, b g Doyen (IRE)—Holmshill Gill (IRE) **D. W. Whillans**
16 **NIGHTS IN VENICE**, 6, ch g Midnight Legend—Well Disguised (IRE) **Mr A. J. M. Duncan**
17 **PAPER TIGER**, 6, b m Califet (FR)—Rose Vic (IRE) **D. W. Whillans**
18 **SEE MY BABY JIVE**, 5, ch m Coach House (IRE)—Lady Fiona **Mrs H. M. Whillans**
19 **SHOESHINE BOY (IRE)**, 6, b br g Valirann (FR)—Godlylady (IRE) **Mousetrap Racing**
20 **SO MANY ROADS**, 5, b g Sulamani (IRE)—Spotthestripe **The The Wellfed Boys**
21 **STAINSBY GIRL**, 8, ch m Shirocco (GER)—Charmaine Wood **Mr A. J. M. Duncan**
22 **STOLEN MONEY (IRE)**, 7, b g Prince Flori (GER)—Dark Daisy (IRE) **D. W. Whillans**
23 **TIME FOR HEROES (IRE)**, 6, b g Libertarian—Be Donn (IRE) **D. W. Whillans**
24 **UNDECIDED (IRE)**, 6, b g Sageburg (IRE)—Your Place Or Mine (IRE) **The Buyers Club**

Other Owners: Mr G. Aitken, J. R. Bewley, Mr J. Fyffe, Mrs A. Gillie, Mr S. P. Gillie, D. W. Whillans, Mrs H. M. Whillans, M. Young.

Assistant Trainer: Mr Callum Whillans.

555 MR EWAN WHILLANS, Hawick
Postal: **Newmill On Slitrig, Hawick, Roxburghshire, TD9 9UQ**
Contacts: **PHONE 01450 372350**
EMAIL ewanwhillans1@gmail.com

1 **ABOUTTIMEYOUTOLDME**, 8, ch g Mastercraftsman (IRE)—Mary Boleyn (IRE) **Miss D. Auld**
2 **AIKIDO (IRE)**, 4, b g Dandy Man (IRE)—Quintessenz (GER) **Mrs K. Spark**
3 **AMAZING ALBA**, 6, ch m Helmet (AUS)—Silcasue **John & Liz Elliot**
4 **ARVICO BLEU (IRE)**, 10, b g Arvico (FR)—Sharifa (GER) **Mrs K. Spark**
5 **BATTLE OF WILLS (IRE)**, 6, b g Lawman (FR)—Maidin Maith (IRE) **The Battle of Wills Partnership**
6 **BELLA BLUESKY**, 6, br m Dylan Thomas (IRE)—Lady Bluesky **A. C. Whillans**
7 **BELLA GLENEAGLES (IRE)**, 5, b br m Gleneagles (IRE)—Miss Lacey (IRE) **The Needlebutt Syndicate**
8 **CHEESE AND WINE**, 5, b m Nathaniel (IRE)—Meet Me Halfway **Miss D. Auld**

MR EWAN WHILLANS - continued

9 **COURT BALOO (IRE)**, 11, b g Court Cave (IRE)—Tremplin (IRE) **A. C. Whillans**
10 **CRACKING DESTINY (IRE)**, 9, b g Dubai Destination (USA)—Cracking Gale (IRE) **Mr A. G. Williams**
11 **DESERT QUEST (IRE)**, 4, b g Footstepsinthesand—Waha (IRE) **Whillans, Orr, Spark, Wright**
12 **DEVIL LOCH**, 5, b g Dawn Approach (IRE)—Historian (IRE) **Mrs E. B. Ferguson**
13 **EMPTY QUARTER**, 7, b g Pivotal—Desert Skies (IRE) **Mr W. J. Muir**
14 **FAYLAQ**, 6, b g Dubawi (IRE)—Danedream (GER) **Bjordan,Brianjordan,Sjordan&nmcconnell**
15 **FOLKS LIKE US (IRE)**, 7, b g Sans Frontieres (IRE)—Nia (IRE) **A. C. Whillans**
16 **GRADY GASTON (IRE)**, 4, b c Dawn Approach (IRE)—Hazium (IRE)
17 **GUIDING STAR**, 8, b m Iffraaj—Still I'm A Star (IRE) **A. C. Whillans**
18 **HEAVENTREE (IRE)**, 5, b m Fame And Glory—Savanna Days (IRE) **Mr A. Turnbull**
19 **HOLD THE NOTE (IRE)**, 8, b g Jeremy (USA)—Keys Hope (IRE) **Bjordan,Brianjordan,Sjordan&nmcconnell**
20 **HUNGRY HELEN**, 4, b f Hellvelyn—Rehlaat (USA) **Mr J D Wright & Mrs S Wright**
21 **JORDAN ELECTRICS**, 6, b g Dandy Man (IRE)—Ruby Slippers **Bjordan,Brianjordan,Sjordan&nmcconnell**
22 **JORDAN SOLAR (IRE)**, 4, ch g Gleneagles (IRE)—Fastnet Mist (IRE) **Bjordan,Brianjordan,Sjordan&nmcconnell**
23 **K C BAILEY**, 6, b m Norse Dancer (IRE)—Wild Child Lucy **John & Liz Elliot**
24 **KAIZER**, 7, ch g Nathaniel (IRE)—Perse **Mrs E. B. Ferguson**
25 **KALAHARRY (IRE)**, 10, b g Kalanisi (IRE)—Full Imperatrice (FR) **A. C. Whillans**
26 **KILCONQUHAR**, 5, b g Hallowed Crown (AUS)—Passing Stranger (IRE) **Mr N. Dalgarno**
27 **LIZZIE LOCH**, 6, br m Maxios—Quenched **Mrs E. B. Ferguson**
28 **NEW RHYTHM**, 7, b m Monsieur Bond (IRE)—Social Rhythm **A. C. Whillans**
29 **PITEMPTON POWER (IRE)**, 7, b g Yeats (IRE)—Western Euro (IRE) **A. J. Brown**
30 **RALPHY BOY TWO (IRE)**, 5, b g Gutaifan (IRE)—St Athan **A. C. Whillans**
31 **ROOM AT THE TOP (IRE)**, 7, b g New Approach (IRE)—Baila Me (GER) **Mrs E. B. Ferguson**
32 **SCOTS POET**, 6, b g Yeats (IRE)—Blue Nymph **Distillery Stud**
33 **SIENNA DREAM**, 7, b m Swiss Spirit—Angry Bark (USA) **A. C. Whillans**
34 **TARQUIN STARDUST (FR)**, 7, gr g Great Pretender (IRE)—Turgotine (FR)
35 **TARTAN COOKIE (IRE)**, 6, b g Leading Light (IRE)—Morning Breeze (IRE) **Mrs M. A. Scott**
36 **THE BRORA POBBLES**, 7, b m Helmet (AUS)—Snow Blossom **Mrs L. M. Whillans**
37 **TOPKAPI STAR**, 5, b m Golden Horn—Burlesque Star (IRE) **Mr M. McLafferty**
38 **TOUTATIS (USA)**, 5, b g Karakontie (JPN)—Afleet Lass (USA) **Stuart Hogg Chris Spark**
39 **YOU BIG DOSSER (IRE)**, 6, b g Getaway (GER)—Sharifa (GER)
40 **ZEALOUS (IRE)**, 9, br g Intense Focus (USA)—Velvet Kiss (IRE) **Mrs M. A. Scott**

THREE-YEAR-OLDS
41 **ACT OF PASSION**, b f Mondialiste (IRE)—Silver Act (IRE) **W.Orr C.Spark A.C.Whillans**
42 **ITIRAZ (IRE)**, b g Iffraaj—Taqdees (IRE) **Mrs E. B. Ferguson**

Other Owners: Mrs E. J. Elliot, Mr J. J. Elliot, Mr S. W. Hogg, Mr B. Jordan, Mr B. A. Jordan, Mr S. Jordan, Mrs N. McConnell, Mr W. Orr, Mr C. Spark, A. C. Whillans, J. D. Wright, Mrs S. L. Wright.

---

556   MR SIMON WHITAKER, Scarcroft
Postal: **Hellwood Lane, Scarcroft, Leeds, West Yorkshire, LS14 3BP**
Contacts: **MOBILE 07771 821955**
WORK EMAIL simonwhitakerracing@gmail.com WEBSITE simonwhitakerracing.co.uk

1 **BILLY ROBERTS (IRE)**, 9, b g Multiplex—Mi Amor (IRE) **Country Lane Partnership**
2 **CAMMY (IRE)**, 4, ch g Camacho—Swan Sea (USA) **Lilling Hall Racing**
3 **COUNTRY CHARM**, 4, b f Charming Thought—Alushta **Mrs Y Mee & Mrs E Whitaker**
4 **DAWN BREAKING**, 7, b g Firebreak—Jubilee Dawn **D Gration, G Sutcliffe, N Farman, Jeaton**
5 **JILL ROSE**, 6, ch m Coach House (IRE)—Wotatomboy **J.W.'s Wotafun Club**
6 **LE FILS DE FORCE**, 4, b g Slade Power (IRE)—Hot Wired **Mr K Walters & Partners**
7 **LIBERTY BREEZE**, 4, b f Equiano (FR)—Avon Breeze **Grange Park RacingXVII**
8 **MYTHICAL (FR)**, 5, b g Camelot—Inchinna **Mrs J. Sivills**
9 **PENNY POT LANE**, 9, b m Misu Bond (IRE)—Velvet Band **Mr A. Melville**
10 **ROUND THE ISLAND**, 9, b g Royal Applause—Luanshya **Nice Day Out Partnership**
11 **STONEY LANE**, 7, b g Mayson—Spin A Wish **Mr R. M. Whitaker**
12 **YASMIN FROM YORK**, 6, b m Sixties Icon—Bonnie Burnett (IRE) **Mrs Greta Sparks & Mr Andrew Sparks**

MR SIMON WHITAKER - continued

THREE-YEAR-OLDS
13 LIL BIT OF MAGIC, ch f Spill The Beans (AUS)—Mey Blossom **Mr P. G. F. Ziegler**
14 MISS WILLOWS, b f Outstrip—Wotatomboy **Mr R. M. Whitaker**
15 Bl g Lethal Force (IRE)—Rio's Rosanna (IRE) **Mr James Marshall & Mr Chris Marshall**
16 SPEAR FIR, b f Spill The Beans (AUS)—Tumblewind **Mr R. M. Whitaker**
17 VARIETY ISLAND, b g Spill The Beans (AUS)—Love Island **Grange Park Racing Xvi & Partners**
18 B g Spill The Beans (AUS)—Velvet Band **Mr R. M. Whitaker**

TWO-YEAR-OLDS
19 B g 25/04 Brazen Beau (AUS)—Sweentnessandlight (Aussie Rules (USA)) **Mr R. M. Whitaker**
20 Gr f 05/03 Pastoral Pursuits—Velvet Band (Verglas (IRE)) **Mr R. M. Whitaker**

Other Owners: Country Lane Partnership, Mr A. D. Crombie, Mr N. Farman, Grange Park Racing XV1, Mr D. Gration, Jeaton Ltd, Mr C. R. Marshall, J. R. Marshall, Mrs Y. E. Mee, Mr A. J. Sparks, Mrs G. Sparks, Mr G. Sutcliffe, Mr K. Walters, Mrs R. M. Whitaker, Mr S. R. Whitaker.

557 **MR HARRY WHITTINGTON, Sparsholt**
Postal: **Harry Whittington Racing Ltd, Hill Barn, Sparsholt, Wantage, Oxfordshire, OX12 9XB**
Contacts: **PHONE 01235 751869 MOBILE 07734 388357**
EMAIL info@harrywhittington.co.uk WEBSITE www.harrywhittington.co.uk

1 BREAKING WAVES (IRE), 8, b g Yeats (IRE)—Acoola (IRE) **Colin Peake & Julie Slater**
2 CALIDAD (IRE), 6, b g Califet (FR)—La Feuillarde (FR) **The Original Investors**
3 DOCPICKEDME (IRE), 6, ch g Getaway (GER)—Hard Luck (IRE) **Jockey Club Ownership (SW 2020) Limited**
4 FAIRE PART SIVOLA (FR), 7, b g Noroit (GER)—Lettre d'Estruval (FR) **Old Gold Racing 6**
5 FITZ IN (IRE), 6, b g Getaway (GER)—Tastytimes (IRE) **J & Starters Orders**
6 FRANIGANE (FR), 7, ch g Coastal Path—Nobless d'Aron (FR) **Edgedale & Robinson**
7 GALUDON (FR), 6, b g Saddler Maker (IRE)—Nobless d'Aron (FR) **The Queue Partnership**
8 HARRY'S HOTTIE (IRE), 5, b m Cloudings (IRE)—Really Royale (FR) **The Atkin Family**
9 HE KNOWS BETTER (IRE), 4, ch g Jet Away—She Knows Best (IRE) **Isobel & Julie Fowler**
10 ICED TEA, 5, br m Sageburg (IRE)—Stone Light (FR) **Mr D. J. Burke**
11 JUNIPER, 8, b m Malinas (GER)—Prescelli (IRE) **Gin n It**
12 MANY DOVES, 5, b g Multiplex—Clover Dove **G. R. Prest**
13 OLD PAINLESS (IRE), 6, b g Imperial Monarch (IRE)—Baby Goose (IRE) **The Racing Demon Partnership**
14 POLDARK CROSS (IRE), 7, b g Shantou (USA)—Diaconate (IRE) **The Racing Demons**
15 RAFFLES GITANE (FR), 5, b m Kapgarde (FR)—Gitane du Berlais (FR) **Mr Simon Munir & Mr Isaac Souede**
16 ROGUE QUEEN (IRE), 4, b f Malinas (GER)—Menepresents (IRE) **The Rogues Gallery**
17 4, B g Champs Elysees—Romantic Fashion (IRE)
18 RULING DE ROOST (IRE), 6, b g Rule of Law (USA)—Silent Memory (IRE)
19 SAVE FACE (FR), 6, b g Planteur (IRE)—Queen Dream (FR)
20 SEDDON (IRE), 9, b g Stowaway—Andreas Benefit (IRE) **McNeill Family Ltd**
21 SHEILA NASH (IRE), 7, b m Flemensfirth (USA)—Hollygrove Rumba (IRE) **Mr C. T. Nash**
22 SHORE SHANTY (IRE), 7, b m Shantou (USA)—Close To Shore (IRE) **A Holt J Robinson I Macnabb & C Clark**
23 TORIGNI (FR), 6, b g Palace Episode (USA)—Princesse Stesa (FR) **Mr Simon Munir & Mr Isaac Souede**
24 TRANSFER FRIENDLY (IRE), 6, b g Mahler—Ballynagall (IRE) **Lead The Way Syndicate**
25 YOUNG BULL (IRE), 8, b g Dubai Destination (USA)—Jane Hall (IRE) **Nash & Webb**

Other Owners: Mr C. N. Clark, Mr T. P. Clover, Mr J. W. Edgedale, Mr A. R. Elliott, Mrs J. G. Emerson, Mrs J. A. Fowler, Mr A. Holt, Mr B. L. Little, Mr K. Little, Mr I. Macnabb, S. E. Munir, Mr C. T. Nash, Mr C. Peake, Mr J. D. Robinson, Mr P. J. Robinson, Mrs J. E. Slater, Mr I. Souede, The Under Starters Orders Syndicate, Mr C. Underwood, Mrs S. H. Underwood, Exors of the late Mr H. J. M. Webb, Mrs I. M. Webb.

Assistant Trainer: Joe Quintin.

NH Jockey: Harry Bannister.

558 MR MICHAEL WIGHAM, Newmarket
Postal: Hamilton Stables, Hamilton Road, Newmarket, Suffolk, CB8 7JQ
Contacts: PHONE 01638 668806 MOBILE 07831 456426
EMAIL michaelwigham@hotmail.co.uk WEBSITE www.michaelwighamracing.co.uk

1 COASE, 5, b g Zoffany (IRE)—Sharnberry D Hassan & Jerry Stevens
2 DEPUTISE, 6, b g Kodiac—Dolly Colman (IRE) Mr Glenn Simons & Id Heerowa
3 EGRECIO, 6, b g Intello (GER)—Aspiring Diva (USA) Five Of Us & Michael Wigham
4 EXCELINTHEJUNGLE (IRE), 6, b g Bungle Inthejungle—Kannon Ms I. D. Heerowa
5 FEMININE FELICITY, 5, b m Dawn Approach (IRE)—Emirates Holidays (IRE) Glenn Simons & Michael Wigham
6 LOUGH CUTRA, 5, b g Oasis Dream—Zulema Mr P. Trainor
7 MUJID (IRE), 7, b g Frankel—Bethrah (IRE) Glenn Simons & Jerry Stevens
8 MY TARGET (IRE), 11, b g Cape Cross—Chercheuse (USA) G Linder,M Wigham,J Williams,A Dearden
9 POOL FUND (IRE), 5, b m Tagula (IRE)—Perfect Pursuit M. Wigham
10 SANAADH, 9, ch g Exceed And Excel (AUS)—Queen's Logic (IRE) M. Wigham, G.D.J. Linder, S Hassiakos
11 SEPTEMBER POWER (IRE), 5, b m Mastercraftsman (IRE)—Lisanor The Gin & Tonic Partnership
12 SMOKE WITHOUT FIRE, 4, ch f Lethal Force (IRE)—Kelowna (IRE) M. Wigham
13 THE YELLOW MINI, 4, b f Cannock Chase (USA)—Cheap N Chic Mr P. J. Edwards
14 VERNE CASTLE, 9, ch g Sakhee's Secret—Lochangel M. Wigham

THREE-YEAR-OLDS

15 STORM ASSET, b g Postponed (IRE)—Clear Water (IRE) Mr T. Akman

Other Owners: Mr C. T. Appleton, Mr A. Dearden, Mr P. J. Edwards, Five of Us, D. Hassan, S. Hassiakos, Ms I. D. Heerowa, G. D. J. Linder, Mr G. Simons, Mr J. Stevens, Mr D. Tate, M. Wigham, Mr J. B. Williams.

Assistant Trainer: Sharon Kenyon.

559 MR CHRISTIAN WILLIAMS, Bridgend
Postal: Ogmore Farm, Ogmore-By-Sea, Bridgend, Mid Glamorgan, CF32 0QP
HOME EMAIL christianrpwilliams@gmail.com

1 AYE AYE CHARLIE, 10, b g Midnight Legend—Trial Trip Lawson Statham & Warren
2 BARDEN BELLA (IRE), 6, b m Mahler—Princess Bella (IRE) All Stars Sports Racing
3 CAP DU NORD (FR), 9, br g Voix du Nord (FR)—Qualite Controlee (FR) The Can't Say No Partnership
4 CARRIG COCH (IRE), 5, b g Sea Moon—Carrig Rua Lady (IRE) G. A. Moore
5 CASTING VOTE (IRE), 5, br g New Approach (IRE)—Masarah (IRE) Mr S. R. Middleton
6 DAYDREAM AULMES (FR), 9, b g Linda's Lad—My Wish Aulmes (FR) Ms S. A. Howell
7 DEFUTURE IS BRIGHT (IRE), 8, b g Westerner—Dustys Delight (IRE) The Can't Say No Partnership
8 FIVE STAR GETAWAY (IRE), 8, b g Getaway (GER)—Hapeney (IRE) Carl Hinchy & Mark Scott
9 GOLDENCARD (IRE), 9, b g Golden Lariat (USA)—Flemensfirth Lady (IRE) Deva Racing Value
10 JOEY STEEL (IRE), 9, b g Craigsteel—Tower Project (IRE) Christian Williams Racing Club
11 JONY MAX (IRE), 7, b g Mahler—Supreme Sunday (IRE) Stquintonmauleintplyw'dvordermans-daniel
12 KITTY'S LIGHT, 6, b g Nathaniel (IRE)—Daraiyna (FR) J & Stars Racing
13 LABEI VITESSE, 8, b g Kayf Tara—Labelthou (FR)
14 LIMITED RESERVE (IRE), 10, b g Court Cave (IRE)—Lady Blackie (IRE) All Stars Sports Racing
15 LOUP DE MAULDE (FR), 5, b g Loup Breton (FR)—Onolita Saulaie (FR) J & Stars Racing
16 MAID ON MENDIP, 8, b m Schiaparelli (GER)—Sericina (FR) GDM Partnership
17 MANSOLINE (FR), 6, ch m Brave Mansonnien (FR)—Line Mai (FR) Kate & Andrew Brooks
18 MIDNIGHT SOLDIER (IRE), 5, b g Soldier of Fortune (IRE)—Midnight Macarena Deva Racing Midnight Soldier
19 MODREENEY (IRE), 5, ch g Famous Name—Give Me High Five Mr M. J. Powell
20 MOSSY FEN (IRE), 7, b g Milan—Inch Native (IRE) Carl Hinchy & Mark Scott
21 MOTOWN LAKE (IRE), 6, b g Valirann (FR)—Montello Ms S. A. Howell
22 MUDDLE THINKING (IRE), 8, b g Haafhd—Just Josie Saloop
23 POTTERS CORNER (IRE), 12, b g Indian Danehill (IRE)—Woodford Beauty (IRE)
All Stars Sports, Davies & RacehorseClub
24 POWERFUL POSITION (IRE), 7, b g Mahler—Molly Con (IRE) J & Stars Racing
25 PRIMAL FOCUS (IRE), 8, b g Intense Focus (USA)—Churn Dat Butter (USA)
John & Paul Stanaway & Nicola Reed
26 ROOTLESS TREE (IRE), 7, b g Jeremy (USA)—Miss Compliance (IRE) Boys on the Black Stuff

MR CHRISTIAN WILLIAMS - continued

27 **ROSE KAR (FR)**, 6, b g Spider Flight (FR)—Rose Wells (FR) **Smerdon Tree Services Ltd**
28 **SEE THE EAGLE FLY (IRE)**, 5, ch m Free Eagle (IRE)—Glassatura (IRE) **Sullivan Racing**
29 **STRICTLYADANCER (IRE)**, 8, b g Yeats (IRE)—Feale Dancer (IRE) **Encore Racing**
30 **TAMGHO BORGET (FR)**, 6, gr g Martaline—Ges (FR)
31 **TIK TOK (FR)**, 5, b g Sri Putra—Lamboghina (GER) **Kate & Andrew Brooks**
32 **TIME FOR BELL (IRE)**, 6, b m Mahler—Bell Walks Eve (IRE) **Mr C. S. Hinchy**
33 **UNO MAS**, 8, b g Morozov (USA)—Broomhill Lady **Christian Williams Racing Club**
34 **WAITING PATIENTLY (IRE)**, 11, b g Flemensfirth (USA)—Rossavon (IRE) **Mr R. Collins**
35 **WHAT A MUDDLE (IRE)**, 8, ch g Haafhd—Spatham Rose **Saloop**
36 **WILLIAM EWART (IRE)**, 5, b g Sageburg (IRE)—Romantic Fashion (IRE) **Ms S. A. Howell**
37 **WIN MY WINGS (IRE)**, 9, b m Gold Well—Telstar (IRE) **Ms S. A. Howell**
38 **YOU SAY NOTHING (IRE)**, 7, b g Epaulette (AUS)—Joyride (GER) **Chiefs and a Dragon**

Other Owners: All Stars Sports Racing, Mr R. J. Bedford, Mr A. L. Brooks, Mrs K. L. Brooks, Mr D. Charlesworth, G. Charlesworth, Mr J. J. V. Davies, Equiclub Ltd, Mr C. S. Hinchy, International Plywood (Importers) Ltd, Mr A. James, Ms L. Judah, Mr J. B. Lawson, Mr G. C. Maule, RacehorseClub.com, Mr M. S. Scott, Mr J. D. Simpson-Daniel, Mr M. Smith, Mr M. G. St Quinton, Mr N. J. Statham, Ms C. J. Vorderman, Mr M. K. Warren.

Assistant Trainer: Nicky Williams.

560

MR EVAN WILLIAMS, Llancarfan
Postal: **Fingerpost Farm, Llancarfan, Nr Barry, Vale of Glamorgan, CF62 3AE**
Contacts: **PHONE** 01446 754069 **MOBILE** 07950 381227 **FAX** 01446 754069
EMAIL cath@evanwilliams.co.uk **WEBSITE** www.evanwilliamsracing.co.uk

1 **ALLSET (IRE)**, 4, b g Anodin (IRE)—Not Ready (USA) **Norwester Racing Club & Partner**
2 **ANNIE WICKS**, 5, b m Kayf Tara—Bathwick Annie **Wayne Clifford & Ian Gosden**
3 **ANNSAM**, 7, b g Black Sam Bellamy (IRE)—Bathwick Annie **H. M. W. Clifford**
4 **ARIZONA GLORY**, 6, gr g Universal (IRE)—Phoenix City (USA) **H. M. W. Clifford**
5 **ASTRA VIA**, 7, b m Multiplex—Wou Oodd **Mrs J. Davies**
6 **BALKARDY (FR)**, 5, ch g Balko (FR)—Kalimnos (FR) **Balkardy Breezers**
7 **BALLINSKER (IRE)**, 7, b g Court Cave (IRE)—Brownie Points (IRE) **Gg Thoroughbreds Xii & Partner**
8 **BALLYBREEN (IRE)**, 9, b g Gold Well—Miss Colclough (IRE) **R. E. R. Williams**
9 **BLACKO (FR)**, 6, gr g Balko (FR)—Ascella (FR) **R J Gambarini Racing**
10 **BLUEBERG (IRE)**, 6, br g Sageburg (IRE)—Swell Sister (IRE) **Chris Trigg & Rer Williams**
11 **BOLD PLAN (IRE)**, 8, b g Jeremy (USA)—Kings Orchid (IRE) **Mr & Mrs William Rucker**
12 **BRANDY COVE (IRE)**, 5, b g Getaway (GER)—Gently Go (IRE) **Mr D. M. Williams**
13 **BROOKSWAY FAIR (IRE)**, 6, b g Mahler—Brook Style (IRE) **Opulence Thorougbreds Nh & Partner**
14 **BULLION (FR)**, 9, ch g Full of Gold (FR)—Ryde (FR) **Mrs C. A. Williams**
15 **CAN YOU CALL**, 7, b g Passing Glance—Call Me A Legend **Mr & Mrs William Rucker**
16 **CANFORD LIGHT (IRE)**, 5, b g Canford Cliffs (IRE)—Way of Light (IRE) **Mrs Janet Davies**
17 **CASWELL BAY**, 7, b g Fame And Glory—Lauderdale (GER) **Mr David M. Williams**
18 **CHAMPAGNE RHYTHM (IRE)**, 7, b g Oscar (IRE)—Before (IRE) **Mrs Janet Davies**
19 **COCONUT SPLASH (IRE)**, 7, ch g Stowaway—Presenting Chaos (IRE) **Mr & Mrs William Rucker**
20 **COOLE CODY (IRE)**, 11, b g Dubai Destination (USA)—Run For Cover (IRE) **H. M. W. Clifford**
21 **COURT DANCER (IRE)**, 7, b g Court Cave (IRE)—Windsor Dancer (IRE) **Mrs J. Davies**
22 **COURT ROYALE (IRE)**, 9, b g Court Cave (IRE)—Windsor Dancer (IRE) **Mrs Janet Davies**
23 **CURRENT MOOD**, 7, ch m Sulamani (IRE)—Lambrini Queen **Mr W Corrigan Racing**
24 **DANS LE VENT (FR)**, 9, b g Skins Game—Boreade (FR) **R J Gambarini Racing**
25 **DIAMON DES FLOS (FR)**, 6, b g Balko (FR)—Marie Royale (FR) **Mr & Mrs William Rucker**
26 **EMORELLE (IRE)**, 5, ch m Shirocco (GER)—Flemerelle (IRE) **Mrs C. A. Williams**
27 **ESPRIT DU LARGE (FR)**, 8, b g No Risk At All (FR)—Tuffslolyloly (FR) **Mr & Mrs William Rucker**
28 **FADO DES BROSSES (FR)**, 7, b g Balko (FR)—Nanou des Brosses (FR) **Mr & Mrs William Rucker**
29 **GILWEN GUS**, 5, b g Multiplex—Gilwen Glory (IRE) **Keith & Sue Lowry**
30 **GOLDEN WHISKY (IRE)**, 9, ch g Flemensfirth (USA)—Derry Vale (IRE) **Mr & Mrs William Rucker**
31 **GREEN OR BLACK (IRE)**, 10, gr m Zebedee—Boucheron **Mr M. Rees**
32 **HELIOS DE GRUGY (FR)**, 5, b g No Risk At All (FR)—Diane de Grugy (FR) **Walters Plant Hire Ltd**
33 **HENRY BOX BROWN (IRE)**, 5, ch g Getaway (GER)—Lough Coyne (IRE) **Old Gold Racing 7**

MR EVAN WILLIAMS - continued

34 **HERONORD (FR),** 5, b g Robin du Nord (FR)—Queen of Colours **Hush Hush Partnership**
35 **HOLLY JAMES,** 8, b g Black Sam Bellamy (IRE)—Miss Chinchilla **Spiers & Hartwell Ltd**
36 **HOWDYALIKEMENOW (IRE),** 6, b g Westerner—Jopa (IRE) **Vale Racing 1**
37 **KAYF KOLI,** 4, b g Kayf Tara—Koliakhova (FR) **Mr D. M. Mathias**
38 **KITAWAY (IRE),** 5, b g Getaway (GER)—Kitara (GER) **Mr & Mrs William Rucker**
39 **L'ASTROBOY (GER),** 5, b g Kamsin (GER)—La Martina (GER) **Mr & Mrs William Rucker**
40 **LOCKDOWN LEADER (IRE),** 6, b g Leading Light (IRE)—Holy Vow (IRE) **Mr & Mrs William Rucker**
41 **LOVED OUT (IRE),** 5, b g Requinto (IRE)—Love Thirty **Mrs Janet Davies**
42 **LUSITANIEN (FR),** 6, b g Muhtathir—Easter Rose (FR) **Mr & Mrs William Rucker**
43 **MAC BE LUCKY,** 5, b g Yorgunnabelucky (USA)—Macnance (IRE) **Keith & Sue Lowry**
44 **MACK THE MAN (IRE),** 8, b g Flemensfirth (USA)—Nifty Nuala (IRE) **Mr & Mrs William Rucker**
45 **MISS WEST (IRE),** 5, b m Westerner—Windmillsfirst (IRE) **Mr W. P. Bates**
46 **MISTER SPLASH (IRE),** 5, b g Shantou (USA)—Presenting Chaos (IRE) **Mr & Mrs William Rucker**
47 **MOUSEINTHEHOUSE (IRE),** 8, b g Milan—Mandysue (IRE) **R J Gambarini Racing**
48 **NIKAP (FR),** 8, b m Kapgarde (FR)—Nika Glitters (FR) **W J Evans & S Williams**
49 **NO REMATCH (IRE),** 8, b g Westerner—Loadsofability (IRE) **Mr & Mrs William Rucker**
50 **NOT LONG NOW,** 6, b g Flemensfirth (USA)—Drop of Spirit (IRE) **Mr & Mrs William Rucker**
51 **NOTER LE (FR),** 5, b g No Risk At All (FR)—Omememo Has (FR) **Mrs C. A. Williams**
52 **OLYMPIC HONOUR (FR),** 6, b g Olympic Glory (IRE)—Shamah **Mr R Abbott & Mr M Stavrou**
53 **ON THE QUIET (FR),** 7, b m Ballingarry (IRE)—Royale Sulawesie (FR) **Hush Hush Partnership**
54 **ON TIME (IRE),** 6, b m Dylan Thomas (IRE)—Fly Town (IRE) **R. E. R. Williams**
55 **ONLY THE BOLD (IRE),** 7, b g Jeremy (USA)—Cloghoge Lady (IRE) **Mr & Mrs William Rucker**
56 **OXWICH BAY (IRE),** 10, b g Westerner—Rose de Beaufai (FR) **T Hywel Jones Racing**
57 **PAGEANT MATERIAL (IRE),** 5, b m Soldier of Fortune (IRE)—House-of-Hearts (IRE) **W J Evans Racing**
58 **PETERBOROUGH (IRE),** 9, b g Fuisse (FR)—Peony Girl (IRE) **Norwester Racing Club & Partner**
59 **PRIME PRETENDER,** 7, b g Great Pretender (IRE)—The Prime Viper (IRE) **Mrs Janet Davies**
60 **PRIME VENTURE (IRE),** 11, br g Primary (USA)—Next Venture (IRE) **Mrs Janet Davies**
61 **QUOI DE NEUF (FR),** 8, b g Anzillero (GER)—Qualite Controlee (FR) **Mr & Mrs William Rucker**
62 **RING THE MOON,** 8, b g Spanish Moon (USA)—Get The Ring (FR) **W J. Evans**
63 **ROCAMBOLAS (FR),** 5, b g Muhtathir—Trudente (FR) **Mr & Mrs William Rucker**
64 **SABBATHICAL (FR),** 7, b g Sunday Break (JPN)—Ulcy Pressive (FR) **R. E. R. Williams**
65 **SECRET REPRIEVE (IRE),** 8, b g Flemensfirth (USA)—Oscar's Reprieve (IRE) **Mr & Mrs William Rucker**
66 **SILVER STREAK (IRE),** 9, gr g Dark Angel (IRE)—Happy Talk (IRE) **Mr T. L. Fell**
67 **SOCIAL CITY,** 6, b g Cityscape—Society Rose **H. M. W. Clifford**
68 **SONNEMOSER (IRE),** 5, b g Great Pretender (IRE)—Rainallday (IRE) **Mr & Mrs William Rucker**
69 **SPIDER CULLEN (IRE),** 9, b g Craigsteel—Carrolleena (IRE) **Mb Racing**
70 **STATE CROWN (IRE),** 5, ch g New Approach (IRE)—Patroness **Six Franks**
71 **SUPREME ESCAPE (IRE),** 8, b g Milan—Silent Whisper (IRE) **Walters Plant, Spiers & Hartwell, Pt Eng**
72 **THE BOAT (IRE),** 6, b g Dylan Thomas (IRE)—Whenever Wherever (IRE) **W J Evans Racing**
73 **THE LAST DAY (IRE),** 10, b g Oscar (IRE)—The Last Bank (IRE) **Mr & Mrs William Rucker**
74 **THREE CLIFFS BAY (GER),** 4, b g Jukebox Jury (IRE)—The Beauty (GER) **Mr D. M. Williams**
75 **TO BE SURE,** 7, b g Sulamani (IRE)—Egretta Island (IRE) **T Hywel Jones Racing**
76 **TREASURE DILLON (IRE),** 8, b g Sans Frontieres (IRE)—Treasure Trix (IRE) **Mr R Abbott & Mr M Stavrou**
77 **VIANS HILL (IRE),** 5, br g Sageburg (IRE)—Carleys Flight (IRE) **R. E. R. Williams**
78 **VOODOO DOLL (IRE),** 9, b g Getaway (GER)—Voodoo Magic (GER)
79 **WALKINTHEWOODS (IRE),** 5, b g Walk In The Park (IRE)—Mercy Mission **Vale Racing 1**
80 **WINDS OF FIRE (USA),** 7, b g Kitten's Joy (USA)—Laureldean Gale (USA) **Mr T. L. Fell**

THREE-YEAR-OLDS

81 **QUICKDRAWMCGRAW (IRE),** b g Kodi Bear (IRE)—Silk Affair (IRE) **Mrs Janet Davies**

Other Owners: R. J. Abbott, Mr J. M. Basquill, Mr M. Bilton, H. M. W. Clifford, Mr W. Corrigan, Mrs J. Davies, W. J. Evans, Mr E. H. M. Frost, GG Thoroughbreds XII, Mr R. J. Gambarini, Mr G. Gill, Mr I. F. Gosden, Mr T. H. Jones, Mr A. Lobo, Mr D. G. Long, K. R. Lowry, Mrs S. B. Lowry, W. J. G. Morse, Norwester Racing Club, Opulence Thoroughbreds NH, P T Civil Engineering Ltd, Spiers & Hartwell Ltd, M. Stavrou, Mr K. J. Strangeway, Mr C. Trigg, Vale Racing, Walters Plant Hire Ltd, Mrs C. A. Williams, Mr D. M. Williams, R. E. R. Williams, Mr S. Williams.

Assistant Trainer: Cath Williams.

NH Jockey: Conor Ring, Adam Wedge. **Conditional Jockey:** Isabel Williams.

561 MR IAN WILLIAMS, Alvechurch
Postal: **Dominion Racing Stables, Seafield Lane, Alvechurch, Birmingham, B48 7HL**
Contacts: **PHONE 01564 822392 MOBILE 07976 645384 FAX 01564 829475**
EMAIL info@ianwilliamsracing.com WEBSITE www.ianwilliamsracing.com

1 **ABEL TASMAN,** 8, b g Mount Nelson—Helena Molony (IRE) **Mr I. Furlong**
2 **AILES D'AMOUR (IRE),** 7, gr g Winged Love (IRE)—Ally Rose (IRE) **Mr A. Cocum**
3 **ALMOST GOLD (IRE),** 9, b g Gold Well—Shining Lights (IRE) **Mr S. Cox**
4 **ANGELS LANDING (IRE),** 4, b f Fascinating Rock (IRE)—Kalinka Malinka (IRE) **The Piranha Partnership**
5 **ANIMAL INSTINCT,** 5, ch h Leroidesanimaux (BRZ)—Alea Iacta **The JAM Partnership**
6 **AQWAAM,** 4, gr g Sea The Stars (IRE)—Aghaany **A. Ownership Change Pending**
7 4, B f Sixties Icon—Asinara (GER) **Bolingbroke, Mickley**
8 **AUTUMN WAR (IRE),** 7, ch g Declaration of War (USA)—Autumn Leaves (FR) **The JAM Partnership**
9 **BEAUTY OF FREEDOM (IRE),** 4, b f Free Eagle (IRE)—The Last Alzao (IRE) **TopSpeed Thoroughbreds**
10 7, B g Oscar (IRE)—Bobs Star (IRE) **John Nicholls Racing**
11 **BOY IN THE BAR,** 11, ch g Dutch Art—Lipsia (IRE) **First Chance Racing**
12 **BUXTED TOO,** 4, ch g Iffraaj—Much Promise **Buxted Partnership**
13 **BYRON FLYER,** 11, b g Byron—Nursling (IRE) **Mr A. Cocum**
14 **C'MON KENNY,** 6, gr g Dutch Art—Bite of The Cherry **Ne-Chance**
15 **C'MON SHARPY (IRE),** 6, b g Sageburg (IRE)—Shining Lights (IRE) **Ne Chance & Partner Iii**
16 **CAP FRANCAIS,** 6, b g Frankel—Miss Cap Ferrat **Coomes Parmar Turner Dale**
17 **CAVE BLEU,** 4, b c Arvico (FR)—Glan Lady (IRE) **Mrs C. L. Voce**
18 **CHEROKEE DANCE (USA),** 4, b br f Honor Code (USA)—Keowee Clai (USA) **I. P. Williams**
19 **CHICA BOOM (IRE),** 4, ch g Tamayuz—Chicane **John Nicholls Racing**
20 **CHOSEN SHANT (IRE),** 6, b br m Shantou (USA)—Ratheniska (IRE) **Golden Equinox Racing**
21 **DONYA (IRE),** 4, b f Dawn Approach (IRE)—Ibiza Dream **I. P. Williams**
22 **DRAGON BONES,** 7, br m Passing Glance—Sainte Kadette (FR) **The DTTW Partnership**
23 **DYNALI,** 6, b g Dansili—Lunar Phase (IRE) **Golden Equinox Racing**
24 **EAST ASIA (IRE),** 7, b g Iffraaj—Chan Tong (BRZ) **Mr S. Hashish**
25 **ENEMY,** 5, b g Muhaarar—Prudenzia (IRE) **Tracey Bell & Caroline Lyons**
26 **ERNESTO (GER),** 7, ch g Reliable Man—Enrica **Midtech**
27 **FAMOUS LAST WORD (IRE),** 7, b br g Fame And Glory—Presenting Tara (IRE) **Mr T. J. & Mrs H. Parrott**
28 **FIFRELET (FR),** 7, br g Diamond Boy (FR)—Unique Star (FR) **ASD Contracts Ltd**
29 **GENERATOR CITY (IRE),** 9, b g Primary (USA)—Sabbatical (IRE) **Dove Valley Holdings Ltd**
30 **GETAWAY MISSION (IRE),** 8, b g Getaway (GER)—Emeranna (IRE) **Andrew Dick & Steve Roberts**
31 6, B g Sholokhov (IRE)—Ginger Bazouka (FR)
32 **GLEN AGAIN (IRE),** 4, b g Gleneagles (IRE)—Four Eleven (CAN) **Teme Valley**
33 **GOD OF LIGHT (IRE),** 7, ch g Sholokhov (IRE)—Chiltern Hills (IRE) **I. P. Williams**
34 **HALIPHON,** 5, b g Showcasing—Harem Lady (FR) **I. P. Williams**
35 **HEAD ON (IRE),** 6, br g Robin des Champs (FR)—Miss Baloo (IRE) **Mr S. Cox**
36 **HIGHLAND DRESS,** 6, b g Shamardal (USA)—Crinoline (USA) **Coomes Parmar Turner Dale**
37 **HYDROPLANE (IRE),** 6, b g Pour Moi (IRE)—Walk On Water **John Nicholls Racing**
38 **INDIANAPOLIS (IRE),** 7, b g Galileo (USA)—Adoration (USA) **Mr K. McKenna**
39 **IVAHUNCH,** 5, b g Ivawood (IRE)—Galante (FR) **Strictly Legal**
40 **JAYTEE,** 7, ch g Schiaparelli (GER)—Archway Copse **J. Tredwell**
41 **JUSTUS (IRE),** 4, ch g Galileo (IRE)—Landikusic (IRE) **Coomes Parmar Turner Dale**
42 **KANGAROO POINT (IRE),** 5, b g Australia—Magic Hale (IRE) **Ne Chance & Partner Iii**
43 **KIMBERLEY EVE,** 4, b f Black Sam Bellamy (IRE)—Ma Councha (FR) **Mr K. M. Harris**
44 **LIBERATED LAD,** 4, b g Muhaarar—Puzzler (IRE) **Mr S. Coomes**
45 **LINDAKA (FR),** 5, b g Linda's Lad—Chamanka (FR) **A. Stennett**
46 **MALAKAHNA (FR),** 4, b f Manduro (GER)—Alakhana (FR) **Macable Partnership**
47 4, B g Great Pretender (IRE)—Mewstone **The Ferandlin Peaches**
48 **MICHAEL'S MOUNT,** 9, ch g Mount Nelson—Dumnoni **Andrew Dick & Mark Dennis**
49 **MINELLA CHOICE (IRE),** 6, b g Beat Hollow—Termsconditonsaply (IRE) **The DTTW Partnership**
50 **MOKAATIL,** 7, br g Lethal Force—Moonlit Garden (IRE) **Midtech**
51 **MOUNT SOUTH (IRE),** 5, b g Well Chosen—Hurry Up Helen (IRE)
52 **MR TRICK (IRE),** 4, b g Kodiac—Alkhawarah (USA)
53 **MRS DIBBLE (FR),** 4, b br f Dabirsim (FR)—Ossun (FR) **Mr A. Grant**
54 **MRS DOUBTFIRE,** 8, b m Jeremy (USA)—Monsignorita (IRE) **M. C. Denmark**
55 **MUSTARRID (IRE),** 8, b g Elzaam (AUS)—Symbol of Peace (IRE) **Mr A. Dale**
56 **NIGHT FORCE (IRE),** 4, gr g Dark Angel (IRE)—Sleeping Beauty (IRE)

MR IAN WILLIAMS - continued

57 **OCEAN VOYAGE (IRE)**, 7, b m Most Improved (IRE)—Minshar **Please Run Faster**
58 **OF ALL THE GREYS**, 5, gr g Trans Island—Grey Lady Grey **Mick Fitzgerald Racing Club**
59 **OI THE CLUBB OI'S**, 7, gr g Champs Elysees—Red Boots (IRE) **The Albatross Club**
60 **ONE MORE FLEURIE (IRE)**, 8, b g Mustameet (USA)—Auburn Cherry (IRE) **Mr K. McKenna**
61 **OUR IDIC BOY (IRE)**, 8, b g Royal Anthem (USA)—Next Best Thing (IRE) **Mr K. McKenna**
62 **PADDY THE CHEF (IRE)**, 7, b g Dandy Man (IRE)—The Reek **Mr & Mrs H. Parmar**
63 **PARTY BUSINESS (IRE)**, 6, b g Shantou (USA)—Marias Dream (IRE) **Eventmasters Racing**
64 **PSYCHEDELIC ROCK**, 11, b g Yeats (IRE)—Gemini Lucy (IRE) **John Nicholls Racing**
65 **RED INFANTRY (IRE)**, 12, ch g Indian River (FR)—Red Rover **Mr R. Little**
66 **REGABY (IRE)**, 7, b g Stowaway—Anjum (USA) **P. Kelly**
67 **RESET BUTTON**, 4, b g Yorgunnabelucky (USA)—Reset City **R. S. Brookhouse**
68 **RESTORER**, 10, gr g Mastercraftsman (IRE)—Moon Empress (FR) **Dr M. B. Q. S. Koukash**
69 **ROBELLI (IRE)**, 7, b g Getaway (GER)—Marhab Dancer (IRE) **John Nicholls Racing**
70 **ROCK CHANT (USA)**, 4, b g Flintshire—High Chant (USA)
71 **RON BURGUNDY (IRE)**, 5, ch g Presenting—Diklers Oscar (IRE) **The DTTW Partnership**
72 **SAINT RIQUIER (FR)**, 4, gr c Le Havre (IRE)—Salamon **Mr D. W. Fox**
73 **SHIP OF THE FEN**, 7, b g Champs Elysees—Ruffled **Midtech, McKenna, Macable**
74 **SOMETIMES ALWAYS (IRE)**, 7, b g Presenting—Noras Fancy (IRE) **Mr S. Cox**
75 **SOPHOSC (IRE)**, 6, ch g Society Rock (IRE)—Ichiuma (USA) **The Harefield Racing Club**
76 **SPEEDO BOY (FR)**, 8, ch g Vision d'Etat (FR)—Shamardanse (USA) **Mr P. R. Williams**
77 **STARLYTE (IRE)**, 5, b m Sir Percy—Virevolle (FR) **Mr A. Grant**
78 **TEEMLUCKY**, 6, ch m Yorgunnabelucky (USA)—Dream Esteem **R. S. Brookhouse**
79 **THUNDER FLASH**, 5, b g Night of Thunder (IRE)—Sultanah Heyam **John Nicholls Racing**
80 **TIDE TIMES (IRE)**, 8, gr g Vinnie Roe (IRE)—Lady Wagtail (IRE) **The DTTW Partnership**
81 **TIKK TOCK BOOM (IRE)**, 10, gr m Tikkanen (USA)—Henrietta (IRE) **The Ferandlin Peaches**
82 **TRIBAL COMMANDER**, 6, gr g Intikhab (USA)—Jessica Ennis (USA) **Mr T. J. & Mrs H. Parrott**
83 **TWOJAYSLAD**, 13, b g Kayf Tara—Fulwell Hill **J. Tredwell**
84 **TYPICAL MAN**, 4, b g Territories (IRE)—Just Like A Woman **Mascalls Stud**
85 **VISSANI (FR)**, 4, gr g Dariyan (FR)—Visorama (IRE) **Ms S. A. Howell**
86 **WALK IN THE STORM (IRE)**, 5, b m Walk In The Park (IRE)—Mucho Macabi (IRE) **TopSpeed Thoroughbreds**
87 **ZEALANDIA (FR)**, 5, b g Sea The Moon (GER)—Belle Ambre

THREE-YEAR-OLDS

88 **ALWAJD (IRE)**, gr f Dark Angel (IRE)—Relation Alexander (IRE)
89 **BATTANI (IRE)**, b g Kodiac—Garra Molly (IRE) **Coomes Parmar Turner Dale**
90 **BUXTED REEL (IRE)**, b g Highland Reel (IRE)—Blue Lightning **Buxted Partnership**
91 **DESERT WILLIAM**, b g Intello (GER)—Desert Kiss **Mr K. M. Harris**
92 **DON BEKAR (USA)**, b g Vancouver (AUS)—Little Sandy (USA) **I. P. Williams**
93 **GYPSY LADY**, ch f Mayson—Reveille **Mr J. D. A. Smith**
94 B g Ardad (IRE)—Highly Spiced
95 B f Australia—Julia Dream **The Albatross Club**
96 **KEMERTON (IRE)**, b g Kodi Bear (IRE)—Moynsha Lady (IRE) **Mr T. J. & Mrs H. Parrott**
97 **KITAAB**, b g Showcasing—Life of Pi
98 B g Garswood—Lady Gibraltar
99 B g Highland Reel (IRE)—Moraine
100 **ONEFORTHEGUTTER**, b c Muhaarar—Rainbow Springs **Tracey Bell & Caroline Lyons**
101 **PERTEMPS DIAMOND**, gr g Dartmouth—Luna June (IRE) **Pertemps Ltd**
102 **RITA'S WISH**, b f Oasis Dream—Lizzie Siddal **I. P. Williams**
103 **SARSONS RISK (IRE)**, b g Caravaggio (USA)—Pink Damsel (IRE) **R. S. Brookhouse**
104 B f Sea The Stars (IRE)—Simple Elegance (USA) **The Albatross Club**
105 **TEAM ENDEAVOUR**, b g Bated Breath—Olympic Medal **Deva Racing Team Endeavour**
106 **TESTING FAITH**, b g Time Test—Midnight (IRE) **Midtech 3**
107 **TYPICAL WOMAN**, ch f Nathaniel (IRE)—Just Like A Woman **Mascalls Stud**

TWO-YEAR-OLDS

108 B c 15/03 Ulysses (IRE)—Giennah (IRE) (Tamayuz) (45000)
109 **I STILL HAVE FAITH**, b c 12/04 Expert Eye—The Thrill Is Gone (Bahamian Bounty) (43810) **R. S. Brookhouse**

Other Owners: Mr G. Anderson, Mr A. J. Bell, Mrs T. Bell, Mr P. R. Billington, Blythe Stables LLP, Mr L. A. Bolingbroke, S. Cannon, Mr S. Coomes, Mr A. Dale, Mr M. N. Dennis, Mr A. I. Derry, Mr J. I. Derry, Mr A. D. Dick, Mr N. D. Ford, Mr C. Hall, Ms

MR IAN WILLIAMS - continued

R. J. Harris, B. M. W. Hearn, Mrs S. J. Hearn, Mr M. Hilton, R. Kent, Mrs C. Lyons, Mr F. Lyons, Fergus & Caroline Lyons, Mr S. Mackintosh, Mr C. R. Mander, Mr K. McKenna, Ne-Chance, Mr J. A. M. Nicholls, Mrs J. J. Nicholls, Mr H. Parmar, Mrs K. Parmar, Mrs H. Parrott, T. J. Parrott, Mr M. Rapley, Mr S. Roberts, Mr S. W. Turner, I. P. Williams.

MRS JANE WILLIAMS, South Molton
Postal: **Culverhill Farm, George Nympton, South Molton, Devon, EX36 4JE**
Contacts: **HOME 01769 574174 MOBILE 07977 457350**

1 ADMIRAL BALKO (FR), 5, b br g Balko (FR)—Singaminnie (FR) **Culverhill Racing Club III**
2 AFTER THE FOX, 7, b g Universal (IRE)—Foxglove **You Can Be Sure**
3 AGRAPART (FR), 11, b br g Martaline—Afragha (IRE) **Gascoigne Brookes Barker & Jakeman**
4 AUBUSSON (FR), 13, b g Ballingarry (IRE)—Katioucha (FR) **Mrs J. R. Williams**
5 BALKO SAINT (FR), 5, b g Balko (FR)—Sainte Cupid (FR) **Mrs J. R. Williams**
6 ERICK LE ROUGE (FR), 8, ch g Gentlewave (IRE)—Imperia II (FR) **The Culverhill Racing Club**
7 ESPRIT DE SOMOZA (FR), 8, b g Irish Wells (FR)—Topaze de Somoza (FR) **Chasing Gold Limited**
8 FOLLY GATE (FR), 7, b g Montmartre (FR)—Cate Bleue (FR) **Mrs J Williams & Mr R Stark**
9 FOX PRO (FR), 7, b g Coastal Path—Devise II (FR) **Mrs J. R. Williams**
10 GALICE MACALO (FR), 6, b m Saddler Maker (IRE)—Victoire de Forme (FR) **Culverhill Racing Club II**
11 GLADIATEUR ALLEN (FR), 6, b g Saint des Saints (FR)—Une Epoque (FR) **Mrs J. R. Williams**
12 HERMES BOY (FR), 5, b g Diamond Boy (FR)—Roche Brune (FR) **The Culverhill Racing Club IV**
13 HONNEUR D'AJONC (FR), 5, b g Diamond Boy (FR)—Fleur d'Ajonc (FR) **J & Jane Williams**
14 ILFONCE (FR), 4, ch g Coastal Path—Une Bile (FR) **Len,Mason,Ray,Nicol,Cowell,Stevens&Booth**
15 IN REM (FR), 7, b g Kapgarde (FR)—Etoile des Iles (FR) **Chasing Gold Limited**
16 MOKA DE VASSY (FR), 4, b g Karaktar (IRE)—Mona Vassy (FR) **Mrs J. R. Williams**
17 MONSIEUR LECOQ (FR), 8, b g Diamond Boy (FR)—Draga (FR) **Knightriders Racing**
18 MOORLAND RAMBLER, 4, b g Telescope (IRE)—Fragrant Rose **Mr R Stark & Mrs J Williams**
19 PATAILLE (FR), 4, ch g Martaline—Panzella (FR) **Gascoigne Brookes Barker & Jakeman**
20 PEPE LE MOKO (FR), 4, b c Saint des Saints (FR)—Jolie Menthe (FR) **Gascoigne Brookes Barker & Jakeman**
21 SAINT SEGAL (FR), 4, b g Saint des Saints (FR)—Bal Celtique (FR) **Culverhill Racing V**
22 SORELLINA ROYALE, 5, b m Kayf Tara—Benefique Royale **Len,Burleigh,Downes,Jess,Jon,Ray,Booth**
23 TEA FOR TWO, 13, b g Kayf Tara—One For Me **Mrs Jane Williams & Mr Len Jakeman**

THREE-YEAR-OLDS

24 JAMINSKA (FR), b f Manatee—Pacifie du Charmil (FR) **Larkhills Racing Partnership III**
25 KAP HORN (FR), b g Manatee—Palma du Charmil (FR)
26 KOOKY (FR), b g Kamsin (GER)—Kotkicha (FR)
27 ROMANCERO LE DUN (FR), b g Spanish Moon (USA)—Uranus Le Dun (FR) **Mrs J. R. Williams**
28 B c Great Pretender (IRE)—Rouvraie (FR)

TWO-YEAR-OLDS

29 INSIDE MAN (FR), b c 28/04 Manatee—Rockburn (FR) (Saint des Saints (FR)) (12755) **Mrs J. R. Williams**

Other Owners: Mr J. Allison, K. Barker, J. N. W. Brookes, D. A. Gascoigne, Mr L. J. Jakeman, KnightRiders, Mr R. Stark, Mrs J. R. Williams.

MR NICK WILLIAMS, South Molton
Postal: **Culverhill Farm, George Nympton, South Molton, Devon, EX36 4JE**
Contacts: **PHONE 01769 574174 MOBILE 07855 450379**
EMAIL nandjwilliams@live.co.uk

1 AIMEE DE SIVOLA (FR), 8, ch m Network (GER)—Neva de Sivola (FR) **Larkhills Racing Partnership IV**
2 FAVORI DE SIVOLA (FR), 7, b g Noroit (GER)—Suave de Sivola (FR) **John White & Anne Underhill**
3 GALAHAD QUEST (FR), 6, b g American Post—Atacames (FR) **Holt, Macnabb, Robinson & Jeffrey**
4 GINGEMBRE MENTHE (FR), 6, ch g Barastraight—Jolie Menthe (FR) **French Gold**
5 HELIOS ALLEN (FR), 5, b g Coastal Path—Silane (FR) **French Gold Racing**
6 HURRICANE SIVOLA (FR), 5, b g Noroit (GER)—Surprise de Sivola (FR) **Mr N. S. L. Williams**

MR NICK WILLIAMS - continued

7 I'M THE DIVA (FR), 4, b f Network (GER)—Sunny Vic (FR) Mr N. S. L. Williams
8 ILIADE ALLEN (FR), 4, b f Rail Link—Atacames (FR) Mr N. S. L. Williams
9 INTERNE DE SIVOLA (FR), 4, b g Noroit (GER)—Kerrana (FR) Mr R. C. Watts
10 KEPLERIAN, 5, b g Telescope (IRE)—Countess Camilla Huw & Richard Davies & Friends
11 LADY GWEN, 4, b f Haafhd—Countess Camilla
12 LE CAMELEON, 7, b br g Great Pretender (IRE)—Countess Camilla The Pretenders & Partner
13 MASKED SPIRIT (FR), 4, ch g Masked Marvel—Locyborg Royale (FR) John White & Anne Underhill
14 MOONLIGHTER, 9, b g Midnight Legend—Countess Camilla Huw & Richard Davies & Friends Racing
15 YGGDRASIL (FR), 5, b g Kapgarde (FR)—Margerie (FR) John White & Anne Underhill

THREE-YEAR-OLDS

16 JAVERT ALLEN (FR), ch g No Risk At All (FR)—Une Epoque (FR) Holtmacnabbrobinsonmiltontuckerweedon
17 JUPITER ALLEN (FR), ch g Castle du Berlais (FR)—Bienvenue Allen (FR) Mr N. S. L. Williams
18 JUST DO IT ALLEN (FR), b g Rail Link—Tromboline (FR) Mr N. S. L. Williams

TWO-YEAR-OLDS

19 EXCELERO (FR), b c 31/05 Castle du Berlais (FR)—Si St Eloi (FR) (Limnos (JPN)) (41667)
                                                          Holt, Macnabb, Robinson & Jeffrey
20 FIDUCIARY DUTY (FR), b g 05/01 Night Wish (GER)—Fadas (FR) (Davidoff (GER))
                                                          Holt, Macnabb, Robinson & Jeffrey
21 KING ALLEN (FR), b c 05/05 Masterstroke (USA)—Atacames (FR) (Dom Alco (FR))
                                                          Holt, Macnabb, Robinson & Jeffrey

Other Owners: Mr T. H. Chadney, Mrs V. J. Chadney, Mr H. G. Davies, Mr R. L. Davies, French Gold, Mr A. Holt, Huw & Richard Davies & Friends, Miss A. Jeffrey, Mr I. Macnabb, Mr C. J. Milton, Mr J. D. Robinson, The Pretenders, Mr A. J. Tucker, Mrs A. Underhill, Mr J. Weedon, Mr A. J. White, Mr N. S. L. Williams.

Conditional Jockey: Chester Williams.

---

564   MR NOEL WILLIAMS, Blewbury
Postal: **Churn Stables, Churn Estate, Blewbury, Didcot, Oxfordshire, OX11 9HG**
Contacts: **PHONE** 01235 850806 **MOBILE** 07887 718678
EMAIL info@noelwilliamsracing.co.uk **WEBSITE** www.noelwilliamsracing.co.uk

1 ANOTHER CRICK, 9, b g Arcadio (GER)—Suetsu (IRE) Mr D. J. S. Sewell
2 BRIERY EXPRESS, 9, b m Rail Link—Blackbriery Thyne (IRE) Helen Plumbly & Kathryn Leadbeater
3 4, B g Vendangeur (IRE)—Contradeal (IRE)
4 CUILLIN (USA), 7, b m Arch (USA)—Zahrah (USA) Mr N. Williams
5 DELIGHT OF DUBAI (IRE), 8, b br m Dubai Destination (USA)—Bonny Hall (IRE) Daniel MacAuliffe & Anoj Don
6 ELLOFAGETAWAY (IRE), 6, b g Getaway (GER)—Ellaway Rose (IRE) Didntt Partnership
7 FARNE (IRE), 8, b m Stowaway—Bonnies Island (IRE) Blyth Currie & Royle
8 GINO WOTIMEAN (USA), 6, b br g Gio Ponti (USA)—Promulgation (USA) Mr D. J. S. Sewell
9 JUST SOPHIE, 4, b f Scorpion (IRE)—Theatre Goer Mr N. Williams, Ms Kate Waddington
10 KALINIHTA (IRE), 8, b g Kalanisi (IRE)—Valamareha (IRE) Mr J Allison & Mr A Allison
11 KISS MY LUCKY EGG, 4, br f Mukhadram—Dayia (IRE) Beswick Brothers Bloodstock
12 LARGY G (IRE), 8, b m Shantou (USA)—G Day Sile (IRE) Mr N. Berry
13 LUCKY ROSE (IRE), 4, b f Soldier of Fortune (IRE)—Shantou Rose (IRE) Allison, Allison, Williams
14 MISS KHARIZMA (IRE), 5, b m Kalanisi (IRE)—Aunt Kate (IRE) Elaine Chivers Racing
15 SOUND OF MUSIC, 7, ch m Universal (IRE)—Sounds Familiar (IRE) Mrs M. L. Luck
16 SPEECH BUBBLE (IRE), 7, b m Well Chosen—Teamplin (IRE) Mr T. D. J. Syder
17 THEDEVILYOUKNOW (IRE), 5, b m Darsi (FR)—Pear Tart (IRE) Mrs S. I. Jeffery
18 TWIN STAR (IRE), 8, ch g Tagula (IRE)—Chronicle Happy Star Partnership
19 VINNIE DEV (IRE), 8, b g Vinnie Roe (IRE)—Nifty Milan (IRE) David J S Sewell & Tim Leadbeater
20 WONDER KING (FR), 4, b g Creachadoir (IRE)—Walk Folie (FR) Mr N. Williams

MR NOEL WILLIAMS - continued

THREE-YEAR-OLDS
21 **MAXIMUM EFFORT,** br g Dartmouth—Theatre Goer **Mr N. Williams, Ms Kate Waddington**

TWO-YEAR-OLDS
22 **BANKSY,** b g 14/04 Passing Glance—Theatre Goer (King's Theatre (IRE)) **Mr N. Williams, Ms Kate Waddington**

Other Owners: Mr J. Allison, S. A. Allison, Mrs H. D. Blyth Currie, Miss C. I. Chivers, Ms E. C. Chivers, Ms L. D. Chivers, Mr Andrew L. Cohen, Mr E. T. D. Leadbeater, Mrs K. B. Leadbeater, Mrs D Ludlow, Mrs H. Plumbly, Mrs H. M. Royle, Mr D. J. S. Sewell, Mr N. Williams.

NH Jockey: Tom O'Brien.

---

565 ## MR OLLY WILLIAMS, Market Rasen
Postal: **Stone Cottage, Nettleton Top, Market Rasen, Lincolnshire, LN7 6SY**
Contacts: **MOBILE 07793 111600**
EMAIL williams.olly@yahoo.co.uk WEBSITE www.ollywilliamsracing.co.uk

1 **CORIANO RIDGE,** 4, b g Al Kazeem—Melodica **Olly Williams Rhys Williams James Hanna**
2 **GAME OF WAR (IRE),** 10, b g Shantou (USA)—Carrig Eden Lass (IRE) **Mr M. Robinson**
3 **GOING NATIVE,** 7, ch m Speightstown (USA)—Latin Love (IRE) **Mr O. R. Williams**
4 **JACK D'OR,** 6, b g Raven's Pass (USA)—Inchberry **Mr M. Robinson**
5 **LINCOLN RED,** 6, ch g Monsieur Bond (IRE)—Roxy Hart **Top of the Wolds Racing**
6 **NORTHERN GENERAL (IRE),** 4, ch g Ivawood (IRE)—Cealtra Star (IRE) **Mrs H. R. Townsend**
7 4, B f Scorpion (IRE)—Our Jess (IRE)
8 5, B m Mountain High (IRE)—Our Jess (IRE)
9 **RASPBERRY,** 6, b m Avonbridge—Spennymoor (IRE) **Olly Williams Rhys Williams James Hanna**
10 **ROMULAN PRINCE,** 4, b g Holy Roman Emperor (IRE)—Nur Jahan (IRE) **D. L. Bayliss**

Other Owners: Mr J. Hanna, Mr T. A. Pocklington, Mr E. Williams, Mr O. R. Williams, Mr R. T. Williams.

Assistant Trainer: Lynsey Williams.

---

566 ## MR STUART WILLIAMS, Newmarket
Postal: **Diomed Stables, Hamilton Road, Newmarket, Suffolk, CB8 0PD**
Contacts: **HOME 01638 560143 PHONE 01638 663984 MOBILE 07730 314102**
EMAIL stuart@stuartwilliamsracing.co.uk WEBSITE www.stuartwilliamsracing.co.uk
TWITTER @Williamsstuart INSTAGRAM stuartwilliams_racing

1 **ABOVE (FR),** 5, b g Anjaal—Broken Applause (IRE) **Mr N. R. Boyden, Mr C. Harrold**
2 **ABSTINENCE,** 4, ch f Lope de Vega (IRE)—Stone Roses (FR) **SRB Equine**
3 **AKKERINGA,** 4, b g Dutch Art—Annie's Fortune (IRE) **Mr G Johnson & Mr J W Parry**
4 **ALHAMMAAM (IRE),** 4, b g Lope de Vega (IRE)—Jadhwah **Mr Glenn Thompson & Partner**
5 **DAWN VIEW (IRE),** 5, b m Dawn Approach (IRE)—Viletta (GER) **Diomed Racing**
6 **DOOLIN DANCER (IRE),** 4, b g Fast Company (IRE)—Anayid **Mrs M. J. Morley**
7 **DWYFRAN,** 5, b m Multiplex—Buddug **Mr J. E. Lloyd**
8 **EQUITATION,** 8, b g Equiano (FR)—Sakhee's Song (IRE) **Mr A Lyons & Mr T W Morley**
9 **EXCELLENT GEORGE,** 10, b g Exceed And Excel (AUS)—Princess Georgina **Mr Stuart Williams & Mr J W Parry**
10 **EXISTENT,** 4, b g Kingman—Entity **Mrs M. J. Morley**
11 **FORD MADOX BROWN,** 4, gr g Oasis Dream—Bruxcalina (FR) **Opulence Thoroughbreds**

MR STUART WILLIAMS - continued

12 **GELLHORN**, 5, b m Showcasing—Lady Correspondent (USA) **Mr W. Slattery**
13 **GOOD HUMOR**, 5, b g Distorted Humor (USA)—Time On **T Mr Reynolds, C Watkins**
14 **GOT NO DOLLARS (IRE)**, 4, b g Showcasing—Canada Water **Mr W Enticknap & Mr B Ralph**
15 **GOT THE MOVES (IRE)**, 4, br f Vadamos (FR)—Johara (IRE) **Mrs M. J. Morley**
16 **HURAIZ (IRE)**, 5, ch g Sepoy (AUS)—Samaah (USA) **Opulence Thoroughbreds**
17 **LIBERTINE BELLE**, 4, b f Helmet (AUS)—Cordial **Mr J W Parry & Partner**
18 **LIGHT OF THUNDER (IRE)**, 4, ch f Night of Thunder (IRE)—Exempt **Mr David N Reynolds & Mr C D Watkins**
19 **LORD NEIDIN**, 5, br g Outstrip—Cosmea **Mr S. C. Williams**
20 **LORD RAPSCALLION (IRE)**, 6, gr g Alhebayeb (IRE)—Simply Topping (IRE) **Mr T. W. Morley**
21 **ONALEDGE**, 4, gr f Toronado (IRE)—Tipping Over (IRE) **Diomed Racing**
22 **PAPA STOUR (USA)**, 7, b g Scat Daddy (USA)—Illaunglass (IRE) **Mr T. W. Morley**
23 **PINNATA (IRE)**, 8, b g Shamardal (USA)—Lavande Violet (GER) **Mr David N Reynolds & Mr C D Watkins**
24 **PRETTY SHIFTWELL**, 4, ch f Equiano (FR)—Holley Shiftwell **J. W. Parry**
25 **PUERTO DE VEGA**, 4, ch g Lope de Vega (IRE)—Exotic Isle **Ballylinch Stud**
26 **QUEEN KAHLUA**, 5, b m Kingman—Kahlua Kiss **Mr R. C. Watts**
27 **REVOLUTIONISE (IRE)**, 6, gr g Lope de Vega (IRE)—Modeeroch (IRE) **T W Morley & Regents Racing**
28 **RHYTHMIC INTENT (IRE)**, 6, ch g Lope de Vega (IRE)—Kerry Gal (IRE) **Proceed Nominees Pty Ltd**
29 **ROYAL BIRTH**, 11, b g Exceed And Excel (AUS)—Princess Georgina **The Morley Family**
30 **SHAMSHON (IRE)**, 11, b g Invincible Spirit (IRE)—Greenisland (IRE) **Mr S. C. Williams**
31 **SOYOUNIQUE (IRE)**, 5, ch g Siyouni (FR)—Adventure Seeker (FR) **Mrs M. J. Morley**
32 **TONE THE BARONE**, 6, ch g Lope de Vega (IRE)—A Huge Dream (IRE) **Mr B Piper & Partner**
33 **TRIBUTO (IRE)**, 4, b g Dragon Pulse (IRE)—Auntie Myrtle (IRE) **Opulence Thoroughbreds**

THREE-YEAR-OLDS

34 **ACCELERANDO (IRE)**, br f No Nay Never (USA)—Keystone Gulch (USA) **Flexford Partners**
35 **AMANDA HUG'N'KISS**, b f Dabirsim (FR)—Percolator **R. Kent**
36 **BEAR PROFIT (IRE)**, b c Profitable (IRE)—Orikawa (FR)
37 **BELLE BOUTEILLE (IRE)**, b f Zoffany (IRE)—Malmoosa (IRE) **Mr J W Parry and Mrs C Shekells**
38 **CHEQUER SQUARE (IRE)**, b g Lope de Vega (IRE)—Newsletter (IRE) **Mr N. R. Boyden, Mr C. Harrold**
39 **CIRCLE TIME (IRE)**, b g Oasis Dream—Maybe Grace (IRE) **Mr J. M. Norris**
40 **DESERT DREAMER**, b f Oasis Dream—Pure Innocence (IRE) **Mr J W Parry and Mrs C Shekells**
41 **DIRTY MARTINI (IRE)**, b f Bungle Inthejungle—Misplace (IRE) **Mr C. J. Haughey**
42 **ELMIRA (IRE)**, b f Dark Angel (IRE)—Hilltop Ranger (IRE) **Mr W. Slattery**
43 **ENZOS ANGEL**, gr g Dark Angel (IRE)—Along Came Casey (IRE) **Opulence T/breds, Regents Racing Et Al**
44 **LORD CHERRY (IRE)**, ch g Profitable (IRE)—Winning Sequence (FR) **Mr B Piper & Mr D Cobill**
45 **MANETTINO (IRE)**, b g Aclaim (IRE)—Step Sequence **Opulence T/breds, Regents Racing Et Al**
46 **MASHKUUR (IRE)**, b g El Kabeir (USA)—Glimmer of Peace (IRE) **Mr M. M. M. Owaimer**
47 **ROSEQUIANO**, b f Equiano (FR)—Warden Rose **The Secretly Hopeful Partnership**
48 **ROYAL SHOWQUEEN**, b f Showcasing—Radio Gaga **Mr Allan Stennett & Mickley Stud**
49 **SEN DING (IRE)**, ch g Mehmas (IRE)—Marol (IRE) **Mr T W Morley & Partner**
50 **SHANKO**, b g Oasis Dream—Beach Bunny (IRE) **Opulence Thoroughbreds**
51 **SHIFTER**, b f Muhaarar—Holley Shiftwell **Chasemore Farm LLP**
52 **SINGAPORE FLYER**, b f Exceed And Excel (AUS)—Miss Marina Bay **Mr R. C. Watts**
53 **VOLOS (IRE)**, b g Belardo (IRE)—Earth Goddess **Star Bloodstock Racing & Partners**
54 **WYVERN**, br g Bated Breath—Miramont **Mrs M. J. Morley**

TWO-YEAR-OLDS

55 **BAILAR CONTIGO (IRE)**, b f 25/04 Gleneagles (IRE)—Slieve Mish (IRE) (Cape Cross (IRE)) (42857)

Mr P Brosnan

56 B c 19/04 Profitable (IRE)—Capote West (USA) (Capote (USA)) (14286)
57 B c 12/02 Fast Company (IRE)—Condensed (Dansili) (30000) **Opulence Thoroughbreds**
58 B c 11/04 Charm Spirit (IRE)—Dainty Dandy (IRE) (Dandy Man (IRE)) (14000)
59 B c 06/02 Muhaarar—Loreto (IRE) (Holy Roman Emperor (IRE)) (110000) **Opulence Thoroughbreds**
60 Ch c 03/04 Exceed And Excel (AUS)—Magic Nymph (IRE) (Galileo (IRE)) (30000) **Opulence Thoroughbreds**
61 Ch c 05/04 Lope de Vega (IRE)—One Spirit (IRE) (Invincible Spirit (IRE)) (80000)

Patrick B Doyle (Construction) Ltd

62 B f 28/03 Oasis Dream—Orpha (New Approach (IRE)) (12000) **Mr J W Parry and Mrs C Shekells**
63 B f 19/02 Expert Eye—Paris Winds (IRE) (Galileo (IRE)) (15000)
64 B c 19/02 Muhaarar—Perfect Blessings (IRE) (Kheleyf (USA)) (48000) **Opulence Thoroughbreds**

MR STUART WILLIAMS - continued

65 B f 27/02 Massaat (IRE)—Piranha (IRE) (Exceed And Excel (AUS)) (40000) **Opulence Thoroughbreds**
66 Gr c 12/05 Oasis Dream (IRE)—Raaqy (IRE) (Dubawi (IRE)) (48000) **Opulence Thoroughbreds**
67 B f 18/02 Fast Company (IRE)—Redoutable (IRE) (Invincible Spirit (IRE)) (19048) **Mr J W Parry and Mrs C Shekells**
68 B f 15/02 Churchill (IRE)—Rosie's Premiere (IRE) (Showcasing) (160000) **Mr R. C. Watts**
69 B c 17/02 Zoustar (AUS)—Spiced (Dansili) (75000) **Mr N. R. Boyden, Mr C. Harrold**
70 B f 14/02 Gleneagles (IRE)—Stellar Surprise (Notnowcato) (45000) **Mr R Levitt, J. W. Parry**
71 Ch c 20/03 Gleneagles (IRE)—Tears In My Eyes (Lilbourne Lad (IRE)) (11429)
72 Ch c 16/05 Showcasing—Zamoura (Azamour (IRE)) (45000) **Opulence Thoroughbreds**

Apprentice Jockey: Muhammad Adeel, Lorenzo Atzori, Luke Catton.

567
MISS VENETIA WILLIAMS, Hereford
Postal: **Aramstone, Kings Caple, Hereford, Herefordshire, HR1 4TU**
Contacts: PHONE **01432 840646** MOBILE **07770 627108**
EMAIL **office@venetiawilliams.com** WEBSITE **www.venetiawilliams.com**

1 ACHILLE (FR), 12, gr g Dom Alco (FR)—Hase (FR) **Mrs V. A. Bingham**
2 ASO (FR), 12, b br g Goldneyev (USA)—Odyssee du Cellier (FR) **The Bellamy Partnership**
3 BALLINGERS CORNER (IRE), 7, br m Jeremy (USA)—Dances With Waves (IRE) **Mr M. G. Roberts**
4 BELAMI DES PICTONS (FR), 11, b g Khalkevi (IRE)—Nina des Pictons (FR) **Hills of Ledbury Ltd**
5 BELLATRIXSA (IRE), 5, gr m Gregorian (IRE)—Aloisi **Mrs S. A. J. Kinsella**
6 BRAVE SEASCA (FR), 7, bl g Brave Mansonnien (FR)—Miss Laveron (FR) **Brooks & Taylor Families**
7 BRESILIANT (FR), 5, b g Blue Bresil (FR)—Ismene (FR) **My Racing Manager Friends**
8 BRIANSTORM (IRE), 10, b g Brian Boru—Coco Moon (IRE) **David & Carol Shaw**
9 BURROWS PARK (FR), 10, b g Astarabad (USA)—La Vie de Boitron (FR)
Venetia Williams Racehorse Syndicate III
10 CEPAGE (FR), 10, b g Saddler Maker (IRE)—Sience Fiction (FR) **The Bellamy Partnership**
11 CHAMBARD (FR), 10, b g Gris de Gris (IRE)—Regina Park (FR) **David & Carol Shaw**
12 CHRISTOPHER WOOD (IRE), 7, b g Fast Company (IRE)—Surf The Web (IRE) **Mrs S. A. J. Kinsella**
13 CLOUDY GLEN (IRE), 9, b g Cloudings (IRE)—Ribble (IRE) **Exors of the Late Mr T. J. Hemmings**
14 COMMIS D'OFFICE (FR), 10, b g Califet (FR)—Pas de Bal (FR) **Mrs C. Maclay**
15 COMMODORE (FR), 10, gr g Fragrant Mix (IRE)—Morvandelle (FR) **Mrs C Watson & Mrs S Graham**
16 COO STAR SIVOLA (FR), 10, b g Assessor (IRE)—Santorine (FR) **Babbitt Racing**
17 CRAAN RUN (IRE), 6, ch m Watar (IRE)—Miss Sinnott (IRE) **B. Hawkins**
18 CRYPTO (IRE), 8, b g Gold Well—Top Lot (IRE) **Mr P. Davies**
19 CUBAN PETE (IRE), 10, b g Flemensfirth (USA)—Gee Whizz (FR) **Mrs J. Jones**
20 DEMNAT (FR), 5, b g Doctor Dino (FR)—Sandside (FR) **Mr P. Davies**
21 DESQUE DE L'ISLE (FR), 9, b g Special Kaldoun (FR)—Naiade de L'Isle (FR) **The Hon Lady M. J. Heber-Percy**
22 DESTINEE ROYALE (FR), 9, b m Balko (FR)—Viana (FR) **Mr C. Boultbee-Brooks**
23 DIDERO VALLIS (FR), 9, b g Poliglote—Oreade Vallis (FR) **Normans, Ramsay, Tufnell & Bishop**
24 DON HERBAGER (FR), 8, b g Saddler Maker (IRE)—Marie d'Altoria (FR) **M Willcocks & V Williams**
25 EASY AS THAT (IRE), 7, b g Sans Frontieres (IRE)—Bell Storm (IRE) **Kate & Andrew Brooks**
26 ECEPARTI (FR), 8, b g Enrique—La Pommeraie (FR) **Mrs S. M. Champ**
27 EDEN FLIGHT (FR), 8, b g Great Pretender (IRE)—Traviata (FR) **Flight Attendants**
28 ELEANOR BOB (FR), 7, b m Midnight Legend—Red And White (IRE) **F. M. P. Mahon**
29 EMINENT POET (FR), 11, b g Montjeu (IRE)—Contare **B. C. Dice**
30 ENZO D'AIRY (FR), 8, b g Anzillero (GER)—Panzara d'Airy (FR) **Dr M. A. Hamlin**
31 ESPOIR DE GUYE (FR), 8, b g Khalkevi (IRE)—Penelope de Guye (FR) **Mrs J. Hitchings**
32 FANION D'ESTRUVAL (FR), 7, b g Enrique—Urfe d'Estruval (FR) **Mr D. C. A. Wilson**
33 FARINET (FR), 7, gr g Lord du Sud (FR)—Mendy Tennise (FR) **Hammond, Coombs T Henriques**
34 FARRANTS WAY (IRE), 8, b g Shantou (USA)—Shuil A Hocht (IRE) **Exors of the Late Mr T. J. Hemmings**
35 FAUTINETTE (FR), 4, b f Bathyrhon (GER)—Fautina (FR) **Dfa Racing (Anderson & Edwards)**
36 FIRST FIGARO (GER), 12, ch g Silvano (GER)—Felina (GER) **Venetia Williams Racehorse Syndicate V**

MISS VENETIA WILLIAMS - continued

37 **FLY SMART (FR)**, 7, b g Day Flight—Abacab (FR) **David & Carol Shaw**
38 **FONTAINE COLLONGES (FR)**, 7, b m Saddler Maker (IRE)—Saturne Collonges (FR) **Mr P. Davies**
39 **FRANCO D'AUNOU (FR)**, 7, b g Saint des Saints (FR)—Jimagine II (FR) **Wrap Up Warm Partnership**
40 **FRENCHY DU LARGE (FR)**, 7, gr g Al Namix (FR)—Quadence de Sivola (FR) **Mr A. O. Wiles**
41 **FRERO BANBOU (FR)**, 7, b g Apsis—Lady Banbou (FR) **Mr P. Davies**
42 **FUJI FLIGHT (FR)**, 7, b g Day Flight—Silverlea (FR) **George & Drury**
43 **FUNAMBULE SIVOLA (FR)**, 7, b g Noroit (GER)—Little Memories (IRE) **My Racing Manager Friends**
44 **GALOP DE CHASSE (FR)**, 6, b g Boris de Deauville (IRE)—Mousse des Bois (FR) **The Winter Partnership**
45 **GAMARET (FR)**, 6, b g Coastal Path—Oppale (FR) **Kate & Andrew Brooks**
46 **GARDEFORT (FR)**, 13, b g Agent Bleu (FR)—La Fresnaie (FR) **Venetia Williams' Stable Staff**
47 **GEMIRANDE (FR)**, 6, b g Al Namix (FR)—Queenjo (FR) **The Bellamy Partnership**
48 **GEORGES SAINT (FR)**, 6, gr g Lord du Sud (FR)—Une Deux Trois (FR) **Mrs C. G. Watson**
49 **GRAND TURINA**, 11, b m Kayf Tara—Cesana (IRE) **Nora's Playmates**
50 **GREEN BOOK (FR)**, 5, b g Authorized (IRE)—Mantissa **Price, Shaw, Boylan I Tagg**
51 **GRIZZLY JAMES (FR)**, 6, b g Montmartre (FR)—Mariyara (FR) **Mr G. Hannon**
52 **HERMES DU GOUET (FR)**, 5, b g Saddler Maker (IRE)—Dolly du Gouet (FR) **My Racing Manager Friends**
53 **HEROS (FR)**, 5, b g Voiladenuo—La Colombe d'Or (FR) **Mr & Mrs Simon E Bown**
54 **HEVA ROSE (FR)**, 5, gr m Saint des Saints (FR)—Wild Rose Bloom (FR) **The Hon Lady M. J. Heber-Percy**
55 **HILL OF TARA**, 5, b g Kayf Tara—Patsie Magern **B B Racing Club**
56 **HOLD THAT TAUGHT**, 7, b g Kayf Tara—Belle Magello (FR) **Mr P. Davies**
57 **HOUI CHERIE (FR)**, 5, gr m Cima de Triomphe (IRE)—Joslaine (FR) **B B Racing Club**
58 **HUNTER LEGEND (FR)**, 5, b g Buck's Boum (FR)—Sience Fiction (FR) **Gaskins Family**
59 **JURYS OUT (IRE)**, 9, b g Witness Box (USA)—No Complaints But (IRE) **Venetia Williams Racehorse Syndicate III**
60 **KAPGA DE LILY (FR)**, 9, ch m Kapgarde (FR)—Louvisy (FR) **Lady Judith Price & Mrs Carol Shaw**
61 **L'HOMME PRESSE (FR)**, 7, b g Diamond Boy (FR)—Romance Turgot (FR) **Dfa Racing (Pink & Edwards)**
62 **LASKALIN (FR)**, 7, b g Martaline—Laskadya (FR) **David & Carol Shaw**
63 **MAKO OF THE GLADE (FR)**, 4, ch g Masterstroke (USA)—Tachibana (USA) **Cliff, Hagenbuch, Siegle & Stevens**
64 **MARTATOR (FR)**, 5, b g Martaline—Tornada (FR) **Camilla Norton**
65 **MOUNTAIN LEOPARD (IRE)**, 7, b g Shantou (USA)—Laurel Gift (IRE) **The Shantou Partnership**
66 **NATTY NIGHT**, 6, b g Nathaniel (IRE)—Danehill Dreamer (USA) **The Gs & Js Partnership**
67 **OTTOLINE**, 6, b m Kayf Tara—Lily Grey (FR) **Ottoline Syndicate**
68 **PASEO**, 6, b g Champs Elysees—Posteritas (USA) **My Racing Manager Friends**
69 **PINK LEGEND**, 8, b m Midnight Legend—Red And White (IRE) **F. M. P. Mahon**
70 **PONIENTE**, 8, br m Shirocco (GER)—Tazzarine (FR) **Hereford Racing Club**
71 **QUICK WAVE (FR)**, 9, b m Gentlewave (IRE)—Magicaldoun (FR) **Mrs S. A. J. Kinsella**
72 **RAMO (FR)**, 5, b g Kapgarde (FR)—Djeville (FR) **C B Compton & L Di Franco**
73 **REALM KEEPER (USA)**, 9, b g Arch (USA)—La Lodola (USA) **Venetia Williams Racehorse Syndicate V**
74 **REALM OF GLORY (IRE)**, 7, b g Fame And Glory—Ebony Queen **Venetia Williams Racehorse Syndicate V**
75 **ROCK OF FAME**, 5, b m Fastnet Rock (AUS)—Familliarity **Caroline Wilson & Lavinia Taylor**
76 **ROYALE PAGAILLE (FR)**, 8, b g Blue Bresil (FR)—Royale Cazoumaille (FR) **Mrs S. Ricci**
77 **SHALAKAR (FR)**, 9, b g Cape Cross (IRE)—Shalanaya (IRE) **Sheila Schwartz & Lady Eliza Mays-Smith**
78 **SNUFF BOX (IRE)**, 11, b g Witness Box (USA)—Dara Supreme (IRE) **Mr J. R. L. Young**
79 **SOLE SOLUTION (IRE)**, 4, ch g Sans Frontieres (IRE)—Bell Storm (IRE) **Sir W. J. A. Timpson**
80 **STAR ACADEMY (IRE)**, 8, b g Stowaway—Academy Miss (IRE) **John Nicholls Racing**
81 **SUBCONTINENT (IRE)**, 10, b g Dubawi (IRE)—Saree **Shire Birds**
82 **SUPERVISOR (IRE)**, 8, b g Flemensfirth (USA)—Coolamaine Star (IRE) **Sarah Williams & Charles Barlow**
83 **TANGANYIKA (FR)**, 4, b g Martaline—Norita Has (FR) **Mrs C. S. Wilson**
84 **TANGO DE JUILLEY (FR)**, 14, b g Lesotho (FR)—Lasalsa de Juilley (FR) **Venetia Williams' Stable Staff**
85 **THE CROONER (FR)**, 7, gr g Martaline—Viva Maria (FR) **The Crooner Partnership**
86 **THE FAMOUS FIVE (FR)**, 4, b c Camelot—Palme Royale (FR) **Mr P. Davies**
87 **TILLY TOUGHNUT**, 5, b m Blue Bresil (FR)—Presenting Diva (IRE) **Mrs S. M. Newell**
88 **TOKYO LIVE (FR)**, 5, gr g Ivory Land (FR)—Tracja (POL) **Old Gold Racing 10**
89 **TOP AND DROP**, 11, b m Kayf Tara—Ismene (FR) **Lady Judith Price & Mrs Carol Shaw**
90 **UN PROPHETE (FR)**, 11, gr g Carlotamix (FR)—Pollita (FR) **Sir W. J. A. Timpson**
91 **VALFORTORE (IRE)**, 4, ch g Olympic Glory (IRE)—Sabaidee (IRE) **Mr L. DI Franco**

NH Jockey: Charlie Deutsch. **Conditional Jockey:** Ned Fox, Hugh Nugent, Shane Quinlan.

Amateur Jockey: Miss Lucy Turner.

568 MRS LISA WILLIAMSON, Tarporley
Postal: **Kelsall Hill Equestrian Centre, Middlewich Road, Tarporley, Cheshire, CW6 0SR**
Contacts: **PHONE 07970 437679**
EMAIL info@lisawilliamson.co.uk WEBSITE www.lisawilliamson.co.uk

1 **BARNEY TOO**, 5, b g Mazameer (IRE)—Ballin Toy Bay **Mrs L. V. Williamson**
2 **BRANDY STATION (IRE)**, 7, b g Fast Company (IRE)—Kardyls Hope (IRE) **A V Wilding (Chester) Ltd**
3 **BRAZEN LADY**, 5, br m Brazen Beau (AUS)—Turin (IRE) **Mrs L. V. Williamson**
4 **CELERITY (IRE)**, 8, ch m Casamento (IRE)—Shinko Dancer (IRE) **Heath House Racing**
5 6, B g Universal (IRE)—Dusky Dancer
6 **INDEPENDENT BEAUTY**, 4, b f Outstrip—Verus Decorus (IRE) **Mr I. Furlong**
7 **ISABELLA RUBY**, 7, b m Power—Scarlet Rocks (IRE) **Heath House Racing**
8 **LA CHICA LOBO**, 5, b m Captain Gerrard (IRE)—Senora Lobo (IRE) **Miss H. J. Roberts**
9 **LOCO LOBO**, 4, ch f Captain Gerrard (IRE)—Senora Lobo (IRE) **Miss H. J. Roberts**
10 **MARIA DI FEBBO**, 5, b m Norse Dancer (IRE)—Sacco d'Oro **Mr P. R. D'Amato**
11 **MRS TIFFEN**, 5, b m Finjaan—Fancy Rose (USA) **A V Wilding (Chester) Ltd**
12 **NEW LOOK (FR)**, 7, gr g Style Vendome (FR)—Tara's Force (IRE) **Heath House Racing**
13 **ORANGE JUSTICE**, 5, ch m Harbour Watch (IRE)—Jord (IRE) **Mr J. E. Lloyd**
14 **RED DEREK**, 6, b g Steele Tango (USA)—Maydream **Mr G. L. Shepherd**
15 **RED STRIPES (USA)**, 10, b g Leroidesanimaux (BRZ)—Kaleidoscopic (USA) **E. H. Jones (Paints) Ltd**
16 **RED WALLS**, 4, b g Heeraat (IRE)—Gemini Glory (USA) **E. H. Jones (Paints) Ltd**
17 **WHITLEY NEILL (IRE)**, 10, b g Shantou (USA)—Maidrin Rua (IRE) **Mrs L. V. Williamson**

TWO-YEAR-OLDS

18 B f 28/04 Bungle Inthejungle—Kardyls Hope (IRE) (Fath (USA)) (15306) **JMH Racing Limited**
19 **MAX STRIPES**, b g 08/04 Heeraat (IRE)—Lily Jicaro (IRE) (Choisir (AUS)) **Miss H. J. Roberts**
20 **PINK STRIPES**, gr f 12/02 Heeraat (IRE)—Mariah's Melody (IRE) (Graydar (USA)) **E. H. Jones (Paints) Ltd**
21 **PINK WALLS**, b f 11/02 Heeraat (IRE)—Gemini Glory (USA) (Tale of Ekati (USA)) **E. H. Jones (Paints) Ltd**

569 MR ANDREW WILSON, Penrith
Postal: **Silver Howe, Orton, Penrith, Cumbria, CA10 3RQ**
Contacts: **PHONE 015396 24071 MOBILE 07813 846768**
EMAIL andywilsonorton@gmail.com

1 **KINGS ECLIPSE (IRE)**, 12, b g Double Eclipse (IRE)—Good Times Ahead (IRE) **Mr A. C. Wilson**
2 **MOORE CLOUDS (IRE)**, 7, gr m Cloudings (IRE)—Wednesday Girl (IRE) **Clouds of Orton**
3 **SAINT JUDE (IRE)**, 9, ch g Presenting—Native Monk (IRE) **Mr A. C. Wilson**
4 **ZANAVI (IRE)**, 5, gr g Champs Elysees—Zindana (IRE) **Mr A. C. Wilson**

570 MR KEN WINGROVE, Bridgnorth
Postal: **6 Netherton Farm Barns, Netherton Lane, Highley, Bridgnorth, Shropshire, WV16 6NJ**
Contacts: **HOME 01746 861534 MOBILE 07974 411267**
EMAIL kenwingrove@btinternet.com

1 **CAMRON DE CHAILLAC (FR)**, 10, br g Laverock—Hadeel **Mr D. G. Wingrove**
2 **EMPIRION (IRE)**, 8, b g Court Cave (IRE)—Della Rose (IRE) **Mr D. G. Wingrove**
3 **HEY PRETTY (IRE)**, 7, b g Society Rock (IRE)—Coffee Date (USA) **Mr D. G. Wingrove**
4 **HOMEGROWNALLIGATOR**, 5, b g Poet's Voice—Samar Qand **Mr D. G. Wingrove**
5 **JAFFATHEGAFFA**, 4, ch g Havana Gold (IRE)—Actionplatinum (IRE) **Mr J. M. Wingrove**
6 **RAHA**, 6, b m Mukhadram—Cefira (USA) **Mr J. M. Wingrove**
7 **SHIFTING GOLD (IRE)**, 6, b m Fast Company (IRE)—Elusive Gold (IRE) **Mr D. G. Wingrove**

Assistant Trainer: Isobel Willer.

571 MR PETER WINKS, Barnsley
Postal: **Homefield, Rotherham Road, Little Houghton, Barnsley, South Yorkshire, S72 0HA**
Contacts: **MOBILE 07846 899993**
EMAIL pwracing@outlook.com

1 **BALLYFARSOON (IRE)**, 11, ch g Medicean—Amzara (IRE) **Barnsley Burglars**
2 **CAVALRY**, 7, b g Exceed And Excel (AUS)—Queen's Best
3 **GROW NASA GROW (IRE)**, 11, ch g Mahler—Dereenavurrig (IRE) **Nature and Science Agriculture Limited**
4 **HARTSIDE (GER)**, 13, b g Montjeu (IRE)—Helvellyn (USA) **Peter Winks Racing Club**
5 **LOUGH SALT (IRE)**, 11, b g Brian Boru—Castlehill Lady (IRE) **Mr J Toes & Mr J O'Loan**
6 **RHYME SCHEME (IRE)**, 5, b m Poet's Voice—Tidal Moon **M. & P. Winks**
7 **SCOTA BESS**, 4, b f Bobby's Kitten (USA)—Gotcha Good (USA) **Mr J Toes & Mr J O'Loan**
8 **SCOTTSDALE**, 9, b g Cape Cross (IRE)—High Praise (USA) **Mr Mr. P W O'Mara & Mr. P Winks**

Other Owners: Mr P Connor, Mr John O'Loan, Mr P. W. O'Mara, Mr M. Simmons, Mr J. Toes, Mr P. Winks.

Assistant Trainer: Ryan Winks.

572 MR ADRIAN WINTLE, Westbury-On-Severn
Postal: **Yew Tree Stables, Rodley, Westbury-On-Severn, Gloucestershire, GL14 1QZ**
Contacts: **MOBILE 07767 351144**

1 **AMLOVI (IRE)**, 9, b m Court Cave (IRE)—Portanob (IRE) **Mr S. R. Whistance**
2 **BARATINEUR (FR)**, 11, ch g Vendangeur (IRE)—Olmantina (FR) **A. A. Wintle**
3 **BLUE HERO (CAN)**, 4, b g Air Force Blue (USA)—Pomarine (USA) **A. A. Wintle**
4 **BOLD SPECTRUM**, 5, b m Assertive—Reengaroga Rainbow (IRE) **Mr G. Ivall**
5 **CREEK HARBOUR (IRE)**, 7, b g Kodiac—Allegheny Creek (IRE) **Mrs H. Hawkins**
6 **ESPINATOR (FR)**, 8, b br g Spider Flight (FR)—Santalisa (FR) **Mr S. R. Whistance**
7 **FLATLEY**, 5, ch g Kendargent (FR)—Premiere Danseuse **Mr D. A. Smerdon**
8 **KEEPER'S CHOICE (IRE)**, 8, ch m Intikhab (USA)—Crossing **Wintle Racing Club**
9 **KENSTONE (FR)**, 9, gr g Kendargent (FR)—Little Stone (FR) **Wintle Racing Club**
10 **MAYSON MOUNT**, 5, b g Mayson—Epernay **Mrs Shelley Tucker Partnership**
11 **MISTY MOUNTAIN (USA)**, 8, gr m Lemon Drop Kid (USA)—Saratoga Fling (USA) **A. A. Wintle**
12 **MY BOY CHARLES (USA)**, 4, b g Air Force Blue (USA)—Sense of Class (USA) **Oracle Horseracing**
13 **ORIENTAL BEAUTY**, 4, b f Oasis Dream—Mitre Peak
14 **PLANSINA**, 7, b m Planteur (IRE)—Sina (GER) **Mr S. Davies**
15 **RED BRAVO (IRE)**, 6, b g Acclamation—Vision of Peace (IRE) **Mr D. A. Smerdon**
16 **RED RIPPLE**, 4, ch g Gentlewave (IRE)—Brackets (USA) **Mrs P Corbett & Mrs A Thomas**
17 4, B f Harbour Watch (IRE)—Rioliina (IRE)
18 **ROCKHAMTOM (IRE)**, 6, b g Leading Light (IRE)—Glencree Rose (IRE) **B. Hawkins**
19 **RUNNING CLOUD (IRE)**, 7, b g Cacique (IRE)—Nimbus Star **Mr A. Jordan**
20 **SEAFORTH (IRE)**, 10, b g Acclamation—Hendrina (IRE) **Wintle Racing Club**
21 **STEVE BACKSHALL**, 5, b g Toronado (IRE)—Black Baroness **A. A. Wintle**
22 **TAWAAFOQ**, 8, b g Showcasing—Gilt Linked **Mr S. R. Whistance**
23 **TEDDY THE KNIGHT**, 7, b g Kayf Tara—Michelle's Ella (IRE) **A. A. Wintle**
24 **THAIS TOIR (FR)**, 7, b g Diamond Boy (FR)—Scotland Act (FR) **Mr S. R. Whistance**
25 **WIFF WAFF**, 7, b g Poet's Voice—Eraadaat (IRE) **A. A. Wintle**
26 **WILD FLOWER (IRE)**, 10, b m Approve (IRE)—Midsummernitedream (GER) **Mrs Shelley Tucker Partnership**

THREE-YEAR-OLDS

27 **GO BEYOND (IRE)**, b f No Nay Never (USA)—Pure Greed (IRE) **Oracle Horseracing**
28 **MIST OF THE DEEP (IRE)**, b f Starspangledbanner (AUS)—Come Softly **Oracle Horseracing**
29 **MONEY TREE (IRE)**, b f Profitable (IRE)—Abhajat (IRE) **Mr S. Davies**
30 **SATELLITE CALL (IRE)**, b c Kodiac—Ball Girl (IRE) **Mr S. Davies**

Other Owners: Mrs P. Corbett, Mrs A. P. Thomas, Mr K. Tucker, Mrs S. M. Tucker.

573 **MISS REBECCA WOODMAN, Chichester**
Postal: **Souters Cottage, 21 East Lavant, Chichester, West Sussex, PO18 0AG**
Contacts: **PHONE 01243 527260 MOBILE 07821 603063**
EMAIL rebeccawoodman@msn.com

1 CLOONEY, 7, b g Dansili—Love Divine **Miss R. E. Woodman**
2 ECHO BRAVA, 12, gr g Proclamation (IRE)—Snake Skin **Miss R. E. Woodman**
3 MILLDEAN FELIX (IRE), 6, br g Red Jazz (USA)—Plausabelle **Miss R. E. Woodman**

THREE-YEAR-OLDS
4 GIN AND TEA, b f Swiss Spirit—Deep Blue Diamond **Burtons Geegees & Budling Bloodstock**

Other Owners: Miss H. Burton, Mrs R. A. Gedge-Gibson.

574 **MR STEVE WOODMAN, Chichester**
Postal: **Parkers Barn Stables, East Lavant, Chichester, West Sussex, PO18 0AU**
Contacts: **PHONE 01243 527136 MOBILE 07889 188519 FAX 01243 527136**
EMAIL stevewoodman83@msn.com

1 BLACK LACE, 7, b m Showcasing—Ivory Lace **The Lacemakers**

THREE-YEAR-OLDS
2 MY BONNIE LASSIE, b f Highland Reel (IRE)—Bonnie Arlene (IRE) **Mrs S. B. Woodman**

575 **MRS CYNTHIA WOODS, Crowborough**
Postal: **Green Hedges Farm, Mark Cross, CROWBOROUGH, East Sussex, TN6 3PA**
Contacts: **PHONE 01892 750567**
EMAIL chaydon@hotmail.co.uk

1 AULD SOD (IRE), 9, b g Court Cave (IRE)—Didn't You Know (FR) **The Abergavenny Arms Sporting Club**
2 GLORIOUS LADY (IRE), 8, b m Fame And Glory—Lady Secret (FR) **Glorious Days Racing**
3 INVINCIBLE CAVE (IRE), 9, b g Court Cave (IRE)—Bespoke Baby (IRE) **Green Hedges Racing**
4 POUCOR, 7, b g Pour Moi (IRE)—Corinium (IRE) **Mr G. Woods**

576 **MR SEAN WOODS, Newmarket**
Postal: **Shalfleet Stables, 17 Bury Road, Newmarket, Suffolk, CB8 7BX**
WORK EMAIL sean@seanwoods.co.uk EMAIL cheryl@seanwoods.co.uk

1 BLACK CAESAR (IRE), 11, b g Bushranger (IRE)—Evictress (IRE) **The Long Furlong**

THREE-YEAR-OLDS
2 APPIER (IRE), b g Holy Roman Emperor (IRE)—Dame Lucy (IRE) **Ignited**
3 BORGI (IRE), b c Anjaad—One Time (IRE) **S. P. C. Woods**
4 BOULIVAR (IRE), ch g Tagula (IRE)—Concra Girl (IRE) **S. P. C. Woods**
5 EIGHT OF DIAMONDS, ch g Ulysses (IRE)—Mirror City **Lifecycle Bloodstock & Brook Stud**
6 ELSAAB, gr f El Kabeir (USA)—Miss Mediator (USA) **The Storm Again Syndicate**
7 FRANCESI (IRE), gr c Caravaggio (USA)—Show Me The Music **S. P. C. Woods**
8 GLORIOUS PEACHES, b f Iffraaj—Anna Sophia (USA) **Teme Valley**
9 GOLDEN KEEPER, b c Pivotal—Celeste **S. P. C. Woods**
10 LITE AND AIRY, b c Twilight Son—Spin Doctor **Mr N. O'Keeffe**
11 MENG TIAN, b g Territories (IRE)—Yearbook **S. P. C. Woods**
12 MUMCAT, b f Bobby's Kitten (USA)—Tell Mum **The Storm Again Syndicate**
13 ONE FOR THE FROG (IRE), b c Dabirsim (FR)—Delicate **Ignited**
14 Ch c Cityscape—Paradise Way **S. P. C. Woods**

MR SEAN WOODS - continued

15 **PRINCESS SHABNAM (IRE),** b f Gregorian (IRE)—Green Vision (IRE) **A. Ali**
16 **SAVVY KNIGHT (IRE),** b g Caravaggio (USA)—Seagull (IRE) **Mr J. C. H. Hui**
17 **SAVVY VICTORY (IRE),** b c New Bay—Highlands Queen (FR) **Mr J. C. H. Hui**
18 **SHAKENOTSTIRRED,** b f Havana Gold (IRE)—So Funny (USA) **Mrs M. Bryce**
19 **SUNNINGHILL,** b c Pride of Dubai (AUS)—Cephalonie (USA) **Davies, Brown, Govier & Woods**
20 **TIME PASSENGER,** b c Time Test—Poly Pomona **Red Room Partnership**
21 **UDABERRI (IRE),** gr g Mastercraftsman (IRE)—Eccellente Idea (IRE) **S. P. C. Woods**

TWO-YEAR-OLDS

22 B f 30/03 Expert Eye—Amanda Carter (Tobougg (IRE)) (26667)
23 **AYYAB,** B f 27/02 Adaay (IRE)—Astrantia (Dansili) (65000)
24 B f 25/02 Cracksman—Bella Varenna (IRE) (Lawman (FR))
25 B c 08/03 Almanzor (FR)—Borja (IRE) (Lope de Vega (IRE)) (70000)
26 B f 09/05 Poet's Word (IRE)—Cape Dollar (IRE) (Cape Cross (IRE))
27 Ch f 21/03 Profitable (IRE)—Cynthiana (FR) (Siyouni (FR)) (425000)
28 **DAYTONA LADY (IRE),** b f 10/04 Bungle Inthejungle—Roseau City (Cityscape) (45000)
29 B c 15/03 Poet's Word (IRE)—Dreaming Beauty (Oasis Dream)
30 B c 21/02 Iffraaj—Final Set (IRE) (Dark Angel (IRE))
31 B f 06/04 Kodiac—Flat White (IRE) (Elusive Quality (USA)) (110000)
32 **GULMARG (IRE),** b c 12/05 Dandy Man (IRE)—Baileys Pursuit (Pastoral Pursuits) (55238)
33 Ch c 07/03 Night of Thunder (IRE)—Harlequin Girl (Where Or When (IRE)) (375000)
34 B f 06/05 Twilight Son—High Class Girl (Royal Applause)
35 B f 22/02 Acclamation—Kiss of Spring (IRE) (Dansili) (63776)
36 **LADY NAGIN (IRE),** b f 03/05 Kodiac—Top Dollar (Elusive Quality (USA)) (47619)
37 B f 14/02 Sea The Moon (GER)—Marmalady (IRE) (Duke of Marmalade (IRE)) (26000)
38 **MASKED QUEEN,** b f 18/03 Hawkbill (USA)—Cephalonie (USA) (Kris S (USA))
39 B c 11/03 Cracksman—Pongee (Barathea (IRE)) (180000)
40 B c 22/01 Territories (IRE)—Sami (Champs Elysees)
41 **SEA ME DANCE,** b f 09/02 Sea The Stars (IRE)—Whirly Dancer (Danehill Dancer (IRE)) (80000)
42 B c 07/02 Golden Horn—Shama's Crown (IRE) (New Approach (IRE))
43 Gr c 11/04 Havana Grey—Starboard Watch (Harbour Watch (IRE)) (57000)
44 B c 13/04 Havana Gold (IRE)—Strictly Silca (Danehill Dancer (IRE)) (70000)
45 **TERRIMIA,** b f 07/02 Territories (IRE)—Miaplacidus (IRE) (Shamardal (USA)) (10500)
46 B c 30/04 Dandy Man (IRE)—Vaudeville (New Approach (IRE)) (30000)
47 B f 25/04 U S Navy Flag (USA)—Wrood (USA) (Invasor (ARG)) (246599)

Other Owners: Mr G. W. Brickwood, Brook Stud, G. S. Brown, Mr R. H. Cooper, Mr J. Davies, Mr A. Duarte, R. T. Goodes, Mr P. Govier, Mr P. F. Govier, Govier & Brown, Mr R. Hine, Lifecycle Bloodstock Ltd, Mr P. A. Moroney, Mr J. Singh, Mr B. Stewart, Mr N. A. D. Thomas, Mr W. A. Tinkler, Mr E. J. Williams, D. G. A. E. Woods, Mr E. W. J. Woods, S. P. C. Woods.

577	**MRS KAYLEY WOOLLACOTT, South Molton**

Postal: **Big Brook Park, Rose Ash, South Molton, Devon, EX36 4RQ**
Contacts: PHONE **01769 550483**
EMAIL **info@richardwoollacottracing.co.uk** WEBSITE **www.richardwoollacottracing.co.uk**

1 **CASPERS COURT (IRE),** 8, gr g Court Cave (IRE)—Kindle Ball (FR) **Mr D Stevens & Mrs S Stevens**
2 **DORRANA (IRE),** 8, br m Darsi (FR)—Arts Theater (IRE) **Gale Force Five**
3 **ENORMOUSE,** 9, b g Crosspeace (IRE)—Mousiemay **M. H. Dare**
4 **EROS (FR),** 8, b g Diamond Boy (FR)—Madame Lys (FR) **Mr D Stevens & Mrs S Stevens**
5 **GETAWAY CORY (IRE),** 7, br g Getaway (GER)—Annaru (IRE) **Mr I. G. Thompson**
6 **GETAWAY LUCY (IRE),** 8, br m Getaway (GER)—Courtmac Memories (IRE) **Mr I. G. Thompson**
7 **MORNING GLORIA (IRE),** 6, b m Fame And Glory—Leading Article (IRE) **4Racing Owners Club**
8 **NICKELSONTHEDIME (IRE),** 8, b g Shantou (USA)—Penny Fiction (IRE) **T Hamlin, J E Gardener**
9 **NO RISK WITH LOU (FR),** 5, b g No Risk At All (FR)—Miss Meteore (FR) **Mrs K. Woollacott**
10 **OSTUNI (FR),** 9, b g Great Pretender (IRE)—Mamassita (FR) **Mr D Stevens & Mrs S Stevens**
11 **SHANNON LODGE (IRE),** 8, b m Doyen (IRE)—Lady Cadia (FR)
12 **SHANNON ROCCO (IRE),** 7, b m Shirocco (GER)—Coco Moon (IRE) **Mr I. G. Thompson**
13 **STRATTON OAKMONT (IRE),** 6, b g Ask—Foxwood Girl (IRE) **Kayley Woollacott Racing Club**

MRS KAYLEY WOOLLACOTT - continued

14 SURDOUE DE BALLON (FR), 9, gr g Turgeon (USA)—Nile Breeze (FR) **4Racing Owners Club**
15 THE KINGS WRIT (IRE), 11, b g Brian Boru—Letterwoman (IRE) **Mr D Stevens & Mrs S Stevens**
16 URABAMBA (IRE), 7, b g Arctic Cosmos (USA)—Glaisdale **Kayley Woollacott Racing Club**

Other Owners: Mr J. E. Gardener, T. Hamlin, Mr D. J. Stevens, Mrs S. E. Stevens.

---

578 MR PHILLIP YORK, Effingham Common
Postal: **Mornshill Farm, Banks Lane, Effingham, Leatherhead, Surrey, KT24 5JB**
Contacts: **PHONE 01372 457102**

1 BARB WIRE, 8, b br m Amber Life—Eastern Point **Mrs K. H. York**
2 DELIGHTFUL GUEST (IRE), 9, b m Beneficial—Saddlers Green (IRE) **Mrs K. H. York**
3 GLORIFY (IRE), 8, b g Fame And Glory—Georgia On My Mind (FR) **Mrs K. H. York**
4 HAPPY LARRY (IRE), 8, b g Stowaway—Lucky Start (IRE) **Mrs K. H. York**
5 LEGAL OK (IRE), 10, b g Echo of Light—Desert Trail (IRE) **P. York**
6 MAGEN'S MOON (IRE), 8, b m Henrythenavigator (USA)—Magen's Star (IRE) **P. York**
7 MOUNT CORBITT (IRE), 7, b g Robin des Champs (FR)—Hanora O'Brien (IRE) **P. York**
8 ROBIN DES MANA (IRE), 11, br g Robin des Pres (FR)—Kokopelli Mana (IRE) **P. York**
9 SPENDABLE, 10, ch m Spendent—Eastern Point **Mrs K. H. York**
10 SPIRITOFCHARTWELL, 14, ch g Clerkenwell (USA)—Rollin Rock **Mrs K. H. York**
11 TOUCH TIGHT (IRE), 10, b g Touch of Land (FR)—Classic China **Mrs K. H. York**

---

579 MRS LAURA YOUNG, Bridgwater
Postal: **Rooks Castle Stables, Broomfield, Bridgwater, Somerset, TA5 2EW**
Contacts: **PHONE 01278 664595 MOBILE 07766 514414 FAX 01278 661555**
EMAIL ljyracing@hotmail.com WEBSITE www.laurayoungracing.com

1 AUENWIRBEL (GER), 11, b g Sholokhov (IRE)—Auentime (GER) **Mrs L. J. Young**
2 BUCEPHALUS (GER), 5, b g Soldier Hollow—Batya (IRE) **C. E. Handford**
3 MEGAUDAIS SPEED (FR), 10, b g Puit d'Or (IRE)—La Rouadiere (FR) **The Isle Of Frogs Partnership**
4 RITHA, 7, b m Poet's Voice—Danat Al Atheer **Mr B. R. Brereton**
5 ROMAN KNOWS, 5, b g Holy Roman Emperor (IRE)—Entre Nous (IRE) **C. E. Handford**
6 ST ESTEPHE, 6, br g Lethal Force (IRE)—Ha'penny Beacon **Mrs L. J. Young**
7 THEDANCINGMAN, 9, b g Jeremy (USA)—Broadway Dancer **Mrs L. J. Young**
8 TOUT PARIS (FR), 7, b g Kapgarde (FR)—Parice de La Borie (FR) **The Isle Of Frogs Partnership**
9 TRUE THOUGHTS (IRE), 7, b g So You Think (NZ)—True Joy (IRE) **Mrs L. J. Young**
10 VALSHAN TIME (IRE), 10, b br g Atraf—Valshan (IRE) **Mrs L. J. Young**

Other Owners: Mr C. V. Vining, Mr G. C. Vining.

Assistant Trainer: James Young.

NH Jockey: Robert Dunne.

---

580 MR MAX YOUNG, Droitwich
Postal: **Little Acton Farm, Sneads Green, Droitwich, Worcestershire, WR9 0PZ**
Contacts: **PHONE 01905 827795**
EMAIL max.young@hotmail.com

1 BATTLE OF ACTIUM (IRE), 7, b g Fame And Glory—Flying Flame (IRE) **Mr D. R. Broadhurst**
2 BAZOOKA (IRE), 11, b g Camacho—Janadam (IRE) **D Jennings & Partner**
3 CATWALK SWAGGER (IRE), 5, b m Walk In The Park (IRE)—Hello Kitty (IRE) **Mr M. J. Young**
4 DANNY PARK (IRE), 6, b g Ocovango—Kilbarry Flame (IRE) **Mr M. J. Young**
5 DOYENS DE ANTE (IRE), 6, b g Doyen (IRE)—De Street (IRE) **Mrs D. Prosser**
6 FERROBIN (IRE), 8, br g Robin des Champs (FR)—Fedaia (IRE) **Mrs D. Prosser**

MR MAX YOUNG - continued

7 **HELOVAPLAN (IRE)**, 8, b g Helmet (AUS)—Watsdaplan (IRE) **Mrs D. Prosser**
8 **JEU DE MOTS (FR)**, 9, b g Saint des Saints (FR)—Nanouska (GER) **Max Young Racing Club**
9 **MINNIE MIA (IRE)**, 6, b m Mahler—Our Deadly (IRE) **Mr D. R. Broadhurst**
10 **MOVED IN MARCH (IRE)**, 6, b g Sans Frontieres (IRE)—Inishbeg House (IRE) **Mr M. J. Young**
11 **ON THE RISE (IRE)**, 6, b g Valirann (FR)—High Sunshine (IRE) **Max Young Racing Club**
12 **OXFORD BLU**, 8, b g Aqlaam—Blue Zealot (IRE) **Lady Brooke**
13 **REGAL PRETENDER**, 7, b g Great Pretender (IRE)—McKyla (IRE) **Mr M. J. Young**
14 **SECOND CHAPTER (IRE)**, 7, b g Arcadio (GER)—Tosca Shine (IRE) **Mr D. R. Broadhurst**
15 **SILVRETTA SCHWARZ (IRE)**, 7, b m Silver Frost (IRE)—Perruche Grise (FR) **Max Young Racing Club**
16 **STEVIE MCKEANE**, 5, b m Bated Breath—Eventfull Meet (IRE) **Mr M. J. Young**
17 **STINGGREY (IRE)**, 9, gr g Scorpion (IRE)—Northinn Lady (IRE) **Max Young Racing Club**
18 **THE FECKENHAM FOX**, 8, ch m Malinas (GER)—Broughton Melody **Mr K. E. Hay**
19 **TOP BEAK (IRE)**, 9, b g Lawman (FR)—Tree Tops **Mr M. J. Young**

Other Owners: Mr D. Jennings, Mr M. J. Young.

---

581 MR WILLIAM YOUNG, Carluke
Postal: **Watchknowe Lodge, Crossford, Carluke, Lanarkshire, ML8 5QT**
Contacts: **PHONE 01555 860226, 01555 860856 MOBILE 07900 408210 FAX 01555 860137**
EMAIL watchknowe@talktalk.net

1 **ARDERA CROSS (IRE)**, 11, ch g Shantou (USA)—Fair Maid Marion (IRE) **W. G. Young**
2 **COOL VALLEY (IRE)**, 13, b g Zerpour (IRE)—Jilly Jaffa Cake (IRE) **W. G. Young**
3 **DARKEST DAY (IRE)**, 7, b g Aizavoski (IRE)—Dempseys Luck (IRE) **W. G. Young**
4 **GRIPPER**, 7, b g Thewayyouare (USA)—Hold On Tight (IRE) **W. G. Young**
5 **MISS VALENTINE (IRE)**, 6, ch m Shantou (USA)—Couture Daisy (IRE) **W. G. Young**
6 **SOME AMBITION (IRE)**, 9, b g Westerner—Heath Heaven **W. G. Young**

Assistant Trainer: William G Young Snr.

INDEX TO HORSES

The figure before the name of the horse refers to the number of the team in which it appears and
The figure after the horse supplies a ready reference to each animal. Horses are indexed strictly alphabetically, e.g.
THE CON MAN appears in the T's, MR NICE GUY In the MR's, ST BASIL in the ST'S etc.
Unnamed animals are listed under their dam, along with their sex.

373 **AGGAGIO** (FR) 4
476 **AGGY WITH IT** (IRE) 2
231 **AGHAREED** C 123
251 **AGONYCLITE** 34
117 **AGOSTINO** 43
562 **AGRAPART** (FR) 3
300 **AGREEABILITY** 37
47 **AGUAPLANO** 26
385 **AGUSTA GOLD** (IRE) 2
25 **AHAMOMENT** (IRE) 27
491 **AHANDFULOFSUMMERS** 1
60 **AHDAAF** (USA) G 1
177 **AHEAD OF SCHEDULE** (IRE) 1
323 **AHEAD OF THE FIELD** (IRE) 1
78 **AHORSECALLEDWANDA** 1
258 **AHORSEWITHNONAME** 1
458 **AHOY SENOR** (IRE) 1
313 **AIDE MEMOIRE** (IRE) 1
1 **AIGHEAR** 1
373 **AIGUILLETTE** 5
455 **AIKENBREAKINHEART** (IRE) 1
402 **AIKHAL** (IRE) 12
555 **AIKIDO** (IRE) 2
561 **AILES D'AMOUR** (IRE) 2
404 **AILISH** T 220
6 **AIM OF ARTEMIS** (IRE) F 90
475 **AIM STRAIGHT** 58
563 **AIMEE DE SIVOLA** (FR) 1
528 **AIMERIC** 40
484 **AIMIGAYLE** G 16
39 **AIMING FOR RIO** (FR) F 91
475 **AIMING HIGH** 31
458 **AIN'T MY FAULT** (IRE) 2
127 **AIN'T NO SUNSHINE** (IRE) 2
385 **AIONE** (FR) 3
550 **AIR HAIR LAIR** (IRE) 1
238 **AIR OF APPROVAL** (IRE) 2
245 **AIR OF YORK** (IRE) 1
405 **AIR RAID** 2
48 **AIR TO AIR** 1
483 **AIRE VALLEY LAD** 2
243 **AIRGLOW** (USA) 76
367 **AIRSHOW** 2
270 **AIRTON** 1
529 **AIRTOTHETHRONE** (IRE) 1
117 **AISH** 1
240 **AJA** (IRE) C 118
404 **AJAY'S WAYS** (IRE) 2
13 **AJERO** (IRE) 1
317 **AJRAD** 1
414 **AKA FLIPPER** (IRE) 30
528 **AKAARIM** (IRE) 41
482 **AKAMANTO** 1
354 **AKENTRICK** 2
528 **AKHU NAJLA** 42
517 **AKI BOMAYE** (IRE) 1
566 **AKKERINGA** 3
402 **AKTORIA** (FR) C 104
231 **AL AASY** (IRE) 2
122 **AL AGAILA** (IRE) 13
48 **AL AMEEN** (IRE) 16
520 **AL AZHAR** (IRE) 18
105 **AL BAREZ** 1
385 **AL BOUM PHOTO** (FR) 4
509 **AL DANCER** (FR) 1
417 **AL DWEHA** (IRE) C 48
410 **AL GAIYA** (FR) 1

240 **AL HARGAH** (IRE) 119
528 **AL HUSN** (IRE) 43
142 **AL JAMAL** F 2
52 **AL KHERB** 1
342 **AL KOUT** 1
16 **AL MAHMEYAH** C 143
94 **AL MANAAL** F 1
16 **AL MARMAR** (IRE) 55
231 **AL MUBHIR** 39
295 **AL MUFFRIH** (IRE) 1
174 **AL MUHAAJIR** (IRE) 1
262 **AL MUQDAD** 58
528 **AL MUZN** (IRE) 149
6 **AL NAFIR** (IRE) 26
240 **AL NOAAMAN** 120
406 **AL QAASIM** (IRE) 1
73 **AL QAREEM** (IRE) 30
428 **AL ROC** (FR) 4
170 **AL ROWAIYAH** F 62
217 **AL RUFAA** (FR) 1
6 **AL SAHARA** (IRE) 27
273 **AL SIMMO** 1
6 **AL SUHAIL** 2
248 **AL SUIL EILE** (FR) 1
163 **AL SULTANA** C 65
91 **AL TARMAAH** (IRE) 1
142 **AL TILAL** (IRE) 41
544 **AL ZARAQAAN** 1
174 **ALABLAQ** (IRE) 2
356 **ALAFDHAL** (IRE) 1
76 **ALAFLAAK** (USA) F 15
374 **ALALA** (IRE) 1
243 **ALALCANCE** 133
404 **ALAPHILIPPE** (IRE) 3
302 **ALASKAN JEWEL** (IRE) 12
340 **ALASKAN WIND** (IRE) 22
544 **ALAZWAR** (IRE) 2
77 **ALBA DE TORMES** (IRE) 3
61 **ALBA DEL SOLE** (IRE) 2
26 **ALBA LONGA** 85
97 **ALBA POWER** (IRE) 2
300 **ALBA ROSE** 1
26 **ALBAFLORA** 1
6 **ALBAHR** 28
26 **ALBANY** 86
39 **ALBASHARAH** (USA) F 92
76 **ALBASHEER** (IRE) 1
475 **ALBAYAADER** (IRE) 32
164 **ALBEGONE** 1
164 **ALBEGREY** 102
265 **ALBERIC** (FR) 4
185 **ALBERT** (IRE) 28
186 **ALBERT BRIDGE** 7
373 **ALBERT VAN ORNUM** (FR) 6
163 **ALBERT'S BACK** 1
319 **ALBERTINE ROSE** F 31
101 **ALBION PRINCESS** 11
386 **ALBORKAN** (FR) 1
91 **ALBUM** (IRE) 2
8 **ALBURN** 1
195 **ALBUS ANNE** 10
398 **ALCALA** (FR) 3
508 **ALCAZAN** 1
527 **ALCHEMIST'S DREAM** 23
273 **ALCHEMYSTIQUE** (IRE) 2
16 **ALCOHOL FREE** (IRE) 1
231 **ALDAARY** 3

434 **ALDABRA** 14
48 **ALDANA** F 57
173 **ALDBOURNE** (IRE) 9
228 **ALDERSON** 1
262 **ALDHAJA** (USA) 23
217 **ALDOUS HUXLEY** (IRE) 38
157 **ALDRICH BAY** (IRE) 2
312 **ALDSWORTH** 1
480 **ALEATORIC** (IRE) 2
540 **ALEEF** (IRE) 3
460 **ALEEZDANCER** (IRE) 21
231 **ALENQUER** (FR) 4
434 **ALERTA ROJA** 1
145 **ALETHIOMETER** (FR) 35
160 **ALETOILE** 1
142 **ALEX GRACIE** 3
7 **ALEXANDER JAMES** (IRE) 1
508 **ALEXANDER QUEEN** C 48
550 **ALEXANDRA ROMANOV** (IRE) 2
434 **ALEXANDRETTA** 43
402 **ALEXANDROVA** (IRE) C 105
491 **ALEXIADE** (IRE) C 30
540 **ALEXIS CARRINGTON** (IRE) G 25
299 **ALEZAN** 3
441 **ALF 'N' DOR** (IRE) 1
51 **ALFA DAWN** (IRE) 1
76 **ALFLAILA** 6
83 **ALFRED BOUCHER** 1
514 **ALFSBOY** (IRE) 1
101 **ALGERNON** 65
483 **ALGESIRAS** 3
333 **ALGHAZAAL** (IRE) 2
335 **ALGHEED** (IRE) 2
312 **ALHABOR** 135
566 **ALHAMMAAM** (IRE) 4
240 **ALHAWDAJ** (USA) C 121
248 **ALI STAR BERT** 1
460 **ALIA CHOICE** 22
183 **ALIBABA** 1
361 **ALICE DIAMOND** (IRE) 68
273 **ALICE KAZEEM** 3
402 **ALICE SPRINGS** (IRE) C 106
315 **ALICESTAR** 1
311 **ALIEN ENCOUNTER** 1
333 **ALIEN STORM** (IRE) 2
414 **ALIGNAK** 1
246 **ALIOMAANA** 2
68 **ALIOSKI** 1
475 **ALIYANA** (IRE) C 59
240 **ALIYFA** (IRE) C 122
243 **ALIZARINE** 77
16 **ALJAAZYA** (USA) C 144
377 **ALJARDAA** (IRE) 1
47 **ALJARI** 1
418 **ALJARYAAL** (FR) 1
318 **ALJASRA UNITED** (FR) 1
318 **ALJASRAPRINCESS** (FR) 2
147 **ALKHATTAAF** 1
371 **ALKHAWARAH** (USA) C 27
324 **ALKOPOP** (GER) 1
480 **ALL ABOUT ALICE** (IRE) 7
406 **ALL ABOUT FREEDOM** 54
32 **ALL ABOUT LOGAN** 1
475 **ALL ARE MINE** (GER) 33
39 **ALL CLEAR** F 93
398 **ALL DANCER** (FR) 4
414 **ALL DUNN** 49

16 **ALL GO** 56
88 **ALL IN GREEN** (IRE) G 20
346 **ALL ON RED** (IRE) C 41
17 **ALL THE FAME** (IRE) 1
409 **ALL THE GLORY** 2
97 **ALL THE KING'S MEN** (FR) 3
131 **ALL THINGS BRIGHT** (IRE) 1
240 **ALL TO DO WITH IT** (IRE) C 123
124 **ALL YOURS** (FR) 1
385 **ALLAHO** (FR) 5
222 **ALLANAH'S BOY** (IRE) 2
259 **ALLARDYCE** 2
300 **ALLARMISTA** 38
388 **ALLAVINA** (IRE) 3
262 **ALLAYAALI** (IRE) 24
163 **ALLE STELLE** C 66
302 **ALLEGHANY** (IRE) 13
385 **ALLEGORIE DE VASSY** (FR) 6
346 **ALLEGRAMENTE** C 42
243 **ALLEGRETTO** (IRE) C 134
155 **ALLEGREZZA** C 54
345 **ALLEGRO JETE** (FR) 1
26 **ALLEMANDE** 25
454 **ALLERTHORPE** 1
406 **ALLIGATOR ALLEY** 2
476 **ALLMANKIND** 3
434 **ALLONS DANSER** 15
26 **ALLOWED** 2
560 **ALLSET** (IRE) 1
517 **ALLSFINEANDANDY** (IRE) 2
118 **ALLURING PARK** (IRE) C 84
403 **ALLURINGLY** (USA) F 22
300 **ALMA MATER** C 121
490 **ALMAAN** (USA) 1
416 **ALMARIN** (IRE) 8
333 **ALMAZHAR GARDE** (FR) 3
252 **ALMINAR** (IRE) 2
47 **ALMODOVAR DEL RIO** (IRE) 27
73 **ALMOHANDESAH** 31
561 **ALMOST GOLD** (IRE) 3
349 **ALMOST GOTAWAY** (IRE) 1
124 **ALMUFEED** (IRE) 2
217 **ALMUHIT** (IRE) 39
476 **ALNADAM** (FR) 4
6 **ALNILAM** (FR) 29
13 **ALNITAK** 2
318 **ALNOOD** (IRE) 3
173 **ALNWICK CASTLE** 10
173 **ALNWICK ROSE** 11
314 **ALOISA** 2
505 **ALOISI** C 47
346 **ALONG CAME CASEY** (IRE) C 43
233 **ALOOQAAL** (IRE) 21
186 **ALORS QUOI** (IRE) C 25
217 **ALOTAIBI** (IRE) 40
16 **ALOUNAK** (FR) 3
231 **ALPHA CAPTURE** (IRE) 124
388 **ALPHA CARINAE** (IRE) 4
243 **ALPHA CENTAURI** (IRE) C 135
406 **ALPHA CRU** (IRE) 3
100 **ALPHA KING** 1
243 **ALPHA LUPI** (IRE) C 136
266 **ALPHABA** (FR) C 19
434 **ALPHABETICAL** 2
155 **ALPHONSE LE GRANDE** (IRE) 15
182 **ALPINE GIRL** (IRE) 43
544 **ALPINE LADY** 38

127 **ALPINE SIERRA** (IRE) 3
138 **ALPINE STROLL** 1
434 **ALPINISTA** 3
220 **ALQABEELA** (IRE) 1
370 **ALQAMAR** 1
208 **ALRAMZ** 1
374 **ALREADY GONE** (IRE) 13
426 **ALREHB** (USA) 2
4 **ALRIGHT CHIEF** (IRE) 1
116 **ALRIGHT MARLENE** (IRE) 1
127 **ALRIGHT SUNSHINE** (IRE) 4
485 **ALRIGHTJACK** (IRE) 1
229 **ALSAADEN** F 26
76 **ALSAAQY** (IRE) 7
371 **ALSAMYAH** 9
240 **ALSINDI** (IRE) C 124
163 **ALSITHEE** 3
300 **ALTA COMEDIA** 122
26 **ALTERNATIVA** 26
312 **ALTERNATIVE FACT** 3
500 **ALTJERINGA** 27
216 **ALTO ALTO** (FR) 1
201 **ALTOBELLI** (IRE) 1
370 **ALTRUISM** (IRE) 2
4 **ALTUMANINA** 2
378 **ALVARITA** C 57
231 **ALVEDISTON** (IRE) 40
561 **ALWAJD** (IRE) 88
472 **ALWAYS ABLE** (IRE) 1
335 **ALWAYS DREAMING** 3
240 **ALWAYS FEARLESS** (IRE) 1
528 **ALWAYS LOVE YOU** 44
270 **ALWAYS TEA TIME** 2
371 **ALWAYS THANKFUL** F 28
233 **ALWAYSANDFOREVER** (IRE) C 38
496 **ALYA'S GOLD AWARD** (IRE) 22
73 **ALYARA** 2
378 **ALYTH** 31
388 **AM I WRONG** (IRE) 5
94 **AMAANY** C 53
404 **AMADORIO** (FR) 4
94 **AMAHORO** F 54
296 **AMAL** (IRE) 2
101 **AMALFI BAY** 1
127 **AMALFI DOUG** (FR) 5
389 **AMALFI GEM** (IRE) 9
47 **AMALFI SALSA** (IRE) 2
530 **AMANDA ADVENTURE** (GER) 28
576 **AMANDA CARTER** F 22
566 **AMANDA HUG'N'KISS** 35
86 **AMANHA** (FR) 2
547 **AMANI** 1
220 **AMANIRENAS** (IRE) 16
231 **AMANZOE** (IRE) 41
262 **AMARANTHE** (FR) C 59
517 **AMARILLO SKY** (IRE) 3
185 **AMARILLO STAR** (IRE) 1
255 **AMASOVA** 1
189 **AMATEUR** (IRE) 1
93 **AMATHUS** (IRE) 1
555 **AMAZING ALBA** 3
470 **AMAZING AMAYA** 1
164 **AMAZING ARTHUR** 163
340 **AMAZING MOLLIE** 23
155 **AMAZING RED** (IRE) 1
509 **AMAZING TANGO** (GER) 2
394 **AMAZON PRINCESS** 1

367 **AMAZONIAN DREAM** (IRE) 24
304 **AMBASSADOR** (IRE) 1
98 **AMBASSADORIAL** (USA) 1
142 **AMBER DEW** 42
334 **AMBER ISLAND** (IRE) 1
238 **AMBER RUN** (IRE) 3
517 **AMBION HILL** (IRE) 4
170 **AMELIA GRACE** (IRE) G 63
120 **AMELIA R** (IRE) 1
536 **AMELIA'S DANCE** (IRE) 1
530 **AMELY ADVENTURE** (GER) 29
398 **AMENON** (FR) 5
483 **AMERDALE** 4
16 **AMERICA NOVA** (FR) C 145
535 **AMERICAN ANTHEM** (IRE) 1
182 **AMERICAN BELLE** 44
47 **AMERICAN ENDEAVOUR** (USA) C 57
378 **AMERICAN GERRY** (IRE) 2
240 **AMERICAN KESTREL** (IRE) 34
222 **AMERICAN LEGACY** 2
491 **AMERICAN SPIRIT** (IRE) F 31
537 **AMERICAN STAR** (IRE) 32
231 **AMETIST** 5
528 **AMEYNAH** (IRE) 45
404 **AMI DESBOIS** (FR) 5
240 **AMIGA MEU** 35
104 **AMINATU** 52
518 **AMISI** 1
403 **AMJAAD** C 23
174 **AMJAD** 21
572 **AMLOVI** (IRE) 1
365 **AMMA LORD** (IRE) 1
122 **AMMOLITE** (IRE) 14
59 **AMNAA** 1
26 **AMONA** (IRE) C 87
551 **AMOOD** (IRE) 1
476 **AMOOLA GOLD** (GER) 5
544 **AMOR DE MI VIDA** (IRE) 15
346 **AMOR VINCIT OMNIA** (IRE) 15
127 **AMOUGE** (IRE) 49
398 **AMOUR DE NUIT** (IRE) 6
106 **AMOUR FOU** (IRE) F 17
120 **AMOURI GLEAM** 2
120 **AMOURIE** 3
346 **AMPLE POWER** (FR) 16
173 **AMSBY** 1
174 **AMTHAL** (IRE) F 37
217 **AMTIYAZ** 2
406 **AMURRA** C 97
94 **AMY BEACH** (IRE) 2
317 **AMZAAN** (IRE) 14
240 **AN ANGEL'S DREAM** (FR) 36
212 **AN BANOG** (IRE) G 2
409 **AN TAILLIUR** (IRE) 3
76 **ANA EMARAATY** 16
361 **ANA LUNA** F 85
122 **ANAAMIL** (IRE) C 15
460 **ANADORA** 23
104 **ANAMANDA** (IRE) 15
62 **ANANDA KANDA** (USA) F 27
76 **ANASHEED** C 17
434 **ANATOMIC** 16
125 **ANAX** (IRE) 1
528 **ANBELLA** (FR) C 150
505 **ANCESTRAL** F 48
402 **ANCHORAGE** (IRE) 13
410 **ANCIENT CAPITAL** 5

434 **ARCLIGHT** 19
544 **ARCTIC EMPEROR** 4
519 **ARCTIC FOX** 2
212 **ARCTIC LADY** (IRE) C 3
223 **ARCTIC ROAD** 3
13 **ARCTIC SAINT** (IRE) 3
385 **ARCTIC WARRIOR** (GER) 10
146 **ARCTICIAN** (IRE) 1
112 **ARD CHROS** (IRE) 4
10 **ARD UP** 31
302 **ARDAT** 1
240 **ARDBRACCAN** (IRE) 37
581 **ARDEA CROSS** (IRE) 1
233 **ARDLA** (IRE) 2
501 **ARDMAYLE** (IRE) 3
25 **ARDOM'S LADY** 28
174 **ARE YOU ABLE** 3
117 **ARECIBO** (FR) 3
97 **AREGAI** (FR) 17
146 **ARENAS DEL TIEMPO** 2
364 **ARENDELLE** C 43
365 **AREYOUWITHUS** (IRE) 3
142 **ARFINN ROSE** 4
426 **ARGIRL** 18
118 **ARGONAULT** 29
320 **ARGONAUTA** (IRE) 2
157 **ARGUS** (IRE) 4
387 **ARIA ROSE** 1
265 **ARIAN** (IRE) 6
530 **ARIELLA** (GER) 31
48 **ARIES LAD** 18
172 **ARIJ** (IRE) 1
98 **ARIKA** (USA) 22
529 **ARINI** 2
417 **ARION** 13
186 **ARISTOBULUS** 8
395 **ARISTOCRATE** (FR) 1
198 **ARIYFA** (IRE) F 10
167 **ARIZONA CARDINAL** 2
560 **ARIZONA GLORY** 4
402 **ARK** (IRE) 15
179 **ARKID** 12
527 **ARLECCHINO'S GIFT** 24
527 **ARLECCHINO'S STAR** 32
255 **ARLO'S SUNSHINE** 2
93 **ARMADAR** 2
354 **ARMATTIEKAN** (IRE) 3
404 **ARMCHAIR FARMER** (IRE) 9
163 **ARMO** 35
240 **ARMOR** 38
240 **ARMOUR PROPRE** (IRE) 126
238 **ARMOURED** (IRE) 92
528 **ARMUM** (IRE) C 151
80 **ARMY OF INDIA** (IRE) 1
282 **ARMY OF ONE** (GER) 1
39 **ARMY SERGEANT** (IRE) 65
44 **ARMY'S DREAM** (IRE) 1
1 **ARNICA** 1
151 **ARNOLD** 1
265 **AROKA** (FR) G 7
231 **AROUSING** 7
183 **ARPINA** (IRE) 2
293 **ARQOOB** (IRE) 1
519 **ARRANGE** (IRE) 3
406 **ARRANMORE** 4
306 **ARRIANNIE** 11
409 **ARRIVEDERCI** (FR) 9

229 **ARRIVISTE** 2
460 **ARROW OF GOLD** (IRE) 1
430 **ARSONIST** (GER) 1
404 **ART APPROVAL** (FR) 10
536 **ART DECCO** 2
334 **ART EXPERT** 29
378 **ART INSTITUTE** (USA) C 58
404 **ART MAN** (FR) 1
78 **ART OF AMERICA** 2
395 **ART OF DIPLOMACY** 2
222 **ART OF ILLUSION** (IRE) 5
164 **ART POWER** (IRE) 3
122 **ARTAOIS** 20
476 **ARTEMIS KIMBO** 8
520 **ARTEMIS SKY** 1
296 **ARTEMISIA GENTILE** (IRE) 21
231 **ARTEMISIA LOMI** (IRE) 8
420 **ARTEMISION** 5
130 **ARTHALOT** (IRE) 3
314 **ARTHUR MAC** (IRE) 4
459 **ARTHUR'S ANGEL** (IRE) 1
155 **ARTHUR'S REALM** (IRE) 2
72 **ARTHUR'S SEAT** (IRE) 1
418 **ARTHUR'S VICTORY** (IRE) 2
1 **ARTIC MANN** 2
53 **ARTILLERY** 2
549 **ARTISAN BLEU** (IRE) 1
300 **ARTISAN DANCER** (FR) 124
122 **ARTISTI** F 21
403 **ARTISTIC CHOICE** (IRE) 4
454 **ARTISTIC DAWN** (IRE) C 2
454 **ARTISTIC DAWN** (IRE) F 9
7 **ARTISTIC DREAMER** 98
529 **ARTISTIC ENDEAVOUR** 3
34 **ARTISTIC RIFLES** (IRE) 1
483 **ARTS THEATER** (IRE) F 6
418 **ARTWORK GENIE** (IRE) F 19
331 **ARTY CAMPBELL** (IRE) 2
387 **ARUAN** F 24
299 **ARUMADAAY** 42
555 **ARVICO BLEU** (IRE) 4
203 **ARVIKA ROYAL** 1
544 **ARWAAG** (IRE) 40
540 **ARZAAK** (IRE) 1
6 **AS GOOD AS GOLD** (IRE) C 94
516 **AS IF BY CHANCE** 2
528 **ASAASSI** (FR) 47
460 **ASAAYIL** 24
7 **ASAD** (IRE) 2
62 **ASADJUMEIRAH** 3
118 **ASCENDING** (IRE) 30
118 **ASCOT ADVENTURE** 2
331 **ASCOT DAY** (FR) 3
178 **ASCOT DE BRUYERE** (FR) 1
266 **ASCOT JUNGLE** (IRE) 1
372 **ASCRAEUS** 1
417 **ASEAN LEGEND** (IRE) 14
373 **ASENSE** 137
69 **ASHBURY** (IRE) G 2
243 **ASHDALE BOB** (IRE) 4
409 **ASHFIELD PADDY** (IRE) 10
170 **ASHINGTON** 1
193 **ASHJAN** 1
101 **ASHKY** (IRE) 13
477 **ASHLEY GOLD** 21
364 **ASHMORE** (IRE) 44
476 **ASHOKA** (IRE) 9

483 **ASHOVER HILLS** (IRE) 7
422 **ASHTEAD** (IRE) 7
162 **ASHTON COURT** (IRE) 1
476 **ASHTOWN LAD** (IRE) 10
317 **ASHURA** 15
327 **ASHUTOR** (FR) 4
73 **ASIA MINOR** (IRE) F 81
117 **ASIAN QUEEN** 44
561 **ASINARA** (GER) F 7
277 **ASJAD** 1
404 **ASK A HONEY BEE** (IRE) 12
404 **ASK DILLON** (IRE) 13
398 **ASK FOR GLORY** (IRE) 7
404 **ASK HENRY** (IRE) 14
201 **ASK ME EARLY** (IRE) 2
403 **ASK ME NICELY** (IRE) F 24
113 **ASK MY HEATHER** (IRE) 2
365 **ASK PADDINGTON** (IRE) 4
172 **ASK PADDY** (IRE) 2
300 **ASK PETER** (FR) 41
223 **ASK THE DOC** (IRE) 4
82 **ASK THE JUDGE** (IRE) 2
38 **ASKALLI** 1
131 **ASKGARMOR** (IRE) 2
519 **ASKING FOR ANSWERS** (IRE) 4
2 **ASKING PRICE** (USA) F 60
385 **ASLUKWOODHAVIT** 11
185 **ASMEEN** (IRE) C 60
88 **ASMUND** (IRE) 1
567 **ASO** (FR) 2
50 **ASOCKASTAR** (IRE) 1
418 **ASPASI** C 29
378 **ASPATRE** 59
97 **ASPEN** (FR) 18
528 **ASRAABB** (IRE) 48
300 **ASSAULT ON ROME** (IRE) F 125
46 **ASSEMBLED** 1
500 **ASSESSMENT** 28
446 **ASTAPOR** 2
243 **ASTELIA** (IRE) 78
385 **ASTERION FORLONGE** (FR) 12
428 **ASTIGAR** (FR) 6
478 **ASTLEY PARK** C 35
166 **ASTONBURY** (IRE) 8
560 **ASTRA VIA** 5
437 **ASTRAL AFFAIR** (IRE) F 1
437 **ASTRAL AFFAIR** (IRE) C 7
317 **ASTRAL BEAT** (IRE) 16
477 **ASTRAL BEAU** 22
16 **ASTRELLE** (IRE) C 148
73 **ASTRO JAKK** (IRE) 3
500 **ASTRO KING** (IRE) 2
173 **ASTROBRIO** 12
395 **ASTROMACHIA** 3
173 **ASTROMAN** 3
208 **ASTRONOMIC VIEW** 2
89 **ASTROPHYSICS** 2
482 **ASTUTE BOY** (IRE) 2
122 **ASWAN** (IRE) 22
47 **AT A CLIP** F 58
173 **AT A PINCH** 4
28 **AT LIBERTY** (IRE) 13
434 **AT THE DOUBLE** (FR) 20
404 **AT THE POUND CROSS** (IRE) F 15
18 **AT YOUR SERVICE** 1
200 **ATACAMA DESERT** (IRE) 1
517 **ATAKAN** (FR) 5

520 **ATALANTA BREEZE** 2
364 **ATALANTA'S BOY** 1
117 **ATALIS BAY** 4
334 **ATAMANA** (IRE) C 58
310 **ATASER** 1
98 **ATHEBY** 23
43 **ATHEEB** 1
402 **ATHENA** (IRE) F 108
149 **ATHGARVAN** (IRE) 1
60 **ATHINEA** (FR) G 2
87 **ATHMAD** (IRE) 1
398 **ATHOLL STREET** (IRE) 8
516 **ATHOLLBLAIR BOY** (IRE) 3
25 **ATIYAH** 1
130 **ATJIMA** (IRE) 4
414 **ATLAAL** F 50
317 **ATLANNA** 17
403 **ATLANTIC BREEZE** (IRE) 5
30 **ATLANTIC CYCLE** (IRE) F 9
1 **ATLANTIC DANCER** (IRE) 3
28 **ATLANTIC DREAM** (IRE) 44
319 **ATLANTIC HEART** (IRE) 12
503 **ATLANTIC STORM** (IRE) 1
217 **ATLANTIS** 42
364 **ATLANTIS BLUE** 17
113 **ATOMIC ANGEL** 3
15 **ATOMIC JACK** 1
164 **ATOMIC LADY** (FR) 104
185 **ATOMISE** 29
65 **ATRAFAN** (IRE) 1
185 **ATRIUM** 30
258 **ATTACCA** (IRE) 4
14 **ATTACHE** (IRE) 59
73 **ATTAGIRL** 33
402 **ATTIRE** (IRE) C 109
315 **ATTRACTED TO YOU** (IRE) C 23
243 **ATTRACTION** C 138
350 **ATTY'S EDGE** 1
204 **ATYAAF** 1
163 **AU JUS** 4
265 **AUBA ME YANG** (IRE) 8
182 **AUBAZINE** (IRE) 45
445 **AUBIS WALK** (IRE) 1
174 **AUBRIETIA** F 38
562 **AUBUSSON** (FR) 4
216 **AUCUNRISQUE** (IRE) 3
217 **AUDIENCE** 43
145 **AUDIT** (IRE) 36
360 **AUDITOR** 9
388 **AUDITORIA** 7
579 **AUENWIRBEL** (GER) 4
112 **AUGHARUE** (IRE) 5
295 **AUGHNACURRA KING** (IRE) 2
334 **AUGMENTARIUM** (IRE) 30
47 **AUGUST PLACE** 28
73 **AUGUSTA ADA** F 82
575 **AULD SOD** (IRE) 1
544 **AUNT BETHANY** (IRE) 41
139 **AUNT MINNIE** C 19
64 **AUNTIE JUNE** 1
300 **AUNTIE MARGARET** (FR) 42
16 **AURELIA** C 149
146 **AURELIA GOLD** 22
16 **AURIA** 4
16 **AURIFEROUS** (IRE) 5
130 **AURIGNY MILL** (FR) 5
48 **AURORA BUTTERFLY** (IRE) F 61

422 **AURORA GLORY** (IRE) 17
39 **AURORA LEIGH** C 94
243 **AURORA PRINCESS** (IRE) 5
240 **AURORA SPRING** (IRE) C 127
378 **AURORA STAR** (FR) 3
458 **AURORA THUNDER** 4
346 **AUSDAISIA** (IRE) 45
280 **AUSSIE BANKER** 22
20 **AUSSIE BREEZE** 1
505 **AUSSIE WARRIOR** (IRE) 7
415 **AUSTIN FRIARS** 2
16 **AUSTRALIAN ANGEL** 60
528 **AUSTRALIAN HARBOUR** 3
26 **AUSTRALIAN QUEEN** C 89
300 **AUSTRIAN THEORY** (IRE) 43
4 **AUTHARI** (IRE) 4
317 **AUTHOR'S DREAM** 2
373 **AUTHORISED SPEED** (IRE) 1
385 **AUTHORIZED ART** (FR) 13
223 **AUTHORIZO** (FR) 5
424 **AUTOLYCUS** 21
404 **AUTONOMOUS CLOUD** (IRE) 16
314 **AUTONOMY** 5
186 **AUTUMN** (IRE) 9
89 **AUTUMN ANGEL** (IRE) 96
243 **AUTUMN EVENING** 6
406 **AUTUMN FESTIVAL** 56
117 **AUTUMN FLIGHT** (IRE) 2
6 **AUTUMN LILY** (AUS) F 95
118 **AUTUMN MAGIC** 31
215 **AUTUMN SYMPHONY** (IRE) 38
229 **AUTUMN TRAIL** 3
561 **AUTUMN WAR** (IRE) 8
83 **AUTUMNAL DANCER** (IRE) 17
217 **AUYOUNI** 44
164 **AVA GO JOE** (IRE) 4
110 **AVABELLA** (IRE) 1
340 **AVAILABLE ANGEL** 1
323 **AVALANCHE PEAK** (IRE) 2
77 **AVARICE** (IRE) 5
101 **AVE MARIA** 14
45 **AVEC LAURA** 1
232 **AVEC PERMISSION** (FR) 2
274 **AVENTIA** (IRE) F 2
54 **AVENTURINA** 2
16 **AVERAMI** C 150
528 **AVESSIA** F 152
300 **AVIACION** (BRZ) F 126
162 **AVICHI** (IRE) F 2
404 **AVIEWTOSEA** (IRE) 17
214 **AVITHOS** 1
418 **AVIZARE** (IRE) F 30
113 **AVOID DE MASTER** (IRE) 4
127 **AVOMCIC** (IRE) F 70
6 **AVONGROVE** F 96
521 **AWARD DANCER** (IRE) 2
6 **AWARD WINNING** (IRE) F 97
354 **AWAY AT DAWN** (IRE) 4
246 **AWAY FOR SLATES** (IRE) 4
371 **AWAY HE GOES** (IRE) 1
255 **AWAY WIT DA FAIRYS** (IRE) 11
420 **AWAYTHELAD** (IRE) 6
528 **AWESOME** C 153
15 **AWESOME DANCER** (IRE) 30
96 **AWESOME TUNES** (IRE) 1
428 **AWESOMEDUDE** 7
18 **AXEL JACKLIN** 3

186 **AXOPAR** 10
266 **AYDA** (FR) 2
559 **AYE AYE CHARLIE** 1
218 **AYE RIGHT** (IRE) 1
302 **AYLING** 15
127 **AYR EMPRESS** (IRE) 6
7 **AYR HARBOUR** 3
233 **AYR MISSILE** C 39
295 **AYR OF ELEGANCE** 3
215 **AYR POET** 3
576 **AYYAB** 23
406 **AZANO** 5
101 **AZEEMA** (IRE) G 15
98 **AZETS** 3
145 **AZHAR** C 54
38 **AZOF DES MOTTES** (FR) 2
34 **AZPEITIA** C 33
455 **AZTEC DREAMS** 2
16 **AZTEC EMPIRE** (IRE) 61
145 **AZURE BLUE** (IRE) 37
231 **BAAEED** 9
395 **BAASEM** (USA) 4
80 **BABA REZA** 3
334 **BABABOBO** (IRE) 31
7 **BABE ALICIOUS** (IRE) 4
431 **BABY BAY** 19
404 **BABY BEN** (IRE) 18
15 **BABY BILL** 50
44 **BABY JANE** (IRE) 4
212 **BABY KING** (IRE) 4
254 **BABY MOONBEAM** 1
384 **BABY SHAM** 1
473 **BABY SPICE** 2
334 **BABY STEPS** 3
383 **BABYDUKE** 1
385 **BACARDYS** (FR) 14
26 **BACCARAT BABY** 90
385 **BACHASSON** (FR) 15
53 **BACK FROM DUBAI** (IRE) 3
304 **BACK ON THE LASH** 2
286 **BACKINFORGLORY** (IRE) 1
73 **BACKSTAGE** 34
5 **BAD COMPANY** 3
216 **BADDESLEY** (IRE) 4
287 **BADENSCOTH** 3
531 **BADINAGE** 38
460 **BADR** (USA) 25
87 **BADRI** 2
364 **BAEZ** 18
22 **BAFANA BLUE** 1
384 **BAGAN** 2
527 **BAGATELLE** 1
379 **BAGGY POINT** (IRE) 32
309 **BAGHDAD CENTRAL** (IRE) 1
426 **BAGIRA** (USA) C 44
538 **BAGUE D'OR** (IRE) 3
516 **BAHAARAH** (IRE) C 41
415 **BAHAMIAN HEIGHTS** 3
231 **BAHEEJA** C 125
122 **BAHEEJA** F 23
16 **BAHIA BREEZE** C 151
229 **BAHIA STAR** 4
76 **BAHJTEE** F 8
122 **BAHJTEE** C 77
384 **BAHRI SUGAR** (IRE) F 36
460 **BAIKAL** 26
566 **BAILAR CONTIGO** (IRE) 55

300 **BAILEYS ACCOLADE** 44
386 **BAILEYS BLING** 30
300 **BAILEYS DERBYDAY** 2
386 **BAILEYS EMINENCE** (FR) 31
386 **BAILEYS EXCELERATE** (FR) 2
300 **BAILEYS LIBERTY** 45
386 **BAILEYS SHOWGIRL** (FR) C 41
426 **BAILEYSGUTFEELING** (IRE) 19
42 **BAILY GORSE** (IRE) 1
409 **BAISE MON TCHU** (IRE) 11
6 **BAISSE** C 98
514 **BAK ROCKY** (IRE) 2
360 **BAKE** (IRE) 1
490 **BAKED ALASKA** 17
346 **BAKERSBOY** 1
488 **BAKOURA** C 40
516 **BAKR** 4
345 **BAL AMIE** (FR) 2
94 **BALAAWY** G 55
340 **BALADIO** (IRE) 2
313 **BALAGAN** 2
155 **BALAKERA** (IRE) C 56
26 **BALANCE PLAY** (IRE) 91
231 **BALANKIYA** C 126
258 **BALCO COASTAL** (FR) 5
7 **BALDOMERO** (IRE) 5
105 **BALGAIR** 2
231 **BALGOWAN** (IRE) 42
500 **BALHAMBAR** (FR) 29
395 **BALI BODY** (IRE) 5
75 **BALINACARY** G 1
472 **BALIYAD** (IRE) 2
229 **BALIYANA** (IRE) F 27
22 **BALKALIN** (FR) 2
560 **BALKARDY** (FR) 6
258 **BALKEO** (FR) 1
463 **BALKING** (FR) 1
562 **BALKO SAINT** (FR) 5
238 **BALKOTIC** (FR) 5
473 **BALLAQUANE** (IRE) 3
424 **BALLET BLANC** 14
240 **BALLET OF DUBAI** (IRE) 39
460 **BALLET STEPS** 27
13 **BALLETICON** (IRE) 4
452 **BALLIN BAY** (IRE) 1
567 **BALLINGERS CORNER** (IRE) 3
384 **BALLINLINA** F 37
560 **BALLINSKER** (IRE) 7
140 **BALLINSLEA BRIDGE** (IRE) 1
219 **BALLINTOGHER BOY** (IRE) 1
366 **BALLINTOY HARBOUR** (IRE) 1
525 **BALLINTUBBER BOY** (IRE) 1
339 **BALLISTIC BERRY** 11
212 **BALLON ONABUDGET** (IRE) 5
96 **BALLY DUN** (IRE) 2
525 **BALLYANDY** 2
458 **BALLYARE** 5
263 **BALLYATTY** 1
357 **BALLYBAY** (FR) 1
357 **BALLYBAYMOONSHINER** (FR) 2
509 **BALLYBEEN** (IRE) 4
325 **BALLYBEGG** (IRE) 1
467 **BALLYBLACK** (IRE) 1
525 **BALLYBOUGH MARY** (IRE) 3
560 **BALLYBREEN** (IRE) 8
149 **BALLYBREEZE** 2
514 **BALLYBROWNEY HALL** (IRE) G 3

309 **BALLYCALLAN FAME** (IRE) 2
525 **BALLYCAMUS** (IRE) 4
88 **BALLYCOMMON** (IRE) 2
80 **BALLYCONNEELY BAY** (IRE) 3
413 **BALLYCORR** (IRE) 1
258 **BALLYCROSS** 7
404 **BALLYDOYLE** (IRE) F 110
259 **BALLYEGAN HERO** (IRE) 3
571 **BALLYFARSOON** (IRE) 1
404 **BALLYGAMBON GIRL** (IRE) G 19
324 **BALLYGLASS** (IRE) 2
147 **BALLYGOE** (IRE) 2
476 **BALLYGRIFINCOTTAGE** (IRE) 11
313 **BALLYHAWKISH** 3
258 **BALLYHIGH** (IRE) 4
252 **BALLYMAGROARTY BOY** (IRE) 3
381 **BALLYMILAN** 3
525 **BALLYMILLSY** 5
194 **BALLYNAGRAN** (IRE) 1
73 **BALLYNAVEEN BOY** (IRE) 35
239 **BALLYRATH** (IRE) 3
193 **BALLYTOBIN** (IRE) 2
248 **BALLYVIL** (IRE) 3
294 **BALLYWHATSIT** (IRE) 1
81 **BALLYWOOD** (FR) 1
204 **BALQAA** 2
235 **BALRANALD** (FR) 1
101 **BALTIC** 67
217 **BALTIC BIRD** 45
26 **BALTIC DUCHESS** (IRE) C 92
28 **BALTIMORE BOY** (IRE) 14
329 **BALZAC** 7
367 **BAMA LAMA** 3
97 **BAMBITA** (IRE) 19
314 **BAMBOO BAY** (IRE) 6
222 **BAMFORD EDGE** (IRE) 6
387 **BAMO MC** 2
467 **BAMPTON STAR** 2
457 **BANANA JOE** (IRE) 1
7 **BANCNUANAHEIREANN** (IRE) 6
6 **BANDINELLI** 3
238 **BANDIT D'AINAY** (FR) 6
489 **BANDSMAN RICE** 1
284 **BANG ON** (IRE) 1
296 **BANG ON THE BELL** 22
420 **BANGERS AND CASH** (IRE) 7
163 **BANKAWI** 1
18 **BANKRUPT** (IRE) 20
564 **BANKSY** 22
378 **BANNED** 32
214 **BANNERGIRL** (IRE) 2
212 **BANNISTER** (FR) 6
455 **BANNIXTOWN BOY** (IRE) 3
153 **BANNSIDE** (IRE) 1
410 **BANSHEE** (IRE) 6
271 **BARAAYA** (IRE) G 1
390 **BARABOY** (IRE) 1
429 **BARACALU** (FR) 2
528 **BARADAR** (IRE) 2
530 **BARAKATLE** 1
158 **BARATHEA DANCER** (IRE) G 1
572 **BARATINEUR** (FR) 2
578 **BARB WIRE** 1
243 **BARBADOS** (IRE) 7
398 **BARBADOS BUCK'S** (IRE) 9
521 **BARBARA'S INCHARGE** 42
71 **BARBARIAN** 1

361 **BARBARY MASTER** 2
335 **BARBILL** (IRE) 5
550 **BARD OF BRITTANY** 4
407 **BARDD** (IRE) 1
559 **BARDEN BELLA** (IRE) 2
247 **BARE GRILS** (IRE) 1
118 **BARE NECESSITY** (IRE) 32
354 **BAREBACK JACK** (IRE) 5
406 **BAREFOOT CONTESSA** (FR) F 98
94 **BAREST OF MARGINS** (IRE) 3
282 **BARFORD DIVA** 2
475 **BARGAIN BLITZ** (USA) C 34
544 **BARGING THRU** 42
16 **BARI** (IRE) F 152
246 **BARI BREEZE** (IRE) 5
360 **BARLEY** (IRE) 10
314 **BARLEY BREEZE** 7
299 **BARLEYBROWN** 43
373 **BARN OWL** 9
354 **BARNABAS COLLINS** (IRE) 6
125 **BARNARD CASTLE** (IRE) 2
381 **BARNARDS GREEN** (IRE) 4
60 **BARNAVIDDAUN** (IRE) 3
82 **BARNAY** 3
399 **BARNEY STINSON** (IRE) 1
568 **BARNEY TOO** 1
164 **BARNEY'S BAY** 5
314 **BARNEYS GIFT** (FR) 87
240 **BARNEZET** (GR) F 128
223 **BARNIE BEETLE** 6
514 **BARON BRIGGS** (IRE) 4
170 **BARON DE MIDLETON** (IRE) 2
97 **BARON PALATCHI** (FR) 20
73 **BARON RUN** 4
520 **BARON SLICK** (IRE) 3
388 **BARONY LEGENDS** (IRE) 8
94 **BAROQUE STAR** (IRE) 23
371 **BARQ AL EMARAT** (IRE) 10
404 **BARRAKHOV** (IRE) 20
388 **BARRICANE** 9
354 **BARRICHELLO** 7
428 **BARRIER PEAKS** (FR) 8
7 **BARRINGTON** (IRE) 7
243 **BARRINGTON COURT** 8
30 **BARRISTER BLASTER** 1
354 **BARROWDALE** (IRE) 8
384 **BARROWMOUNT** (IRE) 3
354 **BARRULE PARK** 9
421 **BARTHOLOMEW J** (IRE) 3
340 **BARTON KNOLL** 3
231 **BARTZELLA** 10
25 **BARYSHNIKOV** 5
299 **BASCINET** 22
280 **BASCULE** (FR) 1
122 **BASE NOTE** 24
82 **BASFORD** (IRE) 4
296 **BASHARAT** 3
92 **BASHERS REFLECTION** 2
223 **BASHFUL** 7
428 **BASHFUL BOY** (IRE) 9
231 **BASHKIROVA** 11
528 **BASHOSH** (IRE) 3
25 **BASIRA** (FR) C 39
514 **BASS ROCK** (FR) 5
94 **BASS STRAIT** 24
240 **BASSMAH** F 129
164 **BASTET** (IRE) G 105

174 **BASTOGNE** 22
290 **BATCH ME** 1
205 **BATCHELOR BOY** (IRE) 1
404 **BATHIVA** (FR) 21
398 **BATHSHEBA BAY** (IRE) 10
16 **BATISTET** 153
365 **BATMAN FOR EVER** (GER) 5
365 **BATOCCHI** 6
561 **BATTANI** (IRE) 89
417 **BATTERED** 1
535 **BATTLE ANGEL** (IRE) 3
147 **BATTLE MARCH** (USA) 3
580 **BATTLE OF ACTIUM** (IRE) 3
459 **BATTLE OF MARATHON** (USA) 2
92 **BATTLE OF PAVIA** (IRE) 3
370 **BATTLE OF TORO** (IRE) 3
555 **BATTLE OF WILLS** (IRE) 5
240 **BATTLE POINT** (IRE) 40
434 **BATYA** (IRE) C 44
299 **BAULAC** 44
163 **BAVARDAGES** (IRE) 6
230 **BAVINGTON BOB** (IRE) 1
511 **BAWAADER** (IRE) 1
164 **BAY BREEZE** 106
500 **BAY BRIDGE** 3
155 **BAY OF BAKU** (FR) 16
6 **BAY OF HONOUR** (IRE) 30
404 **BAY OF INTRIGUE** 22
260 **BAY OF NAPLES** (IRE) 3
549 **BAY TREE** (IRE) G 50
430 **BAY WATCH** (IRE) 2
48 **BAYLASAN** 19
506 **BAYRAAT** 1
76 **BAYRAQ** (USA) 9
528 **BAYSIDE BOY** (IRE) 50
527 **BAYSTON HILL** 2
94 **BAZALGETTE** (IRE) 25
580 **BAZOOKA** (IRE) 2
223 **BAZZA THE BARREL** 94
395 **BBOLD** (IRE) 4
426 **BE A GRIZZLY** 45
160 **BE BE EX** (IRE) 13
381 **BE EASY** (GER) 5
89 **BE FAIR** 3
173 **BE GLORIOUS** 1
26 **BE LUCKY MY SON** (IRE) 28
277 **BE MY ANGEL** F 9
101 **BE MY GAL** F 68
89 **BE MY SEA** (IRE) 4
59 **BE PREPARED** 2
215 **BE PROUD** (IRE) 4
543 **BE SASSY** (IRE) 28
304 **BE THANKFUL** 3
474 **BE THE BEST** (USA) 3
314 **BE THE DIFFERENCE** (IRE) 8
354 **BEACH BREAK** 10
6 **BEACH FROLIC** C 99
317 **BEACH KITTY** (IRE) 38
240 **BEACH WEDDING** (IRE) C 130
262 **BEACHES** 25
361 **BEACON EDGE** (IRE) 3
200 **BEAGNACH SASTA** (IRE) 2
476 **BEAKSTOWN** (IRE) 12
373 **BEALACH** (IRE) 10
110 **BEALATH CHAMP** (IRE) F 2
6 **BEAN FEASA** F 100
409 **BEAN IN TROUBLE** 12

320 **BEAN NORTY** 3
431 **BEAR FORCE** 36
508 **BEAR FORCE ONE** 2
349 **BEAR GHYLLS** (IRE) 2
426 **BEAR ON THE LOOSE** (IRE) 46
566 **BEAR PROFIT** (IRE) 36
233 **BEAR STORY** (IRE) 3
10 **BEAR TO DREAM** (IRE) 32
378 **BEARAWAY** (IRE) 4
179 **BEARCARDI** (IRE) 13
335 **BEARING BOB** 44
178 **BEAT BOX** (IRE) 2
201 **BEAT THE BAT** (IRE) 3
54 **BEAT THE HEAT** 4
48 **BEAT THE STARS** (IRE) F 62
157 **BEAT THE STORM** (IRE) 5
262 **BEATIFY** (IRE) F 62
424 **BEATRICE AURORE** (IRE) F 15
205 **BEATRIX ENCHANTE** 2
125 **BEATTHEBULLET** (IRE) 3
243 **BEAU BRIDGET** (IRE) C 9
373 **BEAU FRENCH** (FR) 11
89 **BEAU GESTE** (IRE) 5
129 **BEAU HAZE** 1
59 **BEAU JARDINE** (IRE) 3
67 **BEAU LILLY** 8
217 **BEAU NASH** (IRE) 3
122 **BEAU RIVAGE** 25
48 **BEAU ROC** 63
366 **BEAU STRATA** (IRE) G 44
10 **BEAUEN ARROWS** 33
286 **BEAUFORT WEST** (IRE) 2
220 **BEAUMADIER** (IRE) 22
525 **BEAUPORT** (IRE) 6
458 **BEAUTE NOIRE** (IRE) 6
375 **BEAUTIFUL BEN** (IRE) 4
39 **BEAUTIFUL COLOUR** 66
297 **BEAUTIFUL CROWN** 2
229 **BEAUTIFUL FOREST** F 28
362 **BEAUTIFUL MIX** 1
422 **BEAUTIFUL MUM** 18
186 **BEAUTIFUL SUNRISE** (IRE) 26
417 **BEAUTIFUL SURPRISE** 15
293 **BEAUTY CHOICE** 2
561 **BEAUTY OF FREEDOM** (IRE) 9
406 **BEAUZON** 57
219 **BEBSIDE BANTER** (IRE) 2
404 **BECKY THE BOO** 23
418 **BEDFORD BLAZE** (IRE) 3
179 **BEDFORD FLYER** (IRE) 1
466 **BEDFORD HOUSE** 9
6 **BEDOUIN QUEEN** 31
39 **BEDOUIN'S STORY** 2
438 **BEEBEE** 4
463 **BEENO** (IRE) 2
525 **BEEP BEEP** (IRE) 7
23 **BEERENBERG** 16
361 **BEESCATTY** (IRE) 69
509 **BEFORE MIDNIGHT** 5
378 **BEGGARMAN** 5
73 **BEGGARMANS ROAD** (IRE) 36
12 **BEGIN THE LUCK** (IRE) 3
243 **BEGINISH** 79
306 **BEGOODTOYOURSELF** (IRE) 1
458 **BEHINDTHELINES** (IRE) 7
485 **BEHOLDEN** 4
97 **BEL ARISTO** (FR) 4

222 **BEL MARE** 7
567 **BELAMI DES PICTONS** (FR) 4
213 **BELARGUS** (FR) 1
16 **BELDALE MEMORY** (IRE) F 154
89 **BELEK BULLFINCH** 6
173 **BELHAVEN** (IRE) 14
528 **BELIEVE IN LOVE** (IRE) 4
500 **BELIEVE IN STARS** (IRE) 30
388 **BELIEVE JACK** (FR) 10
431 **BELISA DE VEGA** (IRE) 20
454 **BELL BOTTOM BLUES** (IRE) 4
398 **BELL EX ONE** (IRE) 11
377 **BELL HEATHER** (IRE) 3
16 **BELL ROCK** 6
262 **BELL SHOT** (IRE) 26
398 **BELL WALKS DAY** (IRE) G 12
252 **BELLA BEAU** (IRE) 4
555 **BELLA BLUESKY** 6
492 **BELLA BLUR** 1
32 **BELLA COLOROSSA** 2
243 **BELLA ESTRELLA** (IRE) C 139
249 **BELLA FEVER** (URU) 1
555 **BELLA GLENEAGLES** (IRE) 7
516 **BELLA KOPELLA** (IRE) 42
369 **BELLA LAZANIA** 1
576 **BELLA VARENNA** (IRE) F 24
229 **BELLA VENETA** 14
62 **BELLAGIO MAN** (IRE) 4
221 **BELLAMY'S GREY** 1
155 **BELLARENA LADY** 17
567 **BELLATRIXSA** (IRE) 5
299 **BELLAZZO** (IRE) 45
417 **BELLE ABOVE ALL** C 49
566 **BELLE BOUTEILLE** (IRE) 37
39 **BELLE BOYD** C 95
274 **BELLE DE MANECH** (FR) 3
300 **BELLE ISLE** F 127
216 **BELLE JOUR** (IRE) 5
385 **BELLE METAL** (IRE) 16
381 **BELLE NA BANN** (IRE) 6
127 **BELLE OF ANNANDALE** (IRE) 50
243 **BELLECHANCE** C 140
399 **BELLELOISE** 2
436 **BELLEVARDE** (IRE) 1
511 **BELLEVUE LAD** 2
477 **BELLICA** 2
364 **BELLOCCIO** (FR) 2
98 **BELLOSA** (IRE) 4
529 **BELLS OF PETERBORO** (IRE) 4
529 **BELLS OF RUTLAND** (IRE) 5
529 **BELLS OF STAMFORD** (IRE) 6
184 **BELLSHILL BEAUTY** (IRE) 24
127 **BELLSLEA** (IRE) 51
28 **BELLSTREET BRIDIE** 15
403 **BELONG** (IRE) F 25
537 **BELOVED** (IRE) 1
158 **BELOVED OF ALL** (IRE) 14
217 **BELT BUCKLE** 46
127 **BELTANE** (IRE) 52
302 **BELVEDERE BLAST** (IRE) 4
473 **BEMBRIDGE** (IRE) 4
4 **BEMPTON CLIFFS** (IRE) 5
451 **BEN ASKER** (IRE) 1
295 **BEN BRODY** (IRE) 4
304 **BEN BUIE** (IRE) 4
201 **BEN BULBEN** (IRE) 4

428 **BEN LILLY** (IRE) 11
414 **BEN LOMOND** (IRE) 51
460 **BEN MACDUI** (IRE) 2
361 **BEN SIEGEL** 4
361 **BEN THOMSON** (IRE) 5
178 **BENACK** (IRE) 3
300 **BENACRE** (IRE) 128
490 **BEND HASCHE** (IRE) 18
181 **BENADALID** 1
23 **BENANDGONE** 2
288 **BENDIS** (GER) F 19
57 **BENDY BOW** 1
185 **BENEDICT WILDES** (IRE) 31
258 **BENEFACT** (IRE) 9
73 **BENEFICIARY** 37
118 **BENEFIT** 33
505 **BENEVENTA** C 50
373 **BENEVOLENTDICTATOR** 12
388 **BENIGN DICTATOR** (IRE) 11
320 **BENITO** (FR) 4
243 **BENITOITE** (IRE) 80
312 **BENJAMIN BEAR** (IRE) 136
315 **BENNY AND THE JETS** (IRE) 2
149 **BENNY'S BRIDGE** (IRE) 3
476 **BENNYS KING** (IRE) 13
395 **BENSON** 7
471 **BENVILLE BRIDGE** 1
280 **BENY NAHAR ROAD** (IRE) 23
406 **BENZEMA** 58
122 **BENZINE** 26
28 **BEOWULF** (IRE) 2
496 **BERAGON** 23
476 **BERAZ** (FR) 14
262 **BEREKA** C 63
6 **BERENGARIA** (IRE) C 101
385 **BERET ROUGE** (IRE) 17
460 **BERGERAC** (IRE) 3
312 **BERINGER** 3
16 **BERKSHIRE BRAVE** (IRE) 155
16 **BERKSHIRE BREEZE** (IRE) 62
16 **BERKSHIRE CRUZ** 156
16 **BERKSHIRE PHANTOM** 157
16 **BERKSHIRE REBEL** (IRE) 63
16 **BERKSHIRE ROCCO** (FR) 7
385 **BERKSHIRE ROYAL** 18
16 **BERKSHIRE SHADOW** 64
16 **BERKSHIRE SUNDANCE** 158
332 **BERMACHA** G 1
118 **BERMUDA** 28
364 **BERMUDIANA** (FR) 19
540 **BERNARD SPIERPOINT** 5
488 **BERNARDO O'REILLY** 5
164 **BERRA GO** (IRE) 107
32 **BERRAHRI** (IRE) 3
326 **BERRY BABY** (IRE) F 15
145 **BERRY EDGE** (IRE) 4
339 **BERRY QUICK** 12
342 **BERRYGAR** 19
25 **BERT KIBBLER** 6
252 **BERT WILSON** (IRE) 5
323 **BERTIE BLUE** 3
517 **BERTIE WOOSTER** (IRE) 6
463 **BERTIE'S BALLET** 3
409 **BERTIE'S BANDANA** (IRE) 13
256 **BERTIELICIOUS** 1
340 **BERTOG** 4
300 **BERWICK LAW** (IRE) 129

31 **BERYL BURTON** 1
426 **BERYL THE PERIL** (IRE) 3
231 **BESHARAH** F 127
173 **BESHAYER** (FR) F 25
520 **BESSICHKA** C 26
118 **BEST BOY ALFIE** (IRE) 35
292 **BEST CHECKER** 53
402 **BEST IN THE WORLD** (IRE) C 111
149 **BEST PAL** (IRE) 4
314 **BEST SIDE** (IRE) F 97
6 **BEST TERMS** F 102
388 **BEST TRITION** (IRE) 12
44 **BESTIARIUS** (IRE) 2
47 **BETA TAURI** (USA) F 59
280 **BETHERSDEN BOY** (IRE) 24
409 **BETHKA** (IRE) 14
240 **BETSHOOF** 41
300 **BETTER HALF** 46
312 **BETTERFOREVERYONE** 4
16 **BETTERMENT** 159
164 **BETTY BALOO** 6
173 **BETTY BROWN** 22
409 **BETTY'S BANJO** (IRE) 15
420 **BETTY'S BELLE** 8
173 **BETWEEN THE COVERS** (IRE) 26
28 **BETWEEN THE SHEETS** (IRE) 16
485 **BETWEEN THE WATERS** (IRE) 5
457 **BEWARE THE BEAR** (IRE) 2
16 **BEWITCHMENT** C 160
207 **BEXANDELLA** G 6
277 **BEYCHELLA** (USA) C 10
516 **BEYLERBEY** (USA) F 43
316 **BEYOND BOUNDARIES** (IRE) 8
388 **BEYOND EQUAL** 1
480 **BEYOND EVERYTHING** (IRE) 13
260 **BEYOND FASHION** C 8
73 **BEYOND INFINITY** 3
443 **BEYOND REPROACH** (IRE) 83
333 **BEYOND SUPREMACY** (IRE) 1
404 **BEYOND THE CLOUDS** 3
89 **BEYOND THE PALE** (IRE) 24
231 **BEZZAS LAD** (IRE) 7
404 **BHAGEERATHI** (IRE) C 128
99 **BHALOO** (IRE) 25
185 **BHARANI STAR** (GER) 1
93 **BHUBEZI** 3
83 **BIBULOUS** (IRE) 2
185 **BIBURY** C 61
521 **BICEP** (IRE) 43
508 **BICKERSTAFFE** 3
460 **BIELSA** (IRE) 4
529 **BIELSA'S BUCKET** 39
341 **BIG 'N BETTER** 1
218 **BIG ARTHUR** 2
445 **BIG BAD BEAR** (IRE) 2
432 **BIG BAD BUZZ** (IRE) 2
373 **BIG BARD** 13
549 **BIG BEAR HUG** 30
298 **BIG BOLD GOLD** (IRE) 1
312 **BIG BOY BOBBY** (IRE) 5
212 **BIG BRESIL** 7
34 **BIG CHEESE** (FR) 13
420 **BIG DIFFERENCE** (IRE) 9
10 **BIG DRIFT** 44
344 **BIG DUTCHIE** (IRE) 1
314 **BIG EARS** (IRE) 9
323 **BIG FISH** (IRE) 4

61 **BIG IMPACT** 6
222 **BIG JIM BEAM** (IRE) 8
80 **BIG LES** (IRE) 4
414 **BIG LITTLE LIE** (IRE) 3
39 **BIG MEETING** (IRE) 3
489 **BIG MUDDY** 5
488 **BIG NARSTIE** (FR) 2
304 **BIG NASTY** 5
182 **BIG NEWS** (IRE) 17
31 **BIG PETE** 2
299 **BIG** R 46
458 **BIG RIVER** (IRE) 8
163 **BIG STAR** 36
39 **BIG TEAM** (USA) 4
10 **BIG TIME MAYBE** (IRE) 1
162 **BIG TREE** (IRE) 3
240 **BIG WING** (IRE) 2
380 **BIGBADBOY** (IRE) 2
178 **BIGBADMATTIE** (IRE) 4
516 **BIGGER PICTURE** (IRE) C 5
26 **BIGGLES** 3
143 **BIGIRONONHISHIP** (IRE) 2
209 **BIGNORM** (IRE) 1
436 **BILBOA RIVER** (IRE) 2
130 **BILINGUAL** 3
246 **BILL AND BARN** (IRE) 6
222 **BILL BAXTER** (IRE) 9
80 **BILL CODY** (IRE) 5
361 **BILL DOOLIN** 6
356 **BILL PLUMB** (IRE) 15
101 **BILLABONG** 69
404 **BILLAMS LEGACY** 26
385 **BILLAWAY** (IRE) 19
314 **BILLIAN** (IRE) 10
549 **BILLIE LOU** 51
200 **BILLIEBROOKEDIT** (IRE) 3
440 **BILLINGSLEY** (IRE) 2
404 **BILLY BOI BLUE** 27
196 **BILLY DYLAN** (IRE) 2
67 **BILLY MCGARRY** 9
367 **BILLY MILL** 4
145 **BILLY NO MATES** (IRE) 5
172 **BILLY RAY** 3
556 **BILLY ROBERTS** (IRE) 1
362 **BILLY WEDGE** 2
151 **BILLYB** (FR) 19
39 **BIN BATTUTA** 5
406 **BIN HAYYAN** (IRE) 59
156 **BINGLEY CROCKER** (IRE) 17
370 **BINGOO** 4
39 **BINT ALMATAR** (USA) F 96
490 **BINT ALSARAB** (IRE) 19
460 **BINT ALSHARF** 28
409 **BIOWAVEGO** (IRE) 16
533 **BIPLANE** (USA) 1
527 **BIRD FOR LIFE** 3
354 **BIRD ON THE WIRE** (FR) 11
527 **BIRD TO LOVE** 4
511 **BIRDIE BOWERS** (IRE) 3
300 **BIRDIE PUTT** (IRE) 47
517 **BIRDMAN BOB** (IRE) 7
398 **BIRDS OF PREY** (IRE) 13
366 **BIRKENHEAD** 7
374 **BIRKIE GIRL** 14
312 **BIRTH HARSH** (IRE) 137
535 **BIT OF A QUIRKE** 4
194 **BIT ON THE SIDE** (IRE) 2

122 **BOLD PRESENCE** 27
258 **BOLD REACTION** (FR) 13
528 **BOLD RIBB** 51
222 **BOLD SOLDIER** 11
572 **BOLD SPECTRUM** 4
110 **BOLD TARA** G 4
145 **BOLD TERRITORIES** (IRE) 8
85 **BOLD VISION** (IRE) 2
12 **BOLDMERE** 4
125 **BOLEY BAY** (IRE) 5
92 **BOLEYN BOY** 4
229 **BOLEYNA** (USA) C 29
395 **BOLINTLEA** (IRE) 8
164 **BOLLIN JOAN** 9
164 **BOLLIN MARGARET** 10
164 **BOLLIN NEIL** 11
164 **BOLLIN PHOENIX** 12
458 **BOLLINGERANDKRUG** (IRE) 11
411 **BOLLY BULLET** (IRE) 1
402 **BOLSHOI BALLET** (IRE) 1
222 **BOLSOVER BILL** (IRE) 11
122 **BOLSTER** 78
153 **BOLT MAN** 2
307 **BOLT N BROWN** 1
28 **BOLTHOLE** (IRE) 17
327 **BOLTISSIME** (FR) 5
365 **BOLTON** 7
374 **BOMB SQUAD** (IRE) 2
61 **BOMBASTIC** (IRE) 8
220 **BOMBAY GLORY** (IRE) 3
83 **BOMBINATE** 18
531 **BOMBYX** 4
445 **BON RETOUR** (IRE) 3
327 **BONBON AU MIEL** (FR) 6
142 **BOND ANGEL** 5
7 **BOND BOY** 84
478 **BOND CHAIRMAN** 14
478 **BOND POWER** 15
2 **BOND SPIRIT** 6
251 **BOND'S GIFT** F 2
330 **BONDESIRE** C 8
98 **BONDI GIRL** (IRE) 24
280 **BONDI MAN** 25
15 **BONDI SPICE** (IRE) 31
94 **BONITA** B 27
163 **BONNE** C 69
238 **BONNE VITESSE** (IRE) 7
15 **BONNET** 2
542 **BONNIE BANJO** 1
280 **BONNIE LAD** 2
431 **BONNSIE** (IRE) 37
118 **BONNY ANGEL** 85
554 **BONNY HOUXTY** 1
404 **BONTTAY** (IRE) 33
54 **BONUS** 5
467 **BONZA BOY** 3
47 **BOODLEY** C 61
73 **BOOGIE TIME** (IRE) 5
232 **BOOK OF GOLD** (IRE) 3
476 **BOOK OF SECRETS** (IRE) 17
335 **BOOKMARK** 1
243 **BOOLA BOOLA** (IRE) 10
157 **BOOLAMORE GLORY** (IRE) 9
258 **BOOM BOOM** (IRE) 14
26 **BOOM BOOM POW** 93
89 **BOOM THE GROOM** (IRE) 10
476 **BOOMBAWN** (IRE) 18

100 **BOONGA ROOGETA** C 8
460 **BOONIE** (IRE) 29
231 **BOOSALA** (IRE) 12
365 **BOOT 'N' SHOE** (IRE) 8
201 **BOOTHILL** (IRE) 5
131 **BOOTLEGGER** (IRE) 3
243 **BOPEDRO** (FR) 11
390 **BORDER VICTOR** 2
304 **BORDERLINE** (IRE) 7
388 **BOREEN BOY** (IRE) 16
323 **BOREHAM BILL** (IRE) 5
576 **BORGI** (IRE) 3
576 **BORJA** (IRE) C 25
523 **BORN AT MIDNIGHT** 1
517 **BORN IN BORRIS** (IRE) 9
434 **BORN RULER** 45
73 **BORN TO BE ALIVE** (IRE) 6
433 **BORN TO FINISH** (IRE) 2
279 **BORN TO FROLIC** (IRE) 1
527 **BORN TO PLEASE** 6
540 **BORN TO SIRE** (IRE) 6
73 **BORN TO SPEND** (IRE) F 84
424 **BORNTOBEALEADER** (IRE) 16
307 **BORO LASS** 2
240 **BOSH** (IRE) 42
476 **BOSS MAN FRED** (IRE) 19
500 **BOSS POWER** (IRE) 4
164 **BOSSIPOP** 13
125 **BOSTON JOE** (IRE) 6
15 **BOTANIST** 32
554 **BOTH BARRELS** 2
263 **BOTHIE LADY** (IRE) 2
258 **BOTHWELL BRIDGE** (IRE) 15
373 **BOTOX HAS** (FR) 15
178 **BOTTLE HILL** 6
150 **BOTUS FLEMING** 1
5 **BOUDICA BAY** (IRE) 1
255 **BOUDICA WARRIOR** (IRE) 13
548 **BOUGHTBEFORELUNCH** (IRE) 1
252 **BOULETTE** (IRE) 4
576 **BOULIVAR** (IRE) 4
313 **BOULTING FOR GLORY** (IRE) 4
544 **BOUNCE BACK** 5
16 **BOUNCE THE BLUES** (IRE) 9
519 **BOUNCING BOBBY** (IRE) 5
6 **BOUND** (IRE) C 105
7 **BOUNDLESS POWER** (IRE) 9
223 **BOUNDSY BOY** 10
43 **BOUNTY PURSUIT** 3
217 **BOUQUET** 48
517 **BOURBALI** (FR) 10
232 **BOURBON BEAUTY** 4
365 **BOURBON BORDERLINE** (IRE) 9
163 **BOW BRIDGE** C 37
365 **BOWLAND BELLE** 3
319 **BOWLAND PARK** 2
164 **BOWLAND PRINCE** (IRE) 164
15 **BOWLING RUSSIAN** (IRE) 3
372 **BOWMAN** (IRE) 3
420 **BOWTOGREATNESS** (IRE) 11
346 **BOX TO BOX** (IRE) 17
300 **BOY ABOUT TOWN** 49
299 **BOY BROWNING** 50
187 **BOY GEORGE** 1
561 **BOY IN THE BAR** 11
458 **BOY'S ON TOUR** (IRE) 12
212 **BOYHOOD** (IRE) 12

413 **BOYS OF WEXFORD** 2
356 **BRACE FOR IMPACT** (IRE) 16
361 **BRACE YOURSELF** (IRE) 8
402 **BRACELET** (IRE) C 113
215 **BRAES OF DOUNE** 6
385 **BRAHMA BULL** (IRE) 24
414 **BRAINS** (IRE) 4
327 **BRAINSTORM** (FR) 7
373 **BRAMBLEDOWN** 16
170 **BRANCASTER** (IRE) 3
531 **BRANDISOVA** (IRE) 5
164 **BRANDY BAY** 14
560 **BRANDY COVE** (IRE) 12
286 **BRANDY CROSS** (IRE) 4
385 **BRANDY LOVE** (IRE) 25
218 **BRANDY MCQUEEN** (IRE) 3
568 **BRANDY STATION** (IRE) 2
156 **BRANSON MISSOURI** (IRE) 2
508 **BRANSTON PIKKLE** 5
48 **BRASIL POWER** (FR) 20
405 **BRASINGAMAN BELLA** 21
120 **BRASS CASTLE** 9
61 **BRASS CLANKERS** 9
367 **BRATISLAVA** C 33
490 **BRAULIA** 21
365 **BRAVANTINA** 11
258 **BRAVE EAGLE** (IRE) 16
124 **BRAVE GOZZY** (BEL) 3
258 **BRAVE JEN** 17
398 **BRAVE KINGDOM** (FR) 15
434 **BRAVE KNIGHT** 46
567 **BRAVE SEASCA** (FR) 6
505 **BRAVE THE STORM** (IRE) 8
485 **BRAVEHEART** (IRE) 6
398 **BRAVEMANSGAME** (FR) 16
223 **BRAVETHEWAVES** 7
434 **BRAVURA** 47
101 **BRAYDEN STAR** 16
178 **BRAYHILL** (IRE) 7
344 **BRAZEN AKOYA** 11
158 **BRAZEN ARROW** 2
507 **BRAZEN BELLE** 1
77 **BRAZEN GIRL** 51
568 **BRAZEN LADY** 3
164 **BRAZILIAN BEACH** (IRE) 108
47 **BRAZILIAN BRIDE** (IRE) C 62
317 **BRAZILIAN LORD** 18
319 **BREAK TIME** F 33
111 **BREAKEVEN** (IRE) 1
22 **BREAKING RECORDS** (IRE) 3
38 **BREAKING THE ICE** (IRE) 3
557 **BREAKING WAVES** (IRE) 1
346 **BREATHALYZE** (FR) 2
198 **BREATHLESSLY** (IRE) 1
187 **BRECKLAND** 2
387 **BREEZYANDBRIGHT** (IRE) 3
265 **BREFFNIBOY** (FR) 9
10 **BREGUET BOY** (IRE) 2
304 **BREIZH ALKO** (FR) 8
251 **BRELAN D'AS** (FR) 3
280 **BRENTFORD HOPE** 3
567 **BRESILIANT** 7
262 **BREVITY** (USA) C 65
398 **BREWERS PROJECT** (IRE) 17
388 **BREWIN'UPASTORM** (IRE) 17
231 **BREWING** 3
549 **BRIAC** (FR) 3

400 **BRIAN BORANHA** (IRE) 1
377 **BRIAN THE SNAIL** (IRE) 4
304 **BRIANNA ROSE** (IRE) 9
567 **BRIANSTORM** (IRE) 8
34 **BRIARDALE** (IRE) 2
238 **BRICKADANK** (IRE) 8
187 **BRICKLAGGER** (IRE) 3
402 **BRIDAL DANCE** (IRE) C 114
258 **BRIDAL KNOT** (IRE) 18
280 **BRIDES BAY** (IRE) 26
48 **BRIDGE POSEIDON** F (IRE) F 64
82 **BRIDGE ROAD** (IRE) 5
361 **BRIDGEHEAD** (IRE) 70
80 **BRIDGETOWN** 6
94 **BRIDIE FFRENCH** F 56
404 **BRIEF AMBITION** 34
381 **BRIEF TIMES** (IRE) 9
564 **BRIERY EXPRESS** 2
280 **BRIGANTES WARRIOR** 27
505 **BRIGHT APPROACH** (IRE) C 51
304 **BRIGHT BLAZE** (IRE) G 10
34 **BRIGHT BLUE** (IRE) 14
454 **BRIGHT DAWN** (IRE) 3
350 **BRIGHT EDGE** F 11
240 **BRIGHT EYED** (IRE) F 131
284 **BRIGHT FOCUS** 2
233 **BRIGHT GLORY** 4
537 **BRIGHT NEW DAY** (IRE) F 60
266 **BRIGHT SAFFRON** 3
26 **BRIGHT SIDE GIRL** (IRE) 94
104 **BRIGHT SPIRIT** 16
39 **BRIGHT START** (USA) 6
373 **BRILLIANT BLUE** (IRE) 138
240 **BRILLIANT COLOURS** (IRE) 132
39 **BRILLIANT LIGHT** 7
280 **BRILLIANT NEWS** (IRE) 28
258 **BRILLIANT PRESENT** (IRE) 19
56 **BRIN MÔ** 1
385 **BRING ON THE NIGHT** 26
252 **BRING THE ACTION** (IRE) 7
345 **BRING THE MONEY** (IRE) 3
127 **BRINGITONBORIS** (USA) 7
428 **BRINKLEY** (FR) 12
6 **BRISTOL BAY** (IRE) C 106
525 **BRISTOL DE MAI** (FR) 10
204 **BRISTOL HILL** (IRE) 3
16 **BRITANNICA** 161
431 **BROAD APPEAL** 1
378 **BROADLANDS** F 60
471 **BROADOAK** 2
528 **BROADSPEAR** 52
233 **BROADWAY DUCHESS** (IRE) F 41
1 **BROADWAY JOE** (IRE) 5
374 **BROCKAGH CAILIN** 3
458 **BROCKWELL PARK** G 13
44 **BROCTUNE RED** 4
277 **BRODERIE ANGLAISE** (IRE) F 11
516 **BROKEN APPLAUSE** (IRE) F 44
398 **BROKEN HALO** 18
35 **BROKEN RIFLE** 1
119 **BROKEN SPEAR** 1
431 **BROLLY** 21
385 **BRONN** (IRE) 27
488 **BRONTE FLYER** F 41
170 **BRONTE SISTER** (IRE) F 65
520 **BRONZE ANGEL** (IRE) 4
7 **BRONZE RIVER** 10

232 **BROOKLYN BELLE** 5
385 **BROOKLYNN GLORY** (IRE) 28
560 **BROOKSWAY FAIR** (IRE) 13
402 **BROOME** (IRE) 2
258 **BROOMFIELD BURG** (IRE) 20
38 **BROOMFIELDS KAN** (IRE) 4
365 **BROOMHILL DAISY** 12
460 **BROOMY LAW** 5
304 **BRORSON** (IRE) 11
354 **BROTHER PAT** 15
514 **BROTHERLY COMPANY** (IRE) 6
41 **BROUGHTONS CHARM** (IRE) F 8
373 **BROUGHTONS COMPASS** 17
335 **BROUGHTONS FLARE** (IRE) 8
353 **BROUGHTONS PEACE** 1
426 **BROUGHTONS REVIVAL** C 47
284 **BROUGHTONS RHYTHM** 3
535 **BROUGHTONS SECRET** G 46
427 **BROWN ARROW** (IRE) G 1
286 **BROWN BULLET** (IRE) 5
220 **BROWN EAGLE** (IRE) 17
284 **BROWN MOUSE** (IRE) 20
25 **BROWNLEE** (IRE) 40
287 **BROXI** (IRE) 4
473 **BRUMMIE BOYS** (IRE) 5
280 **BRUNEL CHARM** 4
506 **BRUNELLO BREEZE** 10
417 **BRUNNERA** 2
508 **BRUNO HEINKE** G 32
544 **BRUNO'S GOLD** (IRE) 44
83 **BRUSH CREEK** 19
432 **BRUSHED UP** 3
508 **BRUTE FORCE** 6
287 **BRUXCALINA** (FR) F 29
331 **BRYANWOOD** (IRE) 4
147 **BRYHER** 4
414 **BRYNTEG** 32
20 **BUACHAILL** (IRE) 25
167 **BUBBLE DUBI** (FR) 5
388 **BUBBLES OF GOLD** (IRE) 18
123 **BUBBLES'N'TROUBLES** 1
299 **BUCCABAY** (IRE) 51
579 **BUCEPHALUS** (GER) 2
27 **BUCK DANCING** (IRE) 1
130 **BUCK N SKIP** 7
398 **BUCK'S BABE** (IRE) G 192
212 **BUCK'S BOGGLE** (FR) 13
517 **BUCKHORN GEORGE** 11
517 **BUCKHORN ROCCO** 12
124 **BUCKLAND BOY** (IRE) 4
485 **BUCKO'S BOY** 7
112 **BUDARRI** 6
458 **BUDDHA SCHEME** (IRE) 14
205 **BUDDY'S BEAUTY** 14
521 **BUFORD** 4
394 **BUG BOY** (IRE) 2
164 **BUGGERLUGS** 165
231 **BUGLE BEADS** 130
217 **BUGLE BOY** 49
280 **BUGLE MAJOR** (USA) 5
361 **BUGS MORAN** (IRE) 9
397 **BUILD ME UP** (IRE) 9
249 **BUILDING YEAR** (IRE) 2
308 **BUKELA** 4
26 **BULLACE** 4
300 **BULLDOG SPIRIT** (IRE) 130
238 **BULLDOZE** (IRE) 9

293 **BULLEIT** 8
73 **BULLET FORCE** (IRE) 38
560 **BULLION** (FR) 14
445 **BULLION BOSS** (IRE) 4
47 **BULLISH** (IRE) 29
292 **BULLS AYE** (IRE) 5
16 **BULRUSHES** C 162
496 **BUMBLE BAY** 1
371 **BUMPTIOUS** F 11
428 **BUMPY JOHNSON** (IRE) 13
212 **BUN DORAN** (IRE) 14
302 **BUNGLE BAY** (IRE) 16
296 **BUNGLEDUPINBLUE** (IRE) 4
164 **BUNGLEY** (IRE) 109
366 **BUNIANN** (IRE) 3
317 **BUNKER BAY** (IRE) 19
122 **BUNTINGFORD** (IRE) C 79
32 **BURABACK** (IRE) 25
370 **BURBANK** (IRE) 5
238 **BURDIGALA** (FR) 10
81 **BURGUNDY MAN** (IRE) 2
397 **BURJ MALINKA** (IRE) 2
238 **BURNAGE BOY** (IRE) 11
155 **BURNING BUSH** (IRE) 18
366 **BURNING CASH** (IRE) 4
80 **BURNING EMOTION** 31
385 **BURNING VICTORY** (IRE) 29
404 **BURRISTO** (IRE) 35
405 **BURROW SEVEN** 3
483 **BURROWS DIAMOND** (FR) 8
258 **BURROWS EDGE** (FR) 21
483 **BURROWS HALL** (FR) 9
567 **BURROWS LIGHT** (FR) 10
483 **BURROWS PARK** (FR) 9
385 **BURROWS SAINT** (FR) 30
314 **BURROWS SEESIDE** (FR) 12
201 **BURROWS TREAT** (FR) 6
94 **BURTONLODGE BEAUTY** (IRE) 28
80 **BURTONWOOD** 7
314 **BUSBY** (IRE) 13
378 **BUSHFIRE** 33
314 **BUSHYPARK** (IRE) 14
83 **BUSSELTON** 20
299 **BUSSENTO** 4
323 **BUSTER THOMAS** (IRE) 6
535 **BUSTER VALENTINE** (IRE) 7
44 **BUSY STREET** 5
272 **BUT YOU SAID** (IRE) 1
388 **BUTCH** 19
61 **BUTCHEROFSTOCKHOLM** 10
440 **BUTLER'S BRIEF** (IRE) 4
163 **BUTOOLAT** C 70
47 **BUTTERCROSS** F 63
402 **BUTTERFLIES** (IRE) C 115
403 **BUTTERFLY COVE** (USA) F 26
402 **BUTTERFLY ROSE** (IRE) 17
517 **BUTTERFLYCOLLECTOR** (IRE) 13
528 **BUTTERSCOTCH** (IRE) F 155
517 **BUTTERWICK BROOK** (IRE) 14
235 **BUTTEVANT LADY** (IRE) 2
326 **BUTTONHOLE** C 2
326 **BUTTONHOLE** F 20
434 **BUTTRESS** 21
258 **BUTTSBURY LADY** 22
258 **BUVEUR D'AIR** (FR) 23
364 **BUXLOW BELLE** (FR) C 46
561 **BUXTED REEL** (FR) 90

561 **BUXTED TOO** 12
335 **BUY ME BACK** 9
26 **BUYING TROUBLE** (USA) F 95
258 **BUZZ** (FR) 24
149 **BUZZ DE TURCOING** (FR) 5
7 **BY JOVE** 11
260 **BY MOONLIGHT** 22
89 **BY RIGHTS** F 97
83 **BY STARLIGHT** (IRE) 3
155 **BY YOUR SIDE** 19
454 **BYDAY** 11
426 **BYEFORNOW** 48
204 **BYFORD** (FR) 4
549 **BYHOOKORBYCROOK** 31
240 **BYKER** 43
561 **BYRON FLYER** 13
522 **BYRON HILL** (IRE) 1
122 **BYSTANDER** (IRE) 80
404 **BYZANTINE EMPIRE** 36
333 **BYZANTIUM LAD** (IRE) 5
403 **C'EST MA SOUER** (IRE) C 27
268 **C'EST NO MOUR** (GER) 1
124 **C'EST QUELQU'UN** (FR) 5
561 **C'MON KENNY** 14
561 **C'MON SHARPY** (IRE) 15
375 **CABALGATA** (IRE) 6
127 **CABALLERO** (IRE) 8
108 **CABAYO LADY** 1
108 **CABAYO LORD BRYAN** 2
108 **CABAYO LORD GEORGE** 3
344 **CABELO** (IRE) F 17
10 **CABEZA DE LLAVE** 34
228 **CABHFUILLFUNGI** (IRE) 2
300 **CABINET MAKER** (IRE) 50
299 **CABINET OF CLOWNS** (IRE) 23
146 **CABLE MOUNTAIN** 23
476 **CABOT CLIFFS** (IRE) 20
458 **CABOY** (FR) 15
240 **CABRAKAN** (IRE) 44
48 **CACHET** (IRE) 21
220 **CACTUS TREE** (IRE) 4
402 **CADABOMOSTO** (IRE) 18
82 **CADDYHILL** (IRE) 6
428 **CADEAU D'OR** (FR) 14
84 **CADEAU DU BRESIL** (FR) 1
243 **CADILLAC** (IRE) 12
216 **CADMAR** 9
86 **CADMOON** (FR) 3
146 **CADMUS** (IRE) 67
402 **CADOGAN SQUARE** 19
402 **CADOGAN SQUARE** 20
262 **CAESAR NERO** 27
376 **CAESAR ROCK** (IRE) 1
122 **CAESAR'S PALACE** 28
262 **CAESONIA** 1
18 **CAFE ESPRESSO** 4
206 **CAFE LASSERE** (USA) G 1
146 **CAFE MILANO** 4
525 **CAFE PUSHKIN** (FR) 11
89 **CAFE SYDNEY** (IRE) 11
90 **CAHORS** 2
143 **CAILIN DEARG** (IRE) 3
260 **CAILIN MEIDHREACH** (IRE) F 4
122 **CAIRNCROSS** (IRE) F 81
194 **CAIRNSHILL** (IRE) 3
364 **CAIUS CHORISTER** (IRE) 21
488 **CAIUS COLLEGE GIRL** (IRE) F 42

445 **CAIUS MARCIUS** (IRE) 5
367 **CAJUN MOON** F 34
6 **CALARE** (IRE) C 107
529 **CALARULES** 2
171 **CALCULUS** (IRE) 2
163 **CALCUTTA DREAM** (IRE) 7
482 **CALDERBANK** 37
469 **CALDWELL** 3
251 **CALEVADE** (IRE) 4
137 **CALGARY TIGER** 1
182 **CALIBRE** 46
476 **CALICO** (GER) 21
51 **CALICOJACK** (IRE) 2
557 **CALIDAD** (IRE) 2
117 **CALIFORNIA CHERRY** 29
89 **CALIN'S LAD** 12
388 **CALIPSO COLLONGES** (FR) 20
1 **CALIVIGNY** (IRE) 6
281 **CALL AT MIDNIGHT** F 2
525 **CALL BLUE** 12
102 **CALL HIS BLUFF** (IRE) 1
312 **CALL ME A STAR** F 7
215 **CALL ME GINGER** 7
292 **CALL ME HARRY** (IRE) 6
110 **CALL ME JEZZA** (IRE) 5
258 **CALL ME LORD** (FR) 25
212 **CALL ME RAFA** (IRE) 15
252 **CALL ME SAINTE** (IRE) 8
404 **CALL ME TARA** 37
187 **CALL MY BLUFF** (IRE) 4
312 **CALL OF THE WILD** (IRE) 8
373 **CALL OFF THE DOGS** (IRE) 18
349 **CALL SIMON** (IRE) 3
395 **CALL THE FAIRIES** (IRE) 9
458 **CALL MALVA** (IRE) 16
403 **CALLING ALL ANGELS** (IRE) 28
280 **CALLING THE WIND** (IRE) 6
463 **CALLIOPE** 4
476 **CALLISTO'S KING** (IRE) 22
251 **CALLSIGN PHOENIX** (IRE) 36
310 **CALM ATTITUDE** (IRE) F 9
61 **CALONNE** (IRE) 11
2 **CALTON HILL** (IRE) 1
511 **CALUM GILHOOLEY** (IRE) 5
398 **CALVA D'AUGE** (FR) 19
354 **CALZA NERA** (IRE) 16
353 **CAMACHESS** (IRE) 2
89 **CAMACHO MAN** (IRE) 13
118 **CAMBAY SCOUT** (IRE) 36
476 **CAMDONIAN** (IRE) 23
409 **CAME FROM NOTHING** (IRE) 19
537 **CAME FROM THE DARK** (IRE) 2
353 **CAMELOPARDALIS** G 5
320 **CAMEMBERT ELECTRIC** (IRE) 6
490 **CAMERATA** (GER) 2
142 **CAMILLE'S SECRET** (FR) F 6
376 **CAMINO ROCK** 2
280 **CAMISOLE** (IRE) C 59
556 **CAMMY** (IRE) 2
398 **CAMMY BEAR** (IRE) 20
458 **CAMP BELAN** (IRE) 17
61 **CAMPACHOOCHOO** (IRE) 12
26 **CAMPAIGN TRAIL** (IRE) 96
404 **CAMPDEN LAD** (IRE) 38
300 **CAMPESE** (IRE) 1
265 **CAMPROND** (FR) 10
570 **CAMRON DE CHAILLAC** (FR) 1

67 **CAN CAN GIRL** (IRE) 1
349 **CAN YOU BELIEVE IT** (IRE) 4
560 **CAN YOU CALL** 15
243 **CAN'T IMAGINE** (IRE) 13
216 **CAN'T STOP NOW** (IRE) 10
488 **CAN'TSMILEWITHOUTU** (IRE) 3
381 **CANADA KID** 10
491 **CANADA WATER** F 34
146 **CANAGAT** 5
331 **CANAL ROCKS** 5
164 **CANARIA PRINCE** 15
265 **CANASTERO** (IRE) 11
1 **CANCAN** (FR) 1
535 **CANDESCENCE** 8
417 **CANDLE LIT** (IRE) C 50
280 **CANDLE OF HOPE** 60
97 **CANDLE STICK** (IRE) 23
231 **CANDLEFORD** (IRE) 13
28 **CANDY KITCHEN** (IRE) 18
510 **CANDY LOU** 2
364 **CANDY SHACK** (IRE) 22
142 **CANDY WARHOL** (USA) 43
284 **CANDYMAN CAN** (IRE) 4
434 **CANDYTUFT** 22
312 **CANELO** (IRE) 9
62 **CANFORD BAY** (IRE) 5
560 **CANFORD LIGHT** (IRE) 16
189 **CANFORD STAR** (IRE) 3
14 **CANFORD'S JOY** (IRE) 3
86 **CANICHETTE** (FR) 4
305 **CANIMAR** 1
528 **CANNY FETTLE** (FR) 53
197 **CANNY TOM** (IRE) 1
231 **CANONIZED** 44
537 **CANOODLED** (IRE) 1
61 **CANTALOUPE** F 59
378 **CANTATA** 34
231 **CANTERBURY BELL** (IRE) 45
90 **CANTERS WELL** (IRE) 13
48 **CANTORA** 65
323 **CANTY BAY** (IRE) 7
313 **CANYON CITY** 5
226 **CANZONE** 5
449 **CAP D'ANTIBES** (IRE) 2
537 **CAP DRAMONT** 34
398 **CAP DU MATHAN** (FR) 21
559 **CAP DU NORD** (FR) 3
561 **CAP FRANCAIS** 16
104 **CAP SAN ROMAN** (FR) 17
404 **CAP ST VINCENT** (FR) 39
549 **CAP'N** (IRE) 4
549 **CAPALA** (IRE) 5
397 **CAPALL MEAR** (IRE) 10
518 **CAPE CORNWALL ROSE** (IRE) 8
576 **CAPE DOLLAR** (IRE) F 26
332 **CAPE GRECO** (USA) 2
163 **CAPE JOY** (IRE) C 71
529 **CAPE ROBIN** (IRE) 9
16 **CAPE SPIRIT** (IRE) C 163
229 **CAPE SUNSET** 5
404 **CAPE TOWN ERIN** (IRE) 40
274 **CAPE VIDAL** 7
83 **CAPE VINCENT** 37
403 **CAPED LADY** (IRE) C 29
280 **CAPELLA'S SONG** (IRE) C 61
145 **CAPERCAILIE** (IRE) 38
528 **CAPH STAR** 54

63 **CONTREBASSE** 1
77 **CONTROL** 52
104 **CONTROL TOWER** (FR) 3
26 **CONVECTION** 30
418 **CONVERSATIONAL** (IRE) F 31
567 **COO STAR SIVOLA** (FR) 16
185 **COOKIES AND CREME** 33
89 **COOL ANGEL** (IRE) G 18
463 **COOL BARANCA** (GER) G 6
519 **COOL COUNTRY** (IRE) 6
170 **COOL JET** (IRE) 4
292 **COOL MIX** 7
226 **COOL SPIRIT** 2
312 **COOL STONE** 15
404 **COOL TARA** 48
505 **COOL THUNDER** (IRE) F 10
581 **COOL VALLEY** (IRE) 2
61 **COOL VIXEN** (IRE) 16
61 **COOLAGH MAGIC** 17
167 **COOLAMAINE LAD** (IRE) 7
514 **COOLBANE BOY** (IRE) 9
404 **COOLDINE BOG** (IRE) 49
560 **COOLE CODY** (IRE) 20
143 **COOLE HALL** (IRE) 6
12 **COOLE LION** (IRE) 5
115 **COOLE WELL** (IRE) 2
514 **COOLKILL** (IRE) 10
406 **COOLMEEN ROYAL** (FR) 62
406 **COOLMEEN VEGA** (IRE) 63
546 **COOLMOYNE** 1
265 **COOLNAUGH HAZE** (IRE) 17
216 **COOLVALLA** (IRE) 14
112 **COOPER'S CROSS** (IRE) 9
117 **COOPERATION** (IRE) 9
260 **COPAKE** (IRE) 5
98 **COPINET** 6
87 **COPPER AND FIVE** 6
483 **COPPER BEACH** (IRE) 12
469 **COPPER COIN** 6
409 **COPPER COVE** (IRE) 28
164 **COPPER KNIGHT** (IRE) 20
163 **COPPER MOUNTAIN** 39
517 **COPPERHEAD** 19
367 **COPPERKIN** 5
373 **COPPERKNOB** (IRE) 139
388 **COPPERLESS** 32
164 **COPPERLINE** (IRE) 116
280 **COPPERPLATE** 32
274 **COQUELICOT** (FR) 10
308 **COQUET** F 63
6 **COQUETTE NOIRE** (IRE) F 99
458 **CORACH RAMBLER** (IRE) 21
48 **CORAJE** 68
404 **CORAL** (FR) 50
49 **CORAL BLUE** (IRE) 1
505 **CORAL GARDEN** C 52
346 **CORAL SHELL** (IRE) C 48
48 **CORAZON** (IRE) 26
146 **CORAZON ESPINADO** (IRE) 6
371 **CORAZONADA** (IRE) 2
4 **CORDEY DANCER** (FR) 51
217 **CORDOUAN** (FR) 5
388 **COREY'S COURAGE** 33
565 **CORIANO RIDGE** 1
544 **CORINTHIA KNIGHT** (IRE) 7
177 **CORINTO** (IRE) 3
170 **CORMIER** (IRE) 5

300 **CORNAKILL** (USA) F 135
87 **CORNDAVON LAD** (IRE) 7
132 **CORNELL** 3
238 **CORNERSTONE LAD** 14
485 **CORNICELLO** (FR) 11
316 **CORNISH STORM** 9
109 **CORNLAW** C 19
6 **COROEBUS** (IRE) 33
216 **CORONADO JOE** 15
462 **CORONATION COTTAGE** 2
229 **CORPS DE BALLET** (IRE) F 31
17 **CORRAN CROSS** (IRE) 3
427 **CORRANY** (IRE) 2
458 **CORRIGEEN ROCK** (IRE) 22
360 **CORSINI** (IRE) 14
127 **CORTON LASS** 11
117 **CORVAIR** (IRE) 10
215 **COSA SARA** (IRE) 8
82 **COSHESTON** 10
47 **COSMIC GEORGE** (IRE) 5
143 **COSMIC OUTLAW** (IRE) 7
179 **COSMIC STAR** 3
233 **COSMIC VEGA** (IRE) 7
406 **COSMOS RAJ** 8
473 **COSSACK DANCER** 9
346 **COSTA ADEJE** (IRE) 19
239 **COSTLY DIAMOND** (IRE) 2
430 **COTAI BEAR** (IRE) 4
505 **COTAI BEAUTY** (IRE) 11
344 **COTAI CLASS** (IRE) 12
405 **COTAI GREY** (IRE) 23
544 **COTAI STAR** (IRE) 46
460 **COTAI WEST** (IRE) 33
179 **COTE D'AZUR** 4
460 **COTTAM LANE** 6
368 **COTTON CLUB** (IRE) 1
329 **COTTON END** (IRE) 2
417 **COTTONMOUTH** (IRE) C 57
212 **COTTUN** (FR) 24
402 **COUGAR** (JPN) 27
51 **COUGAR'S GOLD** (IRE) 3
354 **COULD BE TROUBLE** (IRE) 25
402 **COULD IT BE LOVE** (USA) C 120
517 **COULD TALKABOUTIT** (IRE) 20
420 **COULDBEAWEAPON** (IRE) 16
549 **COULDN'T COULD HE** 33
549 **COULDN'T COULD SHE** 7
217 **COUNSEL** 6
164 **COUNT D'ORSAY** (IRE) 21
424 **COUNT OTTO** (IRE) 7
484 **COUNTERACT** 4
505 **COUNTERATTACK** 12
1 **COUNTERMAND** 11
32 **COUNTERPOISE** F 32
238 **COUNTESS OLIVIA** (IRE) 15
251 **COUNTISTER** (FR) 6
556 **COUNTRY CHARM** 3
75 **COUNTRY DELIGHTS** (IRE) 2
398 **COUNTRY LADY** 29
379 **COUNTRY PYLE** 1
243 **COUNTRYSIDE** F 148
47 **COUNTY WICKLOW** (USA) 6
316 **COUP DE FORCE** 12
511 **COUP DE GOLD** (IRE) 8
69 **COUP DE PINCEAU** (FR) 4
104 **COUP DE SOLEIL** (FR) 53
212 **COUPDEBOL** (FR) 25

217 **COURAGE MON AMI** 51
240 **COURAGETOCONTINUE** (IRE) F 48
164 **COURT AT SLIP** (IRE) 22
365 **COURT CASE** (IRE) 15
560 **COURT DANCER** (IRE) 21
445 **COURT DREAMING** (IRE) 10
354 **COURT JURADO** (IRE) 26
469 **COURT MASTER** (IRE) 7
122 **COURT OF SESSION** 30
149 **COURT PRINCESS** G 8
560 **COURT ROYALE** (IRE) 22
404 **COURTANDBOULD** (IRE) 52
474 **COURTLY LOVE** 7
77 **COURTSIDE** (FR) 8
354 **COUSIN OSCAR** (IRE) 27
476 **COUSU MAIN** (FR) 29
213 **COVE** (IRE) F 4
34 **COVERDALE** (IRE) 35
417 **COVERT LEGEND** 58
426 **COVERT MISSION** (FR) 4
83 **COVETABLE** 38
554 **COWBOY COOPER** (IRE) 3
243 **COWBOY JUSTICE** 84
521 **COWBOY SOLDIER** (IRE) 7
300 **COYOTE** C 136
516 **COZICAN** (IRE) 23
567 **CRAAN RUN** (IRE) 17
82 **CRACK DU NINIAN** (FR) 11
490 **CRACK REGIMENT** (FR) 4
555 **CRACKING DESTINY** (IRE) 10
483 **CRACKING FIND** (IRE) 13
327 **CRACKING SMART** (FR) 10
142 **CRACKLING** (IRE) 9
182 **CRACKSKING** 47
371 **CRAFT IN SILK** (IRE) 13
335 **CRAFTER** (IRE) 13
16 **CRAFTY** (AUS) F 169
98 **CRAFTY LADY** 27
506 **CRAGGAKNOCK** 2
164 **CRAGSIDE** 23
330 **CRAIC AGUS SPRAOI** (IRE) C 9
349 **CRAIC MAGIC** (IRE) 5
258 **CRAIGNEICHE** (IRE) 35
123 **CRAKEHALL LAD** (IRE) 2
404 **CRAMBO** 53
551 **CRANK EM UP** (IRE) 3
361 **CRASSUS** (IRE) 13
155 **CRAVIN RAVEN** (USA) C 60
57 **CRAWFORD** 2
37 **CRAZY JACK** (IRE) 1
367 **CRAZY LUCK** 6
204 **CRAZY MAISIE** (IRE) 38
204 **CRAZY SPIN** 9
243 **CRAZY VOLUME** (IRE) F 149
262 **CRAZYFORLOVINGYOU** (USA) C 68
212 **CREALION** (FR) 26
1 **CREAM OF THE WEST** (IRE) 12
91 **CREATIONIST** (USA) 3
354 **CREATIVE CONTROL** (IRE) 28
6 **CREATIVE FORCE** (IRE) 4
103 **CREATIVE INERTA** (IRE) 5
274 **CREDO** (IRE) 11
572 **CREEK DANCER** (IRE) 5
404 **CREGGAN WHITE HARE** (IRE) 54
58 **CREM FRESH** 1
414 **CREMA INGLESA** (IRE) 8

381 **CREMANT** (IRE) 19
28 **CREME CHANTILLY** (IRE) 46
131 **CRESSWELL QUEEN** 4
360 **CRESTA** (FR) 15
26 **CRESTA DE VEGA** (IRE) 31
418 **CRESTWOOD** 4
528 **CREWE ALEXANDRA** 160
504 **CRIMSON FLOWER** (IRE) F 3
7 **CRIMSON KING** (IRE) 17
528 **CRIMSON ROSETTE** (IRE) F 161
280 **CRIMSON SAND** (IRE) 7
231 **CRIOLLO** 48
16 **CRISTIELLE** (FR) 170
334 **CRITICAL THINKING** (IRE) 8
44 **CRIXUS'S ESCAPE** (IRE) 6
528 **CROACHILL** (IRE) 58
172 **CROAGH PATRICK** (IRE) 5
176 **CROESO CYMRAEG** 1
176 **CROESO CYNNES** 20
132 **CREAMFREE** F 9
475 **CROMARTY** (FR) 40
232 **CRONK Y KNOX** (IRE) 6
95 **CROSS SECTION** (USA) F 8
514 **CROSSGALESFAMEGAME** (IRE) 11
361 **CROSSGUNS** 14
243 **CROSSHILL** (IRE) 16
428 **CROSSING LINES** (IRE) 16
265 **CROSSING THE BAR** (IRE) 18
12 **CROSSPARK** 7
391 **CROSSPOINT** 1
404 **CROSSRAIL** 55
28 **CROSSTITCH** 47
391 **CROUCHING HARRY** (IRE) 2
122 **CROUPIER** (IRE) 31
182 **CROWN POWER** (IRE) 2
422 **CROWN PRINCESS** (IRE) 1
528 **CROWN QUEEN** (USA) C 162
185 **CRUMBIES** (IRE) 34
307 **CRUNCHIE** (IRE) 5
280 **CRUSH AND RUN** (IRE) 33
164 **CRUYFF TURN** 24
320 **CRUZ CONTROL** (FR) 8
366 **CRUZ DA ASSUMADA** 46
229 **CRY HAVOC** (IRE) 6
505 **CRY ME A RIVER** (IRE) F 53
212 **CRY OF LOVE** (SPA) G 77
157 **CRY WOLF** 12
567 **CRYPTO** (IRE) 18
473 **CRYPTO CURRENCY** (IRE) 10
460 **CRYPTO QUEST** (IRE) 34
500 **CRYSTAL CAPRICE** (IRE) 34
367 **CRYSTAL CASQUE** 7
231 **CRYSTAL CAVES** (FR) 49
39 **CRYSTAL CLOUD** 68
500 **CRYSTAL DELIGHT** 35
402 **CRYSTAL DIAMOND** C 121
500 **CRYSTAL ESTRELLA** 36
182 **CRYSTAL GAL** (IRE) F 24
445 **CRYSTAL GLORY** 11
292 **CRYSTAL GUARD** (IRE) 8
548 **CRYSTAL MER** 28
312 **CRYSTAL MOON** (IRE) 16
186 **CRYSTAL STARLET** 2
550 **CRYSTAL TIARA** 7
381 **CRYSTAL TIMES** (IRE) 20
73 **CRYSTAL WAR** (IRE) F 85
305 **CTHULHU** (USA) G 8

417 **CUBAN BEAT** 17
174 **CUBAN BREEZE** 4
240 **CUBAN CIGAR** 4
313 **CUBAN COURT** (IRE) 7
117 **CUBAN GREY** 45
307 **CUBAN HOPE** (IRE) 4
567 **CUBAN PETE** (IRE) 19
477 **CUBANISTA** 23
340 **CUBANO** (IRE) 5
125 **CUBAO** (IRE) 9
313 **CUBSWIN** (IRE) 9
375 **CUDDLY DUDLEY** (FR) 9
542 **CUDGEL** 3
155 **CUE'S FOLLY** F 61
475 **CUERNAVACA** (FR) 41
262 **CUILAPHUCA** (IRE) C 69
564 **CUILLIN** (USA) 4
543 **CULTURE** (FR) 4
304 **CULVERWELL** 14
231 **CUMBFREE** (IRE) C 135
185 **CUMULONIMBUS** (IRE) 35
149 **CUP OF COFFEE** (FR) 9
151 **CUPPACOCO** 9
130 **CURB APPEAL** 21
514 **CURRAMORE** (IRE) 12
77 **CURRANAITOR** 9
560 **CURRENT MOOD** 23
390 **CURTANA** 4
378 **CURTIZ** 7
421 **CURVATURUS** 3
402 **CURVY** F 122
511 **CUSACK** 9
71 **CUSHUISH** 2
521 **CUSTARD** 8
340 **CUSTARD THE DRAGON** 6
288 **CUSTODIAN** (IRE) 12
304 **CUT AND RUN** 15
346 **CUT SHORT** (USA) F 20
398 **CUT THE MUSTARD** (FR) 30
540 **CWTCH** (IRE) 2
243 **CYCLADIC** (IRE) 17
402 **CYCLAMEN** (IRE) 28
26 **CYGNETURE** 32
122 **CYNICAL POINT** (USA) 32
28 **CYNTHIA CALHOUN** C 48
576 **CYNTHIANA** (FR) F 27
398 **CYRNAME** (FR) 31
294 **CYRUS KEEP** (IRE) 2
83 **CYRUS KINGOFPERSIA** 24
469 **CZECH HER OUT** (IRE) 8
426 **D DAY ARVALENREEVA** (IRE) 50
335 **D DAY HERO** (IRE) 45
522 **D DAY ODETTE** 11
433 **D'AMBONNAY** (IRE) 3
549 **D'CRAICOFDAWN** 34
432 **D'EDGE OF GLORY** (IRE) 4
428 **D'JANGO** (IRE) 17
206 **D'ORVEL** (FR) 2
194 **DA VINCI HAND** (IRE) 5
62 **DAAFR** (IRE) 6
470 **DAAFY** (USA) 4
549 **DAANY** (IRE) 8
73 **DABIRSTAR** (FR) 7
403 **DADAO** C 33
104 **DADDY LONG LEGS** (FR) 19
238 **DADDYJACKS SPECIAL** (FR) 16
402 **DADDYS LIL DARLING** (USA) F 123

61 **DADS ARMY** 62
413 **DAENERYS STORMBORN** (IRE) 6
323 **DAGUENEAU** (IRE) 11
335 **DAHEER** (USA) 14
249 **DAIJOOR** 3
518 **DAINTILY DONE** F 11
182 **DAINTILY DONE** F 25
566 **DAINTY DANDY** (IRE) C 58
493 **DAINTY DIVA** (IRE) G 3
493 **DAINTY DIVA** (IRE) F 12
186 **DAINTY'S DAUGHTER** F 28
360 **DAIQUIRI** (IRE) 16
26 **DAIQUIRI DREAM** 33
26 **DAIQUIRI FRANCAIS** 34
28 **DAIRERIN** 19
292 **DAJARUS** 55
401 **DAKOTA BEAT** (IRE) 2
145 **DAKOTA GOLD** 10
123 **DAKOTA MOIRETTE** (FR) 3
508 **DAKOTA POWER** 33
312 **DAL MALLART** 139
529 **DALAMOI** (IRE) 12
94 **DALANIJUJO** (IRE) 6
319 **DALASYLA** (IRE) F 36
475 **DALBY FOREST** 42
25 **DALEY T** (IRE) 41
62 **DALGLISH** (IRE) 23
51 **DALKINGSTOWN** 4
481 **DALLAS COWBOY** (IRE) 1
402 **DALMATIAN COAST** (IRE) 29
361 **DALY TIGER** (FR) 15
365 **DALYOTIN** (FR) 16
217 **DAMAAR** 52
110 **DAMASCENA** (GER) G 7
297 **DAMASCUS FINISH** (IRE) 13
300 **DAME D'HONNEUR** (IRE) F 137
491 **DAME DU ROI** (IRE) C 38
60 **DAME DU SOIR** (FR) 7
217 **DAME ETHEL SMYTH** 53
367 **DAME HELEN** F 36
170 **DAME HESTER** (IRE) C 66
346 **DAME JUDI** (IRE) C 49
549 **DAME PLUME** (IRE) F 35
488 **DAME PLUME** (IRE) F 45
101 **DAMSELFLY** (IRE) C 73
440 **DAMUT I'M OUT** (IRE) 7
164 **DAN DE LIGHT** (IRE) 25
546 **DAN GUN** (IRE) 2
23 **DAN MCGRUE** (IRE) 4
265 **DAN'S CHOSEN** (IRE) 19
409 **DANA'S GEM** (IRE) 29
516 **DANAMIGHT** (IRE) C 46
87 **DANBY WISKE** (IRE) 33
317 **DANCE AWHILE** (IRE) F 21
537 **DANCE EAST** C 62
118 **DANCE FEVER** (IRE) 5
417 **DANCE FLOOR DIVA** (IRE) 18
118 **DANCE HALL GIRL** (IRE) C 87
164 **DANCE KING** 26
94 **DANCE OF DRAGONS** 29
300 **DANCE THE DREAM** F 138
455 **DANCE TO FAME** (IRE) 7
531 **DANCE TO PARIS** 8
312 **DANCE WITH FIRE** 17
514 **DANCING BALOO** (IRE) F 13
177 **DANCING DANI** (IRE) 4
58 **DANCING DORIS** 2

287 **DOR'S DIAMOND** 7
551 **DORA DE JANEIRO** (IRE) 4
174 **DORA PENNY** 24
359 **DORA'S SISTER** (IRE) F 6
92 **DORADO DOLLAR** (IRE) 10
435 **DORAN'S BRIDGE** (IRE) 1
240 **DORCAS LANE** F 142
306 **DORETTE** (IRE) 7
491 **DORIS MARIE** (IRE) F 40
476 **DORISA QUEEN** 36
320 **DORKING BOY** 10
373 **DORKING LAD** 27
530 **DORMIO** 5
300 **DORNOCH CASTLE** (IRE) 142
185 **DOROTHEE** 36
530 **DOROTHY** (FR) 33
256 **DOROTHY'S FLAME** 3
16 **DORRAAR** (IRE) C 173
577 **DORRANA** (IRE) 2
287 **DORS TOYBOY** (IRE) 8
108 **DORUNRON** (IRE) 4
543 **DOUBLE CHERRY** (IRE) 25
392 **DOUBLE COGNAC** 1
118 **DOUBLE DARE YOU** 42
259 **DOUBLE FOR FUN** 5
340 **DOUBLE HIGH** F 28
164 **DOUBLE HIGH** F 31
285 **DOUBLE LEGEND** (IRE) 1
157 **DOUBLE MEAD** F 7
346 **DOUBLE OBAN** 50
538 **DOUBLE OR BUBBLE** (IRE) 5
212 **DOUBLE SHUFFLE** (IRE) 29
518 **DOUBLE TIME** 7
531 **DOUBLETHETROUBLE** 10
516 **DOUGIES DREAM** (IRE) 25
458 **DOUGLAS TALKING** (IRE) 27
124 **DOUKAROV** (FR) 7
93 **DOURADO** (IRE) 6
528 **DOUX ESPRIT** (IRE) 62
327 **DOUX PRETENDER** (FR) 12
424 **DOVENA** 22
158 **DOVES CRY** (IRE) 4
383 **DOVES DELIGHT** 5
28 **DOVES OF PEACE** (IRE) 49
491 **DOWAGER** C 41
204 **DOWN TO THE KID** (IRE) 40
402 **DOWNING STREET** (IRE) 31
54 **DOWNSMAN** (IRE) 8
1 **DOWNTOWN GETAWAY** (IRE) 6
19 **DOYANNIE** (IRE) 3
514 **DOYEN BREED** (IRE) 19
452 **DOYEN DU BAR** (IRE) 3
428 **DOYEN LA LUTTE** (IRE) 21
259 **DOYEN QUEEN** (IRE) 6
580 **DOYENS DE ANTE** (IRE) 5
195 **DOYOUKNOWMYUNCLES** 1
476 **DOYOUKNOWWHATIMEAN** 37
924 **DOZEN** (FR) F 60
293 **DR BRERETON** (IRE) 10
51 **DR DES** (IRE) 7
409 **DR HEGARTY** (IRE) 33
103 **DR KANANGA** 6
113 **DR LYNAS** 7
413 **DR OAKLEY** (IRE) 7
366 **DR RIO** (IRE) 8
251 **DR SANDERSON** (IRE) 7
388 **DR SEB** (FR) 37

193 **DR SHIROCCO** (IRE) 6
388 **DR T J ECKLEBURG** (IRE) 38
428 **DRAG RACE** (IRE) 22
561 **DRAGON BONES** 22
528 **DRAGON SYMBOL** 6
232 **DRAGON'S FIRE** 9
223 **DRAGONFRUIT** 21
238 **DRAGONS WILL RISE** (IRE) 19
89 **DRAGOON SPRINGS** (IRE) 23
67 **DRAKEHOLES** 10
402 **DRAMATICALLY** (USA) C 126
467 **DRASH ON RUBY** 11
478 **DRAWDOWN** 17
155 **DRAWING CLOCKS** 23
222 **DREADPOET'SSOCIETY** (IRE) 14
176 **DREAM** (USA) C 23
47 **DREAM A LITTLE** 8
300 **DREAM BOOK** C 143
217 **DREAM BY DAY** 57
404 **DREAM CHASER** (FR) 62
371 **DREAM CHILD** (IRE) C 32
176 **DREAM COMPOSER** (FR) 3
63 **DREAM DEAL** 16
121 **DREAM GAME** 2
414 **DREAM HARDER** (IRE) 36
323 **DREAM IN THE PARK** (IRE) 4
271 **DREAM LOFTY DREAMS** 5
500 **DREAM OF DREAMS** (IRE) 7
424 **DREAM OF MISCHIEF** 23
243 **DREAM OF TARA** (IRE) F 152
83 **DREAM ON ME** (GER) F 39
375 **DREAM POINT** (FR) 12
215 **DREAM SCENARIO** C 45
262 **DREAM SHOW** 31
91 **DREAM TALE** 4
405 **DREAM TOGETHER** (IRE) 5
122 **DREAM WEDDING** C 35
521 **DREAMCASING** 9
299 **DREAMING** 25
576 **DREAMING BEAUTY** C 29
274 **DREAMING BLUE** 14
404 **DREAMING OF GLORY** (IRE) 63
134 **DREAMINGOFASONG** 4
537 **DREAMLOPER** (IRE) 7
51 **DREAMS OF DIAMONDS** (IRE) 8
272 **DREAMS OF GOLD** 6
354 **DREAMS OF HOME** (IRE) 32
117 **DREAMS OF THUNDER** (IRE) 31
164 **DREAMSELLER** (IRE) 32
304 **DREAMSUNDERMYFEET** (IRE) 17
414 **DREAMT** C 9
395 **DREAMWEAVER** (IRE) 14
440 **DRENAGH** (IRE) 9
122 **DRESDEN DOLL** (USA) F 85
51 **DRIFT ROCK** 9
397 **DRILL TO DREAM** 11
482 **DROMOD MOUR** (IRE) G 6
74 **DROP THE HAMMER** G 3
223 **DRUK** (FR) 22
166 **DRUM BRAE BOY** 14
104 **DRUM ROLL** (FR) 55
302 **DRUMCONNOR LAD** (IRE) 4
113 **DRUMFIRE** 1
222 **DRUMLEE WATAR** (IRE) 15
210 **DRUMNAGREAGH** (IRE) 2
46 **DRUNKEN PIRATE** 2
317 **DUAL IDENTITY** (IRE) 3

259 **DUARIGLE** (IRE) 7
319 **DUBAI AFFAIR** F 37
414 **DUBAI BOUNTY** C 53
528 **DUBAI CLOVER** (IRE) 63
319 **DUBAI CYCLONE** (USA) G 38
1 **DUBAI DAYS** (IRE) 15
470 **DUBAI ELEGANCE** 6
475 **DUBAI EMPEROR** (IRE) 4
182 **DUBAI FASHION** (IRE) F 48
39 **DUBAI FUTURE** 11
388 **DUBAI GUEST** (IRE) 39
505 **DUBAI HARBOUR** 55
231 **DUBAI HONOUR** (FR) 14
39 **DUBAI HOPE** (IRE) 12
39 **DUBAI HORIZON** (IRE) 13
39 **DUBAI ICON** 14
47 **DUBAI IMMO** (IRE) 32
260 **DUBAI JEANIUS** (IRE) 6
16 **DUBAI JEWEL** 72
48 **DUBAI LADY** (IRE) 6
300 **DUBAI LEADER** 57
39 **DUBAI LEGACY** (USA) 15
39 **DUBAI LOVE** 16
537 **DUBAI MANIA** (CAN) C 64
97 **DUBAI MEMORIES** (FR) 31
300 **DUBAI MILE** (IRE) 144
39 **DUBAI MIRAGE** (IRE) 17
528 **DUBAI POET** 64
117 **DUBAI STATION** 11
334 **DUBAI WARRIOR** 10
39 **DUBAI WELCOME** 19
186 **DUBARA** C 29
417 **DUBAWI LEGEND** (IRE) 20
500 **DUBIAN TO** (IRE) G 38
185 **DUBIOUS AFFAIR** (IRE) 5
404 **DUBLIN FOUR** (IRE) 64
201 **DUBROVNIK HARRY** (IRE) 10
428 **DUC DE BEAUCHENE** (FR) 23
398 **DUC DE BOURBON** (FR) 39
514 **DUC DE GRISSAY** (FR) 20
617 **DUC KAUTO** (FR) 21
108 **DUCA DE THAIX** (FR) 5
16 **DUCAL CROWN** 73
292 **DUCHESS DORA** (IRE) G 56
6 **DUCHESS OF BERRY** C 118
97 **DUCHESS OF DUBAI** (IRE) 32
299 **DUE A RUM** 26
478 **DUE A WIN** 4
118 **DUE DATE** 89
333 **DUE REWARD** (IRE) 16
185 **DUEL IN THE SUN** 1
240 **DUELIST** 51
379 **DUFOOF** (IRE) F 34
301 **DUHALLOW LAD** (IRE) 3
476 **DUKE OF BRONTE** 38
135 **DUKE OF CHALFONT** (FR) 2
223 **DUKE OF DECEPTION** (IRE) 23
226 **DUKE OF FIRENZE** 3
304 **DUKE OF LUCKLEY** (IRE) 18
28 **DUKE OF OXFORD** 50
388 **DUKE OF ROCKINGHAM** 40
293 **DUKE OF VERONA** (IRE) 3
217 **DUKEDOM** (IRE) 58
122 **DUKEMAN** (IRE) 36
262 **DUKINTA** (IRE) C 71
361 **DULJANAH** F 89

94 **EL CHE** C 61
538 **EL CUERPO E L'ALMA** (USA) F 28
140 **EL DIABLO** (IRE) 3
528 **EL DRAMA** (IRE) 8
385 **EL FABIOLO** (FR) 58
47 **EL FELICIA** (IRE) 34
505 **EL HADEEYAH** (IRE) 15
373 **EL HAGEB ROSE** (FR) 32
89 **EL HIBRI** (IRE) 100
335 **EL HOMBRE** 16
62 **EL JAD** (IRE) 7
236 **EL JEFE** (IRE) 1
334 **EL MAXIMO** (IRE) 36
455 **EL PACO** 10
428 **EL PASO WOOD** (FR) 26
335 **EL PATRON** (IRE) 17
146 **EL PEQUENO PULPO** 32
127 **EL PICADOR** (IRE) 13
13 **EL PRESENTE** 13
228 **EL SCORPIO** (IRE) 3
220 **ELANORA** (IRE) 5
319 **ELATION** (IRE) C 39
243 **ELAYSA** C 153
402 **ELBASANA** (IRE) C 127
16 **ELBERETH** F 175
431 **ELBOW BEACH** C 39
528 **ELDAR ELDAROV** 65
241 **ELDELBAR** (SPA) 1
139 **ELDERBERRY** F 7
62 **ELDEYAAR** (IRE) 24
517 **ELDORADO ALLEN** (FR) 25
184 **ELDRICKJONES** (IRE) 25
567 **ELEANOR BOB** 28
16 **ELEANOR CROSS** 176
477 **ELEANOR DUMONT** 7
92 **ELECTORAL LADY** (IRE) 11
26 **ELECTRIS** 10
19 **ELECTRIC AVENUE** (IRE) 7
15 **ELECTRIC AVENUE** 51
105 **ELECTRIC LOVE** 4
39 **ELECTRICAL STORM** 20
101 **ELEGANCIA** 76
490 **ELEGANT ANNIE** F 22
366 **ELEGANT ERIN** (IRE) 7
517 **ELEGANT ESCAPE** (IRE) 26
89 **ELEGANT LOVE** 26
217 **ELEGANT VERSE** 59
7 **ELEKTRONIC** (IRE) 24
238 **ELENA DE LA VEGA** 20
26 **ELENA'S GIFT** 41
118 **ELETTARIA** (IRE) 43
10 **ELEUSIS** C 45
493 **ELEVATED** (IRE) 5
204 **ELEVEN ELEVEN** (FR) 13
240 **ELEVENTH HOUR** (IRE) C 144
514 **ELF DE RE** (FR) 21
296 **ELF RISING** 23
333 **ELFLORA** G 12
427 **ELFRIDE** 4
340 **ELHAFEI** (USA) 7
404 **ELHAM VALLEY** (FR) 67
163 **ELIGIBLE** (IRE) 10
385 **ELIMAY** (FR) 59
536 **ELIOS D'OR** (FR) 7
373 **ELISEZMOI** (FR) 33
288 **ELISHEVA** (IRE) 3
122 **ELITE ARTIST** 37

431 **ELITE ETOILE** 22
390 **ELIXER** (IRE) 6
385 **ELIXIR D'AINAY** (FR) 60
517 **ELIXIR DE NUTZ** (FR) 27
524 **ELIXSOFT** (IRE) 1
406 **ELIZABELLE** (IRE) F 103
31 **ELJAYTEE** (IRE) 7
12 **ELKSTONE** 8
551 **ELLA NUTRARGILE** (IRE) F 5
20 **ELLA ROSIE** F 27
20 **ELLA ROSIE** G 26
240 **ELLADE** 52
468 **ELLADORA** 4
340 **ELLAND ROAD BOY** (IRE) 8
495 **ELLAS EREN** 1
476 **ELLE EST BELLE** 40
182 **ELLE GALA** (IRE) F 49
319 **ELLEN CLACY** 15
187 **ELLEN GATES** F 15
222 **ELLEON** (FR) 16
61 **ELLIE PIPER** 22
403 **ELLIPTIC** (IRE) 9
554 **ELLISTRIN STAR** 5
564 **ELLOFAGETAWAY** (IRE) 6
361 **ELLTAAF** G 72
525 **ELMDALE** (FR) 15
32 **ELMEJOR** (IRE) 5
566 **ELMIRA** (FR) 42
458 **ELMONO** (FR) 28
16 **ELOGIO** (IRE) 75
1 **ELOI DU PUY** (FR) 18
491 **ELOPE** (GER) F 42
403 **ELOQUENT** (IRE) F 37
32 **ELOUNTA** G 26
576 **ELSAAB** 6
426 **ELSALS** 24
300 **ELSHAADIN** F 147
200 **ELSHAAMEQ** 21
20 **ELSPETH ROSE** 6
89 **ELUSIVE ARTIST** (IRE) 27
277 **ELUSIVE BEAUTY** (IRE) C 14
258 **ELUSIVE BELLE** (IRE) 41
5 **ELUSIVE ELLEN** (IRE) G 8
69 **ELUSIVE INTENTIONS** (IRE) 6
220 **ELUSIVE NICOLE** (IRE) 6
469 **ELUSIVE POLLY** 11
390 **ELUSIVE RED** (IRE) 7
1 **ELVIS MAIL** (FR) 19
548 **ELWING** (FR) 29
17 **ELYAQIM** (FR) 8
279 **ELYSEE** (IRE) C 15
366 **ELZAAL** (IRE) 8
247 **ELZAAM'S DREAM** (IRE) 4
233 **ELZAAMSAN** (IRE) 8
381 **EMANATE** 25
460 **EMARAATY ANA** 10
521 **EMARATY HERO** 10
467 **EMBERSCOMBE** (IRE) 12
65 **EMBLA** 6
217 **EMBLEM EMPIRE** (IRE) 27
266 **EMBOLDEN** (FR) 8
87 **EMBOUR** (IRE) 8
16 **EMBRACE** (IRE) 177
163 **EMBROIDERY** (IRE) G 73
164 **EMERALD DUCHESS** 166
93 **EMERALD FOX** 7
73 **EMERALD LADY** (IRE) 42

26 **EMERIYA** (USA) F 102
402 **EMILY DICKINSON** (IRE) 32
34 **EMILY POST** 18
217 **EMILY UPJOHN** 60
476 **EMILY'S STAR** 41
319 **EMINENT ANGEL** 16
93 **EMINENT HIPSTER** (IRE) 8
567 **EMINENT POET** 29
258 **EMIR SACREE** (FR) 42
458 **EMIRAT DE CATANA** (FR) 29
491 **EMIRATE JEWEL** (USA) F 43
417 **EMIRATES JOY** (USA) F 61
6 **EMIRATES REWARDS** C 120
537 **EMIRATES VOICE** 65
222 **EMITOM** (IRE) 17
88 **EMIYN** (FR) 3
223 **EMMA BLUE** (IRE) 26
290 **EMMAS DILEMMA** (IRE) 2
476 **EMMAS JOY** (IRE) 42
208 **EMMPRESSIVE LADY** (IRE) 5
98 **EMOJIE** 7
560 **EMORELLE** (IRE) 26
217 **EMOTION** 61
295 **EMOTIONAL MEMORIES** (IRE) 7
478 **EMPEROR CARADOC** (FR) 18
525 **EMPHATIC QUALM** (IRE) 16
178 **EMPIRE DE MAULDE** (FR) 11
514 **EMPIRE STEEL** (IRE) 22
570 **EMPIRION** (IRE) 2
403 **EMPORIO** (IRE) 1
123 **EMPORTEPARLAFOULE** (FR) 5
402 **EMPOWERING** (IRE) C 128
426 **EMPRESS ELLA** (IRE) F 51
163 **EMPRESS ROCK** (IRE) G 42
475 **EMPRESS WU** 61
555 **EMPTY QUARTER** 13
51 **EMRAAN** (IRE) 11
540 **EMULATE** G 17
16 **EMULATION** 76
274 **EMZARA** (IRE) 15
385 **EN BETON** (FR) 61
384 **EN COEUR** (FR) 4
314 **EN MEME TEMPS** (FR) 19
288 **ENAMAY** 4
16 **ENBORNE** 178
488 **ENCANTAR** C 46
420 **ENCASHMENT** 23
158 **ENCHANTED NIGHT** 3
540 **ENCHANTED PRINCESS** G 26
139 **ENCHANTEE** (IRE) 8
243 **ENCORE L'AMOUR** F 154
101 **ENCORE MOI** C 77
440 **ENCOUNTER A GIANT** (IRE) 10
277 **ENCOURAGEABLE** (IRE) 4
182 **ENCOURAGED** (IRE) 4
184 **END ZONE** 7
366 **ENDERMAN** 9
447 **ENDLESS ADVENTURE** 2
6 **ENDLESS CHARM** C 121
208 **ENDLESS FLIGHT** (IRE) 6
300 **ENDLESS NIGHT** (GER) F 148
233 **ENDLESS SEASON** (IRE) 23
118 **ENDOW** (IRE) C 44
89 **ENDOWED** 28
160 **ENDURED** (IRE) 3
299 **ENDURING** 5
295 **ENEMENEMYNEMO** (IRE) 8

561 **ENEMY** 25
554 **ENEMY AT THE GATE** (IRE) 6
388 **ENEMY COAST AHEAD** 43
385 **ENERGUMENE** (FR) 62
265 **ENERGY ONE** 29
403 **ENEZA** (IRE) C 38
327 **ENFANT ROI** (FR) 13
262 **ENFIJAAR** (IRE) C 72
238 **ENFIN PHIL** (FR) 21
528 **ENFORCED** (IRE) 66
304 **ENFORCEMENT** (IRE) 19
300 **ENFRANCHISE** (IRE) 5
402 **ENGAGEMENT RING** (IRE) 33
78 **ENGAGING SAM** 3
458 **ENGLES ROCK** (IRE) 30
342 **ENGLISH SPIRIT** 8
163 **ENGLISHWOMAN** (FR) 74
183 **ENGRAVE** 2
418 **ENIGMATIC** (IRE) 5
414 **ENIGMATIQUE** F 37
300 **ENKINDLE** 58
163 **ENLIGHTEN** 11
387 **ENLIGHTENMENT** (IRE) 15
466 **ENLIVEN** C 26
431 **ENOCHDHU** 40
577 **ENORMOUSE** 3
91 **ENOUGH ALREADY** 6
395 **ENQARDE** (FR) 16
80 **ENRAGED** 34
60 **ENRICHISSANT** (FR) 10
398 **ENRILO** (FR) 42
109 **ENROL** C 20
20 **ENSEL DU PERCHE** (FR) 7
528 **ENSEMBLE** (IRE) 9
231 **ENSHRINE** 50
300 **ENTERTAINMENT** F 149
6 **ENTERTAINS** (AUS) C 122
418 **ENTHUSED** (IRE) 6
231 **ENTICING** C 139
156 **ENTRANCEMENT** (FR) 19
259 **ENTRE DEUX** 8
469 **ENVOL DE LA COUR** (FR) 12
567 **ENZO D'AIRY** (FR) 30
566 **ENZOS ANGEL** 43
403 **EOS** (FR) F 39
398 **EOZ** (IRE) G 43
258 **EPATANTE** (FR) 43
277 **EPATHA** (IRE) C 15
456 **EPIC CHALLENGE** 2
406 **EPIC EFFECT** 104
160 **EPIC EXPRESS** 4
23 **EPIC PASS** (IRE) 8
273 **EPICENTRE** 14
6 **EPITOME** (IRE) C 123
8 **EPONINA** (IRE) 25
460 **EPPING ROSE** (IRE) C 85
60 **EPPLETON COLLIER** (FR) 11
425 **EPSOM FAITHFUL** 2
155 **EPSOM ICON** F 62
500 **EQUAL SHARE** (IRE) 41
262 **EQUALITY** 4
247 **EQUALLY FAST** 5
353 **EQUIAMI** 9
506 **EQUIANO SPRINGS** 4
292 **EQUIDAE** 12
262 **EQUILATERAL** 5
525 **EQUINUS** (IRE) 17

89 **EQUION** 29
566 **EQUITATION** 8
51 **EQUUS DANCER** (IRE) 12
13 **EQUUS DREAMER** (IRE) 14
133 **EQUUS MILLAR** (IRE) 5
373 **ERAGON DE CHANAY** (FR) 34
238 **ERAGONE** (FR) 22
174 **ERICA BING** F 39
150 **ERICAS LAD** 2
184 **ERICH BLOCH** (IRE) 8
562 **ERICK LE ROUGE** (FR) 6
97 **ERIDA** (FR) 33
178 **ERIMITIS** 12
398 **ERITAGE** (FR) 44
425 **ERMYNS DOTTIE** 3
309 **ERNE RIVER** (IRE) 5
312 **ERNEST GRAY** (IRE) 23
561 **ERNESTO** (GER) 26
276 **ERNIE BILKO** (IRE) 2
109 **ERNIE'S VALENTINE** 8
577 **EROS** (FR) 4
231 **ERTIYAD** F 140
164 **ERUPTION** (IRE) 118
312 **ES PERFECTO** (IRE) 24
223 **ESCALADE** (IRE) 27
156 **ESCAPE FREE** (IRE) 12
178 **ESCAPEANDEVADE** (IRE) 13
286 **ESCAPEFROMALCATRAZ** (FR) 9
406 **ESCOBAR** (FR) 12
246 **ESCOBEDO** 10
426 **ESEDRA** (IRE) F 52
528 **ESHAADA** 10
460 **ESKEN ROSE** (USA) 38
233 **ESMAGGIE** F 43
354 **ESME SHELBY** (IRE) 34
16 **ESPADA** (IRE) 77
469 **ESPECIALLY SO** 13
572 **ESPINATOR** (FR) 6
567 **ESPOIR DE GUYE** (FR) 31
13 **ESPOIR DE ROMAY** (FR) 15
212 **ESPOIR DE TEILLEE** (FR) 30
457 **ESPOIR DES FORGES** (FR) 9
143 **ESPOIR MORIVIERE** (FR) 12
496 **ESPRESSO FREDDO** (IRE) 3
300 **ESPRESSOO** 59
562 **ESPRIT DE SOMOZA** (FR) 7
560 **ESPRIT DU LARGE** (FR) 27
458 **ESPRIT DU POTIER** (FR) 88
89 **ESSAKA** (IRE) 30
47 **ESSENCIAL** (IRE) 35
373 **ESSENTIAL JACO** (GER) 35
61 **ESSGEE NICS** (IRE) 23
59 **ESSME** 5
133 **EST ILLIC** (IRE) 7
157 **ESTATE ITALIANA** (USA) 16
538 **ESTEEMED LADY** F 29
490 **ESTEFAN** 23
48 **ESTEHWADH** (IRE) 70
78 **ESTIBDAAD** (IRE) 4
25 **ESTICKY END** (IRE) 10
231 **ESTIDAMA** 51
501 **ESTRELA STAR** (IRE) 3
94 **ESTRELLADA** F 62
299 **ET TU BRUTE** (FR) 6
476 **ETALON** (IRE) 43
474 **ETAT MAJOR AULMES** (FR) 10
97 **ETATIQUE** (FR) 34

300 **ETERNAL GLORY** (IRE) 60
127 **ETERNAL HALO** (IRE) 55
215 **ETERNAL INSTINCT** G 39
188 **ETERNAL LEGACY** (IRE) G 1
6 **ETERNAL PEARL** 34
217 **ETERNAL SUMMER** 11
215 **ETERNALIST** F 40
554 **ETERNALLY YOURS** 7
314 **ETESIAN** (FR) F 99
155 **ETESIAN FLOW** F 63
490 **ETHEL C** (IRE) 6
294 **ETHELWYN** G 21
6 **ETHEREAL SKY** (IRE) C 124
521 **ETIKAAL** 11
471 **ETINCELLE ARTISTE** (FR) 3
157 **ETOILE BRILLANTE** (IRE) 17
1 **ETOILE D'ECOSSE** (FR) 20
243 **ETOILE FILANTE** F 155
15 **ETON BLUE** (IRE) 11
414 **ETON COLLEGE** (IRE) 11
240 **ETONIAN** (FR) 3
178 **ETTILA DE SIVOLA** (FR) 14
482 **EUCHAN FALLS** (IRE) 9
215 **EUCHEN GLEN** 9
403 **EUPHRASIA** (IRE) C 40
182 **EURAQUILO** 26
323 **EUREKA CREEK** (IRE) 17
267 **EUREU DU BOULAY** (FR) 5
548 **EURKASH** (FR) 6
361 **EUROBOT** 18
243 **EUROCRAT** 89
252 **EUROWORK** (FR) 12
550 **EVA ICON** 10
529 **EVA'S OSKAR** (IRE) 14
127 **EVALUATION** 14
223 **EVANDER** (IRE) 28
94 **EVANESCE** F 63
217 **EVANIA** 12
61 **EVASIVE POWER** (USA) 24
185 **EVE LODGE** 38
118 **EVENING FROST** (IRE) C 91
229 **EVENING SONG** 7
48 **EVENSTAR** 71
535 **EVENT OF SIVOLA** (IRE) 11
33 **EVENTFUL** 1
541 **EVEQUE** (FR) 1
346 **EVER GIVEN** (IRE) 22
32 **EVER LOVE** (BRZ) F 33
243 **EVER PRESENT** 21
49 **EVER READY EDDIE** (IRE) 3
163 **EVERGLADES** F 75
361 **EVERGLOW** 19
361 **EVERGREEN AND RED** 20
522 **EVERLOVING** (IRE) 12
500 **EVERY BLUE MOON** (IRE) 42
263 **EVERY BREAKIN WAVE** (IRE) 4
516 **EVERY TIME** C 47
315 **EVERYBODY DANCE** (IRE) 14
445 **EVERYDAY CHAMPAGNE** (IRE) 12
333 **EVERYONESGAME** (IRE) 13
405 **EVERYTHINGSHEWANTS** 37
550 **EVIE MAY** 11
417 **EVIL SPELL** F 62
171 **EVISCERATING** (IRE) 5
49 **EVITA DU MESNIL** (FR) 4
76 **EVITA PERON** C 19
417 **EVOCATIVE SPARK** (IRE) 22

388 **EWOOD PARK** (IRE) 44
98 **EX GRATIA** 8
513 **EX S'ELANCE** (FR) 3
231 **EXACTING** C 141
73 **EXALTED ANGEL** (FR) 10
371 **EXCEEDINGLY REGAL** (IRE) 5
466 **EXCEEDINGLY SONIC** 12
544 **EXCEL POWER** (IRE) 8
292 **EXCELCIUS** (USA) 13
563 **EXCELERO** (FR) 19
240 **EXCELING** (IRE) 53
558 **EXCELINTHEJUNGLE** (IRE) 4
566 **EXCELLENT GEORGE** 9
164 **EXCESSABLE** 35
344 **EXCHEQUER** (IRE) 4
300 **EXCLUSIVE TIMES** 61
366 **EXCUISITE** 10
126 **EXECUTIVE** 1
373 **EXECUTIVE POOL** 140
381 **EXELERATOR EXPRESS** (FR) 26
528 **EXIMIOUS** (IRE) 164
566 **EXISTENT** 10
243 **EXIT POLL** (IRE) 22
292 **EXIT TO WHERE** (FR) 14
34 **EXMINSTER** (IRE) 19
130 **EXMOOR EXPRESS** (IRE) 9
337 **EXMOOR FOREST** (IRE) 3
485 **EXOD'ELA** (FR) 17
15 **EXPECTING TO FLY** (USA) C 52
490 **EXPERT OPINION** 7
117 **EXPLICIT THOUGHTS** 33
243 **EXQUISITE ACCLAIM** (IRE) 90
6 **EXTRA MILE** C 125
17 **EXTRACURICULAR** 9
60 **EXTRAORDINARY MAN** (FR) 12
528 **EXTRICATE** (IRE) C 165
528 **EXTRICATION** 67
367 **EXUDING** 8
119 **EY UP IT'S MAGGIE** 2
54 **EY UP ITS JAZZ** 18
119 **EY UP ITS MICK** 3
119 **EY UP ITS THE BOSS** 10
528 **EYDON** (IRE) 68
164 **EYE KNEE** 36
324 **EYE OF AN EAGLE** (FR) 3
247 **EYE OF THE WATER** (IRE) 6
485 **EYE TO THE SKY** 18
548 **EYED** 7
404 **EYEOFTHESCORPION** (IRE) 68
339 **EYES** (IRE) 4
460 **EYES ON ASHA** (IRE) C 86
187 **EYESHINE** C 16
232 **EZ TIGER** (IRE) 10
10 **EZZRAH** 7
174 **FABIOSA** 25
258 **FABLE** (FR) 44
105 **FABRICATED** 5
312 **FABRIKA** G 25
388 **FABRIQUE EN FRANCE** (FR) 45
551 **FABULEUX DU CLOS** (FR) 6
385 **FACILE VEGA** (FR) 63
485 **FACT OF THE MATTER** (IRE) 19
374 **FACT OR FABLE** (FR) 5
371 **FADING LIGHT** F 15
560 **FADO DES BROSSES** (FR) 28
94 **FAEROES** (IRE) F 64
232 **FAGAN** 11

185 **FAI FAI** 39
245 **FAINT HOPE** 2
247 **FAIR AND SQUARE** 19
55 **FAIR DAMSEL** (IRE) 2
13 **FAIR FRONTIERES** (IRE) 16
530 **FAIR HURRICANE** (GER) 6
243 **FAIR JOE** (IRE) 91
514 **FAIR MINX** 23
77 **FAIR POWER** (IRE) 11
201 **FAIR PRESENT** (IRE) G 11
170 **FAIR STAR** (IRE) 6
133 **FAIR TO DREAM** 7
557 **FAIRE PART SIVOLA** (FR) 4
405 **FAIRFIELD FERRATA** 6
51 **FAIRLAWN FLYER** 13
388 **FAIRLY FAMOUS** (IRE) 46
300 **FAIRMAC** 6
213 **FAIRWAY FREDDY** (IRE) 6
539 **FAIRY ALISHA** G 1
204 **FAIRY FOOTPRINTS** 42
201 **FAIRY GEM** (IRE) 12
220 **FAIRY LOVE** (IRE) 18
381 **FAIRY SLIPPER** F 2
166 **FAIRYWREN** (IRE) G 10
118 **FAITH FULL SPIRIT** 45
335 **FAITHHOPEANDGLORY** 18
469 **FAITQUE DE L'ISLE** (FR) 14
476 **FAIVOIR** (FR) 44
385 **FAKIR RODINO** (FR) 64
354 **FALANGHINA** 35
326 **FALCO BLITZ** (FR) 45
449 **FALCON SUN** (FR) 4
326 **FALDAL** F 16
431 **FALESIA BEACH** 23
549 **FALINE** 10
364 **FALLEN FROM HEAVEN** 26
6 **FALLING SHADOW** (IRE) 35
6 **FALLS OF LORA** (IRE) C 126
515 **FALMOUTH BALLERINA** 8
515 **FALMOUTH QUEEN** 1
117 **FALSIFY** F 46
253 **FAMA ET GLORIA** (IRE) 1
179 **FAME AND ACCLAIM** (IRE) 5
409 **FAME AND CONCRETE** (IRE) 35
398 **FAME AND FUN** (IRE) 45
44 **FAME AND HOPE** (IRE) 7
243 **FAME AND JOY** (IRE) 23
15 **FAME N FORTUNE** 12
153 **FAME VALLEY** (IRE) 4
528 **FAMILIAR DREAMS** 69
528 **FAMILLE VERTE** 70
267 **FAMILY BUSINESS** (FR) 6
341 **FAMILY FORTUNES** 28
450 **FAMILY MAN** (IRE) 2
329 **FAMILY POT** (FR) 3
232 **FAMILY TIME** 12
69 **FAMOSO** (IRE) 7
445 **FAMOUS BRIDGE** (IRE) 13
229 **FAMOUS FOOTSTEPS** (IRE) 27
561 **FAMOUS LAST WORD** (IRE) 8
143 **FAMOUS MOMENT** (IRE) 13
136 **FAMOUS OISIN** (IRE) 1
38 **FAMOUS RESPONSE** (IRE) 7
385 **FAN DE BLUES** (FR) 65
426 **FAN THE FLAMES** (IRE) 25
125 **FANAMIX** (FR) 10

300 **FANCY** (IRE) F 150
240 **FANCY MAN** (IRE) 9
469 **FANCY SHAPES** (IRE) 15
476 **FANCY STUFF** (IRE) 45
265 **FANCY YOUR CHANCES** (IRE) 30
239 **FANDABIDOZI** (IRE) 7
212 **FANFAN DU SEUIL** (FR) 31
274 **FANFARON DINO** (FR) 16
94 **FANGORN** 8
567 **FANION D'ESTRUVAL** (FR) 32
405 **FANTA DIELO** (USA) F 38
361 **FANTASIA ROQUE** (FR) 21
501 **FANTASTIC ACCOUNT** C 22
528 **FANTASTIC FOX** 11
258 **FANTASTIC LADY** (FR) 46
514 **FANTASTIC ROCK** (IRE) 24
525 **FANTASTIKAS** (FR) 18
537 **FANTASY BELIEVER** (IRE) 8
525 **FANTOMAS** (FR) 19
267 **FANZIO** (FR) 7
14 **FANZONE** (IRE) 6
16 **FAR AWAY THOUGHTS** 78
334 **FAR FROM A RUBY** 11
469 **FAR HORIZON** (IRE) 16
10 **FAR TOO BEAUTIFUL** 8
543 **FARASI LANE** (IRE) 8
254 **FARCEUR DE MAULNE** (FR) 3
361 **FARCEUR DU LARGE** (FR) 22
43 **FARD** 5
61 **FAREWELL KISS** (IRE) 25
528 **FAREWELL TO YOU** F 166
77 **FARHAN** (IRE) 12
240 **FARHH NORTH** 54
347 **FARHH TO SHY** 3
470 **FARHHSICAL** 7
567 **FARINET** (FR) 33
22 **FARLAM KING** 7
115 **FARM THE ROCK** (IRE) 3
564 **FARNE** (FR) 7
399 **FARNE ISLAND** 4
223 **FARO** (FR) 29
212 **FARO DE KERSER** (FR) 32
22 **FAROCCO** (GER) 8
258 **FAROUK DE CHENEAU** (FR) 47
385 **FAROUT** (FR) 66
567 **FARRANTS WAY** (IRE) 34
373 **FASCINATING LIPS** (IRE) 36
63 **FASCINATING NEWS** 4
48 **FASCINATOR** C 72
127 **FASHION ADVICE** 15
466 **FASHION CENTRAL** C 27
32 **FASHION DARLING** (IRE) F 27
225 **FASHION DELIGHT** (USA) 16
7 **FASHION FREE** 26
26 **FASHION LOVE** 42
404 **FASHION NOVA** (IRE) 69
426 **FASHION PARADE** C 53
109 **FASHION STATEMENT** C 21
16 **FASHION THEORY** C 179
262 **FASHION TRADE** C 73
329 **FASHION'S MODEL** (IRE) 4
73 **FASHIONABLE SPIRIT** (IRE) G 43
470 **FASLEN** (USA) C 28
182 **FAST AFFAIR** 50
460 **FAST AND LOOSE** 39
159 **FAST ART** (IRE) 3
122 **FAST ATTACK** (IRE) 38

34 **FAST BEAUTY** (IRE) 20
476 **FAST BUCK** (FR) 46
522 **FAST DANSEUSE** (IRE) 13
95 **FAST DEAL** 1
158 **FAST FLO** 16
312 **FAST FORWARD** (FR) 140
537 **FAST LILY** (IRE) C 66
99 **FAST MEDICINE** (IRE) 3
73 **FAST RESPONSE** (IRE) 9
178 **FAST SCENIC** (FR) 15
367 **FAST STEPS** (IRE) 9
4 **FAST STYLE** (IRE) 22
491 **FASTNET MIST** (IRE) F 44
15 **FAT GLADIATOR** (IRE) 34
460 **FATAL ATTRACTION** F 87
258 **FATHER JOHN** (FR) 48
528 **FATHER OF JAZZ** 12
482 **FATHER'S ADVICE** (IRE) 10
85 **FAUCON** F 3
262 **FAURAN** (IRE) C 74
517 **FAUSTINOVICK** 28
117 **FAUSTUS** 12
567 **FAUTINETTE** (FR) 35
229 **FAUVETTE** (IRE) 8
563 **FAVORI DE SIVOLA** (FR) 2
151 **FAVOURITE NIECE** 5
316 **FAWN AT PLAY** 13
420 **FAWSLEY SPIRIT** (IRE) 24
325 **FAY CE QUE VOUDRAS** (IRE) 8
555 **FAYLAQ** 14
504 **FAZAYTE** (FR) 4
240 **FAZENDERA** (IRE) C 55
34 **FEARBY** (IRE) 21
388 **FEARLESS** (IRE) 47
219 **FEARLESS ACTION** (IRE) 6
334 **FEARLESS ANGEL** (IRE) 37
155 **FEARLESS BAY** (IRE) 24
391 **FEARSOME FRED** 3
404 **FEAST** (IRE) 70
94 **FEATHERWEIGHT** (IRE) C 65
557 **FEDE GALIZIA** (IRE) 35
323 **FEDELTA** (IRE) 18
544 **FEDERAL STREET** (IRE) 48
122 **FEEDYAH** (USA) C 86
232 **FEEL LA DUE DE BAUNE** (FR) 13
39 **FEEL THE MOMENT** 70
404 **FEEL THE PINCH** 71
142 **FEEL THE THUNDER** 12
385 **FEIGH** (IRE) 67
163 **FEINT** C 76
395 **FEIVEL** (IRE) 17
240 **FELISSA** (GER) F 145
47 **FELIX** 9
80 **FELIX ADLER** 35
361 **FELIX GOLD** G 73
5 **FELIX NATALIS** (IRE) 10
317 **FELLOWSHIP** (IRE) 22
92 **FELTON BELLEVUE** (FR) 12
558 **FEMININE FELICITY** 5
73 **FEMME PATRONNE** (IRE) 45
34 **FEN ALI** C 37
183 **FEN TIGER** (IRE) 3
42 **FENELON** (FR) 4
172 **FENLAND TIGER** 6
27 **FENNAAN** (IRE) 27
243 **FENNELA** (IRE) 92
19 **FENRIR BINDING** 8

473 **FEODORA** 13
231 **FERDOOS** C 142
300 **FEREVIA** (IRE) F 151
127 **FERGIE TIME** (IRE) 56
382 **FERGUSSINGSDABLUES** 9
361 **FERMOYLE** 23
206 **FERN ARABLE** 4
92 **FERN HILL** (IRE) 13
118 **FERNANDO RAH** 7
445 **FERNEY GREEN** 14
1 **FERNHILL LAD** (IRE) 7
385 **FERNY HOLLOW** (IRE) 68
163 **FERRIER** F 77
200 **FERRO D'ORR** (IRE) 22
580 **FERROBIN** (IRE) 6
94 **FERROUS** (IRE) 66
155 **FESTIVAL OF LIGHT** 25
404 **FESTIVE GLORY** (IRE) 72
143 **FETE CHAMPETRE** (IRE) 14
458 **FETHARD GLORY** (IRE) 31
365 **FEVER ROQUE** (FR) 20
349 **FEVERTRE** (FR) 6
16 **FEYHA** (IRE) 180
334 **FFION** 12
223 **FFREE PEDRO** (IRE) 30
219 **FIADH** (IRE) 7
134 **FIAMETTE** (IRE) 5
46 **FIBONACCI** 3
280 **FICTIONAL** (IRE) 65
122 **FIDAAHA** (IRE) C 87
517 **FIDDLERONTHEROOF** (IRE) 29
125 **FIDDLERS TRACKER** (IRE) 11
174 **FIDHA** 26
563 **FIDUCIARY DUTY** (FR) 20
312 **FIDUX** (FR) 26
89 **FIELDSMAN** (USA) 31
85 **FIERCELY PROUD** (IRE) 5
163 **FIERY DAWN** (IRE) 14
16 **FIESTA DE VEGA** 14
561 **FIFRELET** (FR) 28
115 **FIFTEEN SUMMERS** (IRE) 15
47 **FIFTEENTHAMENDMENT** (USA) 36
373 **FIFTY BALL** (FR) 37
28 **FIFTY SENT** 21
238 **FIFTYSHADESAREDEV** (FR) 93
200 **FIFTYSHADESOFRED** (FR) 6
411 **FIGHT FOR IT** (IRE) 3
385 **FIGHTER ALLEN** (IRE) 69
251 **FIGHTFORTHEROSES** (IRE) 8
551 **FIGHTING CHANCE** 21
414 **FIGHTING POET** (IRE) 12
287 **FIGHTING TEMERAIRE** (IRE) 9
378 **FILANDERER** 9
16 **FILBERT POWER** 79
382 **FILE AND PAINT** (IRE) G 10
409 **FILE ILLICO** (FR) 8
217 **FILISTINE** (IRE) 62
314 **FILLE D'AVIGNON** (IRE) 20
276 **FILLE D'HONFLEUR** G 3
551 **FILOU D'ANJOU** (FR) 7
27 **FILOU DES ISSARDS** (FR) 4
258 **FILS D'OUDAIRIES** (FR) 49
385 **FILS SPIRITUEL** (FR) 70
268 **FINAIR** 4
272 **FINAL ATTACK** (IRE) 7
285 **FINAL CHOICE** 2
231 **FINAL DECISION** 52

378 **FINAL ENCORE** 10
87 **FINAL FRONTIER** (IRE) 9
245 **FINAL LIST** (IRE) 3
404 **FINAL NUDGE** (IRE) 73
1 **FINAL REMINDER** (IRE) 22
404 **FINAL RUN** (IRE) G 74
576 **FINAL SET** (IRE) C 30
39 **FINAL SONG** (IRE) 21
240 **FINAL TREAT** (IRE) C 146
315 **FINALE** G 27
457 **FINALSHOT** 10
325 **FINANCIER** 9
233 **FINANS BAY** (IRE) 9
6 **FINATA** C 127
388 **FINAWN BAWN** (IRE) 48
217 **FIND** 63
364 **FINDONO** (FR) 4
445 **FINDTHETIME** (IRE) 15
199 **FINDUSATGORCOMBE** 4
122 **FINE BALANCE** (IRE) 39
479 **FINE BY HER** 3
525 **FINE BY ME** (IRE) 20
420 **FINE CASTING** (IRE) 25
500 **FINE CHINA** 43
48 **FINE IF** (IRE) C 73
240 **FINE JUDGMENT** C 147
427 **FINE THEATRE** (IRE) 5
122 **FINE TIME** F 40
142 **FINE WINE** (FR) 13
7 **FINERY** 28
304 **FINESCOPE** 4
385 **FINEST EVERMORE** (IRE) 71
122 **FINEST SOUND** (IRE) 3
312 **FINEST VIEW** 27
9 **FINGAL'S HILL** (IRE) 3
381 **FINGERONTHESWITCH** (IRE) 28
354 **FINISK RIVER** 36
300 **FINN'S CHARM** 152
286 **FINNEGAN'S GARDEN** (IRE) 10
327 **FINNISTON FARM** 14
6 **FINTRY** (IRE) C 128
48 **FIORINA** 27
476 **FIRAK** (FR) 47
314 **FIRCOMBE HALL** 21
375 **FIRE AWAY** (IRE) 13
300 **FIRE DANCING** 7
382 **FIRE EYES** (FR) 1
398 **FIRE FLYER** (IRE) 46
547 **FIRE HEART** 12
163 **FIRE IN THE RAIN** 12
246 **FIRE LAKE** (IRE) 11
231 **FIRE ORCHID** F 143
28 **FIREBOLT** (IRE) 22
478 **FIREBOMB** 19
233 **FIRECROWN** (IRE) F 44
199 **FIREFLY LANE** (IRE) 5
415 **FIREGUARD** 6
59 **FIRENZE ROSA** (IRE) 6
536 **FIRENZO** (FR) 8
379 **FIREPOWER** (FR) 2
258 **FIRESTEP** (IRE) 50
274 **FIRESTREAM** 17
226 **FIREWATER** 4
231 **FIREWORKS** (FR) 15
406 **FIRMAMENT** 13
361 **FIROZA** C 91
127 **FIRST ACCOUNT** 16

414 **GOLD MAZE** 14
280 **GOLD MEDAL** 35
170 **GOLD MINER** 7
532 **GOLD RING** 2
173 **GOLD ROBBER** 28
172 **GOLD RUNNER** (IRE) 9
505 **GOLD SANDS** (IRE) C 58
493 **GOLD SOUK** (IRE) 7
105 **GOLD SPLASH** 17
89 **GOLD STANDARD** (IRE) 35
521 **GOLD TERMS** 12
111 **GOLD VENTURE** (IRE) 2
117 **GOLDEN AGE** (FR) 13
330 **GOLDEN ALBA** (IRE) 11
164 **GOLDEN APOLLO** 41
373 **GOLDEN BOY GREY** 44
49 **GOLDEN CHANCER** 6
300 **GOLDEN DISC** 66
162 **GOLDEN DOVE** 4
516 **GOLDEN DUKE** (IRE) 6
381 **GOLDEN EMBLEM** (IRE) 36
300 **GOLDEN FLAME** (IRE) 9
185 **GOLDEN FORCE** 9
422 **GOLDEN GAL** (IRE) 9
164 **GOLDEN GEORGE** (IRE) 124
122 **GOLDEN GLANCE** 42
496 **GOLDEN GLORY** (IRE) 6
576 **GOLDEN KEEPER** 9
300 **GOLDEN LILAC** (IRE) C 163
231 **GOLDEN LYRA** (IRE) 56
243 **GOLDEN LYRIC** 27
386 **GOLDEN MAYFLOWER** 33
164 **GOLDEN MELODY** (IRE) 42
162 **GOLDEN MILLIE** 5
317 **GOLDEN MOON** 40
74 **GOLDEN POET** (IRE) 4
119 **GOLDEN PROSPERITY** (IRE) 11
241 **GOLDEN RAINBOW** 9
483 **GOLDEN ROBIN** (IRE) 20
222 **GOLDEN ROC** (IRE) 22
387 **GOLDEN ROMANCE** (IRE) 16
300 **GOLDEN SANDS** (IRE) 67
527 **GOLDEN SECRET** F 26
101 **GOLDEN SHEEN** 28
434 **GOLDEN SHOT** 30
265 **GOLDEN SOVEREIGN** (IRE) 35
347 **GOLDEN SPICE** (USA) 9
517 **GOLDEN SUNRISE** (IRE) 33
404 **GOLDEN TAIPAN** (IRE) 86
370 **GOLDEN TOWN** (IRE) 7
233 **GOLDEN TWILIGHT** (IRE) 10
122 **GOLDEN VALENTINE** (IRE) C 91
405 **GOLDEN VINTAGE** 26
231 **GOLDEN VOICE** 57
47 **GOLDEN WARRIOR** (IRE) 38
560 **GOLDEN WHISKY** (IRE) 30
544 **GOLDEN WHISPER** 50
559 **GOLDCARD** (IRE) 9
538 **GOLDIE HAWK** 8
269 **GOLDRAPPER** (IRE) 3
16 **GOLDSBOROUGH** 189
364 **GOLDSMITH** (IRE) 29
6 **GOLDSPUR** (FR) 37
388 **GOLEIRIHEM** (IRE) 61
314 **GOLFE CLAIR** (FR) 26
299 **GOLSPIE** 53
127 **GOMETRA GINTY** (IRE) 20

6 **GONBARDA** (GER) C 134
232 **GONE IN SIXTY** 17
16 **GONE SAILING** C 190
479 **GONE TO TEXAS** (IRE) 4
324 **GONE WALKABOUT** (IRE) 7
364 **GONNETOT** (FR) 30
29 **GONZAGA** 1
354 **GOOBINATOR** (USA) 48
321 **GOOCHYPOOCHYPRADER** F 1
26 **GOOD AMERICAN** 44
404 **GOOD AND HARDY** (IRE) 87
16 **GOOD BIRTHDAY** (IRE) 20
525 **GOOD BOY BOBBY** (IRE) 23
301 **GOOD BYE** (GER) 4
260 **GOOD EARTH** (IRE) 9
371 **GOOD EFFORT** (IRE) 4
231 **GOOD GRACIOUS** 145
336 **GOOD GREEF** 3
522 **GOOD HEALTH** F 19
566 **GOOD HUMOR** 13
340 **GOOD LISTENER** (IRE) 9
274 **GOOD LOOK CHARM** (FR) 23
366 **GOOD LUCK FOX** (IRE) 12
375 **GOOD MAN PAT** (IRE) 19
259 **GOOD MAN VINNIE** (IRE) 9
231 **GOOD MEASURE** 58
94 **GOOD MORNING LADY** C 68
444 **GOOD NEWS** 4
532 **GOOD NIGHT MR TOM** (IRE) 3
39 **GOOD PLACE** (USA) C 101
371 **GOOD REGAL** 5
509 **GOOD RISK AT ALL** (FR) 11
417 **GOOD SOUL** 5
33 **GOOD TIME AHEAD** (IRE) 5
296 **GOOD TO GO** 24
223 **GOOD WORK** (FR) 43
138 **GOODISON GIRL** 13
97 **GOODNESS** (FR) 39
202 **GOODNIGHT CHARLIE** 1
488 **GOODNIGHTSUZY** (IRE) C 47
516 **GOODTHINGSTAKETIME** (IRE) F 48
32 **GOODTHYNE MISS** (IRE) G 6
514 **GOODTIMES BADTIMES** (IRE) 30
432 **GOODWILLHUNTING** (IRE) 8
216 **GOODWIN RACING** (IRE) 3
127 **GOODWOOD GLEN** 21
364 **GOODWOOD VISION** 48
16 **GOOLWA** (IRE) 21
466 **GOOSE ROCK** (IRE) 28
486 **GOOSEWOOD** 2
199 **GORCOMBE MOONSHINE** 8
199 **GORCOMBE'S RASCAL** 3
55 **GORDON BENNETT** (IRE) 3
170 **GORDON'S JET** (IRE) 8
411 **GORDONONTHEORGAN** (IRE) 7
434 **GORDONS AURA** (IRE) 31
14 **GORDONSTOUN** (IRE) 8
382 **GORGEOUS GENERAL** 2
113 **GORGEOUS GOBOLINA** 10
334 **GORGEOUS STAR** (FR) 41
373 **GORHAM'S CAVE** 45
385 **GORKI D'AIRY** (FR) 88
404 **GORTROE JOE** (IRE) 88
373 **GOSHEN** (FR) 46
265 **GOSHEVEN** (IRE) 36
83 **GOSMORE** 41
146 **GOSNAY GOLD** (FR) 7

395 **GOSPELUS** (FR) 24
438 **GOSSAMER SILK** 3
142 **GOSSIP** 16
155 **GOT CARTER** (IRE) 27
566 **GOT NO DOLLARS** (IRE) 14
566 **GOT THE MOVES** (IRE) 15
514 **GOT TRUMPED** 31
433 **GOTCHA GOOD** (USA) F 13
201 **GOUDHURST STAR** (IRE) 19
223 **GOUET DES BRUYERES** (FR) 44
385 **GOVEN** (FR) 89
417 **GOVERNMENT** (IRE) 23
440 **GOVERNOR GREEN** (IRE) 15
217 **GOVERNOR OF INDIA** (IRE) 71
113 **GOWANBUSTER** 19
314 **GOWANLAD** 27
525 **GOWEL ROAD** (IRE) 24
398 **GRACE A VOUS ENKI** (FR) 61
271 **GRACE ANGEL** 12
516 **GRACE HULL** C 49
195 **GRACEFUL JAMES** (IRE) 2
20 **GRACEFUL MOMENT** (IRE) 11
199 **GRACEFUL DANCER** 1
508 **GRACEFULALFIE** 36
164 **GRACELANDS GIRL** 125
388 **GRACES ORDER** (IRE) 62
215 **GRACES QUEST** 13
195 **GRACIOUS GEORGE** (IRE) 3
555 **GRADY GASTON** (IRE) 16
158 **GRAFFA** 5
94 **GRAFFITI** 32
404 **GRAGEELAGH GIRL** (IRE) 89
15 **GRAIGNES** (FR) 13
354 **GRAIN D'OUDAIRIES** (FR) 49
496 **GRAIN DE BEAUTE** (IRE) F 24
300 **GRAIN OF HOPE** 164
164 **GRAN CANARIA QUEEN** F 126
86 **GRAN DIOSE** (FR) 9
258 **GRAN LUNA** (FR) 63
299 **GRANARY QUEEN** (IRE) 8
185 **GRAND ALLIANCE** (IRE) 41
205 **GRAND BOBBY** 16
385 **GRAND BORNAND** (IRE) 90
215 **GRAND CANAL** (IRE) 14
109 **GRAND CRU GAGA** 11
238 **GRAND DU NORD** (IRE) 29
229 **GRAND DUCHESS OLGA** 32
124 **GRAND KNIGHT** (FR) 9
105 **GRAND LIBYA** 18
167 **GRAND LORD** (FR) 12
400 **GRAND MARIO** (FR) 4
258 **GRAND MOGUL** (IRE) 64
458 **GRAND MORNING** 34
164 **GRAND PIANOLA** 43
398 **GRAND SANCY** (FR) 62
240 **GRAND SCHEME** (IRE) 10
567 **GRAND TURINA** 49
112 **GRAND VOYAGE** (FR) 13
170 **GRANDAD** 68
423 **GRANDADS BEST GIRL** 2
388 **GRANDADS COTTAGE** (IRE) 63
217 **GRANDE DAME** 72
33 **GRANDEE** (IRE) 6
312 **GRANDEUR D'AME** (FR) 35
117 **GRANDFATHER TOM** 14
501 **GRANDSCAPE** 6
436 **GRANDSTAND** (IRE) 3

272 **HEAD HIGH** (IRE) 11
409 **HEAD LAW** (FR) 48
561 **HEAD ON** (IRE) 35
406 **HEADINGLEY** (IRE) 18
142 **HEADLAND** 20
146 **HEADLEY GEORGE** (IRE) 8
431 **HEADORA** 3
445 **HEADSCARF LIL** (IRE) 23
89 **HEADSHOT** 38
97 **HEALING OASIS** (FR) 42
204 **HEALING POWER** 15
127 **HEAR ME OUT** (IRE) 23
145 **HEAR ME ROAR** (IRE) 19
356 **HEARSAY** G 18
508 **HEART** 49
312 **HEART OF A LION** (IRE) 44
516 **HEART OF ACKLAM** 50
377 **HEART OF SOUL** (IRE) 19
475 **HEART OF THE SUN** 11
478 **HEART THROB** 5
402 **HEART TO HEART** 40
39 **HEART'S CONTENT** (IRE) F 103
402 **HEARTACHE** C 136
354 **HEARTBREAK KID** (IRE) 53
83 **HEARTBREAK LASS** 25
28 **HEARTBREAKER** 4
39 **HEARTILY** (IRE) C 104
505 **HEARTSEASE** F 59
98 **HEAT OF THE MOMENT** 28
12 **HEATH RISE** 12
155 **HEATHEN** 29
488 **HEATHER LARK** (IRE) C 49
28 **HEATHERDOWN HERO** 26
187 **HEATON CHAPEL** (IRE) 7
505 **HEAVEN'S ANGEL** (IRE) C 60
457 **HEAVENLY CLOUDS** (IRE) 11
101 **HEAVENLY SONG** (IRE) C 82
18 **HEAVENS LIGHT** (IRE) 22
555 **HEAVENTREE** (IRE) 18
381 **HEAVEY** 41
231 **HEBRIDES** (IRE) 61
373 **HECOULDBETHEONE** (IRE) 51
240 **HECTIC** 157
15 **HECTOR** (IRE) 36
333 **HECTOR JAVILEX** (FR) 23
146 **HECTOR LOZA** 9
458 **HECTOR MASTER** (FR) 37
204 **HECTOR'S HERE** 16
387 **HEDENHAM** 25
228 **HEDGEBIRD** 6
496 **HEDGEINATOR** (IRE) 8
384 **HEDYCHIUM** (IRE) 5
183 **HEER'S SADIE** 4
527 **HEERATHETRACK** 27
163 **HEEROSE GIRL** 45
522 **HEERS HARRY** 14
476 **HEEZER GEEZER** (FR) 66
385 **HEIA** (FR) 97
127 **HEIGHTS OF ABRAHAM** (IRE) 24
127 **HEIGHTS OF ARAN** (IRE) 58
76 **HEILIG YA MLAY** (IRE) 20
361 **HEISENBERG** (IRE) 29
240 **HELENE** 64
268 **HELETA** 6
517 **HELFORD RIVER** 34
157 **HELIAN** (IRE) 19
378 **HELIANTHUS** 65

475 **HELIOCENTRIC** (FR) F 66
563 **HELIOS ALLEN** (FR) 5
560 **HELIOS DE GRUGY** (FR) 32
57 **HELIX** 4
243 **HELL BENT** (IRE) 29
398 **HELL RED** (FR) 71
431 **HELLAVAPACE** 4
164 **HELLENISTA** 45
546 **HELLFIRE KODE** 4
325 **HELLFIRE PRINCESS** 11
149 **HELLO BOB** 15
237 **HELLO JUDGE** 2
418 **HELLO ME** (IRE) 9
548 **HELLO SUNSHINE** (IRE) 14
231 **HELLO SYDNEY** (IRE) 62
334 **HELLO YOU** (IRE) 42
460 **HELLO ZABEEL** (IRE) 12
48 **HELLOMYDARLIN** (IRE) 30
240 **HELLS BABE** F 158
501 **HELLUVABOY** (IRE) 8
319 **HELM PRINCESS** (IRE) 20
319 **HELM ROCK** 4
7 **HELMORA** 34
580 **HELOVAPLAN** (IRE) 7
80 **HELPFUL** 37
476 **HELTENHAM** (FR) 67
514 **HELTER HELTER** (USA) F 32
200 **HELVETIAN** 9
26 **HELVETIQUE** 47
361 **HELVIC DREAM** 30
361 **HELVIC PRINCESS** 31
540 **HEMSBY PINE** (IRE) 18
402 **HENCE** (IRE) F 137
25 **HENERY HAWK** 31
532 **HENLEY** 5
373 **HENLEY PARK** 52
385 **HENN SEE** (FR) 98
325 **HENRI LE BON** (IRE) 12
398 **HENRI THE SECOND** (FR) 72
560 **HENRY BOX BROWN** (FR) 33
361 **HENRY BROWN** (IRE) 32
409 **HENRY GONDOFF** 49
90 **HENRY THE FIFTH** (FR) 7
222 **HENSCHKE** (IRE) 24
192 **HENZO DES BOULLATS** (FR) 4
312 **HER INDOORS** (IRE) 45
524 **HER WAY** 3
222 **HERAKLES** (FR) 25
223 **HERBIERS** (FR) 45
385 **HERCULE DU SEUIL** (FR) 99
89 **HERE AT NIGHT** 39
167 **HERE COMES HENRY** (IRE) 14
388 **HERE COMES MCCOY** (IRE) 68
21 **HERE COMES MOLLY** (IRE) 2
375 **HERE COMES MR TEE** 22
143 **HERE COMES THE MAN** (IRE) 18
222 **HERE HARE HERE** (IRE) 26
26 **HERE TO ETERNITY** (USA) C 106
375 **HERE WE HAVE IT** (IRE) 23
469 **HERECOMESFREDDIE** 19
304 **HERECOMESHOGAN** (IRE) 24
240 **HEREDIA** 65
430 **HEREIA** (IRE) 7
238 **HERESMAX** (FR) 33
159 **HERESY** 4
417 **HERETIC** (IRE) 24
404 **HEREWEGOHONEY** (IRE) 93

223 **HERITIER** (FR) 46
491 **HERMANA ESTRELLA** 13
308 **HERMANUS** (IRE) 1
398 **HERMES ALLEN** (FR) 73
562 **HERMES BOY** (FR) 12
567 **HERMES DU GOUET** (FR) 52
222 **HERMES LE GRIS** (FR) 2
57 **HERMIN D'OUDAIRIES** (FR) 5
373 **HERMINO AA** (FR) 53
342 **HERMONIE** 24
388 **HERO** (FR) 69
360 **HEROIC HEART** (FR) C 24
312 **HEROIC HOLLY** (IRE) 144
297 **HERON** (USA) 4
395 **HERON CREEK** (IRE) 25
560 **HERONORD** (FR) 34
567 **HEROS** (FR) 53
258 **HEROSS DU SEUIL** (FR) 67
262 **HERSILIA** 32
361 **HE'S A HARDY BLOKE** (IRE) 33
286 **HESBEHINDYOU** (IRE) 14
16 **HESPERANTHA** 87
320 **HESQUE DE L'ISLE** (FR) 16
33 **HESTER LADY** (IRE) F 9
428 **HEURE DE GLOIRE** (FR) 32
567 **HEVA ROSE** (FR) 54
528 **HEXAMETER** 82
364 **HEY BAILS** 31
388 **HEY BOB** (IRE) 70
483 **HEY BOY** 21
284 **HEY BUD** 8
469 **HEY FRANKIE** (IRE) 20
264 **HEY HO LET'S GO** 1
409 **HEY JOE** (IRE) 50
440 **HEY MISTER DJ** (IRE) 17
179 **HEY MR** 6
570 **HEY PRETTY** (IRE) 3
222 **HEY SOUL SISTER** (FR) 28
181 **HEZMIE** (FR) 9
385 **HI HO PHOENIX** 100
538 **HI HO SILVER** 9
41 **HI HOH TONTO** 9
318 **HI MILADY** (IRE) C 9
550 **HI NOTE** F 13
94 **HI NOTE** F 69
267 **HI RIKO** (FR) 9
6 **HIBAAYEB** F 138
182 **HICKORY** (IRE) 8
232 **HICONIC** 21
354 **HIDALGO DE L'ISLE** (FR) 54
404 **HIDDEN BEAUTY** 94
256 **HIDDEN CARGO** (IRE) 4
491 **HIDDEN CHARMS** (IRE) F 48
422 **HIDDEN CODE** (IRE) 21
314 **HIDDEN COMMANDER** (IRE) 31
381 **HIDDEN DEPTHS** (IRE) 42
486 **HIDDEN GLEN** (IRE) 3
6 **HIDDEN GOLD** (IRE) F 139
476 **HIDDEN HEROICS** (FR) 68
31 **HIDDEN PEARL** 8
505 **HIDDEN SANDS** 19
16 **HIDDEN STEPS** F 192
16 **HIDDEN VALLEY** F 193
238 **HIDEO** (FR) 34
421 **HIDING DAVE** (IRE) 6
504 **HIDOR DE BERSY** (FR) 5
154 **HIER ENCORE** (FR) 1

26 **HOSANA** (IRE) 49
87 **HOSTELRY** 12
312 **HOSTILE** 46
287 **HOT CHESNUT** 10
374 **HOT DAY** 6
89 **HOT DESERT** 42
127 **HOT DIGGITY DOG** (IRE) 59
397 **HOT FLUSH** (IRE) 13
89 **HOT HOT HOT** 43
536 **HOT IN THE CITY** 14
522 **HOT LEGS LIL** (IRE) 15
539 **HOT MADRAS** (IRE) 2
7 **HOT MOP** 88
482 **HOT ON HER HEELS** (IRE) F 18
549 **HOT PURSUITS** G 54
201 **HOT ROD LINCOLN** (IRE) 21
183 **HOT ROMANCE** 5
263 **HOT SMOKED** 6
377 **HOT TEAM** (IRE) 12
287 **HOT TICKET** (IRE) F 32
273 **HOTCITY** 4
361 **HOTEL WREN** (IRE) 76
166 **HOTSPUR HARRY** (IRE) 3
406 **HOTTER IN TIME** 71
312 **HOTTER THAN HELL** (FR) 47
567 **HOUI CHERIE** (FR) 57
373 **HOUKA D'OUDAIRIES** (FR) 56
388 **HOURVARI** (FR) 74
125 **HOUSE OF STORIES** (IRE) 9
232 **HOUSTON BERE** (FR) 22
445 **HOUSTON TEXAS** (IRE) 26
360 **HOVER** (IRE) 2
6 **HOW** (IRE) F 141
14 **HOW BIZARRE** 10
32 **HOW HARD CAN IT BE** 7
402 **HOW HIGH THE MOON** (IRE) F 139
417 **HOW IMPRESSIVE** (IRE) 26
374 **HOW LONG** 24
201 **HOW WILL I KNOW** (IRE) 22
402 **HOW'S SHE CUTTIN'** (IRE) C 140
485 **HOWDILYOUDO** (IRE) 27
177 **HOWDY PARTNER** (IRE) 7
560 **HOWDYALIKEMENOW** (IRE) 36
149 **HOWLING MILAN** (IRE) 16
274 **HOWLINGMADMURDOCK** (IRE) 26
402 **HOWTH** (IRE) 45
103 **HOWYA HUN** (IRE) 9
4 **HOWYOUPLAYTHEGAME** (IRE) 11
61 **HOYDAR** 27
238 **HOWZAT HIRIS** (FR) 36
127 **HOWZER BLACK** (IRE) 26
25 **HOY** 44
406 **HOYAMY** C 107
123 **HUBBEL BUBBEL** 7
115 **HUBBLE** 3
385 **HUBRISKO** (FR) 104
25 **HUDDLE UP** (IRE) 12
378 **HUDDLETON MAC** (IRE) 12
373 **HUDSON DE GRUGY** (FR) 57
398 **HUELGOAT** (FR) 77
398 **HUFLOWER** (FR) 78
398 **HUGOS NEW HORSE** (FR) 79
398 **HUGOS OTHER HORSE** 80
508 **HUGOSTHERE** 18
327 **HUGSY** (IRE) 16
76 **HUKUM** (IRE) 3
146 **HUL AH BAH LOO** (IRE) 25

25 **HULA BALLEW** F 32
404 **HULLNBACK** 98
535 **HULTON RANGER** (IRE) 41
293 **HUMAAM** (USA) 13
384 **HUMANISTE** (FR) 6
215 **HUMBLE SPARK** (IRE) 46
186 **HUNDI** (IRE) F 34
94 **HUNDRED ISLES** (IRE) 11
555 **HUNGRY HELEN** 20
409 **HUNGRY HILL** (IRE) 53
12 **HUNGRY TIGER** (IRE) 10
7 **HUNKY** (IRE) 10
404 **HUNNY MOON** 99
328 **HUNSBURY** 3
567 **HUNTER LEGEND** (FR) 58
388 **HUNTERS CALL** (IRE) 75
490 **HUNTERS STEP** 8
385 **HUNTERS YARN** (IRE) 105
323 **HUNTING BROOK** (IRE) 28
320 **HUNTING PERCIVAL** 19
365 **HUNTSMAN'S CALL** (IRE) 27
404 **HUNTSMANS JOG** (IRE) 100
89 **HUNTSMANS MOON** (IRE) 103
566 **HURAIZ** (IRE) 16
46 **HURCLE** (IRE) 5
258 **HURLING MAGIC** (IRE) 70
41 **HURRICANE ALERT** 2
340 **HURRICANE ALI** (IRE) 10
43 **HURRICANE ARCADIO** (FR) 7
531 **HURRICANE BAY** 17
398 **HURRICANE DANNY** (FR) 81
509 **HURRICANE DEAL** (IRE) 14
497 **HURRICANE DYLAN** (IRE) 1
404 **HURRICANE HARVEY** 101
367 **HURRICANE HELEN** 13
231 **HURRICANE IVOR** (IRE) 19
183 **HURRICANE KIKO** (IRE) 19
6 **HURRICANE LANE** (IRE) 8
258 **HURRICANE LE DUN** (IRE) 71
201 **HURRICANE MITCH** (IRE) 23
563 **HURRICANE SIVOLA** (FR) 6
400 **HURSTWOOD** 5
397 **HURT YOU NEVER** (IRE) 14
414 **HUSCARI** (IRE) 39
122 **HUSSAR** F 45
267 **HUSSARD BRUN** (FR) 10
161 **HY BRASIL** (IRE) 3
487 **HY EALES** (IRE) 4
299 **HYANNA** 10
385 **HYBERY** (FR) 106
385 **HYBRIS** (FR) 107
561 **HYDROPLANE** (FR) 37
258 **HYLAND** (FR) 72
201 **HYMAC** (IRE) 24
361 **HYMIE WEISS** 35
471 **HYMN AND A PRAYER** 4
92 **HYMN TO LOVE** (FR) F 15
185 **HYPER DREAM** (IRE) C 64
164 **HYPERFOCUS** (IRE) 48
346 **HYPERSONICAL** (IRE) 27
395 **HYPNOTIK** (FR) 27
26 **HYPOTHETICALLY** (IRE) F 108
504 **HYSTERY BERE** (FR) 7
540 **I AM A DREAMER** 8
360 **I AM BEAUTIFUL** (IRE) C 25
232 **I AM DE CHAILLAC** (FR) 23
98 **I AM LEGEND** (SWE) 40

258 **I AM MAXIMUS** (FR) 73
258 **I AM ROCCO** 74
231 **I AM THE SEA** 64
313 **I HOPE STAR** (FR) 13
388 **I K BRUNEL** 76
80 **I KNOW HOW** (IRE) 10
525 **I LIKE TO MOVE IT** 28
130 **I MATTER** (IRE) 22
384 **I SEE YOU WELL** (FR) 7
517 **I SHUT THAT D'OR** (FR) 36
13 **I SPY A DIVA** 27
561 **I STILL HAVE FAITH** 109
457 **I WILL FOLLOW HER** 12
30 **I'LL BE GOOD** 3
16 **I'LL BE THERE** 90
482 **I'LL HAVE IT** (IRE) F 19
300 **I'M A GAMBLER** (IRE) 70
447 **I'M A STARMAN** 4
206 **I'M DIGBY** (IRE) 8
403 **I'M FEELIN FINE** 9
204 **I'M GRATEFUL** 17
271 **I'M MABLE** 2
301 **I'M NOTAPARTYGIRL** 5
152 **I'M SHEIKRA** (IRE) C 17
395 **I'M SO BUSY** 28
420 **I'M SPELLBOUND** (IRE) 38
563 **I'M THE DIVA** (FR) 7
127 **I'M TO BLAME** (IRE) 27
247 **I'M WATCHING YOU** 8
404 **I'M WISER NOW** (IRE) 102
543 **IAMFINE** (IRE) F 31
239 **IBERIA** (IRE) 12
265 **IBERIO** (GER) 43
346 **IBIZA DREAM** F 54
262 **IBIZA ROCKS** 7
262 **IBN ALDAR** 33
28 **IBRAHIMOVIC** (IRE) 54
385 **ICARE ALLEN** (FR) 108
206 **ICARE COLOMBE** (FR) 9
23 **ICE AGE** (IRE) 8
54 **ICE FURY** (IRE) 20
118 **ICE HAVEN** (IRE) C 95
231 **ICE HOUSE** 65
314 **ICE PYRAMID** (FR) 32
65 **ICE SHADOW** (IRE) 12
265 **ICEBURGH BAY** (IRE) 44
557 **ICED TEA** 11
354 **ICEMAN DENNIS** (FR) 56
398 **ICEO** (FR) 82
431 **ICKYTOO** 24
381 **ICONE D'AUBRELLE** (FR) 45
314 **ICONIC BELLE** 33
89 **ICONIC KNIGHT** (IRE) 44
425 **ICONIC MOVER** 7
373 **ICONIC MUDDLE** 58
222 **ICONIC ROCK** (IRE) 30
406 **ICONICDAAY** 72
185 **ICONIQUE** 10
231 **ICYKEL** (IRE) 66
457 **IDAMIX** (FR) 13
361 **IDAS BOY** (IRE) 36
347 **IDEAL GUEST** (FR) 10
457 **IDEALDES VILLERETS** (FR) 14
458 **IDEM** (FR) 38
463 **IDILICO** (FR) 9
338 **IDOAPOLOGISE** 1
385 **IDOLES DES JEUNES** (FR) 109

375 **INSIDE INFORMANT** (USA) 25
14 **INSIDE INTEL** (IRE) 11
562 **INSIDE MAN** (FR) 29
488 **INSOMNIA** 11
381 **INSPECTOR LYNLEY** 48
217 **INSPIRAL** 79
80 **INSPIRATIONELLIE** (IRE) 38
252 **INSTANT DE BONHEUR** (FR) 19
48 **INSTANT MEMORIES** (FR) 76
170 **INSTANT REPLAY** (IRE) 13
243 **INSTANT RETURN** 31
478 **INSTINCTION** 22
250 **INSTRUCTIVE** (IRE) 4
488 **INSTRUCTRESS** C 50
402 **INSTRUMENTAL** 46
32 **INTEL** 9
509 **INTEL DES BRUYERES** (FR) 15
280 **INTELLIGENTSIA** (IRE) 39
122 **INTENSE PINK** F 93
205 **INTERCESSOR** 4
314 **INTERCONNECTED** 34
48 **INTERMITTENT** F 77
240 **INTERNAL CONFLICT** (IRE) 67
62 **INTERNATIONAL LAW** 9
533 **INTERNATIONAL LION** 6
98 **INTERNATIONALANGEL** (IRE) 11
563 **INTERNE DE SIVOLA** (FR) 9
182 **INTERSTELLA** C 55
7 **INTERVENTION** 36
16 **INTERWEAVE** C 198
110 **INTHESETTLEMENT** G 10
520 **INTISAAR** (USA) C 29
433 **INTO DEBT** 5
535 **INTO OVERDRIVE** 17
451 **INTO THE FIRE** (FR) 6
516 **INTO THE LANE** (IRE) C 53
76 **INTO THE MYSTIC** (IRE) C 21
122 **INTO THE MYSTIC** (IRE) C 46
488 **INTOXICATED** 31
527 **INTOXICATION** 10
100 **INTREPIDLY** (USA) 3
231 **INTRICATELY** C 149
300 **INTRIGUING LADY** (IRE) 71
532 **INTRINSIC BOND** 6
94 **INTRUSION** C 72
122 **INTUITIVE** (IRE) 5
48 **INVER PARK** 7
418 **INVERNATA** (FR) C 32
262 **INVERNESS** (IRE) 35
48 **INVERSE** (IRE) F 78
517 **INVESTMENT MANAGER** 38
216 **INVICTUS DE BRION** (FR) 30
500 **INVIGILATE** 49
575 **INVINCIBLE CAVE** (IRE) 3
32 **INVINCIBLE HEIR** 34
186 **INVINCIBLE KING** (IRE) 16
142 **INVINCIBLE LARNE** (IRE) 21
47 **INVINCIBLE LASS** (IRE) 4
240 **INVINCIBLE ME** (IRE) F 160
118 **INVINCIBLE SOLDIER** (IRE) 10
133 **INVINCIBLE WISH** (IRE) 12
73 **INVINCIBLY** (IRE) 12
16 **INVITE** (IRE) 24
86 **INVITED** (FR) 10
378 **INYA LAKE** F 66
463 **IOLANI** (GER) 10
258 **IOLAOS DU MOU** (FR) 77

231 **IONIC** F 150
440 **IONTACH CHEVAL** 22
216 **IPSO FALCO** (FR) 31
88 **IRELAND'S EYE** (IRE) 5
131 **IRIS DANCER** 9
86 **IRIS DE GRUGY** (FR) 11
231 **IRISH ADMIRAL** (IRE) 21
406 **IRISH APPROACH** (IRE) 74
255 **IRISH CLIFF** (IRE) C 33
282 **IRISH ED** 5
528 **IRISH FLAME** 86
398 **IRISH HILL** (GER) 88
243 **IRISH LULLABY** 95
160 **IRISH MADAM** C 23
209 **IRISH OCTAVE** (IRE) 2
381 **IRISH ODYSSEY** (IRE) 49
323 **IRISH PROPHECY** (IRE) 29
281 **IRISH SOVEREIGN** (IRE) 6
490 **IRISH TIMES** 9
223 **IROKO** (FR) 50
409 **IRON BRIDGE** (IRE) 55
428 **IRON HEART** 35
427 **IRON HORSE** 9
107 **IRON IN THE SOUL** 9
69 **IRON MIKE** 9
184 **IRON SHERIFF** (IRE) 14
252 **IRON WINGS** (FR) 33
386 **IRONHILL** (IRE) 9
231 **IRRESISTABLE** 67
238 **IRV** (IRE) 38
345 **ISAAC D'AUBRELLE** (FR) 8
398 **ISAAC DES OBEAUX** (FR) 89
474 **ISABELLA GLYN** (IRE) F 12
568 **ISABELLA RUBY** 7
118 **ISAKOVA** 50
373 **ISAYALITTLEPRAYER** 62
104 **ISCA** (IRE) 23
182 **ISCHIA** 27
205 **ISEEMIST** (IRE) C 25
240 **ISEMEL** (IRE) 68
420 **ISHKA BAHA** (IRE) G 40
483 **ISKABEG LANE** (IRE) 23
106 **ISKAHEEN** (IRE) 13
227 **ISKRABOB** 1
189 **ISLA DI MILANO** (IRE) 9
486 **ISLA DIAMONDS** 4
516 **ISLA KAI** (IRE) 9
302 **ISLADAAY** (IRE) 21
342 **ISLAND BANDIT** (IRE) 26
342 **ISLAND BRAVE** (IRE) 9
39 **ISLAND FALCON** (IRE) 73
346 **ISLAND ODYSSEY** C 56
265 **ISLAND RUN** 45
345 **ISLAND SONG** (IRE) 9
520 **ISLAND STAR** (IRE) 30
528 **ISLAY OF ANGLESEY** (IRE) 87
529 **ISLE OF ARON** 17
88 **ISLE OF DREAMS** 6
438 **ISLE OF HOPE** 9
99 **ISLE OF LIGHT** 5
117 **ISLE OF LISMORE** (IRE) 17
81 **ISLE OF OIR** (IRE) 5
222 **ISLE OF RONA** 11
35 **ISLE OF WOLVES** 5
354 **ISLEBRIAND** (FR) 57
255 **ISOBEL MOORE** 19
182 **ISOLA ROSSA** 9

312 **ISOLATE** (FR) 49
428 **ISRAEL CHAMP** (IRE) 36
217 **ISRAR** 80
258 **ISSUING AUTHORITY** (IRE) 78
239 **ISTHEBAROPEN** 14
528 **IT IS NOW** 88
535 **IT JUST TAKES TIME** (IRE) 18
77 **IT'S A LOVE THING** 17
60 **IT'S FOR YOU MUM** (FR) 16
82 **IT'S GOOD TO LAUGH** (IRE) 19
487 **IT'S HOW WE ROLL** (IRE) 5
551 **IT'S JUST TOMMY** (IRE) 9
243 **IT'S SNOWING** (IRE) 96
89 **IT'S WONDERFUL** (FR) 46
428 **ITACARE** (FR) 37
388 **ITALIAN SPIRIT** (IRE) 77
388 **ITCHY FEET** (FR) 78
505 **ITIQAD** F 21
555 **ITIRAZ** (IRE) 42
402 **ITQAAN** (USA) C 143
458 **ITS A MIDNIGHT** 39
48 **ITS ALL FOR LUCK** (IRE) C 79
266 **ITS COMING HOME** 20
281 **ITS GONNAHAPPEN** (IRE) 7
393 **ITSABOUTIME** (IRE) 1
189 **ITSALLABOUTLUCK** (IRE) 10
213 **ITSNOTWHATYOUTHINK** (IRE) 9
409 **ITSO FURY** (IRE) 56
340 **ITSY BITSY BEAR** 24
406 **IUR CINN TRA** (FR) 75
561 **IVAHUNCH** 39
540 **IVAN DRAGO** 11
77 **IVASECRET** (IRE) 18
109 **IVATHEENGINE** (IRE) 2
420 **IVETWIGGEDIT** 41
187 **IVILNOBLE** (IRE) 9
288 **IVORS INVOLVEMENT** (IRE) 5
164 **IVORY GALA** (IRE) G 127
222 **IVY AVENUE** (IRE) 32
402 **IVY LEAGUE** (IRE) 47
285 **IVY ROSIE** (IRE) 8
509 **IVY'S SHADOW** (IRE) 16
185 **IVYNATOR** (IRE) 12
509 **IWILLDOIT** 37
77 **IZAR** (GER) 19
431 **IZOLA** F 43
554 **IZONS CROFT** F 10
458 **IZZY'S CHAMPION** (IRE) 40
187 **J J STINGLETON** 3
366 **J R CAVAGIN** (IRE) 15
16 **J WONDER** (USA) C 199
173 **J'ADORE** (IRE) 19
375 **J'AI FROID** (IRE) 26
312 **JABOTICABA** (FR) 50
246 **JACAMAR** (GER) 18
212 **JACHAR** (FR) 72
470 **JACK BEAN** 9
565 **JACK D'OR** 4
88 **JACK DANIEL** (IRE) 7
109 **JACK DARCY** (IRE) 12
143 **JACK DEVINE** (IRE) 20
83 **JACK LESLIE** 26
44 **JACK OF ALL SHAPES** (IRE) 12
459 **JACK RYAN** (IRE) 8
440 **JACK SHARP** (IRE) 23
254 **JACK SNIPE** 9
485 **JACK SPRAT** 28

381 **KANSAS CITY CHIEF** (IRE) 54
372 **KANUHURA** 18
265 **KANUKANKAN** (IRE) 50
73 **KANZINO** (IRE) 52
324 **KAP AUTEUIL** (FR) 10
562 **KAP HORN** (FR) 25
398 **KAPCORSE** (FR) 92
334 **KAPE MOSS** 43
567 **KAPGA DE LILY** (FR) 60
483 **KAPHUMOR** (FR) 26
157 **KAPITALISTE** (FR) 23
184 **KAPONO** 15
426 **KARADOW** (IRE) 56
245 **KARAKORAM** 7
233 **KARAMAYA** (IRE) F 49
442 **KARANNELLE** (IRE) 2
44 **KARAPIRO DOUG** 14
198 **KARATAYKA** (IRE) 5
24 **KARATE QUEEN** G 3
34 **KARDIA** 40
406 **KARDINYA** (IRE) 76
568 **KARDYLS HOPE** (IRE) F 18
6 **KARENINE** C 143
280 **KARIBANA** (IRE) 8
404 **KARL PHILIPPE** (IRE) 117
312 **KARLA JUNE** G 56
469 **KARLIE** 23
530 **KARLITO** (FR) 36
304 **KARMEST** C 41
299 **KARUOKA** 12
92 **KASABA BAY** 16
312 **KASAI RIVER** (IRE) 146
361 **KASAYID** C 95
516 **KASHTAN** C 56
478 **KASINO** 37
5 **KASPERENKO** 6
240 **KASSANDRA** (IRE) C 163
117 **KASSUTA** C 48
14 **KATA HEART'S** 16
77 **KATALAN** (GER) 20
509 **KATATE DORI** (FR) 22
300 **KATCH ME KATIE** F 172
476 **KATEIRA** 77
23 **KATELLI** (IRE) 10
440 **KATESON** 25
280 **KATH'S LUSTRE** 9
280 **KATH'S TOYBOY** 10
87 **KATHEEFA** (USA) 13
523 **KATHERINE PLACE** 5
174 **KATHY SUN** (IRE) F 41
205 **KATIE** K 17
7 **KATIE'S KITTEN** 38
276 **KATIES ESCAPE** (IRE) 5
26 **KATIYRA** (IRE) C 110
395 **KATPOLI** (FR) 31
292 **KATS BOB** 20
7 **KATTANI** (IRE) 39
185 **KATYUSHA** 13
483 **KAUTO D'AMOUR** (FR) 27
225 **KAUTO RIKO** (FR) 6
517 **KAUTO THE KING** (FR) 40
292 **KAVANAGHS CROSS** (IRE) 21
18 **KAWAALEES** 11
537 **KAWIDA** 37
16 **KAY CERAAR** 201
185 **KAYAK** F 65
15 **KAYARNAH** 17

238 **KAYF ADVENTURE** 41
157 **KAYF BAHA** 24
476 **KAYF HERNANDO** 78
560 **KAYF KOLI** 37
398 **KAYF TAOI** 35
354 **KAYFAST WARRIOR** (IRE) 60
295 **KAYLEN'S MISCHIEF** 12
181 **KAYLYN** 2
433 **KAZIMIERZ** (IRE) 6
304 **KAZONTHERAZZ** 26
170 **KEARNEY HILL** (IRE) 16
309 **KEEL OVER** 8
265 **KEELANS CHOICE** (IRE) C 51
491 **KEEP AN EYE OUT** (IRE) 15
26 **KEEP BIDDING** (IRE) 111
423 **KEEP COMING** (IRE) 5
491 **KEEP DANCING** (IRE) C 50
427 **KEEP IT BRIEF** 10
335 **KEEP ME HAPPY** 52
265 **KEEP MOVING** (FR) 52
240 **KEEP RIGHT ON** (IRE) 13
265 **KEEP ROLLING** (IRE) 53
265 **KEEP WONDERING** (IRE) 54
511 **KEEPER CHRIS** (IRE) 12
572 **KEEPER'S CHOICE** (IRE) 8
118 **KEEPING HOPING** (IRE) 51
19 **KEEPITFROMBECKY** (IRE) 11
388 **KEEPYOURDREAMSBIG** (FR) 82
364 **KEHLANI** (IRE) 50
364 **KEKOVA** F 51
460 **KELADORA** (USA) F 93
319 **KELAMITA** (IRE) C 41
418 **KELAPA** 24
97 **KELIADE** (IRE) 45
504 **KELLAHEN** (GER) 9
73 **KELLIA BERE** (FR) 96
89 **KELLS** (IRE) 48
73 **KELLY'S DINO** (FR) 13
467 **KELTUS** (FR) 13
6 **KEMARI** 9
385 **KEMBOY** (IRE) 118
561 **KEMERTON** (IRE) 96
97 **KEN COLT** (IRE) 7
364 **KENAHOPE** (IRE) 8
48 **KENDAL MINT** F 81
118 **KENDAMARA** (FR) C 98
252 **KENDELU** (IRE) 21
190 **KENDERGARTEN KOP** (IRE) 3
405 **KENDRED FIRE** (IRE) 28
420 **KENNACK BAY** (FR) 43
550 **KENNY GEORGE** 15
217 **KENSINGTON** (IRE) 82
89 **KENSINGTON AGENT** (FR) 104
354 **KENSINGTON ART** 61
522 **KENSINGTON GARDENS** G 21
572 **KENSTONE** (FR) 9
409 **KENTANDDOVER** 58
384 **KENTFORD DRAKE** 9
384 **KENTFORD MALLARD** 10
384 **KENTFORD SWANSONG** 11
480 **KENTUCKY HARDBOOT** (IRE) 4
176 **KENTUCKY KINGDOM** (IRE) 8
460 **KENTUCKY ROSE** 46
478 **KENTUCKYCONNECTION** (USA) 6
313 **KENYAN COWBOY** (IRE) 16
204 **KENYX** (IRE) 19
508 **KENZAI WARRIOR** (USA) 21

428 **KEPAGGE** (IRE) 39
157 **KEPALA** 25
563 **KEPLERIAN** 10
265 **KEPY BLANC** (FR) 55
426 **KERENSA** 11
287 **KERRERA** 11
124 **KERRKENNY GOLD** (IRE) 12
472 **KESTREL VALLEY** 4
313 **KEY INSTINCT** 17
334 **KEY LIGHT** (IRE) F 62
241 **KEY LOOK** (IRE) 3
488 **KEYSER SOZE** (IRE) 12
262 **KHAADEM** (IRE) 8
120 **KHABIB** (IRE) 5
139 **KHAJOOL** (IRE) M 12
498 **KHAKI** (IRE) G 12
300 **KHAL** (IRE) 173
274 **KHALINA STAR** 30
531 **KHAMSIN LADY** 39
354 **KHAMSIN MOOR** 62
246 **KHAN** (GER) 21
231 **KHANJAR** (IRE) 70
11 **KHARSHUF** (USA) 4
6 **KHATHAK** 44
7 **KHATWAH** (IRE) 40
6 **KHAWLAH** (IRE) F 144
184 **KHAYRAT** (FR) F 40
511 **KHILWAFY** 13
537 **KHINJANI** 72
511 **KHULU** 14
34 **KHURUMBI** (IRE) 22
16 **KIBARA** C 202
466 **KICK ON GIRL** (IRE) 14
398 **KICK UP A STORM** (IRE) 94
98 **KICKBOX** 29
149 **KICKONMYSON** 18
455 **KICKS AND ALE** (IRE) 12
222 **KICKSAFTERSIX** (IRE) 34
546 **KIDMAN** (IRE) 6
231 **KIDWAH** (IRE) 71
442 **KIERA ROYALE** (IRE) 3
281 **KIERAN'S ANGEL** 10
302 **KIHAVAH** 6
223 **KILBARRY LEADER** (IRE) 53
274 **KILBEG KING** (IRE) 31
92 **KILBREW BOY** (IRE) 59
8 **KILCARAGH BOY** (IRE) 2
169 **KILCASEY GOLD** (IRE) 3
555 **KILCONQUHAR** 26
385 **KILCRUIT** (IRE) 119
295 **KILDIMO** (IRE) 11
420 **KILDISART** (IRE) 44
238 **KILDORAN** (IRE) 42
306 **KILFILUM CROSS** (IRE) 7
548 **KILFILUM WOODS** (IRE) 16
494 **KILFINAN BAY** (IRE) 5
213 **KILFORDS QUEEN** (IRE) 11
97 **KILFRUSH MEMORIES** (IRE) 8
549 **KILGANER QUEEN** (IRE) 12
162 **KILKEASKIN MOLLY** (IRE) 6
398 **KILLALOAN** (IRE) 95
354 **KILLANE** (IRE) 63
262 **KILLEARN** (IRE) 36
323 **KILLER CLOWN** (IRE) 32
517 **KILLER KANE** (IRE) 41
361 **KILLER MODE** (IRE) 42

554 **LADY VILLANELLE** (IRE) 13
44 **LADY VINETTA** 15
74 **LADY WILBERRY** 6
257 **LADY WOLF** 1
182 **LADY WORMSLEY** (IRE) 57
67 **LADY ZIANA** 3
122 **LADY ZONDA** F 96
314 **LADY'S PRESENT** (IRE) 35
520 **LADYBIRD** (IRE) 19
428 **LADYKILLER** (GER) 45
7 **LADYMAC** 91
280 **LADYPACKSAPUNCH** 41
243 **LAELAPS** (IRE) 38
550 **LAETOLI** 16
240 **LAFAN** (IRE) 15
188 **LAFILIA** (GER) 3
299 **LAGUNA VENETA** (IRE) 32
47 **LAHEG** (FR) 40
59 **LAHINA BAY** (IRE) 18
366 **LAHORE** (USA) 17
182 **LAILAH** 28
262 **LAKE ELOISE** (IRE) 86
233 **LAKE LOUISE** (IRE) C 52
501 **LAKE SAND** (IRE) 9
254 **LAKE SHORE DRIVE** (IRE) 7
178 **LAKE TAKAPUNA** (IRE) 23
1 **LAKE VIEW LAD** (IRE) 31
505 **LAKESIDE** 23
384 **LAKESIDE LAD** 12
516 **LAKOTA BLUE** 58
476 **LAKOTA WARRIOR** (IRE) 86
498 **LALANIA** 4
398 **LALLYGAG** (GER) 101
322 **LALOCHEZIA** (IRE) 2
398 **LALOR** (GER) 102
19 **LAMANVER BEL AMI** 12
517 **LAMANVER PIPPIN** 44
320 **LAMANVER WOLD** 25
505 **LAMAR** (IRE) C 63
334 **LAMMAS** 18
164 **LAMPANG** (IRE) 54
300 **LAMYA** (GER) C 176
243 **LAMYAA** F 162
20 **LANCASHIRE LIFE** 14
409 **LAND GENIE** 62
549 **LAND OF EAGLES** 41
39 **LAND OF LEGENDS** (IRE) 28
295 **LAND OF MY DELIGHT** (IRE) 14
229 **LAND OF WINTER** (FR) 11
269 **LANDACRE BRIDGE** 4
404 **LANDING CALLING** (IRE) 120
105 **LANDERMERE** 20
186 **LANDIKUSIC** (IRE) C 37
520 **LANDING STRIP** 20
155 **LANDMARK** (USA) C 68
51 **LANDOFSMILES** (IRE) 24
374 **LANDSHIP** (IRE) 17
529 **LANDSMAN** (IRE) 20
528 **LANEQASH** 16
373 **LANGAFEL** (IRE) 63
476 **LANGER DAN** (IRE) 87
145 **LANGHOLM** (IRE) 22
101 **LANGLAUF** F 83
265 **LANGLEY HUNDRED** (IRE) 57
170 **LANGTON WOLD** (IRE) 56
293 **LANITA** (GER) C 19
517 **LANSPARK** (IRE) 45

401 **LANTANA DANCER** (IRE) 3
64 **LANZAROTE SUNSHINE** 3
393 **LAOCH BEAG** (IRE) 3
30 **LAOCH GACH LA** 13
7 **LARADO** (FR) 43
220 **LARANJAL** (IRE) 25
259 **LARCADIO** (IRE) 13
429 **LARCH HILL** (IRE) 5
398 **LARCHMONT LASS** (IRE) 103
184 **LARGE ACTION** 16
341 **LARGO BAY** (USA) 5
441 **LARGY FIX** (IRE) 4
564 **LARGY G** (IRE) 12
385 **LARGY HILL** (IRE) 124
172 **LARGY MOUTH** 11
333 **LARGY NIGHTS** (IRE) 31
514 **LARGY PERK** (IRE) 35
153 **LARGY PROSPECT** (IRE) 8
354 **LARGY REACH** 65
398 **LARGY TRAIN** 104
530 **LARIO** (GER) 37
91 **LARK LANE** 37
265 **LARKBARROW LAD** 58
346 **LARKIN** (IRE) 29
373 **LARRY** 69
530 **LARRY LOBSTER** (GER) 7
167 **LARUSSO** (IRE) 18
251 **LASKADINE** (FR) 13
567 **LASKALIN** (FR) 62
404 **LASSUE** 121
6 **LAST AMMO** (IRE) 46
299 **LAST CHANCE SALOON** (IRE) 60
73 **LAST CRUSADER** (IRE) 54
204 **LAST DATE** 21
255 **LAST FRONTIER** (IRE) F 34
482 **LAST GLANCE** (IRE) 20
544 **LAST HOORAH** 51
184 **LAST HOORAY** G 27
39 **LAST LOOK** (IRE) 29
176 **LAST MISSION** (FR) 9
201 **LAST OF A LEGEND** 29
143 **LAST ONE TO SHOW** (IRE) 21
182 **LAST PICASSO** (IRE) 11
428 **LAST QUARTER** (IRE) 46
372 **LAST ROAR** (IRE) 19
74 **LAST ROYAL** 7
39 **LAST SUNSET** (IRE) 30
458 **LAST SUPPER** G 93
490 **LAST TO BID** (FR) 10
193 **LASTIN' MEMORIES** 12
77 **LASTING BEAUTY** (FR) 24
185 **LASTING LEGACY** 14
292 **LASTOFTHECOSMICS** 22
276 **LASTORDERSPLEASE** (IRE) 6
163 **LATE ARRIVAL** (IRE) 15
158 **LATE BLOOM** 18
238 **LATE DATE** (IRE) 45
223 **LATE ROMANTIC** (IRE) 56
177 **LATE SHIPMENT** 9
73 **LATENIGHTMISTAKE** (IRE) 55
89 **LATENT HEAT** (IRE) 51
424 **LATER DARLING** 17
122 **LATEST GENERATION** 7
366 **LATIN FIVE** (IRE) 18
173 **LATIN LOVER** (IRE) 20
88 **LATINA REACH** (IRE) C 31
354 **LATINO FLING** (IRE) 66

457 **LATITUDE** (IRE) 16
231 **LATTAM** (IRE) 74
6 **LAUGH ALOUD** F 147
529 **LAUGHARNE** 21
201 **LAUGHING BRAVE** (FR) 30
549 **LAUGHING LUIS** 13
238 **LAUGHING WATER** (IRE) F 46
388 **LAURA BULLION** (IRE) 84
41 **LAUREL STAR** C 10
74 **LAURELDEAN BELLE** (IRE) G 8
232 **LAURELDEAN CROSS** (IRE) 28
287 **LAURENTIA** (IRE) 12
6 **LAVA FLOW** (IRE) C 148
346 **LAVA LIGHT** C 58
122 **LAVANDE** (FR) F 97
16 **LAVENDER AND LACE** C 209
424 **LAVENDER'S BLUE** (IRE) 3
136 **LAVERTEEN** (FR) 7
145 **LAVETTA** G 59
373 **LAVORANTE** (IRE) 70
59 **LAW BROOK BELLE** 8
217 **LAW OF THE SEA** 17
97 **LAW STAR** (FR) 47
474 **LAWD DYLAN** (IRE) 14
293 **LAWMAKER** 20
156 **LAWMANS BLIS** (IRE) 3
10 **LAWN RANGER** 13
81 **LAXEY** (IRE) 7
234 **LAYERTHORPE** (IRE) 3
361 **LAYFAYETTE** (IRE) 43
60 **LAZOUKINE** (FR) G 18
6 **LAZULI** (IRE) 12
104 **LAZY** (GER) 8
369 **LAZY SUNDAY** 2
80 **LAZYITIS** 12
179 **LE BAYOU** (FR) 8
163 **LE BEAU GARCON** 48
388 **LE BON VIVANT** (FR) 85
420 **LE BREUIL** (FR) 46
563 **LE CAMELEON** 12
143 **LE CHEVAL NOIR** (IRE) 22
88 **LE CHEVAL RAPIDE** (IRE) 11
398 **LE CHIFFRE D'OR** (FR) 105
274 **LE COEUR NET** (FR) 33
26 **LE DESIGNE** (IRE) 53
245 **LE FIGARO FAOUDEL** (FR) 8
556 **LE FILS DE FORCE** 6
15 **LE FORBAN** 39
420 **LE GRAND LION** (FR) 47
265 **LE LIGERIEN** (FR) 59
127 **LE MAGNIFIQUE** (GER) 29
529 **LE MILOS** 22
404 **LE MUR** (FR) 122
252 **LE MUSEE** (FR) 22
395 **LE PATRIOTE** (FR) 34
387 **LE REVEUR** (IRE) 8
51 **LE TUEUR** (IRE) 25
73 **LEAD STORY** (IRE) 14
452 **LEAD THE PACK** (IRE) 6
349 **LEADING CHOICE** (IRE) 10
96 **LEADING KNIGHT** (IRE) 6
548 **LEADING MAN** (IRE) 18
536 **LEADING SWOOP** (IRE) 16
404 **LEADING THEATRE** (IRE) 123
101 **LEAF MOTIF** 35
152 **LEAGAN GAEILGE** (IRE) 5
30 **LEANNES LADY** (IRE) 4

109 **LEAP ABROAD** (IRE) 13
460 **LEAP YEAR LAD** (IRE) 94
293 **LEAPING LENA** 14
388 **LEARNTALOT** (IRE) 86
505 **LEARZA** (IRE) C 64
404 **LEAVE HER TO ME** 124
192 **LEAVE MY ALONE** (IRE) 5
216 **LEAVE OF ABSENCE** (FR) 32
335 **LEAVEITWITHME** (IRE) 53
469 **LEBOWSKI** (IRE) 24
500 **LEBSAYER** (FR) 53
491 **LECHRO** 16
239 **LEDHAM** (IRE) 16
204 **LEDNIKOV** 22
170 **LEESWOOD LILY** 20
415 **LEGAL MIND** 10
578 **LEGAL OK** (IRE) 5
204 **LEGAL REFORM** (IRE) 23
373 **LEGAL RIGHTS** (GER) 71
402 **LEGATISSIMO** (IRE) 7
528 **LEGEND OF DUBAI** 17
425 **LEGEND OF FRANCE** 8
275 **LEGEND OF ZORRO** (IRE) 6
378 **LEGENDARY DAY** 14
213 **LEGENDARY GRACE** 13
504 **LEGENDARY RHYTHM** 11
490 **LEGENDE D'ART** (IRE) 11
125 **LEGENDS GOLD** (IRE) 19
485 **LEGENDS RYDE** 31
231 **LEGERETE** F 157
246 **LEGIONAR** (GER) 25
402 **LEINSTER HOUSE** (USA) 50
467 **LEISSIERES EXPRESS** 17
317 **LELABAD** 28
258 **LELANTOS** (IRE) 85
178 **LEMOINE** 31
386 **LEMON ROCK** F 42
294 **LEMON** T 6
219 **LENNY** 12
155 **LENNY'S SPIRIT** (FR) 7
243 **LEO DE FURY** (IRE) 39
366 **LEODIS DREAM** (IRE) 19
428 **LEONCAVALLO** (IRE) 47
335 **LEONNA** (IRE) 63
334 **LEOPOLD BLOOM** 64
314 **LEOPOLDS ROCK** (IRE) 36
89 **LEQUINTO** (IRE) 52
51 **LERMOOS LEGEND** 26
525 **LEROY BROWN** 33
54 **LEROY LEROY** 12
34 **LERWICK** 44
113 **LES'S LEGACY** 13
114 **LESKINFERE** (IRE) 1
80 **LESS IS MORE** 39
279 **LESS OF THAT** (IRE) 6
427 **LESSER** (IRE) 12
255 **LET EM HAVE IT** (IRE) 22
469 **LET IT SHINE** 5
395 **LET ME BE** (IRE) 35
469 **LET ME ENTERTAIN** U 26
456 **LET'S BE HAPPY** (IRE) 4
55 **LET'S BELIEVE** (IRE) 4
118 **LET'S FLY AGAIN** 53
422 **LET'S GO HUGO** (IRE) 23
388 **LET'S HAVE ANOTHER** (IRE) 87
90 **LETHAL ANGEL** 8
59 **LETHAL BLAST** 9

118 **LETHAL NYMPH** 54
314 **LETHAL STEPS** 37
418 **LETHAL TOUCH** 25
67 **LETHAL VISION** 11
398 **LETHERBELUCKY** (IRE) G 106
426 **LETMELIVEMYLIFE** 7
312 **LETMELIVEMYLIFE** 58
409 **LETMETELLUSOMETHIN** 63
212 **LETS GO CHAMP** (IRE) 46
282 **LETS GO DUTCHESS** 4
523 **LETSBE AVENUE** (IRE) 6
373 **LETSCRACKON** (IRE) 72
10 **LETTER AT DAWN** (IRE) 14
438 **LETTER OF THE LAW** (IRE) 10
223 **LETTETHETRUTHBEKNOWN** (IRE) 57
103 **LETTIE LUTZ** (IRE) 10
537 **LETUSGOTHENYOUANDI** 43
528 **LEUVEN POWER** (IRE) 95
424 **LEVEL UP** (IRE) 18
100 **LEVENDI** 4
441 **LEVEROCK LASS** (IRE) 5
300 **LEVITATE** (IRE) 73
33 **LEWESIAN LASS** (IRE) 10
377 **LEXI THE ONE** (IRE) 13
504 **LEXI'S CHOICE** (IRE) 12
337 **LEXINGTON BULLET** 7
240 **LEXINGTON KNIGHT** (IRE) 16
549 **LEYLA'S POWER** (IRE) 42
476 **LEYLAK** (IRE) 88
521 **LEZARDRIEUX** 22
130 **LHEBAYEB** (GER) 13
477 **LIAM'S LASS** (IRE) 13
414 **LIAM'S LEGEND** (USA) 19
73 **LIAMARTY DREAMS** 56
7 **LIAMBA** 44
530 **LIANE** (GER) 44
118 **LIANE DE POUGY** (FR) G 35
165 **LIBBERTY HUNTER** 5
332 **LIBBRETTA** 7
204 **LIBBY AMI** (IRE) 24
238 **LIBBY MAE** (IRE) G 47
243 **LIBER NAUTICUS** (IRE) C 163
561 **LIBERATED LAD** 44
118 **LIBERATING** C 100
7 **LIBERATION POINT** (IRE) 45
173 **LIBERISQUE** F 29
504 **LIBERTARIAN ROYALE** (IRE) 13
566 **LIBERTINE BELLE** 17
182 **LIBERTUS** 29
527 **LIBERTY BAY** 11
556 **LIBERTY BREEZE** 7
17 **LIBERTY POWER** 15
364 **LIBRA TIGER** 33
287 **LIBRISA BREEZE** 13
325 **LICIA ST GOUSTAN** (IRE) 14
164 **LICIT** 55
375 **LICKLIGHTER** (IRE) 27
225 **LICKPENNY LARRY** 7
164 **LIEL** C 169
361 **LIEUTENANT COMMAND** (FR) 44
69 **LIEUTENANT ROCCO** (IRE) 11
403 **LIFE HAPPENED** (USA) F 45
523 **LIFE IS GOLDEN** (USA) C 18
458 **LIFE MADE SIMPLE** 41
6 **LIFE OF DREAMS** 47
240 **LIFE'S A BEACH** (IRE) 71

420 **LIFEISAHIGHWAY** (IRE) 48
327 **LIFESJUSTAFLICKER** 17
243 **LIFETIME AMBITION** 40
313 **LIFETIME LEGEND** (IRE) 18
172 **LIFFEYDALE DREAMER** (IRE) 12
349 **LIGHT EM UP NIGEL** (IRE) 11
432 **LIGHT FLICKER** (IRE) 21
118 **LIGHT GLASS** (IRE) C 101
299 **LIGHT HEARTED** C 61
147 **LIGHT IN THE SKY** (FR) 8
475 **LIGHT INFANTRY** (FR) 50
361 **LIGHT LAUGHTER** F 96
77 **LIGHT LILY** 25
543 **LIGHT MY FIRE** (FR) F 34
323 **LIGHT N STRIKE** (IRE) 35
247 **LIGHT OF ATHENA** (IRE) 9
262 **LIGHT OF LOVE** C 87
566 **LIGHT OF THUNDER** (IRE) 18
16 **LIGHT THE STARS** (IRE) F 210
89 **LIGHT UP OUR STARS** (IRE) 533
251 **LIGHTENING COMPANY** (IRE) 14
73 **LIGHTENING GESTURE** 57
185 **LIGHTENING SHORE** 15
201 **LIGHTLY SQUEEZE** 31
505 **LIGHTNING APPROACH** (IRE) 24
251 **LIGHTNING ATTACK** 15
149 **LIGHTNING BLUE** 20
483 **LIGHTNING BREEZE** (IRE) G 28
484 **LIGHTNING BUG** (IRE) 6
240 **LIGHTNING ELIZA** 167
284 **LIGHTNING GOLD** 10
402 **LIGHTNING THUNDER** C 148
208 **LIGHTONTHEWING** (IRE) 11
500 **LIGHTS ON** 12
82 **LIGNOU** (FR) 20
174 **LIHOU** 9
394 **LIIMARI** 7
164 **LIKE A LION** (IRE) 129
186 **LIKE A TIGER** 38
379 **LIKEABLE** C 36
556 **LIL BIT OF MAGIC** 13
252 **LIL CODEY** (IRE) 23
319 **LIL GUFF** 21
14 **LIL SOPHELLA** (IRE) G 17
28 **LILA GIRL** (IRE) 31
231 **LILAC ROAD** (IRE) 22
189 **LILANDRA** (FR) 11
436 **LILI WEN FACH** (IRE) 4
25 **LILIKOI** (IRE) 13
274 **LILITH** (IRE) 34
271 **LILKIAN** 3
402 **LILLIE LANGTRY** (IRE) F 149
402 **LILY POND** (IRE) 51
179 **LILY'S RAINBOW** (IRE) C 19
532 **LILYWHITE** 8
376 **LIMEKILN ROCK** (IRE) 11
550 **LIMELIGHTER** 17
143 **LIMERICK LEADER** (FR) 23
409 **LIMETREE BOY** (IRE) 64
47 **LIMITED ABILITY** 41
77 **LIMITED EDITION** 26
559 **LIMITED RESERVE** (IRE) 14
204 **LINCOLN GAMBLE** 25
225 **LINCOLN LYN** 4
565 **LINCOLN RED** 5
300 **LINCOLN ROCKS** F 177
561 **LINDAKA** (FR) 45

354 **LINDWALL** (IRE) 67
1 **LINDY LOU** G 33
222 **LINE OF DESCENT** (IRE) 36
388 **LINELEE KING** (FR) 88
483 **LINEN LINE** C 29
207 **LINET** F 11
161 **LINGER** (IRE) 4
375 **LION FACE** (IRE) 28
521 **LION TOWER** (IRE) 23
280 **LION'S DREAM** (FR) 42
523 **LION'S VIGIL** (USA) 7
364 **LIONEL** 34
394 **LIPPY LADY** (IRE) 8
117 **LIPSINK** (IRE) 18
486 **LIQUIDISER** 6
528 **LIR SPECIALE** (IRE) 96
88 **LISA'S DREAM** (IRE) 22
106 **LISDARRAGH** (USA) 3
453 **LISLOAN** (IRE) 1
174 **LISMORE** (USA) F 42
125 **LISNAGAR OSCAR** (IRE) 20
193 **LISSEN TO THE LADY** (IRE) 13
125 **LISSITZKY** (IRE) 21
164 **LISTEN BABY** (IRE) 38
113 **LISTEN TARABLUE** F 14
576 **LITE AND AIRY** 10
69 **LITHAI** (IRE) G 12
548 **LITIGATE** (IRE) 19
201 **LITTERALE CI** (FR) 32
466 **LITTLE AUDIO** (IRE) F 30
473 **LITTLE AWKWARD** (FR) 21
523 **LITTLE BOY BLUE** 8
498 **LITTLE BROWN TROUT** 5
333 **LITTLE BRUCE** (IRE) 32
292 **LITTLE BY LITTLE** 23
551 **LITTLE CHANCE** 12
188 **LITTLE DOTTY** 4
117 **LITTLE EARL** (IRE) 38
170 **LITTLE EMMA LOULOU** 57
30 **LITTLE GEM** 5
523 **LITTLE GIRL BLUE** 15
1 **LITTLE GLENSHEE** (IRE) F 34
246 **LITTLE HERCULES** (IRE) 26
528 **LITTLE HUG** 172
16 **LITTLE HUSTLE** 98
314 **LITTLE INDIA** (FR) 38
103 **LITTLE JESSTURE** (IRE) 11
524 **LITTLE JO** 4
73 **LITTLE KIM** C 99
531 **LITTLE LIGHT** (FR) 18
199 **LITTLE MISS ALICE** 11
388 **LITTLE MISS DANTE** 89
346 **LITTLE MISS DYNAMO** (IRE) 30
118 **LITTLE MISS LILLY** 12
547 **LITTLE MISS SASSY** 6
489 **LITTLE MUDDY** 5
546 **LITTLE ORANGE** 7
118 **LITTLE PALAVER** 13
150 **LITTLE PEACHEY** (IRE) 6
488 **LITTLE PRAYER** (IRE) 32
48 **LITTLE RAVEN** (IRE) 34
428 **LITTLE RED LION** (IRE) 48
265 **LITTLE RIVER BAY** (IRE) 60
498 **LITTLE SUNFLOWER** 6
164 **LITTLE TED** 57
549 **LITTLE TIPSY** 14
432 **LITTLE WINDMILL** (IRE) 13

470 **LITTLEMISSATTITUDE** 13
521 **LITUUS** (IRE) 46
300 **LIV LUCKY** (IRE) 74
338 **LIVA** (IRE) 3
549 **LIVE IN THE DREAM** (IRE) 43
549 **LIVE IN THE MOMENT** (IRE) 31
39 **LIVE YOUR DREAM** (IRE) 31
366 **LIVELIFETOTHEFULL** 36
482 **LIVELIFETOTHEMAX** (IRE) 21
426 **LIVELLA FELLA** (IRE) F 59
385 **LIVELOVELAUGH** (IRE) 125
295 **LIVELY CITIZEN** (IRE) 15
535 **LIVELY LIVVY** 23
426 **LIVERPOOL KNIGHT** 8
312 **LIVERPOOL KNIGHT** 59
300 **LIVING LEGEND** (IRE) 13
533 **LIVING'S BOY AN CO** (FR) 7
240 **LIWA PALACE** F 168
65 **LIZZIANNA** (IRE) 9
204 **LIZZIE JEAN** 47
555 **LIZZIE LOCH** 27
250 **LIZZY'S GIRL** 5
504 **LLANDINABO LAD** 14
440 **LLANTARA** 27
397 **LLEYTON** (IRE) 3
497 **LOBO DEL MAR** 2
406 **LOCAL BAY** 22
300 **LOCAL SPIRIT** (USA) C 178
273 **LOCALLINK** (IRE) 6
239 **LOCH GARMAN ARIS** (IRE) 17
406 **LOCH JIPP** (USA) F 23
44 **LOCH LINNHE** 16
315 **LOCH MIRAGE** F 28
402 **LOCH NESS** (IRE) 52
215 **LOCHNAVER** 17
202 **LOCHSIDE LASS** (IRE) 24
494 **LOCK DOWN LUKE** 6
409 **LOCK'S CORNER** (IRE) 65
15 **LOCKDOWN** 19
404 **LOCKDOWN DREAM** 125
239 **LOCKDOWN LASS** 18
560 **LOCKDOWN LEADER** (IRE) 40
299 **LOCKSMITH** (IRE) 33
568 **LOCO LOBO** 9
170 **LOCOMOTIVE BRETH** (IRE) 21
375 **LOFTY** 29
386 **LOGAN ROCKS** (IRE) 13
321 **LOGAN'S CHOICE** 3
315 **LOGIQUE** (FR) F 15
475 **LOGJAM** (IRE) C 69
231 **LOHENGRIN** 158
220 **LOINGSEOIR** (IRE) 9
334 **LOLA AUGUSTUS** (IRE) 45
507 **LOLA REBEL** (IRE) 4
145 **LOLA RIDGE** (IRE) C 60
334 **LOLA SHOWGIRL** (IRE) 19
300 **LOMAPAMAR** F 179
529 **LONDON** (GER) 23
160 **LONDON EYE** (USA) 9
537 **LONDON PLANE** (IRE) C 73
491 **LONDON WELSH** C 51
360 **LONE EAGLE** (IRE) 4
39 **LONE FIGHTER** (IRE) 32
155 **LONELY ROCK** F 69
89 **LONG CALL** 54
404 **LONG STAY** 126
276 **LONG SYMPHONY** (IRE) 7

10 **LONG TIME COMIN** 35
314 **LONG TO BE** (FR) 39
522 **LONG WEEKEND** 23
475 **LONGING** (IRE) C 70
265 **LONGSHANKS** (IRE) 61
434 **LONGSIDER** (IRE) 7
539 **LONGVILLE LILLY** 3
476 **LONIMOSS BARELIERE** (FR) 89
240 **LOOE BEACH** (IRE) 72
272 **LOOK HERE'S DEE** F 20
80 **LOOK OUT LOUIS** 13
226 **LOOKALIKE** F 10
313 **LOOKAWAY** (IRE) 19
272 **LOOKFORARAINBOW** 13
73 **LOOKING FOR LYNDA** (IRE) 100
117 **LOOKS ALL RIGHT** (IRE) C 49
240 **LOOKS GREAT** F 169
234 **LOOKS LIKE POWER** (IRE) 4
93 **LOOKSEE** 12
56 **LOOKSNOWTLIKEBRIAN** (IRE) 5
127 **LOOSE LIPS** 61
35 **LOPES DANCER** (IRE) 6
243 **LOPES GOLD** (IRE) 98
240 **LOQUACE** (FR) 73
87 **LOQUACIOUS BOY** (IRE) 15
233 **LORD ABAMA** (IRE) 28
381 **LORD ACCORD** (IRE) 57
216 **LORD BADDESLEY** (IRE) 33
245 **LORD BILL** (IRE) 9
51 **LORD BRYAN** (IRE) 27
314 **LORD BUTTONS** 40
251 **LORD CAPRIO** (IRE) 16
566 **LORD CHERRY** (IRE) 44
63 **LORD CONDI** (IRE) 11
267 **LORD DU MESNIL** (FR) 12
176 **LORD GETAWAY** (IRE) 10
406 **LORD GLITTERS** (FR) 24
174 **LORD GORGEOUS** (IRE) 29
99 **LORD MARBURY** (IRE) 6
51 **LORD NAPIER** (IRE) 28
566 **LORD NEIDIN** 19
217 **LORD NORTH** (IRE) 18
73 **LORD OBERON** 18
525 **LORD OF CHESHIRE** (FR) 34
388 **LORD OF KERAK** 90
215 **LORD OF THE GLEN** 18
73 **LORD OF THE LODGE** (IRE) 16
404 **LORD** P 127
528 **LORD PARAMOUNT** 97
26 **LORD PROTECTOR** (GER) 9
566 **LORD RAPSCALLION** (IRE) 30
201 **LORD RAVENSLEY** (IRE) 33
178 **LORD ROCO** 24
385 **LORD ROYAL** (IRE) 126
380 **LORD SERENDIPITY** (IRE) 3
12 **LORD SPARKY** 13
171 **LORD SPRINGFIELD** (IRE) 8
327 **LORD STANLEY** (IRE) 38
314 **LORD TORRANAGA** (FR) 41
459 **LORD VADER** 13
81 **LORD WARBURTON** (IRE) 8
94 **LORD'S BELL** 38
346 **LORDMAN** (IRE) 31
317 **LORDSBRIDGE BOY** 6
317 **LORDSBRIDGE GIRL** 29
231 **LORDSHIP** (GER) 159
164 **LORENZO LOTTO** (IRE) 130

327 **LYGON ROCK** (IRE) 18
475 **LYIN EYES** C 71
326 **LYNCHPIN** (IRE) 7
219 **LYNDALE** 13
189 **LYNDON B** (IRE) 13
438 **LYNNS BOY** 4
431 **LYNWOOD LAD** 46
333 **LYRICAL GENIUS** (IRE) 33
378 **LYRICAL LADY** 38
231 **LYSANDER** 75
385 **M C MULDOON** (IRE) 127
69 **M'LADY MELODY** 14
201 **MA BELLE NOIRE** 35
364 **MA CHERIE** F 52
10 **MAAHI VE** (IRE) 16
361 **MAARIT** C 97
259 **MAASAI WARRIOR** (IRE) 14
91 **MAAZEL** 7
456 **MABAADY** 5
62 **MABDAA** 10
150 **MABEL KINGSMILL** 7
22 **MABLEABLE** 12
174 **MABRE** (IRE) 10
164 **MAC AILEY** 60
560 **MAC BE LUCKY** 43
87 **MAC MCCARTHY** (IRE) 16
51 **MAC TOTTIE** 29
243 **MAC'S XPRESS** (IRE) 41
16 **MACARTHURS PARK** (IRE) F 211
73 **MACCHIAVELLO** (IRE) 59
151 **MACCLOUD** (IRE) 10
133 **MACEY MILAN** (IRE) 15
320 **MACFIN** (IRE) 27
97 **MACHETE** (IRE) 49
346 **MACHITO** (IRE) 60
388 **MACHO MOVER** (IRE) 93
251 **MACHO PRIDE** (IRE) 17
560 **MACK THE MAN** (IRE) 44
388 **MACKELDUFF** (IRE) 94
354 **MACKENBERG** (GER) 71
300 **MACKENZIE ROSE** (IRE) 77
8 **MACKIE DEE** (IRE) 3
473 **MACLAINE** 23
366 **MACMERRY JIM** 20
411 **MACOCHA** (IRE) 12
138 **MACON BELLE** 15
402 **MACQUARIE** (IRE) 7
308 **MACS BLESSINGS** (IRE) 2
411 **MACS DILEMMA** (IRE) 13
7 **MACS GIRL** (IRE) 46
474 **MAD ABOUT SALLY** (IRE) 15
204 **MAD ARTYMAISE** (IRE) 48
436 **MAD BARRY** 5
119 **MAD JAZZ** G 14
265 **MAD MIKE** (IRE) 63
484 **MAD MOLL** (IRE) F 7
484 **MAD MOLL** (IRE) F 19
373 **MADAA** (IRE) 73
32 **MADAM ANNA** (IRE) F 35
181 **MADAM ARKATI** 10
403 **MADAM BAROQUE** F 46
351 **MADAM DELUXE** 2
258 **MADAM FONTAINE** (FR) F 87
300 **MADAM MACHO** 181
525 **MADAM MALARKEY** 35
372 **MADAM MAY** 6
133 **MADAM MILLER** 16

288 **MADAM SCULLY** 9
300 **MADAME AMBASSADOR** 78
23 **MADAME BIJOUX** 11
300 **MADAME BONBON** (FR) 79
26 **MADAME CHIANG** C 114
470 **MADAME FENELLA** 23
151 **MADAME HELEN** (FR) 20
105 **MADAME LAFITE** C 41
204 **MADAME MARMALADE** 49
185 **MADAME PELTIER** (IRE) 16
230 **MADAME POMPADOUR** 3
262 **MADANY** (IRE) C 90
273 **MADASAHATTER** 15
388 **MADE FOR YOU** 95
152 **MADE IN PIMLICO** (IRE) 6
318 **MADE OF GOLD** 5
314 **MADEEH** 44
371 **MADEIRA MOON** (IRE) C 34
240 **MADEMOISELLE MARIE** (FR) F 173
97 **MADEMOISELLE ROSE** 50
529 **MADERA MIST** (IRE) 24
385 **MADIBA PASSION** (FR) 61
385 **MADMANSGAME** 128
402 **MADONNADELROSARIO** (IRE) 56
89 **MADRINHO** (IRE) 55
346 **MAELIA** (USA) C 61
183 **MAEVE'S MEMORY** (IRE) 6
200 **MAFFEO BARBERINI** (IRE) 23
240 **MAFIA POWER** 17
314 **MAGELLAN** 45
578 **MAGEN'S MOON** (IRE) 6
101 **MAGGIE AND ME** 37
369 **MAGGIE GREY** 3
300 **MAGGIE'S DELIGHT** (IRE) 80
73 **MAGGIE'S JOY** 60
239 **MAGHEROARTY STAR** (IRE) 20
262 **MAGHLAAK** 39
325 **MAGIC DANCER** 15
67 **MAGIC GEM** 4
349 **MAGIC MARMALADE** (IRE) 13
74 **MAGIC MINOR** (IRE) F 18
543 **MAGIC MINOR** (IRE) F 35
164 **MAGIC MUSIC** (IRE) F 61
566 **MAGIC NYMPH** (IRE) C 60
172 **MAGIC OF MILAN** (IRE) 13
398 **MAGIC SAINT** (FR) 107
409 **MAGIC SEVEN** (IRE) 66
535 **MAGIC WAVE** 24
340 **MAGICAL DAZE** F 30
240 **MAGICAL DIAS** 75
93 **MAGICAL DRAGON** (IRE) 13
87 **MAGICAL EFFECT** (IRE) 17
13 **MAGICAL ESCAPE** (IRE) 37
243 **MAGICAL LAGOON** (IRE) 102
440 **MAGICAL MAGGIE** 29
535 **MAGICAL MAX** 25
371 **MAGICAL MILE** (IRE) 6
89 **MAGICAL MIST** 56
217 **MAGICAL MORNING** 19
460 **MAGICAL SPIRIT** (IRE) 15
374 **MAGICAL WISH** (IRE) 7
450 **MAGICAL WONDERLAND** G 4
460 **MAGICDOLLAR** 95
332 **MAGICINTHEMAKING** (USA) 8
426 **MAGIQUE** (IRE) F 60
217 **MAGISTERIAL** (IRE) 89
398 **MAGISTRATO** (FR) 108

327 **MAGNA BELLA** 39
327 **MAGNA SAM** 19
300 **MAGNETIC FIELD** 81
475 **MAGNETISED** 14
410 **MAGNIFICENCE** (FR) 3
381 **MAGNIFICENT BEN** 58
243 **MAGNIFICENT LADY** (IRE) 103
156 **MAGNIFICENT MILLIE** 20
11 **MAGNIFIQUE** (FR) 1
544 **MAGURO** (FR) 52
38 **MAH MATE BOB** (IRE) 11
544 **MAHA DEWI** (IRE) 53
94 **MAHALE** 15
164 **MAHANAKHON** 131
365 **MAHANAKHON POWER** 33
260 **MAHARASHTRA** 13
457 **MAHLAND** (IRE) 15
384 **MAHLER'S PROMISE** (IRE) 13
222 **MAHLERVOUS** (IRE) 37
404 **MAHON POINT** 130
231 **MAHRAJAAN** (USA) 23
98 **MAID MILLIE** 2
112 **MAID O'MALLEY** 17
554 **MAID OF ARAGON** (IRE) 16
554 **MAID OF HOUXTY** 14
559 **MAID ON MENDIP** 16
312 **MAID ON THE MOON** 62
417 **MAID TO DREAM** F 72
229 **MAID TO MASTER** (IRE) F 35
83 **MAIDEN CASTLE** 8
262 **MAIDEN'S GREEN** 40
458 **MAIFALKI** (FR) 43
428 **MAIN FACT** (USA) 49
426 **MAIN TARGET** 9
460 **MAIREAD ANNE** (USA) F 96
228 **MAISIEBELLA** 9
148 **MAISON BRILLET** (IRE) 1
481 **MAISON D'OR** (IRE) 3
534 **MAITREE EXPRESS** 2
104 **MAJAL** (FR) 28
94 **MAJESTIC** (IRE) 16
174 **MAJESTIC ALEXANDER** (IRE) C 43
34 **MAJESTIC DANCER** (IRE) F 45
109 **MAJESTIC DAWN** (IRE) 3
101 **MAJESTIC FIGHTER** (IRE) 38
16 **MAJESTIC GLORY** 100
300 **MAJESTIC JASMINE** (IRE) F 182
265 **MAJESTIC MERLIN** 64
543 **MAJESTIC TEJAAN** (IRE) 10
122 **MAJEYDA** (USA) F 99
516 **MAJIL** (IRE) 60
231 **MAJMU** F 161
279 **MAJOR ASSAULT** 1
312 **MAJOR DUNDEE** (IRE) 63
523 **MAJOR GATSBY** (IRE) 16
39 **MAJOR PARTNERSHIP** (IRE) 35
249 **MAJOR PUSEY** 5
33 **MAJOR REWARD** (IRE) 11
428 **MAJOR ROBINSON** (IRE) F 50
365 **MAJOR SNUGFIT** 34
258 **MAJOR STING** (IRE) 88
411 **MAJOR VALENTINE** 14
87 **MAKALU** (IRE) 34
18 **MAKAMBE** (IRE) 13
80 **MAKANAH** 15
100 **MAKARIOS** 5
537 **MAKAROVA** 44

185 **MARTHA EDLIN** 43
405 **MARTHA WILLOW** 9
82 **MARTHA YEATS** (IRE) 21
155 **MARTHAMYDEAR** (USA) C 70
511 **MARTIN'S BRIG** (IRE) 18
99 **MARTINENGO** (IRE) 8
77 **MARTINEO** 28
428 **MARTINHAL** (IRE) 52
402 **MARTINSTOWN** (IRE) 57
13 **MARTON ABBEY** 38
189 **MARTY BYRDE** 14
320 **MARTY TIME** (FR) 28
398 **MARVELLOUS MICK** 112
98 **MARWAD** 30
163 **MARWARI** (IRE) 18
365 **MARY BOLEYN** (IRE) G 36
317 **MARY LOU** (GER) 7
10 **MARY OF MODENA** 37
406 **MARY STEWART** (IRE) C 110
367 **MARY THOMAS** (IRE) F 40
417 **MARY'S CHOICE** (GER) F 73
16 **MARZOCCO** 213
460 **MAS PODER** (IRE) 51
312 **MASACCIO** (IRE) 64
388 **MASADA KNIGHT** (IRE) 97
240 **MASAI QUEEN** (IRE) C 176
403 **MASANDRA** (IRE) F 48
504 **MASCARA PRINCESS** (FR) 18
69 **MASCAT** 15
16 **MASEKELA** (IRE) 101
75 **MASH POTATO** (IRE) 4
181 **MASHAM MOOR** 3
566 **MASHKUUR** (IRE) 46
167 **MASKADA** (FR) 21
354 **MASKED CRUSADER** (FR) 73
335 **MASKED IDENTITY** 25
576 **MASKED QUEEN** 38
563 **MASKED SPIRIT** (IRE) 13
209 **MASKIA** (FR) 3
395 **MASON JAR** (FR) 36
176 **MASQOOL** (IRE) 12
330 **MASQUE OF ANARCHY** (IRE) 3
228 **MASSINI MAN** 10
294 **MASTER ALAN** 8
509 **MASTER AUSTRALIA** (IRE) 50
428 **MASTER BLAZE** (FR) 53
525 **MASTER CHEWY** (IRE) 36
182 **MASTER DANDY** (IRE) 58
201 **MASTER DEBONAIR** 36
145 **MASTER ELLIS** (IRE) 43
97 **MASTER GATSBY** (FR) 51
367 **MASTER GREY** (IRE) 14
238 **MASTER GUSTAV** 48
354 **MASTER MALACHY** (IRE) 74
40 **MASTER MALCOLM** 6
157 **MASTER MEAD** 26
192 **MASTER MIKEY DEE** (IRE) 6
323 **MASTER MILLINER** (IRE) 37
314 **MASTER NEWTON** (IRE) 47
47 **MASTER OF COLOURS** 44
200 **MASTER OF COMBAT** (IRE) 11
99 **MASTER OF SOULS** (IRE) 5
51 **MASTER OF SPIN** (IRE) 30
49 **MASTER OF THE MALT** 7
6 **MASTER OF THE SEAS** (IRE) 15
151 **MASTER RICHARD** 21
217 **MASTER SERGEANT** (IRE) 91

89 **MASTER SULLY** 59
155 **MASTER THE STARS** (GER) 8
369 **MASTER TRADESMAN** (IRE) 4
265 **MASTER WORK** (FR) 66
475 **MASTERCLASS** 52
381 **MASTERDREAM** (FR) 62
342 **MASTERMINDING** (IRE) 29
246 **MASTEROFTHEHEIGHTS** (IRE) 28
265 **MASTERS LEGACY** (IRE) 67
528 **MATAURI PEARL** (IRE) C 175
26 **MATCHED** 55
16 **MATCHING SOX** (IRE) 214
204 **MATCHLESS** (IRE) 26
12 **MATCHMAKING** (GER) 14
484 **MATERIAL WORLD** G 9
484 **MATERIAL WORLD** F 17
95 **MATERIALITY** F 5
33 **MATEWAN** 12
406 **MATRON** C 111
26 **MATRON OF HONOUR** (IRE) C 116
398 **MATTERHORN** (FR) 113
542 **MATTHEW MAN** 5
274 **MATTHIAS** 58
292 **MATTI** (IRE) 63
164 **MATTICE** 135
427 **MATTIE ROSS** 13
406 **MATTINATA** C 112
164 **MATTY TOO** 136
243 **MAUD GONNE SPIRIT** (IRE) 43
445 **MAUGHOLD HEAD** 30
417 **MAUREEN** (IRE) C 74
75 **MAUREEN'S STAR** (IRE) 5
294 **MAURITIAN BOLT** (IRE) 9
7 **MAWKEB** (USA) 47
278 **MAWLOOD** (IRE) 3
40 **MAX DYNAMO** 7
568 **MAX STRIPES** 19
26 **MAX VEGA** (IRE) 11
471 **MAX WOLF** 6
354 **MAXIMILIAN** (GER) 75
326 **MAXIMIZE** 8
212 **MAXIMUM DEX** (IRE) 48
564 **MAXIMUM EFFORT** 21
156 **MAXINE** (IRE) 1
406 **MAY BLOSSOM** 80
539 **MAY MIST** 4
16 **MAY NIGHT** 28
164 **MAY PUNCH** 137
15 **MAY REMAIN** 21
262 **MAY SONIC** 10
142 **MAY THE SIXTH** 26
402 **MAYBE** (IRE) C 151
404 **MAYBE DARK** 135
516 **MAYBE EVEN NEVER** 31
505 **MAYBE TOMORROW** C 65
89 **MAYBE TONIGHT** 105
163 **MAYELF** 19
73 **MAYFAIR ROCK** (IRE) F 102
262 **MAYFAIR STROLL** (IRE) 42
231 **MAYHEM** F 163
275 **MAYHEM MYA** (IRE) 6
296 **MAYKIR** 51
354 **MAYLAH** (IRE) 76
145 **MAYMOON** (IRE) 24
530 **MAYNE** (IRE) 8
445 **MAYO STAR** (IRE) 31
427 **MAYOLYNN** (USA) F 14

409 **MAYPOLE CLASS** (IRE) 69
572 **MAYSON MOUNT** 10
255 **MAYSONG** 3
379 **MAYTREE RESPITE** (IRE) 22
314 **MAYWAY** 48
215 **MAZALITA** 19
41 **MAZAMINSKY** 3
215 **MAZAMIX** 20
385 **MAZE RUNNER** (IRE) 130
547 **MAZZA ROOKS** (IRE) 7
287 **MAZZORBO** 15
424 **MAZZURI** (IRE) 4
418 **MC'TED** 11
98 **MCCANN THE MAN** 13
398 **MCFABULOUS** (IRE) 114
314 **MCGARRY** (IRE) 49
82 **MCGOWAN'S PASS** 22
327 **MCGROARTY** (IRE) 21
223 **MCPHERSON** 59
490 **MCQUEEN** (IRE) 24
97 **MEA DOMINA** (FR) 52
258 **MEADOWSUITE** (IRE) 91
520 **MEADRAM** 3
77 **MEASURED MOMENTS** 55
48 **MEDAL OF GLORY** (IRE) 37
347 **MEDIA GUEST** (FR) 5
491 **MEDICEAN STAR** (IRE) F 53
362 **MEDICINE WHEEL** 4
252 **MEDIMLI** (IRE) G 24
528 **MEDRARA** 101
46 **MEEBO** (IRE) G 11
234 **MEECHLANDS MAGIC** 5
428 **MEEP MEEP MAG** (IRE) 54
271 **MEET ME HALFWAY** F 13
414 **MEETING WATERS** F 55
209 **MEETMELATER** (IRE) 4
379 **MEETYOUATTHEMOON** (IRE) F 38
371 **MEEZNAH** (USA) C 35
7 **MEGA MARVEL** 93
535 **MEGA YEATS** (IRE) 26
217 **MEGALLAN** 21
167 **MEGAN** (GER) 22
26 **MEGAN LILY** (IRE) F 117
492 **MEGANSEIGHTHEEN** 6
290 **MEGASCOPE** 4
579 **MEGAUDAIS SPEED** (FR) 3
544 **MEHMENTO** (IRE) 16
7 **MEHMO** (IRE) 48
535 **MEHRAKI STAR** (IRE) 27
527 **MEISTERZINGER** (IRE) 13
516 **MEJTHAAM** (IRE) 11
240 **MEKBAT** (FR) 77
414 **MEKONG** 21
496 **MELAKAZ** (IRE) 10
482 **MELANAMIX** (IRE) 22
20 **MELANNA** 22
460 **MELAYU KINGDOM** (IRE) 52
1 **MELCHOIR** (FR) 37
81 **MELDRUM WAY** (IRE) 9
537 **MELEAGANT** (FR) 46
54 **MELERI** 22
217 **MELFET** (FR) 92
530 **MELFIRE** (GER) 38
528 **MELINOE** C 176
410 **MELLENCAMP** (IRE) 4
216 **MELLOW BEN** (IRE) 34
16 **MELLOW MAGIC** 29

381 **MISTER SWEETS** (IRE) 67
464 **MISTER SWIFT** 4
373 **MISTER TICKLE** (IRE) 77
420 **MISTER WATSON** 50
354 **MISTER WHITAKER** (IRE) 82
473 **MISTERSISTER** (FR) 28
432 **MISTERTOMMYSHELBY** (IRE) 16
265 **MISTRAL LADY** 69
531 **MISTRAL NELL** 21
531 **MISTRAL REINE** C 40
378 **MISTRAL STAR** 69
466 **MISTRIX** (IRE) 16
127 **MISTY AYR** (IRE) 63
323 **MISTY BLOOM** (IRE) 40
346 **MISTY GREY** (IRE) 9
442 **MISTY MAI** (IRE) 5
400 **MISTY MANI** 8
572 **MISTY MOUNTAIN** (USA) 11
528 **MITBAAHY** (IRE) 103
329 **MITCHELL STREET** 8
246 **MITIGATION** 5
528 **MITIGATOR** 9
379 **MITROSONFIRE** 7
334 **MITSY MOP** 46
94 **MIVVI** 40
440 **MIX OF CLOVER** 31
477 **MIXEDWAVE** (IRE) 14
48 **MIXFEELING** (IRE) C 87
426 **MIYAGI** (IRE) 61
217 **MIZMAR** 96
71 **MIZZ MOONDANCE** 4
229 **MIZZEN YOU** 21
16 **MLLE CHANEL** 216
397 **MO CELITA** (IRE) 4
51 **MO TOTTIE** 31
39 **MO'ASSESS** (IRE) 38
528 **MOBADRA** 18
426 **MOBARHIN** (IRE) 10
47 **MOBASHR** (USA) 12
274 **MOBHI DICK** 39
476 **MOCHACHOCACHINO** (IRE) 98
300 **MODEL** (FR) C 185
6 **MODERN GAMES** (IRE) 49
39 **MODERN IDEALS** F 108
204 **MODERN LOVE** (IRE) C 58
6 **MODERN NEWS** 16
231 **MODEYRA** F 166
559 **MODREENEY** (IRE) 19
25 **MODULAR MAGIC** 14
530 **MODULATION** 11
297 **MOEL ARTHUR** (USA) 6
469 **MOFASA** 27
105 **MOGHAMARAH** C 42
405 **MOGHRAMA** (IRE) F 39
364 **MOGILEVICH** 36
231 **MOHAAFETH** (IRE) 24
7 **MOHAREB** 49
549 **MOHASSANA** (USA) 18
118 **MOHI** 58
26 **MOI MEME** F 120
429 **MOIDORE** 7
47 **MOJAZAFFAH** (IRE) 13
528 **MOJIKA** F 177
369 **MOJITO ROYALE** (FR) 5
240 **MOJO STAR** (IRE) 19
334 **MOJOMAKER** (IRE) 47
562 **MOKA DE VASSY** (FR) 16

561 **MOKAATIL** 50
521 **MOKAMAN** 26
317 **MOKTASAAB** 8
420 **MOLE COURT** (IRE) 51
349 **MOLE TRAP** 14
519 **MOLINARI** (IRE) 9
517 **MOLINEAUX** (IRE) 47
47 **MOLIWOOD** 14
381 **MOLLIANA** 68
537 **MOLLS MEMORY** 15
381 **MOLLY CAREW** 9
208 **MOLLY FLIGHT** (FR) G 13
48 **MOLLY MAYHEM** (IRE) C 88
476 **MOLLY OLLYS WISHES** 99
287 **MOLLY VALENTINE** (IRE) 33
137 **MOLLY'S ANGEL** 2
220 **MOLLYS GLORY** (IRE) 10
201 **MOMELLA** (IRE) 41
16 **MOMENT DE REVE** 102
361 **MOMENTS PAST** (IRE) 49
300 **MOMENTUS** (IRE) C 186
398 **MON FRERE** (IRE) 118
432 **MON RAY** (IRE) 17
87 **MONAADHIL** (IRE) 19
157 **MONAAJEZ** (USA) 28
299 **MONACELLA** (IRE) 35
238 **MONAGHAN BOY** (IRE) 50
426 **MONALEEN** (IRE) F 62
429 **MONARCHOFTHEGRANGE** (IRE) 8
125 **MONBARI** (FR) 24
409 **MONBEG GENIUS** (IRE) 72
62 **MONDAMMEJ** 11
47 **MONELISA** 46
240 **MONET'S SUNRISE** 79
69 **MONETE** (GER) 18
482 **MONETS DREAM** (IRE) G 24
4 **MONEY FOR JAM** (IRE) 13
265 **MONEY SPINNER** (IRE) 70
572 **MONEY TREE** (IRE) 29
388 **MONEYKENNY** (IRE) 100
143 **MONFASS** (IRE) 24
381 **MONGOL EMPEROR** (IRE) 70
423 **MONHAMMER** 8
292 **MONICA** 65
228 **MONITION** (IRE) 11
240 **MONITOR** 80
401 **MONJULES** (FR) 4
385 **MONKFISH** (IRE) 134
346 **MONKMOOR PIP** 63
349 **MONKS CHARM** (IRE) C 15
398 **MONMIRAL** (FR) 119
458 **MONOCHROMIX** (IRE) 47
145 **MONROE** G 44
334 **MONSARAZ** 20
127 **MONSIEUR CO** (FR) 31
411 **MONSIEUR FANTAISIE** (IRE) 15
460 **MONSIEUR JUMBO** (FR) 56
562 **MONSIEUR LECOQ** (FR) 17
61 **MONSIEUR PATAT** 32
302 **MONSIEUR POM POM** (FR) 7
148 **MONSIEUR ROYALE** 2
16 **MONT ATHENA** 103
398 **MONT DES AVALOIRS** (FR) 120
381 **MONT SAINT VINCENT** (FR) 71
51 **MONTANNA** 3
258 **MONTE CRISTO** (FR) 97
223 **MONTE IGUELDO** (FR) 63

431 **MONTEAMIATA** (IRE) C 47
402 **MONTENEGRO** (IRE) 60
274 **MONTEPLEX** 40
316 **MONTERIA** (IRE) 4
300 **MONTEVIDEO** (IRE) 187
362 **MONTICELLO** (IRE) 5
73 **MONTINEY** 61
286 **MONTY'S AWARD** (IRE) 19
177 **MONTY'S MISSION** (IRE) 10
398 **MONTYS MEDOC** (IRE) 121
265 **MONVIEL** (IRE) 71
378 **MONZZA** C 70
475 **MOOAKADA** (IRE) C 73
220 **MOOD INDIGO** F 20
491 **MOODFORAMELODY** 17
528 **MOOJDEE** (IRE) 104
404 **MOON CHIME** 137
403 **MOON DAISY** 2
26 **MOON DE VEGA** 57
434 **MOON FLIGHT** (IRE) 55
164 **MOON FRIEND** (IRE) 170
101 **MOON ISLAND** 42
333 **MOON KING** (FR) 36
140 **MOON OVER GERMANY** (IRE) 8
217 **MOON WATCH** (IRE) 97
112 **MOONACURA** (IRE) 20
312 **MOONAMACAROONA** (IRE) 3
164 **MOONBI** (IRE) 139
528 **MOONIS** (IRE) 105
322 **MOONLIGHT BEAM** (IRE) 3
302 **MOONLIGHT DAWN** (IRE) 25
117 **MOONLIGHT DREAMER** 52
258 **MOONLIGHT FLIT** (IRE) 98
386 **MOONLIGHT FROLIC** 35
473 **MOONLIGHT MUSIC** (IRE) C 29
47 **MOONLIGHT RHAPSODY** (IRE) C 73
182 **MOONLIGHT SONATA** F 30
370 **MOONLIGHT SPIRIT** (IRE) 11
182 **MOONLIGHT TIARA** 31
563 **MOONLINE** F 22
287 **MOONLIT CLOUD** 16
354 **MOONLIT PARK** (IRE) 83
28 **MOONLIT WARRIOR** 34
7 **MOONRAKER** 50
475 **MOONRISE LANDING** (IRE) C 74
406 **MOONS OF JUPITER** (USA) F 114
39 **MOONSAIL** F 109
404 **MOONSHINE SPIRIT** 138
543 **MOONSHINER** (IRE) 12
549 **MOONSHINE ROCK** F 55
569 **MOORE CLOUDS** (IRE) 2
388 **MOORE MARGAUX** (IRE) 101
309 **MOORE ON TOUR** (IRE) 10
562 **MOORLAND RAMBLER** 18
146 **MOOSMEE** (IRE) 11
404 **MOOT COURT** (IRE) 139
7 **MOP'S GEM** 52
28 **MORAG MCCULLAGH** 35
561 **MORAINE** G 99
16 **MORANDO** (FR) 30
480 **MORANI KALI** 6
246 **MORDRED** (IRE) 30
280 **MORE DIAMONDS** (IRE) 46
177 **MORE THAN LIKELY** 1
460 **MORE THAN WELCOME** (USA) 57
25 **MORETHANAFEELING** (IRE) C 45

240 **MUGADER** (FR) 81
371 **MUHADATHAT** F 36
255 **MUHALHEL** (IRE) 5
178 **MUHTAMAR** (FR) 25
155 **MUHTASHIM** 35
300 **MUIR WOOD** 188
402 **MUIRIN** (IRE) C 156
25 **MUJAESCE** (ITY) F 46
6 **MUJARAH** (IRE) F 157
558 **MUJID** (IRE) 7
231 **MUJTABA** 25
528 **MUKADDAMAH** 106
307 **MUKHA MAGIC** 9
404 **MULBERRY HILL** (IRE) 140
222 **MULCAHYS HILL** (IRE) 44
246 **MULLENBEG** (IRE) 32
516 **MULTAMISA** (USA) C 62
387 **MULZIM** 9
335 **MUMAYAZ** (IRE) 54
323 **MUMBO JUMBO** (IRE) 41
576 **MUMCAT** 12
508 **MUMINAMILLION** (IRE) 38
378 **MUMMA MAC** 40
262 **MUMMY'S BOY** 12
240 **MUMS TIPPLE** (IRE) 21
364 **MUNCH** (FR) 54
240 **MUNDANA LILY** 82
231 **MUNEYRA** C 168
18 **MUNIFICENT** 15
184 **MUNTADAB** (IRE) 18
76 **MURAAD** (IRE) 5
182 **MURAU** 12
62 **MURBIH** (IRE) 25
171 **MURCHISON RIVER** 10
444 **MURHIB** (IRE) 5
513 **MUROOR** 6
118 **MURPHY'S DREAM** 59
445 **MURVAGH BEACH** (IRE) 33
406 **MUSCIKA** 26
228 **MUSE OF FIRE** (IRE) 12
186 **MUSIC BANNER** (IRE) 18
88 **MUSIC SEEKER** (IRE) 14
164 **MUSIC SOCIETY** (IRE) 67
327 **MUSICAL** 23
415 **MUSICAL COMEDY** 3
501 **MUSICAL MYSTERY** 18
105 **MUSICAL ROMANCE** 23
265 **MUSICAL SLAVE** (IRE) 72
173 **MUSICAL TRIBUTE** 31
238 **MUSICALITY** 52
314 **MUSIKHANI** G 93
77 **MUSKATEER ONE** 58
77 **MUSKATEER TWO** 59
323 **MUSKOKA** (IRE) 42
167 **MUSSOORIE** (FR) C 38
340 **MUST BE AN ANGEL** (IRE) 13
7 **MUST BE ROYALE** 55
295 **MUSTANG ALPHA** (IRE) 18
297 **MUSTANG KODI** (IRE) 7
561 **MUSTARRID** (IRE) 55
538 **MUSTASEED** (IRE) 12
62 **MUTABAAHY** (IRE) 12
39 **MUTAFAWWIG** 40
90 **MUTALAAQY** (IRE) 9
87 **MUTANAASEQ** (IRE) 20
204 **MUTARAAFEQ** (IRE) 27
77 **MUTARABBY** (IRE) 29

262 **MUTASAABEQ** 13
520 **MUTASALLEM** (IRE) 9
186 **MUTATIS MUTANDIS** (IRE) C 39
292 **MUTAWAARID** 25
76 **MUTEBAH** (IRE) F 24
73 **MUVERAN** 62
402 **MUWAKABA** (USA) C 157
250 **MUWALLA** 8
201 **MUY BIEN** (IRE) 42
146 **MUY MUY GUAPO** 33
375 **MUYAM SPIRIT** (FR) 32
547 **MUZETTA'S WALTZ** (IRE) 8
106 **MY AMBITION** (IRE) 15
243 **MY AQUARIAN** (IRE) C 168
231 **MY ASTRA** (IRE) 26
213 **MY BAD LUCY** 17
16 **MY BETTER HALF** C 218
457 **MY BOBBY DAZZLER** 22
574 **MY BONNIE LASSIE** 2
572 **MY BOY CHARLES** (USA) 12
387 **MY BOY FRANKIE** 10
105 **MY BOY JACK** 24
372 **MY BOY JAMES** (IRE) 9
422 **MY BROTHER JACK** (IRE) 10
497 **MY BROTHER MIKE** (IRE) 3
39 **MY CALL** C 75
300 **MY CALL** F 189
476 **MY DROGO** 101
300 **MY DUBAWI** (IRE) 84
491 **MY EYES ADORE YOU** 18
450 **MY FOREVER FRIEND** (IRE) 6
539 **MY FOXY LADY** 5
11 **MY FRIEND WOODY** 5
548 **MY GIFT TO YOU** (IRE) 21
167 **MY GIRL LOLLIPOP** (IRE) 26
252 **MY GRANNY LILY** 25
240 **MY HENRIETTA** (USA) C 181
243 **MY HOLY FOX** (IRE) 47
356 **MY JEANIE RAI** 4
10 **MY JOKER** (IRE) 39
265 **MY KEEPSAKE** 73
10 **MY KIND OF LADY** 19
93 **MY LADY CLAIRE** 16
517 **MY LADY GREY** 48
349 **MY LAST OSCAR** (IRE) 17
48 **MY LITTLE TIP** (IRE) 39
159 **MY LOVELY SYLV** 11
22 **MY MACHO MAN** (IRE) 14
508 **MY MATE TED** (IRE) 39
243 **MY MINERVINA** (IRE) 48
537 **MY MIRAGE** (IRE) 17
247 **MY NAME'S HOWARD** 21
231 **MY OBERON** (IRE) 27
411 **MY OPINION** (IRE) 25
464 **MY PERFECT COUSIN** 5
223 **MY POEM** 64
231 **MY PROSPERO** (IRE) 79
443 **MY ROCKSTAR** (IRE) 2
252 **MY ROSA'S GOLD** 40
170 **MY ROXANNE** (IRE) 70
155 **MY SILENT SONG** 36
323 **MY SILVER LINING** (IRE) 43
402 **MY SISTER SANDY** (USA) C 158
385 **MY SISTER SARAH** (IRE) 138
277 **MY SPIRIT** (IRE) C 21
314 **MY STRONG MAN** (IRE) 56
558 **MY TARGET** (IRE) 8

216 **MY TICKETYBOO** (IRE) 36
231 **MY TITANIA** F 169
497 **MY TOWN CHICAGO** (USA) 4
238 **MYBOYMAX** (FR) 53
483 **MYBURG** (IRE) 33
238 **MYGIRLMEL** 54
460 **MYKONOS** (IRE) 59
142 **MYKONOS ST JOHN** 27
514 **MYMILAN** (IRE) 37
280 **MYRIAD** (IRE) 47
361 **MYRICA** C 101
164 **MYRISTICA** (IRE) 68
276 **MYSPACENOTYOURS** 9
6 **MYSTERIOUS NIGHT** (IRE) 158
528 **MYSTERY FOX** (IRE) 107
299 **MYSTERY MONARCH** 36
69 **MYSTIC COURT** (IRE) 19
405 **MYSTIC MOONSHADOW** 31
48 **MYSTIC WELLS** (USA) 40
528 **MYSTICAL AIR** 20
173 **MYSTICAL APPLAUSE** 32
402 **MYSTICAL LADY** (IRE) F 159
556 **MYTHICAL** (FR) 8
228 **MYTHICAL FORTUNE** 13
347 **MYTHICAL GUEST** (IRE) 11
406 **MYTHICAL MADNESS** 27
170 **MYTHICAL MOLLY** (IRE) 58
280 **MYTHICAL STAR** 48
76 **MYTURN** (IRE) C 25
521 **MYWAYISTHEONLYWAY** (IRE) 27
105 **MZAHEM** (IRE) 25
243 **MZYOON** (IRE) C 169
151 **N'GOLO** (IRE) 12
491 **NAAHEDH** F 54
401 **NAASIK** 6
460 **NAASMA** (IRE) 60
331 **NABHAN** 10
530 **NABLIRKA** (GER) 13
371 **NABOO** (IRE) 18
428 **NABVUTIKA** (IRE) 58
252 **NACHI FALLS** 26
354 **NACHO** (GER) 85
530 **NACHTFALKE** (GER) 45
460 **NADA** F 99
26 **NADA** (GER) C 122
469 **NADA TO PRADA** 29
420 **NADAITAK** 53
39 **NADER** 76
530 **NADIM** (IRE) 39
451 **NAE BOTHER AT A'** (IRE) 8
145 **NAFA** (IRE) C 62
98 **NAFEE** (IRE) 33
417 **NAGA EYE** (IRE) 29
528 **NAGANO** 21
30 **NAGASAKI DREAM** 6
490 **NAHAAB** (FR) 13
231 **NAHAARR** (IRE) 28
6 **NAHANNI** 50
528 **NAHRAIN** F 108
528 **NAHRI** 109
426 **NAIVASHA** C 63
404 **NAIZAGAI** 141
122 **NAJAT** 52
101 **NAJEEBA** 5
6 **NAJOUM** (USA) F 159
390 **NAKADAM** (FR) 9
517 **NAME IN LIGHTS** (IRE) 49

280 **NAMJONG BOYS** 49
371 **NANCY ASTOR** C 37
537 **NANCY HART** F 76
122 **NANKEEN** 9
319 **NANTOSUELTA** (IRE) 6
47 **NAO DA MAIS** (BRZ) 15
16 **NAPPER TANDY** 31
470 **NARALSAIF** (IRE) F 30
26 **NARANCO** 58
104 **NARIMAN POINT** (IRE) 60
16 **NASHAMA** (IRE) C 219
505 **NASHMIAH** (IRE) F 25
240 **NASHMIAH** (IRE) C 182
324 **NASHVILLE NIPPER** (IRE) 11
217 **NASHWA** 99
340 **NASHY** (IRE) 14
16 **NASIM** 105
76 **NASMATT** F 11
373 **NASSALAM** (FR) 80
131 **NASTASIYA** 10
340 **NAT LOVE** (IRE) 15
434 **NATACATA** 56
251 **NATALEENA** (IRE) 19
293 **NATALIE ROSE** 5
371 **NATALISA** (IRE) F 38
217 **NATASHA** 100
88 **NATCHEZ TRACE** 15
16 **NATE THE GREAT** 32
231 **NATHANAEL GREENE** 80
317 **NATHER** (USA) C 43
231 **NATIONAL CHARTER** (IRE) 81
337 **NATIONAL STAR** (IRE) 14
6 **NATIONS PRIDE** (IRE) 51
417 **NATIVE ANGEL** 30
365 **NATIVE CHOICE** (IRE) 40
370 **NATIVE FIGHTER** (IRE) 12
307 **NATIVE MELODY** (IRE) 24
517 **NATIVE RIVER** (IRE) 50
467 **NATIVE ROBIN** (IRE) 20
6 **NATIVE TRAIL** 52
279 **NATTY DRESSER** (IRE) 9
273 **NATTY MEDDLER** (IRE) 17
567 **NATTY NIGHT** 66
535 **NATURAL APPEAL** (IRE) C 50
373 **NATURAL HISTORY** 81
268 **NATURAL IMPULSE** 14
504 **NATURAL LOOK** (IRE) 23
28 **NATURAL PATH** (IRE) 6
6 **NATURAL WORLD** (IRE) 53
373 **NATURALLY HIGH** (FR) 82
229 **NATURE** (IRE) 12
164 **NAUGHTY MAX** (IRE) 69
133 **NAUGHTY LINES** 18
7 **NAUGHTY NADINE** 95
33 **NAUTICAL HAVEN** 13
504 **NAVAJO INDY** 29
354 **NAVAJO PASS** 86
505 **NAVAJO POET** 26
402 **NAVAJO WARRIOR** (JPN) 61
406 **NAVAL CAPTAIN** (IRE) 28
500 **NAVAL COLLEGE** 61
61 **NAVAL COMMANDER** 33
6 **NAVAL CROWN** 1
61 **NAVAL FLEET** 34
85 **NAVARRA PRINCESS** (IRE) 4
417 **NAVARRE EXPRESS** 75
525 **NAVEGAON GATE** 40

48 **NAVELLO** 41
117 **NAVY DRUMS** (USA) 19
145 **NAVY WREN** (IRE) 63
46 **NAWAR** 6
520 **NAWRAS** 23
48 **NAXOS** 89
354 **NAYATI** (FR) 87
300 **NAYEF ROAD** (IRE) 17
82 **NAYWAY** 24
544 **NAZANIN** (USA) 56
378 **NAZIMOVA** 41
473 **NAZWA** 30
528 **NAZYM** (IRE) C 178
381 **NEACHELLS BRIDGE** (IRE) 73
16 **NEANDRA** (GER) 106
104 **NEAR AMORE** (GER) 61
172 **NEAR KETTERING** 17
164 **NEARLY A GONNA** 70
313 **NEARLY PERFECT** 21
543 **NEARTICA** (FR) F 36
33 **NEAT 'N NIMBLE** F 14
335 **NEAT AND DANDY** 55
530 **NEBRODI** (GER) 46
312 **NEBUCHADNEZZAR** (FR) 73
26 **NECHITA** (AUS) C 123
420 **NECHTAN** (IRE) G 54
185 **NECTAR DE ROSE** (FR) F 67
243 **NECTARIS** 106
1 **NED TANNER** (IRE) 39
48 **NEEDLE LACE** 10
90 **NEEDLELEAF** F 160
90 **NEEDWOOD BLOSSOM** 10
146 **NEFARIOUS** (IRE) 12
361 **NEFETARI** C 102
354 **NEFYN POINT** 88
174 **NEFYN SANDS** 12
73 **NEGWAH** (IRE) 63
163 **NEIGE D'ANTAN** G 51
554 **NEIGH BOTHA** (IRE) 15
258 **NEIL THE LEGEND** 102
106 **NELL QUICKLY** (IRE) 4
537 **NELL THE THIEF** 18
354 **NELL'S BELLS** 89
551 **NELLIE DEEN** (IRE) 14
468 **NELLIE FRENCH** (IRE) 9
424 **NELLIE MOON** 6
445 **NELLS SON** 34
280 **NELSON GAY** (IRE) 13
89 **NELSON RIVER** 62
137 **NELSON'S HILL** 3
517 **NELSONS ROCK** 51
125 **NELSONS STAR** (IRE) 26
325 **NEMEAN LION** (GER) 16
373 **NEMINOS** (FR) 83
310 **NEMORUM** 12
428 **NEON MOON** (IRE) 59
243 **NEOWISE** (USA) 170
97 **NEPALIS** 9
397 **NEPALESIAN** (IRE) 15
83 **NEPHALIST** (IRE) 27
417 **NEPTUNE LEGEND** (IRE) 31
360 **NEPTUNIAN** (IRE) 18
82 **NERO ROCK** (IRE) 25
262 **NESHMEYA** F 94
33 **NESS TA RAH** 15
389 **NESSFIELD BLUE** 3
420 **NESTOR PARK** (FR) 55

458 **NETYWELL** (FR) 48
508 **NEVER IN FOURTH** 40
397 **NEVER NO TROUBLE** 16
345 **NEVER SAID NOTHING** (IRE) 11
335 **NEVER SAID NOTHING** (IRE) 28
412 **NEVER SAY NEVER** (IRE) 3
77 **NEVER SURRENDER** (IRE) 30
80 **NEVERBATSANEYELID** 41
389 **NEVERBEEN TO PARIS** (IRE) 4
402 **NEVERLAND** (USA) 62
243 **NEVERUSHACON** (IRE) 49
163 **NEVERWRONGFORLONG** 37
320 **NEVILLE'S CROSS** (IRE) 29
428 **NEW AGE DAWNING** (IRE) 60
6 **NEW COMEDY** (IRE) 54
292 **NEW DELHI EXPRESS** (IRE) 28
500 **NEW DIMENSION** 62
528 **NEW ENDEAVOUR** (IRE) 179
417 **NEW FORCE** 7
325 **NEW FOUND FAME** (IRE) 17
431 **NEW HEIGHTS** 8
6 **NEW KINGDOM** 55
6 **NEW LONDON** (IRE) 56
568 **NEW LOOK** (FR) 12
26 **NEW MANDATE** (IRE) 12
122 **NEW NATION** (IRE) 53
426 **NEW PURSUIT** (IRE) 31
555 **NEW RHYTHM** 28
156 **NEW ROSE** 14
6 **NEW SCIENCE** 57
166 **NEW SHEPARD** (IRE) 14
6 **NEW STYLE** (USA) F 161
48 **NEW TERMS** F 90
26 **NEW YEAR HONOURS** 59
402 **NEW YORK CITY** (IRE) 63
311 **NEW ZEALANDER** 2
35 **NEWBERRY NEW** (IRE) 8
402 **NEWFOUNDLAND** (IRE) 64
119 **NEWGATE ANGEL** 5
475 **NEWLYWED** (IRE) C 76
372 **NEWS GIRL** (IRE) 20
545 **NEWSPEAK** (IRE) 4
73 **NEWSROOM** (IRE) C 106
186 **NEWTON DANCER** (IRE) 19
316 **NEWTON JACK** 6
473 **NEWTONIAN** 31
127 **NEWTOWN BOY** (IRE) 32
379 **NEWYORKSTATEOFMIND** 8
406 **NEXA BAY** (IRE) 115
505 **NEXT CHAPTER** (IRE) 27
373 **NEXT LEFT** (IRE) 84
87 **NEXT SECOND** 36
232 **NEXTDOORTOALICE** (IRE) 34
287 **NEZAR** (IRE) 17
122 **NEZWAAH** F 102
98 **NIAMH AND OONAGH** (IRE) 34
258 **NIAMH'S AWAY** (IRE) G 103
83 **NIARBYL BAY** 28
549 **NIBLAWI** (IRE) 20
366 **NIBRAS AGAIN** 25
371 **NIBRAS SHADOW** (IRE) 7
1 **NICEANDEASY** (IRE) 40
426 **NICHOLAS GEORGE** 32
215 **NICHOLAS T** 22
61 **NICK VEDDER** 35
243 **NICK'S NIKITA** (IRE) C 171
577 **NICKELSONTHEDIME** (IRE) 8

39 **ONE COLOUR** (IRE) 78
372 **ONE DAY** 10
217 **ONE EVENING** 101
167 **ONE EYE ON VEGAS** 27
472 **ONE FER MAMMA** (IRE) 6
370 **ONE FINE MAN** (IRE) 15
476 **ONE FOR BILLY** 108
30 **ONE FOR BRAD** 7
536 **ONE FOR DUNSTAN** (IRE) 18
172 **ONE FOR NAVIGATION** (IRE) 20
576 **ONE FOR THE FROG** (IRE) 13
216 **ONE FOR THE WALL** (IRE) 39
265 **ONE FOR YOU** (IRE) 19
525 **ONE FORTY SEVEN** (IRE) 44
549 **ONE HANDSOME DUDE** (IRE) 22
521 **ONE HART** (IRE) 28
404 **ONE HUNDRED NOTOUT** (IRE) 147
280 **ONE LAST DANCE** (IRE) 9
225 **ONE LAST GLANCE** 9
215 **ONE LAST HUG** 23
371 **ONE MINUTE** (IRE) F 39
402 **ONE MOMENT IN TIME** (IRE) F 161
280 **ONE MORE DREAM** 51
561 **ONE MORE FLEURIE** (IRE) 60
28 **ONE MORNING** (IRE) 36
127 **ONE NIGHT IN MILAN** (IRE) 33
142 **ONE NIGHT STAND** 29
104 **ONE O'CLOCK JUMP** (FR) 34
302 **ONE PUNCH TERRI** 8
6 **ONE RULER** (IRE) 19
566 **ONE SPIRIT** (IRE) C 61
285 **ONE STEP BEYOND** (IRE) 6
194 **ONE STEP TOO FAR** (IRE) 7
544 **ONE TO GO** 21
420 **ONE TOUCH** (IRE) 62
525 **ONE TRUE KING** (IRE) 45
403 **ONE WAY** (IRE) 12
312 **ONE WILD NIGHT** G 82
298 **ONE YEAR OUT** 6
323 **ONEANDAHALFDEGREES** (IRE) 45
5 **ONEFORSUE** 11
561 **ONEFORTHEGUTTER** 100
170 **ONEHUNDREDPERCENT** (FR) 28
313 **ONEMOREFORTHEROAD** 23
238 **ONENIGHTINTOWN** (IRE) 56
488 **ONEROA** (IRE) C 52
170 **ONESMOOTHOPERATOR** (USA) 29
533 **ONESTEPATATIME** (IRE) 9
213 **ONESTEPTWOSTEPS** (IRE) 19
97 **ONESTO** (IRE) 55
398 **ONETHREEFIVENOTOUT** (IRE) 124
223 **ONETWOBEAT** G 67
19 **ONEUPMANSHIP** (IRE) 16
324 **ONEWAYORTOTHER** (FR) 13
402 **ONLY** (JPN) 68
418 **ONLY DEBRIS** (IRE) 12
486 **ONLY FOR PASCAL** (IRE) 8
216 **ONLY MONEY** (IRE) 40
243 **ONLY SKY** (IRE) 52
560 **ONLY THE BOLD** (IRE) 55
544 **ONLY THE BRAVE** (USA) 22
223 **ONLY TOGETHER** (IRE) G 97
243 **ONLYHUMAN** (IRE) 53
252 **ONNAROLL** (FR) 28
240 **ONSLOW GARDENS** (IRE) 187
538 **ONTHEFRONTFOOT** (IRE) 94
385 **ONTHEROPES** (IRE) 139

400 **ONTHEROUGE** 10
408 **ONURBIKE** 2
365 **ONWARD ROUTE** (IRE) 43
96 **ONWEGOAGAIN** (IRE) G 8
16 **OO DE LALLY** (IRE) 34
174 **OOH IS IT** 14
132 **OOH LA LAH** 4
292 **OOT MA WAY** (FR) 27
378 **OP IT** (IRE) 43
94 **OPAL TIARA** (IRE) F 81
829 **OPEN CHAMPION** (IRE) 112
39 **OPEN MIND** 79
147 **OPENING BID** 14
221 **OPERA FOREVER** 221
16 **OPERA GIFT** 35
217 **OPERATING** (USA) 102
478 **OPERATION GIMCRACK** (IRE) 39
320 **OPERATION MANNA** 31
458 **OPERATION OVERLORD** (IRE) 51
231 **OPERETTIST** C 171
417 **OPERISSIMO** C 77
366 **OPINIONATED LADY** (IRE) F 48
182 **OPPORTUNA** C 60
155 **OPTICA** (FR) C 73
282 **OPTICALITY** 10
420 **OPTIMISE PRIME** (IRE) 63
425 **OPTIMISTIC BELIEF** (IRE) 9
176 **OPTIMISTIC BIAS** (IRE) 15
240 **OPTIVA STAR** (IRE) 188
177 **ORANGE GINA** 13
568 **ORANGE JUSTICE** 13
262 **ORANGE PIP** C 95
262 **ORAZIO** (IRE) 46
406 **ORBAAN** 30
248 **ORBIT OF IOLITE** 4
265 **ORBYS LEGEND** (IRE) 77
325 **ORCHARD GROVE** (IRE) 19
395 **ORCHESTRAL RAIN** (IRE) 44
123 **ORCHID ROSE** (IRE) 11
402 **ORDER OF AUSTRALIA** (IRE) 9
295 **ORDER OF ST JOHN** 19
404 **ORDERED LIVES** (IRE) 148
427 **ORGANDI** (IRE) 17
405 **ORGANZA** G 33
405 **ORGANZA** F 41
366 **ORIENT JEWEL** 40
19 **ORIENTAL ART** 19
572 **ORIENTAL BEAUTY** 13
529 **ORIENTAL CROSS** (IRE) 27
215 **ORIENTAL LILLY** 24
249 **ORIENTAL RELATION** (IRE) 7
316 **ORIENTAL SPIRIT** 7
531 **ORIFLAMME** 41
520 **ORIGINATOR** (IRE) 10
251 **ORIGINTRAIL** (IRE) 41
530 **ORIHIME** (IRE) 15
431 **ORIN SWIFT** (IRE) 9
26 **ORIOLE** 60
535 **ORKAN** 31
139 **ORLANDO LAMMY** 18
113 **ORLAS' ABBEY** 15
226 **ORNATE** 6
537 **ORNELIA RUEE** (FR) F 78
278 **ORNUA** (IRE) 5
526 **ORO COSMICO** 5
566 **ORPHA** F 62
409 **ORRISDALE** (IRE) 77

16 **ORZO** 112
529 **OSCA LOCA** (IRE) 28
286 **OSCAR ASCHE** (IRE) 22
358 **OSCAR BLUE** (IRE) 5
163 **OSCAR DOODLE** 54
517 **OSCAR ELITE** (IRE) 57
333 **OSCAR MONTEL** (IRE) 40
239 **OSCAR NOMINATION** (IRE) 23
212 **OSCAR ROBERTSON** (IRE) 52
112 **OSCAR WILDE** (IRE) 22
82 **OSCARS LEADER** (IRE) 26
398 **OSCARS MOONSHINE** (IRE) 125
484 **OSCARSMAN** (IRE) 10
48 **OSCULA** (IRE) 42
404 **OSLO** 149
184 **OSO RAPIDO** (IRE) 19
440 **OSPREY CALL** (IRE) 32
544 **OSTILIO** 23
577 **OSTUNI** (FR) 10
2 **OTAGO** 14
163 **OTROOHA** (IRE) F 87
199 **OTTER LYNN** 13
364 **OTTILIEN** (FR) 38
25 **OTTO OYL** 18
567 **OTTOLINE** 47
6 **OTTOMAN FLEET** 60
434 **OTTOMAN PRINCE** (IRE) 57
354 **OTTONIAN** 95
183 **OUD METHA BRIDGE** (IRE) 8
300 **OUJA** F 192
155 **OULIANOVSK** (IRE) F 74
232 **OUR BILL'S AUNT** (IRE) 36
317 **OUR BOY SAM** 30
123 **OUR CILLA** 12
404 **OUR COLOSSUS** (IRE) 150
294 **OUR ETHEL** C 10
561 **OUR IDIC BOY** (IRE) 61
565 **OUR JESS** (IRE) F 7
565 **OUR JESS** (IRE) F 8
378 **OUR JESTER** 19
476 **OUR JET** (IRE) 109
118 **OUR JOY** (IRE) F 103
251 **OUR LAURA B** (IRE) 20
382 **OUR LITTLE PONY** 4
458 **OUR MARTY** (IRE) 52
536 **OUR MERLIN** 19
38 **OUR MORRIS** (IRE) 13
212 **OUR NOBBY** 53
501 **OUR NOBLE LORD** 20
509 **OUR POWER** (IRE) 27
370 **OUR SAM** 16
123 **OUR STAR IN HEAVEN** (IRE) 19
201 **OUR SURPRISE** (IRE) 44
422 **OUR VALKYRIE** (IRE) G 26
252 **OURO BRANCO** (FR) 29
432 **OUT BY SIX** (FR) 18
435 **OUT FOR JUSTICE** (IRE) 6
101 **OUT FROM UNDER** 48
15 **OUT OF CAMELOPARDALIS** 53
504 **OUT OF EXILE** (IRE) 25
405 **OUT OF MISCHIEF** 42
198 **OUT OF SIGHT** (IRE) 6
387 **OUT OF TIME** (IRE) C 29
4 **OUT ON THE TEAR** (IRE) 14
293 **OUT RULE** (IRE) 22
388 **OUT THE GLEN** (IRE) 105
223 **OUTBACK BOY** (IRE) 68

411 **OUTBACK FRONTIERS** (IRE) 16
544 **OUTBOX** 24
300 **OUTBREAK** 86
189 **OUTER SPACE** 15
530 **OUTFIT** 16
319 **OUTGATE** 23
398 **OUTLAW PETER** (IRE) 126
454 **OUTOFTHEGLOOM** 6
312 **OUTONPATROL** 83
240 **OUTRACE** (IRE) 189
319 **OUTRAGE** 7
94 **OUTSIDE ART** C 82
300 **OUTSIDE WORLD** 87
422 **OUTSMART** (IRE) 11
264 **OUTTATHEBLUE** 4
186 **OUTWARD BOUND** 40
414 **OUZO** 26
402 **OVER THE RAINBOW** (IRE) 69
393 **OVER THE RIVER** 6
26 **OVERACTIVE** 127
212 **OVERALL MAJORITY** (IRE) 54
383 **OVERCHURCH** 10
514 **OVERCOURT** 40
138 **OVERHAUGH STREET** 7
18 **OVERLAND** 27
379 **OVERNIGHT OATS** 40
258 **OVERPRICED MIXER** 106
388 **OVERTHETOP** (IRE) 106
429 **OVERTOUGEORGE** 9
121 **OWEN LITTLE** 4
200 **OWENS LAD** 14
240 **OWER INDEPENDENCE** 85
580 **OXFORD BLU** 12
508 **OXTED** 26
560 **OXWICH BAY** (IRE) 56
18 **OXYGEN THIEF** (IRE) 24
48 **OZIRIS** F 91
373 **OZZIE MAN** (IRE) 89
146 **PABLO DEL PUEBLO** (IRE) 14
32 **PABLO PRINCE** 13
300 **PABOUCHE** (IRE) C 193
428 **PACHACUTI** (IRE) 67
217 **PACIFIC** 103
371 **PACIFIC ANGEL** (IRE) C 40
377 **PACINO** 15
523 **PACO LOCO** 11
528 **PACO'S PRIDE** 180
445 **PADDOCK COTTAGE** (IRE) 36
170 **PADDLERY** (IRE) 30
381 **PADDY HUSSEYS TAXI** (IRE) 80
205 **PADDY K** 19
561 **PADDY THE CHEF** (IRE) 62
38 **PADDY THE HORSE** (IRE) 14
49 **PADDY THE PANDA** (IRE) 10
262 **PADDY'S DAY** (IRE) 96
223 **PADDY'S FANCY** 95
213 **PADDY'S POEM** 20
509 **PADDYS MOTORBIKE** (IRE) 28
476 **PADLEYOUROWNCANOE** 110
560 **PAGEANT MATERIAL** (IRE) 57
104 **PAGGANE** 35
243 **PAHLAVI** (IRE) 54
312 **PAINLESS POTTER** (IRE) 84
404 **PAINT THE DREAM** 151
235 **PAINTERS LAD** (IRE) 6
323 **PAISLEY PARK** (IRE) 46
82 **PAKIE'S DREAM** (IRE) 27

509 **PALACIO** (FR) 29
240 **PALAMON** (IRE) 190
478 **PALAZZO** 7
417 **PALE ORCHID** (IRE) F 78
98 **PALIFICO** 15
170 **PALLAS DANCER** 31
170 **PALLAS LORD** (IRE) 32
409 **PALMERS HILL** (IRE) 78
215 **PAMMI** 25
508 **PANAMA** 51
164 **PANAMA CITY** 144
246 **PANDA SEVEN** (FR) 33
460 **PANDORA'S BOX** (IRE) C 100
6 **PANEGYRIC** C 163
312 **PANGLOSS** 148
428 **PANIC ATTACK** (IRE) 68
48 **PANOVA** F 92
543 **PAOLO PANINI** 26
105 **PAPA COCKTAIL** (IRE) 26
262 **PAPA DON'T PREACH** (IRE) 47
243 **PAPA K** 108
566 **PAPA STOUR** (USA) 22
409 **PAPA TANGO CHARLY** (FR) 79
316 **PAPABELLA** 18
331 **PAPAS BOY** (IRE) 11
374 **PAPAS GIRL** (IRE) 8
426 **PAPAVER** C 64
554 **PAPER TIGER** 17
376 **PAPION LADY** (IRE) M 12
204 **PARACELSUS** (IRE) 50
19 **PARACHUTE** 19
185 **PARADE MILITAIRE** (IRE) F 92
312 **PARADIAS** (GER) 149
428 **PARADISE ISLAND** (IRE) 69
516 **PARADISE OF LOVE** 33
570 **PARADISE WAY** C 14
262 **PARAKOPI** (IRE) C 97
73 **PARALLEL WORLD** (IRE) 18
292 **PARAMARIBO** (IRE) 28
500 **PARAMETER** 63
13 **PARC D'AMOUR** (IRE) 41
541 **PARELLI POWER** 2
483 **PARELLIROC** 35
428 **PARICOLOR** (FR) 70
155 **PARIKARMA** (IRE) 9
243 **PARIS LIGHTS** (IRE) 109
243 **PARIS PEACOCK** (IRE) 110
535 **PARIS PROTOCOL** 32
566 **PARIS WINDS** (IRE) F 63
445 **PARISENCORE** (IRE) 37
478 **PARISIAC** (IRE) 24
258 **PARISIAN BLUE** 107
346 **PARISIAN CHIC** (IRE) F 64
29 **PARISIAN PRINCESSE** 2
267 **PARISIENNE GOLD** (FR) 13
387 **PARK FARM PRINCE** 194
338 **PARK PADDOCKS** (IRE) 4
485 **PARK THIS ONE** (IRE) 36
476 **PARKIN FINE** 111
61 **PARLANDO** 61
388 **PARLIAMENT HILL** 107
385 **PARMENION** 140
26 **PARNELL'S DREAM** C 128
258 **PAROS** (FR) 108
333 **PARRAMOUNT** 41
232 **PARSONS PLEASURE** (FR) 37
320 **PARTY BELLE** G 32

561 **PARTY BUSINESS** (IRE) 63
13 **PARTY FUZZ** 42
106 **PARTY ISLAND** (IRE) 5
300 **PARTY LINE** C 194
296 **PARTY PLANNER** 11
164 **PARYS MOUNTAIN** (IRE) 72
88 **PASCHA** 23
50 **PASCHALS DREAM** (IRE) 4
60 **PASDATTENTES** (FR) 19
567 **PASEO** 68
423 **PASHA BAY** 15
240 **PASHMINA** (IRE) C 191
398 **PASO DOBLE** (IRE) 127
491 **PASO ROBLES** 19
428 **PASQUALITA** 71
17 **PASS ME BY** 17
312 **PASS THE LOVE ON** 85
161 **PASSAM** 7
496 **PASSIN' THRU** 12
10 **PASSING CLOUDS** 21
245 **PASSING KATE** 12
225 **PASSING SECRETS** 10
39 **PASSION AND GLORY** (IRE) 42
15 **PASSIONOVA** (IRE) 22
546 **PASSNOTALEGEND** 9
500 **PASTEL POWER** (IRE) 64
462 **PASTFACT** 5
48 **PASTICHE** 93
94 **PASTORAL STAR** F 83
458 **PASTURE BEACH** (IRE) 53
216 **PASVOLSKY** (IRE) 41
539 **PAT'S LIGHT** 6
223 **PATAGONIA** (FR) 69
562 **PATAILLE** (FR) 19
56 **PATCH ME UP** 6
27 **PATEEN** (IRE) 7
360 **PATENT JOY** (IRE) F 29
130 **PATH HILL** 16
414 **PATH OF PEACE** C 57
223 **PATIENT DREAM** (FR) 70
413 **PATIENT OWNER** (IRE) 11
406 **PATONTHEBACK** (IRE) 31
372 **PATRIOCTIC** (IRE) 11
258 **PATROCLUS** (IRE) 109
6 **PATRONESS** F 164
106 **PATROON** (USA) 6
125 **PATS FANCY** (IRE) 27
372 **PATSY'S NUMBER ONE** 12
406 **PATTERNED** C 116
491 **PATTI O'RAHY** (USA) C 55
69 **PAUDIE** (IRE) 21
385 **PAUL MARVEL** (FR) 141
543 **PAULO PANINI** 27
432 **PAULS HILL** (IRE) 19
240 **PAVILLON** F 86
451 **PAVLIK** (IRE) 9
118 **PAVLODAR** (FR) 61
231 **PAWAPURI** 82
548 **PAWPAW** 22
346 **PAWS FOR THOUGHT** (IRE) 10
268 **PAY FOR ADAAY** 15
13 **PAY THE PILOT** 43
237 **PAY THE PIPER** (IRE) 5
304 **PAY THE WOMAN** (IRE) 29
24 **PAY TIME** G 5
89 **PAYMASTER** 66
513 **PC DIXON** 7

119 **PEACE ANGEL** 12
543 **PEACE FONIC** (FR) F 37
277 **PEACE IN MOTION** (USA) F 22
217 **PEACE MAN** 104
258 **PEACE OF ROME** (GER) 110
54 **PEACE PREVAILS** 15
312 **PEACE RIVER** 86
6 **PEACE TRAIL** F 165
402 **PEACH BLOSSOM** (IRE) 70
186 **PEACH MELBA** C 41
383 **PEACHEY CARNEHAN** 11
217 **PEACHY KEEN** 105
24 **PEAK TIME** 17
13 **PEAKED TOO SOON** 44
535 **PEAL OF BELLS** F 43
83 **PEARL BAY** 9
317 **PEARL BEACH** 9
6 **PEARL BORDER** (IRE) 62
271 **PEARL EYE** 14
426 **PEARL GLORY** (IRE) 34
527 **PEARL OF KUWAIT** (IRE) 29
131 **PEARL OF QATAR** 12
268 **PEARL REEF** 16
292 **PEARL WARRIOR** 29
204 **PEARLITAS PASSION** (IRE) F 59
531 **PEARLY ISLAND** 23
83 **PEARLY SPIRIT** (FR) F 43
17 **PEBBLY LUNAR LADY** (IRE) 18
17 **PEBBLY NEW MOON** (IRE) 19
312 **PECKINPAH** (IRE) 87
415 **PEDDERY** 18
190 **PEDESTAL** (IRE) 4
177 **PEDRO DE STYLES** (FR) 14
488 **PEEJAYBEE** (IRE) 17
414 **PEERLESS** (IRE) 27
404 **PEERLESS BEAUTY** 152
501 **PEERLESS PERCY** (IRE) 10
537 **PEGGOTY** 48
460 **PEGGY SIOUX** 61
327 **PEGGYCLARE** (IRE) 8
537 **PEINTRE D'ÉTOILES** (FR) 20
404 **PEKING ROSE** 153
466 **PELOPONNESE** (FR) F 32
381 **PELTWELL** (IRE) 81
323 **PEMBERLEY** (IRE) 47
402 **PEMBINA** (IRE) F 162
476 **PEMBROKE** 112
133 **PEMBROKE HOUSE** 19
293 **PEMBROKESHIRE** 23
402 **PENCHANT** C 163
349 **PENCIL** (IRE) 18
420 **PENCREEK** (FR) 64
145 **PENDLETON** 26
302 **PENELOPEBLUEYES** (IRE) 27
83 **PENGUIN ISLAND** 30
47 **PENNA ROSSA** (IRE) 49
234 **PENNANT EMPRESS** 6
319 **PENNY DROPS** C 42
164 **PENNY GARCIA** F 145
440 **PENNY LOUGH** (IRE) G 33
556 **PENNY POT LANE** 9
1 **PENNY RIVER** 43
319 **PENNY ROSE** F 43
125 **PENNYFORAPOUND** (IRE) 28
217 **PENNYMOOR** 24
460 **PENNYPEACE** 62
478 **PENOMBRE** 8

238 **PENPAL** (FR) 57
409 **PENS MAN** (IRE) 80
155 **PENSA TE** (IRE) 38
45 **PENTAOUR** (FR) 9
32 **PENTIMENTO** 14
398 **PENTIRE HEAD** (IRE) 128
258 **PENTLAND HILLS** (IRE) 111
94 **PENUMBRA** 42
478 **PENWAY** (IRE) 25
562 **PEPE LE MOKO** (FR) 20
426 **PEPITE DE AMOUR** 11
223 **PEPITE DE BELLE** 71
463 **PEPITE FLEURIE** 13
87 **PEPPER ARDEN** 37
397 **PEPPER STREAK** (IRE) 18
544 **PEPPERWORT** (FR) 58
273 **PEPSI CAT** (IRE) 18
517 **PER VINO VERITAS** 58
404 **PERCULATOR** 154
375 **PERCUSSION** 3
299 **PERCY BLAKENEY** 65
378 **PERCY JONES** 44
152 **PERCY PI** 10
544 **PERCY PROSECCO** 25
158 **PERCY TOPLIS** 9
13 **PERCY VEERING** 45
405 **PERCY WILLIS** 15
406 **PERCY'S BIRD** C 117
319 **PERCY'S LAD** 8
317 **PERCY'S PRIDE** (IRE) 10
266 **PERCY'S PRINCE** 11
476 **PERCY'S WORD** 113
204 **PERDIKA** 60
240 **PERFECT ANGEL** (IRE) F 192
566 **PERFECT BLESSINGS** (IRE) C 64
118 **PERFECT CHARMER** 62
91 **PERFECT FOCUS** (IRE) 10
406 **PERFECT FUN** C 118
314 **PERFECT GLORY** (IRE) 94
312 **PERFECT HARMONY** (IRE) 88
537 **PERFECT LADY** F 79
39 **PERFECT LIGHT** (IRE) C 110
238 **PERFECT MAN** (IRE) 58
379 **PERFECT MATCH** (IRE) 9
449 **PERFECT MOMENT** (IRE) 7
313 **PERFECT MYTH** 24
231 **PERFECT NEWS** 83
170 **PERFECT PERSUASION** G 71
488 **PERFECT POSE** (IRE) F 53
245 **PERFECT SIGN** (IRE) 13
499 **PERFECT SOLDIER** (IRE) 2
543 **PERFECT SPIRIT** (FR) F 38
262 **PERFECT STAR** F 98
164 **PERFECT SWISS** 73
419 **PERFECT SYMPHONY** (IRE) 3
528 **PERIPATETIC** 113
48 **PERIPETEIA** 11
16 **PERISTYLE** 222
307 **PERONI** 10
402 **PEROTAN** (IRE) 71
520 **PEROTTO** 11
403 **PERPLEXITY** (IRE) F 50
220 **PERRUCHE GRISE** (FR) C 28
457 **PERRYVILLE** (IRE) 23
175 **PERSAVERANCE** 3
170 **PERSEPTION** 59
182 **PERSEVERANDO** 61

101 **PERSIAN ROYAL** 49
231 **PERSIST** 84
25 **PERSUASION** (IRE) 19
299 **PERSUASIVE POWERS** 16
225 **PERSUER** 11
561 **PERTEMPS DIAMOND** 101
527 **PERTEMPS LIFE** (IRE) 15
364 **PERTINENCE** C 56
497 **PERUVIAN SUMMER** (IRE) 5
217 **PETER THE GREAT** 25
333 **PETER'S PORTRAIT** (IRE) 42
560 **PETERBOROUGH** (FR) 58
267 **PETIT PALAIS** 14
409 **PETIT TONNERRE** (FR) 81
516 **PETITE BOULANGERE** (IRE) C 63
232 **PETITE DAME** (IRE) 38
289 **PETITE JOE** 3
471 **PETITE POIS** G 7
404 **PETITE POWER** (IRE) 155
458 **PETITE RHAPSODY** (IRE) 54
467 **PETITEALFIE** 21
295 **PETRASTAR** 20
398 **PETROSSIAN** (IRE) 129
481 **PETRULER** 5
467 **PETTICOAT LUCY** (IRE) 22
7 **PETTINGER** 58
59 **PETTOCHSIDE** 10
473 **PEUR DE RIEN** (FR) 33
475 **PFINGSTBERG** (GER) 77
48 **PHANTASY MAC** (IRE) 43
277 **PHANTOM FLIGHT** 6
13 **PHANTOM GETAWAY** (IRE) 46
223 **PHIL DE PAIL** (FR) 72
420 **PHIL THE SOCK** (IRE) 65
409 **PHIL THE THRILL** (FR) 82
404 **PHILLAPA SUE** (IRE) 156
246 **PHILLIPSTOWN ELLEN** (IRE) 34
122 **PHILOSOPHY** 55
262 **PHINOW** (IRE) 48
6 **PHIZ** (GER) C 169
140 **PHOEBUS LESCRIBAA** (FR) 10
159 **PHOENIX AQUILUS** (IRE) 5
467 **PHOENIX RISEN** 23
339 **PHOENIX STAR** (IRE) 8
251 **PHOENIX STRIKE** 21
201 **PHOENIX WAY** (IRE) 45
229 **PHOTO BOMB** (IRE) 22
88 **PHOTOGRAPH** (IRE) 16
406 **PHRYNE** (IRE) 83
10 **PHYSICS** (IRE) 22
320 **PIAFF BUBBLES** (IRE) 33
134 **PIANISSIMO** 10
280 **PIANO** F 73
516 **PIASTRELLA** (IRE) 34
398 **PIC D'ORHY** (FR) 130
427 **PICANHA** 18
279 **PICC AN ANGEL** 10
231 **PICCADILLY CIRCUS** 172
312 **PICCADILLY LILLY** 89
240 **PICCO UNO** (USA) C 193
361 **PICK AND CHOOSE** C 103
432 **PICKAMIX** 20
440 **PICKERSLEIGH** (IRE) C 34
372 **PICKYOUROWN** (IRE) 13
10 **PICNIC IN THE PARK** 46
500 **PICUAL** 65
257 **PIDDIES REFLECTION** 3

243 **QUEENSCLIFF** (IRE) F 178
145 **QUEENSFERRY** (USA) 28
398 **QUEL DESTIN** (FR) 135
317 **QUEL KAIMA** (GER) 31
272 **QUELLE VITESSE** (GER) 15
516 **QUENCHED** F 64
417 **QUENELLE D'OR** 10
151 **QUERCUS** (IRE) 14
551 **QUERCUS SINUATA** 15
80 **QUEST FOR FUN** 21
535 **QUEST FOR LIFE** 34
373 **QUIANA** 94
431 **QUICK BREATH** 10
73 **QUICK CHANGE** 67
320 **QUICK DRAW** (IRE) 36
426 **QUICK FLING** 65
448 **QUICK OF THE NIGHT** 5
82 **QUICK PICK** (IRE) 28
567 **QUICK WAVE** (FR) 71
258 **QUICKBUCK** (IRE) 117
560 **QUICKDRAWMCGRAW** (IRE) 81
378 **QUICKTHORN** 20
319 **QUIET ELEGANCE** F 44
39 **QUIET EVENING** (IRE) 44
476 **QUIET FLOW** 120
118 **QUIET LIFE** 107
26 **QUIET OASIS** (IRE) F 135
260 **QUIET PRIDE** (IRE) 14
83 **QUIET PROTEST** (USA) F 44
15 **QUIET QUEEN** F 54
402 **QUIET REFLECTION** F 166
272 **QUIET THUNDER** (IRE) 16
97 **QUIETLY CONFIDENT** 59
56 **QUILAURA** (FR) 8
420 **QUINTA DO MAR** (IRE) 67
118 **QUINTA VERDE** (IRE) C 108
125 **QUINTARA** (IRE) G 29
2 **QUINTILLUS** 20
105 **QUITE SHARP** C 43
240 **QUIXOTIC** F 202
182 **QUIZA QUIZA QUIZA** F 62
373 **QULOOB** 95
560 **QUOI DE NEUF** (FR) 61
238 **QUOTELINE DIRECT** 61
402 **QUSHCHI** C 167
77 **QUTEY ZEE** (IRE) 35
422 **QWELDRYK** (IRE) 12
422 **QWICKEN** (IRE) 13
4 **R BERNARD** 16
522 **RAABEH** 14
39 **RAAEB** (IRE) 45
105 **RAAJIL** (IRE) 7
204 **RAAJIS** (IRE) F 51
475 **RAAKIB ALHAWA** (IRE) 21
566 **RAAQY** (IRE) C 66
76 **RAAQYAH** (USA) C 27
246 **RAASED** (IRE) 37
7 **RAASEL** 60
80 **RAATEA** 22
207 **RABAT** (IRE) 4
212 **RABBLE ROUSER** (IRE) 55
212 **RABELLOISE** (FR) 79
409 **RABSKI** (IRE) 91
123 **RACEMAKER** 14
604 **RACHEL LOUISE** 6
493 **RACING COUNTRY** (IRE) 9
138 **RACING DEMON** 18

1 **RACING PULSE** (IRE) 44
39 **RACING ROYALTY** 80
448 **RACING SPIRIT** 7
218 **RACKS CROSS** (IRE) 8
388 **RACY LACEY** (IRE) 109
273 **RACY STACEY** 10
238 **RADDLE AND HUM** (IRE) 62
147 **RADDON TOP** (IRE) 16
98 **RADETSKY** (USA) 17
375 **RADETZKY MARCH** (IRE) 35
379 **RADIANT LIGHT** 11
104 **RADIANT SKY** (FR) 37
174 **RADIO GAGA** F 45
367 **RADUCANU** 43
143 **RAE DES CHAMPS** (IRE) 28
365 **RAECIUS FELIX** (IRE) 44
375 **RAFFERTY** (IRE) 36
365 **RAFFERTY'S RETURN** 45
457 **RAFFLE TICKET** 25
557 **RAFFLES GITANE** (FR) 15
314 **RAFFLES REBEL** 58
312 **RAFIKI** (FR) 93
373 **RAFIOT** (USA) 96
381 **RAGAMUFFIN** (IRE) 85
299 **RAGE OF BAMBY** (IRE) 67
163 **RAGING ATLANTIC** (USA) G 57
543 **RAGING RASCAL** (IRE) 14
104 **RAGNAROK** (FR) 63
39 **RAGSAH** (IRE) F 113
344 **RAGTIME DANCER** C 22
570 **RAHA** 6
155 **RAHAALA** (IRE) F 78
314 **RAIFF** (IRE) 59
373 **RAIHAAN** (IRE) 97
281 **RAILWAY MUICE** (IRE) 12
446 **RAIN CAP** 4
402 **RAIN GODDESS** (IRE) C 168
308 **RAINBOW BISCUIT** 6
300 **RAINBOW COLOURS** (IRE) 90
312 **RAINBOW DREAMER** 94
217 **RAINBOW FIRE** (IRE) 27
340 **RAINBOW JET** (IRE) 17
447 **RAINBOW MIRAGE** 6
532 **RAINBOW RAIN** 10
419 **RAINBOW SIGN** 4
473 **RAINBOW STORM** (FR) 35
378 **RAINBOW'S ARCH** (IRE) C 73
405 **RAINBOW'S GIFT** 16
406 **RAINCLOUD** 121
292 **RAINS OF CASTAMERE** 32
6 **RAINSWEPT** C 171
215 **RAINY CITY** (IRE) 28
398 **RAINYDAY WOMAN** 136
505 **RAISE THE ROOF** (IRE) 4
38 **RAISE YOUR HAND** (IRE) 15
414 **RAISING SAND** 28
204 **RAJAR** C 61
323 **RAJARAN** (FR) 50
346 **RAJINSKY** (IRE) 11
105 **RAJMEISTER** 8
297 **RAKEMATIZ** 8
295 **RAKHINE STATE** (IRE) 21
177 **RAKISH PADDY** (IRE) 16
217 **RAKURAI** 109
354 **RALF DES NOES** (FR) 99
550 **RALLY DRIVER** 18
555 **RALPHY BOY TWO** (IRE) 30

172 **RAMAMARAS BOY** (IRE) 28
454 **RAMBLING QUEEN** (IRE) G 14
188 **RAMBLING RIVER** 5
388 **RAMBO T** (IRE) 110
460 **RAMBUSO CREEK** (IRE) 64
371 **RAMDON ROCKS** 19
231 **RAMENSKY** 178
385 **RAMILLIES** (IRE) 146
170 **RAMIRO** (IRE) 34
388 **RAMMING SPEED** (IRE) 111
567 **RAMO** (FR) 72
460 **RAMONE** (IRE) C 102
267 **RAMONEX** (GER) 15
216 **RAMORE WILL** (IRE) 46
319 **RAMPAGE** (IRE) 27
312 **RAMPOLDI PLAN** (USA) 150
428 **RAMSES DE TEILLEE** (FR) 73
167 **RAMURE** (FR) 28
16 **RANCH HAND** 37
491 **RANCHO SANTA FE** 21
93 **RANCHO STAR** (IRE) F 24
428 **RANCO** (IRE) 74
537 **RANDOM HARVEST** (IRE) 23
42 **RANGATIRA JACK** 5
509 **RANGE** (IRE) 32
365 **RANGER BOB** (IRE) 46
475 **RANI OF JHANSI** 22
315 **RANIA** (IRE) 7
125 **RANIERI** (IRE) 30
486 **RANN OF KUTCH** (IRE) 9
25 **RANZINI** (IRE) 47
72 **RAPAPORT** 7
513 **RAPID FRITZ** (IRE) 8
458 **RAPID RAIDER** (IRE) 58
243 **RAPID RESPONSE** (FR) 56
460 **RAPID TRANSACTION** (USA) C 103
386 **RAQISA** 22
93 **RAQRAAQ** (USA) 17
162 **RARE CLOUDS** 9
333 **RARE EDITION** (IRE) 44
405 **RARE GROOVE** (IRE) 17
361 **RAREMENT** C 105
334 **RASAN** C 67
327 **RASANGO** (FR) 25
212 **RASCAL** 56
217 **RASHMI** 110
565 **RASPBERRY** 9
260 **RATAFIA** 15
404 **RATFACEMCDOUGALL** (IRE) 165
143 **RATH AN IUIR** (IRE) 29
211 **RATHAGAN** 2
460 **RATHBONE** 16
258 **RATHER BE** (IRE) 118
94 **RATHGAR** 85
38 **RATHLEEK** G 16
202 **RATOUTE YUTTY** 3
405 **RATTLE OWL** 18
240 **RATTLING** 89
228 **RATTLING ROSIE** 16
233 **RAUZAN** (FR) 56
204 **RAVANELLI** (IRE) 62
83 **RAVELLO SUNSET** 31
448 **RAVEN'S RAFT** (IRE) 8
420 **RAVEN'S TOWER** (USA) 68
483 **RAVENHILL ROAD** (IRE) 38
378 **RAVENS ARK** 21
155 **RAVENSBURG** C 79

314 **RAVENSCAR** (IRE) 60
292 **RAVENSCRAIG CASTLE** 33
460 **RAVENSWING** (IRE) 65
505 **RAVI ROAD** (IRE) 31
346 **RAVISH** C 67
491 **RAVISSANTE** (IRE) F 58
15 **RAWYAAN** 40
537 **RAY DAY** 24
373 **RAY'S THE ONE** 98
212 **RAYA TIME** (FR) 57
39 **RAYAT** (IRE) 81
184 **RAYDOUN** (IRE) 35
127 **RAYMOND** (IRE) 35
312 **RAYMOND TUSK** (IRE) 95
73 **RAYONG** 19
282 **RAYS RABBLE** 11
110 **RAYTHEHANDYMAN** (IRE) 15
231 **RAZEYNA** (IRE) 91
313 **RAZOR SHARP** G 26
240 **RAZZLE DAZZLE** 90
163 **REACH** (IRE) 21
217 **REACH FOR THE MOON** 111
422 **READY FREDDIE GO** (IRE) 5
12 **READY TO PLEASE** 15
122 **READY TO SHINE** (IRE) 63
299 **READYFORANYTHING** 38
458 **READYSTEADYBEAU** (FR) 59
243 **REAL APPEAL** (GER) 57
541 **REAL ARMANI** 3
500 **REAL DREAM** (IRE) 67
10 **REAL ESTATE** (IRE) 23
280 **REAL GAIN** (IRE) 75
398 **REAL STEEL** (FR) 137
521 **REAL TERMS** 29
39 **REAL WORLD** (IRE) 46
173 **REALISED** 33
402 **REALISM** (IRE) 75
6 **REALLY SPECIAL** C 172
389 **REALLYRADICAL** (IRE) 6
567 **REALM KEEPER** (USA) 73
567 **REALM OF GLORY** (IRE) 74
2 **REALMS OF FIRE** 5
145 **REALT EILE** (IRE) F 67
324 **REALTA ROYALE** 14
94 **REBECCA ROMERO** F 86
73 **REBEL AT DAWN** (IRE) 20
323 **REBEL INTENTIONS** (IRE) 51
395 **REBEL LEADER** (IRE) 46
371 **REBEL LOVE** (IRE) 20
142 **REBEL REDEMPTION** 31
404 **REBEL ROXY** (IRE) 166
92 **REBEL ROYAL** (IRE) 20
488 **REBEL SURGE** (IRE) C 54
424 **REBEL TERRITORY** 7
6 **REBEL'S ROMANCE** (IRE) 21
26 **RECHERCHER** 66
475 **RECIFE** (GER) C 79
385 **RECITE A PRAYER** (IRE) 147
373 **RECKON I'M HOT** 144
170 **RECLAIM VICTORY** (IRE) 35
89 **RECON MISSION** (IRE) 73
484 **RECORD HIGH** (IRE) 12
517 **RECTORY OAK** (IRE) 60
418 **RECTORY ROAD** 15
146 **RECUERDAME** (USA) 17
89 **RED ALERT** 74
273 **RED ALLURE** 11

238 **RED AMAPOLA** 63
164 **RED ASTAIRE** 147
403 **RED AZALEA** (IRE) 17
414 **RED BLANCHE** (IRE) C 60
127 **RED BOND** (IRE) 36
572 **RED BRAVO** (IRE) 15
491 **RED BUD** 22
153 **RED CARD** (IRE) F 10
532 **RED COMMAND** (IRE) 11
528 **RED DANIELLE** 184
568 **RED DEREK** 14
409 **RED DIRT ROAD** (IRE) 92
326 **RED DWARF** (IRE) 11
421 **RED EVELYN** 9
155 **RED FANTASY** (IRE) F 80
32 **RED FLYER** (IRE) 18
314 **RED FORCE ONE** 61
240 **RED FORT** (FR) 203
82 **RED GIANT** (IRE) 29
415 **RED HANRAHAN** (IRE) 15
428 **RED HAPPY** (FR) 75
80 **RED HOW** 42
561 **RED INFANTRY** (IRE) 65
335 **RED JASPER** 31
300 **RED KITE** (IRE) 91
491 **RED LACEWING** (IRE) 23
409 **RED LION LAD** (IRE) 76
458 **RED MISSILE** (IRE) 60
320 **RED NIKA** (FR) 37
219 **RED OCHRE** 14
417 **RED OCTOBER** (IRE) 11
500 **RED RAMBLER** 68
219 **RED REMINDER** 15
572 **RED RIPPLE** 16
398 **RED RISK** (FR) 138
404 **RED RIVER VALLEY** (IRE) 167
503 **RED ROLY** 3
323 **RED ROOKIE** 52
167 **RED ROYALIST** 29
544 **RED SHOWGIRL** 63
238 **RED SKYE DELIGHT** (IRE) 64
77 **RED STARS** (IRE) C 61
530 **RED STORM** (GER) 20
568 **RED STRIPES** (USA) 15
181 **RED TORNADO** (FR) 4
505 **RED TULIP** F 32
155 **RED VERDON** (USA) 10
379 **RED VINEYARD** (IRE) 25
354 **RED VISION** (FR) 100
568 **RED WALLS** 16
145 **RED WARNING** (IRE) 48
216 **RED WINDSOR** (IRE) 47
463 **REDARNA** 15
281 **REDBRIDGE ROSIE** (IRE) 13
385 **REDEMPTION DAY** 148
118 **REDEMPTION TIME** 109
530 **REDEMPTORIST** (IRE) 21
113 **REDESDALE ANGEL** 16
113 **REDESDALE REBEL** 17
525 **REDFORD ROAD** 47
566 **REDOUTABLE** (IRE) F 67
462 **REDREDROBIN** 6
5 **REDROSEZORRO** 7
265 **REDUNDERTHEBED** (IRE) F 83
478 **REDZONE** 9
476 **REDZOR** (IRE) 121

201 **REE OKKA** 50
425 **REECELTIC** 11
459 **REEL OF FORTUNE** (IRE) 15
217 **REEL POWER** 112
406 **REEL PROSPECT** (IRE) 84
34 **REEL ROSIE** (IRE) 26
179 **REEL TIMBA** (IRE) 18
378 **REELEMIN** 48
460 **REEM THREE** C 104
311 **REETAZEETAJONES** 3
240 **REFINE** (IRE) 204
159 **REFLECT** 7
185 **REFLEX** (IRE) 70
326 **REFORMED CHARACTER** (IRE) 12
505 **REFRESHED** (IRE) F 75
163 **REFUGE** 22
561 **REGABY** (IRE) 66
147 **REGAL 'N BOLD** 17
274 **REGAL ENCORE** (IRE) 45
118 **REGAL ENVOY** (IRE) 63
505 **REGAL HAWK** C 76
185 **REGAL HEIRESS** C 71
164 **REGAL MIRAGE** (IRE) 77
580 **REGAL PRETENDER** 13
500 **REGAL REALITY** 16
531 **REGARDING RUTH** (IRE) 27
354 **REGGAE DE BAUNE** (FR) 101
478 **REGIMENTO** 10
478 **REGINALD CHARLES** 41
233 **REGINALDS TOWER** (IRE) 15
34 **REGIONAL** 7
366 **REGULAR INCOME** (IRE) 27
157 **REGULATOR** (IRE) 30
87 **REIGNING PROFIT** (IRE) 38
415 **REIGNITE** 10
476 **REILLY** (IRE) 122
537 **REINA DEL MAR** (IRE) 25
373 **REINATOR** (FR) 99
222 **REINE ANGEVINE** (FR) F 47
173 **REINE DU BAL** 6
413 **REINE FEE** (IRE) 12
505 **REKINDLE** F 77
277 **RELATION ALEXANDER** (IRE) C 23
338 **RELATIVE EASE** 5
345 **RELAXED BOY** (FR) 13
460 **RELAXEZ VOUS** (IRE) C 105
89 **RELAY RUNNER** (IRE) 75
445 **RELEASE THE KRAKEN** (IRE) 38
506 **RELENTLESS SUN** 7
118 **RELEVANT** (IRE) C 110
164 **RELKADAM** (FR) 78
530 **RELY ON OLD SPORT** (FR) 47
26 **REMARQUEE** 136
428 **REMASTERED** 77
331 **REMEDIUM** 13
509 **REMEMBER ALLY** (FR) 33
313 **REMEMBER THE MAN** (IRE) 27
16 **REMEMBER YOU** (IRE) F 229
231 **REMEMBERING** (IRE) 92
78 **REMEMBERTHETITANS** 9
501 **RENARDEAU** 11
16 **RENDITION** (IRE) 114
381 **RENEGADE ARROW** (FR) 86
379 **RENEGADE ROSE** (IRE) 26
83 **RENOIR** 32
91 **REPARTEE** (IRE) 12
475 **REPERTOIRE** 23

485 **REPRESENTING BOB** (IRE) 39
299 **REPRIEVAL** (FR) F 68
473 **REPUBLICAN** 36
87 **REPUTATION** (IRE) 24
505 **REROUTE** (IRE) F 78
238 **RESDEV THUNDER** 95
517 **RESERVE TANK** (IRE) 61
561 **RESET BUTTON** 67
122 **RESET IN BLUE** (IRE) C 64
377 **RESHOUN** (FR) 17
315 **RESILIENCE** 16
341 **RESPLENDENT ROSE** 7
301 **REST AND BE** (IRE) C 12
388 **RESTANDBETHANKFUL** 112
312 **RESTITUTION** (FR) 96
7 **RESTLESS ENDEAVOUR** (IRE) 61
561 **RESTORER** 68
177 **RESTRICTED AREA** (IRE) 17
16 **RETICENT** 115
423 **RETIREMENT BECKONS** 11
294 **RETRIEVE THE STICK** 11
294 **RETRIEVE THE STICK** F 12
395 **RETROSPECT** (IRE) 47
207 **RETROUVAILLES** 5
458 **RETURN FIRE** (IRE) 61
365 **RETURN TICKET** (IRE) 47
39 **RETURN TO DUBAI** (IRE) 82
118 **RETURN VOYAGE** (USA) 64
531 **REVASSER** (IRE) 28
304 **REVE** 32
404 **REVE DE NIAMH** 168
201 **REVELS HILL** 51
240 **REVEREND HUBERT** (IRE) 24
541 **REVERSE THE CHARGE** (IRE) 4
312 **REVERSION** (FR) 151
488 **REVICH** (IRE) 20
61 **REVOLUTIONARY MAN** (IRE) 38
566 **REVOLUTIONISE** (IRE) 27
434 **REVOLVER** (IRE) 8
164 **REVOUABLE** 148
395 **REWIRED** 48
105 **REY ARTURO** (IRE) 27
475 **REYAMOUR** F 55
47 **RHAGORI** C 76
166 **RHEA OF THE YEAR** 16
473 **RHEBUS ROAD** (IRE) 37
504 **RHIAN DE SIVOLA** 26
402 **RHIANNON** (IRE) C 169
73 **RHINOPLASTY** (IRE) 68
530 **RHODESIEN STAR** (GER) 22
402 **RHODODENDRON** (IRE) C 170
406 **RHOSCOLYN** 34
436 **RHUBARB** 7
10 **RHUBARB BIKINI** (IRE) 24
571 **RHYME SCHEME** (IRE) 6
87 **RHYTHM** (IRE) 25
59 **RHYTHM DANCER** 19
77 **RHYTHM N ROCK** (IRE) 36
566 **RHYTHMIC INTENT** (IRE) 28
326 **RHYTHMICAL** F 22
445 **RIBBLE VALLEY** (IRE) 39
47 **RIBBON ROSE** 50
466 **RIBBON ROYALE** C 34
9 **RIBEYE** 5
520 **RIBHI** (IRE) 25
229 **RIBTICKLER** (IRE) 23
397 **RIBTIDE** 20

146 **RICARDO OFWORTHING** (IRE) 34
233 **RICCARDI MEDIDI** (IRE) 31
145 **RICCIRELLA** 29
34 **RICH DREAM** (IRE) 8
34 **RICH KING** 27
16 **RICH LEGACY** (IRE) C 230
26 **RICH RHYTHM** 67
39 **RICH WATERS** (IRE) 47
155 **RICHARD P SMITH** (IRE) 40
334 **RICHARD R H B** (IRE) 23
228 **RICHARDSON** 17
373 **RICHIDISH** (FR) 100
411 **RICHIE VALENTINE** 19
354 **RICHMOND LAKE** (IRE) 102
338 **RICK BLAINE** (IRE) 6
335 **RICKENBACKER** (IRE) 56
335 **RICKSEN** 32
532 **RIDE SALLY RIDE** 12
312 **RIDEAU CANAL** (IRE) 97
267 **RIDERS ONTHE STORM** (IRE) 16
300 **RIDGE RANGER** (IRE) F 197
476 **RIDGEWAY** (FR) 123
186 **RIDGEWAY AVENUE** (USA) 5
476 **RIGGS** (IRE) 124
80 **RIGGSBY** (IRE) 23
174 **RIGHT ACTION** 16
404 **RIGHT DESTINATION** (IRE) 169
6 **RIGHT DIRECTION** (IRE) C 173
539 **RIGHT ROYALS DAY** 7
483 **RIGHT SAID TED** (IRE) 39
388 **RIGHT TURN** (IRE) 113
433 **RIGHTEOUS RENEE** (USA) F 14
233 **RIHANI** (IRE) 32
395 **RIKOBOY** (FR) 49
146 **RIKONA** 26
15 **RILEY'S AYADA** 41
15 **RILEY'S POSITANO** (IRE) 42
104 **RIMBAULT** (GER) 38
466 **RINARIA** (IRE) C 35
16 **RING FENCED** 116
505 **RING FOR BAILEYS** F 79
280 **RING OF BEARA** (FR) 52
163 **RING OF GOLD** 23
83 **RING OF LIGHT** 11
112 **RING PRETENDER** (FR) 25
560 **RING THE MOON** 62
386 **RINGO STARLIGHT** 37
93 **RINTY MAGINTY** (IRE) 18
388 **RIO SILVA** 114
280 **RIO'S CLIFFS** F 76
556 **RIO'S ROSANNA** (IRE) G 15
373 **RIOHACHA** (FR) 101
572 **RIOLIINA** (IRE) F 17
283 **RIP ROCKS PADDY OK** (IRE) 3
240 **RIPALONG** (FR) F 205
388 **RIPPER ROO** (IRE) 115
514 **RIPPLET** 42
412 **RISE HALL** 4
132 **RISE UP SINGING** F 7
47 **RISING STAR** 18
176 **RISK AND ROLL** (FR) 17
417 **RISK AVERSE** (IRE) 39
440 **RISK D'ARGENT** (FR) 37
476 **RISKINTHEGROUND** (IRE) 125
86 **RISKY GIRL** (FR) 17
390 **RITA R** (IRE) 10
549 **RITA RANA** (IRE) 45

177 **RITA THE CHEETAH** 18
561 **RITA'S WISH** 102
251 **RITCHIE STAR** (IRE) 24
334 **RITEASRAIN** 49
579 **RITHA** 4
365 **RITSON** (IRE) 48
189 **RIVAL** 16
230 **RIVARAMA** 7
333 **RIVARROS** (FR) 45
205 **RIVAS ROB ROY** 8
73 **RIVE GAUCHE** F 109
73 **RIVELLINO** 21
436 **RIVER BEAUTY** F 8
130 **RIVER BRAY** (IRE) 19
356 **RIVER CHORUS** (IRE) 6
476 **RIVER LEGEND** (IRE) 126
56 **RIVER LLYNFI** (IRE) 9
445 **RIVER MEADOW** (IRE) 40
231 **RIVER NAVER** (IRE) 179
118 **RIVER NYMPH** 20
26 **RIVER OF STARS** (IRE) 68
240 **RIVER PRIDE** 91
63 **RIVER RIBBLE** (FR) 18
7 **RIVER SONG** (IRE) 62
402 **RIVER THAMES** (IRE) M 76
213 **RIVER TYNE** 21
354 **RIVER WALK** (IRE) 103
89 **RIVER WHARFE** 76
431 **RIVERCAT** F 12
222 **RIVERS DAYDREAM** (IRE) M 48
61 **RIVERS LAD** 39
233 **RIYAMI** (IRE) 33
528 **RIZG** 119
525 **RIZZARDO** 48
164 **ROACH POWER** (IRE) 149
20 **ROAD TO FREEDOM** (FR) F 17
141 **ROAD TO ROSLEY** 6
365 **ROAD WARRIOR** 49
73 **ROAMIN IN GLOAMIN** 69
292 **ROAN** 34
138 **ROAR** (IRE) 8
101 **ROARIN' SUCCESS** 85
186 **ROARING LEGEND** (FR) 43
204 **ROARING ROSA** (IRE) 52
514 **ROB ROY MACGREGOR** (IRE) 43
115 **ROB ROYAL** (FR) 12
4 **ROB THE GETAWAY** (IRE) 17
334 **ROBASTA** (IRE) 50
162 **ROBBER'S BRIDGE** (IRE) 10
469 **ROBBIE DAZZLER** 32
184 **ROBBIE ROGER** (IRE) 36
383 **ROBEAM** (IRE) 13
561 **ROBELLI** 69
310 **ROBERT FROST** (USA) 7
364 **ROBERT HOOKE** 10
314 **ROBERT JOHNSON** 62
528 **ROBERT WALPOLE** 25
231 **ROBERTO ESCOBARR** (IRE) 30
474 **ROBIN DES FOX** 17
578 **ROBIN DES MANA** (IRE) 8
56 **ROBIN DES PEOPLE** (IRE) 17
427 **ROBIN DES SMOKE** (IRE) 20
469 **ROBIN DES THEATRE** (IRE) 33
442 **ROBIN OF SHERWOOD** (IRE) 6
376 **ROBIN SCHERBATSKY** (IRE) 14
373 **ROBIN'S DREAM** 102
385 **ROBINNIA** (IRE) 149

525 **ROBINSHILL** (IRE) 49
517 **ROBINSVILLE** 62
312 **ROBIOLA** (IRE) 98
240 **ROBJON** 92
373 **ROBS SECRET** 145
304 **ROBSAM** (IRE) 33
434 **ROBUSTO** (IRE) 58
61 **ROBY MILL** (IRE) 40
294 **ROBYN PUD** (IRE) 13
404 **ROBYNDZONE** (IRE) 170
97 **ROC ANGEL** (FR) 11
354 **ROC OF DUNDEE** (IRE) 104
521 **ROCADORA** 47
560 **ROCAMBOLAS** (FR) 63
186 **ROCANA** C 44
525 **ROCCO** (IRE) 50
63 **ROCCO STORM** (IRE) 10
222 **ROCCOWITHLOVE** 49
258 **ROCCSTAR BAY** 119
15 **ROCHEBRUNE** 43
240 **ROCHITTA** (USA) C 206
187 **ROCK AND BEL** (FR) 11
335 **ROCK BOY GREY** (IRE) 33
561 **ROCK CHANT** (USA) 70
26 **ROCK EAGLE** 14
240 **ROCK FOLLIES** F 207
476 **ROCK LEGEND** (IRE) 127
426 **ROCK MELODY** (IRE) 36
243 **ROCK OF CANDY** 114
34 **ROCK OF ENGLAND** (IRE) 49
567 **ROCK OF FAME** 75
157 **ROCK OF STAR** (FR) 31
409 **ROCK OF THE NATION** (IRE) 94
259 **ROCK ON BARNEY** (IRE) 18
381 **ROCK ON RITA** (IRE) 87
212 **ROCK ON ROCCO** (IRE) 58
480 **ROCK ON TEDDY** 9
388 **ROCK ON TOMMY** 116
403 **ROCK ORCHID** (IRE) F 51
500 **ROCK SIREN** 69
388 **ROCK THE HOUSE** (IRE) 117
169 **ROCK UP IN STYLE** 5
383 **ROCK WARBLER** (IRE) 14
440 **ROCKADENN** (FR) 38
361 **ROCKAHOOLABABY** F 106
409 **ROCKED UP** (IRE) 95
356 **ROCKESBURY** 7
204 **ROCKET ACTION** 29
163 **ROCKET DANCER** 24
375 **ROCKET ROBBO** 37
241 **ROCKET ROD** (IRE) 4
466 **ROCKET RODNEY** 36
98 **ROCKET YOGI** 37
334 **ROCKETS RED GLARE** (IRE) 24
105 **ROCKETT MAN** 9
572 **ROCKHAMTOM** (IRE) 18
87 **ROCKIN ROSA** 42
509 **ROCKING MAN** (FR) 51
508 **ROCKING REG** (IRE) 28
102 **ROCKINGHAM SOUTH** 3
367 **ROCKINOVERTHEWORLD** 18
468 **ROCKLEY POINT** 10
535 **ROCKMANN** (FR) 35
460 **ROCKPRINCESS** 66
89 **ROCKSHINE** C 112
476 **ROCKSTAR RONNIE** (IRE) 128
323 **ROCKY LAKE** (IRE) 53

476 **ROCKY MAN** (FR) 129
438 **ROCKY SEA** (IRE) 5
13 **ROCKY'S TREASURE** (IRE) 48
538 **RODOLFO** 22
475 **RODRIGO DIAZ** 24
294 **ROEBUCK BAY** 19
171 **ROGAN'S FANCY** (IRE) 12
320 **ROGER RAREBIT** 38
305 **ROGSKI** 10
105 **ROGUE BEAR** (IRE) 10
105 **ROGUE BULL** 28
105 **ROGUE FORCE** (IRE) 11
105 **ROGUE LION** 44
105 **ROGUE MILLENIUM** (IRE) 29
105 **ROGUE MISSION** (IRE) 30
557 **ROGUE QUEEN** (IRE) 16
105 **ROGUE ROCKET** (FR) 31
105 **ROGUE STAR** (FR) 32
174 **ROHAAN** (IRE) 17
34 **ROHLINDI** C 50
384 **ROKO GEORGE** (IRE) 21
56 **ROKOCOKO BLUE** (IRE) 11
469 **ROLFE REMBRANDT** 34
542 **ROLL OF THUNDER** 6
488 **ROLL WITH IT** (IRE) 21
405 **ROLLAJAM** (IRE) 36
112 **ROLLERRULER** 26
265 **ROLLING DYLAN** (IRE) 84
318 **ROLLING THE DICE** (IRE) 7
538 **ROLLZ ROYZ** 31
549 **ROLYPOLYMOLY** 46
22 **ROMA BANGKOK** 19
76 **ROMAANA** C 28
428 **ROMAIN DE SENAM** (FR) 78
346 **ROMAN DRAGON** 36
418 **ROMAN DYNASTY** (IRE) 16
579 **ROMAN KNOWS** 15
543 **ROMAN MIST** (IRE) 15
146 **ROMAN TEMPEST** (FR) 27
562 **ROMANCERO LE DUN** (FR) 21
384 **ROMANOR** 2
460 **ROMANOVICH** (IRE) 67
231 **ROMANTIC ART** 93
557 **ROMANTIC FASHION** (IRE) G 17
431 **ROMANTIC MEMORIES** 29
498 **ROMANTIC SUNLIGHT** 16
521 **ROMANTIC THOUGHT** 48
105 **ROMANY GYPSY** C 45
483 **ROMEO BROWN** 40
246 **ROMEO'S BOND** 38
565 **ROMULAN PRINCE** 10
143 **ROMULUS DU DONJON** (IRE) 30
561 **RON BURGUNDY** (IRE) 71
179 **RON** O 11
80 **RONGWAYRILEY** (IRE) 24
16 **ROODLE** C 231
381 **ROOKIE TRAINER** (IRE) 88
555 **ROOM AT THE TOP** (IRE) 91
184 **ROONEY O'MARA** F 43
62 **ROOT SIXTY SIX** 15
559 **ROOTLESS TREE** (IRE) 26
347 **ROPEY GUEST** 7
398 **ROQUE IT** (IRE) 139
215 **RORY** 29
238 **RORY AND ME** (FR) 65
475 **ROSA CHINENSIS** 80
460 **ROSA EGLANTERIA** C 106

118 **ROSA GIALLA** (IRE) C 111
280 **ROSA MYSTICA** (IRE) 53
16 **ROSCIOLI** 38
312 **ROSCOE TARA** 99
515 **ROSE ABOVE IT** (IRE) 3
24 **ROSE ALL DAY** 6
13 **ROSE AND THISTLE** 49
426 **ROSE BARTON** (IRE) 37
277 **ROSE BLOSSOM** C 24
538 **ROSE CAMIRA** 23
164 **ROSE ECLAIR** C 172
518 **ROSE FANDANGO** 4
89 **ROSE HIP** 77
559 **ROSE KAR** (FR) 27
501 **ROSE OF AFRICA** (IRE) C 25
213 **ROSE OF AGHABOE** (IRE) 22
517 **ROSE OF ARCADIA** (IRE) 63
434 **ROSE OF ITHACA** 59
300 **ROSE OF KILDARE** (IRE) 20
20 **ROSE OF LANCASHIRE** 18
445 **ROSE OF SIENA** (IRE) 41
485 **ROSE OHARA** 40
258 **ROSE ROW** G 120
395 **ROSE SEA HAS** (FR) 50
394 **ROSE WHISPER** (IRE) 9
343 **ROSE'S EMMA** (IRE) F 1
155 **ROSE'S GIRL** 41
473 **ROSEALAINN** (IRE) G 38
501 **ROSEARELLI** 12
16 **ROSEBERRY TOPPING** 117
25 **ROSECOMB** (IRE) C 48
521 **ROSEHILL ARTIST** (IRE) F 49
435 **ROSEISAROSEISAROSE** (IRE) 8
90 **ROSELEA GIRL** 16
378 **ROSEMARY AND THYME** 22
566 **ROSEQUIANO** 47
158 **ROSETINTEDGLASSES** (IRE) 10
104 **ROSETTA STONE** (FR) 39
80 **ROSHAMBO** 43
174 **ROSIE BOBBIE** 32
273 **ROSIE RED** 19
566 **ROSIE'S PREMIERE** (IRE) F 68
314 **ROSIE'S THUNDER** 95
228 **ROSIERITA** 18
320 **ROSMUC RELAY** (IRE) 39
427 **ROSSBEIGH STRAND** (IRE) 21
337 **ROSSERK ABBEY** (IRE) 11
395 **ROSTELLO** (FR) 51
246 **ROSY REDRUM** (IRE) 39
288 **ROSY RYAN** (IRE) 13
484 **ROSY WORLD** 13
122 **ROTATIONAL** 104
454 **ROTHSON** 7
346 **ROUDEMAIS** (IRE) 37
473 **ROUGE ET BLANC** (FR) 39
398 **ROUGE VIF** (FR) 140
94 **ROUGH COURTE** (IRE) C 87
122 **ROULSTON SCAR** (IRE) 10
34 **ROUND ACRE** 28
556 **ROUND THE ISLAND** 10
146 **ROUNDABOUT SILVER** 28
61 **ROUNDEL** 41
516 **ROUNDHAY PARK** 13
274 **ROUQUINE SAUVAGE** G 46
240 **ROUSAY** 93
562 **ROUVRAIE** (FR) C 28
537 **ROVANIEMI** (IRE) 26

385 **SAINT ROI** (FR) 151
385 **SAINT SAM** (FR) 152
562 **SAINT SEGAL** (FR) 21
398 **SAINT SONNET** (FR) 144
267 **SAINT XAVIER** (FR) 17
83 **SAINTE COLETTE** 33
381 **SAINTE DOCTOR** (FR) 90
199 **SAINTEMILION** (FR) 15
405 **SAISONS D'OR** (IRE) 19
122 **SAJJHAA** C 105
528 **SAKHEER** 121
364 **SAKURA STAR** 60
222 **SALAMANCA SCHOOL** (FR) 50
517 **SALCOMBE** 64
385 **SALDIER** (FR) 153
122 **SALEYMM** (IRE) 11
373 **SALIGO BAY** (IRE) 105
240 **SALITEH** 94
388 **SALLEY GARDENS** (IRE) 118
479 **SALLY'S GIRL** 5
213 **SALLYANN** (IRE) 24
293 **SALOME** (FR) F 25
208 **SALOMON PICO** (FR) 208
48 **SALONICA** 45
315 **SALOUEN** (IRE) 8
170 **SALSADA** (IRE) 36
540 **SALSOUL** (IRE) 13
26 **SALT BAY** (GER) 137
379 **SALT TREATY** (IRE) 27
423 **SALTA RESTA** 23
505 **SALTANAT** (IRE) C 80
123 **SALTMARKET** 12
60 **SALTY BOY** (FR) 22
366 **SALUTI** (IRE) 29
364 **SALVATION** F 61
217 **SALVATOR MUNDI** (IRE) 116
417 **SALVE JAPAN** 40
514 **SALVINO** (IRE) 44
323 **SAM BARTON** 55
274 **SAM BROWN** 48
26 **SAM COOKE** (IRE) 15
129 **SAM HAZE** 4
277 **SAM MAXIMUS** 7
170 **SAM'S ADVENTURE** 37
13 **SAM'S CALL** 25
240 **SAM'S HOPE** 209
435 **SAM'S THE MAN** 10
522 **SAMAAH** C 210
346 **SAMAGON** 69
92 **SAMANDARA** (FR) G 69
142 **SAMARA STAR** 32
398 **SAMARRIVE** (FR) 145
118 **SAMASANA** (IRE) C 114
13 **SAMATIAN** (FR) 51
404 **SAMBA DANCER** (IRE) 173
474 **SAMBEZI** (FR) 18
117 **SAMBURU** 117
263 **SAMBURU SHUJAA** (FR) 7
16 **SAME JURISDICTION** (SAF) F 234
233 **SAMEASITEVERWAS** (IRE) 16
164 **SAMEEM** (IRE) 80
126 **SAMEER** (FR) 3
576 **SAMI** C 40
216 **SAMI BEAR** 49
386 **SAMILLE** (IRE) 23
528 **SAMMARR** 28
228 **SAMMIX** 19

404 **SAMMYLOU** (IRE) 174
531 **SAMOURAI ONE** (FR) 29
7 **SAMPERS SEVEN** (IRE) 64
470 **SAMPHIRE COAST** 16
376 **SAMS PROFILE** 15
463 **SAMS ROSEABELLE** 16
304 **SAMTARA** 34
369 **SAMUEL JACKSON** 7
402 **SAMUEL PEPYS** (IRE) 77
406 **SAMUEL SPADE** (GER) 85
468 **SAMURAI SNEDDZ** 17
320 **SAN AGUSTIN** (IRE) 40
388 **SAN FERMIN** (IRE) 59
185 **SAN FRANCISCO BAY** (IRE) 45
201 **SAN GIOVANNI** (IRE) 52
305 **SAN JUAN** (IRE) 4
314 **SAN MIGUEL** (IRE) 63
259 **SAN PEDRO** (IRE) 19
373 **SAN PEDRO DE SENAM** (FR) 106
164 **SAN ROCH** (FR) 81
97 **SAN TEODORICO** (FR) 60
558 **SANAADH** 10
231 **SANCTION** 181
134 **SAND IN MY SHOES** (FR) 11
6 **SAND VIXEN** F 176
398 **SANDALWOOD** (FR) 146
485 **SANDAROC** 41
34 **SANDBECK** 29
466 **SANDGLASS** C 18
47 **SANDIE'S DREAM** 51
457 **SANDMARTIN** 26
251 **SANDRET** (IRE) 26
16 **SANDRINE** 118
214 **SANDS CHORUS** 13
176 **SANDS COVE** (IRE) 18
243 **SANDSNOW** (IRE) F 180
243 **SANDSTONE** C 181
265 **SANDY BOY** (IRE) 85
216 **SANDY BROOK** (IRE) 50
240 **SANDY PARADISE** (IRE) 95
7 **SANDYMAN** 65
243 **SANDYMOUNT BABY** (IRE) 58
105 **SANFELICE** (IRE) 33
109 **SANITISER** 14
231 **SANIYAAT** C 182
287 **SANNA BAY** (IRE) F 35
1 **SANOSUKE** (IRE) 46
356 **SANTA FLORENTINA** 8
97 **SANTA GIULIA** (FR) 61
404 **SANTACUS** (IRE) F 175
167 **SANTESA** 31
32 **SANTIBURI SPIRIT** 19
230 **SANTINI** 8
59 **SANTORINI SAL** 12
365 **SAO** (FR) 50
178 **SAO MAXENCE** (FR) 27
39 **SAOIRSE ABU** (USA) F 114
23 **SAOIRSE AWAY** (IRE) 14
16 **SAORLA** 119
516 **SAPPHIRE SILVER** (IRE) F 65
493 **SAPPHIRE BOMBAY** 10
89 **SAPPHIRE'S MOON** 108
60 **SAQUEBOUTE** (FR) 23
395 **SAQUON** (IRE) 53
247 **SARAH'S VERSE** 13
243 **SARAHA** C 182
6 **SARANGANI** 67

205 **SARAS HOPE** 9
304 **SARASOTA STAR** (IRE) 35
262 **SARATOGA GOLD** 16
262 **SARATOGA SPIRIT** 101
157 **SARCEAUX** (FR) 32
222 **SARIM** (IRE) 51
155 **SARKHA** (IRE) 42
312 **SARSEN** (USA) 101
475 **SARSHAMPLA** (IRE) C 81
561 **SARSONS RISK** (IRE) 103
37 **SARTENE'S SON** (FR) 3
215 **SARVI** 30
514 **SARYSHAGANN** (FR) 45
469 **SASHENKA** (GER) 35
122 **SASSI NERI** 66
265 **SASSIFIED** (IRE) 86
251 **SASSOON** 27
48 **SASSY RASCAL** (IRE) 46
254 **SASTRUGA** (IRE) 9
300 **SATANIC MOON** 94
572 **SATELLITE CALL** (IRE) 30
498 **SATIN WATERS** C 13
500 **SATONO JAPAN** (JPN) 17
312 **SATURDAY SONG** 102
469 **SATURN 'N SILK** 36
280 **SATURNALIA** (GER) 77
445 **SAUCE OF LIFE** (IRE) 44
164 **SAULIRE STAR** (IRE) 82
118 **SAUSALITO** 67
527 **SAUSALITO SUNRISE** (IRE) 33
241 **SAVALAS** (IRE) 6
118 **SAVANNAH BELLE** F 68
183 **SAVANNAH SONG** 21
404 **SAVASTANO** (IRE) 176
528 **SAVE A FOREST** (IRE) 29
557 **SAVE FACE** (FR) 19
101 **SAVIDA** (IRE) C 86
97 **SAVING GRACE** (FR) 62
518 **SAVING GRACE** C 13
10 **SAVOY BROWN** 25
538 **SAVROLA** (IRE) 24
576 **SAVVY KNIGHT** (IRE) 16
576 **SAVVY VICTORY** (IRE) 17
169 **SAW THE SEA** 6
149 **SAWPIT SAMANTHA** 23
149 **SAWPIT SIENNA** 24
379 **SAXON SCENE** (IRE) 41
240 **SAY GOODNIGHT** (IRE) 96
229 **SAY GRACE** (IRE) 24
371 **SAY NO NOW** (IRE) C 42
232 **SAY NOTHING** 41
13 **SAYADAM** (FR) 52
309 **SAYAR** (IRE) 13
424 **SAYIFYOUWILL** 9
324 **SAYO** 15
307 **SCALE FORCE** 12
1 **SCALLOWAY BAY** (IRE) 47
314 **SCALLOWAY CASTLE** (IRE) 64
375 **SCALLYWAGS** 38
16 **SCAMPI** 39
398 **SCARAMANGA** (IRE) 147
145 **SCARBOROUGH** (IRE) G 49
475 **SCARBOROUGH CASTLE** 25
381 **SCARDURA** (IRE) 91
517 **SCARFACE** (IRE) 65
426 **SCARLET** 66

104 **SELWAN** (IRE) 41
231 **SELYL** C 183
265 **SEMI COLON** (FR) F 87
373 **SEMSER** 109
566 **SEN DING** (IRE) 49
240 **SENADORA** (GER) C 211
89 **SEND IN THE CLOUDS** 80
293 **SENDACARD** 6
398 **SENDING LOVE** (IRE) 151
233 **SENDMYLOVETOROSE** F 57
319 **SENECA CHIEF** 10
312 **SENIOR CITIZEN** 104
46 **SENNEN** 8
526 **SENORITA EVA ROSE** (IRE) 3
89 **SENSA** (FR) C 113
231 **SENSE OF DUTY** 105
6 **SENSE OF POWER** (IRE) 70
15 **SENSE OF SECURITY** 44
6 **SENSE OF WISDOM** 71
91 **SENSE OF WORTH** (IRE) 13
314 **SENTIMENTAL LADY** (IRE) 65
80 **SEPARATE** 2
425 **SEPRANI** 12
548 **SEPTEMBER BLAZE** F 31
62 **SEPTEMBER BLAZE** G 24
212 **SEPTEMBER DAISY** 60
558 **SEPTEMBER POWER** (IRE) 11
101 **SEPTEMBER STARS** (IRE) F 87
480 **SEQUEIRA LADY** (IRE) 69
360 **SEQUESTER** C 31
16 **SERAFINA'S FLIGHT** C 236
293 **SERAPHIA** 60
293 **SERAPHINITE** (IRE) 7
491 **SERASANA** F 60
101 **SERENA'S STORM** (IRE) C 178
6 **SERENADA** C 88
182 **SERENADING** 14
6 **SERENE BEAUTY** (USA) C 179
231 **SERENITY** (IRE) 106
246 **SERGEANT** (FR) 40
61 **SERGEANT TIBBS** 7
505 **SERIFOS** 36
274 **SERIOUS CHARGES** (IRE) 49
445 **SERIOUS EGO** (GER) 45
375 **SERIOUS MOOD** (IRE) 42
420 **SERJEANT PAINTER** 72
409 **SERMANDO** (FR) 98
32 **SERPENTINE RIVER** (IRE) F 20
393 **SERVEONTIME** (IRE) 7
312 **SERVILIA** C 102
355 **SET IN STONE** (IRE) 57
455 **SET IN THE WEST** (IRE) 15
417 **SET POINT** (IRE) 12
SETME STRAIGHTMATE 79
61 **SETTLE PETAL** 44
483 **SEVEN ARCHES** 42
460 **SEVEN BROTHERS** (IRE) 17
143 **SEVEN EYE BRIDGE** (IRE) 31
87 **SEVEN FOR A POUND** (USA) 26
346 **SEVEN MAGICIANS** (USA) C 71
476 **SEVEN NO TRUMPS** (IRE) 133
530 **SEVEN O SEVEN** (IRE) 23
237 **SEVEN POCKETS** (IRE) 30
379 **SEVEN SPRINGS** 28
381 **SEVENOFUS** (IRE) 92
428 **SEVENTEEN O FOUR** (IRE) 80
402 **SEVENTH HEAVEN** (IRE) F 172

414 **SEVENTH KINGDOM** 29
420 **SEVERANCE** 73
240 **SEVERANS STOKE** 98
266 **SEVERUS ALEXANDER** (IRE) 13
127 **SEXTANT** 38
314 **SEXY BEAST** 64
428 **SEXY LOT** (GER) 81
145 **SEYCHELLOISE** C 68
517 **SEYMOUR PROMISE** (IRE) 66
145 **SEZAAM** (IRE) 50
170 **SEZINA** 38
520 **SHAADEN** (IRE) 33
217 **SHAARA** 119
457 **SHABADY** (FR) G 27
537 **SHABANO** (GER) 52
240 **SHABBAB** (FR) 99
480 **SHABS** 10
142 **SHACKABOOAH** 34
337 **SHADDEYA** (IRE) C 12
522 **SHADOW ANGEL** (IRE) 5
402 **SHADOW HUNTER** (IRE) C 173
427 **SHADOW MOUNTAIN** F 26
385 **SHADOW RIDER** (FR) 154
427 **SHADOW WALKER** (IRE) 23
217 **SHADOWFAX** 120
94 **SHADOWS OFTHENIGHT** (IRE) C 90
223 **SHADY CHARACTER** 75
75 **SHADY KATIE** (IRE) 6
482 **SHADY PINES** (IRE) G 28
333 **SHAH AN SHAH** 48
543 **SHAHAB** F 39
185 **SHAHBAZ** (IRE) 73
524 **SHAHNAZ** (IRE) 11
514 **SHAKA THE KING** (IRE) 47
280 **SHAKDARA** (USA) C 79
80 **SHAKE A LEG** (IRE) 27
51 **SHAKE HIM UP** (IRE) 35
346 **SHAKE THE MOON** (GER) C 72
420 **SHAKEM UP'ARRY** (IRE) 74
576 **SHAKENOTSTIRRED** 18
243 **SHAKY OPERATOR** 116
302 **SHALAA ASKER** 9
460 **SHALADAR** (IRE) 70
567 **SHALAKAR** (FR) 77
73 **SHALLOW HAL** 22
404 **SHALLOW RIVER** (IRE) 179
373 **SHALLWEHAVEONEMORE** (FR) 110
68 **SHALOTT** (IRE) 6
576 **SHAMA'S CROWN** (IRE) C 42
523 **SHAMADAAN** 13
325 **SHAMAN DU BERLAIS** (FR) 21
418 **SHAMANDAR** (FR) C 34
39 **SHAMEKH** 83
117 **SHAMILLA** 41
426 **SHAMLAAN** (IRE) 39
16 **SHAMLAHAR** F 237
528 **SHAMPION** (IRE) 124
524 **SHAMROCK SHEILA** (IRE) F 16
566 **SHAMSHON** (IRE) 30
476 **SHAN BLUE** (IRE) 114
13 **SHANACOOLE PRINCE** (IRE) 53
143 **SHANBALLY ROSE** (IRE) 32
323 **SHANG TANG** (IRE) 56
117 **SHANGHAI ROCK** 21
89 **SHANI** 81
155 **SHANJIA** (GER) C 85
566 **SHANKO** 50

476 **SHANNON BRIDGE** (IRE) 135
481 **SHANNON HILL** 7
577 **SHANNON LODGE** (IRE) 11
8 **SHANNON PEARL** G 4
577 **SHANNON ROCCO** (IRE) 12
403 **SHANNON SPREE** F 53
277 **SHANNOW** (IRE) F 25
192 **SHANROE SMOOCH** (IRE) 10
245 **SHANROE TIC TEC** (IRE) 16
515 **SHANTOLIE** (IRE) 5
110 **SHANTOU BOUDICCA** 16
51 **SHANTOU CHAMPAGNE** (IRE) 36
13 **SHANTOU EXPRESS** (IRE) 54
398 **SHANTOU FLYER** (IRE) 152
373 **SHANTOU MASTER** (IRE) 111
265 **SHANTOU SUNSET** 88
409 **SHANTOU'S MELODY** (IRE) 99
531 **SHANTUNG** (IRE) 30
92 **SHANTY ALLEY** 21
467 **SHANXI GIRL** G 26
109 **SHAPES** (IRE) C 26
101 **SHARAAKAH** (IRE) F 52
528 **SHARAC** 125
317 **SHARE THE PROFITS** (IRE) 34
101 **SHARED** 53
426 **SHAREDAH** (IRE) F 67
51 **SHAREEF STAR** 37
204 **SHARIB** 30
385 **SHARJAH** (FR) 155
402 **SHARK BAY** (IRE) 79
508 **SHARLA** 29
361 **SHARP APPLAUSE** C 107
300 **SHARP COMBO** (IRE) 95
287 **SHARP DISTINCTION** 25
16 **SHARP FRANK** 122
483 **SHARP RESPONSE** (IRE) 43
265 **SHARP SHADOW** (IRE) 89
340 **SHARPCLIFF** 18
20 **SHARRABANG** 20
334 **SHARRON MACREADY** (IRE) 52
240 **SHARVARA** 100
235 **SHAUGHNESSY** 7
447 **SHAUNA'S PRINCESS** (IRE) C 73
259 **SHAW'S CROSS** (IRE) 20
238 **SHAWS BRIDGE** (IRE) 70
315 **SHE BELIEVES** (IRE) F 31
528 **SHE DO** 31
300 **SHE GOT THE LOOK** (IRE) 21
304 **SHE HAS NOTIONS** (IRE) 36
380 **SHE IS WHAT SHE IS** 4
265 **SHE RANKS ME** (IRE) G 90
516 **SHE'S A DEVA** 14
390 **SHE'S A GEM** 11
15 **SHE'S A LADY** 45
404 **SHE'S A NOVELTY** (IRE) 180
174 **SHE'S A PISTOL** (IRE) C 47
445 **SHE'S A ROCCA** (IRE) 46
441 **SHE'S A STEAL** (IRE) 7
223 **SHE'S ALL IN GOLD** (IRE) 76
243 **SHE'S COMPLETE** (IRE) F 184
97 **SHE'S COSMIC** 63
540 **SHE'S GOT BOTTLE** 21
73 **SHE'S NO ANGEL** (IRE) 23
69 **SHE'S OUT OF REACH** 25
476 **SHE'S SO LOVELY** (IRE) 136
174 **SHE'S SOPHIE** 34
315 **SHE'S THE BOSS** 18

53 **SHE'S THE DANGER** (IRE) 12
292 **SHE'SASUPERMACK** (IRE) 36
398 **SHEARER** (IRE) 153
419 **SHEARWATER** 6
452 **SHEEPYSHEEPSHEEP** (FR) 8
299 **SHEER ROCKS** 39
409 **SHEES A DANTE** (IRE) G 100
557 **SHEILA NASH** (IRE) 21
65 **SHEILA'S LEGACY** 11
384 **SHELDON** (IRE) 24
517 **SHELIKESTHELIGHTS** (IRE) 67
406 **SHELIR** (IRE) 38
22 **SHEM** (IRE) 22
300 **SHEMIYLA** (FR) F 199
4 **SHEMRIYNA** (IRE) C 18
476 **SHENTRI** (FR) 137
414 **SHENZHEN SUBWAY** (IRE) 45
505 **SHEPHERDIA** (IRE) F 82
517 **SHERBORNE** (IRE) 68
73 **SHERDIL** (IRE) 72
296 **SHERELLA** 12
164 **SHERIFF GARRETT** (IRE) 83
530 **SHERIN** (GER) 24
146 **SHERPA TRAIL** (USA) 18
100 **SHES MY GIRL** 7
386 **SHES QUEEN** (IRE) F 43
508 **SHES RANGER** (IRE) C 41
383 **SHESADABBER** 16
184 **SHESASTAR** C 45
432 **SHESUPINCOURT** 23
223 **SHETLAND TONY** 96
385 **SHEWEARSITWELL** (IRE) 156
217 **SHIBORI** (IRE) 121
537 **SHIBUYA SONG** 9
252 **SHIELDED** (IRE) 32
566 **SHIFTER** 51
570 **SHIFTING GOLD** (IRE) 7
231 **SHIGAR** (IRE) 107
238 **SHIGHNESS** 71
528 **SHIKHOVA** 186
163 **SHIMMERING SANDS** 58
537 **SHIMMY SHOES** (IRE) C 81
544 **SHIN SAW GYI** 64
94 **SHINE HONEY SHINE** 111
94 **SHINE LIKEADIAMOND** F 91
16 **SHINE SO BRIGHT** 41
155 **SHINGWEDZI** (SAF) C 86
54 **SHINING** 17
217 **SHINING AL DANAH** (IRE) 122
39 **SHINING EXAMPLE** (IRE) 51
528 **SHINJI** (IRE) 126
212 **SHINJUKU** (FR) 80
13 **SHINOBI** (FR) 55
19 **SHINTORI** (FR) 17
561 **SHIP OF THE FEN** 73
93 **SHIP TO SHORE** 19
17 **SHIPTON MOYNE** 23
323 **SHIROCCAN ROLL** 57
396 **SHIROCCO'S DELIGHT** (IRE) 4
517 **SHIROCCO'S DREAM** (IRE) 69
323 **SHIROCCY ROAD** 58
258 **SHISHKIN** (IRE) 127
28 **SHIVRAJ** 40
388 **SHOAL BAY** (IRE) 121
262 **SHOBIZ** 17
378 **SHOCKWAVES** 50

554 **SHOESHINE BOY** (IRE) 19
262 **SHOGUN'S KATANA** 103
476 **SHOLOKJACK** (IRE) 138
243 **SHOMEN UCHI** (FR) 35
243 **SHONA MEA** (IRE) 60
61 **SHOOT TO KILL** (IRE) 45
557 **SHORE SHANTY** (IRE) 22
186 **SHORT AFFAIR** F 46
106 **SHORT CALL** (IRE) F 19
551 **SHORT HEAD** (GER) 16
243 **SHORT N SWEET** (IRE) 117
275 **SHORTCROSS STORM** (IRE) 8
240 **SHOT** 212
428 **SHOT BOII** (IRE) 82
18 **SHOT TO THE HEART** 26
87 **SHOTLEY ROYALE** 43
218 **SHOUGHALL'S BOY** (IRE) 9
185 **SHOULDERING** (IRE) 22
26 **SHOUTOUT** 70
6 **SHOW DAY** (IRE) F 180
371 **SHOW MAKER** (USA) 22
117 **SHOW ME A SUNSET** 22
229 **SHOW OF HANDS** 36
471 **SHOW ON THE ROAD** 8
314 **SHOW PROMISE** 67
371 **SHOW RAINBOW** C 43
346 **SHOW WILLING** (IRE) F 73
505 **SHOW YOURSELF** 5
164 **SHOWALONG** 84
229 **SHOWBIRD** F 37
77 **SHOWBIZZY** G 62
424 **SHOWGAL** (IRE) 26
15 **SHOWLAN SPIRIT** 46
378 **SHOWMAN** 51
292 **SHOWMEDEMONEY** (IRE) 67
118 **SHOWSTOPPA** F 117
521 **SHOWTIME MAHOMES** 50
278 **SHROPSHIRELASS** C 8
395 **SHUIL DONN** (IRE) 55
97 **SHUMI LA SHUMI LA** (FR) 64
262 **SHUMOOS** (USA) C 104
48 **SHURUT** 48
216 **SHUT THE BOX** (IRE) 51
414 **SHUT UP AND DANCE** (IRE) 46
16 **SHUTKA** (FR) C 238
487 **SHUTTHEGATE** (IRE) 9
536 **SHUTUPSHIRLEY** 20
379 **SHUV H'PENNY KING** 12
158 **SHYJACK** 11
91 **SHYRON** 14
240 **SIAM FOX** (IRE) 26
240 **SIAMSA** (IRE) 101
429 **SIANNES STAR** (IRE) 10
330 **SIBAYA** F 13
361 **SIBERIAN PRINCE** (IRE) 58
97 **SICILIA** 65
117 **SICILIAN BELLE** 23
459 **SICILIAN VITO** (IRE) 16
232 **SID HOODIE** (IRE) 43
409 **SID'S ANNIE** 30
527 **SIDESHIFT** (IRE) 101
209 **SIDEWAYSINMILAN** (IRE) 5
187 **SIDI ISMAEL** (FR) 83
516 **SIDNEY GIRL** C 66
7 **SIEGE OF ZARA** (IRE) 6
431 **SIENNA BONNIE** (IRE) 31
531 **SIENNA BREEZE** (IRE) 31

555 **SIENNA DREAM** 33
467 **SIENNA ROYALE** (IRE) 27
243 **SIERRA NEVADA** (USA) 118
240 **SIGHTSEEING** F 213
243 **SIGN FROM ABOVE** (IRE) 61
476 **SIGNAL POINT** (IRE) 139
157 **SIGNAL TWENTY NINE** 34
240 **SIGNCASTLE CITY** (IRE) 214
231 **SIGNEE** F 184
73 **SIGNIFICANTLY** 24
365 **SIGNORE PICCOLO** 58
94 **SIGNORINA MERISI** 48
194 **SIGURD** (GER) 9
360 **SIKORSKY** 20
373 **SILASTAR** 112
528 **SILENCE IS GOLDEN** 127
16 **SILENCE PLEASE** (IRE) 42
323 **SILENT ASSISTANT** (IRE) 59
6 **SILENT FILM** 23
367 **SILENT FLAME** 19
39 **SILENT HUNTER** 52
528 **SILENT MONARCH** (IRE) 128
135 **SILENT OCEAN** (IRE) 7
286 **SILENT PARTNER** 24
91 **SILENT QUEEN** (IRE) 15
398 **SILENT REVOLUTION** (IRE) 154
6 **SILENT SPEECH** 72
530 **SILIA** (GER) 40
330 **SILK HILL** 14
1 **SILK OR SCARLET** (IRE) 48
6 **SILK ROMANCE** (IRE) 73
6 **SILK WORDS** F 181
112 **SILKEN MOONLIGHT** 27
353 **SILKEN PETALS** 7
118 **SILKEN SKIES** (IRE) G 71
528 **SILKEN SKIES** (IRE) F 187
460 **SILKEN SOUL** C 108
271 **SILKS DREAM** (IRE) 8
271 **SILKS PASS** 9
63 **SILKSTONE** (IRE) 14
417 **SILKY** (IRE) F 82
73 **SILKY WILKIE** (IRE) 73
483 **SILLY GILLY** (IRE) G 44
483 **SILVA ECLIPSE** 45
326 **SILVEEANNA** 13
222 **SILVER AND GOLD** 52
420 **SILVER ATOM** (IRE) 75
307 **SILVER BUBBLE** 13
101 **SILVER BULLET LADY** (IRE) 55
147 **SILVER CHORD** 20
460 **SILVER CLOUDS** (IRE) F 109
205 **SILVER DIVA** 11
166 **SILVER DOLLAR** (IRE) 4
44 **SILVER DUST** (IRE) 19
354 **SILVER FLYER** 109
398 **SILVER FOREVER** (IRE) 155
516 **SILVER GREY** (IRE) G 67
47 **SILVER GUNN** (IRE) 20
404 **SILVER HALLMARK** 181
484 **SILVER HILL FLYER** (IRE) 18
529 **SILVER IN DISGUISE** 31
300 **SILVER KITTEN** 96
281 **SILVER LILY** (IRE) F 15
466 **SILVER MOON** C 37
305 **SILVER NEMO** (IRE) 6
384 **SILVER NICKEL** (IRE) 25
307 **SILVER NIGHTFALL** 26

28 **SILVER PAGEANT** 61
47 **SILVER SAMURAI** 21
118 **SILVER SCREEN** 72
246 **SILVER SHADE** (FR) 41
243 **SILVER SHEEN** (IRE) 62
461 **SILVER STAR** (FR) 3
514 **SILVER STAR MIX** 48
560 **SILVER STREAK** (IRE) 66
528 **SILVER VISION** 129
249 **SILVERBOOK** 8
431 **SILVERDALE** 32
77 **SILVERHILL STAMP** (IRE) 38
170 **SILVERLODE** (IRE) 74
508 **SILVERSCAPE** 42
580 **SILVRETTA SCHWARZ** (IRE) 15
263 **SIMBALLINA** (IRE) C 32
277 **SIMMIE** (IRE) C 26
47 **SIMMY'S TEMPLE** C 77
561 **SIMPLE ELEGANCE** (USA) F 104
292 **SIMPLE STAR** (IRE) 37
26 **SIMPLE VERSE** (IRE) F 139
403 **SIMPLY GLORIOUS** (USA) 18
481 **SIMPLY LOVELEH** 8
486 **SIMPLY LUCKY** (IRE) 10
400 **SIMPLY MANI** 11
537 **SIMPLY ME** C 82
403 **SIMPLY PERFECT** C 54
223 **SIMPLY RED** 77
381 **SIMPLY SIN** (IRE) 93
48 **SIMPLY SONDHEIM** (IRE) 49
213 **SIMPLY SUPREME** (IRE) 25
398 **SIMPLY THE BETTS** (IRE) 156
295 **SIMPLY TRUE** (IRE) 22
466 **SIMULATION THEORY** (IRE) 5
145 **SIN E SHEKELLS** 30
354 **SINCE DAY ONE** (IRE) 110
238 **SINCERELY RESDEV** 72
252 **SINDABELLA** (FR) 33
277 **SINDJARA** (USA) F 27
28 **SINDRI** 62
392 **SINE NOMINE** 2
566 **SINGAPORE FLYER** 52
240 **SINGAPORE LILLY** (IRE) F 215
395 **SINGASONGSAM** 56
516 **SINGE ANGLAIS** (IRE) 15
367 **SINGING THE BLUES** (IRE) 20
94 **SINGLE** (IRE) 17
431 **SINGUITA** (GER) C 51
475 **SINGYOURSONG** (IRE) F 83
329 **SINISTER MINISTER** 10
101 **SINJAARI** (IRE) 7
4 **SINNDARELLA** (IRE) 19
272 **SINNDARELLA** (IRE) 17
45 **SINNDARILLO** (IRE) 10
469 **SINURITA** (IRE) 37
48 **SIP AND SMILE** (IRE) 50
424 **SIR ALFRED** M 20
172 **SIR APOLLO** (IRE) 22
385 **SIR ARGUS** 157
20 **SIR BENEDICT** (IRE) 21
364 **SIR BOB PARKER** (FR) 40
317 **SIR BUSKER** (IRE) 11
395 **SIR CANFORD** (IRE) 57
215 **SIR CHAUVELIN** 32
292 **SIR CHESTER** (IRE) 38
151 **SIR DUKE** 24
435 **SIR EGBERT** 11

385 **SIR GERHARD** (IRE) 158
7 **SIR GREGORY** (FR) 68
540 **SIR HECTOR** (IRE) 14
16 **SIR HENRY COTTON** (IRE) 123
201 **SIR IVAN** 54
108 **SIR JACK WEST** (IRE) 7
488 **SIR JACK YEATS** (IRE) 22
294 **SIR JIM** (IRE) 15
314 **SIR JIMMY ALLEN** (FR) 68
300 **SIR JOCK BENNETT** (IRE) 200
424 **SIR JOSEPH SWAN** 10
185 **SIR MIN** (IRE) 48
160 **SIR OLIVER** (IRE) 46
83 **SIR PHILIP** 34
367 **SIR PLATO** (IRE) 21
398 **SIR PSYCHO** (IRE) 157
346 **SIR RAJ** (IRE) 74
342 **SIR RANDOLPH** 31
296 **SIR RODNEYREDBLOOD** 13
240 **SIR RUMI** (IRE) 27
88 **SIR SEDRIC** (IRE) 17
547 **SIR TAAJ** 19
313 **SIR TAWEEL** (IRE) 29
89 **SIR TITAN** 82
145 **SIR TITUS** (IRE) 31
239 **SIR TIVO** (FR) 24
528 **SIR WINSTON** (IRE) 130
87 **SIRAJU** 39
346 **SIREN SONG** C 75
94 **SIRI** C 92
104 **SIRIUS** (FR) 42
490 **SIRIUS WHITE** (IRE) 25
60 **SIROBBIE** (IRE) 25
398 **SIROCO JO** (FR) 158
300 **SIRON** (GER) 201
208 **SIROP DE MENTHE** (FR) 15
428 **SIRUH DU LAC** (FR) 84
514 **SIRWILLIAMWALLACE** (IRE) 49
432 **SISSINGHURST** (IRE) 24
404 **SISTER MICHAEL** (IRE) 182
431 **SISTER OF THOR** 52
189 **SISTER RAPHAEL** (IRE) 17
398 **SISTER SAINT** (IRE) 159
337 **SISTER SLEW** (IRE) F 13
352 **SISTER SOPHIE** 2
508 **SISTERS IN THE SKY** 43
113 **SISU** 18
374 **SITTING PRITTY** (IRE) F 26
233 **SIWANI** (IRE) 24
552 **SIX AND OUT** 3
414 **SIX CENTS** (IRE) F 61
61 **SIX DIAMONDS** (IRE) F 67
523 **SIX FIVE SPECIAL** 14
142 **SIX O' HEARTS** 46
219 **SIX ONE NINE** (IRE) 17
470 **SIX STRINGS** 18
61 **SIX TIL TWELVE** (IRE) 46
423 **SIXCOR** 13
164 **SIXSTAR** 151
240 **SIXTH STREET** (FR) 102
550 **SIXTIES SECRET** 19
517 **SIXTY DOLLARS MORE** (FR) 70
487 **SIXTY WEST** 10
467 **SIZABLE SAM** 28
517 **SIZING AT MIDNIGHT** (IRE) 71
517 **SIZING CUSIMANO** 72
243 **SIZING MAURITIUS** (IRE) 63

243 **SIZING POTTSIE** (FR) 64
517 **SIZING TARA** 73
203 **SKANDIBURG** (FR) 2
398 **SKATMAN** (IRE) 160
24 **SKEDADDLED** (IRE) 7
240 **SKETCHING** F 216
39 **SKI DUBAI** (IRE) 84
527 **SKIBBEREEN** 17
22 **SKIDDAW TARA** 21
521 **SKILLED WARRIOR** (IRE) 30
413 **SKINFLINT** (IRE) 13
371 **SKINNY LOVE** F 44
200 **SKINWALKER** 26
164 **SKIPNESS** 85
1 **SKIPTHESCALES** (IRE) 49
346 **SKITTLEBOMBZ** 38
361 **SKOL** 59
26 **SKY BLUE PINK** 71
156 **SKY BLUE THINKING** 10
300 **SKY DEFENDER** 23
546 **SKY IS THE LINNET** 11
417 **SKY LEGEND** 42
409 **SKY PIRATE** 102
26 **SKY POWER** (IRE) 17
240 **SKY SILK** (IRE) 103
385 **SKY SPRINTER** (IRE) 159
501 **SKY STORM** 14
330 **SKY'S THE LIMIT** 15
314 **SKYCUTTER** (FR) 69
34 **SKYE BREEZE** (IRE) 30
412 **SKYEFALL** 8
235 **SKYHILL** (IRE) 8
409 **SKYHILLS BREEZE** (IRE) 103
402 **SKYLARK** 80
163 **SKYLINE DANCER** G 59
231 **SKYRUNNER** (IRE) 34
520 **SKYSAIL** 34
509 **SKYTASTIC** (FR) 36
454 **SKYWARDS MILES** (IRE) G 15
468 **SLAINTE MHATH** 11
458 **SLAINTE MHOR** (IRE) 65
143 **SLANELOUGH** (IRE) 33
219 **SLANEMORE HILL** (IRE) 18
88 **SLATE CRACKER** 25
517 **SLATE HOUSE** (IRE) 74
528 **SLEEK** C 188
101 **SLEEPING LION** (USA) 8
246 **SLEEPYSAURUS** (GER) 42
292 **SLEIGHT** 39
408 **SLEPTWITHMEBOOTSON** 3
328 **SLEVE DONARD** (IRE) 6
475 **SLIABH LUACHRA** (IRE) C 84
233 **SLIEVE BEARNAGH** (IRE) 5
233 **SLIEVE BINNIAN** (IRE) 58
509 **SLIP ROAD** (IRE) 37
420 **SLIPWAY** (IRE) 76
97 **SLOANE RANGER** (FR) 66
334 **SLONACH** (IRE) C 68
550 **SLY MADAM** 20
388 **SMACKWATER JACK** (IRE) 122
259 **SMALL BAD BOB** (IRE) 21
483 **SMALL PRESENT** (IRE) 46
101 **SMALL PRINT** 55
32 **SMARDEN FLYER** (IRE) 31
314 **SMART BOYO** 70
314 **SMART BUCKS** 103
475 **SMART CHAMPION** 26

426 **SUPREME QUEST** F 70
486 **SUPREME STEEL** (IRE) 13
222 **SUPREME SUNSET** 54
375 **SUPREME YEATS** (IRE) 45
118 **SURAC** (IRE) 75
577 **SURDOUE DE BALLON** (FR) 14
471 **SURE LISTEN** (FR) 9
388 **SURE TOUCH** 126
272 **SUREWECAN** 18
258 **SURFMAN** 133
364 **SURGE** (FR) 62
31 **SUROOJ** 12
544 **SURPRISE EXHIBIT** 31
406 **SURPRISE PICTURE** (IRE) 46
528 **SURREALISM** F 192
378 **SURREY BELLE** 77
15 **SURREY CHARM** 56
378 **SURREY GOLD** (IRE) 25
185 **SURREY KNIGHT** (FR) 51
15 **SURREY MIST** (FR) 47
185 **SURREY NOIR** (FR) 76
15 **SURREY PRINCESS** 27
258 **SURREY QUEST** (IRE) 134
297 **SURREY TERRITORIES** (IRE) 16
233 **SURROUNDING** (IRE) 18
404 **SURTITLE** (IRE) 189
118 **SUSAN B ANTHONY** (IRE) F 119
277 **SUSAN STROMAN** F 28
544 **SUSANBEQUICK** (IRE) 66
422 **SUSIE JAVEA** 6
26 **SUSPICIOUS** 75
402 **SUSSEX** (IRE) 86
373 **SUSSEX RANGER** (USA) 115
458 **SUTTON MANOR** (IRE) 73
292 **SUTUE ALSHAMS** (IRE) 73
98 **SUZI'S CONNOISSEUR** 20
299 **SUZY'S SHOES** 40
167 **SWAFFHAM BULBECK** (IRE) 34
431 **SWALLOWDALE** 13
34 **SWANLAND** (IRE) 52
258 **SWAPPED** (FR) 135
98 **SWASHBUCKLER** 39
61 **SWATCH** (IRE) 68
379 **SWAYZE** 31
240 **SWEAR** 224
515 **SWEARER** (IRE) 6
402 **SWEDEN** (IRE) 87
509 **SWEDISHHORSEMAFIA** (IRE) 41
556 **SWEENTNESSANDLIGHT** G 19
544 **SWEEPING** 67
378 **SWEEPING UP** C 78
300 **SWEET ALABAMA** F 103
403 **SWEET AND LOVELY** (IRE) 19
339 **SWEET ANGEL** 9
143 **SWEET AS CANDY** (IRE) 37
354 **SWEET AUBURN** (IRE) 118
231 **SWEET BELIEVER** (IRE) 36
77 **SWEET BERTIE** (IRE) 43
517 **SWEET CARYLINE** 79
319 **SWEET CECILY** (IRE) F 29
402 **SWEET CHARITY** (FR) C 174
31 **SWEET CHILD O'MINE** G 13
475 **SWEET CONNIE** (USA) C 87
191 **SWEET DIME** 3
426 **SWEET DREAM** F 71
26 **SWEET FANTASY** 76
298 **SWEET FLORA** (IRE) 8

101 **SWEET GENTLE KISS** (IRE) C 90
460 **SWEET GLANCE** 75
543 **SWEET IDEA** 40
513 **SWEET JUSTICE** (IRE) 9
524 **SWEET MADNESS** (IRE) 12
16 **SWEET MANDOLIN** F 128
68 **SWEET MARTONI** G 8
478 **SWEET MIST** (USA) 29
230 **SWEET NIGHTINGALE** 10
367 **SWEET PURSUIT** 22
431 **SWEET REWARD** (IRE) 14
379 **SWEET SECRET** C 44
320 **SWEET SPIRIT** (FR) 43
101 **SWEET SUMMER** 57
25 **SWEET SURPRISE** (IRE) C 49
251 **SWEETEST COMPANY** (IRE) F 42
486 **SWEETEST SMILE** (IRE) 14
97 **SWEETHEART** (FR) 70
117 **SWELL SONG** 24
217 **SWIFT ADVANCE** 130
313 **SWIFT CRUSADOR** 31
1 **SWIFT GETAWAY** (IRE) F 51
200 **SWIFT REMARK** 24
16 **SWILCAN BRIDGE** 129
274 **SWINCOMBE FLEAT** 52
118 **SWING OUT SISTER** (IRE) C 120
521 **SWINGING EDDIE** 33
388 **SWINGING LONDON** (IRE) 127
34 **SWINTON** 31
7 **SWINTON NOON** 72
402 **SWIRL** (IRE) 88
87 **SWISS ACE** 29
478 **SWISS CONNECTION** 11
99 **SWISS MISTRESS** (IRE) 12
508 **SWISS PRIDE** (IRE) 30
77 **SWISS ROWE** (IRE) 44
383 **SWISS SANCERRE** 18
39 **SWISS VALLEY** 86
398 **SWITCH HITTER** (IRE) 170
294 **SWITCH PARTNER** (IRE) 17
6 **SWITCHING** (USA) F 187
500 **SWOON** (FR) 20
158 **SWOOPER** 12
312 **SWORD BEACH** (IRE) 107
61 **SWORD EXCEED** (GER) 49
311 **SWORD OF FATE** (IRE) 4
404 **SWORDSMAN** (IRE) 190
300 **SYANN** (IRE) F 208
142 **SYCAMORE** (IRE) 36
151 **SYDNEY BAY** 25
16 **SYDNEY MEWS** (IRE) 243
417 **SYDNEY STREET** 45
349 **SYKES** (IRE) 20
217 **SYLVIA BEACH** 131
31 **SYLVIA PLATH** (IRE) 14
245 **SYMBOL OF HOPE** 18
6 **SYMBOL OF LIGHT** 77
386 **SYMBOLIC SPIRIT** (FR) 25
16 **SYMBOLIZE** (IRE) 48
211 **SYMPATHISE** (IRE) 4
371 **SYMPHONIC DANCER** (USA) F 46
240 **SYMPHONY PERFECT** (IRE) 106
373 **SYMPHORINE** (FR) 116
406 **SYMPOSIUM** C 127
240 **SYSTEM** (IRE) 107
373 **SYSTEMIC** 117
466 **T MAXIE** (IRE) 19

409 **T'ARAISON** (FR) 108
528 **TA AMMOL** C 137
507 **TAAMER** 5
505 **TAAQAT** (FR) 39
155 **TAARKOD** (IRE) F 89
544 **TABDEED** 32
540 **TABEEB** 22
182 **TABERNACLE** 66
504 **TABLE MOUNTAIN** 28
323 **TABLE THIRTY FOUR** 61
500 **TABLES TURNED** 72
365 **TABOU BEACH BOY** 64
416 **TABSHEER** 11
240 **TACARIB BAY** 108
16 **TACK** (FR) 130
61 **TACKLESLIKEAFERRET** (IRE) 50
16 **TACTICAL** 49
208 **TACTICAL MANOEUVRE** (IRE) 17
155 **TADITA TWITCH** 47
10 **TADREEB** (IRE) 28
215 **TAFSIR** (USA) 43
367 **TAGLINE** 46
468 **TAGTALE** (IRE) G 13
544 **TAHANI** (IRE) 68
490 **TAHASUN** (IRE) 26
364 **TAHILLA** F 63
483 **TAHIRA** (GER) G 47
346 **TAHITI** C 79
240 **TAHITIAN PRINCE** (FR) 29
398 **TAHMURAS** (FR) 171
522 **TAHONTA** (IRE) 6
243 **TAIPAN** (FR) 67
73 **TAJ ALOLA** (IRE) 76
73 **TAJ ALRIYADH** (IRE) 77
300 **TAKE A DEEP BREATH** F 209
384 **TAKE A DROP** (IRE) C 41
505 **TAKE A STAND** (IRE) 40
365 **TAKE CENTRE STAGE** (IRE) 65
354 **TAKE ME TO THE SKY** 109
26 **TAKE MY CHANCES** (FR) 20
385 **TAKE TEA** (IRE) 166
398 **TAKE YOUR TIME** (IRE) 172
477 **TAKEIT EASY** 17
335 **TAKEONEFORTHETEAM** 38
7 **TAKEUSTOTHEMOON** 96
69 **TAKODA** (IRE) 26
544 **TALABAAT** 33
516 **TALENT SPOTTER** F 69
13 **TALK OF THE MOON** 58
124 **TALKING ABOUT YOU** 15
485 **TALLOW FOR COAL** (IRE) 49
245 **TALLY'S SON** 19
101 **TALQAA** F 91
240 **TAMAANEE** (AUS) C 225
466 **TAMAARA** (IRE) C 39
243 **TAMADHOR** (IRE) C 188
240 **TAMANGO SANDS** (IRE) 226
388 **TAMAR BRIDGE** (IRE) 128
262 **TAMARAMA** 53
327 **TAMARILLO GROVE** (IRE) 27
373 **TAMARIS** (IRE) 19
398 **TAMAROC DU MATHAN** (FR) 173
406 **TAMASKA** 47
559 **TAMGHO BORGET** (FR) 30
231 **TAMILLA** 112
406 **TAMMANI** 48
155 **TAMMY WYNETTE** (IRE) C 90

266 **THE TURFACCOUNTANT** (IRE) 15
543 **THE TURPINATOR** (IRE) 16
381 **THE TURTLE SAID** 98
381 **THE TWISLER** 99
349 **THE TWO AMIGOS** 21
312 **THE UNIT** 115
243 **THE VERY MAN** (IRE) 71
238 **THE VERY THING** (IRE) 81
375 **THE VOLLAN** (IRE) 49
517 **THE WHERRYMAN** 82
373 **THE WHIPMASTER** (IRE) 124
517 **THE WIDDOW MAKER** 83
375 **THE WILD WESTERNER** (IRE) 50
223 **THE WILD WILD SEA** 84
189 **THE WIRE FLYER** 18
333 **THE WISE TRAVELLER** (IRE) 54
374 **THE WIZARD OF EYE** (IRE) 20
388 **THE WOLF** (FR) 130
89 **THE WORTHY BRAT** (IRE) 85
186 **THE WRITER** 22
558 **THE YELLOW MINI** 13
482 **THEATRE FOOL** (IRE) G 32
258 **THEATRE GLORY** (IRE) 140
219 **THEATRE LEGEND** 20
150 **THEATRE MIX** 10
105 **THEBEAUTIFULGAME** 34
259 **THEBELLSOFSHANDON** (IRE) 23
512 **THECHILDREN'STRUST** (IRE) 3
480 **THECOLOUROFMAGIC** 11
579 **THEDANCINGMAN** 7
361 **THEDEVILSCOACHMAN** (IRE) 6
564 **THEDEVILYOUKNOW** (IRE) 17
488 **THEFASTNTHECURIOUS** 25
404 **THEGALLANTWAY** (IRE) 201
386 **THEGREATESTSHOWMAN** 26
247 **THEGREYVTRAIN** 17
301 **THEHARDERYOUWORK** (IRE) 14
48 **THELADYINQUESTION** F 100
315 **THELADYMISSMAISIE** (IRE) 19
525 **THELASTHIGHKING** (IRE) 62
483 **THELONGWAYAROUND** (IRE) 49
300 **THEMAXWECAN** (IRE) 28
409 **THEME TUNE** (IRE) 111
252 **THEOCRAT** (IRE) 29
312 **THEONLYWAYISWESSEX** (FR) 116
104 **THEORETICAL** (FR) 45
170 **THEORETICAL** (FR) 60
104 **THEORICIENNE** F 70
142 **THEOTHERSIDE** (IRE) 37
40 **THEOULE** (FR) 10
133 **THEQUEENBEE** (IRE) 24
16 **THERAPIST** 246
61 **THEREHEGOES** 69
458 **THEREISNODOUBT** (IRE) 75
142 **THERMOMETER** (IRE) 47
327 **THESE HAPPY DAZE** 29
404 **THESETHINGSHAPPEN** 202
101 **THESIS** 91
549 **THESPINNINGWHEEL** (IRE) 27
104 **THETYS** (FR) 45
34 **THEWAYTOTHESTARS** 32
195 **THEY CALL ME PETE** 8
271 **THEY DON'T KNOW** (IRE) 11
307 **THEYAZIN** (FR) 14
100 **THEYDON GIRLS** F 10
222 **THEYSEEKHIMTHERE** (IRE) 55
549 **THIBAULT** 28

145 **THIN LIZZY** 51
384 **THINK FOR A MINIT** 30
373 **THINK TRIGGER** (IRE) 125
428 **THINKING** (IRE) 87
528 **THIRD REALM** 34
525 **THIRD STREET** (IRE) 63
476 **THIRD TIME LUCKI** (IRE) 148
378 **THIRD WIND** 26
254 **THIRSTY FARMER** 11
395 **THIRTYFOURSTITCHES** (IRE) 64
89 **THIS IS MY HALF** (IRE) 109
426 **THIS IS OUR TIME** 73
312 **THIS ONES FOR FRED** (IRE) 117
546 **THISTIMENEXTYEAR** 12
242 **THOMAS BLOSSOM** (IRE) 2
288 **THOMAS CRANMER** (USA) 15
388 **THOMAS DARBY** (IRE) 131
287 **THOMAS EQUINAS** 27
307 **THOMAS KERSHAW** (IRE) 15
485 **THOMAS MACDONAGH** 51
320 **THOMAS PATRICK** (IRE) 46
375 **THOMAS TODD** 51
469 **THOR DE CERISY** (FR) 42
65 **THORDIAC** 13
205 **THORN** 12
365 **THORNABY EXCEED** 66
507 **THORNABY NASH** 6
397 **THORNABY PEARL** 7
454 **THORNTON MARY** C 19
131 **THORSDA** 16
13 **THOSE TIGER FEET** (IRE) 62
516 **THOUGHT IS FREE** C 70
326 **THOUGHTFUL GIFT** 19
402 **THOUGHTS OF JUNE** (IRE) 94
7 **THRAVE** 19
243 **THRAYA QUEEN** C 189
140 **THREE BULLET GATE** (IRE) 13
127 **THREE CASTLES** 44
560 **THREE CLIFFS BAY** (GER) 74
475 **THREE DIAMONDS** 56
89 **THREE DONS** (IRE) 110
243 **THREE LAWS** (IRE) 121
365 **THREE PLATOON** 67
528 **THREE PRIESTS** (JPN) 138
14 **THREE SAINTS BAY** (IRE) 15
231 **THREE START** (IRE) 115
240 **THREEBARS** (IRE) 230
398 **THREEUNDERTHRUFIVE** (IRE) 177
366 **THRILLA IN MANILA** 31
544 **THRONE HALL** 36
13 **THRUTHELOOKINGLASS** 63
223 **THUMUR** (USA) 85
312 **THUNDER AHEAD** 118
109 **THUNDER BALL** 28
406 **THUNDER BEAUTY** (IRE) 50
25 **THUNDER CHAP** 37
491 **THUNDER ECLIPSE** 28
561 **THUNDER FLASH** 79
506 **THUNDER GAP** 8
458 **THUNDER IN MILAN** (IRE) 76
417 **THUNDER LEGEND** (IRE) 46
159 **THUNDER LILY** (IRE) 8
240 **THUNDER MAX** 110
240 **THUNDER QUEEN** 111
460 **THUNDER ROAR** 77
388 **THUNDER ROCK** (IRE) 132
200 **THUNDER SUN** (FR) 18

323 **THUNDER SURF** 67
318 **THUNDER VALLEY** 1
378 **THUNDERCLAP** (IRE) 27
344 **THUNDERHILL** (IRE) 15
460 **THUNDERING** 78
89 **THUNDEROAD** 86
300 **THUNDEROUS** (IRE) 29
217 **THUNDERSHOWER** (IRE) 134
404 **THUNDERSOCKSSUNDAE** (IRE) 203
323 **THUNDERSTRUCK** (IRE) 68
469 **THYME 'N' TIDE** (IRE) 43
265 **THYME HILL** 98
398 **THYME WHITE** (IRE) 178
426 **TIARE** (FR) 41
316 **TIBBIE DUNBAR** 10
231 **TIBER FLOW** (IRE) 116
516 **TIBERIO SMILE** 37
212 **TIBIA** (FR) 75
48 **TIBURTINA** (IRE) F 101
210 **TICKENWOLF** (IRE) 3
118 **TICKET TO ALASKA** (IRE) 122
232 **TICKET TO L A** (IRE) 48
204 **TICKETS** 54
404 **TICKITY BLEUE** F 204
402 **TICKLED PINK** (IRE) C 176
463 **TICO TIMES** (IRE) 19
537 **TIDAL STORM** 56
561 **TIDE TIMES** (IRE) 80
73 **TIDES** F 17
25 **TIDEWELL** 38
26 **TIEMPO STAR** 79
478 **TIERS OF JOY** (FR) 30
524 **TIFAWT** F 17
434 **TIFFANY** (IRE) 60
496 **TIFFANY ROSE** 19
522 **TIGA TUAN** (FR) 7
500 **TIGER BEETLE** 21
475 **TIGER CRUSADE** (FR) 28
231 **TIGER EYE** C 189
170 **TIGER JET** (IRE) 45
395 **TIGER ORCHID** (IRE) 65
137 **TIGER PRINT** 4
260 **TIGER SPIRIT** (IRE) 20
327 **TIGER TAP TAP** (GER) 30
406 **TIGER TOUCH** (USA) 51
388 **TIGERBYTHETAIL** (IRE) 133
359 **TIGERPOMP** 2
525 **TIGERS ROAR** (IRE) 64
60 **TIGERTEN** 28
402 **TIGGY WIGGY** (IRE) F 177
529 **TIGHT CALL** (IRE) 32
28 **TIGHT LINES** C 63
367 **TIGHTEN UP** 23
243 **TIGRILLA** (IRE) C 190
559 **TIK TOK** (FR) 31
548 **TIKA MOON** (IRE) 24
458 **TIKA TOO** 77
313 **TIKI FIRE** (IRE) 34
457 **TIKITOV** (IRE) 29
561 **TIKK TOCK BOOM** (IRE) 81
467 **TIKKINTHEBOX** (IRE) 36
275 **TILE TAPPER** 9
340 **TILIA CORDATA** (IRE) 20
437 **TILINISI** (IRE) F 6
437 **TILINISI** (IRE) C 9
478 **TILLY THE FILLY** (IRE) 31
567 **TILLY TOUGHNUT** 87

292 **TOSHACK** (IRE) 45
533 **TOSSAPENNY** (IRE) 12
16 **TOSTADO** (IRE) 248
268 **TOTAL COMMITMENT** (IRE) 10
538 **TOTAL JOY** (IRE) 26
77 **TOTAL LOCKDOWN** 68
371 **TOTAL MASTER** 24
48 **TOTALLY CHARMING** 15
83 **TOTALLY LOST** (IRE) F 45
73 **TOTHENINES** (IRE) 79
16 **TOTNES** (IRE) 249
427 **TOTTERDOWN** 24
320 **TOUCAN SAM** 48
551 **TOUCH KICK** (IRE) 19
433 **TOUCH OF THUNDER** (IRE) 11
578 **TOUCH TIGHT** (IRE) 11
134 **TOUCHTHESOUL** (ITY) 12
262 **TOUCHWOOD** (IRE) 21
258 **TOUCHY FEELY** 142
494 **TOUGH OUT** (IRE) 12
212 **TOUNGARA** (FR) C 67
243 **TOURING PRODUCTION** 122
424 **TOUS LES GRIS** 27
300 **TOUSSAROK** 31
361 **TOUT EST PERMIS** (FR) 64
579 **TOUT PARIS** (FR) 8
555 **TOUTATIS** (USA) 38
487 **TOWER PRINCESS** (IRE) 11
235 **TOWERBURN** (IRE) 10
325 **TOWN PARKS** (IRE) 24
69 **TOWTHELINE** 27
480 **TOXICOLOGIST** 12
402 **TOY** (IRE) 95
431 **TOYBOX** 16
238 **TRAC** (FR) 82
246 **TRACEYS JOINT** (IRE) 53
409 **TRACK AND TRACE** (IRE) 113
500 **TRAILA** 22
333 **TRAIN HILL** (IRE) 55
184 **TRAINNAH** F 46
94 **TRAIS FLUORS** 21
268 **TRALEE HILLS** 11
15 **TRAMONTANE** 48
378 **TRANQUIL FLIGHT** C 79
6 **TRANQUIL NIGHT** 79
528 **TRANQUIL STAR** (IRE) C 194
208 **TRANS EXPRESS** (IRE) 20
118 **TRANS MONTANA** 76
373 **TRANSATLANTIC** (FR) 128
557 **TRANSFER FRIENDLY** (IRE) 24
381 **TRANSLINK** 100
406 **TRAPEZE** F 129
1 **TRAVAIL D'ORFEVRE** (FR) 54
528 **TRAVEL** (USA) F 195
365 **TRAVEL LIGHTLY** 69
185 **TRAVESURAS** (USA) 53
217 **TRAWLERMAN** (IRE) 31
223 **TRE A PENI** 87
138 **TREACHEROUS** 9
199 **TREACYS JIM** (IRE) 17
560 **TREASURE DILLON** (IRE) 76
524 **TREASURE TROUBE** (IRE) 13
483 **TREASURED COMPANY** (IRE) 50
91 **TREBLE CLEF** 16
167 **TREEFINCH** 35
13 **TREGELE** (IRE) 65
118 **TREGONY** 25

32 **TREGURRIAN** 22
13 **TRELAWNE** 66
520 **TRELINNEY** (IRE) 14
528 **TREMELO POINTE** (IRE) C 141
312 **TREMWEDGE** 120
297 **TREPIDATION** 10
483 **TRESHNISH** (IRE) 51
243 **TREVAUNANCE** (IRE) 123
238 **TREVELYN'S CORN** (IRE) 83
87 **TREVIE FOUNTAIN** 30
204 **TREVOLLI** 36
473 **TREVOR'S LAD** (IRE) 44
300 **TRIBAL ART** (IRE) 32
561 **TRIBAL COMMANDER** 82
16 **TRIBAL CRAFT** 50
286 **TRIBESMANS GLORY** (IRE) 26
466 **TRIBUNA UFFIZI** (IRE) 7
122 **TRIBUTE** (IRE) 110
566 **TRIBUTO** (IRE) 33
354 **TRICK OF THE TAIL** (IRE) 127
108 **TRICKALIGHT** (IRE) 9
47 **TRICOLORE** (ITY) 24
72 **TRICOMI** 9
292 **TRICORN** (IRE) 46
195 **TRIDEVI** 9
11 **TRIGGER HAPPY** (IRE) 3
335 **TRIGGERED** (IRE) 39
537 **TRIGGERS BROOM** (IRE) F 85
238 **TRIMMERS LANE** (IRE) 84
531 **TRINCOMALEE** 36
183 **TRINIDAD CALYPSO** 23
339 **TRINITY GIRL** 10
88 **TRINITY LAKE** 18
511 **TRINITY STAR** (IRE) 22
404 **TRIOPAS** 208
331 **TRIPLE NICKLE** (IRE) 14
490 **TRIPLE PEEL** (FR) 15
460 **TRIPLE TIME** (IRE) 80
517 **TRIPLE TRADE** 84
312 **TRITONIC** 121
34 **TRIUMPHAL ARCH** (IRE) 53
346 **TRIXIE MALONE** F 81
529 **TRIXSTER** (IRE) 34
275 **TROED Y MELIN** (IRE) 10
81 **TROIS BON AMIS** (IRE) 12
505 **TROIS VALLEES** 42
300 **TROJAN HORSE** (IRE) 108
300 **TROJAN LEGEND** 212
138 **TROJAN TRUTH** 16
34 **TROLLEY BOY** 11
535 **TROMPETTE** (USA) M 37
97 **TROMSO** (IRE) 31
530 **TROOPER** (GER) 48
61 **TROOPER COOPER** (IRE) 52
457 **TROOPER JONES** 30
143 **TROOPER TURNBULL** (IRE) 39
104 **TROPEIRA** (FR) 71
240 **TROPEZ POWER** (IRE) 112
243 **TROPICANA BAY** C 191
287 **TROPICS** (USA) 22
238 **TROUBLE SHOOTER** (IRE) 85
92 **TROUVILLE LADY** 24
398 **TRUCKERS LODGE** (IRE) 183
455 **TRUCKSTERS TIME** (IRE) 19
265 **TRUCKIN AWAY** (IRE) 99
389 **TRUCKIN WITH PADDY** (IRE) 7
297 **TRUE BELIEF** (IRE) 11

164 **TRUE BLUE MOON** (IRE) 93
28 **TRUE COURAGE** 10
508 **TRUE FORCE** 44
67 **TRUE HERO** 7
231 **TRUE ICON** (IRE) 117
73 **TRUE JEM** (FR) 80
434 **TRUE LEGEND** (IRE) 61
344 **TRUE MASON** 10
381 **TRUE ROMANCE** (IRE) 101
579 **TRUE THOUGHTS** (IRE) 9
300 **TRUE VERDICT** (IRE) C 213
460 **TRUE WARFARE** 81
61 **TRUE WARRIOR** 53
231 **TRUEMAN** 118
312 **TRUESHAN** (FR) 122
166 **TRUGANINI** (IRE) 13
53 **TRULIE GOOD** 1
446 **TRULOVE** 6
334 **TRUMBLE** (IRE) 28
69 **TRUMP LADY** (IRE) 28
31 **TRUMPER** 20
432 **TRUMPS BENEFIT** (IRE) 25
516 **TRUST BERTIE** (IRE) 38
403 **TRUSTWORTHY** (IRE) 21
89 **TRUSTY RUSTY** 89
428 **TRUSTY SCOUT** (IRE) 89
516 **TRUTH IN JEST** 17
231 **TRUTHFUL** (IRE) 191
44 **TRY TEESCOMPONENTS** 24
528 **TSUBAKI** 142
122 **TUBEREUSE** (IRE) C 111
500 **TUCSON CLOUD** (IRE) 23
312 **TUDDENHAM GREEN** 154
460 **TUDOR QUEEN** (IRE) 82
496 **TUDORS TREASURE** 20
402 **TUESDAY** (IRE) 96
27 **TUFF MCCOOL** (IRE) 9
427 **TULANE** (IRE) 25
398 **TULIN** 184
528 **TULIPA ROSA** (IRE) F 196
483 **TUMBLING DICE** 52
371 **TUNKWA** (FR) C 8
317 **TUNKWA** (FR) F 37
170 **TUPELO MISSISSIPPI** (IRE) 47
235 **TURBO COMMAND** (IRE) 11
233 **TURBO TWO** (IRE) 36
454 **TURBULENT POWER** 8
382 **TURIN** (IRE) C 12
109 **TURKANA GIRL** C 30
300 **TURN BACK TIME** 109
31 **TURN OF PHRASE** 17
476 **TURNAWAY** (IRE) 151
155 **TURNER GIRL** (IRE) 49
37 **TURNING GOLD** 4
538 **TURNTABLE** 15
496 **TURPIN GOLD** 21
262 **TUSCAN** (IRE) 54
243 **TUT TUT** 124
426 **TUTTI FRUTTI** F 74
122 **TUTU NGURU** (USA) F 112
182 **TUXEDO JUNCTION** 39
258 **TWEED SKIRT** 143
88 **TWEET TWEET** 19
544 **TWELFTH KNIGHT** (IRE) 70
373 **TWENTY TWENTY** (IRE) 129
94 **TWENTYFIRST LANCER** 50
426 **TWENTYSHARESOFGREY** 14

97 **TWICE** (IRE) 72
397 **TWICE ADAAY** 8
189 **TWIGGYS PRIDE** 20
287 **TWILIGHT BAY** 28
41 **TWILIGHT BELLE** (IRE) C 11
83 **TWILIGHT CALLS** 15
529 **TWILIGHT GLORY** 35
159 **TWILIGHT HEIR** 9
268 **TWILIGHT MADNESS** 12
83 **TWILIGHT MISCHIEF** 35
360 **TWILIGHT MYSTERY** C 33
51 **TWILIGHT PRINCE** 39
527 **TWILIGHT REVENGE** 31
521 **TWILIGHT SECRET** 37
386 **TWILIGHT STEEL** 39
367 **TWILIGHT TONE** 32
406 **TWILIGHT TRYST** (IRE) 130
312 **TWILIGHT TWIST** 123
7 **TWILLEY** 74
524 **TWIN APPEAL** (IRE) 7
398 **TWIN POWER** (IRE) 185
564 **TWIN STAR** (IRE) 18
54 **TWINING** (IRE) 25
402 **TWINKLE** (IRE) 97
307 **TWINKLE TWILIGHT** 27
505 **TWINKLE TWINKLE** F 85
7 **TWISTALINE** 97
365 **TWISTED DREAMS** (USA) 70
364 **TWISTED REALITY** 12
488 **TWISTEDFIRESTARTER** (IRE) 26
537 **TWITCH** (IRE) C 86
83 **TWIZ** 46
488 **TWIZZELL** F 55
163 **TWO BROTHERS** 28
13 **TWO FOR GOLD** (IRE) 67
251 **TWO PASS** (IRE) C 47
138 **TWO PLUS TWO** (IRE) 19
302 **TWO SUMMERS** (IRE) 28
327 **TWO TAFFS** (IRE) 31
431 **TWO TEMPTING** (IRE) 34
323 **TWO TO TANGO** 70
561 **TWOJAYSLAD** 83
216 **TWOMINUTES TURKISH** (IRE) 60
365 **TWOSHOTSOFTEQUILA** (IRE) 71
223 **TWOTWOTHREE** (IRE) 88
170 **TYCHE** 48
312 **TYING THE KNOT** (USA) 155
132 **TYKENWEAR** 6
122 **TYLOS** (FR) 73
166 **TYNECASTLE PARK** 6
280 **TYNWALD** 20
16 **TYPEWRITER** (IRE) 132
240 **TYPHOON TEN** (IRE) 31
561 **TYPICAL MAN** 84
561 **TYPICAL WOMAN** 107
528 **TYRRHENIAN SEA** (IRE) 38
488 **TYSON FURY** 27
455 **TZAR DE L'ELFE** (FR) 20
509 **TZARMIX** (FR) 43
255 **U A E FIFTY** (IRE) 26
460 **U A E SPIRIT** (IRE) 116
186 **U S S MICHIGAN** (USA) 6
78 **UAE SOLDIER** (USA) 10
23 **UALLRIGHTHARRY** (IRE) 23
62 **UBAHHA** 21
98 **UBER COOL** (IRE) 21
135 **UBERMAN** (IRE) 9

118 **UBERRIMA FIDES** 77
398 **UBETYA** (IRE) 186
274 **UCANAVER** 53
238 **UCCELLO** (IRE) 86
521 **UCKERBY** 88
576 **UDABERRI** (IRE) 21
378 **UGNEGYA** (IRE) C 80
131 **UGO DU MISSELOT** (FR) 19
164 **UGO GREGORY** 94
375 **UISCE UR** (IRE) 53
388 **UKANTANGO** (IRE) 135
365 **UKNOWMYMEANING** (IRE) 72
490 **ULFAH DREAM** C 29
34 **ULSHAW BRIDGE** (IRE) 12
404 **ULTIMATE FAME** (IRE) 209
404 **ULTIMATE GETAWAY** (IRE) 210
1 **ULTRA VIOLET** (GER) 55
361 **ULTRAPOWER** (IRE) 65
82 **ULVERSTON** (IRE) 33
470 **ULYSSES** (GER) 21
334 **UMAX** (IRE) 56
428 **UMBRIGADO** (IRE) 90
101 **UMM HURAIR** (IRE) 9
11 **UMMSUQUAIM** (USA) 16
265 **UMNDENI** (IRE) 100
505 **UMNEYATI** F 86
73 **UMNIYAH** F 120
567 **UN PROPHETE** (FR) 90
106 **UNA NOTTE** 16
216 **UNANSWERED PRAYERS** (IRE) 61
521 **UNASHAMED** 39
37 **UNBLINKING** 5
32 **UNCHARTED WATERS** (IRE) G 24
240 **UNCLE** 231
445 **UNCLE ALASTAIR** 53
272 **UNCLE BERNIE** (IRE) 19
299 **UNCLE DICK** 21
219 **UNCLE GEZ** (IRE) 21
248 **UNCLE HENRY** (IRE) 6
406 **UNCLE JOHN** 93
457 **UNCLE MAC** (IRE) 31
266 **UNCLE O** 16
385 **UNCLE PHIL** (IRE) 172
233 **UNCONQUERABLE KEEN** (IRE) 37
554 **UNDECIDED** (IRE) 24
89 **UNDER CURFEW** 90
164 **UNDER FOX** (IRE) 95
543 **UNDER THE TWILIGHT** 18
214 **UNDERCOVER AGENT** (IRE) 14
13 **UNDERCOVER LOVER** (IRE) 68
26 **UNDERSTATED** 146
525 **UNDERSUPERVISION** (IRE) 69
548 **UNDOMIEL** 26
313 **UNDOUBTEDLY** 35
231 **UNDRESS** (IRE) F 192
404 **UNE DE LA SENIERE** (FR) 211
231 **UNEQUAL LOVE** 193
476 **UNEXPECTED PARTY** (FR) 152
252 **UNFINISHED BUSINES** 37
488 **UNFINISHEDSYMPATHY** (IRE) 39
83 **UNFOOLISH** (IRE) 16
417 **UNFORGETTABLE FILLY** F 85
124 **UNFORGIVING MINUTE** 16
217 **UNFORGOTTEN** (IRE) 32
92 **UNIKA ETOILE** 25
417 **UNILATERALISM** (IRE) 47
537 **UNION COURT** 87

99 **UNION SPIRIT** 12
547 **UNIQUE COMPANY** (IRE) 11
255 **UNIQUE CUT** (IRE) 9
420 **UNIT SIXTYFOUR** (IRE) 85
73 **UNITARIAN** 121
7 **UNITED FRONT** (USA) 75
402 **UNITED NATIONS** (IRE) 98
125 **UNIVERSAL BROOK** 35
312 **UNIVERSAL DAVE** 124
335 **UNIVERSAL EFFECT** 40
445 **UNIVERSAL FOLLY** 54
318 **UNIVERSAL GRACE** 10
475 **UNIVERSAL ORDER** 29
393 **UNIVERSAL SECRET** (IRE) 8
518 **UNO GRANDE** 16
559 **UNO MAS** 33
163 **UNPLUGGED** (IRE) 29
409 **UNSINKABLE MOLLY** B 114
26 **UNSPOKEN** (IRE) 81
134 **UNSTOPPABLE** (FR) 13
342 **UNSUNG HERO** (IRE) 33
39 **UNTOLD STORY** 59
485 **UP FOR PAROL** (IRE) F 53
1 **UP HELLY AA KING** 56
455 **UP THE STRAIGHT** (IRE) 21
131 **UP THE TEMPO** 20
513 **UP WITH THE PLAY** (IRE) 10
354 **UPAGAINSTIT** (IRE) 128
1 **UPANDATIT** (IRE) 57
26 **UPTIME** 82
16 **UPTON PARK** (FR) 133
469 **UPTON ROAD** (IRE) 44
164 **UPTON SEAS** F 96
164 **UPTON SEAS** G 159
541 **UPTOWN HARRY** (IRE) 5
409 **UPTOWN LADY** (IRE) 115
148 **UR SECRET IS SAFE** (IRE) C 3
577 **URABAMBA** (IRE) 16
60 **URANUS DES BORDES** (FR) 29
378 **URBAN ARTIST** 28
138 **URBAN FOREST** 10
388 **URBAN GRIT** (IRE) 136
89 **URBAN HIGHWAY** (IRE) 91
65 **URBAN ROAD** 15
398 **URBAN SOLDIER** (IRE) 187
94 **URBAN VIOLET** 22
386 **URBAN WAR** (IRE) 28
225 **URBLEREAGH** (IRE) 14
315 **URNEYMAN** (IRE) 21
301 **US AND THEM** (IRE) 15
6 **USHERETTE** (IRE) F 189
346 **USRA** (IRE) C 82
184 **USTATH** 22
374 **UTHER PENDRAGON** (IRE) 9
327 **UTILITY** (GER) 32
97 **UTOPISTE** (IRE) 73
77 **UZINCSO** 46
537 **V TWELVE** (IRE) 57
414 **VA PENSIERO** (FR) F 63
145 **VACCINE** (IRE) 52
385 **VADALY** (FR) 173
366 **VADAMIAH** (IRE) 43
185 **VADREAM** 24

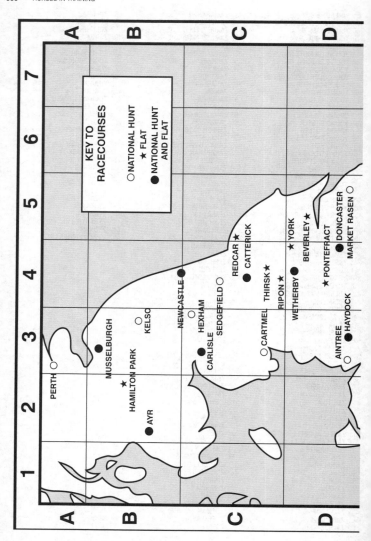

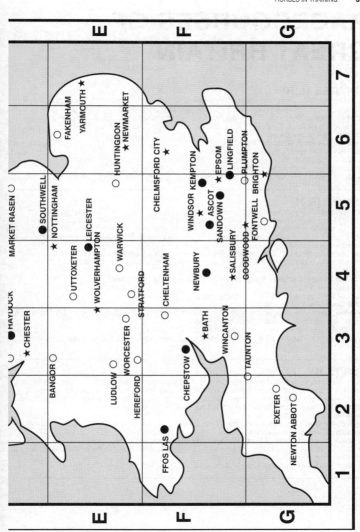

RACECOURSES OF GREAT BRITAIN

AINTREE (L.H)
Grand National Course: Triangular, 2m2f (16 fences) 494y run-in with elbow. Perfectly flat. A severe test for both horse and rider, putting a premium on jumping ability, fitness and courage.
Mildmay Course: Rectangular, 1m4f (8) 260y run-in. A very fast, flat course with sharp bends.
Address: Aintree Racecourse, Ormskirk Road, Aintree, Liverpool, L9 5AS Tel: 0151 523 2600
Website: www.aintree.co.uk
Managing Director: Nicholas Wrigley
Clerk of the Course: Sulekha Varma
By Road: North of the City, near the junction of the M57 and M58 with the A59 (Preston).
By Rail: Aintree Station is adjacent to the Stands, from Liverpool Central.
By Air: Liverpool (John Lennon) Airport is 10 miles. Helicopter landing facility by prior arrangement.

ASCOT (R.H)
Flat: Right-handed triangular track just under 1m6f in length. The Round course descends from the 1m4f start into Swinley Bottom, the lowest part of the track. It then turns right-handed and joins the Old Mile Course, which starts on a separate chute. The course then rises to the right-handed home turn over an underpass to join the straight mile course. The run-in is about 3f, rising slightly to the winning post. The whole course is of a galloping nature with easy turns.
N.H. Triangular, 1m6f (10), 240y run-in mostly uphill. A galloping course with an uphill finish, Ascot provides a real test of stamina. The fences are stiff and sound jumping is essential, especially for novices.
Address: Ascot Racecourse, Ascot, Berkshire SL5 7JX Tel: 08707 271234
Website: www.ascot.co.uk
Clerk of the Course: Chris Stickels 01344 878502 / 07970 621440
Chief Executive: Guy Henderson
By Road: West of the town on the A329. Easy access from the M3 (Junction 3) and the M4 (Junction 6). Car parking adjoining the course and Ascot Heath.
By Rail: Regular service from Waterloo to Ascot (500y from the racecourse).
By Air: Helicopter landing facility at the course. London (Heathrow) Airport 15 miles, White Waltham Airfield 12 miles (01427) 718800.

AYR (L.H)
Flat: A left-handed, galloping, flat oval track of 1m4f with a 4f run-in. The straight 6f is essentially flat.
N.H. Oval, 1m4f (9), 210y run-in. Relatively flat and one of the fastest tracks in Great Britain. It is a well-drained course and the ground rarely becomes testing. The track suits the long-striding galloper.
Address: Ayr Racecourse, Whitletts Road, Ayr, KA8 0JE Tel: 01292 264179
Website: www.ayr-racecourse.co.uk
Clerk of the Course: Graeme Anderson 07768 651261
Managing Director: David Brown
By Road: East of the town on the A758. Free parking for buses and cars.
By Rail: Ayr Station (trains on the half hour from Glasgow Central). Journey time 55 minutes. Buses and taxis also to the course.
By Air: Prestwick International Airport (10 minutes), Glasgow Airport (1 hour).

BANGOR-ON-DEE (L.H)

N.H. Circular, 1m4f (9), 325y run-in. Apart from some 'ridge and furrow', this is a flat course notable for three sharp bends, especially the paddock turn. Suits handy, speedy sorts.

Address: Bangor-On-Dee Racecourse, Overton Road, Bangor-On-Dee, Wrexham, LL13 0DA Tel: 01978 782081

Website: www.bangorondeeraces.co.uk

Clerk of the Course and Racing Manager: Andrew Morris

Chief Executive: Louise Stewart

General Manager: Jeannie Chantler

By Road: 5 miles south-east of Wrexham, off the B5069.

By Rail: Wrexham Station (bus or taxi to the course).

By Air: Helicopters may land by prior arrangement with Clerk of the Course.

BATH (L.H)

Flat: Galloping, left-handed, level oval of 1m4f, with long, stiff run-in of about 4f which bends to the left. An extended chute provides for sprint races.

Address: The Racecourse, Lansdown, Bath, BA1 9BU Tel: 01225 424609

Website: www.bath-racecourse.co.uk

Clerk of the Course: Ben Hicks

Executive Director: Liam Johnson

By Road: 2 miles northwest of the City (M4 Junction 18) at Lansdown. Unlimited free car and coach parking immediately behind the stands. Special bus services operate from Bath to the racecourse.

By Rail: Bath Station (from Paddington).

By Air: Bristol or Colerne Airports. Helicopter landing facilities available by prior arrangement.

BEVERLEY (R.H)

Flat: A right-handed oval of 1m3f, generally galloping, with an uphill run-in of two and a half furlongs. The 5f course is very stiff.

Address: Beverley Race Co. Ltd., York Road, Beverley, Yorkshire HU17 9QZ Tel: 01482 867488 / 882645

Website: www.beverley-racecourse.co.uk

Chief Executive and Clerk of the Course: Sally Iggulden 07850 458605

By Road: 7 miles from the M62 (Junction 38) off the A1035. Free car parking opposite the course. Owners and trainers use a separate enclosure.

By Rail: Beverley Station (Hull-Scarborough line). Occasional bus service to the course (1 mile).

BRIGHTON (L.H)

Flat: Left-handed, 1m4f horseshoe with easy turns and a run-in of three and a half furlongs. Undulating and sharp, the track suits handy types.

Address: Brighton Racecourse, Brighton, East Sussex BN2 2XZ Tel: 01273 603580

Website: www.brighton-racecourse.co.uk

Clerk of the Course: Philip Hide

Executive Director: Paul Ellison

By Road: East of the city on the A27 (Lewes Road). Car park adjoins the course.

By Rail: Brighton Station (from Victoria on the hour, London Bridge or Portsmouth). Special bus service to the course from the station (approx 2 miles).

By Air: Helicopters may land by prior arrangement.

CARLISLE (R.H)

Flat: Right-handed, 1m4f pear-shaped track. Galloping and undulating with easy turns and a stiff uphill run-in of three and a half furlongs. The 6f course begins on an extended chute.
N.H. Pear-shaped, 1m5f (9), 300y run-in uphill. Undulating and a stiff test of stamina, ideally suited to the long-striding thorough stayer.
Address: Carlisle Racecourse, Durdar Road, Carlisle CA2 4TS Tel: 01228 554700
Website: www.carlisle-races.co.uk
Regional Director: Dickon White
Joint Clerks of the Course: Sulekha Varma and Kirkland Tellwright
General Manager: Molly Dingwall
By Road: 2 miles south of the city (Durdar Road). Easy access from the M6 (Junction 42). The car park is free (adjacent to the course).
By Rail: Carlisle Station (2 miles from the course).
By Air: Helicopter landing facility by prior arrangement.

CARTMEL (L.H)

N.H. Oval, 1m1f (6), 800y run-in. Almost perfectly flat but very sharp, with the longest run-in in the country, approximately half a mile. The fences are stiff but fair.
Address: Cartmel Racecourse, Cartmel, nr Grange-Over-Sands, Cumbria LA11 6QF Tel: 01539 536340
Out of season: 01539 533335
Website: www.cartmel-racecourse.co.uk
General Manager: Geraldine McKay
Clerk of the Course: Anthea Morshead 07837 559861
By Road: 1 mile west of the town, 2 miles off the B5277 (Grange-Haverthwaite road). M6 (Junction 36).
By Rail: Cark-in-Cartmel Station (2 miles) (Carnforth-Barrow line). Raceday bus service.
By Air: Light aircraft facilities available at Cark Airport (4 miles from the course). Helicopter landing facility at the course, by prior arrangement only.

CATTERICK (L.H)

Flat: A sharp, left-handed, undulating oval of 1m180y with a downhill run-in of 3f.
N.H. Oval, 1m1f (9), 240y run-in. Undulating, sharp track that favours the handy, front-running sort, rather than the long-striding galloper.
Address: The Racecourse, Catterick Bridge, Richmond, North Yorkshire DL10 7PE Tel: 01748 811478
Website: www.catterickbridge.co.uk
General Manager and Clerk of the Course: Fiona Needham 07831 688625
By Road: The course is adjacent to the A1, 1 mile northwest of the town on the A6136. There is a free car park.
By Rail: Darlington Station (special buses to course - 14-mile journey).
By Air: Helicopters can land by prior arrangement. Fixed wing planes contact RAF Leeming Tel: 01677 423041

CHELMSFORD CITY (L.H)

Flat: A left-handed, floodlit Polytrack oval of 1m with sweeping bends and a 2f home straight. Races over 7f and 1m start from separate chutes.
Address: Chelmsford City Racecourse, Great Leighs, Essex, CM3 1QP Tel: 01245 362412
Website: www.chelmsfordcityracecourse.com
Clerk of the Course: Andy Waitt 07929 915731
By Road: At Great Leighs, five miles north of Chelmsford on the A31
By Rail: Chelmsford station (from Liverpool Street)
By Air: Stansted Airport (17 miles)

CHELTENHAM (L.H)
Old Course: Oval, 1m4f, (9) 350y run-in. A testing, undulating track with stiff fences. The ability to stay is essential.
New Course: Oval, 1m5f (10), 220y run-in. Undulating, stiff fences, testing course, uphill for the final half-mile.
Address: Cheltenham Racecourse, Prestbury Park, Cheltenham, Gloucestershire GL50 4SH Tel: 01242 513014
Website: www.cheltenham.co.uk
Regional Director: Ian Renton
Regional Head of Racing and Clerk of the Course: Jon Pullin 07966 154962
By Road: 1.5 miles north of the town on the A435. M5 (Junction 10 or 11).
By Rail: Cheltenham Spa Station. Buses and taxis to course.
By Air: Helicopter landing site to the northeast of the stands.

CHEPSTOW (L.H)
Flat: A left-handed, undulating oval of about 2m, with easy turns, and a straight run-in of 5f. There is a straight track of 1m14y.
N.H. Oval, 2m (11), 240y run-in. Many changing gradients, five fences in the home straight. Favours the long-striding front-runner, but stamina is important.
Address: Chepstow Racecourse, Chepstow, Monmouthshire NP16 6BE Tel: 01291 622260
Website: www.chepstow-racecourse.co.uk
General Manager: Caroline Williams
Clerk of the Course: Libby O'Flaherty 07970 831987
Executive Director: Phil Bell
By Road: 1 mile north-west of the town on the A466. (1 mile from Junction 22 of the M4 (Severn Bridge) or M48 Junction 2. There is a free public car park opposite the entrance.
By Rail: Chepstow Station (from Paddington, change at Gloucester or Newport). The course is a mile from the station.
By Air: Helicopter landing facility in the centre of the course.

CHESTER (L.H)
Flat: A level, sharp, left-handed, circular course of 1m73y, with a short run-in of 230y.
Chester is a specialists' track which generally suits the sharp-actioned horse.
Address: The Racecourse, Chester CH1 2LY Tel: 01244 304600
Website: www.chester-races.co.uk
Racing Manager and Clerk of the Course: Andrew Morris
Chief Executive: Louise Stewart
By Road: The course is near the centre of the city on the A548 (Queensferry Road). The Owners' and Trainers' car park is adjacent to the Leverhulme Stand. There is a public car park in the centre of the course.
By Rail: Chester Station (3/4 mile from the course). Services from Euston, Paddington and Northgate.
By Air: Hawarden Airport (2 miles). Helicopters are allowed to land on the racecourse by prior arrangement.

DONCASTER (L.H)
Flat: A left-handed, flat, galloping course of 1m7f 110y, with a long run-in which extends to a straight mile.
N.H. Conical, 2m (11), 247y run-in. A very fair, flat track ideally suited to the long-striding galloper.
Address: Doncaster Racecourse, Leger Way, Doncaster, DN2 6BB Tel: 01302 304200
Website: www.doncaster-racecourse.co.uk
Clerk of the Course: Paul Barker 07966 472231
Executive Director: Rachel Harwood
General Manager: Nikki Griffiths
By Road: East of the town, off the A638 (M18 Junctions 3 and 4). Club members' car park reserved. Large public car park free and adjacent to the course.
By Rail: Doncaster Central Station (from King's Cross). Special bus service from the station (1 mile).
By Air: Helicopter landing facility by prior arrangement only. Doncaster Robin Hood Airport is 15 minutes from the racecourse.

EPSOM (L.H)

Flat: Left-handed and undulating with easy turns, and a run-in of just under 4f. The straight 5f course is also undulating and downhill all the way, making it the fastest 5f in the world.
Address: The Racecourse, Epsom Downs, Surrey KT18 5LQ Tel: 01372 726311
Website: www.epsomderby.co.uk
Regional Director: Phil White
Clerk of the Course: Andrew Cooper Tel: 01372 726311 Mobile: 07774 230850
General Manager: Simon Durrant
By Road: Two miles south of the town on the B290 (M25 Junctions 8 and 9). For full car park particulars apply to: The Club Secretary, Epsom Grandstand, Epsom Downs, Surrey KT18 5LQ. Tel: 01372 726311.
By Rail: Epsom, Epsom Downs or Tattenham Corner Stations (trains from London Bridge, Waterloo, Victoria). Regular bus services run to the course from Epsom and Morden Underground Station.
By Air: London (Heathrow) and London (Gatwick) are both within 30 miles of the course. Heliport (Derby Meeting only) - apply to Hascombe Aviation. Tel: 01279 680291.

EXETER (R.H)

N.H. Oval, 2m (11), 300y run-in uphill. Undulating with a home straight of half a mile. A good test of stamina, suiting the handy, well-balanced sort.
Address: Exeter Racecourse, Kennford, Exeter, Devon EX6 7XS Tel: 01392 832599
Website: www.exeter-racecourse.co.uk
Regional Director: Ian Renton
Clerk of the Course: Daniel Cooper 07976 413045
General Manager: Jack Parkinson
By Road: The course is at Haldon, 5 miles south-west of Exeter on the A38 (Plymouth) road, 2 miles east of Chudleigh.
By Rail: Exeter (St Davids) Station. Free bus service to course.
By Air: Helicopters can land by prior arrangement.

FAKENHAM (L.H)

N.H. Square, 1m (6), 200y run-in. On the turn almost throughout and undulating, suiting the handy front-runner. The going rarely becomes heavy.
Address: The Racecourse, Fakenham, Norfolk NR21 7NY Tel: 01328 862388
Website: www.fakenhamracecourse.co.uk
Clerk of the Course and Chief Executive: David Hunter Tel: 01328 862388 Mobile: 07767 802206
By Road: A mile south of the town on the B1146 (East Dereham) road.
By Rail: Norwich Station (26 miles) (Liverpool Street line), King's Lynn (22 miles) (Liverpool Street/Kings Cross).
By Air: Helicopter landing facility in the centre of the course by prior arrangement only.

FFOS LAS (L.H)

Flat The track is a 60m wide, basically flat, 1m4f oval with sweeping bends. Races over 5f and 6f start on a chute.
N.H. A flat, 1m4f oval (9). The going is often testing which places the emphasis on stamina.
Address: Ffos Las Racecourse, Trimsaran, Carmarthenshire SA17 4DE Tel: 01554 811092
Website: www.ffoslasracecourse.com
Executive Director: Phil Bell
Clerk of the Course: Dai Jones 07970 828961
By Road: From the east take J48 from the M4 and join the A4138 to Llanelli, then follow the brown tourist signs to the racecourse. From the west take the A48 to Carmarthen then the A484 to Kidwelly before following the brown signs.
By Air: The course has the facilities to land helicopters on race days.

FONTWELL PARK (Fig. 8)
N.H. 2m (7), 230y run-in with left-hand bend close home. The figure-of-eight chase course suits handy types and is something of a specialists' track. The left-handed hurdle course is oval and one mile round. The bottom bend, which is shared, has been converted to Fibresand.
Address: Fontwell Park Racecourse, nr Arundel, West Sussex BN18 0SX Tel: 01243 543335
Website: www.fontwellpark.co.uk
Clerk of the Course: Philip Hide
Executive Director and General Manager: Jonathan Acott
By Road: South of village at the junction of the A29 (Bognor) and A27 (Brighton-Chichester) roads.
By Rail: Barnham Station (2 miles). Brighton-Portsmouth line (access via London Victoria).
By Air: Helicopter landing facility by prior arrangement with the Clerk of the Course.

GOODWOOD (R.H)
Flat: A sharp, undulating, essentially right-handed track with a long run-in. There is also a straight 6f course.
Address: Goodwood Racecourse Ltd., Goodwood, Chichester, West Sussex PO18 0PX Tel: 01243 755022
Website: www.goodwood.co.uk
Managing Director: Adam Waterworth
General Manager: Alex Eade
Clerk of the Course: Ed Arkell
By Road: 6 miles north of Chichester between the A286 and A285. There is a car park adjacent to the course. Ample free car and coach parking.
By Rail: Chichester Station (from Victoria or London Bridge). Regular bus service to the course (6 miles).
By Air: Helicopter landing facility by prior arrangement 01243 755030. Goodwood Airport 2 miles (taxi to the course).

HAMILTON PARK (R.H)
Flat: A sharp, undulating, right-handed course of 1m5f with a five and a half-furlong, uphill run-in. There is a straight track of 6f.
Address: Hamilton Park Racecourse, Bothwell Road, Hamilton, Lanarkshire ML3 0DW Tel: 01698 283806
Website: www.hamilton-park.co.uk
Clerk of the Course: Harriet Graham
Chief Executive: Vivien Currie 01698 283806
By Road: Off the A72 on the B7071 (Hamilton-Bothwell road). (M74 Junction 5). Free parking for cars and buses.
By Rail: Hamilton West Station (1 mile).
By Air: Glasgow Airport (20 miles).

HAYDOCK PARK (L.H)
Flat: A galloping, almost flat, oval track, 1m5f round, with a run-in of four and a half furlongs and a straight six-furlong course.
N.H. Oval, 1m5f (10), 440y run-in. A flat, galloping chase course using portable fences. The hurdles track, which is sharp, is inside the chase course and has some tight bends.
Address: Haydock Park Racecourse, Newton-le-Willows, Merseyside WA12 0HQ Tel: 01942 402609
Website: www.haydock-park.co.uk
Regional Director: Dickon White
Regional Head of Racing and Clerk of the Course: Kirkland Tellwright 01942 725963 or 07748 181595
By Road: The course is on the A49 near Junction 23 of the M6.
By Rail: Newton-le-Willows Station (Manchester-Liverpool line) is 2.5 miles from the course. Earlstown 3 miles from the course. Warrington Bank Quay and Wigan are on the London to Carlisle/Glasgow line.
By Air: Landing facilities in the centre of the course for helicopters and planes not exceeding 10,000lbs laden weight.

HEREFORD (R.H)

N.H. Square, 1m4f (9), 300y run-in. The turns, apart from the final one that is on falling ground, are easily negotiated, placing the emphasis on speed rather than stamina. A handy position round the home turn is vital, as winners rarely come from behind. The hurdle track is on the outside of the chase course.
Address: Hereford Racecourse, Roman Road, Holmer, Hereford, HR4 9QU Tel: (01432) 273560
Website: www.hereford-racecourse.co.uk
Regional Executive Director: Rebecca Davies
Clerk of the Course: Libby O'Flaherty 07970 831987
By Road: 1 mile north-west of the city centre off the A49 (Leominster) road.
By Rail: Hereford Station (1 mile from the course).

HEXHAM (L.H)

N.H. Oval, 1m4f (10), 220y run-in. An undulating course that becomes very testing when the ground is soft, it has easy fences and a stiff climb to the finishing straight, which is on a separate spur.
Address: Hexham Racecourse, The Riding, Hexham, Northumberland NE46 2JP Tel: 01434 606881 Racedays: 01434 603738
Website: www.hexham-racecourse.co.uk
Chief Executive: Robert Whitelock
Clerk of the Course: James Armstrong 01434 606881 or 07801 166820
By Road: 1.5 miles south-west of the town off the B6305.
By Rail: Hexham Station (Newcastle-Carlisle line). Free bus to the course.
By Air: Helicopter landing facility in centre of course (by special arrangement only).

HUNTINGDON (R.H)

N.H. Oval, 1m4f (9), 200y run-in. A perfectly flat, galloping track with a tricky open ditch in front of the stands. The two fences in the home straight can cause problems for novice chasers. Suits front-runners.
Address: The Racecourse, Brampton, Huntingdon, Cambridgeshire PE28 4NL Tel: 01480 453373
Website: www.huntingdon-racecourse.co.uk
Regional Director: Amy Starkey
Clerk of the Course: Roderick Duncan 07772 958685
General Manager: James Wilcox
By Road: The course is situated at Brampton, 2 miles west of Huntingdon on the A14. Easy access from the A1 (1/2 mile from the course).
By Rail: Huntingdon Station. Buses and taxis to course.
By Air: Helicopter landing facility by prior arrangement.

KELSO (L.H)

N.H. Oval, 1m1f (8), uphill run-in of just over a furlong. Rather undulating with two downhill fences opposite the stands, it suits the nippy, front-running sort, though the uphill finish helps the true stayer. The hurdle course is smaller and very sharp with a tight turn away from the stands.
Address: Kelso Racecourse, Kelso, Roxburghshire TD5 7SX Tel: 01668 280800
Website: www.kelso-races.co.uk
Clerk of the Course: Matthew Taylor 07521 517495
Managing Director: Jonathan Garratt
By Road: 1 mile north of the town, off the B6461.
By Rail: Berwick-upon-Tweed Station. 23-mile bus journey to Kelso.
By Air: Helicopters can land at course by arrangement, fixed wing aircraft at Winfield, regular aircraft at Edinburgh.

KEMPTON PARK (R.H)

Flat: A floodlit Polytrack circuit. A 1m2f outer track accommodates races over 6f, 7f, 1m, 1m3f, 1m4f and 2m. The 1m inner track caters for races over 5f and 1m2f.

N.H. Triangular, 1m5f (10), 175y run-in. A practically flat, sharp course where the long run between the last obstacle on the far side and the first in the home straight switches the emphasis from jumping to speed. The hurdles track is on the outside of the chase track. The course crosses the Polytrack at two points on each circuit.

Address: Kempton Park Racecourse, Sunbury-on-Thames, Middlesex TW16 5AQ Tel: 01932 782292

Website: www.kempton.co.uk

Regional Director: Phil White

Clerk of the Course and Director of Racing: Brian Clifford 07880 784484

Assistant Clerk of the Course: Sarah Dunster

General Manager: Simon Durrant

By Road: On the A308 near Junction 1 of the M3.

By Rail: Kempton Park Station (from Waterloo).

By Air: London (Heathrow) Airport 6 miles.

LEICESTER (R.H)

Flat: A stiff, galloping, right-handed oval of 1m5f, with a 5f run-in. There is a straight course of seven furlongs.

N.H. Rectangular, 1m6f (10), 250y run-in uphill. An undulating course with an elbow 150y from the finish, it can demand a high degree of stamina, as the going can become extremely testing and the last three furlongs are uphill.

Address: Leicester Racecourse, Oadby, Leicester, LE2 4AL Tel: 01162 716515

Website: www.leicester-racecourse.co.uk

Clerk of the Course: Jimmy Stevenson 01162 712115 or 07774 497281

General Manager: Rob Bracken

By Road: The course is 2.5 miles south-east of the city on the A6 (M1, Junction 21). The car park is free.

By Rail: Leicester Station (from St Pancras) is 2.5 miles.

By Air: Helicopter landing facility in the centre of the course.

LINGFIELD PARK (L.H)

Flat, Turf: A sharp, undulating left-handed circuit, with a 7f 140y straight course.

Flat, Polytrack: The left-handed Polytrack is 1m2f round, with an extended chute to provide a 1m5f start. It is a sharp, level track with a short run-in.

N.H. Conical, 1m5f (10), 200y run-in. Severely undulating with a tight downhill turn into the straight, the chase course suits front-runners.

Address: Lingfield Park Racecourse, Lingfield, Surrey RH7 6PQ Tel: 01342 834800

Website: www.lingfield-racecourse.co.uk

Clerk of the Course: George Hill 07581 119984

Executive Director: Amy Smith

General Manager: Russell Bowes

By Road: South-east of the town off the A22; M25 (Junction 6). Ample free parking.

By Rail: Lingfield Station (regular services from London Bridge and Victoria). Half-mile walk to the course.

By Air: London (Gatwick) Airport 10 miles. Helicopter landing facility south of wind-sock.

LUDLOW (R.H)

N.H. Oval, 1m4f (9), 185y run-in. The chase course is flat and has quite sharp bends into and out of the home straight, although long-striding horses never seem to have any difficulties. The hurdle course is on the outside of the chase track and is not so sharp.
Address: Ludlow Race Club Ltd, The Racecourse, Bromfield, Ludlow, Shropshire SY8 2BT Tel: 01584 856221 (Racedays) or see below.
Website: www.ludlowracecourse.co.uk
General Manager and Clerk of the Course: Simon Sherwood 07836 215639
By Road: The course is situated at Bromfield, 2 miles north of Ludlow on the A49.
By Rail: Ludlow Station (Hereford-Shrewsbury line) 2 miles.
By Air: Helicopter landing facility in the centre of the course by arrangement with the Clerk of the Course

MARKET RASEN (R.H)

N.H. Oval, 1m2f (8), 250y run-in. A sharp, undulating course with a long run to the straight, it favours the handy, front-running type.
Address: Market Rasen Racecourse, Legsby Road, Market Rasen, Lincolnshire LN8 3EA Tel: 01673 843434
Website: www.marketrasenraces.co.uk
Regional Director: Amy Starkey
Clerk of the Course: Jack Pryor
General Manager: Nadia Powell
By Road: The town is just off the A46, and the racecourse is one mile east of the town on the A631. Free car parks.
By Rail: Market Rasen Station 1 mile (King's Cross - Cleethorpes line).
By Air: Helicopter landing facility by prior arrangement only.

MUSSELBURGH (R.H)

Flat: A sharp, level, right-handed oval of 1m2f, with a run-in of 4f. There is an additional 5f straight course.
N.H. Rectangular, 1m3f (8), 150y run-in (variable). A virtually flat track with sharp turns, suiting the handy, front-running sort. It drains well. There is a section of Polytrack going away from the stands.
Address: Musselburgh Racecourse, Linkfield Road, Musselburgh, East Lothian EH21 7RG
Tel: 01316 652859
Website: www.musselburgh-racecourse.co.uk
Clerk of the Course & General Manager: Bill Farnsworth 07710 536134
By Road: The course is situated at Musselburgh, 5 miles east of Edinburgh on the A1. Car park, adjoining enclosures, free for buses and cars.
By Rail: Waverley Station (Edinburgh). Local Rail service to Musselburgh.
By Air: Edinburgh (Turnhouse) Airport 30 minutes.

NEWBURY (L.H)

Flat: Left-handed, oval track of about 1m7f, with a slightly undulating straight mile. The round course is level and galloping with a four and a half-furlong straight. Races over the round mile start on the adjoining chute.
N.H. Oval, 1m6f (11), 255y run-in. Slightly undulating, wide and galloping in nature. The fences are stiff and sound jumping is essential. One of the fairest tracks in the country.
Address: Newbury Racecourse, Newbury, Berkshire RG14 7NZ Tel: 01635 40015
Website: www.newbury-racecourse.co.uk
Chief Executive: Julian Thick
Clerk of the Course: Keith Ottesen 07813 043453
By Road: East of the town off the A34 (M4, Junction 12 or 13). Car park, adjoining enclosures, free.
By Rail: Newbury Racecourse Station adjoins the course.
By Air: Light Aircraft landing strip East/West. 830 metres by 30 metres wide. Helicopter landing facilities.

NEWCASTLE (L.H)

Flat: A 1m6f Tapeta track outside the jumps course. The straight mile is floodlit.
N.H. Oval, 1m6f (11), 220y run-in. A gradually rising home straight of four furlongs makes this galloping track a true test of stamina, especially as the ground can become very heavy.
Address: High Gosforth Park, Newcastle-Upon-Tyne, NE3 5HP Tel: 01912 362020
Website: www.newcastle-racecourse.co.uk
Clerk of the Course: Eloise Quayle 07968 751087
Executive Director: David Williamson
By Road: 4 miles north of the city on the A6125 (near the A1). Car and coach park free.
By Rail: Newcastle Central Station (from King's Cross). A free bus service operates from South Gosforth and Regent Metro Station.
By Air: Helicopter landing facility by prior arrangement. The Airport is 4 miles from the course.

NEWMARKET (R.H)

Rowley Mile Course: There is a straight ten-furlong course, which is wide and galloping. Races over 1m4f or more are right-handed. The Rowley Mile course has a long run-in and a stiff finish.
July Course: Races up to a mile are run on the Bunbury course, which is straight. Races over 1m2f or more are right-handed, with a 7f run-in. Like the Rowley Mile course, the July Course track is stiff.
Address: Newmarket Racecourse, Westfield House, The Links, Newmarket, Suffolk CB8 0TG Tel: 01638 663482 (Main Office) 01638 663762 (Rowley Mile) 01638 675416 (July) .
Website: www.newmarketracecourses.co.uk
Clerk of the Course and Racing Director: Michael Prosser 01638 675504 or 07802 844578
Regional Director: Amy Starkey
General Manager: Sophie Able
By Road: South-west of the town on the A1304 London Road (M11 Junction 9). Free car parking at the rear of the enclosure. Annual Badge Holders' car park free all days. Courtesy bus service from Newmarket Station, Bus Station and High Street. , commencing 90 minutes prior to the first race.
By Rail: Infrequent rail service to Newmarket Station from Cambridge (Liverpool Street) or direct bus service from Cambridge (13-mile journey).
By Air: Landing facilities for light aircraft and helicopters on racedays at both racecourses. See Flight Guide. Cambridge Airport 11 miles.

NEWTON ABBOT (L.H)

N.H. Oval, 1m2f (7), 300y run-in. Flat with two tight bends. The nippy, agile sort is favoured. The run-in can be very short on the hurdle course.
Address: Newton Abbot Races Ltd., Kingsteignton Road, Newton Abbot, Devon TQ12 3AF
Tel: 01626 353235
Website: www.newtonabbotracing.com
Clerk of the Course: Jason Loosemore 07766 228109
Managing Director: Pat Masterson Tel: 01626 353235 Mobile: 07917 830144
By Road: North of the town on the A380. Torquay 6 miles, Exeter 17 miles.
By Rail: Newton Abbot Station (from Paddington) 3/4 mile. Buses and taxis operate to and from the course.
By Air: Helicopter landing pad in the centre of the course.

NOTTINGHAM (L.H)

Flat: Left-handed, galloping, oval of about 1m4f, and a straight of four and a half furlongs. Flat with easy turns.
Address: Nottingham Racecourse, Colwick Park, Nottingham, NG2 4BE Tel: 0870 8507634
Website: www.nottinghamracecourse.co.uk
Regional Director: Amy Starkey
Clerk of the Course: Tom Ryall
By Road: 2 miles east of the city centre on the B686.
By Rail: Nottingham (Midland) Station. Regular bus service to course (2 miles).
By Air: Helicopter landing facility in the centre of the course.

PERTH (R.H)
N.H. Rectangular, 1m2f (8), 283y run-in. A flat, easy track with sweeping turns. Not a course for the long-striding galloper.
Address: Perth Racecourse, Scone Palace Park, Perth, PH2 6BB Tel: 01738 551597
Website: www.perth-races.co.uk
Clerk of the Course: Matthew Taylor
General Manager: Hazel Peplinski
By Road: 4 miles north of the town off the A93.
By Rail: Perth Station (from Dundee) 4 miles. There are buses to the course.
By Air: Scone Airport (3.75 miles). Edinburgh Airport 45 minutes.

PLUMPTON (L.H)
N.H. Oval, 1m1f (7), 200y run-in uphill. A tight, undulating circuit with an uphill finish, Plumpton favours the handy, fast jumper. The ground often gets heavy, as the course is based on clay soil.
Address: Plumpton Racecourse, Plumpton, East Sussex BN7 3AL Tel: 01273 890383
Website: www.plumptonracecourse.co.uk
Clerk of the Course: Marcus Waters
Chief Executive: Daniel Thompson
By Road: 2 miles north of the village off the B2116.
By Rail: Plumpton Station (from Victoria) adjoins course.
By Air: Helicopter landing facility by prior arrangement with the Clerk of the Course.

PONTEFRACT (L.H)
Flat: Left-handed oval, undulating course of 2m133y, with a short run-in of 2f. It is a particularly stiff track with the last 3f uphill.
Address: Pontefract Park Race Co. Ltd., The Park, Pontefract, West Yorkshire Tel: 01977 781307
Website: www.pontefract-races.co.uk
Managing Director: Norman Gundill 01977 781307
Assistant Manager and Clerk of the Course: Richard Hamill
By Road: 1 mile north of the town on the A639. Junction 32 of M62. Free car park adjacent to the course.
By Rail: Pontefract Station (Tanshelf, every hour to Wakefield), 1 1/2 miles from the course. Regular bus service from Leeds.
By Air: Helicopters by arrangement only. (Nearest Airfields: Robin Hood (Doncaster), Sherburn-in-Elmet, Yeadon (Leeds Bradford).

REDCAR (L.H)
Flat: Left-handed, level, galloping, oval course of 1m6f with a straight run-in of 5f. There is also a straight mile.
Address: Redcar Racecourse, Redcar, Cleveland TS10 2BY Tel: 01642 484068
Website: www.redcarracing.com
Clerk of the Course: Jonjo Sanderson Tel: 01642 484068 Mobile: 07766 022893
General Manager: Amy Fair
By Road: In the town off the A1085. Free parking adjoining the course for buses and cars.
By Rail: Redcar Station (1/4 mile from the course).
By Air: Landing facilities at Turners Arms Farm (600yds runway) Yearby, Cleveland. Two miles south of the racecourse - transport available. Durham Tees Valley airport (18 miles west of Redcar).

RIPON (R.H)

Flat: A sharp, undulating, right-handed oval of 1m5f, with a 5f run-in. There is also a 6f straight course.
Address: Ripon Racecourse, Boroughbridge Road, Ripon, North Yorkshire HG4 1UG Tel: 01765 530530
Website: www.ripon-races.co.uk
Clerk of the Course and Managing Director: James Hutchinson 07860 679904
By Road: The course is situated 2 miles south-east of the city, on the B6265. There is ample free parking for cars and coaches.
By Rail: Harrogate Station (11 miles) or Thirsk (15 miles). Bus services to Ripon.
By Air: Helicopters only on the course. Otherwise Leeds/Bradford airport.

SALISBURY (R.H)

Flat: Right-handed and level, with a run-in of 4f. There is a straight mile track. The last half-mile is uphill, providing a stiff test of stamina. Galloping.
Address: Salisbury Racecourse, Netherhampton, Salisbury, Wiltshire SP2 8PN Tel: 01722 326461
Website: www.salisburyracecourse.co.uk
Clerk of the Course and General Manager: Jeremy Martin 07880 744999
By Road: 3 miles south-west of the city on the A3094 at Netherhampton. Free car park adjoins the course.
By Rail: Salisbury Station is 3.5 miles (from London Waterloo). Bus service to the course.
By Air: Helicopter landing facility near the 1m2f start.

SANDOWN PARK (R.H)

Flat: An easy right-handed oval course of 1m5f with a stiff, straight uphill run-in of 4f. Separate straight 5f track is also uphill. Galloping.
N.H. Oval, 1m5f (11), 220y run-in uphill. Features seven fences on the back straight; the last three (the Railway Fences) are very close together and can often decide the outcome of races. The stiff climb to the finish puts the emphasis very much on stamina, but accurate-jumping, free-running sorts are also favoured. Hurdle races are run on the Flat course.
Address: Sandown Park Racecourse, Esher, Surrey KT10 9AJ Tel: 01372 464348
Website: www.sandown.co.uk
Regional Director: Phil White
General Manager: Sarah Drabwell
Clerk of the Course: Andrew Cooper: 01372 461213 Mobile: 07774 230850
By Road: Four miles south-west of Kingston-on-Thames, on the A307 (M25 Junction 10).
By Rail: Esher Station (from Waterloo) adjoins the course.
By Air: London (Heathrow) Airport 12 miles.

SEDGEFIELD (L.H)

N.H. Oval, 1m2f (8), 200y run-in. Undulating with fairly tight turns, it doesn't suit big, long-striding horses.
Address: Sedgefield Racecourse, Sedgefield, Stockton-on-Tees, Cleveland TS21 2HW Tel: 01740 621925
Website: www.sedgefield-racecourse.co.uk
Clerk of the Course: Michael Naughton
By Road: ³/₄ mile south-west of the town, near the junction of the A689 (Bishop Auckland) and the A177 (Durham) roads. The car park is free.
By Rail: Darlington Station (9 miles). Durham Station (12 miles).
By Air: Helicopter landing facility in car park area by prior arrangement only.

SOUTHWELL (L.H)

Flat, Tapeta: Left-handed oval, Tapeta course of 1m2f with a 3f run-in. There is a straight 5f. Tapeta replaced Fibresand in late 2021.
N.H. Oval, 1m 1f (7), 220y run-in. A tight, flat track with a short run-in, it suits front-runners.
Address: Southwell Racecourse, Rolleston, Newark, Nottinghamshire NG25 0TS Tel: 01636 814481
Website: www.southwell-racecourse.co.uk
Executive Director: Mark Clayton
Clerk of the Course: Paul Barker 07966 472231
By Road: The course is situated at Rolleston, 3 miles south of Southwell, 5 miles from Newark.
By Rail: Rolleston Station (Nottingham-Newark line) adjoins the course.
By Air: Helicopters can land by prior arrangement.

STRATFORD-ON-AVON (L.H)

N.H. Triangular, 1m2f (8), 200y run-in. Virtually flat with two tight bends, and quite a short home straight. A sharp and turning course, it suits the well-balanced, handy sort.
Address: Stratford Racecourse, Luddington Road, Stratford-upon-Avon, Warwickshire CV37 9SE
Tel: 01789 267949
Website: www.stratfordracecourse.net
Managing Director: Ilona Barnett
Clerk of the Course: Nessie Chanter
By Road: A mile from the town centre, off the A429 (Evesham road).
By Rail: Stratford-on-Avon Station (from Birmingham New Street or Leamington Spa) 1 mile.
By Air: Helicopter landing facility by prior arrangement.

TAUNTON (R.H)

N.H. Elongated oval, 1m2f (8), 150y run-in uphill. Sharp turns, especially after the winning post, with a steady climb from the home bend. Suits the handy sort.
Address: Taunton Racecourse, Orchard Portman, Taunton, Somerset TA3 7BL Tel: 01823 337172
Website: www.tauntonracecourse.co.uk
Clerk of the Course: Jason Loosemore 07766 228109
Chief Executive: Bob Young
By Road: Two miles south of the town on the B3170 (Honiton) road (M5 Junction 25).
By Rail: Taunton Station 2 miles. There are buses and taxis to course.
By Air: Helicopter landing facility by prior arrangement.

THIRSK (L.H)

Flat: Left-handed oval of 1m2f with sharp turns and an undulating run-in of 4f. There is a straight 6f track.
Address: The Racecourse, Station Road, Thirsk, North Yorkshire YO7 1QL Tel: 01845 522276
Website: www.thirskracecourse.net
Clerk of the Course and Managing Director: James Sanderson
By Road: West of the town on the A61. Free car park adjacent to the course for buses and cars.
By Rail: Thirsk Station (from King's Cross), 1/2 mile from the course.
By Air: Helicopters can land by prior arrangement. Tel: Racecourse 01845 522276. Fixed wing aircraft can land at RAF Leeming. Tel: 01677 423041. Light aircraft at Bagby. Tel: 01845 597385 or 01845 537555

UTTOXETER (L.H)
N.H. Oval, 1m2f (8), 170y run-in. A few undulations, easy bends and fences and a flat home straight of over half a mile. Suits front-runners, especially on the 2m hurdle course.
Address: The Racecourse, Wood Lane, Uttoxeter, Staffordshire ST14 8BD Tel: 01889 562561
Website: www.uttoxeter-racecourse.co.uk
Clerk of the Course: Eloise Quayle
General Manager: Brian Barrass
By Road: South-east of the town off the B5017 (Marchington Road).
By Rail: Uttoxeter Station (Crewe-Derby line) adjoins the course.
By Air: Helicopters can land by prior arrangement with the raceday office.

WARWICK (L.H)
N.H. Circular, 1m6f (10), 240y run-in. Undulating with tight bends, five quick fences in the back straight and a short home straight, Warwick favours handiness and speed rather than stamina.
Address: Warwick Racecourse, Hampton Street, Warwick, CV34 6HN Tel: 01926 491553
Website: www.warwickracecourse.co.uk
Regional Director: Ian Renton
Clerk of the Course: Tom Ryall
General Manager: Andre Klein
By Road: West of the town on the B4095 adjacent to Junction 15 of the M40.
By Rail: Warwick or Warwick Parkway Stations.
By Air: Helicopters can land by prior arrangement with the Clerk of the Course.

WETHERBY (L.H)
Flat: First used in 2015, the Flat course is left-handed with a 1m4f circuit.
N.H. Oval, 1m4f (9), 200y run-in slightly uphill. A flat, very fair course which suits the long-striding galloper.
Address: The Racecourse, York Road, Wetherby, LS22 5EJ Tel: 01937 582035
Website: www.wetherbyracing.co.uk
Clerk of the Course and Chief Executive: Jonjo Sanderson 07831 437453
By Road: East of the town off the B1224 (York Road). Adjacent to the A1. Excellent bus and coach facilities. Car park free.
By Rail: Leeds Station 12 miles. Buses to Wetherby.
By Air: Helicopters can land by prior arrangement

WINCANTON (R.H)
N.H. Rectangular, 1m3f (9), 200y run-in. Good galloping course where the going rarely becomes heavy. The home straight is mainly downhill.
Address: Wincanton Racecourse, Wincanton, Somerset BA9 8BJ Tel: 01963 435840
Website: www.wincantonracecourse.co.uk
Regional Director: Ian Renton
Clerk of the Course: Daniel Cooper 07976 413045
General Manager: Jack Parkinson
By Road: 1 mile north of the town on the B3081.
By Rail: Gillingham Station (from Waterloo) or Castle Cary Station (from Paddington). Buses and taxis to the course.
By Air: Helicopter landing area is situated in the centre of the course.

WINDSOR (Fig. 8)
Flat: Figure of eight track of 1m4f 110y. The course is level and sharp with a long run-in. The 6f course is essentially straight.
Address: Royal Windsor Racecourse, Maidenhead Road, Windsor, Berkshire SL4 5JJ Tel: 01753 498400
Website: www.windsor-racecourse.co.uk
Clerk of the Course: Sophie Candy
Executive Director: Simon Williams
By Road: North of the town on the A308 (M4 Junction 6).
By Rail: Windsor Central Station (from Paddington) or Windsor and Eton Riverside Station (from Waterloo).
By Air: London (Heathrow) Airport 15 minutes. Also White Waltham Airport (West London Aero Club) 15 minutes.
River Bus: Seven minutes from Barry Avenue promenade at Windsor.

WOLVERHAMPTON (L.H)
Flat: Left-handed, floodlit, oval Tapeta track of 1m, with a run-in of 380y. A level track with sharp bends.
Address: Wolverhampton Racecourse, Dunstall Park, Gorsebrook Road, Wolverhampton, WV6 0PE Tel: 01902 390000
Website: www.wolverhampton-racecourse.co.uk
Clerk of the Course: Fergus Cameron 07971 531162
General Manager: Dave Roberts
By Road: 1 mile north of the city centre on the A449 (M54 Junction 2 or M6 Junction 12).
Car parking free.
By Rail: Wolverhampton Station (from Euston) 1 mile.
By Air: Halfpenny Green Airport 8 miles.

WORCESTER (L.H)
N.H. Elongated oval, 1m5f (9), 220y run-in. Flat with easy turns, it is a very fair, galloping track.
Address: Worcester Racecourse, Pitchcroft, Worcester, WR1 3EJ Tel: 01905 25364
Website: www.worcester-racecourse.co.uk
Clerk of the Course: Tim Long
Regional Executive Director: Rebecca Davies
General Manager: Michael Thomas
By Road: West of the city centre off the A449 (Kidderminster road) (M5 Junction 8).
By Rail: Foregate Street Station, Worcester (from Paddington) ³/₄ mile.
By Air: Helicopter landing facility in the centre of the course, by prior arrangement only.

YARMOUTH (L.H)
Flat: Left-handed, level circuit of 1m4f, with a run-in of 5f. The straight course is 1m long.
Address: The Racecourse, Jellicoe Road, Great Yarmouth, Norfolk NR30 4AU Tel: 01493 842527
Website: www.greatyarmouth-racecourse.co.uk
Clerk of the Course: Richard Aldous 07738 507643
Executive Director: Glenn Tubby
By Road: 1 mile east of town centre (well signposted from A47 and A12).
By Rail: Great Yarmouth Station (1 mile). Bus service to the course.
By Air: Helicopter landing available by prior arrangement with Racecourse Office

YORK (L.H)
Flat: Left-handed, level, galloping track, with a straight 6f. There is also an adjoining chute for races over 7f.
Address: The Racecourse, York, YO23 1EX Tel: 01904 683932
Website: www.yorkracecourse.co.uk
Clerk of the Course and Chief Executive: William Derby 07812 961176
Assistant Clerk of the Course: Anthea Morshead
By Road: 1 mile south-east of the city on the A1036.
By Rail: 1 1/2 miles York Station (from King's Cross). Special bus service from station to the course.
By Air: Light aircraft and helicopter landing facilities available at Rufforth aerodrome (5,000ft tarmac runway). Leeds Bradford airport (25 miles).

THE BET365
EUROPEAN FREE HANDICAP STAKES
NEWMARKET CRAVEN MEETING 2022
(ON THE ROWLEY MILE COURSE)
TUESDAY, 12TH APRIL

The bet365 European Free Handicap Stakes (Class 1) (Listed Race) with total prize fund of £50,000 for **three-year-olds only** (two-year-olds of 2021 which are included in the European 2-y-o Thoroughbred Rankings or which, in 2021, either ran in Great Britain or ran for a trainer who at the time was licensed by the British Horseracing Authority, and are Rated 100 or above); lowest weight 8st; highest weight 9st 7lb.

Penalty for a winner after 31st December 2021 to be at the discretion of the BHA Handicapper.

To be ran over seven furlongs.

Rating		st	lb
122	**Native Trail** (GB)	9	7
115	**Angel Bleu** (FR)	9	0
115	**Coroebus** (IRE)	9	0
115	**Dubawi Legend** (IRE)	9	0
115	**Luxembourg** (IRE)	9	0
115	**Perfect Power** (IRE)	9	0
115	**Tenebrism** (USA)	9	0
114	**Atomic Force** (IRE)	8	13
114	**Bayside Boy** (IRE)	8	13
114	**Modern Games** (IRE)	8	13
114	**Point Lonsdale** (IRE)	8	13
113	**Ebro River** (IRE)	8	12
113	**Lusail** (IRE)	8	12
113	**Noble Truth** (FR)	8	12
113	**Reach For The Moon** (GB)	8	12
113	**Royal Patronage** (FR)	8	12
113	**Zellie** (FR)	8	12
112	**Ancient Rome** (USA)	8	11
112	**Castle Star** (IRE)	8	11
112	**El Bodegon** (IRE)	8	11
112	**Flotus** (IRE)	8	11
112	**Sea Bay** (GER)	8	11
111	**Albahr** (GB)	8	10
111	**Armor** (GB)	8	10
111	**Discoveries** (IRE)	8	10
111	**Dr Zempf** (GB)	8	10
111	**Go Bears Go** (IRE)	8	10
111	**Hannibal Barca** (IRE)	8	10
111	**Sacred Bridge** (GB)	8	10
111	**Sissoko** (IRE)	8	10
111	**Straight Answer** (IRE)	8	10
111	**Trident** (FR)	8	10
111	**Wild Beauty** (GB)	8	10
110	**Asymmetric** (IRE)	8	9
110	**Berkshire Shadow** (GB)	8	9
110	**Caturra** (IRE)	8	9
110	**Imperial Fighter** (IRE)	8	9
110	**Malavath** (IRE)	8	9
110	**Prosperous Voyage** (IRE)	8	9
110	**Times Square** (FR)	8	9
110	**Twilight Jet** (IRE)	8	9

LONGINES WORLD'S BEST RACEHORSE RANKINGS 2021

For **three-year-olds** rated 115 or greater by the IFHA World's Best Racehorse Rankings Conference.

Rating		Trained
127	Adayar (IRE)	GB
127	St Mark's Basilica (FR)	IRE
125	Baaeed (GB)	GB
124	Efforia (JPN)	JPN
124	Flightline (USA)	USA
124	Life Is Good (USA)	USA
124	Medina Spirit (USA)	USA
123	Essential Quality (USA)	USA
123	Hurricane Lane (IRE)	GB
123	Sealiway (FR)	FR
122	Hot Rod Charlie (USA)	USA
122	Jackie's Warrior (USA)	USA
122	Poetic Flare (IRE)	IRE
121	Dubai Honour (IRE)	GB
121	Golden Pal (USA)	USA
121	Mandaloun (USA)	USA
120	Midnight Bourbon (USA)	USA
120	Shahryar (JPN)	JPN
120	Snowfall (JPN)	IRE
120	State of Rest (IRE)	IRE
120	Yibir (GB)	GB
119	Alcohol Free (IRE)	GB
119	Anamoe (AUS)	AUS
119	Dr Schivel (USA)	USA
119	Lone Eagle (IRE)	GB
119	Schnell Meister (GER)	JPN
119	Stella Veloce (JPN)	JPN
119	Suesa (IRE)	FR
118	Creative Force (IRE)	GB
118	Danon The Kid (JPN)	JPN
118	Home Affairs (AUS)	AUS
118	Mac Swiney (IRE)	IRE
118	Pixie Knight (JPN)	JPN
118	Rombauer (USA)	USA
118	Titleholder (JPN)	JPN
117	Great Magician (JPN)	JPN
117	Master of The Seas (IRE)	GB
117	Rock Your World (USA)	USA
117	Sisfahan (FR)	GER
117	Winter Power (IRE)	GB
116	Drain The Clock (USA)	USA
116	Grenadier Guards (JPN)	JPN
116	Highly Motivated (USA)	USA
116	Hitotsu (AUS)	AUS
116	Irwin (ARG)	ARG
116	Lucky Vega (IRE)	IRE
116	Mendocino (GER)	GER
116	Mojo Star (IRE)	GB
116	Profondo (AUS)	AUS
116	Rougir (FR)	FR
116	Santa Barbara (IRE)	IRE
116	Shantisara (IRE)	USA
116	Tashkhan (IRE)	GB
115	Alenquer (FR)	GB
115	Bubble Gift (FR)	FR
115	Clairiere (USA)	USA
115	Dragon Symbol (GB)	GB
115	Following Sea (USA)	USA
115	Going Global (IRE)	USA
115	Ho O Amazon (JPN)	JPN
115	In The Congo (AUS)	AUS
115	Malathaat (USA)	USA
115	Millebosc (FR)	FR
115	Planetario (BRZ)	BRZ
115	Rebel's Romance (IRE)	UAE
115	Saffron Beach (IRE)	GB
115	Scope (IRE)	GB
115	Snow Lantern (GB)	GB
115	Sodashi (JPN)	JPN
115	Zodiacal (ARG)	ARG

OLDER HORSES 2021

For **four-year-olds and up** rated 115 or greater by the IFHA World's Best Racehorse Rankings Conference.

Rating		Age	Trained
129	Knicks Go (USA)	6	USA
127	Mishriff (IRE)	5	GB
126	Contrail (JPN)	5	JPN
125	Golden Sixty (AUS)	7	HK
125	Palace Pier (GB)	5	GB
124	Torquator Tasso (GER)	5	GER
124	Nature Strip (AUS)	8	AUS
123	Glory Vase (JPN)	7	JPN
123	Verry Elleegant (NZ)	7	AUS
123	Subjectivist (GB)	5	GB
122	Incentivise (AUS)	6	AUS
122	Domestic Spending (GB)	5	USA
122	Mystic Guide (USA)	5	USA
121	Eduardo (AUS)	9	AUS
121	Zaaki (GB)	7	AUS
121	Masked Crusader (AUS)	6	AUS
121	Authority (JPN)	5	JPN
121	Charlatan (USA)	5	USA
121	Deep Bond (JPN)	5	JPN
120	Addeybb (IRE)	8	GB
120	Exultant (IRE) (ex Irishcorrespondent)	8	HK
120	Monomoy Girl (USA)	7	USA
120	Skalleti (FR)	7	FR
120	Chrono Genesis (JPN)	6	JPN
120	Gran Alegria (JPN)	6	JPN
120	Lord North (IRE)	6	GB
120	Tarnawa (IRE)	6	IRE
120	Trueshan (FR)	6	GB
120	Pyledriver (GB)	5	GB
120	T O Keynes (JPN)	5	JPN
119	Do It Again (SAF)	8	SAF
119	Rainbow Bridge (SAF)	8	SAF
119	Village King (ARG)	8	ARG
119	Mugatoo (IRE)	7	AUS
119	World Premiere (JPN)	6	JPN
119	Al Aasy (IRE)	5	GB
119	Aloha West (USA)	5	USA
119	Art Collector (USA)	5	USA
119	Colonel Liam (USA)	5	USA
119	Max Player (USA)	5	USA
119	Starman (GB)	5	GB
118	Southern Legend (AUS)	10	HK
118	Dream of Dreams (IRE)	8	GB
118	Stradivarius (IRE)	8	GB
118	Indy Champ (JPN)	7	JPN
118	Sanrei Pocket (JPN)	7	JPN
118	The Revenant (GB)	7	FR
118	Think It Over (AUS)	7	AUS
118	Waikuku (IRE)	7	HK
118	Broome (IRE)	6	IRE
118	Dalasan (AUS)	6	AUS
118	Danon Kingly (JPN)	6	JPN
118	Letruska (USA)	6	USA
118	Loves Only You (JPN)	6	JPN
118	More Than This (GB)	6	HK
118	Sir Dragonet (IRE)	6	AUS
118	Sir Ron Priestley (GB)	6	GB
118	Space Blues (IRE)	6	GB
118	Unicorn Lion (IRE)	6	JPN
118	Alpinista (GB)	5	GB

Rating		Age	Trained
118	Gamine (USA)	5	USA
118	Lei Papale (JPN)	5	JPN
118	Love (IRE)	5	IRE
118	Mare Australis (IRE)	5	FR
118	Maxfield (USA)	5	USA
118	Order of Australia (IRE)	5	IRE
118	Real World (IRE)	5	GB
118	Russian Camelot (IRE)	5	AUS
117	Furore (NZ)	8	HK
117	Hot King Prawn (AUS) (ex Join In)	8	HK
117	Angel of Truth (AUS)	7	AUS
117	Behemoth (AUS)	7	AUS
117	Cascadian (AUS)	7	AUS
117	Fifty Stars (IRE)	7	AUS
117	Ka Ying Star (GB) (ex Urban Aspect)	7	HK
117	Kolding (NZ)	7	AUS
117	Lone Rock (USA)	7	USA
117	Marianafoot (FR)	7	FR
117	My Sister Nat (FR)	7	USA
117	Hishi Iguazu (JPN)	6	JPN
117	Lady Bowthorpe (GB)	6	GB
117	Mo Forza (USA)	6	USA
117	Probabeel (NZ)	6	NZ
117	Spanish Mission (USA)	6	GB
117	Tetaze (ARG)	6	ARG
117	Zenden (USA)	6	USA
117	Armory (IRE)	5	IRE
117	Gufo (USA)	5	USA
117	Jet Dark (SAF)	5	SAF
117	Kommetdieding (SAF)	5	SAF
117	Lope Y Fernandez (IRE)	5	IRE
117	Malmoos (SAF)	5	SAF
117	Mo'unga (NZ)	5	AUS
117	Salios (JPN)	5	JPN
117	Smooth Like Strait (USA)	5	USA
117	Swiss Skydiver (USA)	5	USA
117	Tripoli (USA)	5	USA
117	Victor Ludorum (GB)	5	FR
117	War Like Goddess (USA)	5	USA
117	Wonderful Tonight (FR)	5	GB
116	Dreamforce (AUS)	10	AUS
116	Lord Glitters (FR)	9	GB
116	Twilight Payment (IRE)	9	IRE
116	Avilius (GB)	8	AUS
116	Kiseki (JPN)	8	JPN
116	Melody Belle (NZ)	8	NZ
116	Aero Trem (BRZ)	7	URU
116	Arcadia Queen (AUS)	7	AUS
116	Avantage (AUS)	7	NZ
116	Chuwa Wizard (JPN)	7	JPN
116	Danon Smash (JPN)	7	JPN
116	George Washington (BRZ)	7	BRZ
116	Gytrash (AUS)	7	AUS
116	Mr Quickie (AUS)	7	AUS
116	Pimper's Paradise (BRZ)	7	BRZ
116	Savatoxl (AUS)	7	AUS
116	Strategos (ARG)	7	ARG
116	Tofane (NZ)	7	AUS
116	Zoutori (AUS)	7	AUS
116	Audarya (FR)	6	GB

Rating		Age	Trained
116	**Emaraaty Ana (GB)**	6	GB
116	**Got The Greenlight (SAF)**	6	SAF
116	**Grand Glory (GB)**	6	FR
116	**Lieutenant Dan (USA)**	6	USA
116	**Lost And Running (NZ)**	6	AUS
116	**Marche Lorraine (JPN)**	6	JPN
116	**Nonconformist (AUS)**	6	AUS
116	**Panfield (CHI) (ex Look Pen)**	6	HK
116	**Riodini (NZ)**	6	AUS
116	**Rio Querari (SAF)**	6	SAF
116	**Sky Field (AUS)**	6	HK
116	**Wellington (AUS)**	6	HK
116	**Aristoteles (JPN)**	5	JPN
116	**Catch Twentytwo (SAF)**	5	SAF
116	**Express Train (USA)**	5	USA
116	**Happy Saver (USA)**	5	USA
116	**Helvic Dream (IRE)**	5	IRE
116	**Hukum (IRE)**	5	GB
116	**Linebacker (SAF)**	5	SAF
116	**Mischevious Alex (USA)**	5	USA
116	**Sonnyboyliston (IRE)**	5	IRE
116	**Tagaloa (AUS)**	5	AUS
116	**Western Empire (NZ)**	5	AUS
115	**Secret Ambition (GB)**	9	UAE
115	**Whitmore (USA)**	9	USA
115	**Benbatl (GB)**	8	GB
115	**C Z Rocket (USA)**	8	USA
115	**Glen Shiel (GB)**	8	GB
115	**Homesman (USA)**	8	AUS
115	**Persian Knight (JPN)**	8	JPN
115	**Streets of Avalon (AUS)**	8	AUS
115	**Trekking (AUS)**	8	AUS
115	**Walton Street (GB)**	8	UAE
115	**Arctos (JPN)**	7	JPN
115	**Belgarion (SAF)**	7	SAF
115	**Classique Legend (AUS)**	7	AUS
115	**Columbus County (NZ) (ex Sword In Stone)**	7	HK
115	**Firenze Fire (USA)**	7	USA
115	**Glorious Dragon (IRE) (ex Stephensons Rocket)**	7	HK
115	**Omega Perfume (JPN)**	7	JPN
115	**Raging Bull (FR)**	7	USA
115	**Regal Power (AUS)**	7	AUS
115	**United (USA)**	7	USA
115	**Atletico El Culano (URU)**	6	URU

Rating		Age	Trained
115	**By My Standards (USA)**	6	USA
115	**Casino Fountain (JPN)**	6	JPN
115	**Ce Ce (USA)**	6	USA
115	**Colette (AUS)**	6	AUS
115	**Duhail (IRE)**	6	FR
115	**Dunbar Road (USA)**	6	USA
115	**Gustavus Weston (IRE)**	6	IRE
115	**Ivar (BRZ)**	6	USA
115	**Japan (GB)**	6	IRE
115	**Lucky Patch (NZ) (ex Paleontologist)**	6	HK
115	**Motakhayyel (GB)**	6	GB
115	**Mozu Bello (JPN)**	6	JPN
115	**Mutually (JPN)**	6	JPN
115	**Nahaarr (IRE)**	6	GB
115	**Oxted (GB)**	6	GB
115	**Royal Flag (USA)**	6	USA
115	**Royal Ship (BRZ)**	6	USA
115	**Search For A Song (IRE)**	6	IRE
115	**Sir Busker (IRE)**	6	GB
115	**Superstorm (AUS)**	6	AUS
115	**Two Emmys (USA)**	6	USA
115	**Vin de Garde (JPN)**	6	JPN
115	**Aegon (NZ)**	5	NZ
115	**Al Suhail (GB)**	5	GB
115	**Althiqa (GB)**	5	GB
115	**Beau Rossa (AUS)**	5	AUS
115	**Cafe Pharoah (USA)**	5	JPN
115	**Cezanne (USA)**	5	USA
115	**Country Grammer (USA)**	5	USA
115	**Daring Tact (JPN)**	5	JPN
115	**Explosive Jack (NZ)**	5	AUS
115	**Gold Trip (FR)**	5	FR
115	**I'm Thunderstruck (NZ)**	5	AUS
115	**Independence Hall (USA)**	5	USA
115	**Jackson Pollock (BRZ)**	5	BRZ
115	**Lauda Sion (JPN)**	5	JPN
115	**Lion's Roar (NZ)**	5	AUS
115	**Luthier Blues (ARG)**	5	ARG
115	**Nerium (IRE)**	5	GER
115	**Prague (AUS)**	5	AUS
115	**Russian Emperor (IRE)**	5	HK
115	**Shedaresthedevil (USA)**	5	USA
115	**Silver State (USA)**	5	USA
115	**Tizamagician (USA)**	5	USA

RACING POST CHAMPIONS 2021

ONLY HORSES WHICH HAVE RUN IN EUROPE ARE INCLUDED

FOUR-YEAR-OLDS AND UP

MISHRIFF	128
PALACE PIER	127
TORQUATOR TASSO	126
STARMAN	124
SPACE BLUES	124
DREAM OF DREAMS	123

THREE-YEAR-OLD COLT

ADAYAR	129
ST MARK'S BASILICA	128
BAAEED	127
HURRICANE LANE	125
POETIC FLARE	124
SEALIWAY	124

THREE-YEAR-OLD FILLY

SUESA	122
ALCOHOL FREE	121
SNOWFALL	121
WINTER POWER	119
SAFFRON BEACH	118
TEONA	118

SPRINTER

STARMAN	124
SPACE BLUES	123
DREAM OF DREAMS	123
MOTAKHAYYEL	121
OXTED	121
CREATIVE FORCE	121
EMARAATY ANA	121

STAYER

SUBJECTIVIST	122
TRUESHAN	122
HURRICANE LANE	122
SONNYBOYLISTON	121
TWILIGHT PAYMENT	120

TWO-YEAR-OLD COLT

NATIVE TRAIL	122
LUXEMBOURG	117
COROEBUS	116
DUBAWI LEGEND	115
PERFECT POWER	115

TWO-YEAR-OLD FILLY

TENEBRISM	116
INSPIRAL	114
FLOTUS	113
ZELLIE	113
DISCOVERIES	110
SACRED BRIDGE	110

MEDIAN TIMES 2021

The following Raceform median times are used in the calculation of the Split Second speed figures. They represent a true average time for the distance, which has been arrived at after looking at the winning times for all races over each distance within the past five years, except for those restricted to two or three-year-olds.

Some current race distances have been omitted as they have not yet had a sufficient number of races run over them to produce a reliable average time.

ASCOT

5f................................1m 1.50	1m Straight....................1m 41.40	1m 7f 209y.....................3m 34.49
6f................................1m 15.11	1m 1f 212y.....................2m 10.75	2m 3f 210y.....................4m 25.11
7f................................1m 30.34	1m 3f 211y.....................2m 35.37	2m 5f 143y.....................4m 52.56
7f 213y Round 1m 41.60	1m 6f 34y.......................3m 10.39	

AYR

5f................................1m 0.42	7f 50y...........................1m 32.76	1m 5f 26y.......................2m 59.10
5f 110y........................1m 7.20	1m................................1m 44.06	1m 7f.............................3m 33.80
6f................................1m 14.73	1m 2f............................2m 13.83	1m 1f 105y.....................4m 0.50

BATH

5f 10y..........................1m 0.60	1m 2f 37y......................2m 12.60	1m 6f.............................3m 4.10
5f 160y........................1m 10.40	1m 3f 137y.....................2m 31.41	2m 1f 24y.......................3m 51.40
1m................................1m 42.66	1m 5f 11y.......................2m 53.77	

BEVERLEY

5f................................1m 4.30	1m 100y........................1m 48.45	1m 4f 23y.......................2m 45.84
7f 96y..........................1m 35.50	1m 1f 207y.....................2m 10.80	2m 32y..........................3m 37.30

BRIGHTON

5f 60y..........................1m 3.32	7f 211y..........................1m 37.15	1m 3f 198y.....................2m 36.56
5f 215y........................1m 11.30	7f 216y..........................1m 38.70	
6f 210y........................1m 23.10	1m 1f 207y.....................2m 6.40	

CARLISLE

5f................................1m 2.10	6f 195y..........................1m 28.00	1m 3f 39y.......................2m 29.70
5f 182y........................1m 12.70	7f 173y..........................1m 41.90	1m 6f 32y.......................3m 13.00
5f 193y........................1m 15.10	1m 1f.............................2m 1.00	2m 1f 47y.......................3m 55.00

CATTERICK

5f................................1m 0.00	7f 6y.............................1m 26.60	1m 5f 192y.....................3m 0.00
5f 212y........................1m 14.20	1m 4f 13y......................2m 39.50	1m 7f 189y.....................3m 39.00

CHELMSFORD (A.W)

5f................................59.40	1m................................1m 38.50	1m 6f.............................3m 0.20
6f................................1m 12.20	1m 2f............................2m 6.10	2m................................3m 29.00
7f................................1m 25.80	1m 5f 66y......................2m 53.60	

CHEPSTOW

5f 16y..........................1m 0.30	1m 14y..........................1m 35.80	2m................................3m 39.10
6f 16y..........................1m 12.30	1m 2f............................2m 10.00	
7f 16y..........................1m 24.40	1m 4f............................2m 37.30	

CHESTER

5f 15y..........................1m 3.50	7f 127y..........................1m 35.70	1m 5f 84y.......................3m 0.60
5f 110y........................1m 7.00	1m 2f 70y......................2m 14.30	1m 6f 87y.......................3m 10.00
6f 17y..........................1m 16.40	1m 3f 75y......................2m 30.40	1m 7f 196y.....................3m 34.00
7f 1y............................1m 28.00	1m 4f 63y......................2m 44.00	2m 2f 140y.....................4m 4.60

DONCASTER

5f 3y	1m 0.30	7f 6y	1m 26.40	1m 3f 197y	2m 33.20
5f 143y	1m 8.10	7f 213y Round	1m 38.00	1m 6f 115y	3m 9.00
6f 2y	1m 13.10	1m Straight	1m 37.70	2m 109y	3m 40.40
6f 111y	1m 19.60	1m 2f 43y	2m 12.30	2m 1f 197y	3m 55.00

EPSOM

5f	55.23	7f 3y	1m 24.40	1m 2f 17y	2m 11.18
6f 3y	1m 9.10	1m 113y	1m 46.90	1m 4f 6y	2m 40.19

FFOS LAS

5f	59.30	1m	1m 42.90	1m 6f	3m 9.60
6f	1m 10.90	2f	2m 11.30	2m	3m 33.70
7f 80y	1m 34.10	1m 3f 209y	2m 38.20		

GOODWOOD

5f	59.80	1m 1f 11y	2m 0.57	1m 6f	3m 7.44
6f	1m 13.42	1m 1f 197y	2m 11.14	2m	3m 40.26
7f	1m 29.09	2m 30.58	2m 4f 134y	4m 38.31	
1m	1m 42.50	1m 3f 218y	2m 44.48		

HAMILTON

5f 7y	1m 0.40	1m 1f 35y	1m 59.10	1m 5f 16y	2m 52.60
6f 6y	1m 13.20	1m 3f 15y	2m 24.60		
1m 68y	1m 48.40	1m 4f 15y	2m 39.60		

HAYDOCK

5f	1m 0.60	7f 212yl	1m 42.70	1m 6fl	3m 9.40
5fl	1m 0.60	1m 37y	1m 45.60	6fl	3m 9.40
6f	1m 14.60	2f 42yl	2m 13.80	1m 6f 1y	3m 9.00
6fl	1m 14.60	1m 2f 100y	2m 16.60	2m 45y	3m 36.70
6f 212yl	1m 28.80	1m 3f 140yl	2m 32.60		
7f 37y	1m 32.20	1m 3f 175y	2m 37.50		

KEMPTON (A.W)

5f	1m 0.50	1m	1m 39.40	1m 3f 219y	2m 34.50
6f	1m 12.80	1m 1f 219y	2m 8.00	1m 7f 218y	3m 30.10[rt\n\x\x [rt
7f	1m 26.20	1m 2f 219y	2m 21.00		

LEICESTER

5f	1m 0.50	7f	1m 24.70	1m 2f	2m 8.70
6f	1m 11.90	1m 53y	1m 46.80	1m 3f 179y	2m 37.40

LINGFIELD

4f 217y	58.70	7f 135y	1m 31.70	1m 3f 133y	2m 34.00
6f	1m 11.50	1m 1f	1m 56.90	1m 6f	3m 6.20
7f	1m 24.30	1m 2f	2m 12.20	2m 68y	3m 36.00

LINGFIELD (A.W)

5f 6y	58.30	1m 1y	1m 37.30	1m 5f	2m 46.00
6f 1y	1m 11.90	1m 2f	2m 5.30	1m 7f 169y	3m 25.70
7f 1y	1m 24.80	1m 4f	2m 32.10		

MUSSELBURGH

5f 1y	1m 0.10	1m 208y	1m 53.10	1m 5f 216y	3m 3.90
7f 33y	1m 29.00	1m 4f 104y	2m 44.50	1m 7f 217y	3m 31.50
1m 2y	1m 40.00	2m 5f	2m 51.70		

NEWBURY

5f 34y	1m 2.40	1m Straight	1m 40.90	1m 5f 61y	2m 54.40
5f	1m 13.20	1m 2f	2m 9.50	2m	3m 39.40
6f 110y	1m 22.10	1m 3f	2m 24.20	2m 110y	3m 46.30
7f Straight	1m 26.90	1m 4f	2m 36.90		

NEWCASTLE (A.W)

5f	1m 0.90	1m 5y	1m 41.95	2m 56y	3m 41.22
6f	1m 13.59	1m 2f 42y	2m 13.98		
7f 14y	1m 27.60	1m 4f 98y	2m 44.69		

NEWMARKET

5f	1m 0.90	1m 1f	1m 53.10	2m	3m 27.30
6f	1m 12.50	1m 2f	2m 6.60	2m 2f	3m 53.00
7f	1m 27.40	1m 4f	2m 34.50		
1m	1m 40.00	1m 6f	3m 2.00		

NEWMARKET (JULY)

5f	58.80	1m	1m 39.90	1m 5f	2m 45.52
6f	1m 12.50	1m 2f	2m 6.30	1m 6f	3m 0.81
7f	1m 27.39	1m 4f	2m 36.25		

NOTTINGHAM

5f 8yl	1m 1.50	1m 75yl	1m 47.80	1m 6f	3m 9.80
5f 8y	1m 1.50	1m 2f	2m 13.50	2m	3m 40.00
6f 18y	1m 15.00	1m 2f 50yl	2m 18.50	2ml	3m 40.00
1m 75y	1m 47.80	1m 6fl	3m 9.80		

PONTEFRACT

5f 3y	1m 4.10	1m 2f 5y	2m 15.00	2m 2f 2y	4m 9.80
6f	1m 17.10	1m 4f 5y	2m 41.10	2m 5f 139y	4m 58.00
1m 6y	1m 45.90	2m 1f 27y	3m 52.30		

REDCAR

5f	58.50	7f 219y	1m 38.10	1m 5f 218y	3m 5.00
5f 217y	1m 11.80	1m 1f	1m 54.50	1m 7f 217y	3m 33.70
7f	1m 21.10	1m 2f 1y	2m 8.40		

RIPON

5f	1m 1.00	1m 1f 170y	2m 5.60	1m 6f	3m 4.40
6f	1m 13.50	1m 2f 190y	2m 22.00	2m	3m 30.40
1m	1m 42.50	1m 4f 10y	2m 39.30		

SALISBURY

5f	1m 2.50	1m	1m 43.50	1m 6f 44y	3m 8.00
6f	1m 16.50	1m 1f 201y	2m 9.30		
6f 213y	1m 30.50	1m 4f 5y	2m 43.60		

SANDOWN PARK

5f 10y	1m 0.30	1m 1f	1m 59.30	2m 50y	3m 39.87
7f	1m 30.70	1m 1f 209y	2m 12.34		
1m	1m 44.89	1m 6f	3m 12.70		

SOUTHWELL (A.W)

Previous median times no longer relevant following installation of new Tapeta surface in late 2021.

THIRSK

5f.. 59.40	7f 218y............................ 1m 42.50	2m 13y............................ 3m 32.00
6f.................................... 1m 12.10	1m 4f 8y......................... 2m 41.90	
7f.................................... 1m 28.50	1m 6f.............................. 3m 3.00	

WETHERBY

5f 110y............................ 1m 6.00	1m.................................. 1m 43.60	1m 6f............................... 3m 8.00
7f.................................... 1m 28.20	1m 2f.............................. 2m 11.50	2m................................... 3m 30.70

WINDSOR

5f 21y.............................. 1m 1.10	1m 31y............................ 1m 46.10	1m 3f 99y........................ 2m 32.40
6f 12y............................ 1m 13.20	1m 2f.............................. 2m 11.50	

WOLVERHAMPTON (A.W)

5f 21y.............................. 1m 1.90	1m 142y.......................... 1m 50.10	1m 5f 219y...................... 3m 1.00
6f 20y............................ 1m 14.50	1m 4f 104y...................... 2m 0.80	2m 120y.......................... 3m 39.30
7f 36y............................ 1m 28.80	1m 4f 51y........................ 2m 40.80	

YARMOUTH

5f 42y.............................. 1m 2.00	1m 3y.............................. 1m 38.20	1m 3f 104y...................... 2m 29.90
6f 3y.............................. 1m 13.50	1m 1f 21y........................ 1m 54.00	1m 6f 17y........................ 3m 4.70
7f 3y.............................. 1m 27.10	1m 2f 23y........................ 2m 8.80	

YORK

5f.. 58.88	7f 192y............................ 1m 39.00	1m 5f 188y...................... 3m 0.20
5f 89y............................ 1m 4.82	1m 177y.......................... 1m 50.40	2m 56y............................ 3m 36.50
6f.................................... 1m 12.60	1m 2f 56y........................ 2m 12.30	
7f.................................... 1m 25.50	1m 3f 188y...................... 2m 32.20	

RACING POST RECORD TIMES (FLAT)

ASCOT

DISTANCE	TIME	AGE	WEIGHT	GOING	HORSE	DATE
5f	58.80	2	9-1	Good To Firm	NO NAY NEVER	Jun 20 2013
5f	57.44	6	9-1	Good To Firm	MISS ANDRETTI	Jun 19 2007
6f (Str)	1m 12.39	2	9-1	Good To Firm	RAJASINGHE	Jun 20 2017
6f	1m 11.05	3	9-1	Good To Firm	BLUE POINT	May 3 2017
6f 110y	1m 21.15	2	8-6	Good	PENNY'S GIFT	Sep 26 2008
6f 110y	1m 20.21	3	9-2	Good To Firm	KHABFAIR	Sep 24 2004
7f	1m 25.73	2	9-3	Good	PINATUBO	Jun 22 2019
7f	1m 24.28	4	8-11	Good To Firm	GALICIAN	Jul 27 2013
7f 213y (Rnd)	1m 39.55	2	8-12	Good	JOSHUA TREE	Sep 26 2009
7f 213y (Rnd)	1m 35.89	3	9-0	Good To Firm	ALPHA CENTAURI	Jun 22 2018
1m (Str)	1m 36.60	4	9-0	Good To Firm	RIBCHESTER	Jun 20 2017
1m 1f 212y	2m 1.90	5	8-11	Good To Firm	THE FUGUE	Jun 18 2014
1m 3f 211y	2m 24.60	4	9-7	Good To Firm	NOVELLIST	Jul 27 2013
1m 5f 211y	2m 59.36	3	9-4	Good	BIG ORANGE	Oct 3 2014
1m 7f 209y	3m 24.12	4	8-12	Good To Firm	MIZZOU	Apr 29 2015
2m 3f 210y	4m 16.92	6	9-2	Good To Firm	RITE OF PASSAGE	Jun 17 2010
2m 5f 143y	4m 45.24	9	9-2	Good To Firm	PALLASATOR	Jun 23 2018

AYR

DISTANCE	TIME	AGE	WEIGHT	GOING	HORSE	DATE
5f	56.89	2	8-12	Good To Firm	VERTIGINOUS (IRE)	Sep 17 2021
5f	55.68	3	8-11	Good To Firm	LOOK BUSY	Jun 21 2008
6f	1m 9.73	2	7-10	Firm	SIR BERT	Sep 17 1969
6f	1m 8.37	5	8-6	Good To Firm	MAISON DIEU	Jun 21 2008
7f 50y	1m 28.99	2	9-0	Good	TAFAAHUM	Sep 19 2003
7f 50y	1m 26.43	4	9-4	Good To Firm	HAJJAM	May 22 2018
1m	1m 39.18	2	9-7	Good	MOONLIGHTNAVIGATOR	Sep 18 2014
1m	1m 36.00	4	7-13	Firm	SUFI	Sep 16 1959
1m 1f 20y	1m 50.30	4	9-3	Good	RETIREMENT	Sep 19 2003
1m 2f	2m 4.02	4	9-9	Good To Firm	ENDLESS HALL	Jul 17 2000
1m 5f 26y	2m 45.81	4	9-7	Good To Firm	EDEN'S CLOSE	Sep 18 1993
1m 7f	3m 13.16	3	9-4	Good	ROMANY RYE	Sep 19 1991
2m 1f 105y	3m 45.20	4	6-13	Firm	CURRY	Sep 16 1955

BATH

DISTANCE	TIME	AGE	WEIGHT	GOING	HORSE	DATE
5f 10y	59.50	2	9-2	Firm	AMOUR PROPRE	Jul 24 2008
5f 10y	58.75	3	8-12	Firm	ENTICING	May 1 2007
5f 160y	1m 8.70	2	8-12	Firm	QALAHARI	Jul 24 2008
5f 160y	1m 7.40	4	9-10	Firm	MOTAGALLY	Sep 14 2020
1m 5y	1m 39.51	2	9-2	Firm	NATURAL CHARM	Sep 14 2014
1m 5y	1m 37.20	5	8-12	Good To Firm	ADOBE	Jun 17 2000
1m 5y	1m 37.24	3	9-4	Good To Firm	EMERGING (IRE)	Jun 30 2021
1m 2f 37y	2m 5.80	3	9-0	Good To Firm	CONNOISSEUR BAY	May 29 1998
1m 3f 137y	2m 25.74	3	9-0	Hard	TOP THE CHARTS	Sep 8 2005
1m 5f 11y	2m 47.20	4	10-0	Firm	FLOWN	Aug 13 1991
1m 6f	2m 58.97	4	9-10	Firm	CHARLIE D	Sep 15 2019
2m 1f 24y	3m 43.41	6	7-9	Firm	YAHESKA	Jun 14 2003

BEVERLEY

DISTANCE	TIME	AGE	WEIGHT	GOING	HORSE	DATE
5f	1m 0.85	2	9-5	Good To Firm	BILLIAN	Aug 12 2020
5f	59.51	7	9-2	Good To Firm	TIS MARVELLOUS	Aug 28 2021
7f 96y	1m 31.10	2	9-7	Good To Firm	CHAMPAGNE PRINCE	Aug 10 1995
7f 96y	1m 31.10	2	9-0	Firm	MAJAL	Jul 30 1991
7f 96y	1m 29.50	3	7-8	Firm	WHO'S TEF	Jul 30 1991
1m 100y	1m 43.30	2	9-0	Firm	ARDEN	Sep 24 1986
1m 100y	1m 42.20	3	8-4	Firm	LEGAL CASE	Jun 14 1989
1m 1f 207y	2m 1.00	3	9-7	Good To Firm	EASTERN ARIA	Aug 29 2009
1m 4f 23y	2m 33.35	5	9-2	Good To Firm	TWO JABS	Apr 23 2015
2m 32y	3m 28.62	4	9-11	Good To Firm	CORPUS CHORISTER	Jul 18 2017

BRIGHTON

DISTANCE	TIME	AGE	WEIGHT	GOING	HORSE	DATE
5f 60y	1m 0.10	2	9-0	Firm	BID FOR BLUE	May 6 1993
5f 60y	59.30	3	8-9	Firm	PLAY HEVER GOLF	May 26 1993
5f 215y	1m 8.10	2	8-9	Firm	SONG MIST	Jul 16 1996
5f 215y	1m 7.01	6	9-8	Good To Firm	KENDERGARTEN KOP &	Jun 1 2021
		4	9-7		BATCHELOR BOY	
6f 210y	1m 19.90	2	8-11	Hard	RAIN BURST	Sep 15 1988
6f 210y	1m 19.53	4	9-2	Good To Firm	ARABIC CHARM	Jun 1 2021
7f 211y	1m 32.80	2	9-7	Firm	ASIAN PETE	Oct 3 1989
7f 211y	1m 30.50	5	8-11	Firm	MYSTIC RIDGE	May 27 1999
1m 1f 207y	2m 4.70	2	9-0	Good To Soft	ESTEEMED MASTER	Nov 2 2001
1m 1f 207y	1m 57.20	3	9-0	Firm	GET THE MESSAGE	Apr 30 1984
1m 3f 198y	2m 25.80	4	8-2	Firm	NEW ZEALAND	Jul 4 1985

CARLISLE

DISTANCE	TIME	AGE	WEIGHT	GOING	HORSE	DATE
5f	1m 0.10	2	8-5	Firm	LA TORTUGA	Aug 2 1999
5f	58.80	3	9-8	Good To Firm	ESATTO	Aug 21 2002
5f 193y	1m 12.30	2	9-2	Good To Firm	BURRISHOOLE ABBEY	Jun 22 2016
5f 193y	1m 10.83	4	9-0	Good To Firm	BO MCGINTY	Sep 11 2005
6f 195y	1m 26.34	2	8-12	Good	MAKALU	Aug 26 2021
6f 195y	1m 24.30	3	8-9	Good To Firm	MARJURITA	Aug 21 2002
7f 173y	1m 35.84	5	8-12	Good To Firm	WAARIF	Jun 27 2018
1m 1f	1m 53.84	2	9-0	Firm	LITTLE JIMBOB	Jun 14 2004
1m 3f 39y	2m 20.46	5	10-0	Good To Firm	AASHEQ	Jun 27 2018
1m 3f 206y	2m 29.13	5	9-8	Good To Firm	TEMPSFORD	Sep 19 2005
1m 6f 32y	3m 2.20	6	8-10	Firm	EXPLOSIVE SPEED	May 26 1994

CATTERICK

DISTANCE	TIME	AGE	WEIGHT	GOING	HORSE	DATE
5f	57.60	2	9-0	Firm	H HARRISON	Oct 8 2002
5f	57.10	4	8-7	Firm	KABCAST	Jul 6 1989
5f 212y	1m 11.40	2	9-4	Firm	CAPTAIN NICK	Jul 11 1978
5f 212y	1m 9.86	9	8-13	Good To Firm	SHARP HAT	May 30 2003
7f 6y	1m 24.10	2	8-11	Firm	LINDA'S FANTASY	Sep 18 1982
7f 6y	1m 22.56	3	8-7	Firm	DIFFERENTIAL	May 31 2003
1m 5f 192y	2m 54.80	3	8-5	Firm	GERYON	May 31 1984
1m 7f 189y	3m 20.80	4	7-11	Firm	BEAN BOY	Jul 8 1982

CHELMSFORD (AW)

DISTANCE	TIME	AGE	WEIGHT	GOING	HORSE	DATE
5f	58.19	2	9-2	Standard	SHALAA ASKER	Sep 13 2020
5f	57.30	7	8-13	Standard	BROTHER TIGER	Feb 7 2016
6f	1m 10.62	2	9-4	Standard	KOEPP	Oct 8 2020
6f	1m 9.87	3	9-2	Standard	TRUMBLE	Oct 9 2021
7f	1m 22.53	4	9-2	Standard	JUMAIRA BAY	Jun 16 2021
1m	1m 37.15	2	9-3	Standard	DRAGON MALL	Sep 26 2015
1m	1m 35.09	6	8-8	Standard	EXTRODINAIR	Jun 17 2021
1m 2f	2m 1.81	5	9-7	Standard	BIN BATTUTA	Sep 28 2019
1m 5f 66y	2m 47.00	4	8-7	Standard	COORG	Jan 6 2016
1m 6f	2m 55.61	3	9-0	Standard	BRASCA	Sep 5 2019
2m	3m 22.37	5	9-3	Standard	NOTARISED	Mar 3 2016

CHEPSTOW

DISTANCE	TIME	AGE	WEIGHT	GOING	HORSE	DATE
5f 16y	57.60	2	8-11	Firm	MICRO LOVE	Jul 8 1986
5f 16y	56.80	3	8-4	Firm	TORBAY EXPRESS	Sep 15 1979
6f 16y	1m 8.50	2	9-2	Firm	NINJAGO	Jul 27 2012
6f 16y	1m 8.10	3	9-7	Firm	AMERICA CALLING	Sep 18 2001
7f 16y	1m 20.48	2	9-0	Good	FESTIVAL DAY	Sep 17 2019
7f 16y	1m 19.30	3	9-0	Firm	TARANAKI	Sep 18 2001
1m 14y	1m 33.10	2	8-11	Good To Firm	SKI ACADEMY	Aug 28 1995
1m 14y	1m 31.60	3	8-13	Firm	STOLI	Sep 18 2001
1m 2f	2m 3.37	3	9-2	Good	BALEARIC	Jul 15 2021
1m 2f 36y	2m 4.10	3	8-5	Good To Firm	ELA ATHENA	Jul 23 1999
1m 2f 36y	2m 4.10	5	8-9	Hard	LEONIDAS	Jul 5 1983
1m 2f 36y	2m 4.10	5	7-8	Good To Firm	IT'S VARADAN	Sep 9 1989
1m 4f 23y	2m 31.00	5	8-11	Hard	THE FRIEND	Aug 29 1983
1m 4f 23y	2m 31.00	3	8-9	Good To Firm	SPRITSAIL	Jul 13 1989
2m 49y	3m 27.70	4	9-0	Good To Firm	WIZZARD ARTIST	Jul 1 1989
2m 2f	3m 56.40	5	8-7	Good To Firm	LAFFAH	Jul 8 2000

CHESTER

DISTANCE	TIME	AGE	WEIGHT	GOING	HORSE	DATE
5f 15y	59.94	2	9-2	Good To Firm	LEIBA LEIBA	Jun 26 2010
5f 15y	58.88	3	8-7	Good To Firm	PETERKIN	Jul 11 2014
5f 110y	1m 6.39	2	8-7	Good To Soft	KINEMATIC	Sep 27 2014
5f 110y	1m 4.54	5	8-5	Good	BOSSIPOP	Sep 1 2018
6f 17y	1m 12.54	2	8-12	Good	GLASS SLIPPERS	Sep 1 2018
6f 17y	1m 12.02	5	9-5	Good To Firm	DEAUVILLE PRINCE	Jun 13 2015
7f 1y	1m 25.29	2	9-0	Good To Firm	DUE RESPECT	Sep 25 2002
7f 1y	1m 23.75	5	8-13	Good To Firm	THREE GRACES	Jul 9 2005
7f 127y	1m 32.29	2	9-0	Good To Firm	BIG BAD BOB	Sep 25 2002
7f 127y	1m 30.62	5	9-10	Good	OH THIS IS US	Sep 1 2018
1m 2f 70y	2m 7.15	3	8-8	Good To Firm	STOTSFOLD	Sep 23 2006
1m 3f 75y	2m 22.17	3	8-12	Good To Firm	PERFECT TRUTH	May 6 2009
1m 5f 84y	2m 45.43	5	8-11	Firm	RAKAPOSHI KING	May 7 1987
1m 7f 196y	3m 20.33	4	9-0	Good To Firm	GRAND FROMAGE	Jul 13 2002
2m 2f 140y	3m 58.89	7	9-2	Good To Firm	GREENWICH MEANTIME	May 9 2007

DONCASTER

DISTANCE	TIME	AGE	WEIGHT	GOING	HORSE	DATE
5f 3y	58.04	2	9-1	Good	GUTAIFAN	Sep 11 2015
5f 3y	57.30	5	9-11	Good To Firm	KHAADEM	Sep 8 2021
5f 143y	1m 5.38	4	9-7	Good	MUTHMIR	Sep 13 2014
6f 2y	1m 10.33	2	9-4	Good To Firm	COMEDY	Jun 29 2018
6f 2y	1m 9.36	3	9-9	Good To Firm	STARMAN	Aug 15 2020
6f 111y	1m 17.19	2	8-9	Good	MR LUPTON	Sep 10 2015
6f 111y	1m 16.62	4	8-10	Good	BADR AL BADOOR	Sep 12 2014
7f 6y	1m 22.78	2	9-5	Good	BASATEEN	Jul 24 2014
7f 6y	1m 21.81	6	8-7	Good To Firm	SIGNOR PELTRO	May 30 2009
7f 213y (Rnd)	1m 38.37	2	8-6	Good To Soft	ANTONIOLA	Oct 23 2009
7f 213y (Rnd)	1m 34.46	4	8-12	Good To Firm	STAYING ON	Apr 18 2009
1m (Str)	1m 36.45	2	9-0	Good To Firm	LILAC ROAD	Aug 15 2020
1m (Str)	1m 34.95	6	8-9	Firm	QUICK WIT	Jul 18 2013
1m 2f 43y	2m 4.81	4	8-13	Good To Firm	RED GALA	Sep 12 2007
1m 3f 197y	2m 27.48	3	8-4	Good To Firm	SWIFT ALHAARTH	Sep 10 2011
1m 6f 115y	3m 0.27	3	9-1	Good To Firm	LOGICIAN	Sep 14 2019
2m 109y	3m 34.52	7	9-0	Good To Firm	INCHNADAMPH	Nov 10 2007
2m 1f 197y	3m 48.41	4	9-4	Good To Firm	SEPTIMUS	Sep 14 2007

EPSOM

DISTANCE	TIME	AGE	WEIGHT	GOING	HORSE	DATE
5f	55.02	2	8-9	Good To Firm	PRINCE ASLIA	Jun 9 1995
5f	54.00	6	8-13	Good To Firm	ORNATE	Jun 1 2019
6f 3y	1m 7.85	2	8-11	Good To Firm	SHOWBROOK	Jun 5 1991
6f 3y	1m 6.20	9	8-11	Good To Firm	WATCHABLE	Jun 1 2019
7f 3y	1m 21.30	2	8-9	Good To Firm	RED PEONY	Jul 29 2004
7f 3y	1m 19.88	7	9-5	Good	SAFE VOYAGE	Jul 4 2020
1m 113y	1m 42.80	2	8-5	Good To Firm	NIGHTSTALKER	Aug 30 1988
1m 113y	1m 40.46	4	9-6	Good To Firm	ZAAKI	Jun 1 2019
1m 2f 17y	2m 3.50	5	7-11	Firm	CROSSBOW	Jun 7 1967
1m 4f 6y	2m 31.33	3	9-0	Good To Firm	WORKFORCE	Jun 5 2010

FFOS LAS

DISTANCE	TIME	AGE	WEIGHT	GOING	HORSE	DATE
5f	57.06	2	9-3	Good To Firm	MR MAJEIKA	May 5 2011
5f	56.35	5	8-8	Good	HAAJES	Sep 12 2009
6f	1m 9.00	2	9-5	Good To Firm	WONDER OF QATAR	Sep 14 2014
6f	1m 7.46	6	10-2	Good To Firm	HANDYTALK	Jul 29 2019
7f 80y	1m 30.15	2	9-2	Good To Firm	FOX TAL	Jul 24 2018
7f 80y	1m 28.26	6	8-12	Good	MABO	Aug 3 2021
1m	1m 39.36	2	9-2	Good To Firm	HALA HALA	Sep 2 2013
1m	1m 37.12	5	9-0	Good To Firm	ZEBRANO	May 5 2011
1m 2f	2m 4.85	8	8-12	Good To Firm	PELHAM CRESCENT	May 5 2011
1m 3f 209y	2m 31.18	3	9-9	Good	TRUESHAN	Aug 29 2019
1m 6f	2m 58.61	4	9-7	Good To Firm	LADY ECLAIR	Jul 12 2010
2m	3m 25.42	4	9-3	Good To Firm	LONG JOHN SILVER	Jul 24 2018

GOODWOOD

DISTANCE	TIME	AGE	WEIGHT	GOING	HORSE	DATE
5f	57.14	2	9-1	Good	YALTA	Jul 27 2016
5f	55.62	6	9-7	Good To Firm	BATTAASH	Jul 31 2020
6f	1m 9.81	2	8-11	Good To Firm	BACHIR	Jul 28 1999
6f	1m 9.10	6	9-0	Good To Firm	TAMAGIN	Sep 12 2009
7f	1m 24.99	2	8-11	Good To Firm	EKRAAR	Jul 19 1999
7f	1m 23.62	4	9-3	Good To Firm	TORO STRIKE	Aug 29 2021
1m	1m 37.21	2	9-0	Good	CALDRA	Sep 9 2006
1m	1m 35.28	3	8-13	Good	BEAT LE BON	Aug 2 2019
1m 1f 11y	1m 56.27	2	9-3	Good To Firm	DORDOGNE	Sep 22 2010
1m 1f 11y	1m 52.81	3	9-6	Good	VENA	Jul 27 1995
1m 1f 197y	2m 2.81	3	9-3	Good To Firm	ROAD TO LOVE	Aug 3 2006
1m 3f 44y	2m 22.77	3	9-3	Good	KHALIDI	May 26 2017
1m 3f 218y	2m 31.39	3	9-1	Good To Firm	CROSS COUNTER	Aug 4 2018
1m 6f	2m 57.61	4	9-6	Good To Firm	MEEZNAH	Jul 28 2011
2m	3m 21.55	5	9-10	Good To Firm	YEATS	Aug 3 2006
2m 4f	4m 11.75	3	7-10	Firm	LUCKY MOON	Aug 2 1990

HAMILTON

DISTANCE	TIME	AGE	WEIGHT	GOING	HORSE	DATE
5f 7y	57.95	2	8-8	Good To Firm	ROSE BLOSSOM	May 29 2009
5f 7y	57.20	5	9-4	Good To Firm	DAPPER MAN	Jun 27 2019
6f 6y	1m 10.00	2	8-12	Good To Firm	BREAK THE CODE	Aug 24 1999
6f 6y	1m 9.03	6	9-5	Good To Firm	GEORGE BOWEN	Jul 20 2018
1m 65y	1m 45.46	2	9-5	Good To Firm	LAAFIRAAQ	Sep 20 2015
1m 65y	1m 42.70	6	7-7	Firm	CRANLEY	Sep 25 1972
1m 1f 35y	1m 53.60	5	9-6	Good To Firm	REGENT'S SECRET	Aug 10 2005
1m 3f 15y	2m 18.66	3	9-3	Good To Firm	POSTPONED	Jul 18 2014
1m 4f 15y	2m 30.52	5	9-10	Good To Firm	RECORD BREAKER	Jun 10 2009
1m 5f 16y	2m 45.10	6	9-6	Firm	MENTALASANYTHIN	Jun 14 1995

HAYDOCK

DISTANCE	TIME	AGE	WEIGHT	GOING	HORSE	DATE
5f	58.56	2	8-2	Good To Firm	BARRACUDA BOY	Aug 11 2012
5f	56.39	5	9-4	Firm	BATED BREATH	May 26 2012
5f (Inner)	58.51	2	9-1	Good	FOUR DRAGONS	Oct 14 2016
5f (Inner)	57.38	7	9-12	Good To Firm	FOXY FOREVER	Jul 21 2017
6f	1m 10.98	4	9-9	Good To Firm	WOLFHOUND	Sep 4 1993
6f	1m 8.56	3	9-0	Firm	HARRY ANGEL	May 27 2017
6f (Inner)	1m 10.58	2	9-2	Good To Firm	PRESTBURY PARK	Jul 21 2017
6f (Inner)	1m 9.04	3	8-11	Good To Firm	PRINCES DES SABLES	Aug 8 2019
6f 212y (Inner)	1m 26.15	2	9-9	Good To Firm	ALBAHR	Jul 17 2021
6f 212y (Inner)	1m 23.52	4	9-1	Good To Firm	AL SUHAIL	Sep 2 2021
7f 37y	1m 27.57	2	9-2	Good To Firm	CONTRAST	Aug 5 2016
7f 37y	1m 25.50	3	8-11	Good	FORGE	Sep 1 2016
7f 212y (Inner)	1m 39.38	2	9-0	Good To Firm	NEW KINGDOM	Sep 2 2021
7f 212y (Inner)	1m 37.80	3	9-4	Good To Firm	SIDEWINDER	May 26 2017
1m 37y	1m 41.21	2	9-2	Good To Firm	TRIPLE TIME	Sep 4 2021
1m 37y	1m 38.50	4	8-11	Good To Firm	EXPRESS HIMSELF	Jun 10 2015
1m 2f 42y (Inner)	2m 7.25	3	8-9	Good To Firm	LARAAIB	May 26 2017
1m 2f 100y	2m 7.53	4	9-5	Good To Firm	TEODORO	Aug 11 2018
1m 3f 140y (Inner)	2m 25.52	5	9-9	Good To Firm	DECEMBER SECOND	Aug 8 2019
1m 3f 175y	2m 25.53	4	8-12	Good To Firm	NUMBER THEORY	May 24 2012
1m 6f	2m 55.20	5	9-9	Good To Firm	HUFF AND PUFF	Sep 7 2012
2m 45y	3m 26.98	5	8-13	Good To Firm	DE RIGUEUR	Jun 8 2013

KEMPTON (AW)

DISTANCE	TIME	AGE	WEIGHT	GOING	HORSE	DATE
5f	58.96	2	8-6	Standard	GLAMOROUS SPIRIT	Nov 28 2008
5f	58.07	5	8-12	Standard	A MOMENTOFMADNESS	Apr 7 2018
6f	1m 11.02	2	9-1	Standard To Slow	INVINCIBLE ARMY	Sep 9 2017
6f	1m 9.79	4	8-11	Standard	TRINITYELITEDOTCOM	Mar 29 2014
7f	1m 23.79	2	8-0	Standard	ELSAAKB	Nov 8 2017
7f	1m 23.10	6	9-9	Standard	SIRIUS PROSPECT	Nov 20 2014
1m	1m 37.26	2	9-0	Standard	CECCHINI	Nov 8 2017
1m	1m 35.73	3	8-9	Standard	WESTERN ARISTOCRAT	Sep 15 2011
1m 1f 219y	2m 2.93	3	8-11	Standard To Slow	PLY	Sep 25 2017
1m 2f 219y	2m 15.65	4	8-8	Standard To Slow	FORBIDDEN PLANET	Mar 30 2019
1m 3f 219y	2m 28.99	6	9-3	Standard	SPRING OF FAME	Nov 7 2012
1m 7f 218y	3m 21.50	4	8-12	Standard	COLOUR VISION	May 2 2012

LEICESTER

DISTANCE	TIME	AGE	WEIGHT	GOING	HORSE	DATE
5f 2y	58.40	2	9-0	Firm	CUTTING BLADE	Jun 9 1986
5f 2y	57.85	5	9-5	Good To Firm	THE JOBBER	Sep 18 2006
5f 218y	1m 9.99	2	9-0	Good	EL MANATI	Aug 1 2012
5f 218y	1m 9.12	6	8-12	Good To Firm	PETER ISLAND	Apr 25 2009
7f	1m 22.83	2	9-5	Good To Firm	CLOUDBRIDGE	Aug 2 2020
7f	1m 22.24	5	9-2	Good To Firm	HOME OF THE BRAVE	Apr 29 2017
1m 53y	1m 44.05	2	8-11	Good To Firm	CONGRESSIONAL	Sep 6 2005
1m 53y	1m 41.89	5	9-7	Good To Firm	VAINGLORY	Jun 18 2009
1m 1f 216y	2m 5.30	2	9-1	Good To Firm	WINDSOR CASTLE	Oct 14 1996
1m 1f 216y	2m 2.40	4	9-6	Good To Firm	LADY ANGHARAD	Jun 18 2000
1m 1f 216y	2m 2.40	3	8-11	Firm	EFFIGY	Nov 4 1985
1m 3f 179y	2m 27.10	5	8-12	Good To Firm	MURGHEM	Jun 18 2000

LINGFIELD (TURF)

DISTANCE	TIME	AGE	WEIGHT	GOING	HORSE	DATE
4f 217y	56.76	2	9-2	Good	GLORY FIGHTER	May 11 2018
4f 217y	56.09	3	9-4	Good To Firm	WHITECREST	Sep 16 2011
6f	1m 9.41	2	9-0	Good To Firm	COMPANY MINX	Jul 10 2019
6f	1m 8.48	4	9-6	Good To Firm	REWAAYAT	Jul 17 2019
7f	1m 20.55	2	8-11	Good To Firm	HIKING	Aug 17 2013
7f	1m 20.44	3	9-5	Good	ADDITIONAL	Jun 26 2020
7f 135y	1m 29.32	2	9-3	Good To Firm	DUNDONNELL	Aug 4 2012
7f 135y	1m 26.73	3	8-6	Good To Firm	HIAAM	Jul 11 1987
1m 1f	1m 50.45	4	9-3	Good To Firm	ENZEMBLE	May 30 2019
1m 2f	2m 4.83	5	9-8	Good To Firm	HAIRDRYER	Jul 21 2018
1m 3f 133y	2m 23.95	3	8-5	Firm	NIGHT-SHIRT	Jul 14 1990
1m 6f	2m 58.88	3	8-13	Good To Firm	TIMOSHENKO	Jul 21 2018
2m 68y	3m 23.71	3	9-5	Good To Firm	LAURIES CRUSADOR	Aug 13 1988

LINGFIELD (AW)

DISTANCE	TIME	AGE	WEIGHT	GOING	HORSE	DATE
5f 6y	56.94	2	10-3	Standard	BEDFORD FLYER	Nov 25 2020
5f 6y	56.65	5	8-2	Standard	STRONG POWER	Jan 7 2022
6f 1y	1m 9.76	2	9-4	Standard	RED IMPRESSION	Nov 24 2018
6f 1y	1m 8.32	6	9-0	Standard	KACHY	Feb 2 2019
7f 1y	1m 22.67	2	9-3	Standard	COMPLICIT	Nov 23 2013
7f 1y	1m 21.90	4	9-9	Standard	CARDSHARP	Mar 13 2019
1m 1y	1m 35.70	2	8-13	Standard	QAADDIM	Oct 3 2019
1m 1y	1m 33.90	6	9-5	Standard	LUCKY TEAM	Mar 30 2018
1m 2f	2m 0.54	4	9-0	Standard	BANGKOK	Feb 1 2020
1m 4f	2m 26.99	6	9-11	Standard	PINZOLO	Jan 21 2017
1m 5f	2m 39.70	3	8-10	Standard	HIDDEN GOLD	Oct 30 2014
1m 7f 169y	3m 15.18	4	9-1	Standard	WINNING STORY	Apr 14 2017

MUSSELBURGH

DISTANCE	TIME	AGE	WEIGHT	GOING	HORSE	DATE
5f 1y	57.66	2	9-2	Good To Firm	IT DONT COME EASY	Jun 3 2017
5f 1y	56.77	9	9-10	Good To Firm	CASPIAN PRINCE	Jun 9 2018
7f 33y	1m 27.46	2	8-8	Good	DURHAM REFLECTION	Sep 14 2009
7f 33y	1m 25.00	9	8-8	Good To Firm	KALK BAY	Jun 4 2016
1m 2y	1m 40.34	2	8-12	Good To Firm	SUCCESSION	Sep 26 2004
1m 2y	1m 36.83	3	9-5	Good To Firm	GINGER JACK	Jul 13 2010
1m 208y	1m 50.42	8	8-11	Good To Firm	DHAULAR DHAR	Sep 3 2010
1m 4f 104y	2m 36.80	3	8-3	Good To Firm	HARRIS TWEED	Jun 5 2010
1m 5f	2m 46.41	3	9-5	Good To Firm	ALCAEUS	Sep 29 2013
1m 5f 216y	2m 57.98	7	8-5	Good To Firm	JONNY DELTA	Apr 18 2014
1m 7f 217y	3m 25.62	4	8-3	Good To Firm	ALDRETH	Jun 13 2015

NEWBURY

DISTANCE	TIME	AGE	WEIGHT	GOING	HORSE	DATE
5f 34y	1m 0.54	2	8-10	Good To Firm	GUBBASS	Jul 17 2021
5f 34y	58.40	3	9-0	Good	LAZULI	Sep 19 2020
6f	1m 9.70	2	9-1	Good	ALKUMAIT	Sep 19 2020
6f 8y	1m 9.42	3	8-11	Good To Firm	NOTA BENE	May 13 2005
6f 110y	1m 18.06	2	9-5	Good To Firm	TWIN SAILS	Jun 11 2015
7f (Str)	1m 23.04	2	8-11	Good To Firm	HAAFHD	Aug 15 2003
7f (Str)	1m 20.80	3	9-0	Good To Firm	MUHAARAR	Apr 18 2015
1m (Str)	1m 37.66	2	8-12	Good	YIBIR	Sep 18 2020
1m (Rnd)	1m 36.98	3	9-1	Good To Firm	HE'S OUR STAR	Jun 26 2018
1m (Str)	1m 35.07	4	8-11	Good To Firm	RHODODENDRON	May 19 2018
1m 1f	1m 49.65	3	8-0	Good To Firm	HOLTYE	May 21 1995
1m 2f	2m 1.29	3	8-7	Good To Firm	WALL STREET	Jul 20 1996
1m 3f 5y	2m 16.54	3	8-9	Good To Firm	GRANDERA	Sep 22 2001
1m 4f 5y	2m 28.26	4	9-7	Good To Firm	AZAMOUR	Jul 23 2005
1m 5f 61y	2m 44.90	5	10-0	Good To Firm	MYSTIC HILL	Jul 20 1996

NEWCASTLE (AW)

Distance	Time	Age	Weight	Going	HORSE	Date
5f	58.05	2	8-6	Standard	SPIN DOCTOR	Oct 25 2016
5f	57.78	3	8-9	Standard	ASTRAEA	Dec 15 2018
6f	1m 9.95	2	9-2	Standard	MAZYOUN	Oct 25 2016
6f	1m 9.86	3	9-2	Standard	UNABATED	Mar 22 2017
7f 14y	1m 25.50	2	9-5	Standard	COMMANDER COLE	Oct 18 2016
7f 14y	1m 24.10	3	9-0	Standard	NORTHERNPOWERHOUSE	Dec 18 2019
1m 5y	1m 36.26	2	9-1	Standard	KAMEKO	Nov 1 2019
1m 5y	1m 36.10	4	9-8	Standard	ALFRED RICHARDSON	Nov 9 2018
1m 2f 42y	2m 4.88	3	8-6	Standard	PALISADE	Oct 16 2016
1m 4f 98y	2m 36.76	3	8-7	Standard	AJMAN PRINCE	Oct 14 2016
2m 56y	3m 29.87	4	9-8	Standard	DANNYDAY	Jun 25 2016

NEWMARKET (ROWLEY MILE)

DISTANCE	TIME	AGE	WEIGHT	GOING	HORSE	DATE
5f	58.04	2	9-5	Good To Firm	EYE OF HEAVEN	Jun 4 2020
5f	56.81	6	9-2	Good To Firm	LOCHSONG	Apr 30 1994
6f	1m 9.31	2	9-0	Good	EARTHLIGHT	Sep 28 2019
6f	1m 9.55	3	9-1	Good	CAPTAIN COLBY	May 16 2015
7f	1m 22.37	2	9-1	Good	U S NAVY FLAG	Oct 14 2017
7f	1m 21.98	3	9-0	Good To Firm	TUPI	May 16 2015
1m	1m 35.13	2	9-0	Good	ROYAL DORNOCH	Sep 28 2019
1m	1m 34.07	4	9-0	Good To Firm	EAGLE MOUNTAIN	Oct 3 2008
1m 1f	1m 46.94	4	8-8	Good	MAJESTIC DAWN	Sep 26 2020
1m 2f	2m 2.76	2	9-2	Good	KEW GARDENS	Oct 14 2017
1m 2f	2m 0.13	3	8-12	Good	NEW APPROACH	Oct 18 2008
1m 4f	2m 25.89	5	9-0	Good To Firm	GHAIYYATH	Jun 5 2020
1m 6f	2m 51.59	3	8-7	Good	ART EYES	Sep 29 2005
2m	3m 18.64	5	9-6	Good To Firm	TIMES UP	Sep 22 2011
2m 2f	3m 45.59	4	8-8	Good	WITHHOLD	Oct 14 2017

NEWMARKET (JULY COURSE)

Following remeasurement of the track by the BHA and RCA in 2017, some starts were moved to retain traditional race distances.

DISTANCE	TIME	AGE	WEIGHT	GOING	HORSE	DATE
5f	57.31	4	9-2	Good To Firm	MOUNTAIN PEAK	Jul 12 2019
6f	1m 9.09	2	9-3	Good To Firm	RAFFLE PRIZE	Jul 12 2019
6f	1m 9.31	3	9-0	Good To Firm	TEN SOVEREIGNS	Jul 13 2019
7f	1m 23.33	2	9-1	Good To Firm	BIRCHWOOD	Jul 11 2015
7f	1m 21.78	3	8-13	Good To Firm	LIGHT AND DARK	Jul 12 2019
1m	1m 37.47	2	8-13	Good	WHIPPERS LOVE	Aug 28 2009
1m	1m 35.89	4	9-7	Good To Firm	VERACIOUS	Jul 12 2019
1m 2f	2m 0.61	3	9-7	Good To Firm	WALKINTHESAND	Jul 12 2019
1m 4f	2m 27.26	3	8-9	Good To Firm	KATARA	Aug 1 2020
1m 5f	2m 39.96	3	9-1	Good To Firm	SPANISH MISSION	Jul 11 2019
1m 6f	2m 53.40	7	9-3	Good To Firm	WITHHOLD	Aug 1 2020

NOTTINGHAM

DISTANCE	TIME	AGE	WEIGHT	GOING	HORSE	DATE
5f 8y (Inner)	59.05	2	9-0	Good To Firm	MAIN DESIRE	May 2 2017
5f 8y (Inner)	57.01	3	8-12	Good To Firm	GARRUS	Apr 10 2019
5f 8y	57.90	2	8-9	Firm	HOH MAGIC	May 13 1994
5f 8y	57.58	5	7-11	Good To Firm	PENNY DREADFUL	Jun 19 2017
6f 18y	1m 11.40	2	8-11	Firm	JAMEELAPI	Aug 8 1983
6f 18y	1m 10.00	4	9-2	Firm	AJANAC	Aug 8 1988
1m 72y (Inner)	1m 45.14	2	9-6	Good	RASHFORD'S DOUBLE	Nov 2 2016
1m 72y (Inner)	1m 43.22	4	9-7	Good To Firm	REAVER	Apr 22 2017
1m 75y	1m 43.50	2	9-7	Good	FABILIS	Sep 27 2020
1m 75y	1m 41.75	3	9-1	Good To Firm	SIAM FOX	Jun 2 2021
1m 2f 50y	2m 7.13	5	9-8	Good To Firm	VASILY	Jul 19 2013
1m 2f 52y (Inner)	2m 16.66	2	9-3	Soft	LETHAL GLAZE	Oct 1 2008
1m 2f 52y (Inner)	2m 9.40	3	9-5	Good	CENTURIUS	Apr 20 2013
1m 6f	2m 57.80	3	8-10	Firm	BUSTER JO	Oct 1 1985
1m 7f 219y (Inner)	3m 34.39	3	8-0	Good	BENOZZO GOZZOLI	Oct 28 2009
2m	3m 25.25	3	9-5	Good	BULWARK	Sep 27 2005

PONTEFRACT

DISTANCE	TIME	AGE	WEIGHT	GOING	HORSE	DATE
5f 3y	1m 1.10	2	9-0	Firm	GOLDEN BOUNTY	Sep 20 2001
5f 3y	1m 0.49	5	9-5	Good To Firm	JUDICIAL	Apr 24 2017
6f	1m 14.00	2	9-3	Firm	FAWZI	Sep 6 1983
6f	1m 12.60	3	7-13	Firm	MERRY ONE	Aug 29 1970
1m 6y	1m 42.80	2	9-13	Firm	STAR SPRAY	Sep 6 1983
1m 6y	1m 42.80	2	9-0	Firm	ALASIL	Sep 26 2002
1m 6y	1m 40.60	4	9-10	Good To Firm	ISLAND LIGHT	Apr 13 2002
1m 2f 5y	2m 10.10	2	9-0	Firm	SHANTY STAR	Oct 7 2002
1m 2f 5y	2m 8.20	4	7-8	Hard	HAPPY HECTOR	Jul 9 1979
1m 2f 5y	2m 8.20	3	7-13	Hard	TOM NODDY	Aug 21 1972
1m 4f 5y	2m 33.72	3	8-7	Firm	AJAAN	Aug 8 2007
2m 1f 27y	3m 40.67	4	8-7	Good To Firm	PARADISE FLIGHT	Jun 6 2005
2m 2f 2y	3m 51.10	3	8-8	Good To Firm	KUDZ	Sep 9 1986
2m 5f 139y	4m 47.80	4	8-4	Firm	PHYSICAL	May 14 1984

REDCAR

DISTANCE	TIME	AGE	WEIGHT	GOING	HORSE	DATE
5f	56.88	2	9-7	Good To Soft	WOLFOFWALLSTREET	Oct 27 2014
5f	56.01	10	9-3	Firm	HENRY HALL	Sep 20 2006
5f 217y	1m 8.84	2	8-3	Good To Firm	OBE GOLD	Oct 2 2004
5f 217y	1m 8.60	3	9-2	Good To Firm	SIZZLING SAGA	Jun 21 1991
7f	1m 21.28	2	9-3	Firm	KAROO BLUE	Sep 20 2006
7f	1m 20.67	3	9-0	Good To Firm	DREAMLOPER	Jul 27 2020
7f 219y	1m 34.37	2	9-0	Firm	MASTERSHIP	Sep 20 2006
7f 219y	1m 32.42	4	10-0	Firm	NANTON	Sep 20 2006
1m 1f	1m 52.44	2	9-0	Firm	SPEAR	Sep 13 2004
1m 1f	1m 48.50	5	8-12	Firm	MELLOTTIE	Jul 25 1990
1m 2f 1y	2m 10.10	2	8-11	Good	ADDING	Nov 10 1989
1m 2f 1y	2m 1.40	5	9-2	Firm	ERADICATE	May 28 1990
1m 5f 218y	2m 59.54	6	8-5	Good To Firm	LEODIS	Jun 23 2018
1m 7f 217y	3m 24.90	3	9-3	Good To Firm	SUBSONIC	Oct 8 1991

RIPON

DISTANCE	TIME	AGE	WEIGHT	GOING	HORSE	DATE
5f	57.80	2	8-8	Firm	SUPER ROCKY	Aug 5 1991
5f	57.80	2	9-5	Good	ORNATE	Jul 18 2015
5f	57.28	5	8-12	Good	DESERT ACE	Sep 24 2016
6f	1m 10.40	2	9-2	Good	CUMBRIAN VENTURE	Aug 17 2002
6f	1m 9.09	5	8-13	Good To Firm	SANDRA'S SECRET	May 20 2018
1m	1m 38.77	2	9-4	Good	GREED IS GOOD	Sep 28 2013
1m	1m 36.62	4	8-11	Good To Firm	GRANSTON	Aug 29 2005
1m 1f	1m 49.97	6	9-3	Good To Firm	GINGER JACK	Jun 20 2013
1m 2f	2m 2.60	3	9-4	Firm	SWIFT SWORD	Jul 20 1991
1m 4f 10y	2m 31.04	3	9-7	Good To Firm	JUST HUBERT	Jul 8 2019
2m	3m 23.90	4	9-10	Firm	PANAMA JACK	Jun 23 1988

SALISBURY

DISTANCE	TIME	AGE	WEIGHT	GOING	HORSE	DATE
5f	59.30	2	9-0	Good To Firm	AJIGOLO	May 12 2005
5f	59.18	7	8-10	Good To Firm	EDGED OUT	Jun 18 2017
6f	1m 12.10	2	8-0	Good To Firm	PARISIAN LADY	Jun 10 1997
6f	1m 11.09	3	9-0	Firm	L'AMI LOUIS	May 1 2011
6f 213y	1m 25.97	2	9-0	Firm	MORE ROYAL	Jun 29 1995
6f 213y	1m 24.91	3	9-4	Firm	CHILWORTH LAD	May 1 2011
1m	1m 40.48	2	8-13	Firm	CHOIR MASTER	Sep 17 2002
1m	1m 38.29	3	8-7	Good To Firm	LAYMAN	Aug 11 2005
1m 1f 201y	2m 4.70	3	8-8	Firm	ALPINISTA	Aug 13 2020
1m 4f 5y	2m 31.69	3	9-5	Good To Firm	ARRIVE	Jun 27 2001
1m 6f 44y	3m 0.48	7	9-2	Good To Firm	HIGHLAND CASTLE	May 23 2015

SANDOWN PARK

DISTANCE	TIME	AGE	WEIGHT	GOING	HORSE	DATE
5f 10y	59.48	2	9-3	Firm	TIMES TIME	Jul 22 1982
5f 10y	58.57	3	8-12	Good To Firm	BATTAASH	Jul 8 2017
7f	1m 26.56	2	9-0	Good To Firm	RAVEN'S PASS	Sep 1 2007
7f	1m 26.36	3	9-0	Firm	MAWSUFF	Jun 14 1986
1m	1m 43.90	2	9-5	Good	VIA DE VEGA	Sep 18 2019
1m	1m 39.21	4	8-12	Good To Firm	EL HAYEM	Jul 8 2017
1m 1f	1m 56.18	3	8-11	Good To Firm	DEJAME PASO	Jun 12 2021
1m 1f 209y	2m 2.14	4	8-11	Good	KALAGLOW	May 31 1982
1m 6f	3m 1.08	3	8-9	Good	JUST HUBERT	Jul 25 2019
2m 50y	3m 29.38	6	9-0	Good To Firm	CAUCUS	Jul 6 2013

SOUTHWELL (AW)

Previous records no longer relevant following installation of new Tapeta surface in late 2021.

THIRSK

DISTANCE	TIME	AGE	WEIGHT	GOING	HORSE	DATE
5f	57.20	2	9-7	Good To Firm	PROUD BOAST	Aug 5 2000
5f	56.92	5	9-6	Firm	CHARLIE PARKES	Apr 11 2003
6f	1m 9.20	3	9-6	Good To Firm	WESTCOURT MAGIC	Aug 25 1995
6f	1m 8.80	5	9-4	Firm	JOHAYRO	Jul 23 1999
7f	1m 23.70	2	8-9	Firm	COURTING	Jul 23 1999
7f	1m 22.80	4	8-5	Firm	SILVER HAZE	May 21 1988
7f 218y	1m 37.97	2	9-0	Firm	SUNDAY SYMPHONY	Sep 4 2004
7f 218y	1m 34.80	4	8-13	Firm	YEARSLEY	May 5 1990
1m 4f 8y	2m 29.90	5	9-12	Firm	GALLERY GOD	Jun 4 2001
2m 13y	3m 22.30	3	9-0	Firm	TOMASCHEK	Jul 17 1981

WETHERBY

DISTANCE	TIME	AGE	WEIGHT	GOING	HORSE	DATE
5f 110y	1m 5.01	2	9-3	Good To Firm	FEARBY	Jun 8 2021
5f 110y	1m 4.25	3	9-1	Good To Firm	DAPPER MAN	Jun 19 2017
7f	1m 26.23	2	8-9	Good	RAYAA	Jul 21 2015
7f	1m 24.72	4	9-2	Good	SLEMY	Jul 21 2015
1m	1m 37.75	7	9-2	Good To Firm	SIX STRINGS	Jun 8 2021
1m 2f	2m 5.13	5	9-5	Good	FIRST SARGEANT	Jul 21 2015
1m 6f	3m 0.41	3	9-7	Good To Firm	DAVY'S DILEMMA	Jun 19 2017

WINDSOR

DISTANCE	TIME	AGE	WEIGHT	GOING	HORSE	DATE
5f 21y	58.69	2	9-0	Good To Firm	CHARLES THE GREAT	May 23 2011
5f 21y	58.08	5	8-13	Good To Firm	TAURUS TWINS	Apr 4 2011
6f 12y	1m 10.50	2	9-5	Good To Firm	CUBISM	Aug 17 1998
6f 12y	1m 9.54	5	9-5	Good	ALJADY	Jul 13 2020
1m 31y	1m 41.73	2	9-5	Good To Firm	SALOUEN	Aug 7 2016
1m 31y	1m 39.47	4	9-6	Good To Firm	MATTERHORN	Jun 29 2019
1m 1f 194y	2m 1.62	6	9-1	Good	AL KAZEEM	Aug 23 2014
1m 2f	2m 4.24	7	9-8	Good To Firm	DESERT ENCOUNTER	Aug 24 2019
1m 3f 99y	2m 21.50	3	9-2	Firm	DOUBLE FLORIN	May 19 1980

WOLVERHAMPTON (AW)

DISTANCE	TIME	AGE	WEIGHT	GOING	HORSE	DATE
5f 21y	59.75	2	9-6	Standard	QUATRIEME AMI	Nov 13 2015
5f 21y	59.33	5	9-6	Standard	LOMU	Dec 3 2019
6f 20y	1m 12.16	2	9-2	Standard	MUBAKKER	Nov 1 2018
6f 20y	1m 11.44	5	9-6	Standard	KACHY	Dec 26 2018
7f 36y	1m 26.77	2	8-11	Standard	RICHARD R H B	Nov 23 2019
7f 36y	1m 25.35	4	9-3	Standard	MISTER UNIVERSE	Mar 12 2016
1m 142y	1m 47.38	2	9-5	Standard	JACK HOBBS	Dec 27 2014
1m 142y	1m 45.43	4	9-4	Standard	KEYSTROKE	Nov 26 2016
1m 1f 104y	1m 57.99	2	9-2	Standard	EMISSARY	Oct 12 2019
1m 1f 104y	1m 55.91	6	8-8	Standard	STORM AHEAD	Nov 18 2019
1m 4f 51y	2m 33.44	4	9-5	Standard	PATHS OF GLORY	Oct 19 2019
1m 5f 219y	2m 57.83	4	9-8	Standard	GIVEN CHOICE	Jan 7 2019
2m 120y	3m 31.18	4	9-0	Standard	AIRCRAFT CARRIER	Jan 14 2019

YARMOUTH

DISTANCE	TIME	AGE	WEIGHT	GOING	HORSE	DATE
5f 42y	59.00	2	9-2	Good To Firm	THE LIR JET	Jun 3 2020
5f 42y	58.57	11	9-10	Good To Firm	CASPIAN PRINCE	Sep 16 2020
6f 3y	1m 10.40	2	9-0	Firm	LANCHESTER	Sep 15 1988
6f 3y	1m 8.85	3	9-1	Good To Firm	DESERT GULF	Jul 14 2021
7f 3y	1m 22.20	2	9-0	Good To Firm	WARRSHAN	Sep 14 1988
7f 3y	1m 21.32	3	9-7	Firm	MISTER SNOWDON	Jun 3 2020
1m 3y	1m 35.40	2	9-2	Good To Firm	FOREST FALCON	Sep 17 2020
1m 3y	1m 33.00	4	9-5	Firm	MAYDANNY	Jun 3 2020
1m 1f 21y	1m 52.00	3	9-5	Good To Firm	TOUCH GOLD	Jul 5 2012
1m 2f 23y	2m 2.83	3	8-8	Firm	REUNITE	Jul 18 2006
1m 3f 104y	2m 23.10	3	8-9	Firm	RAHIL	Jul 1 1993
1m 6f 17y	2m 57.80	3	8-2	Good To Firm	BARAKAT	Jul 24 1990
2m	3m 26.70	4	8-2	Good To Firm	ALHESN	Jul 26 1999

YORK

DISTANCE	TIME	AGE	WEIGHT	GOING	HORSE	DATE
5f	57.11	2	9-0	Good	BIG TIME BABY	Aug 20 2016
5f	55.90	5	9-11	Good To Firm	BATTAASH	Aug 23 2019
5f 89y	1m 3.20	2	9-3	Good To Firm	THE ART OF RACING	Sep 9 2012
5f 89y	1m 1.72	4	9-7	Good To Firm	BOGART	Aug 21 2013
6f	1m 8.90	2	9-0	Good	TIGGY WIGGY	Aug 21 2014
6f	1m 8.23	8-11		Good To Firm	MINCE	Sep 9 2012
7f	1m 22.32	2	9-1	Good To Firm	DUTCH CONNECTION	Aug 20 2014
7f	1m 21.00	3	9-1	Good To Firm	SHINE SO BRIGHT	Aug 24 2019
7f 192y	1m 36.92	2	9-5	Good	AWESOMETANK	Oct 14 2017
7f 192y	1m 34.95	3	9-3	Good To Firm	POGO	Aug 23 2019
1m 177y	1m 46.76	5	9-8	Good To Firm	ECHO OF LIGHT	Sep 5 2007
1m 2f 56y	2m 5.29	3	8-11	Good To Firm	SEA THE STARS	Aug 18 2009
1m 3f 188y	2m 25.40	4	8-8	Good To Firm	TAMREER	Aug 23 2019
1m 5f 188y	2m 52.97	6	9-5	Good To Firm	MUSTAJEER	Aug 24 2019
2m 56y	3m 27.06	5	9-6	Good To Firm	STRADIVARIUS	Aug 23 2019

TOP FLAT JOCKEYS IN BRITAIN 2021
(1 JANUARY - 31 DECEMBER)

WINS-RUNS	%	JOCKEY	2ND	3RD	TOTAL PRIZE	WIN PRIZE
183-861	21%	OISIN MURPHY	148	114	2,566,364	4,271,452
176-1068	16%	TOM MARQUAND	133	144	1,826,296	3,330,900
172-1189	14%	HOLLIE DOYLE	152	153	1,701,325	2,936,347
170-803	21%	WILLIAM BUICK	127	90	4,194,609	5,656,144
170-1236	14%	DAVID PROBERT	143	147	1,065,397	2,017,643
128-968	13%	RICHARD KINGSCOTE	146	138	781,227	1,631,482
123-816	15%	BEN CURTIS	110	103	669,608	1,405,703
120-780	15%	ROSSA RYAN	90	108	740,512	1,663,723
118-642	18%	JAMES DOYLE	130	90	1,136,534	2,681,528
116-716	16%	JACK MITCHELL	94	97	705,177	1,179,932
109-1172	9%	LUKE MORRIS	111	136	490,733	1,055,348
105-821	13%	JASON HART	95	89	745,661	1,306,159
101-590	17%	MARCO GHIANI	76	49	576,615	896,982
96-620	15%	DANIEL TUDHOPE	114	82	668,934	1,441,109
91-575	16%	ADAM KIRBY	72	57	1,277,148	1,880,125
90-549	16%	ROBERT HAVLIN	88	72	638,357	1,045,763
89-541	16%	KEVIN STOTT	68	91	509,921	926,020
86-442	19%	RYAN MOORE	63	53	2,685,510	4,244,026
85-421	20%	JIM CROWLEY	57	45	2,123,404	3,238,069
84-602	14%	CIEREN FALLON	75	84	623,076	1,070,009
84-615	14%	DANIEL MUSCUTT	82	68	428,577	750,144
84-766	11%	CALLUM SHEPHERD	79	93	431,434	798,229
81-594	14%	PAUL MULRENNAN	65	83	502,531	876,377
80-634	13%	JOE FANNING	83	88	727,024	1,175,137
80-696	11%	KIERAN SHOEMARK	61	76	852,261	1,480,881
76-553	14%	CALLUM RODRIGUEZ	72	67	427,145	756,844
76-591	13%	DAVID ALLAN	62	70	404,834	830,462
74-538	14%	SILVESTRE DE SOUSA	76	77	1,085,173	1,927,252
72-543	13%	CONNOR BEASLEY	64	63	460,825	819,985
67-665	10%	P J MCDONALD	86	89	377,498	898,563
66-666	10%	DAVID EGAN	78	92	1,211,542	2,519,897
64-392	16%	HECTOR CROUCH	46	43	380,904	702,982
64-457	14%	ANDREA ATZENI	66	67	791,222	1,546,458
64-533	12%	SEAN LEVEY	71	63	578,183	1,153,219
62-465	13%	RAY DAWSON	51	45	385,868	693,903
61-507	12%	PAUL HANAGAN	56	53	401,045	819,372
59-488	12%	JASON WATSON	53	57	300,361	621,902
58-446	13%	CLIFFORD LEE	70	43	326,043	678,124
57-443	13%	SAM JAMES	61	59	216,012	511,529
56-424	13%	FRANNY NORTON	54	63	433,299	832,610
53-570	9%	KIERAN O'NEILL	54	52	225,731	476,012
51-483	11%	ROB HORNBY	44	53	447,274	931,888
50-627	8%	ANDREW MULLEN	58	61	164,036	452,185
48-403	12%	HAYLEY TURNER	37	46	353,674	621,387
46-299	15%	DANE O'NEILL	44	37	235,045	568,722
45-296	15%	MARK CREHAN	50	34	191,432	394,306
45-820	5%	CAM HARDIE	71	79	216,063	569,678
44-360	12%	PAT COSGRAVE	41	46	221,968	475,910
44-363	12%	JOANNA MASON	40	43	193,064	339,902
42-336	13%	BILLY GARRITTY	39	43	214,553	425,930
42-407	10%	LAURA PEARSON	45	49	201,212	425,783
41-194	21%	FRANKIE DETTORI	18	19	2,299,525	3,107,963
41-594	7%	GRAHAM LEE	74	52	157,714	463,248
40-342	12%	SAFFIE OSBORNE	34	39	198,408	404,288
40-343	12%	THORE HAMMER HANSEN	42	52	143,741	361,124
39-418	9%	ROWAN SCOTT	31	40	158,468	352,665
38-358	11%	TREVOR WHELAN	25	41	126,893	266,259
37-330	11%	JAMIE SPENCER	45	46	356,055	1,000,232
37-557	7%	DARRAGH KEENAN	51	38	126,032	301,826
37-617	6%	TOM EAVES	58	60	174,286	463,781

TOP FLAT TRAINERS
IN BRITAIN 2021

TRAINER	LEADING HORSE	W-R	2ND	3RD	4TH	WIN PRIZE	TOTAL PRIZE
CHARLIE APPLEBY	Adayar	116-402	85	54	37	3,903,656	4,911,903
ANDREW BALDING	Alcohol Free	150-922	133	128	105	2,737,834	4,429,331
JOHN & THADY GOSDEN	Mishriff	133-651	113	88	60	2,868,452	4,350,484
WILLIAM HAGGAS	Baaeed	174-700	104	98	81	2,580,178	4,237,832
A P O'BRIEN	Love	11-119	11	14	19	1,863,142	3,353,427
MARK JOHNSTON	Subjectivist	212-1519	215	213	195	1,808,030	3,284,094
RICHARD HANNON	Mojo Star	146-1239	146	168	158	1,401,526	3,129,530
ROGER VARIAN	Eshaada	133-626	96	101	60	1,425,158	2,683,529
TIM EASTERBY	Winter Power	136-1349	145	155	183	1,034,525	2,018,758
RALPH BECKETT	Albaflora	81-514	83	64	65	904,137	1,939,960
RICHARD FAHEY	Perfect Power	130-1253	145	142	155	912,753	1,789,630
DAVID O'MEARA	Rhoscolyn	123-1110	162	135	129	668,508	1,682,567
SIR MICHAEL STOUTE	Dream Of Dreams	67-324	53	48	43	1,052,584	1,573,744
KEVIN RYAN	Emaraaty Ana	79-612	84	88	64	730,788	1,415,158
ARCHIE WATSON	Dragon Symbol	78-501	68	65	56	478,444	1,387,683
ED WALKER	Starman	66-420	53	50	48	879,764	1,378,245
K R BURKE	Significantly	99-768	120	97	107	633,616	1,325,249
CHARLES HILLS	Pogo	77-484	69	61	53	590,862	1,094,195
ALAN KING	Trueshan	28-322	27	48	43	814,281	1,075,223
MICHAEL APPLEBY	Boundless Power	109-978	108	105	120	522,698	1,040,490
CLIVE COX	Caturra	79-458	41	58	51	633,452	989,017
SAEED BIN SUROOR	Real World	61-287	42	30	27	714,981	956,981
GEORGE BOUGHEY	Mystery Angel	85-475	66	63	55	432,575	932,669
SIMON & ED CRISFORD	Flotus	68-394	72	67	48	472,422	931,439
KEITH DALGLEISH	Volatile Analyst	93-657	77	83	92	485,206	929,586
HUGO PALMER	Dubawi Legend	54-331	58	47	45	353,996	925,925
J S BOLGER	Poetic Flare	2-8	1	1	1	425,503	863,279
TOM DASCOMBE	Ever Given	60-447	53	50	45	472,726	846,997
MICHAEL DODS	Commanche Falls	56-506	58	57	50	490,945	817,383
JOHN QUINN	Highfield Princess	52-359	48	35	32	408,825	726,378
CEDRIC ROSSI	Sealiway	1-1	0	0	0	714,546	714,546
WILLIAM JARVIS	Lady Bowthorpe	11-100	9	10	12	424,819	702,134
IAN WILLIAMS	The Grand Visir	42-451	56	51	52	301,053	671,748
EVE JOHNSON HOUGHTON	Chipotle	46-403	46	48	50	398,582	668,918
DAVID EVANS	Rohaan	68-584	59	53	72	409,060	654,719
STUART WILLIAMS	Desert Dreamer	59-463	61	55	46	291,612	653,976
ROGER CHARLTON	Makram	57-356	45	44	44	329,322	640,365
CHARLIE FELLOWES	Vadream	41-326	32	43	49	343,891	621,594
MARCO BOTTI	Tatsumaki	50-399	50	48	56	359,908	614,219
DAVID MENUISIER	Wonderful Tonight	22-196	9	17	28	479,050	607,798
OWEN BURROWS	Hukum	22-126	25	13	23	304,936	603,394
DAVID LOUGHNANE	Hello You	42-348	54	40	39	306,313	594,071
JAMES FANSHAWE	Audarya	30-222	35	33	33	205,788	578,968
TONY CARROLL	Rose Hip	78-891	98	85	86	251,361	578,938
ROGER TEAL	Oxted	38-293	24	37	26	363,253	577,078
WILLIAM MUIR & CHRIS GRASSICK	Pyledriver	34-224	28	31	24	416,645	570,097
MICK CHANNON	Chairmanoftheboard	46-559	76	62	58	208,451	562,068
DAVID SIMCOCK	Indigo Times	48-349	45	47	44	267,449	561,825
JANE CHAPPLE-HYAM	Saffron Beach	34-242	26	32	32	332,880	556,759
RICHARD HUGHES	Calling The Wind	49-401	45	41	55	270,068	534,519
HUGHIE MORRISON	Quickthorn	45-263	28	25	27	262,851	531,050
MICHAEL BELL	Prince Alex	51-335	40	31	45	286,416	521,853
J P MURTAGH	Sonnyboyliston	3-16	0	4	2	439,742	511,088
ROBERT COWELL	Arecibo	34-315	41	45	34	175,479	507,279
JIM GOLDIE	Nicholas T	38-310	32	35	23	322,341	498,321
ROGER FELL	Cockalorum	41-449	59	40	44	202,331	491,476
SIR MARK PRESCOTT BT	Alpinista	42-232	23	31	29	245,091	415,438
BRIAN ELLISON	Tashkhan	31-301	37	28	41	149,176	387,646
JAMES TATE	Top Ranked	31-223	26	40	31	172,953	379,342
EDWARD BETHELL	Fearby	22-149	21	22	20	186,911	377,891

TOP FLAT OWNERS IN BRITAIN 2021

OWNER	LEADING HORSE	W-R	2ND	3RD	4TH	WIN PRIZE	TOTAL PRIZE
GODOLPHIN	Adayar	187-763	140	93	67	4,598,867	5,902,236
SHADWELL ESTATE COMPANY LTD	Baaeed	132-630	97	76	81	2,568,126	3,803,405
KING POWER RACING CO LTD	Winter Power	56-439	67	73	54	1,037,658	1,940,834
DERRICK SMITH & MRS JOHN MAGNIER & MICHAEL TABOR	Snowfall	5-33	6	5	2	1,046,299	1,627,119
J C SMITH	Alcohol Free	17-152	27	10	20	963,674	1,206,537
CHEVELEY PARK STUD	Inspiral	48-239	30	40	23	828,320	1,094,495
SHEIKH HAMDAN BIN MOHAMMED AL MAKTOUM	Palace Pier	29-188	23	23	21	700,812	1,086,320
AMO RACING LIMITED	Mojo Star	48-242	33	30	32	390,245	1,079,692
SHEIKH MOHAMMED OBAID AL MAKTOUM	Emaraaty Ana	39-220	39	30	30	548,416	1,053,400
PRINCE A A FAISAL	Mishriff	4-23	5	5	3	590,860	931,664
MRS J S BOLGER	Poetic Flare	2-7	1	1	1	425,503	863,279
MICHAEL TABOR & DERRICK SMITH & MRS JOHN MAGNIER	Love	1-26	3	5	3	396,970	790,855
MISS K RAUSING	Albaflora	26-163	28	26	19	330,920	775,878
LE HARAS DE LA GOUSSERIE	Sealiway	1-1	0	0	0	714,546	714,546
SAEED SUHAIL	Dream Of Dreams	20-109	6	17	15	582,063	702,646
SHEIKH AHMED AL MAKTOUM	Addeybb	45-184	32	26	20	311,929	680,837
MS E L BANKS	Lady Bowthorpe	2-18	2	2	1	391,299	629,834
JUDDMONTE	Tilsit	38-164	32	19	23	325,945	625,543
THE QUEEN	King's Lynn	36-166	26	24	20	366,079	584,399
SINGULA PARTNERSHIP	Trueshan	2-3	0	0	0	577,733	577,733
AL SHAQAB RACING	Lusail	28-139	17	13	23	371,627	575,043
CLIPPER LOGISTICS	Last Empire	37-209	32	20	18	262,460	531,150
MOHAMED OBAIDA	Dubai Honour	8-52	10	8	4	111,167	500,758
DAVID WARD	Starman	8-56	8	7	6	392,176	488,310
GEORGE STRAWBRIDGE	Suesa	14-52	7	6	4	343,456	415,606
SHEIKH RASHID DALMOOK AL MAKTOUM	Perfect Power	11-49	10	8	4	283,057	383,796
M M STABLES	Alenquer	3-11	3	0	3	129,254	365,013
ROCKCLIFFE STUD	Snow Lantern	5-26	1	5	2	142,622	353,304
YOSHIRO KUBOTA	Dragon Symbol	4-10	4	1	0	29,243	341,194
CHRISTOPHER WRIGHT	Wonderful Tonight	4-37	4	4	8	286,072	338,204
B E NIELSEN	Stradivarius	8-29	2	5	6	217,061	324,351
SHEIKH JUMA DALMOOK AL MAKTOUM	Symbolize	21-140	19	21	19	132,185	324,297
KILDARE RACING CLUB	Sonnyboyliston	1-3	0	1	0	300,000	309,640
DR ALI RIDHA	Dubawi Legend	11-54	13	8	6	96,073	307,768
MRS JOHN MAGNIER & MICHAEL TABOR & DERRICK SMITH	Armory	2-32	2	5	4	92,788	297,355
DR J WALKER	Subjectivist	3-40	4	8	7	221,548	287,409
MRS B V SANGSTER, J WIGAN & O SANGSTER	Saffron Beach	2-6	2	0	0	187,143	277,443
HAMBLETON RACING XXXVI & PARTNER	Glen Shiel	0-8	2	0	0	0	274,430
S PIPER,T HIRSCHFELD,D FISH & J COLLINS	Oxted	1-4	1	2	0	198,485	273,876
SAEED MANANA	Top Rank	24-141	13	26	18	141,497	264,740
DAVID W ARMSTRONG	Blackrod	12-97	16	13	8	147,067	259,678
A E OPPENHEIMER	Megallan	16-66	11	6	11	144,285	249,579
MARC CHAN	Kinross	5-16	2	1	1	235,117	248,242
MRS FITRI HAY	Bell Rock	19-144	19	18	23	98,523	247,200
T W MORLEY	Arecibo	7-74	12	11	11	38,663	243,116
SUNDERLAND HOLDING INC	Sea La Rosa	14-46	9	7	2	133,487	242,231
LA PYLE PARTNERSHIP	Pyledriver	2-10	3	4	0	211,528	239,936
DR MARWAN KOUKASH	Gabrial The Devil	19-180	16	16	25	130,278	235,018
QATAR RACING LIMITED	Mise En Scene	16-103	13	19	12	102,369	231,254
STONESTREET STABLES LLC	Campanelle	1-3	1	0	0	198,485	216,397
ISA SALMAN AL KHALIFA	Wings Of War	15-64	6	14	10	115,443	207,607
PAUL DEAN	Sir Ron Priestley	3-16	1	2	1	131,992	203,039
THE HORSE WATCHERS	Rhoscolyn	13-58	9	5	7	110,362	197,012
THE GREDLEY FAMILY	Save A Forest	10-49	5	3	10	110,290	188,243
P K SIU	Came From The Dark	8-40	7	4	5	107,096	184,139
SAEED H AL TAYER	Zain Claudette	13-67	12	6	8	148,845	181,039
P BOYLE	Tashkhan	3-9	4	0	0	60,476	179,849
THURLOE FOR ROYAL MARSDEN CANCER CHARITY	Buzz	4-15	2	3	3	159,075	179,220
LORDSHIP STUD	Loving Dream	6-27	3	4	2	153,097	174,964
STRAIGHTLINE BLOODSTOCK	Platinumcard	18-98	9	9	14	91,934	174,586

TOP FLAT HORSES IN BRITAIN 2021

HORSE (AGE)	WIN & PLACE £	W-R	TRAINER	OWNER	BREEDER
ADAYAR (3)	1,190,855	2-5	Charlie Appleby	Godolphin	Godolphin
MISHRIFF (4)	887,321	1-4	John & Thady Gosden	Prince A A Faisal	Nawara Stud Limited
ALCOHOL FREE (3)	881,475	3-7	Andrew Balding	J C Smith	Churchtown House Stud
BAAEED (3)	719,756	5-5	William Haggas	Shadwell Estate Company Ltd	Shadwell Estate Company Limited
SEALIWAY (3)	714,546	1-1	Cedric Rossi	Le Haras De La Gousserie & Guy Pariente	Guy Pariente Holding
PALACE PIER (4)	700,104	3-4	John & Thady Gosden	Sheikh Hamdan bin Mohammed Al Maktoum	Highclere Stud And Floors Farming
HURRICANE LANE (3)	644,346	3-4	Charlie Appleby	Godolphin	Normandie Stud Ltd
POETIC FLARE (3)	640,503	2-3	J S Bolger	Mrs J S Bolger	J S Bolger
LADY BOWTHORPE (5)	627,805	2-6	William Jarvis	Ms E L Banks	Scuderia Archi Romani
LOVE (5)	598,720	1-3	A P O'Brien	Michael Tabor & Derrick Smith & Mrs John Magnier	Coolmore
TRUESHAN (5)	594,933	2-4	Alan King	Singula Partnership	Didier Blot
SNOWFALL (3)	547,177	3-4	A P O'Brien	Derrick Smith & Mrs John Magnier & Michael Tabor	Roncon, Chelston Ire & Wynatt
CREATIVE FORCE (3)	442,395	5-8	Charlie Appleby	Godolphin	Owenstown Bloodstock Ltd
DREAM OF DREAMS (7)	419,654	2-2	Sir Michael Stoute	Saeed Suhail	Prostock Ltd
MOJO STAR (3)	412,554	1-4	Richard Hannon	Amo Racing Limited	Barbara Prendergast
STARMAN (4)	407,928	2-3	Ed Walker	David Ward	D Ward
MOTHER EARTH (3)	388,266	1-5	A P O'Brien	Derrick Smith & Mrs John Magnier & Michael Tabor	Grenane House Stud
INSPIRAL (2)	375,514	4-4	John & Thady Gosden	Cheveley Park Stud	Cheveley Park Stud Limited
ESHAADA (3)	360,528	2-4	Roger Varian	Shadwell Estate Company Ltd	Shadwell Estate Company Limited
NATIVE TRAIL (2)	353,812	3-3	Charlie Appleby	Godolphin	Le Haras D'Haspel
DRAGON SYMBOL (3)	341,194	4-10	Archie Watson	Yoshiro Kubota	Whitsbury Manor Stud
ST MARK'S BASILICA (3)	340,260	1-1	A P O'Brien	Derrick Smith & Mrs John Magnier & Michael Tabor	Robert Scarborough
ALENQUER (3)	338,854	2-3	William Haggas	M M Stables	Gestut Romerhof
SNOW LANTERN (3)	331,292	2-6	Richard Hannon	Rockcliffe Stud	Rockcliffe Stud
DUBAI HONOUR (3)	314,310	1-3	William Haggas	Mohamed Obaida	Macha Bloodstock/Meridian International
SONNYBOYLISTON (4)	309,688	1-3	J P Murtagh	Kildare Racing Club	Ms Diane O'Neill
WINTER POWER (3)	282,982	3-4	Tim Easterby	King Power Racing Co Ltd	Newlands House Stud
WONDERFUL TONIGHT (4)	282,306	2-3	David Menuisier	Christopher Wright	Ecurie Taos
SAFFRON BEACH (3)	277,443	2-6	Jane Chapple-Hyam	Mrs B V Sangster, J Wigan & O Sangster	China Horse Club International Ltd
EMARAATY ANA (5)	276,557	2-8	Kevin Ryan	Sheikh Mohammed Obaid Al Maktoum	Rabbah Bloodstock Limited
OXTED (5)	273,876	1-4	Roger Teal	S Piper,T Hirschfeld,D Fish & J Collins	Homecroft Wealth Racing
GLEN SHIEL (7)	273,765	0-5	Archie Watson	Hambleton Racing Xxxvi & Partner	Darley
ALBAFLORA (4)	268,754	1-6	Ralph Beckett	Miss K Rausing	Miss K Rausing
STRADIVARIUS (7)	261,076	3-5	John & Thady Gosden	B E Nielsen	Bjorn Nielsen
PYLEDRIVER (3)	230,878	2-3	William Muir & Chris Grassick	La Pyle Partnership	Knox & Wells Limited & R Devlin
MAC SWINEY (3)	222,776	0-3	J S Bolger	Mrs J S Bolger	J S Bolger
SUBJECTIVIST (4)	213,016	1-1	Mark Johnston	Dr J Walker	Mascalls Stud
PERFECT POWER (2)	207,380	3-5	Richard Fahey	Sheikh Rashid Dalmook Al Maktoum	Tally-Ho Stud
SIR RON PRIESTLEY (5)	200,722	3-6	Mark Johnston	Paul Dean	Mascalls Stud
CAMPANELLE (3)	198,485	1-1	Wesley A Ward	Stonestreet Stables LLC	Tally-Ho Stud
SUESA (3)	191,570	1-3	F Rohaut	George Strawbridge	Thomastown Farm Ltd
YIBIR (3)	190,655	2-6	Charlie Appleby	Godolphin	Godolphin
HUKUM (4)	189,945	4-7	Owen Burrows	Shadwell Estate Company Ltd	Shadwell Estate Company Limited
ALDAARY (3)	189,507	3-7	William Haggas	Shadwell Estate Company Ltd	M E Broughton
AL AASY (3)	181,656	2-6	William Haggas	Shadwell Estate Company Ltd	Sunderland Holding Inc
ZEYAADH (3)	175,926	1-4	Roger Varian	Shadwell Estate Company Ltd	Shadwell Estate Company Limited
TASHKHAN (3)	173,104	2-7	Brian Ellison	P Boyle	His Highness The Aga Khan's Studs S C
ROHAAN (3)	166,988	4-10	David Evans	Chris Kiely Racing Ltd & J Tomkins	Liam Phelan
AUDARYA (5)	166,640	0-2	James Fanshawe	Mrs A M Swinburn	Haras D'Ecouves
BAYSIDE BOY (2)	165,966	2-5	Roger Varian	Teme Valley & Ballylinch Stud	Ballylinch Stud
EVER GIVEN (4)	161,505	4-7	Tom Dascombe	Dandy Boys	Rathbarry Stud
TENEBRISM (2)	160,914	1-1	A P O'Brien	Westerberg/Coolmore/Merribelle Stables	Merribelle Stables & Orpendale/Chelston/Wynatt
LUSAIL (2)	157,532	4-6	Richard Hannon	Al Shaqab Racing	Tally-Ho Stud
SANDRINE (2)	155,432	3-5	Andrew Balding	Miss K Rausing	Miss K Rausing
BANGKOK (5)	152,092	3-7	Andrew Balding	King Power Racing Co Ltd	Barronstown Stud
HARROW (2)	150,578	3-7	Andrew Balding	Highclere Thoroughbred Racing - Wisteria	School Run Bloodstock
REAL WORLD (4)	147,029	3-3	Saeed bin Suroor	Godolphin	Godolphin
PROSPEROUS VOYAGE (2)	146,328	1-6	Ralph Beckett	M Chan & A Rosen	Lynch Bages & Camas Park Stud
ADDEYBB (7)	146,010	0-2	William Haggas	Sheikh Ahmed Al Maktoum	Rabbah Bloodstock Limited
QUICKTHORN (4)	145,573	3-6	Hughie Morrison	Lady Blyth	Lemington Grange Stud

TOP NH JOCKEYS IN BRITAIN 2020/21

WINS-RUNS	%	JOCKEY	2ND	3RD	TOTAL PRIZE	WIN PRIZE
152-683	22%	HARRY SKELTON	116	88	1,185,168	1,888,853
142-890	16%	BRIAN HUGHES	145	140	727,497	1,260,498
123-582	21%	HARRY COBDEN	94	74	941,923	1,532,941
85-410	21%	NICO DE BOINVILLE	63	42	717,304	1,046,063
83-638	13%	SAM TWISTON-DAVIES	95	90	433,874	884,953
82-446	18%	PADDY BRENNAN	76	61	419,561	683,417
73-521	14%	RICHARD JOHNSON	66	86	463,058	784,515
68-410	17%	SEAN BOWEN	42	40	374,238	541,040
66-347	19%	DAVID BASS	36	33	542,936	702,651
65-430	15%	TOM SCUDAMORE	48	46	636,476	875,464
64-335	19%	AIDAN COLEMAN	50	41	627,524	1,063,624
63-521	12%	SEAN QUINLAN	51	58	382,945	593,286
62-423	15%	JONJO O'NEILL JR	63	55	468,172	764,442
54-383	14%	DARYL JACOB	42	45	520,081	805,263
52-384	14%	TOM CANNON	47	44	337,089	556,063
48-373	13%	JONATHAN BURKE	41	46	324,329	563,120
47-318	15%	BRYONY FROST	42	31	506,651	690,513
46-320	14%	DANNY MCMENAMIN	25	27	230,025	382,133
45-306	15%	ADAM WEDGE	39	31	344,472	504,086
44-369	12%	GAVIN SHEEHAN	45	49	205,699	426,128
44-397	11%	ROBERT DUNNE	45	38	208,433	364,195
43-333	13%	RYAN MANIA	48	35	317,975	525,570
41-348	12%	CONOR O'FARRELL	42	35	266,005	430,003
40-261	15%	JOSHUA MOORE	35	30	243,402	379,610
38-258	15%	CHARLIE DEUTSCH	37	32	296,498	528,917
37-332	11%	TOM BELLAMY	34	39	214,517	355,483
35-337	10%	JAMES BOWEN	55	47	198,820	432,625
34-259	13%	BRYAN CARVER	27	34	169,189	277,233
32-253	13%	A P HESKIN	26	40	194,918	342,013
32-273	12%	JACK QUINLAN	39	27	169,755	319,905
32-310	10%	RICHIE MCLERNON	33	25	209,370	376,883
32-403	8%	KIELAN WOODS	46	59	150,811	355,119
31-184	17%	MAX KENDRICK	20	22	138,364	207,439
31-304	10%	BRENDAN POWELL	35	28	143,691	325,460
31-411	8%	TOM O'BRIEN	53	43	371,111	590,192
29-185	16%	JORDAN NAILOR	16	14	149,708	200,587
29-196	15%	CHARLIE TODD	21	22	162,472	222,434
29-246	12%	CHARLIE HAMMOND	25	26	199,242	282,050
29-309	9%	HENRY BROOKE	16	46	148,148	241,596
27-275	10%	JACK TUDOR	23	26	175,669	325,690
24-237	10%	JAMIE MOORE	36	20	111,510	249,099
24-241	10%	REX DINGLE	21	22	106,936	207,078
24-254	9%	HARRY BANNISTER	20	24	151,157	249,110
24-274	9%	CIARAN GETHINGS	32	31	134,179	252,281
23-151	15%	KEVIN BROGAN	20	19	104,554	176,600
22-150	15%	FERGUS GILLARD	22	7	148,597	226,925
21-172	12%	LORCAN WILLIAMS	22	18	107,551	186,001
21-179	12%	DEREK FOX	16	17	137,443	194,664
21-209	10%	RICHARD PATRICK	20	17	188,843	277,084
20-183	11%	HARRY REED	12	16	89,864	137,683
19-162	12%	ROBBIE POWER	16	19	212,941	410,251
18-203	9%	CONNOR BRACE	22	20	92,627	176,521
18-328	5%	JAMES DAVIES	27	31	70,788	172,969
17-156	11%	NIALL HOULIHAN	17	15	83,985	132,917
17-210	8%	NATHAN MOSCROP	16	29	68,069	127,397
17-224	8%	NICK SCHOLFIELD	22	24	104,132	168,556
17-227	7%	BEN JONES	34	36	94,644	205,885
17-399	4%	JAMES BEST	34	33	66,250	185,837
16-158	10%	MITCHELL BASTYAN	17	15	67,635	117,406
16-211	8%	JAMIE HAMILTON	16	19	75,912	129,283

TOP NH TRAINERS IN BRITAIN 2020/21

TRAINER	LEADING HORSE	W-R	2ND	3RD	4TH	WIN PRIZE	TOTAL PRIZE
PAUL NICHOLLS	Frodon	173-688	109	87	64	1,657,662	2,457,758
DAN SKELTON	Nube Negra	141-731	121	88	93	1,124,874	1,828,628
HENRY DE BROMHEAD	Minella Times	8-39	4	2	5	1,176,211	1,524,042
NICKY HENDERSON	Shishkin	98-512	75	60	40	869,572	1,470,853
JONJO O'NEILL	Cloth Cap	63-479	63	61	57	673,957	903,194
W P MULLINS	Allaho	7-64	7	6	4	452,041	837,744
FERGAL O'BRIEN	Hurricane Harvey	101-546	87	80	60	467,737	783,797
ALAN KING	Sceau Royal	52-386	46	54	53	469,054	783,060
NIGEL TWISTON-DAVIES	Bristol De Mai	58-494	60	53	55	412,429	742,092
VENETIA WILLIAMS	Royale Pagaille	53-302	50	38	36	400,010	692,495
COLIN TIZZARD	Native River	36-430	53	50	51	267,631	681,406
PHILIP HOBBS	Thyme Hill	53-456	53	63	53	407,083	678,522
KIM BAILEY	First Flow	59-312	41	32	25	500,219	669,513
EVAN WILLIAMS	Silver Streak	44-409	53	45	37	434,387	664,480
DAVID PIPE	Adagio	52-342	43	34	32	436,367	633,833
OLLY MURPHY	Brewin'upastorm	78-560	78	76	63	331,688	625,882
DONALD McCAIN	Navajo Pass	63-457	75	67	40	351,660	580,380
GARY MOORE	Editeur Du Gite	57-403	59	41	45	337,085	575,465
NEIL MULHOLLAND	Milkwood	62-439	48	49	57	307,350	467,409
DR RICHARD NEWLAND	Beau Bay	49-310	41	46	45	295,352	444,017
LUCINDA RUSSELL	Mighty Thunder	34-371	39	43	49	281,872	439,596
MRS DENISE FOSTER	Abacadabras	5-40	4	2	5	249,881	436,248
TOM GEORGE	Clondaw Castle	27-246	31	37	21	236,985	422,553
EMMA LAVELLE	Paisley Park	31-235	35	31	20	231,234	387,762
SANDY THOMSON	Seeyouatmidnight	28-171	30	16	18	199,501	338,018
HARRY FRY	Metier	31-193	22	19	19	211,117	330,245
NICKY RICHARDS	Takingrisks	33-249	36	30	25	186,231	320,536
TOM LACEY	Tea Clipper	32-232	28	26	26	187,977	317,656
OLIVER GREENALL	Herbiers	37-328	35	38	36	197,248	303,110
TOM SYMONDS	Song For Someone	30-155	18	18	14	201,392	267,889
CHARLIE LONGSDON	Snow Leopardess	30-251	20	25	28	163,178	264,153
BEN PAULING	The Cob	33-333	41	34	42	123,558	263,967
ANTHONY HONEYBALL	Regal Encore	27-138	17	12	18	166,647	257,597
BRIAN ELLISON	Sam's Adventure	17-168	20	32	15	162,960	253,671
JAMIE SNOWDEN	Ga Law	23-220	37	36	27	129,033	248,201
LUCY WADHAM	Potters Legend	24-135	22	17	13	155,083	247,550
MICHAEL SCUDAMORE	Do Your Job	23-160	20	22	23	142,438	247,383
JEREMY SCOTT	Dashel Drasher	20-202	16	34	18	170,753	246,422
SUE SMITH	Vintage Clouds	20-197	17	17	21	152,993	244,030
IAN WILLIAMS	One More Fleurie	26-181	16	19	18	161,743	230,543
CHRIS GORDON	Annual Invictus	33-200	26	23	21	137,060	223,283
CHRISTIAN WILLIAMS	Kitty's Light	16-208	15	13	15	117,953	219,503
ALEX HALES	For Pleasure	21-140	16	17	14	127,911	208,197
N W ALEXANDER	Lake View Lad	21-205	28	27	14	116,081	207,116
HARRY WHITTINGTON	Rouge Vif	18-174	20	27	21	101,548	206,218
JOSEPH PATRICK O'BRIEN	Fakir D'oudairies	1-19	3	2	1	104,963	203,538
GRAEME McPHERSON	Ratfacemcdougall	24-192	29	19	18	124,035	197,858
GAVIN CROMWELL	Flooring Porter	2-13	0	1	1	190,175	193,025
STUART EDMUNDS	Hometown Boy	17-126	21	15	14	121,025	189,623
JENNIE CANDLISH	Mint Condition	22-162	20	20	18	106,667	182,086
OLIVER SHERWOOD	Jersey Bean	22-177	16	21	19	108,647	170,982
HENRY DALY	Chilli Filli	14-140	19	13	18	90,121	169,907
EMMET MULLINS	The Shunter	4-9	2	0	0	151,716	168,653
PETER BOWEN	Mac Tottie	20-226	30	20	25	86,965	166,923
KEITH DALGLEISH	Amalfi Doug	20-190	15	26	28	96,670	166,567
REBECCA MENZIES	Return Ticket	20-194	16	25	25	101,915	162,713
PHILIP KIRBY	Whoshotthesheriff	16-284	15	21	22	85,953	162,298
WARREN GREATREX	Another Emotion	16-229	20	22	24	79,833	161,371
ROSE DOBBIN	Le Cheval Noir	21-167	21	18	19	98,080	161,246
SAM THOMAS	Good Risk At All	24-87	17	9	7	116,094	157,248

TOP NH OWNERS IN BRITAIN 2020/21

OWNER	LEADING HORSE	W-R	2ND	3RD	4TH	WIN PRIZE	TOTAL PRIZE
JOHN P MCMANUS	Minella Times	78-506	64	52	51	1,173,483	1,811,184
SIMON MUNIR & ISAAC SOUEDE	Sceau Royal	27-168	24	28	17	344,682	594,451
TREVOR HEMMINGS	Cloth Cap	24-101	15	12	4	313,982	380,548
CHEVELEY PARK STUD	Allaho	4-12	3	0	3	239,174	365,292
MRS S RICCI	Monkfish	5-15	1	1	2	198,180	363,542
MRS J DONNELLY	Shishkin	7-19	3	5	0	167,633	265,090
BARRY MALONEY	Minella Indo	1-2	0	0	0	263,765	263,765
GIGGINSTOWN HOUSE STUD	Abacadabras	2-32	1	1	5	135,229	237,637
KENNETH ALEXANDER	Honeysuckle	4-14	3	0	0	232,767	236,696
MR & MRS WILLIAM RUCKER	Secret Reprieve	12-71	14	9	5	172,496	224,644
COLM DONLON	Shan Blue	14-55	11	7	6	130,876	223,493
ONE FOR LUCK RACING SYNDICATE	Put The Kettle On	2-3	0	0	1	204,046	210,175
CHRIS GILES	Greaneteen	6-23	1	3	6	128,536	190,124
P J VOGT	Frodon	4-12	0	1	1	174,006	189,980
SIR A FERGUSON G MASON J HALES & L HALES	Monmiral	9-12	3	0	0	160,969	170,481
KATE & ANDREW BROOKS	Rouge Vif	8-75	9	13	9	67,654	170,148
BROCADE RACING	Native River	12-63	6	6	6	101,971	169,774
MCNEILL FAMILY	Threeunderthrufive	14-65	5	14	5	90,388	166,346
MRS JOHNNY DE LA HEY	Cyrname	11-57	8	5	8	102,089	158,004
IAN HAMILTON	Nuts Well	12-36	4	1	1	103,698	156,693
MR & MRS P K BARBER, G MASON & SIR A FERGUSON	Clan Des Obeaux	2-6	2	1	0	88,731	154,216
ALLSON SPARKLE LTD	Mighty Thunder	5-15	3	1	1	116,144	150,425
RACEHORSECLUB	Balko Des Flos	0-1	1	0	0	0	150,000
T G LESLIE	Navajo Pass	14-66	10	13	7	103,773	143,894
PAUL BYRNE	The Shunter	3-4	0	0	0	138,902	138,902
J HALES	Politologue	6-19	6	0	2	90,604	136,980
MR & MRS R KELVIN-HUGHES	My Drogo	7-19	4	3	0	102,489	136,547
FLOORING PORTER SYNDICATE	Flooring Porter	1-1	0	0	0	135,048	135,048
THE ENGLANDS AND HEYWOODS	Thyme Hill	2-8	2	1	2	112,670	134,251
MRS CAROLYN KENDRICK	Ratfacemcdougall	18-71	12	12	10	89,741	125,797
L FELL	Silver Streak	3-12	5	0	0	81,790	120,686
J FRENCH, D MCDERMOTT, S NELSON, T SYDER	Clondaw Castle	2-6	3	1	0	61,480	120,289
JAMES & JEAN POTTER LTD	Potterman	4-43	4	0	4	80,500	118,663
MALCOLM C DENMARK	Next Destination	13-27	3	1	1	84,718	118,214
MRS B TULLY AND R LOCK	Dashel Drasher	3-7	0	2	1	111,232	115,918
MRS SARAH FAULKS	Roksana	3-19	5	5	1	49,612	115,395
SIR PETER & LADY GIBBINGS	Song For Someone	5-15	3	2	1	96,375	112,034
TIM SYDER	Killer Clown	11-62	11	9	4	60,521	110,457
T SPRAGGETT	Nube Negra	1-2	1	0	0	46,364	109,964
WAYNE CLIFFORD	Coole Cody	3-23	5	2	5	87,727	108,526
MIKE AND EILEEN NEWBOULD	Wilde About Oscar	8-34	2	1	6	83,947	105,423
P HICKEY	Soaring Glory	6-28	3	5	3	88,531	104,045
WALTERS PLANT HIRE LTD	Al Dancer	14-43	8	3	4	75,908	103,537
STRAIGHTLINE BLOODSTOCK	Taxmeifyoucan	14-103	9	17	15	61,810	103,401
R A BARTLETT	Galvin	4-12	0	2	2	83,887	102,583
HILLS OF LEDBURY LTD	Secret Investor	5-17	2	1	1	70,815	101,319
BRADLEY PARTNERSHIP	The Two Amigos	5-61	8	10	7	24,562	95,065
SULLIVAN BLOODSTOCK LIMITED	Duc Des Genievres	3-49	9	8	5	11,306	93,325
GEOFF AND ELSPETH ADAM	Aye Right	2-24	5	3	2	7,537	91,491
A N SOLOMONS	First Flow	3-4	0	0	0	87,114	91,164
THE BELLAMY PARTNERSHIP	Ibleo	4-21	4	1	2	41,045	89,617
DIRECT BLOODSTOCK LIMITED	Belfast Banter	2-5	0	1	0	84,441	88,969
JOHN WHITE & ANNE UNDERHILL	Umbrigado	6-26	2	2	2	69,144	88,852
M TEDHAM	Sky Pirate	3-15	3	1	2	73,458	88,180
ANDREW GEMMELL	Paisley Park	2-10	2	1	1	49,068	88,098
ROBCOUR	Bob Olinger	1-7	1	0	2	52,753	87,948
BRYAN DREW AND FRIENDS / PROF C TISDALL	Adagio	3-6	3	0	0	44,755	86,087
VIVIAN HEALY	Chatham Street Lad	2-9	0	0	1	75,437	85,503
WALTERS PLANT HIRE & POTTER GROUP	Before Midnight	8-66	15	10	9	38,467	83,660
R S BROOKHOUSE	Summerville Boy	5-46	6	8	2	48,329	83,339

TOP NH HORSES IN BRITAIN 2020/21

HORSE (AGE IN 2021)	WIN & PLACE £	W-R	TRAINER	OWNER	BREEDER
MINELLA TIMES (7)	375,000	1-1	Henry De Bromhead	John P McManus	Cathal Ennis
MINELLA INDO (7)	263,765	1-1	Henry De Bromhead	Barry Maloney	Mrs R H Lalor
PUT THE KETTLE ON (6)	210,175	2-3	Henry De Bromhead	One For Luck Racing Syndicate	Butlersgrove Stud
HONEYSUCKLE (6)	189,911	1-1	Henry De Bromhead	Kenneth Alexander	Dr G W Guy
FRODON (9)	185,355	3-5	Paul Nicholls	P J Vogt	Philippe Gasdoue
FAKIR D'OUDAIRIES (5)	162,378	1-2	Joseph Patrick O'Brien	John P McManus	Comte Michel De Gigou
THE SHUNTER (7)	154,885	3-3	Emmet Mullins	John P McManus	James O'Connor
SHISHKIN (6)	153,854	5-5	Nicky Henderson	Mrs J Donnelly	C J & E B Bennett
CLAN DES OBEAUX (9)	150,448	1-4	Paul Nicholls	Mr & Mrs P K Barber, G Mason & Sir A Ferguson	Mme Marie Devilder
ALLAHO (6)	150,350	1-1	W P Mullins	Cheveley Park Stud	Eric Leffray
BALKO DES FLOS (9)	150,000	0-2	Henry De Bromhead	RacehorseClub	Clovis Bardin & Mme Florence Bardin
GREANETEEN (6)	144,180	2-5	Paul Nicholls	Chris Giles	Bertrand Compignie
CLOTH CAP (8)	144,074	2-4	Jonjo O'Neill	Trevor Hemmings	S Spillane
MIGHTY THUNDER (7)	138,165	4-7	Lucinda Russell	Allson Sparkle Ltd	C And Mrs Wilson
CHANTRY HOUSE (6)	135,515	4-5	Nicky Henderson	John P McManus	M Conaghan
FLOORING PORTER (6)	135,048	1-1	Gavin Cromwell	Flooring Porter Syndicate	Sean Murphy
THYME HILL (6)	129,766	2-3	Philip Hobbs	The Englands And Heywoods	Overbury Stallions Ltd
SCEAU ROYAL (8)	122,000	3-8	Alan King	Simon Munir & Isaac Souede	Guy Vimont
CLONDAW CASTLE (8)	120,289	2-6	Tom George	J French, D McDermott, S Nelson, T Syder	Carl Beame
DASHEL DRASHER (8)	115,275	3-4	Jeremy Scott	Mrs B Tully And R Lock	Mrs C C Scott
NUBE NEGRA (7)	109,964	1-2	Dan Skelton	T Spraggett	Cuadra Internorte
SILVER STREAK (7)	108,933	2-6	Evan Williams	L Fell	Yeomanstown Stud
ABACADABRAS (7)	104,983	1-2	Mrs Denise Foster	Gigginstown House Stud	Mme Evelyne Van Haaren
EPATANTE (6)	104,061	1-3	Nicky Henderson	John P McManus	Francois-Xavier & Anne Doulce Lefeuvre
BRISTOL DE MAI (9)	100,765	1-3	Nigel Twiston-Davies	Simon Munir & Isaac Souede	Jean-Yves Touzaint
POLITOLOGUE (9)	100,526	1-3	Paul Nicholls	J Hales	Mme Henri Devin
A PLUS TARD (6)	99,374	0-1	Henry De Bromhead	Cheveley Park Stud	Mme Henri Devin
SECRET REPRIEVE (6)	98,085	2-3	Evan Williams	Mr & Mrs William Rucker	R McCarthy
COOLE CODY (9)	96,456	2-8	Evan Williams	Wayne Clifford	Timothy Considine
SONG FOR SOMEONE (5)	94,743	2-4	Tom Symonds	Sir Peter & Lady Gibbings	J Bervoets
NUTS WELL (9)	92,727	2-4	Ann Hamilton	Ian Hamilton	Chesters Stud Ltd
POTTERMAN (8)	92,252	2-7	Alan King	James & Jean Potter Ltd	James & Jean Potter
FIRST FLOW (8)	91,164	3-4	Kim Bailey	A N Solomons	Mrs Kathleen Flood
ROKSANA (8)	89,639	2-5	Dan Skelton	Mrs Sarah Faulks	John O'Leary
MY DROGO (5)	88,408	4-5	Dan Skelton	Mr & Mrs R Kelvin-Hughes	H & C Group Ltd
BELFAST BANTER (5)	87,121	2-4	Peter Fahey	Direct Bloodstock Limited	Seamus Cooney
ADAGIO (3)	86,087	3-6	David Pipe	Bryan Drew And Friends/Prof C Tisdall	Gestut Schlenderhan
SKY PIRATE (7)	84,345	3-6	Jonjo O'Neill	M Tedham	C B Brookes
MONMIRAL (3)	84,185	4-4	Paul Nicholls	Sir A Ferguson G Mason J Hales & L Hales	S A R L Carion Emm
SHAN BLUE (6)	83,867	3-6	Dan Skelton	Colm Donlon	Desmond Amond
SOARING GLORY (5)	82,969	2-6	Jonjo O'Neill	P Hickey	A V Bloodstock
MASTER TOMMYTUCKER (9)	82,642	3-7	Paul Nicholls	A G Fear	A G Fear
PAISLEY PARK (8)	81,709	1-4	Emma Lavelle	Andrew Gemmell	M Conaghan
AYE RIGHT (7)	79,688	0-6	Harriet Graham	Geoff And Elspeth Adam	Patrick Cashman
TIME TO GET UP (7)	79,303	2-4	Jonjo O'Neill	John P McManus	Mrs E Moore
BUZZ (6)	79,148	1-5	Nicky Henderson	Thurloe For Royal Marsden Cancer Charity	Christian Maillaut & Matthieu Maillaut
MONKFISH (6)	75,151	1-1	W P Mullins	Mrs S Ricci	Cyril O'Hara
NATIVE RIVER (10)	75,009	1-4	Colin Tizzard	Brocade Racing	Fred Mackey
ANY SECOND NOW (8)	75,000	0-1	T M Walsh	John P McManus	Mrs Noreen McManus
SHARJAH (7)	71,550	0-1	W P Mullins	Mrs S Ricci	Ecurie Haras De Beauvoir
ALLMANKIND (4)	71,488	4-6	Dan Skelton	The Gredley Family	Stetchworth & Middle Park Studs Ltd
ROYALE PAGAILLE (6)	70,315	3-4	Venetia Williams	Mrs S Ricci	Philippe Mace
PROTEKTORAT (5)	69,898	3-5	Dan Skelton	Sir A Ferguson G Mason J Hales & L Hales	Guy Cherel & Mme Isabelle Pacault
SAM'S ADVENTURE (8)	69,832	2-6	Brian Ellison	Julie & Phil Martin	R Johnson
HAPPYGOLUCKY (6)	68,885	3-5	Kim Bailey	Lady Dulverton	Mrs Maura Canavan
KITTY'S LIGHT (4)	68,040	4-11	Christian Williams	R J Bedford & All Stars Sports Racing	The Darailya Syndicate
VIEUX LION ROUGE (11)	67,955	1-4	David Pipe	Prof Caroline Tisdall & John Gent	F M Cattin
NOT SO SLEEPY (8)	67,219	1-4	Hughie Morrison	Lady Blyth	Lord Blyth
CHATHAM STREET LAD (8)	66,817	1-2	Michael Winters	Vivian Healy	P Magee
FIDDLERONTHEROOF (6)	65,753	1-7	Colin Tizzard	Taylor, Burley & O'Dwyer	Treaty Pals Syndicate

LEADING SIRES OF 2021 IN GREAT BRITAIN AND IRELAND

STALLION	BREEDING	RNRS	WNRS	WINS	TOTAL	BEST HORSE
FRANKEL	by Galileo	186	87	144	£5,209,199	Adayar
GALILEO	by Sadler's Wells	200	57	73	£3,649,289	Love
DUBAWI	by Dubai Millennium	187	101	164	£3,589,522	Creative Force
SEA THE STARS	by Cape Cross	165	77	123	£3,396,446	Baaeed
DARK ANGEL	by Acclamation	292	134	208	£3,097,663	Art Power
LOPE DE VEGA	by Shamardal	204	91	136	£2,337,266	Lucky Vega
KINGMAN	by Invincible Spirit	153	68	104	£2,270,956	Palace Pier
KODIAC	by Danehill	326	125	181	£2,237,251	Campanelle
ZOFFANY	by Dansili	200	67	88	£2,043,107	Mother Earth
NO NAY NEVER	by Scat Daddy	142	49	79	£1,936,455	Alcohol Free
AUSTRALIA	by Galileo	139	55	93	£1,926,415	Broome
SIYOUNI	by Pivotal	112	46	63	£1,737,636	St Mark's Basilica
DANDY MAN	by Mozart	190	76	132	£1,603,174	Mooneista
MEHMAS	by Acclamation	158	76	115	£1,576,679	Lusail
CAMELOT	by Montjeu	141	57	83	£1,502,719	Luxembourg
NIGHT OF THUNDER	by Dubawi	102	47	76	£1,495,136	Suesa
INVINCIBLE SPIRIT	by Green Desert	158	68	99	£1,442,862	Arecibo
MAYSON	by Invincible Spirit	131	53	96	£1,417,743	Oxted
SHAMARDAL	by Giant's Causeway	98	50	62	£1,380,979	Emaraaty Ana
MUHAARAR	by Oasis Dream	138	53	70	£1,369,808	Eshaada
OASIS DREAM	by Green Desert	140	43	64	£1,349,623	Native Trail
MAKE BELIEVE	by Makfi	68	27	34	£1,348,195	Mishriff
DAWN APPROACH	by New Approach	95	35	53	£1,339,117	Poetic Flare
NATHANIEL	by Galileo	116	34	47	£1,319,929	Lady Bowthorpe
GLENEAGLES	by Galileo	115	50	85	£1,258,773	Loving Dream
EXCEED AND EXCEL	by Danehill	146	66	102	£1,238,227	Great Ambassador
MASTERCRAFTSMAN	by Danehill Dancer	133	45	60	£1,208,424	Discoveries
ACCLAMATION	by Royal Applause	157	62	95	£1,183,065	Oh This Is Us
IFFRAAJ	by Zafonic	170	70	102	£1,161,829	Live Your Dream
SHOWCASING	by Oasis Dream	193	67	101	£1,129,618	Asymmetric

LEADING TWO-YEAR-OLD SIRES OF 2021 IN GREAT BRITAIN AND IRELAND

STALLION	BREEDING	RNRS	WNRS	WINS	TOTAL	BEST HORSE
MEHMAS	by Acclamation	76	38	53	£822,430	Lusail
OASIS DREAM	by Green Desert	40	15	20	£791,792	Native Trail
DARK ANGEL	by Acclamation	77	33	43	£789,359	Berkshire Shadow
FRANKEL	by Galileo	47	18	29	£711,078	Inspiral
KODIAC	by Danehill	99	41	52	£665,250	Atomic Lady
CARAVAGGIO	by Scat Daddy	64	19	23	£573,872	Tenebrism
DUBAWI	by Dubai Millennium	52	26	33	£573,157	Dubawi Legend
STARSPANGLEDBANNER	by Choisir	52	19	24	£534,394	Castle Star
SHOWCASING	by Oasis Dream	70	27	34	£512,776	Asymmetric
HAVANA GOLD	by Teofilo	59	25	36	£498,378	Chipotle
COTAI GLORY	by Exceed And Excel	71	26	36	£493,774	King X J
ARDAD	by Kodiac	57	20	29	£489,941	Perfect Power
NO NAY NEVER	by Scat Daddy	47	21	28	£479,784	Zain Claudette
PROFITABLE	by Invincible Spirit	70	23	31	£465,110	Quick Suzy
KODI BEAR	by Kodiac	35	11	18	£419,909	Ever Given
GALILEO GOLD	by Paco Boy	51	18	24	£400,533	Ebro River
BATED BREATH	by Dansili	41	13	21	£370,465	Sacred Bridge
AUSTRALIA	by Galileo	42	11	14	£351,659	Point Lonsdale
CHURCHILL	by Galileo	64	18	22	£321,733	Ladies Church
NEW BAY	by Dubawi	30	14	16	£318,309	Bayside Boy
WOOTTON BASSETT	by Iffraaj	11	6	10	£315,424	Royal Patronage
ACCLAMATION	by Royal Applause	46	16	23	£314,864	Canonized
ZOFFANY	by Dansili	39	9	10	£306,082	Prosperous Voyage
FAST COMPANY	by Danehill Dancer	43	11	17	£305,402	Symphony Perfect
EL KABEIR	by Scat Daddy	37	7	11	£294,895	Harrow
MASTERCRAFTSMAN	by Danehill Dancer	33	7	9	£274,228	Discoveries
ACLAIM	by Acclamation	54	21	23	£273,402	Cachet
GLENEAGLES	by Galileo	26	10	16	£269,972	Velocidad
LOPE DE VEGA	by Shamardal	49	19	21	£240,941	Duke de Sessa
CAMELOT	by Montjeu	22	5	7	£238,266	Luxembourg

LEADING FIRST CROP SIRES OF 2021 IN GREAT BRITAIN AND IRELAND

STALLION	BREEDING	RNRS	WNRS	WINS	TOTAL	BEST HORSE
CARAVAGGIO	by Scat Daddy	64	19	23	£573,872	Tenebrism
COTAI GLORY	by Exceed And Excel	71	26	36	£493,774	King X J
ARDAD	by Kodiac	57	20	29	£489,941	Perfect Power
PROFITABLE	by Invincible Spirit	70	23	31	£465,110	Quick Suzy
GALILEO GOLD	by Paco Boy	51	18	24	£400,533	Ebro River
CHURCHILL	by Galileo	64	18	22	£321,733	Ladies Church
EL KABEIR	by Scat Daddy	37	7	11	£294,895	Harrow
ACLAIM	by Acclamation	54	21	23	£273,402	Cachet
RIBCHESTER	by Iffraaj	43	10	16	£204,786	Flaming Rib
TIME TEST	by Dubawi	38	9	12	£196,444	Sunset Shiraz
ULYSSES	by Galileo	40	15	17	£136,457	Implore
HIGHLAND REEL	by Galileo	29	8	11	£84,542	Highland Premiere
DECORATED KNIGHT	by Galileo	21	5	6	£69,622	Wind Your Neck In
POSTPONED	by Dubawi	34	3	3	£67,482	Past Time
MATTMU	by Indesatchel	5	2	4	£64,757	Favourite Child
MONDIALISTE	by Galileo	25	4	4	£53,201	Vieux Carre
ALMANZOR	by Wootton Bassett	16	5	6	£52,876	Abbado
NATIONAL DEFENSE	by Invincible Spirit	10	0	0	£28,788	Twilight Gleaming
SPILL THE BEANS	by Snitzel	6	2	3	£24,432	Dairerin
ZELZAL	by Sea The Stars	6	2	3	£20,281	Migdam
JOHNNY BARNES	by Acclamation	3	2	2	£17,928	Grey Belle
ZARAK	by Dubawi	5	1	1	£16,814	Island Bandit
DIVINE PROPHET	by Choisir	12	1	1	£16,138	Scarlet Dancer
BIRCHWOOD	by Dark Angel	3	0	0	£12,665	Buckshaw Village
ECTOT	by Hurricane Run	2	1	1	£9,937	Devasboy
RECORDER	by Galileo	7	0	0	£7,700	Pavlodar
AL WUKAIR	by Dream Ahead	2	2	2	£7,304	Destiny Queen
ELM PARK	by Phoenix Reach	2	1	1	£6,109	Upton Park
JACK HOBBS	by Halling	2	0	0	£5,800	The Gadget Man
HOOTENANNY	by Quality Road	1	1	1	£3,887	Eskin Rose

LEADING MATERNAL GRANDSIRES OF 2021 IN GREAT BRITAIN AND IRELAND

STALLION	BREEDING	RNRS	WNRS	WINS	TOTAL	BEST HORSE
GALILEO	by Sadler's Wells	464	197	294	£6,178,353	St Mark's Basilica
PIVOTAL	by Polar Falcon	322	138	204	£3,425,090	Love
DANEHILL DANCER	by Danehill	243	94	156	£3,207,167	Empress Josephine
OASIS DREAM	by Green Desert	346	149	229	£3,020,770	Quickthorn
DANSILI	by Danehill	294	110	173	£2,912,947	Dream of Dreams
DUBAWI	by Dubai Millennium	174	73	117	£2,535,795	Adayar
CAPE CROSS	by Green Desert	216	94	156	£2,483,008	Emaraaty Ana
MONTJEU	by Sadler's Wells	160	62	97	£2,426,432	Starman
SHAMARDAL	by Giant's Causeway	211	89	130	£1,873,001	Al Aasy
RAVEN'S PASS	by Elusive Quality	77	25	37	£1,814,438	Mishriff
INVINCIBLE SPIRIT	by Green Desert	263	87	143	£1,753,827	Harrow
KINGMAMBO	by Mr. Prospector	64	32	50	£1,669,104	Baaeed
NAYEF	by Gulch	105	37	67	£1,646,770	Palace Pier
ACCLAMATION	by Royal Applause	186	70	100	£1,612,989	Broome
EXCEED AND EXCEL	by Danehill	202	83	134	£1,609,379	Blackod
SHIROCCO	by Monsun	30	13	24	£1,506,680	Hurricane Lane
DANEHILL	by Danzig	120	42	61	£1,484,727	Highfield Princess
TEOFILO	by Galileo	140	50	71	£1,452,372	Mac Swiney
ROCK OF GIBRALTAR	by Danehill	118	32	52	£1,443,908	Poetic Flare
SELKIRK	by Sharpen Up	130	44	78	£1,408,189	Inspiral
SADLER'S WELLS	by Northern Dancer	178	49	69	£1,247,250	Bedouin's Story
GREEN DESERT	by Danzig	121	38	63	£1,228,411	Mother Earth
SEA THE STARS	by Cape Cross	92	48	71	£1,219,669	Mohaafeth
DALAKHANI	by Darshaan	137	46	73	£1,200,125	Royal Patronage
HARD SPUN	by Danzig	20	10	20	£1,137,884	Alcohol Free
STREET CRY	by Machiavellian	105	51	83	£1,118,093	Spanish Mission
ROYAL APPLAUSE	by Waajib	166	57	91	£1,048,516	Hurricane Ivor
VERGLAS	by Highest Honor	70	23	33	£956,961	Lady Bowthorpe
CHOISIR	by Danehill Dancer	35	12	27	£923,113	Creative Force
HIGH CHAPARRAL	by Sadler's Wells	113	45	66	£887,166	Armor
MARJU	by Last Tycoon	88	28	39	£628,964	Happy Romance

FLAT STALLIONS' EARNINGS FOR 2021

(Includes every stallion who sired a winner on the Flat in Great Britain and Ireland in 2021)

STALLIONS	RNRS	WNRS	WINS	PLACES	TOTAL (£)
ACCLAMATION (GB)	157	62	95	220	1190597
ACLAIM (IRE)	54	21	23	58	275468
ADAAY (IRE)	95	26	38	102	412691
ADLERFLUG (GER)	2	1	2	4	343251
AIR CHIEF MARSHAL (IRE)	3	1	1	2	9807
AIR FORCE BLUE (USA)	15	3	4	17	42713
AJAYA (GB)	13	4	5	13	106593
AL KAZEEM (GB)	28	8	19	32	165948
AL WUKAIR (IRE)	2	2	2	0	11140
ALBAASIL (IRE)	7	2	2	6	14469
ALHEBAYEB (IRE)	57	13	25	63	392746
ALMANZOR (FR)	16	5	6	9	53876
AMERICAN PHAROAH (USA)	24	7	7	19	231132
ANIMAL KINGDOM (USA)	6	2	3	8	32741
ANJAAL (GB)	41	15	23	34	188053
ANTONIUS PIUS (USA)	2	1	1	1	5945
APPROVE (IRE)	10	5	7	11	77900
AQLAAM (GB)	11	6	10	14	96552
ARABIAN GLEAM (GB)	5	2	2	2	10565
ARCADIO (GER)	5	1	1	1	38387
ARCANO (IRE)	36	9	16	38	147953
ARCHIPENKO (USA)	30	15	25	36	191873
ARDAD (IRE)	57	20	29	41	492082
ART CONNOISSEUR (IRE)	4	2	3	11	34119
ARTIE SCHILLER (USA)	1	1	1	2	5757
ASK (GB)	3	1	1	3	13819
ASSERTIVE (GB)	8	3	3	14	49669
ATRAF (GB)	1	1	1	1	5672
AUSSIE RULES (USA)	11	3	4	14	56187
AUSTRALIA (GB)	139	55	93	130	1959244
AUTHORIZED (IRE)	29	12	16	26	406881
AVONBRIDGE (GB)	4	2	2	4	12960
AWTAAD (IRE)	73	30	53	91	643688
BAHAMIAN BOUNTY (GB)	10	6	14	23	158152
BAHRI (USA)	4	2	5	3	26647
BALTIC KING (GB)	7	1	3	6	17346
BASHKIROV (GB)	4	1	2	4	17978
BATED BREATH (GB)	136	50	82	168	1002868
BATTLE OF MARENGO (IRE)	17	5	9	10	63213
BEAT HOLLOW (GB)	8	1	2	3	16007
BELARDO (IRE)	59	27	46	75	424327
BERNARDINI (USA)	3	1	1	2	8303
BIG BAD BOB (IRE)	21	5	5	27	63630
BLAME (USA)	4	1	1	6	14849
BOBBY'S KITTEN (USA)	56	16	24	69	357667
BORN TO SEA (IRE)	55	14	24	52	440077
BOW CREEK (IRE)	2	1	1	2	4661
BRAZEN BEAU (AUS)	82	31	52	91	517961
BRILLIANT SPEED (USA)	1	1	1	1	3934
BUNGLE INTHEJUNGLE (GB)	66	22	35	91	625568
BURATINO (IRE)	42	10	13	31	165580
BURWAAZ (GB)	3	3	6	7	52258
BUSHRANGER (IRE)	9	1	2	2	10643
CABLE BAY (IRE)	89	38	62	134	1127778
CACIQUE (IRE)	15	5	10	11	96698
CAMACHO (GB)	140	44	66	165	609133
CAMELOT (GB)	138	57	83	137	1522460

STALLIONS	RNRS	WNRS	WINS	PLACES	TOTAL (£)
CAMPANOLOGIST (USA)	1	1	3	3	80644
CANFORD CLIFFS (IRE)	66	17	22	64	262971
CANNOCK CHASE (USA)	10	1	1	4	13218
CAPE CROSS (IRE)	41	12	19	31	409096
CAPPELLA SANSEVERO (GB)	14	1	1	15	36427
CAPTAIN GERRARD (IRE)	15	6	8	11	58444
CARAVAGGIO (USA)	64	19	23	49	586775
CASAMENTO (IRE)	45	10	13	45	179163
CHAMPS ELYSEES (GB)	60	21	32	70	450989
CHARM SPIRIT (IRE)	46	22	31	83	259962
CHARMING THOUGHT (GB)	33	13	23	42	221834
CHOISIR (AUS)	12	6	15	21	161265
CHURCHILL (IRE)	64	18	22	49	328231
CITYSCAPE (GB)	53	17	28	62	243942
CLODOVIL (IRE)	41	14	19	55	225853
COACH HOUSE (IRE)	65	23	43	75	280428
COCKNEY REBEL (IRE)	2	1	2	2	8269
COMPTON PLACE (GB)	12	3	4	13	47519
CONDUIT (IRE)	1	1	1	2	5070
COTAI GLORY (GB)	71	26	36	54	501107
COULSTY (IRE)	25	8	13	15	92990
DABIRSIM (FR)	47	16	19	49	205884
DAIWA MAJOR (JPN)	1	1	1	3	61371
DALAKHANI (IRE)	8	3	5	8	67077
DANDY MAN (IRE)	190	76	132	321	1613541
DANSILI (GB)	59	27	45	60	521852
DARK ANGEL (IRE)	290	134	208	396	3115662
DAWN APPROACH (IRE)	93	33	51	99	1351539
DECLARATION OF WAR (USA)	30	9	14	37	212162
DECORATED KNIGHT (GB)	21	5	6	11	69634
DEEP IMPACT (JPN)	11	5	9	6	823806
DELEGATOR (GB)	22	11	15	46	186261
DENOUNCE (GB)	2	1	3	0	28389
DIALED IN (USA)	3	2	5	8	39384
DICK TURPIN (IRE)	10	7	8	12	61207
DISTORTED HUMOR (USA)	10	5	10	15	134444
DIVINE PROPHET (AUS)	12	1	1	5	16286
DRAGON PULSE (IRE)	85	31	48	88	406686
DREAM AHEAD (USA)	53	22	40	66	805380
DUBAWI (IRE)	186	101	163	185	3591530
DUE DILIGENCE (USA)	58	20	38	66	390351
DUNADEN (FR)	11	3	5	9	116369
DUNKERQUE (FR)	2	1	1	0	6554
DUTCH ART (GB)	66	28	43	79	862970
DYLAN THOMAS (IRE)	22	6	16	23	141929
ECTOT (GB)	2	1	1	3	9938
EL KABEIR (USA)	37	7	11	26	296792
ELM PARK (GB)	2	1	1	2	6109
ELNADIM (USA)	6	5	7	6	69460
ELUSIVE CITY (USA)	5	3	3	17	42096
ELUSIVE PIMPERNEL (USA)	22	4	6	17	121970
ELUSIVE QUALITY (USA)	8	4	10	6	52116
ELVSTROEM (AUS)	1	1	1	1	12555
ELZAAM (AUS)	99	37	57	93	603978
ENGLISH CHANNEL (USA)	3	2	2	7	37938
EPAULETTE (AUS)	65	26	42	81	364192
EQUIANO (FR)	124	44	65	149	752061
ES QUE LOVE (IRE)	13	5	13	19	111622
ESTIDHKAAR (IRE)	54	16	24	46	187579
EXCEED AND EXCEL (AUS)	146	66	102	181	1242077
EXCELEBRATION (IRE)	58	22	35	66	572611

STALLIONS	RNRS	WNRS	WINS	PLACES	TOTAL (£)
EXCELLENT ART (GB)	6	1	2	6	22044
EXCHANGE RATE (USA)	4	2	6	9	53168
FAIRLY RANSOM (USA)	1	1	2	1	10871
FAMOUS NAME (GB)	15	1	2	12	91651
FARHH (GB)	47	16	26	57	600099
FASCINATING ROCK (IRE)	35	10	14	43	171500
FAST COMPANY (IRE)	138	42	59	149	869626
FASTNET ROCK (AUS)	91	35	57	82	639907
FINJAAN (GB)	6	2	3	2	13300
FINSCEAL FIOR (IRE)	8	2	3	10	24717
FIREBREAK (GB)	4	1	1	7	14056
FIRST DEFENCE (USA)	7	2	3	5	77893
FLEMENSFIRTH (USA)	3	1	1	2	8377
FLINTSHIRE (GB)	10	4	4	10	40046
FOOTSTEPSINTHESAND (GB)	145	41	65	149	734885
FOUNTAIN OF YOUTH (IRE)	44	10	17	42	137046
FOXWEDGE (AUS)	19	9	15	26	131276
FRACAS (IRE)	14	4	4	7	46812
FRANKEL (GB)	186	87	144	204	5235257
FREE EAGLE (IRE)	54	21	42	55	457065
FRENCH FIFTEEN (FR)	7	1	1	0	11734
FRENCH NAVY (GB)	22	5	9	20	153249
FROZEN POWER (IRE)	11	2	4	12	33963
FUISSE (FR)	1	1	1	5	34986
FULBRIGHT (GB)	23	2	2	13	30390
G FORCE (IRE)	3	1	2	2	9871
GALE FORCE TEN (GB)	25	14	29	33	264363
GALILEO (IRE)	198	56	71	179	3705879
GALILEO GOLD (GB)	51	18	24	28	408722
GALIWAY (GB)	1	1	1	0	714546
GARSWOOD (GB)	68	16	23	62	361030
GEMOLOGIST (USA)	1	1	1	1	10629
GEORDIELAND (FR)	2	1	1	0	3300
GETAWAY (GER)	10	2	3	3	24609
GIO PONTI (USA)	2	1	1	2	8942
GLENEAGLES (IRE)	115	50	85	155	1276241
GOKEN (FR)	4	2	3	5	18311
GOLDEN HORN (GB)	98	42	61	120	947533
GOLDEN LARIAT (USA)	1	1	4	3	46893
GREGORIAN (IRE)	38	12	24	44	201888
GUTAIFAN (IRE)	117	40	72	128	714529
HAAFHD (GB)	10	6	14	24	84622
HAATEF (USA)	6	2	3	2	32519
HALLING (USA)	3	1	1	5	57199
HALLOWED CROWN (AUS)	17	9	15	28	145041
HARBOUR WATCH (IRE)	47	17	30	71	680583
HARD SPUN (USA)	9	2	2	10	25076
HARLAN'S HOLIDAY (USA)	1	1	1	1	4492
HARZAND (IRE)	26	11	14	31	134720
HAVANA GOLD (IRE)	114	41	63	111	724734
HEERAAT (IRE)	100	20	30	77	362245
HELLVELYN (GB)	31	7	10	30	81100
HELMET (AUS)	116	40	64	146	518012
HENRYTHENAVIGATOR (USA)	15	3	5	10	43034
HIGH CHAPARRAL (IRE)	15	1	1	12	56276
HIGHLAND REEL (IRE)	29	8	11	10	86362
HIT IT A BOMB (USA)	2	1	2	6	12218
HOLY ROMAN EMPEROR (IRE)	104	32	44	117	497695
HONOR CODE (USA)	2	1	1	6	13020
HOOTENANNY (USA)	1	1	1	0	3888
HOT STREAK (IRE)	58	13	25	59	308698

STALLIONS	RNRS	WNRS	WINS	PLACES	TOTAL (£)
HUNTER'S LIGHT (IRE)	10	2	10	12	43241
IFFRAAJ (GB)	170	70	102	209	1164536
INCLUDE (USA)	2	1	1	1	8809
INTELLO (GER)	51	10	17	49	227468
INTENSE FOCUS (USA)	16	5	7	13	110505
INTIKHAB (USA)	11	3	4	11	39988
INTRINSIC (GB)	9	4	4	10	39267
INVINCIBLE SPIRIT (IRE)	156	68	99	216	1467788
IVAWOOD (IRE)	42	16	29	53	374853
JEREMY (USA)	8	1	1	2	10581
JOHNNY BARNES (IRE)	3	2	2	4	17929
JUKEBOX JURY (IRE)	9	1	2	8	117790
KALANISI (IRE)	9	1	1	5	11897
KARAKONTIE (JPN)	10	6	9	9	102002
KENDARGENT (FR)	30	12	23	37	224388
KHELEYF (USA)	19	4	5	13	61898
KINGMAN (GB)	153	68	104	168	2280037
KING'S THEATRE (IRE)	3	1	1	0	8817
KINGSTON HILL (GB)	12	4	5	6	43906
KITTEN'S JOY (USA)	34	11	17	33	231766
KODI BEAR (IRE)	83	34	50	85	924126
KODIAC (GB)	326	125	181	406	2257809
KUROSHIO (AUS)	3	2	4	7	23446
KYLLACHY (GB)	46	17	29	61	262751
LAWMAN (FR)	87	23	32	100	374205
LE CADRE NOIR (IRE)	5	2	3	4	43478
LE HAVRE (IRE)	58	30	45	61	890943
LEMON DROP KID (USA)	7	4	6	4	93209
LEROIDESANIMAUX (BRZ)	6	3	4	16	69652
LETHAL FORCE (IRE)	102	44	91	154	870871
LIBERTARIAN (GB)	1	1	2	2	6999
LILBOURNE LAD (IRE)	18	8	8	20	161071
LITERATO (FR)	1	1	1	1	5996
LOPE DE VEGA (IRE)	203	91	136	249	2350618
LORD OF ENGLAND (GER)	7	3	6	6	68262
LORD SHANAKILL (USA)	11	7	7	18	67271
LOVELACE (GB)	1	1	1	2	31009
LUCKY LION (GB)	1	1	1	0	2622
MAGICIAN (IRE)	8	3	5	13	48718
MAINSAIL (GB)	1	1	3	0	19527
MAJESTIC MISSILE (IRE)	4	1	3	3	12680
MAJOR CADEAUX (GB)	6	4	5	9	41811
MAKE BELIEVE (GB)	68	27	34	77	1334753
MAKFI (GB)	11	6	10	9	61890
MANDURO (GER)	10	2	2	11	28112
MARCEL (IRE)	5	1	2	3	11317
MARKAZ (IRE)	38	16	22	43	179436
MARTALINE (GB)	3	1	1	0	9058
MASTERCRAFTSMAN (IRE)	133	45	60	135	1220261
MATTMU (GB)	5	2	4	8	64757
MAXIOS (GB)	21	7	10	40	182682
MAYSON (GB)	130	53	96	188	1421748
MAZAMEER (IRE)	13	1	3	4	29607
MEDAGLIA D'ORO (USA)	8	1	1	7	35199
MEDICEAN (GB)	21	3	4	16	57889
MEHMAS (IRE)	158	76	115	186	1592626
MIDNIGHT LEGEND (GB)	1	1	1	3	42512
MILAN (GB)	1	1	1	2	6056
MIZZEN MAST (USA)	6	1	2	18	43101
MONDIALISTE (IRE)	25	4	4	18	53198
MONSIEUR BOND (IRE)	37	7	11	52	143494

STALLIONS	RNRS	WNRS	WINS	PLACES	TOTAL (£)
MONTMARTRE (FR)	3	1	1	0	22139
MOOHAAJIM (IRE)	7	1	1	10	17999
MORE THAN READY (USA)	10	3	5	12	69546
MORPHEUS (GB)	36	13	25	36	260932
MOST IMPROVED (IRE)	16	4	5	17	55377
MOTIVATOR (GB)	19	5	6	8	250649
MOUNT NELSON (GB)	30	11	20	37	177418
MOURAYAN (IRE)	1	1	1	1	11455
MR MEDICI (IRE)	1	1	1	1	3696
MSHAWISH (USA)	5	3	5	7	30793
MUHAARAR (GB)	138	53	70	149	1374199
MUHTATHIR (GB)	6	1	2	6	11923
MUKHADRAM (GB)	68	31	51	88	411614
MULTIPLEX (GB)	14	5	7	16	81679
MUSIC MASTER (GB)	8	2	2	10	17297
MUSTAJEEB (GB)	8	1	1	7	37136
MYBOYCHARLIE (IRE)	4	2	4	10	19796
NATHANIEL (IRE)	112	31	44	112	1306653
NAYEF (USA)	25	3	4	20	69549
NEW APPROACH (IRE)	106	31	45	98	880930
NEW BAY (GB)	63	34	60	72	1116510
NIGHT OF THUNDER (IRE)	102	47	76	114	1507074
NO NAY NEVER (USA)	142	49	79	126	1949889
NO RISK AT ALL (FR)	5	3	3	6	24889
NOBLE MISSION (GB)	23	7	9	22	261884
NORTH LIGHT (IRE)	1	1	1	2	6827
OASIS DREAM (GB)	140	43	64	165	1357938
OLDEN TIMES (GB)	3	1	1	6	18223
OLYMPIC GLORY (IRE)	23	12	14	22	96384
ORB (USA)	1	1	1	4	7651
ORIENTOR (GB)	16	7	16	30	130959
OUTSTRIP (GB)	79	21	40	93	322837
PACO BOY (IRE)	29	10	17	48	185976
PARISH HALL (IRE)	4	1	1	4	12375
PASSING GLANCE (GB)	5	1	1	1	4887
PASTORAL PURSUITS (GB)	33	14	21	38	171054
PASTORIUS (GER)	6	3	5	2	29146
PEACE ENVOY (FR)	2	1	1	0	3300
PEARL SECRET (GB)	28	8	9	29	79980
PEDRO THE GREAT (USA)	5	2	3	6	74440
PENNY'S PICNIC (IRE)	1	1	1	2	10132
PHOENIX REACH (IRE)	8	1	1	2	5886
PICCOLO (GB)	13	2	2	10	46668
PIONEEROF THE NILE (USA)	2	1	1	7	36935
PIVOTAL (GB)	66	21	37	79	945087
PLANTEUR (IRE)	6	4	10	13	638370
POET'S VOICE (GB)	67	26	42	91	363271
POINT OF ENTRY (USA)	6	1	1	5	11162
POSTPONED (IRE)	34	3	3	20	68356
POUR MOI (IRE)	21	4	5	18	134569
POWER (GB)	46	17	26	54	993224
PRESENTING (GB)	2	1	1	0	2922
PRIDE OF DUBAI (AUS)	58	19	32	64	746909
PRINCE GIBRALTAR (FR)	2	1	1	1	11057
PRINCE OF LIR (IRE)	41	14	19	33	179383
PROFITABLE (IRE)	70	23	31	63	473865
PROTECTIONIST (GER)	5	2	4	6	71520
QUALITY ROAD (USA)	6	2	3	3	13959
RAIL LINK (GB)	5	3	5	9	129679
RAJSAMAN (FR)	10	1	2	4	14441
RAVEN'S PASS (USA)	50	17	26	57	575208

STALLIONS	RNRS	WNRS	WINS	PLACES	TOTAL (£)
RED CLUBS (IRE)	3	1	1	1	5338
RED JAZZ (USA)	42	9	11	39	186655
REDOUTE'S CHOICE (AUS)	6	2	2	4	26623
REFUSE TO BEND (IRE)	2	1	2	0	11451
RELIABLE MAN (GB)	8	1	1	11	29718
REQUINTO (IRE)	50	19	33	63	380575
RIBCHESTER (IRE)	43	10	16	29	206075
RIO DE LA PLATA (USA)	8	2	2	13	38396
RIP VAN WINKLE (IRE)	25	6	11	27	81112
ROCK OF GIBRALTAR (IRE)	33	9	14	25	192626
RODERIC O'CONNOR (IRE)	24	10	19	48	284405
ROYAL APPLAUSE (GB)	19	1	4	22	67605
RULER OF THE WORLD (IRE)	23	5	13	14	256994
SAKHEE (USA)	3	1	1	3	6344
SAKHEE'S SECRET (GB)	13	4	10	16	90786
SAMUM (GER)	3	1	2	1	12637
SANS FRONTIERES (IRE)	1	1	1	0	19754
SAYIF (IRE)	12	2	4	7	98608
SCAT DADDY (USA)	8	5	8	14	77755
SCHIAPARELLI (GER)	3	2	3	1	13997
SEA MOON (GB)	1	1	2	3	15080
SEA THE MOON (GER)	63	16	26	58	265228
SEA THE STARS (IRE)	165	77	123	189	3401998
SEPOY (AUS)	73	24	42	78	501851
SHALAA (IRE)	44	11	16	41	415501
SHAMARDAL (USA)	97	50	62	120	1393143
SHANTOU (USA)	4	2	3	2	57357
SHIROCCO (GER)	12	1	1	4	15063
SHOLOKHOV (IRE)	2	1	1	1	4776
SHOWCASING (GB)	193	67	99	167	1129526
SIDESTEP (AUS)	2	1	3	6	133197
SIR PERCY (GB)	70	20	31	99	372551
SIR PRANCEALOT (IRE)	61	24	41	80	492654
SIXTIES ICON (GB)	56	11	24	56	169402
SIYOUNI (FR)	112	46	63	124	1766449
SLADE POWER (IRE)	85	34	54	102	681302
SLEEPING INDIAN (GB)	9	3	3	9	27111
SMART STRIKE (CAN)	4	1	1	6	14377
SO YOU THINK (NZ)	8	6	12	11	68058
SOAVE (GER)	1	1	1	2	4908
SOCIETY ROCK (IRE)	32	19	31	62	268934
SOLDIER HOLLOW (GB)	4	3	3	4	55568
SPEIGHTSTOWN (USA)	22	8	11	16	105199
SPILL THE BEANS (AUS)	6	2	3	4	24432
STARSPANGLEDBANNER (AUS)	121	43	64	139	1049626
STEELE TANGO (USA)	2	2	2	7	17448
STIMULATION (IRE)	15	7	17	12	74737
STORM THE STARS (USA)	1	1	1	0	3780
STORMY ATLANTIC (USA)	4	2	2	9	63168
STRATEGIC PRINCE (GB)	2	1	1	0	7248
STRATH BURN (GB)	6	2	3	8	28807
STREET BOSS (USA)	2	1	2	5	19375
STREET CRY (IRE)	5	4	5	8	36472
STREET SENSE (USA)	7	3	5	12	40998
SULAMANI (IRE)	3	1	1	6	13885
SUMMER FRONT (USA)	2	1	1	1	7059
SWISS SPIRIT (GB)	90	30	51	104	441611
TAGULA (IRE)	26	6	10	21	86561
TAMARKUZ (USA)	4	1	1	7	28382
TAMAYUZ (GB)	69	17	25	54	388010
TAPIT (USA)	2	1	1	4	11510

STALLIONS	RNRS	WNRS	WINS	PLACES	TOTAL (£)
TELESCOPE (IRE)	6	1	1	2	8534
TEMPLE CITY (USA)	2	1	1	1	5424
TEOFILO (IRE)	108	41	56	104	1115216
TERRITORIES (IRE)	72	32	44	77	755301
THE CARBON UNIT (USA)	4	1	1	0	8629
THE FACTOR (USA)	6	2	2	3	12598
THE GURKHA (IRE)	71	30	44	73	511208
THE LAST LION (IRE)	34	8	9	33	118434
THE WOW SIGNAL (IRE)	3	1	1	2	6543
THEWAYYOUARE (USA)	11	2	3	11	30850
THOUSAND WORDS (GB)	2	1	1	2	5982
TIME TEST (GB)	38	9	12	28	200286
TOBOUGG (IRE)	2	1	3	3	28045
TONALIST (USA)	1	1	1	1	3562
TORONADO (IRE)	66	32	46	101	545075
TOUGH AS NAILS (IRE)	14	3	4	12	47577
TWILIGHT SON (GB)	101	39	63	103	661020
TWIRLING CANDY (USA)	2	1	1	4	9376
ULYSSES (IRE)	40	15	17	25	137652
UNCLE MO (USA)	5	1	1	3	15136
UNIVERSAL (IRE)	5	3	5	3	20892
URGENT REQUEST (IRE)	1	1	1	2	5204
VADAMOS (FR)	51	18	24	44	257617
VALE OF YORK (IRE)	9	3	3	12	32109
VALIRANN (FR)	4	2	3	2	21696
VERGLAS (IRE)	2	2	4	5	25958
VERRAZANO (USA)	1	1	1	0	2922
VIOLENCE (USA)	4	1	1	3	8181
VIRTUAL (GB)	1	1	3	3	11265
VISION D'ETAT (FR)	1	1	1	5	27170
VOCALISED (USA)	32	7	9	15	106000
WAR COMMAND (USA)	59	18	29	44	314442
WAR FRONT (USA)	45	20	28	61	423104
WESTERNER (GB)	4	1	1	0	6623
WESTLAKE (GB)	1	1	1	1	8453
WHERE OR WHEN (IRE)	1	1	1	1	7763
WINDSOR KNOT (IRE)	5	1	2	0	21984
WOOTTON BASSETT (GB)	34	16	28	32	778949
WORTHADD (IRE)	7	2	3	10	25181
XTENSION (IRE)	7	3	4	8	45481
YEATS (IRE)	6	3	3	6	29027
YORGUNNABELUCKY (USA)	7	4	7	13	60450
YOUMZAIN (IRE)	6	1	1	1	8983
ZAMINDAR (USA)	1	1	1	4	34840
ZANZIBARI (USA)	2	1	2	1	13613
ZARAK (FR)	5	1	1	5	17001
ZEBEDEE (GB)	70	31	46	98	653852
ZELZAL (FR)	6	2	3	7	20282
ZOFFANY (IRE)	199	67	88	227	2066899

BY KIND PERMISSION OF WEATHERBYS

NH STALLIONS' EARNINGS FOR 2020/21
(Includes every stallion who sired a winner over jumps in Great Britain and Ireland in 2020/21)

STALLIONS	RNRS	WNRS	WINS	PLACES	TOTAL (£)
ACAMBARO (GER)	6	2	3	6	36156
ACCLAMATION (GB)	5	1	1	1	8736
AIR CHIEF MARSHAL (IRE)	6	6	11	6	64033
AIZAVOSKI (IRE)	37	17	27	34	207500
AL NAMIX (FR)	40	9	12	41	224513
ALBERTO GIACOMETTI (IRE)	4	3	5	7	36820
ALEXANDROS (GB)	1	1	1	1	7168
ALFLORA (IRE)	16	3	3	6	54851
ALHEBAYEB (IRE)	14	4	7	7	57352
ALKAADHEM (GB)	14	4	6	3	27847
ALKAASED (GB)	3	1	3	1	32067
AMADEUS WOLF (GB)	4	1	1	1	4623
AMERICAN POST (GB)	4	1	1	3	15098
ANABAA BLUE (GB)	7	1	1	4	10347
AND BEYOND (IRE)	7	2	2	5	24810
ANJAAL (GB)	5	1	1	0	4329
ANODIN (IRE)	2	1	1	1	11427
ANZILLERO (GER)	9	2	3	6	50490
APSIS (GB)	3	1	1	2	13115
AQLAAM (GB)	8	2	2	5	15284
ARAKAN (USA)	66	16	20	58	229440
ARCADIO (GER)	169	39	55	114	511296
ARCANO (IRE)	20	5	7	15	47620
ARCH (USA)	3	1	2	1	14146
ARCHIPENKO (USA)	16	3	3	11	27890
ARCTIC COSMOS (USA)	40	5	7	28	94476
ARISTOTLE (IRE)	3	1	1	0	3555
ARTAN (IRE)	4	1	1	0	4500
ARVICO (FR)	32	7	13	11	83236
ASK (GB)	104	23	38	74	346906
ATRAF (GB)	2	1	1	0	3844
AUSSIE RULES (USA)	7	2	3	5	16610
AUSTRALIA (GB)	17	1	1	7	18551
AUTHORIZED (IRE)	67	29	41	68	568812
AXXOS (GER)	4	2	2	4	17845
AZAMOUR (IRE)	20	6	8	19	80740
BACH (IRE)	8	1	1	6	13651
BALKO (FR)	37	9	12	34	260700
BALLINGARRY (IRE)	28	8	10	20	97850
BARASTRAIGHT (GB)	3	1	3	2	82175
BATED BREATH (GB)	7	1	1	5	8704
BATTLE OF MARENGO (IRE)	11	4	4	8	32345
BEAT ALL (USA)	7	1	1	4	10703
BEAT HOLLOW (GB)	70	23	34	50	663340
BENEFICIAL (GB)	131	43	65	135	1023302
BERNEBEAU (FR)	6	2	4	1	66804
BIENAMADO (USA)	6	1	1	3	8368
BIG BAD BOB (IRE)	29	2	2	9	29216
BLACK SAM BELLAMY (IRE)	110	26	36	69	408038
BLAME (USA)	1	1	1	0	47159
BLUE BRESIL (FR)	33	8	12	21	173209
BLUEPRINT (IRE)	9	2	2	7	22938
BOLLIN ERIC (GB)	16	1	1	7	16565
BONBON ROSE (FR)	9	1	1	6	13923
BORN KING (JPN)	4	2	4	4	36412
BORN TO SEA (IRE)	53	17	22	43	313087
BRAVE MANSONNIEN (FR)	7	4	6	5	73038

STALLIONS	RNRS	WNRS	WINS	PLACES	TOTAL (£)
BRIAN BORU (GB)	60	9	10	53	200655
BUCK'S BOUM (FR)	19	7	12	23	240474
BUSHRANGER (IRE)	8	1	1	5	12292
CABLE BAY (IRE)	5	1	1	0	3618
CACIQUE (IRE)	10	4	5	12	58471
CALIFET (FR)	82	20	28	37	224742
CAMACHO (GB)	17	1	4	2	25743
CAMELOT (GB)	45	13	21	34	227218
CAMPANOLOGIST (USA)	2	1	1	0	4342
CANFORD CLIFFS (IRE)	38	11	16	26	158857
CAPE CROSS (IRE)	27	6	7	10	46721
CAPTAIN RIO (GB)	7	1	1	6	14980
CARLO BANK (IRE)	5	2	2	2	12075
CARLOTAMIX (FR)	32	5	9	20	85263
CASAMENTO (IRE)	33	4	5	15	49117
CELTIC SWING (GB)	1	1	2	0	8187
CENTENNIAL (IRE)	1	1	1	1	10644
CENTRAL PARK (IRE)	12	4	5	13	59292
CHAMPS ELYSEES (GB)	64	15	22	46	187875
CHEVALIER (IRE)	1	1	1	2	10901
CHINEUR (FR)	1	1	1	0	3327
CITY HONOURS (USA)	3	2	2	4	13333
CITYSCAPE (GB)	15	3	3	3	13590
CLODOVIL (IRE)	8	1	1	5	10905
CLOUDINGS (IRE)	39	7	7	15	109924
COASTAL PATH (GB)	35	14	24	34	366488
COKORIKO (FR)	30	6	9	16	173000
COMPTON PLACE (GB)	1	1	2	2	9598
CORONER (IRE)	4	1	1	2	12612
CORRI PIANO (FR)	2	1	1	3	7280
COUNTRY REEL (USA)	1	1	1	0	6803
COURT CAVE (IRE)	176	51	73	119	693838
CRAIGSTEEL (GB)	37	10	18	28	177703
CREACHADOIR (IRE)	6	2	2	3	36817
CRILLON (FR)	9	2	3	7	41949
CROSSPEACE (IRE)	6	1	1	4	7649
CURTAIN TIME (IRE)	20	3	5	8	285197
DADARISSIME (FR)	1	1	1	3	20872
DAHJEE (USA)	5	1	1	3	7351
DAIWA MAJOR (JPN)	1	1	1	0	5268
DALAKHANI (IRE)	6	1	1	3	12718
DANDY MAN (IRE)	7	1	2	5	16732
DANEHILL DANCER (IRE)	3	1	1	3	10290
DANSANT (GB)	14	4	4	19	59461
DANSILI (GB)	26	2	2	15	47065
DAPPER (GB)	4	1	2	2	8912
DARAMSAR (FR)	1	1	1	2	6821
DARK ANGEL (IRE)	32	5	8	26	188885
DARSI (FR)	15	2	3	15	67661
DAVIDOFF (GER)	7	3	4	8	239292
DAWN APPROACH (IRE)	19	3	3	3	15451
DAY FLIGHT (GB)	8	2	4	5	35338
DAYLAMI (IRE)	11	2	2	9	25804
DECLARATION OF WAR (USA)	16	4	6	12	47146
DEFINITE ARTICLE (GB)	27	7	8	27	103335
DELEGATOR (GB)	4	1	1	2	8182
DELLA FRANCESCA (USA)	11	5	6	8	33191
DENHAM RED (FR)	7	1	4	10	162919
DEPORTIVO (GB)	2	1	2	1	29203
DESERT KING (IRE)	5	2	2	3	19140
DESIR D'UN SOIR (FR)	3	2	3	4	25347

STALLIONS	RNRS	WNRS	WINS	PLACES	TOTAL (£)
DIAMOND BOY (FR)	29	8	11	22	137251
DICK TURPIN (IRE)	9	2	3	8	49820
DINK (FR)	1	1	1	2	130053
DOCTOR DINO (FR)	15	8	11	12	345813
DOM ALCO (FR)	5	1	3	6	55507
DOUBLE ECLIPSE (IRE)	10	2	3	5	24731
DOYEN (IRE)	136	34	53	111	680900
DR MASSINI (IRE)	40	6	9	21	117736
DRAGON DANCER (GB)	5	1	1	0	7213
DRAGON PULSE (IRE)	19	4	4	13	39076
DREAM WELL (FR)	7	3	4	5	184319
DUBAI DESTINATION (USA)	64	19	29	63	492635
DUBAWI (IRE)	20	6	8	17	60590
DUKE OF MARMALADE (IRE)	14	3	4	7	22713
DUNADEN (FR)	16	4	6	4	42760
DURBAN THUNDER (GER)	3	1	1	1	7806
DUTCH ART (GB)	10	3	3	2	12698
DYLAN THOMAS (IRE)	119	26	36	70	435721
ECHO OF LIGHT (GB)	11	2	2	4	21401
ELUSIVE CITY (USA)	2	1	1	1	5132
ELUSIVE PIMPERNEL (USA)	57	12	20	35	235089
ELUSIVE QUALITY (USA)	2	1	1	1	6073
ENDOLI (USA)	1	1	1	2	7999
ENRIQUE (GB)	12	1	1	12	41798
EPALO (GER)	2	1	1	2	9287
EPAULETTE (AUS)	9	1	2	3	16789
EXCELEBRATION (IRE)	24	3	6	11	63905
EXCELLENT ART (GB)	7	1	1	2	6385
EXCHANGE RATE (USA)	3	1	1	3	11419
EXIT TO NOWHERE (USA)	6	3	4	6	89036
FAIR MIX (IRE)	50	7	11	34	138212
FAIRLY RANSOM (USA)	6	2	3	14	98696
FALCO (USA)	12	5	7	14	90373
FAME AND GLORY (GB)	285	64	91	210	1070851
FAMOUS NAME (GB)	21	4	12	14	80718
FARHH (GB)	9	2	4	2	41313
FAST COMPANY (IRE)	28	9	14	22	122860
FINE GRAIN (JPN)	1	1	1	2	32154
FINSCEAL FIOR (IRE)	12	1	2	4	32762
FIRST DEFENCE (USA)	3	1	1	2	6204
FLEMENSFIRTH (USA)	254	85	132	209	1836569
FLYING LEGEND (USA)	11	2	2	9	20045
FOOTSTEPSINTHESAND (GB)	21	2	2	6	22630
FORESTIER (FR)	4	1	3	3	13263
FRACAS (IRE)	18	5	9	18	79461
FRAGRANT MIX (IRE)	8	3	4	9	42170
FRAMMASSONE (IRE)	10	5	8	10	59193
FRANKEL (GB)	12	2	5	3	39143
FREE EAGLE (IRE)	10	4	4	8	35094
FRENCH FIFTEEN (FR)	5	3	4	4	29535
FRENCH NAVY (GB)	4	1	1	1	12198
FROZEN FIRE (GER)	12	1	2	1	12539
FROZEN POWER (IRE)	9	2	3	6	23932
FRUITS OF LOVE (USA)	30	5	8	15	66201
FUISSE (FR)	11	5	8	10	66786
FULL OF GOLD (FR)	6	1	1	4	11728
GALE FORCE TEN (GB)	10	2	2	2	12716
GALILEO (IRE)	57	12	17	53	198876
GAMUT (IRE)	24	2	3	11	39200
GENEROUS (IRE)	10	6	7	5	63128
GENTLEWAVE (IRE)	32	4	5	21	112925

STALLIONS	RNRS	WNRS	WINS	PLACES	TOTAL (£)
GEORDIELAND (FR)	22	5	7	13	45689
GEORGE VANCOUVER (USA)	3	1	2	1	9559
GERMANY (USA)	7	2	2	6	23754
GETAWAY (GER)	348	99	136	278	1262496
GIANT'S CAUSEWAY (USA)	1	1	2	2	24504
GLENEAGLES (IRE)	7	2	5	4	26679
GOLAN (IRE)	22	8	9	15	106572
GOLD AWAY (IRE)	2	1	1	1	5457
GOLD WELL (GB)	179	58	95	155	926226
GOLDEN HORN (GB)	4	1	1	0	4966
GOLDEN LARIAT (USA)	19	4	6	14	90926
GOLDEN TORNADO (IRE)	6	3	4	4	93467
GRAND COUTURIER (GB)	1	1	1	6	7887
GREAT JOURNEY (JPN)	4	1	1	2	5850
GREAT PRETENDER (IRE)	51	21	35	54	455907
GREEN TUNE (USA)	1	1	1	1	7908
GREGORIAN (IRE)	11	2	2	6	15097
GRIS DE GRIS (IRE)	16	4	5	13	58995
HAAFHD (GB)	11	1	1	8	29065
HALLING (USA)	5	1	1	8	21303
HALLOWED CROWN (AUS)	4	2	5	4	123031
HARBOUR WATCH (IRE)	20	2	2	11	30766
HELISSIO (FR)	6	3	4	0	26740
HELLO SUNDAY (FR)	1	1	1	0	20725
HELMET (AUS)	26	1	2	4	20875
HENRYTHENAVIGATOR (USA)	9	2	2	2	18208
HERNANDO (FR)	2	1	1	1	9495
HIGH CHAPARRAL (IRE)	30	4	4	15	90050
HIGH ROCK (IRE)	2	1	1	3	19647
HOLY ROMAN EMPEROR (IRE)	17	4	5	10	66384
HURRICANE CAT (USA)	3	2	2	3	12501
HURRICANE RUN (IRE)	6	1	1	4	12043
IFFRAAJ (GB)	23	7	12	9	72969
IMPERIAL MONARCH (IRE)	56	7	9	18	74089
INCLUDE (USA)	1	1	2	1	7608
INDIAN DAFFODIL (IRE)	2	1	2	2	74003
INDIAN DANEHILL (IRE)	12	3	4	4	25283
INDIAN RIVER (FR)	15	5	6	7	150943
INSATIABLE (IRE)	2	2	2	2	11817
INTELLO (GER)	14	3	3	9	29916
INTENSE FOCUS (USA)	10	2	2	9	17683
INTIKHAB (USA)	12	1	2	9	18810
INVINCIBLE SPIRIT (IRE)	14	4	4	10	31341
IRISH WELLS (FR)	9	3	3	7	23399
IT'S GINO (GER)	7	2	5	8	31931
JEREMY (USA)	160	62	101	169	1301910
JET AWAY (GB)	33	6	9	6	54348
JOSHUA TREE (IRE)	6	2	3	3	17658
JUKEBOX JURY (IRE)	16	5	8	14	167567
KADEED (IRE)	2	1	2	3	32856
KALANISI (IRE)	140	35	44	95	500160
KAMSIN (GER)	8	2	2	6	24050
KAP ROCK (FR)	10	3	5	10	40957
KAPGARDE (FR)	87	30	48	89	1098659
KAYF TARA (GB)	201	43	61	132	869151
KELTOS (FR)	1	1	1	1	2579
KENDARGENT (FR)	8	2	5	8	41036
KENTUCKY DYNAMITE (USA)	7	3	4	8	50360
KHALKEVI (IRE)	12	4	6	10	107140
KHELEYF (USA)	4	1	1	0	6674
KING'S THEATRE (IRE)	77	25	34	68	616420

STALLIONS	RNRS	WNRS	WINS	PLACES	TOTAL (£)
KINGSALSA (USA)	6	1	1	4	21144
KINGSTON HILL (GB)	8	1	1	1	5120
KIRKWALL (GB)	3	1	1	4	6096
KITTEN'S JOY (USA)	2	2	4	4	30053
KODIAC (GB)	18	3	3	8	22553
KONIG TURF (GER)	9	2	3	11	89597
KONIGSTIGER (GER)	2	1	2	0	5804
KOTKY BLEU (FR)	2	1	1	3	6149
KUTUB (IRE)	8	1	1	3	9252
KYLLACHY (GB)	9	1	1	4	16616
LAURO (GER)	6	4	6	5	51851
LAVERON (GB)	5	2	2	5	12828
LAWMAN (FR)	26	5	6	15	69225
LE FOU (IRE)	39	9	16	21	142931
LE HAVRE (IRE)	20	9	12	11	126267
LE HOUSSAIS (FR)	1	1	2	1	7045
LEADING LIGHT (IRE)	73	4	5	37	84299
LEMON DROP KID (USA)	1	1	1	0	5288
LESOTHO (USA)	1	1	1	1	5138
LET THE LION ROAR (GB)	8	3	6	4	42003
LETHAL FORCE (IRE)	6	1	1	0	9266
LIBERTARIAN (GB)	11	1	1	2	7757
LIBRETTIST (USA)	6	1	1	5	23390
LILBOURNE LAD (IRE)	10	3	6	7	28272
LINDA'S LAD (GB)	17	6	8	13	99932
LOPE DE VEGA (IRE)	25	7	8	14	93689
LORD AMERICO	1	1	1	2	8308
LORD DU SUD (FR)	21	7	8	24	97520
LORD OF ENGLAND (GER)	6	2	2	4	22360
LORD SHANAKILL (USA)	12	2	3	6	26879
LOUP SOLITAIRE (USA)	2	1	1	5	9624
LOVELACE (GB)	3	1	2	2	13091
LUCARNO (USA)	32	7	8	8	53977
MAGICIAN (IRE)	1	1	2	3	9567
MAHLER (GB)	241	73	94	181	1011027
MAJESTIC MISSILE (IRE)	2	1	1	0	5743
MAKE BELIEVE (GB)	8	3	3	10	31243
MAKFI (GB)	12	3	3	13	56242
MALINAS (GER)	96	32	46	79	562655
MAMOOL (IRE)	4	2	3	7	39699
MANDURO (GER)	18	4	7	11	85794
MARESCA SORRENTO (FR)	26	9	12	21	162004
MARIENBARD (IRE)	8	1	1	3	8638
MARIGNAN (USA)	1	1	1	0	4669
MARTALINE (GB)	117	53	75	106	818965
MASKED MARVEL (GB)	9	3	5	12	65228
MASTERCRAFTSMAN (IRE)	69	16	24	53	265684
MASTEROFTHEHORSE (IRE)	15	6	7	7	49472
MASTERSTROKE (USA)	11	2	2	4	19678
MAWATHEEQ (USA)	4	1	1	5	8445
MAXIOS (GB)	32	10	17	30	281590
MEDAALY (GB)	4	1	1	3	27736
MEDICEAN (GB)	21	4	6	14	146476
MIDNIGHT LEGEND (GB)	147	53	79	161	999310
MILAN (GB)	292	70	91	211	1063196
MILLENARY (GB)	19	4	4	19	74840
MONSUN (GER)	4	2	4	1	143606
MONTMARTRE (FR)	44	17	26	29	208595
MOON BALLAD (IRE)	1	1	1	1	3162
MORE THAN READY (USA)	1	1	1	1	2407
MORES WELLS (GB)	5	1	1	2	5251

STALLIONS	RNRS	WNRS	WINS	PLACES	TOTAL (£)
MOROZOV (USA)	62	11	15	38	145635
MOSCOW SOCIETY (USA)	1	1	1	0	6373
MOST IMPROVED (IRE)	16	1	1	5	17567
MOTIVATOR (GB)	19	7	10	13	252352
MOUNT NELSON (GB)	39	8	10	21	84821
MOUNTAIN HIGH (IRE)	62	8	14	27	114366
MR DINOS (IRE)	12	3	6	14	57374
MUHAARAR (GB)	4	1	1	4	8442
MUHAYMIN (USA)	3	1	1	3	8958
MUHTATHIR (GB)	27	6	9	20	169551
MUKHADRAM (GB)	8	1	1	2	9798
MULTIPLEX (GB)	44	12	13	26	115400
MUSTAMEET (USA)	41	8	11	21	111429
MYBOYCHARLIE (IRE)	3	1	1	2	23481
NATHANIEL (IRE)	66	25	39	62	452166
NATIVE RULER (GB)	16	1	1	5	10877
NAYEF (USA)	18	3	4	8	33390
NAZAR (IRE)	2	1	3	3	19291
NETWORK (GER)	60	26	34	73	507693
NEVER ON SUNDAY (FR)	1	1	1	0	2274
NEW APPROACH (IRE)	24	8	15	19	95101
NICKNAME (FR)	7	4	6	5	278785
NICOBAR (GB)	2	1	1	2	12582
NIDOR (FR)	4	1	1	4	13305
NO RISK AT ALL (FR)	42	15	20	46	556310
NOBLE MISSION (GB)	2	1	1	1	11693
NOROIT (GER)	15	6	11	12	110588
NORSE DANCER (IRE)	24	5	7	16	57398
NORTHERN LEGEND (GB)	1	1	1	1	8181
NORWICH	2	1	1	5	9681
NOTNOWCATO (GB)	23	3	3	5	24684
OCOVANGO (GB)	57	2	3	19	72156
OLD VIC	7	1	1	3	16365
OLDEN TIMES (GB)	8	3	3	7	21669
OLYMPIC GLORY (IRE)	12	2	2	12	26261
ORPEN (USA)	2	1	6	0	22627
OSCAR (IRE)	210	55	81	177	1681776
OVERBURY (IRE)	20	6	10	12	60416
PALACE EPISODE (USA)	3	1	1	6	12654
PAPAL BULL (GB)	21	8	14	20	165810
PASSING GLANCE (GB)	61	22	33	48	357106
PASTERNAK (GB)	9	1	1	8	16409
PASTORIUS (GER)	5	1	1	4	7898
PEDRO THE GREAT (USA)	1	1	1	2	6058
PEINTRE CELEBRE (USA)	2	1	1	1	10530
PERUGINO (USA)	3	2	3	3	25219
PHOENIX REACH (IRE)	19	3	5	23	56476
PIERRE (GB)	2	1	1	1	7241
PIVOTAL (GB)	14	3	3	8	21194
PLANTEUR (IRE)	8	2	2	2	12759
POET'S VOICE (GB)	30	9	11	23	126159
POLICY MAKER (IRE)	8	2	5	6	325123
POLIGLOTE (GB)	26	12	17	33	409698
PORTRAIT GALLERY (IRE)	11	3	3	5	38612
POUR MOI (IRE)	27	9	13	32	134197
POWER (GB)	16	2	2	4	23561
PRESENTING (GB)	254	68	93	192	1160571
PRIMARY (USA)	9	4	9	1	131097
PROCLAMATION (IRE)	12	1	1	5	15341
PROTEKTOR (GER)	4	1	1	0	9787
PUBLISHER (USA)	8	2	2	6	25762

STALLIONS	RNRS	WNRS	WINS	PLACES	TOTAL (£)
PUIT D'OR (IRE)	3	1	1	2	7094
QUWS (GB)	1	1	1	0	5795
RACINGER (FR)	9	5	9	11	94309
RAIL LINK (GB)	18	4	4	10	27503
RAJJ (IRE)	3	1	2	0	14333
RAJSAMAN (FR)	8	3	6	9	41490
RAVEN'S PASS (USA)	15	2	3	10	54221
RECITAL (FR)	9	1	1	5	12112
RED JAZZ (USA)	11	3	7	6	41081
RED ROCKS (IRE)	4	1	2	8	19050
REDOUTE'S CHOICE (AUS)	4	2	4	6	32398
REFUSE TO BEND (IRE)	2	1	1	0	11039
RELIABLE MAN (GB)	2	2	2	2	14339
REQUINTO (IRE)	7	1	2	10	22996
RESPLENDENT CEE (IRE)	1	1	2	4	21649
REVOQUE (IRE)	2	1	1	0	3509
RIP VAN WINKLE (IRE)	30	5	8	15	62336
ROB ROY (USA)	5	1	1	3	8274
ROBIN DES CHAMPS (FR)	88	19	33	56	264411
ROBIN DES PRES (FR)	42	12	15	25	126302
ROCK OF GIBRALTAR (IRE)	27	9	10	19	84919
RODERIC O'CONNOR (IRE)	16	3	3	6	23506
ROMAN SADDLE (IRE)	1	1	1	1	4818
ROYAL ANTHEM (USA)	15	5	9	13	56186
RULER OF THE WORLD (IRE)	11	1	1	4	11630
SABIANGO (GER)	1	1	1	0	67955
SADDEX (GB)	10	4	6	5	89695
SADDLER MAKER (IRE)	46	20	31	46	404951
SAGAMIX (FR)	6	2	2	5	13849
SAGEBURG (IRE)	49	4	8	18	108743
SAINT DES SAINTS (FR)	61	23	35	69	811117
SAKHEE (USA)	11	2	2	4	15595
SAKHEE'S SECRET (GB)	6	1	1	1	7222
SALUTINO (GER)	15	6	9	13	83498
SAMUM (GER)	9	4	6	13	154130
SANDMASON (GB)	11	6	8	12	70027
SANS FRONTIERES (IRE)	57	14	18	32	139592
SANTIAGO (GER)	1	1	1	0	4211
SATRI (IRE)	5	1	1	2	10084
SAYARSHAN (FR)	1	1	1	1	6229
SAYIF (IRE)	5	2	3	1	15801
SCALO (GB)	2	1	1	1	6586
SCHIAPARELLI (GER)	75	17	20	41	221157
SCORPION (IRE)	185	41	53	116	505256
SEA THE MOON (GER)	20	6	11	7	121286
SEA THE STARS (IRE)	29	6	7	24	81791
SECRET SINGER (FR)	11	1	1	4	12686
SEPTEMBER STORM (GER)	41	6	9	21	118486
SHAMARDAL (USA)	10	2	2	8	15963
SHANTOU (USA)	164	59	87	141	1233879
SHIROCCO (GER)	233	58	84	141	696487
SHOLOKHOV (IRE)	98	35	54	68	613198
SHOOTING TO WIN (AUS)	1	1	1	3	11502
SHOWCASING (GB)	9	2	3	2	11819
SILVER FROST (IRE)	5	1	1	4	12936
SINNDAR (IRE)	22	6	9	24	94391
SIR HARRY LEWIS (USA)	5	1	1	0	12024
SIR PERCY (GB)	35	10	14	26	108445
SIXTIES ICON (GB)	43	6	14	25	139296
SKINS GAME (GB)	1	1	1	1	25195
SLADE POWER (IRE)	6	1	1	5	11371

STALLIONS	RNRS	WNRS	WINS	PLACES	TOTAL (£)
SMADOUN (FR)	8	2	2	6	26956
SO YOU THINK (NZ)	22	8	10	12	56221
SOCIETY ROCK (IRE)	7	3	4	6	27058
SOLDIER HOLLOW (GB)	13	6	8	13	55479
SOLDIER OF FORTUNE (IRE)	25	9	11	17	195150
SPADOUN (FR)	7	3	3	3	14758
SPANISH MOON (USA)	23	10	13	25	147771
SPECIAL KALDOUN (IRE)	6	3	5	2	31609
SPIRIT ONE (FR)	5	1	3	5	26831
SRI PUTRA (GB)	2	1	1	2	5613
STARSPANGLEDBANNER (AUS)	6	2	3	6	21469
STIMULATION (IRE)	2	1	1	4	16803
STORMY RIVER (FR)	1	1	1	0	3509
STOWAWAY (GB)	243	73	115	225	2008786
STREET CRY (IRE)	4	3	3	3	15173
SUBTLE POWER (IRE)	7	3	3	8	53370
SULAMANI (IRE)	83	25	45	84	846191
SUNDAY BREAK (JPN)	9	3	4	10	40388
TAGULA (IRE)	6	1	2	3	15487
TAJRAASI (USA)	7	1	1	8	14735
TAMAYUZ (GB)	11	4	5	11	36060
TELESCOPE (IRE)	9	1	1	2	3731
TEOFILO (IRE)	37	5	5	29	77388
TERTULLIAN (USA)	1	1	1	4	6481
THE CARBON UNIT (USA)	2	1	1	1	4583
THEWAYYOUARE (USA)	21	5	5	10	43000
THOUSAND WORDS (GB)	4	1	1	8	23197
TIGER GROOM (GB)	14	3	5	10	112530
TIGER HILL (IRE)	5	2	2	3	16042
TIKKANEN (USA)	27	6	9	17	75464
TIMOS (GER)	1	1	2	1	88466
TIN HORSE (IRE)	3	2	2	4	26101
TIRWANAKO (FR)	3	3	5	4	50970
TOBOUGG (IRE)	25	7	9	19	82519
TOUCH OF LAND (FR)	19	4	5	13	48929
TRANS ISLAND (GB)	40	13	19	49	157997
TURGEON (USA)	15	6	9	20	99396
TURTLE BOWL (IRE)	5	2	3	4	36046
TURTLE ISLAND (IRE)	10	1	1	2	19257
UNIVERSAL (IRE)	31	6	7	23	64762
VALE OF YORK (IRE)	11	1	1	4	10913
VALIRANN (FR)	29	3	5	7	51974
VENDANGEUR (IRE)	2	1	1	3	4949
VERTICAL SPEED (FR)	7	1	2	9	23039
VERTIGINEUX (FR)	2	1	1	6	14060
VINNIE ROE (IRE)	42	9	15	23	140743
VIRTUAL (GB)	9	2	3	10	23133
VISION D'ETAT (FR)	13	5	7	9	80553
VITA VENTURI (IRE)	4	1	1	3	9492
VOCALISED (USA)	14	3	6	3	28335
VOIX DU NORD (FR)	20	6	10	21	328520
WALDPARK (GER)	2	2	4	2	65108
WALK IN THE PARK (IRE)	51	14	16	31	232531
WAR COMMAND (USA)	16	5	5	12	36895
WAREED (IRE)	6	2	5	3	28184
WAVENEY (UAE)	2	1	1	1	5763
WAY OF LIGHT (USA)	3	1	2	1	5529
WELL CHOSEN (GB)	44	13	17	33	215017
WELL MADE (GER)	2	2	4	1	28371
WESTERNER (GB)	194	65	89	174	1010250

STALLIONS	RNRS	WNRS	WINS	PLACES	TOTAL (£)
WHERE OR WHEN (IRE)	4	2	3	3	15969
WHITMORE'S CONN (USA)	18	7	7	17	60613
WIENER WALZER (GER)	1	1	3	3	86087
WINDSOR KNOT (IRE)	19	7	9	13	67350
WINGED LOVE (IRE)	53	12	15	42	153890
WITNESS BOX (USA)	14	6	9	16	78058
WOOTTON BASSETT (GB)	5	1	1	2	14164
WORTHADD (IRE)	3	1	1	1	6273
YEATS (IRE)	286	82	130	274	1777075
YORGUNNABELUCKY (USA)	20	5	8	10	43962
YOUMZAIN (IRE)	11	2	2	5	24078
ZAMBEZI SUN (GB)	7	1	3	8	67472
ZAMINDAR (USA)	3	1	1	3	7702
ZANZIBARI (USA)	2	1	2	2	51496
ZEBEDEE (GB)	11	2	4	6	34570
ZOFFANY (IRE)	35	9	12	31	141959

BY KIND PERMISSION OF WEATHERBYS

HIGH-PRICED YEARLINGS OF 2021 AT TATTERSALLS SALES

The following yearlings realised 120,000 guineas and over at Tattersalls Sales in 2021:

Name and Breeding	Purchaser	Guineas
CH F SEA THE STARS (IRE) - BEST TERMS (GB)	GODOLPHIN	1500000
CH F DUBAWI (IRE) - WALDLERCHE (GB)	AL SHIRA'AA FARMS	1250000
ASTRODOME (GB) B C SEA THE STARS (IRE) - SO MI DAR (GB)	C GORDON-WATSON	1200000
B C GALILEO (IRE) - ANTHEM ALEXANDER (IRE)	M V MAGNIER	1100000
B C KINGMAN (GB) - TURRET ROCKS (IRE)	M V MAGNIER & WHITE BIRCH	1100000
B C FRANKEL (GB) - QUSHCHI (GB)	M V MAGNIER	1100000
B F NO NAY NEVER (USA) - ALTA ANNA (FR)	AL SHIRA'AA FARMS	925000
B C FRANKEL (GB) - AS GOOD AS GOLD (GB)	GODOLPHIN	925000
NEVER ENDING (GB) B F NO NAY NEVER (USA) - LADY EDERLE (USA)	CHEVELEY PARK STUD	900000
B F GALILEO (IRE) - QUIET OASIS (IRE)	A C ELLIOTT, AGENT	825000
OTTERY (GB) CH F DUBAWI (IRE) - LONGINA (GER)	JUDDMONTE FARMS	800000
VIVA BOLIVIA (GB) B F GALILEO (IRE) - ALJAZZI (GB)	HADDEN BS	800000
B C KINGMAN (GB) - BRISTOL BAY (IRE)	GODOLPHIN	750000
GR C DARK ANGEL (IRE) - ANNA LAW (IRE)	M V MAGNIER	750000
B C LOPE DE VEGA (IRE) - GOD GIVEN (GB)	GODOLPHIN	750000
B F SEA THE STARS (IRE) - TIME CONTROL (GB)	ONE AGENCY	725000
LMAY (IRE) B F FRANKEL (GB) - ALIENATE (GB)	THADY GOSDEN	680000
B C GALILEO (IRE) - LIGHTNING THUNDER (GB)	M V MAGNIER	650000
SOUNDS OF HEAVEN (GB) B F KINGMAN (GB) - RING THE BELL (GB)	GLEN HILL FARM	650000
APOLO (GB) GR C KINGMAN (GB) - SKY LANTERN (IRE)	OLIVER ST LAWRENCE BS	650000
B C DUBAWI (IRE) - SERENA'S STORM (IRE)	GODOLPHIN	625000
CH C FRANKEL (GB) - AULD ALLIANCE (IRE)	GODOLPHIN	625000
B F GALILEO (IRE) - MISS FRANCE (IRE)	M V MAGNIER	625000
CH C DUBAWI (IRE) - MARIGOLD HOTEL (IRE)	GODOLPHIN	600000
B C GALILEO (IRE) - KOORA (GB)	M V MAGNIER	600000
B C SHAMARDAL (USA) - BIRDWOOD (GB)	CHAUVIGNY GLOBAL EQUINE	560000
B C DUBAWI (IRE) - BOUND (IRE)	GODOLPHIN	550000
CH C LOPE DE VEGA (IRE) - VIA CONDOTTI (IRE)	GODOLPHIN	550000
CH F GALILEO (IRE) - ROCK ORCHID (IRE)	M V MAGNIER	540000
ZIRYAB (GB) B C KINGMAN (GB) - REEM (AUS)	JUDDMONTE FARMS	525000
B C KINGMAN (GB) - EARTHA KITT (GB)	GODOLPHIN	525000
B F KINGMAN (GB) - GALILEO GAL (IRE)	VENDOR	500000
B F INVINCIBLE SPIRIT (IRE) - SPARKLING SURF (GB)	BEN MCELROY AGENT	480000
B G NO NAY NEVER (USA) - LAGANORE (IRE)	HONG KONG JOCKEY CLUB	475000
B C KODIAC (GB) - ALLURING PARK (IRE)	VENDOR	475000
B F LOPE DE VEGA (IRE) - SWEEPSTAKE (IRE)	AL SHIRA'AA FARMS	475000
B F LOPE DE VEGA (IRE) - HOW (IRE)	GODOLPHIN	475000
B F KODIAC (GB) - DIAMINDA (IRE)	WESTERBERG	470000
B C JUSTIFY (USA) - HOURGLASS (IRE)	ELLIOTT / MCELROY	450000
B/GR C ROARING LION (USA) - RECKONING (IRE)	DAVID REDVERS BS	450000
B C DUBAWI (IRE) - J WONDER (USA)	MYRACEHORSE.COM	450000
B C SEA THE STARS (IRE) - VOW (GB)	OLIVER ST LAWRENCE BS	450000
B C NO NAY NEVER (USA) - SEATONE (USA)	PETER & ROSS DOYLE BS	450000
B C SHOWCASING (GB) - FURBELOW (GB)	KEVIN RYAN	450000
CH F AUSTRALIA (GB) - FALLING PETALS (IRE)	BLANDFORD BS	450000
B C FRANKEL (GB) - SHADOW HUNTER (IRE)	M V MAGNIER	450000
B C CHURCHILL (IRE) - TACHUM (GB)	SACKVILLEDONALD	440000
CH C DUBAWI (IRE) - PHIZ (GER)	GODOLPHIN	425000
B C DUBAWI (IRE) - ATTRACTION (GB)	BBA IRELAND	425000
B C KINGMAN (GB) - MISCHIEF MAKING (USA)	ROBSON AGUIAR/AMO RACING	425000
CH C ALMANZOR (FR) - BEACH FROLIC (GB)	GODOLPHIN	425000
CH F PROFITABLE (IRE) - CYNTHIANA (FR)	OLIVER ST LAWRENCE BS	425000
B C SIYOUNI (FR) - VORDA (FR)	VENDOR	425000
B C KINGMAN (GB) - WALDLIED (GB)	MIKE RYAN AGENT	425000
B F OASIS DREAM (GB) - SPLASHDOWN (GB)	MY RACEHORSE	420000
B C KODIAC (GB) - ZYKINA (GB)	CHAUVIGNY GLOBAL EQUINE	420000
B C DUBAWI (IRE) - SPECTRE (FR)	BBA IRELAND	410000
B F CRACKSMAN (GB) - COOLMINX (IRE)	WINDFIELD BS	410000
B C TIME TEST (GB) - AURELIA (GB)	SACKVILLEDONALD	400000
CH F SEA THE STARS (IRE) - DORCAS LANE (GB)	PETER & ROSS DOYLE BS	400000
B/BR F DUBAWI (IRE) - PEACE IN MOTION (USA)	MANOR HOUSE STUD	400000
B/BR F DUBAWI (IRE) - PRICELESS (GB)	MIKE RYAN AGENT	400000
B C KINGMAN (GB) - CERCLE D'OR (IRE)	STROUD COLEMAN BS	400000
B F FRANKEL (GB) - PERMISSION SLIP (IRE)	A C ELLIOTT, AGENT	400000
B F SEA THE STARS (IRE) - BELLA QATARA (IRE)	ONE AGENCY	380000
CH C NIGHT OF THUNDER (IRE) - HARLEQUIN GIRL (GB)	DWAYNE WOODS	380000
CH F DUBAWI (IRE) - CHARTREUSE (GB)	VENDOR	375000
B C DARK ANGEL (IRE) - GOODNIGHT AND JOY (IRE)	BLANDFORD BS	370000
RED BIRD (IRE) CH F AUSTRALIA (GB) - TISSIAK (GB)	STEPHEN HILLEN BS	370000
B C LOPE DE VEGA (IRE) - MATAURI PEARL (IRE)	BLANDFORD BS	360000
COCO ROYALE (GB) B F FRANKEL (GB) - COCONUT CREME (GB)	VENDOR	360000
B G DARK ANGEL (IRE) - SILK BOW (GB)	THE HONG KONG JOCKEY CLUB	360000

Name and Breeding	Purchaser	Guineas
CH C FRANKEL (GB) - WITHOUT YOU BABE (USA)	VENDOR	360000
B F KODIAC (GB) - KELTIE (GB)	BSW/CROW EURO VENTURE II	360000
CH C AUSTRALIA (GB) - ROCANA (GB)	BSW/CROW EURO VENTURE II	360000
B C LOPE DE VEGA (IRE) - ANISEED (IRE)	AVENUE BS	350000
B G RIBCHESTER (IRE) - VITELLO (GB)	GODOLPHIN	350000
CARL SPACKLER (IRE) CH C LOPE DE VEGA (IRE) - ZINDAYA (USA)	THE HONG KONG JOCKEY CLUB	350000
SALT BAY (GER) CH C FARHH (GB) - SALTITA (IRE)	VENDOR	350000
SUNBELT (IRE) CH F ZOFFANY (IRE) - CURTSY (IRE)	A C ELLIOTT, AGENT	350000
MILL STREAM (IRE) B C GLENEAGLES (IRE) - SWIRRAL EDGE (GB)	THADY GOSDEN	350000
B C KINGMAN (GB) - HORSEPLAY (GB)	STROUD COLEMAN BS	350000
B F WOOTTON BASSETT (GB) - DANCE TOUPIE (FR)	GODOLPHIN	350000
B F KODIAC (GB) - TIGGY TWO (IRE)	STROUD COLEMAN BS	350000
NAAEY (GB) B F LOPE DE VEGA (IRE) - MATERIALISTIC (GB)	SOLIS / LITT	350000
BR C CAMELOT (GB) - ELBASANA (IRE)	THADY GOSDEN	340000
B F CAMELOT (GB) - FREQUENTIAL (GB)	JAMIE MCCALMONT BS	340000
B F DUBAWI (GB) - KNOCKNAGREE (IRE)	BROADHURST AGENCY	340000
B F KODIAC (GB) - SHEHILA (IRE)	MIKE RYAN AGENT	340000
B C CAMELOT (GB) - COPPERTOP (GB)	BEN MCELROY AGENT	340000
B C GALILEO (IRE) - ALLEZ ALAIA (IRE)	BLANDFORD BS	340000
B F KINGMAN (GB) - SECRET SENSE (USA)	M V MAGNIER	340000
B F SIYOUNI (FR) - PINKSTER (GB)	MIKE RYAN AGENT	340000
FOEDERATI (GB) B F SAXON WARRIOR (JPN) - ARCHANGEL GABRIEL (USA)	HARAS D'ETREHAM	330000
GR C FRANKEL (GB) - PERSUASIVE (IRE)	BLANDFORD BS	325000
VELVET CRUSH (IRE) B F INVINCIBLE SPIRIT (IRE) - SHIP OF DREAMS (IRE)	VOUTE SALES / NAWARA STUD	325000
PRIDE OF SPAIN (IRE) CH C LOPE DE VEGA (IRE) - PRIDE (FR)	D WHITE & PARTNERS	325000
WITCHING HOUR (GB) B C FRANKEL (GB) - CURSORY GLANCE (IRE)	PETER & ROSS DOYLE BS	320000
GR F GALILEO (IRE) - MRS DANVERS (GB)	VENDOR	320000
B C KODIAC (GB) - STARS IN YOUR EYES (GB)	BBA IRELAND	320000
B C SEA THE STARS (IRE) - WALDNAH (IRE)	M V MAGNIER	320000
ALEXIS ZORBA (GB) B C ZOUSTAR (AUS) - RUE CAMBON (IRE)	C GORDON WATSON BS	320000
BRITANNICA (GB) CH F LOPE DE VEGA (IRE) - GUERRIERE (IRE)	WHITE BIRCH/D O'BYRNE	310000
LA FILOMENA (IRE) B F LOPE DE VEGA (IRE) - SAGACIOUSLY (IRE)	BLANDFORD BS	310000
NIGIRI (IRE) CH F LOPE DE VEGA (IRE) - DISCLOSE (GB)	WHITE BIRCH/D O'BYRNE	310000
B C SAXON WARRIOR (JPN) - AKTORIA (FR)	A C ELLIOTT, AGENT	300000
B F KINGMAN (GB) - FINE TIME (GB)	AMANDA SKIFFINGTON	300000
LIGHTNING ELIZA (GB) CH C NIGHT OF THUNDER (IRE) - ELIS ELIZ (IRE)	KLARAVICH STABLES	300000
B F KINGMAN (GB) - MIDNIGHT THOUGHTS (USA)	PETER & ROSS DOYLE BS	300000
B G KINGMAN (GB) - HUNAINA (IRE)	BLANDFORD BS	300000
RIVER NAVER (FR) CH F SHOWCASING (GB) - IMPERIALISTIC DIVA (IRE)	THE HONG KONG JOCKEY CLUB	300000
CHILLAXING (IRE) CH C GALILEO (IRE) - DANETIME OUT (IRE)	BLANDFORD BS	300000
NINE TENTHS (IRE) B F KODIAC (GB) - COVETOUS (GB)	BBA IRELAND	300000
B C SEA THE MOON (GER) - PURE SONG (GB)	BLANDFORD BS	300000
CH F SEA THE STARS (IRE) - MAMBO LIGHT (GB)	CHAUVIGNY GLOBAL EQUINE	300000
B C LOPE DE VEGA (IRE) - LUCKY CLIO (IRE)	MANOR HOUSE STUD	300000
B F SEA THE STARS (IRE) - AMAZONE (GER)	BLANDFORD BS	300000
B C ULYSSES (IRE) - SACRE CAROLINE (USA)	THADY GOSDEN	300000
B C FRANKEL (GB) - NOYELLES (IRE)	BLANDFORD BS	300000
PALM LILY (IRE) B F EXPERT EYE (GB) - LADY LIVIUS (IRE)	D FARRINGTON	300000
B F NO NAY NEVER (USA) - SALAMAH (IRE)	JUDDMONTE FARMS	290000
B C KODIAC (GB) - TASTE THE SALT (IRE)	A C ELLIOTT, AGENT	290000
ELEGANCIA (GB) B F LOPE DE VEGA (IRE) - SO SLEEK (GB)	BEN MCELROY AGENT	285000
THE PARENT (GB) B C FRANKEL (GB) - SOPHIE P (GB)	BLANDFORD BS	285000
B G ACCLAMATION (GB) - ABOVE THE MARK (USA)	PETER & ROSS DOYLE BS	280000
SAMYR (FR) B C SEA THE MOON (GER) - SHIMRANA (USA)	THE HONG KONG JOCKEY CLUB	280000
CAPTAIN WIERZBA (GB) CH C NIGHT OF THUNDER (IRE) - RETURN ACE (GB)	A C ELLIOTT, AGENT	280000
BALANCE PLAY (IRE) CH C LOPE DE VEGA (IRE) - BEZIQUE (GB)	A C ELLIOTT, AGENT	280000
GEMSTAR (GB) B F ZOUSTAR (AUS) - PERMISSION (GB)	A C ELLIOTT, AGENT	280000
AESTHETIC (GB) CH F LOPE DE VEGA (IRE) - IONIC (GB)	AMANDA SKIFFINGTON	280000
BR F NATHANIEL (IRE) - THELADYINQUESTION (GB)	SACKVILLEDONALD	270000
B F SEA THE STARS (IRE) - AFFABILITY (IRE)	STROUD COLEMAN/CLANCY BS	270000
CLASSIC (GB) B C DUBAWI (IRE) - DATE WITH DESTINY (IRE)	MIKE RYAN AGENT	265000
FLEET ADMIRAL (GB) BR C NO NAY NEVER (USA) - FLEETING FANCY (FR)	PETER & ROSS DOYLE BS	260000
B F DARK ANGEL (IRE) - STELLAR PATH (FR)	ANDREW BALDING	260000
B C SEA THE STARS (IRE) - GUMRIYAH (GB)	A C ELLIOTT, AGENT	260000
CH C NEW BAY (GB) - PRADEN (USA)	KARL BURKE	260000
B C NO NAY NEVER (USA) - ALJAAZYA (USA)	ROGER VARIAN	260000
B C LOPE DE VEGA (IRE) - BLOOMFIELD (IRE)	AGUIAR BS / AMO RACING	260000
B F LOPE DE VEGA (IRE) - SECRET GAZE (GB)	SACKVILLEDONALD	260000
BR G OASIS DREAM (GB) - BROM FELINITY (AUS)	ROGER VARIAN	260000
CH C MEHMAS (IRE) - C'EST MA SOEUR (IRE)	AL SHIRAA FARMS	260000
CH F MEHMAS (IRE) - COUNTRY MADAM (IRE)	THE HONG KONG JOCKEY CLUB	255000
CHARYN (IRE) GR C DARK ANGEL (IRE) - FUTOON (GB)	DONNACHA O'BRIEN	250000
B C JUSTIFY (USA) - I'M WONDERFUL (USA)	MIKE RYAN AGENT	250000
B C CAMELOT (GB) - MONA BROWN (IRE)	SUMBE	250000
	VENDOR	250000
	CHARLES SHANAHAN	250000

Name and Breeding	Purchaser	Guineas
B/BR F CHURCHILL (IRE) - MORA BAI (IRE)	BSW/CROW EURO VENTURE II	250000
B C LOPE DE VEGA (IRE) - KAMBURA (FR)	NOEL WILSON	250000
B C LOPE DE VEGA (IRE) - DREAMLIKE (GB)	MIKE RYAN AGENT	250000
B F SEA THE STARS (IRE) - BUYING TROUBLE (USA)	A C ELLIOTT, AGENT	250000
CH F LOPE DE VEGA (IRE) - LIPSTICK ROSE (IRE)	KLARAVICH STABLES	250000
B C AUSTRALIA (GB) - BITOOH (GB)	MCKEEVER BS	240000
B F KINGMAN (GB) - POLLY'S MARK (IRE)	KLARAVICH STABLES	240000
B C SEA THE STARS (IRE) - BRIDGE ROYAL GAME (GB)	PETER & ROSS DOYLE BS	240000
CH C SEA THE STARS (IRE) - INSTANCE (GB)	BLANDFORD BS	240000
B F LOPE DE VEGA (IRE) - PECKING ORDER (IRE)	KERN/LILLINGSTON	240000
B C CAMELOT (GB) - JAZZ CAT (IRE)	M V MAGNIER	240000
B F SHOWCASING (GB) - DELEVIGNE (GB)	ROGER VARIAN	240000
AMLETO (IRE) BR C SEA THE STARS (IRE) - HOLY MOON (IRE)	SUNDERLAND HOLDING	240000
BR F BATED BREATH (GB) - DARLING GRACE (GB)	STEPHEN HILLEN BS	230000
TARLO (IRE) B C KODIAC (GB) - PIOUS ALEXANDER (GB)	GAINSBOROUGH TB	230000
B C LOPE DE VEGA (IRE) - FREE REIN (GB)	MIKE RYAN AGENT	230000
B C LE HAVRE (IRE) - LADY FRANCESCA (GB)	HIGHCLERE AGENCY	230000
B F FRANKEL (GB) - PANMOLLE (GB)	TOKYO THOROUGHBRED CLUB	230000
B C GALILEO (IRE) - HERE TO ETERNITY (USA)	A C ELLIOTT, AGENT (P.S.)	230000
BR F DARK ANGEL (IRE) - PIXELEEN (GB)	KEVIN RYAN	225000
OPERA GHOST (IRE) B C CAMELOT (GB) - MALAYAN MIST (IRE)	STROUD COLEMAN BS	225000
NO NO NO NEVER (IRE) B/GR F NO NAY NEVER (USA) - LLEW LAW (GB)	VENDOR	220000
CH F STARSPANGLEDBANNER (AUS) - GREENISLAND (IRE)	HUGO MERRY BS	220000
B C LOPE DE VEGA (IRE) - PACHARANA (GB)	FREEDMAN RACING	220000
B F FRANKEL (GB) - ALDERRY (SAF)	BLANDFORD BS	220000
B C KINGMAN (GB) - ASTRONOMY'S CHOICE (GB)	MIKE RYAN AGENT	220000
MADAM MACHO (GB) CH F CAMACHO (GB) - MADAM PRESIDENT (GB)	BLANDFORD BS	220000
CH F JUSTIFY (USA) - BUTTERSCOTCH (IRE)	KOJI MAEDA	220000
B C SIOUX NATION (USA) - KNOCK STARS (USA)	M V MAGNIER	215000
AUBAZINE (IRE) B F SHAMARDAL (USA) - AMBASSADRICE (GB)	SUZANNE ROBERTS	210000
MISKA (IRE) B F KODIAC (GB) - SHOBOBB (GB)	GAINSBOROUGH TB	210000
B C MEHMAS (IRE) - FIDAAHA (IRE)	STROUD COLEMAN BS	210000
B C KINGMAN (GB) - FATE (FR)	LONGWAY STABLES	210000
B C CAMELOT (GB) - SILVER RAIN (GB)	JOSEPH O'BRIEN	205000
B F CARAVAGGIO (USA) - MORNING LINE (FR)	BLUE EYES BS	205000
CHINDWIN (GB) B C SAXON WARRIOR (JPN) - CAY DANCER (GB)	SYLVESTER KIRK RACING	205000
B F KINGMAN (GB) - SMART CHANGE (USA)	TOKYO THOROUGHBRED CLUB	200000
B C WOOTTON BASSETT (GB) - FOREST CROWN (GB)	SACKVILLEDONALD	200000
B C CRACKSMAN (GB) - ASTRELLE (IRE)	SACKVILLEDONALD	200000
B F KINGMAN (GB) - ARIS (IRE)	BSW/CROW EURO VENTURE II	200000
ATARAMA (GB) B F SEA THE STARS (IRE) - FLY (GB)	THADY GOSDEN	200000
B F FRANKEL (GB) - ALTESSE IMPERIALE (IRE)	DAVID HILTON	200000
CH C SEA THE STARS (IRE) - CUP CAKE (IRE)	C GORDON WATSON BS	200000
B C CAMELOT (GB) - DELTA DREAMER (GB)	AVENUE BS	200000
CH C SIYOUNI (FR) - SAMBA BRAZIL (GER)	JP MURTAGH RACING	200000
CH C JUSTIFY (USA) - SARROCCHI (IRE)	VENDOR	200000
B F SEA THE STARS (IRE) - MEGERA (FR)	VENDOR	200000
LUCKY FIFTEEN (FR) CH C LOPE DE VEGA (IRE) - BESS OF HARDWICK (GB)	A C ELLIOTT, AGENT	200000
B C KINGMAN (GB) - LONGING (IRE)	SACKVILLEDONALD	200000
B C AUSTRALIA (GB) - NATIONS ALEXANDER (IRE)	NOEL WILSON	200000
B C SEA THE STARS (IRE) - TADPOLE (GB)	STROUD COLEMAN BS	200000
B C INVINCIBLE SPIRIT (IRE) - CHICAGO DANCER (GB)	JP MURTAGH RACING	200000
B C SIYOUNI (FR) - FAAY (IRE)	LONGWAYS STABLES	200000
B C CAMELOT (GB) - WANNABE SPECIAL (GB)	JOSEPH O'BRIEN	200000
B C STARSPANGLEDBANNER (AUS) - PRINCESS DESIRE (IRE)	STROUD COLEMAN BS	200000
B F INVINCIBLE SPIRIT (IRE) - GHURRA (US)	VENDOR	200000
B C CRACKSMAN (GB) - MONDELICE (IRE)	STROUD COLEMAN BS	200000
ALMATY STAR (IRE) B C KODIAC (GB) - SANTE (IRE)	SUMBE	200000
B C SHAMARDAL (USA) - THE FUGUE (GB)	VENDOR	200000
B C KINGMAN (GB) - DAWN OF HOPE (IRE)	MIKE RYAN AGENT	200000
BR C SHOWCASING (GB) - PACIFICA HIGHWAY (USA)	STROUD COLEMAN BS	200000
BR F SEA THE STARS (IRE) - DEVERON (GB)	C GORDON WATSON	200000
B F LE HAVRE (IRE) - EXTREME GREEN (GB)	BLANDFORD BS	200000
B C CHURCHILL (IRE) - KATIYRA (IRE)	A C ELLIOTT, AGENT	200000
B F DUBAWI (GB) - BLACK RUBY (IRE)	VENDOR	200000
HIGH FASHION (IRE) B F SIYOUNI (FR) - FASHION FAMILY (FR)	SACKVILLEDONALD	200000
B C SHOWCASING (GB) - LANDMARK (USA)	VENDOR	200000
B C DUBAWI (GB) - POSSET (GB)	VENDOR	200000
B F NO NAY NEVER (USA) - CANADA WATER (GB)	DE BURGH EQUINE	200000
B C GALILEO (IRE) - MADAME CHIANG (GB)	D FARRINGTON	200000
INDEMNITY (IRE) B C LOPE DE VEGA (IRE) - ORIENTAL MAGIC (GER)	HIGHCLERE AGENCY	200000
CH F FRANKEL (GB) - CHRYSANTHEMUM (IRE)	JOSEPH O'BRIEN	200000
B C SIYOUNI (FR) - FUSION (IRE)	MANOR HOUSE STUD	200000
B C SEA THE STARS (IRE) - LA MORTOLA (GB)	KEVIN PHILIPPART DE FOY	200000
B F KINGMAN (GB) - LA DOROTEA (IRE)	BEN MCELROY AGENT	200000

Name and Breeding	Purchaser	Guineas
B C FRANKEL (GB) - PEPITA (IRE)	ROGER VARIAN	200000
CH G ZOUSTAR (AUS) - HERECOMESTHESUN (IRE)	THE HONG KONG JOCKEY CLUB	200000
CH C SHOWCASING (GB) - CHERUBIC (GB)	MIKE RYAN AGENT	200000
B F INVINCIBLE SPIRIT (IRE) - HYPOTHETICALLY (IRE)	SACKVILLEDONALD	200000
B F ARDAD (IRE) - BE MY ANGEL (GB)	MANOR HOUSE STUD	190000
B C KINGMAN (GB) - TWITCH (GB)	SACKVILLEDONALD	190000
B C INVINCIBLE SPIRIT (IRE) - FRESH TERMS (GB)	R AGUIAR / COMPAS EQUINE	190000
B C MEHMAS (IRE) - SINGLE THOUGHT (GB)	VENDOR	190000
B F MEHMAS (IRE) - WARDA (GB)	SACKVILLEDONALD	190000
B F DARK ANGEL (IRE) - SILVER SHOON (IRE)	RICHARD RYAN/P TWOMEY	185000
BR/GR C AUSTRALIA (GB) - LADY AQUITAINE (USA)	MICHAEL WATT	185000
BR F ZOUSTAR (AUS) - FELISSA (GER)	PETER & ROSS DOYLE BS	185000
B C SEA THE STARS (IRE) - OH SEDULOUS (IRE)	VENDOR	180000
B C SEA THE STARS (IRE) - SELYL (GB)	WILLIAM HAGGAS	180000
B F FRANKEL (GB) - BRUXCALINA (FR)	PETER & ROSS DOYLE BS	180000
B C NO NAY NEVER (USA) - BALANKIYA (IRE)	M BUCKLEY	180000
CH F STARSPANGLEDBANNER (AUS) - INTERMITTENT (GB)	AVENUE BS FOR MV MAGNIER	180000
B F KODIAC (GB) - JAWLAAT (IRE)	BSW/CROW EURO VENTURE II	180000
B C CRACKSMAN (GB) - PONGEE (GB)	DWAYNE WOODS	180000
CROWN BOARD (IRE) B C LOPE DE VEGA (IRE) - AGAINST RULES (FR)	STROUD COLEMAN BS	180000
B F KINGMAN (GB) - APPLAUDED (IRE)	C GORDON WATSON	180000
GR F DARK ANGEL (GB) - BY REQUEST (GB)	VENDOR	180000
B C KODIAC (GB) - CHAMPAGNE OR WATER (IRE)	MIKE RYAN AGENT	180000
B C DARK ANGEL (GB) - FRANKEL LIGHT (IRE)	SUZANNE ROBERTS	180000
CH C LOPE DE VEGA (IRE) - FARADAY LIGHT (IRE)	BROWN ISLAND STABLES	175000
B F ZOUSTAR (AUS) - MOONS OF JUPITER (USA)	JASON KELLY BS	175000
B C KODI BEAR (IRE) - FINAL TREAT (IRE)	SACKVILLEDONALD	175000
CH F LOPE DE VEGA (IRE) - BLUE BUTTERFLY (GB)	MIKE RYAN AGENT	170000
BEAUTY BLAZE (IRE) CH C MASTERCRAFTSMAN (IRE) - ARTISTI (GB)	GAELIC BS	170000
CH F SEA THE STARS (IRE) - SHAHAH (GB)	STROUD COLEMAN BS	170000
B C KINGMAN (GB) - SHAPES (GB)	D FARRINGTON	170000
B C KODIAC (GB) - RAMONE (IRE)	KEVIN RYAN	170000
B F SEA THE MOON (GER) - PLUME ROSE (GB)	ANDREW BALDING	170000
B F SHOWCASING (GB) - SACRE COEUR (GB)	A O'RYAN / R FAHEY	170000
CH C SIYOUNI (IRE) - BAL DE LA ROSE (IRE)	BLM BS	170000
B C KODIAC (GB) - FINE IF (IRE)	VENDOR	170000
BR/GR C INVINCIBLE SPIRIT (IRE) - ENJOYABLE (IRE)	KLARAVICH STABLES	170000
B F SEA THE STARS (IRE) - NEWTON'S ANGEL (IRE)	BRIDLEWOOD & MADAKET	170000
SENTIMENTALITY (GB) B F FARHH (GB) - HURRICANE HARRIET (GB)	THADY GOSDEN	170000
B F IFFRAAJ (GB) - EGO (GB)	HIGHCLERE AGENCY	170000
CH C FRANKEL (GB) - SCARLETT ROSE (GB)	VENDOR	170000
B F EXCEED AND EXCEL (AUS) - IMMEDIATE (GB)	MOUNT ARMSTRONG	165000
GR C DARK ANGEL (GB) - TEBEE (GB)	STROUD COLEMAN BS	165000
MISTER MISTER (GER) CH C SEA THE MOON (GER) - MISS GERMANY (GER)	JOSEPH O'BRIEN	165000
B C SEA THE STARS (IRE) - CRYSTAL PATH (IRE)	JOSEPH O'BRIEN	165000
OPERATION GIMCRACK (IRE) CH C SHOWCASING (GB) - FOLK MELODY (IRE)	BRYAN SMART RACING	160000
B C SHOWCASING (GB) - KILLERMONT STREET (IRE)	KARL & KELLY BURKE	160000
B F NO NAY NEVER (USA) - STEEL PRINCESS (IRE)	SOLIS / LITT	160000
B C FRANKEL (GB) - WOODLAND ARIA (GB)	JOSEPH O'BRIEN	160000
KOLSAI (GB) B C OASIS DREAM (GB) - FIZZI TOP (GB)	SUMBE	160000
CH C SEA THE STARS (IRE) - SOLTADA (IRE)	PETER & ROSS DOYLE BS	160000
B F LOPE DE VEGA (IRE) - MOI MEME (GB)	HUGO MERRY BS	160000
BR C SEA THE STARS (IRE) - CHACHAMAIDEE (IRE)	SACKVILLEDONALD	160000
B C FRANKEL (GB) - SEA OF GRACE (IRE)	J BRUMMITT / D O'BRIEN	160000
TWIN EARTH (IRE) B C TEOFILO (IRE) - SULARINA (GB)	ANDREW BALDING	160000
B C KODIAC (GB) - CHUPALLA (GB)	AMANDA SKIFFINGTON	160000
B F NATHANIEL (GB) - ATLANTIC DRIFT (GB)	JOHN GOSDEN	160000
B F KODIAC (GB) - VINTAGE MOLLY (GB)	BEN MCELROY AGENT	160000
B C OASIS DREAM (GB) - TRIPLE STAR (GB)	C GORDON WATSON/AL SHAQAB	160000
B C CHURCHILL (IRE) - MYTURN (GB)	OWEN BURROWS	160000
B C ALMANZOR (FR) - LOREDANA (FR)	A C ELLIOTT	160000
BLANCHLAND (IRE) B C FARHH (GB) - EXAMINEE (GER)	STROUD COLEMAN BS	160000
B F KODIAC (GB) - EAVESDROP (IRE)	KLARAVICH STABLES	160000
CH F EXCEED AND EXCEL (AUS) - SUPEREGO (GB)	OLIVER ST LAWRENCE BS	160000
B/BR C CHURCHILL (IRE) - HURRICANE EMMA (USA)	VENDOR	160000
DOLCE COURAGE (GB) B C SIYOUNI (IRE) - VALIANT GIRL (GB)	M V MAGNIER	160000
B C LOPE DE VEGA (IRE) - ENNAYA (GB)	MARGARET O'TOOLE	160000
B F SIOUX NATION (USA) - NOVANTAE (GB)	JAMIE MCCALMONT BS	160000
BR C SHOWCASING (GB) - DRUMFAD BAY (IRE)	ROBSON AGUIAR/AMO RACING	160000
CH C NO NAY NEVER (USA) - ASHLEY HALL (GB)	BLANDFORD BS	160000
B F CHURCHILL (IRE) - ROSIE'S PREMIERE (GB)	GALLOWAY STUD	160000
B C ACCLAMATION (GB) - KASSANDRA (IRE)	PETER & ROSS DOYLE BS	155000
B C SIYOUNI (FR) - PRETTY PAPER (IRE)	STROUD COLEMAN BS	155000
B F KODIAC (GB) - EMERIYA (GB)	ATLAS BS, AGENT	155000
GLENEAGLE BAY (IRE) B C GLENEAGLES (IRE) - CHARLOTTE RUA (IRE)	JOSEPH O'BRIEN	155000

Name and Breeding	Purchaser	Guineas
CH F NIGHT OF THUNDER (IRE) - LA CHAPELLE (IRE)	A SKIFFINGTON/PEGASUS BS	155000
B C ARDAD (IRE) - SANDY TIMES (IRE)	GROVE STUD	150000
B F LOPE DE VEGA (IRE) - ANNA'S ROCK (IRE)	M PRICE RACING AUS	150000
GR C CAMELOT (GB) - MOONRISE LANDING (IRE)	BLANDFORD BS	150000
B C ZOUSTAR (AUS) - SANIYAAT (GB)	JILL LAMB BS	150000
B F KINGMAN (GB) - ALL OUT (GB)	SOLIS / LITT	150000
GR F DARK ANGEL (IRE) - ASTONISHING (IRE)	VENDOR	150000
PADDY THE SQUIRE (GB) B C GOLDEN HORN (GB) - PROVENANCE (GB)	IAIN JARDINE	150000
B C MEHMAS (IRE) - JUXTAPOSED (GB)	KEVIN RYAN	150000
MICKEY MONGOOSE (GB) B C LOPE DE VEGA (IRE) - MIDNIGHT CROSSING (IRE)	JOHNSTON RACING	150000
WALLOP (IRE) B C HARRY ANGEL (IRE) - SAMAAH (IRE)	PETER & ROSS DOYLE BS	150000
B C INVINCIBLE SPIRIT (IRE) - MARIE CELESTE (IRE)	JAMIE MCCALMONT BS	150000
B C LOPE DE VEGA (IRE) - LAMPS OF HEAVEN (IRE)	J B BS	150000
B F LOPE DE VEGA (IRE) - CRIMSON ROSETTE (IRE)	EBONOS	150000
B C NO NAY NEVER (USA) - BOATER (IRE)	CREIGHTON SCHWARTZ BS	150000
BE A GRIZZLY (GB) B C KODIAC (GB) - BRISTOL FASHION (GB)	A C ELLIOTT, AGENT	150000
B C ACCLAMATION (GB) - CASUAL REMARK (IRE)	C GORDON WATSON BS	150000
CH C CHURCHILL (IRE) - AMJAAD (GB)	CORMAC MCCORMACK	150000
B C KINGMAN (GB) - PRICELESS JEWEL (GB)	HUGO PALMER	150000
B C ULYSSES (IRE) - REGAL HEIRESS (GB)	STROUD COLEMAN/CLANCY BS	150000
B C NEW APPROACH (IRE) - MELINDE (GB)	SACKVILLEDONALD	150000
B F LOPE DE VEGA (IRE) - SHOMARIA (FR)	BRIDLEWOOD & MADAKET	150000
B C FREE EAGLE (IRE) - QATAR PRINCESS (IRE)	J BRUMMITT / D O'BRIEN	150000
B F NIGHT OF THUNDER (IRE) - CUTTY SARK (GB)	STROUD COLEMAN BS	150000
B F FASTNET ROCK (AUS) - STARS AT NIGHT (IRE)	J FERGUSON RACING	150000
SHOT OF LOVE (GB) B C INVINCIBLE SPIRIT (IRE) - DUFAY (IRE)	WHITE BIRCH/D O'BYRNE	150000
B F SEA THE MOON (GER) - FIND IT WITHIN (IRE)	SOLIS / LITT	150000
KING'S VANITY (GB) B C KINGMAN (GB) - POET'S VANITY (GB)	VENDOR	150000
B F LOPE DE VEGA (IRE) - UNPRETENTIOUS (IRE)	JOSEPH O'BRIEN	150000
B F TEOFILO (IRE) - CELESTE DE LA MER (IRE)	BLANDFORD BS	150000
BR C CARAVAGGIO (USA) - AURORA SPRING (IRE)	D FARRINGTON	150000
B C WOOTTON BASSETT (GB) - LOVE ON MY MIND (IRE)	JOSEPH O'BRIEN	150000
B F KODIAC (GB) - MONTEFINO (IRE)	VENDOR	150000
CH F AUSTRALIA (GB) - MADAM BAROQUE (GB)	BBA IRELAND/M V MAGNIER	150000
B C NIGHT OF THUNDER (IRE) - ROMP (IRE)	JOE FOLEY	150000
GREAT BEDWYN (GB) B C SHOWCASING (GB) - MISTRESS QUICKLY (IRE)	PETER & ROSS DOYLE BS	150000
GR F MASTERCRAFTSMAN (IRE) - IL PALAZZO (USA)	HUGO MERRY BS	150000
CH F LOPE DE VEGA (IRE) - STONE ROSES (FR)	MERIDIAN INTERNATIONAL	150000
BYSTANDER (IRE) B C DARK ANGEL (GB) - WITNESSED (GB)	GAINSBOROUGH TB	150000
BR F NO NAY NEVER (USA) - NOW YOU'RE TALKING (IRE)	PETER & ROSS DOYLE BS	150000
LOST ANGEL (IRE) GR F DARK ANGEL (GB) - LAST BID (GB)	A C ELLIOTT, AGENT	150000
B F TEOFILO (IRE) - SWAY ME NOW (USA)	JOSEPH O'BRIEN	150000
B F INVINCIBLE SPIRIT (IRE) - GHURRA (USA)	AVENUE BS / HUGO PALMER	150000
B F KODIAC (GB) - TOQUETTE (IRE)	BSW/CROW EURO VENTURE II	145000
B/BR C SIOUX NATION (USA) - SWING OUT SISTER (IRE)	CLIVE COX RACING	140000
B C CARAVAGGIO (USA) - BRIGHT SAPPHIRE (IRE)	NAJD STUD	140000
B C LOPE DE VEGA (IRE) - MAUREEN (IRE)	C GORDON WATSON/AL SHAQAB	140000
B C OASIS DREAM (GB) - BEYCHELLA (USA)	MANOR HOUSE STUD	140000
STAR AHOY (GB) B C SEA THE STARS (IRE) - INFALLIBLE (GB)	VENDOR	140000
GR F SEA THE STARS (IRE) - REAL SMART (USA)	ROBERT ROULSTON BS	140000
CH F LOPE DE VEGA (IRE) - MINNALOUSHE (IRE)	MIKE RYAN AGENT	140000
MINKA (IRE) B F KODIAC (GB) - QUEEN'S CODE (IRE)	C GORDON WATSON BS	140000
B C KINGMAN (GB) - CASCATA (IRE)	MIKE RYAN AGENT	140000
B/BR F DANDY MAN (IRE) - SUVENNA (IRE)	PETER & ROSS DOYLE BS	140000
B C KODIAC (GB) - AN CAILIN ORGA (IRE)	VENDOR	140000
GR C MASTERCRAFTSMAN (IRE) - SHANJIA (GER)	ED DUNLOP RACING	140000
THUNDER SEA (GB) B F NIGHT OF THUNDER (IRE) - TIDAL MOON (IRE)	PETER & ROSS DOYLE BS	140000
APRICOT TWIST (IRE) B F EXPERT EYE (GB) - ERYSIMUM (GB)	JUDDMONTE FARMS	140000
B C SIOUX NATION (USA) - EDESSA (IRE)	SACKVILLEDONALD	140000
GR C AUSTRALIA (GB) - PROSPER (GB)	AVENUE BS	140000
ONIGHT (GB) B C OASIS DREAM (GB) - SURCINGLE (USA)	BBA IRELAND	140000
B C ZOFFANY (IRE) - SOLAR ECHO (IRE)	KOJI MAEDA	140000
B F KINGMAN (GB) - HARGEISA (USA)	VENDOR	140000
B F NO NAY NEVER (USA) - BRODERIE ANGLAISE (GB)	MANOR HOUSE STUD	140000
B C LOPE DE VEGA (IRE) - LAMAZONIA (IRE)	M O'TOOLE / OAK TREE	135000
B C CAMELOT (GB) - DO RE MI FA SOL (FR)	A C ELLIOTT, AGENT	135000
B C TWILIGHT SON (GB) - SAMASANA (IRE)	CLIVE COX RACING	135000
B C KINGMAN (GB) - SPEEDY BOARDING (IRE)	TOKYO THOROUGHBRED CLUB	135000
B C ZOUSTAR (AUS) - WHITE BULLET (GB)	LONGWAYS STABLES	135000
BRILLIANT COLOURS (IRE) B C EXCEED AND EXCEL (AUS) - INDIGO BUTTERFLY (FR)	PETER & ROSS DOYLE BS	135000
B F TEOFILO (IRE) - DUBAI FASHION (IRE)	STROUD COLEMAN BS	135000
WHERE DO YOU GO TO (IRE) B F AUSTRALIA (GB) - PLEASANTRY (GB)	A C ELLIOTT, AGENT	130000
BL C CAMELOT (GB) - MILL SPRINGS (GB)	VENDOR	130000
B F COTAI GLORY (GB) - INVINCIBLE ME (IRE)	PETER & ROSS DOYLE BS	130000
GR C EL KABEIR (USA) - EXTRICATE (IRE)	SACKVILLEDONALD	130000

Name and Breeding	Purchaser	Guineas
CH C SHOWCASING (GB) - ROODLE (GB)	ANDREW BALDING	130000
B C KINGMAN (GB) - PIROUETTE (GB)	STROUD COLEMAN BS	130000
B F KINGMAN (GB) - RUBY ROCKET (IRE)	JS BS / G BOUGHEY	130000
B F IFFRAAJ (GB) - MOONLIFE (IRE)	MCKEEVER BS / C HILLS	130000
B F NO NAY NEVER (USA) - CRY ME A RIVER (IRE)	RABBAH BS	130000
B C TAMAYUZ (GB) - ALORS QUOI (IRE)	JAMES FERGUSON RACING	130000
GR C DARK ANGEL (IRE) - MISS INFINITY (IRE)	VENDOR	130000
CH C ROARING LION (USA) - DIBAJJ (FR)	EBONOS	130000
B F KINGMAN (GB) - IMPRESSIONIST (IRE)	VENDOR	130000
GR C DARK ANGEL (IRE) - ANDRY BRUSSELLES (GB)	VENDOR	130000
B C SHAMARDAL (USA) - LAMAR (IRE)	VENDOR	130000
VITERBO (IRE) B C MEHMAS (IRE) - STATENICE (GB)	JILL LAMB BS	130000
JUST BRING IT (IRE) CH C HARRY ANGEL (IRE) - JUST JOAN (IRE)	A C ELLIOTT, AGENT	130000
B C LOPE DE VEGA (IRE) - HIBISCUS (GB)	VENDOR	130000
B F INVINCIBLE SPIRIT (IRE) - PRANCE (IRE)	VENDOR	130000
B C SHOWCASING (GB) - FLOWER FASHION (FR)	MANOR HOUSE STUD	130000
CH F SHOWCASING (GB) - INTENSE PINK (IRE)	ARTHUR HOYEAU AGENT	130000
B C BATED BREATH (GB) - SLEEK (GB)	EBONOS	130000
B C ALMANZOR (FR) - NICKY'S BROWN MISS (USA)	C GORDON WATSON/AL SHAQAB	125000
BLOOMIN ROBBERY (IRE) B F KODIAC (GB) - ANNE BONNEY (GB)	RICHARD KNIGHT/S QUINN	125000
B C SHOWCASING (GB) - AWESOME (GB)	SACKVILLEDONALD	125000
B C MEHMAS (GB) - STRANGE MAGIC (IRE)	C GORDON WATSON/AL SHAQAB	125000
HARRY MAGNUS (IRE) B C HARRY ANGEL (IRE) - MUSIC AND DANCE (GB)	HOWSON & HOULDSWORTH BS	125000
B F LOPE DE VEGA (IRE) - STELLAR GLOW (IRE)	RABBAH BS	125000
GR F DARK ANGEL (IRE) - CLEM FANDANGO (FR)	VENDOR	125000
B C KODIAC (GB) - SAY NO NOW (IRE)	RABBAH BS	125000
B C AUSTRALIA (GB) - PERFECT FUN (GB)	JASON KELLY BS	125000
B C AUSTRALIA (GB) - LA DYNAMITE (IRE)	JOSEPH O'BRIEN	125000
CH C NEW BAY (GB) - YOUNG SPECIAL (IRE)	C GORDON WATSON BS	125000
CH F SHAMARDAL (USA) - TRANQUIL STAR (IRE)	EBONOS	125000
B C GLENEAGLES (IRE) - ENROL (GB)	SACKVILLEDONALD	125000
B C AUSTRALIA (GB) - CUMBFREE (IRE)	NAJD STUD	125000
B C OASIS DREAM (GB) - DIRAYAH (IRE)	M O'TOOLE / OAK TREE	125000
B C KODIAC (GB) - LADY RO (GB)	C GORDON WATSON/AL SHAQAB	125000
GR C ZOFFANY (IRE) - SHREYAS (IRE)	DAVID REDVERS	125000
B C LOPE DE VEGA (IRE) - COTTONMOUTH (IRE)	AVENUE BS / HUGO PALMER	125000
B C FARHH (GB) - FORMIDABLE KITT (GB)	KARL & KELLY BURKE	125000
LE LEVRE (IRE) CH F LE HAVRE (IRE) - SUNNY AGAIN (GB)	SACKVILLEDONALD	125000
BALMAHA (IRE) GR F DARK ANGEL (IRE) - LIWA PALACE (GB)	PETER & ROSS DOYLE BS	125000
B C NEW BAY (GB) - CROSSOVER (GB)	PETER & ROSS DOYLE BS	125000
B F NATHANIEL (IRE) - MIX AND MINGLE (IRE)	CUADRA BERNARDO	120000
B F FASTNET ROCK (AUS) - FASHIONABLE (GB)	KOJI MAEDA (P.S.)	120000
B C NIGHT OF THUNDER (IRE) - LABISE (IRE)	PETER & ROSS DOYLE BS	120000
B F DARK ANGEL (IRE) - VENUS DE MILO (IRE)	FORENAGHTS STUD	120000
B F KODIAC (GB) - RAINFALL RADAR (USA)	HUGO MERRY BS	120000
B C OASIS DREAM (GB) - RUFFLED (IRE)	FEDERICO BARBERINI	120000
SIOUX LOVE (IRE) B F SIOUX NATION (USA) - SONNING ROSE (IRE)	A O'RYAN / R FAHEY	120000
B C CAMELOT (GB) - SWEET GENTLE KISS (IRE)	VENDOR	120000
CH F SHOWCASING (GB) - PILATES (IRE)	BLANDFORD BS	120000
B F INVINCIBLE SPIRIT (IRE) - MEHRONISSA (GB)	VENDOR	120000
B C LOPE DE VEGA (IRE) - ALONG CAME CASEY (IRE)	SACKVILLEDONALD	120000
B F ULYSSES (IRE) - MISS PINKERTON (GB)	BLANDFORD BS	120000
HOLLINGBERRY (IRE) B C LOPE DE VEGA (IRE) - PLAYFULL SPIRIT (GB)	STROUD COLEMAN BS	120000
CH F LOPE DE VEGA (IRE) - MEGAN LILY (IRE)	DE BURGH EQUINE	120000
B F CAMELOT (GB) - FASTNET MIST (IRE)	RICHARD RYAN	120000
GR C EL KABEIR (USA) - PREQUEL (IRE)	SACKVILLEDONALD	120000
B C SEA THE STARS (IRE) - POTENT EMBRACE (USA)	GLOBAL EQUINE GROUP	120000
B C TWILIGHT SON (GB) - BAILEYS JUBILEE (GB)	OLIVER ST LAWRENCE BS	120000
BRAVE KNIGHT (GB) B C SIR PERCY (GB) - BELLADONNA (GB)	NAJD STUD	120000
PACO'S PRIDE (GB) GR F ROARING LION (USA) - PACO'S ANGEL (GB)	WHITE BIRCH/D O'BYRNE	120000
BATAAN (GB) B F SHOWCASING (GB) - THE BEGUM (GB)	HIGHCLERE AGENCY	120000
TRUTHFUL (IRE) B F SEA THE STARS (IRE) - MY TIMING (GB)	D FARRINGTON	120000
B C PROFITABLE (GB) - ZENELLA (GB)	VENDOR	120000
B F SEA THE STARS (IRE) - KATYUSHA (USA)	CLEARWATER BS	120000
B C KINGMAN (GB) - SEAL OF APPROVAL (GB)	CRISPIN DE MOUBRAY SARL	120000
STORY TO TELL (IRE) B F NO NAY NEVER (USA) - SARAH LYNX (IRE)	RICHARD HUGHES RACING	120000
B/BR C SEA THE MOON (GER) - FORCE ONE (GB)	RABBAH BS	120000
B C MEHMAS (IRE) - OLIVE BRANCH (GB)	LINA BS	120000
B C SAXON WARRIOR (JPN) - LOVE AND BUBBLES (USA)	VENDOR	120000
GR C ROARING LION (USA) - STREAM SONG (GB)	HIGHCLERE AGENCY	120000
VERMILION (IRE) B F KODIAC (GB) - WESTERN SKY (GB)	BLANDFORD BS	120000
B F U S NAVY FLAG (USA) - PYREAN (GB)	MANOR HOUSE STUD	120000
B C KODIAC (GB) - MILANA (FR)	EASTWIND RACING	120000
JUST A NOTION (GB) B F LE HAVRE (IRE) - QUEEN CORDELIA (IRE)	LONGWAYS STABLES	120000
B F INVINCIBLE SPIRIT (IRE) - TALAAYEB (GB)	LONGWAYS STABLES	120000

HIGH-PRICED YEARLINGS OF 2021 AT GOFFS IRELAND

The following yearlings realised 76,000 euros and over at Goffs Ireland Sales in 2021:

Name and Breeding	Purchaser	Euros
B F GALILEO (IRE) - NICKNAME (USA)	M V MAGNIER	1500000
B C CAMELOT (GB) - ATTIRE (IRE)	M V MAGNIER	1200000
CH C FRANKEL (GB) - BELESTA (GB)	KENNETH MCPEEK, AGENT	900000
B F FRANKEL (GB) - SOPHIE GERMAIN (IRE)	AL SHIRA'AA FARM	650000
B C FOOTSTEPSINTHESAND (GB) - QUEEN OF CARTHAGE (USA)	BBA IRE/YULONG INVEST.	630000
B C NO NAY NEVER (USA) - SWEET CHARITY (FR)	M V MAGNIER	620000
B C SAXON WARRIOR (JPN) - CASSANDRA GO (IRE)	BBA IRELAND	540000
B F KINGMAN (GB) - FINSCEAL BEO (IRE)	J MURTAGH / E LINEHAN	500000
B C GALILEO (IRE) - POCKETFULLOFDREAMS (FR)	KENNETH MCPEEK, AGENT	440000
B F GALILEO (IRE) - TAKE ME WITH YOU (USA)	NEWTOWN ANNER STUD	360000
B C CHURCHILL (IRE) - ARYA TARA (IRE)	JUSTIN CASSE, AGENT	360000
B F KODIAC (GB) - FIKRAH (GB)	PETER & ROSS DOYLE BS	340000
MIDNIGHT TOKER (IRE) B C ACCLAMATION (GB) - BIG BONED (USA)	WHITE BIRCH/D O'BYRNE	330000
B C MENDELSSOHN (USA) - SPIRIT QUEEN (IRE)	DR R TALLAT/A WALLACE	325000
B F RIBCHESTER (IRE) - SCRIBONIA (IRE)	BADGERS BS	310000
B F NO NAY NEVER (USA) - SURPRISINGLY (IRE)	ELLIOTT/MCELROY	300000
B C DANDY MAN (IRE) - RUGGED UP (IRE)	STROUD COLEMAN BS	290000
B F U S NAVY FLAG (USA) - WROOD (USA)	DWAYNE WOODS	290000
CH C SAXON WARRIOR (JPN) - GILT EDGE GIRL (GB)	P ANTONACCI & PARTNERS	270000
B C SIYOUNI (FR) - LEGENDE BLEUE (FR)	BEN MCELROY, AGENT	260000
CH C SHOWCASING (GB) - DADAO (GB)	A.C.ELLIOTT,AGENT	260000
YOU SAW BRIGADOON (IRE) B C KINGMAN (GB) - STIRRING BALLAD (GB)	STROUD COLEMAN/CLANCY BS	260000
B F DANDY MAN (IRE) - KAYAK (GB)	PETER & ROSS DOYLE BS	260000
B F SHOWCASING (GB) - DARING DAY (GB)	BBA IRE/YULONG INVEST.	250000
B C GALILEO (IRE) - LADY LARA (IRE)	WEST BS	250000
STARLIGHT SONG (IRE) CH F STARSPANGLEDBANNER (AUS) - SIBLING HONOUR (GB)	PETER & ROSS DOYLE BS	250000
CH F LOPE DE VEGA (IRE) - ONLY MINE (IRE)	PATTERN BS	250000
B F LOPE DE VEGA (IRE) - WILLOUGHBY (IRE)	AL SHIRA'AA FARM	230000
B F SIOUX NATION (USA) - MANY COLOURS (GB)	AMANDA SKIFFINGTON	230000
B F DARK ANGEL (IRE) - CHOOSE ME (IRE)	JASON KELLY/BRYAN SMART	230000
MARGARET ELIZABETH (IRE) B F KODIAC (GB) - SAGELY (IRE)	PETER & ROSS DOYLE BS	225000
CH C MEHMAS (IRE) - VIDA AMOROSA (GB)	AMANDA SKIFFINGTON	225000
B F KODIAC (GB) - INVERSE (IRE)	HKJC	220000
CH G STARSPANGLEDBANNER (AUS) - FRENCH FLIRT (GB)	AL SHIRA'AA FARM	220000
B F U S NAVY FLAG (USA) - MARIA LEE (IRE)	ERIC LONG	210000
B F ZOFFANY (IRE) - INNOCENT AIR (GB)	MANOR HOUSE STUD	210000
BR C SEA THE STARS (IRE) - MY SPIRIT (IRE)	RICHARD RYAN	200000
NEW ENDEAVOUR (IRE) B C NEW BAY (GB) - MOODY BLUE (IRE)	VENDOR	200000
GR C DARK ANGEL (IRE) - SOMMORELL (IRE)	D HAYDEN	200000
GR F CAMELOT (GB) - PAKORA (FR)	JUSTIN CASSE, AGENT	200000
B C PROFITABLE (IRE) - SLEEPING BEAUTY (IRE)	WEST BS	200000
B F NO NAY NEVER (USA) - SILENT THOUGHTS (IRE)	D HAVEY/HIGHLAND YARD LLC	200000
B F SAXON WARRIOR (JPN) - ONLINE ALEXANDER (IRE)	TINA RAU BS	200000
NARIMAN POINT (IRE) CH F DUBAWI (IRE) - TRAFFIC JAM (IRE)	VENDOR	200000
B C KINGMAN (GB) - ALEXANDER GOLDRUN (IRE)	RICHARD RYAN	200000
B C TEOFILO (IRE) - DAWN OF DAY (IRE)	KENNETH MCPEEK, AGENT	200000
B F CAMELOT (GB) - WILD CHILD (IRE)	RICHARD KNIGHT/SEAN QUINN	200000
MICHAEL'S PLEDGE (IRE) B C CHURCHILL (IRE) - PROMISE ME (IRE)	PHILIP ANTONACCI	190000
CH F AUSTRALIA (GB) - GEMS (GB)	BBA IRELAND (P.S.)	185000
CHARMING STAR (IRE) B C SEA THE STARS (IRE) - BAINO HOPE (FR)	GAELIC BS	180000
BEAUTY CRESCENT (IRE) B C ACCLAMATION (GB) - UP IN TIME (GB)	ADAM DRIVER	180000
B C DARK ANGEL (IRE) - MOGHAMARAH (GB)	ANTHONY DUTROW	180000
B F DANDY MAN (IRE) - REPOSE (USA)	SUNDERLAND HOLDING INC	180000
CH F SEA THE STARS (IRE) - CREGGS PIPES (IRE)	HIGHFLYER BS	180000
ALPHA CAPTURE (IRE) B C COTAI GLORY (GB) - YORK EXPRESS (GB)	P ANTONACCI	170000
B F ZOFFANY (IRE) - TOI ET MOI (IRE)	KILBRIDE EQUINE	170000
BR F SHAMARDAL (USA) - ELSHAADIN (GB)	FLURRY RACING STABLES	170000
SNEACHTA (IRE) B F INVINCIBLE SPIRIT (IRE) - AIMHIRGIN LASS (IRE)	JAMIE MCCALMONT	160000
B C SIOUX NATION (USA) - RHIANNON (IRE)	FILIP ZWICKY	160000
LAUGHINGDALE FEAR (IRE) B C LOPE DE VEGA (IRE) - BISCAYA BAY (GB)	ROCKFIELD FARM	160000
CH F CHURCHILL (IRE) - TARBELA (IRE)	A.C. ELLIOTT, AGENT	160000
HE'S A MONSTER (IRE) BR C NO NAY NEVER (USA) - AL JOZA (IRE)	JOSEPH O'BRIEN	160000
CH C SEA THE STARS (IRE) - WANNABE LOVED (GB)	BEN MCELROY, AGENT	160000
B F U S NAVY FLAG (USA) - HUMBLE AND PROUD (IRE)	MERIDIAN MANAGEMENT	160000
B F SAXON WARRIOR (JPN) - LOVE MAGIC (GB)	FEDERICO BARBERINI	160000
B/BR F ZOUSTAR (AUS) - UTTERLY CHARMING (IRE)	ADAM DRIVER	160000
B F DARK ANGEL (IRE) - MAQAASID (GB)		155000

Name and Breeding	Purchaser	Guineas
B/BR F NO NAY NEVER (USA) - BELLE ISLE (GB)	JOHNSTON RACING	150000
B F NIGHT OF THUNDER (IRE) - ADHWAA (GB)	D GREATHOUSE/PURA VIDA	150000
B C STARSPANGLEDBANNER (AUS) - SAMPERS (IRE)	COPPER BEECH RACING	150000
CH F NO NAY NEVER (USA) - ORNELIA RUEE (FR)	SACKVILLEDONALD	150000
B C LOPE DE VEGA (IRE) - GALLITEA (IRE)	AMANDA SKIFFINGTON	150000
B C WOOTTON BASSETT (GB) - ENEZA (IRE)	M V MAGNIER	150000
B F LOPE DE VEGA (IRE) - QUEEN GUENEVERE (IRE)	RABBAH BS	150000
SKI JUMP (IRE) GR C DARK ANGEL (IRE) - CUT NO ICE (IRE)	R O'RYAN/R FAHEY	145000
B F SHOWCASING (GB) - JASMINE BLUE (IRE)	RICHARD RYAN	145000
EASTERN LEGEND (IRE) B C TEOFILO (IRE) - RAWAAQ (GB)	KERR & CO	140000
BRIGHT LEGEND (IRE) B C ZOUSTAR (AUS) - ALEXIADE (IRE)	AVENUE BS	140000
GR F DARK ANGEL (IRE) - GHAZAAWAT (FR)	BRIAN GRASSICK BS	140000
BEECHWOOD (IRE) B F LE HAVRE (IRE) - STATUESQUE (GB)	GLYN DAVIES	140000
B/BR F RIBCHESTER (IRE) - ETESIAN FLOW (GB)	BLANDFORD BS	140000
B F ALMANZOR (FR) - SHALANAYA (IRE)	HUGO MERRY BS	140000
SALOMON PICO (FR) B C ALMANZOR (FR) - ALTA STIMA (IRE)	PETER & ROSS DOYLE BS	135000
CH C STARSPANGLEDBANNER (AUS) - MIMITEH (USA)	M R BS	135000
KINGSWOOD (GB) GR C ROARING LION (USA) - ALL AT SEA (GB)	GLYN DAVIES	130000
AMI DE VEGA (IRE) B C LOPE DE VEGA (IRE) - AMIE NOIRE (GER)	PETER & ROSS DOYLE BS	130000
B F INVINCIBLE SPIRIT (IRE) - MAURESMO (IRE)	D GREATHOUSE/R MASTERSON	130000
CH F FOOTSTEPSINTHESAND - INIS BOFFIN (GB)	DE BURGH EQUINE	130000
INTELLOTTO (IRE) CH C LOPE DE VEGA (IRE) - EBEYINA (IRE)	HIGHFLYER BS	130000
GOT A LOT (IRE) B F CAMELOT (GB) - STEALTH MISSILE (IRE)	FILIP ZWICKY/SOREN JENSEN	130000
B F ZOFFANY (IRE) - GENUINE QUALITY (IRE)	HUGO MERRY BS	130000
RAMAZAN (IRE) B C KODIAC (GB) - HANALEI MEMORIES (USA)	STROUD COLEMAN BS	130000
B F CHURCHILL (IRE) - QUEENSCLIFF (IRE)	BBA IRE/YULONG INVEST.	125000
B C NO NAY NEVER (USA) - KITTY LOVE (IRE)	BBA IRELAND	125000
B C SIOUX NATION (USA) - ALL TIME HIGH (IRE)	MAGNOLIA RACING	125000
B C NO NAY NEVER (USA) - CATCH THE EYE (IRE)	W DE BURGH/F STACK	125000
CH F BUNGLE INTHEJUNGLE (GB) - GUANA (IRE)	SACKVILLEDONALD	125000
B F KODIAC (GB) - WELSH ANTHEM (GB)	BOBBY O'RYAN/BEN HASLAM	125000
B C DUBAWI (IRE) - I AM BEAUTIFUL (IRE)	D FARRINGTON	125000
BR/GR F NO NAY NEVER (USA) - SUTTON VENY (IRE)	BEN MCELROY, AGENT	120000
BR C SEA THE STARS (IRE) - OLYMPIENNE (IRE)	A.C. ELLIOTT, AGENT	120000
BR C KODIAC (GB) - CUTE (GB)	B GRASSICK/R FITZPATRICK	120000
B F LOPE DE VEGA (IRE) - SPECIAL GAL (FR)	TINA RAU BS (P.S.)	120000
B C KUROSHIO (AUS) - MY BETTER HALF (GB)	SACKVILLEDONALD	120000
ARABIAN LEGEND (IRE) B/BR C NIGHT OF THUNDER (IRE) - ARABESCATTA (IRE)	AVENUE BS	120000
B F DANDY MAN (IRE) - DUCHESS OF FOXLAND (IRE)	B O'RYAN/RICHARD FAHEY	120000
B F NO NAY NEVER (USA) - ZEE ZEE GEE (GB)	RABBAH BS	120000
BAREFOOT ANGEL (IRE) B F DARK ANGEL (IRE) - LOVE IN THE DESERT (GB)	R O'RYAN/NORMAN STEEL	120000
HOPE YOU CAN RUN (IRE) CH C LOPE DE VEGA (IRE) - SHELBYSMILE (USA)	JOHNSTON RACING	115000
B C CARAVAGGIO (USA) - BRIONIYA (GB)	PEARLY BAKER	115000
B F DARK ANGEL (IRE) - FLAME OF GIBRALTAR (IRE)	BLANDFORD BS	110000
OH SWEET TABU (IRE) B F ZOUSTAR (AUS) - THREETIMESALADY (GB)	P & R DOYLE/M HERINCKX	110000
CH C SEA THE STARS (IRE) - ALAMODE (GB)	JOHNSTON RACING	110000
CH F AUSTRALIA (GB) - NOURAH (IRE)	NEW APPROACH BS	110000
B F ZOFFANY (IRE) - BEAT THE STARS (IRE)	AOR/MIDDLEHAM PARK RACING	110000
B C SIYOUNI (FR) - MISS AIGLONNE (USA)	POWERSTOWN STUD	105000
NUNCA (IRE) B F NO NAY NEVER (USA) - INCA WOOD (UAE)	JONATHAN GREEN DJ STABLES	105000
B C INVINCIBLE SPIRIT (IRE) - PRIMA LUCE (IRE)	BBA IRELAND/YULONG	105000
B F KODIAC (GB) - RAZZMATAZZ (GB)	PADDY TWOMEY	105000
B F INVINCIBLE SPIRIT (IRE) - SEEHARN (IRE)	N BRENNAN / A DUTROW	100000
B F CHURCHILL (IRE) - CRAZY VOLUME (IRE)	BBA IRE/YULONG INVEST.	100000
B C NO NAY NEVER (USA) - BALIYANA (IRE)	JOSEPH O'BRIEN	100000
B C DANDY MAN (IRE) - SOUZIE (IRE)	RICHARD RYAN	100000
B F LOPE DE VEGA (IRE) - WILD IRISH ROSE (IRE)	MIKE AKERS, JBTC	100000
GR F DARK ANGEL (IRE) - ANDORRA (IRE)	GROVE STUD	100000
B C FOOTSTEPSINTHESAND (GB) - PAPER DREAMS (IRE)	MAGNOLIA RACING	100000
B C INVINCIBLE SPIRIT (IRE) - LIBERATING (GB)	CLIVE COX RACING	100000
B F U S NAVY FLAG (USA) - CONVOCATE (USA)	TOP LINE SALES, USA	100000
B C NO NAY NEVER (USA) - PRINCESS SINEAD (USA)	BBA IRELAND	100000
B C GLENEAGLES (IRE) - FIRST BLUSH (IRE)	JOSEPH O'BRIEN	100000
APEX (IRE) B C KESSAAR (IRE) - BISOUS Y BESOS (IRE)	HIGHCLERE AGENCY	100000
B C SHALAA (IRE) - CHANTILLY PEARL (USA)	KENNETH MCPEEK/C DIAMOND	100000
CH C BELARDO (IRE) - TOUGH SPIRIT (IRE)	ELLIOTT/MCELROY	100000
B F KINGMAN (GB) - MADLY TRULY (USA)	PEARLY BAKER	100000
CH C NOBLE MISSION (GB) - PICK AND CHOOSE (USA)	PETER NOLAN/NOEL MEADE	100000
B F KODIAC (GB) - REMEMBER ALEXANDER (GB)	JOE FOLEY	100000

Name and Breeding	Purchaser	Guineas
B F KINGMAN (GB) - CARTE DE VISITE (USA)	J MURTAGH / E LINEHAN	100000
JUST A SPLASH (IRE) B F SEA THE STARS (IRE) - AARAMM (USA)	N BRENNAN / A DUTROW	100000
BEAR ON THE LOOSE (IRE) B C FOOTSTEPSINTHESAND (GB) - IHTIRAAM (IRE)	A.C. ELLIOTT, AGENT	100000
B F FRANKEL (GB) - DREAM OF TARA (IRE)	J HARRINGTON RACING	100000
CH C ZOFFANY (IRE) - RIBBLE (FR)	MAGNOLIA RACING	100000
B C ACLAIM (IRE) - DOUGH ON THE GO (USA)	CANNING DOWNS, AUSTRALIA	100000
EXCELIA (IRE) B F EXCEED AND EXCEL (AUS) - NARUKO (USA)	JOHN MCCORMACK BS	100000
B C KINGMAN (GB) - SWEET ACCLAIM (IRE)	NIALL BRENNAN	100000
CH C SEA THE MOON (GER) - TEGARA (GB)	BARRY LYNCH & PARTNERS	100000
TRACHONITUS (IRE) B C TEOFILO (IRE) - AQUAMARINE (JPN)	BOHERGUY STUD	100000
B F SAXON WARRIOR (JPN) - YELLOWHAMMER (GB)	BBA IRELAND	95000
DUTCH GOLD (IRE) B C GALILEO GOLD (GB) - DUTCH MONARCH (GB)	PETER NOLAN BS	95000
GREEN SKY (IRE) B F MASTERCRAFTSMAN (IRE) - HEROINE CHIC (IRE)	HIGHFLYER BS	95000
OSTRAKA (IRE) B F PROFITABLE (IRE) - OSTATNIA (IRE)	GARRETT FREYNE	95000
HUTTON (IRE) B C AUSTRALIA (GB) - SO LONG MARIANNE (IRE)	RICHARD RYAN	95000
B F KODIAC (GB) - CAPRIOLE (GB)	BOBBY O'RYAN/BEN HASLAM	95000
B F SEA THE STARS (IRE) - THE FAIRY (IRE)	SACKVILLEDONALD	95000
B C EXCEED AND EXCEL (AUS) - ARIENA (IRE)	HELEN MACPHAIL	95000
B C INVINCIBLE SPIRIT (IRE) - TAMADHOR (IRE)	BBA IRE/YULONG INVEST.	92000
B F SAXON WARRIOR (JPN) - MISS UNDERSTOOD (IRE)	VENDOR	92000
B F CARAVAGGIO (USA) - LADY FASHION (GB)	A WALLACE/LEWIS LAKIN	90000
B F INVINCIBLE SPIRIT (IRE) - QAREENAH (USA)	MARCO BOZZI BS	90000
CALLING ALL ANGELS (IRE) B/BR F DARK ANGEL (IRE) - SINGLE (FR)	K VALERIO, AGENT	90000
B F BUNGLE INTHEJUNGLE (GB) - PRINCESS JANIE (USA)	R GONCALVES/AGUIAR BS	90000
B F DARK ANGEL (IRE) - PLAGIARISM (USA)	VENDOR	90000
B F GLENEAGLES (IRE) - ON LOCATION (USA)	BO BROMAGEN, AGENT	90000
B C DANDY MAN (IRE) - ZEHRAH (IRE)	F TYLICKI BS/S BRADLEY	90000
KODERA (IRE) CH F ZOFFANY (IRE) - SHAMWARI LODGE (IRE)	HIGHFLYER BS	90000
B F SEA THE STARS (IRE) - SINDJARA (USA)	MANOR HOUSE STUD	90000
B/BR C ROARING LION (USA) - KANES PASS (IRE)	DURCAN BS/S LAVERY	90000
B C HOLY ROMAN EMPEROR (IRE) - ELAYSA (GB)	BBA IRELAND	90000
B C INVINCIBLE SPIRIT (IRE) - OAKLEY GIRL (GB)	VENDOR	90000
LONDON LEGEND (IRE) B C ZOUSTAR (AUS) - LONDON WELSH (GB)	AVENUE BLOODSTOCK	90000
DELLAROC QUEEN (IRE) B F LE HAVRE (FR) - VRAI (FR)	PETER & ROSS DOYLE BS	90000
KITTYKARMA (IRE) B F KITTEN'S JOY (USA) - SPRING LEAF (FR)	R O'RYAN/NORMAN STEEL	85000
LADY VENETA (IRE) B F ACCLAMATION (GB) - BROADWAY DUCHESS (IRE)	NEW APPROACH BS	85000
B F PROFITABLE (IRE) - SINGAPORE LILLY (IRE)	SACKVILLEDONALD	85000
B C BUNGLE INTHEJUNGLE (GB) - TITIAN SAGA (IRE)	JOHNSTON RACING	85000
B F NOBLE MISSION (GB) - GIANNA SCHICCHI (USA)	POWERSTOWN STUD	85000
B F NO NAY NEVER (USA) - ELDALIL (GB)	C O'CONNOR / L LAKIN	85000
B C DARK ANGEL (IRE) - SPESIALTA (GB)	JOHNSTON RACING	85000
LORD OF ADMIRALTY (IRE) B C CHURCHILL (IRE) - ENDURE (IRE)	FRANCISCO CASTRO	85000
GR C HAVANA GREY (GB) - KENDAMARA (FR)	CLIVE COX RACING	85000
B C STARSPANGLEDBANNER (AUS) - FOU RIRE (IRE)	NEW APPROACH BS	85000
BR F U S NAVY FLAG (USA) - HER HONOUR (IRE)	MONTGOMERY MOTTO	82000
B F SEA THE STARS (IRE) - WO DE XIN (GB)	GLENDING STABLES	82000
B C OASIS DREAM (GB) - ABBAKOVA (IRE)	PETER & ROSS DOYLE BS	82000
CH C STARSPANGLEDBANNER (AUS) - VIRGINIA CELESTE (IRE)	DE BURGH EQUINE	82000
WARDOG (IRE) CH F CHURCHILL (IRE) - GUARANDA (GB)	JONATHAN GREEN DJ STABLES	82000
B F EXPERT EYE (GB) - CATCHMENT (GB)	OAK TREE FARM	80000
B C PROFITABLE (IRE) - SNOOZE (IRE)	OAK TREE FARM (P.S.)	80000
CHIKETTO (IRE) B C DANDY MAN (IRE) - NIVVO (IRE)	HIGHFLYER BS	80000
B C CARAVAGGIO (USA) - HEIGHT OF ELEGANCE (IRE)	P ANTONACCI/J O'BRIEN	80000
B/BR F MENDELSSOHN (USA) - MOANIN (FR)	D J STABLES	80000
B F JUSTIFY (USA) - COSTA DEL SOL (USA)	N & C BRENNAN (P.S.)	80000
B F CAMELOT (GB) - HIGH FIDELITY (GER)	J BRUMMITT QUANTUM LEAP	80000
SULEIMAN ARTIST (IRE) B C ZOFFANY (IRE) - TANYELI (IRE)	RICHARD RYAN	80000
B C SHOWCASING (GB) - CAMPION (GB)	R O'RYAN/R FAHEY	80000
B F STARSPANGLEDBANNER (AUS) - CALLISTO STAR (IRE)	KEVIN ROSS BS	80000
B F SIYOUNI (FR) - TROPHEE (FR)	VENDOR	80000
GR C KENDARGENT (FR) - ALMA MATER (USA)	JOHNSTON RACING	80000
B C ACCLAMATION (GB) - FASHION THEORY (GB)	ANDREW BALDING	80000
BR F AWTAAD (IRE) - ZAAKHIR (IRE)	JOE FOLEY	78000
B C LOPE DE VEGA (IRE) - SARAHA (GB)	BBA IRE/YULONG INVEST.	78000
B C INVINCIBLE SPIRIT (IRE) - LETHAL QUALITY (GB)	LONGWAYS STABLES	78000
B C KESSAAR (IRE) - PRINCESS ROSE (GB)	VENDOR	78000
B F ACCLAMATION (GB) - QUALITY TIME (IRE)	RABBAH BS	78000
DOVES OF PEACE (IRE) B C CAMACHO (GB) - PETITS POTINS (IRE)	A C ELLIOTT/M L W BELL	77000
SCHUMANN (IRE) B C DANDY MAN (IRE) - BIBLIOTHECA (JPN)	RICHARD HUGHES	76000

HIGH-PRICED YEARLINGS OF 2021 AT GOFFS UK (DONCASTER)
The following yearlings realised £39,000 and over at Goffs UK Sales in 2021:

Name and Breeding	Purchaser	Pounds
REDEMPTION TIME (GB) B C HARRY ANGEL (IRE) - RED BOX (GB)	A.C. ELLIOTT	220000
B C KODIAC (GB) - STUNNER (GB)	BLANDFORD BS	210000
CH F STARSPANGLEDBANNER (AUS) - UNDER OFFER (IRE)	M V MAGNIER	160000
POWERDRESS (IRE) B F DANDY MAN (IRE) - NUCLEAR OPTION (IRE)	PETER & ROSS DOYLE	130000
CH C RIBCHESTER (IRE) - MIRABILE DICTU (IRE)	RICHARD HUGHES	125000
CH C MEHMAS (IRE) - INTERWEAVE (GB)	MANOR HOUSE STUD	120000
HAVANA BLUE (GB) GR C HAVANA GREY (GB) - EXRATING (GB)	RICHARD RYAN	115000
B C HAVANA GOLD (IRE) - GOLDEN SPELL (GB)	OLIVER ST LAWRENCE	110000
B C ACCLAMATION (GB) - DUKINTA (IRE)	B.HILLS/MCKEEVER	105000
FIFTY YEAR STORM (IRE) B F MEHMAS (IRE) - FAINLEOG (IRE)	A.C.ELLIOTT	100000
B C ARDAD (IRE) - PIGEON POINT (GB)	BLANDFORD BS	100000
B F KINGMAN (GB) - DABAN (IRE)	LONGWAYS STABLES	100000
REGINALD CHARLES (GB) B C ZOUSTAR (AUS) - MELBOURNE MEMORIES (GB)	BRYAN SMART	95000
CH C NO NAY NEVER (USA) - POETIC IMAGINATION (GB)	RABBAH BS	95000
BR F SHOWCASING (GB) - GIRLS TALK (GB)	MANOR HOUSE STUD	95000
CH C NIGHT OF THUNDER (IRE) - KENTUCKY BELLE (IRE)	SAM SANGSTER BS	92000
B C SHOWCASING (GB) - IMPEDE (GB)	PETER & ROSS DOYLE	92000
UNCLE (GB) B C HARRY ANGEL (IRE) - HELIOGRAPH (GB)	PETER & ROSS DOYLE	90000
GR F EL KABEIR (USA) - LITTLE AUDIO (IRE)	JS BS/G.SCOTT RACING	90000
B C KESSAAR (IRE) - BELLE DIVA (IRE)	ROBSON AGUIAR	90000
LAKE ELOISE (IRE) B F KODIAC (GB) - BRONZE BABY (USA)	C.HILLS/MCKEEVER	90000
DARK THIRTY (IRE) B C STARSPANGLEDBANNER (AUS) - BEACH WEDDING (IRE)	PETER & ROSS DOYLE	90000
EXPERT AGENT (GB) B C EXPERT EYE (GB) - OEUVRE D'ART (IRE)	PETER & ROSS DOYLE	90000
THREEBARS (GB) CH F COTAI GLORY (GB) - LADY MEGA (IRE)	PETER & ROSS DOYLE	88000
TALHA (GB) CH C HAVANA GREY (GB) - MY LEA (IRE)	STROUD COLEMAN	85000
MIYAGI (IRE) B C JAMES GARFIELD (IRE) - OMANOME (IRE)	A.C. ELLIOTT	85000
B C SEA THE MOON (GER) - LAUGHING DOVE (IRE)	J MURTAGH / E LINEHAN	85000
B C SHOWCASING (GB) - FIG ROLL (GB)	MEGAN EVANS	85000
B F MEHMAS (IRE) - DORIS MARIE (IRE)	CORMAC MCCORMACK	82000
BR C MEHMAS (IRE) - LUNA ROSA (IRE)	TALLY HO STUD	82000
DRAGON GLORY (IRE) CH F COTAI GLORY (GB) - STRAIT POWER (IRE)	A.C. ELLIOTT	82000
B C DARK ANGEL (IRE) - RELATION ALEXANDER (IRE)	MANOR HOUSE STUD	82000
B C NIGHT OF THUNDER (IRE) - OPERETTIST (GB)	AVENUE BS	82000
B C FAST COMPANY (IRE) - TILTHE END OF TIME (IRE)	ARMANDO DUARTE	80000
B C HOLY ROMAN EMPEROR (IRE) - SACRIFICE MY SOUL (IRE)	OLIVER ST LAWRENCE	80000
B C HARRY ANGEL (IRE) - EXACTING (GB)	JILL LAMB BS	80000
B C U S NAVY FLAG (USA) - CHERISHED (IRE)	CLIVE COX RACING	80000
B C KODIAC (GB) - LIGHT GLASS (IRE)	MIDDLEHAM PARK RACING	80000
SHOT (GB) B F ACCLAMATION (GB) - GLADIATRIX (GB)	PETER & ROSS DOYLE	80000
B C FAST COMPANY (IRE) - CHANTILLY CREAM (IRE)	J D MOORE	78000
B F OASIS DREAM (GB) - SOMMERS DAUGHTER (IRE)	OLIVER ST LAWRENCE	75000
B C MEHMAS (IRE) - LUMINOUS GOLD (IRE)	B O'RYAN/B HASLAM	75000
B C KODIAC (GB) - CHATHAM ISLANDS (USA)	B O'RYAN/B HASLAM	75000
CH F NIGHT OF THUNDER (IRE) - PEAK PRINCESS (IRE)	FREDERIK TYLICKI BS	75000
B F KODIAC (GB) - SHEMDA (IRE)	KEVIN ROSS BS	75000
B C MAYSON (GB) - DANCE EAST (GB)	SACKVILLEDONALD	75000
B C EXCEED AND EXCEL (AUS) - SIMMY'S TEMPLE (GB)	BLANDFORD BS	72000
B C COTAI GLORY (GB) - MAJESTIC ALEXANDER (IRE)	PD.EVANS	72000
BACCARAT BABY (GB) B F GLENEAGLES (IRE) - VOLUNTEER POINT (IRE)	A.C. ELLIOTT	72000
B C SIOUX NATION (USA) - JEWEL IN THE SAND (IRE)	PETER & ROSS DOYLE	70000
B C EXPERT EYE (GB) - LOOKS A MILLION (GB)	CHURCH FM/HORSE PARK	70000
B C EXPERT EYE (GB) - SHAMANDAR (FR)	OLIVER HARRIS	70000
B F TWILIGHT SON (GB) - ZAWIYAH (GB)	KEVIN ROSS BS	70000
B F ZOUSTAR (AUS) - NATURAL (GB)	CHURCH FM/HORSE PARK	70000
B C SHALAA (IRE) - ROWAN BRAE (GB)	CLIVE COX RACING	68000
B C KODI BEAR (IRE) - SLOVAK (IRE)	COMPAS EQUINE	68000
B F DARK ANGEL (IRE) - MEYDAN PRINCESS (IRE)	N BRADLEY RACING/K BURKE	68000
B C KINGMAN (GB) - EARRING (USA)	RABBAH BS (PS.)	67000
B F IFFRAAJ (GB) - MISKIN DIAMOND (IRE)	JILL LAMB BS	65000
B F NIGHT OF THUNDER (IRE) - SILVER CLOUDS (IRE)	HILLEN/RYAN	65000
CH F GALILEO GOLD (GB) - RAHAALA (IRE)	NICK BELL	65000
B F NIGHT OF THUNDER (IRE) - COILLTE CAILIN (IRE)	SACKVILLEDONALD	65000
COVERT LEGEND (GB) B C ZOUSTAR (AUS) - MISS YOU TOO (GB)	AVENUE BS	65000
CH F HAVANA GREY (GB) - SHOWSTOPPA (GB)	CLIVE COX RACING	65000
B F DANDY MAN (IRE) - LAHABAH (IRE)	JOE FOLEY	62000
B C ARDAD (IRE) - RELAXEZ VOUS (IRE)	HILLEN/RYAN	60000
CH C ZOUSTAR (AUS) - WORSHIP (IRE)	HILLEN/RYAN	60000
B C U S NAVY FLAG (USA) - SHOW RAINBOW (IRE)	RABBAH BS	60000

Name and Breeding	Purchaser	Guineas
B C KODIAC (GB) - MARIAN HALCOMBE (USA)	HILLEN/RYAN	60000
B C ACCLAMATION (GB) - VASTITAS (IRE)	ROBSON AGUIAR	60000
B F ZOFFANY (IRE) - HOPE SO (IRE)	N BRADLEY RACING/G TUER	60000
CH C STARSPANGLEDBANNER (AUS) - FRANZY (IRE)	CORMAC MCCORMACK	60000
B C SHOWCASING (GB) - MAGICAL FIRE (IRE)	VENDOR	60000
ADVANTAGE (IRE) CH C PROFITABLE (IRE) - DUTCH ROSE (IRE)	MEGAN NICHOLLS	60000
GR C HAVANA GREY (GB) - FOXCATCHER (GB)	R. O'RYAN/R. FAHEY	60000
CH C HAVANA GREY (GB) - SEVEN MAGICIANS (USA)	SACKVILLEDONALD	55000
RO/GR C STARSPANGLEDBANNER (AUS) - SAVVY (IRE)	CHURCH FM/HORSE PARK	55000
DUE DATE (GB) B C DUE DILIGENCE (IRE) - HARRYANA TO (GB)	CLIVE COX RACING	55000
B C KESSAAR (IRE) - APPLAUDING (IRE)	SYPS	55000
BODORGAN (IRE) GR C EL KABEIR (USA) - SILVER ROSE (IRE)	B.HILLS/MCKEEVER	55000
B F ACCLAMATION (GB) - FREE TO ROAM (GB)	PETER & ROSS DOYLE	54000
ZEBADAAY (GB) B C ADAAY (IRE) - SPRINGING BARONESS (GB)	JASON KELLY	52000
B C EXPERT EYE (GB) - DEEP DREAM (GB)	R. O'RYAN/R. FAHEY	52000
B F KODIAC (GB) - CLIP ART (GB)	HILLEN/RYAN	50000
TICKET TO ALASKA (IRE) B C KODIAC (GB) - JIRA (IRE)	CLIVE COX RACING	50000
B F ACLAIM (IRE) - QUIET PROTEST (USA)	MATTHEW EVES	50000
SAMAGON (GB) B C LIGHTNING SPEAR (GB) - VELVET REVOLVER (IRE)	SACKVILLEDONALD	50000
CH C HARRY ANGEL (IRE) - DANCE HALL GIRL (GB)	A. ALMALEK ALSABAH	50000
B F EXPERT EYE (GB) - ISLAND MAGIC (GB)	JOSEPH O'BRIEN	50000
B F HAVANA GOLD (IRE) - CHICAS AMIGAS (IRE)	RICHARD HUGHES	50000
RADIO GOO GOO (GB) B/GR F HAVANA GREY (GB) - RADIO GAGA (GB)	P.D.EVANS	48000
B C EXCEED AND EXCEL (AUS) - DUQUESA (GB)	HOWSON & HOULDSWORTH B/S	48000
B F PROFITABLE (IRE) - SCHOLARLY (GB)	JOHNNY MURTAGH/ED LINEHAN	48000
CH C COTAI GLORY (GB) - BISHOP'S LAKE (GB)	BLANDFORD BS	48000
I STILL HAVE FAITH (GB) B C EXPERT EYE (GB) - THE THRILL IS GONE (GB)	IAN WILLIAMS RACING	46000
B F HAVANA GOLD (IRE) - BOUNTY BOX (GB)	KEVIN ROSS BS	46000
B F ZOFFANY (IRE) - SACRAMENT (IRE)	PATTERN BS	46000
B C DANDY MAN (IRE) - DUTCH COURAGE (GB)	SACKVILLEDONALD	46000
B C BUNGLE INTHEJUNGLE (GB) - THE SHREW (GB)	R KNIGHT/S QUINN	46000
ZIVANIYA (GB) CH C CITYSCAPE (GB) - ROSIE ROYCE (GB)	SACKVILLEDONALD	45000
B F MASSAAT (IRE) - DELIZIA (IRE)	KILBRIDE EQUINE	45000
B F BUNGLE INTHEJUNGLE (GB) - KHAYRAT (IRE)	N BRADLEY RACING/R FELL	45000
B F ZOUSTAR (AUS) - STREET MARIE (USA)	DONNACHA O'BRIEN	45000
HECTIC (GB) B C MASSAAT (IRE) - CEEDWELL (GB)	HIGHCLERE AGENCY	44000
B C ZOUSTAR (AUS) - ALWAYS A DRAMA (IRE)	LONGWAYS STABLES	44000
B C BLUE BRESIL (FR) - MARY ELEANOR (GB)	R.B.S.LTD	44000
GR F CARAVAGGIO (USA) - NEW TERMS (GB)	JAMAL ALOTAIBI	43000
B F HARRY ANGEL (IRE) - GIMME SOME LOVIN (GB)	VENDOR	42000
B C BATED BREATH (GB) - SPATE (IRE)	SAM SANGSTER BS	42000
SAM'S HOPE (GB) B F AWTAAD (IRE) - DELIGHTFUL BELLE (USA)	PETER & ROSS DOYLE	42000
B G PETHER'S MOON (IRE) - FABRIKA (GB)	ALAN KING/HIGHFLYER BS	42000
PROSPERING (IRE) B C PROFITABLE (IRE) - HEAVENLY ANGEL (GB)	SACKVILLEDONALD	42000
GLAMOROUS STAR (IRE) B F GUTAIFAN (IRE) - GLAMOROUS AIR (IRE)	RON HARRIS	42000
STATU OF LIBERTY (GB) B F WASHINGTON DC (IRE) - MANIA (IRE)	SAM SANGSTER BS	42000
JAM NATION (IRE) B F SIOUX NATION (USA) - HOLY CAT (IRE)	R KNIGHT/S QUINN	42000
B F COTAI GLORY (GB) - DARK MISSILE (GB)	OLIVER ST LAWRENCE	42000
BR C ROARING LION (USA) - RICH LEGACY (IRE)	JS BS/A BALDING	42000
CH C IFFRAAJ (GB) - INALA (GB)	KARL BURKE	42000
B C BLUE BRESIL (FR) - SHALLTOO (IRE)	PINE TREE	42000
B C GALILEO GOLD (GB) - GOLDEN FLOWER (GB)	M.CLEERE	41000
CH F WASHINGTON DC (IRE) - RHAL (IRE)	BRYAN SMART	40000
B F HAVANA GOLD (IRE) - BYBROOK (GB)	SAM SANGSTER BS	40000
CH C CAMACHO (GB) - DESERT WAY (IRE)	HILLEN/RYAN	40000
B C HAVANA GREY (GB) - LADY ESTELLA (IRE)	PETER & ROSS DOYLE/MPR	40000
B C HAVANA GOLD (IRE) - EPATHA (GB)	MANOR HOUSE (P.S.)	40000
B C SIOUX NATION (USA) - SIMPLE LOVE (USA)	PARAGON BS	40000
DEGUELLO (IRE) B C DARK ANGEL (IRE) - LADY SPRINGBANK (IRE)	COMPAS EQUINE	40000
B C PROFITABLE (IRE) - INCA HUSKY (IRE)	STAMINA TURF/EIB	40000
MISS HELEN (IRE) B F U S NAVY FLAG (USA) - FLUVIAL (IRE)	PETER & ROSS DOYLE	40000
B F ZOUSTAR (AUS) - VALONIA (GB)	TIM EASTERBY	40000
B C TWILIGHT SON (GB) - FASCINATOR (GB)	HIGHCLERE AGENCY	40000
SHAHBAZ (IRE) B C FREE EAGLE (IRE) - MIDDLE PERSIA (IRE)	CHARLIE FELLOWES	40000
CH C PIVOTAL (GB) - DUSTY RED (GB)	MIDDLEHAM PARK RACING	40000
B C U S NAVY FLAG (USA) - PRINCESS CLEOPATRA (USA)	MARK GRANT	40000
B F EXPERT EYE (GB) - GARRAUN (IRE)	B.HILLS/MCKEEVER	40000
GEORDIE MACKEM (GB) B G JACK HOBBS (GB) - THE PIRATE'S QUEEN (IRE)	BRIAN ELLISON	40000
B C GUSTAV KLIMT (IRE) - GLITTER BABY (IRE)	O'BYRNE & GRASSICK	39000

HIGH-PRICED YEARLINGS OF 2021 AT TATTERSALLS IRELAND SALES

The following yearlings realised 34,000 euros and over at Tattersalls Ireland Sales in 2021:

Name and Breeding	Purchaser	Euros
CH F EXCEED AND EXCEL (AUS) - CLAUDETTE (USA)	RABBAH BS	224000
CH C NO NAY NEVER (USA) - PINK DAMSEL (IRE)	GLOBAL EQUINE GROUP	145600
SMOOTH RYDER (IRE) B C SMOOTH DADDY (USA) - SILESIE (USA)	JOHNSTON RACING	134400
B C CHURCHILL (IRE) - KOMEDY (IRE)	GLOBAL EQUINE GROUP	123200
GOOSE ROCK (IRE) B C MEHMAS (IRE) - DRIFTING SPIRIT (IRE)	JS BS / G SCOTT RACING	117600
B C ARDAD (IRE) - MARA GREY (IRE)	ROBSON AGUIAR/AMO RACING	117600
B C FOOTSTEPSINTHESAND (GB) - CAPED LADY (IRE)	SACKVILLE DONALD	106400
CH C FAST COMPANY (IRE) - PORTICO (GB)	ED DUNLOP RACING/J MOORE	100800
CH F FARRH (GB) - IMASUMAQ (IRE)	PETER & ROSS DOYLE BS	100800
CH C NEW BAY (GB) - POYLE MEG (GB)	KEVIN ROSS BS	98560
B C STARSPANGLEDBANNER (AUS) - TAMMY WYNETTE (IRE)	BLANDFORD BS	95200
REFINE (IRE) B F STARSPANGLEDBANNER (AUS) - DIVERT (IRE)	PETER & ROSS DOYLE BS	95200
FICTIONAL (IRE) B C MAKE BELIEVE (GB) - HIDDEN GIRL (IRE)	RICHARD HUGHES RACING	95200
GR/RO F DARK ANGEL (IRE) - LIGHT MY FIRE (IRE)	WARD / STEVE BRADLEY	89600
B F ACCLAMATION (GB) - UP AT LAST (GB)	MARK GRANT	89600
B C WALK IN THE PARK (IRE) - WINDERMERE SKY (IRE)	PARK FARM	85000
B C AUSTRALIA (GB) - CHATTING (IRE)	KILBRIDE EQUINE	84000
B F FASCINATING ROCK (IRE) - MISE (IRE)	JOSEPH O'BRIEN	84000
CH F ZOUSTAR (AUS) - SERAFINA SUNSET (IRE)	KEVIN ROSS BS	78400
CH C TAMAYUZ (GB) - MIKANDY (IRE)	D FARRINGTON	78400
B C GALILEO GOLD (GB) - MISS SALLY (IRE)	PETER NOLAN BS	78400
B C SIOUX NATION (USA) - CARTOGRAPHER (GB)	BLANDFORD BS	78400
B C KODIAC (GB) - GET UP AND DANCE (GB)	FEDERICO BARBERINI	76160
B C FASTNET ROCK (AUS) - HEROIC HEART (FR)	D FARRINGTON	75040
B F U S NAVY FLAG (USA) - QUEEN ANDORRA (IRE)	GAELIC BS	72800
B F GARSWOOD (GB) - ROYAL SEAL (GB)	BLANDFORD BS	72800
LADY BRYANSTON (IRE) CH F ULYSSES (IRE) - PIANO (GB)	RICHARD HUGHES RACING	69440
B C FOOTSTEPSINTHESAND (GB) - FINE JUDGMENT (IRE)	PETER & ROSS DOYLE BS	69440
B F PROFITABLE (GB) - TEELINE (IRE)	NICK BRADLEY RACING	69440
LADY DREAMER (IRE) B F DANDY MAN (IRE) - WEEKEND GETAWAY (IRE)	LILLINGSTON BS	69440
CH G TAMAYUZ (GB) - INTO THE LANE (IRE)	STROUD COLEMAN BS	69440
B C SOLDIER OF FORTUNE (IRE) - MO BURY (IRE)	TALLY-HO STUD	68000
KEEP ME STABLE (IRE) B F GALILEO GOLD (GB) - SKETCHING (GB)	PETER & ROSS DOYLE BS	67200
FOREST DEMON (IRE) B C GUSTAV KLIMT (IRE) - BLACK MEYEDEN (IRE)	KUBLER RACING	67200
B F STARSPANGLEDBANNER (AUS) - SHANNOW (IRE)	MANOR HOUSE STUD	67200
CINAMMON ROLL (FR) B G NO RISK AT ALL (FR) - LUNAYA (FR)	ALAN HARTE	65000
B C AUSTRALIA (GB) - ESPRIT DE TAUBER (FR)	VENDOR	64960
B F MEHMAS (IRE) - BALLET OF DOHA (IRE)	CHURCH FARM & HORSE PARK	64960
GR C HAVANA GREY (GB) - ROXIE LOT (GB)	ANDREW BALDING	64960
GULMARG (IRE) B C DANDY MAN (IRE) - BAILEYS PURSUIT (GB)	DWAYNE WOODS	64960
GR F STARSPANGLEDBANNER (AUS) - SERASANA (GB)	DE BURGH EQUINE/F STACK	64960
B C SIOUX NATION (USA) - XEMA (GB)	PETER & ROSS DOYLE BS	64960
B C ACLAIM (IRE) - SELFARA (GB)	SACKVILLEDONALD	63840
B F MEHMAS (IRE) - STAR OF KINGS (GB)	HURWORTH BS / CARL WATERS	62720
B C MEHMAS (IRE) - BETTER CHANCE (IRE)	JOE FOLEY	61600
ATLANTIC DREAM (IRE) B C STARSPANGLEDBANNER (AUS) - TAFAWOQ (GB)	NICK BELL	61600
B C COTAI GLORY (GB) - MASAI QUEEN (IRE)	PETER & ROSS DOYLE BS	61600
B C NOBLE MISSION (GB) - BECKONING (GB)	CATHERINE ERICHSEN	61600
B F KODI BEAR (IRE) - LYNN'S MEMORY (GB)	ROBSON BS/DAVE LOUGHNANE	61600
B C WAR COMMAND (USA) - DUNDEL'S SPIRIT (IRE)	PETER CROKE	61600
KROCODILE ROCK (FR) BL C JEU ST ELOI (FR) - JOLY NELSA (FR)	ALAN HARTE	60000
CH F DANDY MAN (IRE) - KENDAL MINT (GB)	CARL WATERS	58240
PARISH GREEN (IRE) B C PARISH HALL (IRE) - GEARANAI (USA)	BBA IRELAND	58240
B C GUSTAV KLIMT (IRE) - CARAMEL SUNDAE (GB)	PETER & ROSS DOYLE BS	58240
B F CAMACHO (GB) - WAVEBREAK (GB)	PD EVANS	57120
CH F AUSTRALIA (GB) - SUNBIRD (GB)	JOE FOLEY	56000
LADY NAGIN (IRE) B F KODIAC (GB) - TOP DOLLAR (GB)	DWAYNE WOODS	56000
B C KODI BEAR (IRE) - TOP ROW (GB)	HAMISH MACAULEY BS	56000
B C GOLDEN HORN (GB) - SADILLA (GB)	SAM SANGSTER BS	56000
CH F NO NAY NEVER (USA) - SPRING GARDEN (IRE)	VENDOR	56000
B F KODIAC (GB) - TWO FOR TEA (IRE)	EDWARD LYNAM	56000
PALAMON (IRE) CH C DECORATED KNIGHT (GB) - SESCHAT (IRE)	PETER & ROSS DOYLE BS	56000
B C PROFITABLE (IRE) - FLICK SHOW (IRE)	PETER & ROSS DOYLE BS	56000
B C STARSPANGLEDBANNER (AUS) - DESTALINK (GB)	PETER NOLAN / NOEL MEADE	56000
B F SIOUX NATION (USA) - SCHOOL RUN (IRE)	SHAMROCK THOROUGHBREDS	56000
B F STARSPANGLEDBANNER (AUS) - STAR OF SPRING (IRE)	GAELIC BS	56000
B C KESSAAR (IRE) - MISS PURITY PINKER (GB)	PETER & ROSS DOYLE BS	56000
SYDNEY MEWS (IRE) CH F NEW BAY (GB) - LA SUPERBA (IRE)	BLANDFORD BS	56000
B C MEHMAS (IRE) - KIBARA (GB)	ANDREW BALDING	53760

Name and Breeding	Purchaser	Guineas
ARMOUR PROPRE (IRE) CH F PROFITABLE (IRE) - FOOT OF PRIDE (IRE)	PETER & ROSS DOYLE BS	5376
MAJIL (IRE) B F MEHMAS (IRE) - DAMASK (IRE)	J PIGGOTT / N TINKLER	5376
B C KESSAAR (IRE) - RED IVY (IRE)	KEVIN ROSS BS	5264
B C ORDER OF ST GEORGE (IRE) - SEE THE LIGHTNING (IRE)	HENRIETTA KNIGHT	5200
B C DRAGON PULSE (IRE) - ROSA GIALLA (IRE)	CLIVE COX RACING	5152
B C CAMACHO (IRE) - MOTS CROISES (GB)	PETER & ROSS DOYLE BS	5152
B C PROFITABLE (IRE) - MYSTERIOUS BURG (FR)	CH THOROUGHBREDS	5040
BAILAR CONTIGO (IRE) B F GLENEAGLES (IRE) - SLIEVE MISH (IRE)	D OLVER / PAUL HARLEY BS	5040
DANDY ALYS (IRE) B F DANDY MAN (IRE) - ALYSSUM (IRE)	A C ELLIOTT, AGENT	5040
LEAP YEAR LAD (IRE) GR/RO C HAVANA GREY (GB) - SKELETON (IRE)	RJ & R MARLEY	5040
B C WALK IN THE PARK (IRE) - SUPREME PRESENT (GB)	RICHARD FRISBY	5000
CH C STARSPANGLEDBANNER (AUS) - VICTORIA BEAR (GB)	CREIGHTON SCHWARTZ BS	4928
B F ACCLAMATION (GB) - PIACERE (IRE)	ANTONIO DA SILVA	4928
B C MASSAAT (IRE) - MISS LESLEY (GB)	ED DUNLOP RACING/J MOORE	4816
B F DARK ANGEL (IRE) - MISS ALBANE (FR)	VENDOR	4704
CH F EL KABEIR (USA) - RURAL CELEBRATION (GB)	OLIVER ST LAWRENCE BS	4704
B C COTAI GLORY (GB) - DIAMOND FINESSE (IRE)	MANOR HOUSE STUD	4704
B F AUSTRALIA (GB) - SHANNON SPREE (GB)	DONNACHA O'BRIEN	4704
B F DANDY MAN (IRE) - DUBAYA (GB)	MARK GRANT RACING	4704
B F ZOUSTAR (AUS) - EVIL SPELL (GB)	HUGO PALMER	4704
QUEEN OF THRONES (IRE) B F PROFITABLE (IRE) - THRONE (GB)	CLIVE COX RACING	4480
DAYYAN (IRE) B C KODIAC (GB) - DUTCH DESTINY (GB)	C GORDON WATSON BS	4480
REFLEX (IRE) GR C EL KABEIR (USA) - KNAPTON HILL (GB)	C GORDON WATSON BS	4480
B C EXPERT EYE (GB) - GOLD AGAIN (USA)	SACKVILLEDONALD	4480
B F KUROSHIO (AUS) - MIDNIGHT DESTINY (IRE)	COMPAS EQUINE	4480
B C KODIAC (GB) - PLEASE ME (IRE)	AGUIAR BS	4480
B C EXPERT EYE (GB) - COOL KITTEN (GB)	KILBREW STABLES	4480
B F SHOWCASING (GB) - MIDNIGHTLY (GB)	W CLIFFORD	4480
TOSTADO (IRE) B C KESSAAR (IRE) - ZAINDERA (IRE)	ANDREW BALDING	4480
B F FARHH (GB) - BLUE ILLUSION (GB)	PADDY TWOMEY	4480
B C ZOFFANY (IRE) - KAMILI (IRE)	EDWARD LYNAM	4480
B C CHURCHILL (GB) - GLASS SLIPPER (IRE)	PETER NOLAN BS	4256
GR C DANDY MAN (IRE) - SWEET ALABAMA (GB)	OPULENCE THOROUGHBREDS	4256
GR C MASTERCRAFTSMAN (IRE) - BELLE ABOVE ALL (GB)	AVENUE BS / HUGO PALMER	4256
B C WELL CHOSEN (GB) - BELSALSA (FR)	T HILLMAN	4200
B C CARAVAGGIO (USA) - HAND ON HEART (IRE)	MICHAEL DODS	4144
B C MAKE BELIEVE (GB) - UNCHARTED HAVEN (GB)	CON MARNANE	4144
B C WAR COMMAND (USA) - PEIG (IRE)	O'BYRNE & GRASSICK	4032
B C ZOFFANY (IRE) - WILD BLOOM (GB)	CHURCH FARM & HORSE PARK	4032
B F GLENEAGLES (GB) - WEEK END (GB)	VENDOR	3920
CONCON CANDY (IRE) GR F HAVANA GREY (GB) - CHILD BRIDE (USA)	BBA IRELAND	3920
BR F DANDY MAN (IRE) - ALABAMA MONROE (IRE)	EDDIE LINEHAN BS	3920
B C MASTERCRAFTSMAN (IRE) - ONDEAFEARS (IRE)	GRANT TUER	3920
BUCCABAY (IRE) B C SAXON WARRIOR (JPN) - FIFTH COMMANDMENT (IRE)	HIGHFLYER BS	3920
THE ANGELUS BELLE (IRE) B F DANDY MAN (IRE) - ANNAMANAMOUX (USA)	JASON KELLY BS	3920
STENTON GLIDER (IRE) B F DANDY MAN (IRE) - CRYSTAL MALT (IRE)	SACKVILLEDONALD	3920
B F SEA THE MOON (GER) - ROCK FOLLIES (IRE)	PETER & ROSS DOYLE BS	3920
B F ELZAAM (AUS) - BOUNTY'S SPIRIT (GB)	BBA IRELAND	3920
B F DANDY MAN (IRE) - TILLY TROTTER (GB)	KARL BURKE	3920
B F CHURCHILL (GB) - MILANOVA (AUS)	SAM SANGSTER BS	3920
STAMFORD BLUE (IRE) B C FAST COMPANY (IRE) - CHELSEA CORSAGE (IRE)	PETER & ROSS DOYLE BS	3920
CH C DRAGON PULSE (IRE) - PROUD MARIA (GB)	SACKVILLEDONALD	3808
B C SMOOTH DADDY (USA) - LUMINANCE (IRE)	CON MARNANE	3808
CH F STARSPANGLEDBANNER (AUS) - NONETHELESS (IRE)	VENDOR	3808
B C SOLDIER OF FORTUNE (IRE) - A PLUS MA PUCE (FR)	VENDOR	3700
B C HOLY ROMAN EMPEROR (IRE) - IFFA RED (IRE)	OLIVER ST LAWRENCE BS	3696
STAR PLAYER (GB) B C ZOFFANY (IRE) - LUNAR PHASE (GB)	STROUD COLEMAN BS	3696
B C ORDER OF ST GEORGE (IRE) - SWINCOMBE FLAME (GB)	MOSSY FEN STABLES	3600
CH C HARRY ANGEL (IRE) - SILVER RAINBOW (IRE)	LONGWAYS STABLES	3584
GR C COTAI GLORY (GB) - DAY CREEK (GB)	CREIGHTON SCHWARTZ BS	3584
B C CAMACHO (GB) - DAME JUDI (IRE)	SACKVILLEDONALD	3584
B C EXCEED AND EXCEL (AUS) - GHANY (IRE)	PETER NOLAN BS	3584
B C FAST COMPANY (IRE) - RUSSIAN SPIRIT (GB)	RICHARD KNIGHT BS/S QUINN	3584
B C VADAMOS (FR) - FIGURANTE (IRE)	HIGHFLYER BS / A KING	3584
B F BLAME (USA) - GOODTHINGSTAKETIME (IRE)	JEREMY GLOVER	3584
B F FLEMENSFIRTH (USA) - STEPHANIE FRANCES (IRE)	T GREDLEY/STETCHWORTH PARK	3500
B C JUKEBOX JURY (IRE) - BOBAWAY (GB)	VENDOR	3500
B/BR C FAST COMPANY (IRE) - KINDLING (GB)	J OXX	4720
B C KESSAAR (IRE) - CLASSIC IMAGE (GB)	ALICE HAYNES RACING	4720
METAL MERCHANT (IRE) B C MAKE BELIEVE (GB) - WHIPPED (IRE)	KILBRIDE EQUINE	4720
B C WALK IN THE PARK (IRE) - MAIFITZ'S MADONNA (IRE)	RICHARD FRISBY	34000

STAY AHEAD OF THE FIELD WITH

RACING POST MEMBERS' CLUB

ACCESS PREMIUM CONTENT AND FEATURES

FIND OUT MORE AT RACINGPOST.COM/MEMBERS-CLUB

2000 GUINEAS STAKES (3y) Newmarket - 1 mile

Year	Owner	Winner and Price	Jockey	Trainer	Second	Third	Ran	Time
1984	R Sangster's	EL GRAN SENOR (15/8)	P Eddery	V O'Brien	Chief Singer	Lear Fan	9	1 37.41
1985	Maktoum Al Maktoum's	SHADEED (4/5)	L Piggott	M Stoute	Bairn	Supreme Leader	14	1 37.41
1986	K Abdullah's	DANCING BRAVE (15/8)	G Starkey	G Harwood	Green Desert	Huntingdale	15	1 40.00
1987	J Hogan's	DON'T FORGET ME (9/1)	W Carson	R Hannon	Bellotto	Midyan	13	1 36.74
1988	H H Aga Khan's	DOYOUN (4/5)	W R Swinburn	M Stoute	Charmer	Bellefella	9	1 41.73
1989	Hamdan Al-Maktoum's	NASHWAN (3/1)	W Carson	W Hern	Exbourne	Danehill	14	1 36.44
1990	John Horgan's	TIROL (9/1)	M Kinane	R Hannon	Machiavellian	Anshan	14	1 35.84
1991	Lady Beaverbrook's	MYSTIKO (13/2)	M Roberts	C Brittain	Lycius	Ganges	14	1 37.83
1992	R Sangster's	RODRIGO DE TRIANO (6/1)	L Piggott	P Chapple-Hyam	Lucky Lindy	Pursuit of Love	16	1 38.37
1993	K Abdullah's	ZAFONIC (5/6)	P Eddery	A Fabre	Barathea	Bin Alwaad	14	1 35.32
1994	G R Bailey Ltd's	MISTER BAILEYS (16/1)	J Weaver	M Johnston	Grand Lodge	Colonel Collins	16	1 35.08
1995	Sheikh Mohammed's	PENNEKAMP (9/2)	T Jarnet	A Fabre	Celtic Swing	Bahri	23	1 35.16
1996	Godolphin's	MARK OF ESTEEM (8/1)	L Dettori	S bin Suroor	Even Top	Bijou D'Inde	11	1 37.59
1997	M Tabor & Mrs J Magnier's	ENTREPRENEUR (11/2)	M Kinane	A O'Brien	Revoque	Poteen	16	1 35.64
1998	M Tabor & Mrs J Magnier's	KING OF KINGS (7/2)	M Kinane	A O'Brien	Lend A Hand	Border Arrow	18	1 39.25
1999	Godolphin's	ISLAND SANDS (10/1)	L Dettori	S Bin Suroor	Enrique	Mujahid	16	1 37.14
	(Run on July Course)							
2000	Saeed Suhail's	KING'S BEST (13/2)	K Fallon	Sir M Stoute	Giant's Causeway	Barathea Guest	27	1 37.75
2001	Lord Weinstock's	GOLAN (11/1)	K Fallon	Sir M Stoute	Tamburlaine	Frenchmans Bay	18	1 37.48
2002	Sir A Ferguson & Mrs J Magnier's	ROCK OF GIBRALTAR (9/1)	J Murtagh	A O'Brien	Hawk Wing	Redback	22	1 36.50
2003	Moyglare Stud Farm's	REFUSE TO BEND (9/2)	P J Smullen	D Weld	Zafeen	Norse Dancer	20	1 37.98
2004	Hamdan Al Maktoum's	HAAFHD (11/2)	R Hills	B Hills	Snow Ridge	Azamour	14	1 36.60
2005	Mr M Tabor & Mrs John Magnier's &	FOOTSTEPSINTHESAND (13/2)	K Fallon	A O'Brien	Rebel Rebel	Kandidate	19	1 36.10
2006	Mr M Tabor & Mr D Smith's	GEORGE WASHINGTON (6/4)	K Fallon	A O'Brien	Sir Percy	Olympian Odyssey	14	1 36.80
2007	P Cunningham's	COCKNEY REBEL (25/1)	O Peslier	G Huffer	Vital Equine	Dutch Art	24	1 35.84
2008	Mrs J Magnier's	HENRYTHENAVIGATOR (11/1)	J Murtagh	A O'Brien	New Approach	Stubbs Art	15	1 39.14
2009	C Tsui's	SEA THE STARS (8/1)	M Kinane	J Oxx	Delegator	Gan Amhras	15	1 35.68
2010	K Abdullah's	MAKFI (33/1)	C Lemaire	M Delzangles	Dick Turpin	Canford Cliffs	19	1 36.35
2011	D Smith, Mrs J Magnier & M Tabor's	FRANKEL (1/2)	T Queally	H Cecil	Dubawi Gold	Native Khan	13	1 37.30
2012	M Tabor's	CAMELOT (15/8)	J O'Brien	A O'Brien	French Fifteen	Hermival	18	1 42.46
2013	Godolphin's	DAWN APPROACH (11/8)	K Manning	J Bolger	Glory Awaits	Van Der Neer	13	1 35.84
2014	Saeed Manana's	NIGHT OF THUNDER (40/1)	K Fallon	R Hannon Jnr	Kingman	Australia	14	1 36.61
2015	M Tabor, D Smith & Mrs J Magnier's	GLENEAGLES (4/1)	R Moore	A O'Brien	Territories	Ivawood	18	1 37.55
2016	Al Shaqab Racing's	GALILEO GOLD (14/1)	L Dettori	H Palmer	Massaat	Ritchester	13	1 35.91
2017	M Tabor, D Smith & Mrs J Magnier's	CHURCHILL (6/4)	R Moore	A O'Brien	Barney Roy	Al Wukair	10	1 36.61
2018	D Smith, Mrs J Magnier & M Tabor's	SAXON WARRIOR (3/1)	D O'Brien	A O'Brien	Tip Two Win	Masar	14	1 36.55
2019	D Smith/Mrs J Magnier/M Tabor & Flaxman Stables's	MAGNA GRECIA (11/2)	D O'Brien	A O'Brien	King of Change	Skardu	19	1 36.84
2020	Qatar Racing Limited's	KAMEKO (10/1)	O Murphy	A Balding	Wichita	Pinatubo	15	1 34.72
2021	Mrs J Magnier's							

1000 GUINEAS STAKES (3y fillies) Newmarket - 1 mile

Year	Owner	Winner and Price	Jockey	Trainer	Second	Third	Ran	Time
1984	M Lemos's	PEBBLES (8/1)	P Robinson	C Brittain	Meis El-Reem	Desirable	15	1 38.18
1985	Sheikh Mohammed's	OH SO SHARP (2/1)	S Cauthen	H Cecil	Al Bahathri	Bella Colora	17	1 36.85
1986	H Ranier's	MIDWAY LADY (10/1)	R Cochrane	B Hanbury	Maysoon	Sonic Lady	15	1 41.54
1987	S Niarchos's	MESQUE (15/8)	F Head	F Boutin	Milligram	Interval	14	1 38.48
1988	Ecurie Aland's	RAVINELLA (4/5)	G W Moore	Mme C Head	Dabaweyaa	Diminuendo	12	1 40.88
1989	Sheikh Mohammed's	MUSICAL BLISS (7/2)	W R Swinburn	M Stoute	Kerrera	Aldbourne	7	1 42.69
1990	Hamdan Al-Maktoum's	SALSABIL (6/4)	W Carson	J Dunlop	Heart of Joy	Negligent	10	1 38.06
1991	Hamdan Al-Maktoum's	SHADAYID (4/6)	W Carson	J Dunlop	Kooyonga	Crystal Gazing	14	1 38.18
1992	Maktoum Al-Maktoum's	HATOOF (5/1)	W R Swinburn	Mme C Head	Marling	Kenbu	14	1 39.45
1993	Mohamed Obaida's	SAYYEDATI (4/1)	W R Swinburn	C Brittain	Niche	Ajfan	12	1 37.34
1994	R Sangster's	LAS MENINAS (12/1)	J Reid	T Stack	Balanchine	Coup de Genie	15	1 36.71
1995	Hamdan Al-Maktoum's	HARAYIR (5/1)	R Hills	Major W R Hern	Aqaarid	Moonshell	14	1 36.72
1996	Wafic Said's	BOSRA SHAM (10/11)	Pat Eddery	H Cecil	Matiya	Bint Shadayid	13	1 37.75
1997	Greentay Stables Ltd's	SLEEPYTIME (5/1)	K Fallon	H Cecil	Oh Nellie	Dazzle	17	1 37.66
1998	Godolphin's	CAPE VERDI (100/30)	L Dettori	S Bin Suroor	Shahtoush	Exclusive	16	1 37.86
1999	K Abdullah's	WINCE (4/1)	K Fallon	H Cecil	Wannabe Grand	Valentine Waltz	22	1 37.91
	(Run on July Course)							
2000	Hamdan Al-Maktoum's	LAHAN (14/1)	R Hills	J Gosden	Princess Ellen	Petrushka	18	1 36.38
2001	Sheikh Ahmed Al Maktoum's	AMEERAT (11/1)	P Robinson	M Jarvis	Muwakleh	Toroca	15	1 38.36
2002	Godolphin's	KAZZIA (14/1)	L Dettori	S Bin Suroor	Snowfire	Alasha	17	1 37.85
2003	Cheveley Park Stud's	RUSSIAN RHYTHM (12/1)	K Fallon	Sir M Stoute	Six Perfections	Intercontinental	19	1 38.43
2004	Duke of Roxburghe's	ATTRACTION (11/2)	K Darley	M Johnston	Sundrop	Hathrah	16	1 36.70
2005	Mrs John Magnier & Mr M Tabor's	VIRGINIA WATERS (12/1)	K Fallon	A O'Brien	Maids Causeway	Vista Bella	20	1 36.50
2006	M Sly, Dr Davies & Mrs P Sly's	SPECIOSA (10/1)	M Fenton	Mrs P Sly	Confidential Lady	Nasheej	14	1 40.50
2007	M Ryan's	FINSCEAL BEO (5/4)	K Manning	J Bolger	Arch Swing	Simply Perfect	21	1 34.94
2008	S Friborg's	NATAGORA (11/4)	C Lemaire	P Bary	Spacious	Saoirse Abu	15	1 38.99
2009	Hamdan Al-Maktoum's	GHANAATI (20/1)	R Hills	B Hills	Cuis Ghaire	Super Sleuth	14	1 34.22
2010	K Abdullah's	SPECIAL DUTY (9/2)	S Pasquier	Mme C Head-Maarek	Jacqueline Quest	Gile Na Greine	17	1 39.66
	(The first two placings were reversed by the Stewards)							
2011	Godolphin's	BLUE BUNTING (16/1)	L Dettori	M Al Zarooni	Together	Maqaasid	18	1 39.27
2012	Mrs John Magnier, M Tabor & D Smith's	HOMECOMING QUEEN (25/1)	R Moore	A O'Brien	Starscope	Maybe	17	1 40.45
2013	B Keswick's	SKY LANTERN (9/1)	R Hughes	R Hannon	Just The Judge	Moth	15	1 36.38
2014	Ballymore Thoroughbred Ltd's	MISS FRANCE (7/1)	M Guyon	A Fabre	Lightning Thunder	Ihtimal	17	1 37.40
2015	M Tabor, D Smith & Mrs J Magnier's	LEGATISSIMO (13/2)	R Moore	D Wachman	Lucida	Tiggy Wiggy	13	1 34.60
2016	D Smith, Mrs J Magnier & M Tabor's	MINDING (11/10)	R Moore	A O'Brien	Ballydoyle	Alice Springs	16	1 36.53
2017	Mrs John Magnier, M Tabor & D Smith's	WINTER (9/1)	W Lordan	A O'Brien	Rhododendron	Daban	14	1 35.66
2018	Pall Mall Partners & Partners	BILLESDON BROOK (66/1)	S Levey	R Hannon	Laurens	Happily	15	1 36.62
2019	M Tabor, D Smith & Mrs John Magnier's	HERMOSA (14/1)	W Lordan	A O'Brien	Lady Kaya	Qabala	15	1 36.89
2020	M Tabor, D Smith & Mrs John Magnier's	LOVE (4/1)	R Moore	A O'Brien	Cloak Of Spirits	Quadrilateral	15	1 35.80
2021	D Smith, Mrs J Magnier & M Tabor's	MOTHER EARTH (10/1)	L Dettori	A O'Brien	Saffron Beach	Fev Rover	11	1 36.37

OAKS STAKES (3y fillies) Epsom - 1 mile 4 furlongs 6 yards

Year	Owner	Winner and Price	Jockey	Trainer	Second	Third	Ran	Time
1984	Sir R McAlpine's	CIRCUS PLUME (4/1)	L Piggott	J Dunlop	Media Luna	Poquito Queen	15	2 38.97
1985	Sheikh Mohammed's	OH SO SHARP (6/4)	S Cauthen	H Cecil	Triptych	Dubian	12	2 41.37
1986	H Ranier's	MIDWAY LADY (15/8)	S Cochrane	B Hanbury	Untold	Maysoon	15	2 36.60
1987	Sheikh Mohammed's	UNITE (11/1)	W R Swinburn	M Stoute	Bourbon Girl	Three Tails	11	2 38.11
1988	Sheikh Mohammed's	DIMINUENDO (7/4)	S Cauthen	H Cecil	Sudden Love	Animatrice	11	2 35.02
1989	Saeed Maktoum Al Maktoum's	SNOW BRIDE (13/2)	S Cauthen	H Cecil	Roseate Tern	Mamaluna	9	2 34.22
	(Aliysa finished first but was subsequently disqualified)							
1990	Hamdan Al-Maktoum's	SALSABIL (2/1)	W Carson	J Dunlop	Game Plan	Knight's Baroness	8	2 38.70
1991	Maktoum Al-Maktoum's	JET SKI LADY (50/1)	C Roche	J Bolger	Shamshir	Shadayid	9	2 37.30
1992	W J Gredley's	USER FRIENDLY (5/1)	G Duffield	C Brittain	All At Sea	Pearl Angel	7	2 39.77
1993	Sheikh Mohammed's	INTREPIDITY (5/1)	M Roberts	A Fabre	Royal Ballerina	Oakmead	14	2 34.19
1994	Godolphin's	BALANCHINE (6/1)	L Dettori	H Ibrahim	Wind In Her Hair	Hawajiss	10	2 40.37
1995	Maktoum Al Maktoum/Godolphin's	MOONSHELL (3/1)	L Dettori	S Bin Suroor	Dance A Dream	Pure Grain	10	2 35.44
1996	Wafic Said's	LADY CARLA (100/30)	P Eddery	H Cecil	Pricket	Mezzogiorno	11	2 35.55
1997	K Abdulla's	REAMS OF VERSE (5/6)	K Fallon	H Cecil	Gazelle Royale	Crown of Light	12	2 35.59
1998	Mrs D Nagle & Mrs J Magnier's	SHAHTOUSH (12/1)	M Kinane	A O'Brien	Bahr	Midnight Line	8	2 38.23
1999	F Salman's	RAMRUMA (3/1)	K Fallon	H Cecil	Noushkey	Zahrat Dubai	8	2 38.72
2000	Lordship Stud's	LOVE DIVINE (9/4)	L Dettori	H Cecil	Kalypso Katie	Melikah	16	2 43.11
2001	Mrs D. Nagle & Mrs J Magnier's	IMAGINE (3/1)	M Kinane	A O'Brien	Flight Of Fancy	Relish The Thought	16	2 36.70
2002	Godolphin's	KAZZIA (100/30)	L Dettori	S Bin Suroor	Quarter Moon	Shadow Dancing	14	2 44.52
2003	W S Farish III's	CASUAL LOOK (10/1)	M Dwyer	A Balding	Yesterday	Summitville	15	2 36.07
2004	Lord Derby's	OUIJA BOARD (7/2)	K Fallon	E Dunlop	All Too Beautiful	Punctilious	7	2 35.40
2005	Hamdan Al Maktoum's	ESWARAH (11/4)	R Hills	M Jarvis	Something Exciting	Pictavia	7	2 35.40
2006	Mrs J Magnier, Mr M Tabor & Mr D Smith's	ALEXANDROVA (9/4)	K Fallon	A O'Brien	Rising Cross	Short Skirt	10	2 37.70
2007	Niarchos Family's	LIGHT SHIFT (13/2)	T Durcan	H Cecil	Peeping Fawn	All My Loving	14	2 40.38
2008	J H Richmond-Watson's	LOOK HERE (33/1)	S Sanders	R Beckett	Moonstone	Katiyra	16	2 36.89
2009	Lady Bamford's	SARISKA (9/4)	J Spencer	M Bell	Midday	High Heeled	15	2 35.28
2010	Aranaeum Ltd's	SNOW FAIRY (9/1)	R Moore	E Dunlop	Remember When	Rumoush	15	2 35.77
	(Meezan finished second but was subsequently disqualified)							
2011	M J & L A Taylor's	DANCING RAIN (20/1)	J Murtagh	W Haggas	Wonder of Wonders	Izzi Top	13	2 41.73
2012	M Tabor's	WAS (20/1)	S Heffernan	A O'Brien	Shirocco Star	The Fugue	12	2 38.68
2013	D Smith, Mrs J Magnier & M Tabor's	TALENT (20/1)	R Hughes	R Beckett	Secret Gesture	The Lark	11	2 42.00
2014	Hamdan Al Maktoum's	TAGHROODA (5/1)	P Hanagan	J Gosden	Tarfasha	Volume	17	2 34.89
2015	Mrs C C Regalado-Gonzalez's	QUALIFY (50/1)	C O'Donoghue	A O'Brien	Legatissimo	Lady of Dubai	11	2 37.41
2016	D Smith, Mrs J Magnier & M Tabor's	MINDING (10/11)	R Moore	A O'Brien	Architecture	Harlequeen	9	2 42.66
2017	K Abdulla's	ENABLE (6/1)	L Dettori	J Gosden	Rhododendron	Alluringly	9	2 34.13
2018	M Tabor, D Smith & Mrs J Magnier's	FOREVER TOGETHER (7/1)	D O'Brien	A O'Brien	Wild Illusion	Bye Bye Baby	9	2 40.39
2019	Helena Springfield Ltd's	ANAPURNA (8/1)	L Dettori	J Gosden	Pink Dogwood	Fleeting	14	2 36.90
2020	M Tabor, D Smith & Mrs J Magnier's	LOVE (11/10)	R Moore	A O'Brien	Ennistymon	Frankly Darling	8	2 34.06
2021	D Smith, Mrs J Magnier & M Tabor's	SNOWFALL (11/2)	L Dettori	A O'Brien	Mystery Angel	Divinely	14	2 42.67

DERBY STAKES (3y) Epsom - 1 mile 4 furlongs 6 yards

Year	Owner	Winner and Price	Jockey	Trainer	Second	Third	Ran	Time
1984	L Miglitti's	SECRETO (14/1)	C Roche	D O'Brien	El Gran Senor	Mighty Flutter	17	2 39.12
1985	Lord H. de Walden's	SLIP ANCHOR (9/4)	S Cauthen	H Cecil	Law Society	Damister	14	2 36.23
1986	H H Aga Khan's	SHAHRASTANI (11/2)	W Swinburn	M Stoute	Dancing Brave	Mashkour	17	2 37.13
1987	L Freedman's	REFERENCE POINT (6/4)	S Cauthen	H Cecil	Most Welcome	Bellotto	19	2 33.90
1988	H H Aga Khan's	KAHYASI (11/1)	R Cochrane	L Cumani	Glacial Storm	Doyoun	14	2 33.84
1989	Hamdan Al-Maktoum's	NASHWAN (5/4)	W Carson	R Hern	Terimon	Cacoethes	12	2 34.90
1990	K Abdulla's	QUEST FOR FAME (7/1)	Pat Eddery	R Charlton	Blue Stag	Elmaamul	18	2 37.26
1991	F Salman's	GENEROUS (9/1)	A Munro	P Cole	Marju	Star of Gdansk	13	2 34.00
1992	Sidney H Craig's	DR DEVIOUS (8/1)	J Reid	P Chapple-Hyam	St Jovite	Silver Wisp	18	2 36.19
1993	K Abdulla's	COMMANDER IN CHIEF (15/2)	M Kinane	H Cecil	Blue Judge	Blues Traveller	16	2 34.51
1994	Hamdan Al-Maktoum's	ERHAAB (7/2)	W Carson	J Dunlop	King's Theatre	Colonel Collins	25	2 34.16
1995	Saeed Maktoum Al Maktoum's	LAMMTARRA (14/1)	W Swinburn	S Bin Suroor	Tamure	Presenting	15	2 32.31
1996	K Dasmal's	SHAAMIT (12/1)	M Hills	W Haggas	Dushyantor	Shantou	20	2 35.05
1997	L Knight's	BENNY THE DIP (11/1)	W Ryan	J Gosden	Silver Patriarch	Romanov	13	2 35.77
1998	Sheikh Mohammed Obaid Al Maktoum's	HIGH-RISE (20/1)	O Peslier	L Cumani	City Honours	Border Arrow	15	2 33.88
1999	The Thoroughbred Corporation's	OATH (13/2)	K Fallon	H Cecil	Dalapour	Beat All	16	2 37.43
2000	H H Aga Khan's	SINNDAR (7/1)	J Murtagh	J Oxx	Sakhee	Beat Hollow	15	2 36.75
2001	M Tabor & Mrs J Magnier's	GALILEO (11/4)	M Kinane	A O'Brien	Golan	Tobougg	12	2 33.27
2002	M Tabor & Mrs J Magnier's	HIGH CHAPARRAL (7/2)	J Murtagh	A O'Brien	Hawk Wing	Moon Ballad	12	2 39.45
2003	Saeed Suhail's	KRIS KIN (6/1)	K Fallon	Sir M Stoute	The Great Gatsby	Alamshar	20	2 33.35
2004	Ballymacoll Stud's	NORTH LIGHT (7/2)	K Fallon	Sir M Stoute	Rule Of Law	Let The Lion Roar	14	2 33.70
2005	The Royal Ascot Racing Club's	MOTIVATOR (3/1)	J Murtagh	M Bell	Walk In The Park	Dubawi	13	2 35.60
2006	A E Pakenham's	SIR PERCY (6/1)	M Dwyer	M Tregoning	Dragon Dancer	Dylan Thomas	18	2 35.20
2007	Saleh Al Homaizi & Imad Al Sagar's	AUTHORIZED (5/4)	L Dettori	P Chapple-Hyam	Eagle Mountain	Aqaleem	17	2 34.77
2008	HRH Princess Haya of Jordan's	NEW APPROACH (5/1)	K Manning	J Bolger	Tartan Bearer	Casual Conquest	16	2 36.50
2009	C Tsui's	SEA THE STARS (11/4)	M Kinane	J Oxx	Fame And Glory	Masterofthehorse	12	2 36.74
2010	K Abdulla's	WORKFORCE (6/1)	R Moore	Sir M Stoute	At First Sight	Rewilding	12	2 31.33
2011	Mrs John Magnier, M Tabor & D Smith's	POUR MOI (4/1)	M Barzalona	A Fabre	Treasure Beach	Carlton House	13	2 34.54
2012	D Smith, Mrs J Magnier & M Tabor's	CAMELOT (8/13)	J O'Brien	A O'Brien	Main Sequence	Astrology	9	2 33.90
2013	Mrs John Magnier, Michael Tabor & Derrick Smith's	RULER OF THE WORLD (7/1)	R Moore	A O'Brien	Libertarian	Galileo Rock	12	2 39.06
2014	D Smith, Mrs J Magnier, M Tabor & T Ah King's	AUSTRALIA (11/8)	J O'Brien	A O'Brien	Kingston Hill	Romsdal	16	2 33.63
2015	A E Oppenheimer's	GOLDEN HORN (13/8)	L Dettori	J Gosden	Jack Hobbs	Storm The Stars	12	2 32.32
2016	H H Aga Khan's	HARZAND (13/2)	P Smullen	D Weld	US Army Ranger	Idaho	16	2 40.09
2017	D Smith, Mrs J Magnier, M Tabor's	WINGS OF EAGLES (40/1)	P Beggy	A O'Brien	Cliffs of Moher	Cracksman	18	2 33.02
2018	Godolphin's	MASAR (16/1)	W Buick	C Appleby	Dee Ex Bee	Roaring Lion	12	2 34.93
2019	Mrs J Magnier, M Tabor & D Smith's	ANTHONY VAN DYCK (13/2)	S Heffernan	A O'Brien	Madhmoon	Japan	13	2 33.38
2020	Mrs J Magnier, M Tabor & D Smith's	SERPENTINE (25/1)	E McNamara	A O'Brien	Khalifa Sat	Amhran Na Bhfiann	16	2 34.43
2021	Godolphin's	ADAYAR (16/1)	A Kirby	C Appleby	Mojo Star	Hurricane Lane	11	2 36.85

ST LEGER STAKES (3y) Doncaster - 1 mile 6 furlongs 115 yards

Year	Owner	Winner and Price	Jockey	Trainer	Second	Third	Ran	Time
1984	I Allan's	COMMANCHE RUN (7/4)	L Piggott	L Cumani	Baynoun	Alphabatim	11	3 9.93
1985	Sheikh Mohammed's	OH SO SHARP (8/11)	S Cauthen	H Cecil	Phardante	Lanfranco	6	3 7.13
1986	Duchess of Norfolk's	MOON MADNESS (9/2)	Pat Eddery	J Dunlop	Celestial Storm	Untold	8	3 5.03
1987	L Freedman's	REFERENCE POINT (4/11)	S Cauthen	H Cecil	Mountain Kingdom	Dry Dock	7	3 5.91
1988	Lady Beaverbrook's	MINSTER SON (15/2)	W Carson	N A Graham	Diminuendo	Sheriff's Star	6	3 6.80
1989	C St George's (Run at Ayr)	MICHELOZZO (6/4)	S Cauthen	H Cecil	Sapience	Roseate Tern	8	3 20.72
1990	M Arbib's	SNURGE (7/2)	T Quinn	P Cole	Hellenic	River God	8	3 8.78
1991	K Abdullah's	TOULON (5/2)	Pat Eddery	A Fabre	Saddlers' Hall	Micheletti	10	3 3.12
1992	W J Gredley's	USER FRIENDLY (7/4)	G Duffield	C Brittain	Sonus	Bonny Scot	7	3 3.48
1993	Mrs G A E Smith's	BOB'S RETURN (3/1)	P Robinson	M Tompkins	Armiger	Edbaysaan	8	3 7.85
1994	Sheikh Mohammed's	MOONAX (40/1)	Pat Eddery	B Hills	Broadway Flyer	Double Trigger	8	3 4.19
1995	Godolphin's	CLASSIC CLICHE (100/30)	L Dettori	S Bin Suroor	Minds Music	Istidaad	10	3 9.74
1996	Sheikh Mohammed's	SHANTOU (8/1)	L Dettori	J Gosden	Dushyantor	Samraan	11	3 5.10
1997	P Winfield's	SILVER PATRIARCH (5/4)	Pat Eddery	J Dunlop	Vertical Speed	The Fly	10	3 5.92
1998	Godolphin's	NEDAWI (5/2)	J Reid	S Bin Suroor	High and Low	Sunshine Street	9	3 6.92
1999	Godolphin's	MUTAFAWEQ (11/2)	R Hills	S Bin Suroor	Ramruma	Adair	9	3 3.61
2000	N Jones	MILLENARY (11/4)	T Quinn	J Dunlop	Air Marshall	Chimes At Midnight	11	3 2.75
2001	M Tabor & Mrs J Magnier's	MILAN (13/8)	M Kinane	A O'Brien	Demophilis	Mr Combustible	11	3 2.58
2002	Sir Neil Westbrook's	BOLLIN ERIC (7/1)	K Darley	T Easterby	Highest	Bandari	8	3 5.16
2003	Mrs J Magnier's	BRIAN BORU (5/4)	J P Spencer	A O'Brien	High Accolade	Phoenix Reach	12	3 2.92
2004	Godolphin's	RULE OF LAW (10/11)	K McEvoy	S Bin Suroor	Quiff	Tycoon	6	3 4.64
2005	Mrs J Magnier & M Tabor's	SCORPION (10/11)	L Dettori	A O'Brien	The Geezer	Tawqiee	6	3 19.00
2006	Mrs S Roy's (Run at York)	SIXTIES ICON (11/8)	L Dettori	J Noseda	The Last Drop	Red Rocks	11	2 57.20
2007	G Strawbridge's	LUCARNO (7/2)	J Fortune	J Gosden	Mahler	Honolulu	10	3 1.90
2008	Ballymacoll Stud's	CONDUIT (8/1)	L Dettori	Sir M Stoute	Unsung Heroine	Look Here	14	3 7.92
2009	Godolphin's	MASTERY (14/1)	T Durcan	S Bin Suroor	Kite Wood	Monitor Closely	8	3 4.81
2010	Ms R Hood & R Geffen's	ARCTIC COSMOS (12/1)	W Buick	J Gosden	Midas Touch	Corsica	10	3 3.12
2011	B Nielsen's	MASKED MARVEL (15/2)	W Buick	J Gosden	Brown Panther	Sea Moon	9	3 0.44
2012	Godolphin's	ENCKE (25/1)	M Barzalona	M Al Zarooni	Camelot	Michelangelo	9	3 3.81
2013	Derrick Smith & Mrs John Magnier & Michael Tabor's	LEADING LIGHT (7/2)	J O'Brien	A O'Brien	Talent	Galileo Rock	11	3 9.20
2014	Paul Smith's	KINGSTON HILL (9/4)	A Atzeni	R Varian	Romsdal	Snow Sky	12	3 5.42
2015	ORL, Sheikh Suhaim Al Thani & M Al Kubaisi's	SIMPLE VERSE (8/1)	A Atzeni	R Beckett	Bondi Beach	Fields of Athenry	7	3 7.12
2016	Mrs Jackie Cornwell's	HARBOUR LAW (22/1)	G Baker	Mrs L Mongan	Ventura Storm	Housesofparliament	9	3 5.48
2017	Derrick Smith & Mrs John Magnier & Michael Tabor's	CAPRI (3/1)	R Moore	A O'Brien	Crystal Ocean	Stradivarius	11	3 4.04
2018	Derrick Smith & Mrs John Magnier & Michael Tabor's	KEW GARDENS (3/1)	R Moore	A O'Brien	Lah Ti Dar	Southern France	12	3 3.34
2020	Galileo Chrome Partnership's	GALILEO CHROME (4/1)	T Marquand	J O'Brien	Berkshire Rocco	Pyledriver	11	3 1.94
2021	Godolphin's	HURRICANE LANE (8/11)	W Buick	C Appleby	Mojo Star	The Mediterranean	10	3 4.28

KING GEORGE VI AND QUEEN ELIZABETH STAKES Ascot - 1 mile 3 furlongs 211 yards

Year	Owner	Winner and Price	Jockey	Trainer	Second	Third	Ran	Time
1984	E Moller's	TEENOSO 4-9-7 (13/2)	L Piggott	G Wragg	Sadler's Wells	Tolomeo	13	2:27.95
1985	Lady Beaverbrook's	PETOSKI 3-8-8 (12/1)	W Carson	R Hern	Oh So Sharp	Rainbow Quest	12	2:27.61
1986	K Abdullah's	DANCING BRAVE 3-8-8 (6/4)	Pat Eddery	G Harwood	Shardari	Triptych	9	2:29.49
1987	L Freedman's	REFERENCE POINT 3-8-8 (11/10)	S Cauthen	H Cecil	Celestial Storm	Triptych	9	2:34.63
1988	Sheikh Ahmed Al Maktoum	MTOTO 5-9-7 (4/1)	M Roberts	A C Stewart	Unfuwain	Tony Bin	10	2:37.33
1989	Hamdan Al-Maktoum's	NASHWAN 3-8-8 (2/9)	W Carson	R Hern	Cacoethes	Top Class	7	2:32.27
1990	Sheikh Mohammed's	BELMEZ 3-8-9 (15/2)	M Kinane	H Cecil	Old Vic	Assatis	10	2:30.76
1991	F Salman's	GENEROUS 3-8-9 (4/6)	A Murro	P Cole	Sanglamore	Rock Hopper	11	2:28.99
1992	Mrs V K Payson's	ST JOVITE 3-8-9 (4/5)	S Craine	J Bolger	Saddlers' Hall	Opera House	8	2:30.85
1993	Sheikh Mohammed's	OPERA HOUSE 5-9-7 (8/1)	M Roberts	M Stoute	White Muzzle	Commander in Chief	8	2:33.94
1994	Sheikh Mohammed's	KING'S THEATRE 3-8-9 (12/1)	M Kinane	H Cecil	White Muzzle	Wagon Master	12	2:28.92
1995	Saeed Maktoum Al Maktoum's	LAMMTARRA 3-8-9 (9/4)	L Dettori	S Bin Suroor	Pentire	Strategic Choice	7	2:31.01
1996	Mollers Racing's	PENTIRE 4-9-7 (100/30)	M Hills	G Wragg	Classic Cliche	Shaamit	8	2:28.11
1997	Godolphin's	SWAIN 5-9-7 (16/1)	J Reid	S Bin Suroor	Pilsudski	Helissio	8	2:36.45
1998	Godolphin's	SWAIN 6-9-7 (11/2)	L Dettori	S Bin Suroor	High-Rise	Royal Anthem	8	2:29.06
1999	Godolphin's	DAYLAMI 5-9-7 (3/1)	L Dettori	S Bin Suroor	Nedawi	Fruits Of Love	8	2:29.35
2000	M Tabor's	MONTJEU 4-9-7 (1/3)	M Kinane	J Hammond	Fantastic Light	Daliapour	8	2:29.98
2001	Mrs J Magnier & M Tabor's	GALILEO 3-8-9 (1/2)	M Kinane	A O'Brien	Fantastic Light	Hightori	7	2:27.71
2002	Exors of the late Lord Weinstock's	GOLAN 4-9-7 (11/2)	K Fallon	Sir M Stoute	Nayef	Zindabad	12	2:29.70
2003	H H Aga Khan	ALAMSHAR 3-8-9 (3/2)	J Murtagh	J Oxx	Sulamani	Kris Kin	9	2:33.26
2004	Godolphin's	DOYEN 4-9-7 (11/10)	L Dettori	S Bin Suroor	Hard Buck	Sulamani	11	2:33.10
2005	H H Aga Khan's	AZAMOUR 4-9-7 (5/2)	M Kinane	J Oxx	Norse Dancer	Bago	12	2:28.20
2006	H H Aga Khan's (Run at Newbury)	HURRICANE RUN 4-9-7 (5/6)	C Soumillon	A Fabre	Electrocutionist	Heart's Cry	6	2:30.20
2007	Mrs J Magnier & M Tabor's	DYLAN THOMAS 4-9-7 (5/4)	J Murtagh	A O'Brien	Youmzain	Maraahel	7	2:31.10
2008	Mrs J Magnier & M Tabor's	DUKE OF MARMALADE 4-9-7 (4/6)	J Murtagh	A O'Brien	Papal Bull	Youmzain	8	2:27.91
2009	Ballymacoll Stud's	CONDUIT 4-9-7 (13/8)	R Moore	Sir M Stoute	Tartan Bearer	Ask	8	2:28.73
2010	Highclere Thoroughbred Racing (Adm. Rous)'s	HARBINGER 4-9-7 (4/1)	O Peslier	Sir M Stoute	Cape Blanco	Youmzain	6	2:26.78
2011	Lady Rothschild's	NATHANIEL 3-8-8 (11/2)	W Buick	J Gosden	Workforce	St Nicholas Abbey	5	2:35.07
2012	Gestut Burg Eberstein & Teruya Yoshida's	DANEDREAM 4-9-4 (9/1)	A Starke	P Schiergen	Nathaniel	St Nicholas Abbey	10	2:31.62
2013	Dr Christophe Berglar's	NOVELLIST 4-9-7 (13/2)	J Murtagh	A Wohler	Trading Leather	Hillstar	8	2:24.60
2014	Hamdan Al Maktoum Obaid	TAGHROODA 3-8-6 (7/2)	P Hanagan	J Gosden	Telescope	Mukhadram	8	2:28.13
2015	Sheikh Mohammed Obaid Al Maktoum's	POSTPONED 4-9-7 (6/1)	A Atzeni	L Cumani	Eagle Top	Romsdal	7	2:31.25
2016	D Smith, Mrs J Magnier & M Tabor's	HIGHLAND REEL 4-9-7 (13/8)	R Moore	A O'Brien	Wings of Desire	Dartmouth	7	2:28.97
2017	K Abdullah's	ENABLE 3-8-7 (5/4)	L Dettori	J Gosden	Ulysses	Idaho	10	2:36.22
2018	S Suhail's	POET'S WORD 5-9-7 (7/4)	J Doyle	Sir M Stoute	Crystal Ocean	Coronet	5	2:25.84
2019	K Abdullah's	ENABLE 5-9-4 (8/15)	L Dettori	J Gosden	Crystal Ocean	Waldgeist	11	2:32.42
2020	K Abdullah's	ENABLE 6-9-4 (4/9)	L Dettori	J Gosden	Sovereign	Japan	3	2:28.92
2021	Godolphin's	ADAYAR 3-8-10 (9/4)	W Buick	C Appleby	Mishriff	Love	5	2:26.54

PRIX DE L'ARC DE TRIOMPHE ParisLongchamp - 1 mile 4 furlongs

Year	Owner	Winner and Price	Jockey	Trainer	Second	Third	Ran	Time
1984	D Wildenstein's	SAGACE 4-9-4 (29/10)	Y Saint Martin	P Biancone	Northern Trick	All Along	22	2 39.10
1985	K Abdulla's	RAINBOW QUEST 4-9-4 (71/10)	P Eddery	J Tree	Sagace	Kozana	15	2 29.50

(The first two placings are reversed after the Stewards)

Year	Owner	Winner and Price	Jockey	Trainer	Second	Third	Ran	Time
1986	K Abdulla's	DANCING BRAVE 3-8-11 (11/10)	P Eddery	G Harwood	Bering	Triptych	15	2 27.70
1987	P de Moussac's	TREMPOLINO 3-8-11 (20/1)	P Eddery	A Fabre	Tony Bin	Triptych	11	2 26.30
1988	Mrs V Gaucci del Bono's	TONY BIN 5-9-4 (14/1)	J Reid	L Camici	Mtoto	Boyatino	24	2 26.30
1989	A Balzarini's	CARROLL HOUSE 4-9-4 (19/1)	M Kinane	M Jarvis	Behera	Saint Andrews	19	2 30.80
1990	B McNall's	SAUMAREZ 3-8-11 (15/1)	G Mosse	N Clement	Epervier Bleu	Snurge	21	2 29.80
1991	H Chalhoub's	SUAVE DANCER 3-8-11 (37/10)	C Asmussen	J Hammond	Magic Night	Pistolet Bleu	14	2 31.40
1992	O Lecerf's	SUBOTICA 4-9-4 (88/10)	T Jarnet	A Fabre	User Friendly	Vert Amande	14	2 39.00
1993	D Tsui's	URBAN SEA 4-9-1 (37/1)	E Saint Martin	J Lesbordes	White Muzzle	Opera House	18	2 37.90
1994	Sheikh Mohammed's	CARNEGIE 3-8-11 (3/1)	T Jarnet	A Fabre	Hernando	Apple Tree	23	2 31.10
1995	Saeed Maktoum Al Maktoum's	LAMMTARRA 3-8-11 (2/1)	L Dettori	A Fabre	Freedom Cry	Swain	20	2 31.80
1996	E Sarasola's	HELISSIO 3-8-11 (18/10)	O Peslier	E Lellouche	Pilsudski	Oscar Schindler	16	2 24.60
1997	D Wildenstein's	PEINTRE CELEBRE 3-8-11 (22/10)	O Peslier	A Fabre	Pilsudski	Borgia	16	2 34.50
1998	J-L Lagardere's	SAGAMIX 3-8-11 (5/2)	O Peslier	A Fabre	Leggera	Croco Rouge	18	2 38.50
1999	H H Aga Khan's	MONTJEU 3-8-11 (6/4)	M Kinane	J Oxx	El Condor Pasa	Tiger Hill	14	2 25.80
2000	H H Aga Khan's	SINNDAR 3-8-11 (6/4)	J Murtagh	J Oxx	Egyptband	Volvoreta	10	2 36.10
2001	Godolphin's	SAKHEE 4-9-5 (22/10)	L Dettori	S Bin Suroor	Aquarelliste	Sagacity	17	2 26.70
2002	Godolphin's	MARIENBARD 5-9-5 (158/10)	L Dettori	S Bin Suroor	Sulamani	High Chaparral	16	2 32.30
2003	H H Aga Khan's	DALAKHANI 3-8-11 (9/4)	C Soumillon	A De Royer-Dupre	Mubtaker	High Chaparral	13	2 32.30
2004	Niarchos Family's	BAGO 3-8-11 (11/4)	T Gillet	J E Pease	Cherry Mix	Ouija Board	13	2 25.00
2005	M Tabor's	HURRICANE RUN 3-8-11 (11/4)	K Fallon	A Fabre	Westerner	Bago	15	2 27.40
2006	K Abdulla's	RAIL LINK 3-8-11 (8/1)	S Pasquier	A Fabre	Pride	Hurricane Run	8	2 26.30

(Deep Impact disqualified from third place)

Year	Owner	Winner and Price	Jockey	Trainer	Second	Third	Ran	Time
2007	Mrs J Magnier & M Tabor's	DYLAN THOMAS 4-9-5 (11/2)	K Fallon	A O'Brien	Youmzain	Sagara	12	2 28.50
2008	H H Aga Khan's	ZARKAVA 3-8-8 (13/8)	C Soumillon	A De Royer-Dupre	Youmzain	Soldier of Fortune/It's Gino	16	2 28.80
2009	K Abdulla's	SEA THE STARS 3-8-11 (4/6)	M Kinane	J Oxx	Youmzain	Cavalryman	19	2 26.30
2010	K Abdulla's	WORKFORCE 3-8-11 (6/1)	R Moore	Sir M Stoute	Nakayama Festa	Sarafina	18	2 35.30
2011	Gestut Burg Eberstein & T Yoshida's	DANEDREAM 3-8-8 (20/1)	A Starke	Mme C Head-Maarek	Shareta	Snow Fairy	16	2 24.49
2012	Al Thani's	SOLEMIA 4-9-2 (33/1)	O Peslier	Mme C Head-Maarek	Orfevre	Masterstroke	18	2 37.68
2013	H E Sheikh Joaan Bin Hamad	TREVE 3-8-8 (9/2)	T Jarnet	Mme C Head-Maarek	Orfevre	Intello	17	2 32.04
2014	Al Shaqab Racing's	TREVE 4-9-2 (11/1)	T Jarnet	Mme C Head-Maarek	Flintshire	Taghrooda	20	2 26.05
2015	A E Oppenheimer's	GOLDEN HORN 3-8-11 (9/2)	L Dettori	J Gosden	Flintshire	New Bay	17	2 27.23
2016	M Tabor, D Smith & Mrs J Magnier's	FOUND 4-9-2 (6/1)	R Moore	A O'Brien	Highland Reel	Order of St George	16	2 23.61
2017	K Abdulla's (Run at Chantilly)	ENABLE 3-8-9 (10/11)	L Dettori	J Gosden	Cloth of Stars	Ulysses	18	2 28.69
2018	K Abdulla's	ENABLE 4-9-2 (Evs)	L Dettori	J Gosden	Sea Of Class	Cloth Of Stars	19	2 29.24
2019	Gestut Ammerland & Newsells Park's	WALDGEIST 5-9-5 (131/10)	P-C Boudot	A Fabre	Enable	Sottsass	12	2 31.97
2020	White Birch Farm's	SOTTSASS 4-9-5 (73/10)	C Demuro	J-C Rouget	In Swoop	Persian King	11	2 39.30
2021	Gestut Auenquelle's	TORQUATOR TASSO 4-9-5 (72/1)	R Piechulek	M Weiss	Tarnawa	Hurricane Lane	14	2 37.62

GRAND NATIONAL STEEPLECHASE Aintree - 4m 2f 74y (4m 4f before 2013)

Year	Winner and Price	Age & Weight	Jockey	Second	Third	Ran	Time
1976	RAG TRADE (14/1)	10 10:12	J Burke	Red Rum	Eyecatcher	32	9.20.90
1977	RED RUM (9/1)	12 11:8	T Stack	Churchtown Boy	Eyecatcher	42	9.30.30
1978	LUCIUS (14/1)	9 10:9	B R Davies	Sebastian V	Drumroan	37	9.33.90
1979	RUBSTIC (25/1)	10 10:0	M Barnes	Zongalero	Rough and Tumble	34	9.52.90
1980	BEN NEVIS (40/1)	12 10:12	Mr C Fenwick	Rough and Tumble	The Pilgarlic	30	10.17.40
1981	ALDANITI (10/1)	11 10:13	R Champion	Spartan Missile	Royal Mail	39	9.47.20
1982	GRITTAR (7/1)	9 11:5	Mr C Saunders	Hard Outlook	Loving Words	39	9.12.60
1983	CORBIERE (13/1)	8 11:4	B de Haan	Greasepaint	Yer Man	41	9.47.04
1984	HALLO DANDY (13/1)	10 10:2	N Doughty	Greasepaint	Corbiere	40	9.21.04
1985	LAST SUSPECT (50/1)	11 10:5	H Davies	Mr Snugfit	Corbiere	40	9.42.70
1986	WEST TIP (15/2)	9 10:11	R Dunwoody	Young Driver	Classified	40	9.33.00
1987	MAORI VENTURE (28/1)	11 10:13	S C Knight	The Tsarevich	Lean Ar Aghaidh	40	9.19.30
1988	RHYME 'N' REASON (10/1)	9 11:0	B Powell	Durham Edition	Monanore	40	9.53.50
1989	LITTLE POLVEIR (28/1)	12 10:3	J Frost	Durham Edition	The Thinker	40	10.06.80
1990	MR FRISK (16/1)	11 10:6	Mr M Armytage	Durham Edition	Rinus	38	8.47.80
1991	SEAGRAM (12/1)	11 10:6	N Hawke	Garrison Savannah	Auntie Dot	40	9.29.90
1992	PARTY POLITICS (14/1)	8 10:7	C Llewellyn	Romany King	Laura's Beau	40	9.06.30
1993	RACE VOID - FALSE START						
1994	MINNEHOMA (16/1)	11 10:8	R Dunwoody	Just So	Moorcroft Boy	36	10.18.80
1995	ROYAL ATHLETE (40/1)	12 10:6	J Titley	Party Politics	Over The Deel	35	9.04.00
1996	ROUGH QUEST (7/1)	10 10:7	M Fitzgerald	Encore Un Peu	Superior Finish	27	9.00.80
1997	LORD GYLLENE (14/1)	9 10:0	A Dobbin	Suny Bay	Camelot Knight	36	9.05.80
1998	EARTH SUMMIT (7/1)	10 10:5	C Llewellyn	Suny Bay	Samlee	37	10.51.40
1999	BOBBYJO (10/1)	9 10:0	P Carberry	Blue Charm	Call It A Day	32	9.14.00
2000	PAPILLON (10/1)	9 10:12	R Walsh	Mely Moss	Niki Dee	40	9.09.70
2001	RED MARAUDER (33/1)	11 10:11	R Guest	Smarty	Blowing Wind	40	11.00.10
2002	BINDAREE (20/1)	8 10:4	J Culloty	What's Up Boys	Blowing Wind	40	9.09.00
2003	MONTY'S PASS (16/1)	10 10:7	B J Geraghty	Supreme Glory	Amberleigh House	40	9.21.70
2004	AMBERLEIGH HOUSE (16/1)	12 10:10	G Lee	Clan Royal	Lord Atterbury	39	9.20.30
2005	HEDGEHUNTER (7/1)	9 11:1	R Walsh	Royal Auclair	Simply Gifted	40	9.20.80
2006	NUMBERSIXVALVERDE (11/1)	10 10:8	N Madden	Hedgehunter	Clan Royal	40	9.41.00
2007	SILVER BIRCH (33/1)	10 10:6	R M Power	McKelvey	Slim Pickings	40	9.13.60
2008	COMPLY OR DIE (7/1)	9 10:9	T Murphy	King Johns Castle	Snowy Morning	40	9.16.60
2009	MON MOME (100/1)	9 11:0	L Treadwell	Comply Or Die	My Will	40	9.32.90
2010	DON'T PUSH IT (10/1)	10 11:5	A P McCoy	Black Apalachi	State Of Play	40	9.04.60
2011	BALLABRIGGS (14/1)	10 11:0	J Maguire	Oscar Time	Don't Push It	40	9.01.20
2012	NEPTUNE COLLONGES (33/1)	11 11:6	D Jacob	Sunnyhillboy	Seabass	40	9.05.10
2013	AURORAS ENCORE (66/1)	11 10:3	R Mania	Cappa Bleu	Teaforthree	40	9.12.00
2014	PINEAU DE RE (25/1)	11 10:6	L Aspell	Balthazar King	Double Seven	40	9.09.90
2015	MANY CLOUDS (25/1)	8 11:9	L Aspell	Saint Are	Monbeg Dude	39	8.56.80
2016	RULE THE WORLD (33/1)	9 10:7	D Mullins	The Last Samuri	Vics Canvas	39	9.29.00
2017	ONE FOR ARTHUR (14/1)	8 10:11	D Fox	Cause of Causes	Saint Are	40	9.03.50
2018	TIGER ROLL (10/1)	8 10:13	D Russell	Pleasant Company	Bless The Wings	38	9.40.10
2019	TIGER ROLL (4/1)	9 11:5	D Russell	Magic of Light	Rathvinden	40	9.01.00
2020	RACE CANCELLED - CORONAVIRUS PANDEMIC						
2021	MINELLA TIMES (11/1)	8 10:3	R Blackmore	Balko Des Flos	Any Second Now	40	9.15.16

WINNERS OF GREAT RACES

LINCOLN HANDICAP
Doncaster-1m

2012	**BRAE HILL** 6-9-1	22
2013	**LEVITATE** 5-8-4	22
2014	**OCEAN TEMPEST** 5-9-3	17
2015	**GABRIAL** 6-9-0	22
2016	**SECRET BRIEF** 4-9-4	22
2017	**BRAVERY** 4-9-1	22
2018	**ADDEYBB** 4-9-2	20
2019	**AUXERRE** 4-9-3	19
2020	RACE CANCELLED	
2021	**HAQEEQY** 4-8-12	18

GREENHAM STAKES (3y)
Newbury-7f

2012	**CASPAR NETSCHER** 9-0	5
2013	**OLYMPIC GLORY** 9-0	5
2014	**KINGMAN** 9-0	10
2015	**MUHAARAR** 9-0	9
* 2016	**TASLEET** 9-0	3
2017	**BARNEY ROY** 9-0	10
2018	**JAMES GARFIELD** 9-0	7
2019	**MOHAATHER** 9-0	8
2020	RACE CANCELLED	
2021	**CHINDIT** 9-0	11

* Run at Chelmsford City on Polytrack

EUROPEAN FREE HANDICAP (3y)
Newmarket-7f

2012	**TELWAAR** 8-11	7
2013	**GARSWOOD** 9-0	10
2014	**SHIFTING POWER** 9-1	6
2015	**HOME OF THE BRAVE** 8-13	5
2016	**IBN MALIK** 9-6	6
2017	**WHITECLIFFSOFDOVER** 9-7	7
2018	**ANNA NERIUM** 8-11	10
2019	**SHINE SO BRIGHT** 9-3	7
2020	RACE CANCELLED	
2021	**TACTICAL** 9-5	7

CRAVEN STAKES (3y)
Newmarket-1m

2012	**TRUMPET MAJOR** 9-1	12
2013	**TORONADO** 9-1	4
2014	**TOORMORE** 9-3	6
2015	**KOOL KOMPANY** 9-3	7
2016	**STORMY ANTARCTIC** 9-0	6
2017	**EMINENT** 9-0	4
2018	**MASAR** 9-0	6
2019	**SKARDU** 9-0	8
2020	RACE CANCELLED	
2021	**MASTER OF THE SEAS** 9-0	10

JOCKEY CLUB STAKES
Newmarket-1m 4f

2012	**AL KAZEEM** 4-8-12	8
2013	**UNIVERSAL** 4-8-12	4
2014	**GOSPEL CHOIR** 5-9-0	8
2015	**SECOND STEP** 4-9-0	4
2016	**EXOSPHERE** 4-9-0	6
2017	**SEVENTH HEAVEN** 4-9-1	5

2018	**DEFOE** 4-9-1	
2019	**COMMUNIQUE** 4-9-1	
2020	RACE CANCELLED	
2021	**SIR RON PRIESTLEY** 5-9-1	

SANDOWN MILE
Sandown-1m

2012	**PENITENT** 6-9-0	
2013	**TRUMPET MAJOR** 4-9-0	
2014	**TULLIUS** 6-9-1	
2015	**CUSTOM CUT** 6-9-5	
2016	**TOORMORE** 5-9-4	
2017	**SOVEREIGN DEBT** 8-9-1	
2018	**ADDEYBB** 4-9-1	
2019	**BEAT THE BANK** 5-9-1	
2020	RACE CANCELLED	
2021	**PALACE PIER** 4-9-1	

CHESTER VASE (3y)
Chester-1m 4f 63yds

2012	**MICKDAAM** 8-12	
2013	**RULER OF THE WORLD** 8-12	
2014	**ORCHESTRA** 9-0	
2015	**HANS HOLBEIN** 9-0	
2016	**US ARMY RANGER** 9-0	
2017	**VENICE BEACH** 9-0	
2018	**YOUNG RASCAL** 9-0	1
2019	**SIR DRAGONET** 9-0	
2020	RACE CANCELLED	
2021	**YOUTH SPIRIT** 9-0	

CHESTER CUP
Chester-2m 2f 140yds

2012	**ILE DE RE** 6-8-11	1
2013	**ADDRESS UNKNOWN** 6-9-0	1
2014	**SUEGIOO** 5-9-4	1
2015	**TRIP TO PARIS** 4-8-9	1
2016	**NO HERETIC** 8-8-13	1
2017	**MONTALY** 6-9-6	1
2018	**MAGIC CIRCLE** 6-9-3	1
2019	**MAKING MIRACLES** 4-9-0	1
2020	RACE CANCELLED	
2021	**FALCON EIGHT** 6-9-10	1

OAKS TRIAL (3y fillies)
Lingfield-1m 3f 133yds

* 2012	**VOW** 8-12	
2013	**SECRET GESTURE** 8-12	
2014	**HONOR BOUND** 9-0	1
2015	**TOUJOURS L'AMOUR** 9-0	1
2016	**SEVENTH HEAVEN** 9-0	
2017	**HERTFORD DANCER** 9-0	
2018	**PERFECT CLARITY** 9-0	
2019	**ANAPURNA** 9-0	
2020	**MISS YODA** 9-0	8
2021	**SHERBET LEMON** 9-0	

* Run over 1m4f on Polytrack

DERBY TRIAL (3y)
Lingfield-1m 3f 133yds
* 2012	**MAIN SEQUENCE** 8-12	8
2013	**NEVIS** 8-12	4
2014	**SNOW SKY** 9-0	9
2015	**KILIMANJARO** 9-0	5
2016	**HUMPHREY BOGART** 9-0	5
2017	**BEST SOLUTION** 9-0	8
2018	**KNIGHT TO BEHOLD** 9-0	9
2019	**ANTHONY VAN DYCK** 9-0	10
2020	**ENGLISH KING** 9-0	8
2021	**THIRD REALM** 9-0	6

* Run over 1m4f on Polytrack

MUSIDORA STAKES (3y fillies)
York-1m 2f 56yds
2012	**THE FUGUE** 8-12	6
2013	**LIBER NAUTICUS** 8-12	6
2014	**MADAME CHIANG** 9-0	9
2015	**STAR OF SEVILLE** 9-0	5
2016	**SO MI DAR** 9-0	7
2017	**SHUTTER SPEED** 9-0	7
2018	**GIVE AND TAKE** 9-0	7
2019	**NAUSHA** 9-0	10
2020	**ROSE OF KILDARE** 9-0	7
2021	**SNOWFALL** 9-0	7

DANTE STAKES (3y)
York-1m 2f 56yds
2012	**BONFIRE** 9-0	7
2013	**LIBERTARIAN** 9-0	8
2014	**THE GREY GATSBY** 9-0	7
2015	**GOLDEN HORN** 9-0	7
2016	**WINGS OF DESIRE** 9-0	12
2017	**PERMIAN** 9-0	10
2018	**ROARING LION** 9-0	9
2019	**TELECASTER** 9-0	8
2020	**THUNDEROUS** 9-0	6
2021	**HURRICANE LANE** 9-0	10

MIDDLETON STAKES
(fillies and mares)
York-1m 2f 56yds
2012	**IZZI TOP** 4-8-12	9
2013	**DALKALA** 4-9-0	8
2014	**AMBIVALENT** 5-9-0	8
2015	**SECRET GESTURE** 5-9-0	8
2016	**BEAUTIFUL ROMANCE** 4-9-0	7
2017	**BLOND ME** 5-9-0	4
2018	**CORONET** 4-9-0	7
2019	**LAH TI DAR** 4-9-0	6
2020	RACE CANCELLED	
2021	**QUEEN POWER** 5-9-0	5

YORKSHIRE CUP
York-1m 5f 188yds
2012	**RED CADEAUX** 6-9-0	8
2013	**GLEN'S DIAMOND** 5-9-0	8
2014	**GOSPEL CHOIR** 5-9-0	12
2015	**SNOW SKY** 4-9-0	6
2016	**CLEVER COOKIE** 8-9-1	5
2017	**DARTMOUTH** 5-9-1	8
2018	**STRADIVARIUS** 4-9-1	8
2019	**STRADIVARIUS** 5-9-4	8
2020	RACE CANCELLED	
2011	**SPANISH MISSION** 5-9-4	5

DUKE OF YORK STAKES
York-6f
2012	**TIDDLIWINKS** 6-9-7	13
2013	**SOCIETY ROCK** 6-9-13	17
2014	**MAAREK** 7-9-13	13
2015	**GLASS OFFICE** 4-9-8	15
2016	**MAGICAL MEMORY** 4-9-8	12
2017	**TASLEET** 4-9-8	12
2018	**HARRY ANGEL** 4-9-13	5
2019	**INVINCIBLE ARMY** 4-9-8	10
2020	RACE CANCELLED	
2021	**STARMAN** 4-9-8	12

LOCKINGE STAKES
Newbury-1m
2012	**FRANKEL** 4-9-0	6
2013	**FARHH** 5-9-0	12
2014	**OLYMPIC GLORY** 4-9-0	8
2015	**NIGHT OF THUNDER** 4-9-0	16
2016	**BELARDO** 4-9-0	12
2017	**RIBCHESTER** 4-9-0	8
2018	**RHODODENDRON** 4-8-11	14
2019	**MUSTASHRY** 6-9-0	14
2020	RACE CANCELLED	
2021	**PALACE PIER** 4-9-0	11

HENRY II STAKES
Sandown-2m 50yds
2012	**OPINION POLL** 6-9-4	10
2013	**GLOOMY SUNDAY** 4-8-11	10
2014	**BROWN PANTHER** 6-9-4	11
2015	**VENT DE FORCE** 4-9-0	7
2016	**PALLASATOR** 7-9-6	4
2017	**BIG ORANGE** 6-9-2	7
2018	**MAGIC CIRCLE** 6-9-2	8
2019	**DEE EX BEE** 4-9-4	5
2020	**DASHING WILLOUGHBY** 4-9-2	5
2021	**LISMORE** 4-8-12	5

TEMPLE STAKES
Haydock-5f
2012	**BATED BREATH** 5-9-4	12
2013	**KINGSGATE NATIVE** 8-9-4	10
2014	**HOT STREAK** 3-8-10	9
2015	**PEARL SECRET** 6-9-4	11
2016	**PROFITABLE** 4-9-4	11
2017	**PRICELESS** 4-9-1	12
2018	**BATTAASH** 4-9-9	11
2019	**BATTAASH** 4-9-2	5
2020	RACE CANCELLED	
2021	**LIBERTY BEACH** 4-9-1	6

BRIGADIER GERARD STAKES
Sandown-1m 1f 209yds
2012	**CARLTON HOUSE** 4-9-0	6
2013	**MUKHADRAM** 4-9-0	5
2014	**SHARESTAN** 6-9-0	3
2015	**WESTERN HYMN** 4-9-3	5
2016	**TIME TEST** 4-9-5	7
2017	**AUTOCRATIC** 4-9-0	7
2018	**POET'S WORD** 5-9-0	6
2019	**REGAL REALITY** 4-9-0	6
* 2020	**LORD NORTH** 4-9-0	5
2021	**EUCHEN GLEN** 8-9-3	4

* Run at Haydock Park (1m 2f 42yds)

CORONATION CUP
Epsom-1m 4f 6yds

2012	ST NICHOLAS ABBEY 5-9-0	6
2013	ST NICHOLAS ABBEY 6-9-0	5
2014	CIRRUS DES AIGLES 8-9-0	7
2015	PETHER'S MOON 5-9-0	4
2016	POSTPONED 5-9-0	6
2017	HIGHLAND REEL 5-9-0	10
2018	CRACKSMAN 4-9-0	6
2019	DEFOE 5-9-0	9
* 2020	GHAIYYATH 5-9-0	7
2021	PYLEDRIVER 4-9-0	6

* Run at Newmarket

CHARITY SPRINT HANDICAP
York-6f

2012	SHOLAAN 8-9	17
2013	BODY AND SOUL 8-11	19
2014	SEE THE SUN 8-7	20
2015	TWILIGHT SON 8-10	16
2016	MR LUPTON 9-7	17
2017	GOLDEN APOLLO 8-3	18
2018	ENCRYPTED 8-8	20
2019	RECON MISSION 9-2	22
2020	RACE CANCELLED	
2021	FIRST FOLIO 9-3	17

QUEEN ANNE STAKES
Ascot-1m (st)

2012	FRANKEL 4-9-0	11
2013	DECLARATION OF WAR 4-9-0	13
2014	TORONADO 4-9-0	10
2015	SOLOW 5-9-0	8
2016	TEPIN 5-8-11	13
2017	RIBCHESTER 4-9-0	16
2018	ACCIDENTAL AGENT 4-9-0	15
2019	LORD GLITTERS 6-9-0	11
2020	CIRCUS MAXIMUS 4-9-0	15
2021	PALACE PIER 4-9-0	11

PRINCE OF WALES'S STAKES
Ascot-1m 2f

2012	SO YOU THINK 6-9-0	11
2013	AL KAZEEM 5-9-0	11
2014	THE FUGUE 5-8-11	8
2015	FREE EAGLE 4-9-0	9
2016	MY DREAM BOAT 4-9-0	11
2017	HIGHLAND REEL 5-9-0	8
2018	POET'S WORD 5-9-0	7
2019	CRYSTAL OCEAN 5-9-0	8
2020	LORD NORTH 4-9-0	7
2021	LOVE 4-8-11	6

ST JAMES'S PALACE STAKES (3y)
Ascot-7f 213yds (rnd)

2012	MOST IMPROVED 9-0	16
2013	DAWN APPROACH 9-0	9
2014	KINGMAN 9-0	7
2015	GLENEAGLES 9-0	5
2016	GALILEO GOLD 9-0	7
2017	BARNEY ROY 9-0	8
2018	WITHOUT PAROLE 9-0	10
2019	CIRCUS MAXIMUS 9-0	11
2020	PALACE PIER 9-0	7
2021	POETIC FLARE 9-0	13

COVENTRY STAKES (2y)
Ascot-6f

2012	DAWN APPROACH 9-1	22
2013	WAR COMMAND 9-1	15
2014	THE WOW SIGNAL 9-1	15
2015	BURATINO 9-1	17
2016	CARAVAGGIO 9-1	18
2017	RAJASINGHE 9-1	18
2018	CALYX 9-1	23
2019	ARIZONA 9-1	17
2020	NANDO PARRADO 9-1	15
2021	BERKSHIRE SHADOW 9-1	17

KING EDWARD VII STAKES (3y)
Ascot-1m 4f

2012	THOMAS CHIPPENDALE 8-12	5
2013	HILLSTAR 8-12	8
2014	EAGLE TOP 9-0	9
2015	BALIOS 9-0	7
2016	ACROSS THE STARS 9-0	9
2017	PERMIAN 9-0	12
2018	OLD PERSIAN 9-0	9
2019	JAPAN 9-0	8
2020	PYLEDRIVER 9-0	6
2021	ALENQUER 9-0	6

JERSEY STAKES (3y)
Ascot-7f

2012	ISHVANA 8-12	22
2013	GALE FORCE TEN 9-1	21
2014	MUSTAJEEB 9-4	23
2015	DUTCH CONNECTION 9-4	16
2016	RIBCHESTER 9-6	19
2017	LE BRIVIDO 9-1	20
2018	EXPERT EYE 9-1	21
2019	SPACE TRAVELLER 9-1	14
2020	MOLATHAM 9-1	13
2021	CREATIVE FORCE 9-1	18

DUKE OF CAMBRIDGE STAKES
(fillies & mares)
Ascot-1m (st)

2012	JOVIALITY 4-8-12	13
2013	DUNTLE 4-8-12	9
2014	INTEGRAL 4-9-0	14
2015	AMAZING MARIA 4-9-0	6
2016	USHERETTE 4-9-3	14
2017	QEMAH 4-9-0	14
2018	ALJAZZI 5-9-0	11
2019	MOVE SWIFTLY 4-9-0	7
2020	NAZEEF 4-9-0	10
2021	INDIE ANGEL 4-9-0	12

QUEEN MARY STAKES (2y fillies)
Ascot-5f

2012	CEILING KITTY 8-12	27
2013	RIZEENA 8-12	21
2014	ANTHEM ALEXANDER 9-0	21
2015	ACAPULCO 9-0	20
2016	LADY AURELIA 9-0	17
2017	HEARTACHE 9-0	23
2018	SIGNORA CABELLO 9-0	22
2019	RAFFLE PRIZE 9-0	25
2020	CAMPANELLE 9-0	18
2021	QUICK SUZY 9-0	21

CORONATION STAKES (3y fillies)
Ascot-7f 213yds (rnd)

2012	**FALLEN FOR YOU** 9-0	10
2013	**SKY LANTERN** 9-0	17
2014	**RIZEENA** 9-0	12
2015	**ERVEDYA** 9-0	9
2016	**QEMAH** 9-0	13
2017	**WINTER** 9-0	7
2018	**ALPHA CENTAURI** 9-0	12
2019	**WATCH ME** 9-0	9
2020	**ALPINE STAR** 9-0	7
2021	**ALCOHOL FREE** 9-0	11

COMMONWEALTH CUP (3y)
Ascot-6f

2015	**MUHAARAR** 9-3	18
2016	**QUIET REFLECTION** 9-0	10
2017	**CARAVAGGIO** 9-3	12
2018	**EQTIDAAR** 9-3	22
2019	**ADVERTISE** 9-3	9
2020	**GOLDEN HORDE** 9-0	16
2021	**CAMPANELLE** 8-11	15

ROYAL HUNT CUP
Ascot-1m (st)

2012	**PRINCE OF JOHANNE** 6-9-3	30
2013	**BELGIAN BILL** 5-8-11	28
2014	**FIELD OF DREAM** 7-9-1	28
2015	**GM HOPKINS** 4-9-3	30
2016	**PORTAGE** 4-9-5	28
2017	**ZHUI FENG** 4-9-0	29
2018	**SETTLE FOR BAY** 4-9-1	30
2019	**AFAAK** 5-9-3	28
2020	**DARK VISION** 4-9-1	23
2021	**REAL WORLD** 4-8-6	30

QUEEN'S VASE (3y)
Ascot-1m 6f 34yds (2m before 2017)

2012	**ESTIMATE** 8-12	10
2013	**LEADING LIGHT** 9-4	15
2014	**HARTNELL** 9-3	10
2015	**ALOFT** 9-3	13
2016	**SWORD FIGHTER** 9-3	18
2017	**STRADIVARIUS** 9-0	13
2018	**KEW GARDENS** 9-0	12
2019	**DASHING WILLOUGHBY** 9-0	9
2020	**SANTIAGO** 9-0	8
2021	**KEMARI** 9-0	13

DIAMOND JUBILEE STAKES
Ascot-6f (Golden Jubilee Stakes before 2012)

2012	**BLACK CAVIAR** 6-9-1	14
2013	**LETHAL FORCE** 4-9-4	18
2014	**SLADE POWER** 5-9-4	14
2015	**UNDRAFTED** 5-9-3	15
2016	**TWILIGHT SON** 4-9-3	9
2017	**THE TIN MAN** 5-9-3	19
2018	**MERCHANT NAVY** 3-9-3	12
2019	**BLUE POINT** 5-9-3	17
2020	**HELLO YOUMZAIN** 4-9-3	10
2021	**DREAM OF DREAMS** 7-9-3	12

NORFOLK STAKES (2y)
Ascot-5f

2012	**RECKLESS ABANDON** 9-1	11
2013	**NO NAY NEVER** 9-1	14
2014	**BAITHA ALGA** 9-1	9
2015	**WATERLOO BRIDGE** 9-1	10
2016	**PRINCE OF LIR** 9-1	11
2017	**SIOUX NATION** 9-1	17
2018	**SHANG SHANG SHANG** 8-12	10
2019	**A'ALI** 9-1	14
2020	**THE LIR JET** 9-1	12
2021	**PERFECT POWER** 9-1	15

GOLD CUP
Ascot-2m 4f

2012	**COLOUR VISION** 4-9-0	9
2013	**ESTIMATE** 4-8-11	14
2014	**LEADING LIGHT** 4-9-0	12
2015	**TRIP TO PARIS** 4-9-0	12
2016	**ORDER OF ST GEORGE** 4-9-0	17
2017	**BIG ORANGE** 6-9-2	14
2018	**STRADIVARIUS** 4-9-1	9
2019	**STRADIVARIUS** 5-9-2	11
2020	**STRADIVARIUS** 6-9-2	8
2021	**SUBJECTIVIST** 4-9-1	12

RIBBLESDALE STAKES (3y fillies)
Ascot-1m 4f

2012	**PRINCESS HIGHWAY** 8-12	14
2013	**RIPOSTE** 8-12	9
2014	**BRACELET** 9-0	12
2015	**CURVY** 9-0	10
2016	**EVEN SONG** 9-0	14
2017	**CORONET** 9-0	12
2018	**MAGIC WAND** 9-0	10
2019	**STAR CATCHER** 9-0	11
2020	**FRANKLY DARLING** 9-0	11
2021	**LOVING DREAM** 9-0	13

HARDWICKE STAKES
Ascot-1m 4f

2012	**SEA MOON** 4-9-0	12
2013	**THOMAS CHIPPENDALE** 4-9-0	8
2014	**TELESCOPE** 4-9-1	10
2015	**SNOW SKY** 4-9-1	7
2016	**DARTMOUTH** 4-9-1	9
2017	**IDAHO** 4-9-1	12
2018	**CRYSTAL OCEAN** 4-8-12	5
2019	**DEFOE** 5-9-1	8
2020	**FANNY LOGAN** 4-8-12	9
2021	**WONDERFUL TONIGHT** 4-8-12	10

WOKINGHAM STAKES
Ascot-6f

2012	**DANDY BOY** 6-9-8	28
2013	**YORK GLORY** 5-9-2	26
2014	**BACCARAT** 5-9-2	28
2015	**INTERCEPTION** 5-9-3	25
2016	**OUTBACK TRAVELLER** 5-9-1	28
2017	**OUT DO** 8-8-13	28
2018	**BACCHUS** 4-9-6	28
2019	**CAPE BYRON** 5-9-5	26
2020	**HEY JONESY** 5-9-3	22
2021	**ROHAAN** 3-9-8	21

KING'S STAND STAKES
Ascot-5f

2012	**LITTLE BRIDGE** 6-9-4	22
2013	**SOLE POWER** 6-9-4	19
2014	**SOLE POWER** 7-9-4	16
2015	**GOLDREAM** 6-9-4	18
2016	**PROFITABLE** 4-9-4	17
2017	**LADY AURELIA** 3-8-9	17
2018	**BLUE POINT** 4-9-4	14
2019	**BLUE POINT** 5-9-4	12
2020	**BATTAASH** 6-9-4	11
2021	**OXTED** 5-9-5	16

NORTHUMBERLAND PLATE
Newcastle-2m 56y Tapeta (2m 19y turf before 2016)

2012	**ILE DE RE** 6-9-3	16
2013	**TOMINATOR** 6-9-10	18
2014	**ANGEL GABRIAL** 5-8-12	19
2015	**QUEST FOR MORE** 5-9-4	19
2016	**ANTIQUARIUM** 4-9-5	20
2017	**HIGHER POWER** 5-9-9	20
2018	**WITHHOLD** 5-9-1	20
2019	**WHO DARES WINS** 7-9-1	19
2020	**CARAVAN OF HOPE** 4-8-5	18
2021	**NICHOLAS T** 9-8-10	20

ECLIPSE STAKES
Sandown-1m 1f 209yds

2012	**NATHANIEL** 4-9-7	9
2013	**AL KAZEEM** 5-9-7	7
2014	**MUKHADRAM** 5-9-7	9
2015	**GOLDEN HORN** 3-8-10	5
2016	**HAWKBILL** 3-8-10	9
2017	**ULYSSES** 4-9-7	7
2018	**ROARING LION** 3-8-11	8
2019	**ENABLE** 5-9-4	8
2020	**GHAIYYATH** 5-9-3	7
2021	**ST MARK'S BASILICA** 3-8-11	4

LANCASHIRE OAKS
(fillies and mares)
Haydock-1m 3f 175yds

2012	**GREAT HEAVENS** 3-8-6	9
2013	**EMIRATES QUEEN** 4-9-5	8
2014	**POMOLOGY** 4-9-5	9
2015	**LADY TIANA** 4-9-5	10
2016	**ENDLESS TIME** 4-9-5	7
2017	**THE BLACK PRINCESS** 4-9-5	7
2018	**HORSEPLAY** 4-9-5	7
2019	**ENBIHAAR** 4-9-5	6
2020	**MANUELA DE VEGA** 4-9-5	5
2021	**ALPINISTA** 4-9-5	7

DUCHESS OF CAMBRIDGE STAKES
(2y fillies)
Newmarket-6f (Cherry Hinton Stakes before 2013)

2012	**SENDMYLOVETOROSE** 8-12	10
2013	**LUCKY KRISTALE** 8-12	8
2014	**ARABIAN QUEEN** 9-0	5
2015	**ILLUMINATE** 9-0	9
2016	**ROLY POLY** 9-0	10
2017	**CLEMMIE** 9-0	8
2018	**PRETTY POLLYANNA** 9-0	7
2019	**RAFFLE PRIZE** 9-3	7
2020	**DANDALLA** 9-0	7
2021	**SANDRINE** 9-0	8

BUNBURY CUP
Newmarket-7f

2012	**BONNIE BRAE** 5-9-9	15
2013	**FIELD OF DREAM** 6-9-7	19
2014	**HEAVEN'S GUEST** 4-9-3	13
2015	**RENE MATHIS** 5-9-1	17
2016	**GOLDEN STEPS** 5-9-0	16
2017	**ABOVE THE REST** 6-8-10	18
2018	**BURNT SUGAR** 6-9-1	18
2019	**VALE OF KENT** 4-9-4	17
2020	**MOTAKHAYYEL** 4-9-7	17
2021	**MOTAKHAYYEL** 5-9-10	18

PRINCESS OF WALES'S STAKES
Newmarket-1m 4f

2012	**FIORENTE** 4-9-2	7
2013	**AL KAZEEM** 4-9-5	6
2014	**CAVALRYMAN** 8-9-2	8
2015	**BIG ORANGE** 4-9-2	8
2016	**BIG ORANGE** 5-9-2	7
2017	**HAWKBILL** 4-9-2	6
2018	**BEST SOLUTION** 4-9-6	7
2019	**COMMUNIQUE** 4-9-2	6
2020	**DAME MALLIOT** 4-9-3	7
2021	**SIR RON PRIESTLEY** 5-9-9	5

JULY STAKES (2y)
Newmarket-6f

2012	**ALHEBAYEB** 8-12	7
2013	**ANJAAL** 8-12	11
2014	**IVAWOOD** 9-0	12
2015	**SHALAA** 9-0	9
2016	**MEHMAS** 9-0	9
2017	**CARDSHARP** 9-0	12
2018	**ADVERTISE** 9-0	8
2019	**ROYAL LYTHAM** 9-0	7
2020	**TACTICAL** 9-0	9
2021	**LUSAIL** 9-0	11

FALMOUTH STAKES
(fillies & mares)
Newmarket-1m

2012	**GIOFRA** 4-9-5	10
2013	**ELUSIVE KATE** 4-9-5	4
2014	**INTEGRAL** 4-9-7	7
2015	**AMAZING MARIA** 4-9-7	7
2016	**ALICE SPRINGS** 3-8-12	7
2017	**ROLY POLY** 3-8-12	7
2018	**ALPHA CENTAURI** 3-8-12	7
2019	**VERACIOUS** 4-9-7	7
2020	**NAZEEF** 4-9-7	6
2021	**SNOW LANTERN** 3-8-12	13

SUPERLATIVE STAKES (2y)
Newmarket-7f

2012	**OLYMPIC GLORY** 9-0	9
2013	**GOOD OLD BOY LUKEY** 9-0	8
2014	**ESTIDHKAAR** 9-1	8
2015	**BIRCHWOOD** 9-1	8
2016	**BOYNTON** 9-1	9
2017	**GUSTAV KLIMT** 9-1	10
2018	**QUORTO** 9-1	8
2019	**MYSTERY POWER** 9-1	7
2020	**MASTER OF THE SEAS** 9-1	10
2021	**NATIVE TRAIL** 9-1	9

JULY CUP
Newmarket-6f

2012	**MAYSON** 4-9-5	12
2013	**LETHAL FORCE** 4-9-5	14
2014	**SLADE POWER** 5-9-6	13
2015	**MUHAARAR** 3-9-0	14
2016	**LIMATO** 4-9-6	18
2017	**HARRY ANGEL** 3-9-0	10
2018	**U S NAVY FLAG** 3-9-0	13
2019	**TEN SOVEREIGNS** 3-9-0	12
2020	**OXTED** 4-9-6	12
2021	**STARMAN** 4-9-6	19

WEATHERBYS SUPER SPRINT (2y)
Newbury-5f 34 yds

2012	**BODY AND SOUL** 7-12	22
2013	**PENIAPHOBIA** 8-8	24
2014	**TIGGY WIGGY** 9-1	22
2015	**LATHOM** 9-0	22
2016	**MRS DANVERS** 8-8	23
2017	**BENGALI BOYS** 8-7	23
2018	**GINGER NUT** 8-5	25
2019	**BETTYS HOPE** 8-4	24
2020	**HAPPY ROMANCE** 8-5	25
2021	**GUBBASS** 8-10	22

SUMMER MILE
Ascot-7f 213yds (rnd)

2012	**FANUNALTER** 6-9-1	8
2013	**ALJAMAAHEER** 4-9-1	11
2014	**GUEST OF HONOUR** 5-9-1	9
2015	**AROD** 4-9-1	6
2016	**MUTAKAYYEF** 5-9-1	10
2017	**MUTAKAYYEF** 6-9-1	8
2018	**BEAT THE BANK** 4-9-1	8
2019	**BEAT THE BANK** 5-9-4	8
2020	**MOHAATHER** 4-9-1	11
2021	**TILSIT** 4-9-1	9

PRINCESS MARGARET STAKES (2y fillies)
Ascot-6f

2012	**MAUREEN** 8-12	6
2013	**PRINCESS NOOR** 8-12	10
2014	**OSAILA** 9-0	8
2015	**BESHARAH** 9-0	6
2016	**FAIR EVA** 9-0	12
2017	**NYALETI** 9-0	7
2018	**ANGEL'S HIDEAWAY** 9-0	7
2019	**UNDER THE STARS** 9-0	9
2020	**SANTOSHA** 9-0	7
2021	**ZAIN CLAUDETTE** 9-0	10

LENNOX STAKES
Goodwood-7f

2012	**CHACHAMAIDEE** 5-8-13	7
2013	**GARSWOOD** 3-8-9	10
2014	**ES QUE LOVE** 5-9-3	7
2015	**TOORMORE** 4-9-3	7
2016	**DUTCH CONNECTION** 4-9-3	8
2017	**BRETON ROCK** 7-9-3	13
2018	**SIR DANCEALOT** 4-9-3	12
2019	**SIR DANCEALOT** 5-9-3	9
2020	**SPACE BLUES** 4-9-3	11
2021	**KINROSS** 4-9-3	8

STEWARDS' CUP
Goodwood-6f

2012	**HAWKEYETHENOO** 6-9-9	27
2013	**REX IMPERATOR** 4-9-4	27
2014	**INTRINSIC** 4-8-11	24
2015	**MAGICAL MEMORY** 3-8-12	27
2016	**DANCING STAR** 3-8-12	27
2017	**LANCELOT DU LAC** 7-9-5	26
2018	**GIFTED MASTER** 5-9-6	26
2019	**KHAADEM** 3-9-6	27
2020	**SUMMERGHAND** 6-9-10	27
2021	**COMMANCHE FALLS** 4-9-1	27

GORDON STAKES (3y)
Goodwood-1m 4f

2012	**NOBLE MISSION** 9-0	7
2013	**CAP O'RUSHES** 9-0	7
2014	**SNOW SKY** 9-1	7
2015	**HIGHLAND REEL** 9-1	9
2016	**ULYSSES** 9-1	9
2017	**CRYSTAL OCEAN** 9-1	5
2018	**CROSS COUNTER** 9-1	4
2019	**NAYEF ROAD** 9-1	9
2020	**MOGUL** 9-1	6
2021	**OTTOMAN EMPEROR** 9-1	8

VINTAGE STAKES (2y)
Goodwood-7f

2012	**OLYMPIC GLORY** 9-3	10
2013	**TOORMORE** 9-0	12
2014	**HIGHLAND REEL** 9-1	8
2015	**GALILEO GOLD** 9-1	8
2016	**WAR DECREE** 9-1	9
2017	**EXPERT EYE** 9-1	10
2018	**DARK VISION** 9-1	12
2019	**PINATUBO** 9-1	7
2020	**BATTLEGROUND** 9-1	10
2021	**ANGEL BLEU** 9-1	6

SUSSEX STAKES
Goodwood-1m

2012	**FRANKEL** 4-9-7	4
2013	**TORONADO** 3-8-13	7
2014	**KINGMAN** 3-9-0	4
2015	**SOLOW** 5-9-8	8
2016	**THE GURKHA** 3-9-0	10
2017	**HERE COMES WHEN** 7-9-8	7
2018	**LIGHTNING SPEAR** 7-9-8	8
2019	**TOO DARN HOT** 3-9-0	7
2020	**MOHAATHER** 4-9-8	7
2021	**ALCOHOL FREE** 3-8-11	9

RICHMOND STAKES (2y)
Goodwood-6f

2012	**HEAVY METAL** 9-0	8
2013	**SAAYERR** 9-0	10
2014	**IVAWOOD** 9-3	8
2015	**SHALAA** 9-3	8
2016	**MEHMAS** 9-3	4
2017	**BARRAQUERO** 9-0	7
2018	**LAND FORCE** 9-0	9
2019	**GOLDEN HORDE** 9-0	8
2020	**SUPREMACY** 9-0	7
2021	**ASYMMETRIC** 9-0	7

KING GEORGE STAKES
Goodwood-5f
2012	**ORTENSIA** 7-9-5	17
2013	**MOVIESTA** 3-8-12	17
2014	**TAKE COVER** 7-9-1	15
2015	**MUTHMIR** 5-9-6	15
2016	**TAKE COVER** 9-9-2	17
2017	**BATTAASH** 3-8-13	11
2018	**BATTAASH** 4-9-5	11
2019	**BATTAASH** 5-9-5	8
2020	**BATTAASH** 6-9-7	7
2021	**SUESA** 3-8-9	13

GOODWOOD CUP
Goodwood-2m
2012	**SADDLER'S ROCK** 4-9-7	10
2013	**BROWN PANTHER** 5-9-7	14
2014	**CAVALRYMAN** 8-9-8	8
2015	**BIG ORANGE** 4-9-8	11
2016	**BIG ORANGE** 5-9-8	14
2017	**STRADIVARIUS** 3-8-8	14
2018	**STRADIVARIUS** 4-9-9	7
2019	**STRADIVARIUS** 5-9-9	9
2020	**STRADIVARIUS** 6-9-9	7
2021	**TRUESHAN** 5-9-9	8

MOLECOMB STAKES (2y)
Goodwood-5f
2012	**BUNGLE INTHEJUNGLE** 9-0	10
2013	**BROWN SUGAR** 9-0	8
2014	**COTAI GLORY** 9-1	8
2015	**KACHY** 9-1	10
2016	**YALTA** 9-1	9
2017	**HAVANA GREY** 9-1	10
2018	**RUMBLE INTHEJUNGLE** 9-1	11
2019	**LIBERTY BEACH** 8-12	13
2020	**STEEL BULL** 9-1	10
2021	**ARMOR** 9-1	11

NASSAU STAKES
(fillies and mares)
Goodwood-1m 1f 197yds
2012	**THE FUGUE** 3-8-11	8
2013	**WINSILI** 3-8-11	14
2014	**SULTANINA** 4-9-7	6
2015	**LEGATISSIMO** 3-8-12	9
2016	**MINDING** 3-8-11	5
2017	**WINTER** 3-8-13	6
2018	**WILD ILLUSION** 3-8-13	6
2019	**DEIRDRE** 5-9-7	9
2020	**FANCY BLUE** 3-8-12	6
2021	**LADY BOWTHORPE** 5-9-7	6

HUNGERFORD STAKES
Newbury-7f
2012	**LETHAL FORCE** 3-8-12	9
2013	**GREGORIAN** 4-9-3	5
2014	**BRETON ROCK** 4-9-5	6
2015	**ADAAY** 3-9-2	11
2016	**RICHARD PANKHURST** 4-9-6	6
2017	**MASSAAT** 4-9-6	8
2018	**SIR DANCEALOT** 4-9-9	8
2019	**GLORIOUS JOURNEY** 4-9-6	7
2020	**DREAM OF DREAMS** 6-9-6	9
2021	**SACRED** 3-8-11	10

GEOFFREY FREER STAKES
Newbury-1m 5f 61yds
2012	**MOUNT ATHOS** 5-9-4	6
2013	**ROYAL EMPIRE** 4-9-4	10
2014	**SEISMOS** 6-9-4	11
2015	**AGENT MURPHY** 4-9-5	6
2016	**KINGS FETE** 5-9-7	6
2017	**DEFOE** 3-8-10	8
2018	**HAMADA** 4-9-5	6
2019	**TECHNICIAN** 3-8-10	5
2020	**HUKUM** 3-8-9	7
2021	**HUKUM** 4-9-8	10

INTERNATIONAL STAKES
York-1m 2f 56yds
2012	**FRANKEL** 4-9-5	9
2013	**DECLARATION OF WAR** 4-9-5	6
2014	**AUSTRALIA** 3-8-12	6
2015	**ARABIAN QUEEN** 3-8-9	7
2016	**POSTPONED** 5-9-6	12
2017	**ULYSSES** 4-9-6	7
2018	**ROARING LION** 3-8-13	8
2019	**JAPAN** 3-8-13	9
2020	**GHAIYYATH** 5-9-6	5
2021	**MISHRIFF** 4-9-6	5

GREAT VOLTIGEUR STAKES (3y)
York-1m 3f 188yds
2012	**THOUGHT WORTHY** 8-12	6
2013	**TELESCOPE** 8-12	7
2014	**POSTPONED** 9-0	9
2015	**STORM THE STARS** 9-0	7
2016	**IDAHO** 9-0	6
2017	**CRACKSMAN** 9-0	6
2018	**OLD PERSIAN** 9-3	9
2019	**LOGICIAN** 9-0	5
2020	**PYLEDRIVER** 9-3	8
2021	**YIBIR** 9-0	8

LOWTHER STAKES
(2y fillies)
York-6f
2012	**ROSDHU QUEEN** 8-12	10
2013	**LUCKY KRISTALE** 9-1	9
2014	**TIGGY WIGGY** 9-0	9
2015	**BESHARAH** 9-0	9
2016	**QUEEN KINDLY** 9-0	9
2017	**THREADING** 9-0	9
2018	**FAIRYLAND** 9-0	9
2019	**LIVING IN THE PAST** 9-0	10
2020	**MISS AMULET** 9-0	14
2021	**ZAIN CLAUDETTE** 9-0	10

YORKSHIRE OAKS
(fillies and mares)
York-1m 3f 188yds
2012	**SHARETA** 4-9-7	6
2013	**THE FUGUE** 4-9--7	7
2014	**TAPESTRY** 3-8-11	9
2015	**PLEASCACH** 3-8-11	11
2016	**SEVENTH HEAVEN** 3-8-11	12
2017	**ENABLE** 3-8-12	6
2018	**SEA OF CLASS** 3-8-12	8
2019	**ENABLE** 5-9-7	4
2020	**LOVE** 3-8-12	6
2021	**SNOWFALL** 3-8-12	7

EBOR HANDICAP
York-1m 5f 188yds
2012	**WILLING FOE** 5-9-2	19
2013	**TIGER CLIFF** 4-9-0	14
2014	**MUTUAL REGARD** 5-9-4	19
2015	**LITIGANT** 7-9-1	19
2016	**HEARTBREAK CITY** 6-9-1	20
2017	**NAKEETA** 6-9-0	19
2018	**MUNTAHAA** 5-9-9	20
2019	**MUSTAJEER** 6-9-5	22
2020	**FUJAIRA PRINCE** 6-9-8	21
2021	**SONNYBOYLISTON** 4-9-8	20

GIMCRACK STAKES (2y)
York-6f
2012	**BLAINE** 8-12	8
2013	**ASTAIRE** 8-12	7
2014	**MUHAARAR** 9-0	9
2015	**AJAYA** 9-0	9
2016	**BLUE POINT** 9-0	10
2017	**SANDS OF MALI** 9-0	10
2018	**EMARAATY ANA** 9-0	9
2019	**THREAT** 9-0	12
2020	**MINZAAL** 9-0	9
2021	**LUSAIL** 9-3	11

NUNTHORPE STAKES
York-5f
2012	**ORTENSIA** 7-9-8	19
2013	**JWALA** 4-9–8	17
2014	**SOLE POWER** 7-9-11	13
2015	**MECCA'S ANGEL** 4-9-10	19
2016	**MECCA'S ANGEL** 5-9-8	19
2017	**MARSHA** 4-9-8	11
2018	**ALPHA DELPHINI** 7-9-11	15
2019	**BATTAASH** 5-9-11	11
2020	**BATTAASH** 6-9-11	8
2021	**WINTER POWER** 3-9-6	14

LONSDALE CUP
York-2m 56yds
2012	**TIMES UP** 6 9-1	11
2013	**AHZEEMAH** 4 9-3	7
2014	**PALE MIMOSA** 5-9-0	7
2015	**MAX DYNAMITE** 5-9-3	8
2016	**QUEST FOR MORE** 6-9-3	7
2017	**MONTALY** 6-9-3	9
2018	**STRADIVARIUS** 4-9-6	9
2019	**STRADIVARIUS** 5-9-6	4
2020	**ENBIHAAR** 5 9-0	7
2021	**STRADIVARIUS** 7-9-3	4

PRESTIGE STAKES (2y fillies)
Goodwood-7f
2012	**OLLIE OLGA** 9-0	8
2013	**AMAZING MARIA** 9-0	7
2014	**MALABAR** 9-0	8
2015	**HAWKSMOOR** 9-0	9
2016	**KILMAH** 9-0	7
2017	**BILLESDON BROOK** 9-0	10
2018	**ANTONIA DE VEGA** 9-0	8
2019	**BOOMER** 9-0	7
2020	**ISABELLA GILES** 9-0	5
2021	**MISE EN SCENE** 9-0	9

CELEBRATION MILE
Goodwood-1m
2012	**PREMIO LOCO** 8-9-1	5
2013	**AFSARE** 6-9-1	8
2014	**BOW CREEK** 3-8-12	8
2015	**KODI BEAR** 3-8-12	6
2016	**LIGHTNING SPEAR** 5-9-4	5
2017	**LIGHTNING SPEAR** 6-9-4	6
2018	**BEAT THE BANK** 4-9-7	8
2019	**DUKE OF HAZZARD** 3-8-12	6
2020	**CENTURY DREAM** 6-9-4	6
2021	**LAVENDER'S BLUE** 5-9-1	7

SOLARIO STAKES (2y)
Sandown-7f 16yds
2012	**FANTASTIC MOON** 9-0	7
2013	**KINGMAN** 9-0	4
2014	**AKTABANTAY** 9-1	5
2015	**FIRST SELECTION** 9-1	10
2016	**SOUTH SEAS** 9-1	10
2017	**MASAR** 9-1	7
2018	**TOO DARN HOT** 9-1	6
2019	**POSITIVE** 9-1	6
2020	**ETONIAN** 9-1	7
2021	**REACH FOR THE MOON** 9-1	6

SPRINT CUP
Haydock-6f
2012	**SOCIETY ROCK** 5-9-3	13
2013	**GORDON LORD BYRON** 5-9-3	13
2014	**G FORCE** 3-9-1	17
2015	**TWILIGHT SON** 3-9-1	15
2016	**QUIET REFLECTION** 3-8-12	14
2017	**HARRY ANGEL** 3-9-1	11
2018	**THE TIN MAN** 6-9-3	12
2019	**HELLO YOUMZAIN** 3-9-1	11
2020	**DREAM OF DREAMS** 6-9-3	13
2021	**EMARAATY ANA** 6-9-3	16

SEPTEMBER STAKES
Kempton-1m 3f 219yds Polytrack
2012	**DANDINO** 5-9-4	9
2013	**PRINCE BISHOP** 6-9-4	10
2014	**PRINCE BISHOP** 7-9-12	7
2015	**JACK HOBBS** 3-9-3	7
2016	**ARAB SPRING** 6-9-5	6
2017	**CHEMICAL CHARGE** 5-9-5	6
2018	**ENABLE** 4-9-2	4
2019	**ROYAL LINE** 5-9-5	12
2020	**ENABLE** 6-9-9	6
2021	**HAMISH** 5-9-5	5

MAY HILL STAKES
(2y fillies)
Doncaster-1m

2012	CERTIFY 8-12	7
2013	IHTIMAL 8-12	7
2014	AGNES STEWART 9-0	8
2015	TURRET ROCKS 9-0	8
2016	RICH LEGACY 9-0	9
2017	LAURENS 9-0	8
2018	FLEETING 9-0	11
2019	POWERFUL BREEZE 9-0	9
2020	INDIGO GIRL 9-0	9
2021	INSPIRAL 9-0	6

PORTLAND HANDICAP
Doncaster-5f 143yds

2012	DOC HAY 5-8-11	20
2013	ANGELS WILL FALL 4-9-2	21
2014	MUTHMIR 4-9-7	20
2015	STEPS 7-9-7	20
2016	CAPTAIN COLBY 4-9-0	20
2017	SPRING LOADED 5-8-9	22
2018	A MOMENTOFMADNESS 5-9-4	21
2019	OXTED 3-9-4	22
2020	STONE OF DESTINY 3-9-4	21
2021	HURRICANE IVOR 4-9-10	16

PARK HILL STAKES
(fillies and mares)
Doncaster-1m 6f 115yd

2012	WILD COCO 4-9-4	9
2013	THE LARK 3-8--6	9
2014	SILK SARI 4-9-5	13
2015	GRETCHEN 3-8-7	11
2016	SIMPLE VERSE 4-9-5	12
2017	ALYSSA 4-9-5	10
2018	GOD GIVEN 4-9-5	7
2019	ENBIHAAR 4-9-5	8
2020	PISTA 3-8-9	7
2021	FREE WIND 3-8-9	8

DONCASTER CUP
Doncaster-2m 1f 197yds

2012	TIMES UP 6-9-1	10
2013	TIMES UP 7-9-3	7
2014	ESTIMATE 5-9-0	12
2015	PALLASATOR 6-9-3	11
2016	SHEIKHZAYEDROAD 7-9-3	8
2017	DESERT SKYLINE 3-8-5	9
2018	THOMAS HOBSON 8-9-5	8
2019	STRADIVARIUS 5-9-10	5
2020	SPANISH MISSION 4-9-5	7
2021	STRADIVARIUS 7-9-8	6

CHAMPAGNE STAKES (2y)
Doncaster-7f 6yds

2012	TORONADO 8-12	5
2013	OUTSTRIP 8-12	4
2014	ESTIDHKAAR 9-3	6
2015	EMOTIONLESS 9-0	6
2016	RIVET 9-0	6
2017	SEAHENGE 9-0	6
2018	TOO DARN HOT 9-0	6
2019	THREAT 9-3	6
2020	CHINDIT 9-0	7
2021	BAYSIDE BOY 9-0	4

PARK STAKES
Doncaster-7f 6yds

2012	LIBRANNO 4-9-4	8
2013	VIZTORIA 3-8-11	9
2014	ANSGAR 6-9-4	7
2015	LIMATO 3-9-0	15
2016	BRETON ROCK 6-9-4	8
2017	ACLAIM 4-9-4	8
2018	MUSTASHRY 5-9-4	9
2019	SIR DANCEALOT 5-9-7	5
2020	WICHITA 3-9-0	8
2021	GLORIOUS JOURNEY 6-9-4	6

FLYING CHILDERS STAKES (2y)
Doncaster-5f

2012	SIR PRANCEALOT 9-0	9
2013	GREEN DOOR 9-0	7
2014	BEACON 9-1	14
2015	GUTAIFAN 9-1	9
2016	ARDAD 9-1	11
2017	HEARTACHE 8-12	9
2018	SOLDIER'S CALL 9-1	9
2019	A'ALI 9-1	7
2020	UBETTABELIEVEIT 9-1	10
2021	CATURRA 9-1	11

AYR GOLD CUP
Ayr-6f

2012	CAPTAIN RAMIUS 6-9-0	26
2013	HIGHLAND COLORI 5-8-13	26
2014	LOUIS THE PIOUS 6-9-4	27
2015	DON'T TOUCH 3-9-1	25
2016	BRANDO 4-9-10	23
* 2017	DONJUAN TRIUMPHANT 4-9-10	17
2018	SON OF REST 4-9-3 dead heated with	
	BARON BOLT 5-8-12	24
2019	ANGEL ALEXANDER 3-8-13	24
2020	NAHAARR 4-9-5	24
2021	BIELSA 6-9-1	24
*Run at Haydock Park

MILL REEF STAKES (2y)
Newbury-6f 8yds

2012	MOOHAAJIM 9-1	8
2013	SUPPLICANT 9-1	7
2014	TOOCOOLFORSCHOOL 9-1	6
2015	RIBCHESTER 9-1	6
2016	HARRY ANGEL 9-1	7
2017	JAMES GARFIELD 9-1	9
2018	KESSAAR 9-1	7
2019	PIERRE LAPIN 9-1	8
2020	ALKUMAIT 9-1	8
2021	WINGS OF WAR 9-1	9

ROYAL LODGE STAKES (2y)
Newmarket-1m

2012	STEELER 8-12	8
2013	BERKSHIRE 8-12	5
2014	ELM PARK 9-0	6
2015	FOUNDATION 9-0	8
2016	BEST OF DAYS 9-0	8
2017	ROARING LION 9-0	6
2018	MOHAWK 9-0	7
2019	ROYAL DORNOCH 9-0	7
2020	NEW MANDATE 9-0	5
2021	ROYAL PATRONAGE 9-0	7

CHEVELEY PARK STAKES (2y fillies)
Newmarket-6f
2012	**ROSDHU QUEEN** 8-12	11
2013	**VORDA** 8-12	7
2014	**TIGGY WIGGY** 9-0	9
2015	**LUMIERE** 9-0	8
2016	**BRAVE ANNA** 9-0	6
2017	**CLEMMIE** 9-0	11
2018	**FAIRYLAND** 9-0	11
2019	**MILLISLE** 9-0	11
2020	**ALCOHOL FREE** 9-0	8
2021	**TENEBRISM** 9-0	12

SUN CHARIOT STAKES
(fillies and mares)
Newmarket-1m
2012	**SIYOUMA** 4-9-3	8
2013	**SKY LANTERN** 3-8-13	7
2014	**INTEGRAL** 4-9-3	7
2015	**ESOTERIQUE** 5-9-3	9
2016	**ALICE SPRINGS** 3-9-0	8
2017	**ROLY POLY** 3-9-0	13
2018	**LAURENS** 3-9-0	9
2019	**BILLESDON BROOK** 4-9-3	9
2020	**NAZEEF** 4-9-3	12
2021	**SAFFRON BEACH** 3-9-0	12

CAMBRIDGESHIRE
Newmarket-1m 1f
2012	**BRONZE ANGEL** 3-8-8	33
2013	**EDUCATE** 4-9-9	31
2014	**BRONZE ANGEL** 5-8-8	31
2015	**THIRD TIME LUCKY** 3-8-4	34
2016	**SPARK PLUG** 5-9-4	34
2017	**DOLPHIN VISTA** 4-8-7	31
2018	**WISSAHICKON** 3-9-5	33
2019	**LORD NORTH** 3-8-10	30
2020	**MAJESTIC DAWN** 4-8-8	27
2021	**BEDOUIN'S STORY** 6-9-5	26

CUMBERLAND LODGE STAKES
Ascot-1m 4f
2012	**HAWAAFEZ** 4-8-11	6
2013	**SECRET NUMBER** 3-8-7	7
2014	**PETHER'S MOON** 4-9-6	5
2015	**STAR STORM** 3-8-8	8
2016	**MOVE UP** 3-8-13	9
2017	**DANEHILL KODIAC** 4-9-2	9
2018	**LARAAIB** 4-9-2	5
2019	**MORANDO** 6-9-5	7
* 2020	**EUCHEN GLEN** 7-9-0	4
2021	**HUKUM** 4-9-5	7

*Run at York

FILLIES' MILE (2y fillies)
Newmarket-1m
2012	**CERTIFY** 8-12	6
2013	**CHRISELLIAM** 8-12	8
2014	**TOGETHER FOREVER** 9-0	7
2015	**MINDING** 9-0	10
2016	**RHODODENDRON** 9-0	8
2017	**LAURENS** 9-0	11
2018	**IRIDESSA** 9-0	8
2019	**QUADRILATERAL** 9-0	9
2020	**PRETTY GORGEOUS** 9-0	10
2021	**INSPIRAL** 9-0	8

MIDDLE PARK STAKES (2y)
Newmarket-6f
2012	**RECKLESS ABANDON** 8-12	10
2013	**ASTAIRE** 9-0	10
2014	**CHARMING THOUGHT** 9-0	6
2015	**SHALAA** 9-0	7
2016	**THE LAST LION** 9-0	10
2017	**U S NAVY FLAG** 9-0	9
2018	**TEN SOVEREIGNS** 9-0	8
2019	**EARTHLIGHT** 9-0	8
2020	**SUPREMACY** 9-0	8
2021	**PERFECT POWER** 9-0	10

CHALLENGE STAKES
Newmarket-7f
2012	**FULBRIGHT** 3-9-1	11
2013	**FIESOLANA** 4-9-0	9
2014	**HERE COMES WHEN** 4-9-7	13
2015	**CABLE BAY** 4-9-3	10
2016	**ACLAIM** 3-9-1	12
2017	**LIMATO** 5-9-3	11
2018	**LIMATO** 6-9-3	8
2019	**MUSTASHRY** 6-9-8	5
2020	**HAPPY POWER** 4-9-3	9
2021	**AL SUHAIL** 4-9-3	9

DEWHURST STAKES (2y)
Newmarket-7f
2012	**DAWN APPROACH** 9-1	6
2013	**WAR COMMAND** 9-1	6
2014	**BELARDO** 9-1	6
2015	**AIR FORCE BLUE** 9-1	7
2016	**CHURCHILL** 9-1	7
2017	**U S NAVY FLAG** 9-1	9
2018	**TOO DARN HOT** 9-1	7
2019	**PINATUBO** 9-1	9
2020	**ST MARK'S BASILICA** 9-1	14
2021	**NATIVE TRAIL** 9-1	8

CESAREWITCH
Newmarket-2m 2f
2012	**AAIM TO PROSPER** 8-9-10	34
2013	**SCATTER DICE** 4-8-8	33
2014	**BIG EASY** 7-8-7	33
2015	**GRUMETI** 7-8-2	34
2016	**SWEET SELECTION** 4-8-8	33
2017	**WITHHOLD** 4-8-8	34
2018	**LOW SUN** 5-9-2	33
2019	**STRATUM** 6-9-7	30
2020	**GREAT WHITE SHARK** 6-8-6	34
2021	**BUZZ** 7-8-13	32

ROCKFEL STAKES (2y fillies)
Newmarket-7f
2012	**JUST THE JUDGE** 8-12	11
2013	**AL THAKHIRA** 8-12	8
2014	**LUCIDA** 9-0	9
2015	**PROMISING RUN** 9-0	7
2016	**SPAIN BURG** 9-0	8
2017	**JULIET CAPULET** 9-0	10
2018	**JUST WONDERFUL** 9-0	9
2019	**DAAHYEH** 9-0	8
2020	**ISABELLA GILES** 9-0	5
2021	**HELLO YOU** 9-0	9

QIPCO BRITISH CHAMPIONS SPRINT STAKES
Ascot-6f

2012	**MAAREK** 5-9-0	15
2013	**SLADE POWER** 4-9-0	14
2014	**GORDON LORD BYRON** 6-9-2	15
2015	**MUHAARAR** 3-9-1	20
2016	**THE TIN MAN** 4-9-2	13
2017	**LIBRISA BREEZE** 5-9-2	12
2018	**SANDS OF MALI** 3-9-1	14
2019	**DONJUAN TRIUMPHANT** 6-9-2	17
2020	**GLEN SHIEL** 6-9-2	16
2021	**CREATIVE FORCE** 3-9-1	20

QUEEN ELIZABETH II STAKES (BRITISH CHAMPIONS MILE)
Ascot-1m

2012	**EXCELEBRATION** 4-9-3	8
2013	**OLYMPIC GLORY** 3-9-0	12
2014	**CHARM SPIRIT** 3-9-1	11
2015	**SOLOW** 5-9-4	9
2016	**MINDING** 3-8-12	10
2017	**PERSUASIVE** 4-9-1	15
2018	**ROARING LION** 3-9-1	13
2019	**KING OF CHANGE** 3-9-1	16
2020	**THE REVENANT** 5-9-4	14
2021	**BAAEED** 3-9-1	10

QIPCO BRITISH CHAMPIONS LONG DISTANCE CUP
Ascot-2m

2012	**RITE OF PASSAGE** 8-9-7	9
2013	**ROYAL DIAMOND** 7-9-7	12
2014	**FORGOTTEN RULES** 4-9-7	9
2015	**FLYING OFFICER** 5-9-7	13
2016	**SHEIKHZAYEDROAD** 7-9-7	10
2017	**ORDER OF ST GEORGE** 5-9-7	13
2018	**STRADIVARIUS** 4-9-7	6
2019	**KEW GARDENS** 4-9-7	6
2020	**TRUESHAN** 4-9-7	13
2021	**TRUESHAN** 5-9-7	10

QIPCO BRITISH CHAMPIONS FILLIES' AND MARES' STAKES
Ascot-1m 4f

2012	**SAPPHIRE** 4-9-3	10
2013	**SEAL OF APPROVAL** 4-9-3	8
2014	**MADAME CHIANG** 3-8-12	10
2015	**SIMPLE VERSE** 3-8-12	12
2016	**JOURNEY** 4-9-5	13
2017	**HYDRANGEA** 3-8-13	10
2018	**MAGICAL** 3-8-13	11
2019	**STAR CATCHER** 3-8-13	12
2020	**WONDERFUL TONIGHT** 3-8-13	12
2021	**ESHAADA** 3-8-13	8

QIPCO CHAMPION STAKES (BRITISH CHAMPIONS MIDDLE DISTANCE)
Ascot-1m 2f

2012	**FRANKEL** 4-9-3	6
2013	**FARHH** 5-9-3	10
2014	**NOBLE MISSION** 5-9-5	9
2015	**FASCINATING ROCK** 4-9-5	13
2016	**ALMANZOR** 3-9-0	10
2017	**CRACKSMAN** 3-9-1	10
2018	**CRACKSMAN** 4-9-5	8
2019	**MAGICAL** 4-9-2	12
2020	**ADDEYBB** 6-9-5	10
2021	**SEALIWAY** 3-9-1	9

BALMORAL HANDICAP
Ascot-1m

2014	**BRONZE ANGEL** 5-9-2	27
2015	**MUSADDAS** 5-8-2	20
2016	**YUFTEN** 5-9-1	19
2017	**LORD GLITTERS** 6-9-3	20
2018	**SHARJA BRIDGE** 4-9-5	20
2019	**ESCOBAR** 5-9-6	20
2020	**NJORD** 4-9-5	18
2021	**ALDAARY** 3-9-6	20

CORNWALLIS STAKES (2y)
Newmarket-5f (run at Ascot before 2014)

2012	**BUNGLE INTHEJUNGLE** 9-3	6
2013	**HOT STREAK** 9-0	12
2014	**ROYAL RAZALMA** 8-12	12
2015	**QUIET REFLECTION** 8-12	11
2016	**MRS DANVERS** 8-12	9
2017	**ABEL HANDY** 9-1	12
2018	**SERGEI PROKOFIEV** 9-1	14
2019	**GOOD VIBES** 8-12	12
2020	**WINTER POWER** 8-12	11
2021	**TWILIGHT JET** 9-1	12

TWO-YEAR-OLD TROPHY (2y)
Redcar-6f

2012	**BODY AND SOUL** 8-1	21
2013	**VENTURA MIST** 8-7	23
2014	**LIMATO** 8-12	23
2015	**LOG OUT ISLAND** 9-2	20
2016	**WICK POWELL** 8-3	20
2017	**DARKANNA** 8-11	23
2018	**SUMMER DAYDREAM** 8-9	21
2019	**SUMMER SANDS** 8-3	17
2020	**LULLABY MOON** 8-9	21
2021	**CHIPOTLE** 9-1	15

HORRIS HILL STAKES (2y)
Newbury-7f

2012	**TAWHID** 8-12	8
2013	**PIPING ROCK** 8-12	11
2014	**SMAIH** 9-0	6
2015	**CRAZY HORSE** 9-0	6
2016	**PLEASELETMEWIN** 9-0	13
2017	**NEBO** 9-0	8
2018	**MOHAATHER** 9-0	6
2019	ABANDONED	
2020	**MUJBAR** 9-0	12
2021	**LIGHT INFANTRY** 9-0	7

VERTEM FUTURITY TROPHY (2y)
(Racing Post Trophy before 2018)
Doncaster-1m (St)

2012	**KINGSBARNS** 9-0	7
2013	**KINGSTON HILL** 9-0	11
2014	**ELM PARK** 9-1	8
2015	**MARCEL** 9-1	7
2016	**RIVET** 9-1	10
2017	**SAXON WARRIOR** 9-1	12
2018	**MAGNA GRECIA** 9-1	11
* 2019	**KAMEKO** 9-1	11
2020	**MAC SWINEY** 9-1	8
2021	**LUXEMBOURG** 9-1	8

* Run at Newcastle 1m 5yds (Tapeta)

NOVEMBER HANDICAP
Doncaster-1m 3f 197yds

2012	**ART SCHOLAR** 5-8-7	23
2013	**CONDUCT** 6-9-2	23
2014	**OPEN EAGLE** 5-8-12	23
2015	**LITIGANT** 7-9-10	22
2016	**PRIZE MONEY** 3-8-10	15
2017	**SAUNTER** 4-8-13	23
2018	**ROYAL LINE** 4-9-8	23
2019	ABANDONED	
2020	**ON TO VICTORY** 6-9-0	23
2021	**FARHAN** 3-8-3	23

WINNERS OF PRINCIPAL RACES IN IRELAND

IRISH 2,000 GUINEAS (3y)
The Curragh-1m

2012	**POWER** 9-0	10
2013	**MAGICIAN** 9-0	10
2014	**KINGMAN** 9-0	11
2015	**GLENEAGLES** 9-0	11
2016	**AWTAAD** 9-0	8
2017	**CHURCHILL** 9-0	6
2018	**ROMANISED** 9-0	11
2019	**PHOENIX OF SPAIN** 9-0	14
2020	**SISKIN** 9-2	11
2021	**MAC SWINEY** 9-2	11

TATTERSALLS GOLD CUP
The Curragh-1m 2f 110yds

2012	**SO YOU THINK** 6-9-1	5
2013	**AL KAZEEM** 5-9-3	4
2014	**NOBLE MISSION** 5-9-3	5
2015	**AL KAZEEM** 7-9-3	6
2016	**FASCINATING ROCK** 5-9-3	5
2017	**DECORATED KNIGHT** 5-9-3	8
2018	**LANCASTER BOMBER** 4-9-3	5
2019	**MAGICAL** 4-9-0	5
2020	**MAGICAL** 5-9-3	6
2021	**HELVIC DREAM** 4-9-5	8

IRISH 1,000 GUINEAS (3y fillies)
The Curragh-1m

2012	**SAMITAR** 9-0	8
2013	**JUST THE JUDGE** 9-0	15
2014	**MARVELLOUS** 9-0	11
2015	**PLEASCACH** 9-0	18
2016	**JET SETTING** 9-0	10
2017	**WINTER** 9-0	8
2018	**ALPHA CENTAURI** 9-0	13
2019	**HERMOSA** 9-0	10
2020	**PEACEFUL** 9-2	11
2021	**EMPRESS JOSEPHINE** 9-2	14

IRISH DERBY (3y)
The Curragh-1m 4f

2012	**CAMELOT** 9-0	5
2013	**TRADING LEATHER** 9-0	9
2014	**AUSTRALIA** 9-0	5
2015	**JACK HOBBS** 9-0	8
2016	**HARZAND** 9-0	9
2017	**CAPRI** 9-0	9
2018	**LATROBE** 9-0	12
2019	**SOVEREIGN** 9-0	8
2020	**SANTIAGO** 9-2	14
2021	**HURRICANE LANE** 9-2	11

PRETTY POLLY STAKES
(fillies and mares)
The Curragh-1m 2f

2012	**IZZI TOP** 4-9-9	4
2013	**AMBIVALENT** 4-9-10	9
2014	**THISTLE BIRD** 6-9-10	8

2015	**DIAMONDSANDRUBIES** 3-8-12	9
2016	**MINDING** 3-8-12	5
2017	**NEZWAAH** 4-9-8	11
2018	**URBAN FOX** 4-9-8	6
2019	**IRIDESSA** 3-8-12	5
2020	**MAGICAL** 5-9-12	5
2021	**THUNDERING NIGHTS** 4-9-12	11

IRISH OAKS (3y fillies)
The Curragh-1m 4f

2012	**GREAT HEAVENS** 9-0	7
2013	**CHICQUITA** 9-0	7
2014	**BRACELET** 9--0	10
2015	**COVERT LOVE** 9-0	9
2016	**SEVENTH HEAVEN** 9-0	11
2017	**ENABLE** 9-0	10
2018	**SEA OF CLASS** 9-0	7
2019	**STAR CATCHER** 9-0	8
2020	**EVEN SO** 9-2	8
2021	**SNOWFALL** 9-2	8

PHOENIX STAKES (2y)
The Curragh-6

2012	**PEDRO THE GREAT** 9-3	6
2013	**SUDIRMAN** 9-3	6
2014	**DICK WHITTINGTON** 9-3	6
2015	**AIR FORCE BLUE** 9-3	4
2016	**CARAVAGGIO** 9-3	5
2017	**SIOUX NATION** 9-3	4
2018	**ADVERTISE** 9-3	5
2019	**SISKIN** 9-3	5
2020	**LUCKY VEGA** 9-5	10
2021	**EBRO RIVER** 9-5	8

MATRON STAKES (fillies and mares)
Leopardstown-1m

* 2012	**CHACHAMAIDEE** 5-9-5	11
2013	**LA COLLINA** 4-9-5	12
2014	**FIESOLANA** 5-9-5	10
2015	**LEGATISSIMO** 3-9-0	9
2016	**ALICE SPRINGS** 3-9-0	8
2017	**HYDRANGEA** 3-9-0	10
2018	**LAURENS** 3-9-0	7
2019	**IRIDESSA** 3-9-0	7
2020	**CHAMPERS ELYSEES** 3-9-2	11
2021	**NO SPEAK ALEXANDER** 3-9-2	13

* Duntle disqualified from first place

IRISH CHAMPION STAKES
Leopardstown-1m 2f

2012	**SNOW FAIRY** 5-9-4	6
2013	**THE FUGUE** 4-9-4	7
2014	**THE GREY GATSBY** 3-9-0	7
2015	**GOLDEN HORN** 3-9-0	7
2016	**ALMANZOR** 3-9-0	12
2017	**DECORATED KNIGHT** 5-9-7	10
2018	**ROARING LION** 3-9-1	7
2019	**MAGICAL** 4-9-4	8

| 2020 | MAGICAL 5-9-6 | 6 |
| 2021 | ST MARK'S BASILICA 3-9-3 | 4 |

IRISH CAMBRIDGESHIRE
The Curragh-1m

2012	PUNCH YOUR WEIGHT 3-8-6	18
2013	MORAN GRA 6-8-13	20
2014	SRETAW 5-8-8	21
2015	HINT OF A TINT 5-9-3	24
2016	SEA WOLF 4-9-5	22
2017	ELUSIVE TIME 9-8-9	27
2018	KENYA 3-9-2	21
2019	JASSAAR 4-8-8	25
2020	LAUGHIFUWANT 5-9-10	21
2021	BOPEDRO 5-9-3	27

MOYGLARE STUD STAKES
(2y fillies)
The Curragh-7f

2012	SKY LANTERN 9-0	13
2013	RIZEENA 9-0	7
2014	CURSORY GLANCE 9-0	10
2015	MINDING 9-0	9
2016	INTRICATELY 9-0	7
2017	HAPPILY 9-0	8
2018	SKITTER SKATTER 9-0	10
2019	LOVE 9-0	9
2020	SHALE 9-2	13
2021	DISCOVERIES 9-2	8

VINCENT O'BRIEN
NATIONAL STAKES (2y)
The Curragh-7f

2012	DAWN APPROACH 9-3	7
2013	TOORMORE 9-3	5
2014	GLENEAGLES 9-3	5
2015	AIR FORCE BLUE 9-3	5
2016	CHURCHILL 9-3	7
2017	VERBAL DEXTERITY 9-3	7
2018	QUORTO 9-3	7
2019	PINATUBO 9-3	8
2020	THUNDER MOON 9-5	10
2021	NATIVE TRAIL 9-5	7

IRISH ST LEGER
The Curragh-1m 6f

2012	ROYAL DIAMOND 6-9-11	9
2013	VOLEUSE DE COEURS 4-9-8	10
2014	BROWN PANTHER 6-9-11	11
2015	ORDER OF ST GEORGE 3-9-0	11
2016	WICKLOW BRAVE 7-9-11	4
2017	ORDER OF ST GEORGE 5-9-10	10
2018	FLAG OF HONOUR 3-9-1	10
2019	SEARCH FOR A SONG 3-8-11	10
2020	SEARCH FOR A SONG 4-9-8	8
2021	SONNYBOYLISTON 4-9-11	13

IRISH CESAREWITCH
The Curragh-2m

2012	VOLEUSE DE COEURS 3-9-1	27
2013	MONTEFELTRO 5-9-4	30
2014	EL SALVADOR 5-9-5	21
2015	DIGEANTA 8-9-10	20
2016	LAWS OF SPIN 3-8-6	20
* 2017	LORD ERSKINE 4-8-5	24

2018	BRAZOS 4-8-12	24
2019	ROYAL ILLUSION 7-8-5	18
2020	CAPE GENTLEMAN 4-9-0	21
2021	LINE OUT 9-8-9	30
* Run at Navan

LADBROKES HURDLE (HANDICAP)
Leopardstown-2m
(Various sponsors)

2012	CITIZENSHIP 6-10-3	30
2013	ABBEY LANE 8-10-8	28
2014	GILGAMBOA 6-10-9	24
2015	KATIE T 6-10-9	24
2016	HENRY HIGGINS 6-10-10	23
2017	ICE COLD SOUL 7-10-2	20
2018	OFF YOU GO 5-9-10	28
2019	OFF YOU GO 6-11-5	19
2020	THOSEDAYSAREGONE 7-9-12	22
2021	DROP THE ANCHOR 7 10-5	22

IRISH CHAMPION HURDLE
Leopardstown-2m

2012	HURRICANE FLY 8-11-10	5
2013	HURRICANE FLY 9-11-10	5
2014	HURRICANE FLY 10-11-10	4
2015	HURRICANE FLY 11-11-10	6
2016	FAUGHEEN 8-11-10	5
2017	PETIT MOUCHOIR 6 11-10	4
2018	SUPASUNDAE 8-11-10	8
2019	APPLE'S JADE 7-11-3	6
2020	HONEYSUCKLE 6-11-3	9
2021	HONEYSUCKLE 7-11-5	6

IRISH GOLD CUP
Leopardstown-3m(Hennessy Gold Cup before 2016)

2012	QUEL ESPRIT 8-11-10	7
2013	SIR DES CHAMPS 7-11-10	4
2014	LAST INSTALMENT 9-11-10	7
2015	CARLINGFORD LOUGH 9-11-10	8
2016	CARLINGFORD LOUGH 10-11-10	10
2017	SIZING JOHN 7-11-10	7
2018	EDWULF 9-11-10	10
2019	BELLSHILL 9-11-10	4
2020	DELTA WORK 7-11-10	8
2021	KEMBOY 9-11-12	5

IRISH GRAND NATIONAL
Fairyhouse-3m 5f

2012	LION NA BEARNAI 10-10-5	29
2013	LIBERTY COUNSEL 10-9-5	28
2014	SHUTTHEFRONTDOOR 7-10-13	26
2015	THUNDER AND ROSES 7-10-6	28
2016	ROGUE ANGEL 7-10-6	27
2017	OUR DUKE 7-11-4	28
2018	GENERAL PRINCIPLE 9-10-0	30
2019	BURROWS SAINT 6-10-8	30
2020	RACE CANCELLED	
2021	FREEWHEELIN DYLAN 9-10-8	28

WINNERS OF PRINCIPAL RACES IN FRANCE

PRIX GANAY
ParisLongchamp-1m 2f 110yds
2012	**CIRRUS DES AIGLES** 6-9-2	6
2013	**PASTORIUS** 4-9-2	9
2014	**CIRRUS DES AIGLES** 8-9-2	8
2015	**CIRRUS DES AIGLES** 9-9-2	7
* 2016	**DARIYAN** 4-9-2	10
2017	**CLOTH OF STARS** 4-9-2	7
2018	**CRACKSMAN** 4-9-2	7
2019	**WALDGEIST** 5-9-2	5
** 2020	**SOTTSASS** 4-9-2	5
2021	**MARE AUSTRALIS** 4-9-2	7

* Run at Saint-Cloud
** Run at Chantilly

POULE D'ESSAI DES POULAINS (3y)
ParisLongchamp-1m
2012	**LUCAYAN** 9-2	12
2013	**STYLE VENDOME** 9-2	18
2014	**KARAKONTIE** 9-2	12
2015	**MAKE BELIEVE** 9-2	18
* 2016	**THE GURKHA** 9-2	13
* 2017	**BRAMETOT** 9-2	13
2018	**OLMEDO** 9-2	11
2019	**PERSIAN KING** 9-2	10
* 2020	**VICTOR LUDORUM** 9-2	9
2021	**ST MARK'S BASILICA** 9-2	12

* Run at Deauville

POULE D'ESSAI DES POULICHES (3y fillies)
ParisLongchamp-1m
2012	**BEAUTY PARLOUR** 9-0	13
2013	**FLOTILLA** 9-0	20
2014	**AVENIR CERTAIN** 9-0	16
2015	**ERVEDYA** 9-0	14
* 2016	**LA CRESSONNIERE** 9-0	14
* 2017	**PRECIEUSE** 9-0	18
2018	**TEPPAL** 9-0	14
2019	**CASTLE LADY** 9-0	10
* 2020	**DREAM AND DO** 9-0	9
2021	**COUERSAMBA** 9-0	13

* Run at Deauville

PRIX SAINT-ALARY (3y fillies)
ParisLongchamp-1m 2f
2012	**SAGAWARA** 9-0	8
2013	**SILASOL** 9-0	8
* 2014	**VAZIRA** 9-0	8
2015	**QUEEN'S JEWEL** 9-0	9
** 2016	**JEMAYEL** 9-0	9
** 2017	**SOBETSU** 9-0	11
2018	**LAURENS** 9-0	5
2019	**SIYARAFINA** 9-0	11
*** 2020	**TAWKEEL** 9-0	7
2021	**INCARVILLE** 9-0	11

* We Are disqualified from first place
** Run at Deauville
*** Run at Chantilly

PRIX D'ISPAHAN
ParisLongchamp-1m 1f 55yds
2012	**GOLDEN LILAC** 4-8-13	8
2013	**MAXIOS** 5-9-2	7
2014	**CIRRUS DES AIGLES** 8-9-2	6
2015	**SOLOW** 5-9-2	4
* 2016	**A SHIN HIKARI** 5-9-2	9
* 2017	**MEKHTAAL** 4-9-2	5
2018	**RECOLETOS** 4-9-2	6
2019	**ZABEEL PRINCE** 6-9-2	9
* 2020	**PERSIAN KING** 4-9-6	8
2021	**SKALLETI** 6-9-2	6

* Run at Chantilly

PRIX DU JOCKEY CLUB (3y)
Chantilly-1m 2f 110yds
2012	**SAONOIS** 9-2	20
2013	**INTELLO** 9-2	19
2014	**THE GREY GATSBY** 9-2	14
2015	**NEW BAY** 9-2	14
2016	**ALMANZOR** 9-2	16
2017	**BRAMETOT** 9-2	12
2018	**STUDY OF MAN** 9-2	16
2019	**SOTTSASS** 9-3	15
2020	**MISHRIFF** 9-2	16
2021	**ST MARK'S BASILICA** 9-2	19

PRIX DE DIANE (3y fillies)
Chantilly-1m 2f 110yds
2012	**VALYRA** 9-0	12
2013	**TREVE** 9-0	11
2014	**AVENIR CERTAIN** 9-0	12
2015	**STAR OF SEVILLE** 9-0	17
2016	**LA CRESSONNIERE** 9-0	16
2017	**SENGA** 9-1	16
2018	**LAURENS** 9-0	13
2019	**CHANNEL** 9-0	16
2020	**FANCY BLUE** 9-0	11
2021	**JOAN OF ARC** 9-0	17

GRAND PRIX DE SAINT-CLOUD
Saint-Cloud-1m 4f
2012	**MEANDRE** 4-9-2	4
2013	**NOVELLIST** 4-9-2	11
* 2014	**NOBLE MISSION** 5-9-2	7
2015	**TREVE** 5-8-13	7
2016	**SILVERWAVE** 4-9-2	11
2017	**ZARAK** 4-9-2	6
2018	**WALDGEIST** 4-9-3	10
2019	**CORONET** 5-9-0	7
2020	**WAY TO PARIS** 7-9-2	9
2021	**BROOME** 5-9-2	8

* Spiritjim disqualified from first place

PRIX JEAN PRAT (3y)
Chantilly-7f (1m before 2019)
2012	**AESOP'S FABLES** 9-2	8
2013	**HAVANA GOLD** 9-2	12
2014	**CHARM SPIRIT** 9-2	7

2015	**TERRITORIES** 9-2	8
2016	**ZELZAL** 9-2	9
2017	**THUNDER SNOW** 9-3	5
2018	**INTELLOGENT** 9-2	6
2019	**TOO DARN HOT** 9-2	12
2020	**PINATUBO** 9-2	11
2021	**LAWS OF INDICES** 9-2	13

GRAND PRIX DE PARIS (3y)
ParisLongchamp-1m 4f

2012	**IMPERIAL MONARCH** 9-2	9
2013	**FLINTSHIRE** 9-2	8
2014	**GALLANTE** 9-2	11
2015	**ERUPT** 9-2	6
* 2016	**MONT ORMEL** 9-2	8
* 2017	**SHAKEEL** 9-2	9
2018	**KEW GARDENS** 9-3	6
2019	**JAPAN** 9-2	8
2020	**MOGUL** 9-3	10
2021	**HURRICANE LANE** 9-2	11

* Run at Saint-Cloud

PRIX ROTHSCHILD
(fillies and mares)
Deauville-1m

2012	**ELUSIVE KATE** 3-8-9	5
2013	**ELUSIVE KATE** 4-9-2	12
2014	**ESOTERIQUE** 4-9-2	4
2015	**AMAZING MARIA** 4-9-2	8
2016	**QEMAH** 3-8-9	10
2017	**ROLY POLY** 3-8-9	10
2018	**WITH YOU** 3-8-9	10
2019	**LAURENS** 4-9-3	9
2020	**WATCH ME** 4-9-4	6
2021	**MOTHER EARTH** 3-8-11	14

PRIX MAURICE DE GHEEST
Deauville-6f 110yds

2012	**MOONLIGHT CLOUD** 4-8-13	9
2013	**MOONLIGHT CLOUD** 5-8-13	14
2014	**GARSWOOD** 4-9-2	14
2015	**MUHAARAR** 3-8-11	12
2016	**SIGNS OF BLESSING** 5-9-2	15
2017	**BRANDO** 5-9-3	13
2018	**POLYDREAM** 3-8-10	20
2019	**ADVERTISE** 3-8-13	15
2020	**SPACE BLUES** 4-9-4	11
2021	**MARIANAFOOT** 6-9-4	12

PRIX JACQUES LE MAROIS
Deauville-1m

2012	**EXCELEBRATION** 4-9-4	11
2013	**MOONLIGHT CLOUD** 5-9-1	13
2014	**KINGMAN** 3-8-13	5
2015	**ESOTERIQUE** 5-9-1	9
2016	**RIBCHESTER** 3-8-13	11
2017	**AL WUKAIR** 3-8-13	11
2018	**ALPHA CENTAURI** 3-8-9	6
2019	**ROMANISED** 4-9-5	8
2020	**PALACE PIER** 3-8-13	7
2021	**PALACE PIER** 4-9-5	8

PRIX MORNY (2y)
Deauville-6f

2012	**RECKLESS ABANDON** 9-0	11
2013	**NO NAY NEVER** 9-0	10
2014	**THE WOW SIGNAL** 9-0	9
2015	**SHALAA** 9-0	5
2016	**LADY AURELIA** 8-10	5
2017	**UNFORTUNATELY** 9-0	8
2018	**PRETTY POLLYANNA** 8-10	9
2019	**EARTHLIGHT** 9-0	8
2020	**CAMPANELLE** 8-10	9
2021	**PERFECT POWER** 9-0	14

PRIX JEAN ROMANET
(fillies and mares)
Deauville-1m 2f

* 2012	**IZZI TOP** 4-9-0	8
2013	**ROMANTICA** 4-9-0	6
2014	**RIBBONS** 4-9-0	11
2015	**ODELIZ** 4-9-0	11
2016	**SPEEDY BOARDING** 4-9-0	10
2017	**AJMAN PRINCESS** 4-9-0	10
2018	**NONZA** 4-9-0	9
2019	**CORONET** 5-9-0	8
2020	**AUDARYA** 4-9-0	11
2021	**GRAND GLORY** 5-9-0	8

* Snow Fairy disqualified from first place

PRIX DU MOULIN DE LONGCHAMP
ParisLongchamp-1m

2012	**MOONLIGHT CLOUD** 4-8-13	4
2013	**MAXIOS** 5-9-2	7
2014	**CHARM SPIRIT** 3-8-11	10
2015	**ERVEDYA** 3-8-9	6
* 2016	**VADAMOS** 5-9-3	6
* 2017	**RIBCHESTER** 4-9-3	7
2018	**RECOLETOS** 4-9-4	11
2019	**CIRCUS MAXIMUS** 3-8-13	10
2020	**PERSIAN KING** 4-9-3	6
2021	**BAAEED** 3-9-0	6

* Run at Chantilly

PRIX VERMEILLE (fillies and mares)
ParisLongchamp-1m 4f

2012	**SHARETA** 4-9-2	13
2013	**TREVE** 3-8-8	10
2014	**BALTIC BARONESS** 4-9-3	9
2015	**TREVE** 5-9-3	9
* 2016	**LEFT HAND** 3-8-8	6
* 2017	**BATEEL** 5-9-3	11
2018	**KITESURF** 4-9-3	8
2019	**STAR CATCHER** 3-8-9	9
2020	**TARNAWA** 4-9-5	10
2021	**TEONA** 3-8-10	7

* Run at Chantilly

PRIX DE LA FORET
ParisLongchamp-7f

2012	**GORDON LORD BYRON** 4-9-2	11
2013	**MOONLIGHT CLOUD** 5-8-13	11
2014	**OLYMPIC GLORY** 4-9-2	14
2015	**MAKE BELIEVE** 3-9-0	13
* 2016	**LIMATO** 4-9-2	11
* 2017	**ACLAIM** 4-9-2	10
2018	**ONE MASTER** 4-8-13	15
2019	**ONE MASTER** 5-8-13	12

| 2020 | **ONE MASTER** 6-8-13 | 9 |
| 2021 | **SPACE BLUES** 5-9-2 | 15 |

* Run at Chantilly

PRIX DU CADRAN
ParisLongchamp-2m 4f

2012	**MOLLY MALONE** 4-8-13	10
2013	**ALTANO** 7-9-2	10
2014	**HIGH JINX** 6-9-2	8
2015	**MILLE ET MILLE** 5-9-2	10
* 2016	**QUEST FOR MORE** 6-9-2	12
* 2017	**VAZIRABAD** 5-9-2	6
2018	**CALL THE WIND** 4-9-2	8
2019	**HOLDTHASIGREEN** 7-9-2	10
2020	**PRINCESS ZOE** 5-8-13	9
2021	**TRUESHAN** 5-9-2	13

* Run at Chantilly

PRIX DE L'ABBAYE DE LONGCHAMP
ParisLongchamp-5f

2012	**WIZZ KID** 4-9-7	18
2013	**MAAREK** 6-9-11	20
2014	**MOVE IN TIME** 6-9-11	18
2015	**GOLDREAM** 6-9-11	18
* 2016	**MARSHA** 3-9--7	17
* 2017	**BATTAASH** 3-9-11	13
2018	**MABS CROSS** 4-9-7	16
2019	**GLASS SLIPPERS** 3-9-7	16
2020	**WOODED** 3-9-11	11
2021	**A CASE OF YOU** 3-9-11	14

* Run at Chantilly

PRIX JEAN-LUC LAGARDERE (2y)
ParisLongchamp-1m (7f before 2015)

2012	**OLYMPIC GLORY** 9-0	8
2013	**KARAKONTIE** 9-0	8
* 2014	**FULL MAST** 9-0	9
2015	**ULTRA** 9-0	11
** 2016	**NATIONAL DEFENSE** 9-0	6
* 2017	**HAPPILY** 8-10	6
2018	**ROYAL MARINE** 9-0	6
2019	**VICTOR LUDORUM** 9-0	7
2020	**SEALIWAY** 9-0	5
2021	**ANGEL BLEU** 9-0	9

* Gleneagles disqualified from first place
** Run at Chantilly

PRIX MARCEL BOUSSAC (2y fillies)
ParisLongchamp-1m

2012	**SILASOL** 8-11	9
2013	**INDONESIENNE** 8-11	12
2014	**FOUND** 8-11	12
2015	**BALLYDOYLE** 8-11	8
* 2016	**WUHEIDA** 8-11	11
* 2017	**WILD ILLUSION** 8-11	7
2018	**LILY'S CANDLE** 8-11	8
2019	**ALBIGNA** 8-11	9
2020	**TIGER TANAKA** 8-11	12
2021	**ZELLIE** 8-11	8

* Run at Chantilly

PRIX DE L'OPERA (fillies and mares)
ParisLongchamp-1m 2f

2012	**RIDASIYNA** 3-8-11	13
2013	**DALKALA** 4-9-2	9
2014	**WE ARE** 3-8-11	11
2015	**COVERT LOVE** 3-8-11	13
* 2016	**SPEEDY BOARDING** 4-9-2	7
* 2017	**RHODODENDRON** 3-8-11	13
2018	**WILD ILLUSION** 3-8-11	15
2019	**VILLA MARINA** 3-8-11	12
2020	**TARNAWA** 4-9-2	12
2021	**ROUGIR** 3-8-11	14

* Run at Chantilly

PRIX ROYAL-OAK
ParisLongchamp-1m 7f 110yds

2012	**LES BEAUFS** 3-8-9	9
2013	**TAC DE BOISTRON** 6-9-4	15
2014	**TAC DE BOISTRON** 7-9-4	11
2015	**VAZIRABAD** 3-8-10	13
* 2016	**VAZIRABAD** 4-9-4	15
** 2017	**ICE BREEZE** 3-8-10	9
2018	**HOLDTHASIGREEN** 6-9-4	8
2019	**TECHNICIAN** 3-8-10	6
2020	**SUBJECTIVIST** 3-8-10	8
2021	**SCOPE** 3-8-10	12

* Run at Chantilly
** Run at Saint-Cloud

CRITERIUM INTERNATIONAL (2y)
Saint-Cloud-1m (7f 2015-2019)

2012	**LOCH GARMAN** 9-0	6
2013	**ECTOT** 9-0	4
2014	**VERT DE GRECE** 9-0	9
2015	**JOHANNES VERMEER** 9-0	9
2016	**THUNDER SNOW** 9-0	9
2017	ABANDONED	
* 2018	**ROYAL MEETING** 9-0	6
* 2019	**ALSON** 9-0	2
2020	**VAN GOGH** 9-0	6
2021	**ANGEL BLEU** 9-0	6

* Run at Chantilly
** Run at ParisLongchamp

CRITERIUM DE SAINT-CLOUD (2y)
Saint-Cloud-1m 2f

2012	**MORANDI** 9-0	8
2013	**PRINCE GIBRALTAR** 9-0	12
2014	**EPICURIS** 9-0	6
2015	**ROBIN OF NAVAN** 9-0	10
2016	**WALDGEIST** 9-0	13
2017	ABANDONED	
2018	**WONDERMENT** 8-10	9
2019	**MKFANCY** 9-0	8
2020	**GEAR UP** 9-0	7
2021	**EL BODEGON** 9-0	9

WINNERS OF OTHER OVERSEAS RACES

SAUDI CUP
Riyadh-1m 1f dirt
2020	**MAXIMUM SECURITY** 4-9-0	14
2021	**MISHRIFF** 4-9-0	14

PEGASUS WORLD CUP
Gulfstream Park-1m 1f dirt
2017	**ARROGATE** 4-8-12	12
2018	**GUN RUNNER** 5-8-12	12
2019	**CITY OF LIGHT** 5-8-12	12
2020	**MUCHO GUSTO** 4-8-12	10
2021	**KNICKS GO** 5-8-11	12
2022	**LIFE IS GOOD** 4-8-11	9

DUBAI WORLD CUP
Meydan-1m 2f Tapeta
2012	**MONTEROSSO** 5-9-0	13
2013	**ANIMAL KINGDOM** 5-9-0	13
2014	**AFRICAN STORY** 7-9-0	16
2015	**PRINCE BISHOP** 8-9-0	9
2016	**CALIFORNIA CHROME** 5-9-0	12
2017	**ARROGATE** 4-9-0	14
2018	**THUNDER SNOW** 4-9-0	10
2019	**THUNDER SNOW** 5-9-0	12
2020	RACE CANCELLED	
2021	**MYSTIC GUIDE** 4-9-0	12

KENTUCKY DERBY
Churchill Downs-1m 2f dirt
2012	**I'LL HAVE ANOTHER** 9-0	20
2013	**ORB** 9-0	19
2014	**CALIFORNIA CHROME** 9-0	19
2015	**AMERICAN PHAROAH** 9-0	18
2016	**NYQUIST** 9-0	20
2017	**ALWAYS DREAMING** 9-0	20
2018	**JUSTIFY** 9-0	20
2019	**COUNTRY HOUSE** 9-0	19
2020	**AUTHENTIC** 9-0	15
2021	**MEDINA SPIRIT** 9-0	19

* Maximum Security disqualified from first place

BREEDERS' CUP TURF
Various courses-1m 4f
2012	**LITTLE MIKE** 5-9-0	12
2013	**MAGICIAN** 3-8-10	12
2014	**MAIN SEQUENCE** 5-9-0	12
2015	**FOUND** 3-8-7	12
2016	**HIGHLAND REEL** 4-9-0	12
2017	**TALISMANIC** 4-9-0	13
2018	**ENABLE** 4-8-11	13
2019	**BRICKS AND MORTAR** 5-9-0	12
2020	**TARNAWA** 4-8-11	10
2021	**YIBIR** 3-8-10	14

BREEDERS' CUP CLASSIC
Various courses-1m 2f dirt
2012	**FORT LARNED** 4-9-0	12
2013	**MUCHO MACHO MAN** 5-9-0	11
2014	**BAYERN** 3-8-10	14
2015	**AMERICAN PHAROAH** 3-8-10	8
2016	**ARROGATE** 3-8-10	9
2017	**GUN RUNNER** 4-9-0	11
2018	**ACCELERATE** 5-9-0	14
2019	**VINO ROSSO** 4-9-0	11
2020	**AUTHENTIC** 3-8-10	10
2021	**KNICKS GO** 5-9-0	8

MELBOURNE CUP
Flemington-2m
2012	**GREEN MOON** 5-8-6	24
2013	**FIORENTE** 5-8-9	24
2014	**PROTECTIONIST** 4-8-13	22
2015	**PRINCE OF PENZANCE** 6-8-5	24
2016	**ALMANDIN** 6-8-3	24
2017	**REKINDLING** 3-8-2	23
2018	**CROSS COUNTER** 3-8-0	24
2019	**VOW AND DECLARE** 4-8-3	24
2020	**TWILIGHT PAYMENT** 7-8-10	23
2021	**VERRY ELLEEGANT** 6-9-0	23

JAPAN CUP
Tokyo-1m 4f
2012	**GENTILDONNA** 3-8-5	17
2013	**GENTILDONNA** 4-8-9	17
2014	**EPIPHANEIA** 4-9-0	18
2015	**SHONAN PANDORA** 4-8-9	18
2016	**KITASAN BLACK** 4-9-0	17
2017	**CHEVAL GRAND** 5-9-0	17
2018	**ALMOND EYE** 3-8-5	14
2019	**SUAVE RICHARD** 5-9-0	15
2020	**ALMOND EYE** 5-8-9	15
2021	**CONTRAIL** 4-9-0	18

WINNERS OF PRINCIPAL NATIONAL HUNT RACES

PADDY POWER GOLD CUP (HANDICAP CHASE)
Cheltenham-2m 4f 78yds
(BetVictor Gold Cup before 2020)

2012	**AL FEROF** 7-11-8	18
2013	**JOHNS SPIRIT** 6-10-2	20
2014	**CAID DU BERLAIS** 5-10-13	18
2015	**ANNACOTTY** 7-11-0	20
2016	**TAQUIN DU SEUIL** 9-11-11	17
2017	**SPLASH OF GINGE** 9-10-6	17
2018	**BARON ALCO** 7-10-0	18
2019	**HAPPY DIVA** 8-11-0	17
2020	**COOLE CODY** 9-10-5	16
2021	**MIDNIGHT SHADOW** 8-11-5	19

BETFAIR CHASE
Haydock-3m 1f 125yds (3m 24yds before 2017)

2012	**SILVINIACO CONTI** 6-11-7	5
2013	**CUE CARD** 7-11-7	8
2014	**SILVINIACO CONTI** 8-11-7	9
2015	**CUE CARD** 9-11-7	5
2016	**CUE CARD** 10-11-7	6
2017	**BRISTOL DE MAI** 6-11-7	6
2018	**BRISTOL DE MAI** 7-11-7	5
2019	**LOSTINTRANSLATION** 7-11-7	4
2020	**BRISTOL DE MAI** 9-11-7	5
2021	**A PLUS TARD** 7-11-7	7

LADBROKES TROPHY HANDICAP CHASE
Newbury-3m 1f 214yds
(Run as Hennessy Gold Cup before 2017)

2012	**BOBS WORTH** 7-11-6	19
2013	**TRIOLO D'ALENE** 6-11-1	21
2014	**MANY CLOUDS** 7-11-6	19
2015	**SMAD PLACE** 8-11-4	15
2016	**NATIVE RIVER** 6-11-1	19
2017	**TOTAL RECALL** 8-10-8	20
2018	**SIZING TENNESSEE** 10-11-3	24
2019	**DE RASHER COUNTER** 7-10-10	24
2020	**CLOTH CAP** 8-10-0	18
2021	**CLOUDY GLEN** 8-10-8	21

TINGLE CREEK CHASE
Sandown-2m

2012	**SPRINTER SACRE** 6-11-7	7
2013	**SIRE DE GRUGY** 7-11-7	7
2014	**DODGING BULLETS** 6-11-7	10
2015	**SIRE DE GRUGY** 9-11-7	7
2016	**UN DE SCEAUX** 8-11-7	6
2017	**POLITOLOGUE** 6-11-7	6
2018	**ALTIOR** 8-11-7	4
2019	**DEFI DU SEUIL** 6-11-7	8
2020	**POLITOLOGUE** 9-11-7	6
2021	**GREANETEEN** 7-11-7	5

CHRISTMAS HURDLE
Kempton-2m

2012	**DARLAN** 5-11-7	7
2013	**MY TENT OR YOURS** 6-11-7	6
2014	**FAUGHEEN** 6-11-7	6
2015	**FAUGHEEN** 7-11-7	5
2016	**YANWORTH** 6-11-7	5
2017	**BUVEUR D'AIR** 6-11-7	4
2018	**VERDANA BLUE** 6-11-0	5
2019	**EPATANTE** 5-11-0	10
2020	**SILVER STREAK** 7-11-7	5
2021	**EPATANTE** 7-11-0	5

KING GEORGE VI CHASE
Kempton-3m

2012	**LONG RUN** 7-11-10	9
2013	**SILVINIACO CONTI** 7-11-10	9
2014	**SILVINIACO CONTI** 8-11-10	10
2015	**CUE CARD** 9-11-10	9
2016	**THISTLECRACK** 8-11-10	8
2017	**MIGHT BITE** 8-11-10	9
2018	**CLAN DES OBEAUX** 6-11-10	10
2019	**CLAN DES OBEAUX** 7-11-10	5
2020	**FRODON** 8-11-10	9
2021	**TORNADO FLYER** 8-11-10	9

WELSH GRAND NATIONAL (HANDICAP CHASE)
Chepstow-3m 5f 110yds

*	2012	**MONBEG DUDE** 8-10-1	17
	2013	**MOUNTAINOUS** 8-10-0	20
	2014	**EMPEROR'S CHOICE** 7-10-8	19
**	2015	**MOUNTAINOUS** 11-10-6	20
	2016	**NATIVE RIVER** 6-11-12	20
***	2017	**RAZ DE MAREE** 13-10-10	20
	2018	**ELEGANT ESCAPE** 6-11-8	20
	2019	**POTTERS CORNER** 9-10-4	17
****	2020	**SECRET REPRIEVE** 7-10-1	18
	2021	**IWILLDOIT** 8-10-0	20

* Run in January 2013
** Run in January 2016
*** Run in January 2018
**** Run in January 2021

CLARENCE HOUSE CHASE
(Victor Chandler Chase before 2014)
Ascot-2m 167yds

*	2013	**SPRINTER SACRE** 7-11-7	7
	2014	**SIRE DE GRUGY** 8-11-7	7
	2015	**DODGING BULLETS** 7-11-7	5
	2016	**UN DE SCEAUX** 8-11-7	5
*	2017	**UN DE SCEAUX** 9-11-7	7
	2018	**UN DE SCEAUX** 10-11-7	5
	2019	**ALTIOR** 9-11-7	3
	2020	**DEFI DU SEUIL** 7-11-7	7
	2021	**FIRST FLOW** 9-11-7	8
	2022	**SHISHKIN** 8-11-7	5

* Run at Cheltenham

BETFAIR HANDICAP HURDLE
Newbury-2m 69yds

2012	**ZARKANDAR** 5-11-1	20
2013	**MY TENT OR YOURS** 6-11-2	21
2014	**SPLASH OF GINGE** 6-10-3	20
2015	**VIOLET DANCER** 5-10-9	23
2016	**AGRAPART** 5-10-5	22
2017	**BALLYANDY** 6-11-1	16
2018	**KALASHNIKOV** 5-11-5	24
* 2019	**AL DANCER** 6-11-8	14
2020	**PIC D'ORHY** 5-11-5	24
2021	**SOARING GLORY** 6-10-7	23

* run at Ascot over 1m 1 ½f

SUPREME NOVICES' HURDLE
Cheltenham-2m 87yds

2012	**CINDERS AND ASHES** 5-11-7	19
2013	**CHAMPAGNE FEVER** 6-11-7	12
2014	**VAUTOUR** 5-11-7	18
2015	**DOUVAN** 5-11-7	12
2016	**ALTIOR** 6-11-7	14
2017	**LABAIK** 6-11-7	14
2018	**SUMMERVILLE BOY** 6-11-7	19
2019	**KLASSICAL DREAM** 5-11-7	16
2020	**SHISHKIN** 6-11-7	15
2021	**APPRECIATE IT** 7-11-7	8

ARKLE CHALLENGE TROPHY (NOVICES' CHASE)
Cheltenham-1m 7f 199yds

2012	**SPRINTER SACRE** 6-11-7	6
2013	**SIMONSIG** 7-11-7	7
2014	**WESTERN WARHORSE** 6-11-4	9
2015	**UN DE SCEAUX** 7-11-4	11
2016	**DOUVAN** 6-11-4	7
2017	**ALTIOR** 7-11-4	9
2018	**FOOTPAD** 6-11-4	5
2019	**DUC DES GENIEVRES** 6-11-4	12
2020	**PUT THE KETTLE ON** 6-10-11	11
2021	**SHISHKIN** 7-11-4	5

CHAMPION HURDLE
Cheltenham-2m 87yds

2012	**ROCK ON RUBY** 7-11-10	10
2013	**HURRICANE FLY** 9-11-10	9
2014	**JEZKI** 6-11-10	9
2015	**FAUGHEEN** 7-11-10	8
2016	**ANNIE POWER** 8-11-3	12
2017	**BUVEUR D'AIR** 6-11-10	11
2018	**BUVEUR D'AIR** 7-11-10	11
2019	**ESPOIR D'ALLEN** 5-11-10	10
2020	**EPATANTE** 6-11-3	17
2021	**HONEYSUCKLE** 7-11-3	10

QUEEN MOTHER CHAMPION CHASE
Cheltenham-1m 7f 199yds

2012	**FINIAN'S RAINBOW** 9-11-10	8
2013	**SPRINTER SACRE** 7-11-10	7
2014	**SIRE DE GRUGY** 8-11-10	11
2015	**DODGING BULLETS** 7-11-10	11
2016	**SPRINTER SACRE** 10-11-10	10
2017	**SPECIAL TIARA** 10-11-10	10
2018	**ALTIOR** 8-11-10	9
2019	**ALTIOR** 9-11-10	10
2020	**POLITOLOGUE** 9-11-10	5
2021	**PUT THE KETTLE ON** 7-11-3	9

BALLYMORE NOVICES' HURDLE
Cheltenham-2m 5f 26yds

2012	**SIMONSIG** 6-11-7	17
2013	**THE NEW ONE** 5-11-7	8
2014	**FAUGHEEN** 6-11-7	15
2015	**WINDSOR PARK** 6-11-7	10
2016	**YORKHILL** 6-11-7	11
2017	**WILLOUGHBY COURT** 6-11-7	15
2018	**SAMCRO** 6-11-7	14
2019	**CITY ISLAND** 6-11-7	16
2020	**ENVOI ALLEN** 6-11-7	12
2021	**BOB OLINGER** 6-11-7	7

BROWN ADVISORY NOVICES' CHASE
(RSA Insurance Novices' Chase before 2021)
Cheltenham-3m 80yds

2012	**BOBS WORTH** 7-11-4	9
2013	**LORD WINDERMERE** 7-11-4	11
2014	**O'FAOLAINS BOY** 7-11-4	15
2015	**DON POLI** 6-11-4	8
2016	**BLAKLION** 7-11-4	8
2017	**MIGHT BITE** 8-11-4	12
2018	**PRESENTING PERCY** 7-11-4	10
2019	**TOPOFTHEGAME** 7-11-4	10
2020	**CHAMP** 8-11-4	10
2021	**MONKFISH** 7-11-4	6

STAYERS' HURDLE
(World Hurdle before 2017)
Cheltenham-2m 7f 213yds

2012	**BIG BUCK'S** 9-11-10	11
2013	**SOLWHIT** 9-11-10	13
2014	**MORE OF THAT** 6-11-10	10
2015	**COLE HARDEN** 6-11-10	16
2016	**THISTLECRACK** 8-11-10	12
2017	**NICHOLS CANYON** 7-11-10	12
2018	**PENHILL** 7-11-10	15
2019	**PAISLEY PARK** 7-11-10	18
2020	**LISNAGAR OSCAR** 7-11-10	15
2021	**FLOORING PORTER** 6-11-10	15

TRIUMPH HURDLE (4y)
Cheltenham-2m 179yds

2012	**COUNTRYWIDE FLAME** 11-0	20
2013	**OUR CONOR** 11-0	17
2014	**TIGER ROLL** 11-0	16
2015	**PEACE AND CO** 11-0	16
2016	**IVANOVICH GORBATOV** 11-0	15
2017	**DEFI DU SEUIL** 11-0	15
2018	**FARCLAS** 11-0	12
2019	**PENTLAND HILLS** 11-0	14
2020	**BURNING VICTORY** 10-7	13
2021	**QUILIXIOS** 11-0	8

CHELTENHAM GOLD CUP
Cheltenham-3m 2f 110yds

2012	**SYNCHRONISED** 9-11-10	14
2013	**BOBS WORTH** 8-11-10	9
2014	**LORD WINDERMERE** 8-11-10	13
2015	**CONEYGREE** 8-11-10	16
2016	**DON COSSACK** 9-11-10	9
2017	**SIZING JOHN** 7-11-10	13
2018	**NATIVE RIVER** 8-11-10	15
2019	**AL BOUM PHOTO** 7-11-10	16
2020	**AL BOUM PHOTO** 8-11-10	12
2021	**MINELLA INDO** 8-11-10	12

RYANAIR CHASE (FESTIVAL TROPHY)
Cheltenham-2m 4f 166yds
2012	**RIVERSIDE THEATRE** 8-11-10	12
2013	**CUE CARD** 7-11-10	8
2014	**DYNASTE** 8-11-10	11
2015	**UXIZANDRE** 7-11-10	14
2016	**VAUTOUR** 7-11-10	15
2017	**UN DE SCEAUX** 9-11-10	8
2018	**BALKO DES FLOS** 7-11-10	6
2019	**FRODON** 7-11-10	12
2020	**MIN** 9-11-10	8
2021	**ALLAHO** 7-11-10	11

BOWL CHASE
Aintree-3m 210yds
2012	**FOLLOW THE PLAN** 9-11-7	11
2013	**FIRST LIEUTENANT** 8-11-7	8
2014	**SILVINIACO CONTI** 8-11-7	6
2015	**SILVINIACO CONTI** 9-11-7	6
2016	**CUE CARD** 10-11-7	9
2017	**TEA FOR TWO** 8-11-7	7
2018	**MIGHT BITE** 9-11-7	8
2019	**KEMBOY** 7-11-7	6
2020	RACE CANCELLED	
2021	**CLAN DES OBEAUX** 9-11-7	9

MELLING CHASE
Aintree-2m 3f 200yds
2012	**FINIAN'S RAINBOW** 9-11-10	8
2013	**SPRINTER SACRE** 7-11-10	6
2014	**BOSTON BOB** 9-11-10	10
2015	**DON COSSACK** 8-11-10	10
2016	**GOD'S OWN** 8-11-10	6
2017	**FOX NORTON** 7-11-7	9
2018	**POLITOLOGUE** 7-11-7	6
2019	**MIN** 8-11-7	6
2020	RACE CANCELLED	
2021	**FAKIR D'OUDAIRIES** 6-11-7	7

AINTREE HURDLE
Aintree-2m 4f
2012	**OSCAR WHISKY** 7-11-7	5
2013	**ZARKANDAR** 6-11-7	9
2014	**THE NEW ONE** 6-11-7	7
2015	**JEZKI** 7-11-7	6
2016	**ANNIE POWER** 8-11-0	6
2017	**BUVEUR D'AIR** 6-11-7	6
2018	**L'AMI SERGE** 8-11-7	9
2019	**SUPASUNDAE** 9-11-7	7
2020	RACE CANCELLED	
2021	**ABACADABRAS** 7-11-7	11

SCOTTISH GRAND NATIONAL (H'CAP CHASE)
Ayr-3m 7f 176 yds
2012	**MERIGO** 11-10-2	2
2013	**GODSMEJUDGE** 7-11-3	2
2014	**AL CO** 9-10-0	2
2015	**WAYWARD PRINCE** 11-10-1	2
2016	**VICENTE** 7-11-3	2
2017	**VICENTE** 8-11-10	3
2018	**JOE FARRELL** 9-10-6	2
2019	**TAKINGRISKS** 10-10-1	2
2020	RACE CANCELLED	
2021	**MIGHTY THUNDER** 8-11-7	2

BET365 GOLD CUP (H'CAP CHASE)
Sandown-3m 4f 166yds
2012	**TIDAL BAY** 11-11-12	1
2013	**QUENTIN COLLONGES** 9-10-12	1
2014	**HADRIAN'S APPROACH** 7-11-0	1
2015	**JUST A PAR** 8-10-0	2
2016	**THE YOUNG MASTER** 7-10-12	2
2017	**HENLLAN HARRI** 9-10-0	1
2018	**STEP BACK** 8-10-0	2
2019	**TALKISCHEAP** 7-10-11	1
2020	RACE CANCELLED	
2021	**POTTERMAN** 8-11-9	1

DISTANCE CONVERSION
5f	1,000m	10f	2,000m	15f	3,000m	20f	4,000m
6f	1,200m	11f	2,200m	16f	3,200m	21f	4,200m
7f	1,400m	12f	2,400m	17f	3,400m	22f	4,400m
8f	1,600m	13f	2,600m	18f	3,600m		
9f	1,800m	14f	2,800m	19f	3,800m		

LEADING TRAINERS ON THE FLAT: 1905-2021

1905 W T Robinson	1944 Frank Butters	1983 W Hern
1906 Hon G Lambton	1945 W Earl	1984 H Cecil
1907 A Taylor	1946 Frank Butters	1985 H Cecil
1908 C Morton	1947 F Darling	1986 M Stoute
1909 A Taylor	1948 C F N Murless	1987 H Cecil
1910 A Taylor	1949 Frank Butters	1988 H Cecil
1911 Hon G Lambton	1950 C H Semblat	1989 M Stoute
1912 Hon G Lambton	1951 J L Jarvis	1990 H Cecil
1913 R Wootton	1952 M Marsh	1991 P Cole
1914 A Taylor	1953 J L Jarvis	1992 R Hannon Snr
1915 P P Gilpin	1954 C Boyd-Rochfort	1993 H Cecil
1916 R C Dawson	1955 C Boyd-Rochfort	1994 M Stoute
1917 A Taylor	1956 C F Elsey	1995 J Dunlop
1918 A Taylor	1957 C F N Murless	1996 Saeed bin Suroor
1919 A Taylor	1958 C Boyd-Rochfort	1997 M Stoute
1920 A Taylor	1959 C F N Murless	1998 Saeed bin Suroor
1921 A Taylor	1960 C F N Murless	1999 Saeed bin Suroor
1922 A Taylor	1961 C F N Murless	2000 Sir M Stoute
1923 A Taylor	1962 W Hern	2001 A O'Brien
1924 R C Dawson	1963 P Prendergast	2002 A O'Brien
1925 A Taylor	1964 P Prendergast	2003 Sir M Stoute
1926 F Darling	1965 P Prendergast	2004 Saeed bin Suroor
1927 Frank Butters	1966 M V O'Brien	2005 Sir M Stoute
1928 Frank Butters	1967 C F N Murless	2006 Sir M Stoute
1929 R C Dawson	1968 C F N Murless	2007 A O'Brien
1930 H S Persse	1969 A M Budgett	2008 A O'Brien
1931 J Lawson	1970 C F N Murless	2009 Sir M Stoute
1932 Frank Butters	1971 I Balding	2010 R Hannon Snr
1933 F Darling	1972 W Hern	2011 R Hannon Snr
1934 Frank Butters	1973 C F N Murless	2012 J Gosden
1935 Frank Butters	1974 P Walwyn	2013 R Hannon Snr
1936 J Lawson	1975 P Walwyn	2014 R Hannon Jnr
1937 C Boyd-Rochfort	1976 H Cecil	2015 J Gosden
1938 C Boyd-Rochfort	1977 M V O'Brien	2016 A O'Brien
1939 J L Jarvis	1978 H Cecil	2017 A O'Brien
1940 F Darling	1979 H Cecil	2018 J Gosden
1941 F Darling	1980 W Hern	2019 J Gosden
1942 F Darling	1981 M Stoute	2020 J Gosden
1943 W Nightingall	1982 H Cecil	2021 C Appleby

CHAMPION JOCKEYS ON THE FLAT: 1904-2021

1904 O Madden	161	1924 C Elliott	106	1945 G Richards	104
1905 E Wheatley	124	1925 G Richards	118	1946 G Richards	212
1906 W Higgs	149	1926 T Weston	95	1947 G Richards	269
1907 W Higgs	146	1927 G Richards	164	1948 G Richards	224
1908 D Maher	139	1928 G Richards	148	1949 G Richards	261
1909 F Wootton	165	1929 G Richards	135	1950 G Richards	201
1910 F Wootton	137	1930 F Fox	129	1951 G Richards	227
1911 F Wootton	187	1931 G Richards	145	1952 G Richards	231
1912 F Wootton	118	1932 G Richards	190	1953 Sir G Richards	191
1913 D Maher	115	1933 G Richards	259	1954 D Smith	129
1914 S Donoghue	129	1934 G Richards	212	1955 D Smith	168
1915 S Donoghue	62	1935 G Richards	217	1956 D Smith	155
1916 S Donoghue	43	1936 G Richards	174	1957 A Breasley	173
1917 S Donoghue	42	1937 G Richards	216	1958 D Smith	165
1918 S Donoghue	66	1938 G Richards	206	1959 D Smith	157
1919 S Donoghue	129	1939 G Richards	155	1960 L Piggott	170
1920 S Donoghue	143	1940 G Richards	68	1961 A Breasley	171
1921 S Donoghue	141	1941 H Wragg	71	1962 A Breasley	179
1922 S Donoghue	102	1942 G Richards	67	1963 A Breasley	176
1923 S Donoghue	89	1943 G Richards	65	1964 L Piggott	140
1923 C Elliott	89	1944 G Richards	88	1965 L Piggott	160

1966 L Piggott	191	1985 S Cauthen	195	2004 L Dettori	192
1967 L Piggott	117	1986 Pat Eddery	176	2005 J Spencer	163
1968 L Piggott	139	1987 S Cauthen	197	2006 R Moore	180
1969 L Piggott	163	1988 Pat Eddery	183	2007 S Sanders	190
1970 L Piggott	162	1989 Pat Eddery	171	J Spencer	190
1971 L Piggott	162	1990 Pat Eddery	209	2008 R Moore	186
1972 W Carson	132	1991 Pat Eddery	165	2009 R Moore	174
1973 W Carson	164	1992 M Roberts	206	2010 P Hanagan	191
1974 Pat Eddery	148	1993 Pat Eddery	169	2011 P Hanagan	165
1975 Pat Eddery	164	1994 L Dettori	233	2012 R Hughes	172
1976 Pat Eddery	162	1995 L Dettori	211	2013 R Hughes	203
1977 Pat Eddery	176	1996 Pat Eddery	186	2014 R Hughes	161
1978 W Carson	182	1997 K Fallon	196	2015 S De Sousa	132
1979 J Mercer	164	1998 K Fallon	185	2016 J Crowley	148
1980 W Carson	166	1999 K Fallon	200	2017 S De Sousa	155
1981 L Piggott	179	2000 K Darley	152	2018 S De Sousa	148
1982 L Piggott	188	2001 K Fallon	166	2019 O Murphy	168
1983 W Carson	159	2002 K Fallon	144	2020 O Murphy	142
1984 S Cauthen	130	2003 K Fallon	208	2021 O Murphy	153

CHAMPION APPRENTICES ON THE FLAT 1986-2021

1986 G Carter	34	1999 R Winston	49	2010 M Lane	41
1987 G Bardwell	27	2000 L Newman	87	2011 M Harley	57
1988 G Bardwell	39	2001 C Catlin	71	2012 A Ryan	40
1989 L Dettori	71	2002 P Hanagan	74	2013 J Hart	51
1990 J Fortune	46	2003 R Moore	52	2014 O Murphy	74
1991 D Holland	79	2004 T Queally	59	2015 T Marquand	54
1992 D Harrison	56	2005 S Golam	44	2016 J Gordon	50
1993 J Weaver	60	H Turner	44	2017 D Egan	61
1994 S Davies	45	2006 S Donohoe	44	2018 J Watson	77
1995 S Sanders	61	2007 G Fairley	65	2019 C Fallon	50
1996 D O'Neill	79	2008 W Buick	50	2020 C Fallon	48
1997 R Ffrench	77	D Probert	50	2021 M Ghiani	51
1998 C Lowther	72	2009 F Tylicki	60		

LEADING OWNERS ON THE FLAT: 1899-2021

1899 Duke of Westminster	1924 H.H. Aga Khan	1949 H.H. Aga Khan
1900 H.R.H. The Prince of Wales	1925 Ld Astor	1950 M M Boussac
1901 Sir G Blundell Maple	1926 Ld Woolavington	1951 M M Boussac
1902 Mr R S Sievier	1927 Ld Derby	1952 H.H. Aga Khan
1903 Sir James Miller	1928 Ld Derby	1953 Sir Victor Sassoon
1904 Sir James Miller	1929 H.H. Aga Khan	1954 Her Majesty
1905 Col W Hall Walker	1930 H.H. Aga Khan	1955 Lady Zia Wernner
1906 Ld Derby (late)	1931 Mr J A Dewar	1956 Maj L B Holliday
1907 Col W Hall Walker	1932 H.H. Aga Khan	1957 Her Majesty
1908 Mr J B Joel	1933 Ld Derby	1958 Mr J McShain
1909 Mr "Fairie"	1934 H.H. Aga Khan	1959 Prince Aly Khan
1910 Mr "Fairie"	1935 H.H. Aga Khan	1960 Sir Victor Sassoon
1911 Ld Derby	1936 Ld Astor	1961 Maj L B Holliday
1912 Mr T Pilkington	1937 H.H. Aga Khan	1962 Maj L B Holliday
1913 Mr J B Joel	1938 Ld Derby	1963 Mr J R Mullion
1914 Mr J B Joel	1939 Ld Rosebery	1964 Mrs H E Jackson
1915 Mr L Neumann	1940 Lord Rothermere	1965 M J Ternynck
1916 Mr E Hulton	1941 Ld Glanely	1966 Lady Zia Wernher
1917 Mr "Fairie"	1942 His Majesty	1967 Mr H J Joel
1918 Lady James Douglas	1943 Miss D Paget	1968 Mr Raymond R Guest
1919 Ld Glanely	1944 H.H. Aga Khan	1969 Mr D Robinson
1920 Sir Robert Jardine	1945 Ld Derby	1970 Mr C Engelhard
1921 Mr S B Joel	1946 H.H. Aga Khan	1971 Mr P Mellon
1922 Ld Woolavington	1947 H.H. Aga Khan	1972 Mrs J Hislop
1923 Ld Derby	1948 H.H. Aga Khan	1973 Mr N B Hunt

1974 Mr N B Hunt
1975 Dr C Vittadini
1976 Mr D Wildenstein
1977 Mr R Sangster
1978 Mr R Sangster
1979 Sir M Sobell
1980 S Weinstock
1981 H.H. Aga Khan
1982 Mr R Sangster
1983 Mr R Sangster
1984 Mr R Sangster
1985 Sheikh Mohammed
1986 Sheikh Mohammed
1987 Sheikh Mohammed
1988 Sheikh Mohammed
1989 Sheikh Mohammed

1990 Mr Hamdan Al-Maktoum
1991 Sheikh Mohammed
1992 Sheikh Mohammed
1993 Sheikh Mohammed
1994 Mr Hamdan Al-Maktoum
1995 Mr Hamdan Al-Maktoum
1996 Godolphin
1997 Sheikh Mohammed
1998 Godolphin
1999 Godolphin
2000 H.H. Aga Khan
2001 Godolphin
2002 Mr Hamdan Al-Maktoum
2003 K Abdullah
2004 Godolphin
2005 Mr Hamdan Al-Maktoum

2006 Godolphin
2007 Godolphin
2008 HRH Princess Haya of Jordan
2009 Mr Hamdan Al-Maktoum
2010 K Abdullah
2011 K Abdullah
2012 Godolphin
2013 Godolphin
2014 Mr Hamdan Al-Maktoum
2015 Godolphin
2016 Godolphin
2017 Godolphin
2018 Godolphin
2019 Mr Hamdan Al-Maktoum
2020 Mr Hamdan Al-Maktoum
2021 Godolphin

LEADING SIRES ON THE FLAT: 1899-2021

1899 Orme
1900 St Simon
1901 St Simon
1902 Persimmon
1903 St Frusquin
1904 Gallinule
1905 Gallinule
1906 Persimmon
1907 St Frusquin
1908 Persimmon
1909 Cyllene
1910 Cyllene
1911 Sundridge
1912 Persimmon
1913 Desmond
1914 Polymelus
1915 Polymelus
1916 Polymelus
1917 Bayardo
1918 Bayardo
1919 The Tetrarch
1920 Polymelus
1921 Polymelus
1922 Lemberg
1923 Swynford
1924 Son-in-Law
1925 Phalaris
1926 Hurry On
1927 Buchan
1928 Phalaris
1929 Tetratema
1930 Son-in-Law
1931 Pharos
1932 Gainsborough
1933 Gainsborough
1934 Blandford
1935 Blandford
1936 Fairway
1937 Solario
1938 Blandford
1939 Fairway

1940 Hyperion
1941 Hyperion
1942 Hyperion
1943 Fairway
1944 Fairway
1945 Hyperion
1946 Hyperion
1947 Nearco
1948 Big Game
1949 Nearco
1950 Fair Trial
1951 Nasrullah
1952 Tehran
1953 Chanteur II
1954 Hyperion
1955 Alycidon
1956 Court Martial
1957 Court Martial
1958 Mossborough
1959 Petition
1960 Aureole
1961 Aureole
1962 Never Say Die
1963 Ribot
1964 Chamossaire
1965 Court Harwell
1966 Charlottesville
1967 Ribot
1968 Ribot
1969 Crepello
1970 Northern Dancer
1971 Never Bend
1972 Queen's Hussar
1973 Vaguely Noble
1974 Vaguely Noble
1975 Great Nephew
1976 Wolver Hollow
1977 Northern Dancer
1978 Mill Reef (USA)
1979 Petingo
1980 Pitcairn

1981 Great Nephew
1982 Be My Guest (USA)
1983 Northern Dancer
1984 Northern Dancer
1985 Kris
1986 Nijinsky (CAN)
1987 Mill Reef (USA)
1988 Caerleon (USA)
1989 Blushing Groom (FR)
1990 Sadler's Wells (USA)
1991 Caerleon (USA)
1992 Sadler's Wells (USA)
1993 Sadler's Wells (USA)
1994 Sadler's Wells (USA)
1995 Sadler's Wells (USA)
1996 Sadler's Wells (USA)
1997 Sadler's Wells (USA)
1998 Sadler's Wells (USA)
1999 Sadler's Wells (USA)
2000 Sadler's Wells (USA)
2001 Sadler's Wells (USA)
2002 Sadler's Wells (USA)
2003 Sadler's Wells (USA)
2004 Sadler's Wells (USA)
2005 Danehill (USA)
2006 Danehill (USA)
2007 Danehill (USA)
2008 Galileo (IRE)
2009 Danehill Dancer (IRE)
2010 Galileo (IRE)
2011 Galileo (IRE)
2012 Galileo (IRE)
2013 Galileo (IRE)
2014 Galileo (IRE)
2015 Galileo (IRE)
2016 Galileo (IRE)
2017 Galileo (IRE)
2018 Galileo (IRE)
2019 Galileo (IRE)
2020 Galileo (IRE)
2021 Frankel

LEADING BREEDERS ON THE FLAT: 1915-2021

1915 Mr L Neumann
1916 Mr E Hulton
1917 Mr "Fairie"
1918 Lady James Douglas
1919 Ld Derby
1920 Ld Derby
1921 Mr S B Joel
1922 Ld Derby
1923 Ld Derby
1924 Lady Sykes
1925 Ld Astor
1926 Ld Woolavington
1927 Ld Derby
1928 Ld Derby
1929 Ld Derby
1930 Ld Derby
1931 Ld Dewar
1932 H.H. Aga Khan
1933 Sir Alec Black
1934 H.H. Aga Khan
1935 H.H. Aga Khan
1936 Ld Astor
1937 H.H. Aga Khan
1938 Ld Derby
1939 Ld Rosebery
1940 Mr H E Morriss
1941 Ld Glanely
1942 National Stud
1943 Miss D Paget
1944 Ld Rosebery
1945 Ld Derby
1946 Lt- Col H Boyd-Rochfort
1947 H.H. Aga Khan
1948 H.H. Aga Khan
1949 H.H. Aga Khan
1950 M M Boussac

1951 M M Boussac
1952 H. H. Aga Khan
1953 Mr F Darling
1954 Maj L B Holliday
1955 Someries Stud
1956 Maj L B Holliday
1957 Eve Stud
1958 Mr R Ball
1959 Prince Aly Khan and the late
         H.H. Aga Khan
1960 Eve Stud Ltd
1961 Eve Stud Ltd
1962 Maj L B Holliday
1963 Mr H F Guggenheim
1964 Bull Run Stud
1965 Mr J Ternynck
1966 Someries Stud
1967 Mr H J Joel
1968 Mill Ridge Farm
1969 Lord Rosebery
1970 Mr E P Taylor
1971 Mr P Mellon
1972 Mr J Hislop
1973 Claiborne Farm
1974 Mr N B Hunt
1975 Overbury Stud
1976 Dayton Ltd
1977 Mr E P Taylor
1978 Cragwood Estates Inc
1979 Ballymacoll Stud
1980 P Clarke
1981 H.H. Aga Khan
1982 Someries Stud
1983 White Lodge Stud
1984 Mr E P Taylor
1985 Dalham Stud Farms

1986 H.H. Aga Khan
1987 Cliveden Stud
1988 H. H. Aga Khan
1989 Mr Hamdan Al-Maktoum
1990 Capt. Macdonald- Buchanan
1991 Barronstown Stud
1992 Swettenham Stud
1993 Juddmonte Farms
1994 Shadwell Farm & Estate Ltd
1995 Shadwell Farm & Estate Ltd
1996 Sheikh Mohammed
1997 Sheikh Mohammed
1998 Sheikh Mohammed
1999 H. H. The Aga Khan's Studs
2000 H. H. The Aga Khan's Studs
2001 Shadwell Farm & Estate Ltd
2002 Gainsborough Stud
2003 Juddmonte
2004 Juddmonte
2005 Shadwell Farm & Estate Ltd
2006 Darley
2007 Darley
2008 Darley
2009 Darley
2010 Juddmonte
2011 Juddmonte
2012 Juddmonte
2013 Darley
2014 Darley
2015 Darley
2016 Darley
2017 Darley
2018 Godolphin
2019 Godolphin
2020 Godolphin
2021 Godolphin

LEADING TRAINERS OVER JUMPS: 1950-2021

1950-51 T F Rimell
1951-52 N Crump
1952-53 M V O'Brien
1953-54 M V O'Brien
1954-55 H R Price
1955-56 W Hall
1956-57 N Crump
1957-58 F T T Walwyn
1958-59 H R Price
1959-60 P V F Cazalet
1960-61 T F Rimell
1961-62 H R Price
1962-63 K Piggott
1963-64 F T T Walwyn
1964-65 P V F Cazalet
1965-66 H R Price
1966-67 H R Price
1967-68 Denys Smith
1968-69 T F Rimell
1969-70 T F Rimell
1970-71 F T Winter
1971-72 F T Winter
1972-73 F T Winter
1973-74 F T Winter

1974-75 F T Winter
1975-76 T F Rimell
1976-77 F T Winter
1977-78 F T Winter
1978-79 M H Easterby
1979-80 M H Easterby
1980-81 M H Easterby
1981-82 M W Dickinson
1982-83 M W Dickinson
1983-84 M W Dickinson
1984-85 F T Winter
1985-86 N J Henderson
1986-87 N J Henderson
1987-88 D R C Elsworth
1988-89 M C Pipe
1989-90 M C Pipe
1990-91 M C Pipe
1991-92 M C Pipe
1992-93 M C Pipe
1993-94 D Nicholson
1994-95 D Nicholson
1995-96 M C Pipe
1996-97 M C Pipe
1997-98 M C Pipe

1998-99 M C Pipe
1999-00 M C Pipe
2000-01 M C Pipe
2001-02 M C Pipe
2002-03 M C Pipe
2003-04 M C Pipe
2004-05 M C Pipe
2005-06 P F Nicholls
2006-07 P F Nicholls
2007-08 P F Nicholls
2008-09 P F Nicholls
2009-10 P F Nicholls
2010-11 P F Nicholls
2010-11 P F Nicholls
2011-12 P F Nicholls
2012-13 N J Henderson
2013-14 P F Nicholls
2014-15 P F Nicholls
2015-16 P F Nicholls
2016-17 N J Henderson
2017-18 N J Henderson
2018-19 P F Nicholls
2019-20 N J Henderson
2020-21 P F Nicholls

CHAMPION JOCKEYS OVER JUMPS: 1905-2021
Prior to the 1925-26 season the figure relates to racing between January and December

1905	F Mason	73
1906	F Mason	58
1907	F Mason	59
1908	P Cowley	65
1909	R Gordon	45
1910	E Piggott	67
1911	W Payne	76
1912	I Anthony	78
1913	E Piggott	60
1914	Mr J R Anthony	60
1915	E Piggott	44
1916	C Hawkins	17
1917	W Smith	15
1918	G Duller	17
1919	Mr H Brown	48
1920	F B Rees	64
1921	F B Rees	65
1922	J Anthony	78
1923	F B Rees	64
1924	F B Rees	108
1925	E Foster	76
1925-26	T Leader	61
1926-27	F B Rees	59
1927-28	W Stott	88
1928-29	W Stott	65
1929-30	W Stott	77
1930-31	W Stott	81
1931-32	W Stott	77
1932-33	G Wilson	61
1933-34	G Wilson	56
1934-35	G Wilson	73
1935-36	G Wilson	57
1936-37	G Wilson	45
1937-38	G Wilson	59
1938-39	T F Rimell	61
1939-40	T F Rimell	24
1940-41	G Wilson	22
1941-42	R Smyth	12
1942-43	No racing	
1943-44	No racing	

1944-45	H Nicholson	15
	T F Rimell	15
1945-46	T F Rimell	54
1946-47	J Dowdeswell	58
1947-48	B Marshall	66
1948-49	T Moloney	60
1949-50	T Moloney	95
1950-51	T Moloney	83
1951-52	T Moloney	99
1952-53	F Winter	121
1953-54	R Francis	76
1954-55	T Moloney	67
1955-56	F Winter	74
1956-57	F Winter	80
1957-58	F Winter	82
1958-59	T Brookshaw	83
1959-60	S Mellor	68
1960-61	S Mellor	118
1961-62	S Mellor	80
1962-63	J Gifford	70
1963-64	J Gifford	94
1964-65	T Biddlecombe	114
1965-66	T Biddlecombe	102
1966-67	J Gifford	122
1967-68	J Gifford	82
1968-69	B R Davies	77
	T Biddlecombe	77
1969-70	B R Davies	91
1970-71	G Thorner	74
1971-72	B R Davies	89
1972-73	R Barry	125
1973-74	R Barry	94
1974-75	T Stack	82
1975-76	J Francome	96
1976-77	T Stack	97
1977-78	J O'Neill	149
1978-79	J Francome	95
1979-80	J O'Neill	117
1980-81	J Francome	105
1981-82	J Francome	120

	P Scudamore	120
1982-83	J Francome	106
1983-84	J Francome	131
1984-85	J Francome	101
1985-86	P Scudamore	91
1986-87	P Scudamore	123
1987-88	P Scudamore	132
1988-89	P Scudamore	221
1989-90	P Scudamore	170
1990-91	P Scudamore	141
1991-92	P Scudamore	175
1992-93	R Dunwoody	173
1993-94	R Dunwoody	197
1994-95	R Dunwoody	160
1995-96	A P McCoy	175
1996-97	A P McCoy	190
1997-98	A P McCoy	253
1998-99	A P McCoy	186
1999-00	A P McCoy	245
2000-01	A P McCoy	191
2001-02	A P McCoy	289
2002-03	A P McCoy	256
2003-04	A P McCoy	209
2004-05	A P McCoy	200
2005-06	A P McCoy	178
2006-07	A P McCoy	184
2007-08	A P McCoy	140
2008-09	A P McCoy	186
2009-10	A P McCoy	195
2010-11	A P McCoy	218
2011-12	A P McCoy	199
2012-13	A P McCoy	185
2013-14	A P McCoy	218
2014-15	A P McCoy	231
2015-16	R Johnson	235
2016-17	R Johnson	189
2017-18	R Johnson	176
2018-19	R Johnson	200
2019-20	B Hughes	141
2020-21	H Skelton	152

LEADING OWNERS OVER JUMPS: 1950-2021
(Please note that prior to the 1994-95 season the leading owner was determined by win prize money only)

1950-51	Mr J Royle
1951-52	Miss D Paget
1952-53	Mr J H Griffin
1953-54	Mr J H Griffin
1954-55	Mrs W H E Welman
1955-56	Mrs L Carver
1956-57	Mrs Geoffrey Kohn
1957-58	Mr D J Coughlan
1958-59	Mr J E Bigg
1959-60	Miss W H Wallace
1960-61	Mr C Vaughan
1961-62	Mr N Cohen
1962-63	Mr P B Raymond
1963-64	Mr J K Goodman
1964-65	Mrs M Stephenson
1965-66	Duchess of Westminster
1966-67	Mr C P T Watkins
1967-68	Mr H S Alper
1968-69	Mr B P Jenks
1969-70	Mr E R Courage

1970-71	Mr F Pontin
1971-72	Capt T A Forster
1972-73	Mr N H Le Mare
1973-74	Mr N H Le Mare
1974-75	Mr R Guest
1975-76	Mr P B Raymond
1976-77	Mr N H Le Mare
1977-78	Mrs O Jackson
1978-79	Snailwell Stud Co Ltd
1979-80	Mr H J Joel
1980-81	Mr R J Wilson
1981-82	Sheikh Ali Abu Khamsin
1982-83	Sheikh Ali Abu Khamsin
1983-84	Sheikh Ali Abu Khamsin
1984-85	T Kilroe and Son Ltd
1985-86	Sheikh Ali Abu Khamsin
1986-87	Mr H J Joel
1987-88	Miss Juliet E Reed
1988-89	Mr R Burridge
1989-90	Mrs Harry J Duffey

1990-91	Mr P Piller
1991-92	Whitcombe Manor Racing Stables Ltd
1992-93	Mrs J Mould
1993-94	Pell-Mell Partners
1994-95	Roach Foods Limited
1995-96	Mr A T A Wates
1996-97	Mr R Ogden
1997-98	Mr D A Johnson
1998-99	Mr J P McManus
1999-00	Mr R Ogden
2000-01	Sir R Ogden
2001-02	Mr D A Johnson
2002-03	Mr D A Johnson
2003-04	Mr D A Johnson
2004-05	Mr D A Johnson
2005-06	Mr J P McManus
2006-07	Mr D A Johnson
2007-08	Mr D A Johnson
2008-09	Mr J P McManus

2009-10 Mr J P McManus
2010-11 Mr T Hemmings
2011-12 Mr J P McManus
2012-13 Mr J P McManus

2013-14 Mr J P McManus
2014-15 Mr J P McManus
2015-16 Gigginstown House Stud
2016-17 Mr J P McManus

2017-18 Mr J P McManus
2018-19 Mr J P McManus
2019-20 Mr J P McManus
2020-21 Mr J P McManus

LEADING AMATEUR RIDERS OVER JUMPS: 1954-2021

1954-55 Mr A H Moralee 16
1955-56 Mr R McCreery 13
       Mr A H Moralee 13
1956-57 Mr R McCreery 23
1957-58 Mr J Lawrence 18
1958-59 Mr J Sutcliffe 18
1959-60 Mr G Kindersley 22
1960-61 Sir W Pigott-Brown 28
1961-62 Mr A Biddlecombe 30
1962-63 Sir W Pigott-Brown 20
1963-64 Mr S Davenport 32
1964-65 Mr M Gifford 15
1965-66 Mr C Collins 24
1966-67 Mr C Collins 33
1967-68 Mr R Tate 30
1968-69 Mr R Tate 17
1969-70 Mr M Dickinson 23
1970-71 Mr J Lawrence 17
1971-72 Mr W Foulkes 26
1972-73 Mr R Smith 56
1973-74 Mr A Webber 21
1974-75 Mr R Lamb 22
1975-76 Mr P Greenall 25
       Mr G Jones 25
1976-77 Mr P Greenall 27

1977-78 Mr G Sloan 23
1978-79 Mr T G Dun 26
1979-80 Mr O Sherwood 29
1980-81 Mr P Webber 32
1981-82 Mr D Browne 28
1982-83 Mr D Browne 33
1983-84 Mr S Sherwood 28
1984-85 Mr S Sherwood 30
1985-86 Mr T Thomson Jones 25
1986-87 Mr T Thomson Jones 19
1987-88 Mr T Thomson Jones 15
1988-89 Mr P Fenton 23
1989-90 Mr P McMahon 15
1990-91 Mr K Johnson 24
1991-92 Mr M P Hourigan 24
1992-93 Mr A Thornton 26
1993-94 Mr J Greenall 21
1994-95 Mr D Parker 16
1995-96 Mr J Culloty 40
1996-97 Mr R Thornton 30
1997-98 Mr S Durack 41
1998-99 Mr A Dempsey 47
1999-00 Mr P Flynn 41
2000-01 Mr T Scudamore 24
2001-02 Mr D Crosse 19

2002-03 Mr C Williams 23
2003-04 Mr O Nelmes 14
2004-05 Mr T Greenall 31
2005-06 Mr T O'Brien 32
2006-07 Mr T Greenall 31
2007-08 Mr T Greenall 23
2008-09 Mr O Greenall 23
2009-10 Mr O Greenall 41
2010-11 Mr R Mahon 19
2011-12 Miss E Sayer 11
2012-13 Mr N de Boinville 16
2013-14 Mr H Bannister 11
2014-15 Mr H Bannister 16
2015-16 Mr D Noonan 19
2016-17 Mr J King 15
2017-18 Miss P Fuller 16
2018-19 Mr D Maxwell 18
2019-20 Mr D Maxwell 18
*2020-21 Miss G Andrews 4
       Mr J King 4
       Miss B Smith 4
       Miss L Turner 4
* Truncated season for amateurs owing to COVID

LEADING SIRES OVER JUMPS: 1989-2021

1989-90 Deep Run
1990-91 Deep Run
1991-92 Deep Run
1992-93 Deep Run
1993-94 Strong Gale
1994-95 Strong Gale
1995-96 Strong Gale
1996-97 Strong Gale
1997-98 Strong Gale
1998-99 Strong Gale
1999-00 Strong Gale

2000-01 Be My Native (USA)
2001-02 Be My Native (USA)
2002-03 Be My Native (USA)
2003-04 Be My Native (USA)
2004-05 Supreme Leader
2005-06 Supreme Leader
2006-07 Presenting
2007-08 Old Vic
2008-09 Presenting
2009-10 Presenting
2010-11 Presenting

2011-12 King's Theatre
2012-13 Beneficial
2013-14 King's Theatre
2014-15 King's Theatre
2015-16 King's Theatre
2016-17 King's Theatre
2017-18 King's Theatre
2018-19 Flemensfirth
2019-20 Milan
2020-21 Stowaway

JOCKEYS' AGENTS

Jockeys' agents and their contact details

Agent	Telephone	Mobile/Email
NICKY ADAMS	01488 72004/72964	07796547659 nickadams2594@hotmail.com
NEIL ALLAN	01243 543870	aneilallan@aol.com
ROSS BIRKETT	07855 065036	rbirkett1989@hotmail.co.uk
PAUL BRIERLEY		07824828750 bbjockeys@hotmail.co.uk
ADAM BROOK		07399390303 info@brooksportsmanagement.com
GLORIA CHARNOCK	01653 695004	07951576912 gloriacharnock@hotmail.com
PAUL CLARKE	01638 660804	07885914306 paul.clarke79@btinternet.com
GORDON CLARKSON	01451 509496	07493802743 gordonclarkson@live.co.uk
STEVEN CROFT		07809205556 steven.croft6@googlemail.com
CHRIS DIXON	07557129536	dixonbloodstock@gmail.com
SIMON DODDS	01509 734496	07974924735 simon.dodds@btinternet.com
SHELLEY DWYER	01638 493123	07949612256 shelleydwyer4031@outlook.com
SHIPPY ELLIS	01638 668484	07860864864 shippysjockeys@jockeysagent.com

Agent	Telephone	Mobile/Email
MARK FURNASS		07474242332 jockeysagent@gmail.com
AARON GORMAN		07966293350 aarongormanjockeysagent@gmail.com
RICHARD HALE	01768 88699	07909520542 richardhale77@hotmail.co.uk
NIALL HANNITY	01677 423363	07710141084 niallhannity@yahoo.co.uk
ALAN HARRISON	01969 326248	07846187991 ahjockagent60@yahoo.co.uk
TONY HIND	01638 724997	07807908599 tonyhind@jockeysagent.com
GAVIN HORNE	01392 433610	07914897170 renoodriver2@gmail.com
CHRIS HUMPLEBY		07712608969 chris.humpleby13@gmail.com
RUSS JAMES	01653 699466	07947414001 russjames2006@btconnect.com
BRUCE JEFFREY	01750 21521	07747854684 brucejeffrey@live.co.uk
GUY JEWELL	01672 861231	07765248859 guyjewell@btconnect.com
ANDY LEWIS		07838506594 andrew.lewis11@sky.com
SARA-LOUISE METCALFE	01635 269647	07918525354 troopersjockeys@hotmail.co.uk
JOHN NEILSON	01388 730249	07813874970 john@jlnjockeys.co.uk
GARETH OWEN	01603 569390	07958335206 garethowenracing@gmail.com

Agent	Telephone	Mobile/Email
IAN POPHAM		07791225707 ianpopham28@outlook.com
WILSON RENWICK		07860949577 wilsonrenwick@aol.com
SHASHI RIGHTON	01353 688594	07825381350 srighton.sr@googlemail.com
DAVE ROBERTS	01737 221368	07860234342 daveroberts.racing@gmail.com
PHILIP SHEA	01638 667456	07585120297 psheajockeysagent@gmail.com
ANNA WALLACE		07867923642 awallace51@yahoo.com
LAURA WAY	01704 834488	07775777494 laura.way@btconnect.com
IAN WOOD		07733156380 ianwood@chase3c.com

FLAT JOCKEYS

Riding weights and contact details
An index of agents appears on page 714

Jockey	Weight	Agent
DAVID ALLAN	8-10	Mrs G. S. Charnock
ANDREA ATZENI	8-5	Mr S. Croft
DAYVERSON DE BARROS	8-7	Miss A. Wallace
CONNOR BEASLEY	8-6	Mr G. R. Owen
ALED BEECH	7-13	Mr L. R. James
KATHERINE BEGLEY	9-0	01544 267672
CHARLIE BENNETT	8-6	Mr G. D. Jewell
CHARLES BISHOP	8-10	Mr Neil Allan
SEAN BOWEN	8-12	Mr Dave Roberts\ M. Furnass
JOSHUA BRYAN	8-9	Mr G. D. Jewell
WILLIAM BUICK	8-6	Mr Tony Hind
HARRY BURNS	8-4	Mr Christopher Humpleby
NEIL CALLAN	8-10	07710967430
WILLIAM CARSON	8-6	Mr Neil Allan
HOWARD CHENG	8-4	Miss A. Wallace
ROSS COAKLEY	8-10	Mr G. J. Horne
PAT COSGRAVE	8-9	Mr Paul Clarke
DOUGIE COSTELLO	8-10	Mr A. T. Brook
LAURA COUGHLAN	7-13	Mr Paul Brierley
HECTOR CROUCH	8-11	Mr G. D. Jewell
JIM CROWLEY	8-7	Mr Tony Hind
NICOLA CURRIE	8-0	Mr G. J. Horne
BEN CURTIS	8-5	Mr S. T. Dodds
RAY DAWSON	8-4	Mr A. T. Brook
PHIL DENNIS	8-10	Mrs G. S. Charnock
FRANKIE DETTORI	8-9	07703606162
PAT DOBBS	8-9	Mr Tony Hind
STEVIE DONOHOE	8-8	P.C. Shea
GEORGE DOWNING	8-11	Mr R. Birkett
HOLLIE DOYLE	8-0	Mr G. D. Jewell
JAMES DOYLE	8-10	Mr Christopher Humpleby
JACK DUERN	8-4	M. Furnass
MARTIN DWYER	8-3	Mr S. T. Dodds
TOM EAVES	8-7	Mr R. A. Hale
LEWIS EDMUNDS	8-9	Mr S. T. Dodds
DAVID EGAN	8-4	Mr Tony Hind
JOHN EGAN	8-3	Mr Paul Brierley
ANDREW ELLIOTT	8-4	Mrs G. S. Charnock
JANE ELLIOTT	8-0	Mr S. Croft
NATHAN EVANS	8-2	07592324869
JOHN FAHY	8-6	Mr Paul Brierley
CIEREN FALLON	8-5	Mr G. J. Horne
JOE FANNING	8-2	Mr N. Hannity
DURAN FENTIMAN	8-0	Mr Alan Harrison
ROYSTON FFRENCH	8-3	07880702502
JONATHAN FISHER	8-7	M. Furnass
JACK GARRITTY	8-12	K. W. Renwick
MARCO GHIANI	8-5	Mr S. M. Righton
JOSEPHINE GORDON	8-4	Mr A. T. Brook
JAMIE GORMLEY	8-0	Mr R. A. Hale
SHANE GRAY	8-4	Mr N. Hannity
TONY HAMILTON	8-8	Mr N. Hannity
PAUL HANAGAN	8-5	Mr R. A. Hale
CAM HARDIE	8-0	Mr R. A. Hale
MARTIN HARLEY	8-11	Mr Neil Allan
JASON HART	8-9	Mr Alan Harrison
ROBERT HAVLIN	8-7	Mr Neil Allan
JOEY HAYNES	8-5	Mr A. T. Brook
SAM HITCHCOTT	8-5	Mr N. M. Adams
DYLAN HOGAN	8-5	Mr Paul Brierley
ROB HORNBY	8-10	Mr N. M. Adams
SAM JAMES	8-6	K. W. Renwick
LIAM JONES	8-0	Miss A. Wallace
DARRAGH KEENAN	8-0	Mr S. T. Dodds
SHANE KELLY	8-7	Mr N. M. Adams
LIAM KENIRY	8-8	Mr N. M. Adams
RICHARD KINGSCOTE	8-8	Mr G. D. Jewell
ADAM KIRBY	9-0	Mr N. M. Adams
CLIFFORD LEE	8-10	Mr G. R. Owen
GRAHAM LEE	8-9	Mr R. A. Hale
SEAN LEVEY	8-10	Mr S. M. Righton
NICKY MACKAY	8-4	Mr N. A. Baxter
ELLIE MACKENZIE	8-3	Mr S. T. Dodds
GINA MANGAN	8-0	Mr L. R. James
TOM MARQUAND	8-7	Mr S. M. Righton
JOANNA MASON	8-5	Mr N. Hannity
PADDY MATHERS	8-0	Mrs G. S. Charnock
P. J. MCDONALD	8-6	Mr S. T. Dodds
BARRY MCHUGH	8-6	K. W. Renwick
FAYE MCMANOMAN	7-13	Mr Paul Brierley
ADAM MCNAMARA	8-10	P.C. Shea
JACK MITCHELL	8-8	Mr S. Croft
RYAN MOORE	8-9	Mr Tony Hind
LUKE MORRIS	8-0	Mr Neil Allan
PAULA MUIR	8-0	Mr Paul Brierley
ANDREW MULLEN	8-3	Mr R. A. Hale
PAUL MULRENNAN	8-10	Mr R. A. Hale
DANIEL MUSCUTT	8-10	Mr Paul Clarke
MEGAN NICHOLLS	8-4	07792440002
CAMERON NOBLE	8-9	Mr Paul Clarke
DAVID NOLAN	9-1	Mr R. A. Hale
FRANNY NORTON	8-0	Mr N. Hannity
DANE O'NEILL	8-7	Mr N. M. Adams
KIERAN O'NEILL	8-0	Mr N. M. Adams
PHILIP PRINCE	9-0	Miss S. L. Metcalfe
DAVID PROBERT	8-7	Mr Neil Allan
TOM QUEALLY	8-11	Mr S. T. Dodds
JIMMY QUINN	8-0	Miss A. Wallace
ALISTAIR RAWLINSON	8-11	Mr S. Croft
BEN ROBINSON	8-0	Mr R. A. Hale
CALLUM RODRIGUEZ	8-10	Mr R. A. Hale
ROSSA RYAN	8-7	Mr S. Croft
KIERAN SCHOFIELD	8-0	Mr S. T. Dodds
ROWAN SCOTT	8-5	Mr N. Hannity
HARRISON SHAW	8-5	Mr R. A. Hale
CALLUM SHEPHERD	8-9	Mr N. M. Adams
KIERAN SHOEMARK	8-10	Mr G. D. Jewell
JEFFERSON SMITH	8-2	Mr G. J. Horne
SILVESTRE DE SOUSA	8-0	Mrs Shelley Dwyer
RENATO SOUZA	8-8	07818814732
JAMIE SPENCER	8-7	Mr Christopher Humpleby
LOUIS STEWARD	8-11	Mr A. T. Brook

KEVIN STOTT	8 - 11	Mr R. A. Hale
JAMES SULLIVAN	8 - 0	Mr R. A. Hale
DALE SWIFT	8 - 9	Mr R. A. Hale
ROBERT TART	8 - 8	Mr R. Birkett
RYAN TATE	8 - 6	07860584701
DANIEL TUDHOPE	8 - 11	Mrs L. H. Way
HAYLEY TURNER	8 - 2	Mr G. D. Jewell
GEMMA TUTTY	8 - 7	07970095355
EOIN WALSH	8 - 10	Mr N. M. Adams
JASON WATSON	8 - 4	Mr C. Dixon
AMIE WAUGH	7 - 7	Mr J. L. Neilson
TREVOR WHELAN	8 - 7	P.C. Shea
ROBERT WINSTON	8 - 11	Miss A. Wallace
GEORGE WOOD	8 - 8	Mr S. M. Righton

Are your contact details missing or incorrect? If so please update us by email: hitraceform@weatherbys.co.uk

APPRENTICES

Riding weights and contact details

An index of agents appears on page 714

MUHAMMAD ADEEL (Stuart Williams)	8 - 6	c/o 01638 663984
GAVIN ASHTON (Roger Varian)	8 - 0	Mr Paul Brierley
LORENZO ATZORI (Stuart Williams)	8 - 0	c/o 01638 663984
GEORGE BASS (Mick Channon)	8 - 5	Mrs Shelley Dwyer
MIA BIGGS (Kevin Philippart de Foy)	8 - 0	Mr Paul Clarke
CONNOR BRACE (Fergal O'Brien)	8 - 12	Mr Dave Roberts\M. Furnass
JOE BRADNAM (Michael Bell)	8 - 3	c/o 07802264514
ANDREW BRESLIN (Mark Johnston)	7 - 9	Mr N. Hannity
AIDEN BROOKES (Micky Hammond)	7 - 13	K. W. Renwick
LIAM BROWNE (Richard Hannon)	8 - 4	Mr S. M. Righton
TOM BUCKLEY (Paul Nicholls)	9 - 0	Mr Dave Roberts
WILLIAM CARVER (Andrew Balding)	8 - 3	P. C. Shea
LUKE CATTON (Stuart Williams)	8 - 9	Mr G. D. Jewell
STEFANO CHERCHI (Amy Murphy)	8 - 3	Mr Paul Clarke
JACOB CLARK (Tom Clover)	8 - 4	c/o 01638 660055
SOPHIE CLEMENTS (Nigel Tinkler)	7 - 8	Mr Alan Harrison
RHYS CLUTTERBUCK (Gary Moore)	8 - 10	Mr N. M. Adams
MORGAN COLE (Sir Mark Prescott Bt)	7 - 11	M. Furnass
GEORGIA COX (John & Thady Gosden)	8 - 2	07807442009
WILLIAM COX (Andrew Balding)	8 - 2	Mr N. M. Adams
MARK CREHAN (George Boughey)	8 - 7	P. C. Shea
ELLE-MAY CROOT (Ivan Furtado)	8 - 2	c/o 07783520746
HARRY DAVIES (Andrew Balding)	7 - 9	P. C. Shea
ROSE DAWES (Mick Channon)	7 - 10	c/o 01635 281166
GEORGIA DOBIE (Eve Johnson Houghton)	8 - 3	P. C. Shea
JULIA ENGSTROM (Roger Varian)	8 - 10	c/o 01638 661702
ADAM FARRAGHER (William Haggas)	7 - 10	Mr S. M. Righton
SAM FEILDEN (K. R. Burke)	8 - 5	Mr R. Birkett\K. W. Renwick
ISOBEL FRANCIS (Mark Usher)	7 - 7	Mr L. R. James
HANNAH FRASER (Ed Walker)	7 - 4	c/o 01488 674148
KAIYA FRASER (Chris Wall)	8 - 7	c/o 01638 661999
BRADLEY FURNISS (Gay Kelleway)	8 - 0	c/o 07815738779
CATHAL GAHAN (William Muir & Chris Grassick)	8 - 5	353876022636
BILLY GARRITTY (Micky Hammond)	8 - 8	K. W. Renwick
ANNA GIBSON (Gary Moore)	7 - 7	c/o 01403 891912
JADE GOODWIN (Adrian Keatley)	7 - 7	c/o 07934903387
SELMA GRAGE (Kevin Philippart de Foy)	8 - 7	07388629833
THOMAS GREATREX (Roger Charlton)	8 - 6	Mr G. D. Jewell
MOLLY GUNN (Anthony Carson)	8 - 1	c/o 01285 658919
OLIVIA HAINES (David Simcock)	8 - 3	c/o 07808954109
THORE HAMMER HANSEN (Richard Hannon)	8 - 0	Mrs Shelley Dwyer
TYLER HEARD (Darryll Holland)	8 - 2	Mr N. M. Adams
CAMERON HILLHOUSE (Mark Loughnane)	8 - 10	c/o 07805531021
PAIGE HOPPER (Michael Dods)	8 - 6	c/o 07860411590
CHRISTIAN HOWARTH (Marco Botti)	8 - 3	Mr A. T. Brook
WILLIAM HUMPHREY (Simon & Ed Crisford)	7 - 5	Mr S. T. Dodds
CALLUM HUTCHINSON (Andrew Balding)	8 - 0	Mr N. M. Adams
RHIAIN INGRAM (Roger Ingram)	7 - 11	Miss A. Wallace
PIERRE-LOUIS JAMIN (K. R. Burke)	8 - 3	Mr G. D. Jewell
ALEX JARY (Nigel Tinkler)	8 - 3	Mr Paul Brierley
ELINOR JONES (Richard Hughes)	7 - 0	Mr G. D. Jewell
ETHAN JONES (George Baker)	8 - 0	c/o 01428 682059
SOPHIE JONES (J. S. Moore)	8 - 0	c/o 01488 73887
AIDAN KEELEY (Gary Moore)	8 - 2	Mr N. M. Adams**L**
EWIS KENT (T. J. Kent)	8 - 11	Mrs L. H. Way
GEORGIA KING (Alan King)	7 - 10	Mr G. D. Jewell
THEODORE LADD (Michael Appleby)	8 - 0	Mr G. D. Jewell
FREDERICK LARSON (Michael Appleby)	8 - 2	Mr R. Birkett

GEORGIA LEA (Martin Smith)	7 - 4	c/o 07712493589
OWEN LEWIS (Clive Cox)	8 - 2	c/o 01488 73072
ELLA MCCAIN (Tim Easterby)	8 - 0	Mr R. A. Hale
CONNER MCCANN (Lucinda Russell)	8 - 7	K. W. Renwick
GRACE MCENTEE (Phil McEntee)	8 - 7	Mr S. T. Dodds
OISIN MCSWEENEY (Kevin Ryan)	8 - 3	Mr N. Hannity
UGNE MICKUTE (Edward Bethell)	8 - 0	07598128527
SHARIQ MOHD (Sylvester Kirk)	7 - 10	Mr L. R. James
STEPHEN MOONEY (James Ferguson)	8 - 4	Mr Paul Clarke
CONNOR MURTAGH (Richard Fahey)	8 - 6	K. W. Renwick
JACK OSBORNE (Sir Mark Prescott Bt)	8 - 4	c/o 01638 662117
SAFFIE OSBORNE (Jamie Osborne)	8 - 4	Mr N. Hannity
ERIKA PARKINSON (Michael Appleby)	8 - 0	M. Furnass
LAURA PEARSON (Ralph Beckett)	8 - 4	Mr S. Croft
JONNY PEATE (Mark Johnston)	7 - 7	Mrs Shelley Dwyer
MOLLIE PHILLIPS (Tony Carroll)	8 - 0	Miss S. L. Metcalfe
TIA PHILLIPS (John Ryan)	8 - 3	c/o 01638 664172
ABBIE PIERCE (William Knight)	7 - 10	Andy Lewis
RHONA PINDAR (K. R. Burke)	8 - 0	Mr J. L. Neilson
WILLIAM PYLE (Michael & David Easterby)	8 - 0	Mr N. Hannity
SOPHIE REED (Joseph Tuite)	8 - 0	Mr Ian Wood
GEORGE ROOKE (Richard Hughes)	7 - 13	Mr N. M. Adams
DEON LE ROUX (Clive Cox)	8 - 2	c/o 01488 73072
HARRY RUSSELL (Brian Ellison)	8 - 7	Mr R. A. Hale
BEN SANDERSON (Ian Williams)	8 - 7	Mr S. T. Dodds
GIANLUCA SANNA (Bryan Smart)	8 - 8	Mr R. A. Hale
TYLER SAUNDERS (Jonathan Portman)	8 - 7	Mr Ian Wood\Miss A. Wallace
RYAN SEXTON (Adrian Keatley)	8 - 6	K. W. Renwick
OLIVER STAMMERS (Mark Johnston)	8 - 4	Mr S. T. Dodds
MOHAMMED TABTI (Paul & Oliver Cole)	8 - 0	33771633066
EMMA TAFF (Tony Carroll)	8 - 4	Mr R. Birkett
COURTNEY THOMAS (Ronald Harris)	7 - 4	c/o 07831770899
ANGUS VILLIERS (Richard Spencer)	8 - 2	P. C. Shea
SHANNON WATTS (Iain Jardine)	8 - 8	c/o 07944722011
ZAK WHEATLEY (Declan Carroll)	8 - 5	Mr R. A. Hale
ELISHA WHITTINGTON (Mark Loughnane)	7 - 11	Mrs L. H. Way
BRANDON WILKIE (Tim Easterby)	8 - 5	c/o 01653 668566
JORDAN WILLIAMS (Bernard Llewellyn)	8 - 10	Miss S. L. Metcalfe
LEVI WILLIAMS (Jane Chapple-Hyam)	7 - 10	Mr S. T. Dodds
MARK WINN (David O'Meara)	8 - 0	Mr R. A. Hale
SEBASTIAN WOODS (Chris Wall)	8 - 11	Mrs Shelley Dwyer
LIAM WRIGHT (Darryll Holland)	8 - 3	c/o 07901550909

JUMP JOCKEYS

Riding weights and contact details
An index of agents appears on page 714

An index of agents appears on page 714

Jockey	Weight	Agent
AARON ANDERSON	9-7	Mr Paul Brierley
BRIDGET ANDREWS	9-5	Mr I. P. Popham
EDWARD AUSTIN	10-0	K. W. Renwick
HARRY BANNISTER	9-7	Mr Gordon Clarkson
DAVID BASS	10-5	Mr Gordon Clarkson
MATTIE BATCHELOR	10-5	07767400753
TOM BELLAMY	10-5	Mr Gordon Clarkson
JAMES BEST	10-0	Mr Dave Roberts
HARRISON BESWICK	10-0	Mr I. P. Popham
CALLUM BEWLEY	10-0	Mr R. A. Hale
JONATHON BEWLEY	10-0	01450860651
NICO DE BOINVILLE	10-0	Mr Dave Roberts
JAMES BOWEN	10-0	Mr Dave Roberts
SEAN BOWEN	9-7	Mr Dave Roberts\ M. Furnass
CONNOR BRACE	9-3	Mr Dave Roberts\ M. Furnass
PADDY BRENNAN	9-12	Mr Dave Roberts
HENRY BROOKE	10-0	K. W. Renwick
JONATHAN BURKE	10-0	Mr Gordon Clarkson
DANNY BURTON	9-9	Mr L. R. James
BLAIR CAMPBELL	10-0	K. W. Renwick
TOM CANNON	10-5	Mr Dave Roberts
ALAIN CAWLEY	9-10	Mr Dave Roberts
ROSS CHAPMAN	9-8	Mr R. A. Hale
TOM CHEESMAN	9-9	07513109598
HARRY COBDEN	10-0	Mr Dave Roberts
AIDAN COLEMAN	10-0	Mr Dave Roberts
SAM COLTHERD	9-12	Mr J. B. Jeffrey
DOUGIE COSTELLO	10-0	Mr A. T. Brook
PATRICK COWLEY	10-0	Mr I. P. Popham
JAMES DAVIES	10-0	Mr L. R. James
CHARLIE DEUTSCH	10-0	Mr Gordon Clarkson
REX DINGLE	10-2	Mr Dave Roberts
THOMAS DOWSON	10-0	Mr J. L. Neilson
ALAN DOYLE	9-10	Mr R. A. Hale
ROBERT DUNNE	10-7	Mr Dave Roberts
KIERON EDGAR	10-7	07832903378
ALEX EDWARDS	10-0	Mr Gordon Clarkson
LEE EDWARDS	10-0	Mr Gordon Clarkson
DAVID ENGLAND	10-0	Mr I. P. Popham
JONATHAN ENGLAND	9-10	07747390455
DEREK FOX	10-0	Mr J. B. Jeffrey
BRYONY FROST	9-12	Mr Dave Roberts
PAGE FULLER	9-3	Mr L. R. James
LUCY GARDNER	10-0	07814979 699
THOMAS GARNER	10-2	Mr I. P. Popham
BILLY GARRITTY	9-7	K. W. Renwick
JACK GARRITTY	9-0	K. W. Renwick
CIARAN GETHINGS	10-2	Mr Gordon Clarkson
MARC GOLDSTEIN	10-0	Mr Dave Roberts
JAMIE GORMLEY	8-0	Mr R. A. Hale
MATT GRIFFITHS	10-7	Mr I. P. Popham
JAMIE HAMILTON	10-0	Mr R. A. Hale
CHARLIE HAMMOND	9-7	Mr Dave Roberts
A. P. HESKIN	10-0	Mr Dave Roberts
DANIEL HISKETT	9-10	Mr I. P. Popham
SEAN HOULIHAN	9-11	Mr Dave Roberts
BRIAN HUGHES	9-7	Mr R. A. Hale
DARYL JACOB	10-3	Mr Dave Roberts
ALAN JOHNS	10-0	Mr I. P. Popham
ALISON JOHNSON	9-7	07549142203
BEN JONES	10-0	Mr Dave Roberts
CHARLOTTE JONES	8-11	Mr J. L. Neilson
KEVIN JONES	10-0	Mr Dave Roberts
JONJO O'NEILL JR.	10-4	Mr Dave Roberts
MAX KENDRICK	9-9	Mr Dave Roberts
WILLIAM KENNEDY	10-0	Mr Gordon Clarkson
JOHN KINGTON	10-0	Mr R. A. Hale
RYAN MANIA	10-3	K. W. Renwick
JAMES MARTIN	10-13	07815698359
JEREMIAH MCGRATH	10-0	Mr Dave Roberts
RICHIE MCLERNON	9-10	Mr Dave Roberts
DANNY MCMENAMIN	9-7	Mr R. A. Hale
JAMIE MOORE	10-0	Mr Dave Roberts
JOSHUA MOORE	10-5	Mr Dave Roberts
NATHAN MOSCROP	10-5	Mr R. A. Hale
STEPHEN MULQUEEN	10-0	K. W. Renwick
CRAIG NICHOL	10-0	K. W. Renwick
MEGAN NICHOLLS	8-4	07792440002
MICHEAL NOLAN	10-4	Mr Dave Roberts
DAVID NOONAN	10-0	Mr Dave Roberts
HUGH NUGENT	9-9	Mr Gordon Clarkson
PAUL O'BRIEN	10-3	Mr I. P. Popham
TOM O'BRIEN	10-2	Mr Dave Roberts
CONOR O'FARRELL	10-3	K. W. Renwick
KATIE O'FARRELL	9-13	Mr Gordon Clarkson
RICHARD PATRICK	9-7	Mr Dave Roberts
BEN POSTE	9-10	Mr Dave Roberts
BRENDAN POWELL	9-11	Mr Dave Roberts
DAVID PRICHARD	10-0	Mr I. P. Popham
JACK QUINLAN	9-10	Mr Dave Roberts
SHANE QUINLAN	9-7	Mr I. P. Popham
SEAN QUINLAN	10-0	Mr R. A. Hale
HARRY REED	9-7	Mr Dave Roberts
CONOR RING	10-5	Mr I. P. Popham
BEN ROBINSON	8-9	Mr R. A. Hale
DANIEL SANSOM	10-5	Mr L. R. James
JACK SAVAGE	10-5	07778683721
NICK SCHOLFIELD	10-0	Mr Dave Roberts
TOM SCUDAMORE	10-0	Mr Dave Roberts
WILLIAM SHANAHAN	10-3	Mr J. L. Neilson
GAVIN SHEEHAN	10-0	Mr Gordon Clarkson
STAN SHEPPARD	10-4	Mr Gordon Clarkson
HARRY SKELTON	10-0	Mr I. P. Popham
NICK SLATTER	9-0	07716151634
ALEXANDER THORNE	9-7	Mr Dave Roberts
HARRIET TUCKER	9-3	Mr L. R. James
SAM TWISTON-DAVIES	10-0	Mr Gordon Clarkson
CHRIS WARD	9-12	Mr L. R. James
ADAM WEDGE	10-0	Mr Dave Roberts
KIELAN WOODS	10-3	Mr Gordon Clarkson
TABITHA WORSLEY	9-9	Mr L. R. James

CONDITIONALS

Their employer and contact details
An index of agents appears on page 714

BENJAMIN ABBOTT (Tjade Collier)	9 - 10	c/o 07939303933
JOE ANDERSON (Emma Lavelle)	9 - 11	Mr Dave Roberts
JACK ANDREWS (Pam Sly)	10 - 4	Mr I. P Popham
PHILIP ARMSON (David Pipe)	9 - 7	Mr Dave Roberts
MITCHELL BASTYAN (Milton Harris)	10 - 0	Mr Dave Roberts
ARCHIE BELLAMY (D. J. Jeffreys)	9 - 10	Mr Gordon Clarkson
NATHAN BRENNAN (Nicky Henderson)	9 - 12	Mr Dave Roberts
KEVIN BROGAN (Jonjo O'Neill)	10 - 0	Mr Dave Roberts
OAKLEY BROWN (Brian Ellison)	9 - 12	Mr R. A. Hale
KIEREN BUCKLEY (Nigel Hawke)	10 - 10	Mr Dave Roberts
TOM BUCKLEY (Paul Nicholls)	9 - 0	Mr Dave Roberts
BRYAN CARVER (Paul Nicholls)	9 - 7	Mr Dave Roberts
ANGUS CHELEDA (Paul Nicholls)	9 - 10	Mr Dave Roberts
PETER COLEMAN (Rebecca Menzies)	10 - 0	Mr R. A. Hale
ELLIS COLLIER (Christian Williams)	9 - 10	c/o 07702 896759
DAIRE DAVIS (Olly Murphy)	9 - 3	Mr I. P Popham
BEN FFRENCH DAVIS (Nicky Henderson)	9 - 12	Mr L. R. James
LEWIS DOBB (L J Morgan)	9 - 8	c/o 01664 464571
THOMAS DOGGRELL (Tom George)	10 - 4	Mr Gordon Clarkson
EDDIE EDGE (Nigel Twiston-Davies)	9 - 9	Mr Gordon Clarkson
NED FOX (Venetia Williams)	9 - 10	Mr I. P Popham
MARK GALLIGAN (Nicky Richards)	9 - 7	Mr R. A. Hale
FERGUS GILLARD (David Pipe)	9 - 7	Mr Dave Roberts
THEO GILLARD (Donald McCain)	10 - 7	Mr R. A. Hale
BEN GODFREY (Anthony Honeyball)	9 - 4	Mr Dave Roberts
FERGUS GREGORY (Olly Murphy)	10 - 7	Mr I. P Popham
GEAROID HARNEY (Olly Murphy)	10 - 0	Mr I. P Popham
BRADLEY HARRIS (Milton Harris)	9 - 2	Mr S. T. Dodds
LIAM HARRISON (Fergal O'Brien)	9 - 6	Mr Dave Roberts
NIALL HOULIHAN (Gary Moore)	9 - 7	Mr Dave Roberts
DILLAN HURST (George Bewley)	9 - 7	Mr J. L. Neilson
CAMERON ILES (Anthony Honeyball)	9 - 0	c/o 07815898569
MAX JENKINS (Iain Jardine)	9 - 10	c/o 07944722011
ALFIE JORDAN (Oliver Sherwood)	9 - 7	Mr Gordon Clarkson
PETER KAVANAGH (Donald McCain)	9 - 0	Mr R. A. Hale
HARRY KIMBER (Colin Tizzard)	9 - 0	Mr Gordon Clarkson
DYLAN KITTS (Tom Lacey)	9 - 7	c/o 07768398604
FINN LAMBERT (Nigel Twiston-Davies)	10 - 3	Mr Gordon Clarkson
ROBERT LAW-EADIE (Fergal O'Brien)	9 - 8	c/o 07771702829
KAI LENIHAN (Neil King)	9 - 10	Mr I. P Popham
CILLIN LEONARD (Dr Richard Newland)	9 - 11	Mr Dave Roberts
BRUCE LYNN (N. W. Alexander)	10 - 0	K. W. Renwick
WILLIAM MARSHALL (Jonjo O'Neill)	9 - 7	Mr Dave Roberts
JACK MARTIN (Philip Hobbs)	10 - 4	Mr Dave Roberts
MISS ABBIE MCCAIN (Donald McCain)	9 - 9	Mr R. A. Hale
CONNER MCCANN (Lucinda Russell)	8 - 10	K. W. Renwick
DAIRE MCCONVILLE (Kerry Lee)	10 - 0	c/o 07968242663
COREY MCGIVERN (Lucy Wadham)	9 - 6	c/o 07980545776
TOM MIDGLEY (Sam England)	10 - 0	Mr R. A. Hale
LUCA MORGAN (Ben Pauling)	10 - 3	Mr Dave Roberts
LORCAN MURTAGH (Harry Fry)	9 - 11	Mr Gordon Clarkson
JORDAN NAILOR (Nigel Twiston-Davies)	9 - 7	Mr Gordon Clarkson
LILLY PINCHIN (Richard Hobson)	10 - 0	Mr Gordon Clarkson
CHARLIE PRICE (Tim Vaughan)	9 - 2	Mr I. P Popham
CAOILIN QUINN (Warren Greatrex)	9 - 10	Mr Dave Roberts
CONOR RABBITT (Nicky Richards)	9 - 12	Mr R. A. Hale
EMMA SMITH-CHASTON (Micky Hammond)	9 - 7	K. W. Renwick

LEWIS STONES (Olly Murphy)	9 - 7	Mr I. P. Popham
JAY TIDBALL (Alastair Ralph)	10 - 2	Mr Gordon Clarkson
CHARLIE TODD (Ian Williams)	9 - 5	Mr I. P. Popham
JACK TUDOR (Christian Williams)	9 - 7	Mr Dave Roberts
ROSS TURNER (Oliver Greenall)	9 - 7	c/o 07771571000
ELLIE VAUGHAN (Gary Moore)	9 - 8	c/o 01403 891912
PATRICK WADGE (Lucinda Russell)	9 - 0	Mr J. B. Jeffrey
JACK WILDMAN (Emma Lavelle)	9 - 10	Mr Gordon Clarkson
CHESTER WILLIAMS (Mrs Jane Williams)	10 - 2	c/o 07977457350
ISABEL WILLIAMS (Evan Williams)	9 - 7	Mr Dave Roberts
JORDAN WILLIAMS (Bernard Llewellyn)	8 - 10	Miss S. L. Metcalfe
LORCAN WILLIAMS (Paul Nicholls)	10 - 9	Mr I. P. Popham
JOE WILLIAMSON (Philip Kirby)	9 - 7	K. W. Renwick
THOMAS WILLMOTT (Sue Smith)	9 - 7	Mr J. B. Jeffrey

Are your contact details missing or incorrect? If so please update us by email:
hitraceform@weatherbys.co.uk

AMATEUR RIDERS

Riding weights and contact details
An index of agents appears on page 714

An index of agents appears on page 714

JOHNSTONE-BAKER, C. 9 - 7 07808093979
ORTTEWELL, G. 9 - 4 07703351178
WOODS, S. 11 - 4
AGAR, J. 10 - 4
ALEXANDER, C. 9 - 10 07799191093
ALEXANDER, K. 9 - 7 07950989807
ANDREWS, D. I. J. 10 - 10 ....07817 322974
ANDREWS, G. 10 - 0 ....Mr Gordon Clarkson
APRAHAMIAN, B. 10 - 12 07739819804
ATKINS, H. 8 - 8
ATKINSON, P. L. 8 - 5 ....01609 772691
BAILEY, H. G. 12 - 0 07834641078
BAIN, S. A. 8 - 8
BAKER, Z. C. N. 10 - 10 ....Mr Gordon Clarkson
BAMENT, J. J. 9 - 10 07964587682
BARBER, J. 10 - 0
BARFOOT-SAUNT, G. C. 10 - 12 ....01684 833227
BARLOW, P. C. F. 9 - 0
BARR, F. J. A. 11 - 2
BARRATT-ATKIN, N. 9 - 2
BARTLEY, C. A. 8 - 10 ....Mrs G. S. Charnock
BARTON, V. 8 - 10
BEDI, J. I. 8 - 10 ....01642 780202
BELL, A. 9 - 4 07971675180
BEVAN, M. J. 9 - 10
BIDDICK, W. E. T. 11 - 0 07976556823
BIRKETT, R. A. 9 - 10 07855065036
BLAKEMORE, A. 9 - 0
BLOSS, A. Z. 8 - 5 ......Mrs N. Bloss\Miss S. L. Metcalfe
BODDY, C. 10 - 7 07944581502
BOSTOCK, K. L. 8 - 8
BOWEN, S. L. 9 - 0 ....Mr S. M. Righton
BRACE, J. 10 - 0
BRACKENBURY, B. E. 10 - 11
BRADBURN, T. M. 9 - 4
BRADSTOCK, L. A. N. 9 - 6 07972161732
BRAZG-CARRELL, N. 10 - 0
BRIDGER, M. 9 - 4 07961349301
BRISELDEN, P. R. 8 - 13
BROMLEY, B. W. 9 - 9
BROOKES, M. R. 8 - 3
BROOKS, C. 9 - 0
BROPHY, O. 9 - 1
BROTHERTON, S. 8 - 12
BROUGHTON, T. P. 10 - 0 07769311769
BROWN, L. 9 - 12
BROWN, M. W. 9 - 12 ....Mr J. B. Jeffrey
BROWN, P. J. 9 - 5
BRYANT, M. P. 9 - 12 07976217542
BULLOCK, E. 8 - 0
BURNS-LEWIS, B. D. 9 - 7
BUTLER, C. G. 10 - 5
BUTTERFIELD, A. 11 - 0
CAGNEY, E. 9 - 0 ....Mr Paul Brierley
CASE, C. 10 - 10 07807652305
CATER, J. J. 9 - 7
CHADWICK, A. 10 - 0
CHATTERTON, G. 10 - 7

CHERRIMAN, D. J. 10 - 7 07900963271
COLEMAN, A. H. 9 - 0
COLLIER, A. 9 - 0 ....Mrs G. S. Charnock
COOKSON, N. P. 8 - 6 07711910653
COX, A. 8 - 2 07813386642
CRANE, C. R. 9 - 8
CROW, H. 10 - 7 07794379295
DALY, G. 10 - 0 07469811361
DAVIS, J. 9 - 4
DAWSON, J. A. 9 - 0 07540710068
DIXON, J. 9 - 7
DIXON, J. 9 - 7 ....Mr Gordon Clarkson
DODD, M. 9 - 0
DODS, C. A. 8 - 13 07590048619
DODS, S. E. 9 - 0
DURRELL, T. 9 - 7 ....Mr I. P Popham
EASTERBY, E. A. 8 - 7 07854733689
EASTERBY, W. H. 9 - 7 07772216507
EDDERY, G. 9 - 4
EDWARDS, D. M. 11 - 4
EDWARDS, H. 10 - 4 07709506046
ELDIN, D. S. 10 - 2
ELLIS, D. F. 8 - 7
EMSLEY, C. J. R. 9 - 5
ENNIS, M. C. 9 - 11 ....Mrs L. H. Way
EYSTON, T. 9 - 10 ....Mr Gordon Clarkson
FEAKES, G. 9 - 4 07771902739
FEATHERSTONE, W. 9 - 0
FOX, M. 9 - 0
FURNESS, C. J. W. 10 - 6 07871449210
GAMBIN, J. 9 - 6 07934342739
GARVEN, A. 8 - 9 ....Mr Paul Brierley
GERMANY, S. 9 - 0
GIBBS, B. 10 - 10 07818407883
GINGELL, F. L. 9 - 0
GLANVILLE, P. 10 - 0
GLASSONBURY, E. 10 - 12 07917167236
GORDON, F. 9 - 10
GORDON, L. 10 - 10 ....01285 740445
GOWING, K. 10 - 7
GREASBY, H. 10 - 0
GREENWOOD, T. O. M. 10 - 7 07904889779
GREGORY, H. J. 8 - 10 07772008845
HAMPSON, B. 9 - 12
HAMPTON, M. L. 11 - 0
HARDING, J. 9 - 10 ....Miss A. Wallace
HARGREAVES, R. 10 - 5
HAWKER, R. 10 - 12 07891960356
HENDERSON, G. 10 - 5 07765967086
HERBERT, M. 11 - 0
HERBISON, E. 10 - 7 07368385161
HILL, R. L. 9 - 0
HODGINS, L. W. 10 - 5
HOLDER, E. 9 - 0
HOLLIDAY, J. 9 - 10 07553773454
HOLMES, R. J. 9 - 5
HOULIHAN, C. 11 - 7 07808843313
HOWARTH, R. 9 - 2

NOTES

 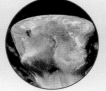 

Injured Jockeys Fund

We are here to help

**Any rider who holds, or has held,
a Professional or Amateur licence
(including Apprentice, Conditional and Point-to-Point)
can access the services we provide**

www.ijf.org.uk

Compassion • Care • Support
Injured Jockeys Fund (Registered Charity No. 1107395)

GALLOP ENGINEERED.

STANDALONE PRO FIBRE

Standalone pro fibre surface is ideal for gallops, ménages and arenas. This product has been developed by racehorse owners and breeders to a specification that is consistent with what they would use for their own horses. Standalone pro fibre surface is made from all recycled fibres.

BENEFITS

● All-weather surface
● Drainage friendly
● 100% Recycled Fibres
● Low Maintenance - rolling needed
● Frost resistant
● Minimal dust
● 20 year plus lifespan

SUITABILITY

Standalone pro fibre surface is an exceptional product for gallops.

● Will reduce deep riding
● Can be used as a complete surface
● Improves fitness

SUSSEX EQUINE
HOSPITAL
-EST 1951-

USSEX EQUINE HOSPITAL

- tate of the art hospital facilities
- outine race yard management
- tud vet services
- BLB accredited laboratory
- eferral service led by European and state oarded specialists
- rthopaedic and soft tissue surgical facilities
- verland endoscopy
- 1RI
- cintigraphy

COMPREHENSIVE THOROUGHBRED VETERINARY SERVICES

Providing a routine and emergency service 24/7 throughout the season.

CVS
CREDITED
ACTICE
QUINE HOSPITAL

further information, please contact us at:

info@sussexequinehospital.co.uk
01903 883050
Facebook: Sussex Equine Hospital
Billingshurst Road, Ashington, West Sussex RH20

www.sussexequinehospital.co.uk